VECTOR
MECHANICS FOR ENGINEERS

STATICS AND DYNAMICS

Vector Mechanics for Engineers

STATICS AND DYNAMICS

FERDINAND P. BEER
Professor and Head, Department of Mechanics
Lehigh University

E. RUSSELL JOHNSTON, JR.
Professor, Department of Civil Engineering
University of Connecticut

1962

McGRAW-HILL BOOK COMPANY
New York, San Francisco, Toronto, London

VECTOR MECHANICS FOR ENGINEERS: STATICS AND DYNAMICS

04309

Library of Congress Catalog Card Number 61-9324

IV

PREFACE

The main objective of a first course in mechanics should be to develop in the engineering student the ability to analyze any problem in a simple and logical manner and to apply to its solution a few, well-understood, basic principles. This text is designed for the first courses in statics and dynamics offered in the sophomore or junior year, and it is hoped that it will help the instructor achieve this goal.†

Vector analysis is introduced early in the text and used throughout the presentation of statics and dynamics. This approach leads to more concise derivations of the fundamental principles of mechanics. It also results in simpler solutions of three-dimensional problems in statics, and makes it possible to analyze many advanced problems in kinematics and kinetics, which could not be solved by the standard scalar methods. The emphasis in this text, however, remains on the correct understanding of the principles of mechanics and on their application to the solution of engineering problems, and vector analysis is presented chiefly as a convenient tool.‡

One of the characteristics of the approach used in this book is that the mechanics of *particles* has been clearly separated from the mechanics of *rigid bodies*. This approach makes it possible to consider simple practical applications at an early stage and to postpone the introduction of the more difficult concepts. In statics, for example, the statics of particles is treated first (Chap. 2); after the rules of addition and subtraction of vectors have been introduced, the principle of equilibrium of a particle is immediately applied to practical situations

† This text is also available in two separate volumes, *Vector Mechanics for Engineers: Statics*, and *Vector Mechanics for Engineers: Dynamics*.

‡ In a parallel text, *Mechanics for Engineers*, second edition, the use of vector algebra is limited to the addition and subtraction of vectors, and vector differentiation is omitted.

involving only concurrent forces. The statics of rigid bodies is considered in Chaps. 3 and 4. In Chap. 3, the vector and scalar products of two vectors are introduced and used to define the moment of a force about a point and about an axis. The presentation of these new concepts is followed by a thorough and rigorous discussion of equivalent systems of forces leading, in Chap. 4, to many practical applications involving the equilibrium of rigid bodies under general force systems. In dynamics, the same division is observed. The basic concepts of force, mass, and acceleration, of work and energy, and of impulse and momentum are introduced and first applied to problems involving only particles. Thus, the student may familiarize himself with the three basic methods used in dynamics and learn their respective advantages before facing the difficulties associated with the motion of rigid bodies.

Since this text is designed for first courses in statics and dynamics, new concepts have been presented in simple terms and every step explained in detail. On the other hand, by discussing the broader aspects of the problems considered, and by stressing methods of general applicability, a definite maturity of approach has been achieved. For example, the concepts of partial constraints and of statical indeterminacy are introduced early in the text and used throughout statics. In dynamics, the concept of potential energy is discussed in the general case of a conservative force. Also, the study of the plane motion of rigid bodies has been designed to lead naturally to the study of their general motion in space. This is true in kinematics as well as in kinetics, where the principle of equivalence of external and effective forces (rather than the method of dynamic equilibrium) is applied directly to the analysis of plane motion, thus facilitating the transition to the study of three-dimensional motion.

A large number of optional sections have been included. These sections are indicated by asterisks and may thus easily be distinguished from those which form the core of the basic mechanics course. They may be omitted without prejudice to the understanding of the rest of the text. Among the topics covered in these additional sections are applications to hydrostatics, shear and bending-moment diagrams for beams, equilibrium of cables, products of inertia and Mohr's circle, the method of virtual work, graphical methods for the solution of rectilinear-motion problems, the motion of a particle under a central force with applications to space mechanics, the deflection of fluid streams, problems involving jet and rocket propulsion, Coriolis acceleration, the kinetics of rigid bodies in three dimensions, damped mechanical vibrations, and electrical analogues. In addition, the method of the force polygon and string polygon for the analysis of coplanar forces has been covered in an Appendix. The sections on beams are especially useful when the course in statics is immediately followed by a course in mechanics of materials, while the additional topics included in dynamics will be found of interest when dynamics is taught in the junior year.

The fact that mechanics is essentially a *deductive* science based on a few fundamental principles has been stressed. Derivations have been presented in their logical sequence and with all the rigor warranted at this level. However, the learning process being largely *inductive,* simple applications have been considered first. Thus the statics of particles precedes the statics of rigid bodies, and problems involving internal forces are postponed until Chap. 6. Also, in Chap. 4, equilibrium problems involving only coplanar forces are considered first and solved by ordinary algebra, while problems involving three-dimensional forces and requiring the full use of vector algebra are discussed in the second part of the chapter. Again, the dynamics of particles precedes the dynamics of rigid bodies; and, in the latter, the fundamental principles of kinetics are first applied to the solution of two-dimensional problems, which can be more easily visualized by the student (Chaps. 16 and 17), while three-dimensional problems are postponed until Chap. 18, where more powerful methods of vector analysis are used.

Free-body diagrams are introduced early, and their importance is emphasized throughout the text. They are used not only to solve equilibrium problems but also to express the equivalence of two systems of forces or, more generally, of two systems of vectors. This approach is particularly useful in the dynamics of rigid bodies. Indeed, by placing the emphasis on "free-body-diagram equations" rather than on the standard algebraic equations of motion, a more intuitive and more complete understanding of the fundamental principles of dynamics may be achieved.

The material presented in the text and most of the problems require no previous mathematical knowledge beyond algebra, trigonometry, and elementary calculus, and all the elements of vector algebra necessary to the understanding of the text have been carefully presented in Chaps. 2 and 3. However, special problems have been included, which make use of a more advanced knowledge of calculus, and certain sections, such as

Secs. 19.8 and 19.9 on damped vibrations, should be assigned only if the students possess the proper mathematical background. In the portions of the text using elementary calculus, a greater emphasis has been placed on the correct understanding and application of the concepts of differentiation and integration than on the nimble manipulation of mathematical formulas. In this connection, it should be mentioned that the determination of the centroids of composite areas precedes the calculation of centroids by integration, making it thus possible to establish firmly the concept of moment of area before introducing the use of integration.

Since students are often given no formal training in the use of the slide rule, special notes have been included in Chap. 2, stressing the proper use of the slide rule in the solution of problems involving proportions or trigonometric relations.

The text has been divided into units, each consisting of one or several theory sections, one or several sample problems, and a large number of problems to be assigned. Each unit corresponds to a well-defined topic and generally may be covered in one lesson. In a number of cases, however, the instructor will find it desirable to devote more than one lesson to a given topic. The sample problems have been set up in much the same form that a student will use in solving the assigned problems. They thus serve the double purpose of amplifying the text and demonstrating the type of neat and orderly work that the student should cultivate in his own solutions. Most of the problems to be assigned are of a practical nature and should appeal to the engineering student. They are primarily designed, however, to illustrate the material presented in the text and to help the student understand the basic principles of mechanics. The problems have been grouped according to the portions of material they illustrate and have been arranged in order of increasing difficulty. Problems requiring special attention have been indicated by asterisks. Answers to all even-numbered problems are given at the end of the book.

The authors wish to acknowledge gratefully the many helpful comments and suggestions offered by the users of the first edition of *Mechanics for Engineers*.

FERDINAND P. BEER
E. RUSSELL JOHNSTON, JR.

CONTENTS

LIST OF SYMBOLS

$\mathbf{a}$, a	Acceleration
a	Constant; radius; distance; semimajor axis of ellipse
$\bar{\mathbf{a}}$, $\bar{a}$	Acceleration of mass center
$\mathbf{a}_{B/A}$	Acceleration of B relative to frame in translation with A
$\mathbf{a}_c$	Coriolis acceleration
$\mathbf{A}, \mathbf{B}, \mathbf{C}, \ldots$	Reactions at supports and connections
$A, B, C, \ldots$	Points
A	Area
b	Width; distance; semiminor axis of ellipse
c	Constant; coefficient of viscous damping
C	Centroid; instantaneous center of rotation; capacitance
d	Distance
e	Coefficient of restitution; base of natural logarithms
E	Voltage
f	Frequency; scalar function
$\mathbf{F}$	Force; friction force
g	Acceleration of gravity
G	Center of gravity; mass center; constant of gravitation
h	Height; sag of cable
$\mathbf{h}_O$	Angular momentum about O
$\mathbf{i}, \mathbf{j}, \mathbf{k}$	Unit vectors along coordinate axes
$\mathbf{i}_n$, $\mathbf{i}_t$	Unit vectors along normal and tangent
$\mathbf{i}_r$, $\mathbf{i}_\theta$	Unit vectors in radial and transverse directions
i	Current
$I, I_x, \ldots$	Moment of inertia
$\bar{I}$	Centroidal moment of inertia
J	Polar moment of inertia
k	Spring constant
k_x, k_y, k_O	Radius of gyration

$\bar{k}$	Centroidal radius of gyration
l	Length
L	Length; span; inductance
m	Mass
$\mathbf{M}$	Couple; moment
$\mathbf{M}_O$	Moment about point O
$\mathbf{M}_O^R$	Moment resultant about point O
M	Magnitude of couple or moment; mass of earth
M_{OL}	Moment about axis OL
n	Normal direction
$\mathbf{N}$	Normal component of reaction
O	Origin of coordinates
p	Pressure; circular frequency
$\mathbf{P}$	Force; vector
$P_{xy}, \ldots$	Product of inertia
q	Electric charge
$\mathbf{Q}$	Force; vector
$\mathbf{r}$	Position vector
r	Radius; distance; polar coordinate
$\mathbf{R}$	Resultant force; resultant vector; reaction
R	Radius of earth; resistance
$\mathbf{s}$	Position vector
s	Distance; length of arc; length of cable
$\mathbf{S}$	Force; vector
t	Time; thickness; tangential direction
$\mathbf{T}$	Force
T	Tension; kinetic energy
$\mathbf{u}$	Velocity
u	Rectangular coordinate; variable
U	Work
$\mathbf{v}, v$	Velocity
v	Speed; rectangular coordinate
$\bar{\mathbf{v}}, \bar{v}$	Velocity of mass center
$\mathbf{v}_{B/A}$	Velocity of B relative to frame in translation with A
$\mathbf{V}$	Vector product; shearing force
V	Volume; potential energy; shear
w	Load per unit length
$\mathbf{W}, W$	Weight; load
x, y, z	Rectangular coordinates; distances
$\bar{x}, \bar{y}, \bar{z}$	Rectangular coordinates of centroid, center of gravity, or mass center
$\boldsymbol{\alpha}, \alpha$	Angular acceleration
α, β, γ	Angles
γ	Specific weight
δ	Elongation

$\delta\mathbf{r}$	Virtual displacement
δU	Virtual work
ε	Eccentricity of conic section or of orbit
$\boldsymbol{\lambda}$	Unit vector along a line
η	Efficiency
θ	Angular coordinate; Eulerian angle; angle; polar coordinate
μ	Coefficient of friction
ρ	Density; radius of curvature
τ	Period; periodic time
ϕ	Angle of friction; Eulerian angle; phase angle; angle
φ	Phase difference
ψ	Eulerian angle
$\boldsymbol{\omega}, \omega$	Angular velocity
ω	Circular frequency of forced vibration
$\boldsymbol{\Omega}$	Angular velocity of frame of reference
ξ, η, ζ	Rectangular coordinates

STATICS

1. INTRODUCTION

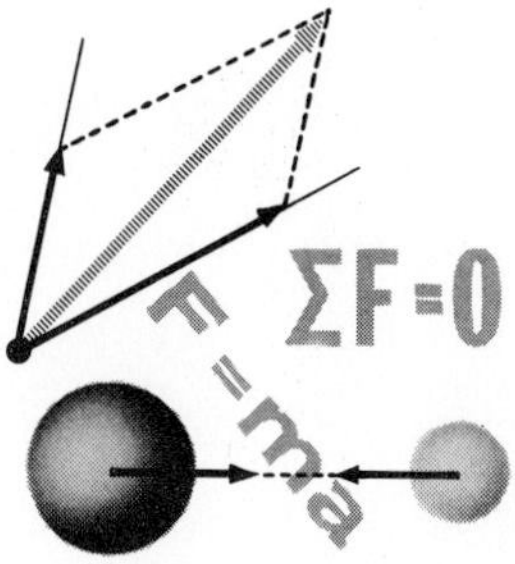

1.1. What Is Mechanics? Mechanics may be defined as that science which describes and predicts the conditions of rest or motion of bodies under the action of forces. It is divided into three parts: mechanics of *rigid bodies,* mechanics of *deformable bodies,* and mechanics of *fluids.*

The mechanics of rigid bodies is subdivided into *statics* and *dynamics,* the former dealing with bodies at rest, the latter with bodies in motion. In this part of the study of mechanics, bodies are assumed to be perfectly rigid. Actual structures and machines, however, are never absolutely rigid and deform under the loads to which they are subjected. But these deformations are usually small and do not appreciably affect the conditions of equilibrium or motion of the structure under consideration. They are important, though, as far as the resistance of the structure to failure is concerned and are studied in mechanics of materials, which is a part of the mechanics of deformable bodies. The third division of mechanics, the mechanics of fluids, is subdivided into the study of *incompressible fluids* and of *compressible fluids.* An important subdivision of the study of incompressible fluids is *hydraulics,* which deals with problems involving liquids.

Mechanics is a physical science, since it deals with the study of physical phenomena. However, some associate mechanics with mathematics, while many consider it as an engineering subject. Both these views are justified in part. Mechanics is the foundation of most engineering sciences and is an indispensable prerequisite to their study. However, it does not have the *empiricism* found in many engineering sciences; by its rigor and the emphasis it places on deductive reasoning it resembles mathematics. But, again, it is not an *abstract* or even a *pure* science; mechanics is an *applied* science. The purpose of mechanics is to explain and predict physical phenomena and thus to lay the foundations for engineering applications.

1.2. Fundamental Concepts and Principles. Although the study of mechanics goes back to the time of Aristotle (384–322 B.C.) and Archimedes (287–212 B.C.), one has to wait until Newton (1642–1727) to find a satisfactory formulation of its fundamental principles. These principles were later expressed in a modified form by D'Alembert, Lagrange, and Hamilton. Their validity remained unchallenged, however, until Einstein formulated his *theory of relativity* (1905). While its limitations have now been recognized, *newtonian mechanics* still remains the basis of today's engineering sciences.

The basic concepts used in mechanics are *space, time, mass,* and *force.* These concepts cannot be truly defined; they should be accepted on the basis of our intuition and experience and used as a mental frame of reference for our study of mechanics.

The concept of *space* is associated with the notion of the position of a point *P*. The position of *P* may be defined by three lengths measured from a certain reference point, or *origin,* in three given directions. These lengths are known as the *coordinates* of *P*.

To define an event, it is not sufficient to indicate its position in space. The *time* of the event should also be given.

The concept of *mass* is used to characterize and compare bodies on the basis of certain fundamental mechanical experiments. Two bodies of the same mass, for example, will be attracted by the earth in the same manner; they will also offer the same resistance to a change in translational motion.

A *force* represents the action of one body on another. It may be exerted by actual contact or at a distance, as in the case of gravitational forces and magnetic forces. A force is characterized by its *point of application,* its *magnitude,* and its *direction;* a force is represented by a *vector* (Sec. 2.2).

In newtonian mechanics, space, time, and mass are absolute concepts, independent of each other. (This is not true in *relativistic mechanics,* where the time of an event depends upon its position, and where the mass of a body varies with its velocity.) On the other hand, the concept of force is not independent of the other three. Indeed, one of the fundamental principles of newtonian mechanics listed below indicates that the resultant force acting on a body is related to the mass of the body and to the manner in which its velocity varies with time.

We shall study the conditions of rest or motion of particles and rigid bodies in terms of the four basic concepts we have introduced. By *particle* we mean a very small amount of matter which may be assumed to occupy a single point in space. A *rigid body* is a combination of a large number of particles occupying fixed positions with respect to each other. The study of the mechanics of particles is obviously a prerequisite to that of rigid bodies. Besides, the results obtained for a particle may be used directly in a large number of problems dealing with the conditions of rest or motion of actual bodies.

The study of elementary mechanics rests on six fundamental principles based on experimental evidence:

The Parallelogram Law for the Addition of Forces. This states that two forces acting on a particle may be replaced by a single force, called their *resultant*, obtained by drawing the diagonal of the parallelogram which has sides equal to the given forces (Sec. 2.1).

The Principle of Transmissibility. This states that the conditions of equilibrium or of motion of a rigid body will remain unchanged if a force acting at a given point of the rigid body is replaced by a force of the same magnitude and same direction, but acting at a different point, provided that the two forces have the same line of action (Sec. 3.2).

Newton's Three Fundamental Laws. Formulated by Sir Isaac Newton in the latter part of the seventeenth century, these laws may be stated as follows:

FIRST LAW. If the resultant force acting on a particle is zero, the particle will remain at rest (if originally at rest) or will move with constant speed in a straight line (if originally in motion) (Sec. 2.9).

SECOND LAW. If the resultant force acting on a particle is not zero, the particle will have an acceleration proportional to the magnitude of the resultant and in the direction of this resultant force.

As we shall see in Sec. 12.1, this law may be stated as

$$\mathbf{F} = m\mathbf{a} \tag{1.1}$$

where $\mathbf{F}$, m, and $\mathbf{a}$ represent, respectively, the resultant force acting on the particle, the mass of the particle, and the acceleration of the particle, expressed in a consistent system of units.

THIRD LAW. The forces of action and reaction between bodies in contact have the same magnitude, same line of action, and opposite sense (Sec. 6.1).

Newton's Law of Gravitation. This states that two particles of mass M and m are mutually attracted with equal and opposite forces **F** and $-$**F** of magnitude F given by the formula

$$F = G\frac{Mm}{r^2} \tag{1.2}$$

where r = distance between the two particles
G = a universal constant called the *constant of gravitation*

A particular case of great importance is that of the attraction of the earth on a particle located on its surface. The force **F** exerted by the earth on the particle is then defined as the *weight* **W** of the particle. Taking M equal to the mass of the earth, m equal to the mass of the particle, and r equal to the radius R of the earth, and introducing the constant

$$g = \frac{GM}{R^2} \tag{1.3}$$

the magnitude W of the weight of a particle of mass m may be expressed as†

$$W = mg \tag{1.4}$$

The value of R in formula (1.3) depends upon the elevation of the point considered; it also depends upon its latitude, since the earth is not truly spherical. The value of g therefore varies with the position of the point considered. As long as the point actually remains on the surface of the earth, it is sufficiently accurate in most engineering computations to assume that g equals 32.2 ft/sec^2.

As noted earlier, the six fundamental principles listed above are based on experimental evidence; they cannot be derived mathematically. On these principles rests most of the intricate structure of newtonian mechanics. For more than two centuries a tremendous number of problems dealing with the conditions of rest and motion of rigid bodies, deformable bodies, and fluids have been solved by applying these fundamental principles. Many of the solutions obtained could be checked experimentally, thus providing a further verification of the principles from which they were derived. It is only recently that Newton's mechanics was found at fault, in the study of the motion of atoms and in the study of the motion of certain planets, where it must be supplemented by the theory of rela-

† A more accurate definition of the weight **W** should take into account the rotation of the earth.

tivity. But on the human or engineering scale, where velocities are small compared with the velocity of light, Newton's mechanics has yet to be disproved.

1.3. Units. With the four basic concepts introduced in the preceding section are associated the units of *length, time, mass,* and *force.* These four units are not independent. As we shall see in greater detail in Sec. 12.2, three of these units may be defined arbitrarily, but the fourth one must be chosen in accordance with formula (1.1).

The fundamental units chosen by engineers everywhere are the units of length, time, and force. The standard unit of length used by American engineers is the *foot* (ft), subdivided into 12 *inches* (in.); a multiple of the foot is the *mile,* equal to 5,280 ft. The standard unit of time is the *second* (sec); a multiple of the second is the *hour* (hr), equal to 3,600 sec. The standard unit of force is the *pound* (lb), defined as the force (weight) with which a certain mass of platinum is attracted by the earth at the latitude of 45° and at sea level. Multiples of the pound frequently used are the *kilopound* (kip, or k), equal to 1,000 lb, and the *ton,* equal to 2,000 lb.

All quantities other than length, time, and force should be expressed in units obtained from the fundamental units ft, sec, and lb. For example, an area, obtained by multiplying a length (ft) by a length (ft), should be expressed in ft^2. A pressure, obtained by dividing a force (lb) by an area (ft^2), should be expressed in lb/ft^2. The magnitude of a velocity, obtained by dividing a length (ft) by a time (sec), should be expressed in ft/sec. An acceleration, obtained by dividing a velocity (ft/sec) by a time (sec), should be expressed in ft/sec^2. Since, according to formula (1.1), a mass may be obtained by dividing the magnitude of a force (lb) by that of an acceleration (ft/sec^2), a mass should be expressed in $lb\text{-}sec^2/ft$.

A useful check of our computations may be obtained if we carry out the computations with the units as well as the numerical values. For example, the magnitude of the moment of a 10-lb force about a point 2 ft from its line of action may be determined as follows (Sec. 3.5):

$$M = Fd = (10 \text{ lb})(2 \text{ ft}) = 20 \text{ lb-ft}$$

The unit lb-ft obtained by multiplying lb by ft is the correct unit for the moment of a force; if another unit had been obtained, we would have known that some mistake had been made.

Sometimes a quantity is expressed in units other than the

standard units. For example, the magnitude of a velocity may be given as $v = 30$ mph (miles per hour). To express this magnitude in ft/sec, we shall proceed as follows:

First we write $$v = 30\,\frac{\text{miles}}{\text{hr}}$$

Since we want to get rid of the unit miles and introduce instead the unit feet, we should multiply the right-hand member of the equation by an expression containing miles in the denominator and feet in the numerator. But, since we do not want to change the value of the right-hand member, the expression used should have a value equal to unity. The quotient 5,280 ft/1 mile is such an expression. Operating in a similar way to transform the unit hour into seconds, we write

$$v = \left(30\,\frac{\text{miles}}{\text{hr}}\right)\left(\frac{5{,}280\text{ ft}}{1\text{ mile}}\right)\left(\frac{1\text{ hr}}{3{,}600\text{ sec}}\right)$$

Carrying out the numerical computations and canceling out units which appear both in the numerator and the denominator, we obtain

$$v = 44\,\frac{\text{ft}}{\text{sec}} = 44\text{ ft/sec}$$

1.4. Method of Problem Solution. The student should approach a problem in mechanics as he would approach an actual engineering situation. By drawing on his own experience and on his intuition, he will find it easier to understand and formulate the problem. Once the problem has been clearly stated, however, there is no place in its solution for the student's particular fancy. *The solution must be based on the six fundamental principles stated above or on theorems derived from them.* Every step taken must be justified on that basis. Strict rules must be followed, which lead to the solution in an almost automatic fashion, leaving no room for the student's intuition or "feeling." After an answer has been obtained, it should be checked. Here again, the student may call upon his common sense and personal experience. If not completely satisfied with the result obtained, he should carefully check his formulation of the problem, the validity of the methods used for its solution, and the accuracy of his computations.

The *statement* of a problem should be clear and precise. It should contain the given data and indicate what information is required. A neat drawing showing all quantities involved should be included. Separate diagrams should be drawn for all bodies involved, indicating clearly the forces acting on each body. These diagrams are known as *free-body diagrams* and are described in detail in Secs. 2.10 and 4.2.

The *fundamental principles* of mechanics listed in Sec. 1.2 *will be used to write equations* expressing the conditions of rest or motion of the bodies considered. Each equation should be clearly related to one of the free-body diagrams. The student will then proceed to solve the problem, observing strictly the usual rules of algebra and recording neatly the various steps taken.

After the answer has been obtained, it should be *carefully checked.* Mistakes in reasoning may often be detected by checking the units, as indicated in Sec. 1.3. Errors in computation will usually be found by substituting the numerical values obtained into an equation which has not yet been used and verifying that the equation is satisfied. The importance of correct computations in engineering cannot be overemphasized.

1.5. Numerical Accuracy. The accuracy of the solution of a problem depends upon two items: (1) the accuracy of the given data; (2) the accuracy of the computations performed.

The solution cannot be more accurate than the less accurate of these two items. For example, if the loading of a bridge is known to be 75,000 lb with a possible error of 100 lb either way, the relative error which measures the degree of accuracy of the data is

$$\frac{100\text{ lb}}{75{,}000\text{ lb}} = 0.0013 = 0.13\text{ per cent}$$

It would then be meaningless, in computing the reaction at one of the bridge supports, to record it as 14,322 lb. The accuracy of the solution cannot be greater than 0.13 per cent, no matter how accurate the computations are, and the possible error in the answer may be as large as $(0.13/100)(14{,}322\text{ lb}) \approx 20$ lb. The solution should be properly recorded as $14{,}320 \pm 20$ lb.

In engineering problems, the data are seldom known with an accuracy greater than 0.2 per cent. It is therefore unnecessary to carry out computations with a greater accuracy. In almost all cases, the slide rule will provide the desired accuracy. On looking at the main scales of a 10-in. slide rule, it will be observed that the number 502 may be easily interpolated between the graduations corresponding, respectively, to 500 and 505. It might possibly be mistaken for 501 or 503, but no larger error in reading or in adjusting the rule will be made if a minimum of care is observed. The error involved is thus at most 1 unit out of 500; the relative error is 0.2 per cent. For other positions on the rule, the absolute error will be different (for example, 2 units out of 1,000); owing to the logarithmic nature of the scales, however, the relative error will remain 0.2 per cent.

It is sometimes said that the accuracy obtained on the slide rule is *three significant figures.* This is correct as far as the central portion of the scale is concerned, where numbers such as 298, 299, 300, 301 may be easily read. The third significant figure, however, becomes doubtful toward the right end of the scale, where it is difficult to tell 997 from 998. On the other hand, one should be able, toward the left end of the scale, to estimate the fourth significant figure within a couple of units. The relative error between 996 and 998 is the same as between 1,002 and 1,004 (0.2 per cent in both cases). We should therefore define the accuracy of a computation by the possible relative error involved, rather than by the number of significant figures obtained, and we shall attempt to obtain all answers with an accuracy of about 0.2 per cent. A practical rule consists in using four figures to record readings taken on a 10-in. slide rule between 1 and 2 and three figures to record readings between 2 and 10. Unless otherwise indicated, the data given in a problem should be assumed known with a comparable degree of accuracy. A force of 40 lb, for example, should actually be read 40.0 lb, and a force of 15 lb should be read 15.00 lb.

2. STATICS OF PARTICLES

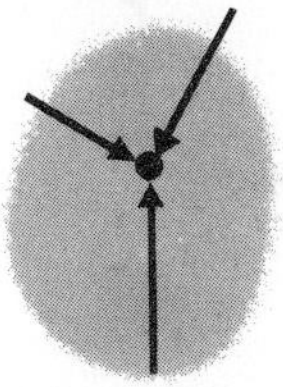

FORCES IN A PLANE

2.1. Force on a Particle. Resultant of Two Forces. A force represents the action of one body on another. It is characterized by its *point of application*, its *magnitude*, and its *direction*. In this chapter we shall study the effect of forces on particles. The use of the word "particles" does not imply that we shall restrict our study to that of small corpuscles. It means that the size and shape of the bodies under consideration will not affect the solution of the problems treated in this chapter and that all the forces acting on a given body will be assumed to have the same point of application. Each force will thus be completely defined by its magnitude and direction.

The magnitude of a force is characterized by a certain number of units; as was indicated in Sec. 1.3, the standard units used by American engineers to measure the magnitude of a force are the pound (lb) and its multiples, the kilopound (kip, or k), equal to 1,000 lb, and the ton, equal to 2,000 lb. The direction of a force is defined by the *line of action* and the *sense* of the force. The line of action is the infinite straight line along which the force acts; it is characterized by the angle it forms with some fixed axis (Fig. 2.1). The force itself is represented by a segment of that line; through the use of an appropriate scale, the length of this segment may be chosen to represent the magnitude of the force. Finally, the sense of the force should be indicated by an arrowhead. It is important, in defining a force, to indicate its sense. Two forces, such as those shown in Figs. 2.1*a* and 2.1*b*, having the same magnitude and the same line of action but different sense, will have directly opposite effects on a particle.

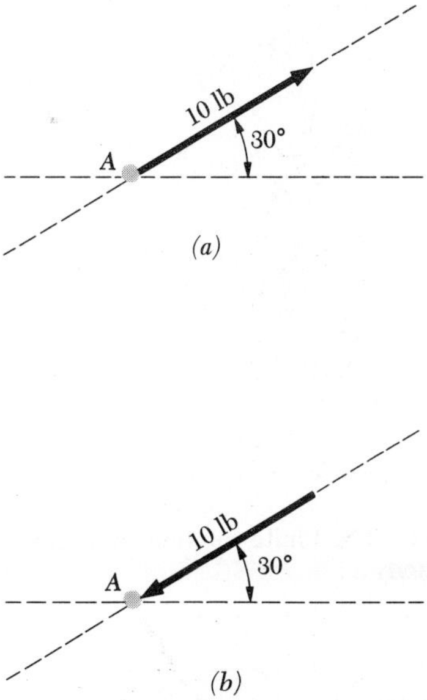

FIG. 2.1

Experimental evidence shows that two forces **P** and **Q** acting on a particle *A* (Fig. 2.2*a*) may be replaced by a single force **R** which has the same effect on the particle (Fig. 2.2*c*). This

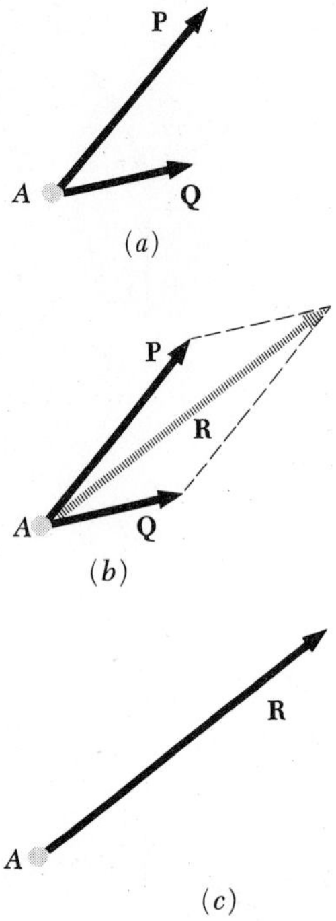

FIG. 2.2

force is called the *resultant* of the forces **P** and **Q** and may be obtained, as shown in Fig. 2.2*b*, by constructing a parallelogram, using **P** and **Q** as two sides of the parallelogram. *The diagonal that passes through A represents the resultant.* This is known as the *parallelogram law* for the addition of two forces. This law is based on experimental evidence; it cannot be proved or derived mathematically.

2.2. Vectors. It appears from the above that forces do not obey the rules of addition defined in ordinary arithmetic or algebra. For example, two forces acting at a right angle to each other, one of 4 lb and the other of 3 lb, add up to a force of 5 lb, *not* to a force of 7 lb. Forces are not the only expressions which follow the parallelogram law of addition. As we shall see later, *displacements, velocities, accelerations, momenta* are other examples of physical quantities possessing magnitude and direction and which are added according to the parallelogram law. All these quantities may be represented mathematically by *vectors,* while those physical quantities which do not have direction, such as *volume, mass,* or *energy,* are represented by ordinary numbers or *scalars.*

Vectors are defined as *mathematical expressions possessing magnitude and direction, which add according to the parallelogram law.*† Vectors are represented by arrows in the illustrations and will be distinguished from scalar quantities in this text through the use of boldface type (**P**). In longhand writing, a vector may be characterized by drawing a short arrow above the letter used to represent it ($\overrightarrow{P}$), or by underlining the letter ($\underline{P}$). The last method is gaining wider acceptance since it can also be used on a typewriter. The magnitude of a vector defines the length of the arrow used to represent the vector.

† Some expressions have magnitude and direction, but do not add according to the parallelogram law. While these expressions may be represented by arrows, they *cannot* be considered as vectors.

A group of such expressions are the finite rotations of a rigid body. Place a closed book on a table in front of you, so that it lies in the usual fashion, with its front cover up and its binding to the left. Now rotate it through 180° about an axis parallel to the binding (Fig. 2.3*a*); this rotation may be represented by an arrow of length equal to 180 units and oriented as shown. Picking up the book as it lies in its new position, rotate it now through 180° about a horizontal

FIG. 2.3. Finite rotations of a rigid body

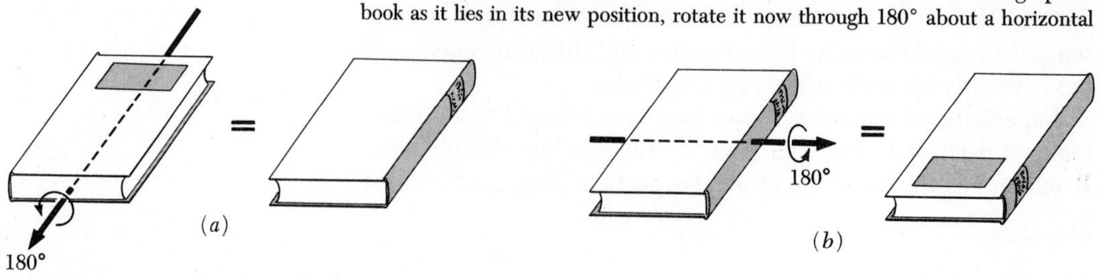

In this text, italic type will be used to denote the magnitude of a vector. Thus, the magnitude of the vector **P** will be referred to as *P*.

A vector used to represent a force acting on a given particle has a well-defined point of application, namely, the particle itself. Such a vector is said to be a *fixed,* or *bound,* vector and cannot be moved without modifying the conditions of the problem. Other physical quantities, however, such as couples (see Chap. 3), are represented by vectors which may be freely moved in space; these vectors are called *free* vectors. Still other physical quantities, such as forces acting on a rigid body (see Chap. 3), are represented by vectors which may be moved, or slid, along their line of action; they are known as *sliding* vectors.

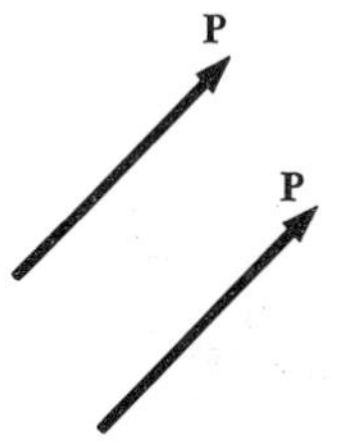

FIG. 2.4

Two vectors which have the same magnitude and the same direction are said to be *equal,* whether or not they also have the same point of application (Fig. 2.4); equal vectors may be denoted by the same letter.

The *negative vector* of a given vector **P** is defined as a vector having the same magnitude as **P** and a direction opposite to that of **P** (Fig. 2.5); the negative of the vector **P** is denoted by $-\mathbf{P}$. The vectors **P** and $-\mathbf{P}$ are commonly referred to as *equal and opposite* vectors. Clearly, we have

$$\mathbf{P} + (-\mathbf{P}) = 0$$

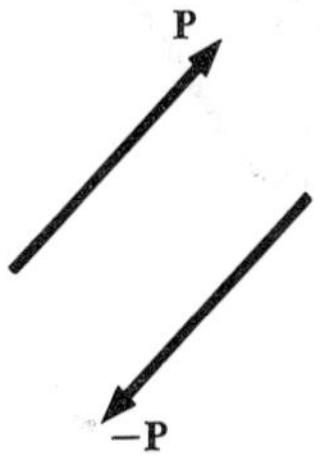

FIG. 2.5

2.3. Addition of Vectors. We saw in the preceding section that, by definition, vectors add according to the parallelogram law. Thus the sum of two vectors **P** and **Q** is obtained by attaching the two vectors to the same point *A* and constructing a parallelogram, using **P** and **Q** as two sides of the parallelo-

---

axis perpendicular to the binding (Fig. 2.3*b*); this second rotation may be represented by an arrow 180 units long and oriented as shown. But the book could have been placed in this final position through a single 180-degree rotation about a vertical axis (Fig. 2.3*c*). We conclude that the sum of the two 180-degree rotations represented by arrows directed respectively along the *z* and *x* axes is a 180-degree rotation represented by an arrow directed along the *y* axis (Fig. 2.3*d*). Clearly, the finite rotations of a rigid body *do not* obey the parallelogram law of addition; therefore they *cannot* be represented by vectors.

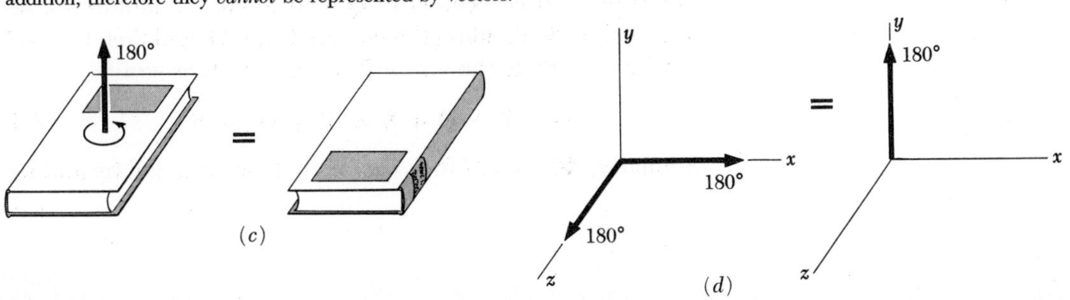

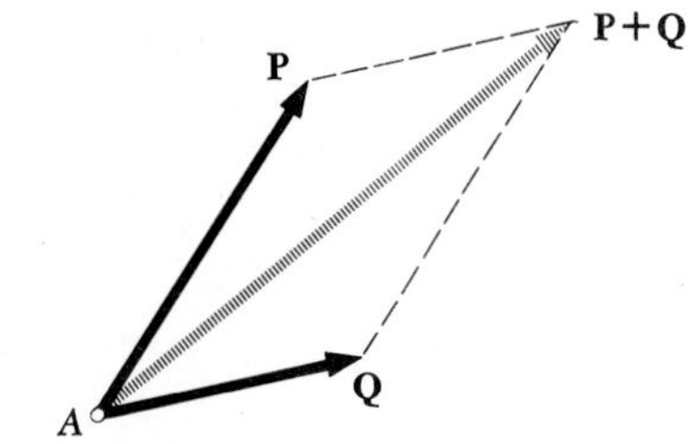

FIG. 2.6

gram (Fig. 2.6). The diagonal that passes through A represents the sum of the vectors **P** and **Q**, and this sum is denoted by **P** + **Q**. The fact that the sign + is used to denote both vector and scalar addition should not cause any confusion if vector and scalar quantities are always carefully distinguished. Thus, we should note that the magnitude of the vector **P** + **Q** is *not,* in general, equal to the sum $P + Q$ of the magnitudes of the vectors **P** and **Q**.

Since the parallelogram constructed on the vectors **P** and **Q** does not depend upon the order in which **P** and **Q** are selected, we conclude that the addition of two vectors is *commutative,* and we write

$$\mathbf{P} + \mathbf{Q} = \mathbf{Q} + \mathbf{P} \tag{2.1}$$

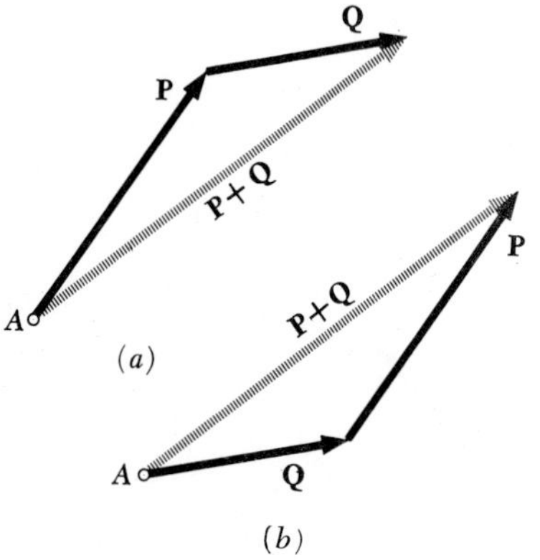

FIG. 2.7

From the parallelogram law, we can derive an alternate method for determining the sum of two vectors. This method, known as the *triangle rule,* is derived as follows: Consider Fig. 2.6, where the sum of the vectors **P** and **Q** has been determined by the parallelogram law. Since the side of the parallelogram opposite **Q** is equal to **Q** in magnitude and direction, we could draw only half of the parallelogram (Fig. 2.7*a*). The sum of the two vectors may thus be found by *arranging* **P** *and* **Q** *in tip-to-tail fashion and then connecting the tail of* **P** *with the tip of* **Q**. In Fig. 2.7*b*, the other half of the parallelogram is considered, and the same result is obtained. This confirms the fact that vector addition is commutative.

The *subtraction* of a vector is defined as the addition of the corresponding negative vector. Thus, the vector **P** − **Q** representing the difference between the vectors **P** and **Q** is obtained by adding to **P** the negative vector −**Q** (Fig. 2.8). We write

$$\mathbf{P} - \mathbf{Q} = \mathbf{P} + (-\mathbf{Q}) \tag{2.2}$$

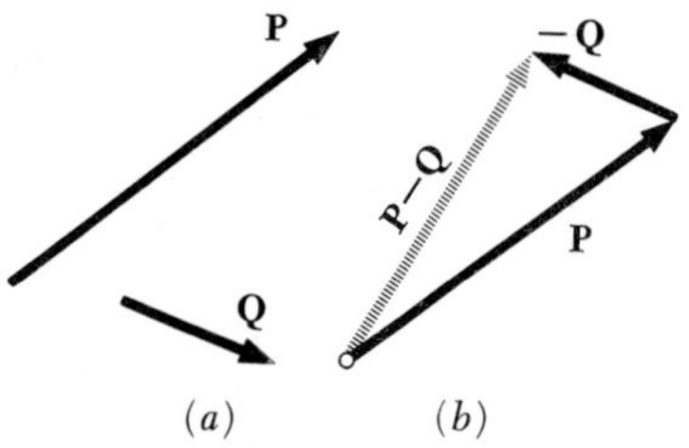

FIG. 2.8

Here again we should observe that, while the same sign is used to denote both vector and scalar subtraction, confusion will be avoided if care is taken to distinguish between vector and scalar quantities.

We shall now consider the *sum of three or more vectors.* The sum of three vectors **P**, **Q**, and **S** will, *by definition,* be obtained by first adding the vectors **P** and **Q**, and then by adding the vector **S** to the vector **P** + **Q**. We thus write

$$\mathbf{P} + \mathbf{Q} + \mathbf{S} = (\mathbf{P} + \mathbf{Q}) + \mathbf{S} \tag{2.3}$$

Similarly, the sum of four vectors will be obtained by adding the fourth vector to the sum of the first three. It follows that the sum of any number of vectors may be obtained by applying repeatedly the parallelogram law to successive pairs of vectors until all the given vectors are replaced by a single vector.

If the given vectors are *coplanar,* i.e., if they are contained in the same plane, their sum may be easily obtained graphically. In that case, the repeated application of the triangle rule will be preferred to the application of the parallelogram law. In Fig. 2.9 the sum of three vectors **P**, **Q**, and **S** was obtained in that manner. The triangle rule was first applied to obtain the sum **P** + **Q** of the vectors **P** and **Q**; it was applied again to obtain the sum of the vectors **P** + **Q** and **S**. The determination of the vector **P** + **Q**, however, could have been omitted and the sum of the three vectors could have been obtained directly, as shown in Fig. 2.10, by *arranging the given vectors in tip-to-tail fashion and connecting the tail of the first vector with the tip of the last one.* This is known as the *polygon rule* for the addition of vectors.

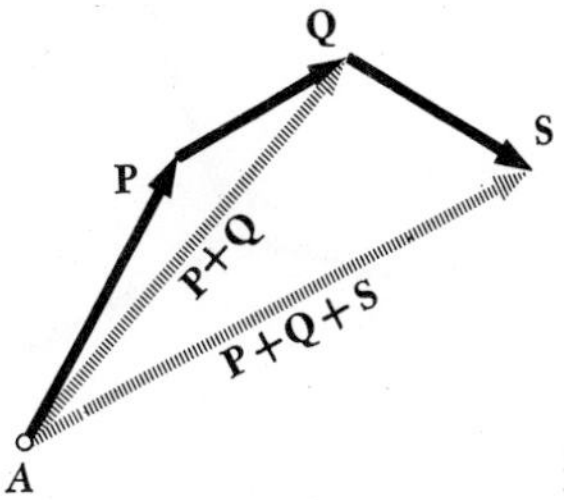

FIG. 2.9

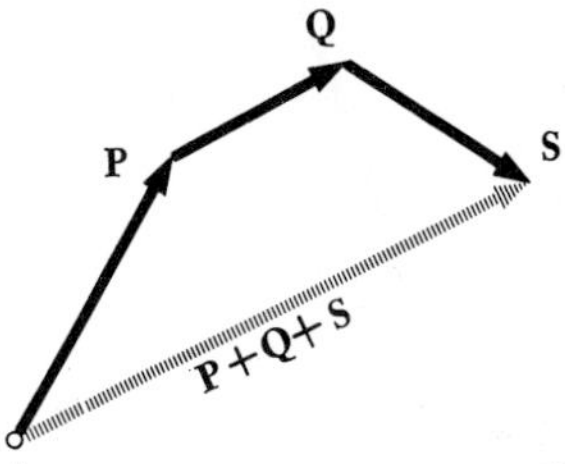

FIG. 2.10

We observe that the result obtained would have been unchanged if, as shown in Fig. 2.11, the vectors **Q** and **S** had been replaced by their sum **Q** + **S**. We may thus write

$$\mathbf{P} + \mathbf{Q} + \mathbf{S} = (\mathbf{P} + \mathbf{Q}) + \mathbf{S} = \mathbf{P} + (\mathbf{Q} + \mathbf{S}) \qquad (2.4)$$

which expresses the fact that vector addition is *associative.* Recalling that vector addition has also been shown, in the case of two vectors, to be commutative, we write

$$\begin{aligned} \mathbf{P} + \mathbf{Q} + \mathbf{S} &= (\mathbf{P} + \mathbf{Q}) + \mathbf{S} = \mathbf{S} + (\mathbf{P} + \mathbf{Q}) \\ &= \mathbf{S} + (\mathbf{Q} + \mathbf{P}) = \mathbf{S} + \mathbf{Q} + \mathbf{P} \qquad (2.5) \end{aligned}$$

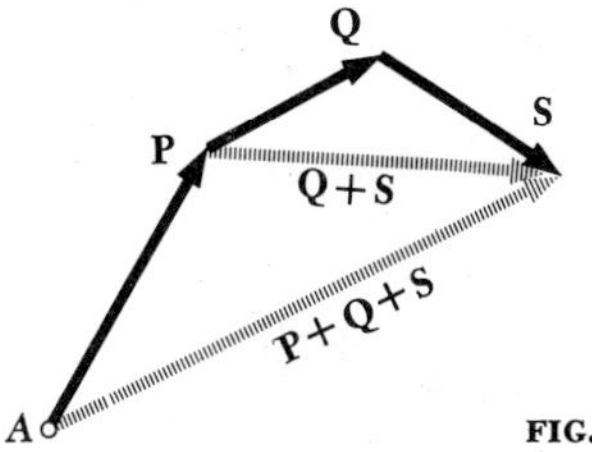

FIG. 2.11

This expression, as well as others which may be obtained in the same way, shows that the order in which several vectors are added together is immaterial (Fig. 2.12).

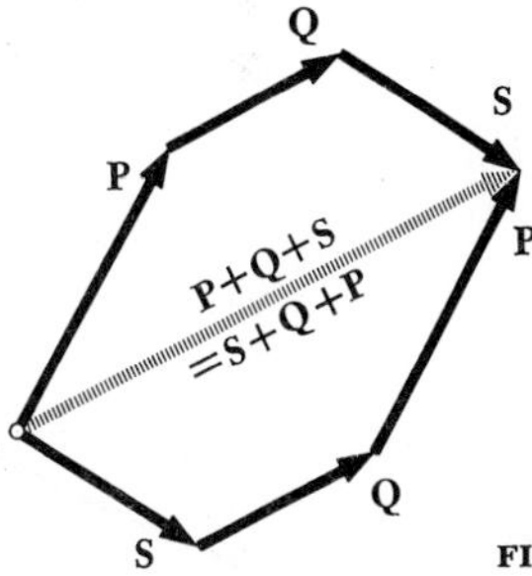

FIG. 2.12

Product of a Scalar and a Vector. Since it is convenient to denote the sum **P** + **P** by 2**P**, the sum **P** + **P** + **P** by 3**P**, and, in general, to represent the sum of n equal vectors **P** by the product n**P**, we shall define the product n**P** of a positive integer n and a vector **P** as a vector having the same direction as **P** and the magnitude nP. Extending this definition to include all scalars, and recalling the definition of a negative vector given in Sec. 2.2, we define the product k**P** of a scalar k and a vector **P** as a vector having the same direction as **P** (if k is positive), or a direction opposite to that of **P** (if k is negative), and a magnitude equal to the product of P and of the absolute value of k (Fig. 2.13).

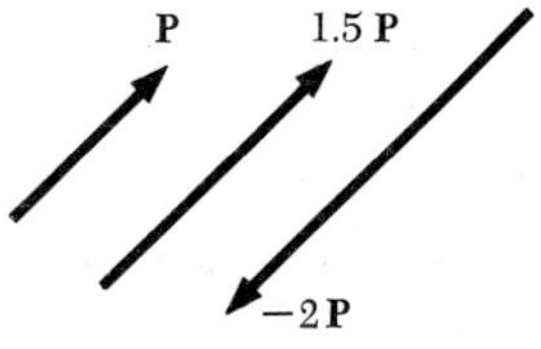

FIG. 2.13

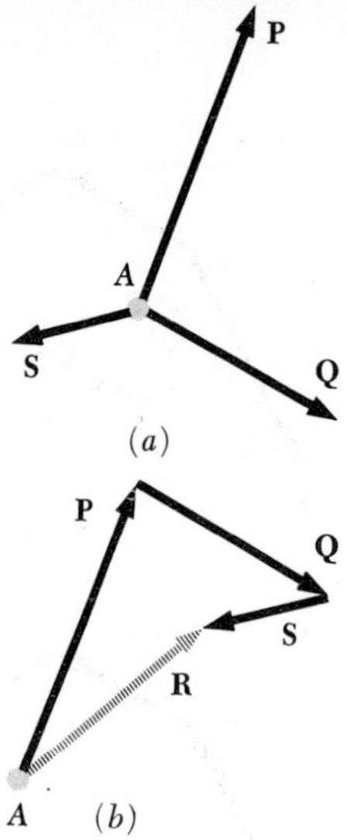

FIG. 2.14

2.4. Resultant of Several Concurrent Forces. Consider a particle A acted upon by several coplanar forces, i.e., by several forces contained in the same plane (Fig. 2.14*a*). Since the forces considered here all pass through A, they are also said to be *concurrent*. The vectors representing the forces acting on A may be added by the polygon rule (Fig. 2.14*b*). Since the use of the polygon rule is equivalent to the repeated application of the parallelogram law, the vector **R** thus obtained represents the resultant of the given concurrent forces, i.e., the single force which has the same effect on the particle A as the given forces. As indicated above, the order in which the vectors **P**, **Q**, and **S** representing the given forces are added together is immaterial.

2.5 Resolution of a Force into Components. We have seen that two or more forces acting on a particle may be replaced by a single force which has the same effect on the particle. Conversely, a single force **F** acting on a particle may be replaced by two or more forces which, together, have the same effect on the particle. These forces are called the *components* of the original force **F**, and the process of substituting them for **F** is called *resolving the force* **F** *into components.*

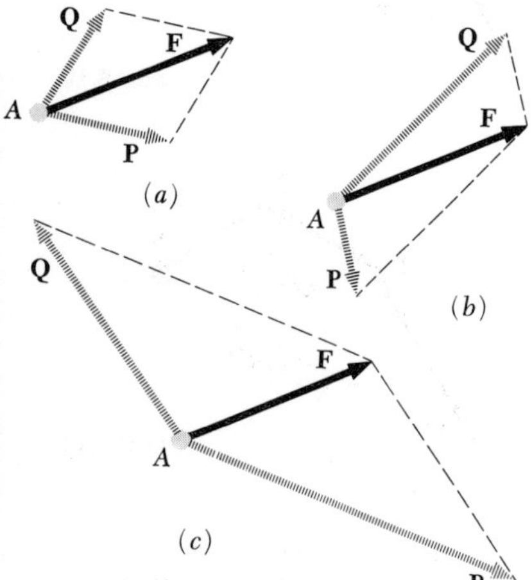

FIG. 2.15

Clearly, for each force **F** there exist an infinite number of possible sets of components. Sets of *two components* **P** *and* **Q** are the most important as far as practical applications are concerned. But, even then, the number of ways in which a given force **F** may be resolved into two components is unlimited (Fig. 2.15). Two cases are of particular interest:

1. *One of the Two Components,* **P**, *Is Known.* The second component, **Q**, is obtained by applying the triangle rule and joining the tip of **P** to the tip of **F** (Fig. 2.16); the magnitude and direction of **Q** are determined graphically or by trigonometry. Once **Q** has been determined, both components **P** and **Q** should be applied at A.

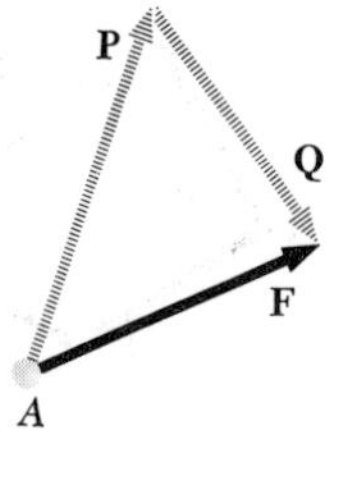

FIG. 2.16

2. *The Line of Action of Each Component Is Known.* The magnitude and sense of the components are obtained by applying the parallelogram law and drawing lines, through the tip of **F**, parallel to the given lines of action (Fig. 2.17). This process leads to two well-defined components, **P** and **Q**, which may be determined graphically or by applying the law of sines.

Many other cases may be encountered; for example, the direction of one component may be known while the magnitude of the other component is to be as small as possible (see Sample Prob. 2.2). In all cases the appropriate triangle or parallelogram is drawn, which satisfies the given conditions.

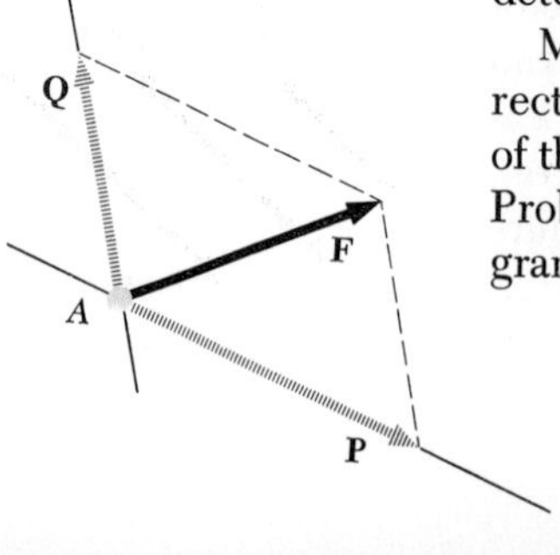

FIG. 2.17

SAMPLE PROBLEM 2.1

The two forces **P** and **Q** act on a bolt A. Determine their resultant.

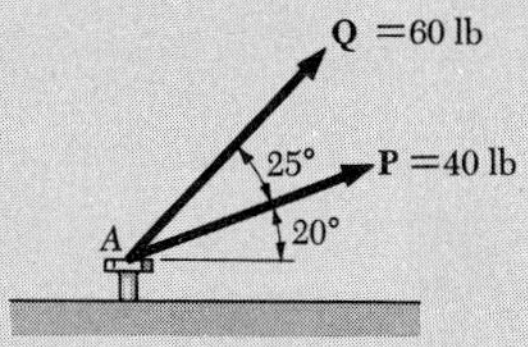

Graphical Solution. A parallelogram with sides equal to **P** and **Q** is drawn to scale. The magnitude and direction of the resultant are measured and found to be

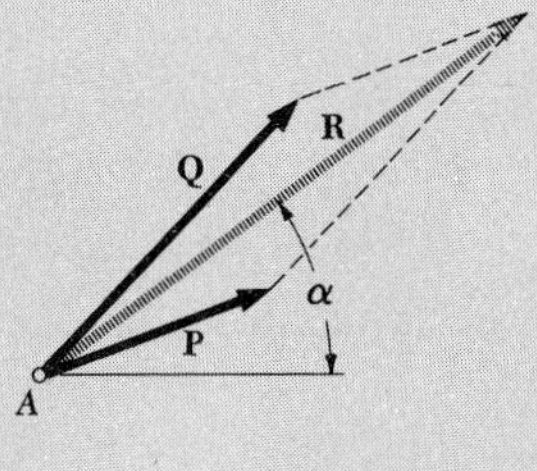

$$R = 98 \text{ lb} \qquad \alpha = 35° \qquad \mathbf{R} = 98 \text{ lb} \measuredangle 35°$$ ◄

The triangle rule may also be used. Forces **P** and **Q** are drawn in tip-to-tail fashion. Again the magnitude and direction of the resultant are measured.

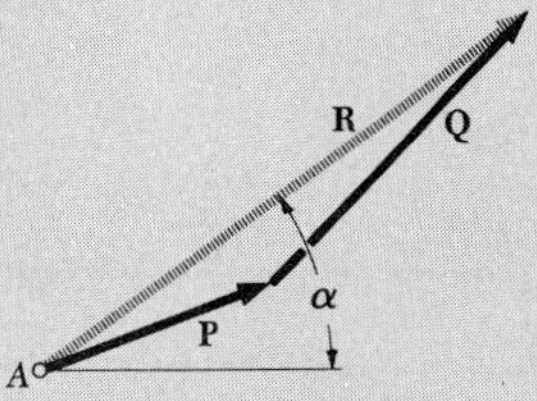

$$R = 98 \text{ lb} \qquad \alpha = 35° \qquad \mathbf{R} = 98 \text{ lb} \measuredangle 35°$$ ◄

Trigonometric Solution. The triangle rule is again used; two sides and the included angle are known. We apply the law of cosines.

$$R^2 = P^2 + Q^2 - 2PQ \cos B$$
$$R^2 = (40 \text{ lb})^2 + (60 \text{ lb})^2 - 2(40 \text{ lb})(60 \text{ lb}) \cos 155°$$
$$R = 97.7 \text{ lb}$$

Now, applying the law of sines, we write

$$\frac{\sin A}{Q} = \frac{\sin B}{R} \qquad \frac{\sin A}{60 \text{ lb}} = \frac{\sin 155°}{97.7 \text{ lb}}$$

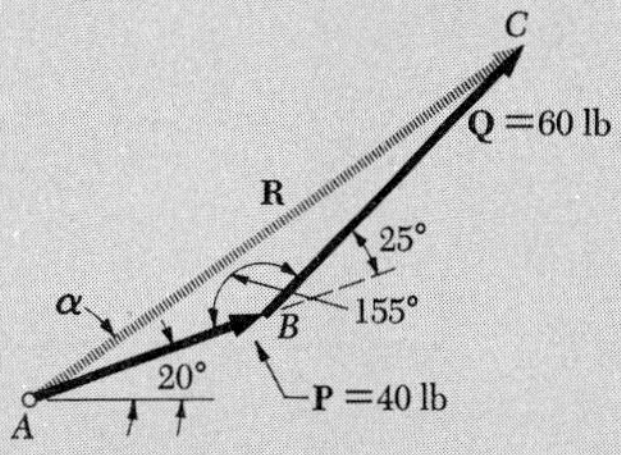

Noting that sin 155° = sin 25°, and setting the slide rule as shown, we read

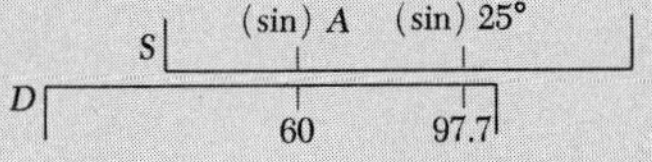

$$A = 15.0° \qquad \alpha = 20° + A = 35.0°$$
$$\mathbf{R} = 97.7 \text{ lb} \measuredangle 35°$$ ◄

Alternate Trigonometric Solution. We construct the right triangle BCD and compute

$$CD = (60 \text{ lb}) \sin 25° = 25.4 \text{ lb}$$
$$BD = (60 \text{ lb}) \cos 25° = 54.4 \text{ lb}$$

Then, using triangle ACD, we obtain

$$\tan A = \frac{25.4 \text{ lb}}{94.4 \text{ lb}} \qquad A = 15.0°$$
$$R \sin A = 25.4 \qquad R = 97.7 \text{ lb}$$

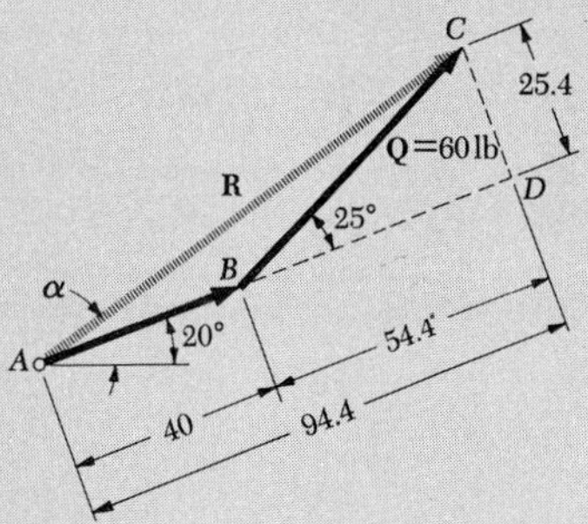

Again,

$$\alpha = 20° + A = 35.0° \qquad \mathbf{R} = 97.7 \text{ lb} \measuredangle 35°$$ ◄

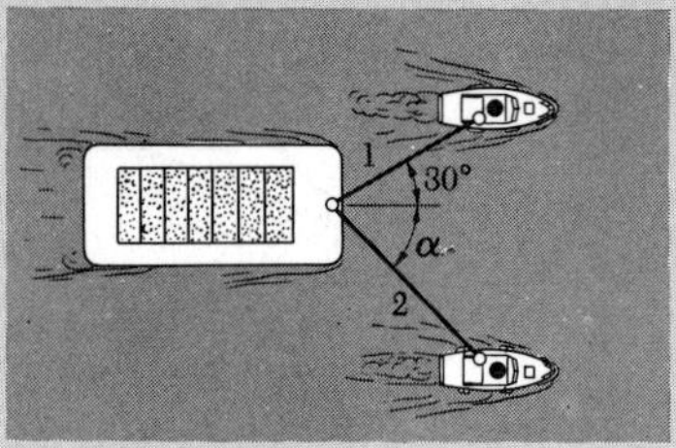

SAMPLE PROBLEM 2.2

A barge is pulled by two tugboats. If the resultant of the forces exerted by the tugboats is a 5,000-lb force directed along the axis of the barge, find (*a*) the tension in each of the ropes, knowing that $\alpha = 45°$, (*b*) the value of α such that the tension in rope 2 is minimum.

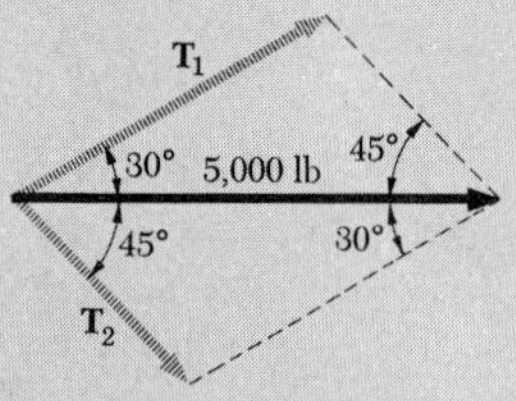

a. **Tension for $\alpha = 45°$.** *Graphical Solution.* The parallelogram law is used; the diagonal (resultant) is known to be equal to 5,000 lb and to be directed to the right. The sides are drawn parallel to the ropes. If the drawing is done to scale, we measure

$$T_1 = 3{,}700 \text{ lb} \qquad T_2 = 2{,}600 \text{ lb} \blacktriangleleft$$

Trigonometric Solution. The triangle rule may be used. We note that the triangle shown represents half of the parallelogram shown above. Using the law of sines, we write

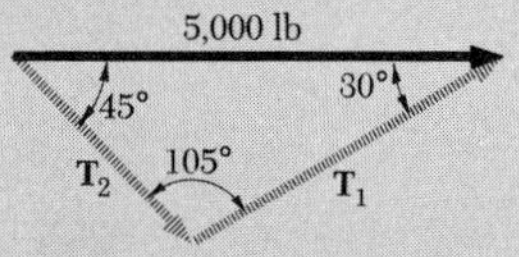

$$\frac{T_1}{\sin 45°} = \frac{T_2}{\sin 30°} = \frac{5{,}000 \text{ lb}}{\sin 105°}$$

or, since $\sin 105° = \sin 75°$,

$$\frac{T_1}{\sin 45°} = \frac{T_2}{\sin 30°} = \frac{5{,}000 \text{ lb}}{\sin 75°}$$

The values of T_1 and T_2 may be obtained in one setting of the slide rule.

$$T_1 = 3{,}660 \text{ lb} \qquad T_2 = 2{,}590 \text{ lb} \blacktriangleleft$$

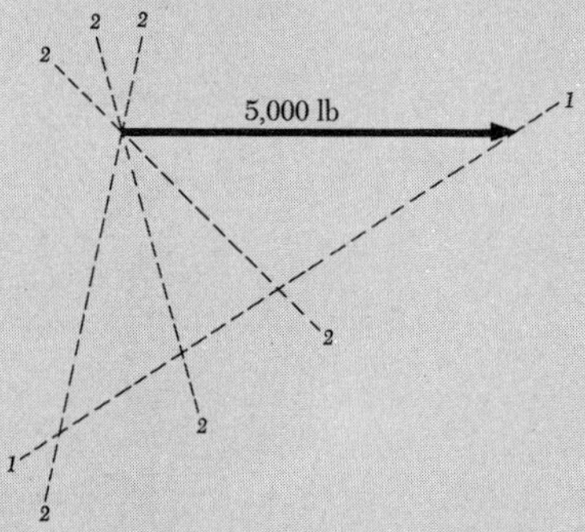

b. **Value of α for Minimum T_2.** To determine the value of α such that the tension in rope 2 is minimum, the triangle rule is again used. In the sketch shown, line *1-1* is the known direction of $\mathbf{T}_1$. Several possible directions of $\mathbf{T}_2$ are shown by the lines *2-2*. We note that the minimum value of T_2 occurs when $\mathbf{T}_1$ and $\mathbf{T}_2$ are perpendicular. The minimum value of T_2 is

$$T_2 = (5{,}000 \text{ lb}) \sin 30° = 2{,}500 \text{ lb}$$

Corresponding values of T_1 and α are

$$T_1 = (5{,}000 \text{ lb}) \cos 30° = 4{,}330 \text{ lb}$$

$$\alpha = 90° - 30° \qquad \qquad \alpha = 60° \blacktriangleleft$$

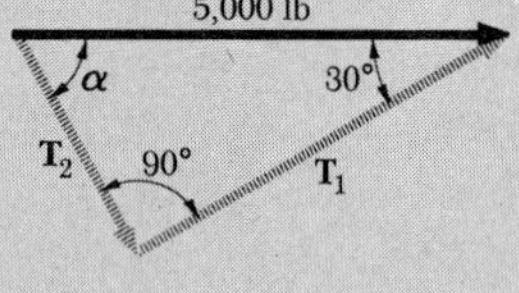

PROBLEMS†

2.1 and 2.2. Determine graphically the magnitude and direction of the resultant of the two forces shown, using in each problem (*a*) the parallelogram law, (*b*) the triangle rule.

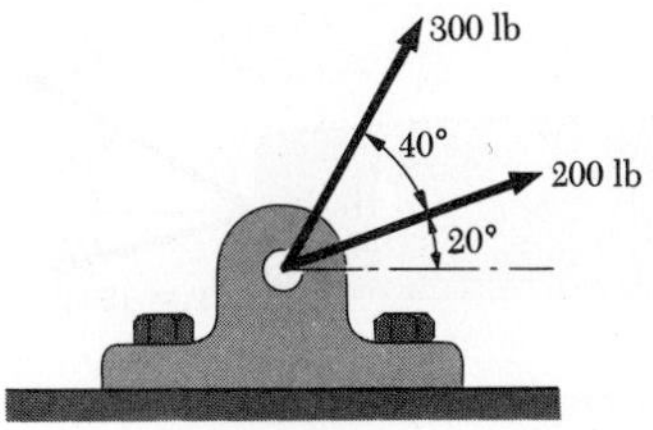

FIG. P 2.1

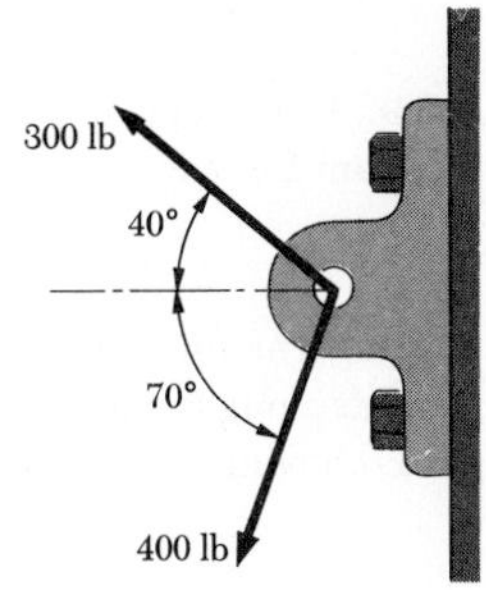

FIG. P 2.2

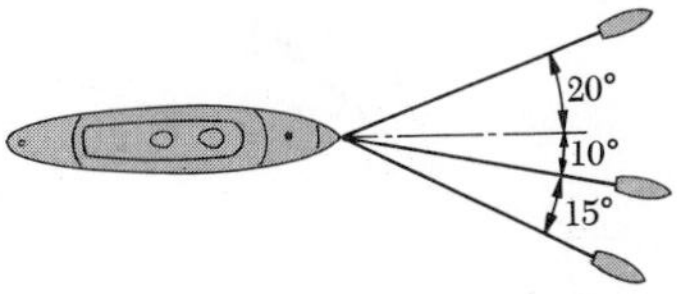

FIG. P 2.3

2.3. A disabled ocean liner is being towed by three tugboats as shown. The tension in each cable is 5,000 lb. (*a*) Determine graphically the resultant force acting on the bow of the liner. (*b*) If the tugboats cannot operate safely when the angle between any two of the cables is less than 10°, where should the tugboats be located in order to produce the largest resultant force parallel to the axis of the liner? What is the magnitude of this resultant?

2.4. Two structural members *B* and *C* are riveted to the bracket *A*. Knowing that the tension in member *B* is 2,500 lb and that the tension in *C* is 2,000 lb, determine graphically the magnitude and direction of the resultant force acting on the bracket.

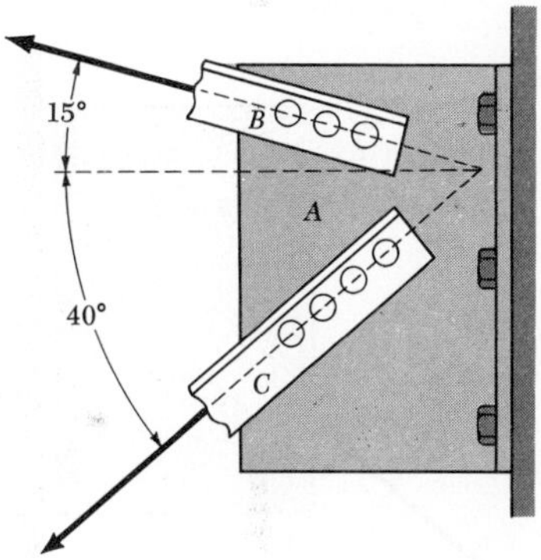

FIG. P 2.4

2.5. Solve Prob. 2.4 by trigonometry.

2.6. In raising the lid of a box, the two forces shown are applied at edge A. Determine by trigonometry the resultant of the two applied forces.

2.7. Determine by trigonometry the magnitude and direction of the force **P** so that the resultant of **P** and the 300-lb force is a vertical force of 900 lb directed downward.

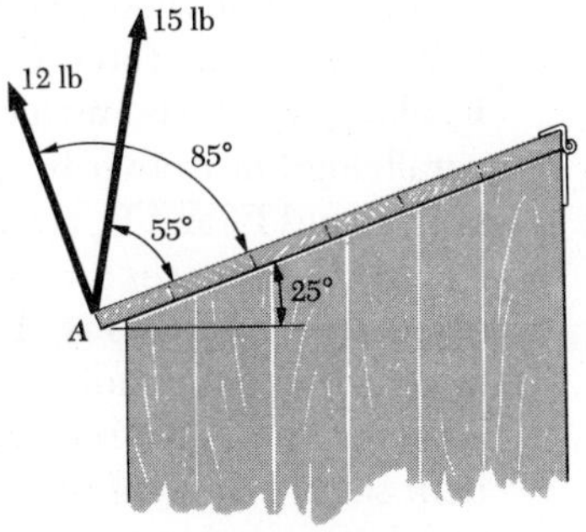

FIG. P 2.6

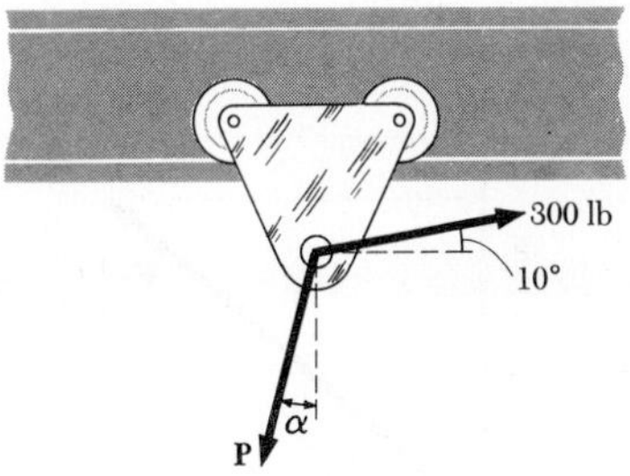

FIG. P 2.7

† Answers to all even-numbered problems are given at the end of the book.

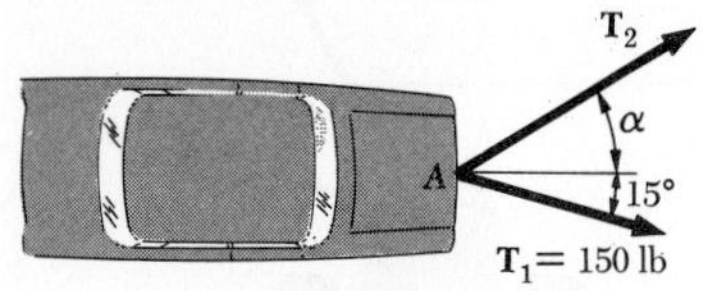

FIG. P 2.8, P 2.9, AND P 2.13

2.8. A disabled automobile is being pulled by means of two ropes. Knowing that the tension in rope *1* is 150 lb, determine the magnitude and direction of the tension in rope 2 so that the resultant is a 200-lb force parallel to the axis of the automobile. Check the answer graphically.

2.9. If the angle α is equal to 30°, determine the tension T_2 so that the resultant force exerted at *A* is parallel to the axis of the automobile.

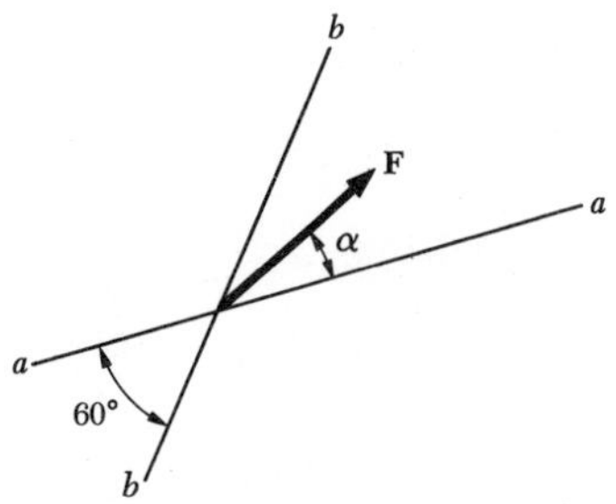

FIG. P 2.10 AND P 2.11

2.10. The force **F** of magnitude 800 lb is to be resolved into two components along the lines *a-a* and *b-b*. Determine by trigonometry the angle α, knowing that the component of **F** along the line *a-a* is to be 500 lb.

2.11. The force **F** of magnitude 800 lb is to be resolved into two components along the lines *a-a* and *b-b*. Determine by trigonometry the angle α, knowing that the component of **F** along the line *b-b* is to be 600 lb.

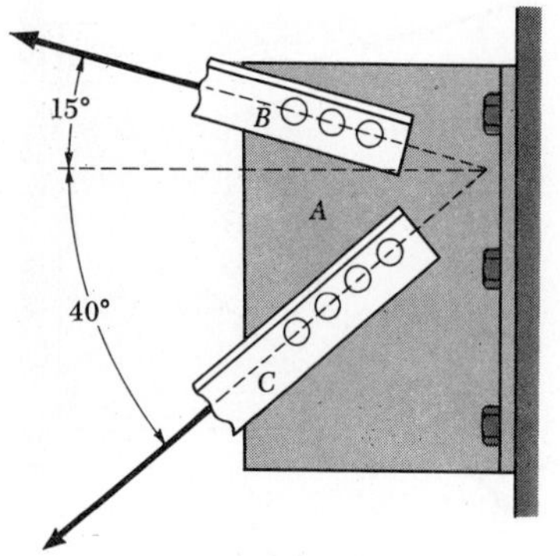

FIG. P 2.12

2.12. The tension in member *B* is 1,500 lb. If the resultant of the forces exerted by members *B* and *C* is to be horizontal, determine the tension in member *C*.

2.13. If the resultant of the two forces $\mathbf{T}_1$ and $\mathbf{T}_2$ is parallel to the axis of the automobile, find the value of α for which the tension T_2 is minimum. What is the corresponding value of T_2?

2.6. Rectangular Components of a Force. Unit Vectors.† In many problems it will be found desirable to resolve a force into two components which are perpendicular to each other. In Fig. 2.18, the force **F** has been resolved into a component $\mathbf{F}_x$ along the x axis and a component $\mathbf{F}_y$ along the y axis. The parallelogram drawn to obtain the two components is a *rectangle*, and $\mathbf{F}_x$ and $\mathbf{F}_y$ are called *rectangular components*.

The x and y axes are usually chosen horizontal and vertical, respectively, as in Fig. 2.18; they may, however, be chosen in any two perpendicular directions, as shown in Fig. 2.19. In determining the rectangular components of a force, the student should think of the construction lines shown in Figs. 2.18 and 2.19 as being *parallel* to the x and y axes, rather than *per-*

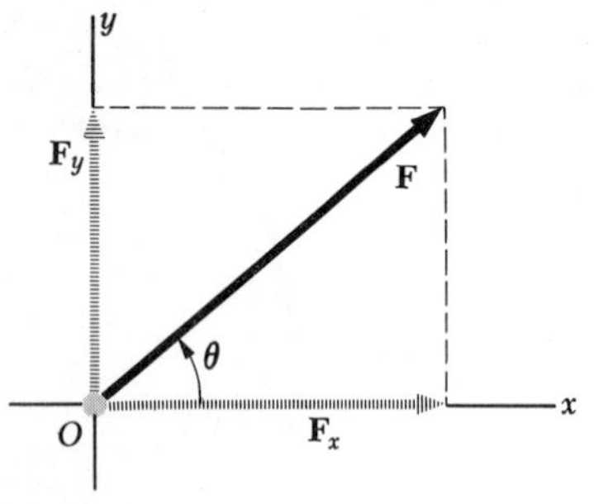

FIG. 2.18

† The properties established in Secs. 2.6 and 2.7 may be readily extended to the rectangular components of any vector quantity.

pendicular to these axes. This practice will help avoid mistakes in determining *oblique* components as in Sec. 2.5.

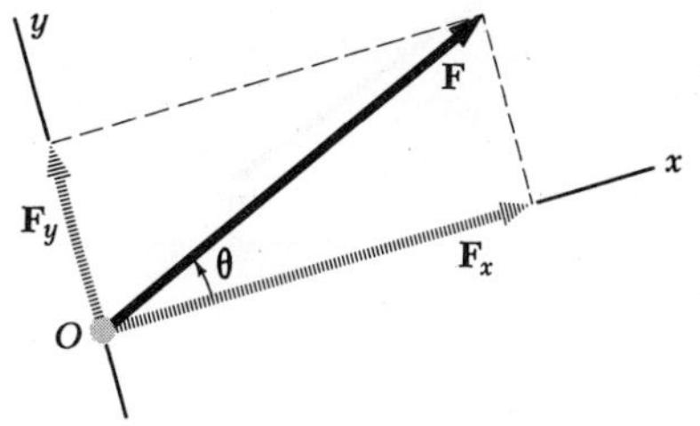

FIG. 2.19

We shall, at this point, introduce two vectors of magnitude 1, directed respectively along the positive x and y axes. These vectors are called *unit vectors* and are denoted by **i** and **j**, respectively (Fig. 2.20). Recalling the definition of the product of a scalar and a vector given in Sec. 2.3, we note that the rectangular components $\mathbf{F}_x$ and $\mathbf{F}_y$ of a force **F** may be obtained by multiplying respectively the unit vectors **i** and **j** by appropriate scalars (Fig. 2.21). We write

$$\mathbf{F}_x = F_x\mathbf{i} \qquad \mathbf{F}_y = F_y\mathbf{j} \tag{2.6}$$

and

$$\mathbf{F} = F_x\mathbf{i} + F_y\mathbf{j} \tag{2.7}$$

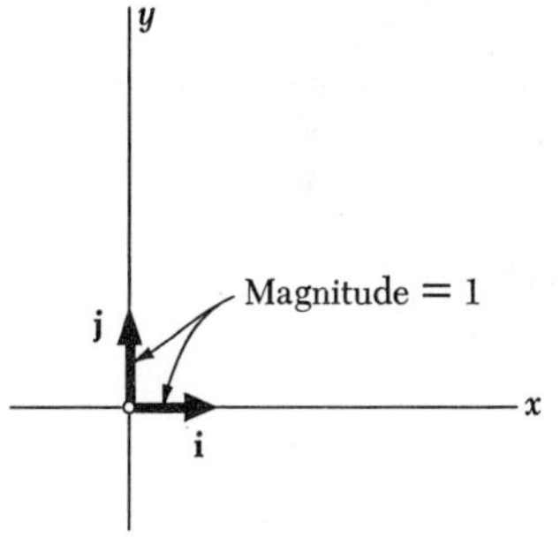

FIG. 2.20

While the scalars F_x and F_y may be positive or negative, depending upon the sense of $\mathbf{F}_x$ and of $\mathbf{F}_y$, their absolute values are respectively equal to the magnitudes of the component forces $\mathbf{F}_x$ and $\mathbf{F}_y$. The scalars F_x and F_y are called the *scalar components* of the force **F**, while the actual component forces $\mathbf{F}_x$ and $\mathbf{F}_y$ should be referred to as the *vector components* of **F**. However, when there exists no possibility of confusion, the vector as well as the scalar components of **F** may be referred to simply as the *components* of **F**. We note that the scalar component F_x is positive when the vector component $\mathbf{F}_x$ has the same sense as the unit vector **i** (i.e., the same sense as the positive x axis) and negative when $\mathbf{F}_x$ has the opposite sense. A similar conclusion may be drawn regarding the sign of the scalar component F_y.

Denoting by F the magnitude of the force **F** and by θ the angle between **F** and the x axis, measured counterclockwise from the positive x axis (Fig. 2.21), we may express the scalar components of **F** as follows:

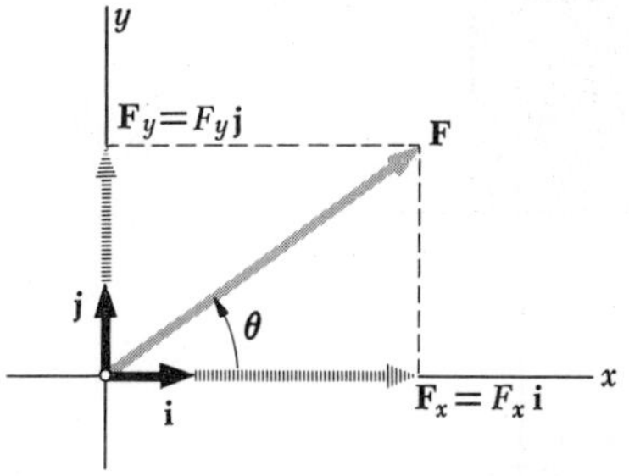

FIG. 2.21

$$F_x = F\cos\theta \qquad F_y = F\sin\theta \tag{2.8}$$

We note that the relations obtained hold for any value of the angle θ from 0° to 360°, and that they define the signs as well as the absolute values of the scalar components F_x and F_y.

Example 1. An 800-lb force is exerted on a bolt A as shown in Fig. 2.22*a*. Determine the horizontal and vertical components of the force.

In order to obtain the correct sign for the scalar components F_x and F_y, the value $\theta = 180° - 35° = 145°$ should be substituted for θ in the relations (2.8). However, it will be found more practical to deter-

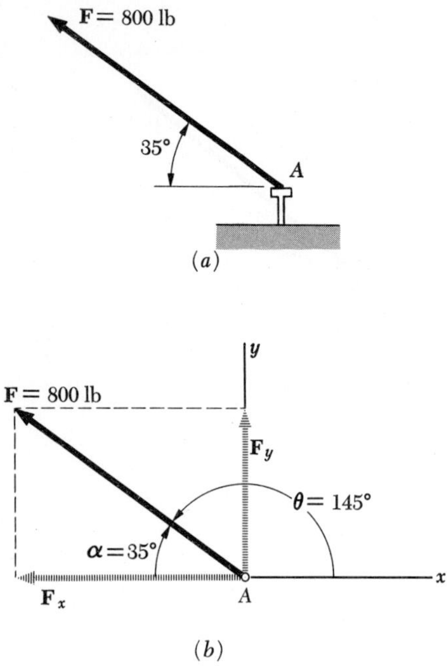

FIG. 2.22

mine by inspection the signs of F_x and of F_y (Fig. 2.22*b*) and to use the trigonometric functions of the angle $\alpha = 35°$, which may be read directly on the slide rule. We write therefore

$$F_x = -F\cos\alpha = -(800 \text{ lb})\cos 35° = -655 \text{ lb}$$
$$F_y = +F\sin\alpha = +(800 \text{ lb})\sin 35° = +459 \text{ lb}$$

The vector components of **F** are thus

$$\mathbf{F}_x = -(655 \text{ lb})\mathbf{i} \qquad \mathbf{F}_y = +(459 \text{ lb})\mathbf{j}$$

and we may write **F** in the form

$$\mathbf{F} = -(655 \text{ lb})\mathbf{i} + (459 \text{ lb})\mathbf{j}$$

Example 2. A man pulls with a force of 75 lb on a rope attached to a building, as shown in Fig. 2.23*a*. What are the horizontal and vertical components of the force exerted by the rope at point *A*?

It is seen from Fig. 2.23*b* that

$$F_x = +(75 \text{ lb})\cos\alpha \qquad F_y = -(75 \text{ lb})\sin\alpha$$

Observing that $AB = 25$ ft, we find from Fig. 2.23*a*

$$\cos\alpha = \frac{20 \text{ ft}}{AB} = \frac{20 \text{ ft}}{25 \text{ ft}} = \frac{4}{5} \qquad \sin\alpha = \frac{15 \text{ ft}}{AB} = \frac{15 \text{ ft}}{25 \text{ ft}} = \frac{3}{5}$$

We thus obtain

$$F_x = +(75 \text{ lb})\frac{4}{5} = +60 \text{ lb} \qquad F_y = -(75 \text{ lb})\frac{3}{5} = -45 \text{ lb}$$

and write

$$\mathbf{F} = (60 \text{ lb})\mathbf{i} - (45 \text{ lb})\mathbf{j}$$

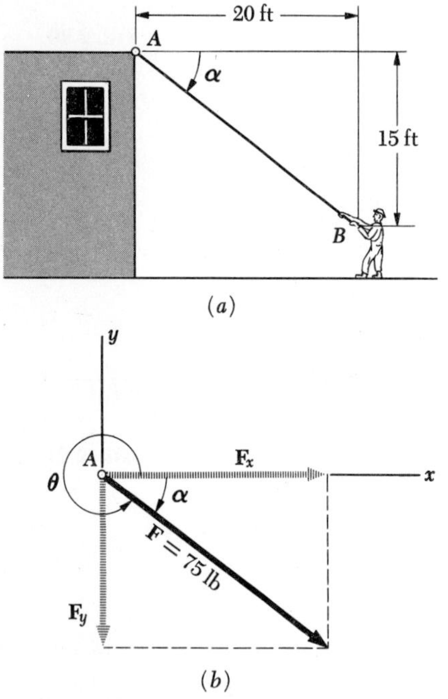

FIG. 2.23

When a force **F** is defined by its rectangular components F_x and F_y (see Fig. 2.21), the angle θ defining its direction can be obtained by writing

$$\tan\theta = \frac{F_y}{F_x} \tag{2.9}$$

The magnitude F of the force may be obtained by applying the Pythagorean theorem and writing

$$F = \sqrt{F_x^2 + F_y^2} \tag{2.10}$$

However, once θ has been found, it is usually easier to determine the magnitude of the force by the process of solving one of the formulas (2.8) for F.

Example 3. A force $\mathbf{F} = (700 \text{ lb})\mathbf{i} + (1{,}500 \text{ lb})\mathbf{j}$ is applied to a bolt A. Determine the magnitude of the force and the angle θ it forms with the horizontal.

First, we draw a diagram showing the two rectangular components of the force and the angle θ (Fig. 2.24*a*). Rather than θ, however, we shall determine its complement β (Fig. 2.24*b*) because β being smaller than 45°, its tangent is more easily found on the slide rule.

We write

$$F_y \tan \beta = F_x$$
$$(1{,}500 \text{ lb}) \tan \beta = 700 \text{ lb} \qquad (2.11)$$

and obtain
$$\beta = 25.0°$$

We then write
$$F \sin \beta = F_x$$
$$F \sin 25.0° = 700 \text{ lb} \qquad (2.12)$$

and obtain
$$F = 1{,}656 \text{ lb}$$

The magnitude of the force is thus 1,656 lb, and the angle θ it forms with the x axis is $\theta = 90.0° - 25.0° = 65.0°$.

Use of the Slide Rule. On most slide rules, β and F may be conveniently determined in the following way (Fig. 2.25):

FIRST STEP. Move the slide until one of the extremities of the trigonometric scale (in the present case the left one) coincides with the *larger* of the two components (1,500 lb) read on the D scale.

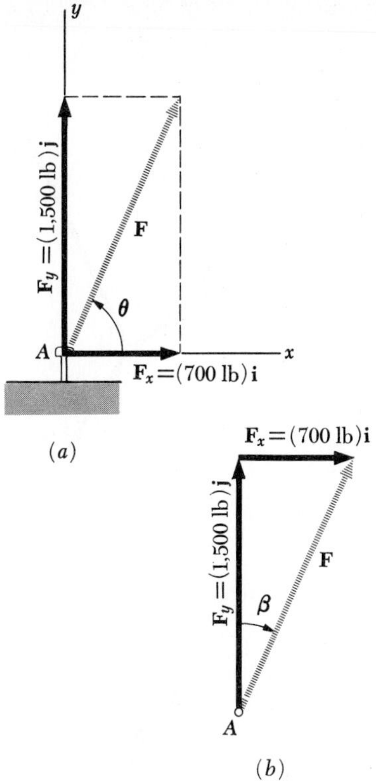

FIG. 2.24

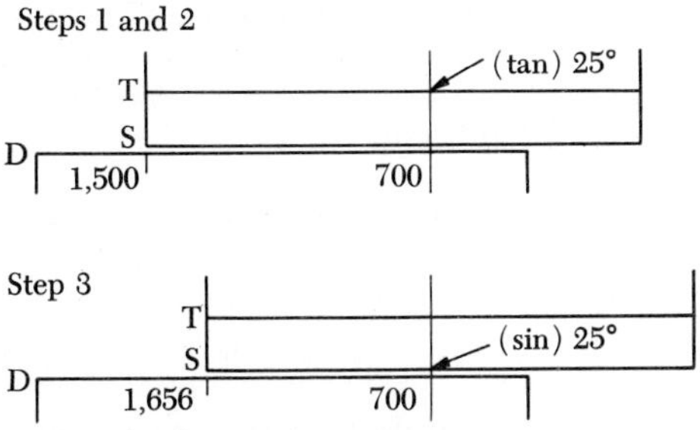

FIG. 2.25

SECOND STEP. Move the indicator until the hairline coincides with the *smaller* of the two components (700 lb). Angle β may then be read *on the* T *scale* under the hairline since the rule is set to perform the product defined by Eq. (2.11).

THIRD STEP. Without touching the indicator, move the slide until angle β (25.0°) is read *on the* S *scale* under the hairline. The value of F (1,656 lb) may then be read on the D scale opposite one of the extremities of the trigonometric scale since the rule is set to perform the product defined by Eq. (2.12).

Remark. If the smaller of the two components is less than one-tenth of the larger one, the ST scale should be used in the second step, instead of the T scale, and the angle found will be less than 5.7°. The third step may then be omitted since, within the accuracy of the slide rule, the magnitude F of the force may be assumed equal to the larger of the two components (see Sample Prob. 2.3).

2.7. Addition of Forces by Summing x and y Components. It was seen in Sec. 2.1 that forces should be added according to the parallelogram law. From this law, two other methods, more readily applicable to the *graphical* solution of problems, were derived in Secs. 2.3 and 2.4: the triangle rule for the addition of two forces and the polygon rule for the addition of three or more forces. It was also seen that the force triangle used to define the resultant of two forces could be used to obtain a *trigonometric* solution.

When three or more forces are to be added, no practical trigonometric solution may be obtained from the force polygon which defines the resultant of the forces. In this case, an *analytic* solution of the problem may be obtained by resolving each force into two rectangular components. Consider, for instance, three forces **P**, **Q**, and **S** acting on a particle A (Fig. 2.26*a*). Their resultant **R** is defined by the relation

$$\mathbf{R} = \mathbf{P} + \mathbf{Q} + \mathbf{S}$$

Resolving each force into its rectangular components, we write

$$\begin{aligned} R_x\mathbf{i} + R_y\mathbf{j} &= P_x\mathbf{i} + P_y\mathbf{j} + Q_x\mathbf{i} + Q_y\mathbf{j} + S_x\mathbf{i} + S_y\mathbf{j} \\ &= (P_x + Q_x + S_x)\mathbf{i} + (P_y + Q_y + S_y)\mathbf{j} \end{aligned}$$

from which it follows that

$$R_x = P_x + Q_x + S_x \qquad R_y = P_y + Q_y + S_y$$

or, for short,

$$R_x = \Sigma F_x \qquad R_y = \Sigma F_y \tag{2.13}$$

We thus conclude that *the scalar components R_x and R_y of the resultant* **R** *of several forces acting on a particle are obtained by adding algebraically the corresponding scalar components of the given forces.*†

In practice, the determination of the resultant **R** is carried out in three steps as illustrated in Fig. 2.26. First, the given forces shown in Fig. 2.26*a* are resolved into their x and y components (Fig. 2.26*b*). Adding these components, we obtain the x and y components of **R** (Fig. 2.26*c*). Finally, the resultant $\mathbf{R} = R_x\mathbf{i} + R_y\mathbf{j}$ is determined by applying the parallelogram law (Fig. 2.26*d*). The procedure just described will be carried out most efficiently if the computations are arranged in a table. While it is the only practical analytic method for adding three or more forces, it is also often preferred to the trigonometric solution in the case of the addition of two forces.

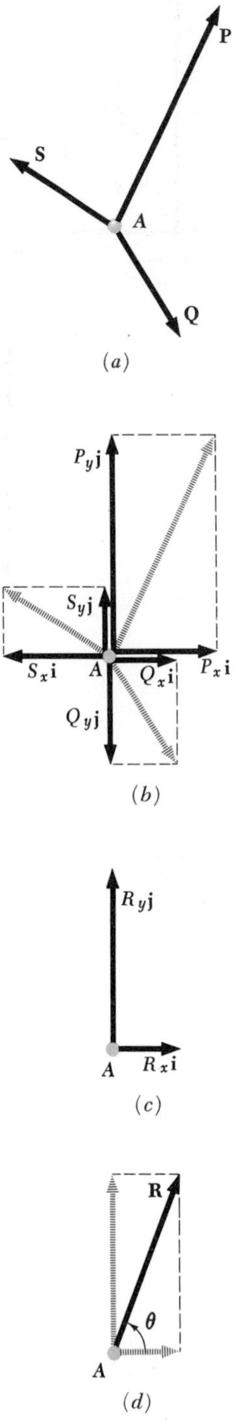

FIG. 2.26

† Clearly, this result also applies to the addition of other vector quantities, such as velocities, accelerations, or momenta.

SAMPLE PROBLEM 2.3

Four forces act on bolt A as shown. Determine the resultant of the forces on the bolt.

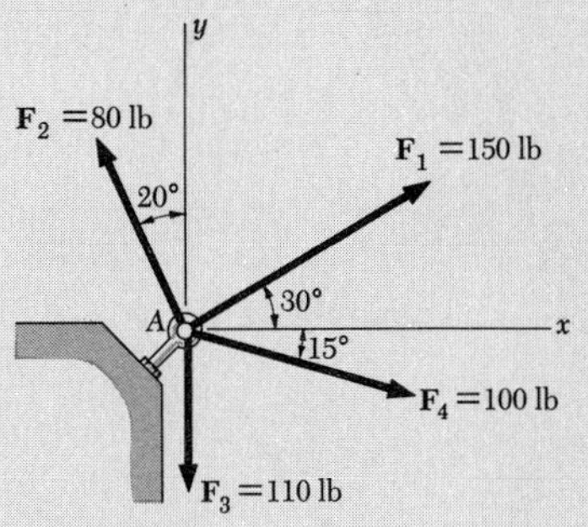

Solution. The x and y components of each force are determined by trigonometry as shown and are entered in the table below. According to the convention adopted in Sec. 2.6, the scalar number representing a force component is positive if the force component has the same sense as the corresponding coordinate axis. Thus, x components acting to the right and y components acting upward are represented by positive numbers.

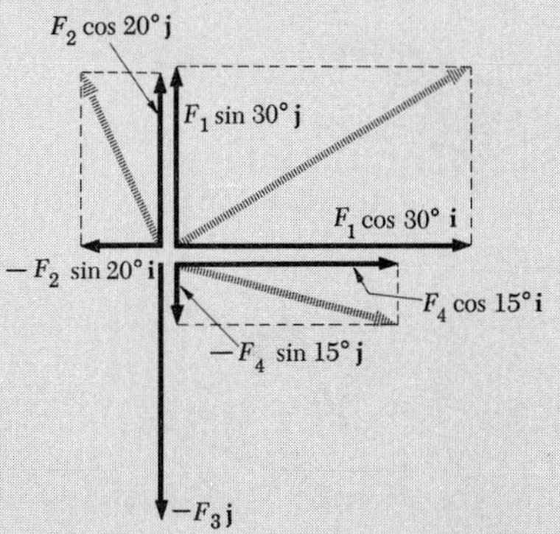

Force	Magnitude, lb	x component, lb	y component, lb
$\mathbf{F}_1$	150	+129.9	+75.0
$\mathbf{F}_2$	80	−27.4	+75.2
$\mathbf{F}_3$	110	0	−110.0
$\mathbf{F}_4$	100	+96.6	−25.9
		$R_x = +199.1$	$R_y = +14.3$

Thus, the resultant $\mathbf{R}$ of the four forces is

$$\mathbf{R} = R_x\mathbf{i} + R_y\mathbf{j} \qquad \mathbf{R} = (199.1 \text{ lb})\mathbf{i} + (14.3 \text{ lb})\mathbf{j} \blacktriangleleft$$

The magnitude and direction of the resultant may now be determined. In the triangle shown,

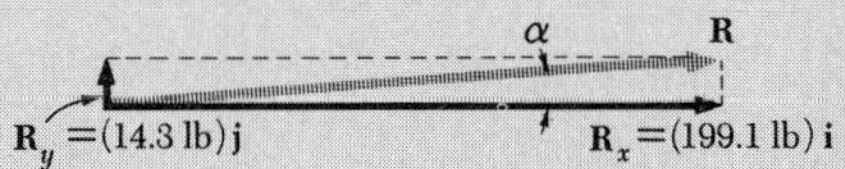

$$R_x \tan \alpha = R_y \qquad (199.1 \text{ lb}) \tan \alpha = 14.3 \text{ lb}$$

The smaller component (14.3 lb) being less than one-tenth of the larger component (199.1 lb), we use the ST scale and read $\alpha = 4.1°$. Since within the accuracy of the slide rule the sine and tangent of this angle are equal, the magnitude of $\mathbf{R}$ may be assumed equal to that of the larger component,

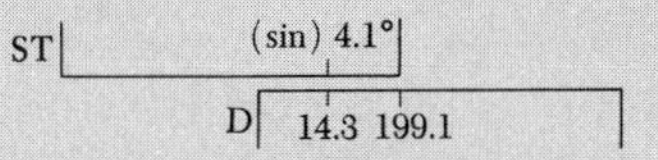

$$\mathbf{R} = 199.1 \text{ lb} \measuredangle 4.1° \blacktriangleleft$$

PROBLEMS

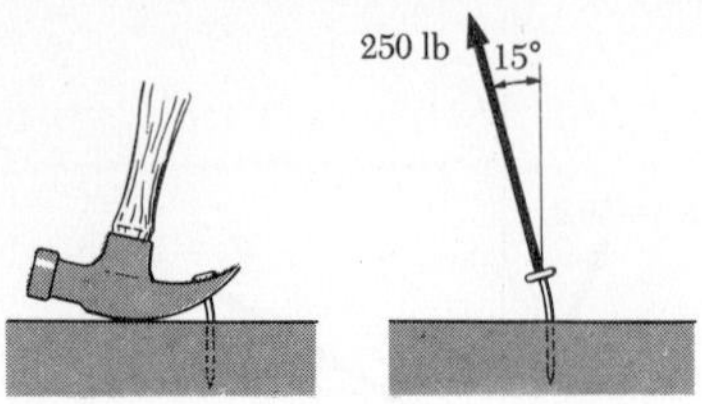

FIG. P 2.14

2.14. In removing a nail, a force of 250 lb is applied by a hammer in the direction shown. What are the horizontal and vertical components of this force?

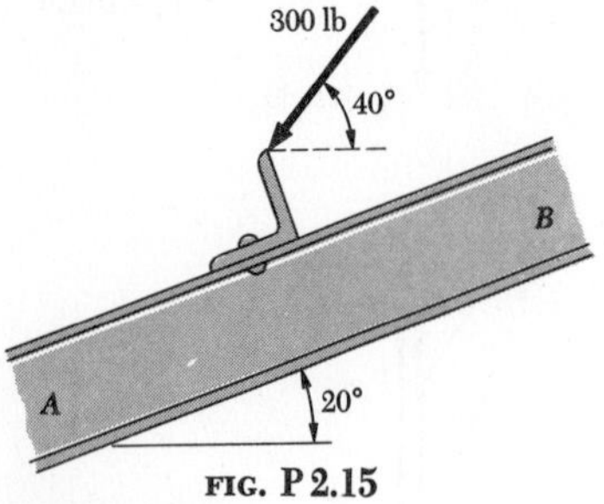

FIG. P 2.15

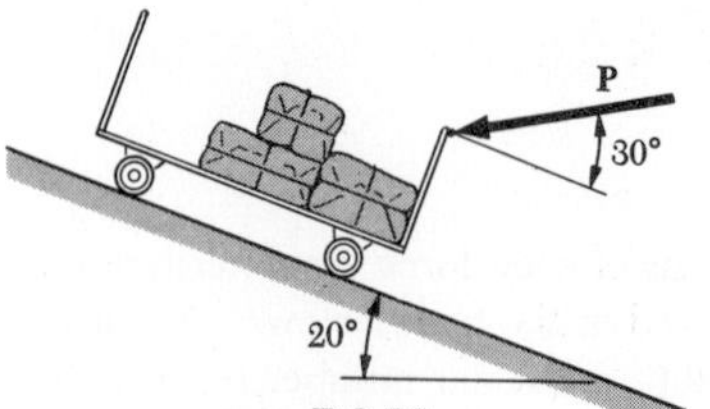

FIG. P 2.16

2.15. Determine the components of the 300-lb force in directions parallel and perpendicular to the beam *AB*.

2.16. The force **P** must have a 60-lb component acting up the incline. Determine the magnitude of **P** and of its component perpendicular to the incline.

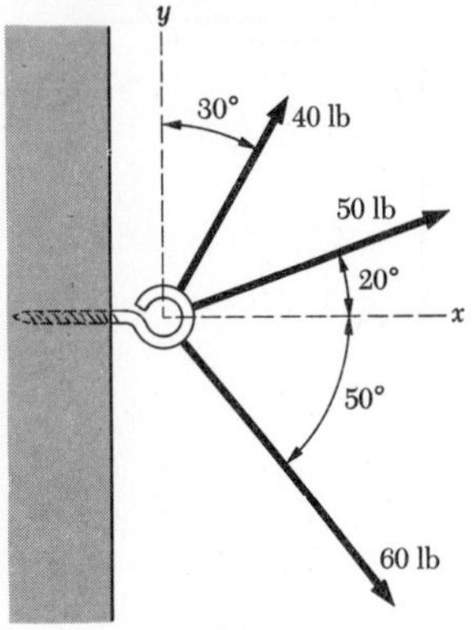

FIG. P 2.17

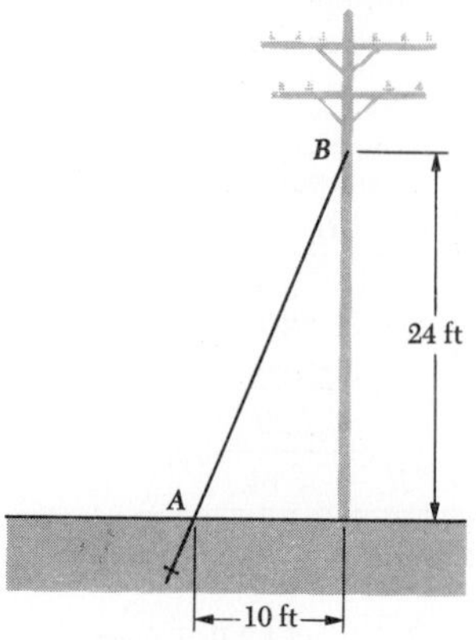

FIG. P 2.18

2.17. Determine the *x* and *y* components of each of the forces shown.

2.18. The tension in the telephone-pole guy wire is 390 lb. Determine the horizontal and vertical components of the force acting on the anchor at *A*.

2.19. Determine the *x* and *y* components of each of the forces shown.

2.20 and 2.21. The *x* and *y* components of a force **F** are as shown. Determine the magnitude and direction of the force **F**.

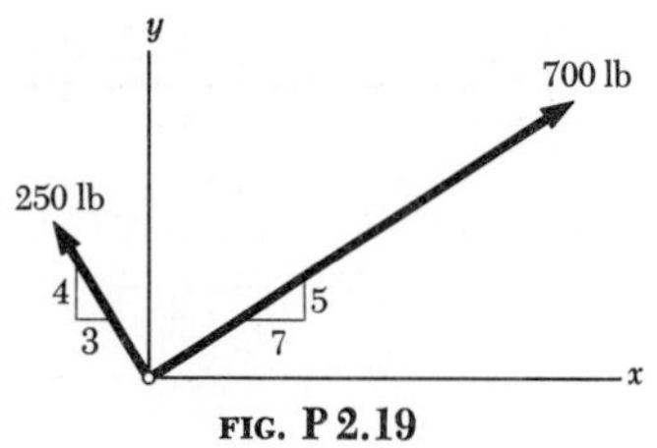

FIG. P 2.19

FIG. P 2.20

2.22. Determine the resultant of the four forces shown.

2.23. Using *x* and *y* components, solve part *a* of Prob. 2.3.

2.24. Using *x* and *y* components, solve Prob. 2.4.

2.25. Determine the resultant of the three forces of Prob. 2.17.

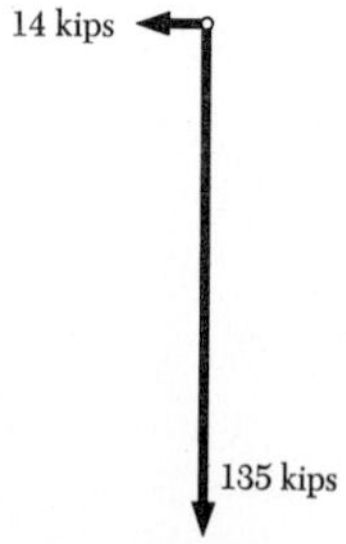

FIG. P 2.21

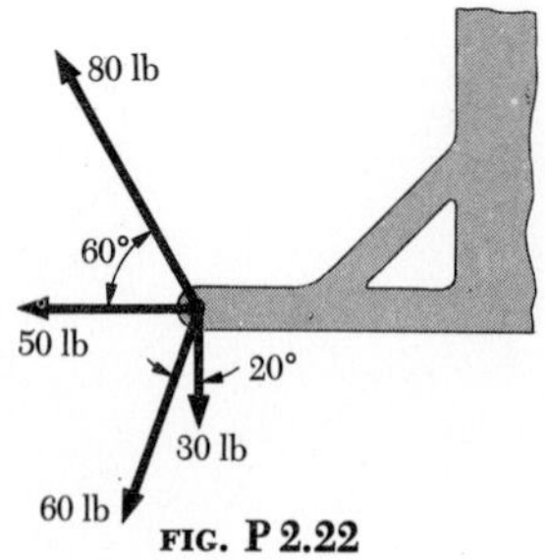

FIG. P 2.22

2.26. A hoist trolley is subjected to the three forces shown. The direction of the force **F** may be varied. If possible, determine the direction of the force **F** so that the resultant of the three forces is vertical, knowing that the magnitude of **F** is (*a*) 240 lb, (*b*) 140 lb.

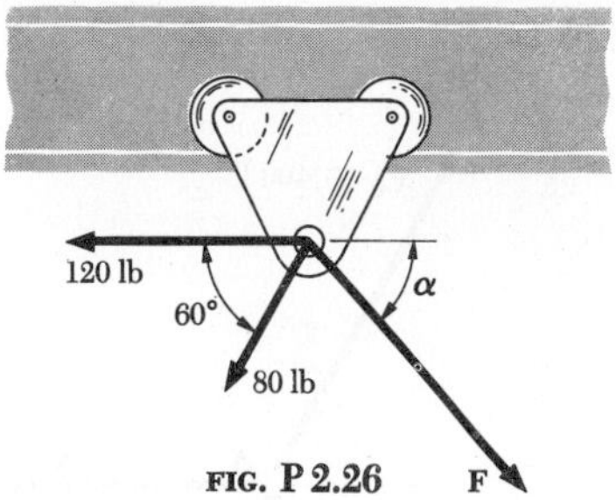

FIG. P 2.26

2.27. Two cables which have known tensions are attached at point B. A third cable AB is used as a guy wire and is also attached at B. Determine the required tension in AB so that the resultant of the forces exerted by the three cables will be vertical.

2.28. The resultant of the three forces shown must be a 100-lb force directed to the right along line *a-a*. Determine the required magnitude and direction of the force **F**.

2.29. Show that the forces $\mathbf{P} = P_x\mathbf{i} + P_y\mathbf{j}$ and $\mathbf{Q} = Q_x\mathbf{i} + Q_y\mathbf{j}$ are perpendicular to each other if and only if $P_xQ_x + P_yQ_y = 0$.

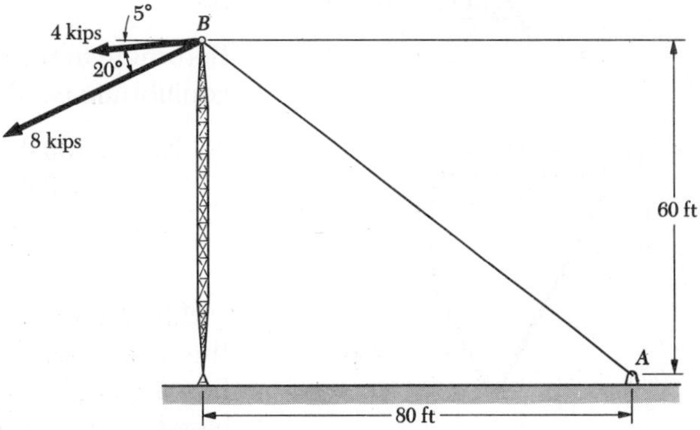

FIG. P 2.27

2.8. Equilibrium of a Particle. In the preceding sections, we discussed the methods for determining the resultant of several forces acting on a particle. Although this has not occurred in any of the problems considered so far, it is quite possible for the resultant to be zero. In such a case, the net effect of the given forces is zero, and the particle is said to be in equilibrium. We thus have the following definition: *When the resultant of all the forces acting on a particle is zero, the particle is in equilibrium.*

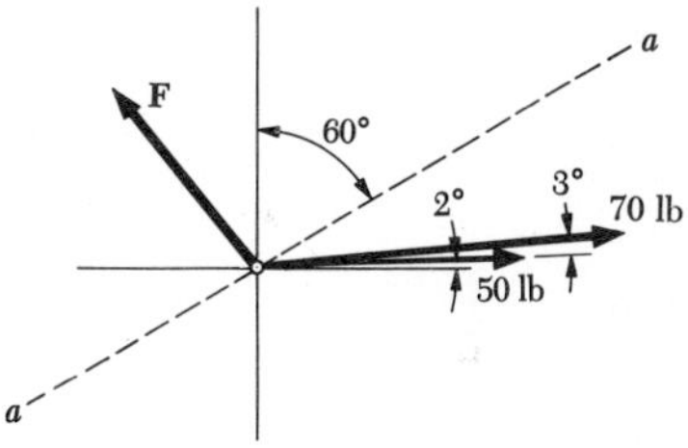

FIG. P 2.28

A particle which is acted upon by two forces will be in equilibrium if the two forces have the same magnitude, same line of action, and opposite sense. The resultant of the two forces is then zero. Such a case is shown in Fig. 2.27.

FIG. 2.27

Another case of equilibrium of a particle is represented in Fig. 2.28*a*, where four forces are shown acting on A. In Fig. 2.28*b*, the resultant of the given forces is determined by the polygon rule. Starting from point O with $\mathbf{F}_1$ and arranging the forces in tip-to-tail fashion, we find that the tip of $\mathbf{F}_4$ coincides with the starting point O. Thus the resultant **R** of the given system of forces is zero, and the particle is in equilibrium.

The closed polygon drawn in Fig. 2.28*b* provides a *graphical* expression of the equilibrium of A. To express *algebraically*

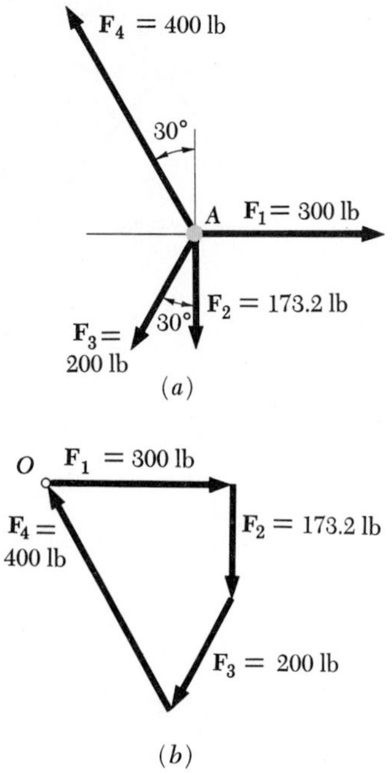

FIG. 2.28

the conditions for the equilibrium of a particle, we write

$$\mathbf{R} = \Sigma \mathbf{F} = 0 \tag{2.14}$$

Resolving each force **F** into rectangular components, we have

$$\Sigma(F_x\mathbf{i} + F_y\mathbf{j}) = 0 \qquad \text{or} \qquad (\Sigma F_x)\mathbf{i} + (\Sigma F_y)\mathbf{j} = 0$$

We conclude that the necessary and sufficient conditions for the equilibrium of a particle are

$$\Sigma F_x = 0 \qquad \Sigma F_y = 0 \tag{2.15}$$

Returning to the particle shown in Fig. 2.28*a* we check that the equilibrium conditions are satisfied.

$$\begin{aligned} \Sigma F_x &= 300 \text{ lb} - (200 \text{ lb}) \sin 30° - (400 \text{ lb}) \sin 30° \\ &= 300 \text{ lb} - 100 \text{ lb} - 200 \text{ lb} = 0 \\ \Sigma F_y &= -173.2 \text{ lb} - (200 \text{ lb}) \cos 30° + (400 \text{ lb}) \cos 30° \\ &= -173.2 \text{ lb} - 173.2 \text{ lb} + 346.4 \text{ lb} = 0 \end{aligned}$$

2.9. Newton's First Law of Motion. In the latter part of the seventeenth century, Sir Isaac Newton formulated three fundamental laws upon which the science of mechanics is based. The first of these laws can be stated as follows:

If the resultant force acting on a particle is zero, the particle will remain at rest (if originally at rest) or will move with constant speed in a straight line (if originally in motion).

From this law and from the definition of equilibrium given in Sec. 2.8, it is seen that a particle in equilibrium either is at rest or is moving in a straight line with constant speed. In the following section, various problems concerning the equilibrium of a particle will be considered.

2.10. Problems Involving the Equilibrium of a Particle. Free-body Diagram. In practice, a problem in engineering mechanics is derived from an actual physical situation. A sketch showing the physical conditions of the problem is known as a *space diagram.*

The methods of analysis discussed in the preceding sections apply to a system of forces acting on a particle. A large number of problems involving actual structures, however, may be reduced to problems concerning the equilibrium of a particle. This is done by choosing a significant particle and drawing a separate diagram showing this particle and all the forces acting on it. Such a diagram is called a *free-body diagram.*

As an example, consider the crate, weighing 140 lb, shown in the space diagram of Fig. 2.29*a*. This crate was lying between two buildings, and it is now being lifted onto a truck, which will remove it. The crate is supported by a vertical cable, which is joined at A to two ropes which pass over pulleys attached to the buildings at B and C. It is desired to determine the tension in each of the ropes AB and AC.

In order to solve this problem, a free-body diagram must be drawn, showing a particle in equilibrium. Since we are interested in the rope tensions, the free-body diagram should include at least one of these tensions and, if possible, both tensions. Point A is seen to be a good free body for this problem. The free-body diagram of point A is shown in Fig. 2.29*b*. It represents point A and the three forces acting on A, namely, the 140-lb force exerted by the crate and the two forces $\mathbf{T}_{AB}$ and $\mathbf{T}_{AC}$ representing respectively the tension in rope AB and the tension in rope AC. These two forces are shown acting away from point A. No other detail is included in the free-body diagram.

Since point A is in equilibrium, the three forces acting on it must form a closed triangle when drawn in tip-to-tail fashion. This *force triangle* has been drawn in Fig. 2.29*c*. The values T_{AB} and T_{AC} of the tension in the ropes may be found graphically if the triangle is drawn to scale, or they may be found by trigonometry. If the latter method of solution is chosen, we use the law of sines and write

$$\frac{T_{AB}}{\sin 60^\circ} = \frac{T_{AC}}{\sin 40^\circ} = \frac{140 \text{ lb}}{\sin 80^\circ}$$

$$T_{AB} = 123.2 \text{ lb} \qquad T_{AC} = 91.4 \text{ lb}$$

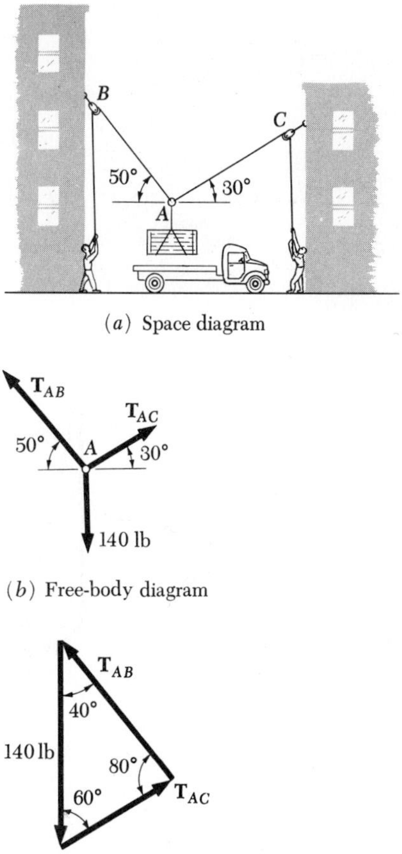

(*a*) Space diagram

(*b*) Free-body diagram

(*c*) Force triangle

FIG. 2.29

When a particle is in *equilibrium under three forces,* the problem may always be solved by drawing a force triangle. When a particle is in *equilibrium under more than three forces,* the problem may be solved graphically by drawing a force polygon. If an analytic solution is desired, the *equations of equilibrium* given in Sec. 2.8 should be solved:

$$\Sigma F_x = 0 \qquad \Sigma F_y = 0 \tag{2.15}$$

These equations may be solved for no more than *two unknowns;* similarly, the force triangle used in the case of equilibrium under three forces may be solved for two unknowns.

The more common types of problems are those where the two unknowns represent (1) the two components (or the magnitude and direction) of a single force, (2) the magnitude of two forces each of known direction. Problems involving the determination of the maximum or minimum value of the magnitude of a force are also encountered (see Probs. 2.34 and 2.37).

SAMPLE PROBLEM 2.4

In a ship-unloading operation, a 3,500-lb automobile is supported by a cable. A rope is tied to the cable at A and pulled in order to center the automobile over its intended position. The angle between the cable and the vertical is $2°$, while the angle between the rope and the horizontal is $30°$. What is the tension in the rope?

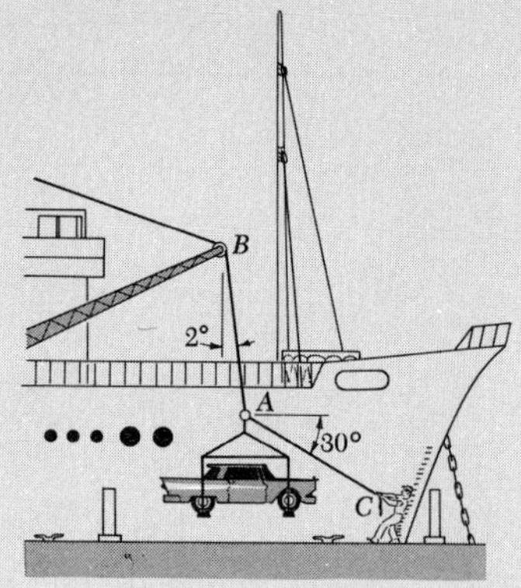

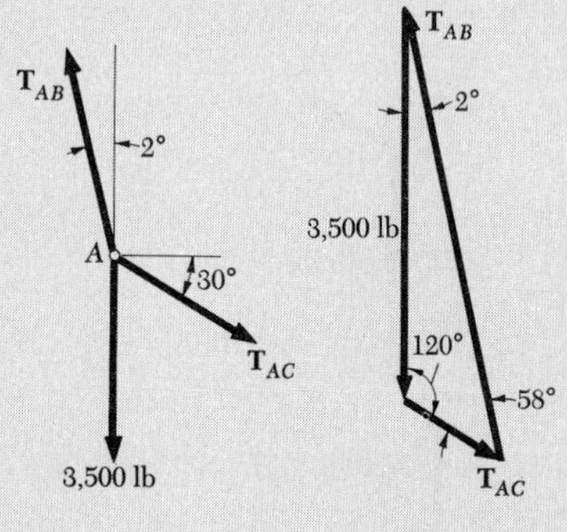

Solution. Point A is chosen as a free body, and the complete free-body diagram is drawn. T_{AB} is the tension in the cable AB, and T_{AC} is the tension in the rope. Drawing the force triangle and using the law of sines, we write

$$\frac{T_{AB}}{\sin 120°} = \frac{T_{AC}}{\sin 2°} = \frac{3{,}500 \text{ lb}}{\sin 58°}$$

$$T_{AB} = 3{,}570 \text{ lb} \qquad T_{AC} = 144 \text{ lb} \blacktriangleleft$$

SAMPLE PROBLEM 2.5

Determine the magnitude and direction of the smallest force **F** which will maintain the package shown in equilibrium. Note that the force exerted by the rollers on the package is perpendicular to the incline.

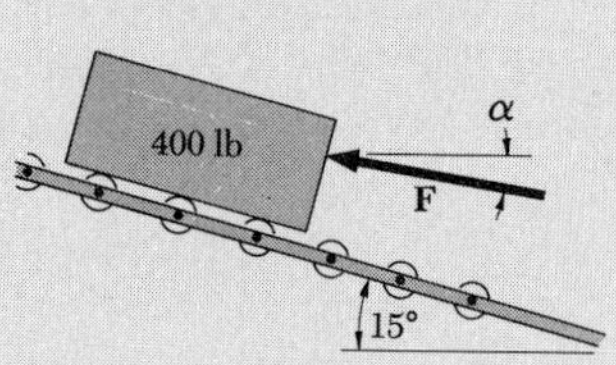

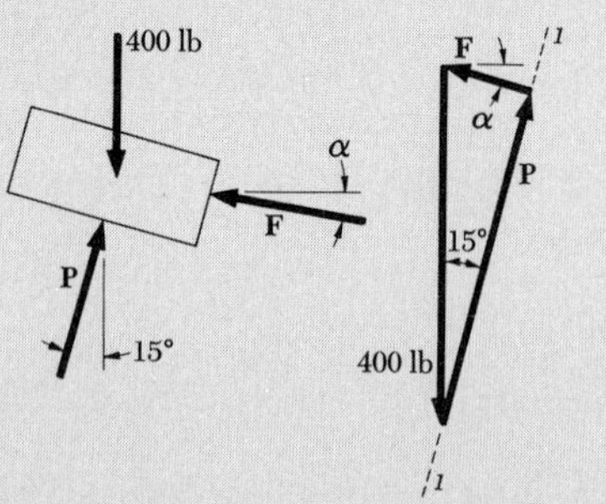

Solution. We choose the package as a free body and assume that it may be treated as a particle. Since three forces act on the free body, we draw a force triangle to express that it is in equilibrium. Line *1-1* represents the known direction of **P**. In order to obtain the minimum value of the force **F**, we choose the direction of **F** perpendicular to that of **P**. From the geometry of the triangle obtained, we find

$$F = (400 \text{ lb}) \sin 15° = 103.6 \text{ lb} \qquad \alpha = 15°$$

$$\mathbf{F} = 103.6 \text{ lb} \measuredangle 15° \blacktriangleleft$$

SAMPLE PROBLEM 2.6

A small boat is moored by means of three ropes tied to posts on the banks of a stream. The stream flow exerts a force on the boat which acts directly downstream. The tensions in ropes A and B are measured and found to be $A = 120$ lb and $B = 80$ lb. Determine the magnitude of the force exerted by the flow and the tension in rope C.

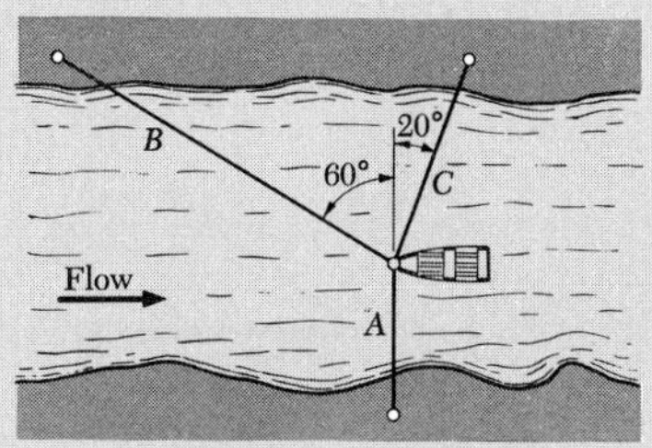

Solution. The boat is taken as a free body. It is acted upon by four forces directed as shown. Each force is resolved into its x and y components.

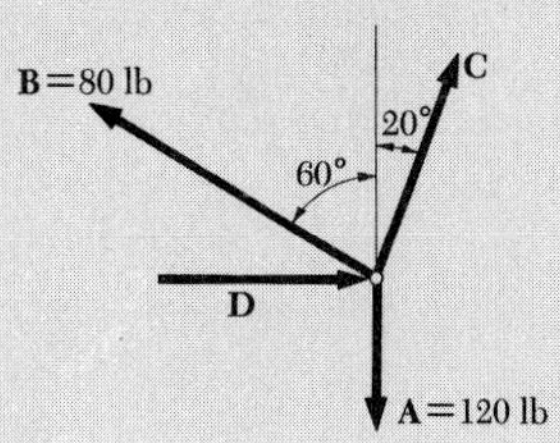

$$\mathbf{A} = -(120\text{ lb})\mathbf{j}$$
$$\mathbf{B} = -(80\text{ lb})\cos 30°\mathbf{i} + (80\text{ lb})\sin 30°\mathbf{j}$$
$$= -(69.3\text{ lb})\mathbf{i} + (40\text{ lb})\mathbf{j}$$
$$\mathbf{C} = C\sin 20°\mathbf{i} + C\cos 20°\mathbf{j}$$
$$= 0.342\,C\mathbf{i} + 0.940\,C\mathbf{j}$$
$$\mathbf{D} = D\mathbf{i}$$

Since the boat is in equilibrium, the resultant of the forces must be zero. Thus

$$\mathbf{R} = \mathbf{A} + \mathbf{B} + \mathbf{C} + \mathbf{D} = 0$$

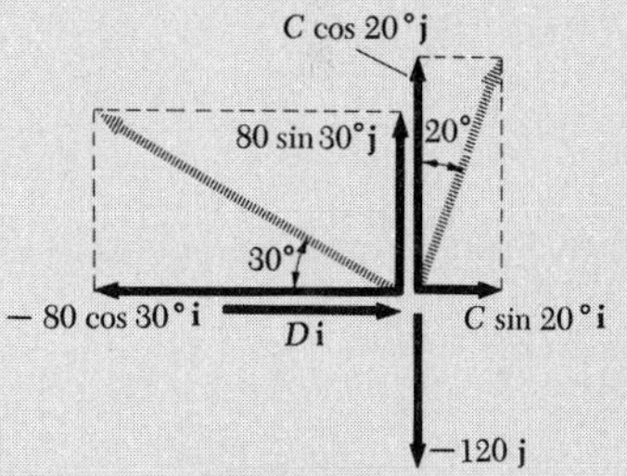

Substituting for **A**, **B**, **C**, and **D** the expressions obtained above, and factoring the unit vectors **i** and **j**, we have

$$(-69.3\text{ lb} + 0.342\,C + D)\mathbf{i} + (-120\text{ lb} + 40\text{ lb} + 0.940\,C)\mathbf{j} = 0$$

This equation will be satisfied if, and only if, the coefficients of **i** and **j** are equal to zero. We thus obtain the following two equilibrium equations, which express, respectively, that the sum of the x components and the sum of the y components of the given forces must be zero.

$$(\Sigma F_x = 0:) \qquad -69.3\text{ lb} + 0.342C + D = 0$$

$$(\Sigma F_y = 0:) \qquad -120\text{ lb} + 40\text{ lb} + 0.940C = 0$$

Solving these equations, we find

$$C = +85.1\text{ lb} \qquad D = +40.2\text{ lb} \quad ◄$$

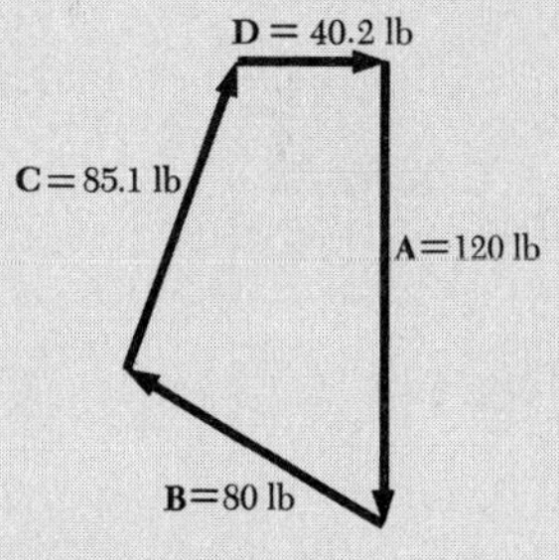

In drawing the free-body diagram, we assumed a sense for each unknown force. A positive sign in the answer indicates that the assumed sense is correct. The complete force polygon may be drawn to check the results.

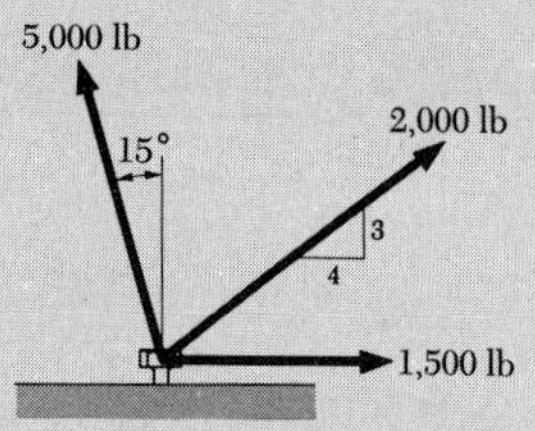

SAMPLE PROBLEM 2.7

A bolt is used to anchor three guy wires as shown. The tension in each wire is given. Determine the magnitude and direction of the force exerted by the foundation on the bolt.

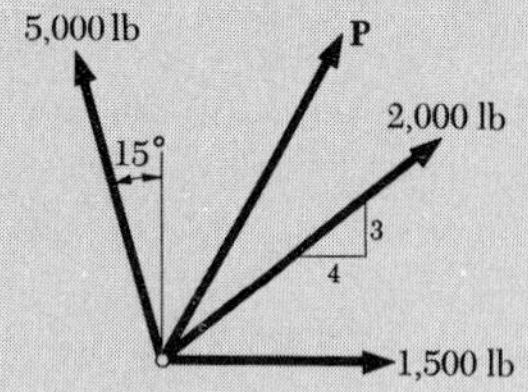

Solution. A free-body diagram of the bolt is drawn; the force exerted by the foundation is **P**. No attempt is made to guess the direction or sense of **P** (although in this case it is easily seen that **P** has a downward component). We assume that **P** is directed to the right and upward and write

$$\mathbf{P} = P_x\mathbf{i} + P_y\mathbf{j}$$

Since the bolt is in equilibrium, the resultant must be zero; therefore,

$$\Sigma F_x = 0 \qquad \Sigma F_y = 0$$

Positive sense is to the right for the x components and upward for the y components. The components of the 2,000-lb force are computed directly from the given slope of the force.

$\Sigma F_x = 0$: $\quad -(5{,}000 \text{ lb}) \sin 15° + (2{,}000 \text{ lb})\frac{4}{5} + 1{,}500 \text{ lb} + P_x = 0$

$$-1{,}294 \text{ lb} + 1{,}600 \text{ lb} + 1{,}500 \text{ lb} + P_x = 0$$
$$+1{,}806 \text{ lb} + P_x = 0 \qquad P_x = -1{,}806 \text{ lb}$$

$\Sigma F_y = 0$: $\quad +(5{,}000 \text{ lb}) \cos 15° + (2{,}000 \text{ lb})\frac{3}{5} + P_y = 0$

$$+4{,}830 \text{ lb} + 1{,}200 \text{ lb} + P_y = 0$$
$$+6{,}030 \text{ lb} + P_y = 0 \qquad P_y = -6{,}030 \text{ lb}$$

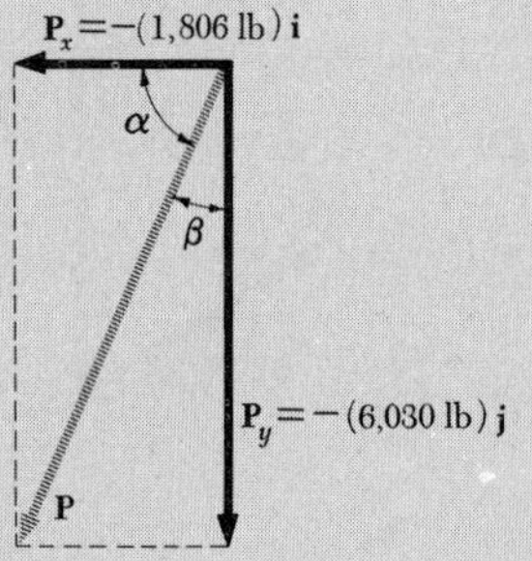

Thus the force **P** is

$$\mathbf{P} = P_x\mathbf{i} + P_y\mathbf{j}$$
$$\mathbf{P} = -(1{,}806 \text{ lb})\mathbf{i} - (6{,}030 \text{ lb})\mathbf{j}$$

The magnitude and direction of **P** are now determined.

$$P_y \tan \beta = P_x$$
$$(6{,}030 \text{ lb}) \tan \beta = 1{,}806 \text{ lb}$$
$$\beta = 16.7° \qquad \alpha = 90° - 16.7° = 73.3°$$
$$P \sin \beta = P_x$$
$$P \sin 16.7° = 1{,}806 \text{ lb}$$
$$\mathbf{P} = 6{,}300 \text{ lb} \measuredangle 73.3° \quad ◄$$

PROBLEMS

2.30 through 2.32. Two cables are tied together at C and loaded as shown. Determine the tension in AC and BC.

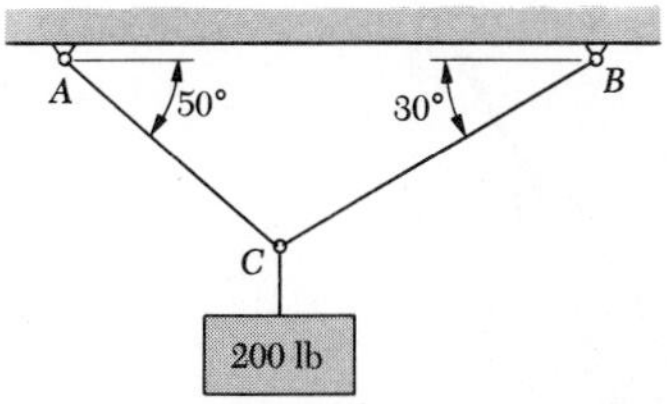

FIG. P 2.30

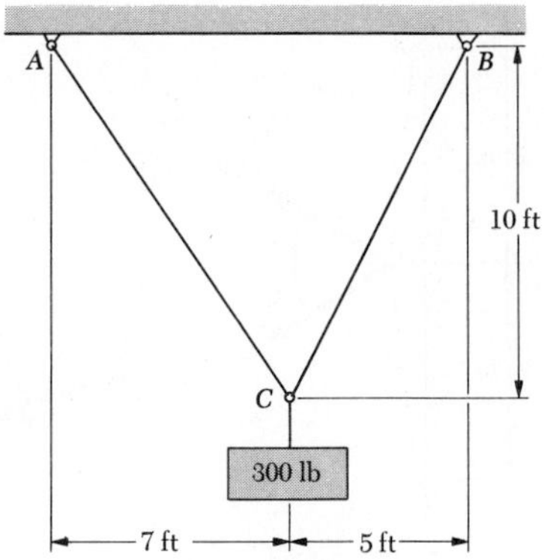

FIG. P 2.31

2.33. If the length of cable BC is increased to 10 ft in Prob. 2.32, determine the new tension in AC and BC.

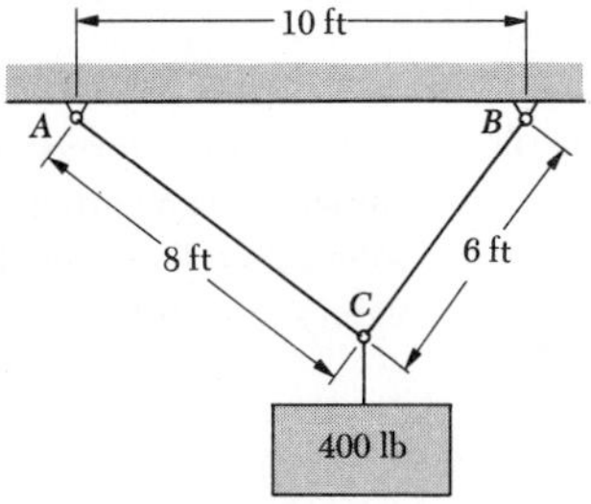

FIG. P 2.32

2.34. A 600-lb block is supported by the two cables AC and BC. (*a*) For what value of α is the tension in cable AC minimum? (*b*) What are the corresponding values of the tension in cables AC and BC?

2.35. A 600-lb block is supported by the two cables AC and BC. Determine (*a*) the value of α for which the larger of the cable tensions is as small as possible, (*b*) the corresponding values of the tension in cables AC and BC.

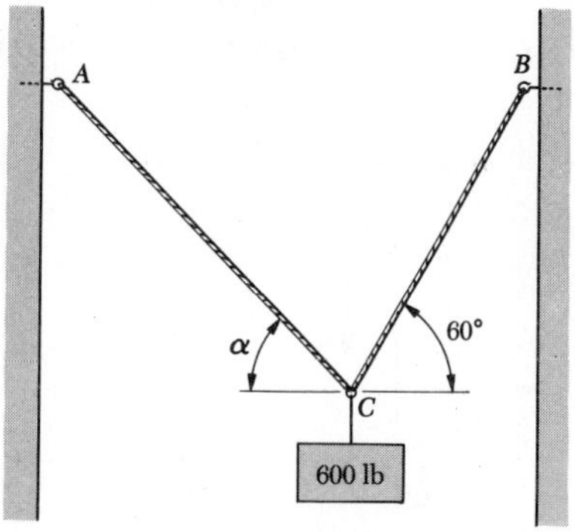

FIG. P 2.34 AND P 2.35

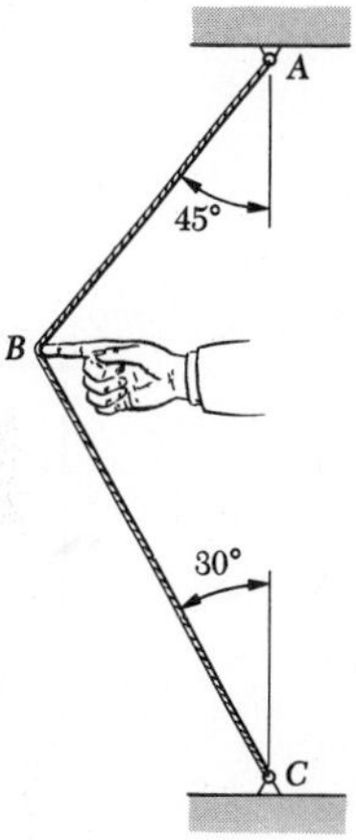

FIG. P 2.36

2.36. A man stretches an elastic cord AC by applying his finger at B. Determine the magnitude and direction of the force exerted by the man, knowing that the tension in both parts of the cord is 5 lb.

2.37. Two ropes are tied together at C. If the maximum permissible tension in each rope is 750 lb, what is the maximum force $\mathbf{F}$ that may be applied? In what direction must this maximum force act?

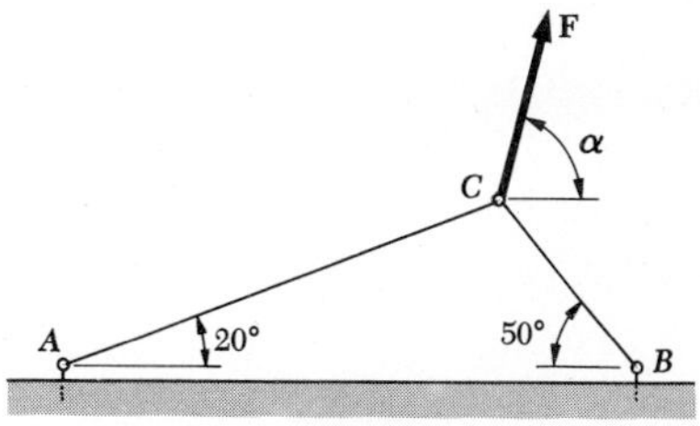

FIG. P 2.37

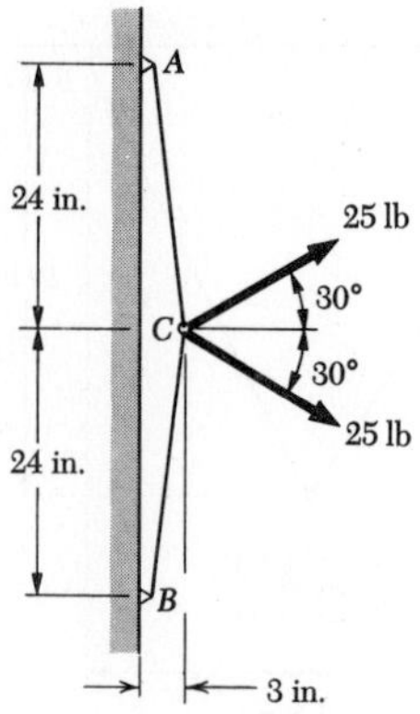

FIG. P 2.38

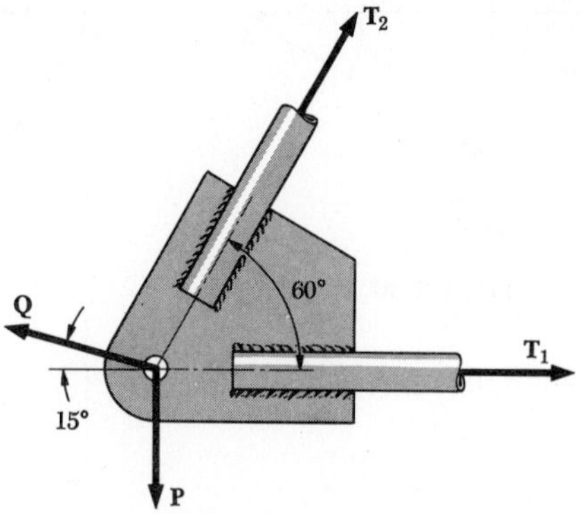

FIG. P 2.39 AND P 2.40

2.38. Two strings are tied together at C and loaded as shown. Determine the tension in AC and BC.

2.39. Two forces **P** and **Q** of magnitude $P = 1{,}000$ lb and $Q = 1{,}200$ lb are applied to the aircraft connection shown. Knowing that the connection is in equilibrium, determine the tensions T_1 and T_2.

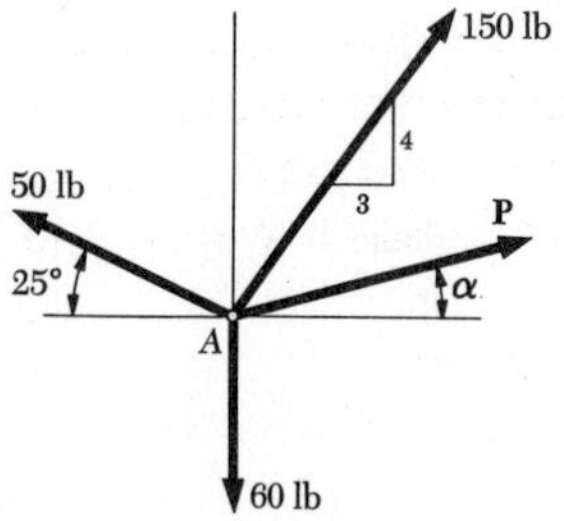

FIG. P 2.41

2.40. Two forces **P** and **Q** are applied to the aircraft connection shown. At a certain instant, when the connection is in equilibrium, it is found that $T_1 = 560$ lb and $T_2 = 120$ lb. Determine the corresponding values of P and Q.

2.41. A particle A is in equilibrium under the action of the four forces shown. Determine the magnitude and direction of **P**.

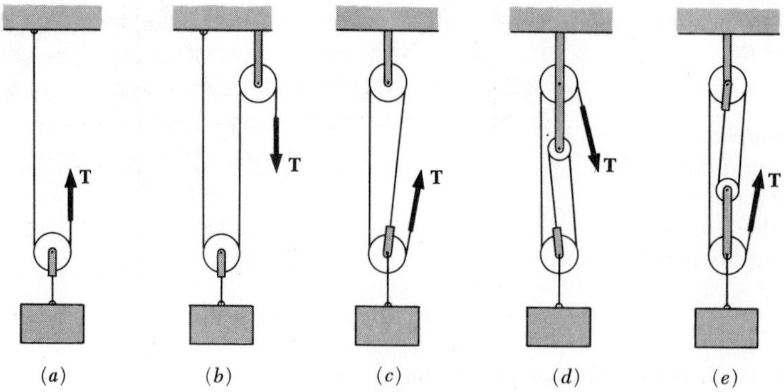

FIG. P 2.42

2.42. A 600-lb crate is supported by several rope-and-pulley arrangements as shown. Determine for each arrangement the tension in the rope. (The tension in the rope is the same on each side of a simple pulley. This can be proved by the methods of Chap. 4.)

2.43. Solve parts b and d of Prob. 2.42 assuming that the free end of the rope is attached to the crate.

2.44. A 1,500-lb crate is lifted by a crane cable *CD*. A cable sling *ACB* is 5 ft long and can be attached to the crate in each of the two ways shown. Determine the tension in the cable sling in each case.

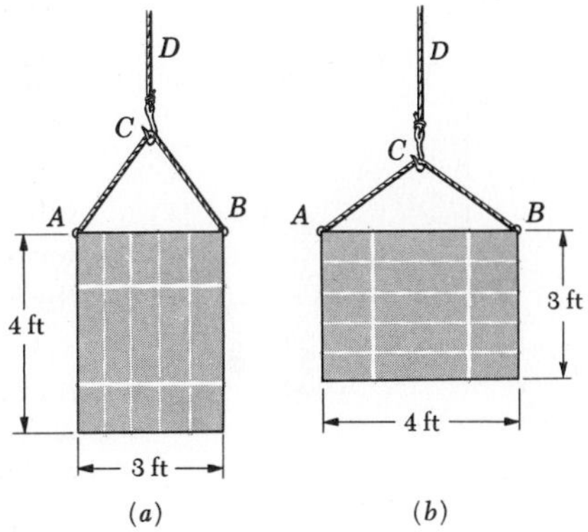

FIG. P 2.44

2.45. A portable bin and its contents weigh 750 lb. Determine the shortest chain sling *ACB* which may be used to lift the loaded bin if the tension in the chain sling is not to exceed 900 lb.

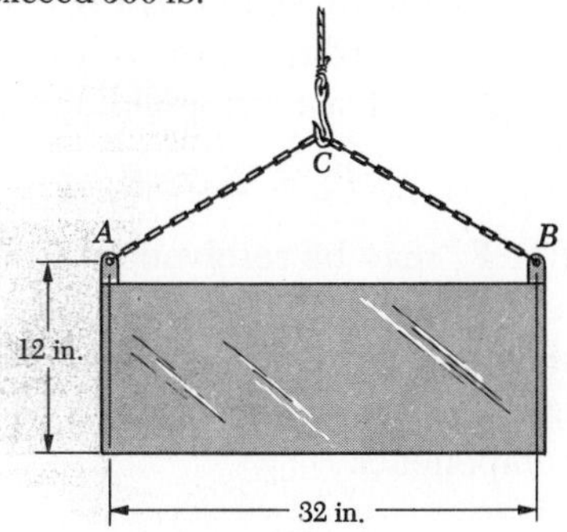

FIG. P 2.45

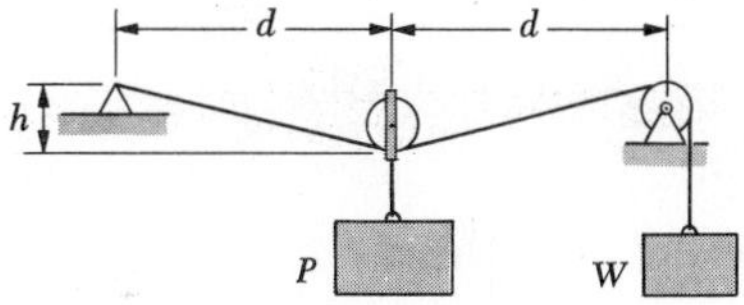

FIG. P 2.46 AND P 2.47

*2.46. If in the diagram shown $W = 80$ lb, $P = 10$ lb, and $d = 20$ in., determine the value of h consistent with equilibrium.

*2.47. Express the weight W required to maintain equilibrium in terms of P, d, and h.

*2.48. A 500-lb crate is to be supported by the rope-and-pulley arrangement shown. Determine the required magnitude and direction of the force **T**.

*2.49. For any given value of α in Prob. 2.37, there is a maximum force **F** which may be applied without exceeding the permissible tension in either of the ropes. Considering only cases in which both ropes remain taut, determine the magnitude of the maximum force **F** as a function of the angle α.

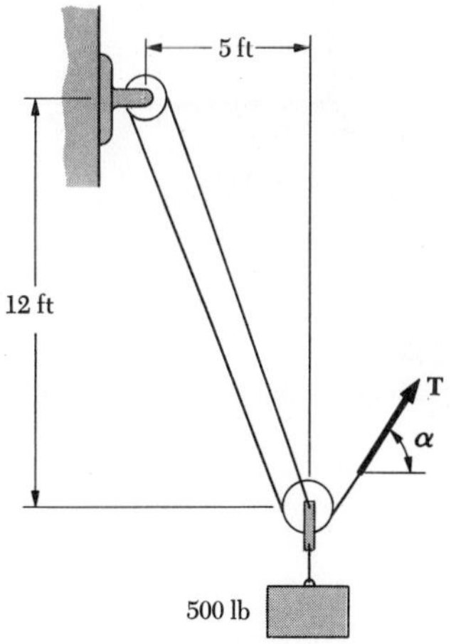

FIG. P 2.48

FORCES IN SPACE

2.11. Rectangular Components of a Force in Space. The problems considered in the first part of this chapter involved only two dimensions; they could be formulated and solved in a single plane. In this section and in the remaining sections of the chapter, we shall discuss problems involving the three dimensions of space.

Consider a force **F** acting at the origin O of the system of rectangular coordinates x, y, z. To define the direction of **F**, we may draw the vertical plane $OBAC$ containing **F** and shown in Fig. 2.30*a*. This plane passes through the vertical y axis; its orientation is defined by the angle ϕ it forms with the xy plane, while the direction of **F** within the plane is defined by the angle θ_y that **F** forms with the y axis. The force **F** may be resolved into a vertical component $\mathbf{F}_y$ and a horizontal component $\mathbf{F}_h$; this operation, shown in Fig. 2.30*b*, is carried out inside plane $OBAC$ according to the rules developed in the first part of the chapter. The corresponding scalar components are

$$F_y = F\cos\theta_y \qquad\qquad F_h = F\sin\theta_y \tag{2.16}$$

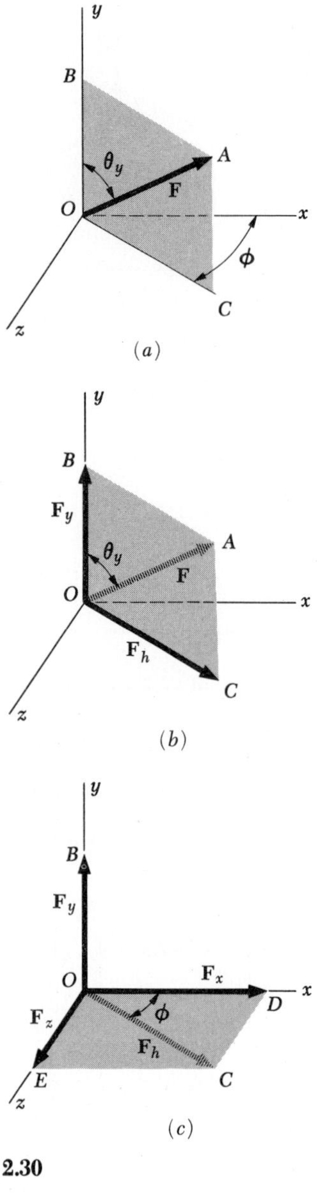

FIG. 2.30

But $\mathbf{F}_h$ may be resolved into two rectangular components $\mathbf{F}_x$ and $\mathbf{F}_z$ along the x and z axes, respectively. This operation, shown in Fig. 2.30*c*, is carried out inside the xz plane. We obtain the following expressions for the corresponding scalar components:

$$\begin{aligned} F_x &= F_h\cos\phi = F\sin\theta_y\cos\phi \\ F_z &= F_h\sin\phi = F\sin\theta_y\sin\phi \end{aligned} \tag{2.17}$$

The given force **F** has thus been resolved into three rectangular vector components $\mathbf{F}_x$, $\mathbf{F}_y$, $\mathbf{F}_z$, directed along the three axes of coordinates.

Applying the Pythagorean theorem to the triangles OAB and OCD of Fig. 2.30, we write

$$\begin{aligned} F^2 &= (OA)^2 = (OB)^2 + (BA)^2 = F_y^2 + F_h^2 \\ F_h^2 &= (OC)^2 = (OD)^2 + (DC)^2 = F_x^2 + F_z^2 \end{aligned}$$

Eliminating F_h^2 from these two equations and solving for F, we obtain the following relation between the magnitude of **F** and its rectangular scalar components:

$$F = \sqrt{F_x^2 + F_y^2 + F_z^2} \tag{2.18}$$

The relationship existing between the force **F** and its three components $\mathbf{F}_x$, $\mathbf{F}_y$, $\mathbf{F}_z$ is more easily visualized if a "box" having $\mathbf{F}_x$, $\mathbf{F}_y$, $\mathbf{F}_z$ for edges is drawn as shown in Fig. 2.31. The force **F** is then represented by the diagonal OA of this box. Fig. 2.31b shows the right triangle OAB used to derive the first of the formulas (2.16): $F_y = F \cos \theta_y$. In Fig. 2.31a and c, two other right triangles have also been drawn: OAD and OAE. These triangles are seen to occupy in the box positions comparable with that of triangle OAB. Denoting by θ_x and θ_z, respectively, the angles that **F** forms with the x and z axes, we may derive two formulas similar to $F_y = F \cos \theta_y$. We thus write

$$F_x = F \cos \theta_x \qquad F_y = F \cos \theta_y \qquad F_z = F \cos \theta_z \tag{2.19}$$

The three angles θ_x, θ_y, θ_z define the direction of the force **F**; they are more commonly used for this purpose than the angles θ_y and ϕ introduced at the beginning of this section. The cosines of θ_x, θ_y, θ_z are known as the direction cosines of the force **F**.

Introducing the unit vectors **i**, **j**, and **k**, directed respectively along the x, y, and z axes (Fig. 2.32), we may express **F** in the form

$$\mathbf{F} = F_x\mathbf{i} + F_y\mathbf{j} + F_z\mathbf{k} \tag{2.20}$$

where the scalar components F_x, F_y, F_z are defined by the relations (2.19).

Example 1. A 100-lb force forms angles of 60, 45, and 120°, respectively, with the x, y, and z axes. Find the components F_x, F_y, and F_z of the force.

Substituting $F = 100$ lb, $\theta_x = 60°$, $\theta_y = 45°$, $\theta_z = 120°$ into formulas (2.19), we write

$$F_x = (100 \text{ lb}) \cos 60° = +50.0 \text{ lb}$$
$$F_y = (100 \text{ lb}) \cos 45° = +70.7 \text{ lb}$$
$$F_z = (100 \text{ lb}) \cos 120° = -50.0 \text{ lb}$$

Carrying into Eq. (2.20) the values obtained for the scalar components of **F**, we have

$$\mathbf{F} = (50.0 \text{ lb})\mathbf{i} + (70.7 \text{ lb})\mathbf{j} - (50.0 \text{ lb})\mathbf{k}$$

As in the case of two-dimensional problems, the plus sign indicates that the component has the same sense as the corresponding axis, and the minus sign that it has the opposite sense.

The angle a force **F** forms with an axis should be measured from the positive side of the axis and will always be comprised between 0 and 180°. An angle θ_x smaller than 90° (acute) indicates that **F** (assumed attached at O) is on the same side of

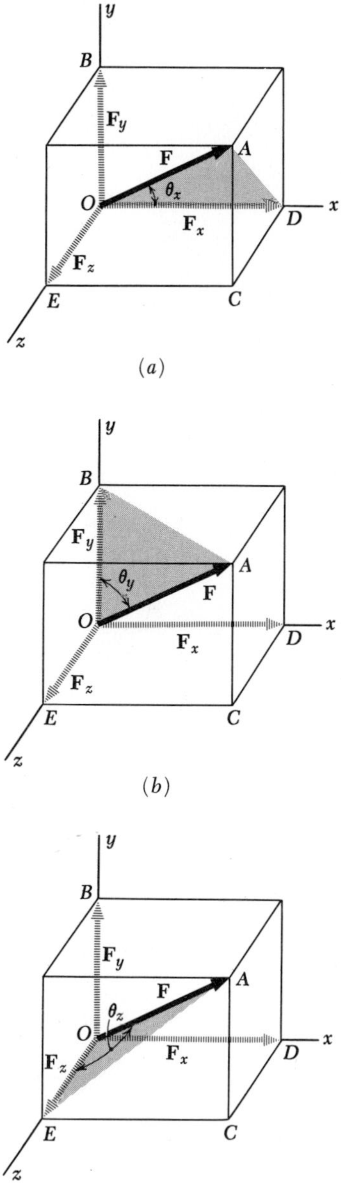

FIG. 2.31

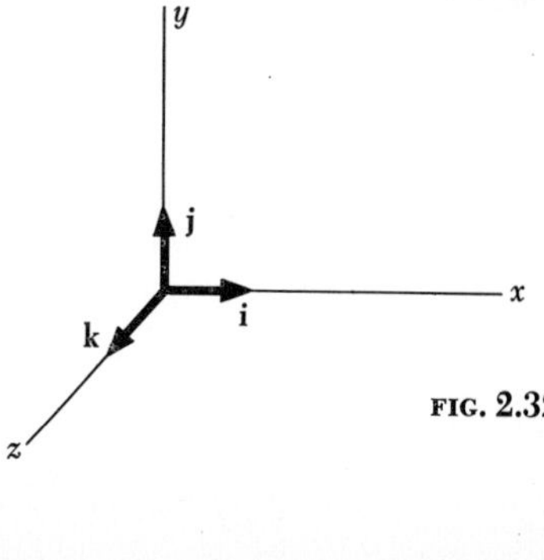

FIG. 2.32

the yz plane as the positive x axis; $\cos \theta_x$ and F_x will then be positive. An angle θ_x larger than 90° (obtuse) would indicate that **F** is on the other side of the yz plane; $\cos \theta_x$ and F_x would then be negative. In Example 1 the angles θ_x and θ_y are acute, while θ_z is obtuse: consequently, F_x and F_y are positive, while F_z is negative.

Substituting into (2.20) the expressions obtained for F_x, F_y, F_z in (2.19), we write

$$\mathbf{F} = F(\cos \theta_x \mathbf{i} + \cos \theta_y \mathbf{j} + \cos \theta_z \mathbf{k}) \qquad (2.21)$$

which shows that the force **F** may be expressed as the product of the scalar F and of the vector

$$\boldsymbol{\lambda} = \cos \theta_x \mathbf{i} + \cos \theta_y \mathbf{j} + \cos \theta_z \mathbf{k} \qquad (2.22)$$

Clearly, the vector $\boldsymbol{\lambda}$ is a vector of magnitude equal to 1 and of the same direction as **F** (Fig. 2.33). We shall refer to $\boldsymbol{\lambda}$

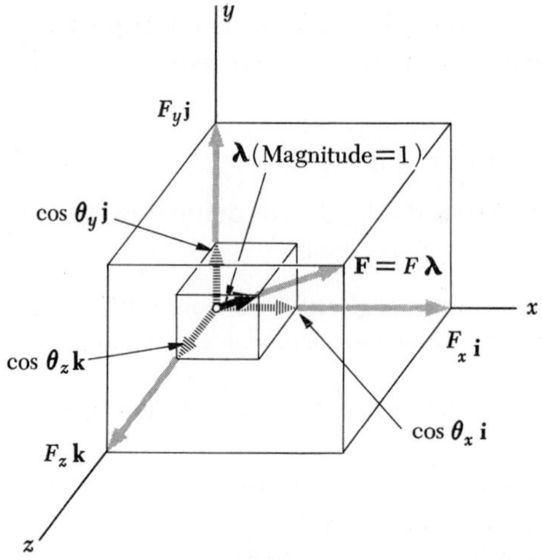

FIG. 2.33

as the *unit vector* along the line of action of **F**. It follows from (2.22) that the components of the unit vector $\boldsymbol{\lambda}$ are respectively equal to the direction cosines of the line of action of **F**:

$$\lambda_x = \cos \theta_x \qquad \lambda_y = \cos \theta_y \qquad \lambda_z = \cos \theta_z \qquad (2.23)$$

We should observe that the values of the three angles θ_x, θ_y, θ_z are not independent. Expressing that the sum of the squares of the components of $\boldsymbol{\lambda}$ is equal to the square of its magnitude, we write

$$\lambda_x^2 + \lambda_y^2 + \lambda_z^2 = 1$$

or, substituting for λ_x, λ_y, λ_z from (2.23),

$$\cos^2\theta_x + \cos^2\theta_y + \cos^2\theta_z = 1 \tag{2.24}$$

In Example 1, for instance, once the values $\theta_x = 60°$ and $\theta_y = 45°$ have been selected, the value of θ_z *must* be equal to 60° or 120° in order to satisfy identity (2.24).

When the components F_x, F_y, F_z of a force **F** are given, the magnitude F of the force is obtained from (2.18). The relations (2.19) may then be solved for the direction cosines, and the angles θ_x, θ_y, θ_z characterizing the direction of **F** may be found. However, these relations may also be written in the form

$$\frac{\cos\theta_x}{F_x} = \frac{\cos\theta_y}{F_y} = \frac{\cos\theta_z}{F_z} = \frac{1}{F} \tag{2.25}$$

which is better adapted to the use of the slide rule. Note that the relations obtained express that the components and the magnitudes of the unit vector $\boldsymbol{\lambda}$ and of the force **F** (i.e., the sides and the diagonals of the two "boxes" shown in Fig. 2.33) must be respectively proportional.

Example 2. A force **F** has the components $F_x = 20$ lb, $F_y = -30$ lb, $F_z = 60$ lb. Determine its magnitude F and the angles θ_x, θ_y, θ_z it forms with the axes of coordinates.

From formula (2.18) we obtain

$$F = \sqrt{F_x^2 + F_y^2 + F_z^2} = \sqrt{(20\text{ lb})^2 + (-30\text{ lb})^2 + (60\text{ lb})^2}$$
$$= \sqrt{4{,}900\text{ lb}} = 70\text{ lb}$$

Substituting the values of the components and of the magnitude of **F** into (2.25), we obtain

$$\frac{\cos\theta_x}{20\text{ lb}} = \frac{\cos\theta_y}{-30\text{ lb}} = \frac{\cos\theta_z}{60\text{ lb}} = \frac{1}{70\text{ lb}}$$

$$\theta_x = 73.4° \qquad \theta_y = 115.4° \qquad \theta_z = 31.0°$$

Note that, F_y being negative, the value of θ_y must be larger than 90°; thus θ_y is equal not to 64.6° but to its supplement, 115.4°.

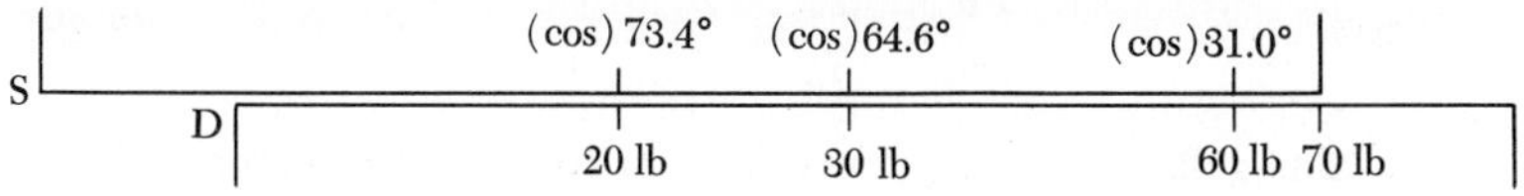

FIG. 2.34

Use of the Slide Rule. The angles θ_x, θ_y, θ_z defined by formula (2.25) are found on the slide rule by bringing one of the extremities of the S scale to coincide with F on the D scale. The values of θ_x, θ_y, θ_z are then read directly on the S scale (using angles corresponding to cosines) above F_x, F_y, F_z, respectively. The sketch of Fig. 2.34 shows the rule set to read the values corresponding to Example 2.

2.12. Force Defined by Its Magnitude and Two Points on Its Line of Action. In many applications, the direction of a force $\mathbf{F}$ is defined by the coordinates of two points, $M(x_1, y_1, z_1)$ and $N(x_2, y_2, z_2)$, located on its line of action (Fig. 2.35). Con-

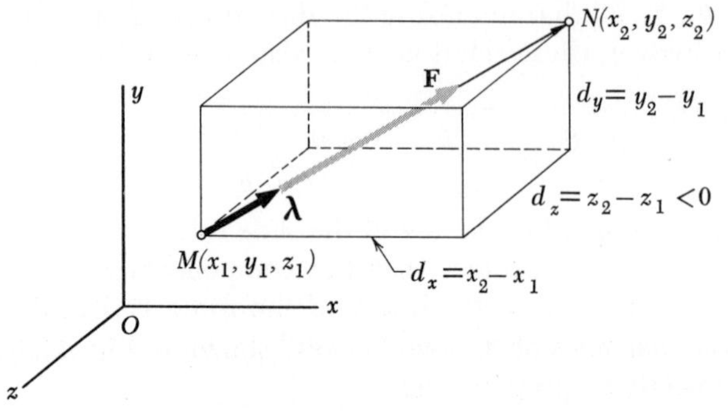

FIG. 2.35

sider the vector $\overrightarrow{MN}$ joining M and N and of the same sense as $\mathbf{F}$; we shall denote its scalar components by d_x, d_y, d_z, respectively, and its magnitude (i.e., the distance from M to N) by d. Since the vector $\overrightarrow{MN}$ has the same direction as $\mathbf{F}$ and, thus, the same direction as the unit vector $\boldsymbol{\lambda}$, we may express it as the product of d and $\boldsymbol{\lambda}$ and write

$$\overrightarrow{MN} = d_x\mathbf{i} + d_y\mathbf{j} + d_z\mathbf{k} = \boldsymbol{\lambda}\, d \tag{2.26}$$

Recalling that $\mathbf{F}$ is equal to the product of F and $\boldsymbol{\lambda}$, we also have

$$\mathbf{F} = F_x\mathbf{i} + F_y\mathbf{j} + F_z\mathbf{k} = \boldsymbol{\lambda}\, F \tag{2.27}$$

Observing that the coefficients of the unit vectors $\mathbf{i}$, $\mathbf{j}$, $\mathbf{k}$, and $\boldsymbol{\lambda}$ in Eqs. (2.26) and (2.27) must be proportional, we write

$$\frac{F_x}{d_x} = \frac{F_y}{d_y} = \frac{F_z}{d_z} = \frac{F}{d} \tag{2.28}$$

The relations (2.28) considerably simplify the determination of the components of a force $\mathbf{F}$ of given magnitude F when the line of action of $\mathbf{F}$ is defined by two points M and N. Subtracting the coordinates of M from those of N, we first determine the components of the vector $\overrightarrow{MN}$ and the distance d

from M to N.

$$d_x = x_2 - x_1 \qquad d_y = y_2 - y_1 \qquad d_z = z_2 - z_1$$

$$d = \sqrt{d_x^2 + d_y^2 + d_z^2} \tag{2.29}$$

Substituting for F and for d_x, d_y, d_z, and d into the relations (2.28), we obtain the components F_x, F_y, F_z of the force. This computation, which is easily performed on the slide rule, has been carried out in Sample Prob. 2.8. Since the vector $\overrightarrow{MN}$ was chosen to have the same sense as **F**, the components F_x, F_y, and F_z will have, respectively, the same signs as d_x, d_y, and d_z.

Comparing Eqs. (2.22) and (2.26), we may also write the proportions

$$\frac{\cos\theta_x}{d_x} = \frac{\cos\theta_y}{d_y} = \frac{\cos\theta_z}{d_z} = \frac{1}{d} \tag{2.30}$$

These relations may be used to obtain the angles θ_x, θ_y, θ_z that **F** forms with the coordinate axes, directly from the components d_x, d_y, d_z, and the distance d.

2.13. Addition of Concurrent Forces in Space. We shall determine the resultant **R** of two or more forces in space by summing their rectangular components. Graphical or trigonometric methods are generally not practical in the case of forces in space.

The method followed here is similar to that used in Sec. 2.7 with coplanar forces. Setting

$$\mathbf{R} = \Sigma\mathbf{F}$$

we resolve each force into its rectangular components and write

$$R_x\mathbf{i} + R_y\mathbf{j} + R_z\mathbf{k} = \Sigma\,(F_x\mathbf{i} + F_y\mathbf{j} + F_z\mathbf{k})$$
$$= (\Sigma F_x)\mathbf{i} + (\Sigma F_y)\mathbf{j} + (\Sigma F_z)\mathbf{k}$$

from which it follows that

$$R_x = \Sigma F_x \qquad R_y = \Sigma F_y \qquad R_z = \Sigma F_z \tag{2.31}$$

The magnitude of the resultant **R** and the angles θ_x, θ_y, θ_z it forms with the axes of coordinates are obtained by the method of Sec. 2.11. We write

$$R = \sqrt{R_x^2 + R_y^2 + R_z^2} \tag{2.32}$$

$$\frac{\cos\theta_x}{R_x} = \frac{\cos\theta_y}{R_y} = \frac{\cos\theta_z}{R_z} = \frac{1}{R} \tag{2.33}$$

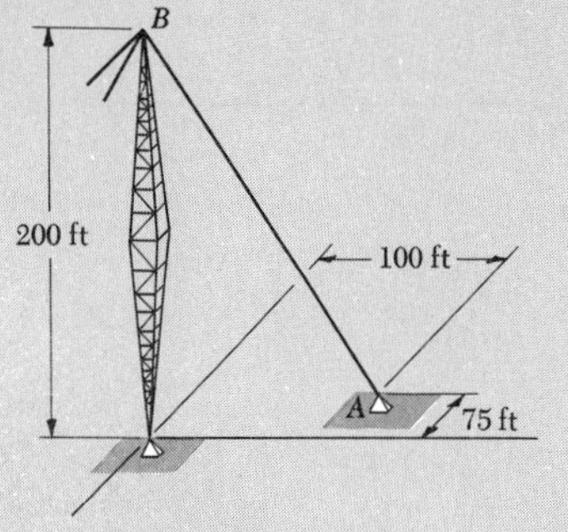

SAMPLE PROBLEM 2.8

A tower guy wire is anchored by means of a bolt at A. The tension in the wire is 2,500 lb. Determine (a) the components F_x, F_y, F_z of the force acting on the bolt, (b) the angles θ_x, θ_y, θ_z defining the direction of the force.

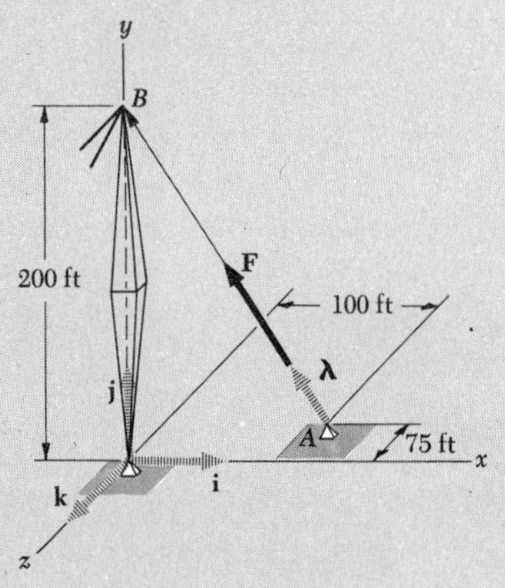

a. **Components of the Force.** The line of action of the force acting on the bolt passes through A and B; and the force is directed from A to B. The components of the vector AB, which has the same direction as the force, are

$$d_x = -100 \text{ ft} \qquad d_y = +200 \text{ ft} \qquad d_z = +75 \text{ ft}$$

The total distance from A to B is

$$d = \sqrt{d_x^2 + d_y^2 + d_z^2} = 236 \text{ ft}$$

Introducing the unit vectors **i**, **j**, **k** along the axes of coordinates, and the unit vector $\boldsymbol{\lambda}$ along AB, we write

$$\overrightarrow{AB} = -(100 \text{ ft})\mathbf{i} + (200 \text{ ft})\mathbf{j} + (75 \text{ ft})\mathbf{k} = (236 \text{ ft})\,\boldsymbol{\lambda} \qquad (1)$$

$$\mathbf{F} = F_x\mathbf{i} + F_y\mathbf{j} + F_z\mathbf{k} = (2{,}500 \text{ lb})\boldsymbol{\lambda} \qquad (2)$$

Expressing that the coefficients of the unit vectors in (1) and (2) are proportional, we write

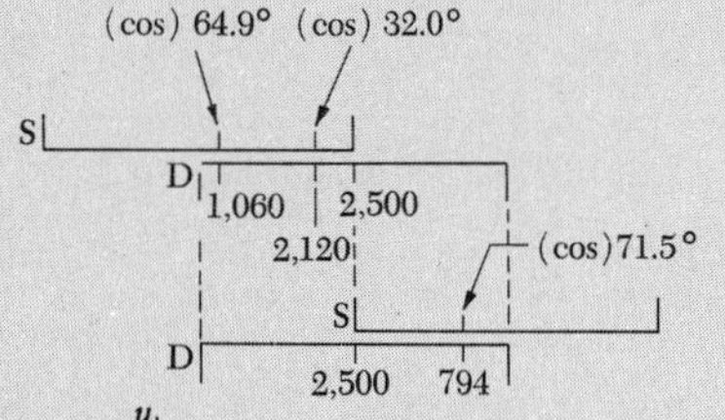

$$\frac{F_x}{-100 \text{ ft}} = \frac{F_y}{+200 \text{ ft}} = \frac{F_z}{+75 \text{ ft}} = \frac{2{,}500 \text{ lb}}{236 \text{ ft}}$$

and obtain

$$F_x = -1{,}060 \text{ lb} \qquad F_y = +2{,}120 \text{ lb} \qquad F_z = +794 \text{ lb}$$ ◄

b. **Direction of Force.** Recalling that the components of the unit vector $\boldsymbol{\lambda}$ are respectively equal to the direction cosines of **F**, we write

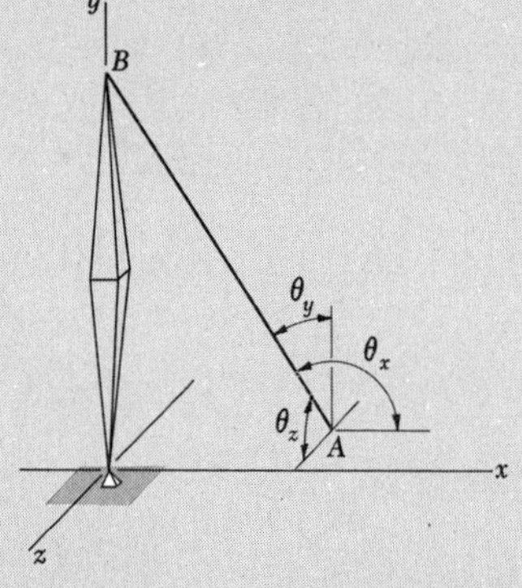

$$\cos\theta_x\mathbf{i} + \cos\theta_y\mathbf{j} + \cos\theta_z\mathbf{k} = \boldsymbol{\lambda} \qquad (3)$$

$$\mathbf{F} = -(1{,}060 \text{ lb})\mathbf{i} + (2{,}120 \text{ lb})\mathbf{j} + (794 \text{ lb})\mathbf{k} = (2{,}500 \text{ lb})\,\boldsymbol{\lambda} \qquad (4)$$

Expressing that the coefficients of the unit vectors in (3) and (4) are proportional, we have

$$\frac{\cos\theta_x}{-1{,}060 \text{ lb}} = \frac{\cos\theta_y}{+2{,}120 \text{ lb}} = \frac{\cos\theta_z}{+794 \text{ lb}} = \frac{1}{2{,}500 \text{ lb}}$$

$$\theta_x = 180° - 64.9° = 115.1° \qquad \theta_y = 32.0° \qquad \theta_z = 71.5°$$ ◄

This result may also be obtained by using proportions involving the components of the vector AB instead of the components of **F**.

SAMPLE PROBLEM 2.9

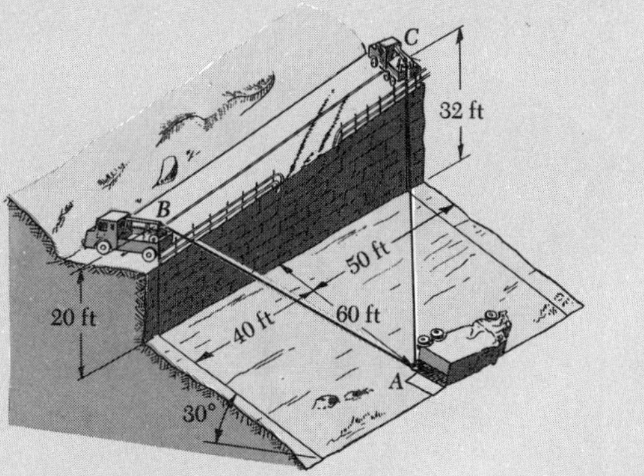

In order to move a wrecked truck, two cables are attached to the truck at A and pulled by winches B and C as shown. Determine the resultant of the forces exerted on the truck by the two cables, knowing that the tension is 2,000 lb in cable AB and 1,500 lb in cable AC.

Solution. The force exerted by each cable on the truck will be resolved into x, y, and z components. We first determine the components and magnitudes of the vectors AB and AC, measuring them from the truck toward each winch.

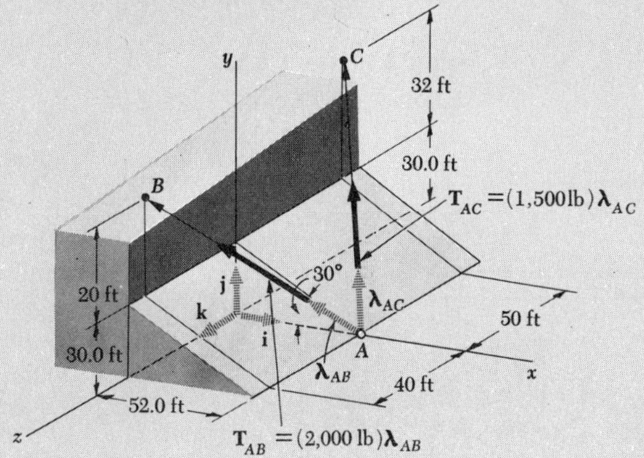

Cable AB (A to B): $\quad d_x = -52$ ft $\quad d_y = +50$ ft $\quad d_z = +40$ ft $\quad d = 82.5$ ft

Cable AC (A to C): $\quad d_x = -52$ ft $\quad d_y = +62$ ft $\quad d_z = -50$ ft $\quad d = 95.1$ ft

Denoting by **i**, **j**, **k** the unit vectors along the coordinate axes, and by $\boldsymbol{\lambda}_{AB}$ the unit vector along AB, we write

$$\overrightarrow{AB} = -(52\text{ ft})\mathbf{i} + (50\text{ ft})\mathbf{j} + (40\text{ ft})\mathbf{k} = (82.5\text{ ft})\boldsymbol{\lambda}_{AB}$$
$$\mathbf{T}_{AB} = F_x\mathbf{i} + F_y\mathbf{j} + F_z\mathbf{k} = (2{,}000\text{ lb})\boldsymbol{\lambda}_{AB}$$

and find the components of $\mathbf{T}_{AB}$ by proportions. We have

$$\mathbf{T}_{AB} = -(1{,}260\text{ lb})\mathbf{i} + (1{,}212\text{ lb})\mathbf{j} + (970\text{ lb})\mathbf{k}$$

Denoting by $\boldsymbol{\lambda}_{AC}$ the unit vector along AC, we write in a similar way

$$\overrightarrow{AC} = -(52\text{ ft})\mathbf{i} + (62\text{ ft})\mathbf{j} - (50\text{ ft})\mathbf{k} = (95.1\text{ ft})\boldsymbol{\lambda}_{AC}$$
$$\mathbf{T}_{AC} = F_x\mathbf{i} + F_y\mathbf{j} + F_z\mathbf{k} = (1{,}500\text{ lb})\boldsymbol{\lambda}_{AC}$$

and, by proportions,

$$\mathbf{T}_{AC} = -(820\text{ lb})\mathbf{i} + (978\text{ lb})\mathbf{j} - (788\text{ lb})\mathbf{k}$$

The resultant **R** of the forces exerted by the two cables is

$$\mathbf{R} = \mathbf{T}_{AB} + \mathbf{T}_{AC} = -(2{,}080\text{ lb})\mathbf{i} + (2{,}190\text{ lb})\mathbf{j} + (182\text{ lb})\mathbf{k}$$

The magnitude R of the resultant is

$$R = \sqrt{(-2{,}080)^2 + (2{,}190)^2 + (182)^2} = 3{,}030\text{ lb} \quad ◄$$

Recalling that the direction cosines of the resultant represent the components of the unit vector $\boldsymbol{\lambda}_R$ directed along **R**, we write

$$\cos\theta_x\mathbf{i} + \cos\theta_y\mathbf{j} + \cos\theta_z\mathbf{k} = \boldsymbol{\lambda}_R$$
$$\mathbf{R} = -(2{,}080\text{ lb})\mathbf{i} + (2{,}190\text{ lb})\mathbf{j} + (182\text{ lb})\mathbf{k} = (3{,}030\text{ lb})\boldsymbol{\lambda}_R$$

and, by proportions,

$$\frac{\cos\theta_x}{-2{,}080\text{ lb}} = \frac{\cos\theta_y}{+2{,}190\text{ lb}} = \frac{\cos\theta_z}{+182\text{ lb}} = \frac{1}{3{,}030\text{ lb}}$$

$$\theta_x = 180° - 46.6° = 133.4° \qquad \theta_y = 43.7° \qquad \theta_z = 86.6° \quad ◄$$

PROBLEMS

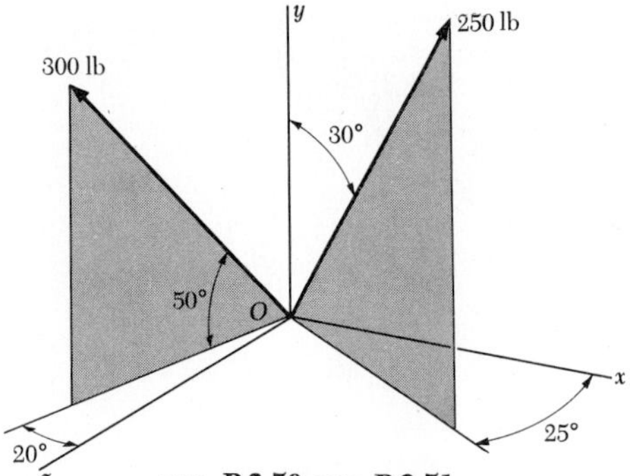

FIG. P 2.50 AND P 2.51

2.50. Determine (*a*) the *x*, *y*, and *z* components of the 250-lb force, (*b*) the angles θ_x, θ_y, and θ_z that the force forms with the coordinate axes.

2.51. Determine (*a*) the *x*, *y*, and *z* components of the 300-lb force, (*b*) the angles θ_x, θ_y, and θ_z that the force forms with the coordinate axes.

2.52. A force of 500 lb, directed along the axis of the boom from *A* to *O*, is exerted on the support at *O*. Knowing that $\alpha = 35°$ and $\beta = 65°$, determine (*a*) the *x*, *y*, and *z* components of the force exerted at *O*, (*b*) the angles θ_x, θ_y, and θ_z for the force exerted at *O*.

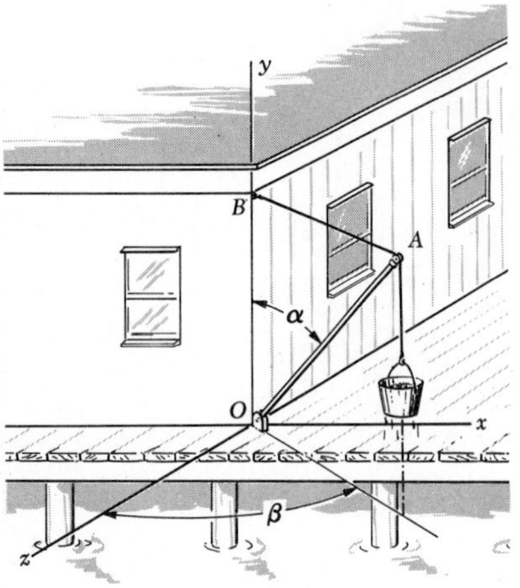

FIG. P 2.52

2.53. A gun is aimed so that it will fire at a point *A* which is 30° east of north and is 15 ft above the gun in elevation. The horizontal distance from the gun to point *A* is 50 ft. If at a given instant the recoil force of the gun is 80 lb, determine (*a*) the *x*, *y*, and *z* components of the recoil force, (*b*) the values of θ_x, θ_y, and θ_z. (Assume the *x* axis is toward the east, the *y* axis is up, and the *z* axis is south.)

2.54. A 400-lb force acts at the origin in a direction defined by the angles $\theta_y = 80.0°$ and $\theta_z = 46.0°$. It is also known that the *x* component of the force is positive. Determine the value of θ_x and the components of the force.

2.55. A force acts at the origin in a direction defined by the angles $\theta_x = 125.0°$ and $\theta_z = 65.0°$. It is known that the *y* component of the force is +3.20 lb. Determine the magnitude of the force and the value of θ_y.

2.56. A precast-concrete wall section is temporarily held by the cables shown. If the tension in cable *AB* is 700 lb, determine the components of the force exerted on the wall section at *A*.

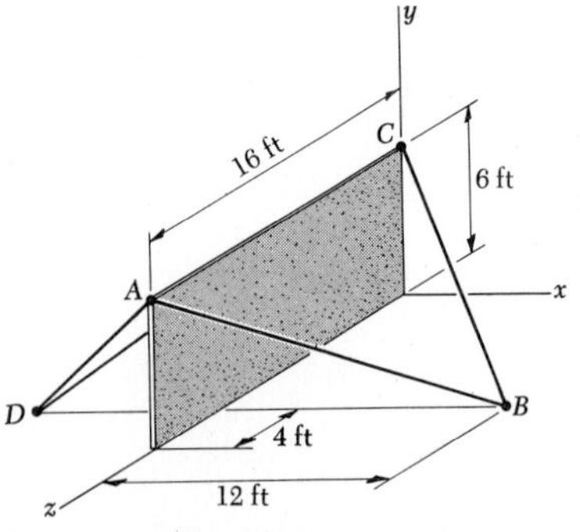

FIG. P 2.56, P 2.57, AND P 2.62

2.57. Knowing that the tension in cable *BC* is 900 lb, determine the components of the force exerted on the wall section at *C*.

2.58. Determine the magnitude and direction of the force $\mathbf{F} = 150\mathbf{i} - 75\mathbf{j} + 200\mathbf{k}$ (lb).

2.59. Determine the magnitude and direction of the force $\mathbf{F} = -150\mathbf{i} - 350\mathbf{j} + 200\mathbf{k}$ (lb).

2.60. Determine the angles θ_x, θ_y, and θ_z which define the direction of the force exerted on point A in Prob. 2.56.

2.61. Determine the angles θ_x, θ_y, and θ_z which define the direction of the force exerted on point C in Prob. 2.57.

2.62. The tension in cable AB is 700 lb and the tension in cable BC is 900 lb. Determine the components of the resultant of the forces exerted by the cables on point B.

2.63. Several guy wires are attached to the top of the tower at A. The tension in AB is 5,200 lb and the tension in AC is 3,500 lb. Determine the resultant of the two forces exerted by these two cables on point A.

2.64. Knowing that the tension in AC is 7,000 lb, determine the required values of the tension in AB and AD so that the resultant of the three forces applied at A is vertical.

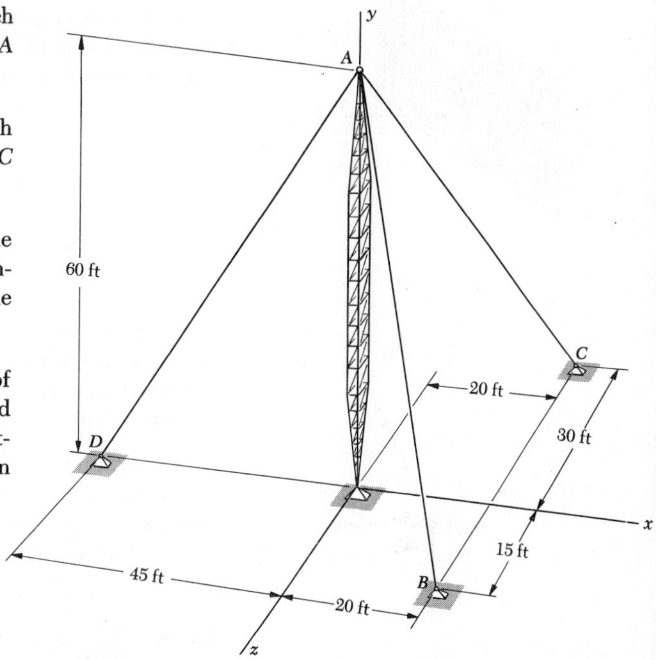

FIG. P 2.63 AND P 2.64

2.65. Determine the two possible values of θ_y for a force **F**, (*a*) if the force forms equal angles with the positive x, y, and z axes, (*b*) if the force forms equal angles with the positive y and z axes and an angle of 45° with the positive x axis.

2.14. Equilibrium of a Particle in Space. According to the definition given in Sec. 2.8, a particle A is in equilibrium if the resultant of all the forces acting on A is zero. The components R_x, R_y, R_z of the resultant are given by the relations (2.31); expressing that the components of the resultant are zero, we write

$$\Sigma F_x = 0 \qquad \Sigma F_y = 0 \qquad \Sigma F_z = 0 \tag{2.34}$$

Equations (2.34) represent the necessary and sufficient conditions for the equilibrium of a particle in space. They may be used to solve problems dealing with the equilibrium of a particle and involving no more than three unknowns.

To solve such problems, we first should draw a free-body diagram showing the particle in equilibrium and *all* the forces acting on it. We may then write the equations of equilibrium (2.34) and solve them for three unknowns. In the more common types of problems, these unknowns will represent (1) the three components of a single force or (2) the magnitude of three forces each of known direction.

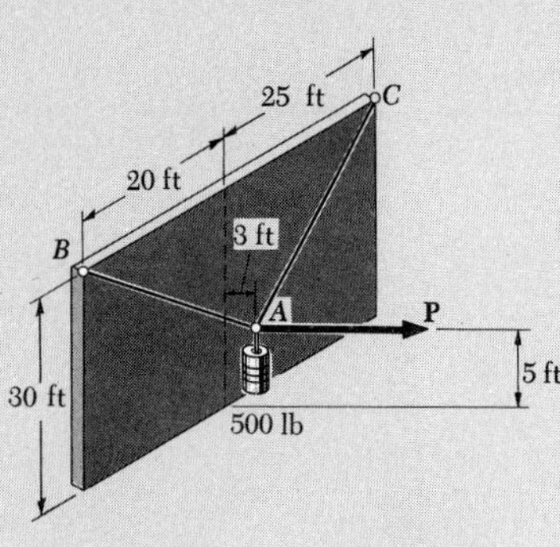

SAMPLE PROBLEM 2.10

A 500-lb weight is hung by means of two cables AB and AC, which are attached to the top of a vertical wall. A horizontal force **P** perpendicular to the wall holds the weight in the position shown. Determine the magnitude of **P** and the tension in each cable.

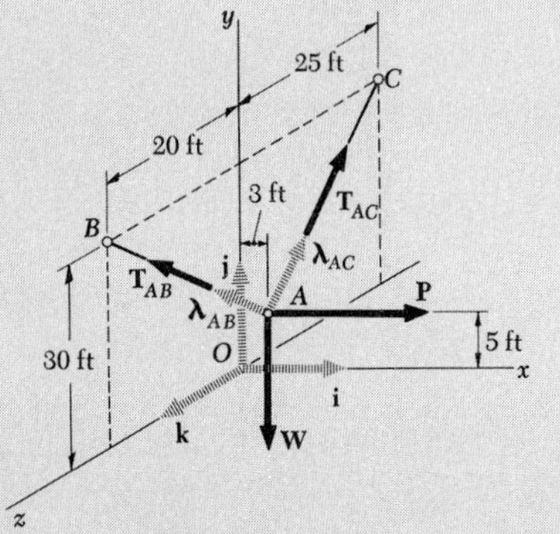

Solution. Point A is chosen as a free body; this point is subjected to four forces, three of which are of unknown magnitude.

Introducing the unit vectors **i**, **j**, **k**, we resolve each force into rectangular components.

$$\mathbf{P} = P\mathbf{i} \qquad \mathbf{W} = -500\mathbf{j} \tag{1}$$

In the case of $\mathbf{T}_{AB}$ and $\mathbf{T}_{AC}$, it is necessary first to determine the components and magnitudes of the vectors $\overrightarrow{AB}$ and $\overrightarrow{AC}$. Denoting by $\boldsymbol{\lambda}_{AB}$ the unit vector along AB, we write

$$\overrightarrow{AB} = -(3\text{ ft})\mathbf{i} + (25\text{ ft})\mathbf{j} + (20\text{ ft})\mathbf{k} \qquad AB = 32.2\text{ ft}$$

$$\boldsymbol{\lambda}_{AB} = \frac{\overrightarrow{AB}}{32.2\text{ ft}} = -0.0932\mathbf{i} + 0.776\mathbf{j} + 0.621\mathbf{k}$$

$$\mathbf{T}_{AB} = T_{AB}\boldsymbol{\lambda}_{AB} = -0.0932T_{AB}\mathbf{i} + 0.776T_{AB}\mathbf{j} + 0.621T_{AB}\mathbf{k} \tag{2}$$

Denoting by $\boldsymbol{\lambda}_{AC}$ the unit vector along AC, we write in a similar way

$$\overrightarrow{AC} = -(3\text{ ft})\mathbf{i} + (25\text{ ft})\mathbf{j} - (25\text{ ft})\mathbf{k} \qquad AC = 35.5\text{ ft}$$

$$\boldsymbol{\lambda}_{AC} = \frac{\overrightarrow{AC}}{35.5\text{ ft}} = -0.0845\mathbf{i} + 0.704\mathbf{j} - 0.704\mathbf{k}$$

$$\mathbf{T}_{AC} = T_{AC}\boldsymbol{\lambda}_{AC} = -0.0845T_{AC}\mathbf{i} + 0.704T_{AC}\mathbf{j} - 0.704T_{AC}\mathbf{k} \tag{3}$$

Since point A is in equilibrium, we must have

$$\Sigma\mathbf{F} = 0: \qquad \mathbf{T}_{AB} + \mathbf{T}_{AC} + \mathbf{P} + \mathbf{W} = 0$$

or, substituting from (1), (2), (3) for the various forces and factoring **i**, **j**, **k**,

$$(-0.0932T_{AB} - 0.0845T_{AC} + P)\mathbf{i} + (0.776T_{AB} + 0.704T_{AC} - 500)\mathbf{j} + (0.621T_{AB} - 0.704T_{AC})\mathbf{k} = 0$$

Setting the coefficients of **i**, **j**, **k** equal to zero, we write three scalar equations, which express that the sums of the x, y, and z components of the forces are respectively equal to zero.

$$(\Sigma F_x = 0:) \qquad -0.0932T_{AB} - 0.0845T_{AC} + P = 0$$
$$(\Sigma F_y = 0:) \qquad +0.776T_{AB} + 0.704T_{AC} - 500 = 0$$
$$(\Sigma F_z = 0:) \qquad +0.621T_{AB} - 0.704T_{AC} = 0$$

Solving these equations, we obtain

$$P = 60\text{ lb} \qquad T_{AB} = 358\text{ lb} \qquad T_{AC} = 316\text{ lb}$$ ◄

PROBLEMS

2.66. A load W is supported by three cables as shown. Determine the value of W, knowing that the tension in cable BD is 200 lb.

2.67. A load W is supported by three cables as shown. Determine the value of W, knowing that the tension in cable CD is 450 lb.

2.68. A load W of magnitude 262 lb is supported by three cables as shown. Determine the tension in each cable.

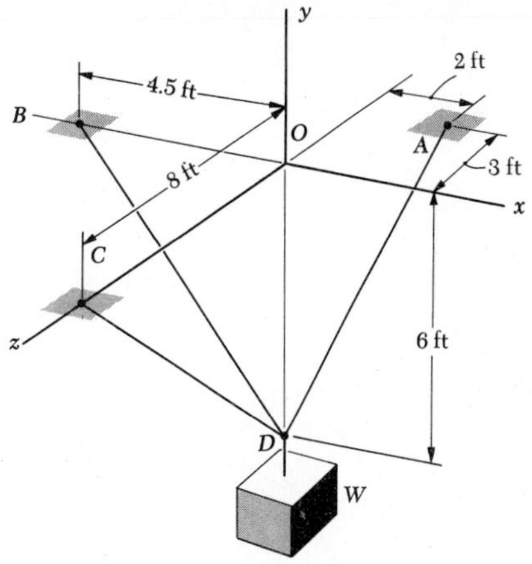

FIG. P 2.66, P 2.67, AND P 2.68

2.69. Three cables are joined at D where an upward force of 6,000 lb is applied. Determine the tension in each cable.

2.70. A 50-lb load is supported by three ropes which are attached to a ceiling as shown. Determine the tension in each rope.

2.71. A pole AB is used to support a 180-lb weight which hangs very close to the intersection of two smooth walls. It is known that the force exerted on point B by the pole must be directed along the pole and that the force exerted on point B by a wall must be perpendicular to the wall. Determine the force exerted on B by the pole and by each wall, when $a = 6$ ft, $b = 2$ ft, and $h = 3$ ft.

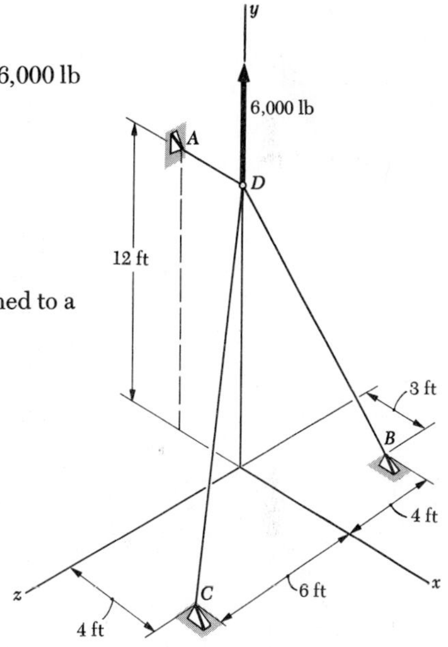

FIG. P 2.69

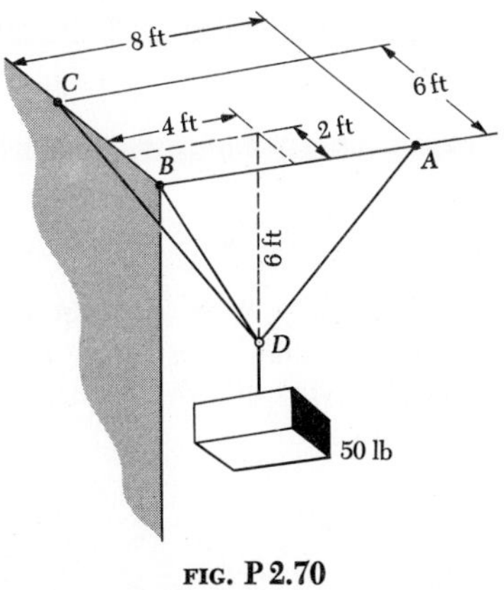

FIG. P 2.70

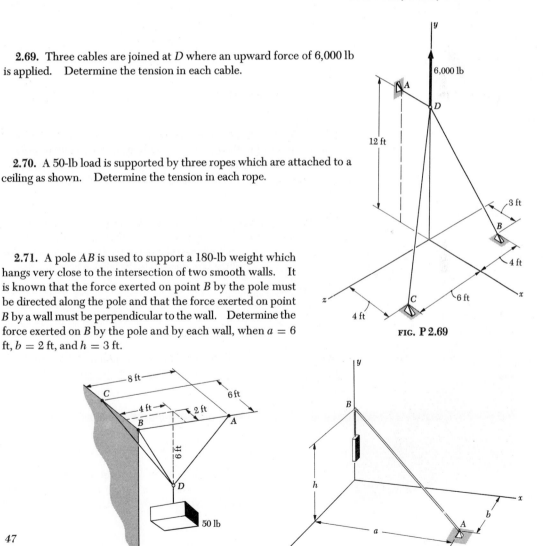

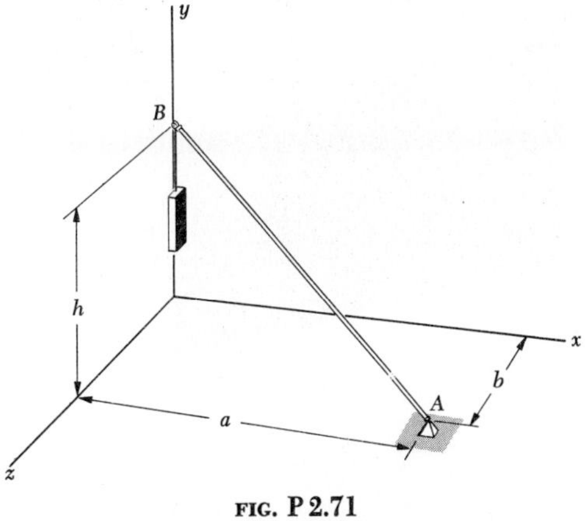

FIG. P 2.71

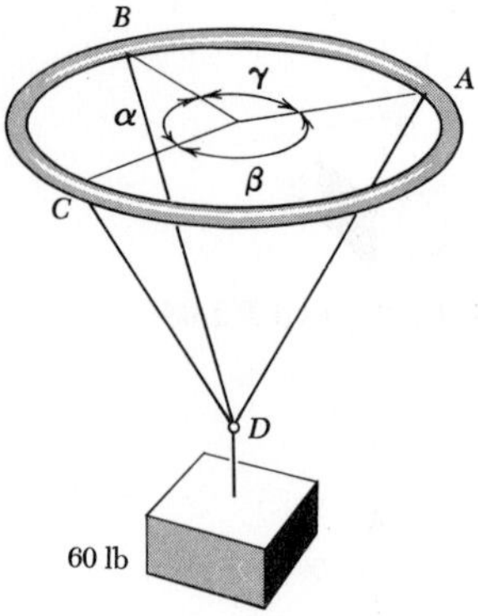

FIG. P 2.72

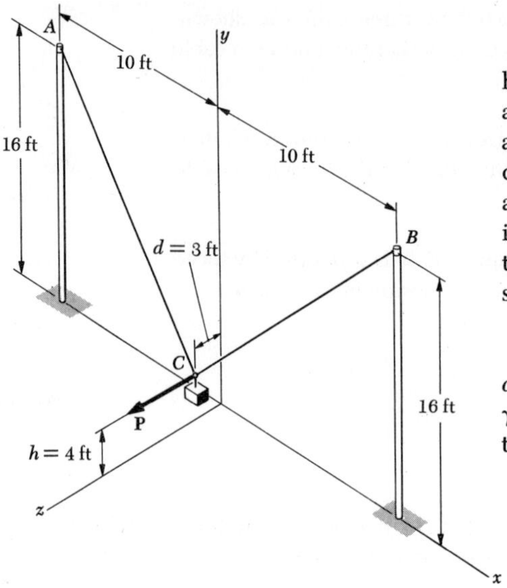

FIG. P 2.74

2.72. A 60-lb weight is hung by three strings which are attached to a ring and are tied together at D. The diameter of the ring is 24 in., and the length of each string is 20 in. If $\alpha = \beta = \gamma$, determine the tension in each string.

2.73. If, in Prob. 2.72, $\alpha = 80°$, $\beta = 130°$, and $\gamma = 150°$, determine the tension in each string.

2.74. A 500-lb weight is hung by means of two cables AC and BC, which are attached to the top of vertical posts. A horizontal force **P**, perpendicular to the plane containing the posts, holds the weight in the position shown. Determine the magnitude of **P** and the tension in each cable.

2.75. A 20-lb instrument is hung inside a box by means of three strings. If the instrument hangs directly in the center of the box and the strings are tied together at a point D, 3 in. below the top of the box, determine the tension in each string.

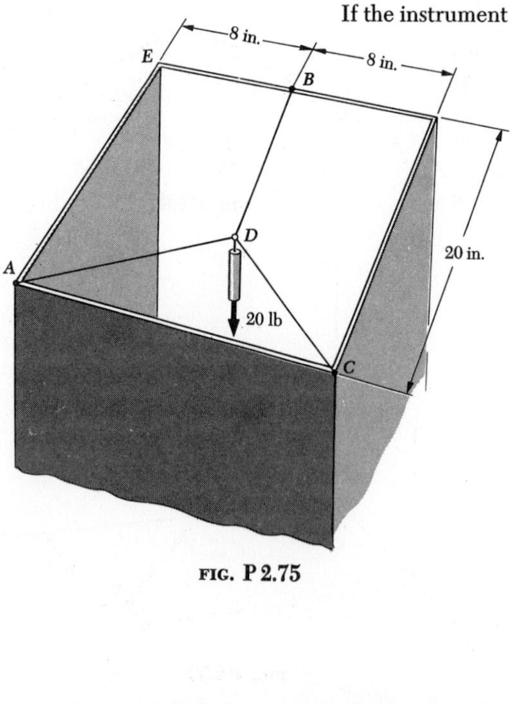

FIG. P 2.75

2.76. Solve Prob. 2.75 assuming that string BD is removed and replaced by a string between D and E.

2.77. Solve Prob. 2.75 assuming that point D is located only ½ in. below the top of the box. (Explain why this arrangement results in higher tensions.)

2.78. A pole AB of length 10 ft is used to support a 180-lb weight as shown in Prob. 2.71. If the force exerted on point B by the pole must not exceed 300 lb, determine (*a*) the smallest value of h that may be used, (*b*) the area of the floor in which point A must be located.

***2.79.** In Prob. 2.74 the weight is held in equilibrium by a force **P** of magnitude 200 lb. Determine the value of d and of h for this equilibrium position.

REVIEW PROBLEMS

2.80. A chain loop of length 5 ft is placed around a 1- by 1-ft piece of lumber as shown. Knowing that the weight lifted by the crane hook is 800 lb, determine the tension in the chain in each case.

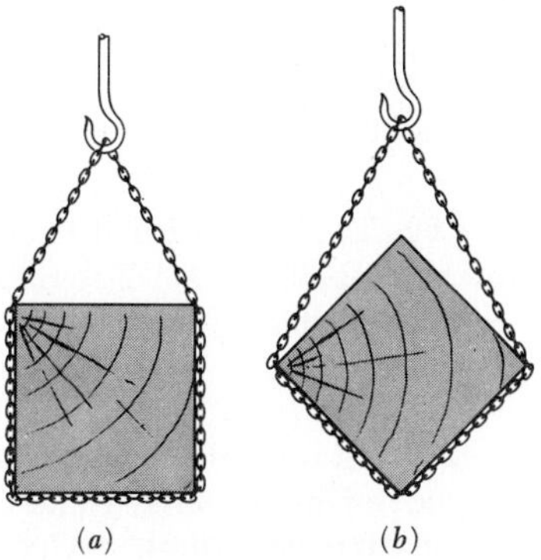

FIG. P 2.80

2.81. Knowing that the magnitude of the force **P** is 500 lb, determine the resultant of the three forces applied at A.

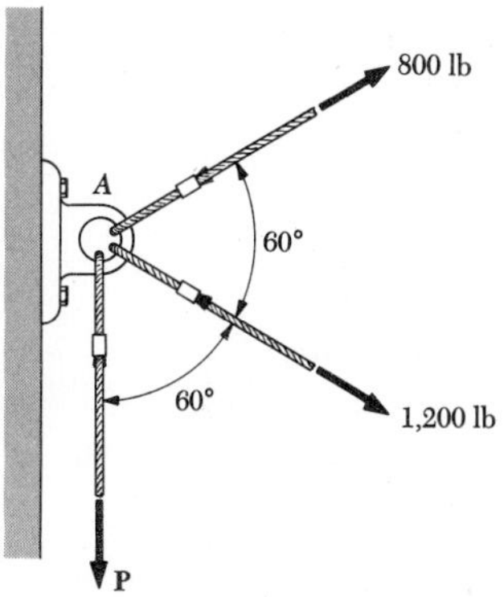

FIG. P 2.81 AND P 2.82

2.82. Determine the magnitude of the force **P** for which the resultant of the three forces applied at A is 2,000 lb.

2.83. Three cables are connected at D, which lies 4 ft below the x axis, and support the load $W = 600$ lb. Determine the tension in each cable.

2.84. Determine the angles θ_x, θ_y, and θ_z for the force exerted (*a*) at A by cable AD, (*b*) at B by cable BD, (*c*) at C by cable CD.

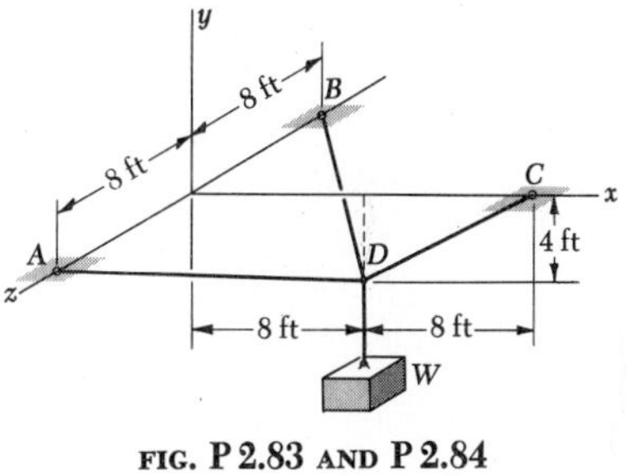

FIG. P 2.83 AND P 2.84

2.85. Resolve the 1,500-lb force into a component directed along the line a-a and a component directed along the line b-b.

2.86. Resolve the 1,500-lb force into a component directed along the line a-a and a component directed along the line c-c.

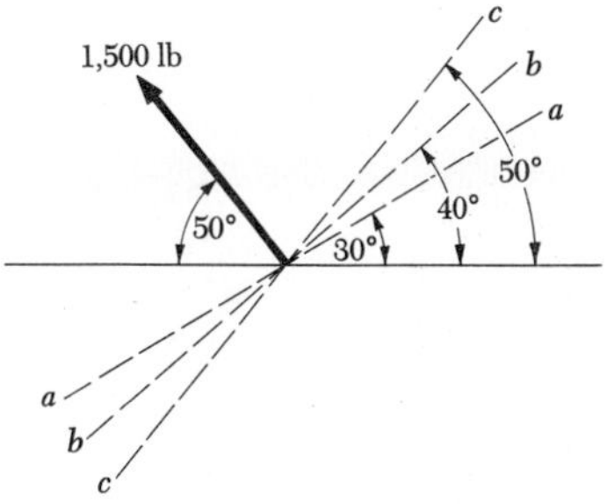

FIG. P 2.85 AND P 2.86

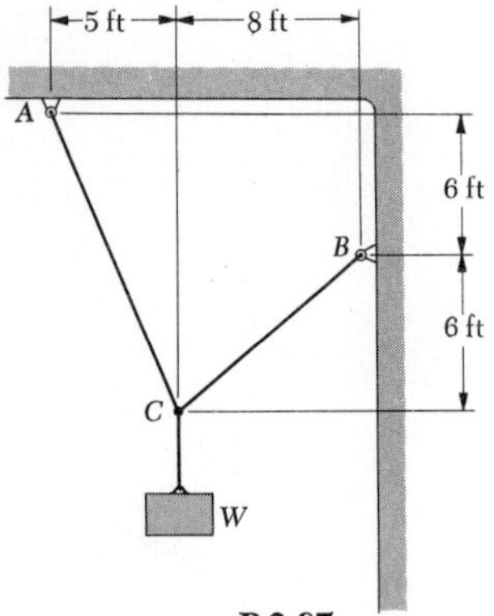

FIG. P 2.87

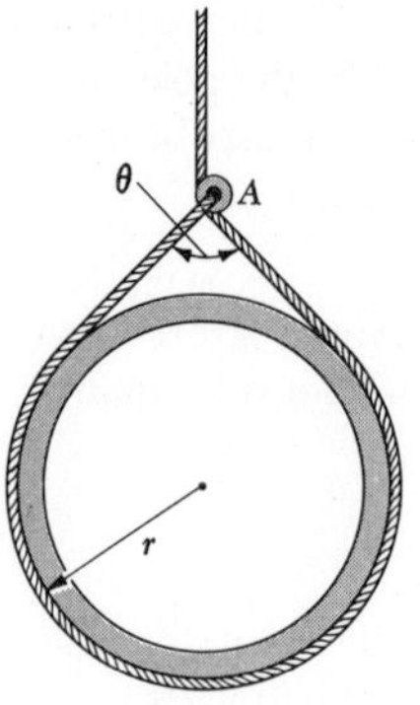

FIG. P 2.88

2.87. Two cables are tied together at C and loaded as shown. Knowing that the maximum permissible tension in AC and in BC is 650 lb, determine the largest weight W which can be safely supported.

2.88. A small pulley is attached to the end of a rope which is looped around a pipe of radius r and weight W. Determine (a) the angle θ, (b) the tension in the rope if $r = 10$ in. and $W = 100$ lb.

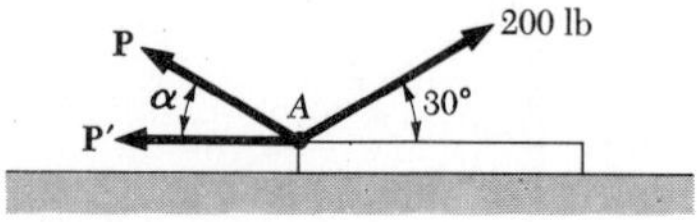

FIG. P 2.89 AND P 2.90

2.89. Two forces, **P** and **P′**, of the same magnitude P, and a 200-lb force are applied at A. Determine the required magnitude P and angle α if the resultant of the three forces is to be a vertical upward force of 250 lb.

2.90. Knowing that $\alpha = 60°$, determine the required common magnitude P of the two forces **P** and **P′** if the resultant of the three forces acting at A is to be vertical. What is the corresponding magnitude of the resultant?

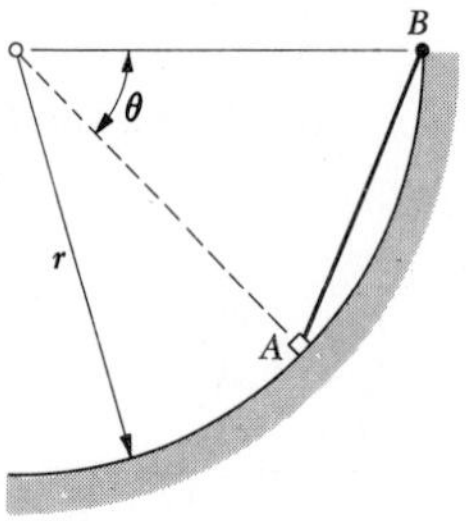

FIG. P 2.91

2.91. A particle A of weight W is supported by a string on a circular cylindrical surface as shown. Assuming that the force **N** exerted on A by the surface is normal to the surface, show that $N = W \tan \theta/2$. What is the corresponding tension in the string?

3. RIGID BODIES. EQUIVALENT SYSTEMS OF FORCES

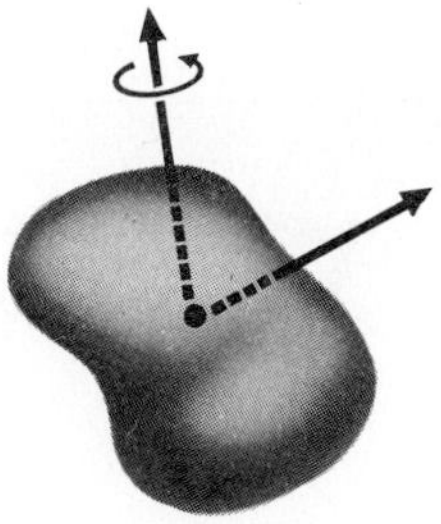

3.1. Rigid Bodies. External and Internal Forces. In the preceding chapter it was assumed that each of the bodies considered could be treated as a single particle. Such a view, however, is not always possible, and a body, in general, should be treated as a combination of a large number of particles. The size of the body will have to be taken into consideration, as well as the fact that forces will act on different particles and thus will have different points of application.

Most of the bodies considered in elementary mechanics are assumed to be *rigid*, a *rigid body* being defined as one which does not deform. Actual structures and machines, however, are never absolutely rigid and deform under the loads to which they are subjected. But these deformations are usually small and do not appreciably affect the conditions of equilibrium or motion of the structure under consideration. They are important, though, as far as the resistance of the structure to failure is concerned, and are considered in the study of mechanics of materials.

Forces acting on rigid bodies may be separated into two groups: (1) *external forces;* (2) *internal forces.*

1. The *external forces* represent the action of other bodies on the rigid body under consideration. They are entirely responsible for the external behavior of the rigid body. They will either cause it to move or assure that it remains at rest. We shall be concerned only with external forces in this chapter and in Chaps. 4 and 5.

2. The *internal forces* are the forces which hold together the particles forming the rigid body. If the rigid body is structurally composed of several parts, the forces holding the component parts together are also defined as internal forces. Internal forces will be considered in Chaps. 6 and 7.

FIG. 3.1

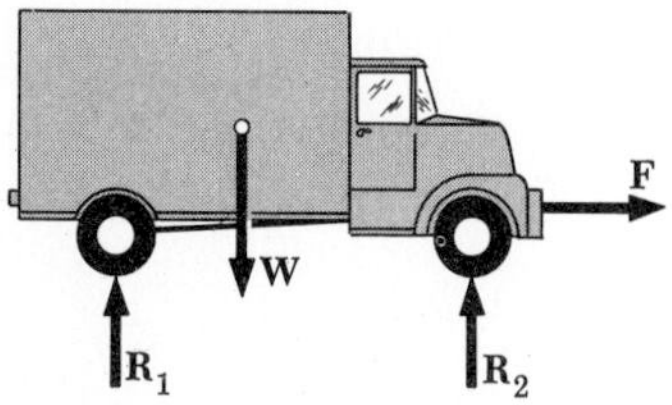

FIG. 3.2

As an example of external forces, we shall consider the forces acting on a disabled truck that men are pulling forward by means of a rope attached to the front bumper (Fig. 3.1). The external forces acting on the truck are shown in a *free-body diagram* (Fig. 3.2). Let us first consider the *weight* of the truck. Although it embodies the effect of the earth's pull on each of the particles forming the truck, the weight may be represented by the single force **W**. The *point of application* of this force, i.e., the point at which the force acts, is defined as the *center of gravity* of the truck. It will be seen in Chap. 5 how centers of gravity may be determined. The weight **W** tends to make the truck move vertically downward. In fact, it would actually cause the truck to move downward, i.e., to fall, if it were not for the presence of the ground. The ground opposes the downward motion of the truck by means of the reactions $\mathbf{R}_1$ and $\mathbf{R}_2$. These forces are exerted *by* the ground *on* the truck and must therefore be included among the external forces acting on the truck.

The men pulling on the rope exert the force **F**. The point of application of **F** is on the front bumper. The force **F** tends to make the truck move forward in a straight line and does actually make it move, since no external force opposes this motion. (Rolling resistance has been neglected here for simplicity.) This forward motion of the truck, during which all straight lines remain parallel to themselves (the floor of the truck remains horizontal, and its walls remain vertical), is known as a *translation.* Other forces might cause the truck to move differently. For example, the force exerted by a jack placed under the front axle would cause the truck to pivot about its rear axle. Such a motion is a *rotation.* It may be concluded, therefore, that each of the *external forces* acting on a *rigid body* is capable, if unopposed, of imparting to the rigid body a motion of translation or rotation, or both.

3.2. Principle of Transmissibility. Equivalent Forces. The *principle of transmissibility* states that the conditions of equilibrium or of motion of a rigid body will remain unchanged if a force **F** acting at a given point of the rigid body is replaced by a force **F′** of the same magnitude and same direction, but acting at a different point, *provided that the two forces have the same line of action* (Fig. 3.3). The two forces **F** and **F′** have the same effect on the rigid body and are said to be *equivalent.* This principle, which states in fact that the action of a force may be *transmitted* along its line of action, is based on experimental evidence. It *cannot* be derived from the properties established so far in this text and must therefore be accepted as an experimental law.

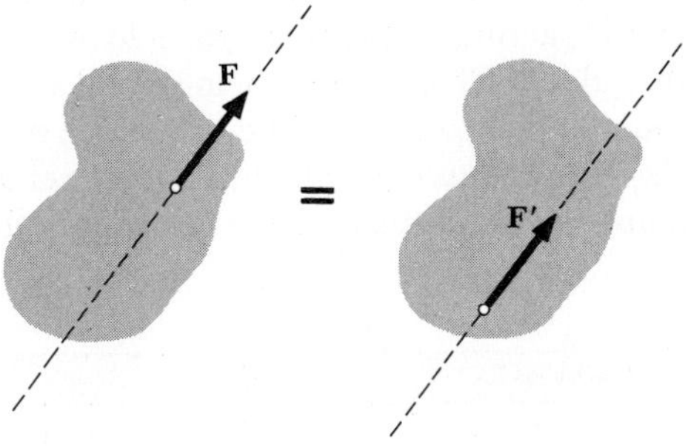

FIG. 3.3

It was indicated in Chap. 2 that the forces acting on a particle are vectors. These vectors had a well-defined point of application, namely, the particle itself, and were therefore fixed, or bound, vectors. In the case of forces acting on a rigid body, however, the point of application of the force does not matter, as long as the line of action remains unchanged. Thus forces acting on a rigid body are *sliding vectors*, i.e., vectors which may be allowed to slide along their line of action.

Returning to the example of the truck, we first observe that the line of action of the force **F** is a horizontal line passing through both the front and the rear bumpers of the truck (Fig. 3.4). Using the principle of transmissibility, we may therefore

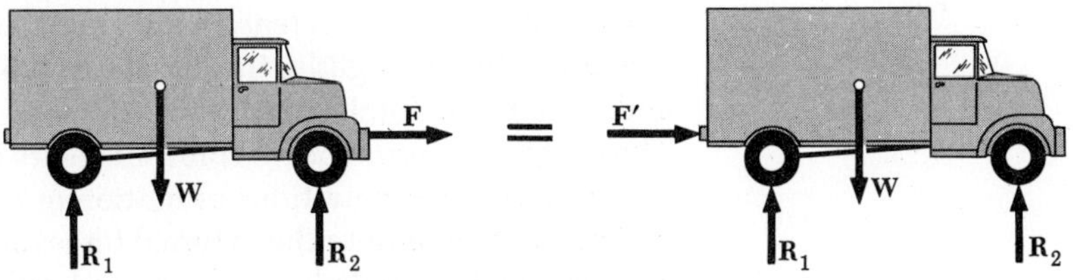

FIG. 3.4

replace **F** by an *equivalent force* **F′** acting on the rear bumper. In other words, the conditions of motion are unaffected, and all the other external forces acting on the truck ($\mathbf{W}$, $\mathbf{R}_1$, $\mathbf{R}_2$) remain unchanged if the men push on the rear bumper instead of pulling on the front bumper.

The principle of transmissibility and the concept of equivalent forces have limitations, however. Consider, for example, a short bar AB acted upon by equal and opposite axial forces $\mathbf{P}_1$ and $\mathbf{P}_2$, as shown in Fig. 3.5*a*. According to the principle of transmissibility, the force $\mathbf{P}_2$ may be replaced by a force $\mathbf{P'}_2$ having the same magnitude, same direction, and same line of action, but acting at A instead of B (Fig. 3.5*b*). The forces $\mathbf{P}_1$ and $\mathbf{P'}_2$ acting on the same particle may be added according to the rules of Chap. 2, and, being equal and opposite, their sum is found equal to zero. The original system of forces shown in Fig. 3.5*a* is thus equivalent to no force at all (Fig. 3.5*c*) from the point of view of the external behavior of the bar.

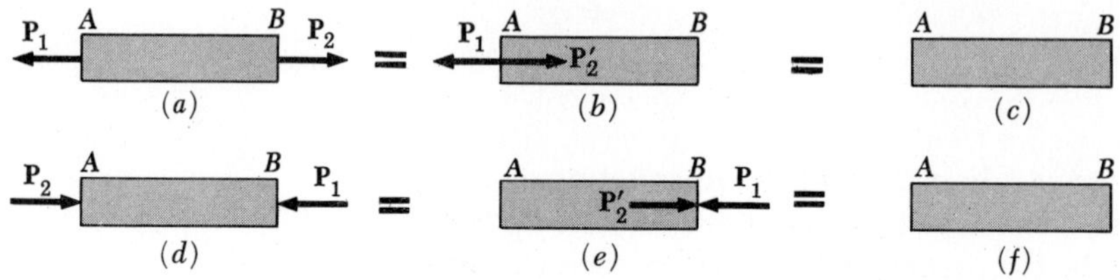

FIG. 3.5

Consider now the two equal and opposite forces $\mathbf{P}_1$ and $\mathbf{P}_2$ acting on the bar AB as shown in Fig. 3.5*d*. The force $\mathbf{P}_2$ may be replaced by a force $\mathbf{P'}_2$ having the same magnitude, same direction, and same line of action, but acting at B instead of A (Fig. 3.5*e*). The forces $\mathbf{P}_1$ and $\mathbf{P'}_2$ may then be added, and their sum is found again to be zero (Fig. 3.5*f*). From the point of view of the mechanics of rigid bodies, the systems shown in Fig. 3.5*a* and *d* are thus equivalent. But the *internal forces* and *deformations* produced by the two systems are clearly different. The bar of Fig. 3.5*a* is in *tension* and, if not absolutely rigid, will increase in length slightly; the bar of Fig. 3.5*d* is in *compression* and, if not absolutely rigid, will decrease in length slightly. Thus, while the principle of transmissibility may be used freely to determine the conditions of motion or equilibrium of rigid bodies and to compute the external forces acting on these bodies, it should be avoided, or at least used with care, in determining internal forces and deformations.

3.3. Vector Product of Two Vectors. In order to gain a better understanding of the effect of a force on a rigid body, we shall introduce a new concept, the concept of *moment of a force about a point*. This concept will be more clearly understood, and we shall be able to apply it more effectively, if we first add to the mathematical tools at our disposal by defining the *vector product* of two vectors.

The vector product of two vectors **P** and **Q** is defined as the vector **V** which satisfies the following conditions:

1. The line of action of **V** is perpendicular to the plane containing **P** and **Q** (Fig. 3.6).
2. The magnitude of **V** is the product of the magnitudes of **P** and **Q** and of the sine of the angle θ formed by **P** and **Q** (the measure of which will always be 180° or less); we thus have

$$V = PQ \sin \theta \qquad (3.1)$$

3. The sense of **V** is such that a man located at the tip of **V** will observe as counterclockwise the rotation through θ which brings the vector **P** in line with the vector **Q**; note that if **P** and **Q** do not have a common point of application, they should first be redrawn from the same point. The three vectors **P**, **Q**, and **V**—taken in that order—are said to form a *right-handed triad*.†

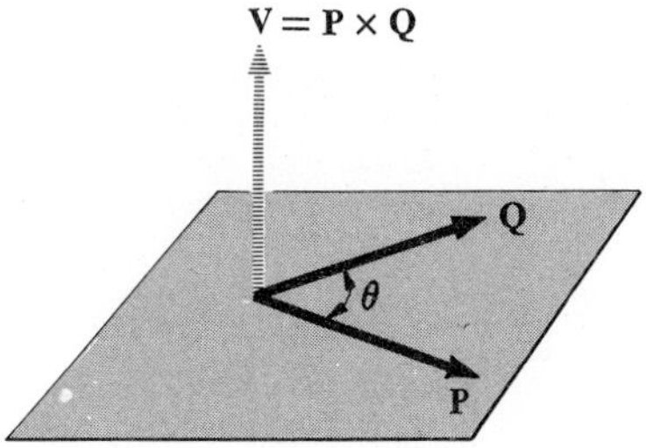

FIG. 3.6

As stated above, the vector **V** satisfying these three conditions (which define it uniquely) is referred to as the vector product of **P** and **Q**; it is represented by the mathematical expression

$$\mathbf{V} = \mathbf{P} \times \mathbf{Q} \qquad (3.2)$$

Because of the notation used, the vector product of two vectors **P** and **Q** is also referred to as the *cross product* of **P** and **Q**.

It follows from Eq. (3.1) that, when two vectors **P** and **Q** have either the same direction or opposite directions, their vector product is zero. In the general case when the angle θ formed by the two vectors is neither 0° nor 180°, Eq. (3.1) may be given a simple geometric interpretation: the magnitude V of the vector product of **P** and **Q** measures the area of the parallelogram which has **P** and **Q** for sides (Fig. 3.7). The vector product **P** × **Q** will therefore remain unchanged if we replace **Q** by a vector **Q′** coplanar with **P** and **Q** and such that the line joining the tips of **Q** and **Q′** is parallel to **P**. We write

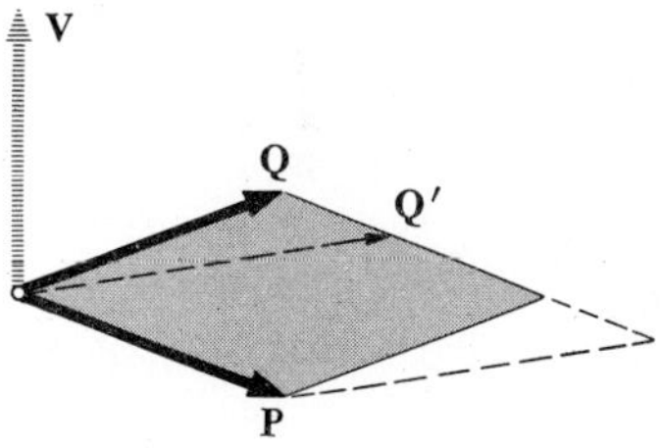

FIG. 3.7

$$\mathbf{V} = \mathbf{P} \times \mathbf{Q} = \mathbf{P} \times \mathbf{Q}' \qquad (3.3)$$

From the third condition used to define the vector product **V** of **P** and **Q**, namely, the condition stating that **P**, **Q**, and **V** must form a right-handed triad, it follows that vector products *are not*

† We should note that the x, y, and z axes used in Chap. 2 form a right-handed system of axes and that the unit vectors **i**, **j**, **k** defined in Sec. 2.11 form a right-handed triad.

commutative, i.e., $\mathbf{Q} \times \mathbf{P}$ is not equal to $\mathbf{P} \times \mathbf{Q}$. Indeed, we may easily check that $\mathbf{Q} \times \mathbf{P}$ is represented by the vector $-\mathbf{V}$ equal and opposite to $\mathbf{V}$. We thus write

$$\mathbf{Q} \times \mathbf{P} = -(\mathbf{P} \times \mathbf{Q}) \tag{3.4}$$

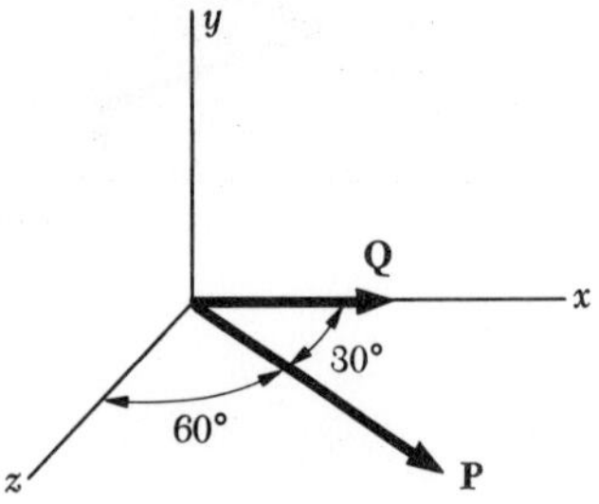

FIG. 3.8

Example. Let us compute the vector product $\mathbf{V} = \mathbf{P} \times \mathbf{Q}$ of the vector $\mathbf{P}$ of magnitude 6 lying in the zx plane at an angle of 30° with the x axis, and of the vector $\mathbf{Q}$ of magnitude 4 lying along the x axis (Fig. 3.8).

It follows immediately from the definition of the vector product that the vector $\mathbf{V}$ must lie along the y axis, have the magnitude

$$V = PQ \sin\theta = (6)\,(4) \sin 30° = 12$$

and be directed upward.

We saw that the commutative property does not apply to vector products. We may wonder whether the *distributive* property holds, i.e., whether the relation

$$\mathbf{P} \times (\mathbf{Q}_1 + \mathbf{Q}_2) = \mathbf{P} \times \mathbf{Q}_1 + \mathbf{P} \times \mathbf{Q}_2 \tag{3.5}$$

is valid. The answer is *yes.* Many readers are probably willing to accept without formal proof an answer which they intuitively feel is correct. However, since the entire structure of vector algebra and of statics depends upon the relation (3.5), we shall take time out actually to derive it.

We may, without any loss of generality, assume that $\mathbf{P}$ is directed along the y axis (Fig. 3.9a). Denoting by $\mathbf{Q}$ the sum of $\mathbf{Q}_1$ and $\mathbf{Q}_2$, we drop perpendiculars from the tips of $\mathbf{Q}$, $\mathbf{Q}_1$, and $\mathbf{Q}_2$ onto the zx plane, defining in this way the vectors $\mathbf{Q}'$, $\mathbf{Q}'_1$, and $\mathbf{Q}'_2$. These vectors will be referred to, respectively, as the *projections* of $\mathbf{Q}$, $\mathbf{Q}_1$, and $\mathbf{Q}_2$ on the zx plane. Recalling the property expressed by Eq. (3.3), we note that the left-hand member of Eq. (3.5) may be replaced by $\mathbf{P} \times \mathbf{Q}'$ and that, similarly, the vector products $\mathbf{P} \times \mathbf{Q}_1$ and $\mathbf{P} \times \mathbf{Q}_2$ may, respectively, be replaced by $\mathbf{P} \times \mathbf{Q}'_1$ and $\mathbf{P} \times \mathbf{Q}'_2$. Thus, the relation to be proved may be written in the form

$$\mathbf{P} \times \mathbf{Q}' = \mathbf{P} \times \mathbf{Q}'_1 + \mathbf{P} \times \mathbf{Q}'_2 \tag{3.5'}$$

We now observe that $\mathbf{P} \times \mathbf{Q}'$ may be obtained from $\mathbf{Q}'$ by multiplying this vector by the scalar P and rotating it counterclockwise through 90° in the zx plane (Fig. 3.9*b*); the other two vector products in (3.5′) may be obtained in the same manner from $\mathbf{Q}'_1$ and $\mathbf{Q}'_2$, respectively. Now, since the projection of a parallelogram onto an arbitrary plane is a parallelogram, the projection $\mathbf{Q}'$ of the sum $\mathbf{Q}$ of $\mathbf{Q}_1$ and $\mathbf{Q}_2$ must be the sum of the projections $\mathbf{Q}'_1$ and $\mathbf{Q}'_2$ of $\mathbf{Q}_1$ and $\mathbf{Q}_2$ on the same plane (Fig. 3.9*a*). This relation between the vectors $\mathbf{Q}'$, $\mathbf{Q}'_1$, and $\mathbf{Q}'_2$ will

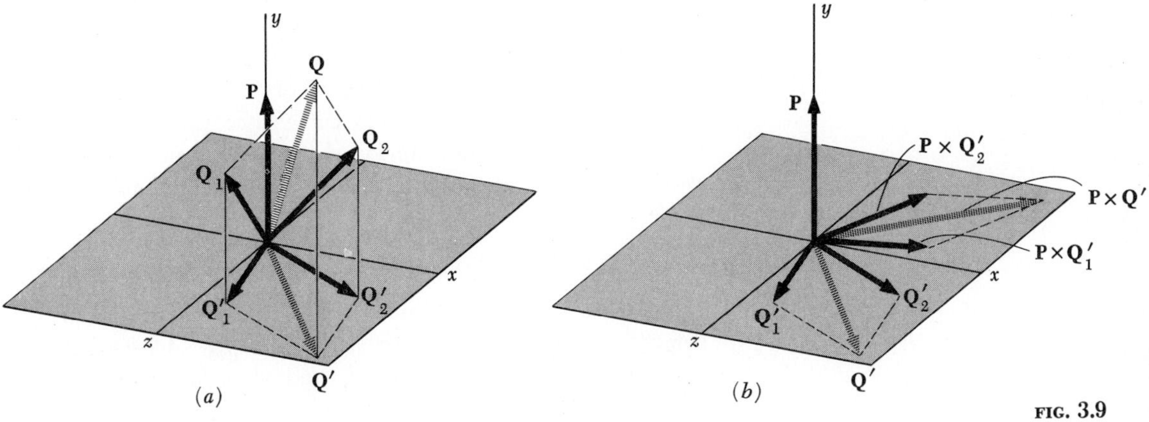

FIG. 3.9

still hold after the three vectors have been multiplied by the scalar P and rotated through 90° (Fig. 3.9*b*). Thus the relation (3.5′) has been proved and we can now be sure that the distributive property holds for vector products.

The third property, the associative property, does not apply to vector products; we have in general

$$(\mathbf{P} \times \mathbf{Q}) \times \mathbf{S} \neq \mathbf{P} \times (\mathbf{Q} \times \mathbf{S}) \tag{3.6}$$

3.4. Vector Products Expressed in Terms of Rectangular Components. We shall now determine the vector product of any two of the unit vectors, **i**, **j**, **k**, defined in Chap. 2. Consider first the product $\mathbf{i} \times \mathbf{j}$ (Fig. 3.10*a*). Since both vectors have a magnitude equal to one and since they are at a right angle to each other, their vector product will also be a unit vector. This unit vector must be **k**, since the vectors **i**, **j**, **k** are mutually perpendicular and form a right-handed triad. On the other hand, the product $\mathbf{j} \times \mathbf{i}$ will be equal to $-\mathbf{k}$ since the 90-degree rotation which brings **j** into **i** is observed as counterclockwise by a man located at the tip of $-\mathbf{k}$ (Fig. 3.10*b*). Finally, it should be observed that the vector product of a unit vector by itself, such as $\mathbf{i} \times \mathbf{i}$, is equal to zero, since both vectors have the same direction. The vector products of the various possible pairs of unit vectors are

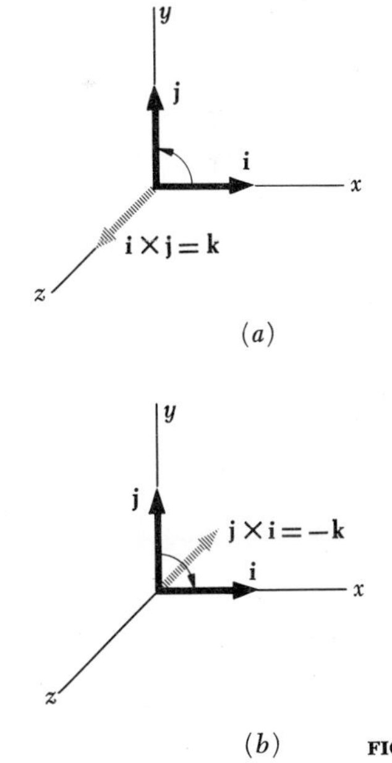

FIG. 3.10

$$\begin{array}{lll} \mathbf{i} \times \mathbf{i} = 0 & \mathbf{j} \times \mathbf{i} = -\mathbf{k} & \mathbf{k} \times \mathbf{i} = \mathbf{j} \\ \mathbf{i} \times \mathbf{j} = \mathbf{k} & \mathbf{j} \times \mathbf{j} = 0 & \mathbf{k} \times \mathbf{j} = -\mathbf{i} \\ \mathbf{i} \times \mathbf{k} = -\mathbf{j} & \mathbf{j} \times \mathbf{k} = \mathbf{i} & \mathbf{k} \times \mathbf{k} = 0 \end{array} \tag{3.7}$$

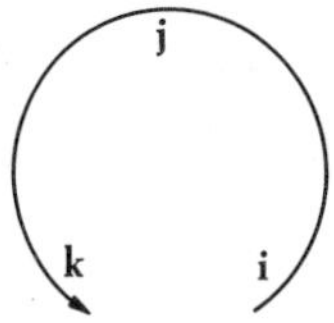

FIG. 3.11

By arranging the three letters representing the unit vectors in a circle (Fig. 3.11), we may simplify the determination of the sign of the vector product of two unit vectors: The product of two unit vectors will be positive if they follow each other in counterclockwise order, and negative otherwise.

We may now easily express the vector product **V** of two given vectors **P** and **Q** in terms of the rectangular components of these vectors. Resolving **P** and **Q** into components, we first write

$$\mathbf{V} = \mathbf{P} \times \mathbf{Q} = (P_x\mathbf{i} + P_y\mathbf{j} + P_z\mathbf{k}) \times (Q_x\mathbf{i} + Q_y\mathbf{j} + Q_z\mathbf{k})$$

Making use of the distributive property, we express **V** as the sum of vector products such as $P_x\mathbf{i} \times Q_y\mathbf{j}$. Observing that each of the expressions obtained is equal to the vector product of two unit vectors, such as $\mathbf{i} \times \mathbf{j}$, multiplied by the product of two scalars, such as P_xQ_y, and recalling the identities (3.7), we obtain, after factoring **i**, **j**, and **k**,

$$\mathbf{V} = (P_yQ_z - P_zQ_y)\mathbf{i} + (P_zQ_x - P_xQ_z)\mathbf{j} + (P_xQ_y - P_yQ_x)\mathbf{k} \tag{3.8}$$

The rectangular components of the vector product **V** are thus found to be

$$\begin{aligned} V_x &= P_yQ_z - P_zQ_y \\ V_y &= P_zQ_x - P_xQ_z \\ V_z &= P_xQ_y - P_yQ_x \end{aligned} \tag{3.9}$$

Returning to Eq. (3.8), we observe that its right-hand member represents the expansion of a determinant. The vector product **V** may thus be expressed in the following form, more easily memorized:†

$$\mathbf{V} = \begin{vmatrix} \mathbf{i} & \mathbf{j} & \mathbf{k} \\ P_x & P_y & P_z \\ Q_x & Q_y & Q_z \end{vmatrix} \tag{3.10}$$

† Any determinant consisting of 3 rows and 3 columns may be evaluated by repeating the first and second columns and forming products along each diagonal line. The sum of the products obtained along the dashed lines is then subtracted from the sum of the products obtained along the solid lines.

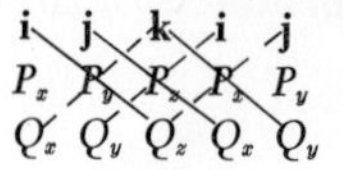

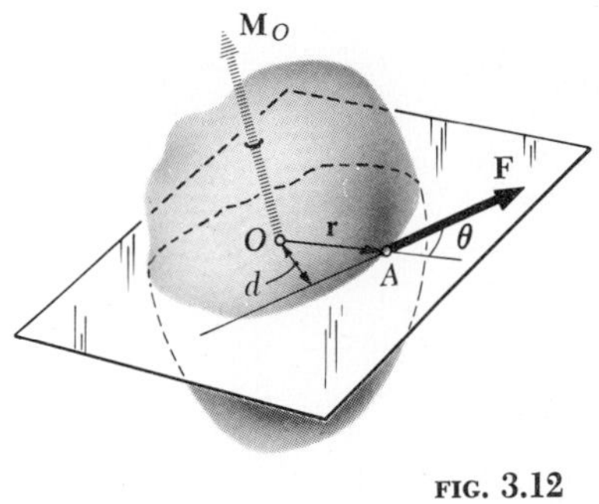

FIG. 3.12

3.5. Moment of a Force about a Point. Let us now consider a force **F** acting on a rigid body (Fig. 3.12). As we know, the force **F** is represented by a vector which defines its magnitude and direction. However, the effect of the force on the rigid body depends also upon its point of application A. The position of A may be conveniently defined by the vector **r** which joins the fixed reference point O with A; this vector is known as the *position vector* of A.† The position vector **r** and the force **F** define the plane shown in Fig. 3.12.

We shall define the *moment of* **F** *about* O as the vector product of **r** and **F**:

$$\mathbf{M}_O = \mathbf{r} \times \mathbf{F} \tag{3.11}$$

According to the definition of the vector product given in Sec. 3.3, the moment $\mathbf{M}_O$ must be perpendicular to the plane containing O and **F**; thus, *the line of action of* $\mathbf{M}_O$ *represents the axis about which the body tends to rotate* when attached at O and subjected to the force **F**.

The sense of $\mathbf{M}_O$ is defined by the sense of the rotation which would bring the vector **r** in line with the vector **F**; but this rotation is the rotation that **F** tends to impart to the body. Thus *the sense of the moment* $\mathbf{M}_O$ *characterizes the sense of the rotation that* **F** *tends to impart to the rigid body;* this rotation will be observed as *counterclockwise* by an observer located at the tip of $\mathbf{M}_O$. Another way of stating the relationship existing between the sense of $\mathbf{M}_O$ and the sense of rotation of the rigid body is furnished by the *right-hand rule:* Close your right hand and hold it so that your fingers are curled in the sense of the rotation that **F** tends to impart to the rigid body; your thumb will indicate the sense of the moment $\mathbf{M}_O$.

Finally, denoting by θ the angle between the lines of action of the position vector **r** and the force **F**, we find that the magnitude of the moment of **F** about O is

$$M_O = rF \sin \theta = Fd \tag{3.12}$$

where d represents the perpendicular distance from O to the line of action of **F**. A force being expressed in pounds and a

† We may easily verify that position vectors obey the law of vector addition and, thus, are truly vectors. Consider, for example, the position vectors **r** and **r′** of A with respect to two reference points O and O', and the position vector **s** of O with respect to O' (Fig. 3.37*a*, Sec. 3.14). We check that the position vector $\mathbf{r}' = \overrightarrow{O'A}$ may be obtained from the position vectors $\mathbf{s} = \overrightarrow{O'O}$ and $\mathbf{r} = \overrightarrow{OA}$ by applying the triangle rule for the addition of vectors.

distance in feet or inches, the moment of a force will be expressed in lb-ft or lb-in. Since the tendency of a force **F** to make a rigid body rotate about an axis perpendicular to the force depends upon the distance of **F** from that axis, as well as upon the magnitude of **F**, we note that *the magnitude of* $\mathbf{M}_O$ *measures the tendency of the force* **F** *to impart to the rigid body a rotational motion* when the body is attached at O.

We may observe that the moment $\mathbf{M}_O$ of a force about a point, while it depends upon the magnitude, the line of action, and the sense of the force, does *not* depend upon the actual position of the point of application of the force along its line of action. Conversely, the moment $\mathbf{M}_O$ of a force **F** does not characterize the position of the point of application of **F**.

However, as we shall see presently, the moment $\mathbf{M}_O$ of a force **F** of given magnitude and direction *completely defines the line of action of* **F**. Indeed, the line of action of **F** must lie in a plane through O perpendicular to the moment $\mathbf{M}_O$; its distance d from O must be equal to the quotient M_O/F of the magnitudes of $\mathbf{M}_O$ and **F**; and the sense of $\mathbf{M}_O$ determines whether the line of action of **F** is to be drawn on one side or the other of the point O.

We recall from Sec. 3.2 that the principle of transmissibility states that two forces **F** and **F′** are equivalent (i.e., have the same effect on a rigid body) if they have the same magnitude, same direction, and same line of action. This principle may now be restated as follows: *Two forces* **F** *and* **F′** *are equivalent if, and only if, they are equal* (i.e., have the same magnitude and same direction) *and have equal moments about a given point* O. The necessary and sufficient condition for two forces **F** and **F′** to be equivalent is thus

$$\mathbf{F} = \mathbf{F}' \qquad \text{and} \qquad \mathbf{M}_O = \mathbf{M}'_O \tag{3.13}$$

We should observe that it follows from this statement that if the relations (3.13) hold for a given point O, they will hold for any other point.

Problems Involving Only Two Dimensions. Many applications deal with two-dimensional structures, i.e., structures which have length and breadth, but only negligible depth, and which are subjected to forces contained in the plane of the structure. Two-dimensional structures and the forces acting on them may be readily represented on a sheet of paper or on a blackboard. Their analysis is therefore considerably simpler than that of three-dimensional structures and forces.

Consider, for example, a rigid slab acted upon by a force **F**

(Fig. 3.13). The moment of **F** about a point O chosen in the plane of the figure is represented by a vector $\mathbf{M}_O$ perpendicular to that plane and of magnitude Fd. In the case of Fig. 3.13*a* the vector $\mathbf{M}_O$ points *out* of the paper, while in the case of Fig. 3.13*b* it points *into* the paper. As we look at the figure, we observe the action of **F** in the first case as counterclockwise, and in the second case as clockwise. Therefore, it is natural to refer to the sense of the moment of **F** about O in Fig. 3.13*a* as counterclockwise ↺, and in Fig. 3.13*b* as clockwise ↻.

Since the moment of a force **F** acting in the plane of the figure must be perpendicular to that plane, we need only specify the *magnitude* and the *sense* of the moment of **F** about O. This may be done by assigning to the magnitude M_O of the moment a positive or negative sign, according to whether the vector $\mathbf{M}_O$ points out of or into the paper.

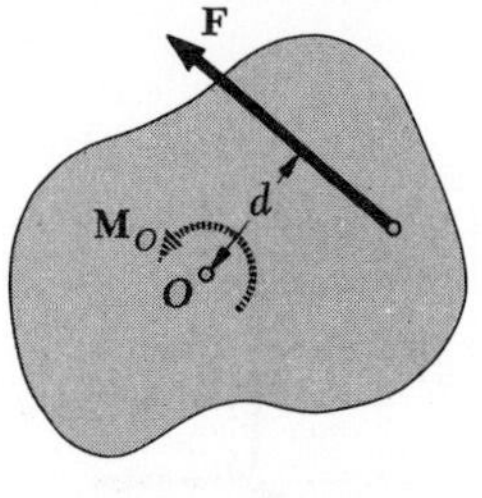

(*a*) $M_O = +Fd$

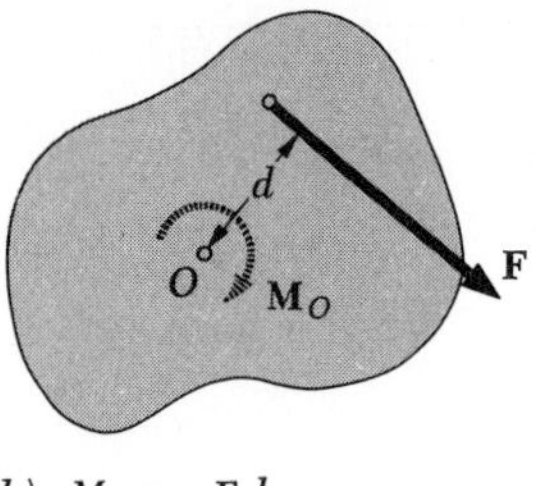

(*b*) $M_O = -Fd$

FIG. 3.13

3.6. Varignon's Theorem. The distributive property of vector products may be used to determine the moment of the resultant of several *concurrent forces*. If several forces $\mathbf{F}_1$, $\mathbf{F}_2$, . . . are applied at the same point A (Fig. 3.14), and if we denote by **r** the position vector of A, it follows immediately from formula (3.5) that

$$\mathbf{r} \times (\mathbf{F}_1 + \mathbf{F}_2 + \cdots) = \mathbf{r} \times \mathbf{F}_1 + \mathbf{r} \times \mathbf{F}_2 + \cdots \quad (3.14)$$

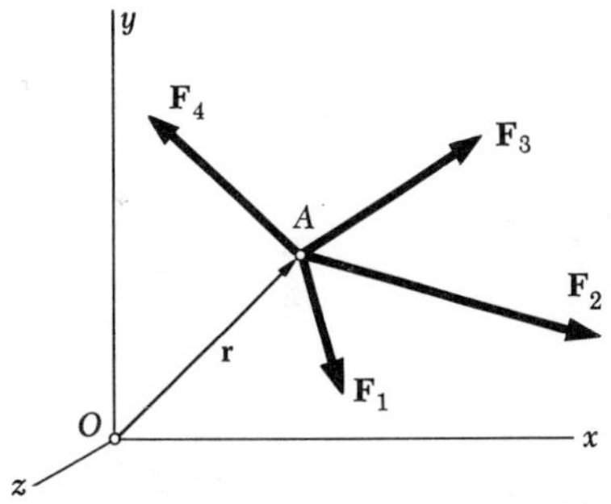

FIG. 3.14

In words, *the moment about a given point O of the resultant of several concurrent forces is equal to the sum of the moments of the various forces about the same point O.* This property was originally established by the French mathematician Varignon (1654–1722), long before the introduction of vector algebra, and is known as *Varignon's Theorem.*

The relation (3.14) makes it possible to replace the direct determination of the moment of a force **F** by the determination of the moments of two or more component forces. As we shall see in the next section, **F** will generally be resolved into components parallel to the coordinate axes. However, it may be found more expeditious in some instances to resolve **F** into components which are not parallel to the coordinate axes (see Sample Prob. 3.3).

3.7. Rectangular Components of the Moment of a Force. In general, the determination of the moment of a force in space will be considerably simplified if the force and the position vector of its point of application are resolved into rectangular x, y, and z components. Consider, for example, the moment $\mathbf{M}_O$ about O of a force **F** of components F_x, F_y, and F_z, applied at a point A of coordinates x, y, and z (Fig. 3.15). Observing that

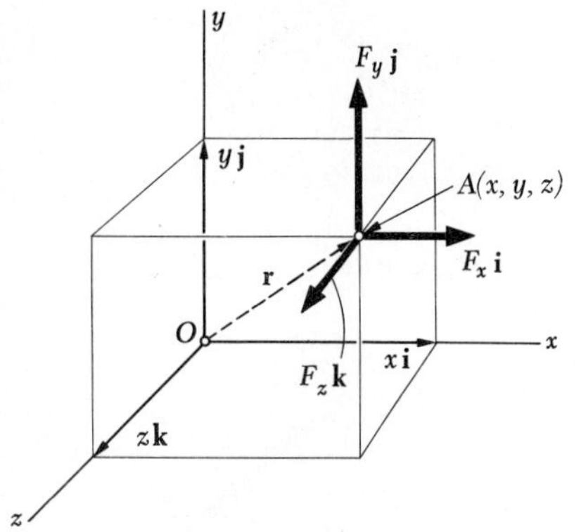

FIG. 3.15

the components of the position vector **r** are respectively equal to the coordinates x, y, and z of the point A, we write

$$\mathbf{r} = x\mathbf{i} + y\mathbf{j} + z\mathbf{k} \qquad (3.15)$$
$$\mathbf{F} = F_x\mathbf{i} + F_y\mathbf{j} + F_z\mathbf{k} \qquad (3.16)$$

Substituting for **r** and **F** from (3.15) and (3.16) into

$$\mathbf{M}_O = \mathbf{r} \times \mathbf{F} \qquad (3.11)$$

and recalling the results obtained in Sec. 3.4, we write the moment $\mathbf{M}_O$ of **F** about O in the form

$$\mathbf{M}_O = M_x\mathbf{i} + M_y\mathbf{j} + M_z\mathbf{k} \qquad (3.17)$$

where the components M_x, M_y, and M_z are defined by the relations

$$\begin{aligned} M_x &= yF_z - zF_y \\ M_y &= zF_x - xF_z \\ M_z &= xF_y - yF_x \end{aligned} \qquad (3.18)$$

As we shall see in Sec. 3.10, the scalar components M_x, M_y, and M_z of the moment $\mathbf{M}_O$ measure the tendency of the force **F** to impart to a rigid body a motion of rotation about the x, y, and z axes, respectively. Substituting from (3.18) into (3.17), we may also write $\mathbf{M}_O$ in the form of the determinant

$$\mathbf{M}_O = \begin{vmatrix} \mathbf{i} & \mathbf{j} & \mathbf{k} \\ x & y & z \\ F_x & F_y & F_z \end{vmatrix} \qquad (3.19)$$

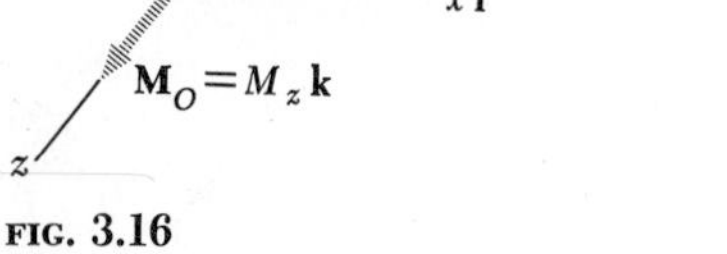

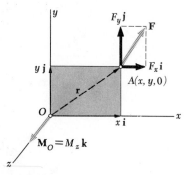

FIG. 3.16

In the case of *problems involving only two dimensions*, the force **F** may be assumed to lie in the xy plane (Fig. 3.16). Carrying $z = 0$ and $F_z = 0$ into the relations (3.19), we obtain

$$\mathbf{M}_O = (xF_y - yF_x)\mathbf{k}$$

We check that the moment of **F** about O is perpendicular to the plane of the figure and that it is completely defined by the scalar

$$M_O = M_z = xF_y - yF_x \qquad (3.20)$$

As noted earlier, a positive value for M_O indicates that the vector $\mathbf{M}_O$ points out of the paper (the force **F** tends to rotate the body counterclockwise about O), and a negative value that the vector $\mathbf{M}_O$ points into the paper (the force **F** tends to rotate the body clockwise about O).

SAMPLE PROBLEM 3.1

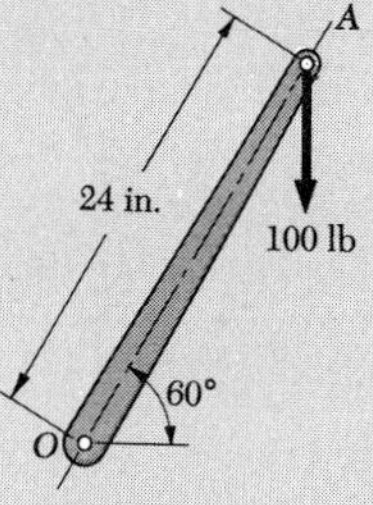

A 100-lb vertical force is applied to the end of a lever which is attached to a shaft at O. Determine (a) the moment of the 100-lb force about O; (b) the magnitude of the horizontal force applied at A which creates the same moment about O; (c) the smallest force applied at A which creates the same moment about O; (d) how far from the shaft a 240-lb vertical force must act to create the same moment about O; (e) whether any one of the forces obtained in parts b, c, and d is equivalent to the original force.

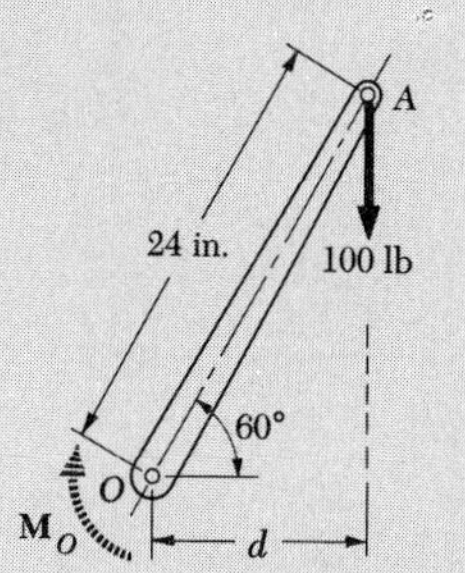

a. **Moment about** O. The perpendicular distance from O to the line of action of the 100-lb force is

$$d = (24 \text{ in.}) \cos 60° = 12 \text{ in.}$$

The magnitude of the moment about O of the 100-lb force is

$$M_O = Fd = (100 \text{ lb})(12 \text{ in.}) = 1{,}200 \text{ lb-in.}$$

Since the force tends to rotate the lever clockwise about O, the moment will be represented by a vector $\mathbf{M}_O$ perpendicular to the plane of the figure and pointing *into* the paper. We express this fact by writing

$$\mathbf{M}_O = 1{,}200 \text{ lb-in. } ↻$$ ◄

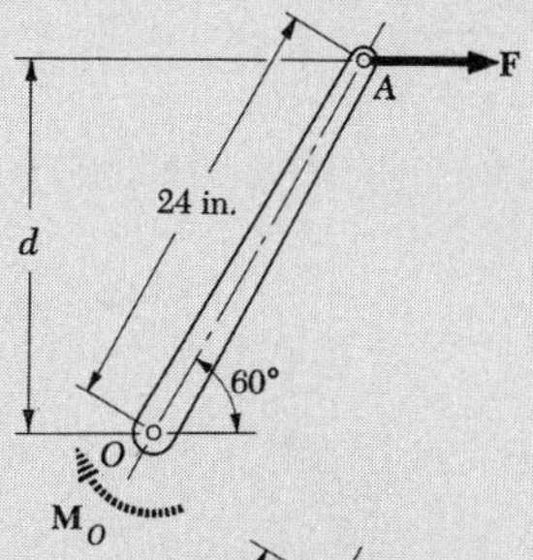

b. **Horizontal Force.** In this case, we have

$$d = (24 \text{ in.}) \sin 60° = 20.8 \text{ in.}$$

Since the moment about O must be 1,200 lb-in., we write

$$M_O = Fd \qquad 1{,}200 \text{ lb-in.} = F(20.8 \text{ in.})$$

$$F = 57.8 \text{ lb} \qquad \mathbf{F} = 57.8 \text{ lb} \rightarrow$$ ◄

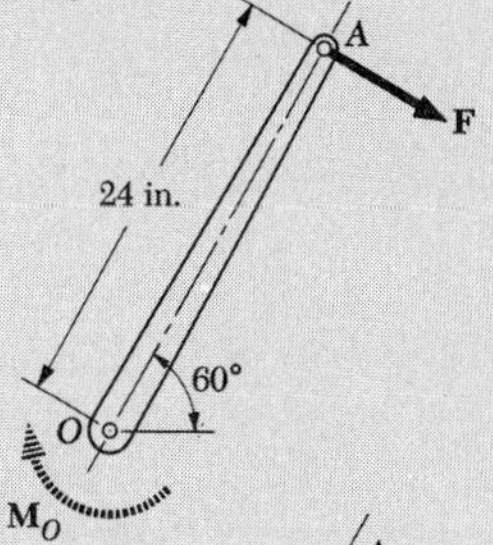

c. **Smallest Force.** Since $M_O = Fd$, the smallest value of **F** occurs when d is maximum. We choose the force perpendicular to OA and find $d = 24$ in.; thus

$$M_O = Fd \qquad 1{,}200 \text{ lb-in.} = F(24 \text{ in.})$$

$$F = 50 \text{ lb} \qquad \mathbf{F} = 50 \text{ lb} \measuredangle 30°$$ ◄

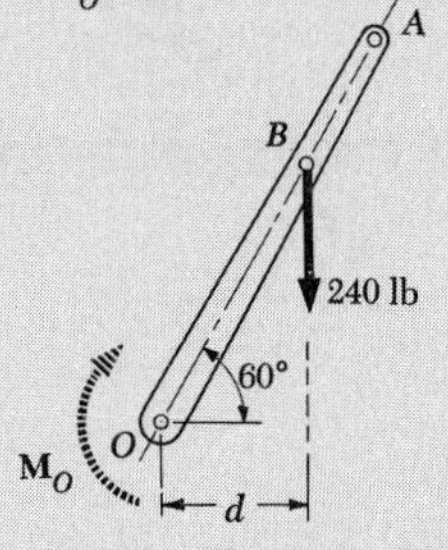

d. **240-lb Vertical Force.** In this case $M_O = Fd$ yields

$$1{,}200 \text{ lb-in.} = (240 \text{ lb})d \qquad d = 5 \text{ in.}$$

but $\qquad OB \cos 60° = d \qquad OB = 10 \text{ in.}$ ◄

e. None of the forces considered in parts b, c, and d is equivalent to the original 100-lb force. Although they have the same moment about O, they have different x and y components. In other words, although each force tends to rotate the shaft in the same manner, each causes the lever to pull on the shaft in a different way.

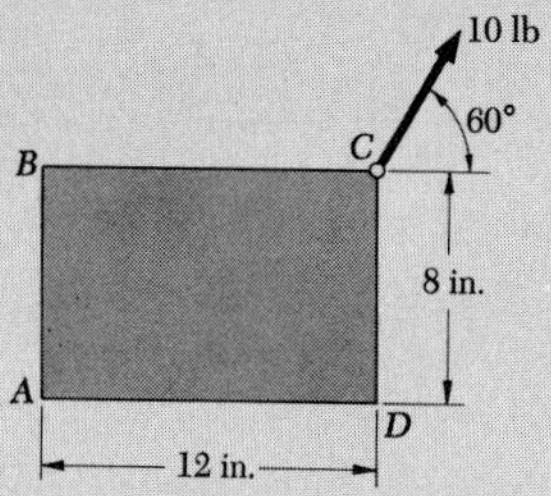

SAMPLE PROBLEM 3.2

A 10-lb force acts on the corner of a 12- by 8-in. plate as shown. Determine the moment $\mathbf{M}_A$ of the force about A.

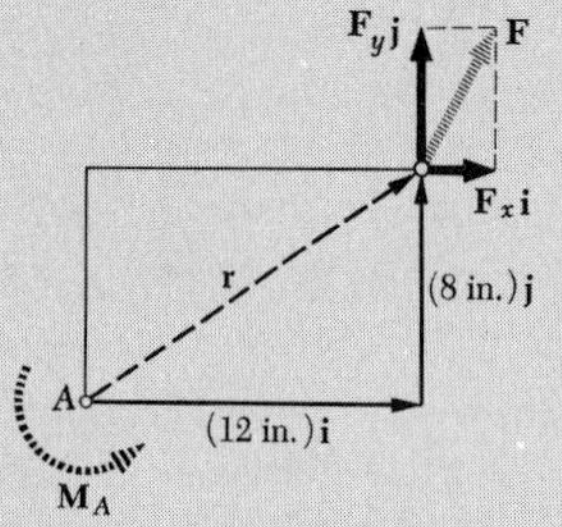

Solution. The moment $\mathbf{M}_A$ is obtained by forming the vector product

$$\mathbf{M}_A = \mathbf{r} \times \mathbf{F}$$

Resolving the position vector $\mathbf{r}$ and the force $\mathbf{F}$ into rectangular components, we write

$$\mathbf{r} = x\mathbf{i} + y\mathbf{j} = (12\text{ in.})\mathbf{i} + (8\text{ in.})\mathbf{j}$$
$$\mathbf{F} = F_x\mathbf{i} + F_y\mathbf{j} = (10\text{ lb})\cos 60°\mathbf{i} + (10\text{ lb})\sin 60°\mathbf{j} = (5\text{ lb})\mathbf{i} + (8.66\text{ lb})\mathbf{j}$$

Recalling the relations (3.7) for the cross products of unit vectors, we obtain

$$\mathbf{M}_A = \mathbf{r} \times \mathbf{F} = [(12\text{ in.})\mathbf{i} + (8\text{ in.})\mathbf{j}] \times [(5\text{ lb})\mathbf{i} + (8.66\text{ lb})\mathbf{j}]$$
$$= (104\text{ lb-in.})\mathbf{k} - (40\text{ lb-in.})\mathbf{k} = +(64\text{ lb-in.})\mathbf{k}$$

The moment $\mathbf{M}_A$ is a vector perpendicular to the plane of the figure and pointing *out* of the paper.

$$\mathbf{M}_A = +(64\text{ lb-in.})\mathbf{k} \qquad M_A = 64\text{ lb-in. } \circlearrowleft \blacktriangleleft$$

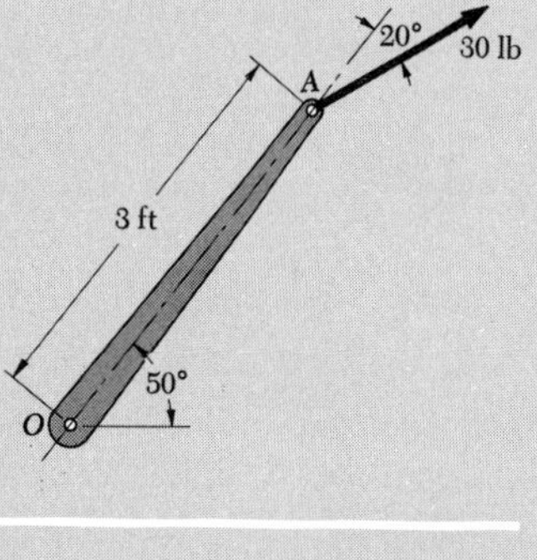

SAMPLE PROBLEM 3.3

A 30-lb force acts on the end of the 3-ft lever as shown. Determine the moment of the force about O.

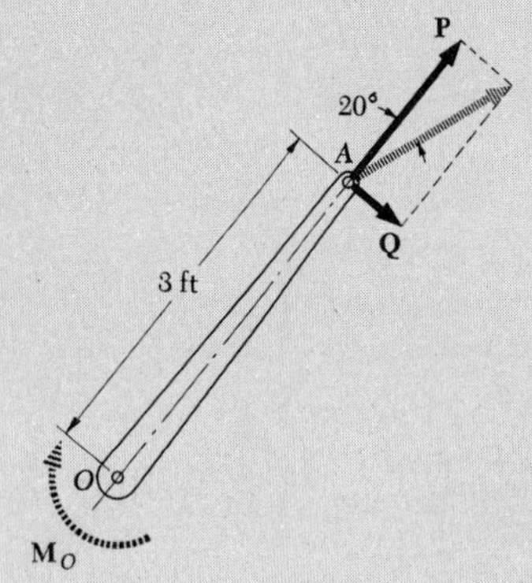

Solution. The force is replaced by two components, one component $\mathbf{P}$ in the direction of OA and one component $\mathbf{Q}$ perpendicular to OA. Since O is on the line of action of $\mathbf{P}$, the moment of $\mathbf{P}$ about O is zero and the moment of the 30-lb force reduces to the moment of $\mathbf{Q}$, which is clockwise and, thus, represented by a negative scalar.

$$Q = (30\text{ lb})\sin 20° = 10.26\text{ lb}$$
$$M_O = -Q(3\text{ ft}) = -(10.26\text{ lb})(3\text{ ft}) = -30.8\text{ lb-ft} \blacktriangleleft$$

Since the value obtained for the scalar M_O is negative, the moment $\mathbf{M}_O$ points *into* the paper. We write

$$M_O = 30.8\text{ lb-ft } \circlearrowright \blacktriangleleft$$

SAMPLE PROBLEM 3.4

A 6-ft pole AB is held by three guy wires as shown. Determine the moment about O of the force exerted by wire BE on point B. The tension in wire BE is known to be 210 lb.

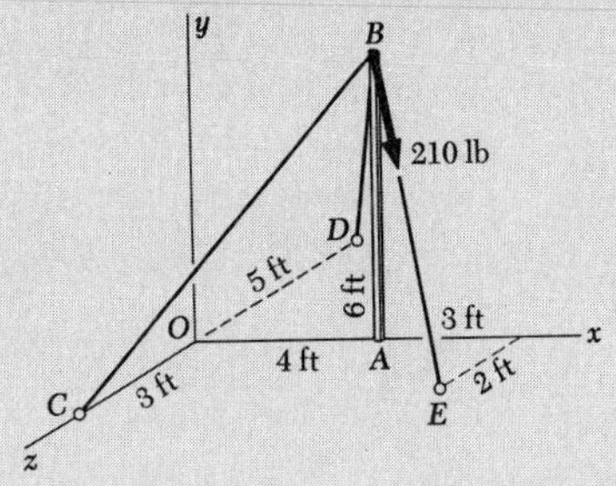

Solution. The moment $\mathbf{M}_O$ about O of the force exerted by wire BE on point B is obtained by forming the vector product

$$\mathbf{M}_O = \mathbf{r} \times \mathbf{F} \qquad (1)$$

where $\mathbf{r}$ is the position vector of point B,

$$\mathbf{r} = (4\text{ ft})\mathbf{i} + (6\text{ ft})\mathbf{j} \qquad (2)$$

and where $\mathbf{F}$ is the 210-lb force exerted by wire BE.

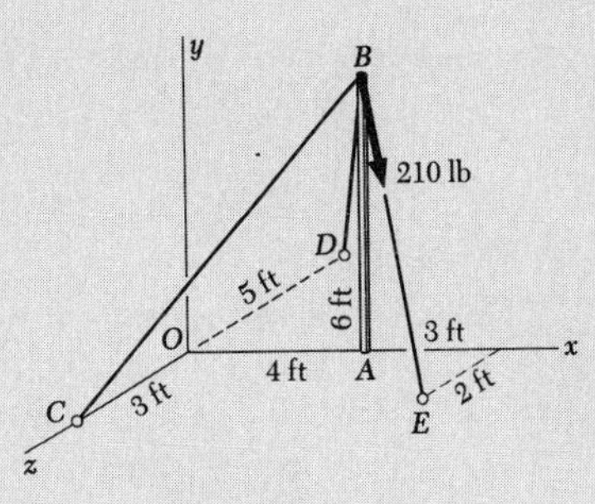

To determine the rectangular components of $\mathbf{F}$, we first compute the components and the magnitude of the vector $\overrightarrow{BE}$ which has the same direction as $\mathbf{F}$.

$$d_x = +3\text{ ft} \qquad d_y = -6\text{ ft} \qquad d_z = +2\text{ ft} \qquad d = 7\text{ ft}$$

Expressing that the components and the magnitudes of the force $\mathbf{F}$ and of the vector $\overrightarrow{BE}$ are proportional, we write

$$\frac{F_x}{+3\text{ ft}} = \frac{F_y}{-6\text{ ft}} = \frac{F_z}{+2\text{ ft}} = \frac{210\text{ lb}}{7\text{ ft}}$$

$$F_x = +90\text{ lb} \qquad F_y = -180\text{ lb} \qquad F_z = +60\text{ lb}$$

$$\mathbf{F} = F_x\mathbf{i} + F_y\mathbf{j} + F_z\mathbf{k} = (90\text{ lb})\mathbf{i} - (180\text{ lb})\mathbf{j} + (60\text{ lb})\mathbf{k} \qquad (3)$$

Substituting for $\mathbf{r}$ and $\mathbf{F}$ from (2) and (3) into (1), and recalling the relations (3.7), we obtain

$$\begin{aligned}\mathbf{M}_O = \mathbf{r} \times \mathbf{F} &= (4\mathbf{i} + 6\mathbf{j}) \times (90\mathbf{i} - 180\mathbf{j} + 60\mathbf{k}) \\ &= (4)(-180)\mathbf{k} + (4)(60)(-\mathbf{j}) + (6)(90)(-\mathbf{k}) + (6)(60)\mathbf{i}\end{aligned}$$

$$\mathbf{M}_O = 360\mathbf{i} - 240\mathbf{j} - 1{,}260\mathbf{k} \quad \text{lb-ft} \blacktriangleleft$$

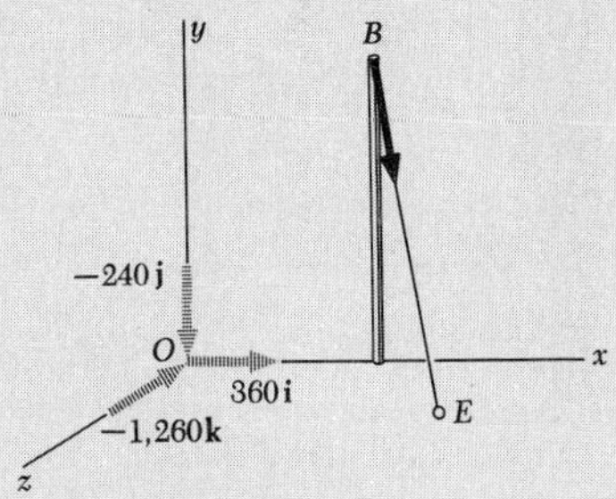

Alternate Solution. As indicated in Sec. 3.7, the moment $\mathbf{M}_O$ may be expressed in the form of a determinant. Substituting for x, y, z the coordinates of point B and for F_x, F_y, F_z the values obtained above for the components of the 210-lb force, we have

$$\mathbf{M}_O = \begin{vmatrix} \mathbf{i} & \mathbf{j} & \mathbf{k} \\ x & y & z \\ F_x & F_y & F_z \end{vmatrix} = \begin{vmatrix} \mathbf{i} & \mathbf{j} & \mathbf{k} \\ 4 & 6 & 0 \\ 90 & -180 & 60 \end{vmatrix}$$

$$\mathbf{M}_O = 360\mathbf{i} - 240\mathbf{j} - 1{,}260\mathbf{k} \quad \text{lb-ft} \blacktriangleleft$$

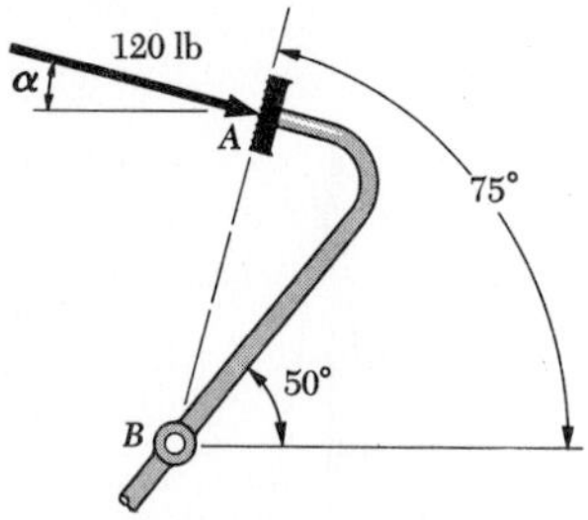

FIG. P 3.1 AND P 3.2

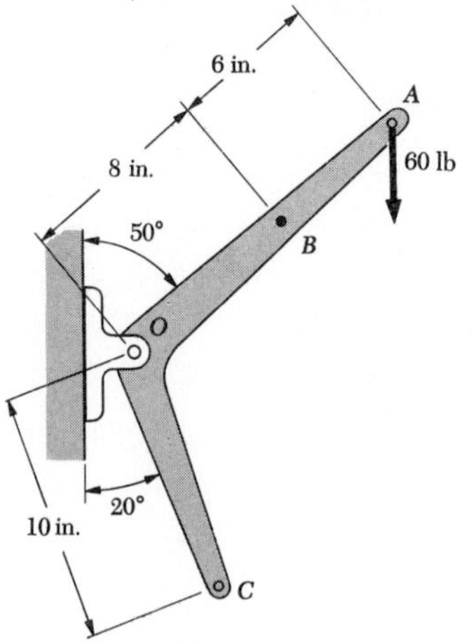

FIG. P 3.3 AND P 3.4

PROBLEMS

3.1. A 120-lb force is applied to the brake pedal at A. Knowing that the distance AB is 8 in., determine the moment of the force about B when α is 30°.

3.2. Knowing that the distance AB is 8 in., determine the maximum moment about B which can be caused by the 120-lb force. In what direction should the force act?

3.3. A 60-lb force is applied at A as shown. Determine (*a*) the moment of the 60-lb force about O, (*b*) the smallest force applied at B which creates the same moment about O.

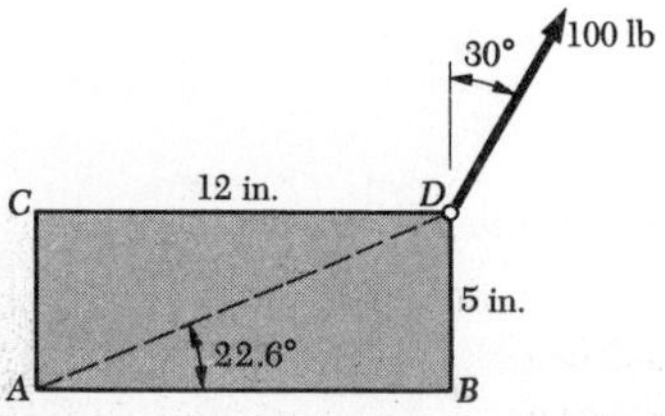

FIG. P 3.5

3.4. A 60-lb force is applied at A. Determine (*a*) the moment of the 60-lb force about O, (*b*) the magnitude and sense of the horizontal force applied at C which creates the same moment about O, (*c*) the smallest force applied at C which creates the same moment about O.

3.5. Compute the moment of the 100-lb force about A (*a*) by using the definition of the moment of a force, (*b*) by resolving the force into components along BD and CD, (*c*) by resolving the force into components along AD and in the direction perpendicular to AD.

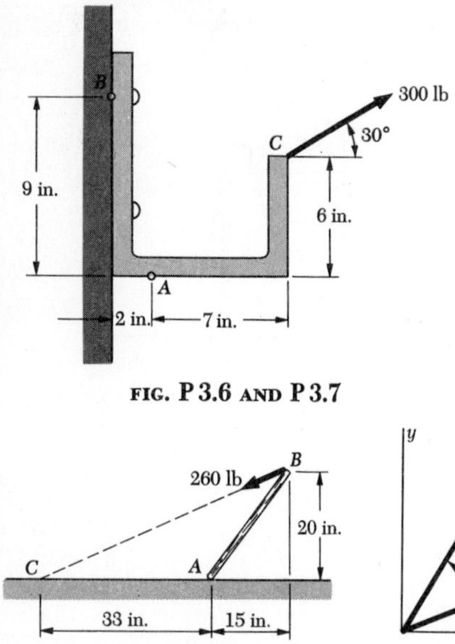

FIG. P 3.6 AND P 3.7

3.6. Determine the moment of the 300-lb force about A.

3.7. Determine the moment of the 300-lb force about B.

3.8. Determine the moment of the 260-lb force about A (*a*) by resolving the force into x and y components acting at B, (*b*) by resolving the force into x and y components acting at C.

3.9. Form the vector product $\mathbf{P}_1 \times \mathbf{P}_2$ and use the result obtained to prove the identity $\sin(\theta_1 - \theta_2) = \sin\theta_1 \cos\theta_2 - \cos\theta_1 \sin\theta_2$.

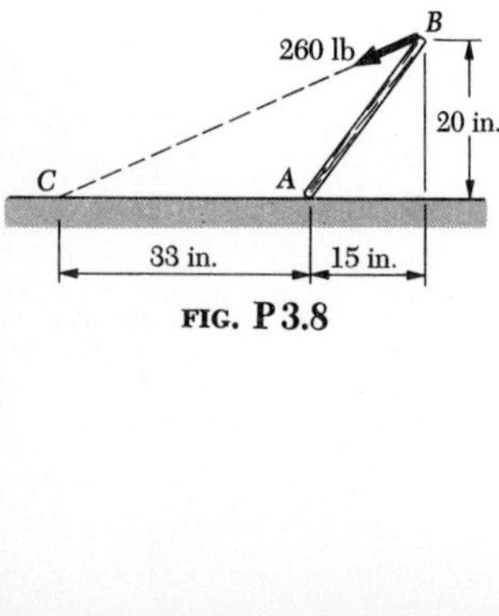

FIG. P 3.8

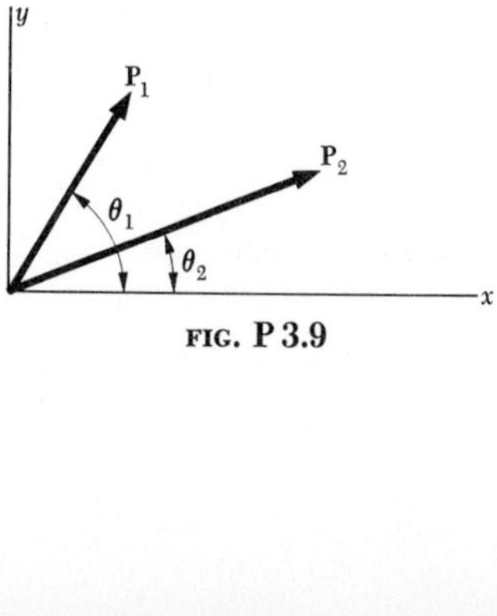

FIG. P 3.9

3.10. A force $\mathbf{F} = F_x\mathbf{i} + F_y\mathbf{j}$ acts at a point A of coordinates x_1 and y_1. Derive an expression for the moment of $\mathbf{F}$ about a second point B of coordinates x_2 and y_2.

3.11. The line of action of a force **P** passes through the two points $A\ (x_1, y_1)$ and $B\ (x_2, y_2)$. If the force is directed from A to B, determine the moment of the force about the origin.

3.12. A force $\mathbf{F} = F_x\mathbf{i} + F_y\mathbf{j}$ acts at a point of coordinates x and y. Derive an expression for the perpendicular distance d from the line of action of **F** to the origin O of the system of coordinates.

3.13. Determine the moment about the origin O of the force $\mathbf{F} = -2\mathbf{i} - 3\mathbf{j} + 5\mathbf{k}$ which acts at a point A. Assume that the position vector of A is (*a*) $\mathbf{r} = \mathbf{i} + \mathbf{j} + \mathbf{k}$, (*b*) $\mathbf{r} = 4\mathbf{i} + 6\mathbf{j} - 10\mathbf{k}$, (*c*) $\mathbf{r} = 4\mathbf{i} + 3\mathbf{j} - 5\mathbf{k}$.

3.14. Determine the moment about the origin O of the force $\mathbf{F} = 4\mathbf{i} + 10\mathbf{j} + 6\mathbf{k}$ which acts at a point A. Assume that the position vector of A is (*a*) $\mathbf{r} = 2\mathbf{i} - 3\mathbf{j} + 4\mathbf{k}$, (*b*) $\mathbf{r} = 2\mathbf{i} + 6\mathbf{j} + 3\mathbf{k}$, (*c*) $\mathbf{r} = 2\mathbf{i} + 5\mathbf{j} + 6\mathbf{k}$.

3.15. A precast-concrete wall section is temporarily held by cables as shown. Knowing that the tension in cable AB is 700 lb, determine the moment about the origin of coordinates O of the force exerted on the wall section at A.

3.16. Knowing that the tension in cable BC is 900 lb, determine the moment about the origin of coordinates O of the force exerted on the wall section at C.

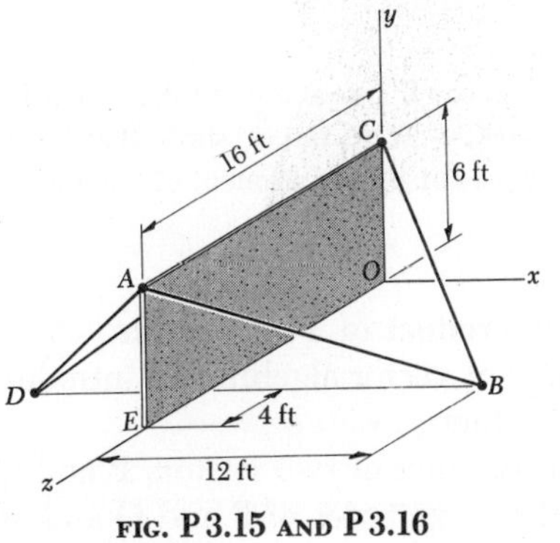

FIG. P3.15 AND P3.16

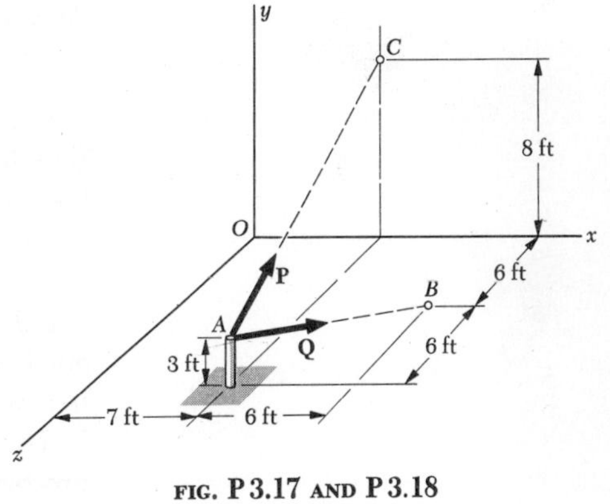

FIG. P3.17 AND P3.18

3.17. A force **P** of magnitude 260 lb is applied at point A as shown. Determine the rectangular components of the moment of **P** about the origin of coordinates O.

3.18. A force **Q** of magnitude 300 lb is applied at a point A as shown. Determine the rectangular components of the moment of **Q** about the origin of coordinates O.

3.19. A force **P** acts along the diagonal of a face of a rectangular box as shown. Determine the moment of **P** about the origin O.

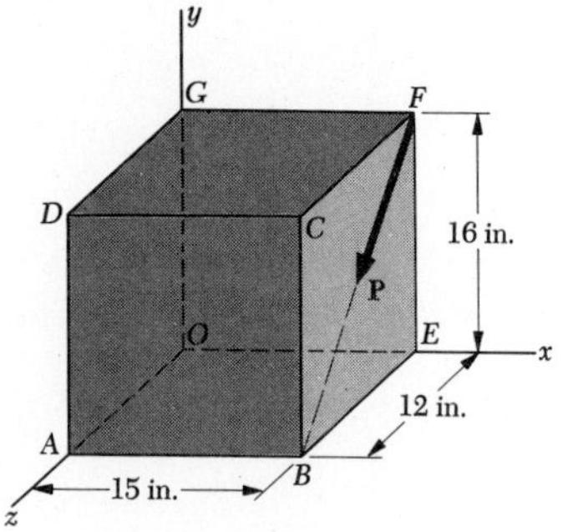

FIG. P 3.19

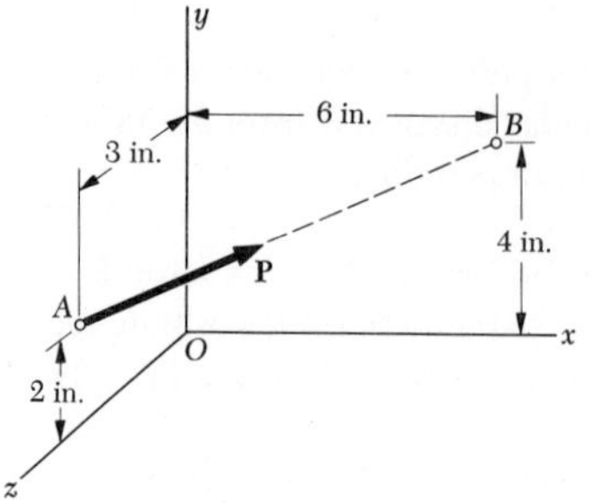

FIG. P 3.20

3.20. The line of action of the force **P** of magnitude 700 lb passes through the two points A and B as shown. Compute the moment of **P** about O using the position vector (*a*) of point A, (*b*) of point B.

3.21. In Prob. 3.19, determine the perpendicular distance from the line of action of **P** to the origin O.

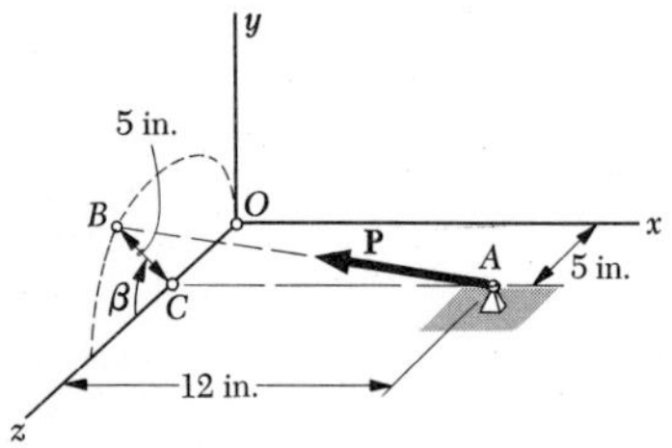

FIG. P 3.23

3.22. In Prob. 3.20, determine the perpendicular distance from the line of action of **P** to the origin O.

3.23. The line of action of the force **P** passes through points A and B. Knowing that the magnitude of **P** is 260 lb, determine the rectangular components of the moment of **P** about the origin O (*a*) in terms of β, (*b*) when $\beta = 60°$, (*c*) when $\beta = 120°$.

3.24. A single force **F** acts at a point A of coordinates $x = y = z = a$. Show that $M_x + M_y + M_z = 0$; i.e., show that the *algebraic* sum of the rectangular components of the moment of **F** about O is zero.

3.8. Scalar Product of Two Vectors.

We shall now expand our knowledge of vector algebra and introduce the *scalar product* of two vectors.

The scalar product of two vectors **P** and **Q** is defined as the product of the magnitudes of **P** and **Q** and of the cosine of the angle θ formed by **P** and **Q** (Fig. 3.17). The scalar product of **P** and **Q** is denoted by $\mathbf{P} \cdot \mathbf{Q}$. We write therefore

$$\mathbf{P} \cdot \mathbf{Q} = PQ \cos \theta \qquad (3.21)$$

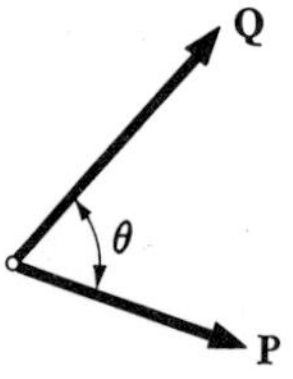

FIG. 3.17

Note that the expression just defined is not a vector, but a *scalar*, which explains the name *scalar product;* because of the notation used, $\mathbf{P} \cdot \mathbf{Q}$ is also referred to as the *dot product* of the vectors **P** and **Q**.

It follows from its very definition that the scalar product of two vectors is *commutative,* i.e., that

$$\mathbf{P} \cdot \mathbf{Q} = \mathbf{Q} \cdot \mathbf{P} \tag{3.22}$$

To prove that the scalar product is also *distributive,* we must prove the relation

$$\mathbf{P} \cdot (\mathbf{Q}_1 + \mathbf{Q}_2) = \mathbf{P} \cdot \mathbf{Q}_1 + \mathbf{P} \cdot \mathbf{Q}_2 \tag{3.23}$$

We may, without any loss of generality, assume that **P** is directed along the y axis (Fig. 3.18). Denoting by **Q** the sum of $\mathbf{Q}_1$ and $\mathbf{Q}_2$, and by θ_y the angle **Q** forms with the y axis, we express the left-hand member of (3.23) as follows:

$$\mathbf{P} \cdot (\mathbf{Q}_1 + \mathbf{Q}_2) = \mathbf{P} \cdot \mathbf{Q} = PQ \cos \theta_y = PQ_y \tag{3.24}$$

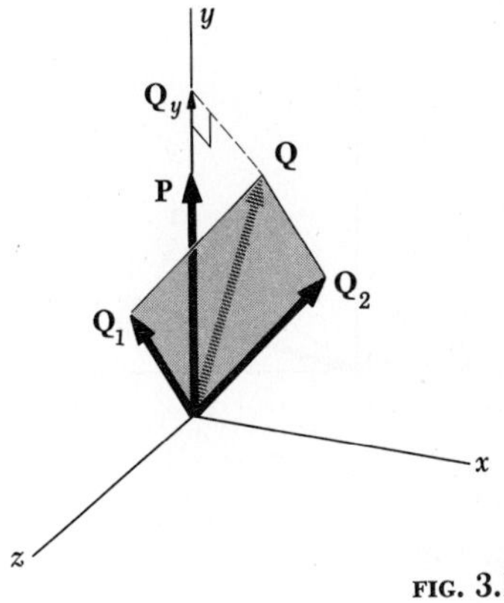

FIG. 3.18

where Q_y is the y component of **Q**. We may, in a similar way, express the right-hand member of (3.23) as

$$\mathbf{P} \cdot \mathbf{Q}_1 + \mathbf{P} \cdot \mathbf{Q}_2 = P(Q_1)_y + P(Q_2)_y \tag{3.25}$$

Since **Q** is the sum of $\mathbf{Q}_1$ and $\mathbf{Q}_2$, its y component must be equal to the sum of the y components of $\mathbf{Q}_1$ and $\mathbf{Q}_2$. Thus, the expressions obtained in (3.24) and (3.25) are equal and the relation (3.23) has been proved.

As far as the third property—the associative property—is concerned, we note that this property cannot apply to scalar products. Indeed, $(\mathbf{P} \cdot \mathbf{Q}) \cdot \mathbf{S}$ has no meaning, since $\mathbf{P} \cdot \mathbf{Q}$ is not a vector, but a scalar.

We shall now express the scalar product of two vectors **P** and **Q** in terms of their rectangular components. Resolving **P** and **Q** into components, we first write

$$\mathbf{P} \cdot \mathbf{Q} = (P_x\mathbf{i} + P_y\mathbf{j} + P_z\mathbf{k}) \cdot (Q_x\mathbf{i} + Q_y\mathbf{j} + Q_z\mathbf{k})$$

Making use of the distributive property, we express $\mathbf{P} \cdot \mathbf{Q}$ as the sum of scalar products such as $P_x\mathbf{i} \cdot Q_x\mathbf{i}$ and $P_x\mathbf{i} \cdot Q_y\mathbf{j}$. But we may easily check from the definition of the scalar product that the scalar products of the unit vectors are either zero or one.

$$\begin{array}{lll} \mathbf{i} \cdot \mathbf{i} = 1 & \mathbf{j} \cdot \mathbf{j} = 1 & \mathbf{k} \cdot \mathbf{k} = 1 \\ \mathbf{i} \cdot \mathbf{j} = 0 & \mathbf{j} \cdot \mathbf{k} = 0 & \mathbf{k} \cdot \mathbf{i} = 0 \end{array} \tag{3.26}$$

Thus, the expression obtained for $\mathbf{P} \cdot \mathbf{Q}$ reduces to

$$\mathbf{P} \cdot \mathbf{Q} = P_xQ_x + P_yQ_y + P_zQ_z \tag{3.27}$$

In the particular case when **P** and **Q** are equal, we check that

$$\mathbf{P} \cdot \mathbf{P} = P_x^2 + P_y^2 + P_z^2 = P^2 \tag{3.28}$$

Applications. 1. *Angle formed by two given vectors.* Let two vectors be given in terms of their components.

$$\mathbf{P} = P_x\mathbf{i} + P_y\mathbf{j} + P_z\mathbf{k}$$
$$\mathbf{Q} = Q_x\mathbf{i} + Q_y\mathbf{j} + Q_z\mathbf{k}$$

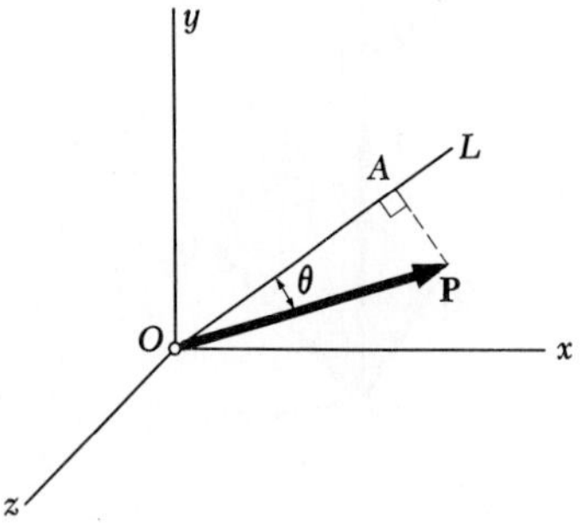

FIG. 3.19

To determine the angle formed by the two vectors we shall equate the expressions obtained in (3.21) and (3.27) for their scalar product:

$$PQ \cos \theta = P_xQ_x + P_yQ_y + P_zQ_z$$

Solving for $\cos \theta$, we write

$$\cos \theta = \frac{P_xQ_x + P_yQ_y + P_zQ_z}{PQ} \tag{3.29}$$

2. *Projection of a Vector on a Given Axis.* Consider a vector **P** forming an angle θ with an axis, or directed line, OL (Fig. 3.19). The *projection of* **P** *on the axis* OL is defined as the scalar

$$P_{OL} = P \cos \theta \tag{3.30}$$

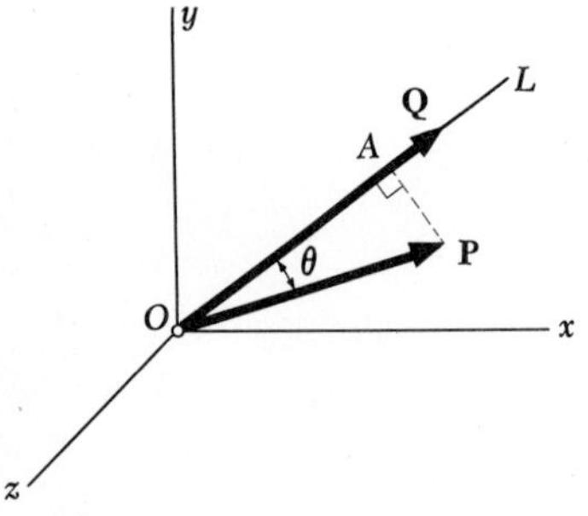

FIG. 3.20

We note that the projection P_{OL} is equal in absolute value to the length of the segment OA; it will be positive if OA has the same sense as the axis OL, i.e., if θ is acute, and negative otherwise. If **P** and OL are at a right angle, the projection of **P** on OL is zero.

Consider now a vector **Q** directed along OL and of the same sense as OL (Fig. 3.20). The scalar product of **P** and **Q** may be expressed as

$$\mathbf{P} \cdot \mathbf{Q} = PQ \cos \theta = P_{OL}Q \tag{3.31}$$

from which it follows that

$$P_{OL} = \frac{\mathbf{P} \cdot \mathbf{Q}}{Q} = \frac{P_xQ_x + P_yQ_y + P_zQ_z}{Q} \tag{3.32}$$

In the particular case when the vector selected along OL is the unit vector $\boldsymbol{\lambda}$ (Fig. 3.21), we write

$$P_{OL} = \mathbf{P} \cdot \boldsymbol{\lambda} \tag{3.33}$$

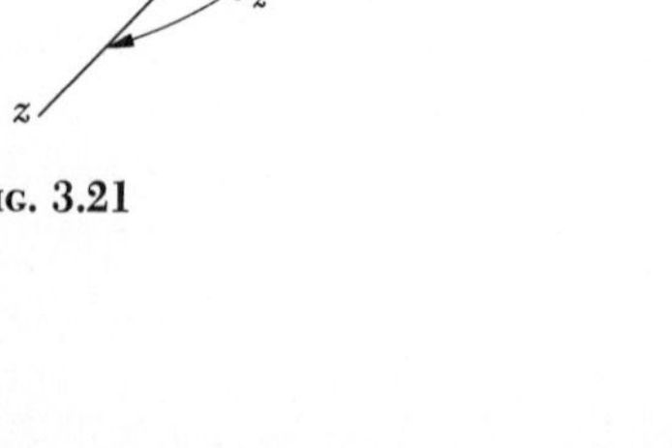

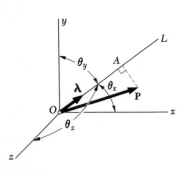

FIG. 3.21

Resolving **P** and $\boldsymbol{\lambda}$ into rectangular components, and recalling from Sec. 2.11 that the components of $\boldsymbol{\lambda}$ along the coordinate axes are respectively equal to the direction cosines of OL, we express the projection of **P** on OL as

$$P_{OL} = P_x \cos \theta_x + P_y \cos \theta_y + P_z \cos \theta_z \tag{3.34}$$

where θ_x, θ_y, and θ_z denote the angles that the axis OL forms with the coordinate axes.

3.9. Mixed Triple Product of Three Vectors. We define the *mixed triple product* of the three vectors **S**, **P**, and **Q** as the scalar expression

$$\mathbf{S} \cdot (\mathbf{P} \times \mathbf{Q}) \tag{3.35}$$

obtained by forming the scalar product of **S** with the vector product of **P** and **Q**.†

A simple geometrical interpretation may be given for the mixed triple product of **S**, **P**, and **Q** (Fig. 3.22). We first recall from Sec. 3.3 that the vector **P** × **Q** is perpendicular to the plane containing **P** and **Q**, and that its magnitude is equal to the area of the parallelogram constructed on **P** and **Q**. On the other hand, Eq. (3.31) indicates that the scalar product of **S** and **P** × **Q** may be obtained by multiplying the magnitude of **P** × **Q** (i.e., the area of the parallelogram built on **P** and **Q**) by the projection of **S** on the vector **P** × **Q** (i.e., by the projection of **S** on the normal to the plane containing the parallelogram). The mixed triple product is thus equal, in absolute value, to the volume of the parallelepiped having the vectors **S**, **P**, and **Q** for sides (Fig. 3.23). We may check that the sign of the mixed triple product will be positive if **S**, **P**, and **Q** form a right-handed triad, and negative if they form a left-handed triad [i.e., **S** · (**P** × **Q**) will be negative if the rotation which brings **P** into line with **Q** is observed as clockwise from the tip of **S**]. The mixed triple product will be zero if **S**, **P**, and **Q** are coplanar.

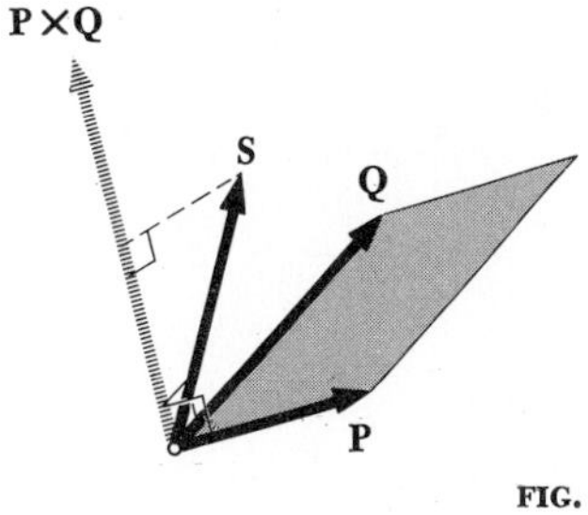

FIG. 3.22

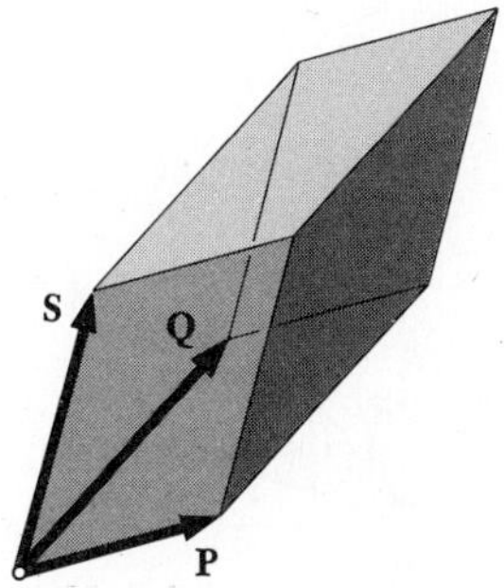

FIG. 3.23

Since the parallelepiped defined in the preceding paragraph is independent of the order in which the three vectors are taken, the six mixed triple products which may be formed with **S**, **P**, and **Q** will all have the same absolute value, although not the same sign. We check that

$$\begin{aligned}\mathbf{S} \cdot (\mathbf{P} \times \mathbf{Q}) &= \mathbf{P} \cdot (\mathbf{Q} \times \mathbf{S}) = \mathbf{Q} \cdot (\mathbf{S} \times \mathbf{P}) \\ &= -\mathbf{S} \cdot (\mathbf{Q} \times \mathbf{P}) = -\mathbf{P} \cdot (\mathbf{S} \times \mathbf{Q}) = -\mathbf{Q} \cdot (\mathbf{P} \times \mathbf{S})\end{aligned} \tag{3.36}$$

Arranging in a circle and in counterclockwise order the letters representing the three vectors (Fig. 3.24), we note that the sign of the mixed triple product is conserved if the vectors are permuted in such a way that they are still read in counterclockwise order. Such a permutation is said to be a *circular permutation*. It also follows from (3.36) that the mixed triple product of **S**, **P**, and **Q** may be defined equally well as **S** · (**P** × **Q**) or (**S** × **P**) · **Q**.

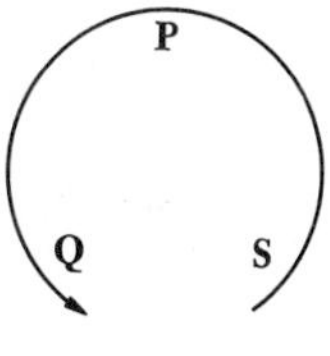

FIG. 3.24

† Another kind of triple product will be introduced later (Chap. 15): the *vector triple product* **S** × (**P** × **Q**).

We shall now express the mixed triple product of the vectors **S**, **P**, and **Q** in terms of the rectangular components of these vectors. Denoting **P** × **Q** by **V**, and using formula (3.27) to express the scalar product of **S** and **V**, we write

$$\mathbf{S} \cdot (\mathbf{P} \times \mathbf{Q}) = \mathbf{S} \cdot \mathbf{V} = S_x V_x + S_y V_y + S_z V_z$$

Substituting from the relations (3.9) for the components of **V**, we obtain

$$\mathbf{S} \cdot (\mathbf{P} \times \mathbf{Q}) = S_x(P_y Q_z - P_z Q_y) + S_y(P_z Q_x - P_x Q_z) + S_z(P_x Q_y - P_y Q_x) \quad (3.37)$$

This expression may be written in a more compact form if we observe that it represents the expansion of a determinant:

$$\mathbf{S} \cdot (\mathbf{P} \times \mathbf{Q}) = \begin{vmatrix} S_x & S_y & S_z \\ P_x & P_y & P_z \\ Q_x & Q_y & Q_z \end{vmatrix} \quad (3.38)$$

By applying the rules governing the permutation of rows in a determinant, we could easily verify the relations (3.36) which were derived earlier from geometrical considerations.

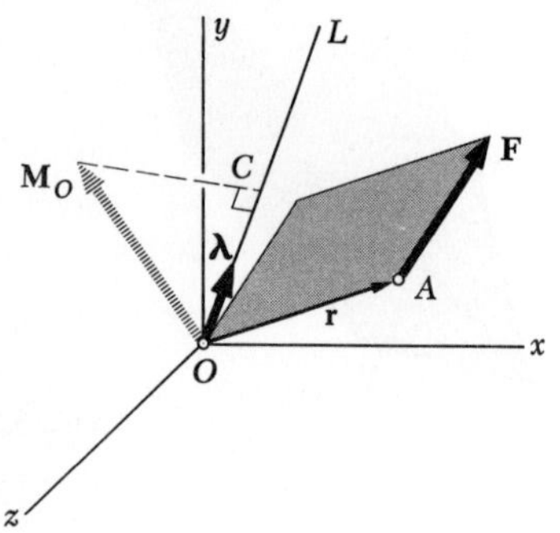

FIG. 3.25

3.10. Moment of a Force about a Given Axis. Now that we have further increased our knowledge of vector algebra, we shall introduce a new concept, the concept of *moment of a force about an axis.* Consider again a force **F** acting on a rigid body and the moment $\mathbf{M}_O$ of that force about O (Fig. 3.25). Let OL be an axis through O; *we define the moment M_{OL} of* **F** *about OL as the projection OC of the moment $\mathbf{M}_O$ on the axis OL.* Denoting by $\boldsymbol{\lambda}$ the unit vector along OL, and recalling the expressions (3.33) and (3.11) obtained earlier for the projection of a vector on a given axis and for the moment $\mathbf{M}_O$ of a force **F**, we write

$$M_{OL} = \boldsymbol{\lambda} \cdot \mathbf{M}_O = \boldsymbol{\lambda} \cdot (\mathbf{r} \times \mathbf{F}) \quad (3.39)$$

which shows that the moment M_{OL} of **F** about the axis OL is the scalar obtained by forming the mixed triple product of $\boldsymbol{\lambda}$, **r**, and **F**. Expressing M_{OL} in the form of a determinant, we write

$$M_{OL} = \begin{vmatrix} \lambda_x & \lambda_y & \lambda_z \\ x & y & z \\ F_x & F_y & F_z \end{vmatrix} \quad (3.40)$$

where $\lambda_x, \lambda_y, \lambda_z$ = direction cosines of axis OL
x, y, z = coordinates of point of application of **F**
F_x, F_y, F_z = components of force **F**

The physical significance of the moment M_{OL} of a force **F** about a fixed axis OL becomes more apparent if we resolve **F** into two rectangular components $\mathbf{F}_1$ and $\mathbf{F}_2$, with $\mathbf{F}_1$ parallel to OL and $\mathbf{F}_2$ lying in a plane P perpendicular to OL (Fig. 3.26). Resolving **r** similarly into two components $\mathbf{r}_1$ and $\mathbf{r}_2$, and substituting for **F** and **r** into (3.39), we write

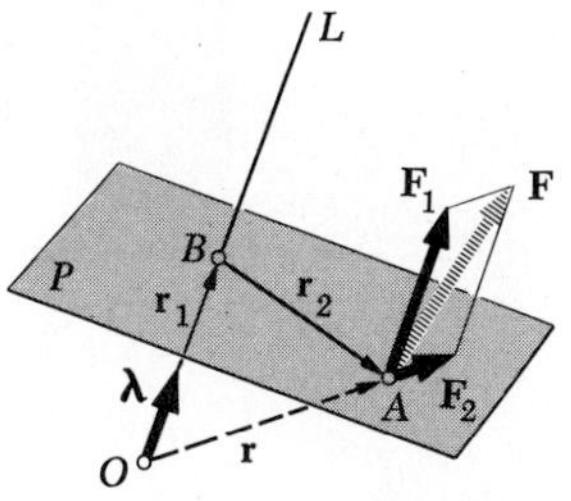

FIG. 3.26

$$\begin{aligned} M_{OL} &= \boldsymbol{\lambda}\cdot[(\mathbf{r}_1 + \mathbf{r}_2) \times (\mathbf{F}_1 + \mathbf{F}_2)] \\ &= \boldsymbol{\lambda}\cdot(\mathbf{r}_1 \times \mathbf{F}_1) + \boldsymbol{\lambda}\cdot(\mathbf{r}_1 \times \mathbf{F}_2) + \boldsymbol{\lambda}\cdot(\mathbf{r}_2 \times \mathbf{F}_1) + \boldsymbol{\lambda}\cdot(\mathbf{r}_2 \times \mathbf{F}_2) \end{aligned}$$

Noting that all mixed triple products, except the last one, involve coplanar vectors and, therefore, are equal to zero, we have†

$$M_{OL} = \boldsymbol{\lambda}\cdot(\mathbf{r}_2 \times \mathbf{F}_2) \tag{3.41}$$

The vector product $\mathbf{r}_2 \times \mathbf{F}_2$ is perpendicular to the plane P and represents the moment of the component $\mathbf{F}_2$ of **F** about the point B where OL intersects P. Therefore, the scalar M_{OL}, which will be positive if $\mathbf{r}_2 \times \mathbf{F}_2$ and OL have the same sense, and negative otherwise, measures the tendency of $\mathbf{F}_2$ to make the rigid body rotate about the fixed axis OL. Since the other component $\mathbf{F}_1$ of **F** does not tend to make the body rotate about OL, we conclude that *the moment M_{OL} of* **F** *about OL measures the tendency of the force* **F** *to impart to the rigid body a motion of rotation about the fixed axis OL.*

It follows from the definition of the moment of a force about an axis that the moment of **F** about a coordinate axis is equal to the component of $\mathbf{M}_O$ along that axis. Substituting successively each of the unit vectors **i**, **j**, and **k** for $\boldsymbol{\lambda}$ in (3.39), we check that the expressions thus obtained for the *moments of* **F** *about the coordinate axes* are respectively equal to the expressions obtained in Sec. 3.7 for the components of the moment $\mathbf{M}_O$ of **F** about O.

$$\begin{aligned} M_x &= yF_z - zF_y \\ M_y &= zF_x - xF_z \\ M_z &= xF_y - yF_x \end{aligned} \tag{3.18}$$

We observe that, just as the components F_x, F_y, and F_z of a force **F** acting on a rigid body measure, respectively, the tendency of **F** to move the rigid body in the x, y, and z directions, the moments M_x, M_y, and M_z of **F** about the coordinate axes measure the tendency of **F** to impart to the rigid body a motion of rotation about the x, y, and z axes, respectively.

† Note that, since the expression (3.41) obtained for M_{OL} does not contain the vector $\mathbf{r}_1$, it is clear that the value of M_{OL} is independent of the choice of the point O used in the original definition of the moment M_{OL}.

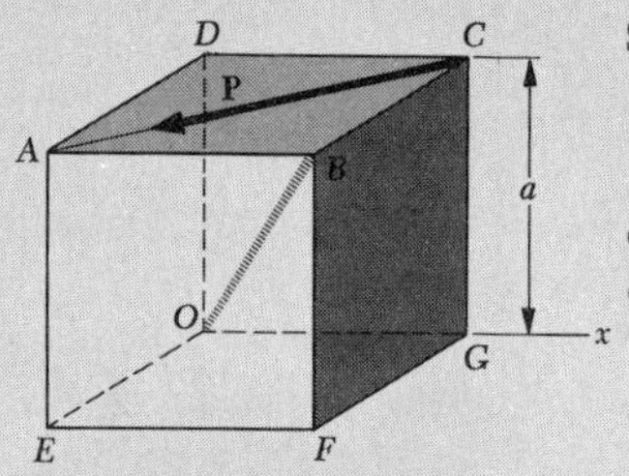

SAMPLE PROBLEM 3.5

A cube of side a is acted upon by a force **P** as shown. Determine the moment of **P** (*a*) about O, (*b*) about the x axis, (*c*) about the diagonal OB of the cube. (*d*) Using the result of part *c*, determine the perpendicular distance from OB to AC.

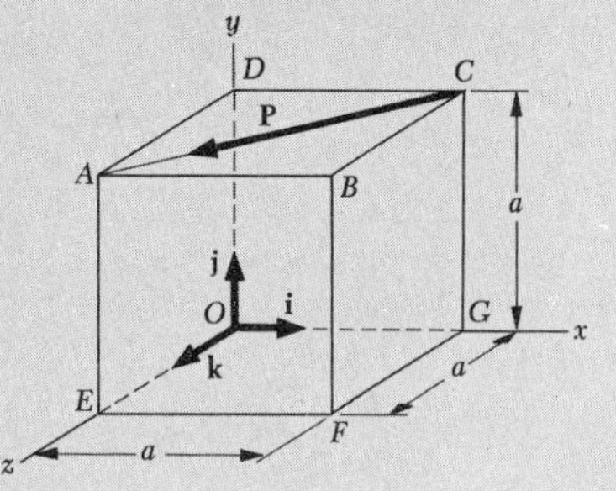

a. **Moment about** O. Choosing x, y, and z axes as shown, we resolve the force **P** and the position vector **r** of its point of application into rectangular components.

$$\mathbf{r} = a\mathbf{i} + a\mathbf{j} = a(\mathbf{i} + \mathbf{j})$$
$$\mathbf{P} = -(P/\sqrt{2})\mathbf{i} + (P/\sqrt{2})\mathbf{k} = (P/\sqrt{2})(-\mathbf{i} + \mathbf{k})$$

The moment of **P** about O is

$$\mathbf{M}_O = \mathbf{r} \times \mathbf{P} = a(\mathbf{i} + \mathbf{j}) \times (P/\sqrt{2})\,(-\mathbf{i} + \mathbf{k})$$
$$\mathbf{M}_O = (aP/\sqrt{2})\,(\mathbf{i} - \mathbf{j} + \mathbf{k}) \quad ◄$$

b. **Moment about** x **axis.** Projecting $\mathbf{M}_O$ on the x axis, we write

$$M_x = \mathbf{i} \cdot \mathbf{M}_O = \mathbf{i} \cdot (aP/\sqrt{2})\,(\mathbf{i} - \mathbf{j} + \mathbf{k})$$
$$M_x = aP/\sqrt{2} \quad ◄$$

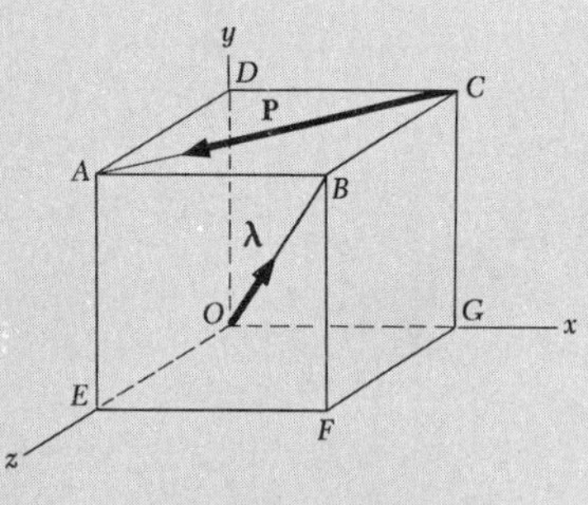

We verify that M_x is also the x component of the moment $\mathbf{M}_O$.

c. **Moment about Diagonal** OB. The moment of **P** about OB is obtained by projecting $\mathbf{M}_O$ on OB. Denoting by $\boldsymbol{\lambda}$ the unit vector along OB, we note that

$$\boldsymbol{\lambda} = \frac{\overrightarrow{OB}}{OB} = \frac{a\mathbf{i} + a\mathbf{j} + a\mathbf{k}}{a\sqrt{3}} = (1/\sqrt{3})\,(\mathbf{i} + \mathbf{j} + \mathbf{k})$$

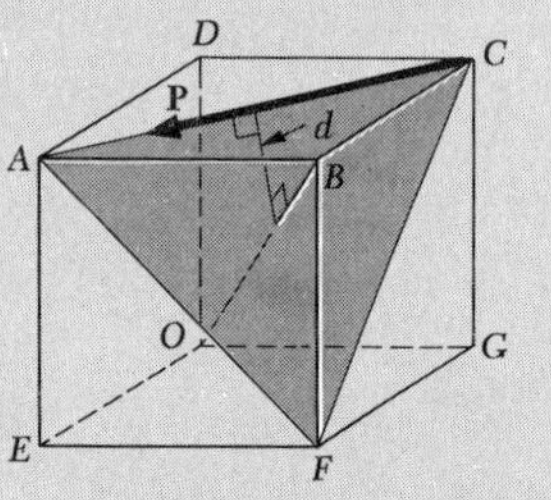

and write

$$M_{OB} = \boldsymbol{\lambda} \cdot \mathbf{M}_O = (1/\sqrt{3})\,(\mathbf{i} + \mathbf{j} + \mathbf{k}) \cdot (aP/\sqrt{2})\,(\mathbf{i} - \mathbf{j} + \mathbf{k})$$
$$M_{OB} = (aP/\sqrt{6})\,(1 - 1 + 1) \qquad M_{OB} = aP/\sqrt{6} \quad ◄$$

Alternate Method. The moment of **P** about OB may also be expressed in the form of a determinant:

$$M_{OB} = \begin{vmatrix} \lambda_x & \lambda_y & \lambda_z \\ x & y & z \\ F_x & F_y & F_z \end{vmatrix} = \begin{vmatrix} 1/\sqrt{3} & 1/\sqrt{3} & 1/\sqrt{3} \\ a & a & 0 \\ -P/\sqrt{2} & 0 & P/\sqrt{2} \end{vmatrix} = aP/\sqrt{6}$$

d. **Perpendicular Distance from** OB **to** AC. We first observe that **P** is perpendicular to the diagonal OB. This may be checked by forming the scalar product of **P** and $\boldsymbol{\lambda}$ and verifying that it reduces to zero:

$$\mathbf{P} \cdot \boldsymbol{\lambda} = (P/\sqrt{2})(-\mathbf{i} + \mathbf{k}) \cdot (1/\sqrt{3})(\mathbf{i} + \mathbf{j} + \mathbf{k}) = (P/\sqrt{6})(-1 + 0 + 1) = 0$$

The moment M_{OB} may then be expressed as the product of P and the perpendicular distance d from OB to AC. Using the value of M_{OB} found in part *c*, we write

$$aP/\sqrt{6} = Pd \qquad d = a/\sqrt{6} \quad ◄$$

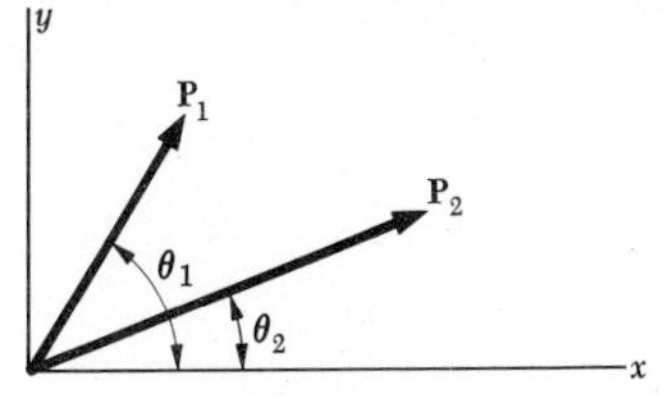

FIG. P 3.26

PROBLEMS

3.25. Given the vectors $\mathbf{P} = 2\mathbf{i} + \mathbf{j} + 2\mathbf{k}$, $\mathbf{Q} = 3\mathbf{i} + 4\mathbf{j} - 5\mathbf{k}$, and $\mathbf{S} = -4\mathbf{i} + \mathbf{j} - 2\mathbf{k}$, compute the scalar products $\mathbf{P} \cdot \mathbf{Q}$, $\mathbf{P} \cdot \mathbf{S}$, and $\mathbf{Q} \cdot \mathbf{S}$.

3.26. Form the scalar product $\mathbf{P}_1 \cdot \mathbf{P}_2$ and use the result obtained to prove the identity $\cos(\theta_1 - \theta_2) = \cos\theta_1 \cos\theta_2 + \sin\theta_1 \sin\theta_2$.

3.27. Several cables are attached to the top of the tower at *A*. Determine the angle formed by cables *AB* and *AC*.

3.28. Determine the angle formed by cables *AD* and *AB*.

3.29. A force **P** of magnitude 420 lb is directed along the line *AB* from point *A* to point *B*. Determine the projection of **P** on the line *AC*.

3.30. A force **Q** of magnitude 420 lb is directed along line *AC* from point *A* to point *C*. Determine the projection of **Q** on line *AB*.

3.31. Knowing that the tension in cable *AB* is 210 lb, determine (*a*) the angle formed by *AB* and *AC*, (*b*) the projection on *AC* of the force exerted by cable *AB* at point *A*.

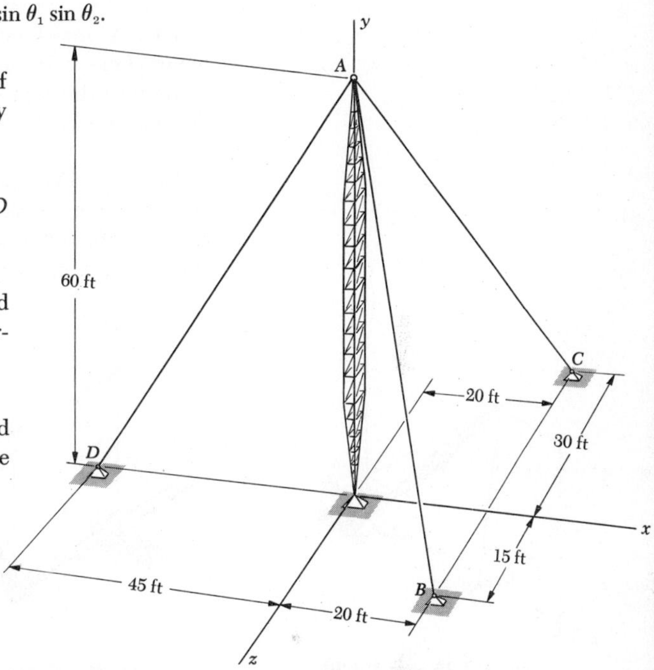

FIG. P 3.27 AND P 3.28

3.32. Knowing that the tension in cable *AB* is 210 lb, determine (*a*) the angle between cable *AB* and a line joining points *B* and *C*, (*b*) the projection on that line of the force exerted by cable *AB* at point *B*.

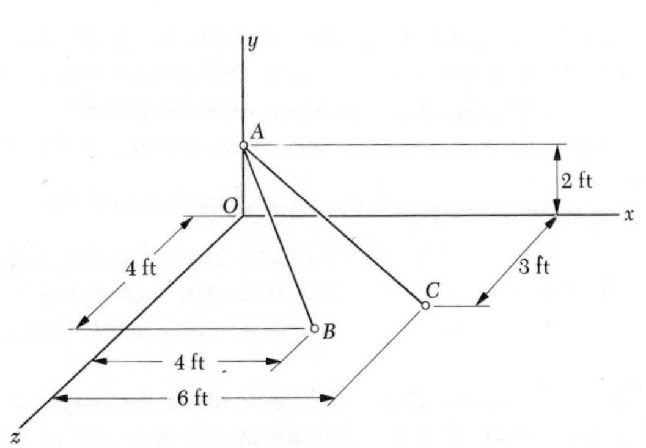

FIG. P 3.29 AND P 3.30

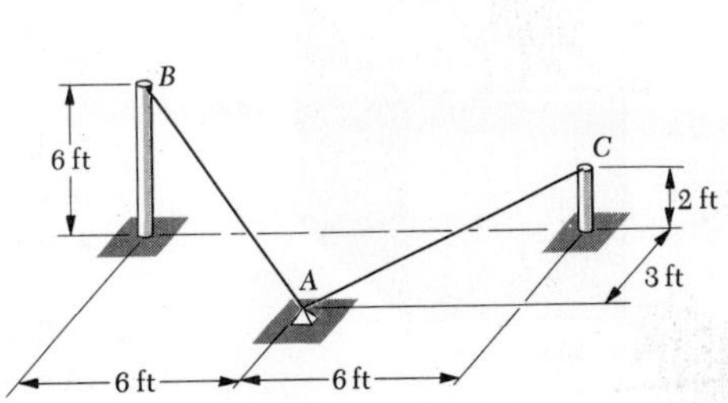

FIG. P 3.31 AND P 3.32

3.33. Given the vectors $\mathbf{P} = \mathbf{i} + \mathbf{j} + \mathbf{k}$, $\mathbf{Q} = \mathbf{i} + \mathbf{j}$, and $\mathbf{S} = \mathbf{i}$, compute $\mathbf{P} \cdot (\mathbf{Q} \times \mathbf{S})$, $(\mathbf{P} \times \mathbf{Q}) \cdot \mathbf{S}$, and $(\mathbf{S} \times \mathbf{Q}) \cdot \mathbf{P}$.

3.34. Given the vectors $\mathbf{P} = \mathbf{i} + 2\mathbf{j} + 3\mathbf{k}$, $\mathbf{Q} = 2\mathbf{i} - \mathbf{j} - 5\mathbf{k}$, and $\mathbf{S} = S_x\mathbf{i} + 3\mathbf{j} + \mathbf{k}$, determine the value of S_x for which the three vectors are coplanar.

3.35. A crane is oriented so that the end of the 50-ft boom AO lies in the yz plane. At the instant shown the tension in cable AB is 1,000 lb. Determine the moment about each of the coordinate axes of the force exerted on A by the cable AB.

3.36. The 50-ft crane boom AO lies in the yz plane. Determine the maximum permissible tension in the cable AB if the absolute value of the moments about the coordinate axes of the force exerted on A must be as follows: $M_x \leqslant 40{,}000$ lb-ft, $M_y \leqslant 8{,}000$ lb-ft, $M_z \leqslant 9{,}000$ lb-ft.

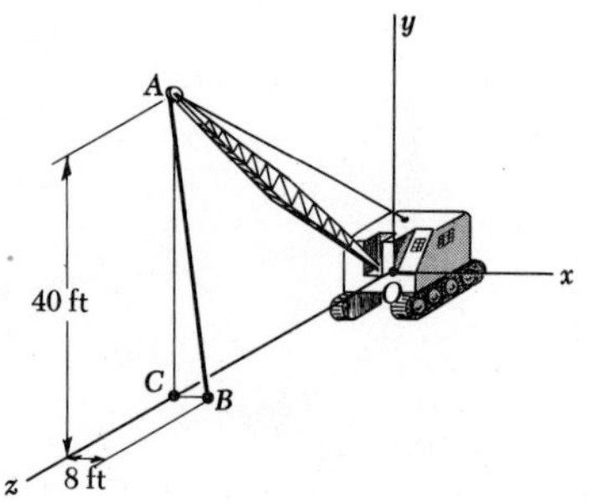

FIG. P3.35 AND P3.36

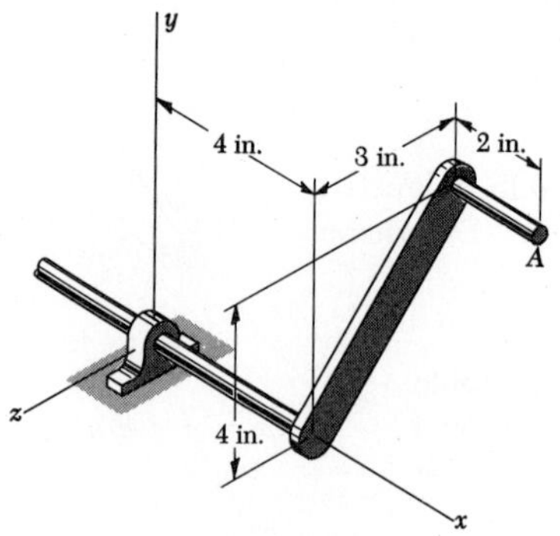

FIG. P3.37 AND P3.38

3.37. A single force $\mathbf{F}$ of unknown magnitude and direction acts at point A of the crank shown. Determine the moment M_x of $\mathbf{F}$ about the x axis, knowing that $M_y = +90$ lb-in. and $M_z = -220$ lb-in.

3.38. The primary purpose of the crank shown is, of course, to produce a moment about the x axis. Show that a single force acting at A and having a moment M_x different from zero about the x axis must also have a moment different from zero about at least one of the other coordinate axes.

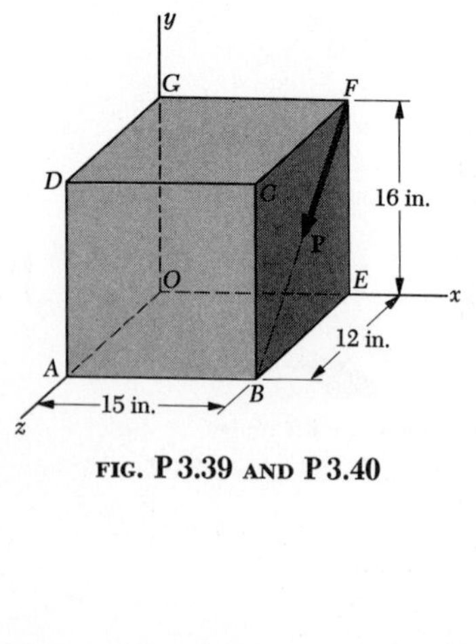

FIG. P3.39 AND P3.40

3.39. A force $\mathbf{P}$ of magnitude 50 lb acts along the diagonal of a face of a rectangular box as shown. Determine the moment of $\mathbf{P}$ about (*a*) a line joining corners G and C, (*b*) a line joining corners O and C.

3.40. A force $\mathbf{P}$ of magnitude 50 lb acts along the diagonal of a face of a rectangular box as shown. Determine the moment of $\mathbf{P}$ about (*a*) a line joining corners A and C, (*b*) a line joining corners D and E.

3.41. An irregular pyramid is acted upon by a force **P** of magnitude 75 lb as shown. Determine the moment of **P** about (*a*) edge *AD*, (*b*) edge *AB*, (*c*) edge *AC*.

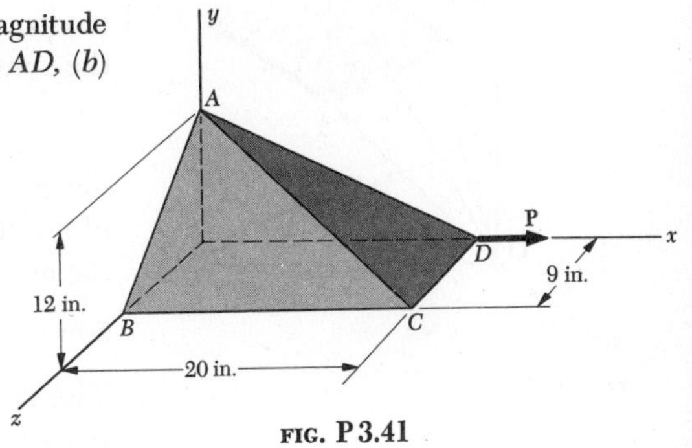

FIG. P 3.41

3.42. Solve Prob. 3.41 assuming that the force **P** is replaced by the force $\mathbf{Q} = 50\mathbf{i} + 25\mathbf{j} + 50\mathbf{k}$ acting at point *D*.

3.43. A 5- by 12-ft rectangular plate has one edge located along the *x* axis as shown. A force **P** of magnitude 1,400 lb is applied to the plate at *C*. Determine the moment of **P** about (*a*) edge *OA*, (*b*) the diagonal *OB*.

3.44. A 5- by 12-ft rectangular plate has one edge located along the *x* axis as shown. A force **P** of magnitude 1,400 lb is applied to the plate at *C*. Determine the moment of **P** about (*a*) the *y* axis, (*b*) the diagonal *DA*.

3.45. A regular tetrahedron has six edges each of length *a*. A single force **P** is directed along one edge. Determine the moment of **P** about each of the other five edges.

3.46. Two forces $\mathbf{F}_1$ and $\mathbf{F}_2$ in space have the same magnitude *F*. Prove that the moment of $\mathbf{F}_1$ about the line of action of $\mathbf{F}_2$ is equal to the moment of $\mathbf{F}_2$ about the line of action of $\mathbf{F}_1$.

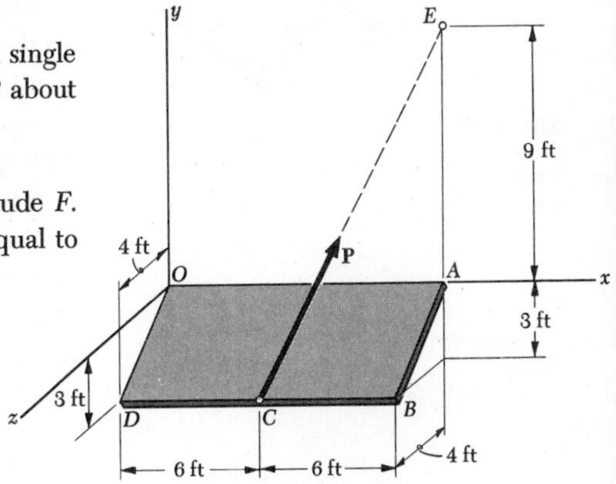

FIG. P 3.43 AND P 3.44

***3.47.** In Prob. 3.39, use the result obtained in part *b* to determine the perpendicular distance between the lines *OC* and *BF*.

***3.48.** In Prob. 3.40, use the result obtained in part *b* to determine the perpendicular distance between the lines *DE* and *BF*.

3.11. Moment of a Couple. *Two forces* **F** *and* −**F**, *having the same magnitude, parallel lines of action, and opposite sense are said to form a couple* (Fig. 3.27). Clearly, the sum of the components of the two forces in any direction is zero. The sum of the moments of the two forces about a given point, however, is not zero. While the two forces will not translate the body on which they act, they will tend to make it rotate.

FIG. 3.27

Denoting by $\mathbf{r}_A$ and $\mathbf{r}_B$, respectively, the position vectors of

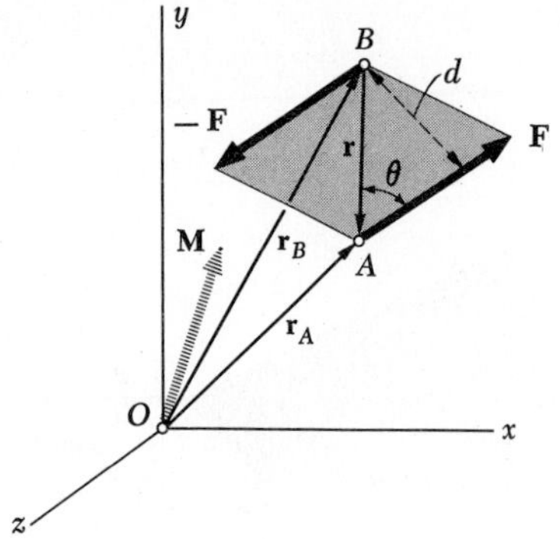

FIG. 3.28

the points of application of **F** and $-$**F** (Fig. 3.28), we find that the sum of the moments of the two forces about O is

$$\mathbf{r}_A \times \mathbf{F} + \mathbf{r}_B \times (-\mathbf{F}) = (\mathbf{r}_A - \mathbf{r}_B) \times \mathbf{F}$$

Setting $\mathbf{r}_A - \mathbf{r}_B = \mathbf{r}$, where **r** is the vector joining the points of application of the two forces, we conclude that the sum of the moments of **F** and $-$**F** about O is represented by the vector

$$\mathbf{M} = \mathbf{r} \times \mathbf{F} \tag{3.42}$$

The vector **M** is called the *moment of the couple;* it is a vector perpendicular to the plane containing the two forces and its magnitude is

$$M = rF \sin\theta = Fd \tag{3.43}$$

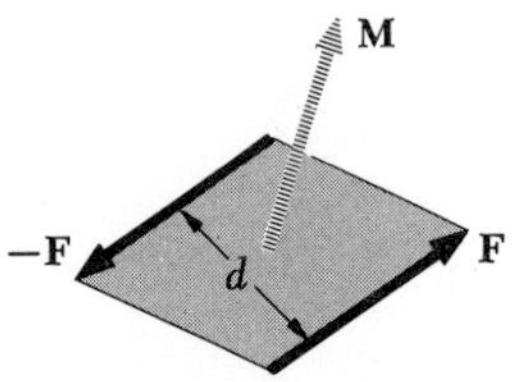

FIG. 3.29

where d is the perpendicular distance between the lines of action of **F** and $-$**F**. The sense of **M** is defined by the right-hand rule.

Since the vector **r** in (3.42) is independent of the choice of the origin O of the coordinate axes, we note that the same result would have been obtained if the moments of **F** and $-$**F** had been computed about a different point O'. Thus, the moment **M** of a couple is a *free vector* (Sec. 2.2) which may be applied at any point (Fig. 3.29).

From the definition of the moment of a couple, it also follows that two couples, one consisting of the forces $\mathbf{F}_1$ and $-\mathbf{F}_1$, the other of the forces $\mathbf{F}_2$ and $-\mathbf{F}_2$ (Fig. 3.30), will have equal moments if

$$F_1 d_1 = F_2 d_2 \tag{3.44}$$

and if the two couples lie in parallel planes (or in the same plane) and have the same sense.

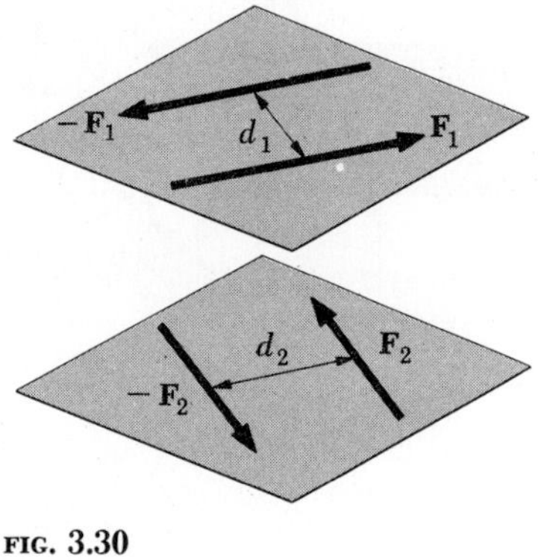

FIG. 3.30

3.12. Equivalent Couples. Consider the three couples shown in Fig. 3.31, which are made to act successively on the same rectangular box. As seen in the preceding section, the only motion a couple may impart to a rigid body is a rotation. Since each of the three couples shown has the same moment **M** (same direction and same magnitude $M = 120$ lb-in.), we may expect the three couples to have the same effect on the box.

As reasonable as this conclusion may appear, we should not accept it hastily. While intuitive feeling is of great help in the study of mechanics, it should not be accepted as a substitute for logical reasoning. Before stating that two systems (or groups) of forces have the same effect on a rigid body, we should prove that fact on the basis of the experimental evidence introduced so far. This evidence consists of the parallelogram law for the addition of two forces (Sec. 2.1) and of the principle of transmissibility (Sec. 3.2). Therefore, we shall state that *two systems of forces are equivalent* (i.e., they have the same effect on a rigid body) *if we can transform one of them into the other by means of one or several of the following operations:* (1) replacing two forces acting on the same particle by their resultant; (2) resolving a force into two components; (3) canceling two equal and opposite forces acting on the same particle; (4) attaching to the same particle two equal and opposite forces; (5) moving a force along its line of action. Each of these operations is easily justified on the basis of the parallelogram law or the principle of transmissibility.

Let us now prove that *two couples having the same moment* **M** *are equivalent.* First, we shall consider two couples contained in the same plane, and we shall assume that this plane coincides with the plane of the figure (Fig. 3.32). The first couple consists of the forces $\mathbf{F}_1$ and $-\mathbf{F}_1$, of magnitude F_1 and at a distance d_1 from each other (Fig. 3.32*a*), and the second couple of the forces $\mathbf{F}_2$ and $-\mathbf{F}_2$, of magnitude F_2 and at a distance d_2 from each other (Fig. 3.32*d*). Since the two couples have the same moment **M** perpendicular to the plane of the figure, they must have the same sense (assumed here counterclockwise) and the relation

$$F_1 d_1 = F_2 d_2 \tag{3.44}$$

must be satisfied. To prove that they are equivalent, we shall show that the first couple may be transformed into the second by means of the operations listed above.

Denoting by A, B, C, D the points of intersection of the lines of action of the two couples, we first slide the forces $\mathbf{F}_1$ and $-\mathbf{F}_1$ until they are attached, respectively, at A and B, as shown in Fig. 3.32*b*. The force $\mathbf{F}_1$ is then resolved into a component **P** along line AB and a component **Q** along AC (Fig. 3.32*c*); similarly, the force $-\mathbf{F}_1$ is resolved into $-\mathbf{P}$ along AB and $-\mathbf{Q}$ along BD. The forces **P** and $-\mathbf{P}$ have the same magnitude, same line of action, and opposite sense; they may be moved along their common line of action until they are applied at the

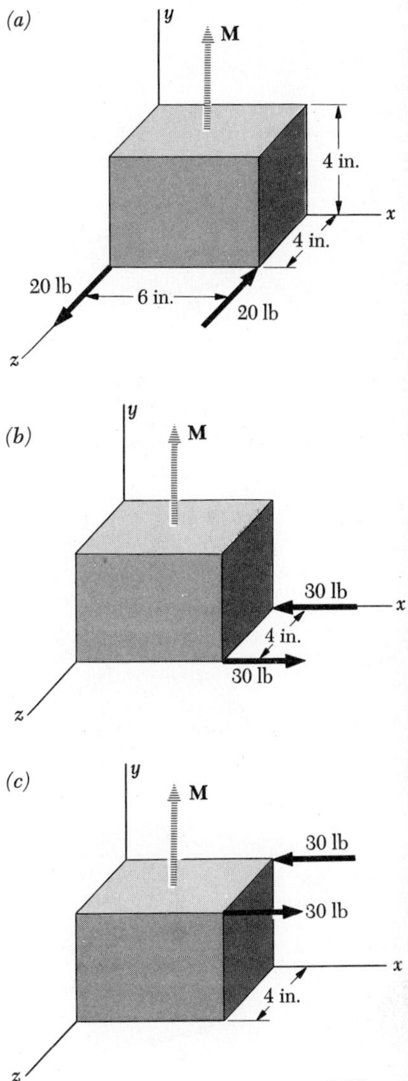

FIG. 3.31

FIG. 3.32

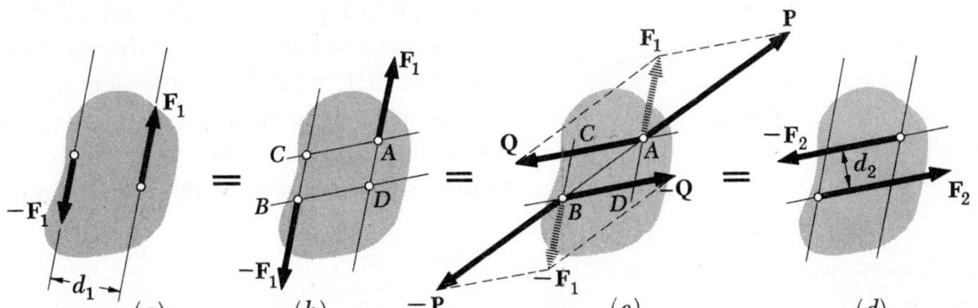

same point and then canceled. Thus the couple formed by $\mathbf{F}_1$ and $-\mathbf{F}_1$ reduces to a couple consisting of $\mathbf{Q}$ and $-\mathbf{Q}$.

We shall now show that the forces $\mathbf{Q}$ and $-\mathbf{Q}$ are respectively equal to the forces $-\mathbf{F}_2$ and $\mathbf{F}_2$. The moment of the couple formed by $\mathbf{Q}$ and $-\mathbf{Q}$ may be obtained by computing the moment of $\mathbf{Q}$ about B; similarly, the moment of the couple formed by $\mathbf{F}_1$ and $-\mathbf{F}_1$ is the moment of $\mathbf{F}_1$ about B. But, by Varignon's theorem, the moment of $\mathbf{F}_1$ is equal to the sum of the moments of its components $\mathbf{P}$ and $\mathbf{Q}$. Since the moment of $\mathbf{P}$ about B is zero, the moment of the couple formed by $\mathbf{Q}$ and $-\mathbf{Q}$ must be equal to the moment of the couple formed by $\mathbf{F}_1$ and $-\mathbf{F}_1$. Recalling (3.44), we write

$$Qd_2 = F_1d_1 = F_2d_2 \qquad \text{and} \qquad Q = F_2$$

Thus the forces $\mathbf{Q}$ and $-\mathbf{Q}$ are respectively equal to the forces $-\mathbf{F}_2$ and $\mathbf{F}_2$, and the couple of Fig. 3.32*a* is equivalent to the couple of Fig. 3.32*d*.

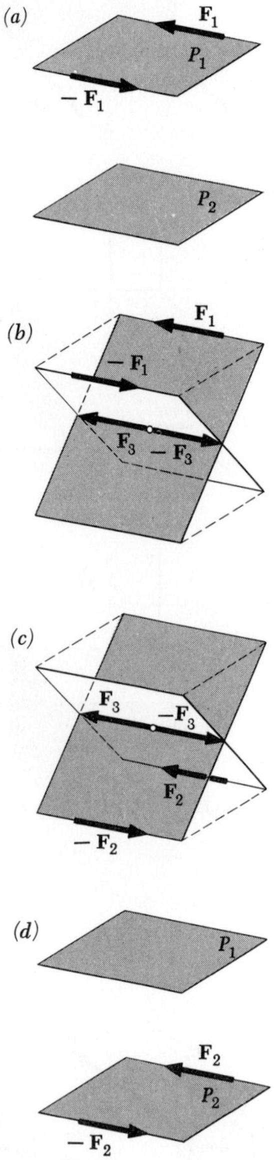

FIG. 3.33

Next we shall consider two couples contained in parallel planes P_1 and P_2 and prove that they are equivalent if they have the same moment. In view of the foregoing we may assume that the couples consist of forces of the same magnitude F acting along parallel lines (Fig. 3.33*a* and *d*). We propose to show that the couple contained in plane P_1 may be transformed into the couple contained in plane P_2 by means of the standard operations listed above.

Let us consider the two planes defined respectively by the lines of action of $\mathbf{F}_1$ and $-\mathbf{F}_2$, and of $-\mathbf{F}_1$ and $\mathbf{F}_2$ (Fig. 3.33*b*). At a point on their line of intersection we attach two forces $\mathbf{F}_3$ and $-\mathbf{F}_3$, respectively equal to $\mathbf{F}_1$ and $-\mathbf{F}_1$. The couple formed by $\mathbf{F}_1$ and $-\mathbf{F}_3$ may be replaced by a couple consisting of $\mathbf{F}_3$ and $-\mathbf{F}_2$ (Fig. 3.33*c*), since both couples have clearly the same moment and are contained in the same plane. Similarly, the couple formed by $-\mathbf{F}_1$ and $\mathbf{F}_3$ may be replaced by a couple consisting of $-\mathbf{F}_3$ and $\mathbf{F}_2$. Canceling the two equal and opposite forces $\mathbf{F}_3$ and $-\mathbf{F}_3$, we obtain the desired couple in plane P_2 (Fig. 3.33*d*). Thus, we conclude that two couples having the same moment $\mathbf{M}$ are equivalent, whether they are contained in the same plane or in parallel planes.

The property we have just established is very important for the correct understanding of the mechanics of rigid bodies. It indicates that, when a couple acts on a rigid body, it does not matter where the two forces forming the couple act, or what magnitude and direction they have. The only thing which counts is the *moment* of the couple (magnitude and direction).

Couples with the same moment will have the same effect on the rigid body.

3.13. Couples May Be Represented by Vectors. Since couples which have the same moment are equivalent, there is no need to draw the actual forces forming a given couple in order to define its effect on a rigid body (Fig. 3.34*a*). It is sufficient to draw a vector equal in magnitude and direction to the moment **M** of the couple (Fig. 3.34*b*); this vector is called a *couple vector.* Note that a solid arrow is used to distinguish the couple vector, *which represents the couple itself,* from the vector representing the *moment* of the couple, and that the symbol ⟲ is added to avoid any confusion with vectors representing forces. A couple vector, like the moment of a couple, is a free vector. Its point of application, therefore, may be chosen at the origin of the system of coordinates, if so desired (Fig. 3.34*c*). Furthermore, the couple vector **M** may be resolved into component vectors $\mathbf{M}_x$, $\mathbf{M}_y$, and $\mathbf{M}_z$, directed along the axes of coordinates (Fig. 3.34*d*) and representing couples acting, respectively, in the *yz, zx,* and *xy* planes.

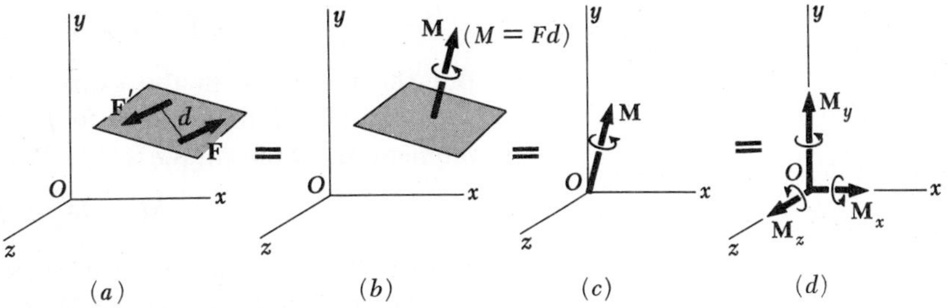

FIG. 3.34

The representation of a couple by means of a vector is convenient. This representation, however, should be *justified,* i.e., we should show that the arrows used to represent couples possess the characteristics of vectors (see Sec. 2.2); more specifically, we should prove that they obey the parallelogram law of addition.

Consider two intersecting planes P_1 and P_2 and two couples acting respectively in P_1 and P_2. We may, without any loss of generality, assume that the couple in P_1 consists of two forces $\mathbf{F}_1$ and $-\mathbf{F}_1$ perpendicular to the line of intersection of the two planes and acting respectively at A and B (Fig. 3.35*a*). Similarly, we assume that the couple in P_2 consists of two forces $\mathbf{F}_2$ and $-\mathbf{F}_2$ perpendicular to AB and acting respectively at A and B. It is clear that the resultant **R** of $\mathbf{F}_1$ and $\mathbf{F}_2$ and the resultant

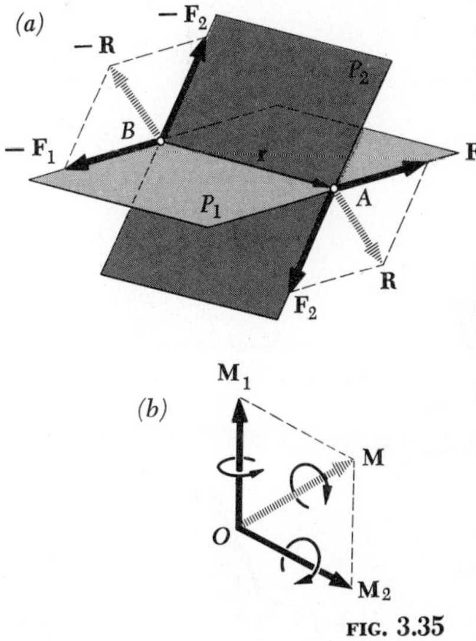

FIG. 3.35

$-\mathbf{R}$ of $-\mathbf{F}_1$ and $-\mathbf{F}_2$ form a couple. Denoting by $\mathbf{r}$ the vector joining B to A, and recalling the definition of the moment of a couple (Sec. 3.11), we express the moment $\mathbf{M}$ of the resulting couple as follows:

$$\mathbf{M} = \mathbf{r} \times \mathbf{R} = \mathbf{r} \times (\mathbf{F}_1 + \mathbf{F}_2)$$

and, by Varignon's theorem,

$$\mathbf{M} = \mathbf{r} \times \mathbf{F}_1 + \mathbf{r} \times \mathbf{F}_2$$

But the first term in the expression obtained represents the moment $\mathbf{M}_1$ of the couple in P_1, and the second term the moment $\mathbf{M}_2$ of the couple in P_2. We have

$$\mathbf{M} = \mathbf{M}_1 + \mathbf{M}_2 \tag{3.45}$$

and we conclude that the sum of two couples of moments $\mathbf{M}_1$ and $\mathbf{M}_2$ is a couple of moment $\mathbf{M}$ equal to the vector sum of $\mathbf{M}_1$ and $\mathbf{M}_2$. Clearly, the same relation holds between the corresponding couple vectors; thus, couple vectors obey the parallelogram law of addition (Fig. 3.35*b*).

Summarizing the results obtained in this section, we conclude that *a couple may be truly represented by a vector.* This vector, called a couple vector, is equal to the moment of the couple; it is a *free vector* and may be applied at any point. Couple vectors may be added or resolved according to the parallelogram law.

3.14. Resolution of a Given Force into a Force at *O* and a Couple. Consider a force $\mathbf{F}$ acting on a rigid body at a point A defined by the position vector $\mathbf{r}$ (Fig. 3.36*a*). Suppose that for some reason we would rather have the force act at point O. We know that we can move $\mathbf{F}$ along its line of action (principle of transmissibility); but we cannot move it to a point O away from the original line of action without modifying the action of $\mathbf{F}$ on the rigid body.

We may, however, attach two forces at point O, one equal to $\mathbf{F}$ and the other equal to $-\mathbf{F}$, without modifying the action of the original force on the rigid body (Fig. 3.36*b*). As a result of this transformation, a force $\mathbf{F}$ is now applied at O; the other two

FIG. 3.36

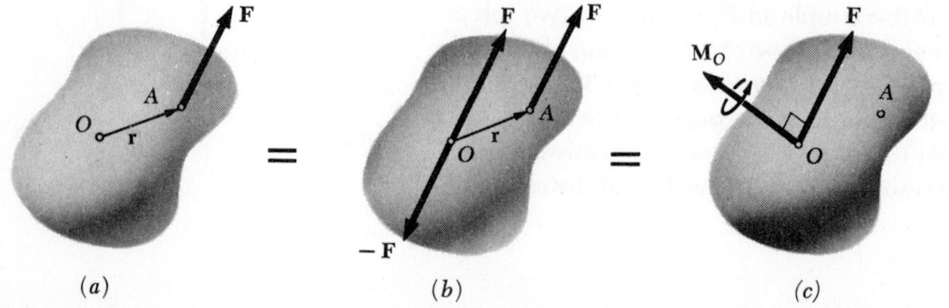

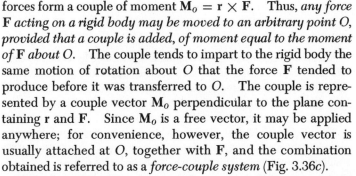

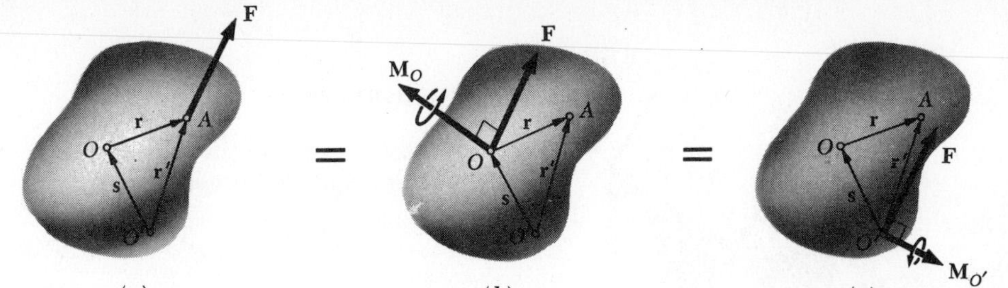

(a) (b) (c)

FIG. 3.37

forces form a couple of moment $\mathbf{M}_O = \mathbf{r} \times \mathbf{F}$. Thus, *any force* $\mathbf{F}$ *acting on a rigid body may be moved to an arbitrary point O, provided that a couple is added, of moment equal to the moment of* $\mathbf{F}$ *about O.* The couple tends to impart to the rigid body the same motion of rotation about O that the force $\mathbf{F}$ tended to produce before it was transferred to O. The couple is represented by a couple vector $\mathbf{M}_O$ perpendicular to the plane containing $\mathbf{r}$ and $\mathbf{F}$. Since $\mathbf{M}_O$ is a free vector, it may be applied anywhere; for convenience, however, the couple vector is usually attached at O, together with $\mathbf{F}$, and the combination obtained is referred to as a *force-couple system* (Fig. 3.36*c*).

If the force $\mathbf{F}$ had been moved from A to a different point O' (Fig. 3.37*a* and *c*), the moment $\mathbf{M}_{O'} = \mathbf{r}' \times \mathbf{F}$ of $\mathbf{F}$ about O' should have been computed, and a new force-couple system, consisting of $\mathbf{F}$ and of the couple vector $\mathbf{M}_{O'}$, would have been attached at O'. The relation existing between the moments of $\mathbf{F}$ about O and O' is obtained by writing

$$\mathbf{M}_{O'} = \mathbf{r}' \times \mathbf{F} = (\mathbf{r} + \mathbf{s}) \times \mathbf{F} = \mathbf{r} \times \mathbf{F} + \mathbf{s} \times \mathbf{F}$$

$$\mathbf{M}_{O'} = \mathbf{M}_O + \mathbf{s} \times \mathbf{F} \qquad (3.46)$$

where $\mathbf{s}$ is the vector joining O' to O. Thus, the moment $\mathbf{M}_{O'}$ of $\mathbf{F}$ about O' is obtained by adding to the moment $\mathbf{M}_O$ of $\mathbf{F}$ about O the vector product $\mathbf{s} \times \mathbf{F}$ representing the moment about O' of the force $\mathbf{F}$ applied at O.

This result could also have been established by observing that, in order to transfer to O' the force-couple system attached at O (Fig. 3.37*b* and *c*), the couple vector $\mathbf{M}_O$ may be freely moved to O'; to move the force $\mathbf{F}$ from O to O', however, it is necessary to add to $\mathbf{F}$ a couple vector $\mathbf{s} \times \mathbf{F}$ representing the moment about O' of the force $\mathbf{F}$ applied at O. Thus, the couple vector $\mathbf{M}_{O'}$ must be the sum of $\mathbf{M}_O$ and $\mathbf{s} \times \mathbf{F}$.

As noted above, the force-couple system obtained by transferring a force $\mathbf{F}$ from a point A to a point O consists of $\mathbf{F}$ and of a couple vector $\mathbf{M}_O = \mathbf{r} \times \mathbf{F}$ perpendicular to $\mathbf{F}$. Conversely, any force-couple system consisting of a force $\mathbf{F}$ and of a couple vector $\mathbf{M}_O$ which are *mutually perpendicular* may be replaced by a single equivalent force. This is done by moving the force $\mathbf{F}$ in the plane perpendicular to $\mathbf{M}_O$ until its moment about O becomes equal to the couple vector $\mathbf{M}_O$ to be eliminated.

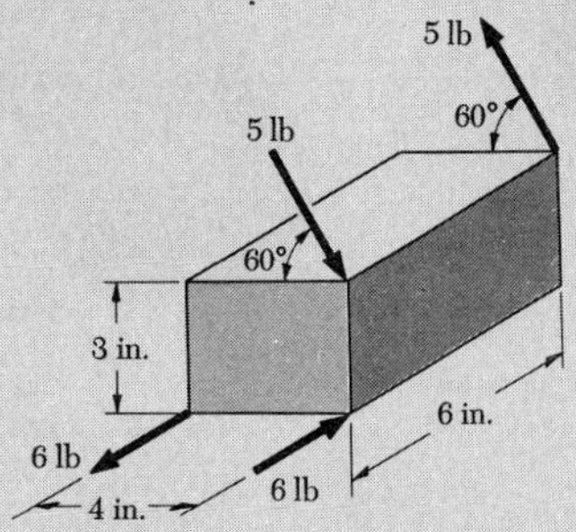

SAMPLE PROBLEM 3.6

Two couples act on a rectangular box as shown. Replace these two couples by a single equivalent couple.

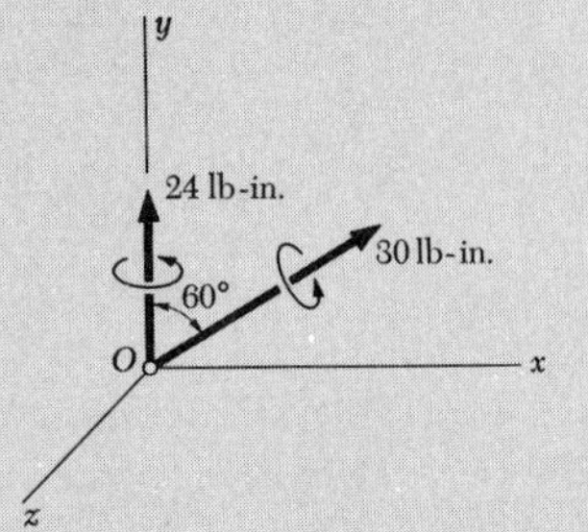

Solution. Each of the given couples is represented by a couple vector which is perpendicular to the plane of the couple and of a magnitude equal to the moment of the couple. The sense of each vector is obtained by applying the right-hand rule, and for convenience both couple vectors are attached at the origin.

The single couple equivalent to the two given couples will be represented by the resultant of the two couple vectors. The magnitude of the resultant couple vector **M** is obtained from the law of cosines.

$$M^2 = (24)^2 + (30)^2 - (2)(24)(30)\cos 120°$$

$$M = 46.9 \text{ lb-in.}$$

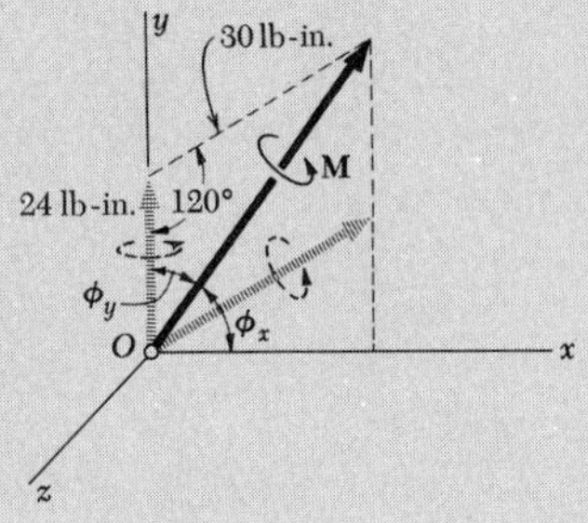

The angle ϕ_y that the resultant couple vector forms with the vertical is obtained from the law of sines.

$$\frac{\sin \phi_y}{30 \text{ lb-in.}} = \frac{\sin 120°}{46.9 \text{ lb-in.}} \qquad \phi_y = 33.6°$$

The angle that the couple vector forms with the x axis is

$$\phi_x = 90° - 33.6° = 56.4°$$

and the angle it forms with the z axis is $\phi_z = 90°$. Thus the resultant couple vector **M** is defined by

$$M = 46.9 \text{ lb-in.} \qquad \phi_x = 56.4° \qquad \phi_y = 33.6° \qquad \phi_z = 90°$$ ◄

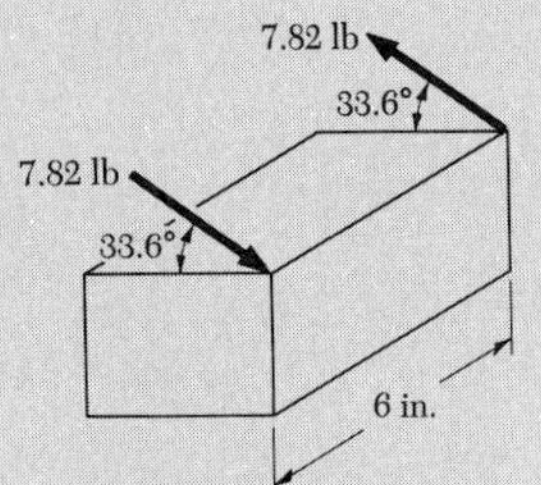

The single couple equivalent to the two original couples is a couple of moment $M = 46.9$ lb-in., acting in a plane parallel to the z axis and forming an angle of 33.6° with the horizontal plane. This couple may be formed in many ways, for example, by the two 7.82-lb forces shown.

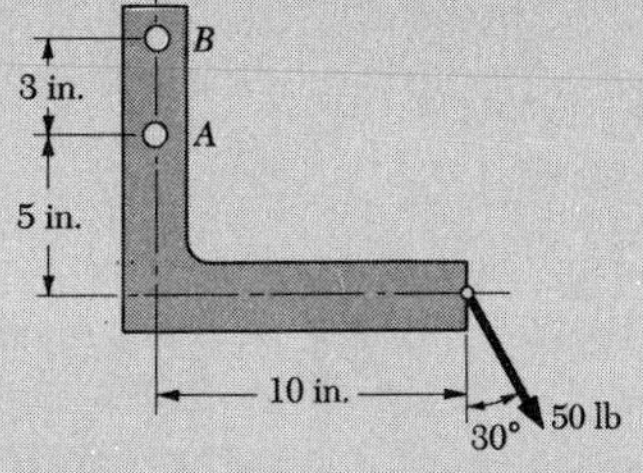

SAMPLE PROBLEM 3.7

A 50-lb force is applied to a corner plate as shown. Determine (*a*) an equivalent force-couple system at *A*, (*b*) an equivalent system consisting of a 150-lb force at *B* and another force at *A*.

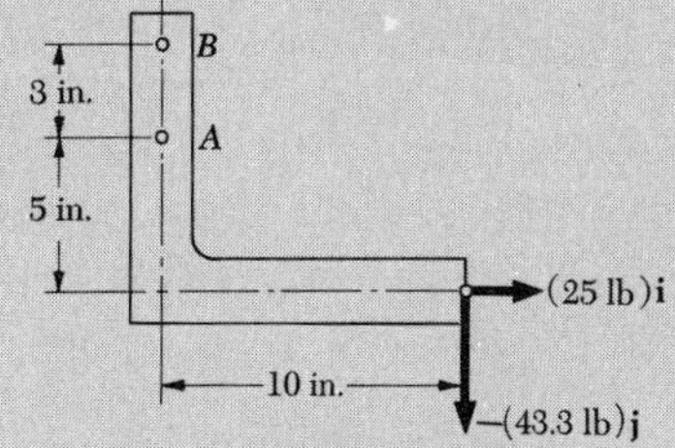

a. **Force-couple System at *A*.** We resolve the 50-lb force into *x* and *y* components.

$$\mathbf{F} = F_x\mathbf{i} + F_y\mathbf{j} = (50 \text{ lb}) \sin 30°\mathbf{i} - (50 \text{ lb}) \cos 30°\mathbf{j}$$

$$\mathbf{F} = (25.0 \text{ lb})\mathbf{i} - (43.3 \text{ lb})\mathbf{j} \quad ◄$$

The force **F** may be moved to *A* if a couple is added, of moment $\mathbf{M}_A$ equal to the moment about *A* of the force **F** in its original position. We write

$$\mathbf{M}_A = \mathbf{r} \times \mathbf{F} = [(10 \text{ in.})\mathbf{i} - (5 \text{ in.})\mathbf{j}] \times [(25.0 \text{ lb})\mathbf{i} - (43.3 \text{ lb})\mathbf{j}]$$

$$= (-433 \text{ lb-in.} + 125 \text{ lb-in.})\mathbf{k}$$

$$\mathbf{M}_A = -(308 \text{ lb-in.})\mathbf{k} \quad ◄$$

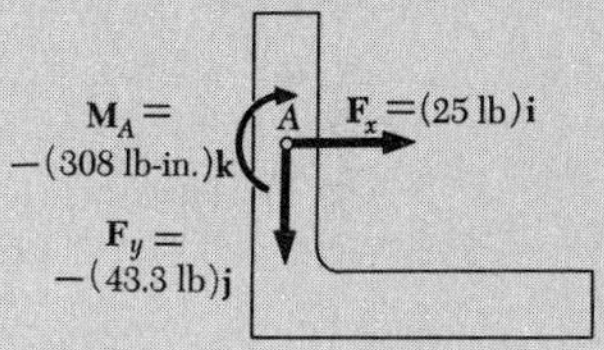

b. **Forces at *A* and *B*.** We shall assume that the couple $\mathbf{M}_A$ found in part *a* consists of two 150-lb forces **P** and −**P** acting respectively at *B* and *A*. The moment of **P** about *A* must be equal to the moment $\mathbf{M}_A$ of the couple. Denoting by θ the angle that **P** forms with the horizontal, we have

$$\mathbf{P} = (150 \text{ lb}) \cos\theta\, \mathbf{i} + (150 \text{ lb}) \sin\theta\, \mathbf{j}$$

$$\mathbf{M}_A = (3 \text{ in.})\mathbf{j} \times \mathbf{P} = -(450 \text{ lb-in.}) \cos\theta\, \mathbf{k}$$

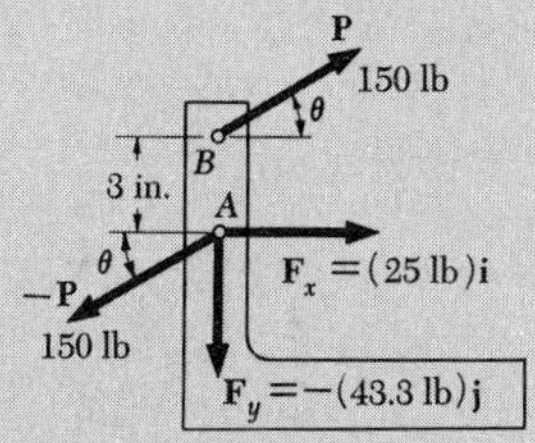

Substituting for $\mathbf{M}_A$ the expression found in part *a* for the moment of the couple, we write

$$-(308 \text{ lb-in.})\mathbf{k} = -(450 \text{ lb-in.}) \cos\theta\, \mathbf{k}$$

$$\cos\theta = \frac{308 \text{ lb-in.}}{450 \text{ lb-in.}} = 0.684 \qquad \theta = \pm 46.8°$$

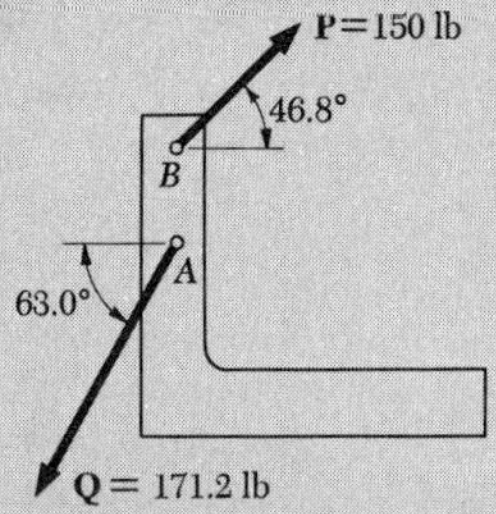

Having found the direction of the forces **P** and −**P**, we complete the solution by determining the resultant **Q** of the forces **F** and −**P** acting at *A*.

$$\mathbf{Q} = \mathbf{F} - \mathbf{P} = (25.0\mathbf{i} - 43.3\mathbf{j}) - (150 \cos\theta\, \mathbf{i} + 150 \sin\theta\, \mathbf{j})$$

$$\mathbf{Q} = (25.0 - 150 \cos\theta)\mathbf{i} - (43.3 + 150 \sin\theta)\mathbf{j}$$

Since we have found two possible values for θ, there will be two pairs of forces **P** and **Q** forming a system equivalent to the original 50-lb force:

$$\mathbf{P} = 150 \text{ lb} \measuredangle 46.8° \text{ at } B \qquad \mathbf{Q} = 171.2 \text{ lb} \measuredangle 63.0° \text{ at } A \quad ◄$$

or

$$\mathbf{P} = 150 \text{ lb} \measuredangle 46.8° \text{ at } B \qquad \mathbf{Q} = 101.8 \text{ lb} \measuredangle 40.3° \text{ at } A \quad ◄$$

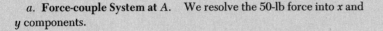

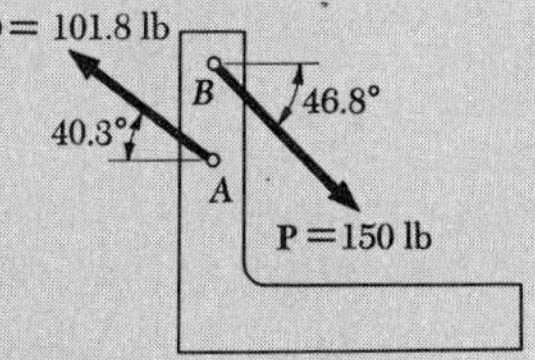

SAMPLE PROBLEM 3.8

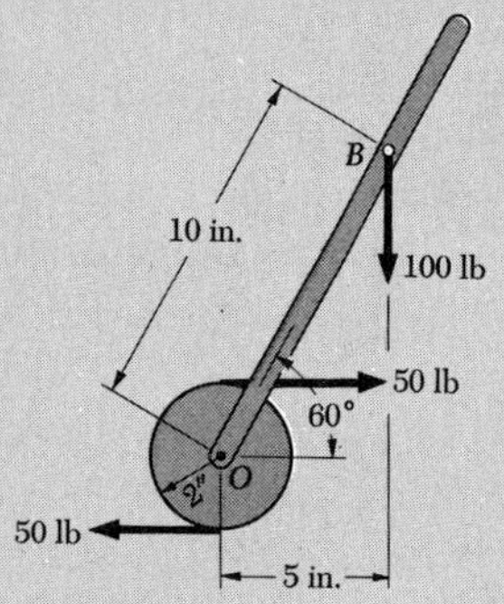

Replace the couple and force shown by an equivalent single force applied to the lever. Determine the distance from the shaft to the point of application of this equivalent force.

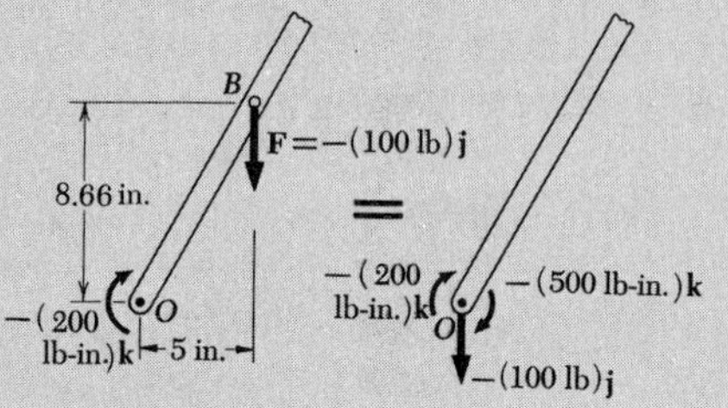

Solution. First the given force and couple are replaced by an equivalent force-couple system at O. We move the force $\mathbf{F} = -(100 \text{ lb})\mathbf{j}$ to O and at the same time add a couple of moment $\mathbf{M}_O$ equal to the moment about O of the force in its original position.

$$\mathbf{M}_O = \overrightarrow{OB} \times \mathbf{F} = (5\mathbf{i} + 8.66\mathbf{j}) \times (-100\mathbf{j}) = -(500 \text{ lb-in.})\mathbf{k}$$

This couple is added to the couple of moment $-(200 \text{ lb-in.})\mathbf{k}$ formed by the two 50-lb forces, and a couple of moment $-(700 \text{ lb-in.})\mathbf{k}$ is obtained. This last couple may be eliminated by applying $\mathbf{F}$ at a point C chosen in such a way that

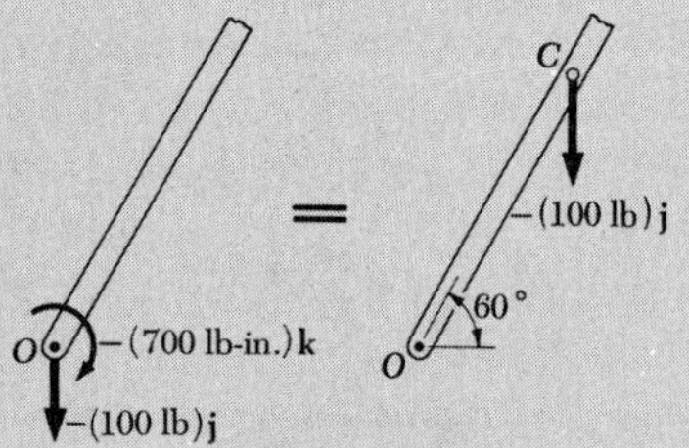

$$\begin{aligned}
-(700 \text{ lb-in.})\mathbf{k} &= \overrightarrow{OC} \times \mathbf{F} \\
&= [(OC)\cos 60°\,\mathbf{i} + (OC)\sin 60°\,\mathbf{j}] \times (-100 \text{ lb})\mathbf{j} \\
&= -(OC)\cos 60°\,(100 \text{ lb})\mathbf{k}
\end{aligned}$$

We conclude that

$$(OC)\cos 60° = 7 \text{ in.} \qquad OC = 14 \text{ in.} ◄$$

Alternate Solution. Since the effect of a couple does not depend on its location, the couple of moment $-(200 \text{ lb-in.})\mathbf{k}$ may be moved to B; we thus obtain a force-couple system at B. The couple may now be eliminated by applying $\mathbf{F}$ at a point C chosen in such a way that

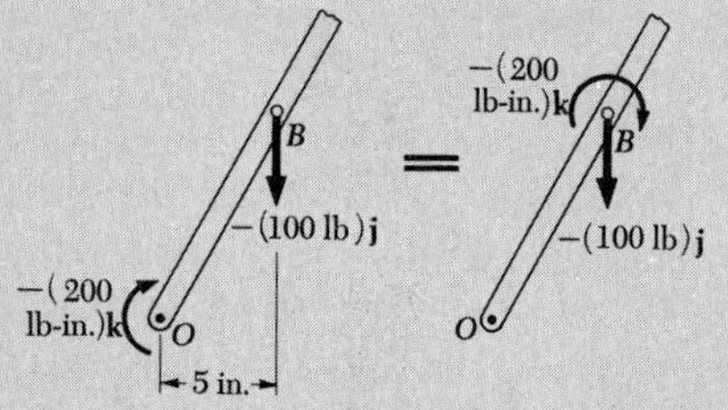

$$\begin{aligned}
-(200 \text{ lb-in.})\mathbf{k} &= \overrightarrow{BC} \times \mathbf{F} \\
&= -(BC)\cos 60°\,(100 \text{ lb})\mathbf{k}
\end{aligned}$$

We conclude that

$$(BC)\cos 60° = 2 \text{ in.} \qquad BC = 4 \text{ in.}$$

$$OC = OB + BC = 10 \text{ in.} + 4 \text{ in.} \qquad OC = 14 \text{ in.} ◄$$

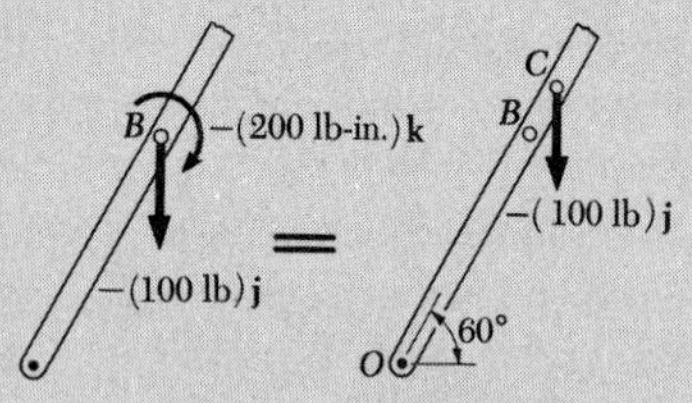

PROBLEMS

3.49. The two couples shown are applied to a 6- by 8-in. plate. Knowing that $P_1 = P_2 = 30$ lb and $Q_1 = Q_2 = 40$ lb, prove that their sum is zero (*a*) by adding their moments, (*b*) by combining $\mathbf{P}_1$ and $\mathbf{Q}_1$ into their resultant $\mathbf{R}_1$, combining $\mathbf{P}_2$ and $\mathbf{Q}_2$ into their resultant $\mathbf{R}_2$, and then showing that $\mathbf{R}_1$ and $\mathbf{R}_2$ are equal and opposite and have the same line of action.

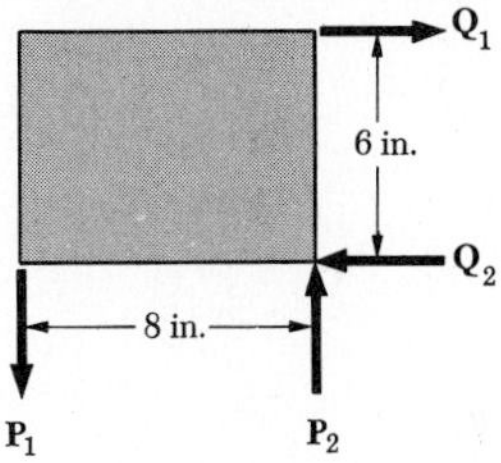

FIG. P 3.49

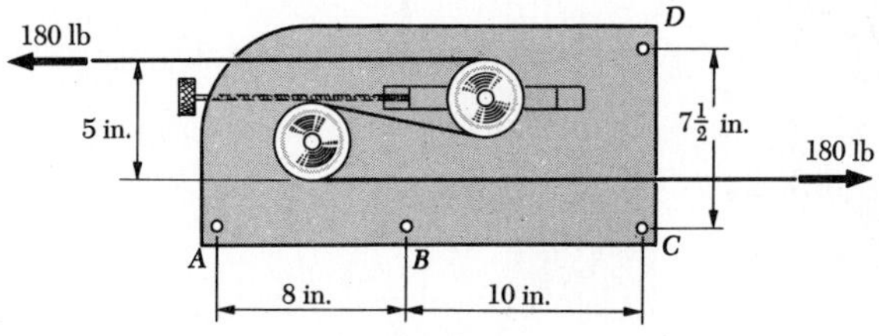

FIG. P 3.50

3.50. A couple formed by two 180-lb forces is applied to the pulley assembly shown. Determine an equivalent couple which is formed by (*a*) vertical forces acting at *A* and *C*, (*b*) the smallest possible forces acting at *B* and *D*, (*c*) the smallest possible forces which can be attached to the assembly.

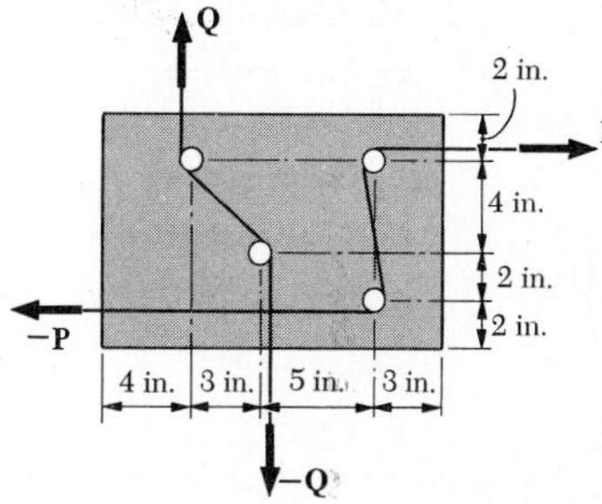

FIG. P 3.51 AND P 3.52

3.51. Four 1-in.-diameter pegs are attached to a board as shown. Two strings are passed around the pegs and pulled with forces of magnitude $P = 16$ lb and $Q = 40$ lb. Determine the resultant couple acting on the board.

3.52. Four pegs are attached to a board as shown. Two strings are passed around the pegs and pulled with forces of magnitude $P = 16$ lb and $Q = 40$ lb. Determine the required diameter of the pegs if the resultant couple applied to the board is to be 300 lb-in. clockwise.

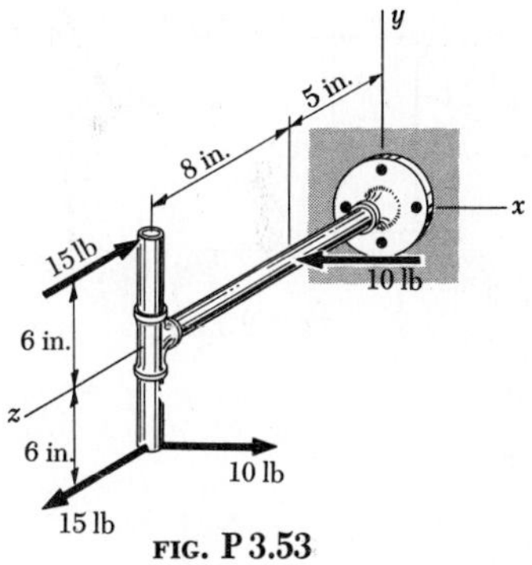

FIG. P 3.53

3.53. Determine the components of a single couple equivalent to the two couples shown. Check the result obtained by adding the moments of the individual forces about the coordinate axes.

3.54. The axles and drive shaft of an automobile are acted upon by the three couples shown. Replace these three couples by a single equivalent couple.

3.55. Three shafts are connected to a gear box as shown. Shaft *A* is horizontal and shafts *B* and *C* lie in the vertical *yz* plane. Determine the components of the resultant couple exerted on the gear box.

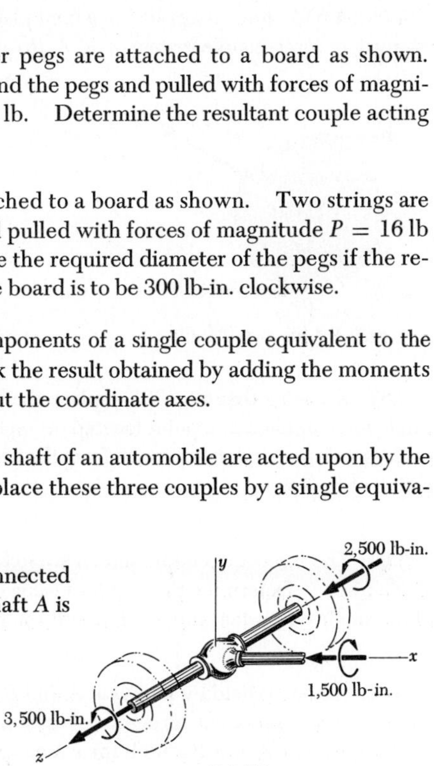

FIG. P 3.54

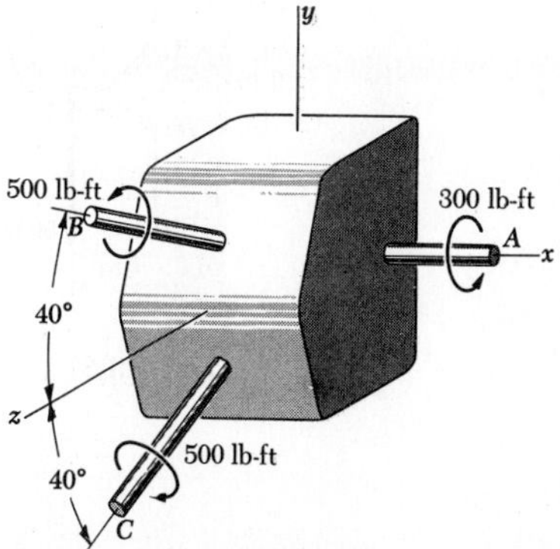

FIG. P 3.55

3.56. The couple vectors $\mathbf{M}_1$ and $\mathbf{M}_2$ represent couples which are contained in the planes *ABC* and *ACD*, respectively. Assuming that $M_1 = M_2 = M$, determine a single couple equivalent to the two given couples.

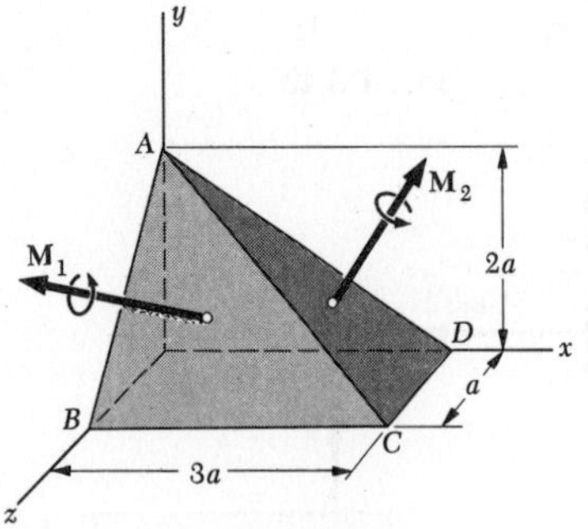

FIG. P3.56

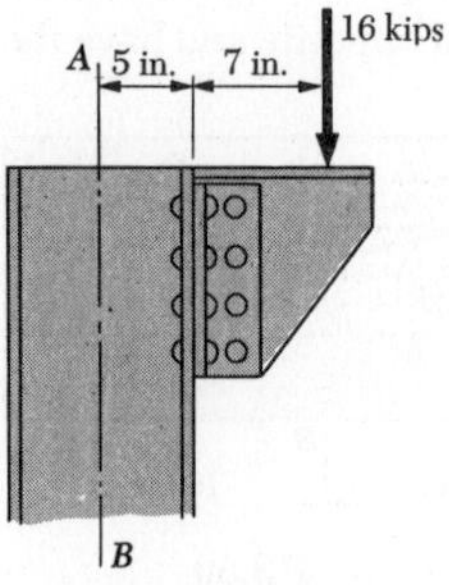

FIG. P3.57

3.57. A crane column supports a 16-kip load as shown. Reduce the load to an axial force along *AB* and a couple.

3.58. A 65-lb force is applied to a bent plate as shown. Determine an equivalent force-couple system (*a*) at *A*, (*b*) at *B*.

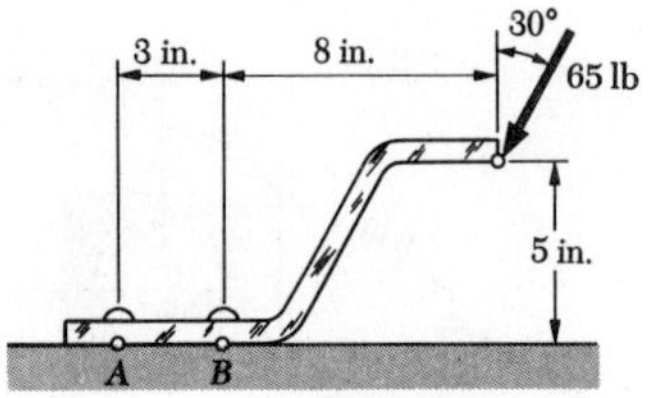

FIG. P3.58

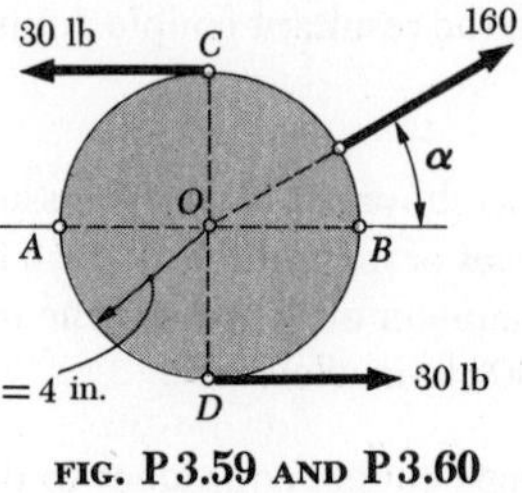

FIG. P3.59 AND P3.60

3.59. Knowing that $\alpha = 30°$, replace the force and couple shown by a single force applied at a point located (*a*) on line *AB*, (*b*) on line *CD*. In each case determine the distance from the center *O* to the point of application of the force.

3.60. The force and couple shown are to be replaced by an equivalent single force. Determine the required value of α so that the line of action of the single equivalent force will pass through point *B*.

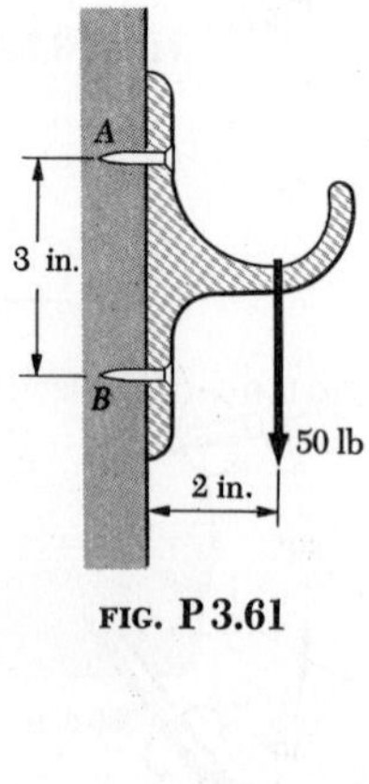

FIG. P3.61

3.61. A hook is held by screws at *A* and *B*. (*a*) Replace the 50-lb load shown by an equivalent force-couple system at *B*. (*b*) Find two horizontal forces at *A* and *B* which form a couple equivalent to the couple found in part *a*.

3.62. A force **P** is applied to a beam *AB* at a point *C* as shown. Find the vertical forces $\mathbf{F}_A$ and $\mathbf{F}_B$, applied, respectively, at *A* and *B*, which form a system equivalent to **P**.

3.63. The 60-lb force is applied in a direction perpendicular to the handle at *A* ($\beta = 0$). When the rod is in the vertical position ($\alpha = 0$), replace the 60-lb force by (*a*) an equivalent force-couple system at *B*, (*b*) an equivalent system formed by two parallel forces at *B* and *C*.

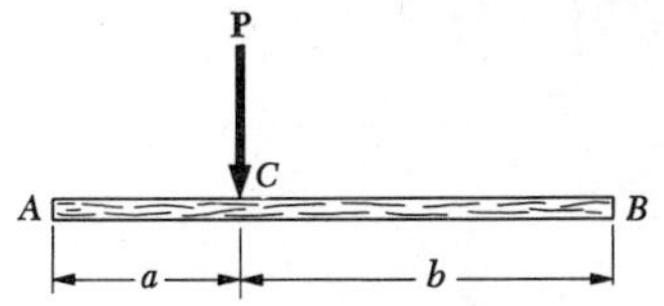

FIG. P 3.62

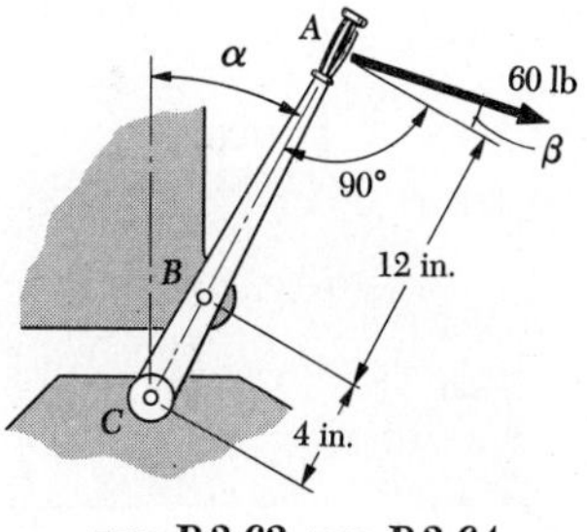

FIG. P 3.63 AND P 3.64

*3.64. Replace the 60-lb force by an equivalent system formed by two parallel forces at *B* and *C*. Show (*a*) that these forces are parallel to the 60-lb force, (*b*) that the magnitude of these forces is independent of both α and β.

3.65. A 25-kip load is applied eccentrically on a column. Determine the components of the force and couple at *G* which are equivalent to the 25-kip load.

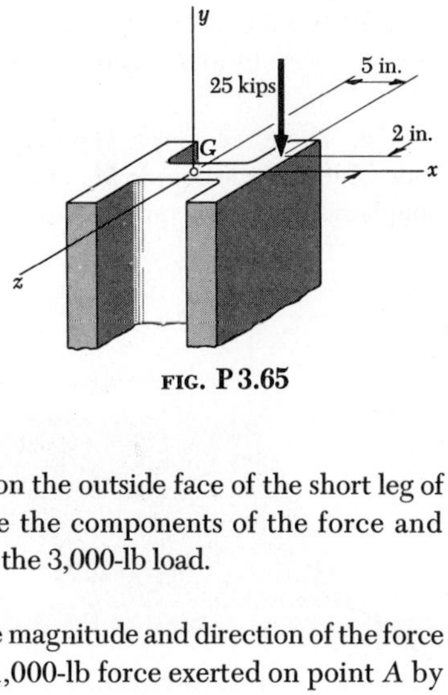

FIG. P 3.65

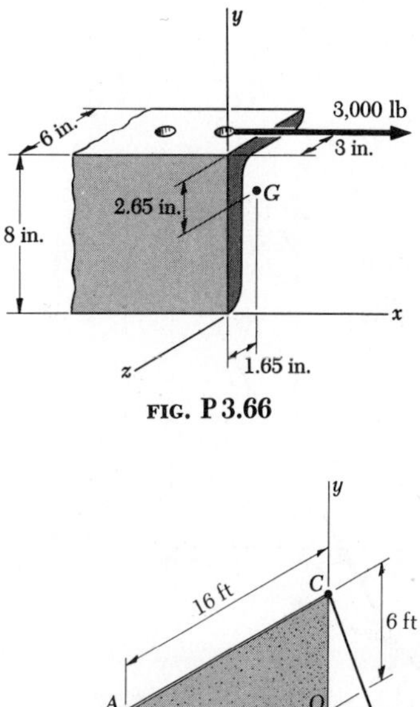

FIG. P 3.66

3.66. A 3,000-lb force is applied on the outside face of the short leg of a rolled angle section. Determine the components of the force and couple at *G* which are equivalent to the 3,000-lb load.

3.67. In Prob. 3.35, determine the magnitude and direction of the force and couple at *O* equivalent to the 1,000-lb force exerted on point *A* by the cable *AB*.

3.68. A precast-concrete wall section is temporarily held by cables as shown. The tension in cable *AB* is 700 lb. Replace the force exerted on the wall section at *A* by a force-couple system located (*a*) at the origin of coordinates *O*, (*b*) at point *E*.

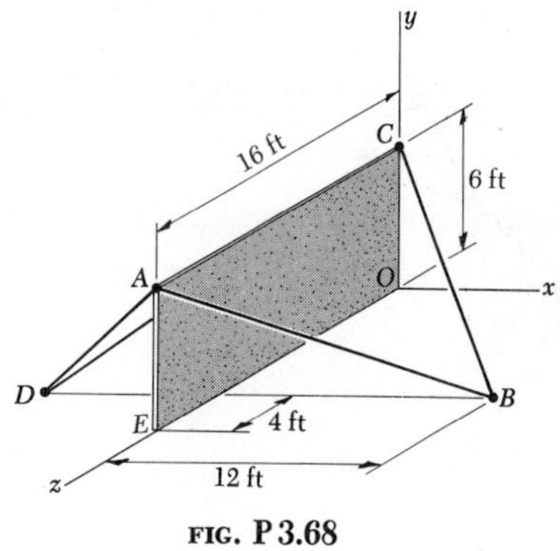

FIG. P 3.68

3.69. Five separate force-couple systems act at the corners of a rectangular box as shown. Find two force-couple systems which are equivalent.

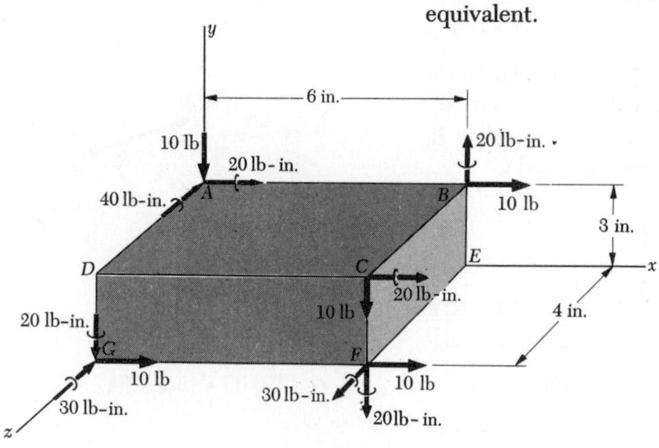

FIG. P3.69

3.70. Determine which of the force-couple systems given in Prob. 3.69 is equivalent to a force-couple system located at the origin *O* and consisting of $\mathbf{F} = -10\mathbf{j}$ and $\mathbf{M}_O = 60\mathbf{i} - 60\mathbf{k}$.

3.71. The force-couple system at *A* consists of the force **F** of magnitude 25 lb and the couple $\mathbf{M}_A$ of moment 250 lb-in. Replace this force-couple system by an equivalent force-couple system at *D*.

3.72. The force-couple system at *A* consists of the force **F** of magnitude 25 lb and the couple $\mathbf{M}_A$ of moment 250 lb-in. Replace this force-couple system by an equivalent force-couple system at *E*.

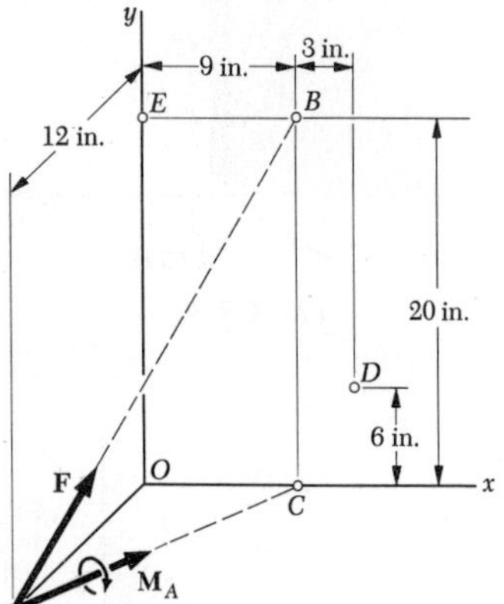

FIG. P3.71 AND P3.72

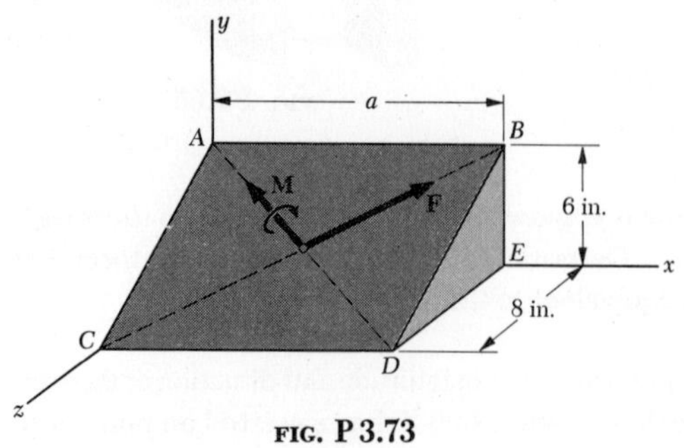

FIG. P3.73

3.73. Determine the dimension *a* for which the force-couple system shown may be replaced by a single equivalent force. If $F = 200$ lb and $M = 1{,}000$ lb-in., determine the point where the line of action of the single equivalent force intersects the *yz* plane.

3.15. Reduction of a System of Forces to One Force and One Couple. Consider a system of forces $\mathbf{F}_1$, $\mathbf{F}_2$, $\mathbf{F}_3$, etc., acting on a rigid body at the points A_1, A_2, A_3, etc., defined by the position vectors $\mathbf{r}_1$, $\mathbf{r}_2$, $\mathbf{r}_3$, etc. (Fig. 3.38*a*). As seen in the preceding section, $\mathbf{F}_1$ may be moved from A_1 to a given point O if a couple of moment $\mathbf{M}_1$ equal to the moment $\mathbf{r}_1 \times \mathbf{F}_1$ of $\mathbf{F}_1$ about O is added to the original system of forces. Repeating this procedure with $\mathbf{F}_2$, $\mathbf{F}_3$, etc., we obtain the system shown in Fig. 3.38*b*, consisting of forces acting at O and of couples. Since the forces are now concurrent, they may be added vectorially and replaced by their resultant $\mathbf{R}$. Similarly, the couple vectors $\mathbf{M}_1$, $\mathbf{M}_2$, $\mathbf{M}_3$, etc., may be added vectorially and replaced by a single couple vector $\mathbf{M}_O^R$. Any system of forces, however complex, may thus be reduced to an *equivalent force-couple system acting at a given point O* (Fig. 3.38*c*). We should note that, while each of the couple vectors $\mathbf{M}_1$, $\mathbf{M}_2$, $\mathbf{M}_3$, etc., in Fig. 3.38*b* is perpendicular to the corresponding force, the resultant force $\mathbf{R}$ and the resultant couple vector $\mathbf{M}_O^R$ in Fig. 3.38*c* will not, in general, be perpendicular to each other.

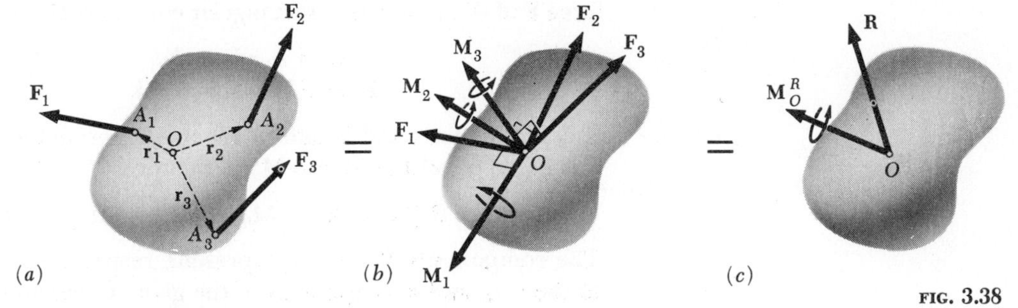

FIG. 3.38

The equivalent force-couple system is defined by the equations

$$\mathbf{R} = \Sigma\mathbf{F} \qquad \mathbf{M}_O^R = \Sigma\mathbf{M}_O = \Sigma(\mathbf{r} \times \mathbf{F}) \tag{3.47}$$

which express that the force $\mathbf{R}$ is obtained by adding all the forces of the system, while the moment $\mathbf{M}_O^R$ of the couple, called *moment resultant* of the system, is obtained by adding the moments about O of all the forces of the system.

Once a given system of forces has been reduced to a force and a couple at a point O, it may easily be reduced to a force and a couple at another point O'. While the resultant force $\mathbf{R}$ will remain unchanged, the new couple vector $\mathbf{M}_{O'}^R$ will be equal to the sum of the couple vector $\mathbf{M}_O^R$ and of the moment about O'

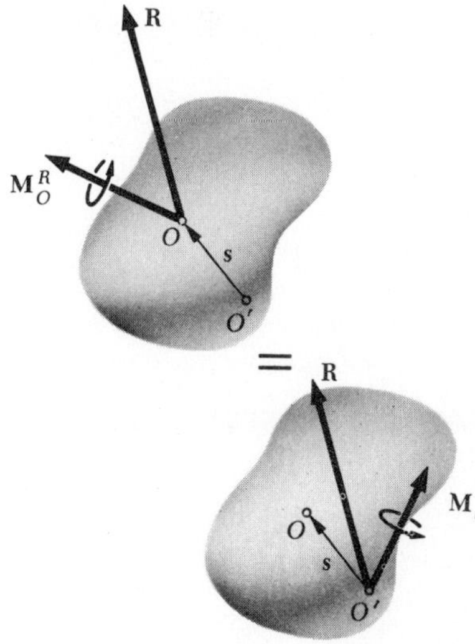

FIG. 3.39

of the force **R** attached at O (Fig. 3.39). We have

$$\mathbf{M}_{O'}^R = \mathbf{M}_O^R + \mathbf{s} \times \mathbf{R} \tag{3.48}$$

In practice, the reduction of a given system of forces to a single force **R** at O and a couple $\mathbf{M}_O^R$ will be carried out in terms of components. Resolving each position vector **r** and each force **F** of the system into rectangular components, we write

$$\mathbf{r} = x\mathbf{i} + y\mathbf{j} + z\mathbf{k} \tag{3.49}$$
$$\mathbf{F} = F_x\mathbf{i} + F_y\mathbf{j} + F_z\mathbf{k} \tag{3.50}$$

Substituting for **r** and **F** into (3.47) and factoring the unit vectors **i**, **j**, **k**, we obtain **R** and $\mathbf{M}_O^R$ in the form

$$\mathbf{R} = R_x\mathbf{i} + R_y\mathbf{j} + R_z\mathbf{k} \qquad \mathbf{M}_O^R = M_x^R\mathbf{i} + M_y^R\mathbf{j} + M_z^R\mathbf{k} \tag{3.51}$$

The components R_x, R_y, R_z represent, respectively, the sums of the x, y, and z components of the given forces and measure the tendency of the system to impart to the rigid body a motion of translation in the x, y, or z direction. Similarly, the components M_x^R, M_y^R, M_z^R represent, respectively, the sums of the moments of the given forces about the x, y, and z axes and measure the tendency of the system to impart to the rigid body a motion of rotation about the x, y, or z axis.

If the magnitude and direction of the force **R** are desired, they may be obtained from the components R_x, R_y, R_z by means of the relations (2.18) and (2.25) of Sec. 2.11; similar computations will yield the magnitude and direction of the couple vector $\mathbf{M}_O^R$.

3.16. Equivalent Systems of Forces. We have seen in the preceding section that any system of forces acting on a rigid body may be reduced to a force-couple system at a given point O. This equivalent force-couple system characterizes completely the effect of the given system on the rigid body. *Two systems of forces are equivalent, therefore, if they may be reduced to the same force-couple system at a given point O.* Recalling that the force-couple system at O is defined by the relations (3.47), we state: *Two systems of forces* $\mathbf{F}_1$, $\mathbf{F}_2$, $\mathbf{F}_3$, *etc., and* $\mathbf{F}_1'$, $\mathbf{F}_2'$, $\mathbf{F}_3'$, *etc., are equivalent if, and only if, the sums of the forces and the sums of the moments about a given point O of the forces of the two systems are, respectively, equal.* Expressed mathematically, the necessary and sufficient conditions for the two systems of forces to be equivalent are

$$\Sigma\mathbf{F} = \Sigma\mathbf{F}' \quad \text{and} \quad \Sigma\mathbf{M}_O = \Sigma\mathbf{M}_O' \tag{3.52}$$

Note that, to prove that two systems of forces are equivalent, the second of the relations (3.52) needs to be established with respect to *only one point O*. It will hold, however, with respect to *any point* if the two systems are equivalent.

Resolving the forces and moments in (3.52) into their rectangular components, we may express the necessary and sufficient conditions for the equivalence of two systems of forces as follows:

$$\begin{aligned} \Sigma F_x &= \Sigma F'_x \qquad \Sigma F_y = \Sigma F'_y \qquad \Sigma F_z = \Sigma F'_z \\ \Sigma M_x &= \Sigma M'_x \qquad \Sigma M_y = \Sigma M'_y \qquad \Sigma M_z = \Sigma M'_z \end{aligned} \tag{3.53}$$

These equations have a simple physical significance. They express that two systems of forces are equivalent if they tend to impart to a given rigid body (1) the same translation in the x, y, and z directions, respectively, and (2) the same rotation about the x, y, and z axes, respectively.

3.17. Further Reduction of a System of Forces. We saw in Sec. 3.15 that any given system of forces may be reduced to an equivalent force-couple system at O, consisting of a force $\mathbf{R}$ equal to the sum of the forces of the system, and of a couple vector $\mathbf{M}_O^R$ equal to the moment resultant of the system.

When $\mathbf{R} = 0$, the force-couple system reduces to the couple vector $\mathbf{M}_O^R$. The given system of forces may then be reduced to a single couple, called the *resultant couple* of the system.

We shall now investigate the conditions under which a given system of forces may be reduced to a single force. It follows from Sec. 3.14 that the force-couple system at O may be replaced by a single force $\mathbf{R}$ acting along a new line of action if $\mathbf{R}$ and $\mathbf{M}_O^R$ are mutually perpendicular. The systems of forces which may be reduced to a single force, or *resultant*, are therefore the systems for which the force $\mathbf{R}$ and the couple vector $\mathbf{M}_O^R$ are mutually perpendicular. While this condition *is generally not satisfied* by systems of forces in space, it *will be satisfied* by systems consisting (1) of concurrent forces, (2) of coplanar forces, or (3) of parallel forces. We shall discuss these cases separately.

1. *Concurrent forces* are applied at the same point and may therefore be added directly into their resultant $\mathbf{R}$. Thus, they always reduce to a single force. Concurrent forces have been discussed in detail in Chap. 2.

2. *Coplanar forces* act in the same plane, which we shall assume here to be the plane of the figure (Fig. 3.40*a*). The sum $\mathbf{R}$ of the forces of the system will also lie in the plane of the figure, while the moment of each force about O, and thus the moment resultant $\mathbf{M}_O^R$, will be perpendicular to that plane. The force-couple system at O consists therefore of a force $\mathbf{R}$

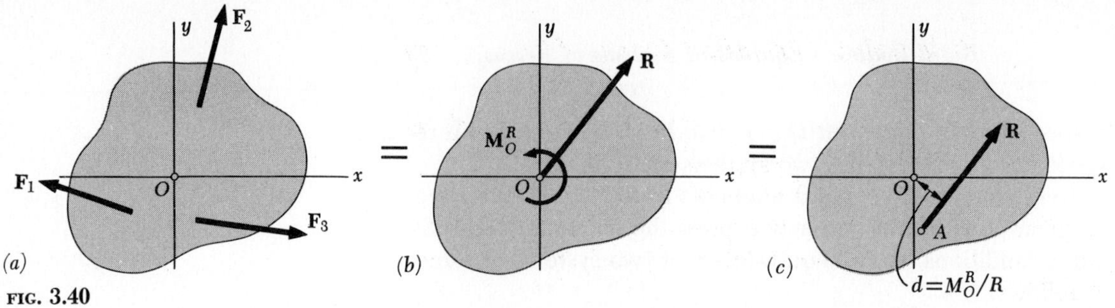

FIG. 3.40

and a couple vector $\mathbf{M}_O^R$ which are mutually perpendicular (Fig. 3.40*b*).† They may be reduced to a single force $\mathbf{R}$ by moving $\mathbf{R}$ in the plane of the figure until its moment about O becomes equal to $\mathbf{M}_O^R$. The distance from O to the line of action of $\mathbf{R}$ is $d = \mathbf{M}_O^R/R$ (Fig. 3.40*c*).

As noted in Sec. 3.15, the reduction of a system of forces is considerably simplified if the forces are resolved into rectangular components. The force-couple system at O is then characterized by the components

$$R_x = \Sigma F_x \qquad R_y = \Sigma F_y \qquad M_z^R = M_O^R = \Sigma M_O \quad (3.54)$$

To reduce the system to a single force $\mathbf{R}$ we shall express that the moment of $\mathbf{R}$ about O must be equal to $\mathbf{M}_O^R$. Denoting by x and y the coordinates of the point of application A of the resultant, and recalling formula (3.20), we write

$$xR_y - yR_x = M_O^R$$

which represents the equation of the line of action of $\mathbf{R}$. We may also determine directly the x and y intercepts of the line of action of the resultant by noting that $\mathbf{M}_O^R$ must be equal to the moment about O of the y component of $\mathbf{R}$ when $\mathbf{R}$ is attached at B (Fig. 3.41*a*), and to the moment of its x component when $\mathbf{R}$ is attached at C (Fig. 3.41*b*).

† Since the couple vector $\mathbf{M}_O^R$ is perpendicular to the plane of the figure, it has been represented by the symbol . A counterclockwise couple corresponds to a vector pointing out of the paper, and a clockwise couple to a vector pointing into the paper.

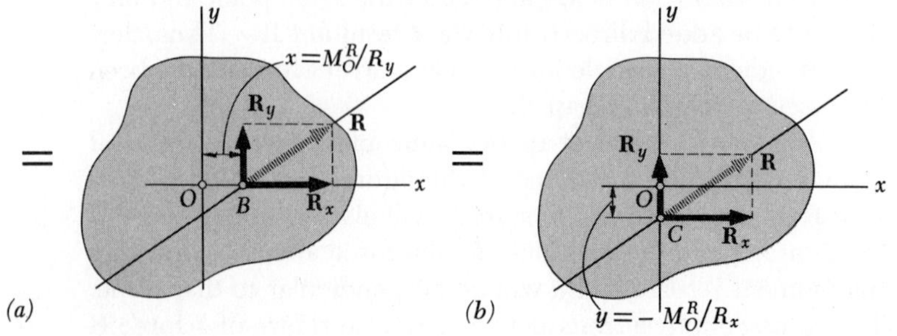

FIG. 3.41

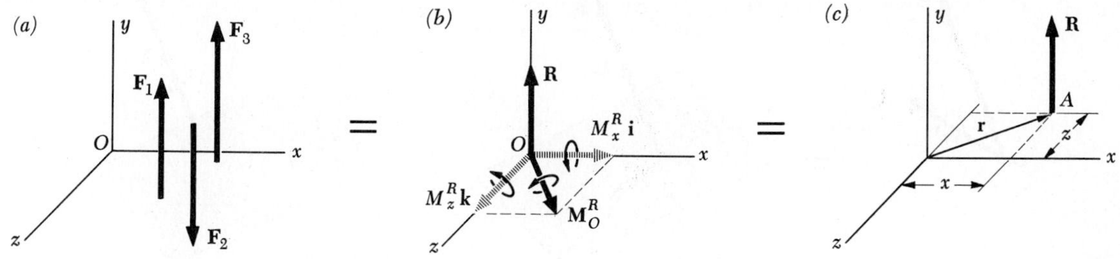

FIG. 3.42

3. *Parallel forces* have parallel lines of action and may or may not have the same sense. Assuming here that the forces are parallel to the y axis (Fig. 3.42*a*), we note that their sum **R** will also be parallel to the y axis. On the other hand, since the moment of a given force must be perpendicular to that force, the moment about O of each force of the system, and thus the moment resultant $\mathbf{M}_O^R$, will lie in the zx plane. The force-couple system at O consists therefore of a force **R** and a couple vector $\mathbf{M}_O^R$ which are mutually perpendicular (Fig. 3.42*b*). They may be reduced to a single force **R** (Fig. 3.42*c*) or, if $\mathbf{R} = 0$, to a single couple of moment $\mathbf{M}_O^R$.

In practice, the force-couple system at O will be characterized by the components

$$R_y = \Sigma F_y \qquad M_x^R = \Sigma M_x \qquad M_z^R = \Sigma M_z \tag{3.55}$$

The reduction of the system to a single force may be carried out by moving **R** to a new point of application $A(x, 0, z)$ chosen so that the moment of **R** about O is equal to $\mathbf{M}_O^R$. We write

$$\mathbf{r} \times \mathbf{R} = \mathbf{M}_O^R$$

$$(x\mathbf{i} + z\mathbf{k}) \times R_y\mathbf{j} = M_x^R\mathbf{i} + M_z^R\mathbf{k}$$

Computing the vector products and equating the coefficients of the corresponding unit vectors in both members of the equation, we obtain two scalar equations which define the coordinates of A:

$$-zR_y = M_x^R \qquad xR_y = M_z^R$$

These equations express that the moments of **R** about the x and z axes must, respectively, be equal to M_x^R and M_z^R.

In the general case of a system of forces in space, the force-couple system at O consists of a force **R** and a couple vector $\mathbf{M}_O^R$ which are not perpendicular, and neither of which is zero (Fig. 3.43*a*). Thus, the system of forces *cannot* be reduced to a single force or a single couple. The couple vector, however, may be replaced by two other couple vectors obtained by resolving $\mathbf{M}_O^R$ into a component $\mathbf{M}_1$ along **R** and a component $\mathbf{M}_2$ in a plane perpendicular to **R** (Fig. 3.43*b*). The couple

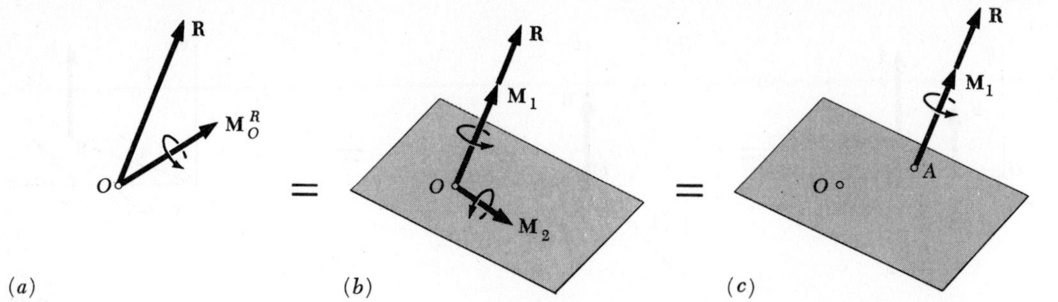

FIG. 3.43

vector $\mathbf{M}_2$ and the force $\mathbf{R}$ may then be replaced by a single force $\mathbf{R}$ acting along a new line of action. The original system of forces thus reduces to $\mathbf{R}$ and to the couple vector $\mathbf{M}_1$ (Fig. 3.43*c*), i.e., to $\mathbf{R}$ and a couple acting in the plane perpendicular to $\mathbf{R}$. This particular force-couple combination is called a *wrench*. The force $\mathbf{R}$ and the couple vector $\mathbf{M}_1$ tend, at the same time, to translate the rigid body on which they act in the direction of $\mathbf{R}$ and to rotate it about the line of action of $\mathbf{R}$. The line of action of $\mathbf{R}$ is known as the *axis of the wrench*, and the ratio M_1/R is called the *pitch* of the wrench.

Recalling the expression (3.32) obtained for the projection of a vector on the line of action of another vector, we note that the projection of $\mathbf{M}_O^R$ on the line of action of $\mathbf{R}$ is

$$M_1 = \frac{\mathbf{R} \cdot \mathbf{M}_O^R}{R} \tag{3.56}$$

We thus have †

$$\text{Pitch of wrench} = \frac{M_1}{R} = \frac{\mathbf{R} \cdot \mathbf{M}_O^R}{R^2} \tag{3.57}$$

An important particular case of the reduction of a system of forces to a force-couple system occurs when both the force $\mathbf{R}$ and the couple vector $\mathbf{M}_O^R$ are equal to zero. The system of forces is said to be *equivalent to zero*. Such a system has no effect on the rigid body on which it acts, and the rigid body is said to be in *equilibrium*. This case will be considered in detail in the next chapter.

† The expressions obtained for the projection of the couple vector on the line of action of $\mathbf{R}$ and for the pitch of the wrench are independent of the choice of point O. Using the relation (3.48), we check that if a different point O' had been used, the numerator in (3.56) and (3.57) would be

$$\mathbf{R} \cdot \mathbf{M}_{O'}^R = \mathbf{R} \cdot (\mathbf{M}_O^R + \mathbf{s} \times \mathbf{R}) = \mathbf{R} \cdot \mathbf{M}_O^R + \mathbf{R} \cdot (\mathbf{s} \times \mathbf{R})$$

Since the mixed triple product $\mathbf{R} \cdot (\mathbf{s} \times \mathbf{R})$ is identically equal to zero, we have

$$\mathbf{R} \cdot \mathbf{M}_{O'}^R = \mathbf{R} \cdot \mathbf{M}_O^R \tag{3.58}$$

and conclude that the scalar product $\mathbf{R} \cdot \mathbf{M}_O^R$ is independent of the choice of point O.

SAMPLE PROBLEM 3.9

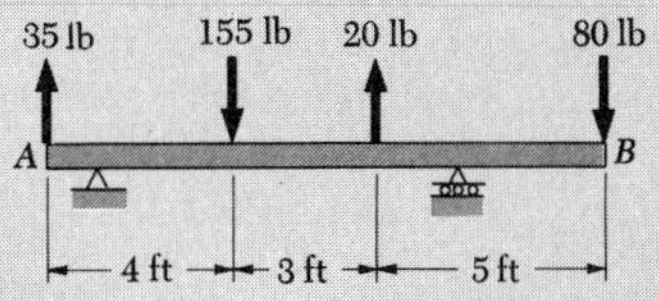

A 12-ft beam is subjected to the forces shown. Reduce the given system of forces to (*a*) an equivalent force-couple system at *A*, (*b*) an equivalent force-couple system at *B*, (*c*) a single force or resultant.

Note. Since the reactions at the supports are not included in the given system of forces, the given system will not maintain the beam in equilibrium.

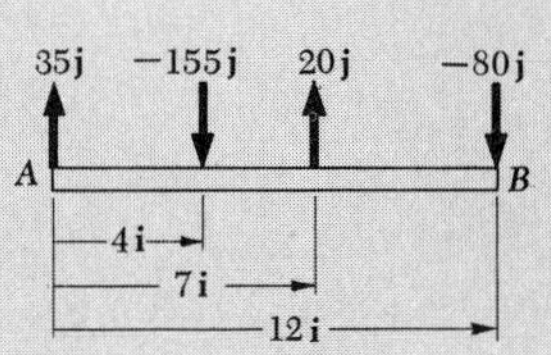

a. **Force-couple System at** *A*. The force-couple system at *A* equivalent to the given system of forces consists of a force **R** and a couple $\mathbf{M}_A^R$ defined as follows:

$$\mathbf{R} = \Sigma\mathbf{F}$$
$$= (35\text{ lb})\mathbf{j} - (155\text{ lb})\mathbf{j} + (20\text{ lb})\mathbf{j} - (80\text{ lb})\mathbf{j} = -(180\text{ lb})\mathbf{j}$$
$$\mathbf{M}_A^R = \Sigma(\mathbf{r} \times \mathbf{F})$$
$$= (4\mathbf{i}) \times (-155\mathbf{j}) + (7\mathbf{i}) \times (20\mathbf{j}) + (12\mathbf{i}) \times (-80\mathbf{j}) = -(1{,}440\text{ lb-ft})\mathbf{k}$$

The equivalent force-couple system at *A* is thus

$$\mathbf{R} = 180\text{ lb}\downarrow \qquad \mathbf{M}_A^R = 1{,}440\text{ lb-ft} \curvearrowright \quad ◄$$

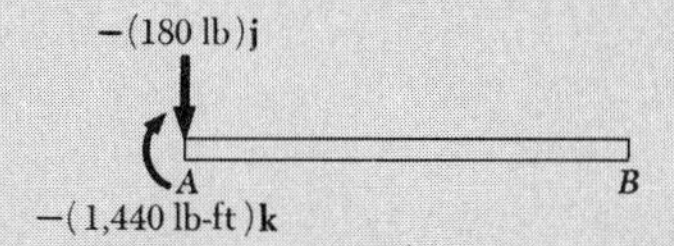

b. **Force-couple System at** *B*. We shall find a force-couple system at *B* equivalent to the force-couple system at *A* determined in part *a*. The force **R** is unchanged, but a new couple $\mathbf{M}_B^R$ must be determined, the moment of which is equal to the moment about *B* of the force-couple system determined in part *a*. Thus, we have

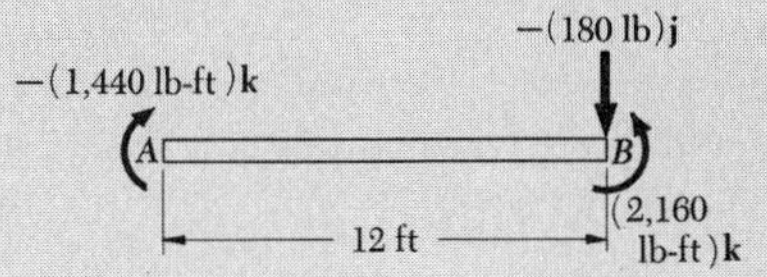

$$\mathbf{M}_B^R = \mathbf{M}_A^R + \overrightarrow{BA} \times \mathbf{R}$$
$$= -(1{,}440\text{ lb-ft})\mathbf{k} + (-12\text{ ft})\mathbf{i} \times (-180\text{ lb})\mathbf{j}$$
$$= -(1{,}440\text{ lb-ft})\mathbf{k} + (2{,}160\text{ lb-ft})\mathbf{k} = +(720\text{ lb-ft})\mathbf{k}$$

The equivalent force-couple system at *B* is thus

$$\mathbf{R} = 180\text{ lb}\downarrow \qquad \mathbf{M}_B^R = 720\text{ lb-ft} \circlearrowleft \quad ◄$$

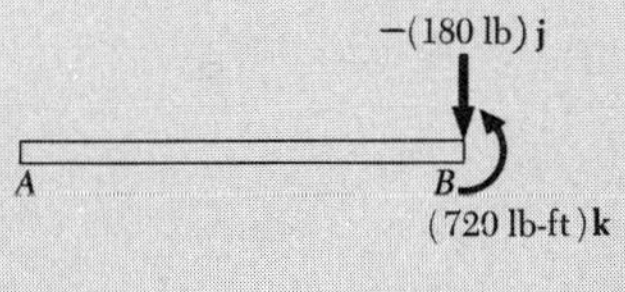

c. **Single Force or Resultant.** The resultant of the given system of forces is equal to **R** and its point of application must be such that the moment of **R** about *A* is equal to $\mathbf{M}_A^R$. We write

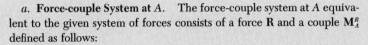

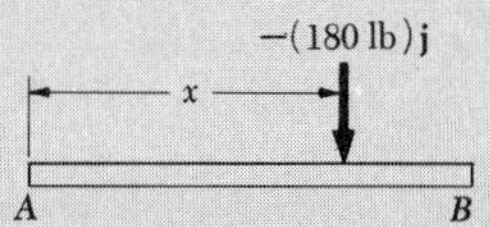

$$\mathbf{r} \times \mathbf{R} = \mathbf{M}_A^R$$
$$x\mathbf{i} \times (-180\text{ lb})\mathbf{j} = -(1{,}440\text{ lb-ft})\mathbf{k}$$
$$-x(180\text{ lb})\mathbf{k} = -(1{,}440\text{ lb-ft})\mathbf{k}$$

and conclude that $x = 8$ ft. Thus, the single force equivalent to the given system is defined as

$$\mathbf{R} = 180\text{ lb}\downarrow \qquad x = 8\text{ ft} \quad ◄$$

SAMPLE PROBLEM 3.10

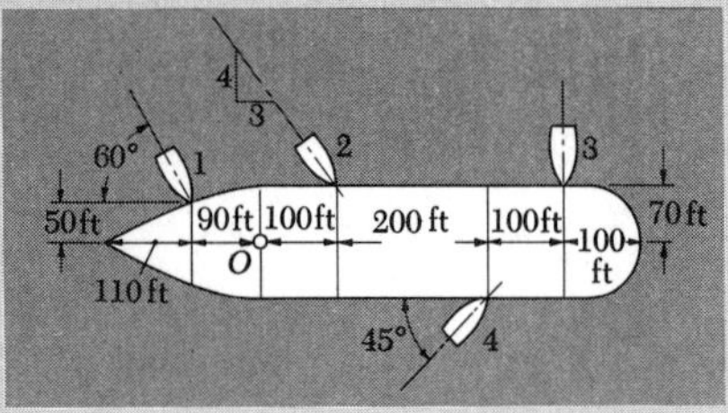

Four tugboats are used to bring an ocean liner to its pier. Each tugboat exerts a 5,000-lb force in the direction shown. Determine (*a*) the equivalent force-couple system at the foremast *O*, (*b*) the point on the hull where a single, more powerful tugboat should push to produce the same effect as the original four tugboats.

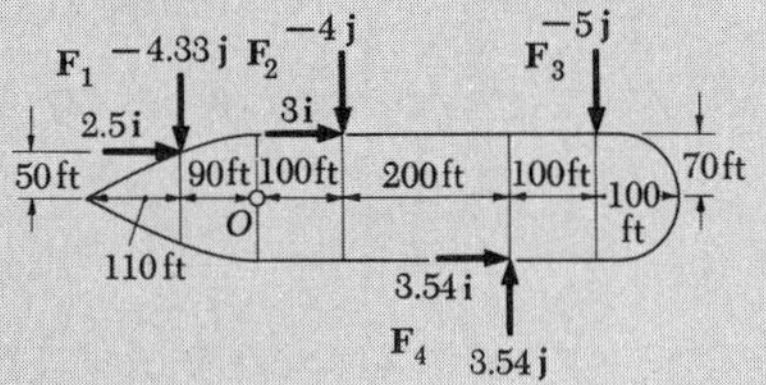

a. **Force-couple System at** *O*. Each of the given forces is resolved into components in the diagram shown (kip units are used). The force-couple system at *O* equivalent to the given system of forces consists of a force **R** and a couple $\mathbf{M}_O^R$ defined as follows:

$$
\begin{aligned}
\mathbf{R} &= \Sigma \mathbf{F} \\
&= (2.50\mathbf{i} - 4.33\mathbf{j}) + (3.00\mathbf{i} - 4.00\mathbf{j}) + (-5.00\mathbf{j}) + (3.54\mathbf{i} + 3.54\mathbf{j}) \\
&= 9.04\mathbf{i} - 9.79\mathbf{j} \\
\mathbf{M}_O^R &= \Sigma(\mathbf{r} \times \mathbf{F}) \\
&= (-90\mathbf{i} + 50\mathbf{j}) \times (2.50\mathbf{i} - 4.33\mathbf{j}) \\
&\quad + (100\mathbf{i} + 70\mathbf{j}) \times (3.00\mathbf{i} - 4.00\mathbf{j}) \\
&\quad + (400\mathbf{i} + 70\mathbf{j}) \times (-5.00\mathbf{j}) \\
&\quad + (300\mathbf{i} - 70\mathbf{j}) \times (3.54\mathbf{i} + 3.54\mathbf{j}) \\
&= (390 - 125 - 400 - 210 - 2{,}000 + 1{,}062 + 248)\mathbf{k} \\
&= -1{,}035\mathbf{k}
\end{aligned}
$$

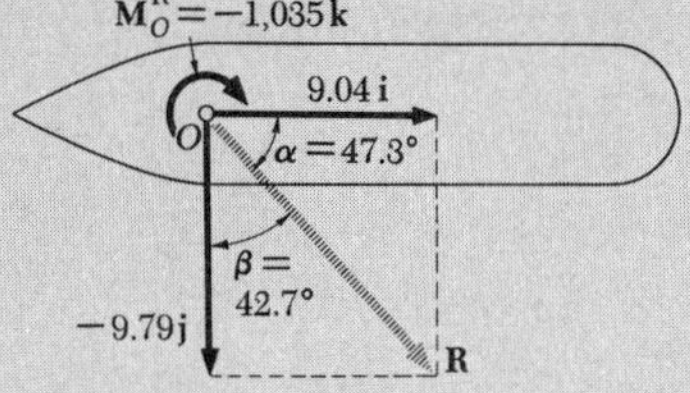

The equivalent force-couple system at *O* is thus

$$\mathbf{R} = (9.04 \text{ kips})\mathbf{i} - (9.79 \text{ kips})\mathbf{j} \qquad \mathbf{M}_O^R = -(1{,}035 \text{ kip-ft})\mathbf{k}$$

or $$\mathbf{R} = 13.33 \text{ kips} \measuredangle 47.3° \qquad \mathbf{M}_O^R = 1{,}035 \text{ kip-ft} \circlearrowright$$ ◄

Remark. Since all the forces are contained in the plane of the figure, we could have expected the sum of their moments to be perpendicular to that plane. Note that the moment of each force component could have been obtained directly from the diagram by forming the product of its magnitude and its perpendicular distance to *O*, and assigning to this product a positive or a negative sign, depending upon the sense of the moment.

b. **Single Tugboat.** The force exerted by a single tugboat must be equal to **R** and its point of application *A* must be such that the moment of **R** about *O* is equal to $\mathbf{M}_O^R$. Observing that the position vector of *A* is

$$\mathbf{r} = x\mathbf{i} + 70\mathbf{j}$$

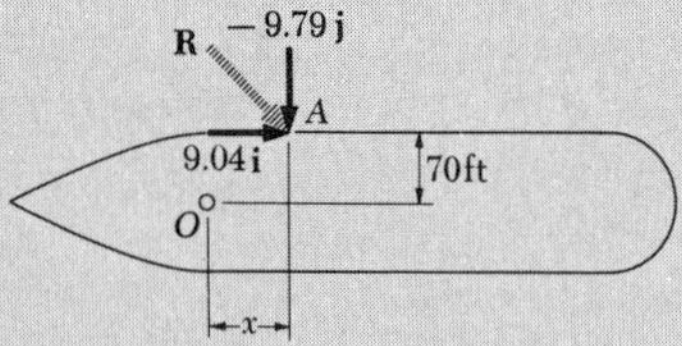

we write

$$
\begin{aligned}
\mathbf{r} \times \mathbf{R} &= \mathbf{M}_O^R \\
(x\mathbf{i} + 70\mathbf{j}) \times (9.04\mathbf{i} - 9.79\mathbf{j}) &= -1{,}035\mathbf{k} \\
-x(9.79)\mathbf{k} - 633\mathbf{k} &= -1{,}035\mathbf{k}
\end{aligned}
$$

$$x = 41.1 \text{ ft}$$ ◄

SAMPLE PROBLEM 3.11

Three cables are attached to a bracket as shown. Replace the forces exerted by the cables by an equivalent force-couple system at A.

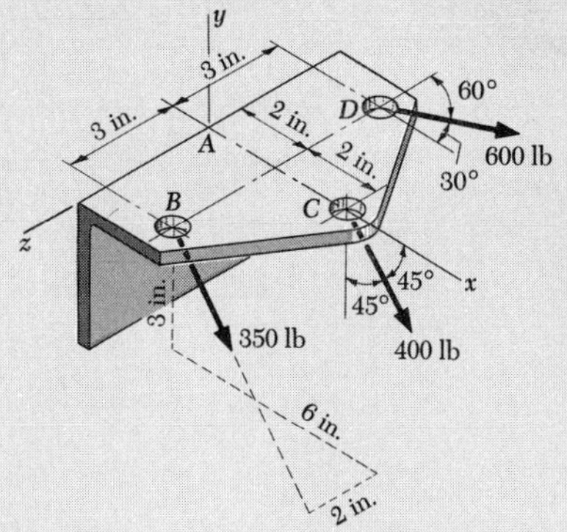

Solution. We first determine the position vectors of the points of application B, C, D and resolve the given forces into rectangular components.

$$\mathbf{r}_B = 2\mathbf{i} + 3\mathbf{k} \qquad \mathbf{F}_B = 300\mathbf{i} - 150\mathbf{j} + 100\mathbf{k}$$
$$\mathbf{r}_C = 4\mathbf{i} \qquad \mathbf{F}_C = 283\mathbf{i} - 283\mathbf{j}$$
$$\mathbf{r}_D = 2\mathbf{i} - 3\mathbf{k} \qquad \mathbf{F}_D = 520\mathbf{i} - 300\mathbf{k}$$

The force-couple system at A equivalent to the given forces consists of a force $\mathbf{R}$ and a couple $\mathbf{M}_A^R$ defined as follows:

$$\mathbf{R} = \Sigma\mathbf{F} \qquad \mathbf{M}_A^R = \Sigma(\mathbf{r} \times \mathbf{F})$$

The force $\mathbf{R}$ is readily obtained by adding respectively the x, y, and z components of the given forces.

$$\mathbf{R} = \Sigma\mathbf{F} = (1{,}103 \text{ lb})\mathbf{i} - (433 \text{ lb})\mathbf{j} - (200 \text{ lb})\mathbf{k} \quad ◄$$

The computation of $\mathbf{M}_A^R$ will be facilitated if we express each of the moments $\mathbf{r} \times \mathbf{F}$ in the form of a determinant (Sec. 3.7).

$$\mathbf{r}_B \times \mathbf{F}_B = \begin{vmatrix} \mathbf{i} & \mathbf{j} & \mathbf{k} \\ 2 & 0 & 3 \\ 300 & -150 & 100 \end{vmatrix} = 450\mathbf{i} + 700\mathbf{j} - 300\mathbf{k}$$

$$\mathbf{r}_C \times \mathbf{F}_C = \begin{vmatrix} \mathbf{i} & \mathbf{j} & \mathbf{k} \\ 4 & 0 & 0 \\ 283 & -283 & 0 \end{vmatrix} = -1{,}132\mathbf{k}$$

$$\mathbf{r}_D \times \mathbf{F}_D = \begin{vmatrix} \mathbf{i} & \mathbf{j} & \mathbf{k} \\ 2 & 0 & -3 \\ 520 & 0 & -300 \end{vmatrix} = -960\mathbf{j}$$

Adding the expressions obtained, we have

$$\mathbf{M}_A^R = \Sigma(\mathbf{r} \times \mathbf{F}) = (450 \text{ lb-in.})\mathbf{i} - (260 \text{ lb-in.})\mathbf{j} - (1{,}432 \text{ lb-in.})\mathbf{k} \quad ◄$$

The components of the force $\mathbf{R}$ and of the couple $\mathbf{M}_A^R$ along the coordinate axes are shown in the adjoining sketch.

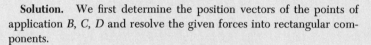

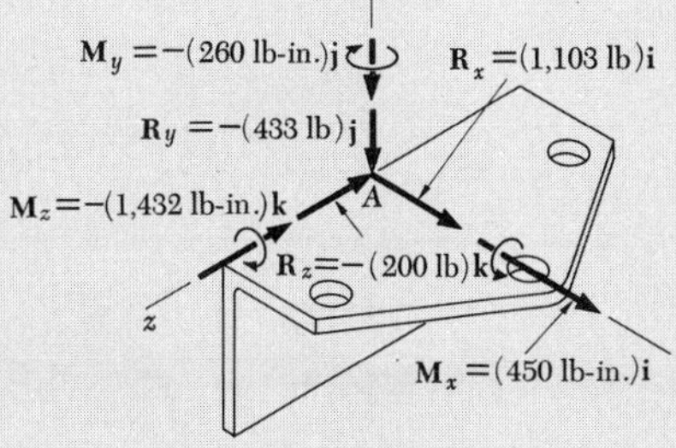

SAMPLE PROBLEM 3.12

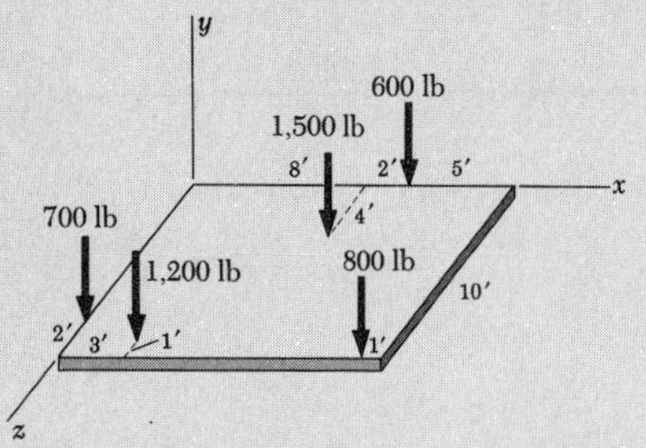

A 10- by 15-ft slab supports five columns which exert on the slab the forces indicated. Determine the magnitude and point of application of the single force equivalent to the given forces.

Solution. We shall first reduce the given system of forces to a force-couple system at the origin O of the coordinates. This force-couple system consists of a force **R** and a couple $\mathbf{M}_O^R$ defined as follows:

$$\mathbf{R} = \Sigma \mathbf{F} \qquad \mathbf{M}_O^R = \Sigma(\mathbf{r} \times \mathbf{F})$$

The position vectors of the points of application of the various forces are determined and the computations are arranged in tabular form.

r, ft	F, lb	r × F, lb-ft
10i	− 600j	− 6,000k
8k	− 700j	5,600i
14i + 10k	− 800j	8,000i − 11,200k
3i + 9k	−1,200j	10,800i − 3,600k
8i + 4k	−1,500j	6,000i − 12,000k
	R = −4,800j	$\mathbf{M}_O^R$ = 30,400i − 32,800k

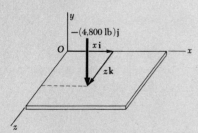

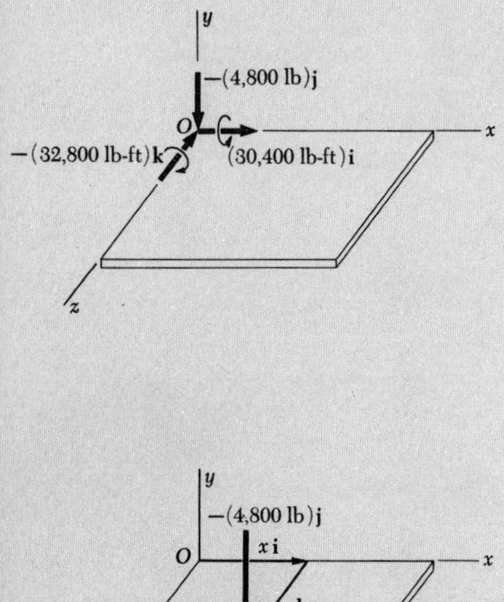

Since the force **R** and the couple vector $\mathbf{M}_O^R$ are mutually perpendicular, the force-couple system obtained may be reduced further to a single force **R**. The new point of application of **R** will be selected in the plane of the slab and in such a way that the moment of **R** about O will be equal to $\mathbf{M}_O^R$. Denoting by **r** the position vector of the desired point of application, and by x and z its coordinates, we write

$$\mathbf{r} \times \mathbf{R} = \mathbf{M}_O^R$$
$$(x\mathbf{i} + z\mathbf{k}) \times (-4{,}800\mathbf{j}) = 30{,}400\mathbf{i} - 32{,}800\mathbf{k}$$
$$-4{,}800x\mathbf{k} + 4{,}800z\mathbf{i} = 30{,}400\mathbf{i} - 32{,}800\mathbf{k}$$

from which it follows that

$$-4{,}800x = -32{,}800 \qquad 4{,}800z = 30{,}400$$
$$x = 6.83 \text{ ft} \qquad z = 6.33 \text{ ft}$$

We conclude that the resultant of the given system of forces is

$$\mathbf{R} = 4{,}800 \text{ lb} \downarrow \quad \text{at} \quad x = 6.83 \text{ ft}, z = 6.33 \text{ ft}$$ ◄

445-9378

US NAVAL SUB. MEDICAL CENTER
WARD 5 GROTON, CONN.
06340

PROBLEMS

3.74. A 12-ft beam is loaded in the various ways represented in the figure. Find two loadings which are equivalent.

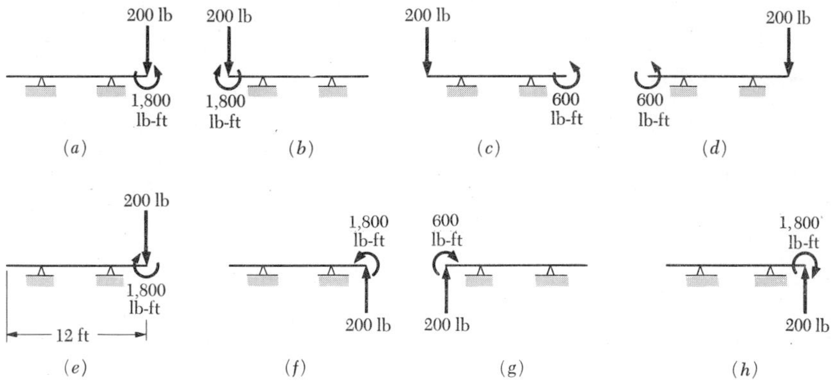

FIG. P3.74

3.75. A 12-ft beam is loaded as shown. Determine the loading of Prob. 3.74 which is equivalent to this loading.

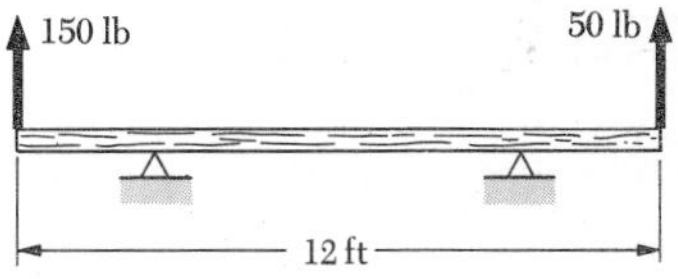

FIG. P3.75

3.76. For the truss and loading shown, determine the resultant of the loads and the distance from point *A* to its line of action.

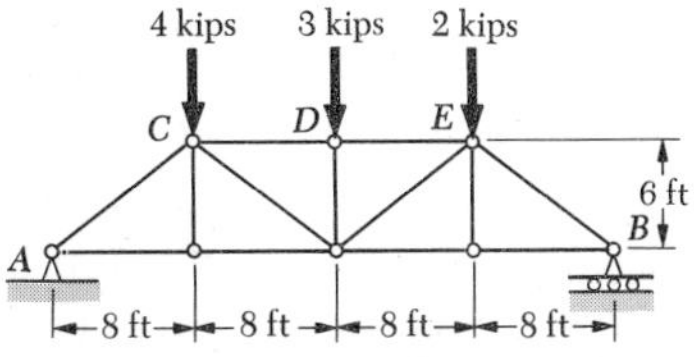

FIG. P3.76

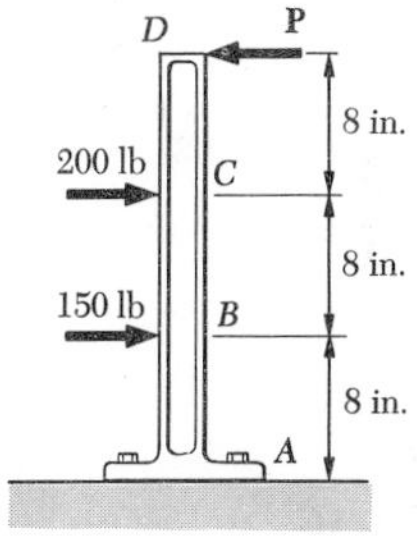

FIG. P3.77

3.77. Three horizontal forces are applied as shown to a machine arm. Determine the resultant of the loads and the point where its line of action intersects *AD* if the magnitude of **P** is (*a*) $P = 50$ lb, (*b*) $P = 500$ lb, (*c*) $P = 350$ lb.

3.78. Replace the three forces acting on the gear by an equivalent force-couple system at *O*.

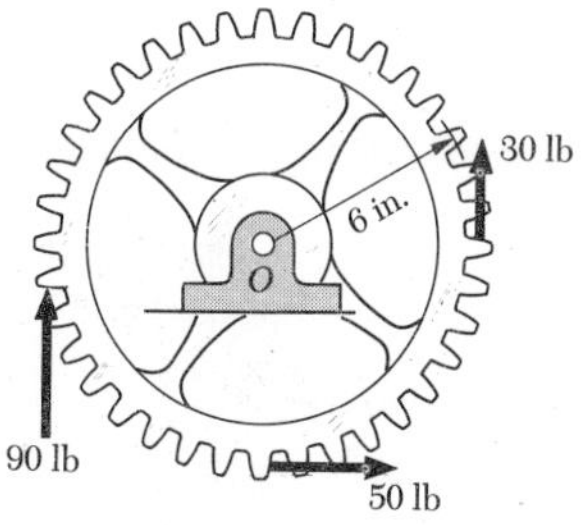

FIG. P3.78

3.79. Replace the two belt tensions by an equivalent force-couple system at *A*.

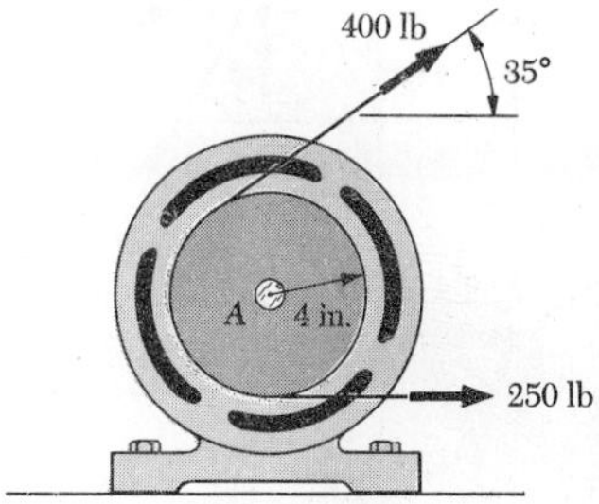

FIG. P3.79

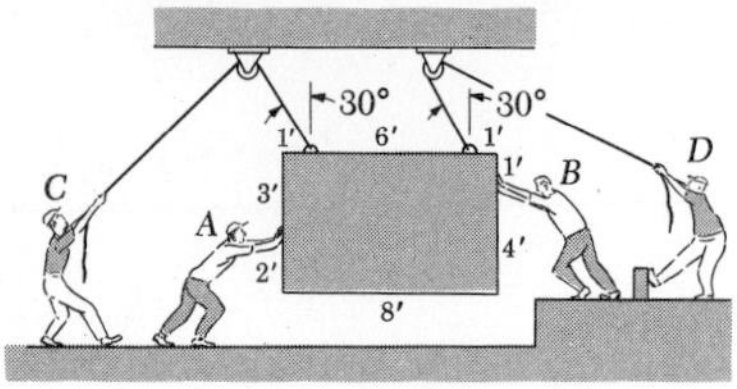

FIG. P3.80

3.80. In order to move a 173-lb crate, two men push on it while two other men pull on it by means of ropes. The force exerted by man A is 150 lb, and that exerted by man B is 50 lb; both forces are horizontal. Man C pulls with a force equal to 80 lb and man D with a force equal to 120 lb. Both cables form an angle of 30° with the vertical. Determine the resultant of all forces acting on the crate.

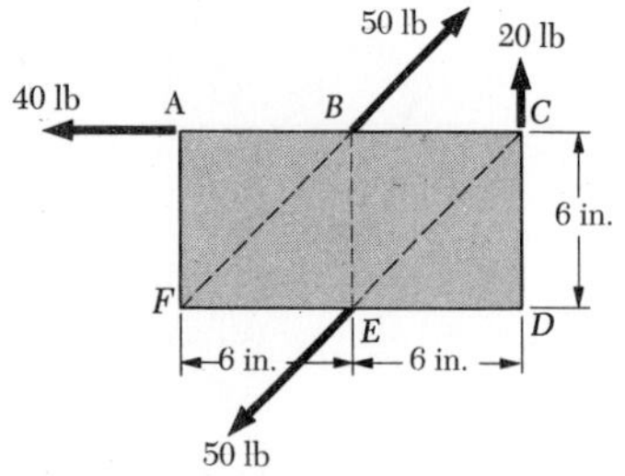

FIG. P3.81

3.81. A 6- by 12-in. plate is subjected to four loads. Find the resultant of the four loads and the two points at which the line of action of the resultant intersects the edge of the plate.

3.82. An angle bracket is subjected to the system of forces shown. Find the resultant of the system and the point of intersection of its line of action with (*a*) line AB, (*b*) line BC.

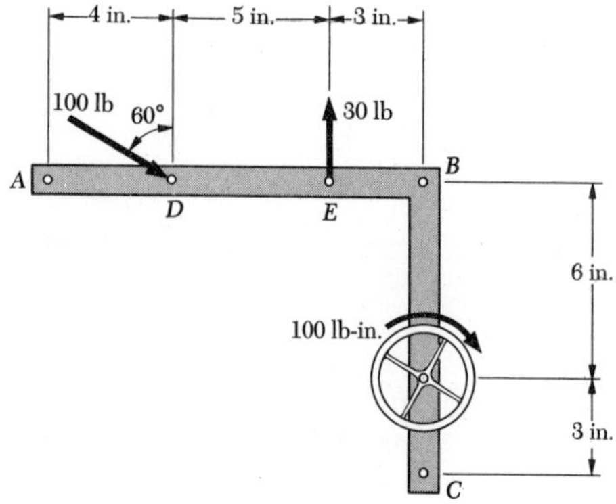

FIG. P3.82

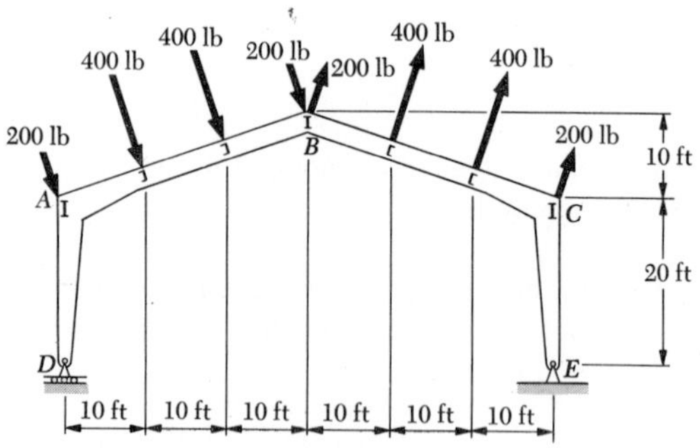

FIG. P3.83

3.83. The roof of a building frame is subjected to the wind loading shown. Determine (*a*) the equivalent force-couple system at D, (*b*) the resultant of the loading and its line of action.

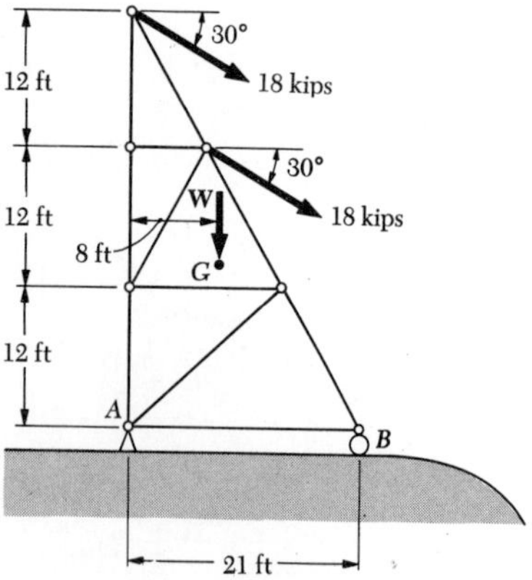

FIG. P3.84

3.84. Two cables exert forces of 18 kips each on a truss of weight $W =$ 40 kips. Find the resultant force acting on the truss and the point of intersection of its line of action with the line AB.

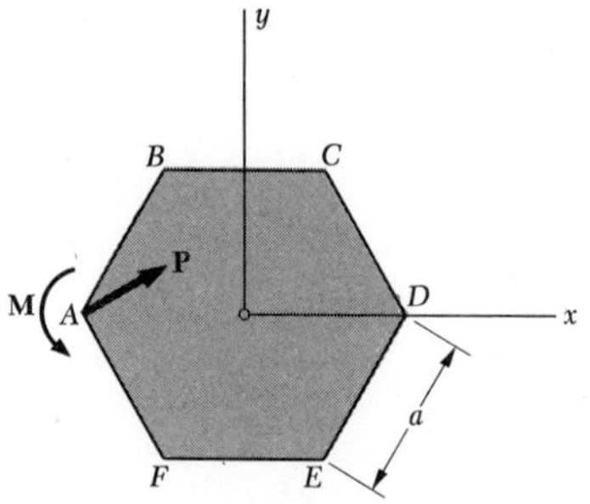

FIG. P3.85

3.85. A force **P** and a couple **M** of moment 200 lb-in. are applied at A to a plate cut in the shape of a regular hexagon of side $a = 5$ in. Determine the force **P** for which the resultant of the system is directed along (*a*) side BC, (*b*) side CD, (*c*) side DE.

3.86. In Prob. 3.85, determine the force **P** for which the resultant of the system is directed along a line joining (*a*) points *F* and *C*, (*b*) points *E* and *B*.

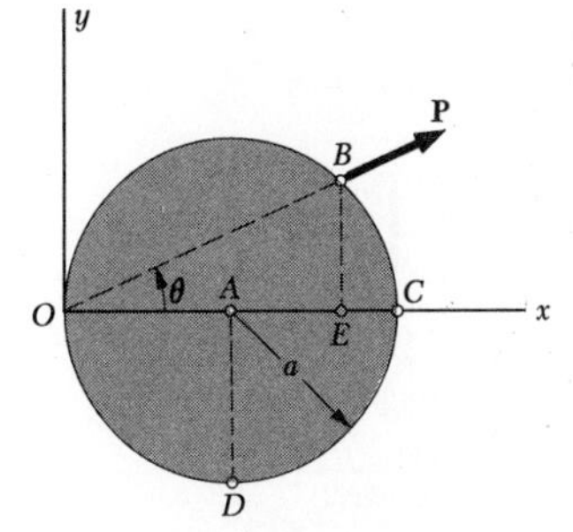

FIG. P 3.87 AND P 3.88

3.87. A force **P** of given magnitude *P* is applied to the edge of a circular plate of radius *a* as shown. (*a*) Replace **P** by a force-couple system at point *D*. (*b*) Determine the value of θ for which the moment of the equivalent force-couple system at *D* is maximum.

3.88. A force **P** of given magnitude *P* is applied to the edge of a circular plate of radius *a* as shown. (*a*) Replace **P** by an equivalent force-couple system at the point *E* obtained by drawing the perpendicular from *B* to the *x* axis. (*b*) Determine the value of θ for which the moment of the equivalent force-couple system at *E* is maximum.

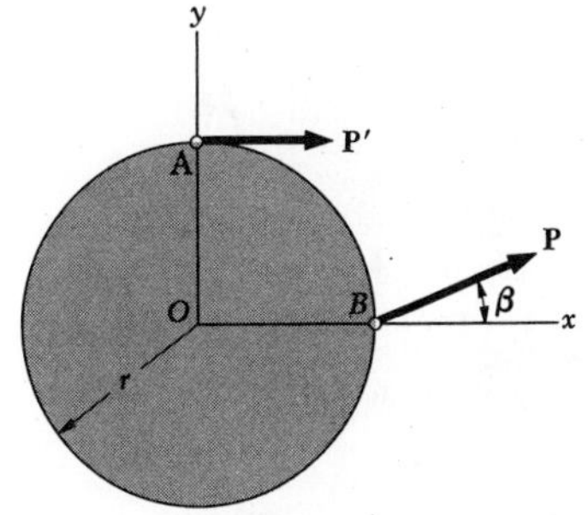

FIG. P 3.89

*3.89. Two forces, each of magnitude *P*, are applied to the edge of a circular disk as shown. Knowing that the line of action of the resultant of the two forces is tangent to the edge of the disk, determine the required value of β.

3.90. Two forces, both parallel to the *yz* plane, are applied to the pipe as shown. Determine the components of the force and couple at *A* equivalent to the two forces.

3.91. Two forces, both parallel to the *yz* plane, are applied to the pipe as shown. Determine the components of the force and couple at *B* equivalent to the two forces.

3.92. What is the smallest additional force **P** that can be applied at point *E* in order to transform the system of forces into a system equivalent to a single force applied at the origin of coordinates?

3.93. In drilling a hole in a wall, a man applies a vertical 30-lb force at *B* on the brace and bit, while pushing at *C* with a 10-lb force. The brace lies in the horizontal *xz* plane. (*a*) Determine the other components of the total force which should be exerted at *C* if the bit is not to be bent about the *y* and *z* axes (i.e., if the system of forces applied on the brace is to have zero moment about both the *y* and *z* axes). (*b*) Reduce the 30-lb force and the total force at *C* to an equivalent force and couple at *A*.

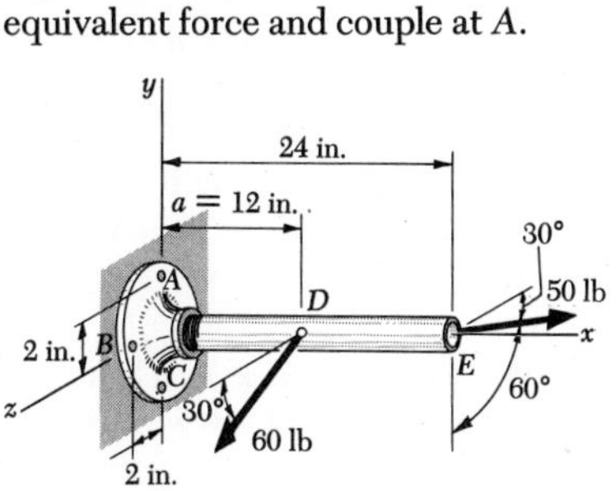

FIG. P 3.90, P 3.91, AND P 3.92

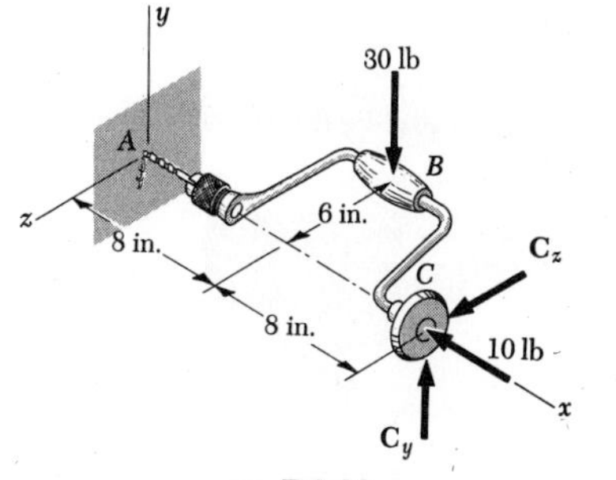

FIG. P 3.93

3.94. A concrete foundation mat of 16-ft radius supports four equally spaced columns, each of which is located 14 ft from the center of the mat. Determine the magnitude and the point of application of the resultant of the four loads.

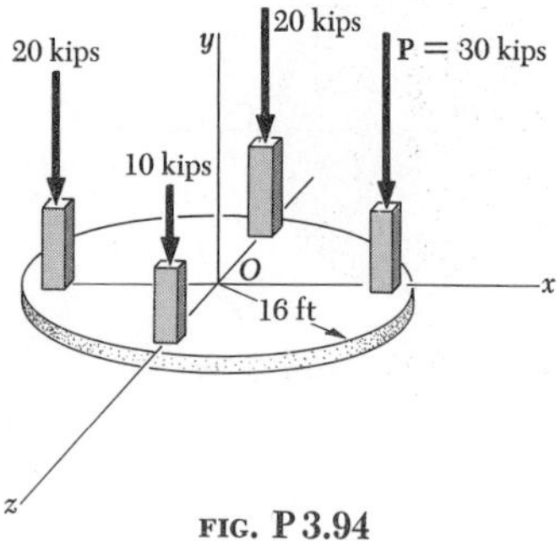

FIG. P 3.94

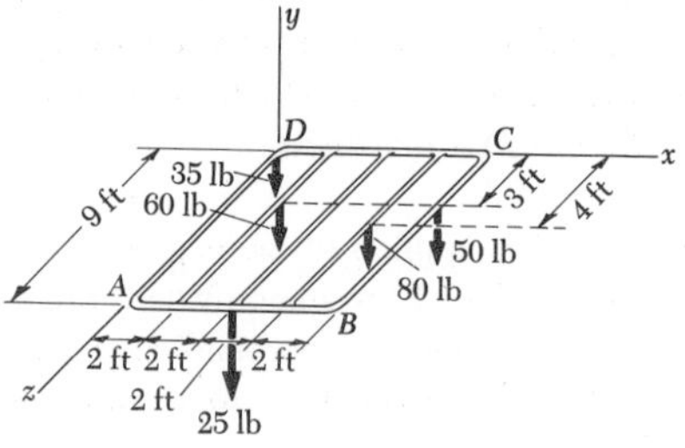

FIG. P 3.95

3.95. Five loads are suspended from the rack shown. Determine the magnitude and line of action of the resultant of the five loads.

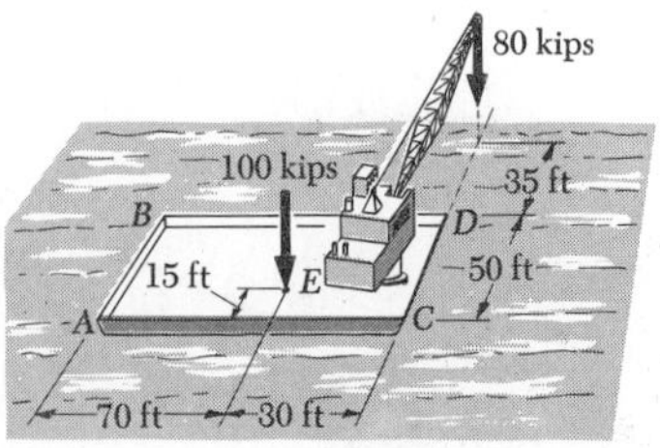

FIG. P 3.96

3.96. A marine crane is mounted on a 100- by 50-ft barge; the crane supports an 80-kip load, and a 100-kip load is stored on the deck at *E*. Determine the magnitude and point of application of the smallest additional load which should be placed on the deck if the resultant of the three loads is to pass through the center of the barge.

3.97. Three vertical loads $\mathbf{P}_1$, $\mathbf{P}_2$, and $\mathbf{P}_3$ are applied at points *A*, *B*, and *C*, respectively, on the perimeter of a horizontal circular plate of radius *r*. Denoting the center of the plate by *O*, determine the angles *AOB* and *AOC* if the resultant of the three loads is to pass through point *O*.

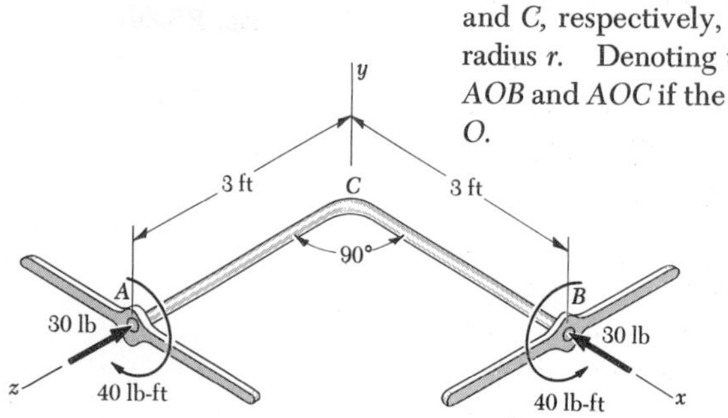

FIG. P 3.98

3.98. Two men are threading the ends of a bent pipe simultaneously. Each of the men applies a 40-lb-ft couple and a force of 30 lb directed along the axis of the section he is threading. The thread at *A* is to be right-handed, and that at *B* is to be left-handed. (*a*) Replace the given system of forces by a force at *C* and a couple. (*b*) Show that the given system may be reduced to a single force and determine the line of action of the force.

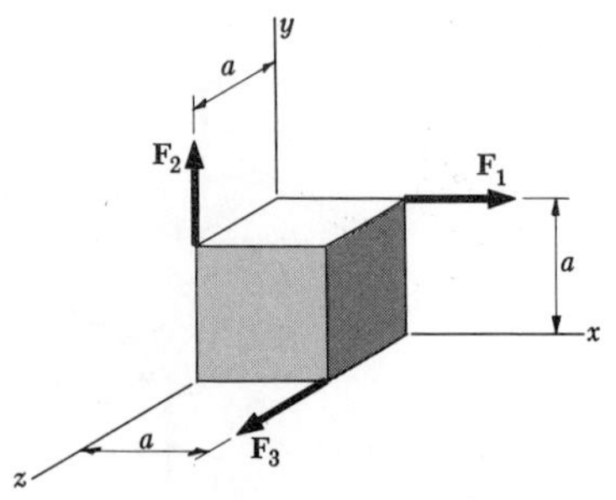

FIG. P 3.99 AND P 3.100

***3.99.** Three forces act on a cube of side *a* as shown. Determine the magnitude of $\mathbf{F}_3$, knowing that $F_1 = F_2 = P$ and that the system may be reduced to a single force **R**. Also determine the magnitude of **R** and its line of action.

3.100. Three forces act on a cube of side *a* as shown. Determine the magnitude and axis of the wrench equivalent to the three forces, if $F_1 = F_2 = F_3 = P$.

3.101. Solve Prob. 3.100 if $F_1 = F_2 = P$ and $F_3 = 0$.

3.102. A rectangular block is acted upon by the five forces shown, which are directed along the edges. Reduce the system of forces to (*a*) a force-couple system at the origin, (*b*) a wrench (specify the axis and pitch of the wrench).

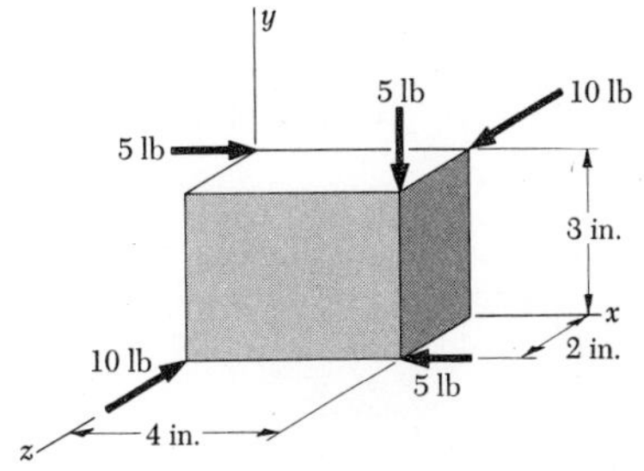

FIG. P3.102

3.103. Solve Prob. 3.102 if the 10-lb forces are replaced by 20-lb forces.

3.104. Two forces of magnitude P act along the diagonals of the faces of a cube of side a as shown. Replace the two forces by a system consisting of (*a*) a single force at O and a couple, (*b*) a wrench (specify the axis and pitch of the wrench).

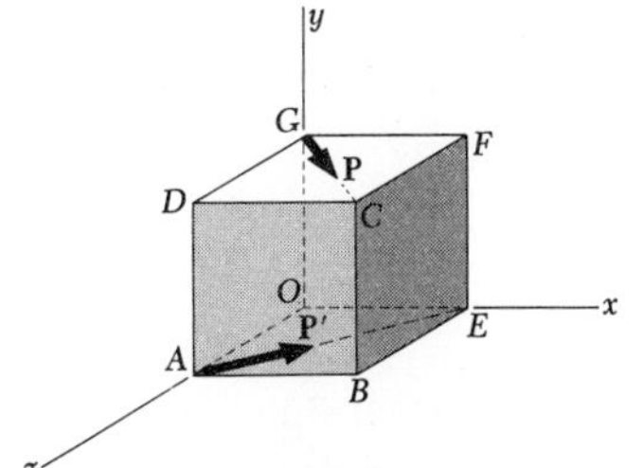

FIG. P3.104

***3.105.** In Prob. 3.94 determine the range of permissible values of the load **P** if the resultant of the four loads must be located so that (*a*) it is not more than 4 ft from the yz plane, (*b*) it is not more than 4 ft from the center of the mat.

***3.106.** In Prob. 3.90 consider the dimension a as a variable and determine the force and couple at the origin of coordinates which are equivalent to the two forces shown. For what value of a is the moment of the couple minimum?

3.107. (*a*) Reduce the wrench shown to a system consisting of two forces perpendicular to the y axis and applied respectively at A and B. (*b*) Solve part *a* assuming $R = 60$ lb, $M = 400$ lb-in., $a = 5$ in., and $b = 10$ in.

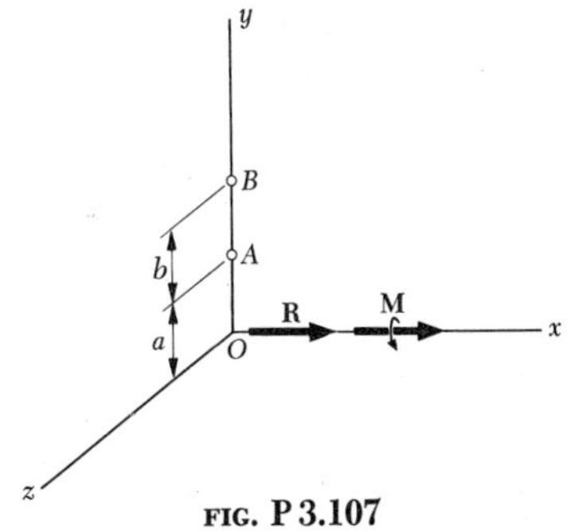

FIG. P3.107

3.108. Knowing that $R = 70$ lb and $M = 140$ lb-in., replace the given wrench by a system of two forces chosen in such a way that one force acts at point B and the other force lies in the xz plane.

3.109. Show that, in general, a wrench may be replaced by two forces chosen in such a way that one force passes through a given point while the other force lies in a given plane.

***3.110.** Show that a wrench may be replaced by two perpendicular forces, one of which is applied at a given point.

***3.111.** Show that a wrench may be replaced by two forces, one of which has a prescribed line of action.

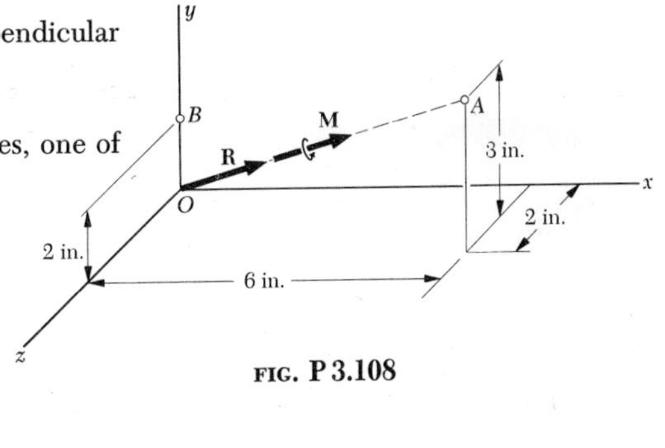

FIG. P3.108

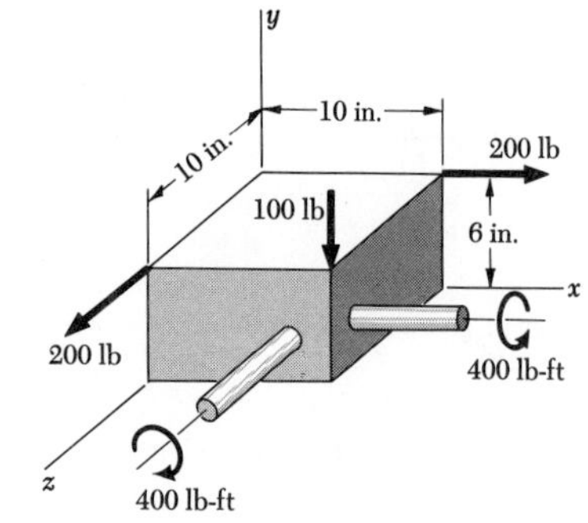

FIG. P3.112 AND P3.113

REVIEW PROBLEMS

3.112. Replace the forces and couples shown by an equivalent force-couple system at the origin of coordinates.

3.113. Determine the magnitude of the single force equivalent to the system shown and find the point where its line of action intersects each of the coordinate planes.

3.114. Find the resultant of the system shown and the point of intersection of its line of action with (*a*) line *AB*, (*b*) line *BD*, (*c*) line *DE*.

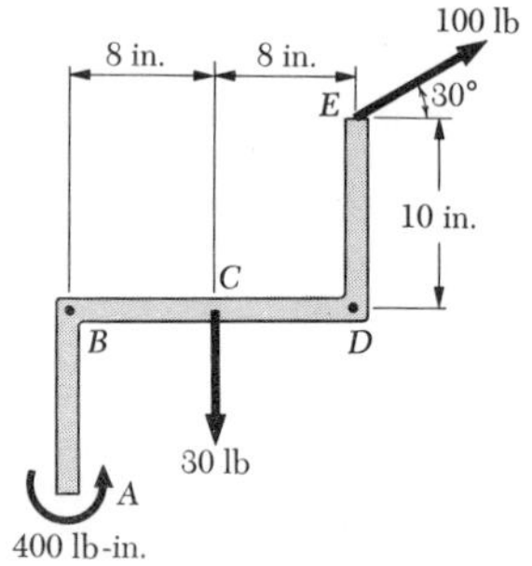

FIG. P3.114 AND P3.115

3.115. Determine the magnitude and sense of the single vertical force **P** which must be applied at *D* if the line of action of the resultant of the entire system is to pass through point *B*.

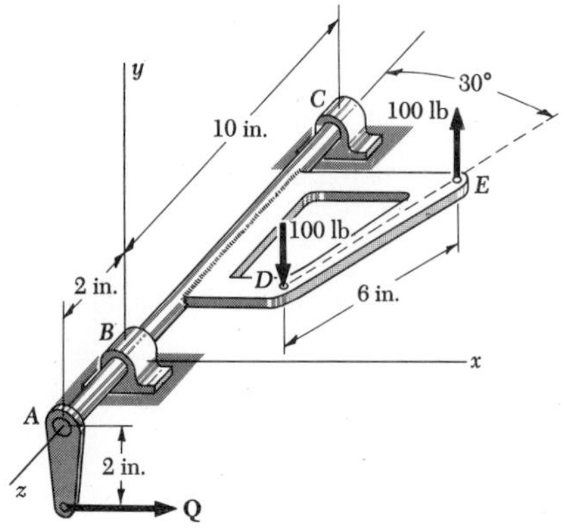

FIG. P3.116

3.116. A 600-lb-in. couple formed by two 100-lb forces and a force **Q** of magnitude 150 lb are applied to the assembly shown. Replace this system of forces (*a*) by an equivalent force-couple system at *B*, (*b*) by an equivalent wrench (specify the pitch and axis of the wrench).

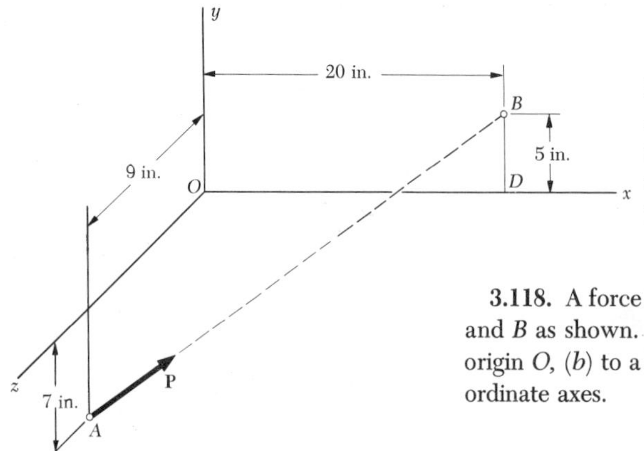

FIG. P3.118

3.117. The corners of a square plate of side *a* are lettered *A*, *B*, *C*, and *D* clockwise as viewed from above. The plate supports loads *W*, 2*W*, 3*W*, and 4*W* at the corners *A*, *B*, *C*, and *D*, respectively. Determine where the line of action of the resultant of the four loads intersects the plate.

3.118. A force **P** of magnitude 500 lb acts along a line joining points *A* and *B* as shown. Determine the moment of **P** with respect (*a*) to the origin *O*, (*b*) to a line forming equal angles with each of the positive coordinate axes.

3.119. Three forces act on a plate as shown. Determine (*a*) an equivalent force-couple system at *C*, (*b*) the points where the line of action of the resultant intersects the edge of the plate.

3.120. Determine the force **Q** which must be applied at *C* if the line of action of the entire system is to pass through both points *B* and *D*.

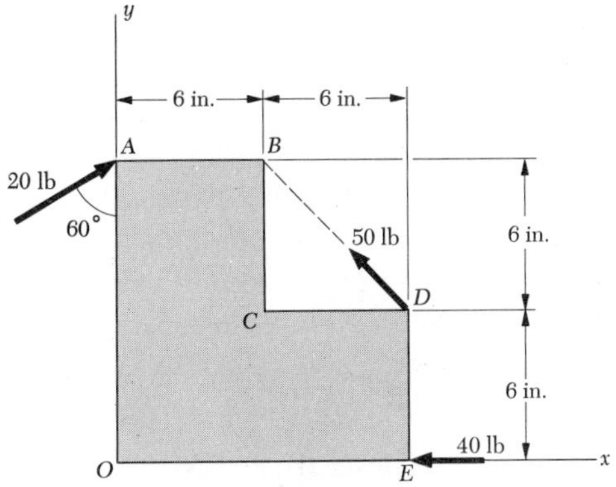

FIG. P3.119 AND P3.120

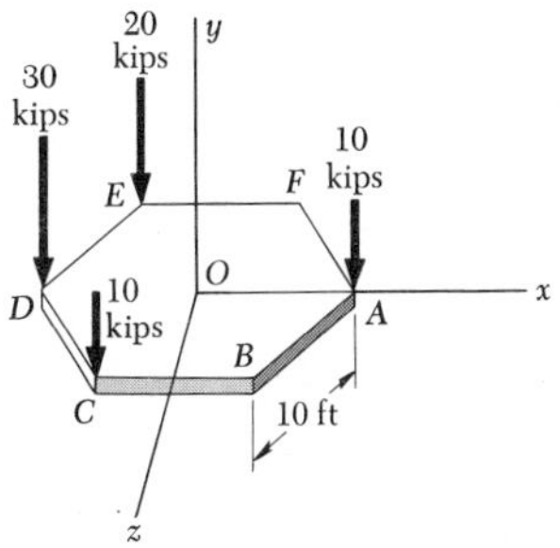

FIG. P3.121

3.121. A concrete foundation mat, in the shape of a regular hexagon of side 10 ft, supports four column loads as shown. Determine where the line of action of the resultant of the four loads intersects the mat.

3.122. In Prob. 3.121 determine the magnitude of the downward loads which must be applied at *B* and *F* if the resultant of all six loads is to pass through the center of the mat.

3.123. Two wrenches, each with its axis perpendicular to the *y* axis, are applied to a gear box as shown. Determine (*a*) an equivalent force-couple system at the origin *O*, (*b*) a single equivalent wrench (specify the axis and pitch of the wrench).

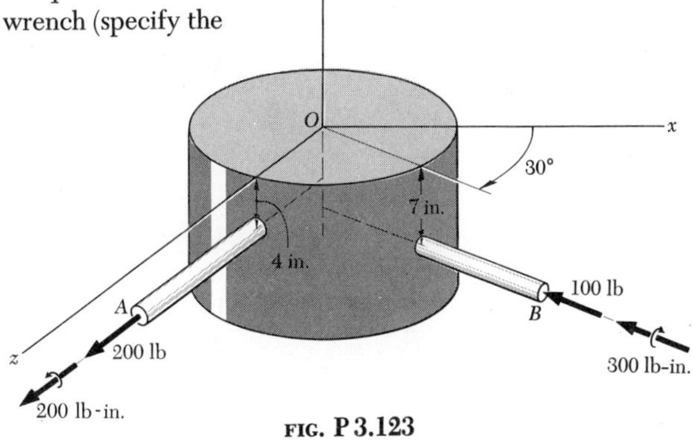

FIG. P3.123

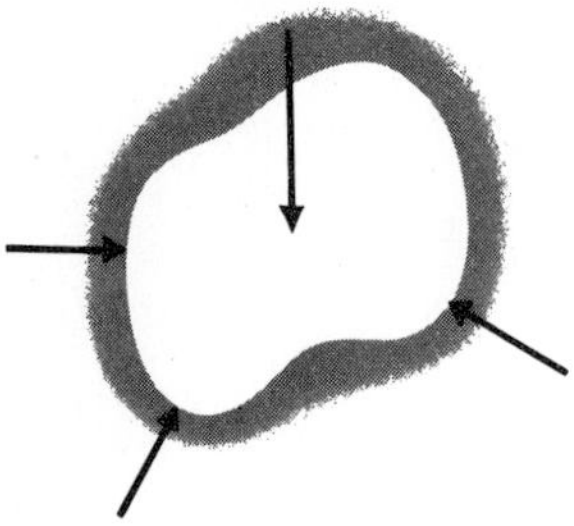

4. EQUILIBRIUM OF RIGID BODIES

4.1. Rigid Body in Equilibrium. *A rigid body is said to be in equilibrium when the external forces acting on it form a system of forces equivalent to zero*, i.e., when the external forces may be reduced to no force and no couple. Setting **R** and $\mathbf{M}_O^R$ equal to zero in the relations (3.47), we obtain the following necessary and sufficient conditions for the equilibrium of a rigid body:

$$\Sigma \mathbf{F} = 0 \qquad \Sigma \mathbf{M}_O = \Sigma(\mathbf{r} \times \mathbf{F}) = 0 \tag{4.1}$$

Resolving each force and each moment into its rectangular components, we find that the necessary and sufficient conditions for the equilibrium of a rigid body may also be expressed by the six scalar equations

$$\Sigma F_x = 0 \qquad \Sigma F_y = 0 \qquad \Sigma F_z = 0 \tag{4.2}$$
$$\Sigma M_x = 0 \qquad \Sigma M_y = 0 \qquad \Sigma M_z = 0 \tag{4.3}$$

Equations (4.2) express the fact that the components of the external forces in the x, y, and z directions are balanced; Eqs. (4.3) express the fact that the moments of the external forces about the x, y, and z axes are balanced. The system of the external forces, therefore, will impart no motion of translation or rotation to the rigid body considered.

4.2. Free-body Diagram. In solving a problem concerning the equilibrium of a rigid body, it is essential to consider *all* the forces acting on the body; it is equally important to exclude any force which is not directly applied on the body. Omitting a force or adding an extraneous one would destroy the conditions of equilibrium. Therefore, the first step in the solution of the problem should consist in drawing a *free-body diagram* of the rigid body under consideration. Free-body diagrams have already been used on many occasions in Chap. 2. However, in view of their importance to the solution of equilibrium problems, we shall summarize here the various steps which must be followed in drawing a free-body diagram.

First, a clear decision is made regarding the choice of the free body to be used. This body is then detached from the ground and separated from any other body. The contour of the body thus isolated is sketched.

All external forces are then indicated. These forces represent the action exerted *on* the free body *by* the ground and the bodies which have been detached; they should be applied at the various points where the free body was supported by the ground or connected to the other bodies. The *weight* of the free body should also be included among the external forces, since it represents the attraction exerted by the earth on the various particles forming the free body. As will be seen in Chap. 5, the weight should be applied at the center of gravity of the body. When the free body is made of several parts, the forces the various parts exert on each other should *not* be included among the external forces. These forces are internal forces as far as the free body is concerned.

The magnitude and direction of the *known external forces* should be clearly marked on the free-body diagram. Care should be taken to indicate the sense of the force exerted *on* the free body, not that of the force exerted *by* the free body. Known external forces generally include the *weight* of the free body and *forces applied* for a given purpose.

Unknown external forces usually consist of the *reactions*—also called sometimes *constraining forces*—through which the ground and other bodies oppose a possible motion of the free body and thus constrain it to remain in the same position. Reactions are exerted at the points where the free body is *supported* or *connected* to other bodies. They will be discussed in detail in Secs. 4.3 and 4.8.

The free-body diagram should also include dimensions, since these may be needed in the computation of moments of forces. Any other detail, however, should be omitted.

EQUILIBRIUM IN TWO DIMENSIONS

4.3. Reactions at Supports and Connections for a Two-dimensional Structure. In the first part of this chapter we shall consider the equilibrium of a two-dimensional structure, i.e., we shall assume that the structure considered and the forces applied to it are contained in the plane of the figure. Clearly, the reactions needed to maintain the structure in the same position will also be contained in the plane of the figure.

The reactions exerted on a two-dimensional structure may be

divided into three groups, corresponding to three types of *supports*, or *connections:*

1. *Reactions Equivalent to a Force with Known Line of Action.* Supports and connections causing reactions of this group include *rollers, rockers, smooth surfaces, short links and cables, collars on smooth rods,* and *pins in smooth slots.* Each of these supports and connections can prevent motion in one direction only. They are shown in Fig. 4.1, together with the reaction they produce. Reactions of this group involve *one unknown,* namely, the magnitude of the reaction; this magnitude should be denoted by an appropriate letter. The line of action of the reaction is known and should be indicated clearly in the free-body diagram. The sense of the reaction must be as shown in Fig. 4.1 in the case of a smooth surface (away from the surface) or of a cable (tension in the direction of the cable). The reaction may be directed either way in the case of double-track rollers, links, collars on rods, and pins in slots. Single-track rollers and rockers are generally assumed to be reversible, and thus the corresponding reactions may also be directed either way.

2. *Reactions Equivalent to a Force of Unknown Direction.* Supports and connections causing reactions of this group include *smooth pins in fitted holes, hinges,* and *rough surfaces.* They can prevent translation of the free body in all directions, but they cannot prevent the body from rotating about the connection. Reactions of this group involve *two unknowns* and are usually represented by their x and y components. In the case of a rough surface, the component normal to the surface must be directed away from the surface.

3. *Reactions Equivalent to a Force and a Couple.* These reactions are caused by *fixed supports* which oppose any motion of the free body and thus constrain it completely. Fixed supports actually produce forces over the entire surface of contact; these forces, however, form a system which may be reduced to a force and a couple. Reactions of this group involve *three unknowns,* namely, the two components of the force and the moment of the couple.

When the sense of an unknown force or couple is not clearly apparent, no attempt should be made at determining it. Instead, the sense of the force or couple should be arbitrarily assumed; the sign of the answer obtained will indicate whether the assumption is correct or not.

4.4. Equilibrium of a Rigid Body in Two Dimensions. The conditions stated in Sec. 4.1 for the equilibrium of a rigid body become considerably simpler in the case of a two-dimensional

Support or Connection	Reaction	Number of Unknowns
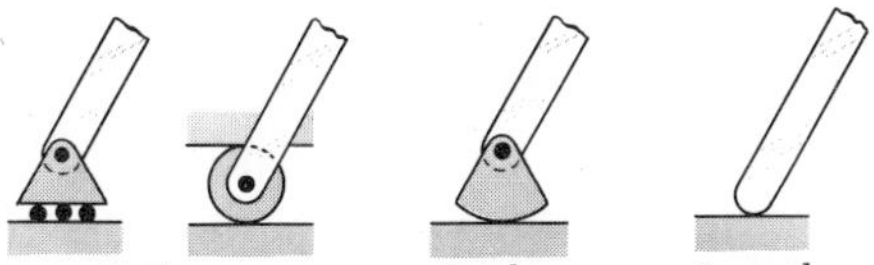 Rollers; Rocker; Smooth surface	 Force with known line of action	1
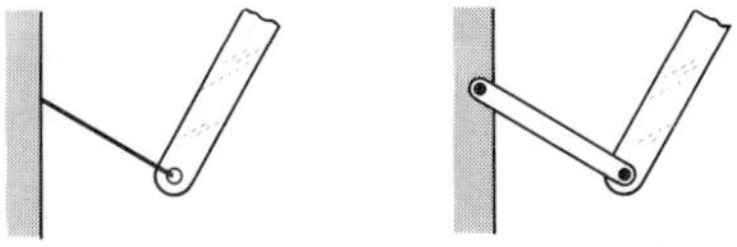 Short cable; Short link	 Force with known line of action	1
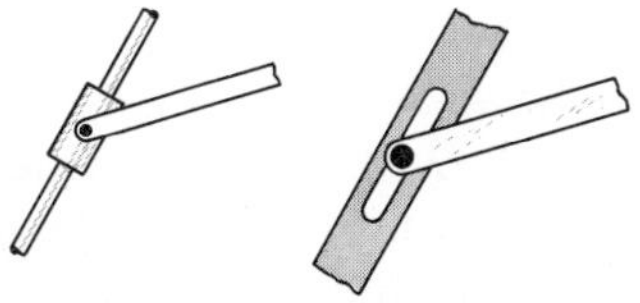 Collar on smooth rod; Pin in smooth slot	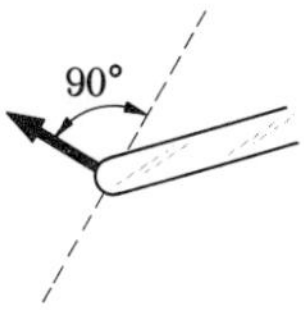 Force with known line of action	1
 Smooth pin or hinge; Rough surface	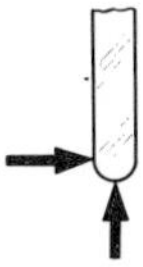 Force of unknown direction	2
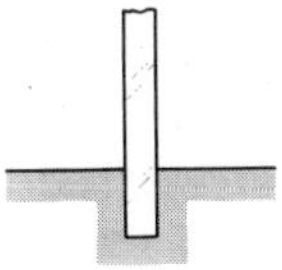 Fixed support	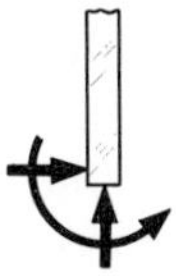 Force and couple	3

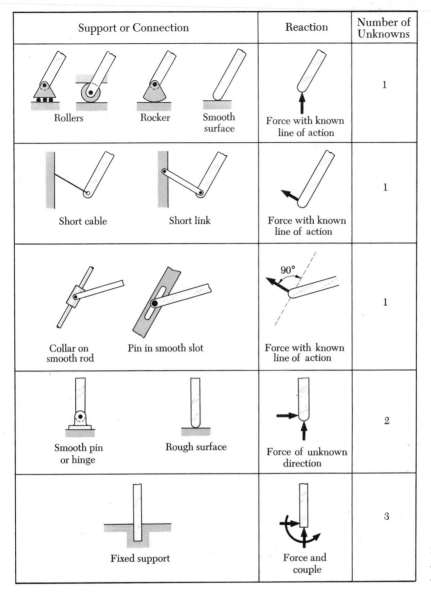

FIG. 4.1. Reactions at supports and connections

structure. Choosing the x and y axes in the plane of the structure, we have

$$F_z = 0 \qquad M_x = M_y = 0 \qquad M_z = M_O$$

for each of the forces applied to the structure. Thus, the six equations of equilibrium derived in Sec. 4.1 reduce to

$$\Sigma F_x = 0 \qquad \Sigma F_y = 0 \qquad \Sigma M_O = 0 \tag{4.4}$$

and to three trivial identities $0 = 0$. Since the third of the equations (4.4) must be satisfied regardless of the choice of the origin O, we may write the equations of equilibrium for a two-dimensional structure in the more general form

$$\Sigma F_x = 0 \qquad \Sigma F_y = 0 \qquad \Sigma M_A = 0 \tag{4.5}$$

where A is any point in the plane of the structure. The three equations obtained may be solved for no more than *three unknowns*.

We saw in the preceding sections that unknown forces usually consist of reactions, and that the number of unknowns corresponding to a given reaction depends upon the type of support or connection causing that reaction. Referring to Sec. 4.3, we check that the equilibrium equations (4.5) may be used to determine the reactions of two rollers and one cable, or of one fixed support, or of one roller and one smooth pin in a fitted hole, etc.

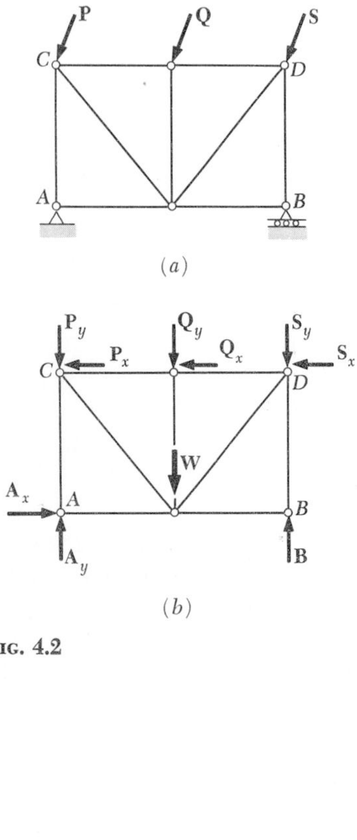

FIG. 4.2

Consider, for instance, the truss shown in Fig. 4.2*a*, which is subjected to the given forces **P**, **Q**, and **S**. The truss is held in place by a smooth pin at A and a roller at B. The pin prevents point A from moving by exerting on the truss a force which may be resolved into the components $\mathbf{A}_x$ and $\mathbf{A}_y$; the roller keeps the truss from rotating about A by exerting the vertical force **B**. The free-body diagram of the truss is shown in Fig. 4.2*b*; it includes the reactions $\mathbf{A}_x$, $\mathbf{A}_y$, and **B** as well as the applied forces **P**, **Q**, **S**, and the weight **W** of the truss. Expressing that the sum of the moments about A of all the forces shown in Fig. 4.2*b* is zero, we write the equation $\Sigma M_A = 0$, which may be solved for the magnitude B since it does not contain A_x or A_y. Expressing, then, that the sum of the x components and the sum of the y components of the forces are zero, we write the equations $\Sigma F_x = 0$ and $\Sigma F_y = 0$, which may be solved for the components A_x and A_y, respectively.

Additional equations could be obtained by expressing that the sum of the moments of the external forces about points other than A is zero. We could write, for instance, $\Sigma M_B = 0$. Such a statement, however, does not contain any new information, since it has already been established that the system of the forces shown in Fig. 4.2*b* is equivalent to zero. The additional equation *is not independent* and cannot be used to determine a fourth unknown. It will be useful, however, for checking the solution obtained from the original three equations of equilibrium.

While the three equations of equilibrium cannot be *augmented* by additional equations, any of them may be *replaced* by another equation. Thus, an alternate system of equations of equilibrium is

$$\Sigma F_x = 0 \qquad \Sigma M_A = 0 \qquad \Sigma M_B = 0 \tag{4.6}$$

where the line AB is chosen in a direction different from the y direction (Fig. 4.2b). These equations are sufficient conditions for the equilibrium of the truss. The first two equations indicate that the external forces must reduce to a single vertical force at A. Since the third equation requires that the moment of this force be zero about a point B which is not on its line of action, the force must be zero and the rigid body is in equilibrium.

A third possible set of equations of equilibrium is

$$\Sigma M_A = 0 \qquad \Sigma M_B = 0 \qquad \Sigma M_C = 0 \tag{4.7}$$

where the points A, B, and C are not in a straight line (Fig. 4.2b). The first equation requires that the external forces reduce to a single force at A; the second equation requires that this force pass through B; the third, that it pass through C. Since the points A, B, C are not in a straight line, the force must be zero and the rigid body is in equilibrium.

The equation $\Sigma M_A = 0$, which expresses that the sum of the moments of the forces about pin A is zero, possesses a more definite physical meaning than either of the other two equations (4.7). These two equations express a similar idea of balance, but with respect to points about which the rigid body is not actually hinged. They are, however, as useful as the first equation, and our choice of equilibrium equations should not be unduly influenced by the physical meaning of these equations. Indeed, it will be desirable in practice to choose equations of equilibrium containing only one unknown, since this eliminates the necessity of solving simultaneous equations. Equations containing only one unknown may be obtained by summing moments about the point of intersection of the lines of action of two unknown forces or, if these forces are parallel, by summing components in a direction perpendicular to their common direction. In the case of the truss of Fig. 4.3, for example, which is held by rollers at A and B and a short link at D, the reactions at A and B may be eliminated by summing x components. The reactions at A and D will be eliminated by summing moments about C and the reactions at B and D by summing moments about D. The equations obtained are

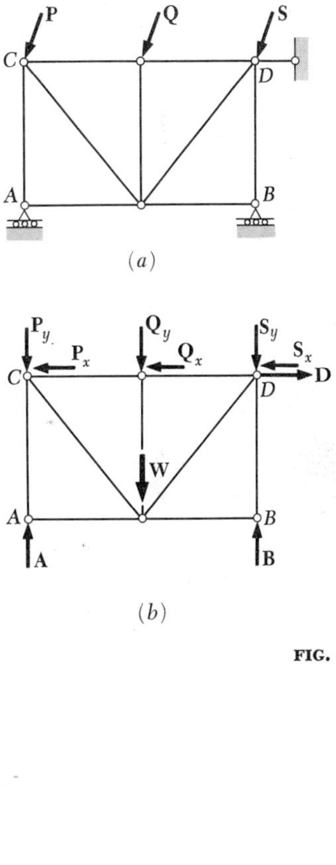

FIG. 4.3

$$\Sigma F_x = 0 \qquad \Sigma M_C = 0 \qquad \Sigma M_D = 0$$

Each of these equations contains only one unknown.

4.5. Statically Indeterminate Reactions. Partial Constraints. In each of the two examples considered in the preceding section (Figs. 4.2 and 4.3), the reactions to be determined involved *three unknowns;* these unknowns were obtained by solving the three equations of equilibrium. Besides, the types of supports used were such that the rigid body could not possibly move under the given loads or under any other loading conditions. In such cases, the reactions are said to be *statically determinate* and the rigid body is said to be *completely constrained.*

Consider now the truss shown in Fig. 4.4*a*, which is held by smooth pins at *A* and *B*. We note from the free-body diagram of Fig. 4.4*b* that the reactions involve *four unknowns.* Since, as was pointed out in Sec. 4.4, only three independent equilibrium equations are available, there are *more unknowns than equations* and all the unknowns cannot be determined. While the equations $\Sigma M_A = 0$ and $\Sigma M_B = 0$ yield the vertical components B_y and A_y, respectively, the equation $\Sigma F_x = 0$ gives only the sum $A_x + B_x$ of the horizontal components of the reactions at *A* and *B*. The components A_x and B_x are said to be *statically indeterminate.* They could be determined by considering the deformations produced in the truss by the given loading, but this method is beyond the scope of statics and belongs to the study of mechanics of materials.

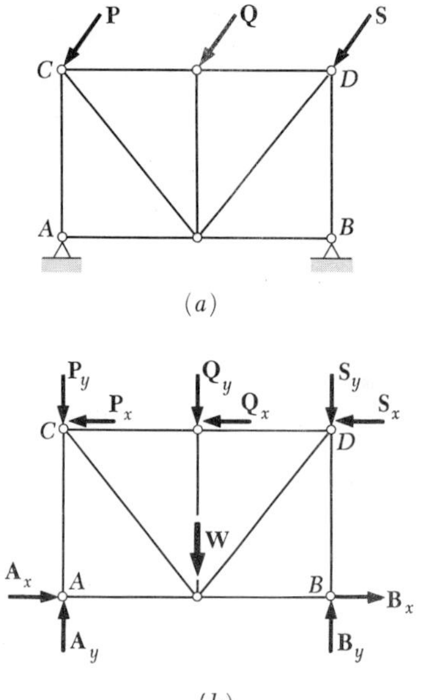

FIG. 4.4. Statically indeterminate reactions

The supports used to hold the truss shown in Fig. 4.5*a* consist of rollers at *A* and *B*. The corresponding reactions, shown in Fig. 4.5*b*, involve *two unknowns.* Since three equations of equilibrium must still be satisfied, there are *fewer unknowns than equations* and one of the equilibrium equations will not be satisfied. While the equations $\Sigma M_A = 0$ and $\Sigma M_B = 0$ can be satisfied by a proper choice of reactions at *A* and *B*, the equation $\Sigma F_x = 0$ will not be satisfied unless the sum of the horizontal components of the applied forces happens to be zero. The physical significance of this result is clear: Equilibrium cannot be maintained under general loading conditions; while any vertical motion is prevented, the truss is free to move horizontally. The truss is said to be only *partially constrained.*†

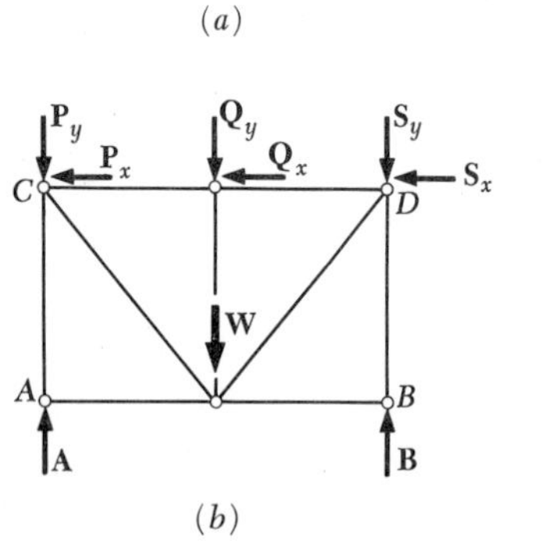

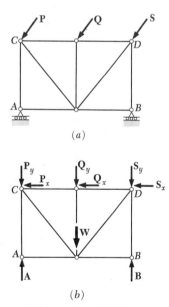

FIG. 4.5. Partial constraints

It appears from the above that, if a rigid body is to be completely constrained and if the reactions at its supports are to be statically determinate, *there must be as many unknowns as there are equations of equilibrium.* We should note, however, that while *necessary* this condition is *not sufficient.*

† Partially constrained bodies are often referred to as *unstable.* However, in order to avoid any confusion between this type of instability, due to insufficient constraints, and the type of instability considered in Chap. 10, which relates to the behavior of a rigid body when its equilibrium is disturbed, we shall restrict the use of the words *stable* and *unstable* to the latter case.

Consider, for example, the truss shown in Fig. 4.6*a*, which is held by rollers at *A*, *B*, and *E*. While there are three unknown reactions, **A**, **B**, and **E** (Fig. 4.6*b*), we find that the equation $\Sigma F_x = 0$ will not be satisfied unless the sum of the horizontal components of the applied forces happens to be zero. There is a sufficient number of constraints, but these constraints are not properly arranged; we say that the truss is *improperly constrained.* Since only two equilibrium equations are left for determining the three unknowns, the reactions will be statically indeterminate. Thus, improper constraints also produce statical indeterminacy.

Another example of improper constraints—and of the accompanying statical indeterminacy—is provided by the truss shown in Fig. 4.7. This truss is held by a smooth pin at *A* and by rollers at *B* and *C*, which altogether involve four unknowns. Choosing the equilibrium equations $\Sigma M_A = 0$, $\Sigma F_x = 0$, and $\Sigma F_y = 0$, we find that the first equation cannot be satisfied under general loading conditions, while the other two yield only the sums $A_x + B$ and $A_y + C$. The examples of Figs. 4.6 and 4.7 lead us to conclude that *a rigid body is improperly constrained whenever the supports,* even though they may provide a sufficient number of reactions, *are arranged in such a way that the reactions must be either concurrent or parallel.*†

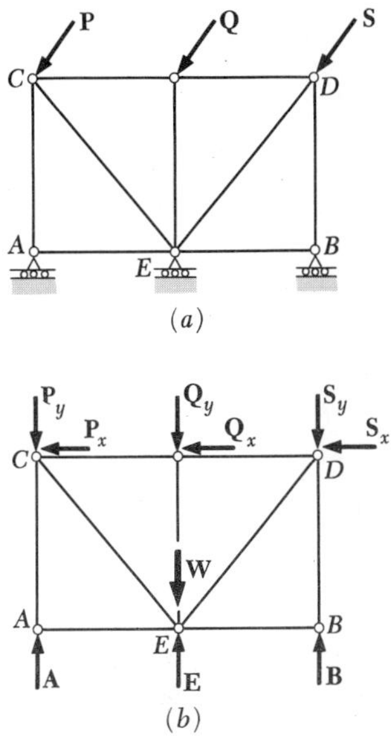

FIG. 4.6. Improper constraints

Supports involving statically indeterminate reactions should be used with care in the *design* of structures, and only with a full knowledge of the problems they may cause. On the other hand, the *analysis* of structures possessing statically indeterminate reactions often may be partially carried out by the methods of statics. In the case of the truss of Fig. 4.4, for example, the vertical components of the reactions at *A* and *B* were obtained from the equilibrium equations.

For obvious reasons, supports producing partial or improper constraints should be avoided in the design of stationary structures. However, a partially or improperly constrained structure will not necessarily collapse; under particular loading conditions, equilibrium may be maintained. For example, the trusses of Figs. 4.5 and 4.6 will be in equilibrium if the applied forces **P**, **Q**, and **S** are vertical. Besides, structures which are designed to move *should* be only partially constrained. A railroad car, for instance, would be of little use if it were completely constrained by having its brakes applied permanently.

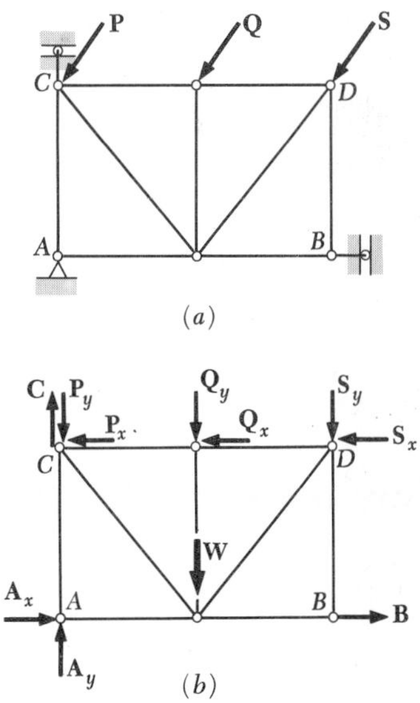

FIG. 4.7. Improper constraints

† Because this situation arises from an inadequate arrangement or *geometry* of the supports, it is often referred to as *geometric instability.*

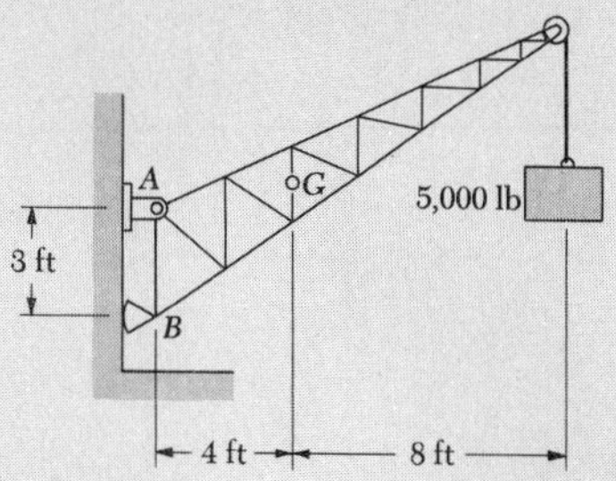

SAMPLE PROBLEM 4.1

A fixed crane weighs 2,000 lb and is used to lift a load of 5,000 lb. It is held in place by a smooth pin at A and a rocker at B. The center of gravity is located at G. Determine the components of the reactions at A and B.

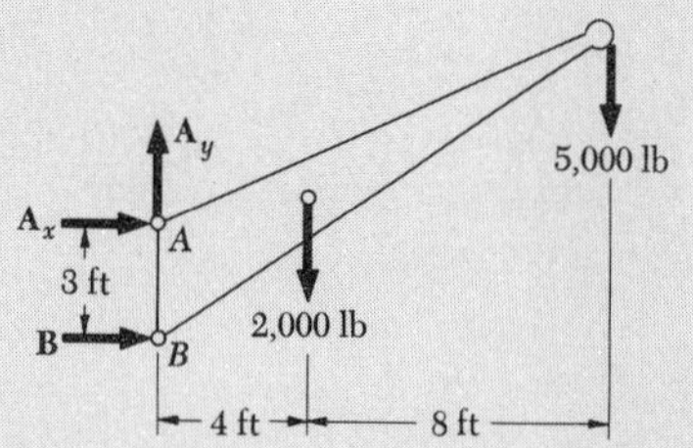

Solution. A free-body diagram of the crane is drawn. Since the reaction at a smooth pin is a force of unknown direction, the reaction at A is represented by its components $\mathbf{A}_x$ and $\mathbf{A}_y$. Since the reaction at a rocker is perpendicular to the rocker surface, the reaction at B will be horizontal. We assume that $\mathbf{A}_x$, $\mathbf{A}_y$, and $\mathbf{B}$ act in the directions shown on the free-body diagram.

Determination of **B**. We express that the sum of the moments of all external forces about point A is zero. The equation obtained will contain neither A_x nor A_y since the moments of $\mathbf{A}_x$ and $\mathbf{A}_y$ about A are zero. Multiplying the magnitude of each force by its perpendicular distance from B, and recalling that counterclockwise is positive, we write

$$+\circlearrowleft \Sigma M_A = 0: \qquad +B(3\text{ ft}) - (2{,}000\text{ lb})(4\text{ ft}) - (5{,}000\text{ lb})(12\text{ ft}) = 0$$

$$B = +22{,}700\text{ lb} \qquad \mathbf{B} = 22{,}700\text{ lb} \rightarrow \blacktriangleleft$$

Since the result is positive, the reaction is directed as assumed.

Determination of $\mathbf{A}_x$. The magnitude A_x is determined by expressing that the sum of the horizontal components of all external forces is zero. We write

$$\overset{+}{\rightarrow} \Sigma F_x = 0: \qquad A_x + B = 0 \qquad A_x + 22{,}700\text{ lb} = 0$$

$$A_x = -22{,}700\text{ lb} \qquad \mathbf{A}_x = 22{,}700\text{ lb} \leftarrow \blacktriangleleft$$

Determination of $\mathbf{A}_y$. The sum of the vertical components must also equal zero.

$$+\uparrow \Sigma F_y = 0: \qquad A_y - 2{,}000\text{ lb} - 5{,}000\text{ lb} = 0$$

$$A_y = +7{,}000\text{ lb} \qquad \mathbf{A}_y = 7{,}000\text{ lb} \uparrow \blacktriangleleft$$

Adding vectorially the components $\mathbf{A}_x$ and $\mathbf{A}_y$, we find that the reaction at A is 23,700 lb ⦪ 17.2°.

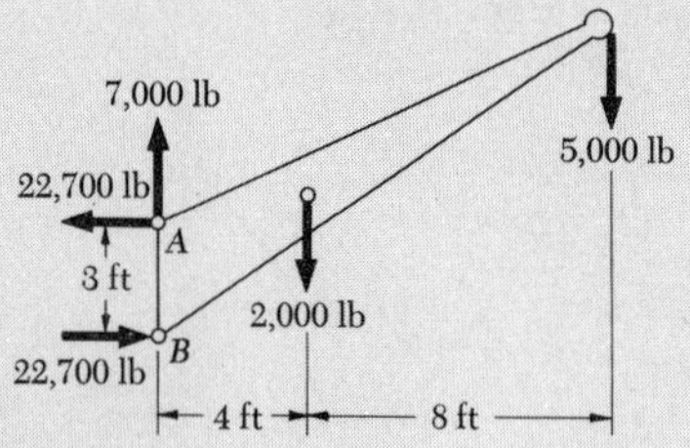

Check. The values obtained for the reactions may be checked by recalling that the sum of the moments of all external forces about any point must be zero. For example, considering point B, we write

$$+\circlearrowleft \Sigma M_B = -(2{,}000\text{ lb})(4\text{ ft}) - (5{,}000\text{ lb})(12\text{ ft}) + (22{,}700\text{ lb})(3\text{ ft}) = 0$$

SAMPLE PROBLEM 4.2

Three loads are applied to a truss as shown. The truss is supported by a roller at A and by a smooth pin at B. Determine the reactions at A and B.

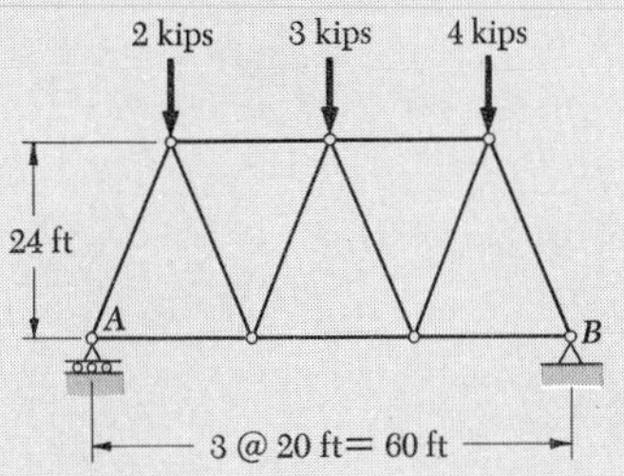

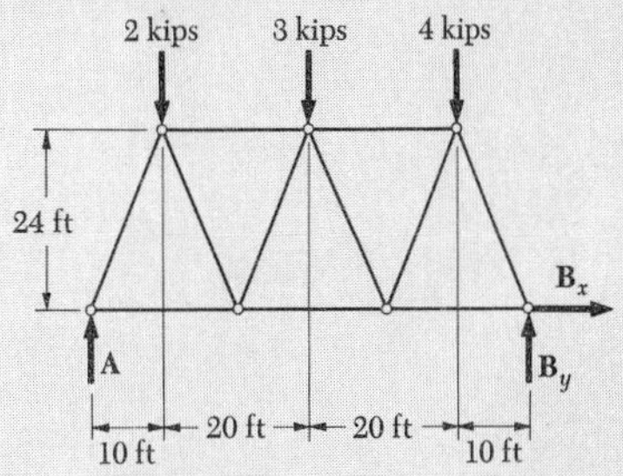

Solution. A free-body diagram of the truss is drawn. The reaction at A is vertical and is denoted by **A**. The reaction at B is represented by components $\mathbf{B}_x$ and $\mathbf{B}_y$. Each component is assumed to act in the direction shown.

Equilibrium Equations. We write the following three equilibrium equations and solve for the reactions indicated:

$\xrightarrow{+} \Sigma F_x = 0$: $\quad B_x = 0 \qquad \mathbf{B}_x = 0$ ◄

$+\circlearrowleft \Sigma M_A = 0$:

$$-(2 \text{ kips})(10 \text{ ft}) - (3 \text{ kips})(30 \text{ ft}) - (4 \text{ kips})(50 \text{ ft}) + B_y(60 \text{ ft}) = 0$$

$$B_y = +5.17 \text{ kips} \qquad \mathbf{B}_y = 5.17 \text{ kips} \uparrow$$ ◄

$+\circlearrowleft \Sigma M_B = 0$:

$$A(60 \text{ ft}) - (2 \text{ kips})(50 \text{ ft}) - (3 \text{ kips})(30 \text{ ft}) - (4 \text{ kips})(10 \text{ ft}) = 0$$

$$A = +3.83 \text{ kips} \qquad \mathbf{A} = 3.83 \text{ kips} \uparrow$$ ◄

Check. The results are checked by adding the vertical components of all the external forces.

$$+\uparrow \Sigma F_y = +5.17 \text{ kips} + 3.83 \text{ kips} - 2 \text{ kips} - 3 \text{ kips} - 4 \text{ kips} = 0$$

Remark. In this problem the reactions at both A and B are vertical; however, these reactions are vertical for different reasons. At A, the truss is supported by a roller; hence the reaction cannot have any horizontal component. At B, the horizontal component of the reaction is zero because it must satisfy the equilibrium equation $\Sigma F_x = 0$ and none of the other forces acting on the truss has a horizontal component.

We could have noticed at first glance that the reaction at B was vertical and dispensed with the horizontal component $\mathbf{B}_x$. This, however, is a bad practice. In following it, we would run the risk of forgetting the component $\mathbf{B}_x$ when the loading conditions require such a component (i.e., when a horizontal load is included). Also, the component $\mathbf{B}_x$ was found to be zero by using and solving an equilibrium equation, $\Sigma F_x = 0$. By setting $\mathbf{B}_x$ equal to zero immediately, we might not realize that we actually make use of this equation and thus might lose track of the number of equations available for solving the problem.

SAMPLE PROBLEM 4.3

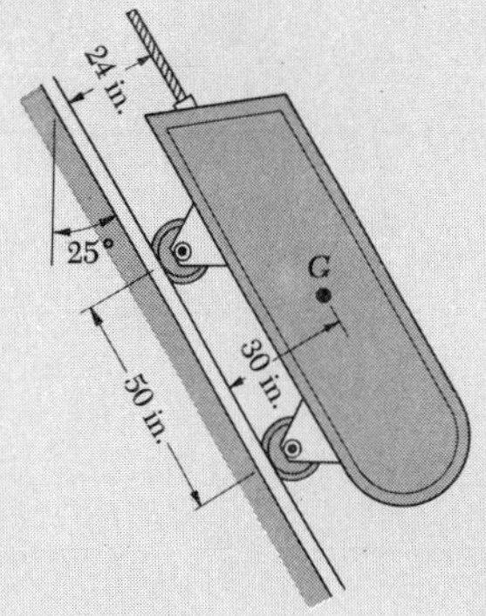

A loading car is at rest on a track forming an angle of 25° with the vertical. The gross weight of the car and its load is 5,500 lb, and it is applied at a point 30 in. from the track, halfway between the two axles. The car is held by a cable attached 24 in. from the track. Determine the tension in the cable and the reaction at each pair of wheels.

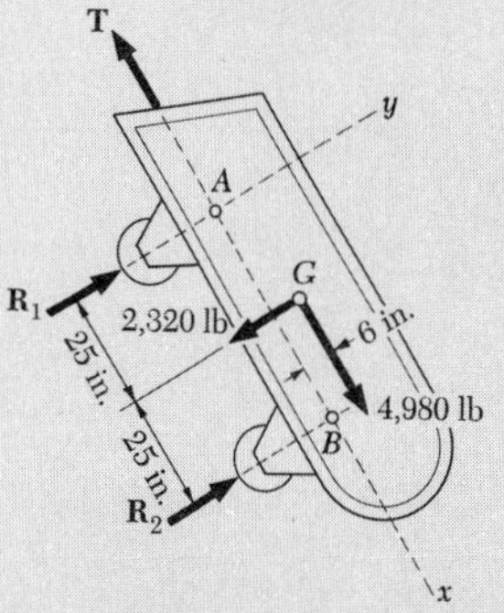

Solution. A free-body diagram of the car is drawn. The reaction at each wheel is perpendicular to the track, and the tension force **T** is parallel to the track. For convenience, we choose the x axis parallel to the track and the y axis perpendicular to the track. The 5,500-lb weight is then resolved into x and y components.

$$W_x = +(5{,}500 \text{ lb}) \cos 25° = +4{,}980 \text{ lb}$$

$$W_y = -(5{,}500 \text{ lb}) \sin 25° = -2{,}320 \text{ lb}$$

Equilibrium Equations. We take moments about A to eliminate **T** and $\mathbf{R}_1$ from the computation.

$+\circlearrowleft \Sigma M_A = 0$:

$$-(2{,}320 \text{ lb})(25 \text{ in.}) - (4{,}980 \text{ lb})(6 \text{ in.}) + R_2(50 \text{ in.}) = 0$$

$$R_2 = +1{,}758 \text{ lb} \qquad \mathbf{R}_2 = 1{,}758 \text{ lb} \nearrow \blacktriangleleft$$

Now, taking moments about B to eliminate **T** and $\mathbf{R}_2$ from the computation, we write

$+\circlearrowleft \Sigma M_B = 0$: $\quad (2{,}320 \text{ lb})(25 \text{ in.}) - (4{,}980 \text{ lb})(6 \text{ in.}) - R_1(50 \text{ in.}) = 0$

$$R_1 = +562 \text{ lb} \qquad \mathbf{R}_1 = 562 \text{ lb} \nearrow \blacktriangleleft$$

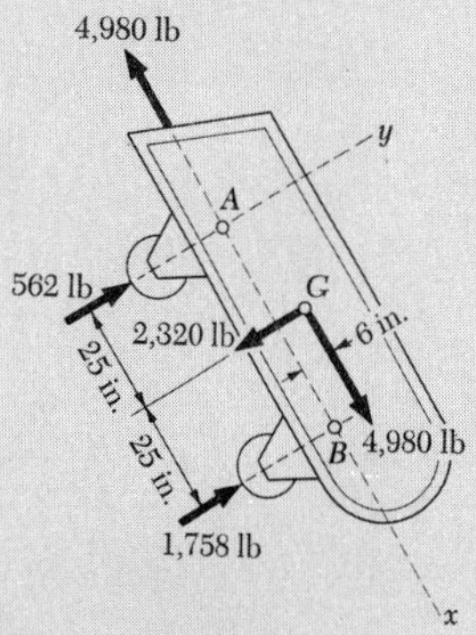

The value of T is found by writing

$\searrow +\Sigma F_x = 0$: $\quad +4{,}980 \text{ lb} - T = 0$

$$T = +4{,}980 \text{ lb} \qquad \mathbf{T} = 4{,}980 \text{ lb} \nwarrow \blacktriangleleft$$

The computed values of the reactions are shown in the adjacent sketch.

Check. The computations are verified by writing

$$\nearrow +\Sigma F_y = +562 \text{ lb} + 1{,}758 \text{ lb} - 2{,}320 \text{ lb} = 0$$

A check could also have been obtained by computing moments about any point except A or B.

SAMPLE PROBLEM 4.4

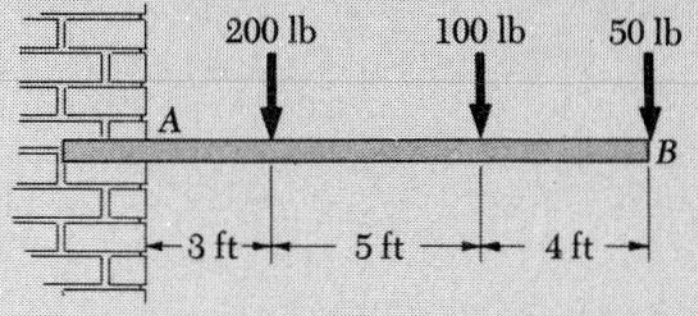

A cantilever beam is loaded as shown. The beam is fixed at the left end and free at the right end. Determine the reaction at the fixed end.

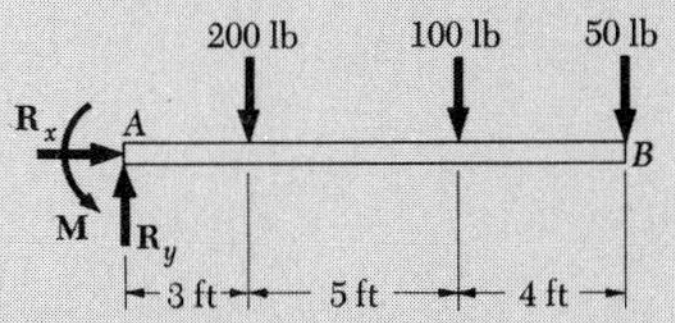

Solution. The portion of the beam which is embedded in the wall is subjected to a large number of forces. These forces, however, are equivalent to a force of components $\mathbf{R}_x$ and $\mathbf{R}_y$ and a couple **M**.

Equilibrium Equations

$\overset{+}{\rightarrow} \Sigma F_x = 0$: $\quad R_x = 0 \qquad \mathbf{R}_x = 0$ ◄

$+\uparrow \Sigma F_y = 0$: $\quad R_y - 200\text{ lb} - 100\text{ lb} - 50\text{ lb} = 0$

$R_y = +350\text{ lb} \qquad \mathbf{R}_y = 350\text{ lb}\uparrow$ ◄

$+\circlearrowleft \Sigma M_A = 0$:

$$-(200\text{ lb})(3\text{ ft}) - (100\text{ lb})(8\text{ ft}) - (50\text{ lb})(12\text{ ft}) + M = 0$$

$M = +2{,}000\text{ lb-ft} \qquad \mathbf{M} = 2{,}000\text{ lb-ft}\circlearrowleft$ ◄

The reaction at the fixed end consists of a vertical upward force of 350 lb and of a 2,000-lb-ft counterclockwise couple.

Check. The results may be checked by computing moments about any point. Choosing point B, we write

$$+\circlearrowleft \Sigma M_B = 2{,}000\text{ lb-ft} - (350\text{ lb})(12\text{ ft}) + (200\text{ lb})(9\text{ ft}) + (100\text{ lb})(4\text{ ft}) = 0$$

SAMPLE PROBLEM 4.5

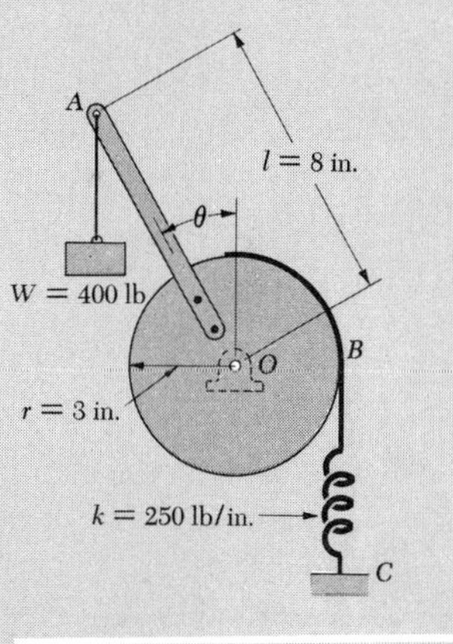

A 400-lb weight is attached to the lever AO as shown. The constant of the spring BC is $k = 250$ lb/in., and the spring is unstretched when $\theta = 0$. Determine the position or positions of equilibrium.

Solution. *Force Exerted by Spring.* Denoting by s the deflection of the spring from its undeformed position, and noting that $s = r\theta$, we write

$$F = ks = kr\theta$$

Equilibrium Equation. Summing the moments of **W** and **F** about O, we write

$+\circlearrowleft \Sigma M_O = 0$: $\quad Wl \sin\theta - r(kr\theta) = 0 \qquad \sin\theta = \dfrac{kr^2}{Wl}\theta$

Substituting the given data, we obtain

$$\sin\theta = \frac{(250\text{ lb/in.})(3\text{ in.})^2}{(400\text{ lb})(8\text{ in.})}\theta \qquad \sin\theta = 0.703\theta$$

Solving by trial and error, we find

$\theta = 0 \qquad \theta = 80.4°$ ◄

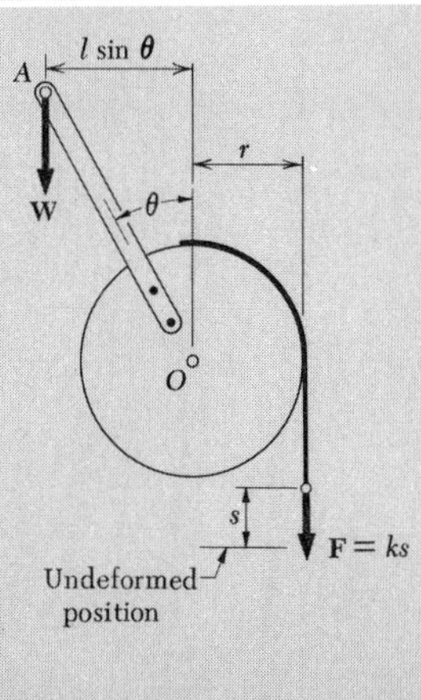

PROBLEMS

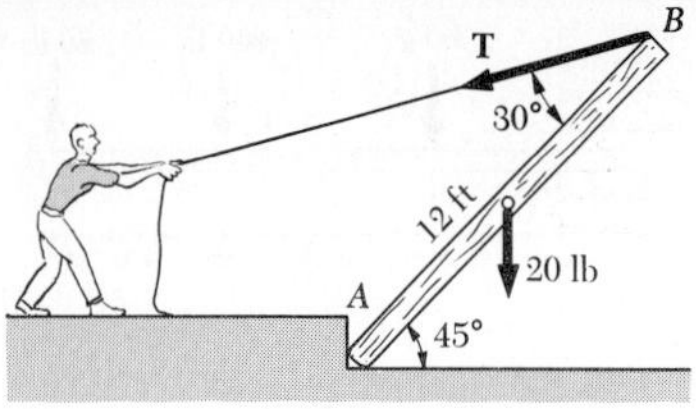

FIG. P 4.1

4.1. A man raises a 12-ft joist weighing 20 lb by pulling on a rope. Find the tension T in the rope and the reaction at A.

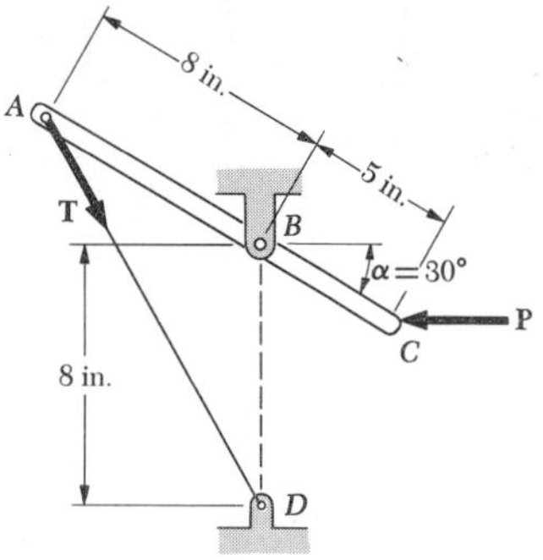

FIG. P 4.2

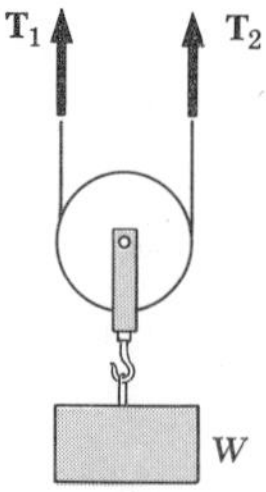

FIG. P 4.3

4.2. A 13-in. lever is hinged at B and attached to a control cable at A. Knowing that the magnitude of the force **P** is 400 lb, find the tension in the cable and the reaction at B.

4.3. A load W is supported by the pulley as shown. Prove that, if the pulley is in equilibrium, the tensions T_1 and T_2 are both equal to $W/2$.

4.4. The chain hoist shown may be used to raise a weight W by pulling on the free end of the chain with a smaller force **T**. (*a*) Derive an expression for the magnitude of **T** in terms of W, r_1, and r_2. (*b*) If $W = 3$ tons, $r_1 = 7$ in., and $r_2 = 7.5$ in., determine the magnitude of the required force **T**.

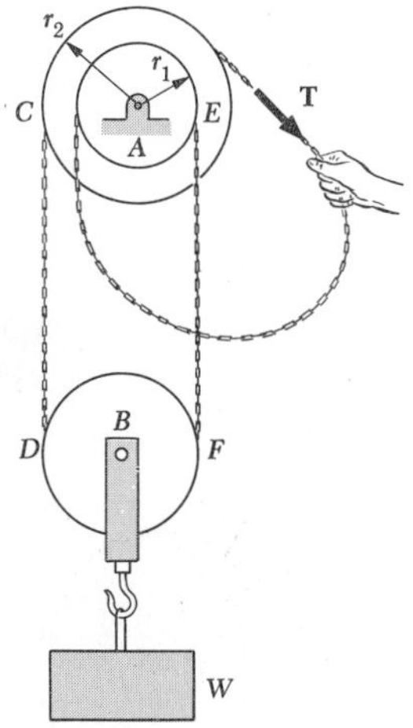

FIG. P 4.4

4.5. The ladder AB, of length L and weight W, can be raised by the cable BC. Determine the tension T required to raise end B just off the floor (*a*) in terms of W and θ, (*b*) if $h = 8$ ft, $L = 10$ ft, and $W = 35$ lb.

4.6. A vertical force **P** is applied to the handle of a winch of weight W. Determine the tension in the hoisting cable (*a*) in terms of P, W, r, a, and θ, (*b*) if $P = 40$ lb, $W = 20$ lb, $r = 4$ in., $a = 12$ in., and $\theta = 75°$.

4.7. Two links AB and CD are connected by a bell crank as shown. The tension in link AB is 100 lb. Determine the tension in CD and the reaction at O.

4.8. Find the maximum force which may be safely exerted by link AB on the bell crank if the maximum allowable value for the reaction at O is 500 lb.

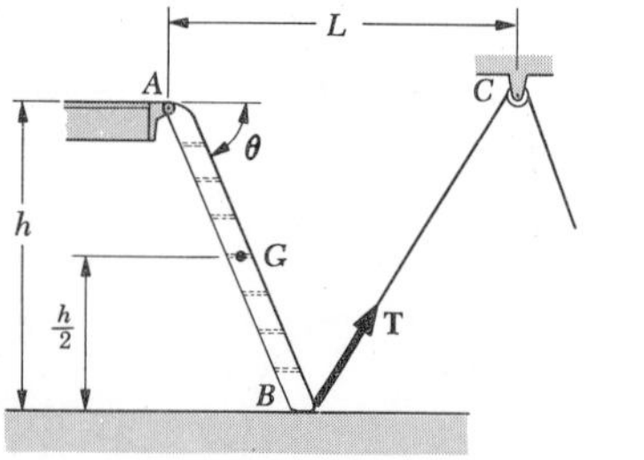

FIG. P 4.5

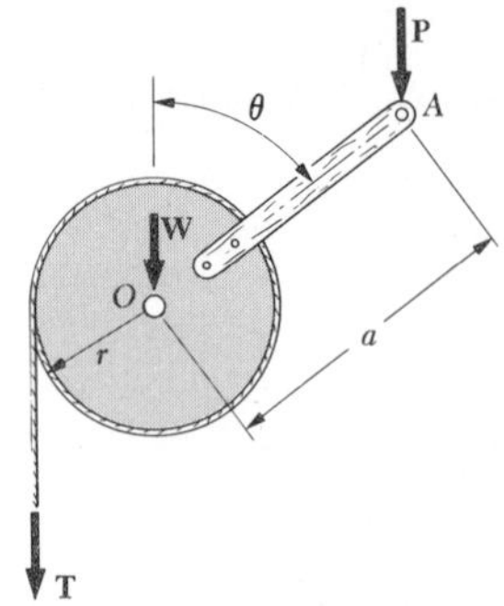

FIG. P 4.6

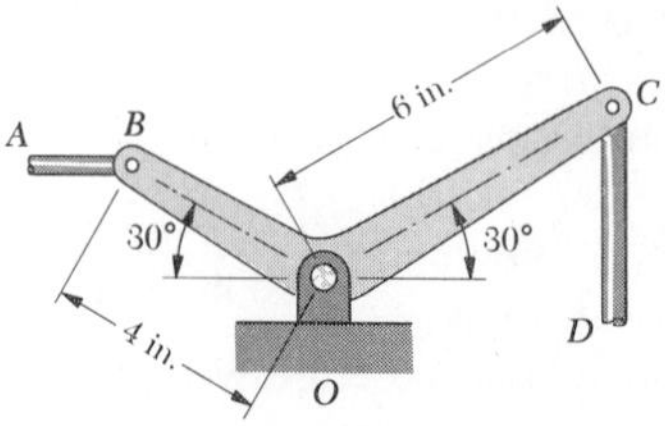

FIG. P 4.7 AND P 4.8

4.9. Determine the reactions at A and B for the truss and loading shown. Note that the roller rests on a 30° incline.

4.10. Determine the reactions at A and B for the truss of Prob. 4.9, if the horizontal 4-kip load is directed to the left.

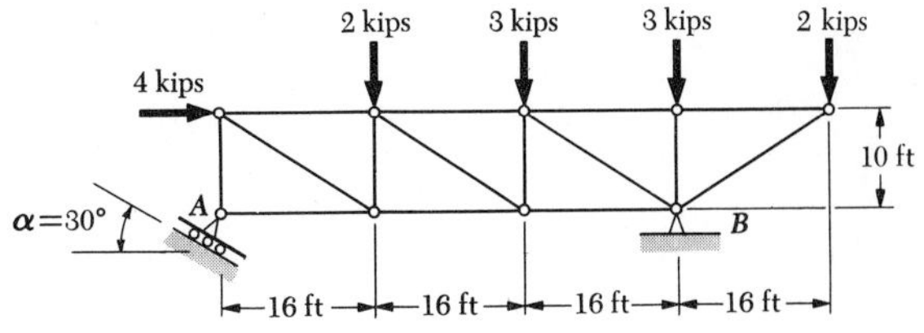

FIG. P 4.9

4.11. Determine the reactions at A and B for the truss of Prob. 4.9, if the horizontal 4-kip load is removed.

4.12. Determine the reaction at A and B for the truss and loading of Prob. 4.9, if the roller at A rests on a horizontal plane.

4.13. A movable bracket is held at rest by a cable attached at C and by frictionless rollers at A and B. For the loading shown, determine the tension in the cable and the reactions at A and B.

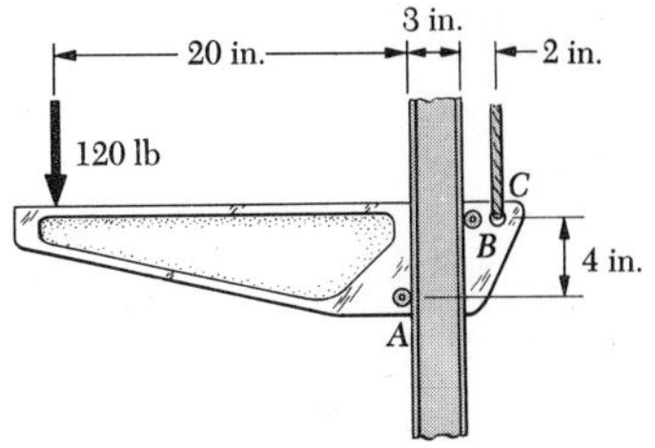

FIG. P 4.13

4.14. A light bar AD is suspended from a cable BE and supports an 800-lb load at point C. The extremities A and D of the bar are in contact with smooth, vertical walls. (*a*) If $d = 8$ in., determine the tension in cable BE and the reactions at A and D. (*b*) Find the maximum distance d which may be safely used if the maximum allowable value for the reaction at A is 500 lb.

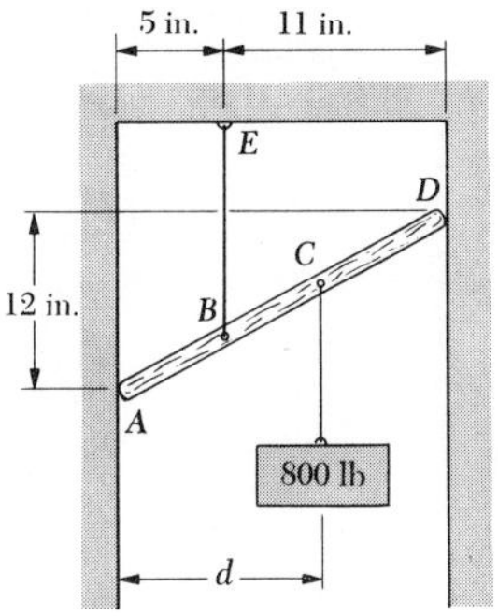

FIG. P 4.14

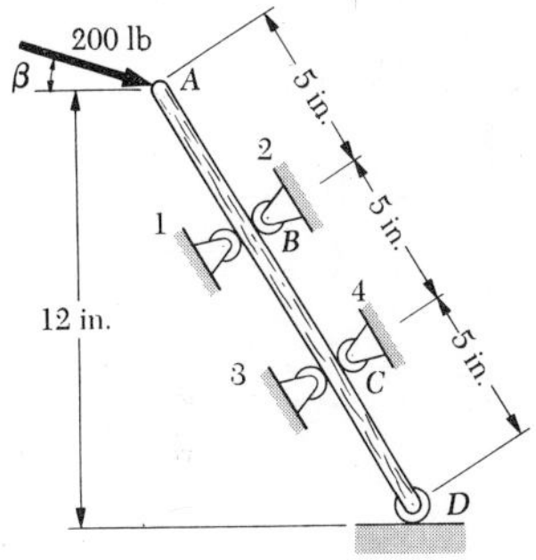

FIG. P 4.15

4.15. A light rod, supported by rollers at B, C, and D, is subjected to a 200-lb force applied at A. If $\beta = 0$, determine (*a*) the reactions at B, C, and D, (*b*) the rollers which may safely be removed for this loading.

4.16. Solve Prob. 4.15 when the 200-lb force is directed vertically downward, i.e., when $\beta = 90°$.

4.17. A man holds a 3-ft wooden bar at both ends while another man tightens screws into the bar with a screw driver, applying a couple of magnitude 10 lb-ft. Find the smallest forces that the first man may apply to hold the bar in place while a screw is being tightened (*a*) in the middle of the bar, (*b*) 1 ft from the end of the bar.

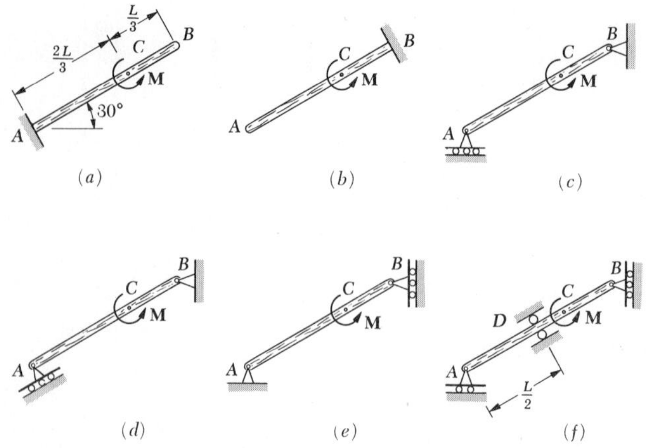

FIG. P 4.18

4.18. A couple **M** is applied to a bar of length L which may be supported in six different ways as shown. In each case determine the reactions at the supports.

4.19. Determine the reactions at the points of support of the pulley assembly of Prob. 3.50, assuming in turn the following types of connections: (*a*) a pin in a fitted hole at A and a pin in a horizontal slot at C, (*b*) a pin in a fitted hole at A and a pin in a vertical slot at D, (*c*) a tightly clinched rivet at A.

4.20. Determine the reactions at the points of support of the pulley assembly of Prob. 3.50, assuming in turn the following types of connections: (*a*) a pin in a horizontal slot at B and a pin in a fitted hole at D, (*b*) a pin in a vertical slot at B and a pin in a fitted hole at D, (*c*) a tightly clinched rivet at B.

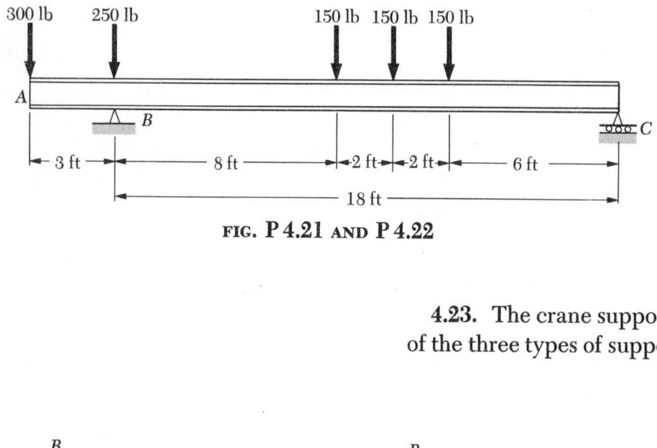

FIG. P 4.21 AND P 4.22

4.21. Determine the reactions at B and C for the beam and loading shown.

4.22. Assuming that the maximum allowable value of the reaction at B is 2,000 lb and that the reaction at C must be directed upward, determine the largest additional downward force **P** which may safely be applied at point A.

4.23. The crane supports a 500-lb load. Find the reactions for each of the three types of supports shown.

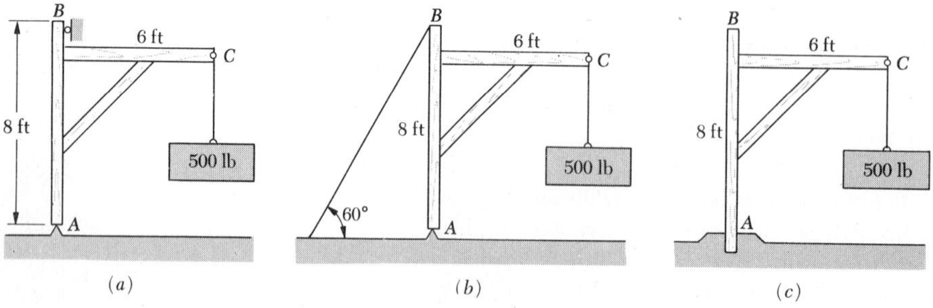

FIG. P 4.23

4.24. A slender, uniform bar is 24 in. long and weighs 15 lb. Determine the reactions for each of the four types of supports shown.

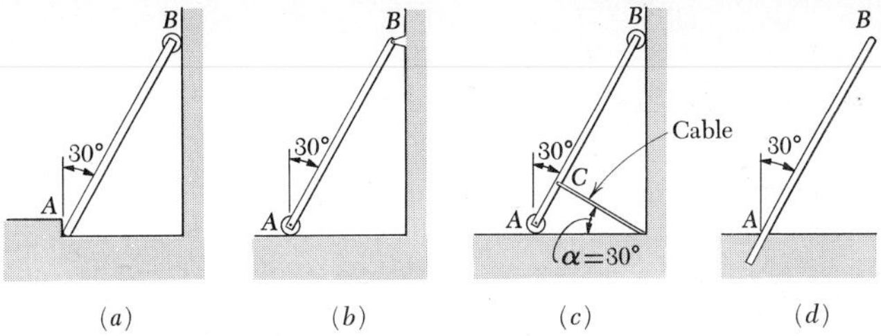

FIG. P 4.24

4.25. Determine the reactions at the points of support of the angle bracket of Prob. 3.82, assuming in turn the following types of connections: (*a*) a pin in a fitted hole at *A* and a pin in a horizontal slot at *B*, (*b*) a pin in a horizontal slot at *A* and a pin in a fitted hole at *B*, (*c*) a firmly clinched rivet at *B*.

4.26. Determine the reactions at the points of support of the angle bracket of Prob. 3.82, assuming in turn the following types of connections: (*a*) a pin in a fitted hole at *A* and a pin in a vertical slot at *C*, (*b*) a pin in a horizontal slot at *A* and a pin in a fitted hole at *C*, (*c*) a firmly clinched rivet at *C*.

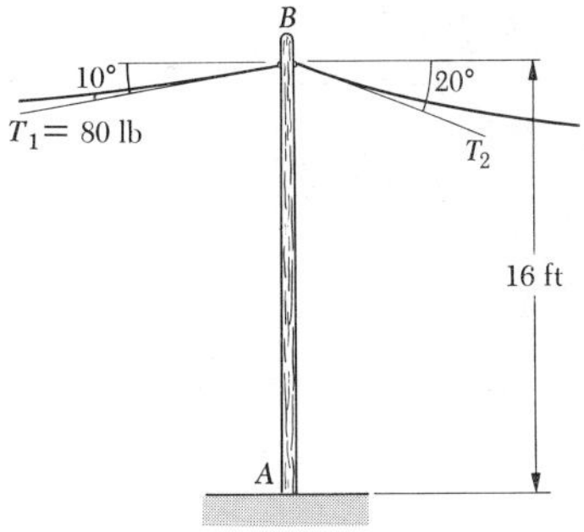

FIG. P 4.27

4.27. A 16-ft telephone pole weighing 300 lb is used to support the ends of two wires. The tension in the wire to the left is 80 lb and, at the point of support, the wire forms an angle of 10° with the horizontal. (*a*) If the tension T_2 is zero, determine the reaction at the base *A*. (*b*) Determine the largest and smallest allowable tension T_2, if the magnitude of the couple at *A* may not exceed 600 lb-ft.

4.28. A workbench seat *ABC* is held in the position shown by a vertical bar *DE* and supports a 175-lb man. (*a*) Determine the reaction at *A*. (*b*) If the inside diameter of the collar is slightly larger than the bar, the collar will bear only at points *G* and *H*. Determine the magnitude of the horizontal forces developed at *G* and *H*.

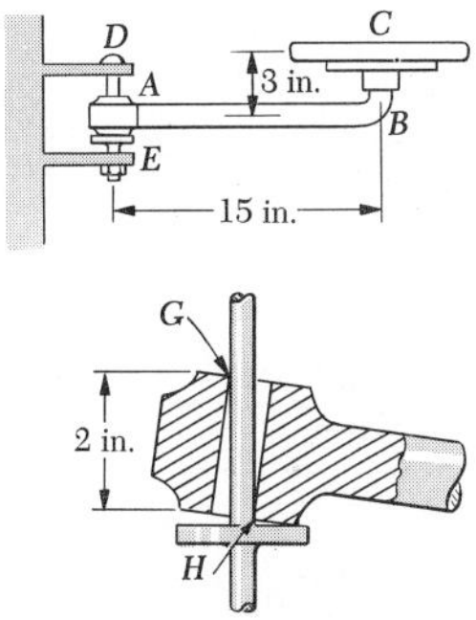

FIG. P 4.28

4.29. In the pivoted motor mount, or Rockwood drive, the weight of the motor is used to maintain tension in the drive belt. When the motor is at rest, the tensions T_1 and T_2 may be assumed equal. The weight of the motor is 175 lb, and the diameter of the drive pulley is 6 in. Assuming that the weight of the platform *AB* is negligible, determine the tension in the belt and the reaction at *C* when the motor is at rest.

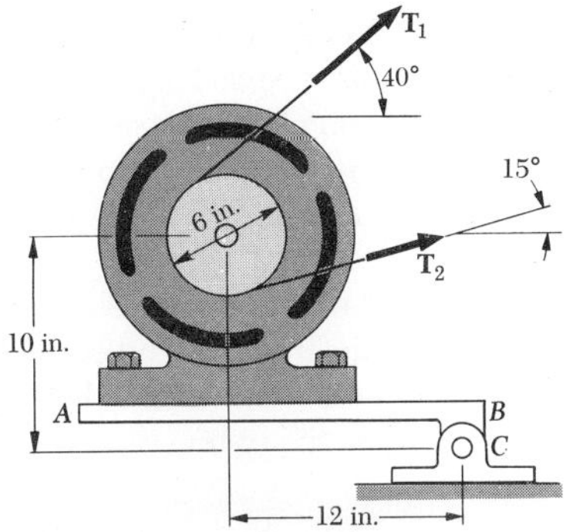

FIG. P 4.29

4.30. A force **P** of magnitude 40 lb is applied to the end of a beam *AB* which is supported by a smooth pin at *D* and by the cable *ACB*. Since the cable passes over a pulley at *C*, the tension may be assumed to be the same in the portions *AC* and *BC* of the cable. Determine the tension in the cable and the reaction at *D*.

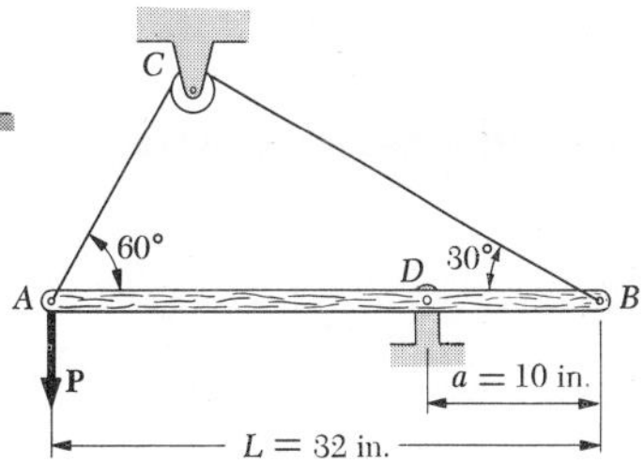

FIG. P 4.30

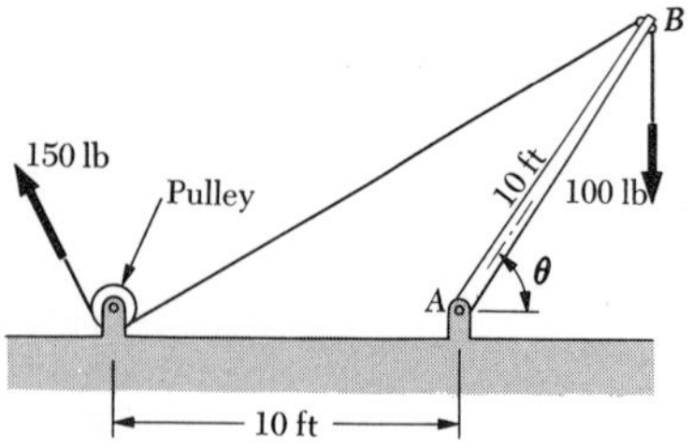

FIG. P 4.31

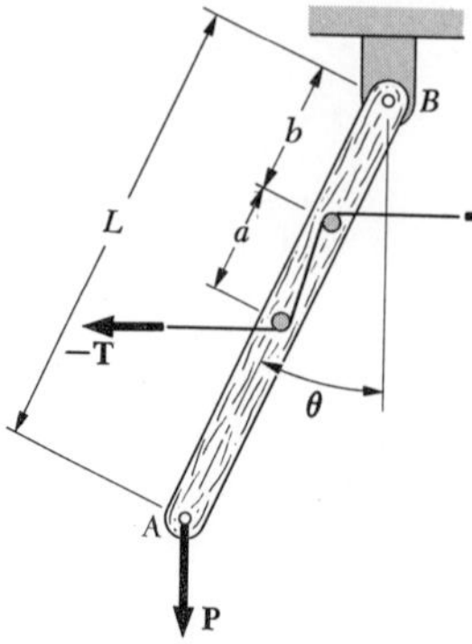

FIG. P 4.33

*4.31. Find the angle θ for which the boom AB is in equilibrium. Neglect the weight of the boom.

*4.32. Solve Prob. 4.31 assuming that the 100-lb force applied at B is directed horizontally to the right.

*4.33. The control rod AB is acted upon by the vertical force **P** and by two forces of magnitude T exerted by the cable which passes over frictionless pulleys of negligible diameter. Assuming that the free ends of the cable remain horizontal, determine the value of θ corresponding to equilibrium.

*4.34. For the control rod of Prob. 4.33 the following values are given: $L = 20$ in., $a = 8$ in., $b = 5$ in., $T = 150$ lb, and $P = 100$ lb. If possible, determine the value of θ corresponding to equilibrium (*a*) neglecting the diameter of the pulleys, (*b*) assuming that the diameter of each pulley is 1 in., (*c*) neglecting the diameter of the pulleys and assuming that the force **P** is directed horizontally to the right.

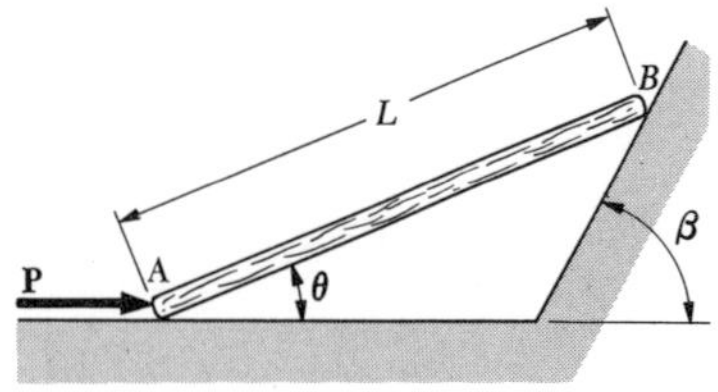

FIG. P 4.35

*4.35. A uniform, slender rod of length L and weight W is held in the position shown by the horizontal force **P**. Knowing that both the floor at A and the surface at B are smooth, determine the angle θ corresponding to equilibrium (*a*) in terms of P, W, L, and β, (*b*) if $P = 10$ lb, $W = 20$ lb, $L = 30$ in., and $\beta = 60°$.

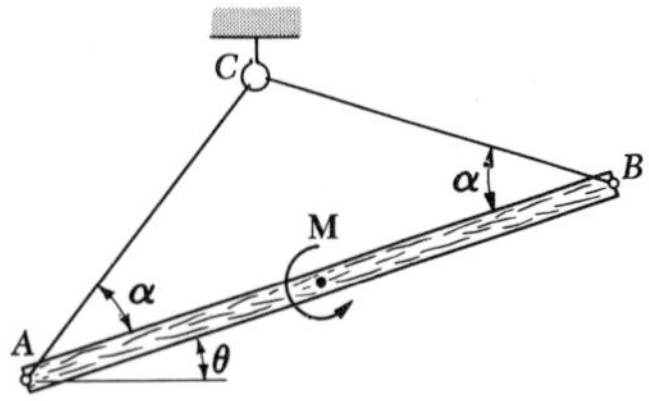

FIG. P 4.36

*4.36. A uniform rod of length L and weight W is suspended by two cords of equal length. If a couple **M** is applied to the rod, find the angle θ formed by the axis of the rod and the horizontal. Also, prove that if both cords are to remain taut, the magnitude of **M** must be less than $\frac{1}{2}WL \sin \alpha$.

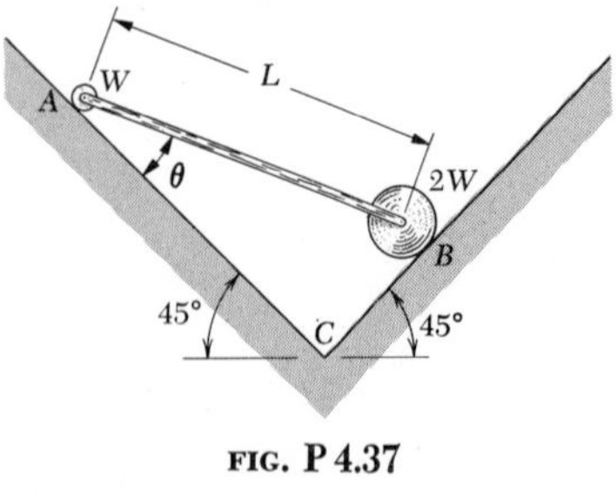

FIG. P 4.37

*4.37. Two wheels A and B, of weight W and $2W$, respectively, are connected by a rod of negligible weight and are free to roll on 45° inclines. Determine the angle θ that the rod forms with the incline AC when the system is in equilibrium.

*4.38. In the problems listed below, the rigid bodies considered were completely constrained and the reactions were statically determinate. For each of these rigid bodies it is possible to create an improper set of constraints by changing either a dimension of the body or the direction of a reaction. In each problem determine the value of α or of a which results in improper constraints. (*a*) Prob. 4.2, (*b*) Prob. 4.9, (*c*) Prob. 4.24*c*, (*d*) Prob. 4.30.

4.39. Twelve identical rectangular plates, 2 by 3 ft, weighing 100 lb each, are held in a vertical plane as shown. All connections consist of smooth pins, rollers, or short links. In each case, determine whether (*a*) the plate is completely, partially, or improperly constrained, (*b*) the reactions are statically determinate or indeterminate, (*c*) the equilibrium of the plate is maintained in the position shown. Also, wherever possible, compute the reactions.

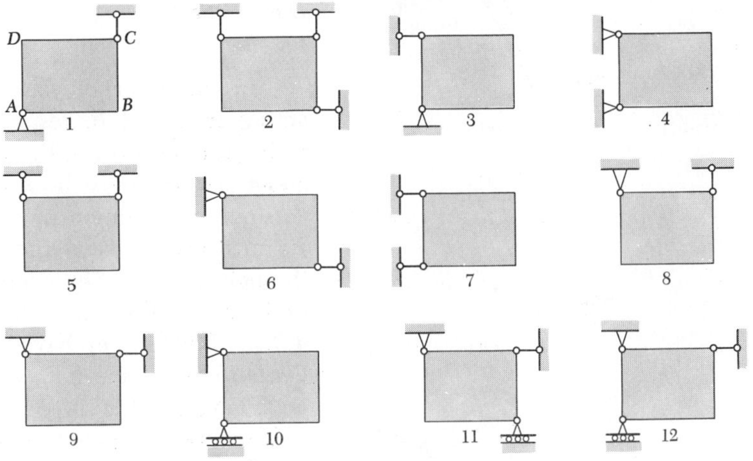

FIG. P 4.39

4.40. A small truss is supported in eight different ways as shown. All connections consist of smooth pins, rollers, or short links. For each structure, answer the questions listed in Prob. 4.39, and, wherever possible, compute the reactions, assuming that the magnitude of the force **P** is 10 kips.

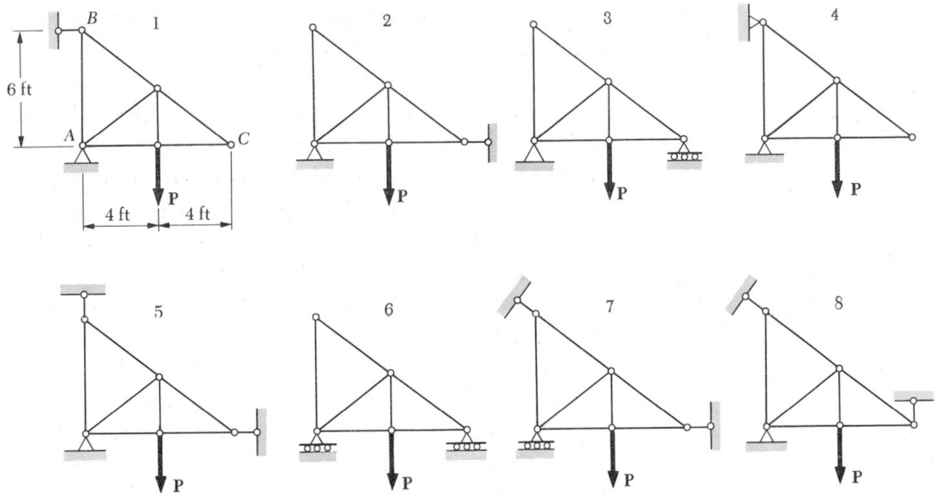

FIG. P 4.40

4.6. Equilibrium of a Two-force Body. A particular case of equilibrium which is of considerable interest is that of a rigid body subjected to two forces. Such a body is commonly called a *two-force body*. We shall show that, *if a two-force body is in equilibrium, the two forces must have the same magnitude, same line of action, and opposite sense.*

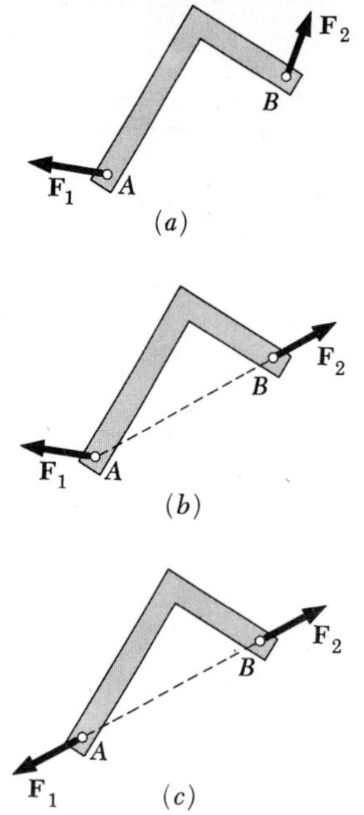

FIG. 4.8

Consider a corner plate subjected to two forces $\mathbf{F}_1$ and $\mathbf{F}_2$ acting at A and B, respectively (Fig. 4.8*a*). If the plate is to be in equilibrium, the sum of the moments of $\mathbf{F}_1$ and $\mathbf{F}_2$ about any axis must be zero. First, we sum moments about A: since the moment of $\mathbf{F}_1$ is obviously zero, the moment of $\mathbf{F}_2$ must also be zero and the line of action of $\mathbf{F}_2$ must pass through A (Fig. 4.8*b*). Summing moments about B, we prove similarly that the line of action of $\mathbf{F}_1$ must pass through B (Fig. 4.8*c*). Both forces have the same line of action (line AB). From the equation $\Sigma F_x = 0$ or $\Sigma F_y = 0$, it is seen that they must have also the same magnitude but opposite sense.

If several forces act at two points A and B, the forces acting at A may be replaced by their resultant $\mathbf{F}_1$ and those acting at B by their resultant $\mathbf{F}_2$. Thus a two-force body may be more generally defined as *a rigid body subjected to forces acting at only two points.* The resultants $\mathbf{F}_1$ and $\mathbf{F}_2$ then must have the same line of action, same magnitude, and opposite sense.

Although problems dealing with the equilibrium of two-force bodies may be solved by the general methods studied in the preceding sections, it is sometimes desirable to make use of the property we have just established to simplify certain problems so that simple trigonometric or geometric relations can be used.

4.7. Equilibrium of a Three-force Body. Another case of equilibrium that is of great interest is that of a *three-force body,* i.e., a rigid body subjected to three forces or, more generally, *a rigid body subjected to forces acting at only three points.* Consider a rigid body subjected to a system of forces which may be reduced to three forces $\mathbf{F}_1$, $\mathbf{F}_2$, and $\mathbf{F}_3$ acting at A, B, and C, respectively (Fig. 4.9*a*). We shall show that, if the body is in equilibrium, *the lines of action of the three forces must be either concurrent or parallel.*

Since the rigid body is in equilibrium, the sum of the moments of $\mathbf{F}_1$, $\mathbf{F}_2$, and $\mathbf{F}_3$ about any axis must be zero. Assuming that the lines of action of $\mathbf{F}_1$ and $\mathbf{F}_2$ intersect, and denoting their point of intersection by D, we sum moments about D (Fig. 4.9*b*); since the moments of $\mathbf{F}_1$ and $\mathbf{F}_2$ about D are zero, the moment of $\mathbf{F}_3$ about D must also be zero and the line of action of $\mathbf{F}_3$ must pass through D (Fig. 4.9*c*). The three lines of action are concurrent. The only exception occurs when none of the lines intersect; the lines of action must then be parallel.

Although problems concerning three-force bodies may be solved by the general methods of Secs. 4.3 to 4.5, the property just established may be used to solve them either graphically or from simple trigonometric or geometric relations.

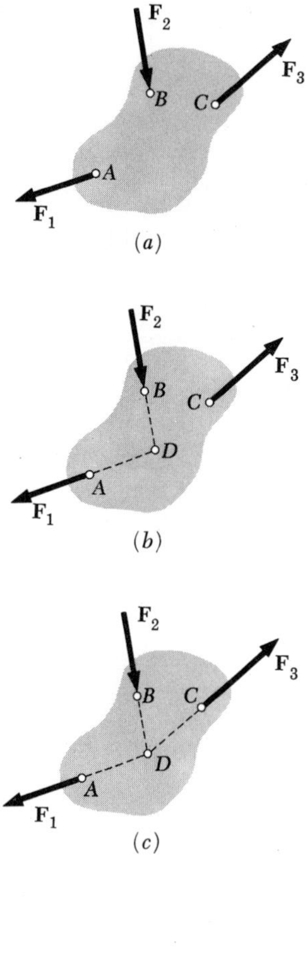

FIG. 4.9

SAMPLE PROBLEM 4.6

A 500-lb cylindrical tank, 8 ft in diameter, is to be raised over a 2-ft obstruction. A cable is wrapped around the tank and pulled horizontally as shown. The corner of the obstruction at A is rough. Find the required tension in the cable and the reaction at A.

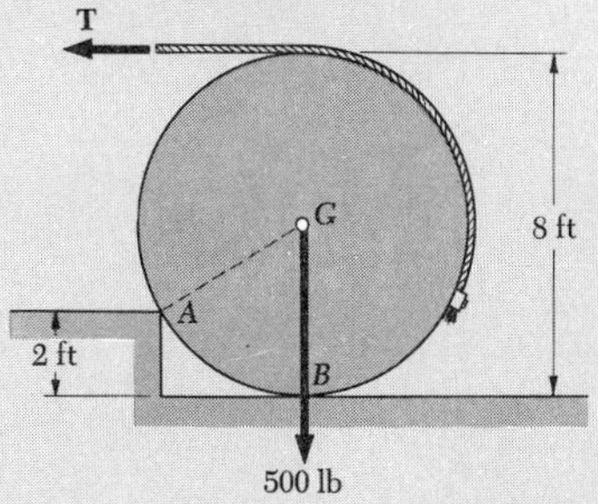

Solution. When the tank is just about to be raised, there is no force acting at B. Since the corner at A is rough, the reaction **R** is of unknown magnitude and direction. The only other forces acting on the tank are its 500-lb weight and the force **T** exerted by the cable. The tank is thus a three-force body, and the three forces must be concurrent. The reaction **R**, therefore, will pass through the point of intersection C of the lines of action of the 500-lb weight and the tension force **T**.

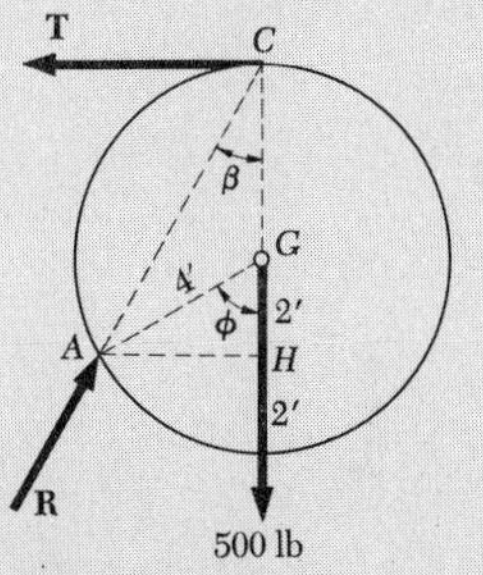

We compute

$$\cos\phi = \frac{GH}{AG} = \frac{2\text{ ft}}{4\text{ ft}} = 0.500 \qquad \phi = 60°$$

Since β is the corresponding inscribed angle, we find

$$\beta = \frac{\phi}{2} = 30°$$

A force triangle is drawn as shown, and we compute

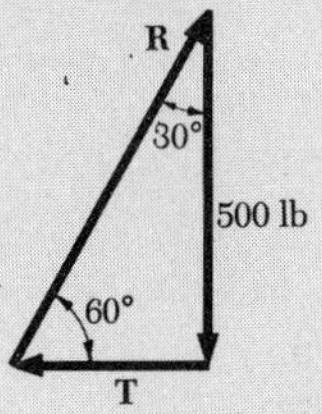

$$T = (500\text{ lb})\tan 30° \qquad T = 288\text{ lb} \blacktriangleleft$$

$$R = \frac{500\text{ lb}}{\cos 30°} = 577\text{ lb} \qquad \mathbf{R} = 577\text{ lb} \angle 60° \blacktriangleleft$$

Remark. It should be noted that **R** is not normal to the surface of the tank. Therefore, the surfaces of the obstruction and of the tank must be rough if the tank is to be raised in the described manner. This point is discussed fully in Chap. 8.

PROBLEMS

4.41. Using the method of Sec. 4.7, solve Prob. 4.1.

4.42. Using the method of Sec. 4.7, solve Prob. 4.2.

4.43. Using the method of Sec. 4.7, solve Prob. 4.7.

4.44. Using the method of Sec. 4.7, solve Prob. 4.8.

4.45. Using the method of Sec. 4.7, solve Prob. 4.23*a* and *b*.

4.46. Using the method of Sec. 4.7, solve Prob. 4.24*a* and *b*.

4.47. In Prob. 4.15, determine (*a*) the value of β for which the reaction at *C* is zero, (*b*) the corresponding reactions at *B* and *D*.

4.48. In Prob. 4.15, determine (*a*) the value of β for which the reaction at *B* is zero, (*b*) the corresponding reactions at *C* and *D*.

4.49. A uniform plate girder weighs 6,000 lb. It is held by two crane cables as shown; the cable attached at *B* forms an angle of 30° with the vertical. If the girder is to be held in a horizontal position, determine the direction of the cable attached at *A* and the tension in each cable.

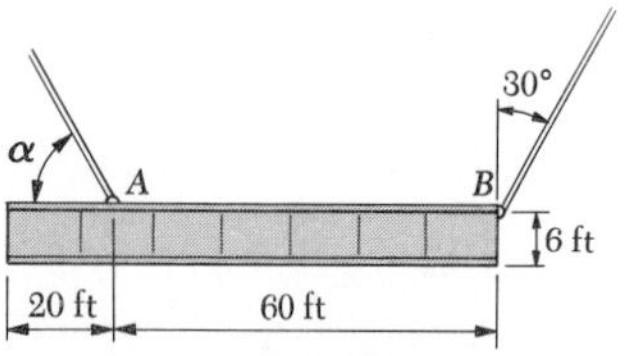

FIG. P4.49

4.50. A weight *W* is to be supported by the bell crank shown. Determine the horizontal force **P** which must be applied at *A* and the magnitude and direction of the reaction at *B*.

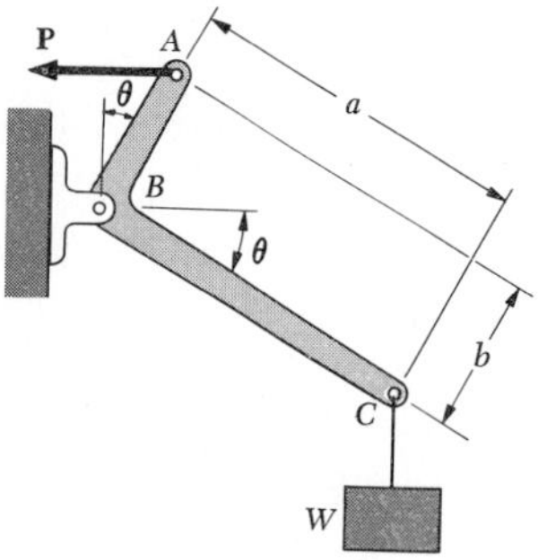

FIG. P4.50

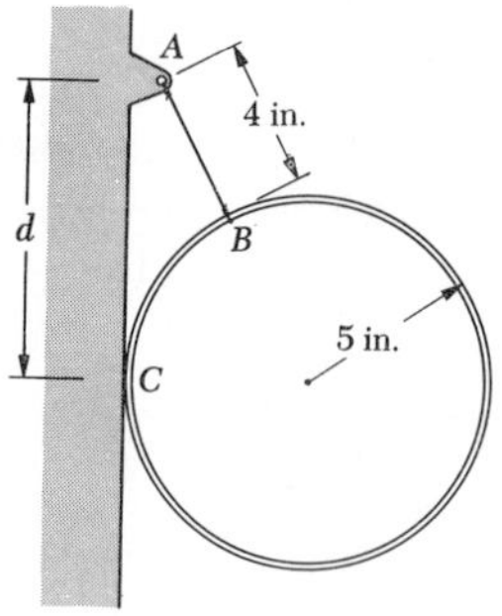

FIG. P4.51

4.51. A thin ring, of radius 5 in., weighs 3 lb and is held against a smooth wall by a 4-in. string *AB*. Determine the angle the string forms with the wall and the tension in the string. Also find the distance *d* and the reaction at *C*.

4.52. A 600-lb roller, 2 ft in diameter, is used on a lawn. Determine the force **F** required to make it roll over a 3-in. obstruction (*a*) if the roller is pushed as shown, (*b*) if the roller is pulled as shown.

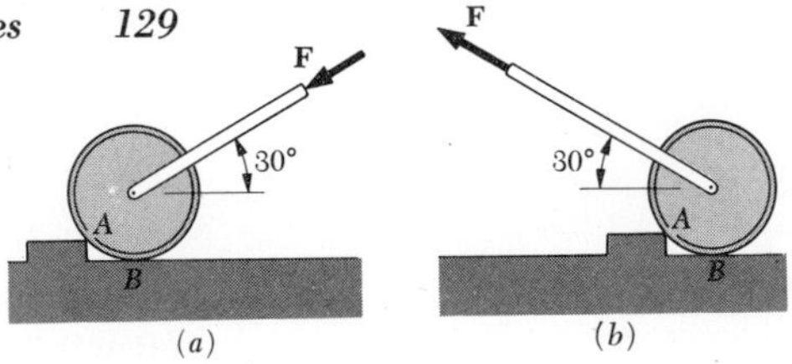

FIG. P 4.52

***4.53.** A slender rod of length $2r$ and weight W is attached to a collar at B and rests on a smooth circular cylinder of radius r. Knowing that the collar may slide freely along a vertical guide, determine the value of θ corresponding to equilibrium.

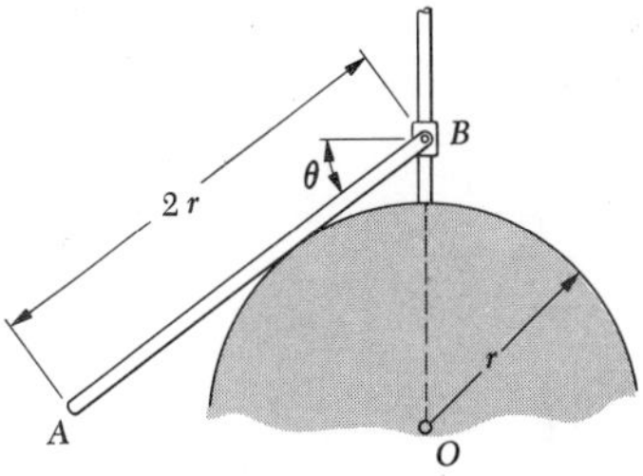

FIG. P 4.53

***4.54.** A slender rod AB of length L and weight W is held by a cable BC and by a pin at A which may slide in a smooth vertical slot. Determine the values of α and θ for which the rod is in equilibrium.

***4.55.** A 4-ft rod, of uniform cross section, is held in equilibrium as shown, with one end against a smooth, vertical wall and the other end attached to a cord. Find the length of the cord.

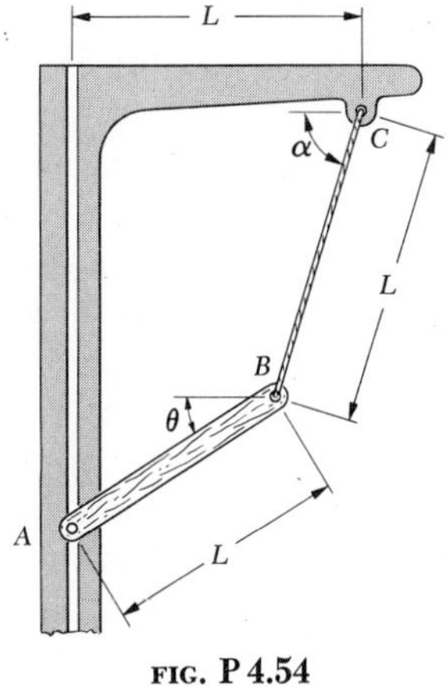

FIG. P 4.54

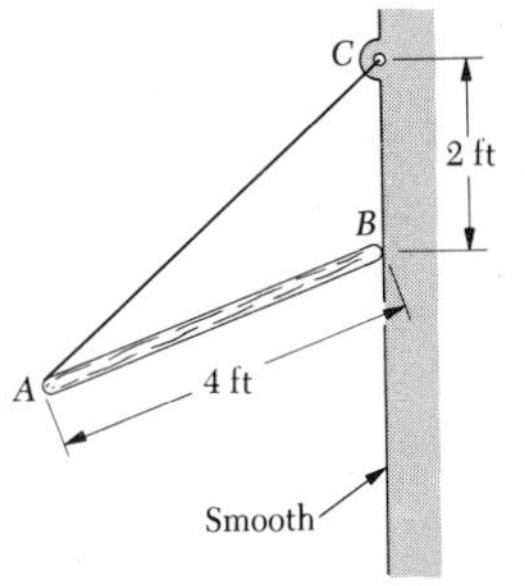

FIG. P 4.55

***4.56.** A slender rod of length L and weight W is lodged between a smooth wall and a smooth peg. Determine the angle θ between the rod and the wall corresponding to equilibrium.

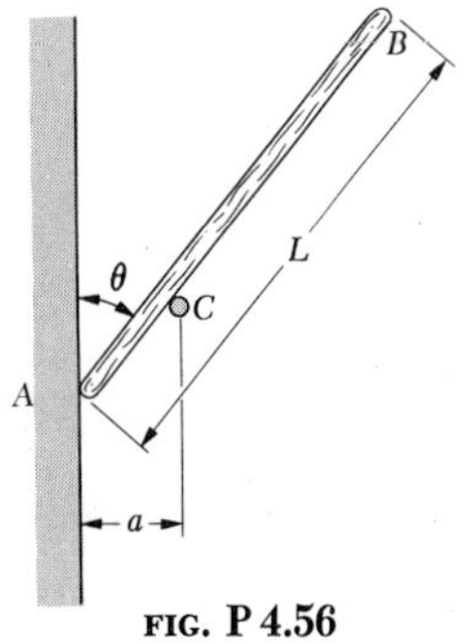

FIG. P 4.56

EQUILIBRIUM IN THREE DIMENSIONS

4.8. Reactions at Supports and Connections for a Three-dimensional Structure. The reactions on a three-dimensional structure range from the single force of known direction exerted by a smooth surface to the force-couple system exerted by a fixed support. Consequently, the number of unknowns associated with the reaction at a support or connection may vary from one to six in problems involving the equilibrium of a three-dimensional structure. Various types of supports and connections are shown in Fig. 4.10 with the corresponding reactions. A simple way of determining the type of reaction corresponding to a given support or connection and the number of unknowns involved is to find which of the six fundamental motions (translation in x, y, and z directions, rotation about the x, y, and z axes) are allowed and which motions are prevented.

Ball supports, smooth surfaces, and cables, for example, prevent translation in one direction only and thus exert a single force of known line of action; they each involve one unknown, namely, the magnitude of the reaction. Rollers on rough surfaces and wheels on rails prevent translation in two directions; the corresponding reactions consist of two unknown force components. Rough surfaces in direct contact and ball-and-socket supports prevent translation in three directions; these supports involve three unknown force components.

Some supports and connections may prevent rotation as well as translation; the corresponding reactions include, then, couples as well as forces. The reaction at a fixed support, for example, which prevents any motion (rotation as well as translation), consists of three unknown forces and three unknown couples. A universal joint, which is designed to allow rotation about two axes, will exert a reaction consisting of three unknown force components and one unknown couple.

Other supports and connections are primarily intended to prevent translation; their design, however, is such that they also prevent some rotations. The corresponding reactions consist essentially of force components but may also include couples. One group of supports of this type includes hinges and bearings designed to support radial loads only (for example, journal bearings, roller bearings). The corresponding reactions consist of two force components but may also include two couples. Another group includes pin-and-bracket supports, hinges, and bearings designed to support an axial thrust as well as a radial load (for example, ball bearings). The corresponding reactions

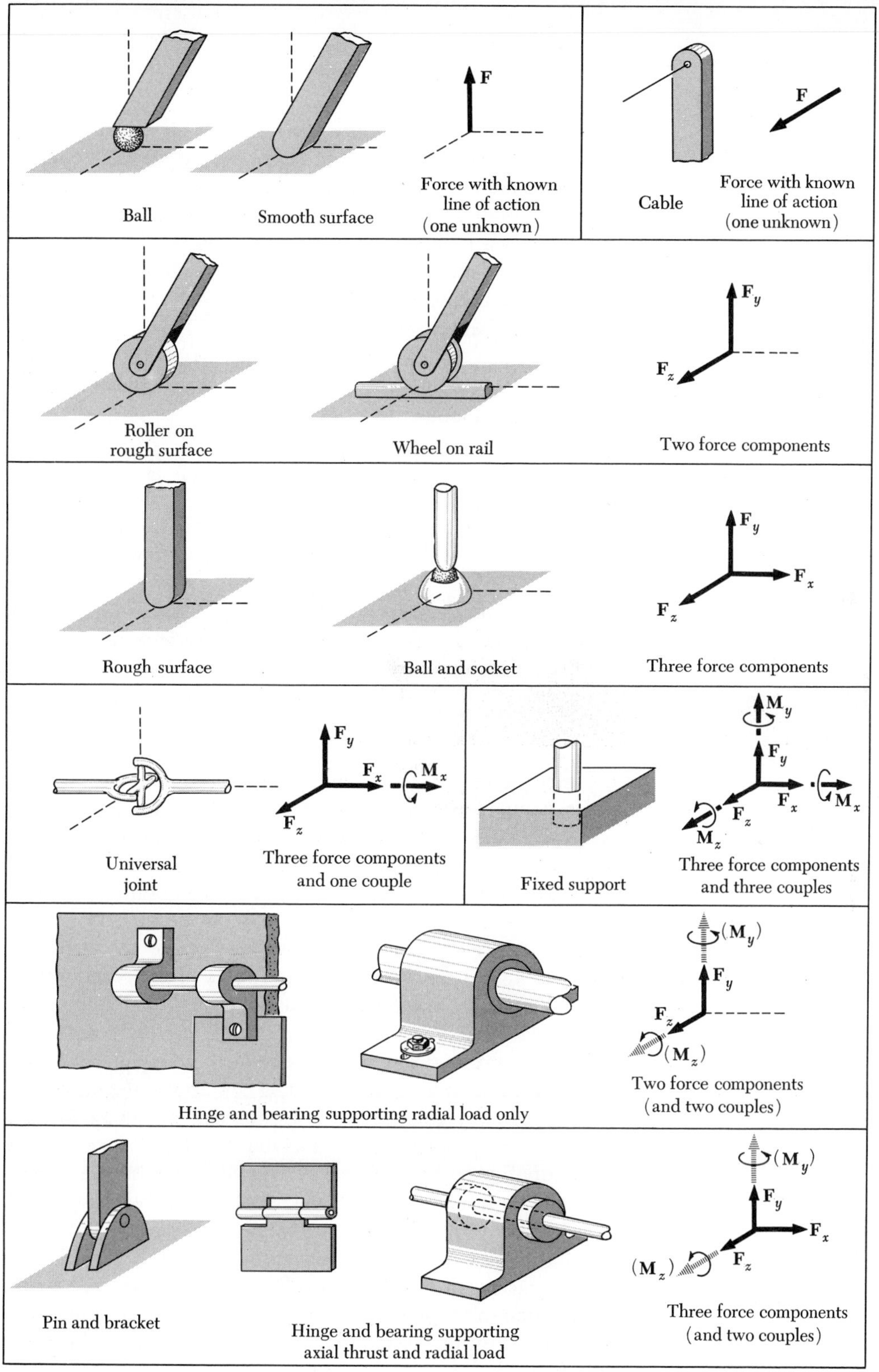

FIG. 4.10. Reactions at supports and connections

consist of three force components but may include two couples. However, these supports will not exert any appreciable couples under normal conditions of use. Therefore, only force components should be included in their analysis, unless it is found that couples are necessary to maintain the equilibrium of the rigid body, or unless the support is known to have been specifically designed to exert a couple.

4.9. Equilibrium of a Rigid Body in Three Dimensions. We saw in Sec. 4.1 that six scalar equations are required to express the conditions for the equilibrium of a rigid body in the general three-dimensional case.

$$\Sigma F_x = 0 \qquad \Sigma F_y = 0 \qquad \Sigma F_z = 0 \tag{4.2}$$
$$\Sigma M_x = 0 \qquad \Sigma M_y = 0 \qquad \Sigma M_z = 0 \tag{4.3}$$

These equations may be solved for no more than *six unknowns*, which generally will represent reactions at supports or connections.

In most problems the scalar equations (4.2) and (4.3) will be more conveniently obtained if we first express in vector form the conditions for the equilibrium of the rigid body considered. We write

$$\Sigma \mathbf{F} = 0 \qquad \Sigma \mathbf{M}_O = \Sigma(\mathbf{r} \times \mathbf{F}) = 0 \tag{4.1}$$

and express the forces **F** and position vectors **r** in terms of scalar components and unit vectors. Next we compute all vector products, either directly, or by means of determinants (see Sec. 3.7). Equating to zero the coefficients of the unit vectors in each of the two relations (4.1), we obtain the desired scalar equations.

If the reactions involve more than six unknowns, there are more unknowns than equations and some of the reactions are *statically indeterminate* (see Sample Prob. 4.9). If the reactions involve less than six unknowns, there are more equations than unknowns and some of the equations of equilibrium cannot be satisfied under general loading conditions; the rigid body is only *partially constrained.* Under the particular loading conditions corresponding to a given problem, however, the extra equations often reduce to trivial identities such as $0 = 0$ and may be disregarded; although only partially constrained, the rigid body remains in equilibrium (see Sample Probs. 4.7 and 4.8). Even with six or more unknowns, it is possible that some equations of equilibrium will not be satisfied. This may occur when the supports are such that the reactions are forces which must either be parallel or intersect the same line; the rigid body is then *improperly constrained.*

SAMPLE PROBLEM 4.7

A ladder used to reach high shelves in a storeroom is supported by two flanged wheels A and B mounted on a rail and by an unflanged wheel C resting against a rail fixed to the wall. A man stands on the ladder and leans to the right. The line of action of the 240-lb combined weight of the man and ladder intersects the floor at point D. Determine the components of the reactions at A, B, and C.

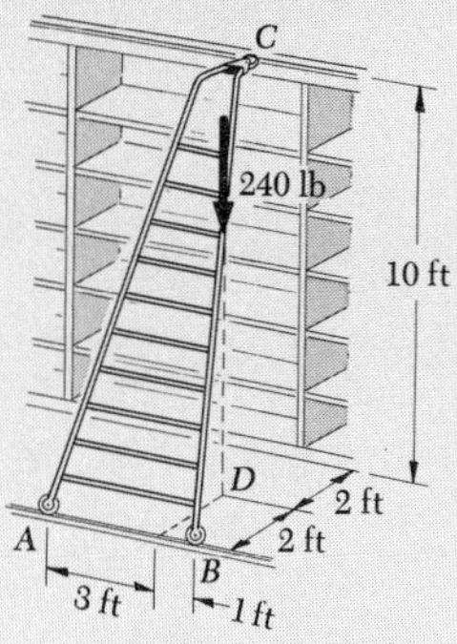

Solution. A free-body diagram of the ladder is drawn; there are five unknown reaction components, two at each flanged wheel and one at the unflanged wheel. The ladder is therefore only partially constrained; it is free to roll along the rails. It is, however, in equilibrium under the given vertical load since the equation $\Sigma F_x = 0$ is satisfied.

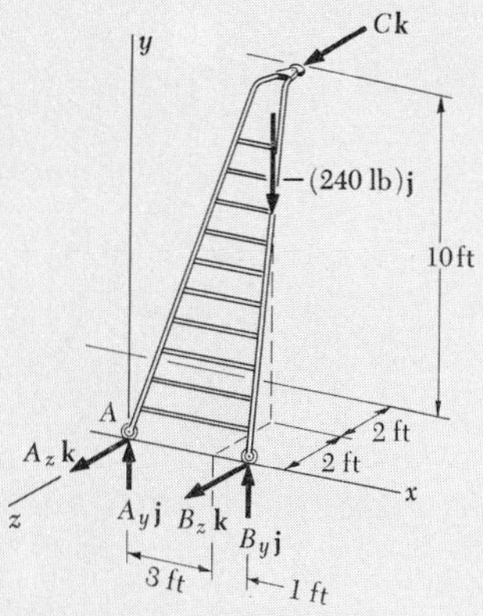

Since the ladder is in equilibrium, the forces acting on it must form a system equivalent to zero. We write therefore

$\Sigma \mathbf{F} = 0$:

$$A_y\mathbf{j} + A_z\mathbf{k} + B_y\mathbf{j} + B_z\mathbf{k} - (240 \text{ lb})\mathbf{j} + C\mathbf{k} = 0$$
$$(A_y + B_y - 240 \text{ lb})\mathbf{j} + (A_z + B_z + C)\mathbf{k} = 0 \qquad (1)$$

$\Sigma \mathbf{M}_A = \Sigma(\mathbf{r} \times \mathbf{F}) = 0$:

$$4\mathbf{i} \times (B_y\mathbf{j} + B_z\mathbf{k}) + (3\mathbf{i} - 2\mathbf{k}) \times (-240\mathbf{j}) + (2\mathbf{i} + 10\mathbf{j} - 4\mathbf{k}) \times C\mathbf{k} = 0$$

Computing the vector products, we have†

$$4B_y\mathbf{k} - 4B_z\mathbf{j} - 720\mathbf{k} - 480\mathbf{i} - 2C\mathbf{j} + 10C\mathbf{i} = 0$$
$$(10C - 480)\mathbf{i} - (4B_z + 2C)\mathbf{j} + (4B_y - 720)\mathbf{k} = 0 \qquad (2)$$

Setting the coefficients of **i**, **j**, **k** equal to zero in Eq. (2), we obtain the following three scalar equations, which express that the sum of the moments about each coordinate axis must be zero:

$$10C - 480 = 0 \qquad C = +48 \text{ lb} \quad ◄$$
$$4B_z + 2C = 0 \qquad B_z = -24 \text{ lb} \quad ◄$$
$$4B_y - 720 = 0 \qquad B_y = +180 \text{ lb} \quad ◄$$

Setting the coefficients of **j** and **k** equal to zero in Eq. (1), we obtain two scalar equations expressing that the sums of the components in the y and z directions are equal to zero. Substituting for B_y, B_z, and C the values obtained above, we write

$$A_y + B_y - 240 = 0 \qquad A_y + 180 - 240 = 0 \qquad A_y = +60 \text{ lb} \quad ◄$$
$$A_z + B_z + C = 0 \qquad A_z - 24 + 48 = 0 \qquad A_z = -24 \text{ lb} \quad ◄$$

†*Remark.* The moments in this Sample Problem and in Sample Probs. 4.8 and 4.9 could also be expressed in the form of determinants (see Sample Prob. 3.11, page 99).

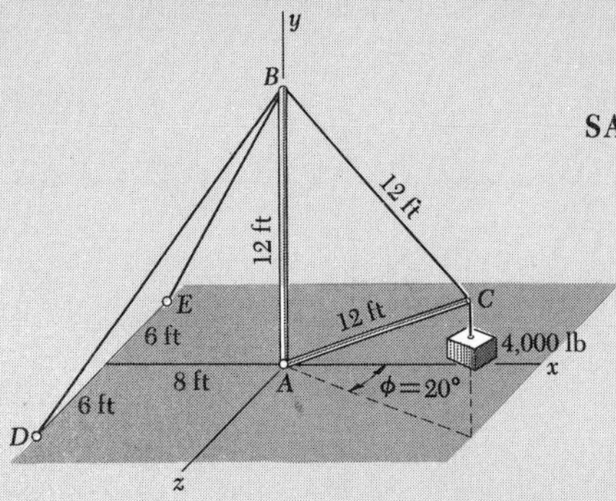

SAMPLE PROBLEM 4.8

The derrick shown supports a 4,000-lb load. It is held by a ball and socket at A and by two cables attached at points D and E. In the position shown, the derrick stands in a vertical plane forming an angle $\phi = 20°$ with the xy plane. Determine the tension in each cable and the components of the reaction at A.

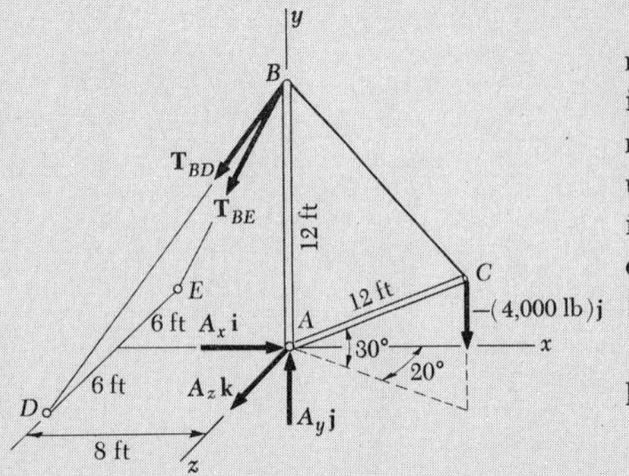

Solution. A free-body diagram of the derrick is drawn. Since the directions of the forces exerted at B by the cables are known, these forces involve one unknown each, namely, the magnitudes T_{BD} and T_{BE}. The reaction at A is a force of unknown direction and is represented by three unknown components. Since there are only five unknowns, the derrick is partially constrained. It may rotate freely about the y axis; it is, however, in equilibrium under the given loading since the equation $\Sigma M_y = 0$ is satisfied.

The components of the forces $\mathbf{T}_{BD}$ and $\mathbf{T}_{BE}$ may be obtained by proportions from the components of the vectors $\overrightarrow{BD}$ and $\overrightarrow{BE}$. We write

$$\overrightarrow{BD} = -(8\text{ ft})\mathbf{i} - (12\text{ ft})\mathbf{j} + (6\text{ ft})\mathbf{k} \qquad BD = 15.62\text{ ft}$$
$$\overrightarrow{BE} = -(8\text{ ft})\mathbf{i} - (12\text{ ft})\mathbf{j} - (6\text{ ft})\mathbf{k} \qquad BE = 15.62\text{ ft}$$
$$\mathbf{T}_{BD} = T_{BD}(\overrightarrow{BD}/BD) = T_{BD}(-0.512\mathbf{i} - 0.768\mathbf{j} + 0.384\mathbf{k})$$
$$\mathbf{T}_{BE} = T_{BE}(\overrightarrow{BE}/BE) = T_{BE}(-0.512\mathbf{i} - 0.768\mathbf{j} - 0.384\mathbf{k})$$

We also resolve the position vector of point C into rectangular components

$$\overrightarrow{AC} = (12\text{ ft})(\cos 30° \cos 20°\mathbf{i} + \sin 30°\mathbf{j} + \cos 30° \sin 20°\mathbf{k})$$

$$\overrightarrow{AC} = (9.77\text{ ft})\mathbf{i} + (6\text{ ft})\mathbf{j} + (3.55\text{ ft})\mathbf{k}$$

Since the derrick is in equilibrium, the forces acting on it must form a system equivalent to zero. We write therefore

$$\Sigma\mathbf{F} = 0: \quad A_x\mathbf{i} + A_y\mathbf{j} + A_z\mathbf{k} + \mathbf{T}_{BD} + \mathbf{T}_{BE} - (4{,}000\text{ lb})\mathbf{j} = 0$$
$$(A_x - 0.512T_{BD} - 0.512T_{BE})\mathbf{i}$$
$$+(A_y - 0.768T_{BD} - 0.768T_{BE} - 4{,}000\text{ lb})\mathbf{j}$$
$$+(A_z + 0.384T_{BD} - 0.384T_{BE})\mathbf{k} = 0 \qquad (1)$$

$$\Sigma\mathbf{M}_A = \Sigma(\mathbf{r}\times\mathbf{F}) = 0:$$
$$12\mathbf{j}\times T_{BD}(-0.512\mathbf{i} - 0.768\mathbf{j} + 0.384\mathbf{k})$$
$$+12\mathbf{j}\times T_{BE}(-0.512\mathbf{i} - 0.768\mathbf{j} - 0.384\mathbf{k})$$
$$+(9.77\mathbf{i} + 6\mathbf{j} + 3.55\mathbf{k})\times(-4{,}000\mathbf{j}) = 0$$

$$(4.61T_{BD} - 4.61T_{BE} + 14{,}200)\mathbf{i}$$
$$+(6.14T_{BD} + 6.14T_{BE} - 39{,}080)\mathbf{k} = 0 \qquad (2)$$

Setting the coefficients of $\mathbf{i}$ and $\mathbf{k}$ equal to zero in Eq. (2), we obtain two scalar equations which may be solved for T_{BD} and T_{BE}:

$$T_{BD} = 1{,}640\text{ lb} \qquad T_{BE} = 4{,}720\text{ lb} \blacktriangleleft$$

Setting the coefficients of $\mathbf{i}$, $\mathbf{j}$, $\mathbf{k}$ equal to zero in Eq. (1), we obtain three more scalar equations which yield

$$A_x = +3{,}260\text{ lb} \qquad A_y = +8{,}880\text{ lb} \qquad A_z = +1{,}183\text{ lb} \blacktriangleleft$$

SAMPLE PROBLEM 4.9

A 500-lb marquee, 8 by 10 ft, is held in a horizontal position by two horizontal hinges at A and B and by a cable CD attached to a point D located 5 ft directly above B. Determine the tension in the cable and the components of the reactions at the hinges.

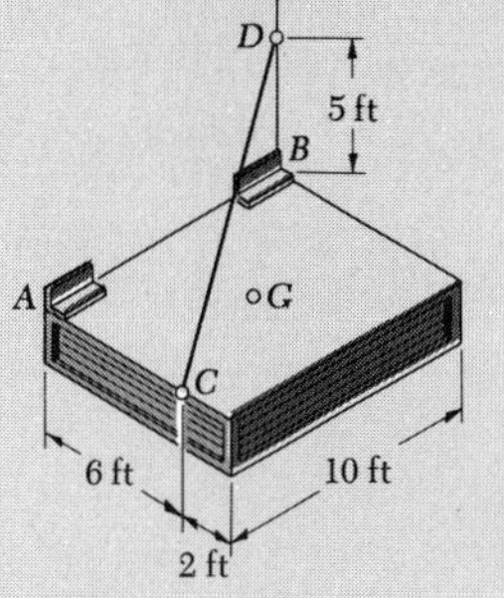

Solution. A free-body diagram of the marquee is drawn. The reactions involve seven unknowns, namely, the force **T** exerted by the cable and three unknown components at each hinge. Since we cannot write more than six independent equations, the problem is indeterminate and cannot be solved completely by the methods of statics.

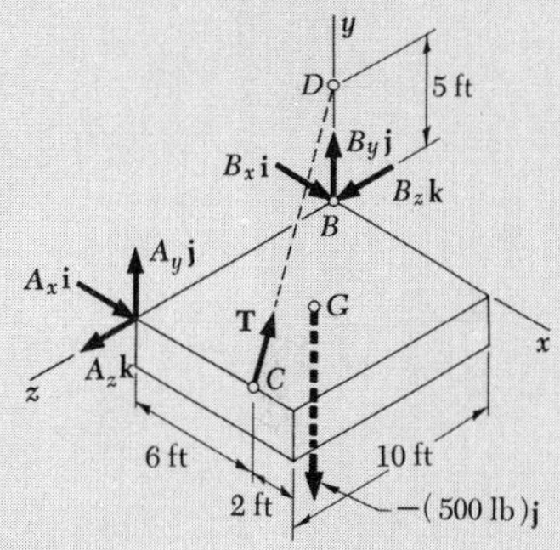

The components of the force **T** may be obtained by proportions from the components of the vector $\overrightarrow{CD}$. We write

$$\overrightarrow{CD} = -(6\text{ ft})\mathbf{i} + (5\text{ ft})\mathbf{j} - (10\text{ ft})\mathbf{k} \qquad CD = 12.69\text{ ft}$$
$$\mathbf{T} = T(\overrightarrow{CD}/CD) = -0.473T\mathbf{i} + 0.394T\mathbf{j} - 0.788T\mathbf{k}$$

Since the marquee is in equilibrium, the forces acting on it must form a system equivalent to zero. We write therefore

$$\Sigma\mathbf{F} = 0: \quad A_x\mathbf{i} + A_y\mathbf{j} + A_z\mathbf{k} + B_x\mathbf{i} + B_y\mathbf{j} + B_z\mathbf{k} + \mathbf{T} - (500\text{ lb})\mathbf{j} = 0$$
$$(A_x + B_x - 0.473T)\mathbf{i} + (A_y + B_y + 0.394T - 500\text{ lb})\mathbf{j} + (A_z + B_z - 0.788T)\mathbf{k} = 0 \qquad (1)$$

$$\Sigma\mathbf{M}_B = \Sigma(\mathbf{r} \times \mathbf{F}) = 0:$$

$$10\mathbf{k} \times (A_x\mathbf{i} + A_y\mathbf{j} + A_z\mathbf{k}) + (6\mathbf{i} + 10\mathbf{k}) \times (-0.473T\mathbf{i} + 0.394T\mathbf{j} - 0.788T\mathbf{k}) + (4\mathbf{i} + 5\mathbf{k}) \times (-500\mathbf{j}) = 0$$
$$(-10A_y - 3.94T + 2{,}500)\mathbf{i} + 10A_x\mathbf{j} + (2.36T - 2{,}000)\mathbf{k} = 0 \qquad (2)$$

Setting the coefficients of the unit vectors equal to zero in Eq. (2), we write three scalar equations which yield

$$T = 846\text{ lb} \qquad A_x = 0 \qquad A_y = -83.3\text{ lb} \quad ◄$$

Setting the coefficients of the unit vectors equal to zero in Eq. (1), we obtain three more scalar equations. After substituting the values of T, A_x, and A_y into these equations, we obtain

$$B_x = +400\text{ lb} \qquad B_y = +250\text{ lb} \qquad A_z + B_z = +667\text{ lb} \quad ◄$$

The z components of the reactions at the hinges cannot be determined separately; only their sum is known. Other equations of equilibrium may be written; such equations, however, are not independent of the six equations used above, and they cannot be used to determine A_z and B_z. If the hinge at B were modified so that it could not exert any axial thrust, we would then obtain $B_z = 0$ and $A_z = +667$ lb.

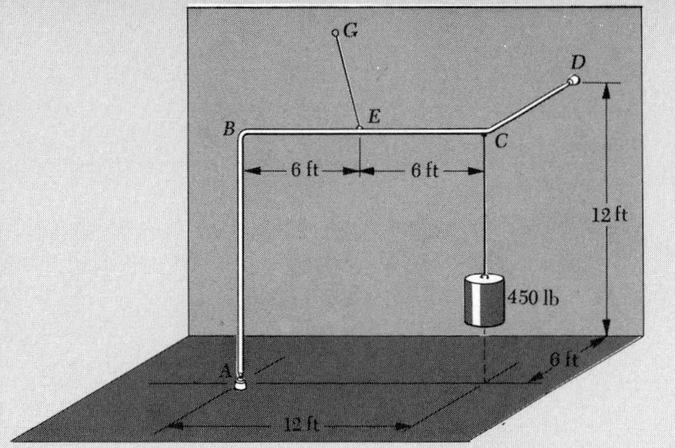

SAMPLE PROBLEM 4.10

A 450-lb load hangs from the corner C of a rigid piece of pipe $ABCD$ which has been bent as shown. The pipe is supported by the ball-and-socket joints A and D fastened, respectively, to the floor and to a vertical wall, and by a cable attached at the mid-point E of the portion BC of the pipe and at a point G on the wall. Determine (*a*) where G should be located if the tension in the cable is to be minimum, (*b*) the corresponding minimum value of the tension.

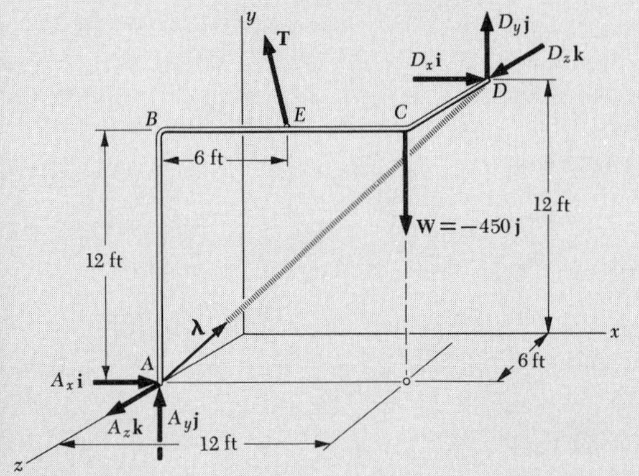

Solution. The free-body diagram of the pipe includes the load $\mathbf{W} = -450\mathbf{j}$, the reactions at A and D, and the force $\mathbf{T}$ exerted by the cable. To eliminate the reactions at A and D from the computations, we express that the sum of the moments of the forces about AD is zero. Denoting by $\boldsymbol{\lambda}$ the unit vector along AD, we write

$$\Sigma M_{AD} = 0: \qquad \boldsymbol{\lambda} \cdot (\overrightarrow{AE} \times \mathbf{T}) + \boldsymbol{\lambda} \cdot (\overrightarrow{AC} \times \mathbf{W}) = 0 \quad (1)$$

The second term in Eq. (1) may be computed as follows:

$$\overrightarrow{AC} \times \mathbf{W} = (12\mathbf{i} + 12\mathbf{j}) \times (-450\mathbf{j}) = -5{,}400\mathbf{k}$$

$$\boldsymbol{\lambda} = \frac{\overrightarrow{AD}}{AD} = \frac{12\mathbf{i} + 12\mathbf{j} - 6\mathbf{k}}{18} = \tfrac{2}{3}\mathbf{i} + \tfrac{2}{3}\mathbf{j} - \tfrac{1}{3}\mathbf{k}$$

$$\boldsymbol{\lambda} \cdot (\overrightarrow{AC} \times \mathbf{W}) = (\tfrac{2}{3}\mathbf{i} + \tfrac{2}{3}\mathbf{j} - \tfrac{1}{3}\mathbf{k}) \cdot (-5{,}400\mathbf{k}) = +1{,}800$$

Substituting the value obtained into Eq. (1), we write

$$\boldsymbol{\lambda} \cdot (\overrightarrow{AE} \times \mathbf{T}) = -1{,}800 \text{ lb-ft} \qquad (2)$$

Minimum Value of Tension. Recalling the commutative property for mixed triple products, we rewrite Eq. (2) in the form

$$\mathbf{T} \cdot (\boldsymbol{\lambda} \times \overrightarrow{AE}) = -1{,}800 \text{ lb-ft} \qquad (3)$$

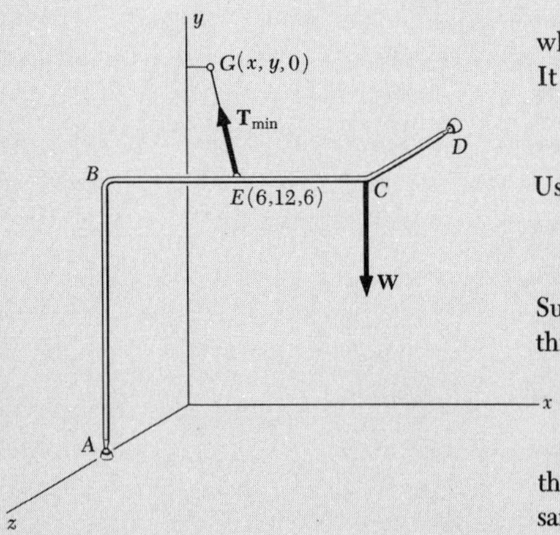

which shows that the projection of $\mathbf{T}$ on the vector $\boldsymbol{\lambda} \times \overrightarrow{AE}$ is a constant. It follows that $\mathbf{T}$ is minimum when parallel to the vector

$$\boldsymbol{\lambda} \times \overrightarrow{AE} = (\tfrac{2}{3}\mathbf{i} + \tfrac{2}{3}\mathbf{j} - \tfrac{1}{3}\mathbf{k}) \times (6\mathbf{i} + 12\mathbf{j}) = 4\mathbf{i} - 2\mathbf{j} + 4\mathbf{k}$$

Using proportions, we write

$$\mathbf{T}_{\min} = T(\tfrac{2}{3}\mathbf{i} - \tfrac{1}{3}\mathbf{j} + \tfrac{2}{3}\mathbf{k}) \qquad (4)$$

Substituting for $\mathbf{T}$ and $\boldsymbol{\lambda} \times \overrightarrow{AE}$ in Eq. (3), we find $T = -300$. Carrying this value into (4), we obtain

$$\mathbf{T}_{\min} = -200\mathbf{i} + 100\mathbf{j} - 200\mathbf{k} \qquad T_{\min} = 300 \text{ lb} \blacktriangleleft$$

Location of G. Denoting by x, y, 0 the coordinates of point G where the cable is attached to the wall, and observing that the vector $\overrightarrow{EG}$ has the same direction as the force $\mathbf{T}_{\min}$, we write

$$\frac{x - 6}{-200} = \frac{y - 12}{+100} = \frac{0 - 6}{-200} \qquad x = 0 \quad y = 15 \text{ ft} \blacktriangleleft$$

PROBLEMS

4.57. The 10-ft flagpole OB forms an angle of 60° with the vertical; it is held by a ball and socket at O and by two braces. Knowing that the distance OA is 3 ft, determine the components of the reaction at O and the tension in each brace caused by the 100-lb load.

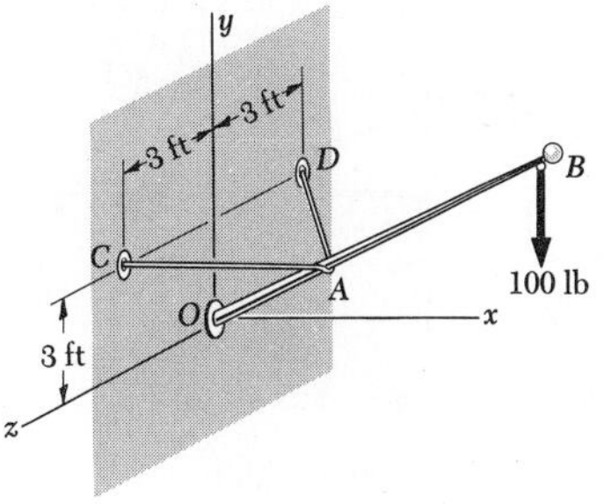

FIG. P 4.57

4.58. A surveying instrument weighing 15 lb is mounted on a tripod. The legs of the tripod are equally spaced and form an angle of 20° with the vertical. Find the reaction of the ground on each leg, neglecting the weight of the tripod and assuming (*a*) that the tripod is rigid and the ground is smooth, (*b*) that the screws connecting the legs to the instrument mount are loose and that the ground is sufficiently rough to keep the legs from sliding.

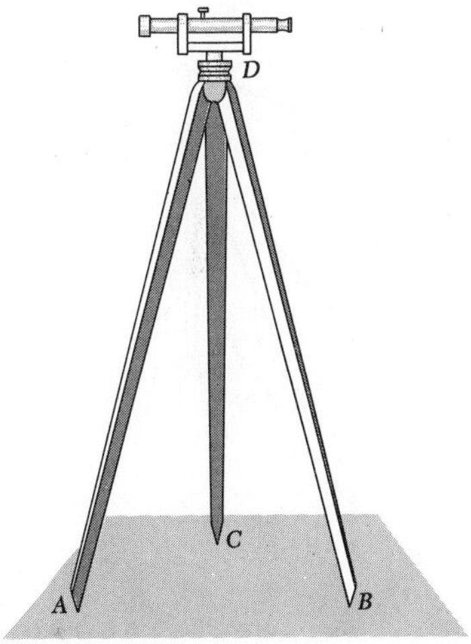

FIG. P 4.58

4.59. A 7-ft boom supports an 1,800-lb load as shown. The boom is held by a ball and socket at A and by the two cables BC and BD. Neglecting the weight of the boom, determine the tension in each cable and the reaction at A.

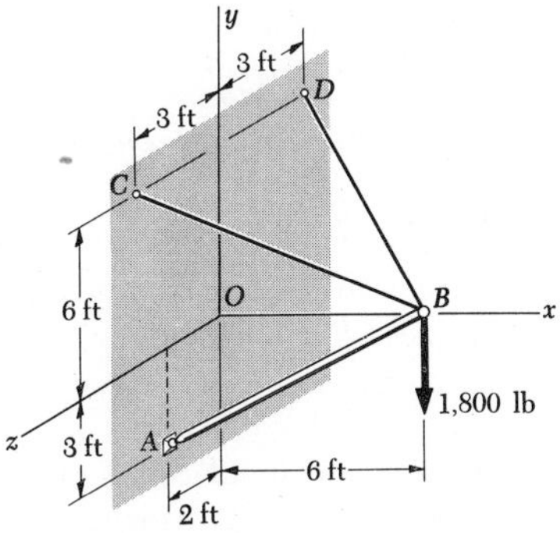

FIG. P 4.59 AND P 4.60

4.60. A 7-ft boom is held by a ball and socket at A and by two cables. In addition to the vertical 1,800-lb load shown, a force of magnitude P is also applied at B in the direction of the positive x axis. Determine (*a*) the required magnitude P if the tension is to be the same in both cables, (*b*) the corresponding reaction at A.

4.61. A 4- by 6-ft plate weighing 900 lb is lifted by three cables which are joined at point D directly above the center of the plate. Determine the tension in each cable.

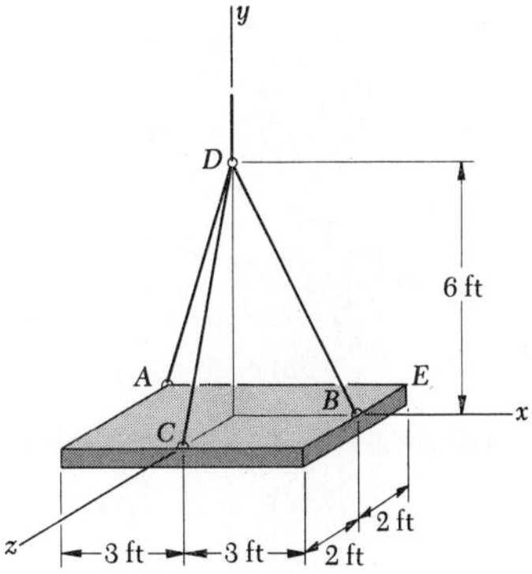

FIG. P 4.61

4.62. Solve Prob. 4.61 assuming that cable BD is replaced by a cable connecting points D and E.

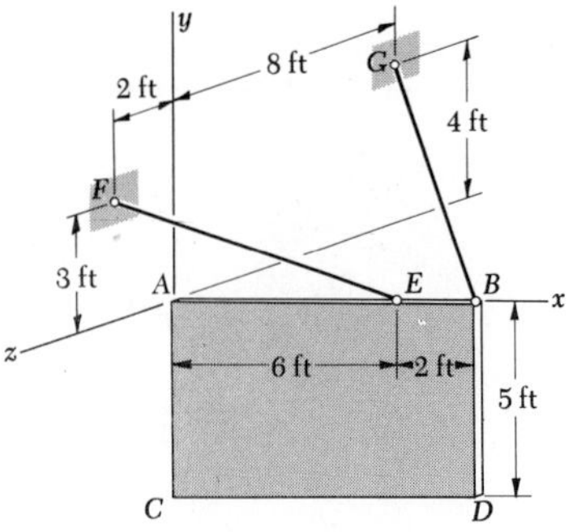

FIG. P 4.63

4.63. A 5- by 8-ft sign of uniform density weighs 270 lb and is supported by a ball and socket at A and by two cables. Determine the tension in each cable and the reaction at A.

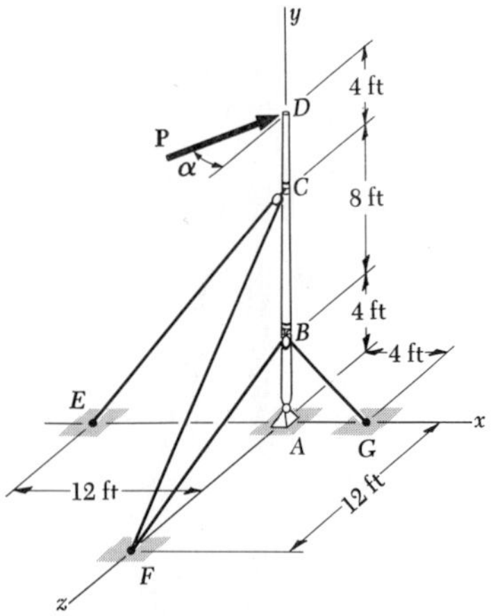

FIG. P 4.64

4.64. A 16-ft boom is held by a ball and socket at A and by two cables ECF and FBG which pass around frictionless pulleys at C and B. A horizontal load **P** of magnitude 900 lb is applied at the top of the boom at D. If **P** is parallel to the z axis ($\alpha = 0$), determine the reaction at A and the tension in each cable.

***4.65.** In Prob. 4.64, determine the limiting values of the horizontal angle α if both the cables are to remain taut.

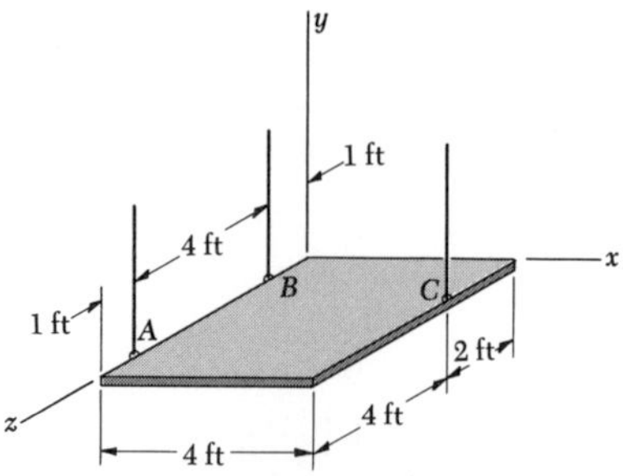

FIG. P 4.67 AND P 4.69

4.66. In Sample Prob. 4.8, determine the horizontal angle ϕ for which the tension in BE is maximum (a) if neither cable may become slack, (b) if cables BE and BD are replaced by rods which can withstand either a tension or a compression force.

4.67. The rectangular plate shown weighs 60 lb and is supported by three wires. Determine the tension in each wire.

4.68. A load W is placed on the plate of Prob. 4.67. Knowing that the weight of the plate is 60 lb, determine the magnitude of the load W and the point where the load should be placed if the tension is to be 50 lb in each of the three wires.

4.69. Determine the magnitude and location of the smallest load which must be placed on the 60-lb plate if the tensions in the three wires are to be equal.

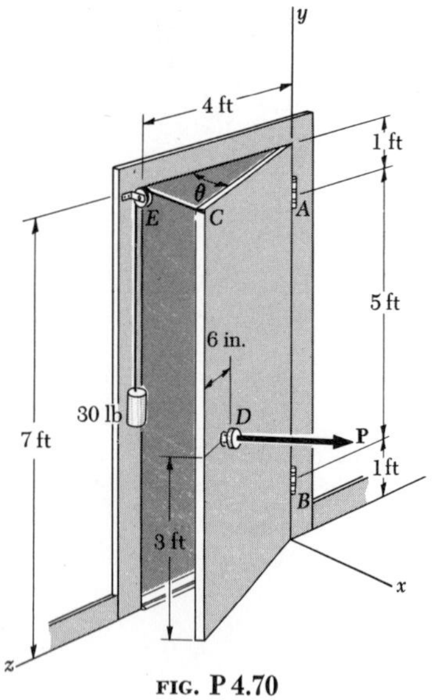

FIG. P 4.70

4.70. A 40-lb door is made self-closing by attaching to it a 30-lb weight by means of a cable CE. The door is held open by a force **P** applied at the knob D, in a direction perpendicular to the door. Determine the magnitude of **P** and the components of the reactions at A and B when $\theta = 90°$. It is assumed that the hinge at A does not exert any axial thrust.

4.71. The door of a bank vault weighs 12,000 lb and is supported by two hinges as shown. Determine the components of the reaction at each hinge.

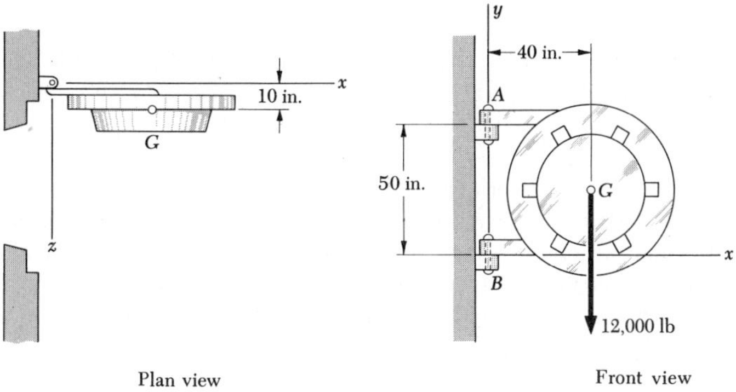

FIG. P 4.71

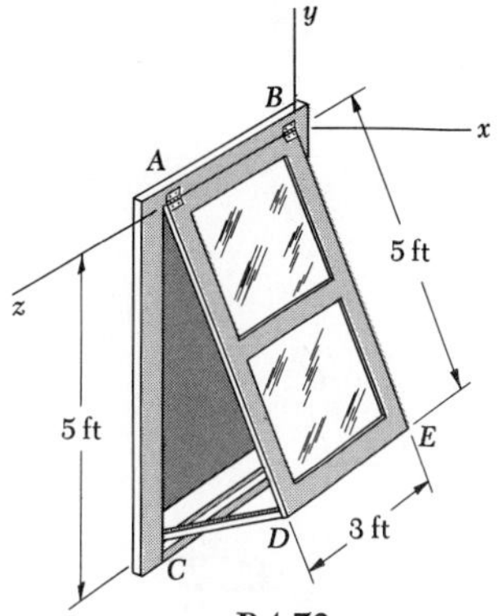

FIG. P 4.72

4.72. A 3- by 5-ft storm window weighs 15 lb and is held by hinges at A and B. In the position shown, it is held away from the side of the house by a 2-ft stick CD. Assuming that the hinge at A does not exert any axial thrust, determine the magnitude of the force exerted by the stick and the components of the reactions at A and B.

4.73. Solve Prob. 4.72 assuming that the hinge at A is removed.

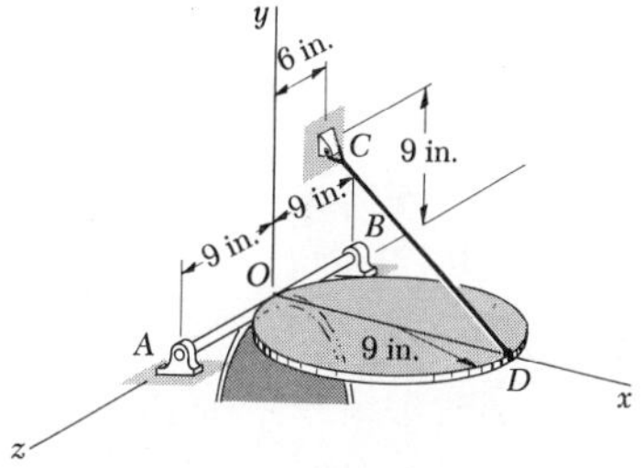

FIG. P 4.74

4.74. A uniform pipe cover of radius 9 in. and weight 60 lb is held in a horizontal position by the cable CD. Assuming that the bearing at B does not exert any axial thrust, determine the tension in the cable and the components of the reactions at A and B.

4.75. Solve Prob. 4.74 assuming that the bearings at A and B are removed and are replaced by a single hinge at O.

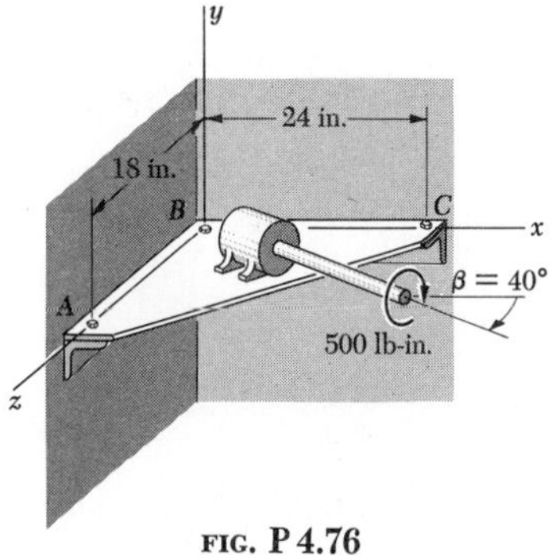

FIG. P 4.76

4.76. A generator is mounted on a platform which is held by bolts at A, B, and C. The generator and platform, as a unit, weigh 60 lb and have a combined center of gravity located at $x = 10$ in. and $z = 8$ in. If a 500-lb-in. couple is applied to the horizontal shaft, determine the vertical component of the reactions at A, B, and C.

4.77. In Prob. 4.76 determine the smallest allowable value of the horizontal angle β, if the bolts are removed and the platform simply rests on its supports.

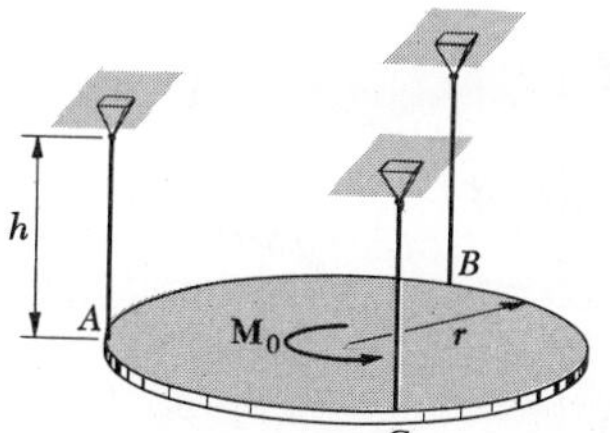

FIG. P 4.78

4.78. A uniform circular plate of radius r and weight W is supported by three vertical wires, each of length h, equally spaced around the edge. Determine the horizontal angle θ through which the plate rotates when a couple $\mathbf{M}_0$ is applied in the plane of the plate. Assume that θ is small.

4.79. In Prob. 4.78, show that the angle θ is independent of the location of the points where the vertical wires are attached to the edge of the plate, provided that A, B, and C do not lie on the same side of a diameter. Assume that θ is small.

***4.80.** In Prob. 4.78, determine the magnitude of the couple $\mathbf{M}_0$ required to rotate the plate through an angle θ. Do *not* assume that θ is small.

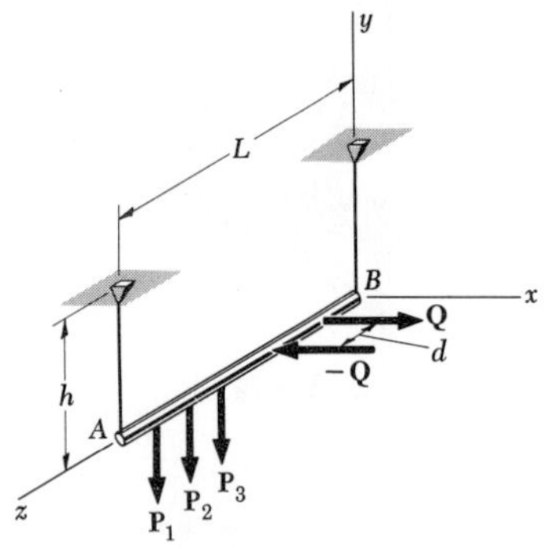

FIG. P 4.81

***4.81.** A bar AB, of negligible weight, is suspended from two wires and supports several vertical loads $\mathbf{P}_1$, $\mathbf{P}_2$, and $\mathbf{P}_3$. Determine the angle θ through which the bar rotates when two horizontal forces forming a couple of magnitude $M_0 = Qd$ are applied to the bar. Also show that the axis of rotation coincides with the axis of the wrench which is equivalent to the total loading. Assume that θ is small.

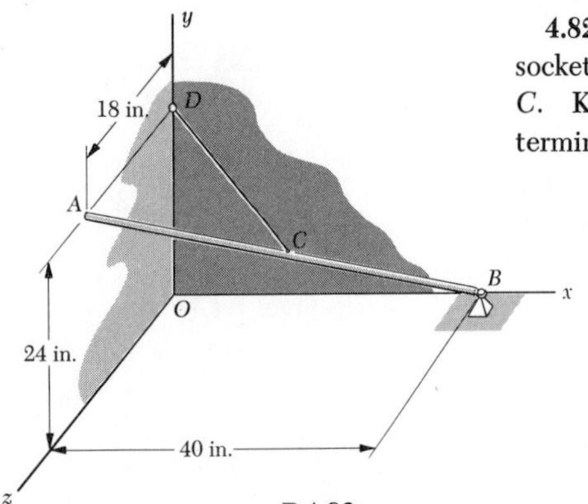

FIG. P 4.82

4.82. The uniform rod AB weighs 24 lb; it is supported by a ball and socket at B and the cord CD which is attached to the mid-point of the rod C. Knowing that the rod leans against a smooth vertical wall at A, determine the tension in the cord and the reactions at A and B.

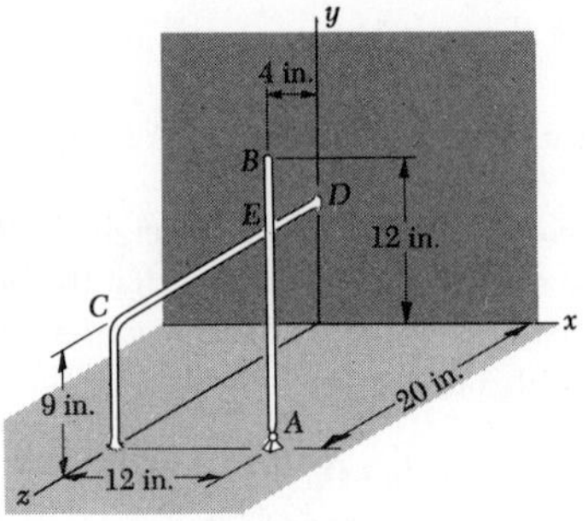

FIG. P 4.83

4.83. The rod AB is uniform and weighs 25 lb. It is supported by a ball and socket at A and leans against both the rod CD and the vertical wall. Assuming the wall and the rods to be smooth, determine (*a*) the components of the force which rod CD exerts on AB, (*b*) the components of the reactions at A and B. (*Hint.* The force exerted by CD on AB must be perpendicular to both rods.)

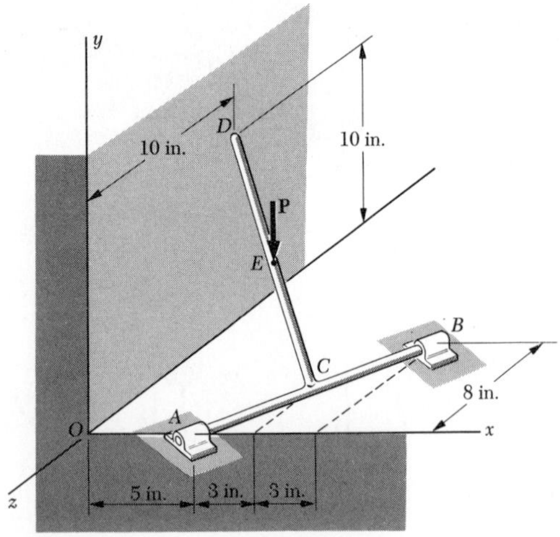

FIG. P 4.84

4.84. Two rods are welded together to form a T-shaped lever which leans against a smooth vertical wall at D and is supported by bearings at A and B. A vertical force $\mathbf{P}$ of magnitude 120 lb is applied at the mid-point of rod DC. Determine the reaction at D.

4.85. Solve Prob. 4.84 assuming that the vertical force P is replaced by a force **Q** of magnitude 300 lb acting at E and directed along a line joining point E and the origin O.

4.86. A bent plate is held by two ball-and-socket joints and a cord AB. Determine the tension in the cord if a 100-lb force is applied at D as shown.

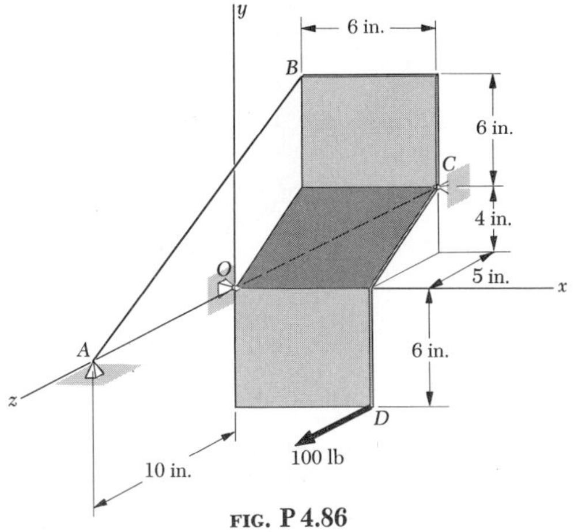

FIG. P 4.86

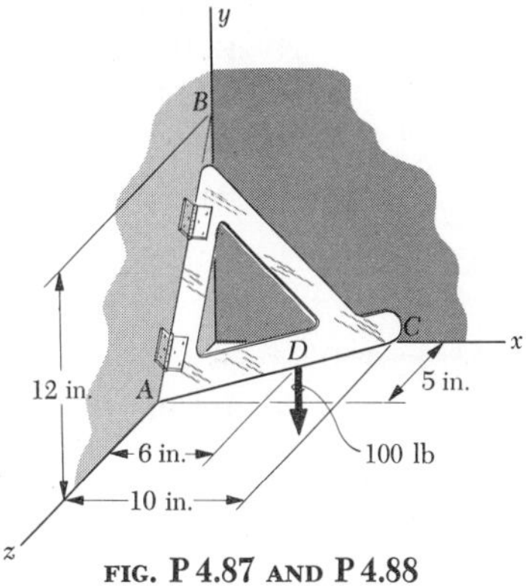

FIG. P 4.87 AND P 4.88

4.87. The bracket shown is held by hinges located along line AB and bears against a smooth vertical wall at C. Neglecting the weight of the bracket, determine the reaction at C when a 100-lb load is applied as shown.

4.88. Determine the magnitude and direction of the smallest force **P** which should be applied at C to keep the bracket from bearing against the wall.

4.89. In Prob. 4.86 the cord AB is removed and replaced by a force **P** applied at B. Determine the magnitude and direction of the smallest force **P** required to hold the plate.

REVIEW PROBLEMS

4.90. The frame shown is held by a pin at A and by a cable BDC which passes over a frictionless pulley at D. Determine the reaction at A and the tension in the cable when $\alpha = 45°$ and $P = 200$ lb.

4.91. The frame shown is held by a pin at A and by a cable BDC which passes over a frictionless pulley at D. If $P = 200$ lb, determine (a) the value of α for which the tension in the cable is maximum, (b) the corresponding reaction at A and tension in the cable.

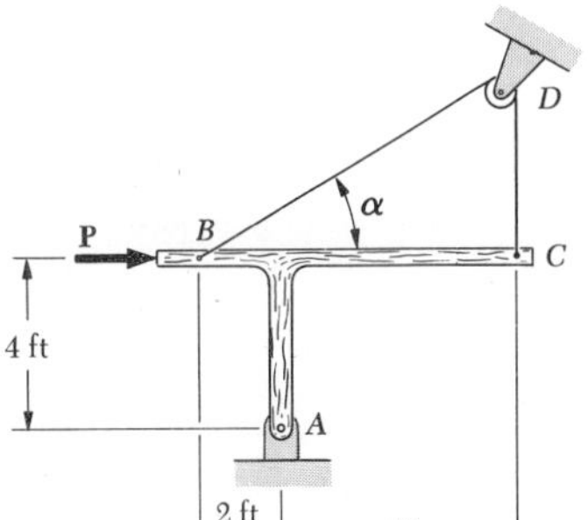

FIG. P 4.90 AND P 4.91

4.92. A 600-lb-in. couple formed by 100-lb forces acting at D and E is applied to the assembly shown. Knowing that a line joining D and E forms an angle of 30° with the yz plane, determine the force $\mathbf{Q}$ required for equilibrium and the components of the reactions at B and C. It is assumed that the bearing at C does not exert any axial thrust.

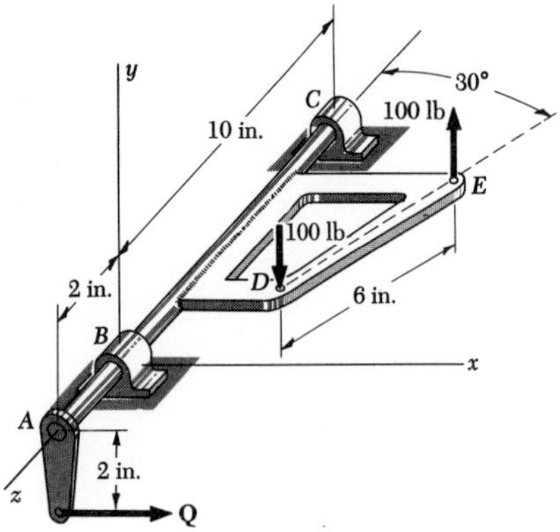

FIG. P 4.92

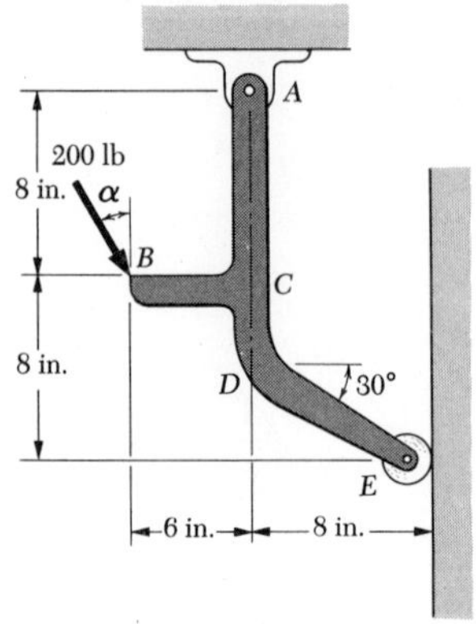

FIG. P 4.93

4.93. (*a*) Determine the reactions at A and E, if $\alpha = 0$. (*b*) Determine the values of α for which the magnitude of the reaction at E is 120 lb.

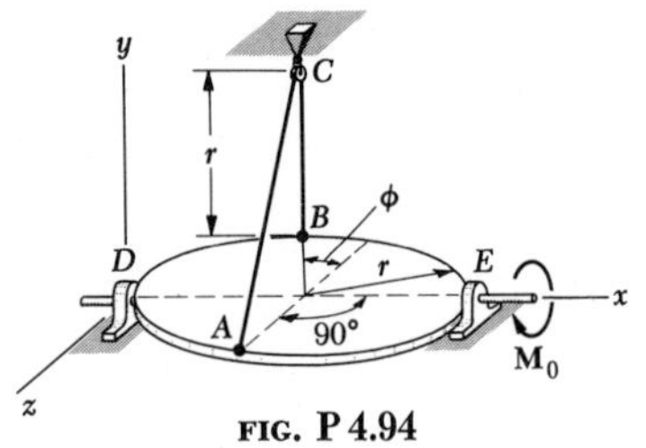

FIG. P 4.94

4.94. The circular plate of radius r is supported by bearings at D and E and by the cable ACB which passes over a frictionless pulley at C. The pulley is located at a distance r directly above point B. A couple $\mathbf{M}_0$ is applied to the plate as shown. (*a*) Express the tension in the cable in terms of M_0, r, and ϕ. (*b*) Determine the tension in the cable and the reactions at D and E when $\phi = 0$. (*c*) Determine the range of values of ϕ for which the bearings and cable can maintain the plate in equilibrium. Bearing E does not exert any axial thrust.

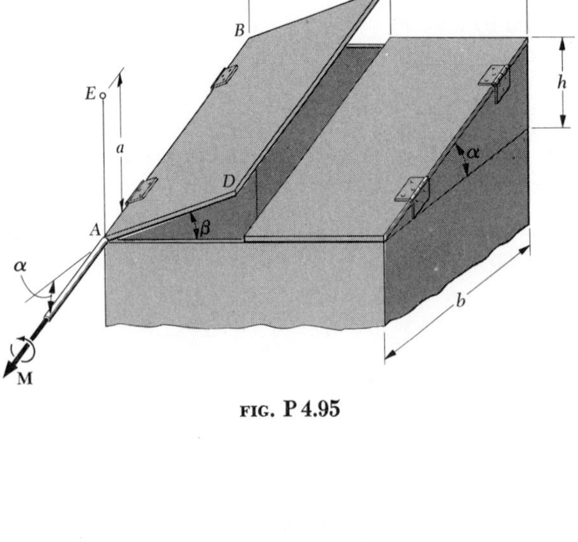

FIG. P 4.95

4.95. A shaft is attached to the left half of the lid of a box so that it is collinear with the axis of the hinges located along edge AB. Denoting by W the weight of $ABCD$, determine the couple $\mathbf{M}$ which must be applied to the shaft in order to hold the left half of the lid in the position shown.

4.96. Three identical rectangular plates, weighing 40 lb each, are held by a pin at A and by a cable as shown. In each case determine (a) the value of θ for which the tension in the cable is minimum, (b) the minimum cable tension and the corresponding reaction at A, (c) the value of θ for which the plate is improperly constrained.

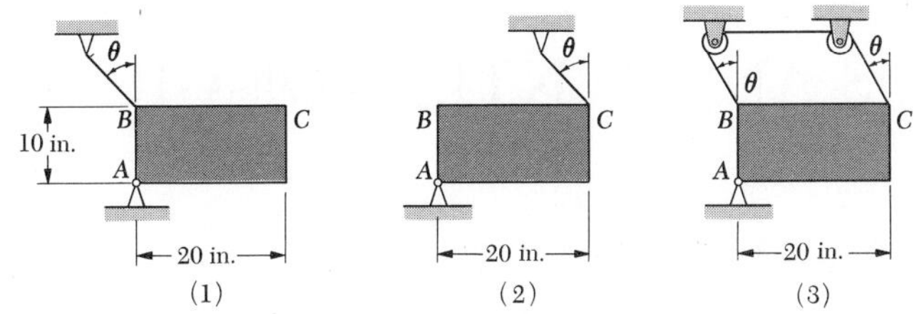

FIG. P 4.96

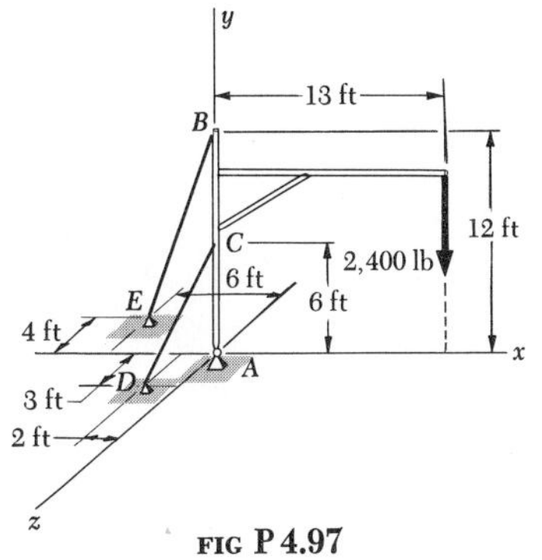

FIG P 4.97

4.97. Determine the tension in cables BE and CD.

4.98. Knowing that $\alpha = 0$, determine the reactions at B, C, and D for the semicircular rod shown.

4.99. Determine the range of values of α for which the semicircular rod can be maintained in equilibrium by the small wheel at D and the rollers at B and C.

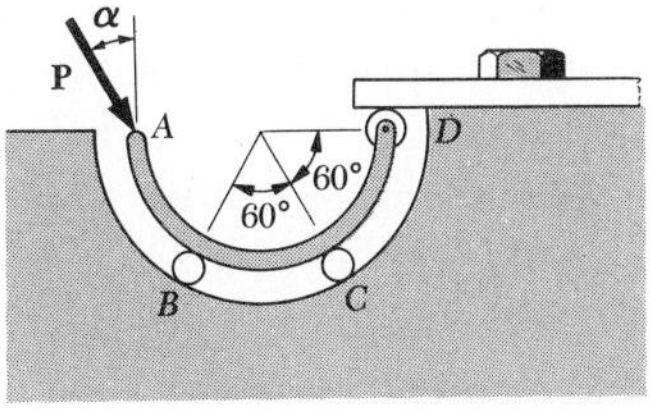

FIG. P 4.98 AND P 4.99

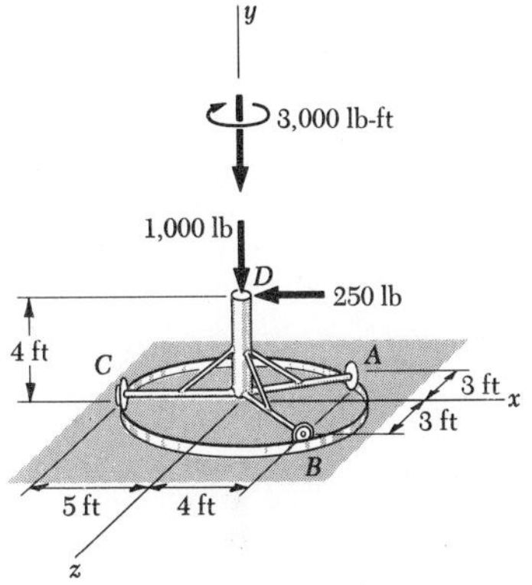

FIG. P 4.100

4.100. An experimental radar antenna is to be mounted on the base shown which may roll on a 5-ft-radius track. Each wheel has a single flange on the inner side of the track. Wheels A and B are free to rotate, but a brake is applied to wheel C to keep it from moving. Determine the components of the reactions at A, B, and C for the loading shown.

4.101. In Prob. 4.84, assuming that the bearing at B does not exert any axial thrust, determine the reactions at A, B, and D.

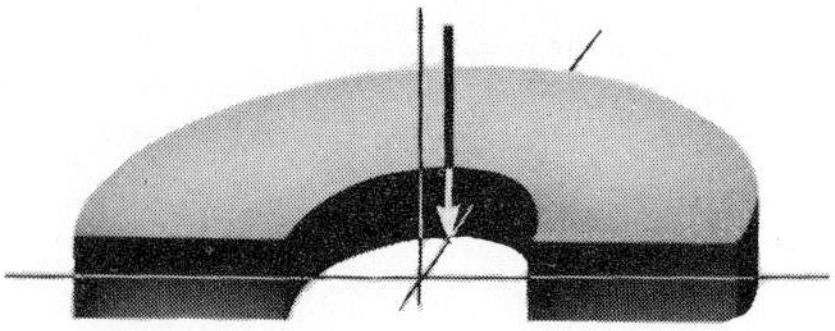

5. DISTRIBUTED FORCES: CENTROIDS AND CENTERS OF GRAVITY

AREAS AND LINES

5.1. Center of Gravity of a Two-dimensional Body. We have assumed so far that the attraction exerted by the earth on a rigid body could be represented by a single force **W**. This force, called the weight of the body, was to be applied at the *center of gravity* of the body (Sec. 3.1). Actually, the earth exerts a force on each of the particles forming the body. The action of the earth on a rigid body should thus be represented by a large number of small forces distributed over the entire body. We shall see in this chapter, however, that all these small forces may be replaced by a single equivalent force **W**. We shall also learn to determine the center of gravity, i.e., the point of application of the resultant **W**, for various shapes of bodies.

Let us first consider a flat horizontal plate (Fig. 5.1). We may divide the plate into n small elements. The coordinates of the first element are denoted by x_1 and y_1, those of the second element by x_2 and y_2, etc. The forces exerted by the earth on the elements of plate will be denoted, respectively, by $\Delta\mathbf{W}_1$, $\Delta\mathbf{W}_2, \ldots, \Delta\mathbf{W}_n$. These forces or weights are directed toward

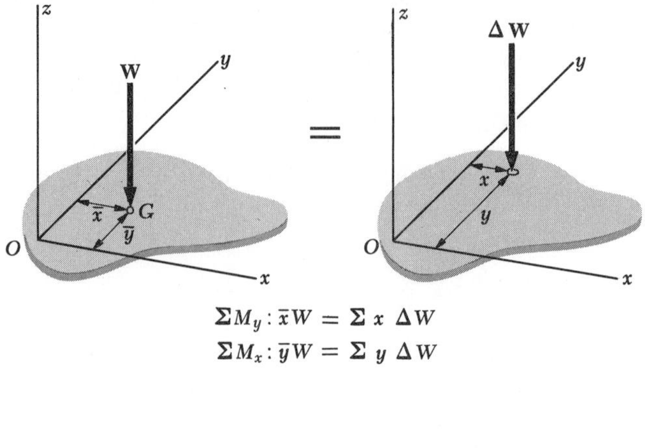

$$\Sigma M_y : \bar{x}W = \Sigma\, x\, \Delta W$$
$$\Sigma M_x : \bar{y}W = \Sigma\, y\, \Delta W$$

FIG. 5.1. Center of gravity of a plate

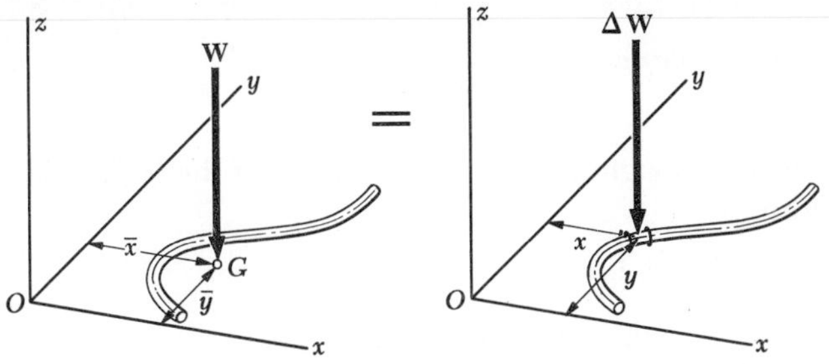

$$\Sigma M_y:\ \bar{x}W = \Sigma\, x\, \Delta W$$
$$\Sigma M_x:\ \bar{y}W = \Sigma\, y\, \Delta W$$

FIG. 5.2. **Center of gravity of a wire**

the center of the earth; however, for all practical purposes they may be assumed parallel. Their resultant is therefore a single force in the same direction. The magnitude W of this force is obtained by adding the magnitudes of the elementary weights,

$$\Sigma F_z: \qquad W = \Delta W_1 + \Delta W_2 + \cdots + \Delta W_n \qquad (5.1)$$

To obtain the coordinates $\bar{x}$ and $\bar{y}$ of the point G where the resultant $\mathbf{W}$ should be applied, we write that the moments of $\mathbf{W}$ about the y and x axes are equal to the sum of the corresponding moments of the elementary weights,

$$\begin{aligned} \Sigma M_y: \quad & \bar{x}W = x_1\Delta W_1 + x_2\Delta W_2 + \cdots + x_n\Delta W_n \\ \Sigma M_x: \quad & \bar{y}W = y_1\Delta W_1 + y_2\Delta W_2 + \cdots + y_n\Delta W_n \end{aligned} \qquad (5.2)$$

If we now increase the number of elements into which the plate is divided and simultaneously decrease the size of each element, we obtain at the limit the following expressions:

$$W = \int dW \qquad \bar{x}W = \int x\, dW \qquad \bar{y}W = \int y\, dW \qquad (5.3)$$

These equations define the weight $\mathbf{W}$ and the coordinates $\bar{x}$ and $\bar{y}$ of the center of gravity G of a flat plate. The same equations may be derived for a wire lying in the xy plane (Fig. 5.2). We shall observe, in the latter case, that the center of gravity G will generally not be located on the wire.

5.2. Centroids of Areas and Lines. In the case of a homogeneous plate of uniform thickness, the magnitude ΔW of the weight of an element of plate may be expressed as

$$\Delta W = \gamma t\, \Delta A$$

where γ = specific weight (weight per unit volume) of material
t = thickness of plate
ΔA = area of element

If γ is expressed in lb/ft^3, t in feet, and ΔA in square feet, we check that ΔW is expressed in pounds. Similarly, we may express the magnitude W of the weight of the entire plate in the form

$$W = \gamma t A$$

where A is the total area of the plate.

Substituting for ΔW and W in the moment equations (5.2) and dividing throughout by γt, we write

$$\begin{aligned} \Sigma M_y: \quad \bar{x}A &= x_1\,\Delta A_1 + x_2\,\Delta A_2 + \cdots + x_n\,\Delta A_n \\ \Sigma M_x: \quad \bar{y}A &= y_1\,\Delta A_1 + y_2\,\Delta A_2 + \cdots + y_n\,\Delta A_n \end{aligned} \tag{5.4}$$

If we increase the number of elements into which the area A is divided and simultaneously decrease the size of each element, we obtain at the limit

$$\bar{x}A = \int x\,dA \qquad \bar{y}A = \int y\,dA \tag{5.5}$$

These equations define the coordinates $\bar{x}$ and $\bar{y}$ of the center of gravity of a homogeneous plate. The point of coordinates $\bar{x}$ and $\bar{y}$ is also known as the *centroid C of the area A* of the plate (Fig. 5.3). If the plate is not homogeneous, the equations cannot be used to determine the center of gravity of the plate; they still define, however, the centroid of the area.

The integral $\int x\,dA$ is known as the *first moment of the area A with respect to the y axis.* Similarly, the integral $\int y\,dA$ defines the *first moment of A with respect to the x axis.* It is seen from Eqs. (5.5) that, if the centroid of an area is located on a coordinate axis, the first moment of the area with respect to that axis is zero.

In the case of a homogeneous wire of uniform cross section, the magnitude ΔW of the weight of an element of wire may be expressed as

$$\Delta W = \gamma a\,\Delta L$$

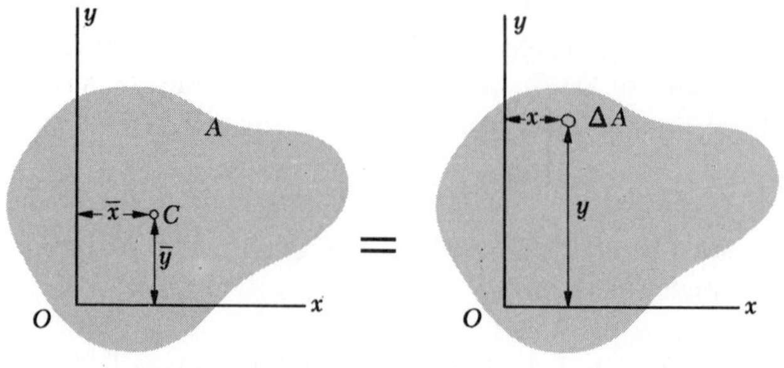

$$\Sigma M_y: \bar{x}A = \Sigma x\,\Delta A$$
$$\Sigma M_x: \bar{y}A = \Sigma y\,\Delta A$$

FIG. 5.3. Centroid of an area

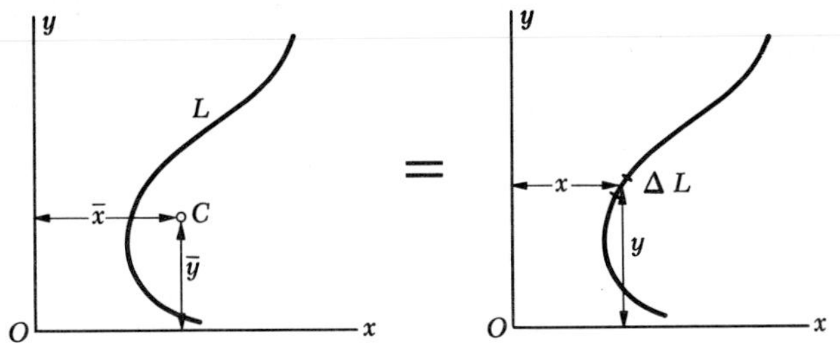

$$\Sigma M_y: \bar{x}\,L = \Sigma\, x\ \Delta L$$
$$\Sigma M_x: \bar{y}\,L = \Sigma\, y\ \Delta L$$

FIG. 5.4. Centroid of a line

where γ = specific weight of material
a = cross-sectional area of wire
ΔL = length of element

The center of gravity of the wire then coincides with the *centroid C of the line L* defining the shape of the wire (Fig. 5.4). The coordinates $\bar{x}$ and $\bar{y}$ of the centroid of the line L are obtained from the equations

$$\bar{x}L = \int x\, dL \qquad \bar{y}L = \int y\, dL \tag{5.6}$$

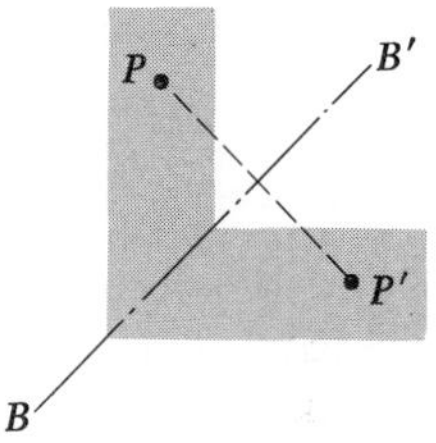

FIG. 5.5

An area A is said to be *symmetrical about an axis BB′* if to every point P of the area corresponds a point P' of the same area such that the line PP' is perpendicular to BB' and is divided into two equal parts by that axis (Fig. 5.5). A line L is said to be symmetrical about BB' if it satisfies similar conditions. When an area A or a line L possesses an axis of symmetry BB', the centroid of the area or line must be located on that axis. If the axis of symmetry is chosen as the y axis, the coordinate $\bar{x}$ of the centroid is found to be zero, since to every product $x\, dA$ or $x\, dL$ appearing in the first integral in Eqs. (5.5) or (5.6) will correspond a product of equal magnitude but of opposite sign. It follows that, if an area or line possesses two axes of symmetry, the centroid of the area or line is located at the intersection of the two axes of symmetry (Fig. 5.6). This property enables us to determine immediately the centroid of areas such as circles, ellipses, squares, rectangles, equilateral triangles, or any other symmetrical figures, as well as the centroid of lines in the shape of the circumference of a circle, the perimeter of a square, etc.

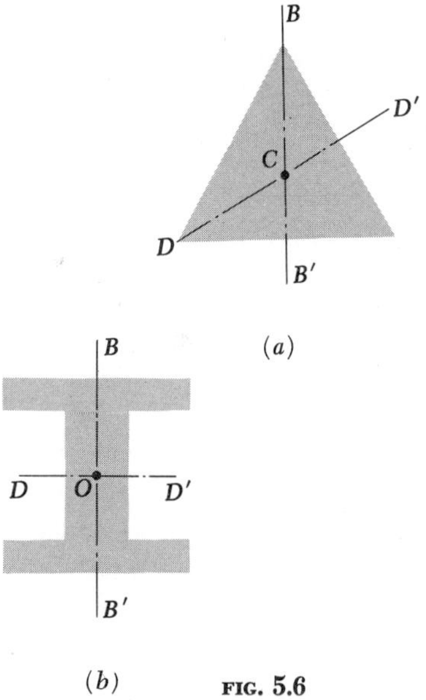

(a)

(b)

FIG. 5.6

An area is said to be *symmetrical about a center O* if to every point P of the area corresponds a point P' of the same area such that the line PP' is divided into two equal parts by O (Fig. 5.7). A line L is said to be symmetrical about O if it satisfies similar conditions. A reasoning similar to that used above would show that, when an area A or line L possesses a center of symmetry O, the point O must be the centroid of the area or line. It

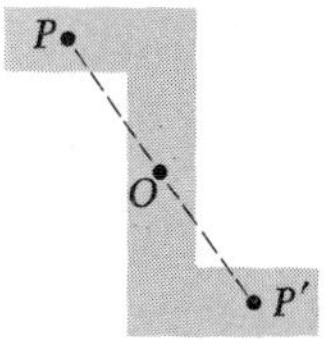

FIG. 5.7

Shape		$\bar{x}$	$\bar{y}$	Area
Triangular area	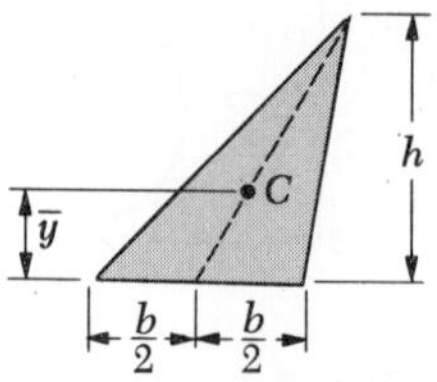		$\frac{h}{3}$	$\frac{bh}{2}$
Quarter-circular area	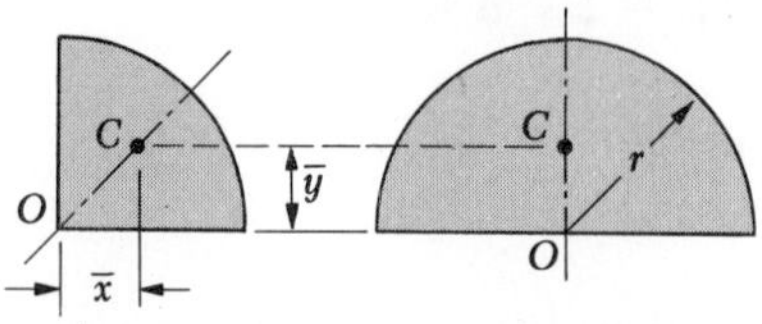	$\frac{4r}{3\pi}$	$\frac{4r}{3\pi}$	$\frac{\pi r^2}{4}$
Semicircular area		0	$\frac{4r}{3\pi}$	$\frac{\pi r^2}{2}$
Quarter-elliptical area	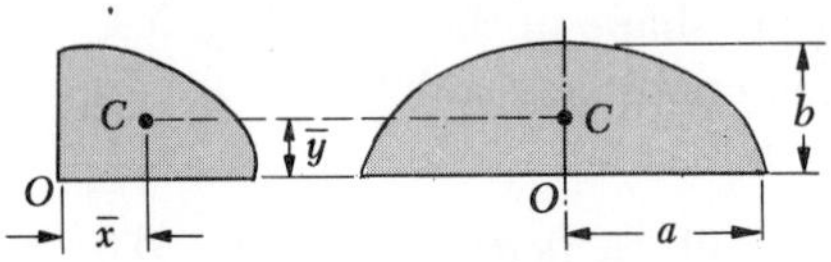	$\frac{4a}{3\pi}$	$\frac{4b}{3\pi}$	$\frac{\pi ab}{4}$
Semielliptical area		0	$\frac{4b}{3\pi}$	$\frac{\pi ab}{2}$
Semiparabolic area	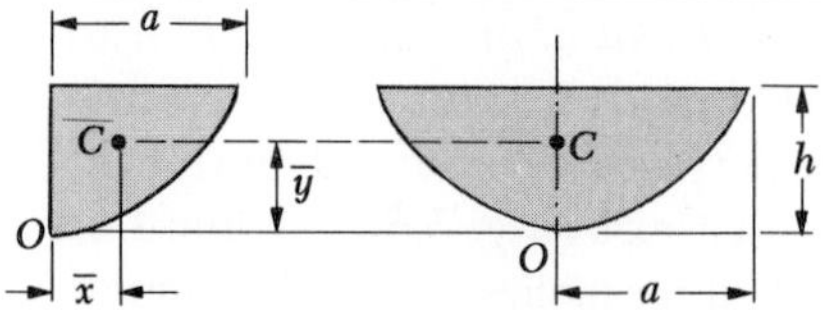	$\frac{3a}{8}$	$\frac{3h}{5}$	$\frac{2ah}{3}$
Parabolic area		0	$\frac{3h}{5}$	$\frac{4ah}{3}$
Parabolic spandrel	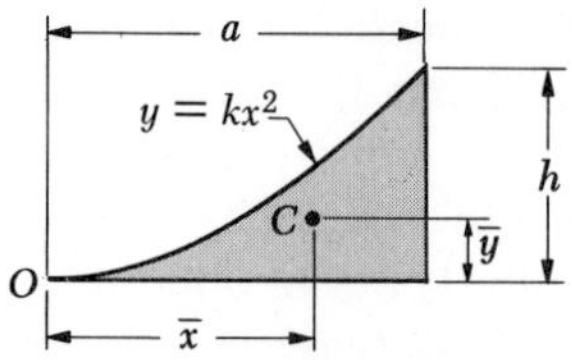	$\frac{3a}{4}$	$\frac{3h}{10}$	$\frac{ah}{3}$
General spandrel	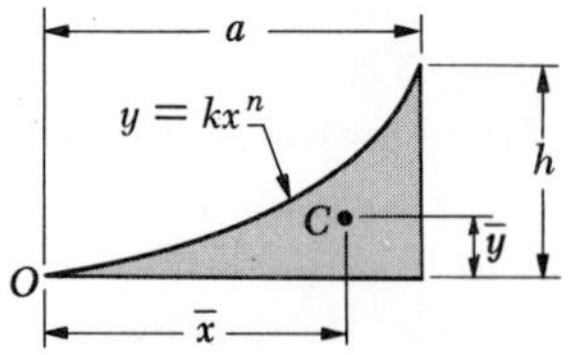	$\frac{n+1}{n+2}a$	$\frac{n+1}{4n+2}h$	$\frac{ah}{n+1}$
Circular sector	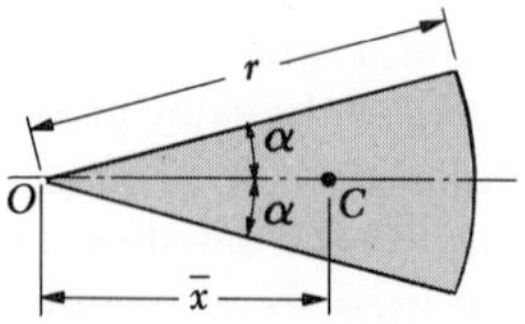	$\frac{2r \sin \alpha}{3\alpha}$	0	αr^2

FIG. 5.8A. Centroids of common shapes of areas

Shape		$\bar{x}$	$\bar{y}$	Length
Quarter-circular arc	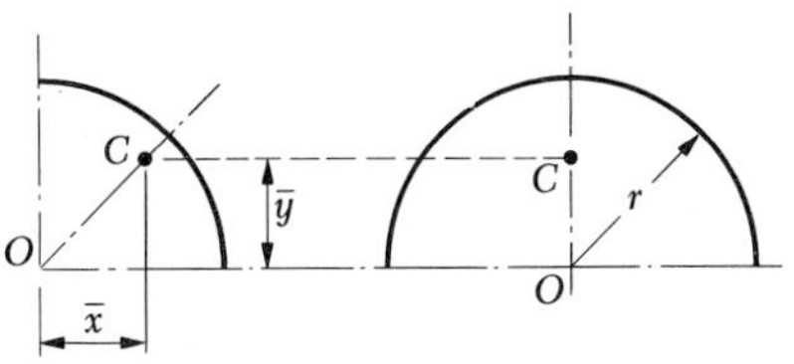	$\frac{2r}{\pi}$	$\frac{2r}{\pi}$	$\frac{\pi r}{2}$
Semicircular arc		0	$\frac{2r}{\pi}$	πr
Arc of circle	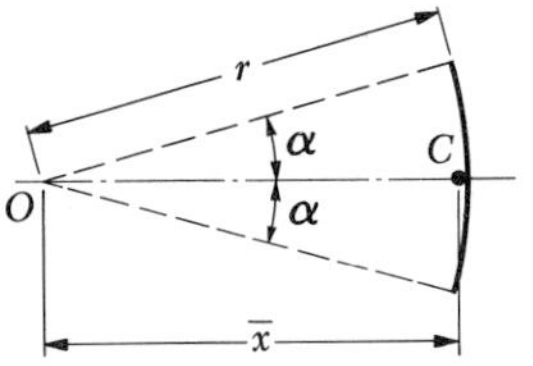	$\frac{r \sin \alpha}{\alpha}$	0	$2\alpha r$

FIG. 5.8*B*. Centroids of common shapes of lines

should be noted that a figure possessing a center of symmetry does not necessarily possess an axis of symmetry (Fig. 5.7), while a figure possessing two axes of symmetry does not necessarily possess a center of symmetry (Fig. 5.6*a*). However, if a figure possesses two axes of symmetry at a right angle to each other, the point of intersection of these axes will be a center of symmetry (Fig. 5.6*b*).

Centroids of unsymmetrical areas and lines and of areas and lines possessing only one axis of symmetry will be determined by the methods of Secs. 5.4 and 5.5. Centroids of common shapes of areas and lines are shown in Fig. 5.8*A* and *B*. The formulas defining these centroids will be derived in the Sample Problems and Problems following Secs. 5.4 and 5.5.

5.3. Composite Plates and Wires. In many instances, a flat plate may be divided into rectangles, triangles, or other common shapes shown in Fig. 5.8*A*. The abscissa $\bar{X}$ of its center of gravity G may be determined from the abscissas $\bar{x}_1$, $\bar{x}_2$, . . .

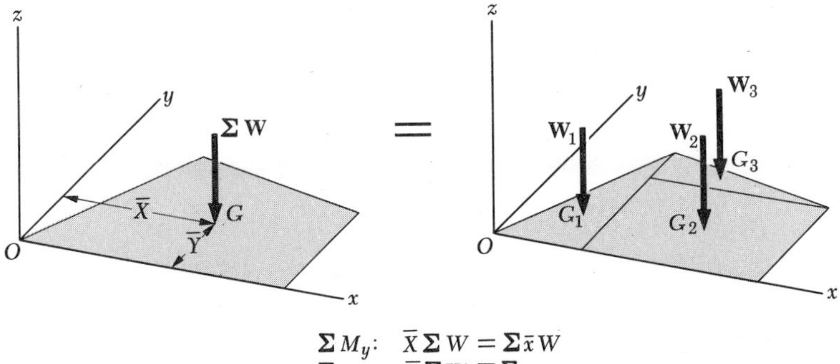

$$\Sigma M_y: \quad \bar{X}\Sigma W = \Sigma \bar{x} W$$
$$\Sigma M_x: \quad \bar{Y}\Sigma W = \Sigma \bar{y} W$$

FIG. 5.9. Center of gravity of a composite plate

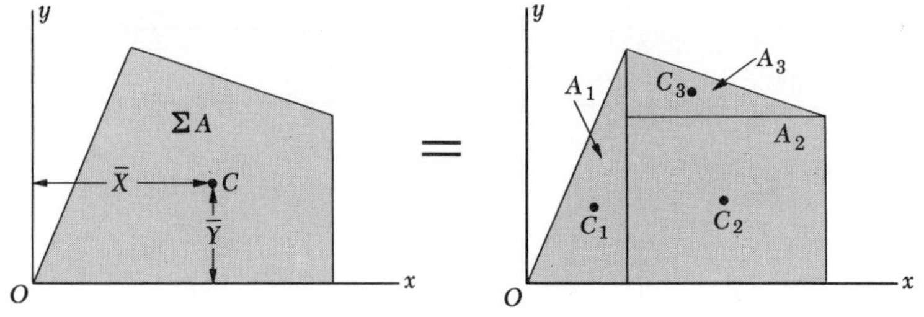

FIG. 5.10. Centroid of a composite area

$$\Sigma M_y:\quad \overline{X}\Sigma A = \Sigma \bar{x} A$$
$$\Sigma M_x:\quad \overline{Y}\Sigma A = \Sigma \bar{y} A$$

of the centers of gravity of the various parts by expressing that the moment of the weight of the whole plate about the y axis is equal to the sum of the moments of the weights of the various parts about the same axis (Fig. 5.9). The ordinate $\overline{Y}$ of the center of gravity of the plate is found in a similar way by equating moments about the x axis.

$$\begin{aligned} \Sigma M_y:\quad & \overline{X}(W_1 + W_2 + \cdots + W_n) \\ & = \bar{x}_1 W_1 + \bar{x}_2 W_2 + \cdots + \bar{x}_n W_n \\ \Sigma M_x:\quad & \overline{Y}(W_1 + W_2 + \cdots + W_n) \\ & = \bar{y}_1 W_1 + \bar{y}_2 W_2 + \cdots + \bar{y}_n W_n \end{aligned} \qquad (5.7)$$

If the plate is homogeneous and of uniform thickness, the center of gravity coincides with the centroid C of its area. The abscissa $\overline{X}$ of the centroid of the area may then be determined by expressing that the first moment of the composite area with respect to the y axis is equal to the sum of the first moments of the elementary areas with respect to the same axis (Fig. 5.10). The ordinate $\overline{Y}$ of the centroid is found in a similar way by equating first moments of areas with respect to the x axis.

$$\begin{aligned} \Sigma M_y:\quad & \overline{X}(A_1 + A_2 + \cdots + A_n) \\ & = \bar{x}_1 A_1 + \bar{x}_2 A_2 + \cdots + \bar{x}_n A_n \\ \Sigma M_x:\quad & \overline{Y}(A_1 + A_2 + \cdots + A_n) \\ & = \bar{y}_1 A_1 + \bar{y}_2 A_2 + \cdots + \bar{y}_n A_n \end{aligned} \qquad (5.8)$$

Care should be taken to record the moment of each area with the appropriate sign. First moments of areas, just like moments of forces, may be positive or negative. For example, an area whose centroid is located to the left of the y axis will have a negative first moment with respect to that axis. Also, the area of a hole should be recorded with a negative sign (Fig. 5.11).

Similarly, it is possible in many cases to determine the center of gravity of a composite wire or the centroid of a composite line by dividing the wire or line into simpler elements (Sample Prob. 5.3).

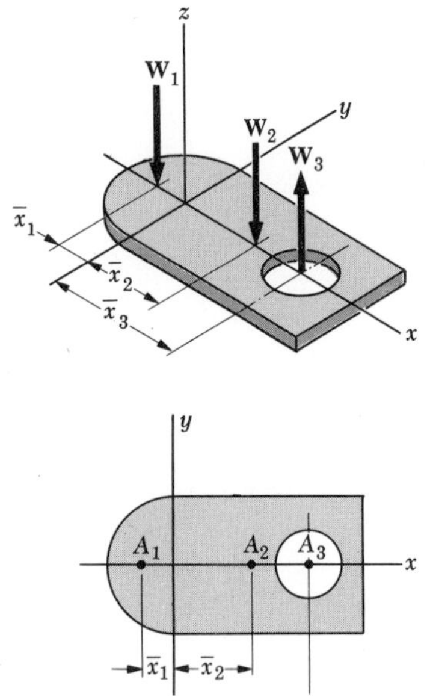

	$\bar{x}$	A	$\bar{x}A$
A_1 Semicircle	−	+	−
A_2 Full rectangle	+	+	+
A_3 Circular hole	+	−	−

FIG. 5.11

SAMPLE PROBLEM 5.1

Determine the center of gravity of the thin homogeneous plate shown.

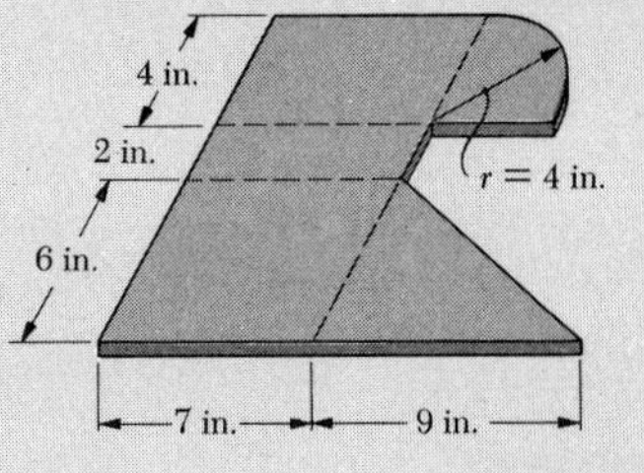

Solution. Since the plate is homogeneous, we may locate the center of gravity by determining the centroid of the area of the plate. The area is divided into its component parts: a rectangle, a triangle, and a quarter circle. Coordinate axes are chosen with the origin at the lower left corner of the plate. The centroid of each component part is indicated in the figure, and $\bar{x}$ and $\bar{y}$ are computed for each component. The moments of the component areas with respect to the coordinate axes are determined in the following table:

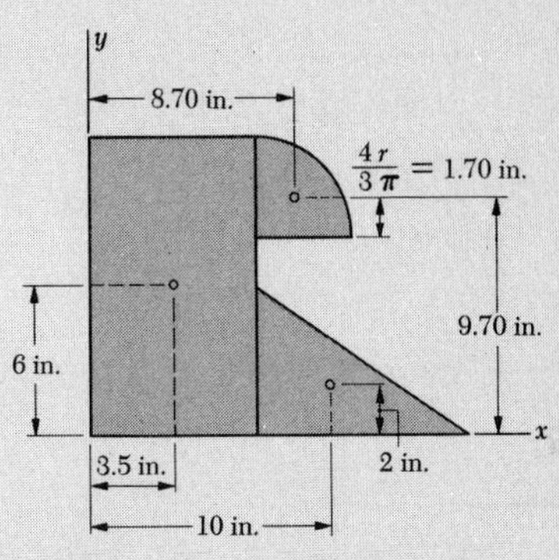

Component	A	$\bar{x}$	$\bar{y}$	$\bar{x}A$	$\bar{y}A$
Rectangle......	84	3.5	6.0	294	504
Triangle.......	27	10.0	2.0	270	54
Quarter circle...	12.56	8.7	9.7	109.2	121.8
	$\Sigma A =$ 123.6	....	...	$\Sigma\bar{x}A =$ 673.2	$\Sigma\bar{y}A =$ 679.8

Substituting the values obtained from the table into the equations defining the centroid of a composite area, we obtain

$\bar{X}\Sigma A = \Sigma\bar{x}A$: $\quad \bar{X}(123.6) = 673.2 \qquad \bar{X} = 5.45$ in. ◄

$\bar{Y}\Sigma A = \Sigma\bar{y}A$: $\quad \bar{Y}(123.6) = 679.8 \qquad \bar{Y} = 5.50$ in. ◄

The above values of $\bar{X}$ and $\bar{Y}$ define the centroid of the area and also the center of gravity of the plate. The center of gravity, of course, is actually located halfway between the upper and lower faces of the plate.

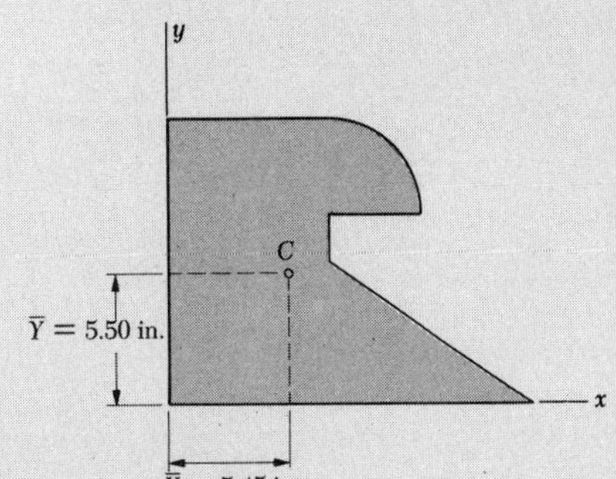

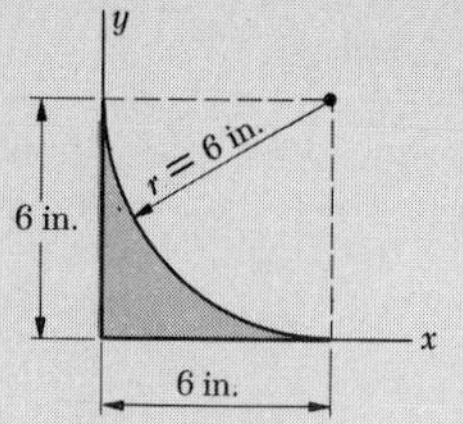

SAMPLE PROBLEM 5.2

Determine the centroid of the area shown.

Solution. Since the area is symmetrical with respect to a line drawn at 45° through the origin, the centroid must be located on this line; therefore, $\bar{X} = \bar{Y}$. The given area may be obtained by subtracting a quarter circle from a square. The centroid of the quarter circle is obtained from Fig. 5.8*A* and the following table is constructed:

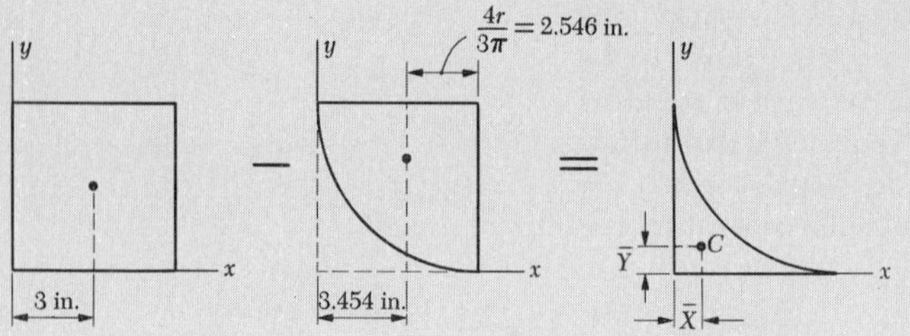

Component	A	$\bar{x}$	$\bar{x}A$
Square........	36.00	3.00	108.00
Quarter circle...	−28.27	3.454	−97.64
	$\Sigma A =$ 7.73	....	$\Sigma \bar{x}A =$ 10.36

Since we are subtracting numbers of about the same magnitude, accuracy greater than standard is required in the table in order to obtain standard accuracy (0.2 per cent) in the result.

$\bar{X}\Sigma A = \Sigma \bar{x}A$: $\quad \bar{X}(7.73) = 10.36 \qquad \bar{X} = \bar{Y} = 1.34$ in. ◄

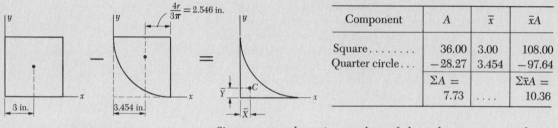

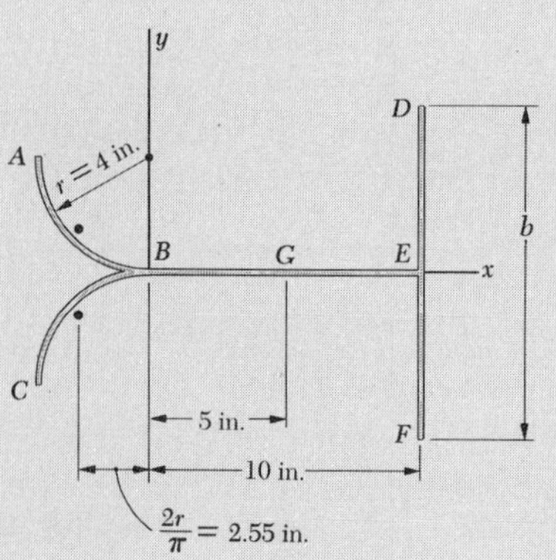

SAMPLE PROBLEM 5.3

The figure shown is made of a thin homogeneous wire. Determine the dimension b such that the center of gravity will be located at point G.

Solution. Since the figure is formed of homogeneous wire, its center of gravity may be located by determining the centroid of the corresponding line. The origin is arbitrarily placed at point B, and the line is divided into three segments ABC, BGE, and DEF.

Segment	L	$\bar{x}$	$\bar{x}L$
ABC	12.56	−2.55	−32.0
BGE	10.00	5.00	50.0
DEF	b	10.00	$10b$
	$\Sigma L =$ $22.56 + b$	......	$\Sigma \bar{x}L =$ $18 + 10b$

Since the value of $\bar{X}$ is known to be 5 in., the value of b is determined as follows:

$\bar{X}\Sigma L = \Sigma \bar{x}L$: $\quad 5(22.56 + b) = 18 + 10b \qquad b = 18.96$ in. ◄

PROBLEMS

5.1 through 5.12. Locate the centroid of the plane area shown.

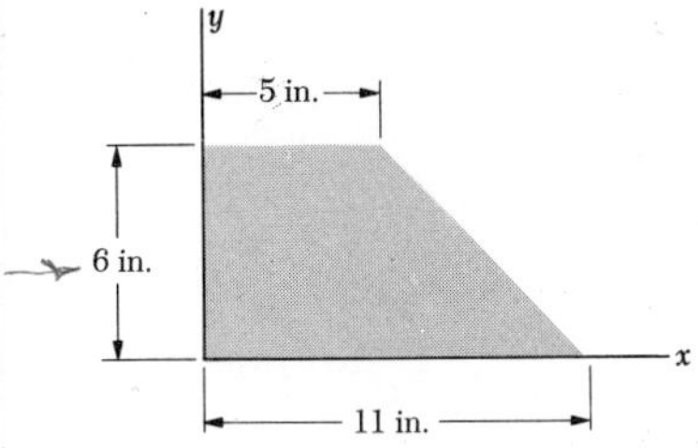

FIG. P 5.1

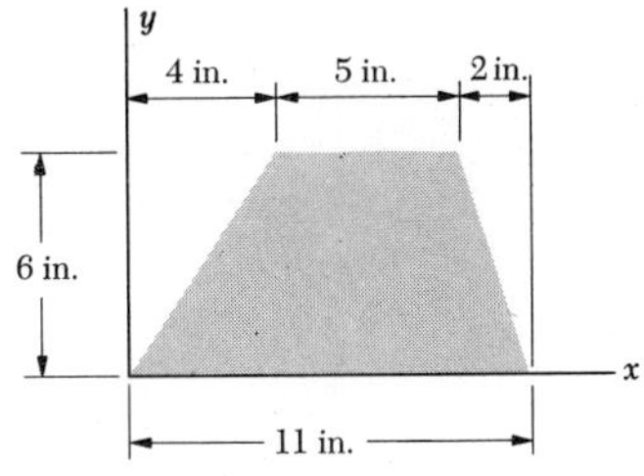

FIG. P 5.2

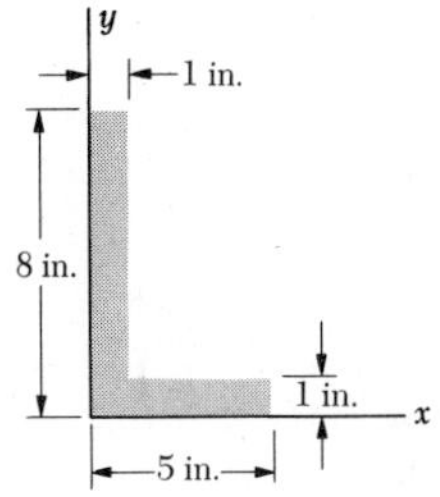

FIG. P 5.3

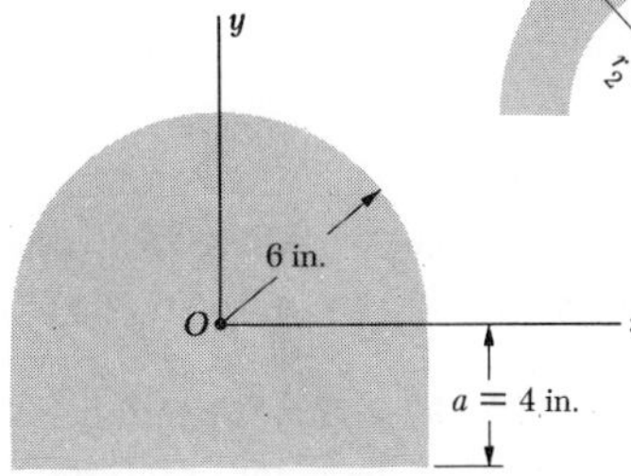

FIG. P 5.4

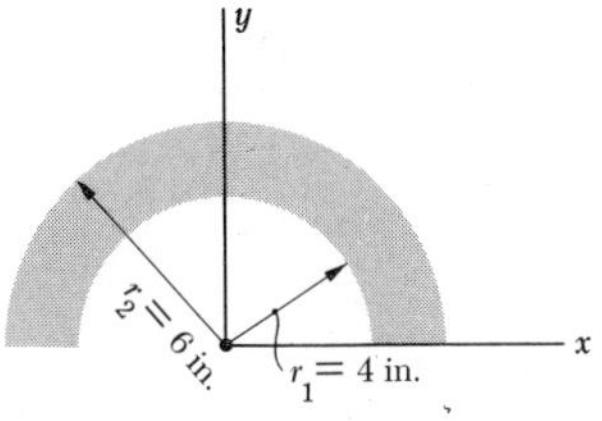

FIG. P 5.5

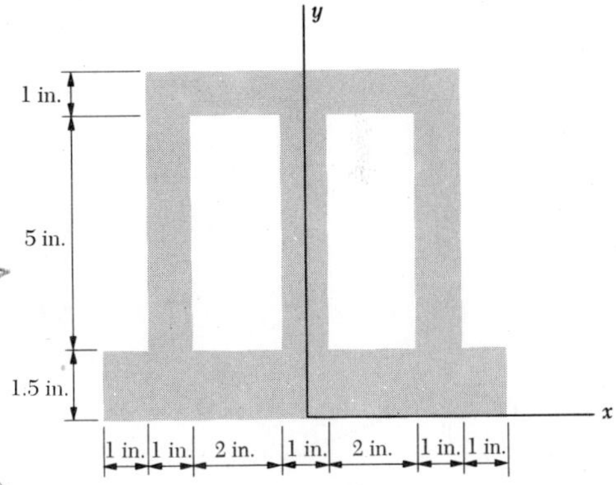

FIG. P 5.6

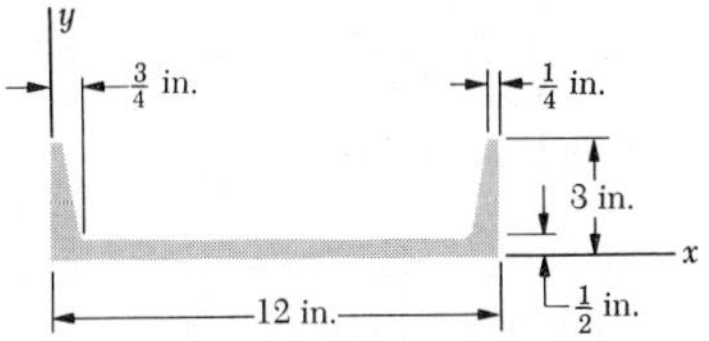

FIG. P 5.7

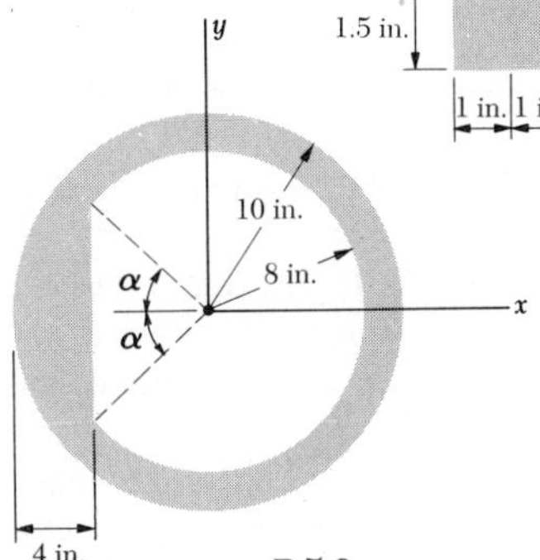

FIG. P 5.8

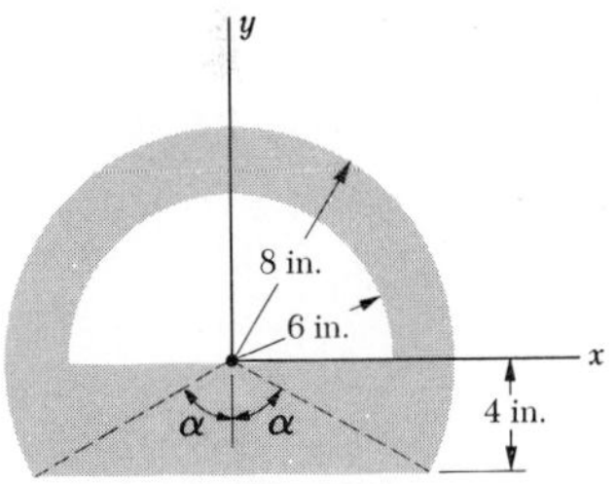

FIG. P 5.9

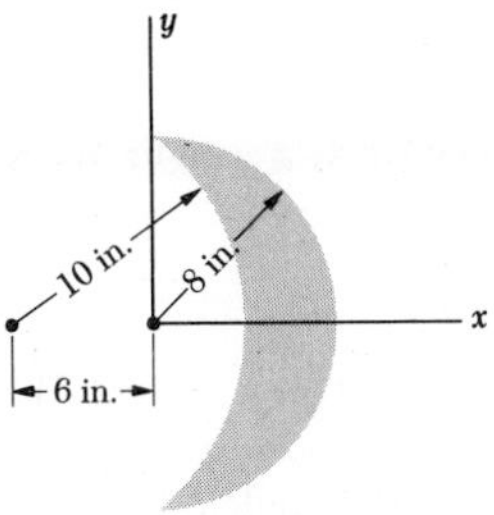

FIG. P 5.10

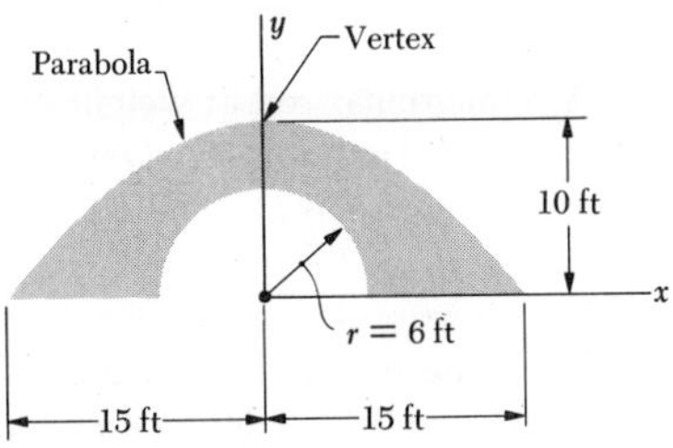

FIG. P 5.11

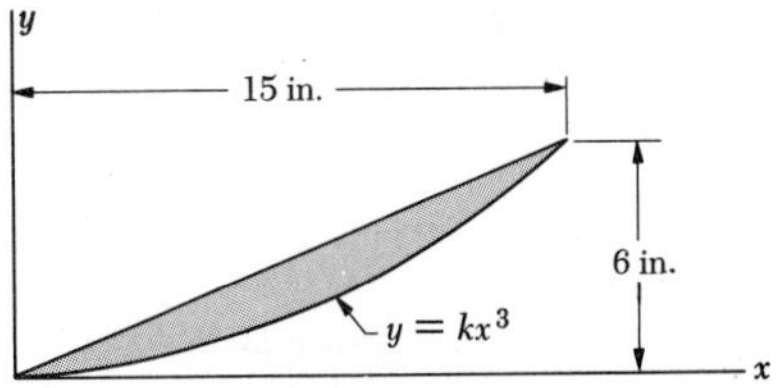

FIG. P 5.12

5.13. Locate the centroid of the shaded area in terms of a, b, and h.

5.14. Determine the abscissa of the centroid of the circular segment in terms of r and α.

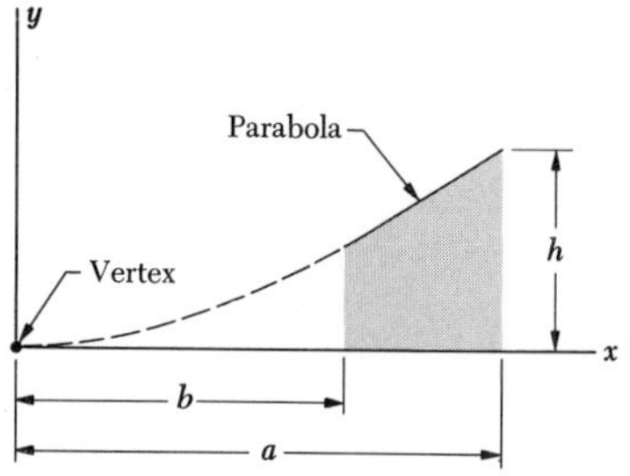

FIG. P 5.13

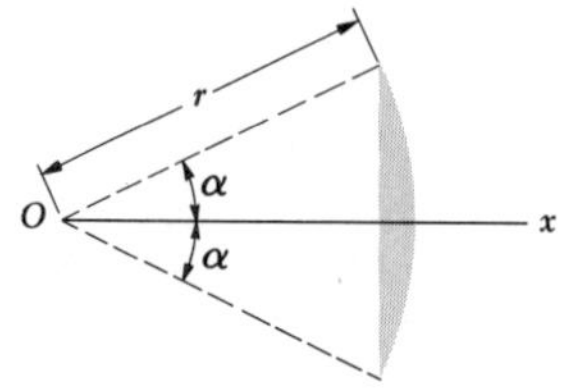

FIG. P 5.14

5.15 through 5.18. A thin homogeneous wire is bent to form the *perimeter* of the figure indicated. Locate the center of gravity of the wire figure thus formed.

5.15. Fig. P 5.1.
5.16. Fig. P 5.4.
5.17. Fig. P 5.10.
5.18. Fig. P 5.14.

5.19. For the plane area of Prob. 5.4, determine the value of the dimension a for which the centroid of the area is located at the origin O.

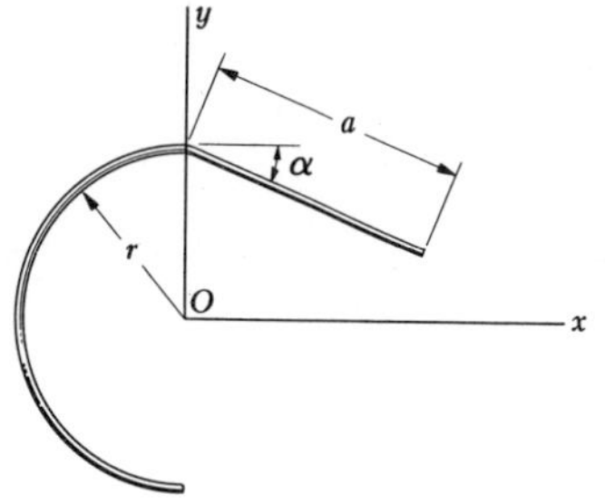

FIG. P 5.21

5.20. For the semiannular area of Prob. 5.5, determine the ratio r_1 to r_2 for which the centroid of the area is located at the point of intersection of the inner circle and the y axis.

5.21. The figure shown is formed of a thin homogeneous wire. Determine the length a of the straight portion and the angle α for which the center of gravity of the entire figure is located at the origin O.

***5.22.** Locate the centroid C in Prob. 5.5 in terms of r_1 and r_2 and show that, as r_1 approaches r_2, the location of C approaches that for a semicircular arc of radius $\frac{1}{2}(r_1 + r_2)$.

5.23. A semicircular rod of weight W and radius r is attached to a pin at A. If the surface at B is smooth, determine the reactions at A and B.

5.24. A semicircular rod of weight W is hinged at A; a weight W_1 is attached to the rod at point B. Derive an expression for the magnitude of θ in terms of W and W_1.

***5.25.** A semicircular rod of weight W is hinged at A; a weight W_1 is attached to the rod at a point D. Denoting by α the angle formed by the radii AO and OD, derive an expression for the angle θ in terms of W, W_1, and α.

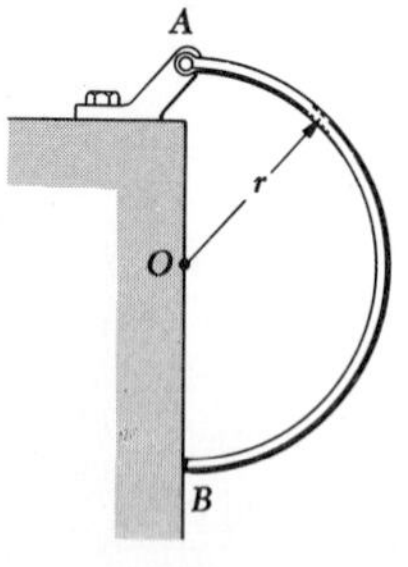

FIG. P 5.23

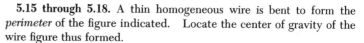

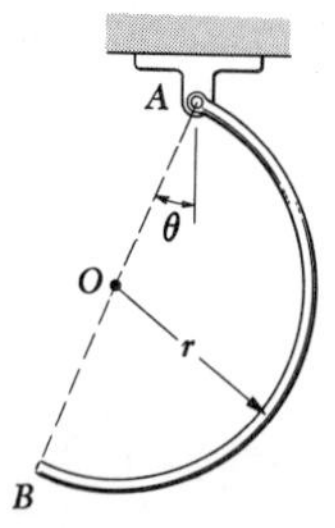

FIG. P 5.24 AND P 5.25

*5.26. If in Prob. 5.25 the weight W_1 is equal in magnitude to the weight of the rod W, determine where W_1 should be attached to the rod so that the angle θ will be maximum. Also determine the corresponding maximum value of θ.

*5.27. A curved slot is cut in a uniform disk of radius r. The disk is mounted on a frictionless shaft at O and is in equilibrium in the position shown. After a weight W_1 has been attached to the rim of the disk at A, the disk takes a new position of equilibrium in which line BOC is vertical. At what point on the rim should a second weight W_2 be attached, and how large should W_2 be, if the center of gravity of the disk and the two weights is to be located at O?

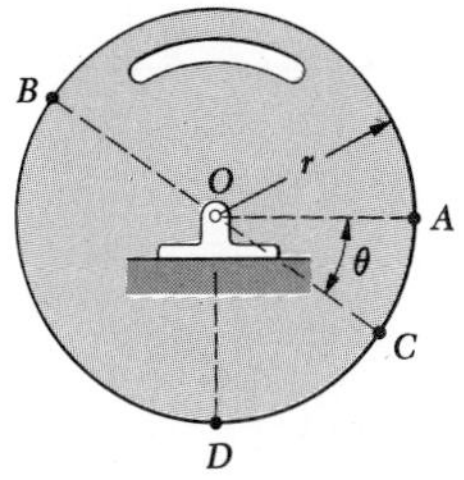

FIG. P 5.27

5.28. The plan view of a cam of uniform thickness is shown. Locate by approximate means the center of gravity of the cam.

5.29. A plate of uniform thickness is cut as shown. Locate by approximate means the center of gravity of the plate.

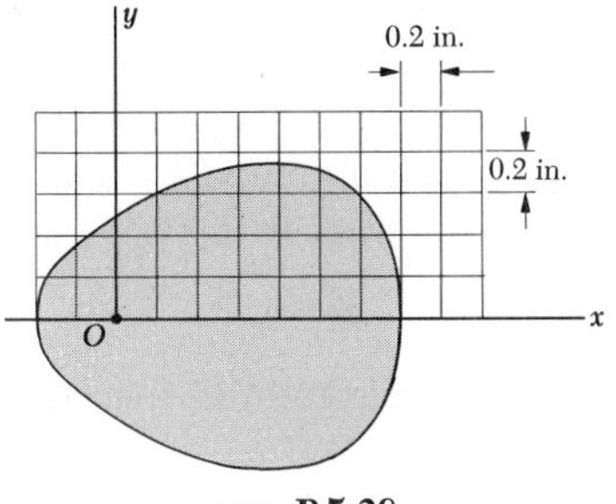

FIG. P 5.28

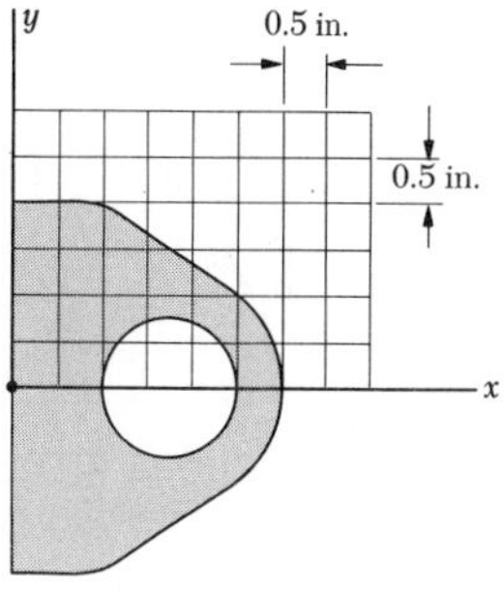

FIG. P 5.29

5.30. Divide the parabolic spandrel shown into five vertical sections and determine by approximate means the x coordinate of its centroid; approximate the spandrel by rectangles of the form $bcc'b'$. What is the percentage error in the answer obtained? (See Fig. 5.8A for exact answer.)

5.31. Solve Prob. 5.30 using rectangles of the form $bdd'b'$.

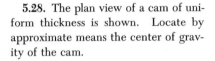

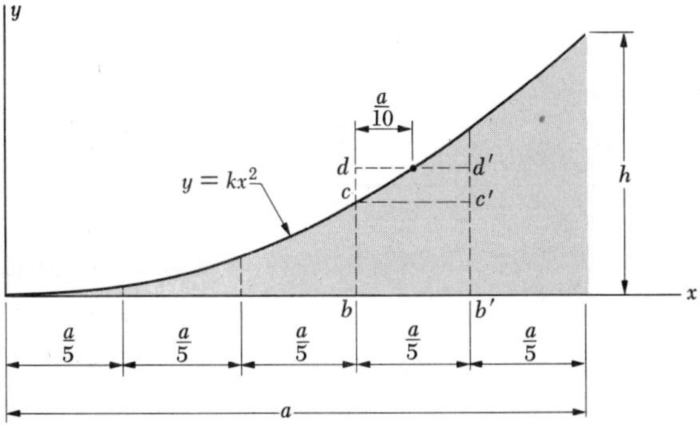

FIG. P 5.30

$\bar{x}_{el} = x$

$\bar{y}_{el} = y/2$

$dA = y\, dx$

(a)

$\bar{x}_{el} = \dfrac{a+x}{2}$

$\bar{y}_{el} = y$

$dA = (a - x)\, dy$

(b)

$\bar{x}_{el} = \dfrac{2r}{3}\cos\theta$

$\bar{y}_{el} = \dfrac{2r}{3}\sin\theta$

$dA = \dfrac{1}{2} r^2\, d\theta$

(c)

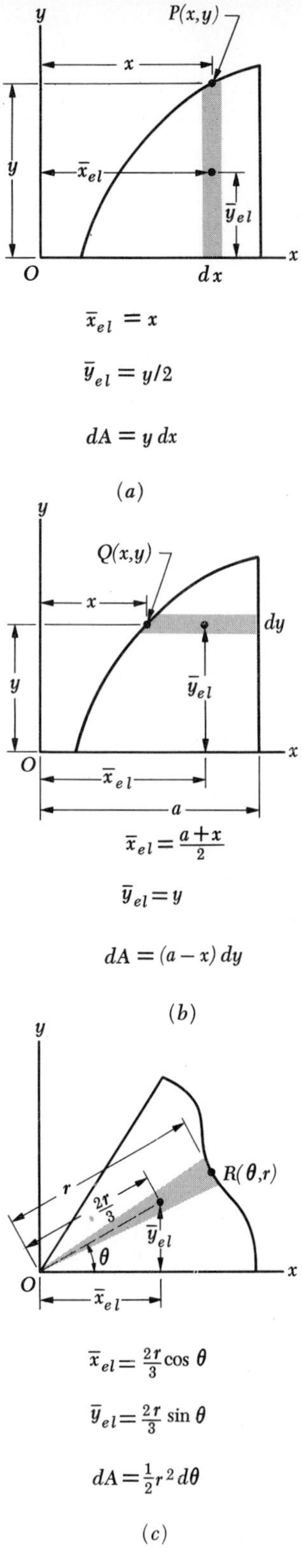

FIG. 5.12. Centroids and areas of differential elements

5.4. Determination of Centroids by Integration. The centroid of an area bounded by analytical curves (i.e., curves defined by algebraic equations) is usually determined by computing the integrals in Eqs. (5.5) of Sec. 5.2.

$$\bar{x}A = \int x\, dA \qquad \bar{y}A = \int y\, dA \qquad (5.5)$$

If the element of area dA is chosen equal to a small square of sides dx and dy, the determination of each of these integrals requires a *double integration* in x and y. A double integration is also necessary if polar coordinates are used and if dA is chosen equal to a small square of sides dr and $r\, d\theta$.

In most cases, however, it is possible to determine the coordinates of the centroid of an area by performing a single integration. This is achieved by choosing for dA a thin rectangle or strip, or a thin sector or pie-shaped element (Fig. 5.12). The coordinates of the centroid of the area under consideration are then obtained by expressing that the first moment of the entire area with respect to each of the coordinate axes is equal to the sum (or integral) of the corresponding moments of the elements of area. Denoting by $\bar{x}_{el}$ and $\bar{y}_{el}$ the coordinates of the centroid of the element dA, we write

▶ ΣM_y: $\bar{x}A = \int \bar{x}_{el}\, dA$

▶ ΣM_x: $\bar{y}A = \int \bar{y}_{el}\, dA$ (5.9)

If the area itself is not already known, it may also be computed from these elements.

The coordinates $\bar{x}_{el}$ and $\bar{y}_{el}$ of the centroid of the element of area should be expressed in terms of the coordinates of a point located on the curve bounding the area under consideration. Also, the element of area dA should be expressed in terms of the coordinates of the point and their differentials. This has been done in Fig. 5.12 for three common types of elements; the pie-shaped element of part c should be used when the equation of the curve bounding the area is given in polar coordinates. The appropriate expressions should be substituted in formulas (5.9), and the equation of the curve should be used to express one of the coordinates in terms of the other. The integration is thus reduced to a single integration which may be performed according to the usual rules of calculus.

The centroid of a line defined by an algebraic equation may be determined by computing the integrals in Eqs. (5.6) of Sec. 5.2.

$$\bar{x}L = \int x\, dL \qquad \bar{y}L = \int y\, dL \qquad (5.6)$$

The element dL should be replaced by one of the following expressions, depending upon the type of equation used to define the line (these expressions may be derived by using the Pythagorean theorem).

$$dL = \sqrt{1 + (dy/dx)^2}\, dx$$
$$dL = \sqrt{1 + (dx/dy)^2}\, dy$$
$$dL = \sqrt{r^2 + (dr/d\theta)^2}\, d\theta$$

The equation of the line is then used to express one of the coordinates in terms of the other, and the integration may be performed by the methods of calculus.

5.5. Theorems of Pappus-Guldinus. These theorems, which were first formulated by the Greek geometer Pappus during the third century A.D. and later restated by the Swiss mathematician Guldinus, or Guldin (1577–1643), deal with surfaces and bodies of revolution.

A *surface of revolution* is a surface which may be generated by rotating a plane curve about a fixed axis. For example (Fig. 5.13), the surface of a sphere may be obtained by rotating a

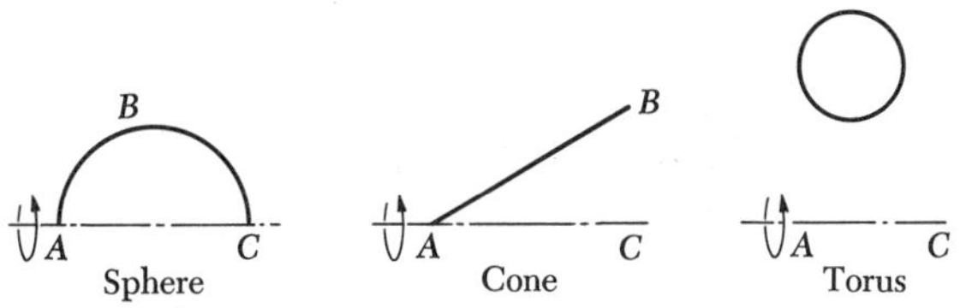

FIG. 5.13. Generating a surface of revolution

semicircular arc ABC about the diameter AC; the surface of a cone by rotating a straight line AB about an axis AC; the surface of a torus or ring by rotating the circumference of a circle about a nonintersecting axis. A *body of revolution* is a body which may be generated by rotating a plane area about a fixed axis. A solid sphere may be obtained by rotating a semicircular area, a cone by rotating a triangular area, and a solid torus by rotating a full circular area (Fig. 5.14).

THEOREM I. *The area of a surface of revolution is equal to the length of the generating curve times the distance traveled by the centroid of the curve while the surface is being generated.*

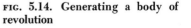

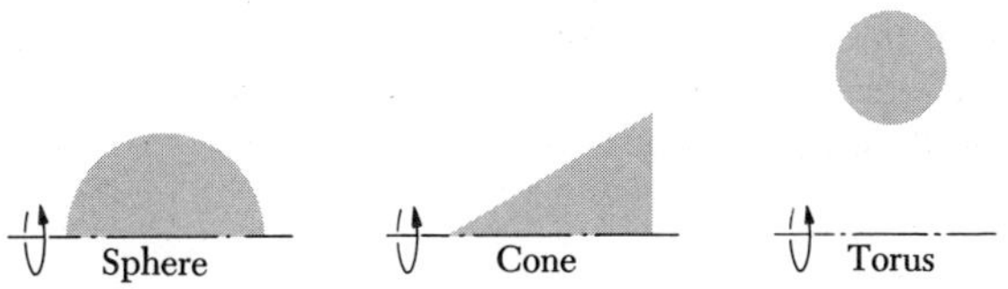

FIG. 5.14. Generating a body of revolution

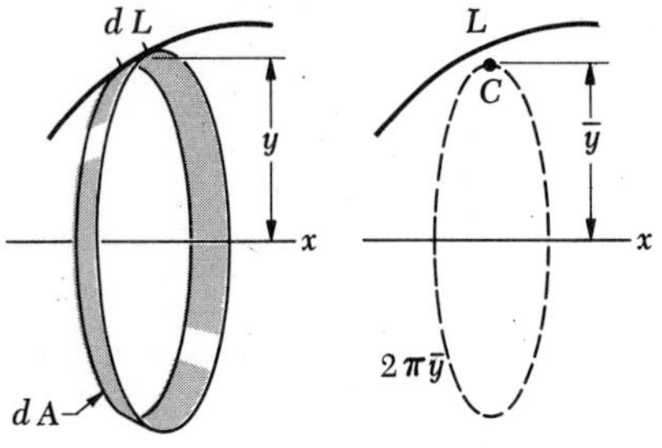

FIG. 5.15

Proof. Consider an element dL of the line L (Fig. 5.15) which is revolved about the x axis. The area dA generated by the element dL is equal to $2\pi y\, dL$. Thus, the entire area generated by L is $A = \int 2\pi y\, dL$. But we saw in Sec. 5.2 that the integral $\int y\, dL$ is equal to $\bar{y}L$. We have therefore

$$A = 2\pi\bar{y}L \tag{5.10}$$

where $2\pi\bar{y}$ is the distance traveled by the centroid of L. It should be noted that the generating curve should not cross the axis about which it is rotated; if it did, the two sections on either side of the axis would generate areas of opposite signs and the theorem would not apply.

THEOREM II. *The volume of a body of revolution is equal to the generating area times the distance traveled by the centroid of the area while the body is being generated.*

Proof. Consider an element dA of the area A which is revolved about the x axis (Fig. 5.16). The volume dV generated by the element dA is equal to $2\pi y\, dA$. Thus, the entire volume generated by A is $V = \int 2\pi y\, dA$. But since the integral $\int y\, dA$ is equal to $\bar{y}A$ (Sec. 5.2), we have

$$V = 2\pi\bar{y}A \tag{5.11}$$

where $2\pi\bar{y}$ is the distance traveled by the centroid of A. Again, it should be noted that the theorem does not apply if the axis of rotation intersects the generating area.

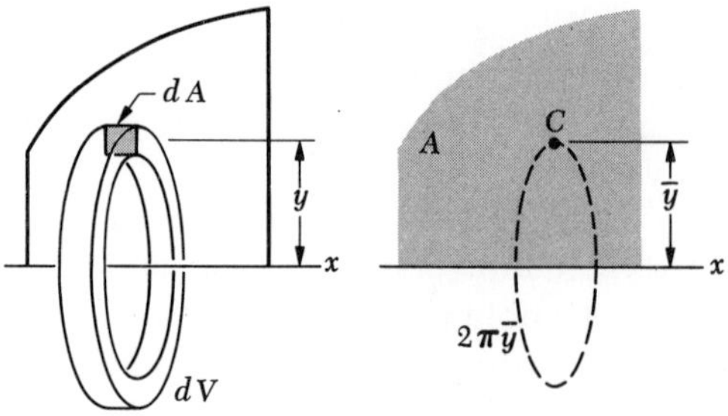

FIG. 5.16

The theorems of Pappus-Guldinus offer a simple way for computing the area of surfaces of revolution and the volume of bodies of revolution. They may also be used conversely to determine the centroid of a plane curve when the area of the surface generated by the curve is known or to determine the centroid of a plane area when the volume of the body generated by the area is known (see Sample Prob. 5.8).

SAMPLE PROBLEM 5.4

Determine by direct integration the centroid of a parabolic spandrel.

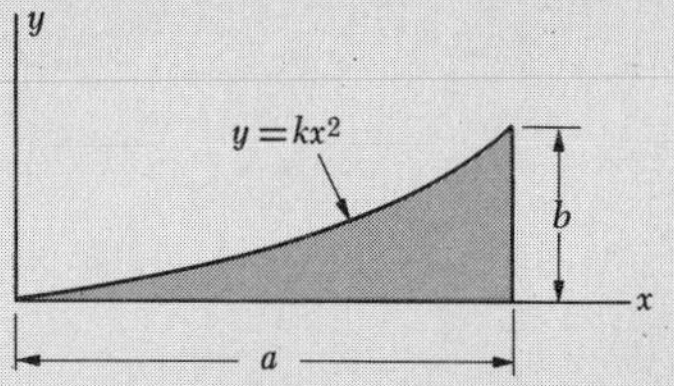

Solution. The value of k is determined by substituting $x = a$ and $y = b$ in the given equation. We have $b = ka^2$ and $k = b/a^2$. The equation of the curve is thus

$$y = \frac{b}{a^2}x^2 \qquad \text{or} \qquad x = \frac{a}{b^{1/2}}y^{1/2}$$

Vertical Differential Element. We choose the differential element shown and find the total area of the figure.

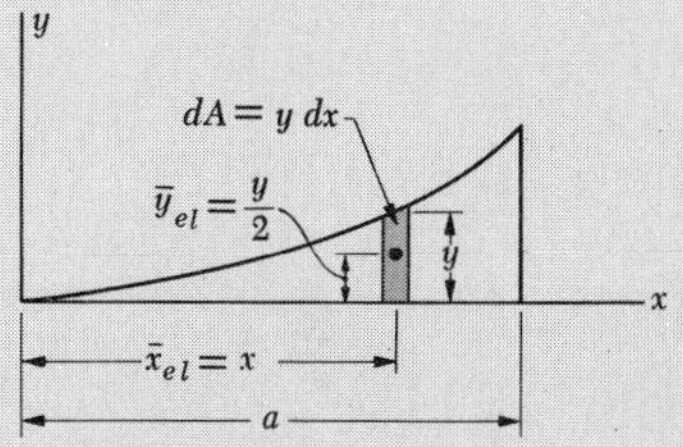

$$A = \int dA = \int y\,dx = \int_0^a \frac{b}{a^2}x^2\,dx = \left[\frac{b}{a^2}\frac{x^3}{3}\right]_0^a = \frac{ab}{3}$$

The moment of the differential element with respect to the y axis is $\bar{x}_{el}\,dA$; hence, the moment of the entire area with respect to this axis is

$$\int \bar{x}_{el}\,dA = \int xy\,dx = \int_0^a x\left(\frac{b}{a^2}x^2\right)dx = \left[\frac{b}{a^2}\frac{x^4}{4}\right]_0^a = \frac{a^2b}{4}$$

Thus, $\quad \bar{x}A = \int \bar{x}_{el}\,dA \qquad \bar{x}\frac{ab}{3} = \frac{a^2b}{4} \qquad \bar{x} = \frac{3}{4}a$ ◄

Likewise, the moment of the differential element with respect to the x axis is $\bar{y}_{el}\,dA$, and the moment of the entire area is

$$\int \bar{y}_{el}\,dA = \int \frac{y}{2}y\,dx = \int_0^a \frac{1}{2}\left(\frac{b}{a^2}x^2\right)^2 dx = \left[\frac{b^2}{2a^4}\frac{x^5}{5}\right]_0^a = \frac{ab^2}{10}$$

Thus, $\quad \bar{y}A = \int \bar{y}_{el}\,dA \qquad \bar{y}\frac{ab}{3} = \frac{ab^2}{10} \qquad \bar{y} = \frac{3}{10}b$ ◄

Horizontal Differential Element. The same result may be obtained by considering a horizontal element. The moments of the area are

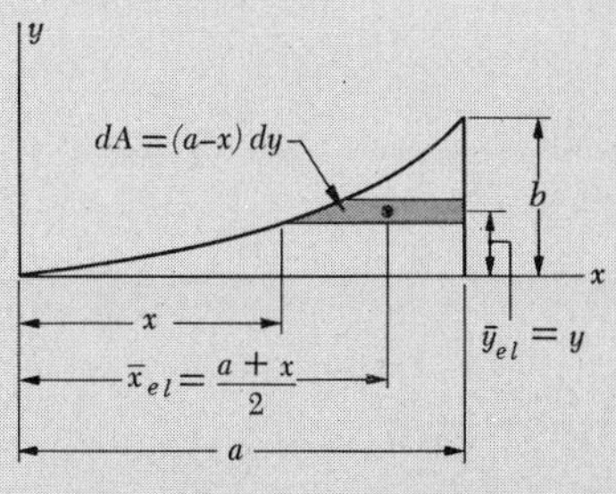

$$\int \bar{x}_{el}\,dA = \int \frac{a+x}{2}(a-x)\,dy = \int_0^b \frac{a^2-x^2}{2}\,dy$$

$$= \frac{1}{2}\int_0^b \left(a^2 - \frac{a^2}{b}y\right)dy = \frac{a^2b}{4}$$

$$\int \bar{y}_{el}\,dA = \int y(a-x)\,dy = \int y\left(a - \frac{a}{b^{1/2}}y^{1/2}\right)dy$$

$$= \int_0^b \left(ay - \frac{a}{b^{1/2}}y^{3/2}\right)dy = \frac{ab^2}{10}$$

These moments are again substituted in the equations defining the centroid of the area to obtain $\bar{x}$ and $\bar{y}$.

SAMPLE PROBLEM 5.5

Determine the centroid of a quarter circle by direct integration.

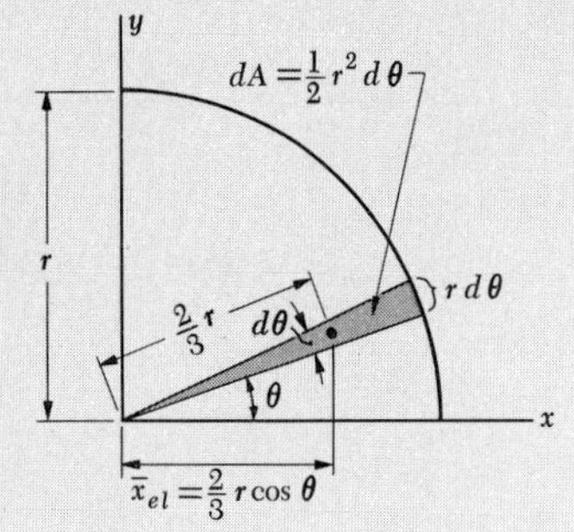

Solution. A differential element is chosen as shown, and the area of the quarter circle is determined.

$$A = \int dA = \int_0^{\pi/2} \tfrac{1}{2}r^2\, d\theta = \tfrac{1}{4}\pi r^2$$

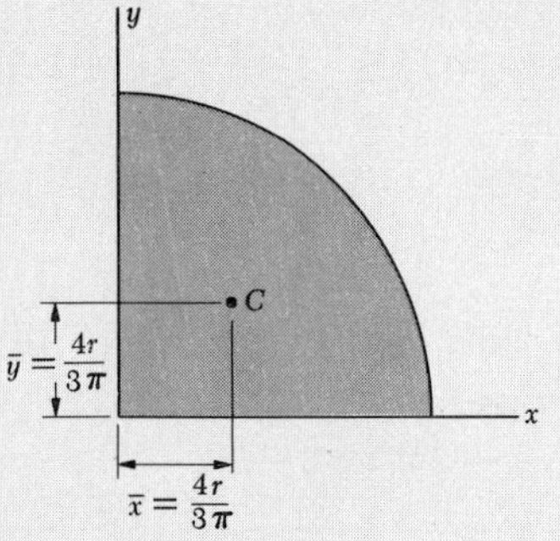

The moment of the area with respect to the y axis is

$$\int_0^{\pi/2} \bar{x}_{el}\, dA = \int_0^{\pi/2} (\tfrac{2}{3}r\cos\theta)(\tfrac{1}{2}r^2\, d\theta) = \tfrac{1}{3}r^3 \int_0^{\pi/2} \cos\theta\, d\theta = \tfrac{1}{3}r^3$$

Thus, $\quad \bar{x}A = \int \bar{x}_{el}\, dA \qquad \bar{x}(\tfrac{1}{4}\pi r^2) = \tfrac{1}{3}r^3 \qquad \bar{x} = \dfrac{4r}{3\pi}$

Since the area is symmetrical with respect to a 45° line drawn through the origin, we have

$$\bar{x} = \bar{y} = \frac{4r}{3\pi} \quad ◄$$

SAMPLE PROBLEM 5.6

Determine the centroid of the 90° circular arc shown.

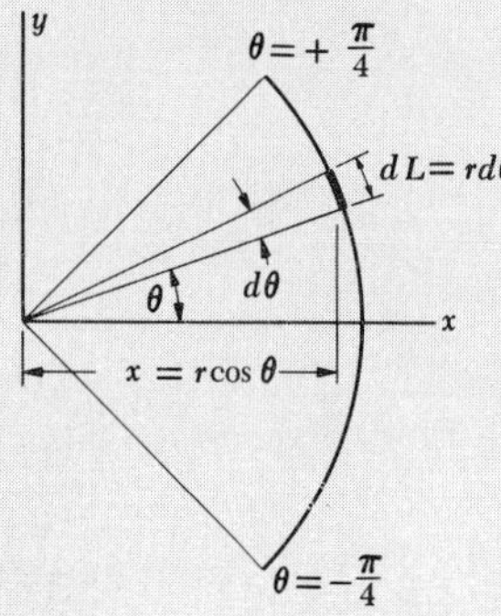

Solution. The arc is symmetrical with respect to the x axis, and we note that $\bar{y} = 0$. Since the arc subtends an angle of $90° = \tfrac{1}{2}\pi$ radians, the length of arc is $L = \tfrac{1}{2}\pi r$. A differential element of arc is chosen as shown, and the moment of the entire arc with respect to the y axis is determined.

$$\int x\, dL = \int_{-\pi/4}^{\pi/4} (r\cos\theta)(r\, d\theta)$$

$$= r^2 \int_{-\pi/4}^{\pi/4} \cos\theta\, d\theta = \sqrt{2}\, r^2$$

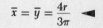

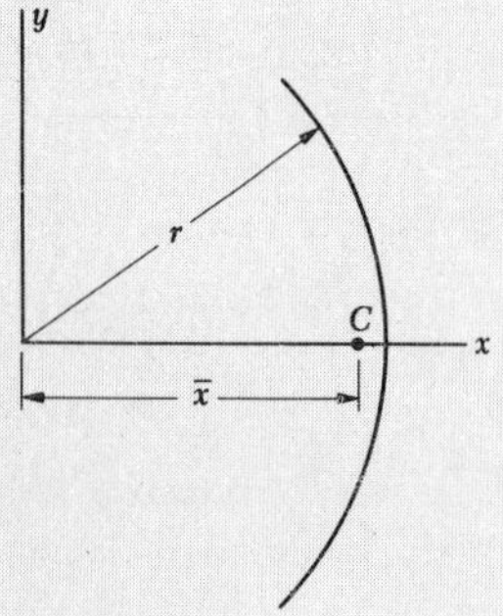

Thus, $\quad \bar{x}L = \int x\, dL \qquad \bar{x}(\tfrac{1}{2}\pi r) = \sqrt{2}\, r^2$

$$\bar{x} = \frac{2\sqrt{2}}{\pi} r \quad ◄$$

SAMPLE PROBLEM 5.7

The outside diameter of a steel flywheel is 8 ft, and the cross section of the rim is as shown. Determine the weight of the rim. Specific weight of steel = 490 lb/ft³.

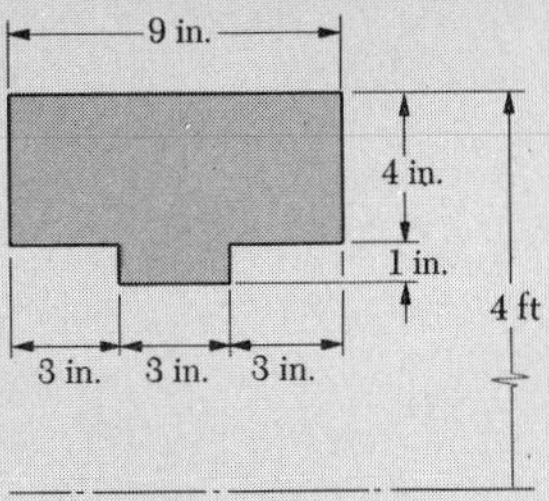

Solution. The volume of the rim may be found by applying Theorem II of Pappus-Guldinus, which states that the volume equals the product of the given cross-sectional area and of the distance traveled by its centroid in one complete revolution. However, the volume may be more easily obtained by considering the cross section as the sum of a 9- by 4-in. rectangle and a 3- by 1-in. rectangle. The volume of the rim is then equal to the sum of the volumes generated by rotating the rectangles about the x axis.

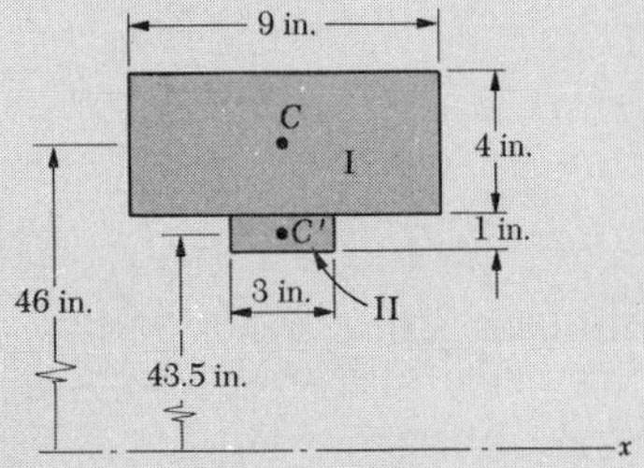

Component	Area	$\bar{y}$	Distance traveled by C	Volume
I	36 in.²	46.0 in.	$2\pi(46.0) = 289$ in.	(36 in.²)(289 in.) = 10,400 in.³
II	3 in.²	43.5 in.	$2\pi(43.5) = 273$ in.	(3 in.²)(273 in.) = 819 in.³
				Volume of rim = 11,220 in.³

Since the specific weight of steel is 490 lb/ft³, the weight of the rim is

$$W = \gamma V = \frac{490 \text{ lb/ft}^3}{1{,}728 \text{ in.}^3/\text{ft}^3}(11{,}220 \text{ in.}^3) \qquad W = 3{,}180 \text{ lb} \blacktriangleleft$$

SAMPLE PROBLEM 5.8

Using the theorems of Pappus-Guldinus, determine (*a*) the centroid of a semicircular area, (*b*) the centroid of a semicircular arc. We recall that the volume of a sphere is $\frac{4}{3}\pi r^3$ and that its surface area is $4\pi r^2$.

Solution. The volume of a sphere is equal to the product of the area of a semicircle and of the distance traveled by the centroid of the semicircle in one revolution about the x axis.

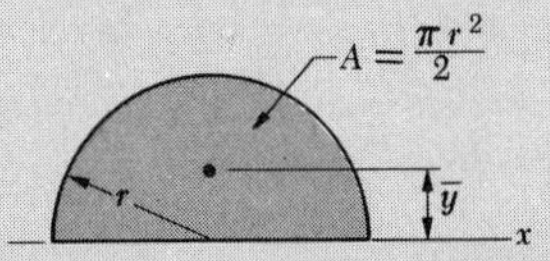

$$V = 2\pi\bar{y}A \qquad \tfrac{4}{3}\pi r^3 = 2\pi\bar{y}(\tfrac{1}{2}\pi r^2) \qquad \bar{y} = \frac{4r}{3\pi} \blacktriangleleft$$

Likewise, the area of a sphere is equal to the product of the length of the generating semicircle and of the distance traveled by its centroid in one revolution.

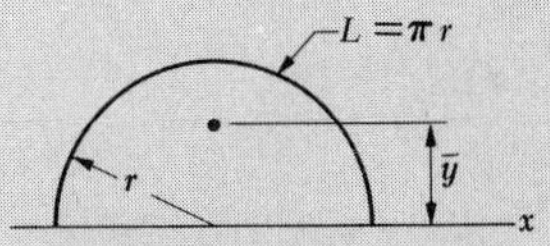

$$A = 2\pi\bar{y}L \qquad 4\pi r^2 = 2\pi\bar{y}(\pi r) \qquad \bar{y} = \frac{2r}{\pi} \blacktriangleleft$$

PROBLEMS

5.32 through 5.35. Determine by direct integration the centroid of the area shown.

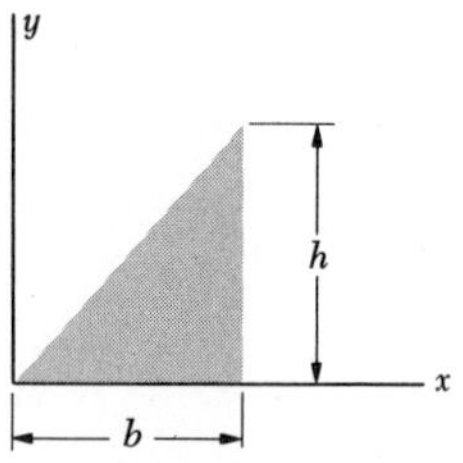

FIG. P 5.32

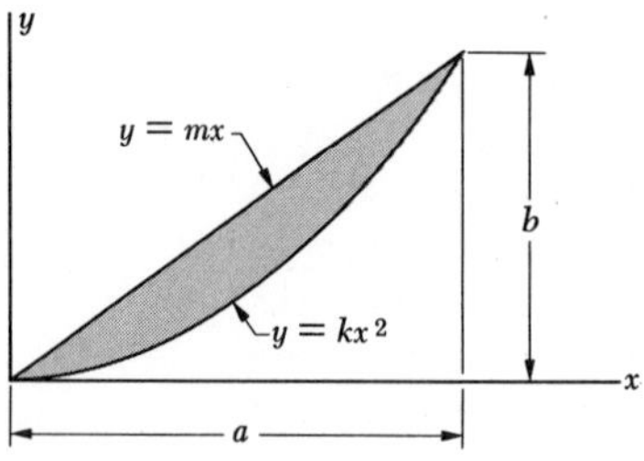

FIG. P 5.33

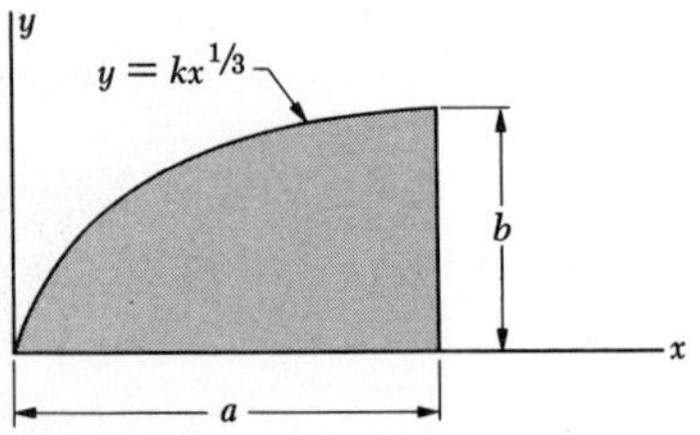

FIG. P 5.34

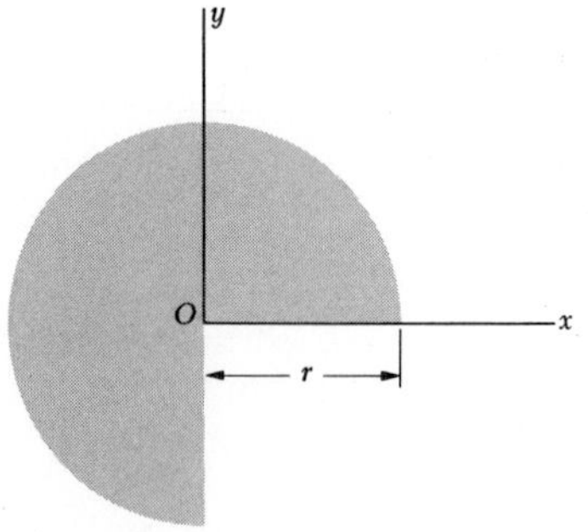

FIG. P 5.35

5.36 through 5.41. Derive by direct integration the expressions for $\bar{x}$ and $\bar{y}$ given in Fig. 5.8 for:

5.36. A semicircular area.
5.37. A quarter-elliptical area.
5.38. A circular sector.
5.39. A semiparabolic area.
5.40. A general spandrel ($y = kx^n$).
5.41. An arc of circle.

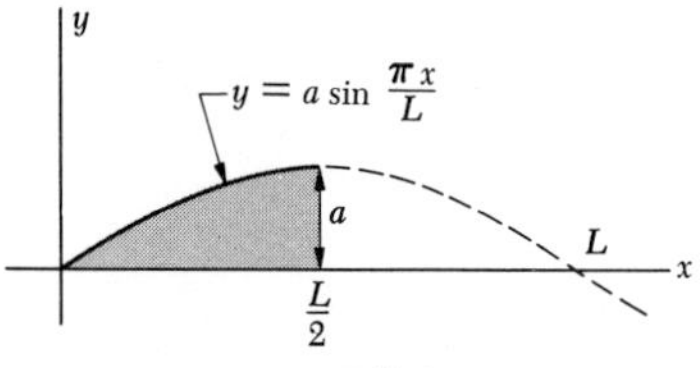

FIG. P 5.44

5.42. Determine by direct integration the centroid of the area bounded by the curves $y = x^2$ and $x = y^2$.

5.43. Determine by direct integration the centroid of the area located in the first quadrant and bounded by the curves $y = x^n$ and $x = y^n$, for $n > 1$.

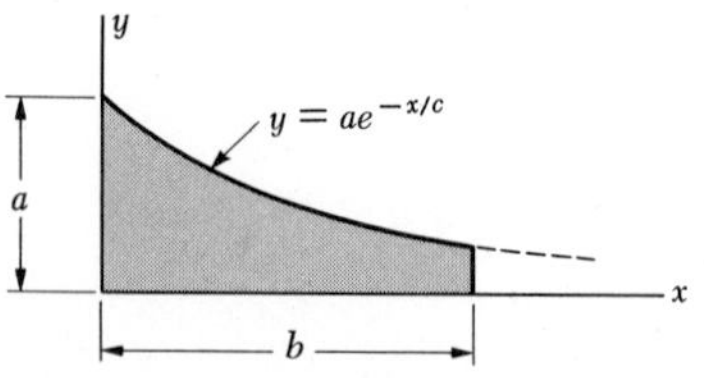

FIG. P 5.45

***5.44.** Determine by direct integration the centroid of the area shown.

***5.45.** Determine by direct integration the centroid of the area shown when $b = c$.

*5.46. Determine the location of the centroid of the area of Prob. 5.45 when b approaches infinity.

*5.47. Determine the centroid of the area shown.

*5.48. Determine the centroid of the area of Prob. 5.47 in terms of a.

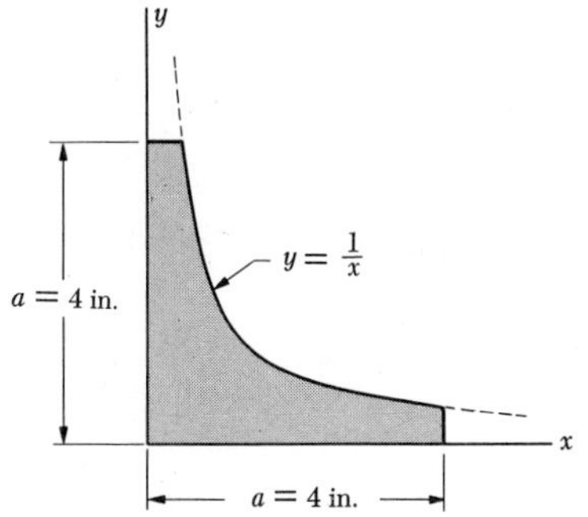

FIG. P 5.47

5.49. Determine the volume and total surface area of a right circular cone of height h and base radius r.

5.50. Determine the volume of the solid obtained by rotating the trapezoid of Prob. 5.1 about (a) the x axis, (b) the y axis.

5.51. Determine the volume of the solid obtained by rotating the semiparabolic area shown about (a) the y axis, (b) the x axis.

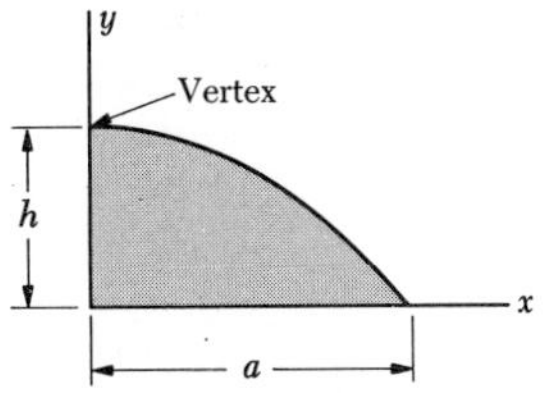

FIG. P 5.51

5.52. Determine the surface area and the volume of the torus shown.

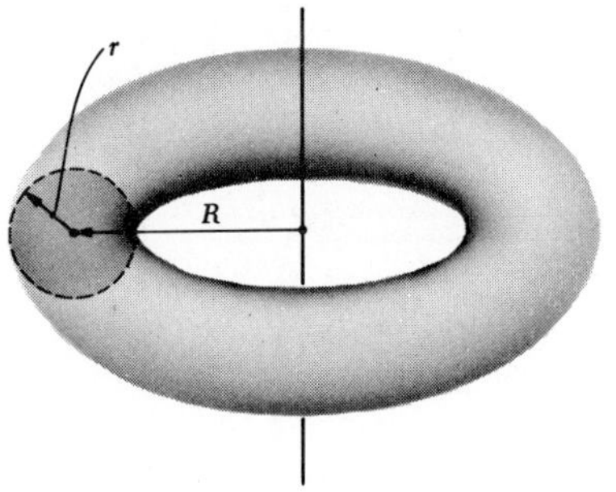

FIG. P 5.52

5.53. The inside diameter of a spherical tank is 6 ft. What volume of liquid is required to fill the tank to a depth of 1.5 ft?

5.54. In Prob. 5.53, determine the area of the inside surface which is below the level of the liquid.

5.55. Determine the latitude of the parallel which divides the area of the northern hemisphere into two equal parts.

5.56. The excavation shown has been dug in a soil with a constant angle of repose $\phi = \tan^{-1}(\frac{3}{4})$. The excavation is to be enlarged until the base radius is $r = 22$ ft and the width of the straight portion is $2r = 44$ ft. Assuming that the angle of repose of the soil will remain constant, determine the volume of soil which must be removed in the portion of the excavation to the left of the vertical plane $ABDE$.

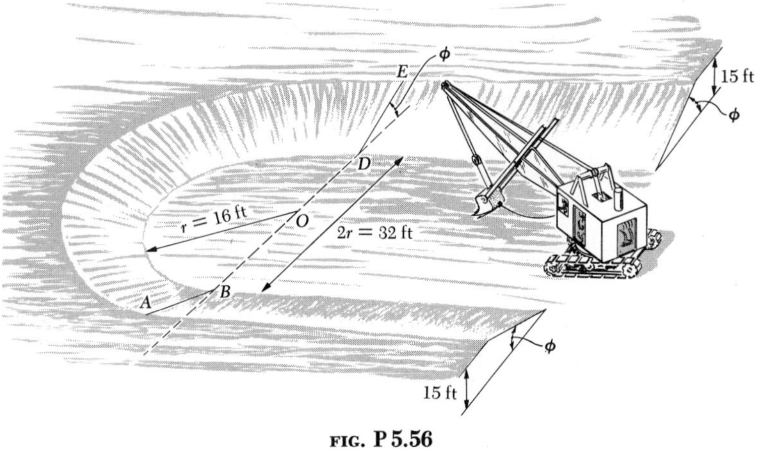

FIG. P 5.56

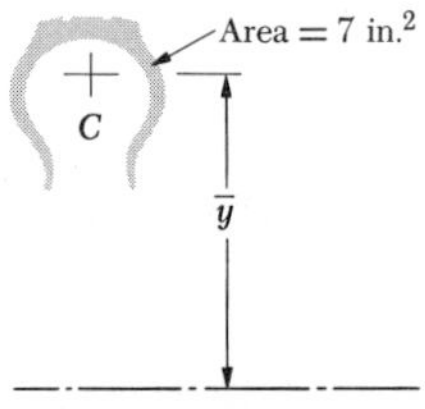

FIG. P 5.57

5.57. An automobile tire weighs 22 lb and has a cross-sectional area of 7 in.^{2}. The specific weight of the rubber used is 80 lb/ft^3; determine the location of the centroid of the cross-sectional area.

5.58. A section of ring is cut into the two portions shown; the cross section of each portion is a semicircle. Determine the volume and the surface area, including the vertical cut, of portion *1*.

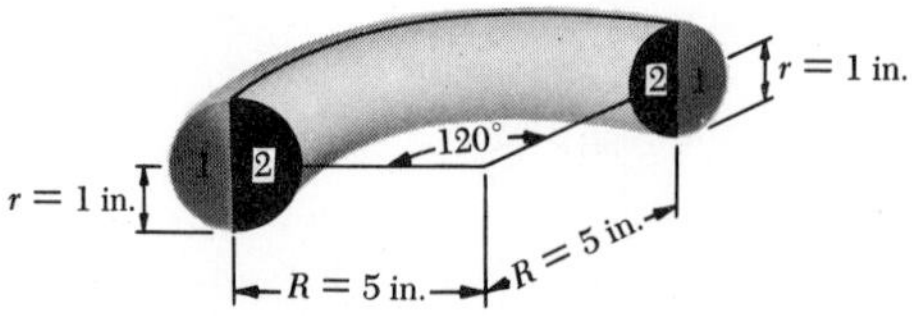

FIG. P 5.58

5.59. Solve Prob. 5.58 for portion *2* of the ring.

5.60. In Prob. 5.58 determine the ratio of r to R for which the volume of portion *1* is twice the volume of portion *2*.

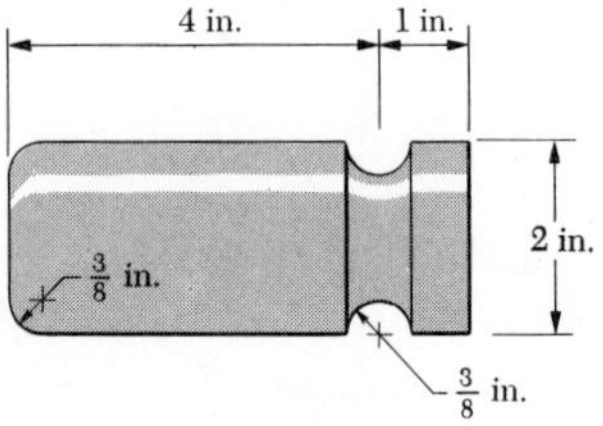

FIG. P 5.61

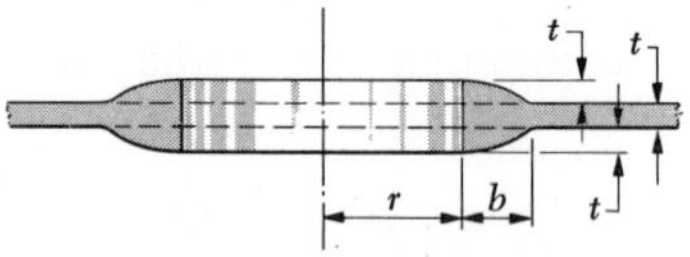

FIG. P 5.63

5.61. A brass plug is made from a 2-in.-diameter cylinder by machining it as shown. Determine the volume of the material removed in forming the semicircular groove.

5.62. In Prob. 5.61 determine the volume of the material removed in machining the quarter-circular rounding on the left end of the plug.

5.63. A hole of radius r is drilled in a flat plate of thickness t. In order to reinforce the plate, a metal "crack stopper" is welded around the hole as shown. Assuming that the cross section of the crack stopper is parabolic, determine the ratio b/r for which the total volume of metal used is the same as that of a plate without a hole.

5.64. Solve Prob. 5.63 assuming that the cross section of the crack stopper is triangular.

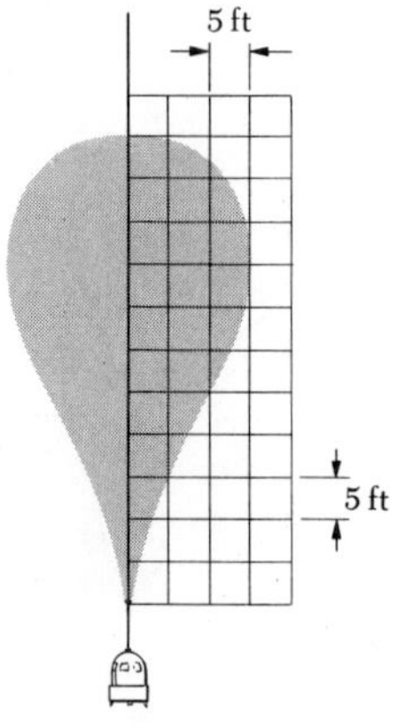

FIG. P 5.65

5.65. An experimental high-altitude balloon at a given time has the shape shown. Determine by approximate means (a) the volume of gas inside the balloon, (b) the surface area of the balloon.

***5.6. Distributed Loads on Beams.** The concept of centroid of an area may be used to solve other problems, besides those dealing with the weight of flat plates. Consider, for example, a beam supporting a *distributed load;* this load may consist of the weight of materials supported directly or indirectly by the beam, or it may be caused by wind or hydrostatic pressure. The distributed load may be represented by plotting the load w supported per unit length (Fig. 5.17). The magnitude of the force exerted on an element of beam of length dx is thus $dW = w\,dx$, and the total load supported by the beam is

$$W = \int_0^L w\,dx$$

But the product $w\,dx$ is equal to the element of area dA shown in Fig. 5.17*a*, and W is thus equal to the total area A under the load curve,

$$W = \int dA = A$$

We shall now determine where a *single concentrated load* **W**, of the same magnitude W as the total distributed load, should be applied on the beam if it is to produce the same reactions at the supports (Fig. 5.17*b*). This concentrated load **W**, which represents the resultant of the given distributed loading, should be equivalent to this loading as far as the free-body diagram of the entire beam is concerned. The point of application P of the equivalent concentrated load **W** will therefore be obtained by expressing that the moment of **W** about point O is equal to the sum of the moments of the elementary loads $d\mathbf{W}$ about O:

$$(OP)W = \int x\,dW$$

or, since $dW = w\,dx = dA$ and $W = A$,

$$(OP)A = \int_0^L x\,dA \tag{5.12}$$

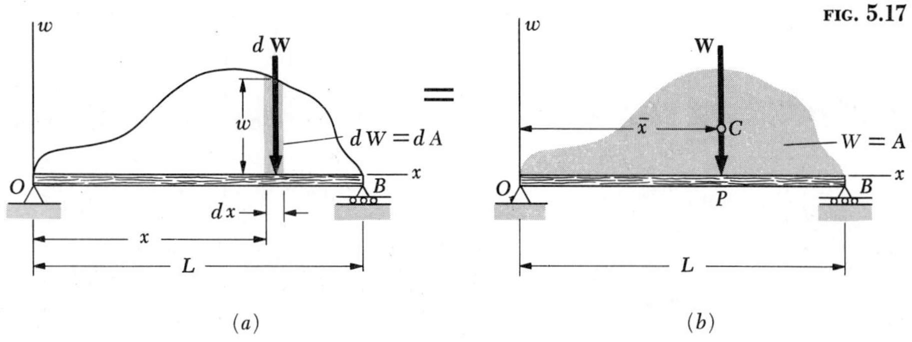

FIG. 5.17

Since the integral represents the first moment with respect to the w axis of the area under the load curve, it may be replaced by the product $\bar{x}A$. We have therefore $OP = \bar{x}$, where $\bar{x}$ is the distance from the w axis to the centroid C of the area A (this is *not* the centroid of the beam).

A distributed load on a beam may thus be replaced by a concentrated load; the magnitude of this single load is equal to the area under the load curve, and its line of action passes through the centroid of that area. It should be noted, however, that the concentrated load is equivalent to the given loading only as far as external forces are concerned. It may be used to determine reactions but should not be used to compute internal forces and deflections.

***5.7. Forces on Submerged Surfaces.** Another example of the use of first moments and centroids of areas is obtained by considering the forces exerted on a *rectangular surface* submerged in a liquid. Consider the rectangular plate shown in Fig. 5.18; it has a length L, and its width, perpendicular to the plane of the figure, is assumed equal to unity. Since the gage pressure in a liquid is $p = \gamma h$, where γ is the specific weight of the liquid and h the vertical distance from the free surface, the pressure on the plate varies linearly with the distance x.

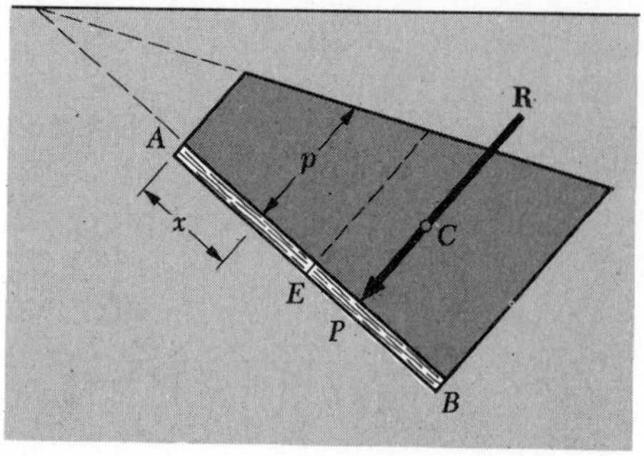

FIG. 5.18

The width of the plate being taken equal to unity, the pressure p is equal to the load w per unit length used in Sec. 5.6. The results obtained in that section may thus be used here, and we find that the magnitude of the resultant **R** of the forces exerted on one face of the plate is equal to the area under the pressure curve; we also find that the line of action of **R** passes through the centroid C of that area.

Noting that the area under the pressure curve is equal to $p_E L$, where p_E is the pressure at the center E of the plate and

L the length (or area) of the plate, we find that the magnitude R of the resultant may be obtained by multiplying the area of the plate by the pressure at the center E of the plate. The resultant **R**, however, *should not* be applied at E; as indicated above, its line of action passes through the centroid C of the area under the pressure curve. The point of application P of the resultant **R** is known as the *center of pressure.*

We shall consider next the forces exerted by a liquid on a curved surface of constant width (Fig. 5.19*a*). Since the de-

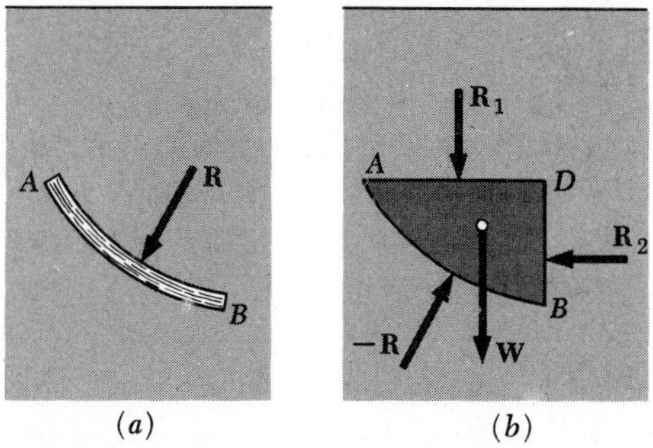

FIG. 5.19

termination of the resultant **R** of these forces by direct integration would not be easy, we shall consider the free body obtained by detaching the volume of liquid ABD bounded by the curved surface AB and by the two plane surfaces AD and DB shown in Fig. 5.19*b*. The forces acting on the free body ABD consist of the weight **W** of the volume of liquid detached, the resultant $\mathbf{R}_1$ of the forces exerted on AD, the resultant $\mathbf{R}_2$ of the forces exerted on BD, and the resultant of the forces exerted *by the curved surface on the liquid.* This last resultant is equal and opposite to, and has the same line of action as, the resultant **R** of the forces exerted *by the liquid on the curved surface;* we shall, therefore, denote it by $-\mathbf{R}$. The forces **W**, $\mathbf{R}_1$, and $\mathbf{R}_2$ may be determined by standard methods; after their values have been found, the force $-\mathbf{R}$ will be obtained by solving the equations of equilibrium for the free body of Fig. 5.19*b*. The resultant **R** of the hydrostatic forces exerted on the curved surface will then be obtained by reversing the sense of $-\mathbf{R}$.

The methods outlined in this section may be used to determine the resultant of the hydrostatic forces exerted on the surface of dams or on rectangular gates and vanes. Resultants of forces on submerged surfaces of variable width should be determined by the methods of Chap. 9.

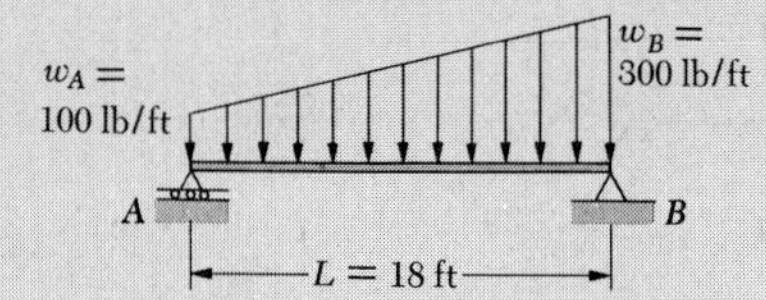

SAMPLE PROBLEM 5.9

A beam supports a distributed load as shown. (*a*) Determine the equivalent concentrated load. (*b*) Determine the reactions at the supports.

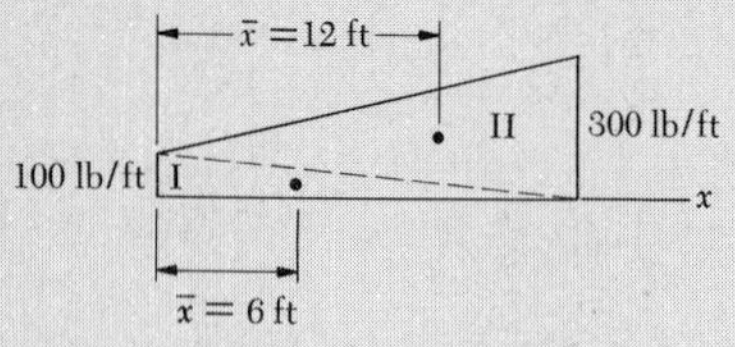

a. **Equivalent Concentrated Load.** The magnitude of the resultant of the load is equal to the area under the load curve, and the line of action of the resultant passes through the centroid of the same area. We divide the area under the load curve into two triangles and construct the following table:

Component	A	$\bar{x}$	$\bar{x}A$
Triangle I.	900	6	5,400
Triangle II	2,700	12	32,400
	$\Sigma A = 3{,}600$	. . .	$\Sigma \bar{x}A = 37{,}800$

Thus,

$$\bar{X}\Sigma A = \Sigma \bar{x}A \qquad \bar{X}(3{,}600) = 37{,}800 \qquad \bar{X} = 10.5 \text{ ft}$$

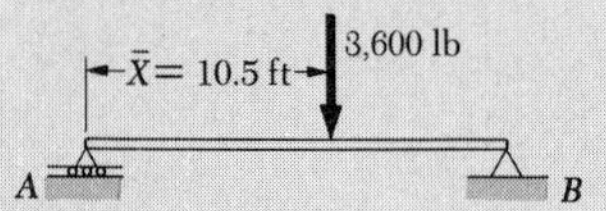

The equivalent concentrated load is

$$\mathbf{W} = 3{,}600 \text{ lb} \downarrow \quad ◄$$

and its line of action is located at a distance

$$\bar{X} = 10.5 \text{ ft to the right of } A \quad ◄$$

b. **Reactions.** The reaction at A is vertical and is denoted by **A**; the reaction at B is represented by its components $\mathbf{B}_x$ and $\mathbf{B}_y$. The given load may be considered as the sum of two triangular loads as shown. The resultant of each triangular load is equal to the area of the triangle and acts at its centroid. We write the following equilibrium equations for the free body shown:

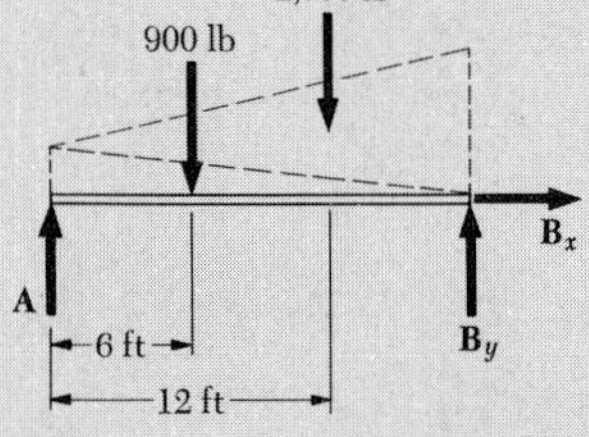

$\xrightarrow{+} \Sigma F_x = 0$: $\qquad \mathbf{B}_x = 0 \quad ◄$

$+\circlearrowleft \Sigma M_A = 0$: $\quad -(900 \text{ lb})(6 \text{ ft}) - (2{,}700 \text{ lb})(12 \text{ ft}) + B_y(18 \text{ ft}) = 0$

$$\mathbf{B}_y = 2{,}100 \text{ lb} \uparrow \quad ◄$$

$+\circlearrowleft \Sigma M_B = 0$: $\quad +(900 \text{ lb})(12 \text{ ft}) + (2{,}700 \text{ lb})(6 \text{ ft}) - A(18 \text{ ft}) = 0$

$$\mathbf{A} = 1{,}500 \text{ lb} \uparrow \quad ◄$$

Alternate Solution. The given distributed load may be replaced by its resultant, which was found in part *a*. The reactions may be determined by writing the equilibrium equations $\Sigma F_x = 0$, $\Sigma M_A = 0$, and $\Sigma M_B = 0$. We again obtain

$$\mathbf{B}_x = 0 \qquad \mathbf{B}_y = 2{,}100 \text{ lb} \uparrow \qquad \mathbf{A} = 1{,}500 \text{ lb} \uparrow \quad ◄$$

SAMPLE PROBLEM 5.10

The cross section of a concrete dam is as shown. Consider a section of the dam 1 ft thick, and determine (*a*) the resultant of the reaction forces exerted by the ground on the base of the dam *AB*, (*b*) the resultant of the pressure forces exerted by the water on the face *BC* of the dam. Specific weight of concrete = 150 lb/ft³; of water = 62.4 lb/ft³.

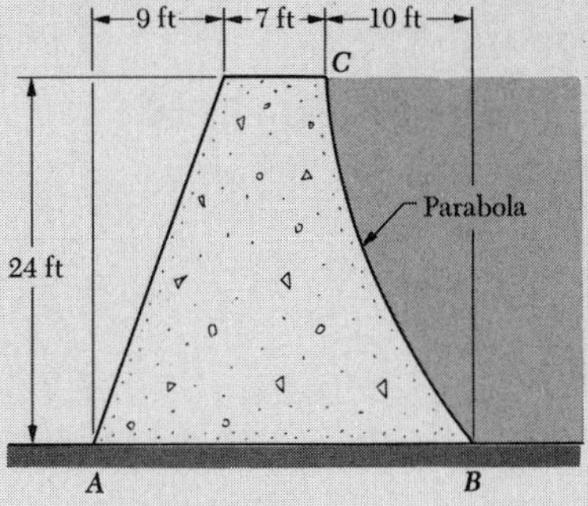

a. **Ground Reaction.** As a free body we choose a section *ABDEA*, 1 ft thick, of the dam and water as shown. The reaction forces exerted by the ground on the base *AB* are represented by an equivalent force-couple system at *A*. Other forces acting on the free body are the weight of the dam, represented by the weights of its components $\mathbf{W}_1$, $\mathbf{W}_2$, and $\mathbf{W}_3$, the weight of the water $\mathbf{W}_4$, and the resultant **P** of the pressure forces exerted on section *BD* by the water to the right of section *BD*. We have

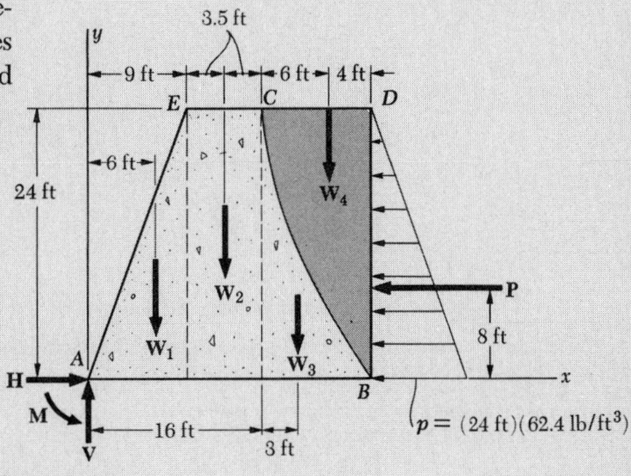

$$W_1 = \tfrac{1}{2}(9\text{ ft})(24\text{ ft})(1\text{ ft})(150\text{ lb/ft}^3) = 16{,}200\text{ lb}$$
$$W_2 = (7\text{ ft})(24\text{ ft})(1\text{ ft})(150\text{ lb/ft}^3) = 25{,}200\text{ lb}$$
$$W_3 = \tfrac{1}{3}(10\text{ ft})(24\text{ ft})(1\text{ ft})(150\text{ lb/ft}^3) = 12{,}000\text{ lb}$$
$$W_4 = \tfrac{2}{3}(10\text{ ft})(24\text{ ft})(1\text{ ft})(62.4\text{ lb/ft}^3) = 9{,}980\text{ lb}$$
$$P = \tfrac{1}{2}(24\text{ ft})(1\text{ ft})(24\text{ ft})(62.4\text{ lb/ft}^3) = 17{,}970\text{ lb}$$

Equilibrium Equations

$\Sigma F_x = 0$: $\quad H - 17{,}970\text{ lb} = 0 \qquad \mathbf{H} = 17{,}970\text{ lb} \rightarrow$ ◄

$\Sigma F_y = 0$: $\quad V - 16{,}200\text{ lb} - 25{,}200\text{ lb} - 12{,}000\text{ lb} - 9{,}980\text{ lb} = 0$

$$\mathbf{V} = 63{,}400\text{ lb} \uparrow$$ ◄

$+\circlearrowleft \Sigma M_A = 0$: $\quad -(16{,}200\text{ lb})(6\text{ ft}) - (25{,}200\text{ lb})(12.5\text{ ft})$
$- (12{,}000\text{ lb})(19\text{ ft}) - (9{,}980\text{ lb})(22\text{ ft}) + (17{,}970\text{ lb})(8\text{ ft}) + M = 0$

$$\mathbf{M} = 716{,}000\text{ lb-ft} \circlearrowleft$$ ◄

We may replace the force-couple system obtained by a single force acting at a distance *d* to the right of *A*, where

$$d = \frac{716{,}000\text{ lb-ft}}{63{,}400\text{ lb}} = 11.30\text{ ft}$$ ◄

b. **Resultant R of Water Forces.** The parabolic section of water *BCD* is chosen as a free body. The forces involved are the resultant $-\mathbf{R}$ of the forces exerted by the dam on the water, the weight $\mathbf{W}_4$, and the force **P**. Since these forces must be concurrent, $-\mathbf{R}$ passes through the point of intersection *F* of $\mathbf{W}_4$ and **P**. A force triangle is drawn from which the magnitude and direction of $-\mathbf{R}$ are determined. The resultant **R** of the forces exerted by the water on the face *BC* is equal and opposite:

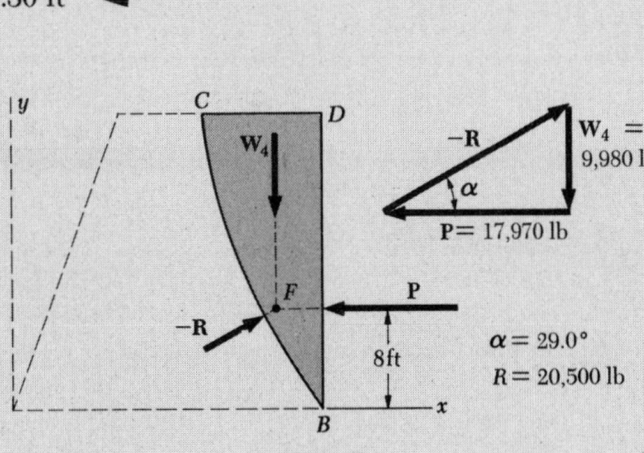

$$\mathbf{R} = 20{,}500\text{ lb} \;\angle\; 29.0°$$ ◄

PROBLEMS

5.66 and 5.67. Determine the magnitude and location of the resultant of the distributed load shown. Also calculate the reactions at A and B.

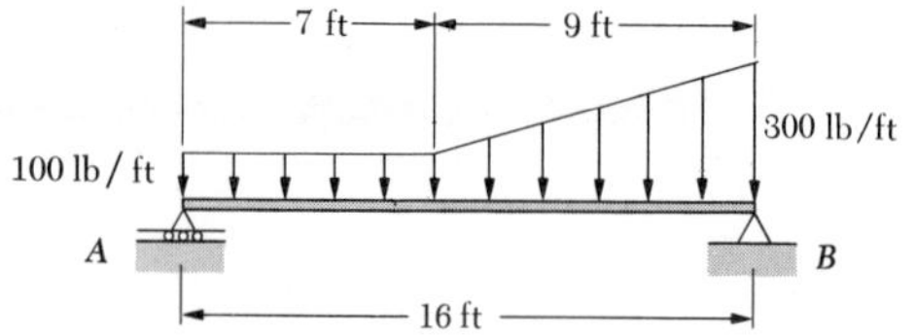

FIG. P 5.66

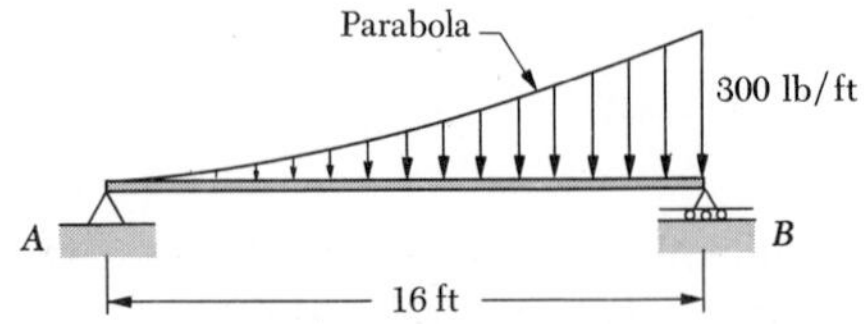

FIG. P 5.67

5.68 through 5.71. Determine the reactions at the beam supports for the given loading condition.

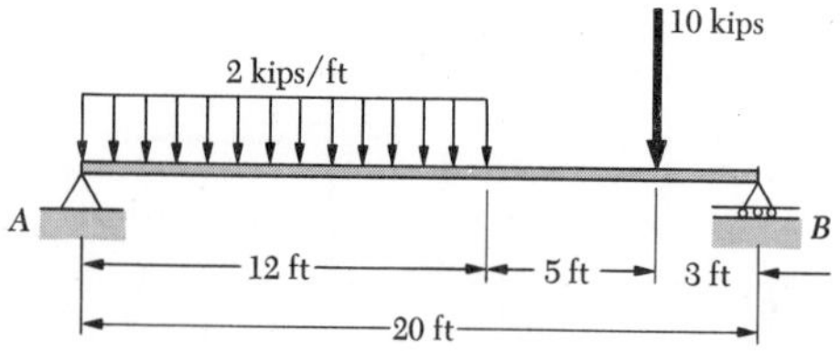

FIG. P 5.68

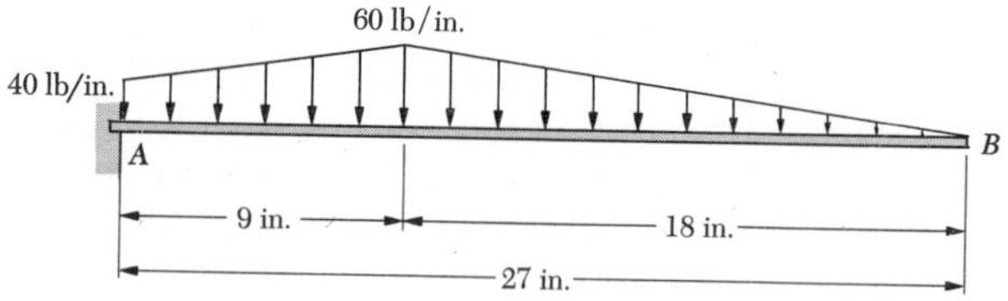

FIG. P 5.69

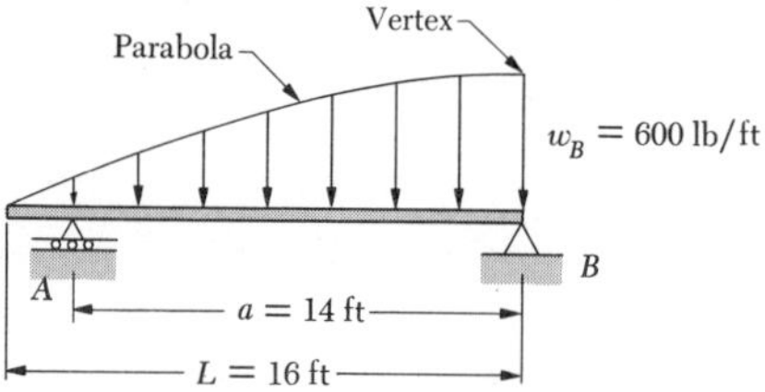

FIG. P 5.70

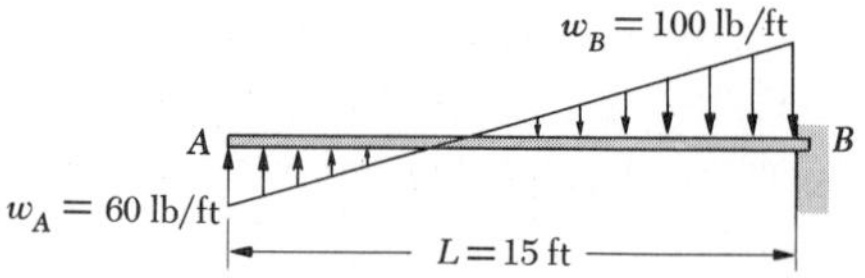

FIG. P 5.71

5.72. In Prob. 5.71 determine the ratio of w_A to w_B for which the reaction at B is equal to (*a*) a force and no couple, (*b*) a couple and no force. In each case express the reaction in terms of w_B and L.

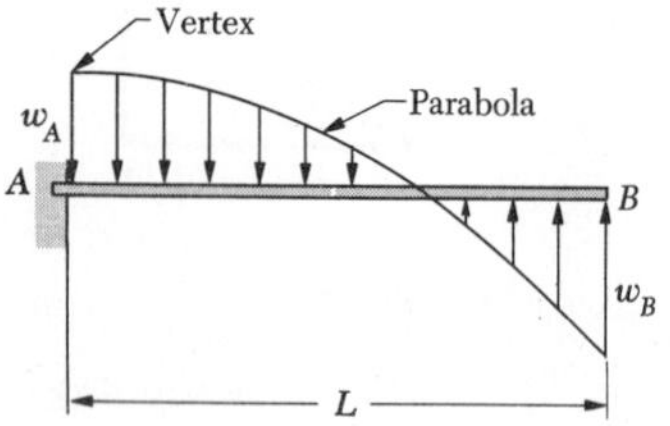

FIG. P 5.73

5.73. Determine the ratio of w_A to w_B for which the reaction at A is equal to (*a*) a couple and no force, (*b*) a force and no couple. In each case express the reaction in terms of w_A and L.

5.74. Solve Sample Prob. 5.9 in terms of the letter quantities w_A, w_B, and L.

5.75. A beam supports a uniformly distributed load w_1 and rests on soil which exerts a uniformly varying upward load as shown. Determine w_2 and w_3, corresponding to equilibrium. Knowing that at any point the soil can exert only an upward loading on the beam, state for what range of values of a/L the results obtained are valid.

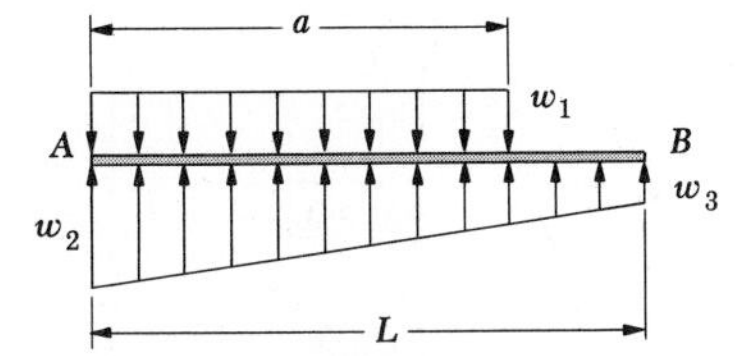

FIG. P 5.75

In the following problems, use $\gamma = 62.4$ lb/ft^3 for the specific weight of fresh water.

5.76. A 3- by 3-ft gate is placed in a wall below water level as shown. (*a*) Determine the magnitude and location of the resultant of the forces exerted by the water on the gate. (*b*) If the gate is hinged at *A*, determine the force exerted by the sill on the gate at *B*.

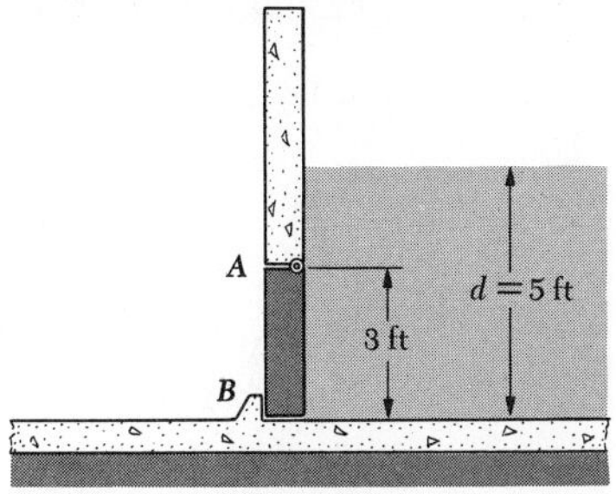

FIG. P 5.76

5.77. In Prob. 5.76 determine the depth of water *d* for which the force exerted by the sill on the gate at *B* is 1,500 lb.

5.78. An automatic valve consists of a square plate, 6 by 6 in., which is pivoted about a horizontal axis through *A* located at a distance $h = 2.5$ in. above the lower edge. Determine the depth of water *d* for which the valve will open.

5.79. If the valve shown is to open when the depth of water is $d = 12$ in., determine the distance *h* from the bottom of the valve to the pivot *A*.

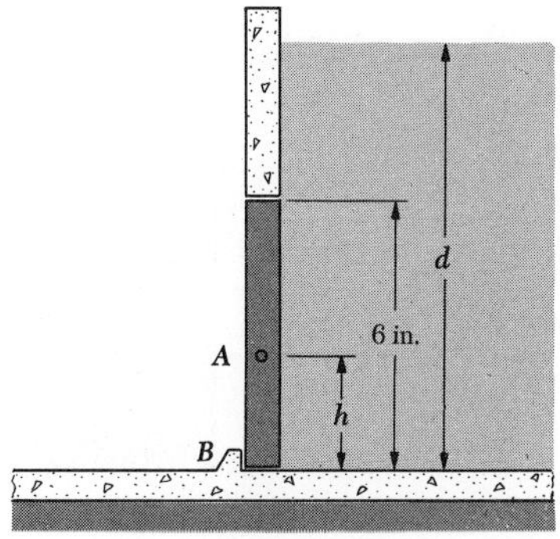

FIG. P 5.78 and P 5.79

5.80. A fresh-water marsh is drained to the ocean through an automatic tide gate which is 4 ft wide and 3 ft high. The gate is held by hinges located along its top edge at *A* and bears on a sill at *B*. At a given time, the water level in the marsh is $h = 6$ ft and in the ocean $d = 9$ ft. Determine the force exerted by the sill on the gate at *B* and the hinge reaction at *A*. (Specific weight of salt water $= 64$ lb/ft^3.)

5.81. The automatic tide gate described in Prob. 5.80 is used to drain a fresh-water marsh into the ocean. If the water level in the marsh is $h = 6$ ft, determine the ocean level *d* for which the gate will open.

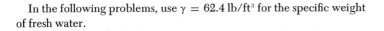

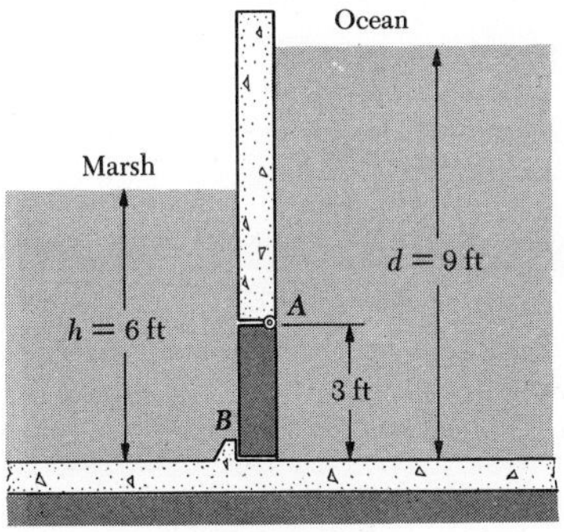

FIG. P 5.80

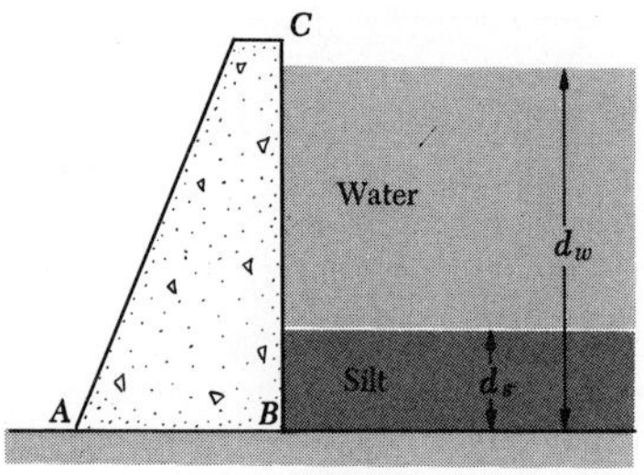

FIG. P 5.82

5.82. At the time of construction no silt was present behind the dam shown. At a later time silt has accumulated to a depth $d_s = 9$ ft. Knowing that $d_w = 24$ ft and assuming that the silt is equivalent to a liquid of specific weight $\gamma_s = 110\ \text{lb/ft}^3$, determine the magnitude and location of the resultant force exerted on the face *BC*. Consider a section of dam 1 ft thick.

5.83. For the dam of Prob. 5.82 determine the ratio of d_s to d_w for which (*a*) the resultant is 15 per cent larger than when $d_s = 0$, (*b*) the moment of the resultant about *A* is 15 per cent larger than when $d_s = 0$.

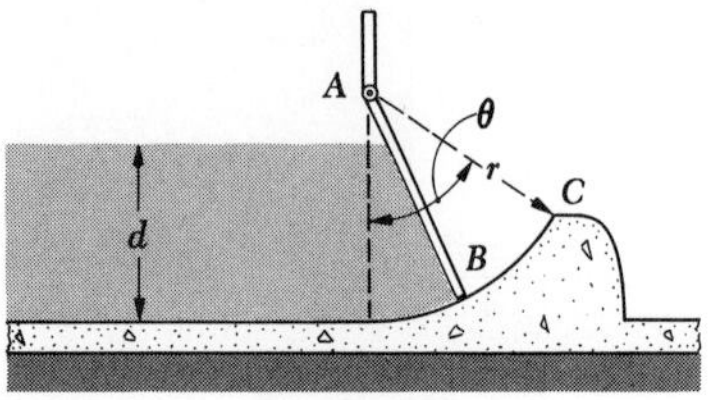

FIG. P 5.84

5.84. A uniform rectangular gate of weight *W*, height *r*, and length *b* is hinged at *A*. Denoting the specific weight of the fluid by γ, determine the required angle θ if the gate is to permit flow when $d = r$.

In the following problems, assume the specific weight of concrete to be $\gamma_c = 150\ \text{lb/ft}^3$.

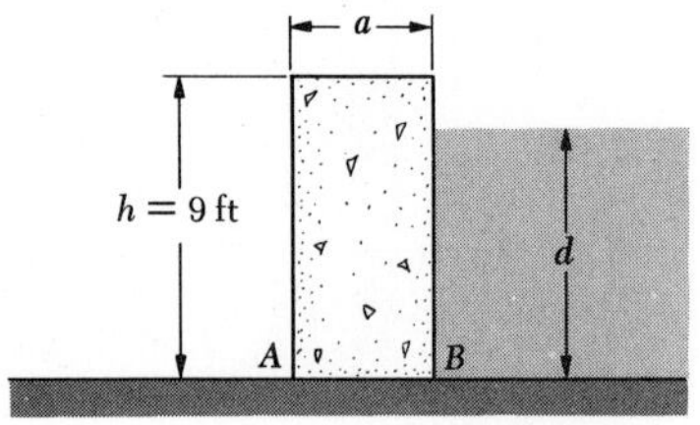

FIG. P 5.85, P 5.87, AND P 5.88

5.85. Determine the minimum allowable value of the width *a* of the rectangular concrete dam if the dam is not to overturn about point *A* when $d = h = 9$ ft.

5.86. Solve Prob. 5.85 assuming that leakage occurs under the dam, causing an upward pressure on the bottom face *AB* which varies linearly from zero at *A* to the full hydrostatic pressure at *B*.

5.87. Concrete is a material which is weak in tension. In order to eliminate tension, the line of action of the resultant of the hydrostatic forces and of the weight of the dam must pass through the middle third of the base. Determine the minimum width *a* for which no tension will occur in the rectangular concrete dam shown when $d = h = 9$ ft.

5.88. Knowing that the width of the rectangular concrete dam is $a = 3$ ft and that its height is $h = 9$ ft, determine the maximum allowable value of the depth *d* of water if the dam is not to overturn about *A*.

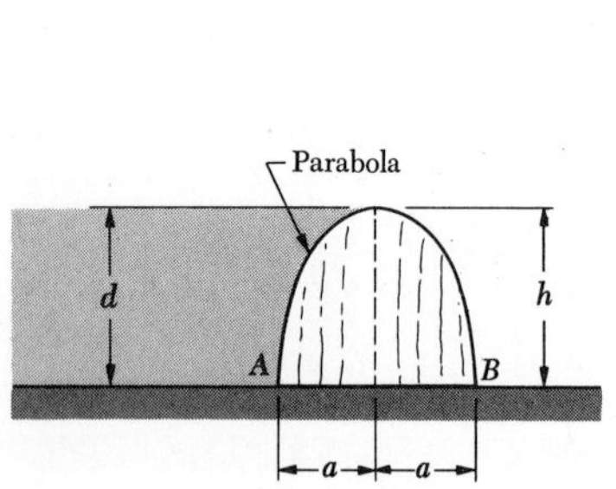

FIG. P 5.89

5.89. A block of wood (specific weight $\gamma_1 = 40\ \text{lb/ft}^3$) is placed in a small channel to stop the flow of water. Assuming that $d = h$ and that no water leaks between the block and the floor of the channel, determine the maximum value of the ratio h/a for which the block will not overturn about point *B*.

5.90. Solve Prob. 5.89 assuming that leakage occurs under the block, causing an upward pressure on the base which varies linearly from zero at B to the full hydrostatic pressure at A.

5.91. A cylindrical drum, 10 ft long, is used as a temporary dam. Determine the resultant (magnitude and line of action) of the water pressure acting on the drum if $h = 2$ ft.

5.92. Solve Prob. 5.91 when $h = 4$ ft.

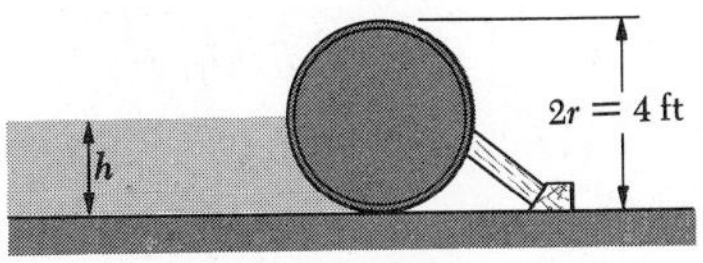

FIG. P 5.91

VOLUMES

5.8. Center of Gravity of a Three-dimensional Body. Centroid of a Volume. The *center of gravity* G of a three-dimensional body is obtained by dividing the body into small elements and expressing that the weight $\mathbf{W}$ of the body attached at G is equivalent to the system of distributed forces $\Delta\mathbf{W}$ representing the weights of the small elements. Choosing the y axis vertical with positive sense upward (Fig. 5.20), and denoting by $\bar{\mathbf{r}}$ the position vector of G, we write that $\mathbf{W}$ is equal to the sum of the elementary weights $\Delta\mathbf{W}$ and that its moment about O is equal to the sum of the moments about O of the elementary weights:

$$\Sigma\mathbf{F}: \qquad -W\mathbf{j} = \Sigma(-\Delta W\mathbf{j}) \qquad (5.13)$$
$$\Sigma\mathbf{M}_O: \qquad \bar{\mathbf{r}} \times (-W\mathbf{j}) = \Sigma[\mathbf{r} \times (-\Delta W\mathbf{j})]$$

Rewriting the last equation in the form

$$\bar{\mathbf{r}}W \times (-\mathbf{j}) = (\Sigma\mathbf{r}\Delta W) \times (-\mathbf{j}) \qquad (5.14)$$

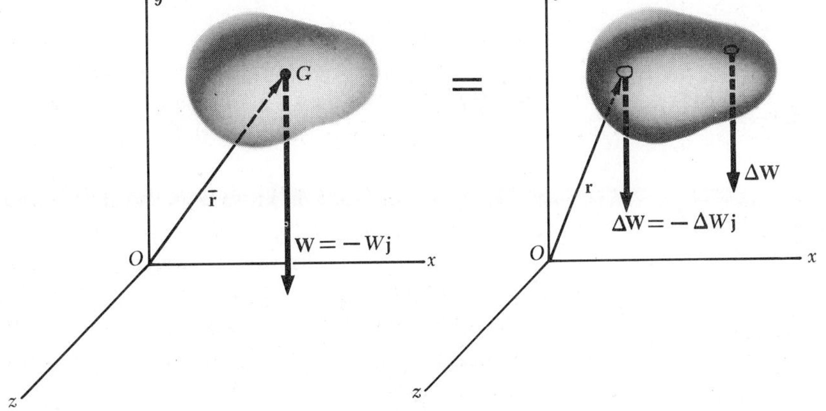

FIG. 5.20

we observe that the weight **W** of the body will be equivalent to the system of the elementary weights $\Delta\mathbf{W}$ if the following conditions are satisfied:

$$W = \Sigma \Delta W \qquad \bar{\mathbf{r}}W = \Sigma \mathbf{r} \Delta W$$

Increasing the number of elements and simultaneously decreasing the size of each element, we obtain at the limit

$$W = \int dW \qquad \bar{\mathbf{r}}W = \int \mathbf{r}\, dW \tag{5.15}$$

We note that the relations obtained are independent of the orientation of the body. For example, if the body and the axes of coordinates were rotated so that the z axis pointed upward, the unit vector $-\mathbf{j}$ would be replaced by $-\mathbf{k}$ in Eqs. (5.13) and (5.14), but the relations (5.15) would remain unchanged. Resolving the vectors $\bar{\mathbf{r}}$ and $\mathbf{r}$ into rectangular components, we verify that the second of the relations (5.15) is equivalent to the three scalar equations

$$\bar{x}W = \int x\, dW \qquad \bar{y}W = \int y\, dW \qquad \bar{z}W = \int z\, dW \tag{5.16}$$

If the body is made of a homogeneous material of specific weight γ, the magnitude dW of the weight of an infinitesimal element may be expressed in terms of the volume dV of the element, and the magnitude W of the total weight in terms of the total volume V. We write

$$dW = \gamma\, dV \qquad W = \gamma V$$

Substituting for dW and W in the second of the relations (5.15), we write

$$\bar{\mathbf{r}}V = \int \mathbf{r}\, dV \tag{5.17}$$

or, in scalar form,

$$\bar{x}V = \int x\, dV \qquad \bar{y}V = \int y\, dV \qquad \bar{z}V = \int z\, dV \tag{5.18}$$

The point of coordinates $\bar{x}$, $\bar{y}$, $\bar{z}$ is also known as the *centroid C of the volume V* of the body. If the body is not homogeneous, Eqs. (5.18) cannot be used to determine the center of gravity of the body; they still define, however, the centroid of the volume.

The integral $\int x\, dV$ is known as the *first moment of the volume with respect to the yz plane.* Similarly, the integrals $\int y\, dV$ and $\int z\, dV$ define the first moments of the volume with respect to the zx plane and the xy plane, respectively. It is seen from Eqs. (5.18) that, if the centroid of a volume is located in a coordinate plane, the first moment of the volume with respect to that plane is zero.

A volume is said to be symmetrical with respect to a given plane if to every point P of the volume corresponds a point P' of the same volume, such that the line PP' is perpendicular to the given plane and divided into two equal parts by that plane. The plane is said to be a *plane of symmetry* for the given volume. When a volume V possesses a plane of symmetry, the centroid of the volume must be located in that plane. When a volume possesses two planes of symmetry, the centroid of the volume must be located on the line of intersection of the two planes. Finally, when a volume possesses three planes of symmetry which intersect in a well-defined point (i.e., not along a common line), the point of intersection of the three planes must coincide with the centroid of the volume. This property enables us to determine immediately the centroid of the volume of spheres, ellipsoids, cubes, rectangular parallelepipeds, etc.

Centroids of unsymmetrical volumes or of volumes possessing only one or two planes of symmetry should be determined by integration (Sec. 5.10). Centroids of common shapes of volumes are shown in Fig. 5.21. It should be observed that the centroid of a volume of revolution in general *does not coincide* with the centroid of its cross section. Thus, the centroid of a hemisphere is different from that of a semicircular area, and the centroid of a cone is different from that of a triangle.

5.9. Composite Bodies. If a body can be divided into several of the common shapes shown in Fig. 5.21, its center of gravity G may be determined by expressing that the moment about O of its total weight is equal to the sum of the moments about O of the weights of the various component parts. Proceeding as in Sec. 5.8, we obtain the following equations defining the coordinates $\bar{X}$, $\bar{Y}$, $\bar{Z}$ of the center of gravity G:

$$\bar{X}\Sigma W = \Sigma\bar{x}W \qquad \bar{Y}\Sigma W = \Sigma\bar{y}W \qquad \bar{Z}\Sigma W = \Sigma\bar{z}W \qquad (5.19)$$

If the body is made of a homogeneous material, its center of gravity coincides with the centroid of its volume and the following equations may be used:

$$\bar{X}\Sigma V = \Sigma\bar{x}V \qquad \bar{Y}\Sigma V = \Sigma\bar{y}V \qquad \bar{Z}\Sigma V = \Sigma\bar{z}V \qquad (5.20)$$

5.10. Determination of Centroids of Volumes by Integration. The centroid of a volume bounded by analytical surfaces may be determined by computing the integrals given in Sec. 5.8.

$$\bar{x}V = \int x\,dV \qquad \bar{y}V = \int y\,dV \qquad \bar{z}V = \int z\,dV \qquad (5.21)$$

Shape		$\bar{x}$	Volume
Hemisphere	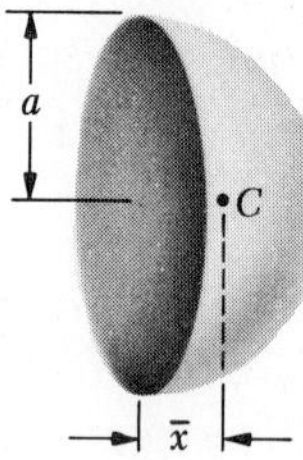	$\frac{3a}{8}$	$\frac{2}{3}\pi a^3$
Semiellipsoid of revolution	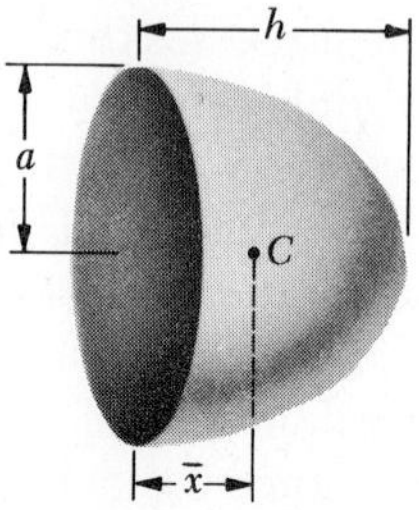	$\frac{3h}{8}$	$\frac{2}{3}\pi a^2 h$
Paraboloid of revolution	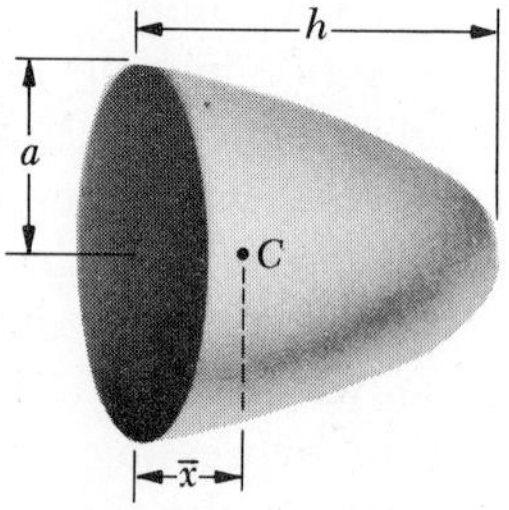	$\frac{h}{3}$	$\frac{1}{2}\pi a^2 h$
Cone	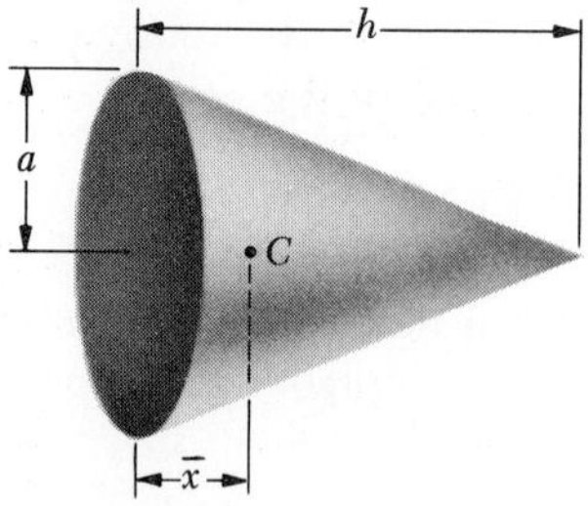	$\frac{h}{4}$	$\frac{1}{3}\pi a^2 h$
Pyramid	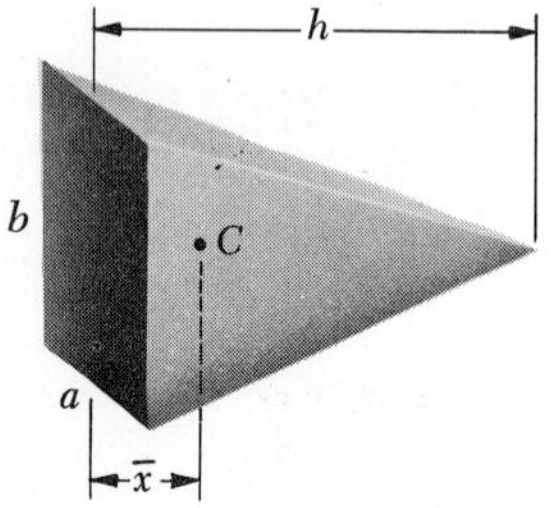	$\frac{h}{4}$	$\frac{1}{3} a b h$

FIG. 5.21. Centroids of common shapes of volumes

If the element of volume dV is chosen equal to a small cube of sides dx, dy, and dz, the determination of each of these integrals requires a *triple integration* in x, y, and z. However, it is possible to determine the coordinates of the centroid of most volumes by *double integration* if dV is chosen equal to the volume of a thin filament as shown in Fig. 5.22. The coordinates of the centroid of the volume are then obtained by writing

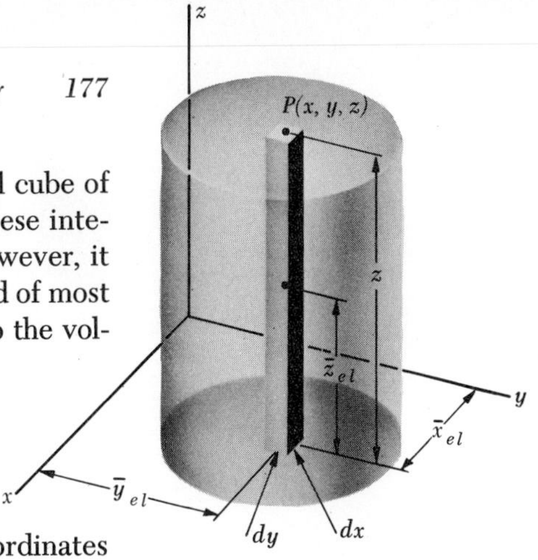

FIG. 5.22. Determination of the centroid of a volume by double integration

$$\bar{x}V = \int \bar{x}_{el}\, dV \qquad \bar{y}V = \int \bar{y}_{el}\, dV \qquad \bar{z}V = \int \bar{z}_{el}\, dV \tag{5.22}$$

and substituting for the volume dV and the coordinates $\bar{x}_{el}$, $\bar{y}_{el}$, $\bar{z}_{el}$ the expressions given in Fig. 5.22. Using the equation of the surface to express z in terms of x and y, the integration is reduced to a double integration in x and y.

If the volume under consideration possesses *two planes of symmetry*, its centroid must be located on their line of intersection. Choosing the x axis along this line, we have

$$\bar{y} = \bar{z} = 0$$

and the only coordinate to determine is $\bar{x}$. This will be done most conveniently by dividing the given volume into thin slabs parallel to the yz plane. In the particular case of a body of revolution, these slabs are circular; their volume dV is given in Fig. 5.23. Substituting for $\bar{x}_{el}$ and dV into the equation

$$\bar{x}V = \int \bar{x}_{el}\, dV \tag{5.23}$$

and expressing the radius r of the slab in terms of x, we may determine $\bar{x}$ by a single integration.

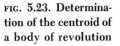

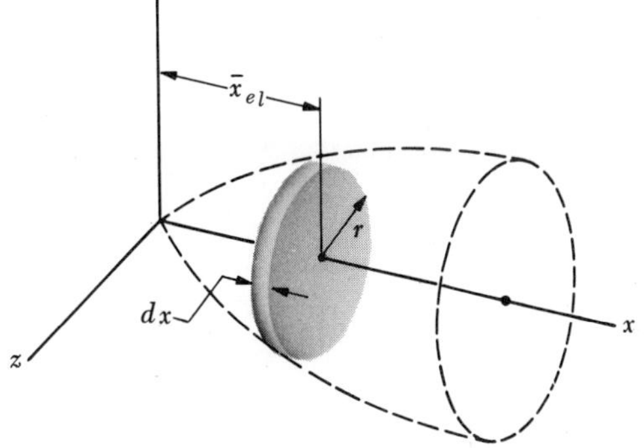

FIG. 5.23. Determination of the centroid of a body of revolution

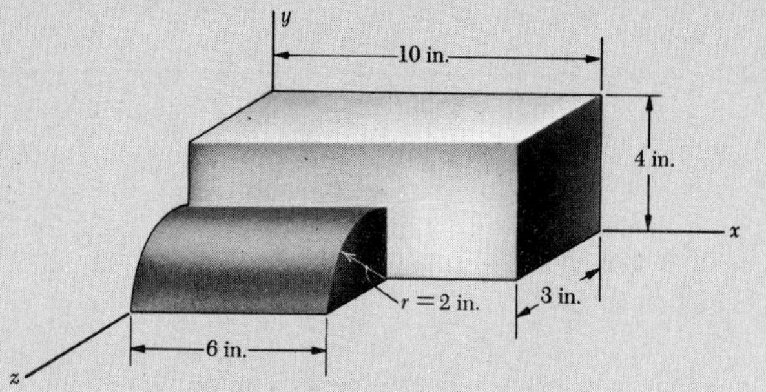

SAMPLE PROBLEM 5.11

Determine the center of gravity of the homogeneous body shown.

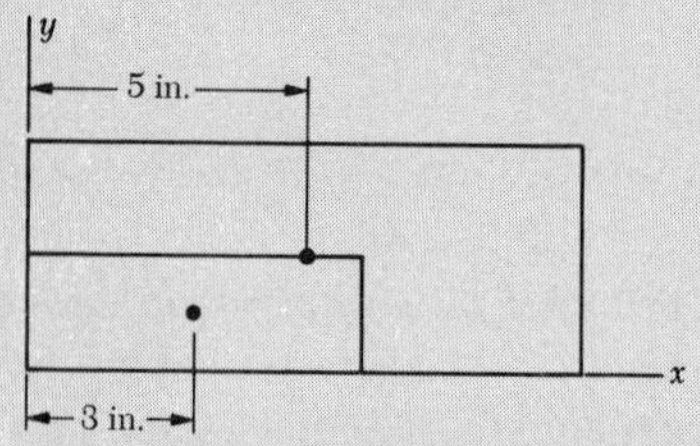

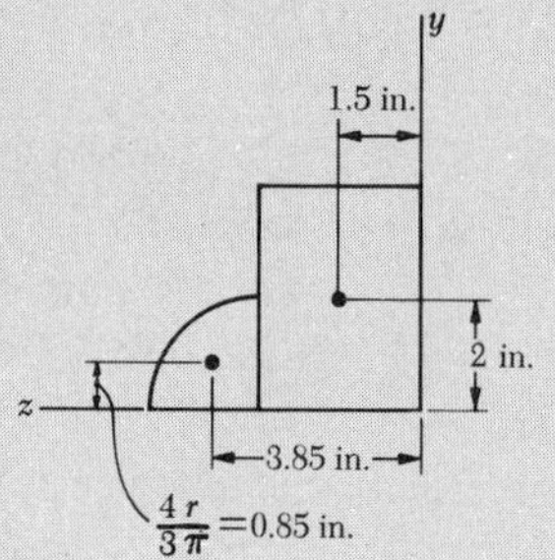

Solution. Since the body is homogeneous, its center of gravity coincides with its centroid. The body is made of a rectangular parallelepiped and a quarter cylinder, whose centroids are shown. The total volume and the moment of the volume with respect to each coordinate plane are determined from the table.

Component	V	$\bar{x}$	$\bar{y}$	$\bar{z}$	$\bar{x}V$	$\bar{y}V$	$\bar{z}V$
Parallelepiped. .	120.0	5	2	1.5	600	240	180
Quarter cylinder	18.85	3	0.85	3.85	56.5	16.0	72.6
	$\Sigma V =$ 138.8	.	. . . .	. . . .	$\Sigma\bar{x}V =$ 656.5	$\Sigma\bar{y}V =$ 256.0	$\Sigma\bar{z}V =$ 252.6

Thus,

$\bar{X}\Sigma V = \Sigma\bar{x}V$: $\quad \bar{X}(138.8) = 656.5 \quad\quad \bar{X} = 4.73 \text{ in.}$ ◄

$\bar{Y}\Sigma V = \Sigma\bar{y}V$: $\quad \bar{Y}(138.8) = 256.0 \quad\quad \bar{Y} = 1.84 \text{ in.}$ ◄

$\bar{Z}\Sigma V = \Sigma\bar{z}V$: $\quad \bar{Z}(138.8) = 252.6 \quad\quad \bar{Z} = 1.82 \text{ in.}$ ◄

SAMPLE PROBLEM 5.12

Determine the center of gravity of the homogeneous body of revolution shown.

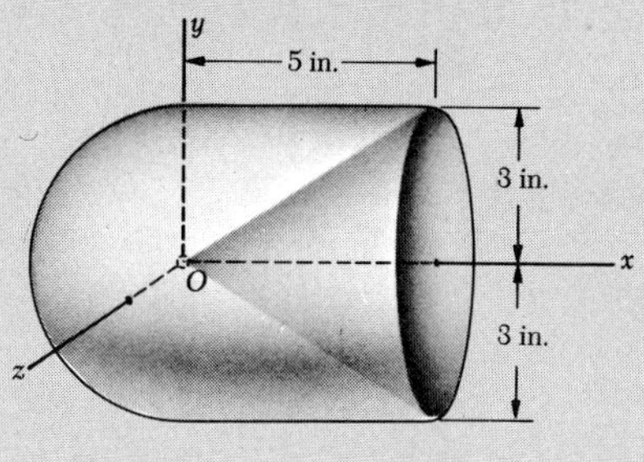

Solution. Because of symmetry, the center of gravity lies on the x axis. The body is seen to consist of a hemisphere, plus a cylinder, minus a cone, as shown.

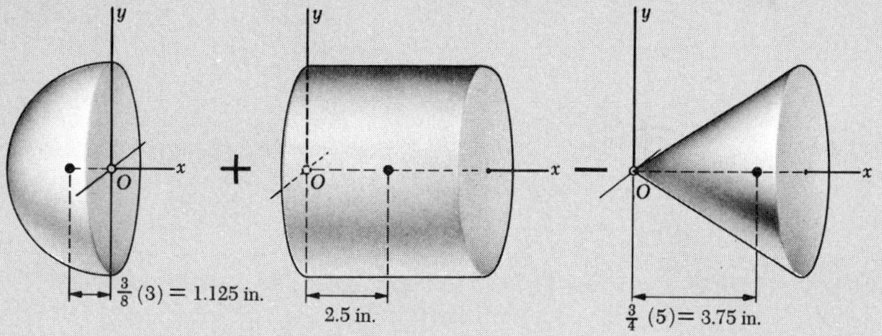

Component	Volume	$\bar{x}$	$\bar{x}V$
Hemisphere. . . .	$\frac{1}{2}\frac{4\pi}{3}(3)^3 = \quad 56.5$	-1.125	-63.6
Cylinder	$\pi(3)^2(5) = \quad 141.4$	$+2.50$	$+353.5$
Cone	$-\frac{\pi}{3}(3)^2(5) = -47.1$	$+3.75$	-176.6
	$\Sigma V = 150.8$	. . . . . .	$\Sigma\bar{x}V = +113.3$

$\bar{X}\Sigma V = \Sigma\bar{x}V$: $\quad \bar{X}(150.8) = 113.3 \qquad \bar{X} = 0.75$ in. ◄

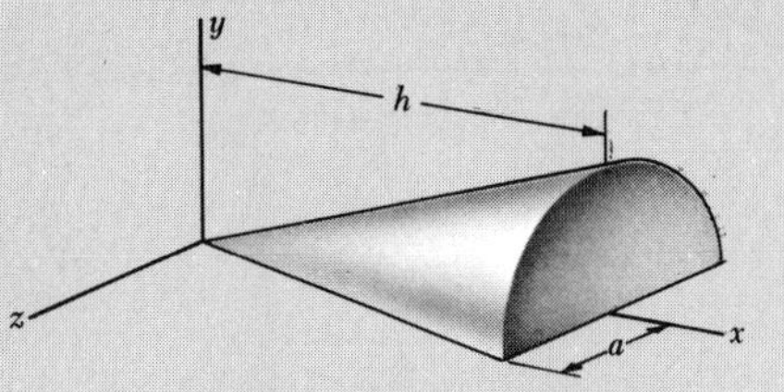

SAMPLE PROBLEM 5.13

Determine the location of the centroid of the half right circular cone shown.

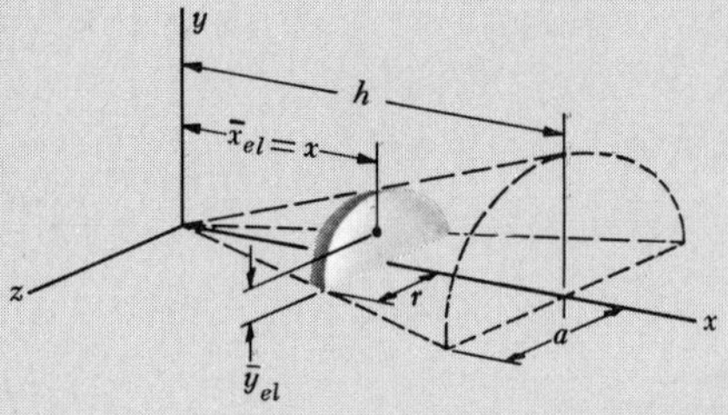

Solution. Since the xy plane is a plane of symmetry, the centroid lies in this plane and $\bar{z} = 0$. A slab of thickness dx is chosen as a differential element. The volume of this element is

$$dV = \tfrac{1}{2}\pi r^2\, dx$$

The coordinates $\bar{x}_{el}$ and $\bar{y}_{el}$ of the centroid of the element are obtained from Fig. 5.8 (semicircular area).

$$\bar{x}_{el} = x \qquad \bar{y}_{el} = \frac{4r}{3\pi}$$

We observe that r is proportional to x and write

$$\frac{r}{x} = \frac{a}{h} \qquad r = \frac{a}{h}x$$

The volume of the body is

$$V = \int dV = \int_0^h \tfrac{1}{2}\pi r^2\, dx = \int_0^h \tfrac{1}{2}\pi \left(\frac{a}{h}x\right)^2 dx = \frac{\pi a^2 h}{6}$$

The moment of the differential element with respect to the yz plane is $\bar{x}_{el}\, dV$; and the total moment of the body with respect to this plane is

$$\int \bar{x}_{el}\, dV = \int_0^h x(\tfrac{1}{2}\pi r^2)\, dx = \int_0^h x(\tfrac{1}{2}\pi)\left(\frac{a}{h}x\right)^2 dx = \frac{\pi a^2 h^2}{8}$$

Thus, $\quad \bar{x}V = \int \bar{x}_{el}\, dV \qquad \bar{x}\frac{\pi a^2 h}{6} = \frac{\pi a^2 h^2}{8} \qquad \bar{x} = \tfrac{3}{4}h$ ◄

Likewise, the moment of the differential element with respect to the xz plane is $\bar{y}_{el}\, dV$; and the total moment is

$$\int \bar{y}_{el}\, dV = \int_0^h \frac{4r}{3\pi}(\tfrac{1}{2}\pi r^2)\, dx = \frac{2}{3}\int_0^h \left(\frac{a}{h}x\right)^3 dx = \frac{a^3 h}{6}$$

Thus, $\quad \bar{y}V = \int \bar{y}_{el}\, dV \qquad \bar{y}\frac{\pi a^2 h}{6} = \frac{a^3 h}{6} \qquad \bar{y} = \frac{a}{\pi}$ ◄

PROBLEMS

5.93. A hemisphere and a cone are attached as shown. Determine the ratio h/a for which the centroid of the composite body is located in the plane between the hemisphere and the cone.

5.94. A paraboloid of revolution and a cylinder of the same radius a and height h are attached as shown. Determine the location of the centroid of the composite body.

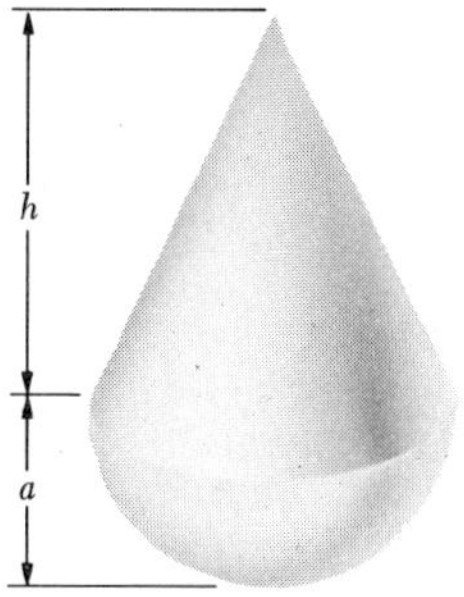

FIG. P 5.93

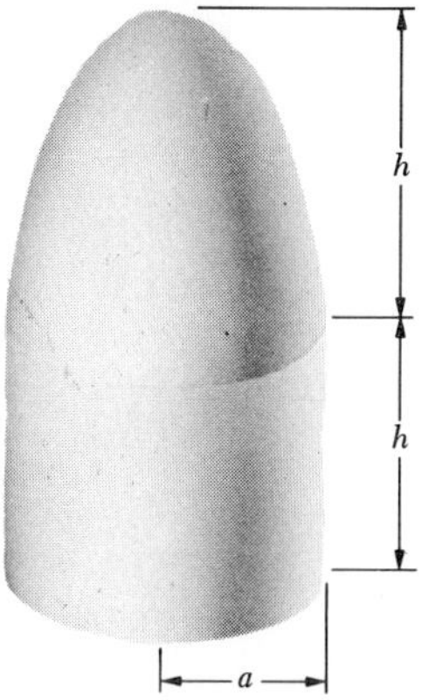

FIG. P 5.94

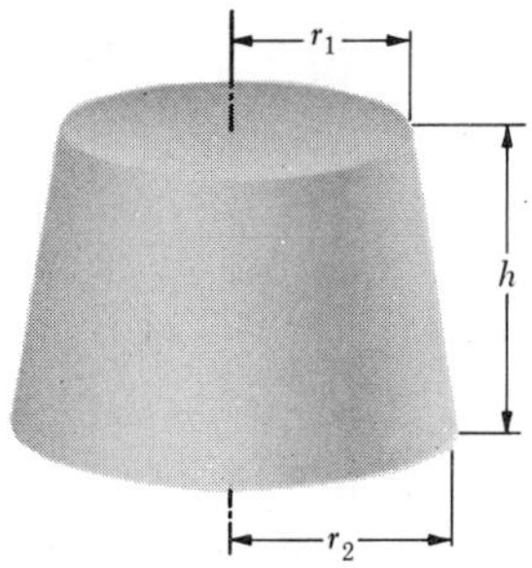

FIG. P 5.95

5.95. Locate the centroid of the frustum of a right circular cone when $r_1 = 8$ in., $r_2 = 10$ in., and $h = 6$ in.

5.96. A $\frac{3}{4}$-in.-diameter hole is drilled through the entire length of a taper as shown. Locate the center of gravity of the taper.

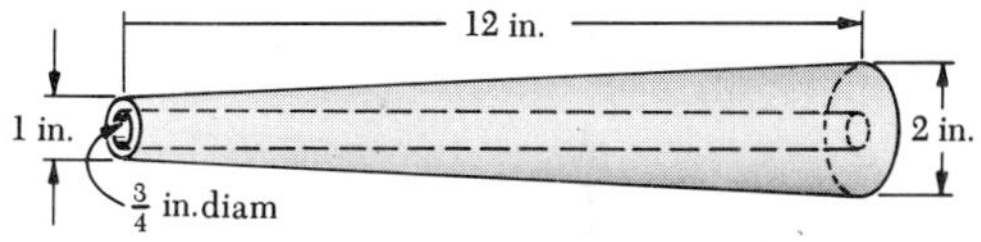

FIG. P 5.96

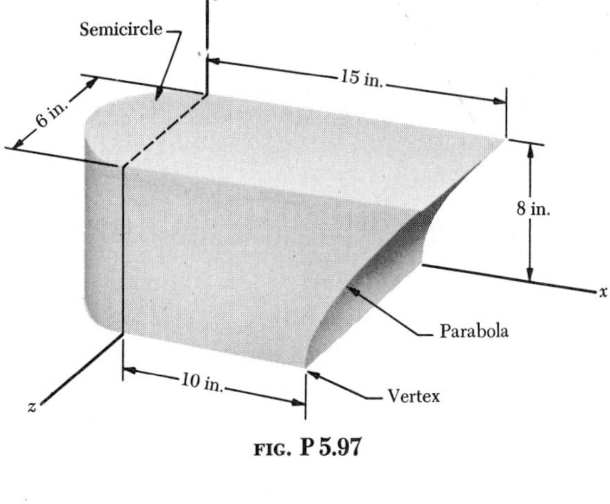

5.97. Locate the center of gravity of the block shown.

FIG. P 5.97

5.98 and 5.99. Locate the center of gravity of the link shown.

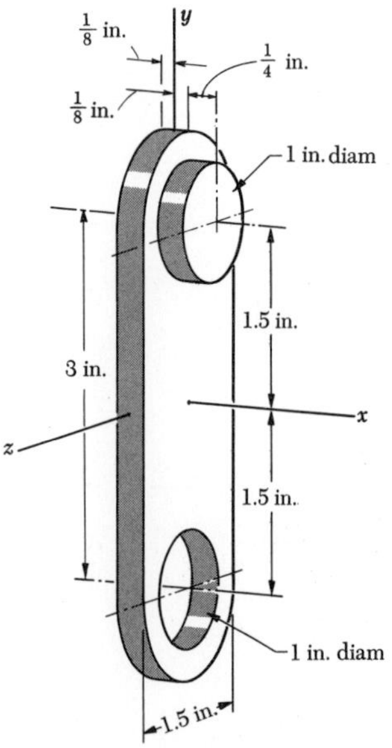

FIG. P 5.98

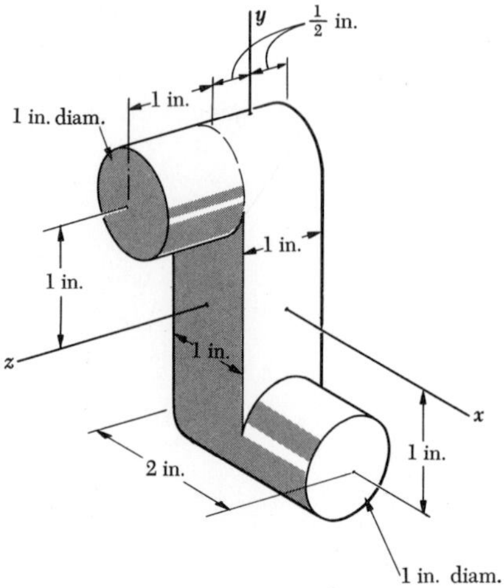

FIG. P 5.99

5.100. The brass sleeve is to be mounted on the pin of a machine part made of aluminum. Locate the center of gravity of the assembly. (Specific weights: brass $= 530\ \mathrm{lb/ft^3}$; aluminum $= 170\ \mathrm{lb/ft^3}$.)

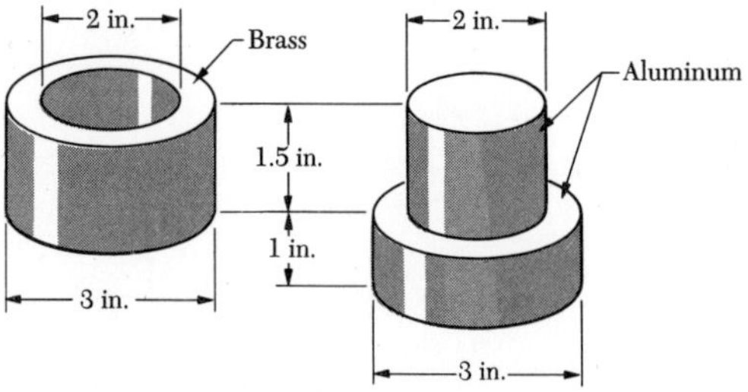

FIG. P 5.100

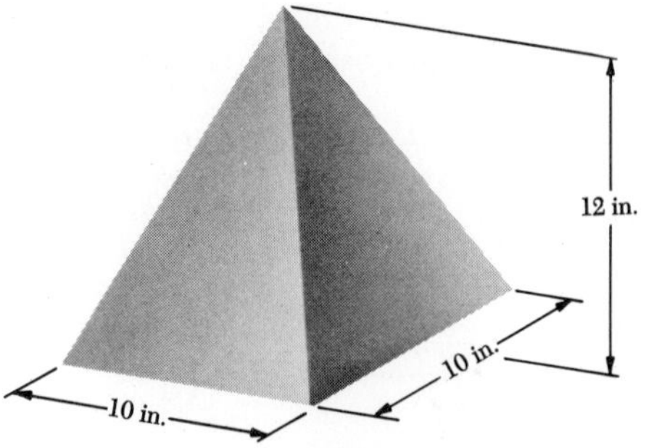

FIG. P 5.101

5.101. A regular pyramid 12 in. high, with a square base of side 10 in., is made of wood. Its four triangular faces are covered with steel sheets $\frac{1}{32}$ in. thick. Locate the center of gravity of the composite body. (Specific weights: steel $= 490\ \mathrm{lb/ft^3}$; wood $= 30\ \mathrm{lb/ft^3}$.)

5.102 and 5.103. Locate the center of gravity of the sheet-metal form shown.

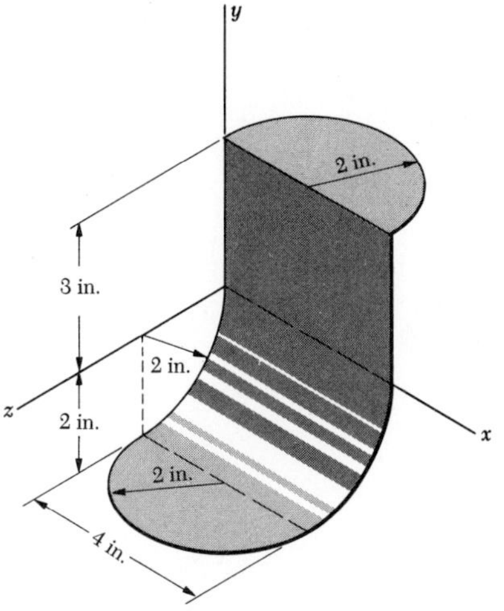

FIG. P 5.102

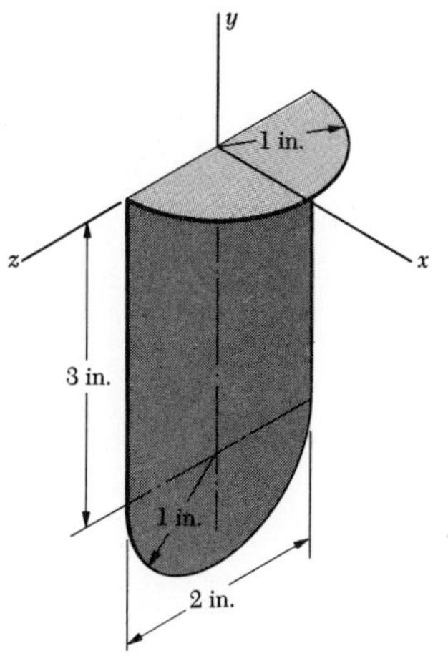

FIG. P 5.103

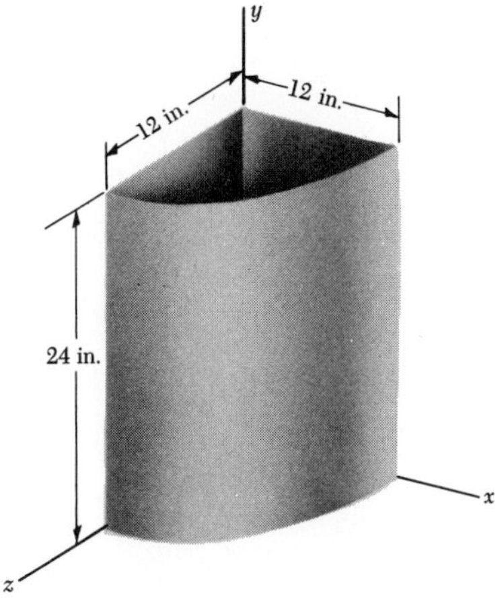

FIG. P 5.104

5.104. A wastebasket, designed to fit in the corner of a room, is 24 in. high and has a base in the shape of a quarter circle of radius 12 in. Locate the center of gravity of the wastebasket, knowing that it is made of sheet metal of uniform thickness.

5.105. Locate the centroid of the frustum of the right circular cone of Prob. 5.95, expressing the result in terms of r_1, r_2, and h.

5.106. Locate the center of gravity of a thin hemispherical shell of radius r and thickness t. (*Hint.* Consider the shell as formed by removing a hemisphere of radius r from a hemisphere of radius $r + t$; then neglect the terms containing t^2 and t^3, and keep those terms containing t.)

5.107. Derive by direct integration the expression given for $\bar{x}$ in Fig. 5.21 for a semiellipsoid of revolution.

5.108. Derive by direct integration the expression given for $\bar{x}$ in Fig. 5.21 for a paraboloid of revolution.

5.109 and 5.110. Locate the centroid of the volume obtained by rotating the area shown about the x axis.

5.111. Locate the centroid of the semiparaboloid of revolution shown.

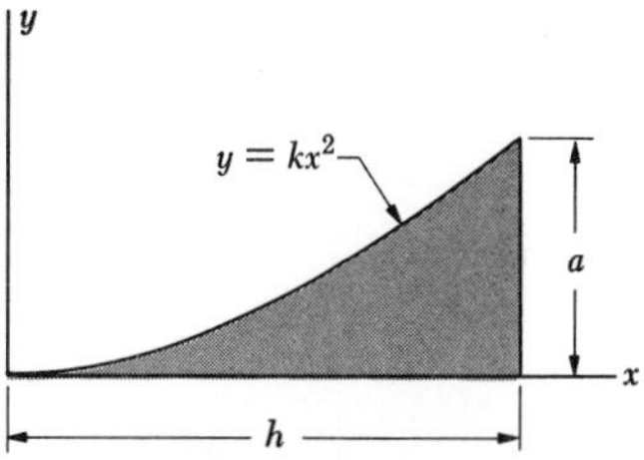

FIG. P 5.109

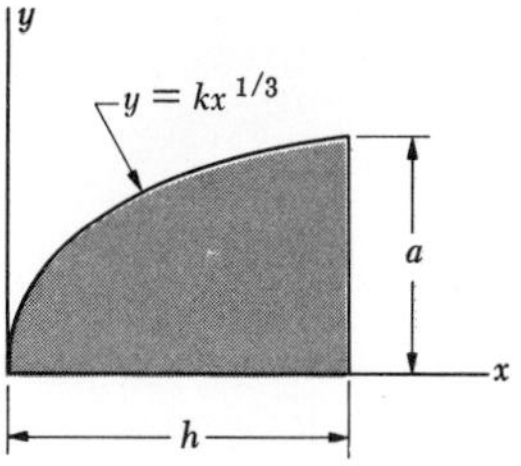

FIG. P 5.110

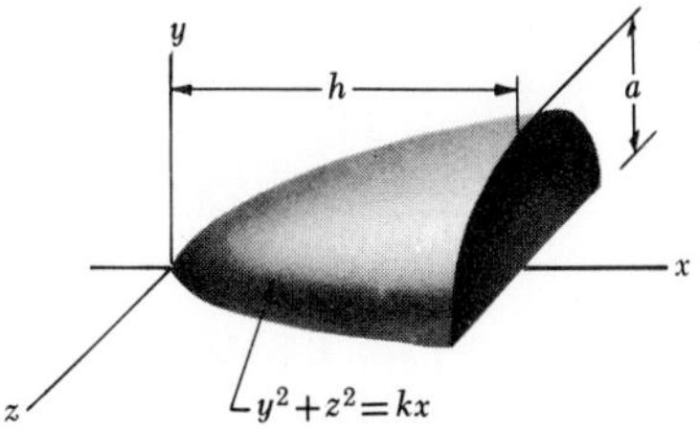

FIG. P 5.111

5.112. Locate the centroid of the volume shown, which was obtained by rotating the area of Fig. P 5.109 through 180° about the x axis.

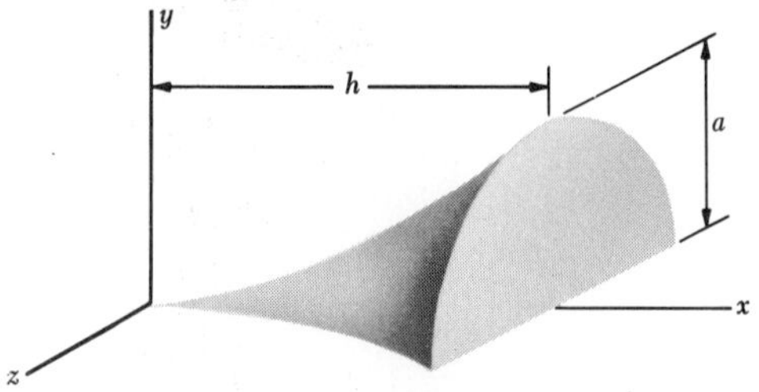

FIG. P 5.112

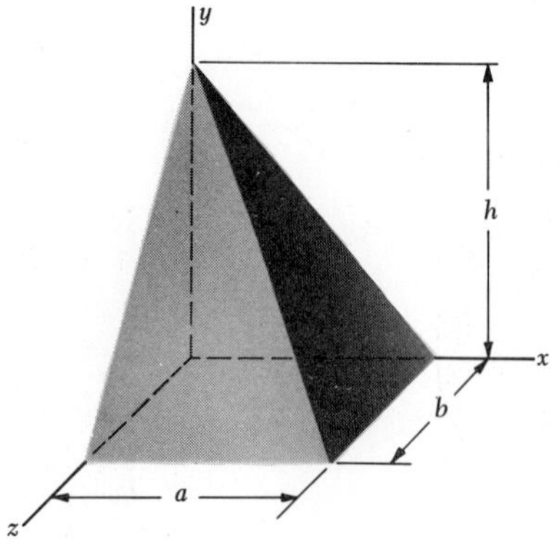

FIG. P 5.113

5.113. Locate the centroid of the volume of the irregular pyramid shown.

***5.114.** Locate the centroid of the volume obtained by rotating the area of Prob. 5.47 about the y axis.

***5.115.** A spherical tank is 12 ft in diameter and is filled with water to a depth of 9 ft. Determine by direct integration the center of gravity of the water in the tank.

***5.116.** A hemispherical shell of radius a is partially filled with water. Using the result obtained in Prob. 5.106, determine for what depth of water the center of gravity of the water will coincide with the center of gravity of the shell.

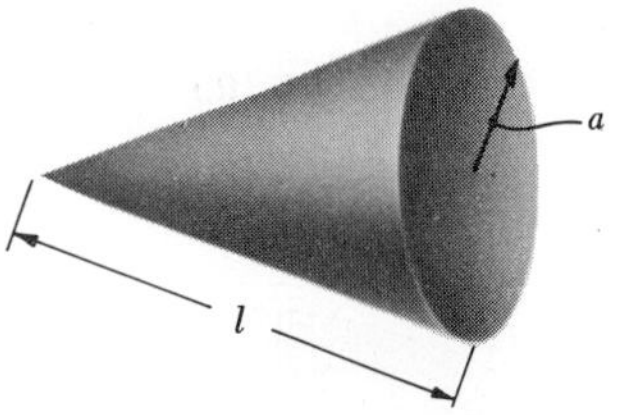

FIG. P 5.117

***5.117.** A right circular cone is made by welding a circular disk of sheet metal of radius a to a conical shell of the same gage and of generatrix l. For what ratio l/a will the center of gravity of this hollow cone coincide with the center of gravity of a solid cone of the same dimensions? (*Hint.* Consider the conical shell as the limiting case of the lateral surface of a regular pyramid when the number of faces of the pyramid approaches infinity.)

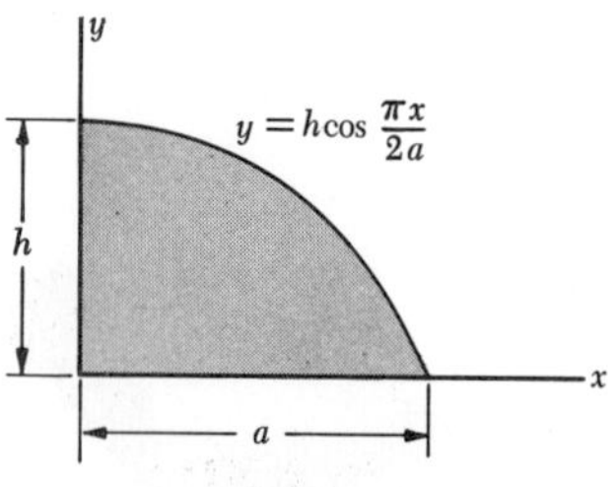

FIG. P 5.118

***5.118.** Locate the centroid of the volume generated by revolving the portion shown of the cosine curve about the y axis. (*Hint.* Use as an element of volume a thin cylindrical shell of radius r and thickness dr.)

*5.119. Determine by direct integration the location of the centroid of the volume between the xz plane and the portion shown of the surface $y = h \sin(\pi x/a) \sin(\pi z/b)$.

*5.120. A circular cylinder of radius a is cut by an oblique plane as shown. Determine by direct integration the location of the centroid.

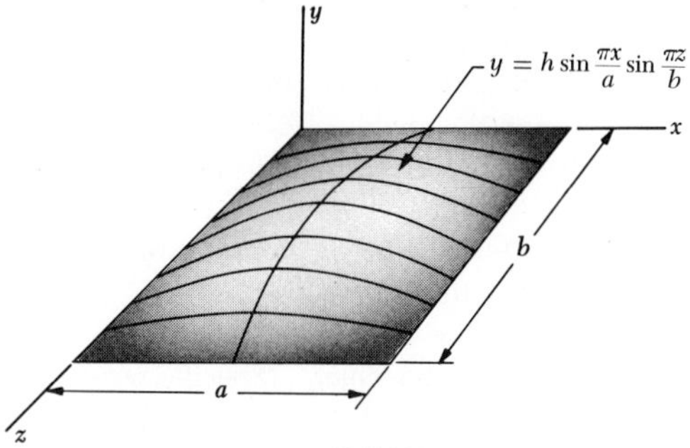

FIG. P5.119

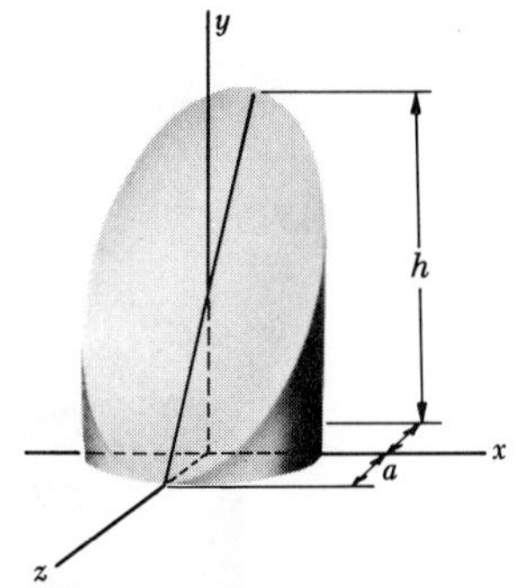

FIG. P5.120

REVIEW PROBLEMS

5.121. Locate the centroid of the plane area shown.

5.122. Determine the volume of the solid generated by rotating the area shown about the y axis.

5.123. Determine the total surface area of the solid generated by rotating the area shown about the y axis.

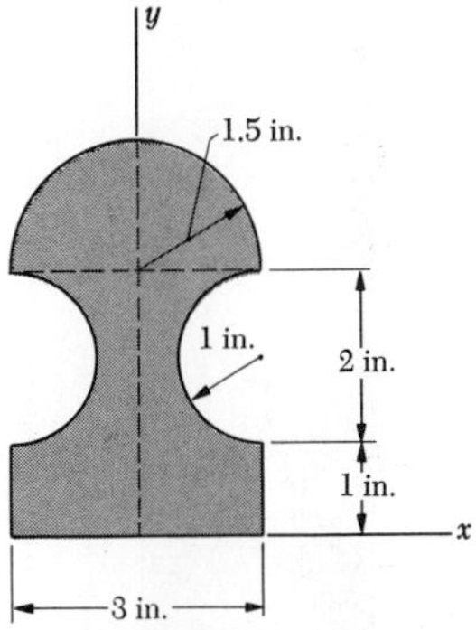

FIG. P5.121, P5.122, AND P5.123

5.124. Determine the reactions at A and B.

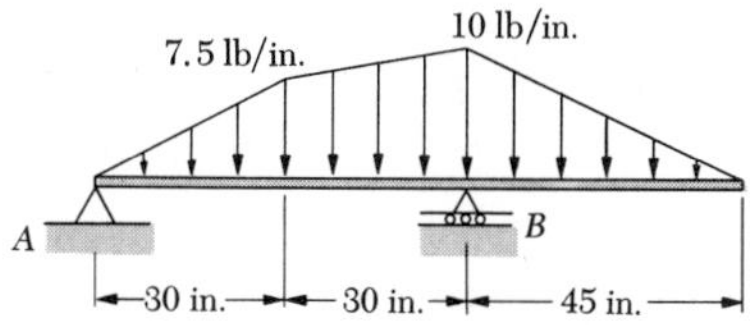

FIG. P5.124

5.125. Locate the center of gravity of the sheet-metal form shown when $a = 1$ ft.

5.126. Determine the distance a so that the center of gravity of the sheet-metal form is located 1 ft from the y axis.

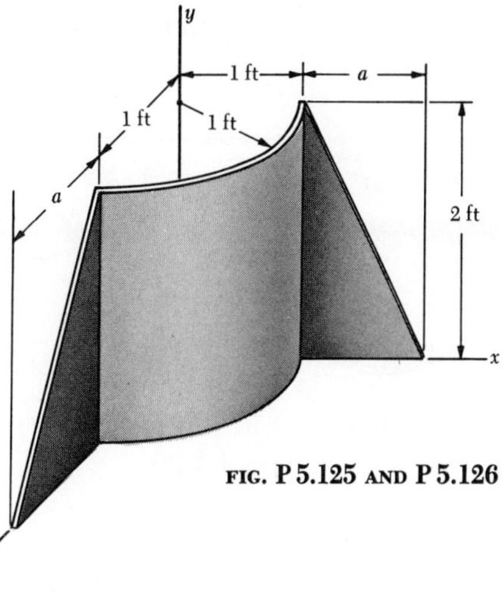

FIG. P5.125 AND P5.126

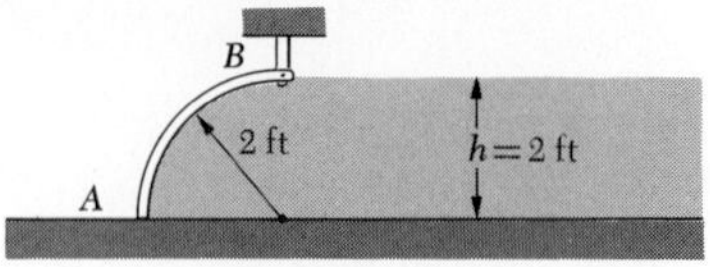

FIG. P 5.127

5.127. The gate shown is supported by hinges located along its top edge at B and rests on the floor of a channel at A. Knowing that the gate is 4 ft wide, determine the magnitude and direction of the resultant of the hydrostatic forces exerted on the gate when $h = 2$ ft.

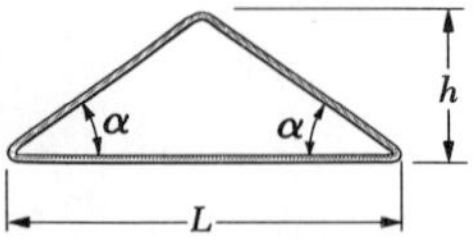

FIG. P 5.129

5.128. Knowing that the gate of Prob. 5.127 is 4 ft wide and is made of sheet metal of uniform gage, determine the required weight of the gate if it is to prevent water from flowing when $h = 2$ ft.

5.129. A homogeneous wire is bent to form an isosceles triangle. Determine the angle α for which the center of gravity of the wire coincides with the centroid of the area enclosed by the wire.

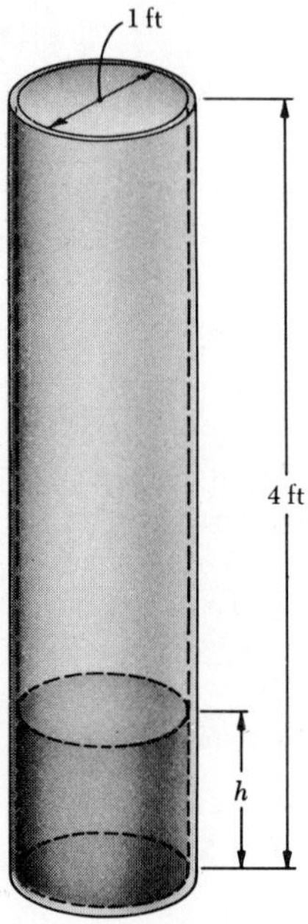

FIG. P 5.130

5.130. Concrete is poured into a steel pipe of length 4 ft, inside diameter 1 ft, and weight 200 lb. To what depth should concrete be poured if the combined center of gravity of the pipe and concrete is to be as low as possible? (Specific weight of concrete = 150 lb/ft³.)

5.131. The production-line balancing of an automobile speedometer cup is done as follows. The unbalanced cup is placed on a frictionless shaft at O and is allowed to come to rest. A hole is then punched at A; the cup rotates through an angle θ and again comes to rest. The balancing is completed by punching additional holes at B and C. Knowing that the three holes are equal in size and are at the same distance from the shaft O, determine the required angle α in terms of the angle θ.

5.132. A simple beam AB of length L supports a distributed load $w = w_0(au^2 + bu^3)$ where $u = x/L$, with x measured from the left end A of the beam. Determine the ratio of b/a for which the reactions are equal in magnitude and direction.

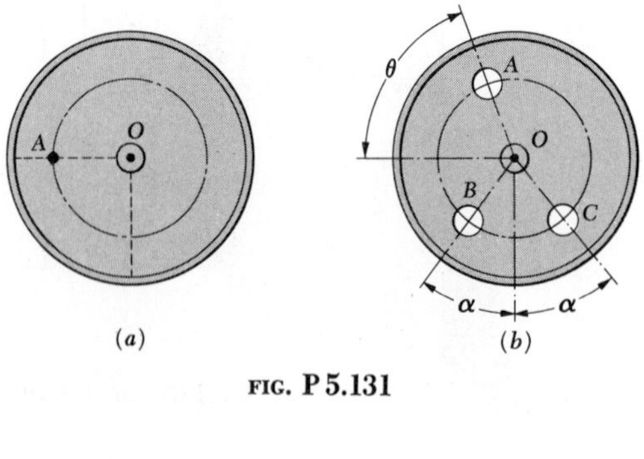

FIG. P 5.131

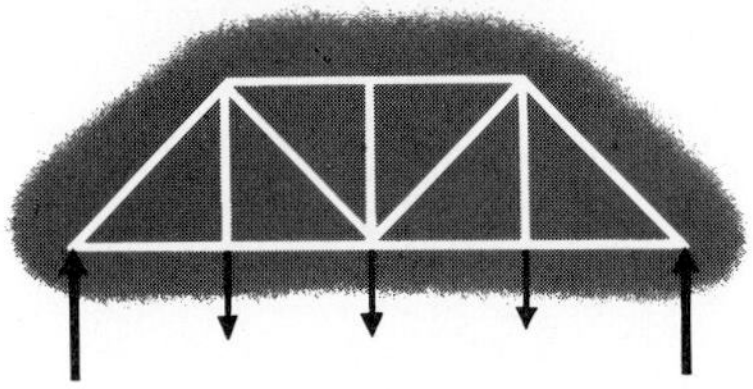

6. ANALYSIS OF STRUCTURES

6.1. Internal Forces. Newton's Third Law. The problems considered in the preceding chapters concerned the equilibrium of a single rigid body, and all forces involved were external to the rigid body. We shall now consider problems dealing with the equilibrium of structures made of several connected parts. These problems call not only for the determination of the external forces acting on the structure but also for the determination of the forces which hold together the various parts of the structure. From the point of view of the structure as a whole, these forces are *internal forces.*

Consider, for example, the crane shown in Fig. 6.1*a*, which carries a load *W*. The crane consists of three beams *AD, CF,* and *BE* connected by smooth pins; it is supported by a smooth pin at *A* and by a cable *DG*. The free-body diagram of the crane has been drawn in Fig. 6.1*b*. The external forces are shown in the diagram and include the weight **W**, the two components $\mathbf{A}_x$ and $\mathbf{A}_y$ of the reaction at *A*, and the force **T** exerted by the cable at *D*. The internal forces holding the various parts of the crane together do not appear in the diagram. If, however, the crane is dismembered and if a free-body diagram is drawn for each of its component parts, the forces holding the three beams together must also be represented, since these forces are external forces from the point of view of each component part (Fig. 6.1*c*).

It will be noted that the force exerted at *B* by member *BE* on member *AD* has been represented as equal and opposite to the force exerted at the same point by member *AD* on member *BE*; similarly, the force exerted at *E* by *BE* on *CF* is shown equal and opposite to the force exerted by *CF* on *BE*; and the components of the force exerted at *C* by *CF* on *AD* are shown equal and opposite to the components of the force exerted by *AD* on *CF*. This is in conformity with Newton's third law,

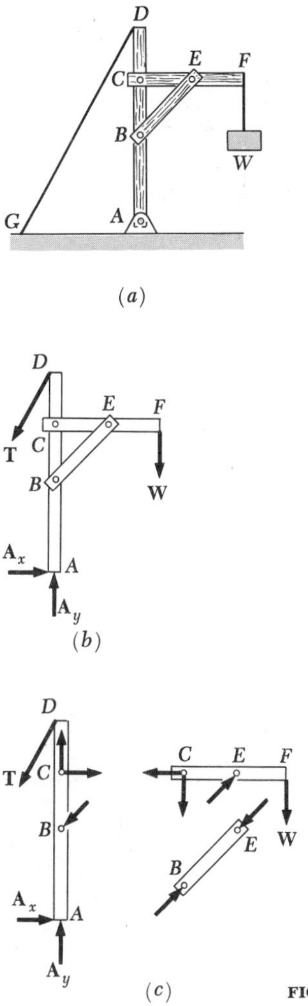

FIG. 6.1

which states that *the forces of action and reaction between bodies in contact have the same magnitude, same line of action, and opposite sense.* As pointed out in Chap. 1, this law is one of the six fundamental principles of elementary mechanics and is based on experimental evidence. Its application is essential to the solution of problems involving connected bodies.

TRUSSES

6.2. Definition of a Truss. The truss is one of the major types of engineering structures. It provides both a practical and an economical solution to many engineering situations, especially in the design of bridges and buildings. A truss consists of straight members connected at joints; a typical truss is shown in Fig. 6.2*a*. Truss members are connected at their extremities only; thus no member is continuous through a joint. In Fig. 6.2*a*, for example, there is no member *AB*; there are instead two distinct members *AD* and *DB*. Actual structures are made of several trusses joined together to form a space framework. Each truss is designed to carry those loads which act in its plane and thus may be treated as a two-dimensional structure.

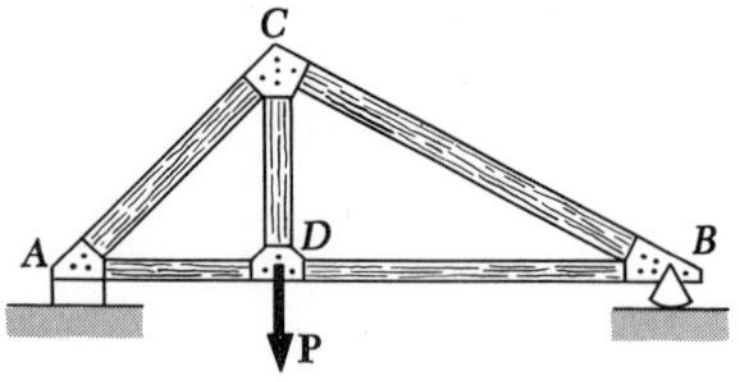

(*a*)

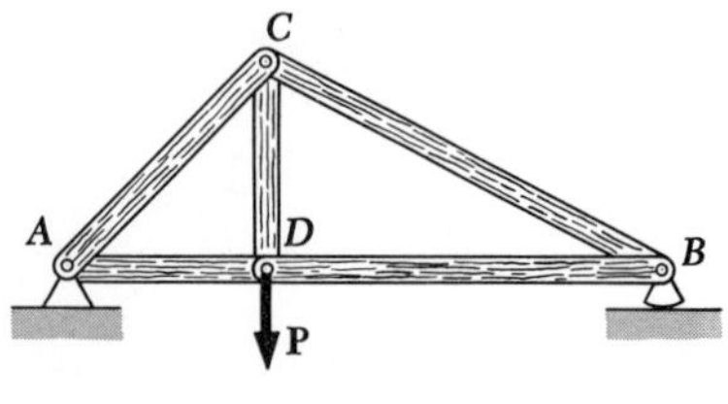

(*b*)

FIG. 6.2

In general, the members of a truss are slender and can support little lateral load; all loads, therefore, must be applied to the various joints, and not to the members themselves. When a concentrated load is to be applied between two joints, or when a distributed load is to be supported by the truss, as in the case of a bridge truss, a floor system must be provided which, through the use of stringers and floor beams, transmits the load to the joints (Fig. 6.3).

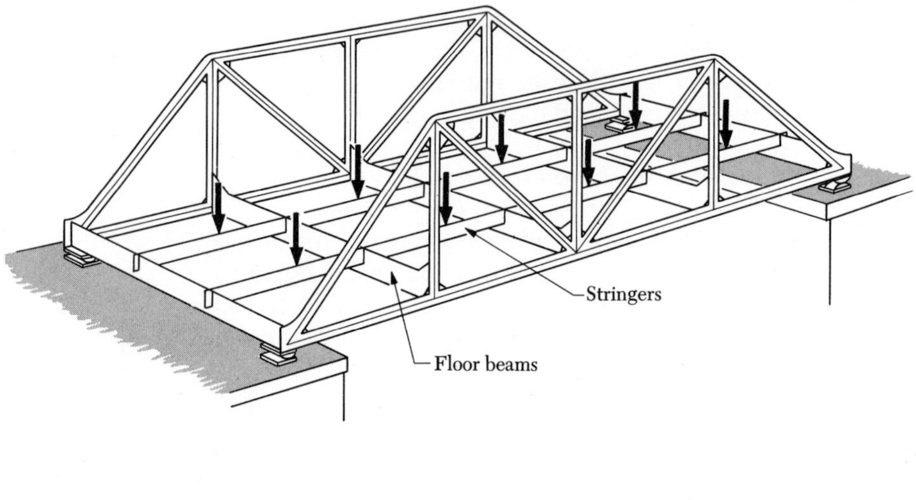

FIG. 6.3

The weights of the members of the truss are also assumed to be applied to the joints, half of the weight of each member being applied to each of the two joints the member connects. Although the members are actually joined together by means of riveted and welded connections, it is customary to assume that the members are pinned together; therefore, the forces acting at each end of a member reduce to a single force and no couple. Thus, the only forces assumed to be applied to a truss member are a single force at each end of the member. Each member may then be treated as a two-force member, and the entire truss may be considered as a group of pins and two-force members (Fig. 6.2*b*). An individual member may be acted upon as shown in either of the two sketches of Fig. 6.4. In the first sketch, the forces tend to pull the member apart, and the member is in tension, while, in the second sketch, the forces tend to compress the member, and the member is in compression. Several typical trusses are shown in Fig. 6.5.

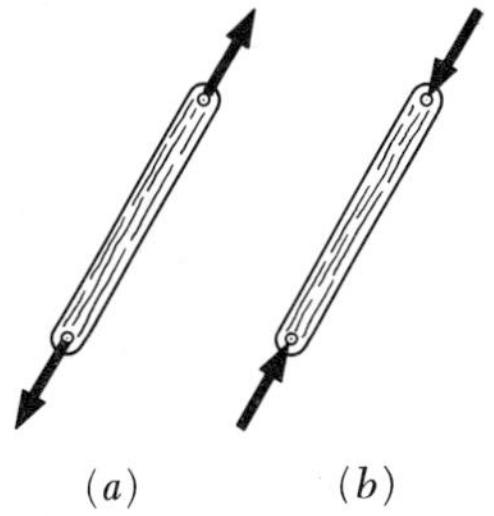

FIG. 6.4

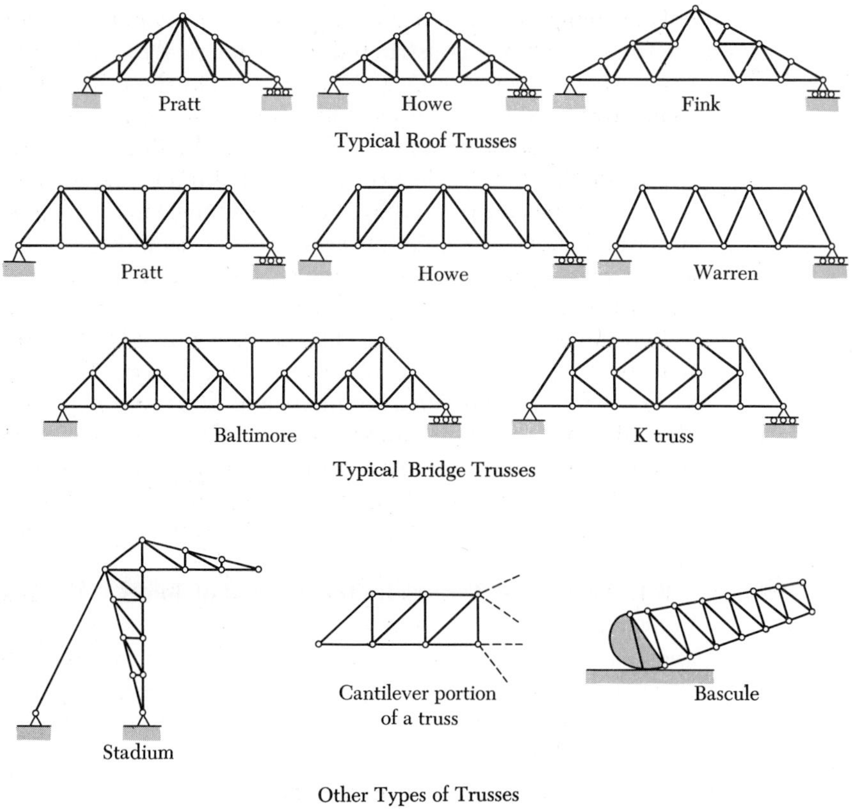

FIG. 6.5. Typical trusses

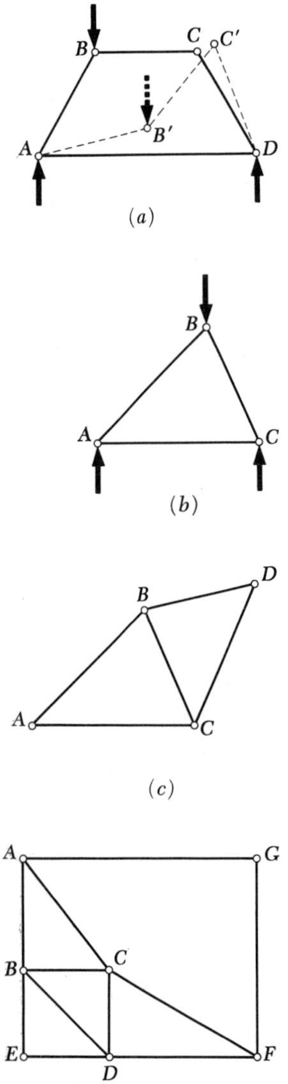

FIG. 6.6

6.3. Simple Trusses. Consider the truss of Fig. 6.6*a*, which is made of four members connected by pins at *A*, *B*, *C*, and *D*. If a load is applied at *B*, the truss will greatly deform and lose completely its original shape. On the other hand, the truss of Fig. 6.6*b*, which is made of three members connected by pins at *A*, *B*, and *C*, will deform only slightly under a load applied at *B*. The only possible deformation for this truss is one involving small changes in the length of its members. The truss of Fig. 6.6*b* is said to be a *rigid truss*, the term rigid being used here to indicate that the truss *will not collapse*.

As shown in Fig. 6.6*c*, a larger rigid truss may be obtained by adding two members *BD* and *CD* to the basic triangular truss of Fig. 6.6*b*. This procedure may be repeated as many times as desired, and the resulting truss will be rigid if, each time we add two new members, we attach them to separate existing joints and connect them at a new joint.† A truss which may be constructed in this manner is called a *simple truss*.

It should be noted that a simple truss is not necessarily made only of triangles. The truss of Fig. 6.6*d*, for example, is a simple truss which was constructed from triangle *ABC* by adding successively the joints *D*, *E*, *F*, and *G*. On the other hand, rigid trusses are not always simple trusses, even when they appear to be made of triangles. The Fink and Baltimore trusses shown in Fig. 6.5, for instance, are not simple trusses, since they cannot be constructed from a single triangle in the manner described above. All the other trusses shown in Fig. 6.5 are simple trusses, as may be easily checked. (For the K truss, start with one of the central triangles.)

Returning to the basic triangular truss of Fig. 6.6*b*, we note that this truss has three members and three joints. The truss of Fig. 6.6*c* has two more members and one more joint, i.e., altogether five members and four joints. Observing that every time two new members are added, the number of joints is increased by one, we find that in a simple truss the total number of members is $m = 2n - 3$, where n is the total number of joints.

6.4. Analysis of Trusses by the Method of Joints. We saw in Sec. 6.2 that a truss may be considered as a group of pins and two-force members. The truss of Fig. 6.2, whose free-body diagram is shown in Fig. 6.7*a*, may thus be dismembered, and a free-body diagram can be drawn for each pin and each

† The three joints must not be in a straight line.

member (Fig. 6.7*b*). Each member is acted upon by two forces, one at each end; these forces have the same magnitude, same line of action, and opposite sense (Sec. 4.6). Besides, Newton's third law indicates that the forces of action and reaction between a member and a pin are equal and opposite. Therefore, the forces exerted by a member on the two pins it connects must be directed along that member and be equal and opposite. The common magnitude of the forces exerted by a member on the two pins it connects is commonly referred to as the *force in the member* considered, even though this quantity is actually a scalar. Since the lines of action of all the internal forces in a truss are known, the analysis of a truss reduces to the computation of the forces in its various members and to the determination of whether each of its members is in tension or in compression.

Since the entire truss is in equilibrium, each pin must be in equilibrium. The fact that a pin is in equilibrium may be expressed by drawing its free-body diagram and writing two equilibrium equations (Sec. 2.8). If the truss contains n pins, there will be therefore $2n$ equations available, which may be solved for $2n$ unknowns. In the case of a simple truss, we have $m = 2n - 3$, that is, $2n = m + 3$, and the number of unknowns which may be determined from the free-body diagrams of the pins is thus $m + 3$. This means that the forces in all the members, as well as the two components of the reaction $\mathbf{R}_1$, and the reaction $\mathbf{R}_2$ may be found by considering the free-body diagrams of the pins.

The fact that the entire truss is a rigid body in equilibrium may be used to write three more equations involving the forces shown in the free-body diagram of Fig. 6.7*a*. Since they do not contain any new information, these equations are not independent from the equations associated with the free-body diagrams of the pins. Nevertheless, they may be used to determine immediately the components of the reactions at the supports. The arrangement of pins and members in a simple

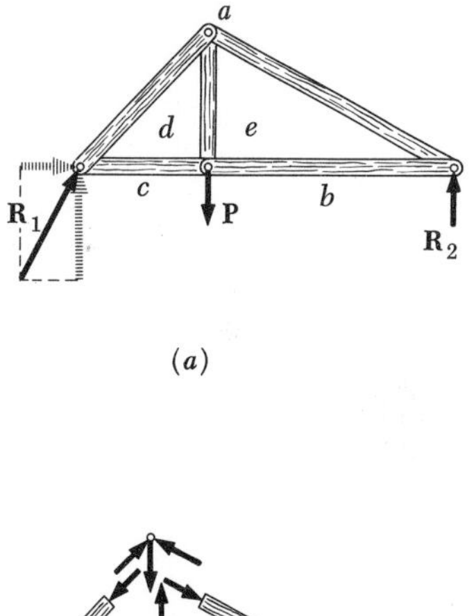

(*a*)

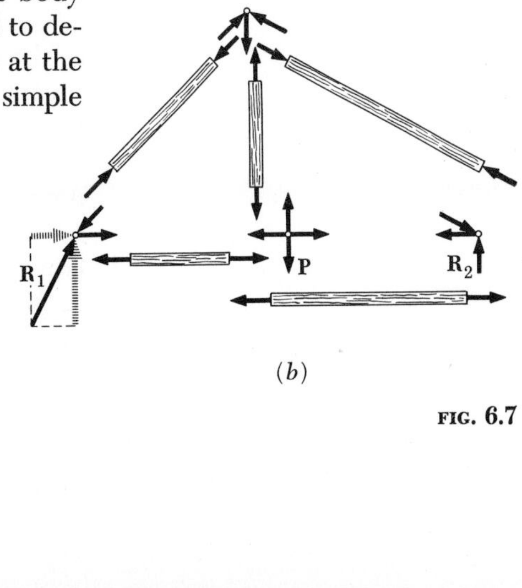

(*b*)

FIG. 6.7

truss is such that it will then always be possible to find a joint involving only two unknown forces. These forces may be determined by the methods of Sec. 2.10 and their values transferred to the adjacent joints and treated as known quantities at these joints. This procedure may be repeated until all unknown forces have been determined.

In order to expedite the analysis of trusses, it is desirable to establish a uniform method for denoting the various joints, members, loads, and forces. This is done by using the following notation, known as *Bow's notation*. A lower-case letter is assigned to every region between loads and reactions, moving clockwise around the truss, and to every area inside the truss (Fig. 6.7*a*). Each joint, member, load, and force may then be denoted as follows:

1. *Joints.* A joint is specified by naming *in clockwise order* the letters corresponding to all the areas adjacent to the joint. For example, the joint at the left support (Fig. 6.7*a*) is joint *adc,* or joint *dca,* or joint *cad.* For convenience, however, joints will be denoted sometimes by a number.

2. *Members.* A member is specified by naming the letters of the two adjacent areas. For example, the vertical member above the load **P** is member *de* or member *ed.*

3. *Loads.* A load is specified by reading *in clockwise order* the letters of the two areas adjacent to the load. The name of the load is then recorded with capital letters surmounted by an arrow. For example, at joint *debc*, the load **P** is denoted by $\overrightarrow{BC}$.

4. *Forces Exerted by Members on Pins.* As noted above, the forces exerted by a member on the two pins it connects must be directed along the member and be equal and opposite. In considering the action of the member on one of the two pins, we denote the force it exerts by reading the letters of the two areas adjacent to the member *in clockwise order* with respect to the joint. For example, the force exerted by member *ad* on pin *adc* is $\overrightarrow{AD}$, while the force exerted by the same member on pin *aed* is $\overrightarrow{DA}$. The common magnitude of these forces commonly referred to as the force in member *ad,* may be denoted by either AD or DA.

We shall now proceed to analyze the truss of Fig. 6.7 by considering successively the equilibrium of each pin, starting with a joint at which only two forces are unknown. In the truss considered, all pins are subjected to at least three unknown forces. Therefore, the reactions at the supports must first be determined by considering the entire truss as a free body and using the equations of equilibrium of a rigid body. We find in this way that $\mathbf{R}_1$ is vertical and determine the magnitudes of $\mathbf{R}_1$ and $\mathbf{R}_2$.

The number of unknown forces at joint *adc* is thus reduced to two; and these forces may be determined by considering the equilibrium of pin *adc*. The magnitude and sense of $\overrightarrow{AD}$ and $\overrightarrow{DC}$ are obtained from the corresponding force triangle (Fig. 6.8).

We may now proceed to joint *debc*, where only two forces, $\overrightarrow{DE}$ and $\overrightarrow{EB}$, are still unknown. $\overrightarrow{BC}$ is the given load $\mathbf{P}$ and hence is known; *CD* is the force exerted on the pin by the mem-

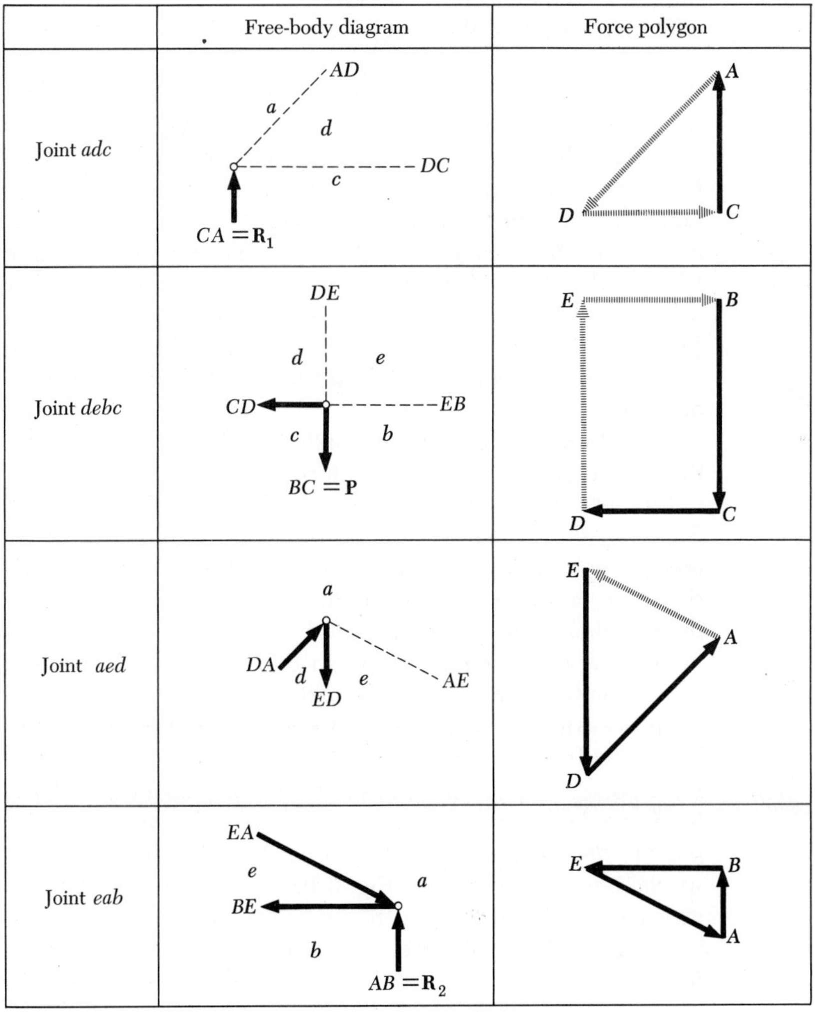

FIG. 6.8

ber *cd* and, as indicated above, is equal and opposite to the force $\overrightarrow{DC}$ exerted by the same member on pin *adc*.

Next, joint *aed* is considered; its free-body diagram is shown in Fig. 6.8. It is noted that both $\overrightarrow{ED}$ and $\overrightarrow{DA}$ are known from the analysis of the preceding joints and that only $\overrightarrow{AE}$ is unknown. Since the equilibrium of each pin provides sufficient information to determine two unknowns, a check of our analysis is obtained at this joint. The force triangle is drawn, and the magnitude and sense of $\overrightarrow{AE}$ are determined. The check is obtained by verifying that the force $\overrightarrow{AE}$ and the member *ae* are parallel.

At joint *eab*, all the forces are known. Since the corresponding pin is in equilibrium, the force triangle must close and an additional check of the analysis is obtained.

From the free-body diagrams shown in Fig. 6.8, it is seen that some forces act away from a given joint and others toward it. If the force acts away from the joint, the corresponding member pulls on the pin and the member is in tension; if the force acts toward the joint, the corresponding member pushes on the pin and the member is in compression. For example, at joint *adc*, it is seen from the free-body diagram and the force triangle that force $\overrightarrow{AD}$ acts toward the joint; hence, member *ad* pushes on the pin and is in compression. If we consider joint *aed*, it is seen that $\overrightarrow{DA}$ also acts toward the joint; hence, member *ad* is again found to push and thus to be in compression.

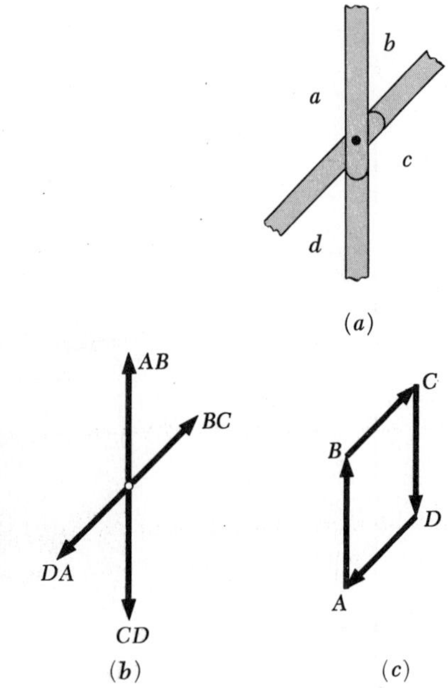

FIG. 6.9

***6.5. Joints under Special Loading Conditions.** Consider the joint shown in Fig. 6.9*a*, which connects four members lying in two intersecting straight lines. The free-body diagram of Fig. 6.9*b* shows that the pin is subjected to two pairs of directly opposite forces. The corresponding force polygon, therefore, must be a parallelogram (Fig. 6.9*c*), and *the forces in opposite members must be equal.*

Consider next the joint shown in Fig. 6.10*a*, which connects three members and supports a load **P**. Two of the members lie in the same line, and the load **P** acts along the third member. The free-body diagram of the pin and the corresponding force polygon again will be as shown in Fig. 6.9*b* and *c*. Thus, *the forces in the two opposite members must be equal, and the force in the other member must equal P.* A particular case of special interest is shown in Fig. 6.10*b*. Since, in this case, no external load is applied to the joint, we have $P = 0$ and the force in member *cd* is zero. Member *cd* is said to be a *zero-force member.*

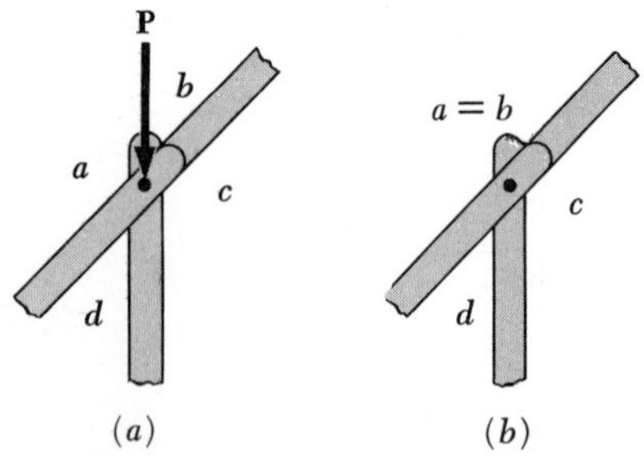

FIG. 6.10

Consider now a joint connecting two members only. From Sec. 2.8, we know that a particle which is acted upon by two forces will be in equilibrium if the two forces have the same magnitude, same line of action, and opposite sense. In the case of the joint of Fig. 6.11*a*, which connects two members lying in the same line, the equilibrium of the pin requires therefore that *the forces in the two members be equal.* In the case of the joint of Fig. 6.11*b*, equilibrium is impossible unless the forces in both members are zero. Members connected as shown in Fig. 6.11*b*, therefore, must be *zero-force members.*

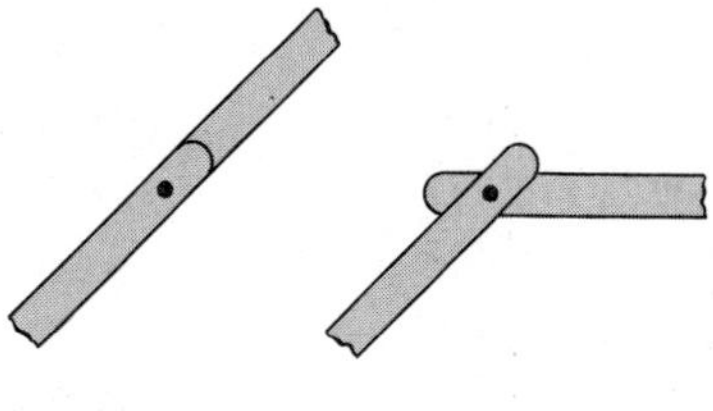

FIG. 6.11

Spotting the joints which are under the special loading conditions listed above will expedite the analysis of a truss. Consider, for example, a Howe truss loaded as shown in Fig. 6.12. All the members represented by dashed lines will be recognized as zero-force members. Joint *3* connects three members, two of which lie in the same line, and is not subjected to any external load; member *hi* is thus a zero-force member. Applying the same reasoning to joint *11*, we find that member *pq* is also a zero-force member. But joint *10* is now in the same situation as joints *3* and *11*, and member *po* must be a zero-force member. The examination of joints *3*, *10*, and *11* also shows that the forces in members *fh* and *if* are equal, that the forces in members *od* and *dq* are equal, and that the forces in members *ep* and *qe* are equal. Furthermore, now turning our attention to joint 9, where the 4-kip load and member *no* are collinear, we note that the force in member *no* is 4 kips (tension) and that the forces in members *fn* and *pe* are equal. Hence, the forces in members *ep*, *eq*, and *fn* are equal.

Students, however, should be warned against misusing the rules established in this section. For example, it would be wrong to assume that the force in member *kj* is 5 kips or that

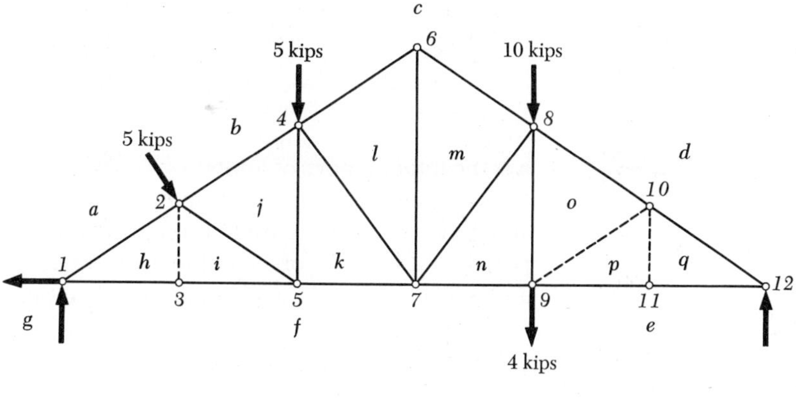

FIG. 6.12

the forces in members *bj* and *ha* are equal. The conditions discussed above do not apply to joints *2* and *4*. The forces in these members and in all remaining members should be found by carrying out the analysis of joints *1, 2, 4, 5, 6, 7, 8,* and *12* in the usual manner. Until they have become thoroughly familiar with the conditions of application of the rules established in this section, students would be well advised to draw the free-body diagrams of all pins and to write the corresponding equilibrium equations (or draw the corresponding force polygons), whether or not the joints considered fall into the categories listed above.

A final remark concerning zero-force members: These members are not useless. While they do not carry any load under the particular loading conditions shown, the zero-force members of Fig. 6.12 will probably carry loads if the loading conditions are changed. Besides, even in the case considered, these members are needed to support the weight of the truss and to maintain the truss in the desired shape.

***6.6. Space Trusses.** When several straight members are joined together at their extremities to form a three-dimensional configuration, the structure obtained is called a *space truss.*

We recall from Sec. 6.3 that the most elementary two-dimensional rigid truss consisted of three members joined at their extremities to form the sides of a triangle; by adding two members at a time to this basic configuration, and connecting them at a new joint, it was possible to obtain a larger rigid structure which was defined as a simple truss. Similarly, the most elementary rigid space truss consists of six members joined at their extremities to form the edges of a tetrahedron *ABCD* (Fig. 6.13*a*). By adding three members at a time to this basic configuration, such as *AE, BE,* and *CE,* attaching them at separate existing joints, and connecting them at a new joint, we can obtain a larger rigid structure which is defined as a *simple space truss* (Fig. 6.13*b*).† Observing that the basic tetrahedron has six members and four joints, and that, every time three members are added, the number of joints is increased by one, we conclude that in a simple space truss the total number of members is $m = 3n - 6$, where n is the total number of joints.

If a space truss is to be completely constrained and if the reactions at its supports are to be statically determinate, the supports should consist of a combination of balls, rollers, and balls and sockets providing six unknown reactions (see Sec. 4.9).

† The four joints must not lie in a plane.

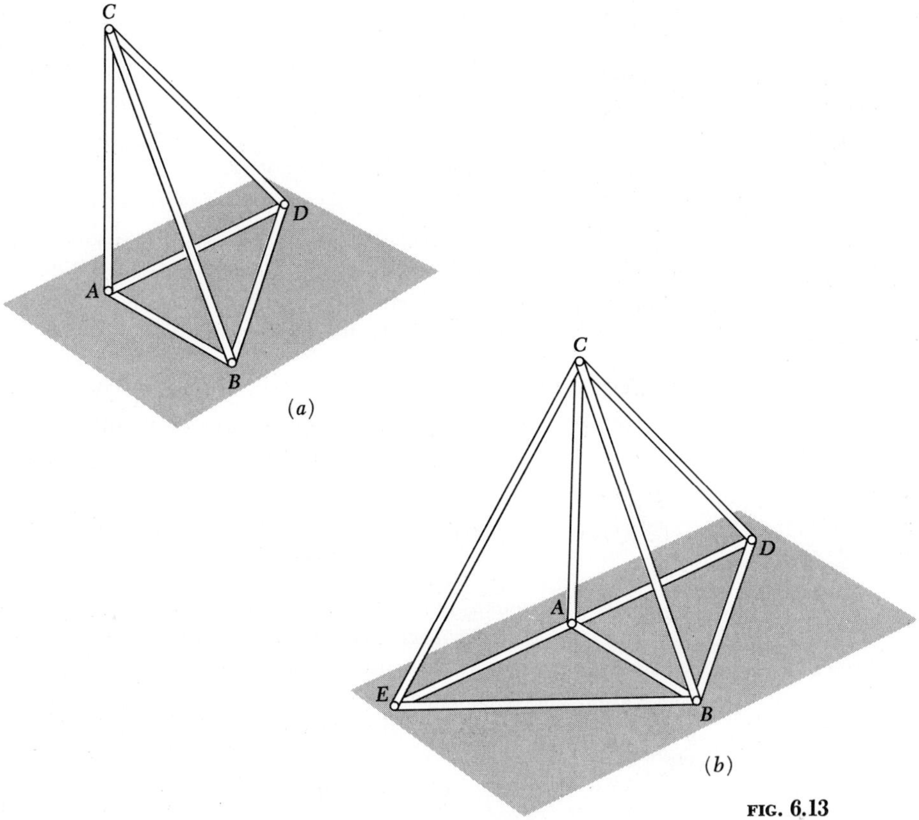

FIG. 6.13

These unknown reactions may be readily determined by solving the six equations expressing that the three-dimensional truss is in equilibrium.

Although the members of a space truss are actually joined together by means of riveted or welded connections, it is assumed that each joint consists of a ball-and-socket connection. Thus, no couple will be applied to the members of the truss and each member may be treated as a two-force member. The conditions of equilibrium for each joint will be expressed by the three equations $\Sigma F_x = 0$, $\Sigma F_y = 0$, and $\Sigma F_z = 0$. In the case of a simple space truss containing n joints, writing the conditions of equilibrium for each joint will thus yield $3n$ equations. Since $m = 3n - 6$, these equations suffice to determine all unknown forces (forces in m members and six reactions at the supports). However, to avoid solving many simultaneous equations, care should be taken to select joints in such an order that no selected joint will involve more than three unknown forces.

SAMPLE PROBLEM 6.1

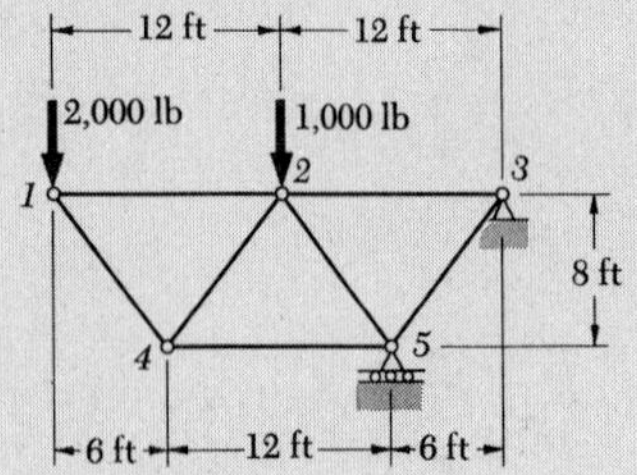

Using the method of joints, determine the force in each member of the truss shown.

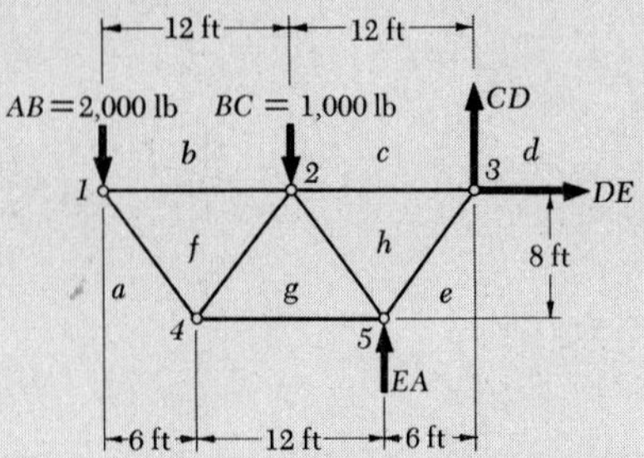

Solution. A free-body diagram of the entire truss is drawn; external forces acting on this free body consist of the applied loads and the reactions. The truss is then lettered, using Bow's notation. The applied loads are thus $\overrightarrow{AB}$ and $\overrightarrow{BC}$; the reactions are $\overrightarrow{CD}$, $\overrightarrow{DE}$, and $\overrightarrow{EA}$.

Equilibrium of Entire Truss

$+\circlearrowleft \Sigma M_3 = 0$: $(2{,}000 \text{ lb})(24 \text{ ft}) + (1{,}000 \text{ lb})(12 \text{ ft}) - (EA)(6 \text{ ft}) = 0$

$EA = +10{,}000 \text{ lb}$ $\qquad EA = 10{,}000 \text{ lb} \uparrow$

$\overset{+}{\rightarrow} \Sigma F_x = 0$: $\qquad \overrightarrow{DE} = 0$

$+\uparrow \Sigma F_y = 0$: $-2{,}000 \text{ lb} - 1{,}000 \text{ lb} + 10{,}000 \text{ lb} + CD = 0$

$CD = -7{,}000 \text{ lb}$ $\qquad \overrightarrow{CD} = 7{,}000 \text{ lb} \downarrow$

Joint 1. This joint is subjected to only two unknown forces, namely, the forces exerted by members *bf* and *fa*. A force triangle is used to determine $\overrightarrow{BF}$ and $\overrightarrow{FA}$. We note that member *bf* pulls on the joint and thus is in tension and that member *fa* pushes on the joint and thus is in compression. The magnitudes of the two forces are obtained from the proportion

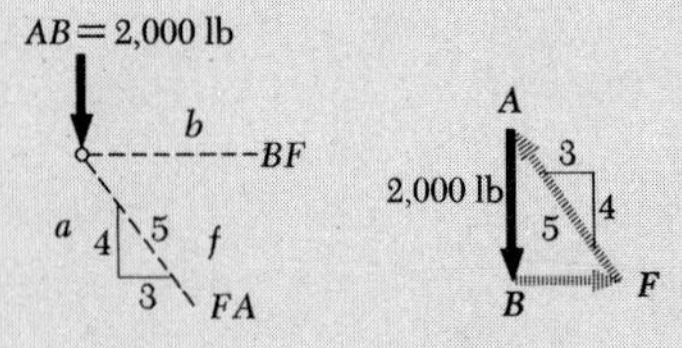

$$\frac{2{,}000 \text{ lb}}{4} = \frac{BF}{3} = \frac{FA}{5}$$

$BF = 1{,}500 \text{ lb } T$ ◄

$FA = 2{,}500 \text{ lb } C$ ◄

Joint 4. Since the force exerted by member *af* has been determined, only two unknown forces are now involved at this joint. Again, a force triangle is used to determine the unknown forces in members *fg* and *ga*.

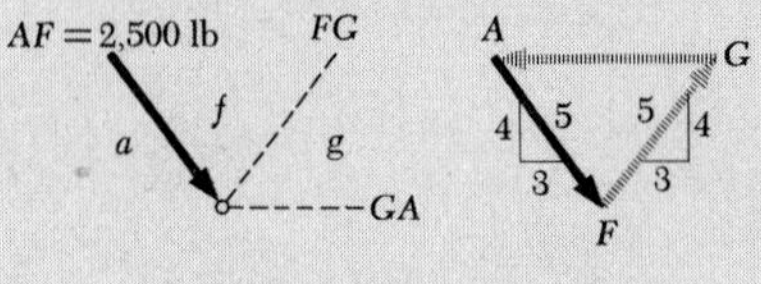

$FG = AF$ $\qquad FG = 2{,}500 \text{ lb } T$ ◄

$GA = (2)(\tfrac{3}{5} AF)$ $\qquad GA = 3{,}000 \text{ lb } C$ ◄

SAMPLE PROBLEM 6.1 *(Continued)*

Joint 2. Since more than three forces act at this joint, we determine the two unknown forces $\overrightarrow{CH}$ and $\overrightarrow{HG}$ by solving the equilibrium equations $\Sigma F_x = 0$ and $\Sigma F_y = 0$. We arbitrarily assume that both unknown forces act away from the joint, i.e., that the members are in tension. The positive value obtained for CH indicates that our assumption was correct; member ch is in tension. The negative value of HG indicates that our assumption was wrong; member hg is in compression.

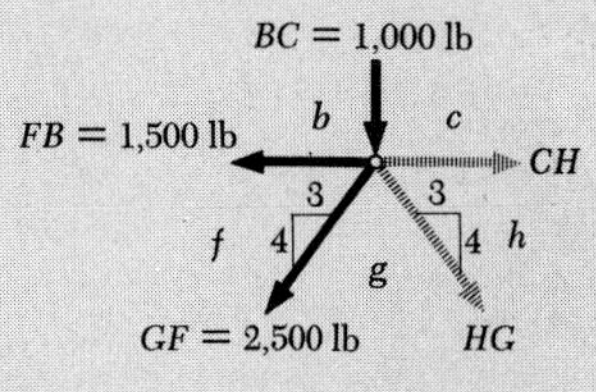

$+\uparrow \Sigma F_y = 0$: $\quad -1{,}000 - (\frac{4}{5})(2{,}500) - \frac{4}{5}HG = 0$

$HG = -3{,}750 \text{ lb} \qquad\qquad HG = 3{,}750 \text{ lb } C$ ◄

$\xrightarrow{+} \Sigma F_x = 0$: $\quad CH - 1{,}500 - (\frac{3}{5})(2{,}500) - (\frac{3}{5})(3{,}750) = 0$

$CH = +5{,}250 \text{ lb} \qquad\qquad CH = 5{,}250 \text{ lb } T$ ◄

Joint 5. The unknown force $\overrightarrow{HE}$ is assumed to act away from the joint. Summing x components, we write

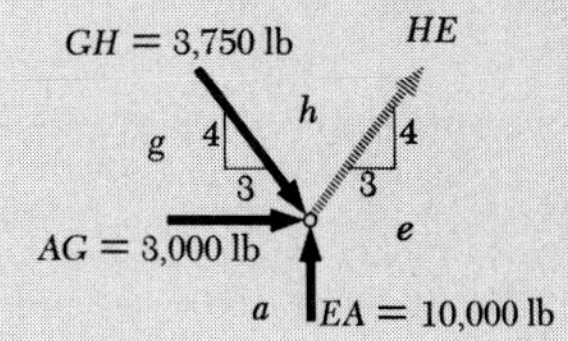

$\xrightarrow{+} \Sigma F_x = 0$: $\quad \frac{3}{5}HE + 3{,}000 + (\frac{3}{5})(3{,}750) = 0$

$HE = -8{,}750 \text{ lb} \qquad\qquad HE = 8{,}750 \text{ lb } C$ ◄

Summing y components, we obtain a check of our computations:

$$+\uparrow \Sigma F_y = 10{,}000 - (\tfrac{4}{5})(3{,}750) - (\tfrac{4}{5})(8{,}750)$$
$$= 10{,}000 - 3{,}000 - 7{,}000 = 0 \qquad \text{(checks)}$$

Joint 3. Using the computed values of $\overrightarrow{HC}$ and $\overrightarrow{EH}$, we may determine the reactions $\overrightarrow{CD}$ and $\overrightarrow{DE}$ by considering the equilibrium of this joint. Since these reactions have already been determined from the equilibrium of the entire truss, we will obtain two checks of our computations. We may also merely use the computed values of all forces acting on the joint (forces in members and reactions) and check that the joint is in equilibrium.

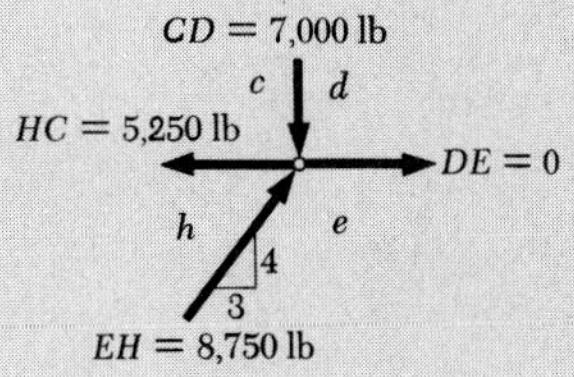

$$\xrightarrow{+} \Sigma F_x = -5{,}250 + (\tfrac{3}{5})(8{,}750) = -5{,}250 + 5{,}250 = 0 \qquad \text{(checks)}$$

$$+\uparrow \Sigma F_y = -7{,}000 + (\tfrac{4}{5})(8{,}750) = -7{,}000 + 7{,}000 = 0 \qquad \text{(checks)}$$

PROBLEMS

6.1 through 6.12. Using the method of joints, determine the force in each member of the truss shown. State whether each member is in tension or compression.

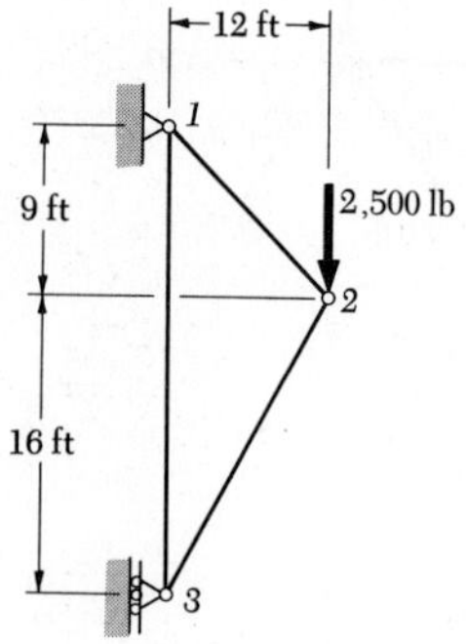

FIG. P 6.1 AND P 6.21

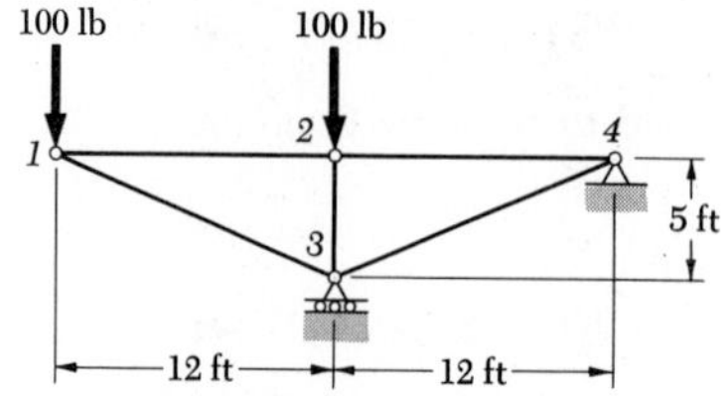

FIG. P 6.2 AND P 6.22

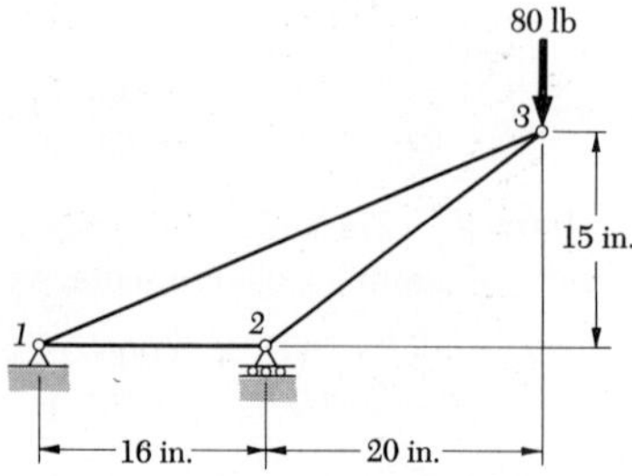

FIG. P 6.3 AND P 6.23

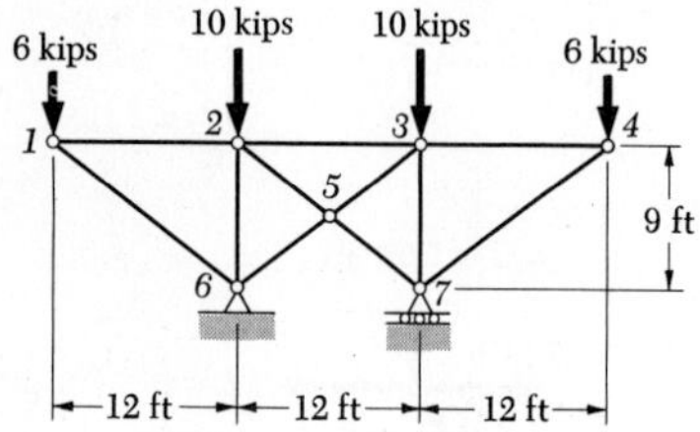

FIG. P 6.4 AND P 6.24

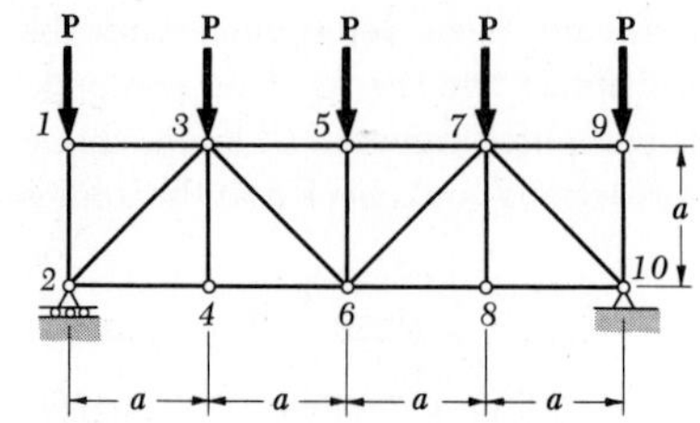

FIG. P 6.5 AND P 6.25

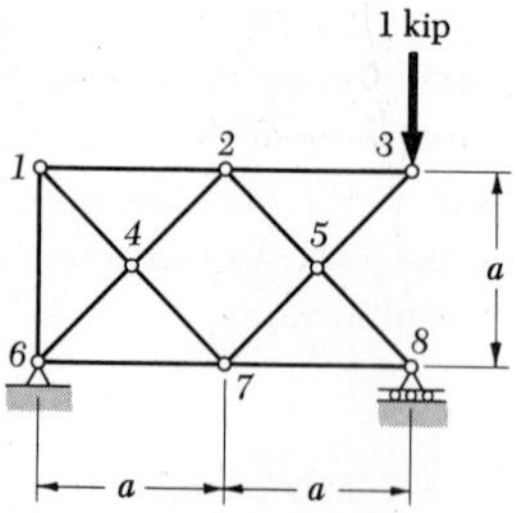

FIG. P 6.6 AND P 6.26

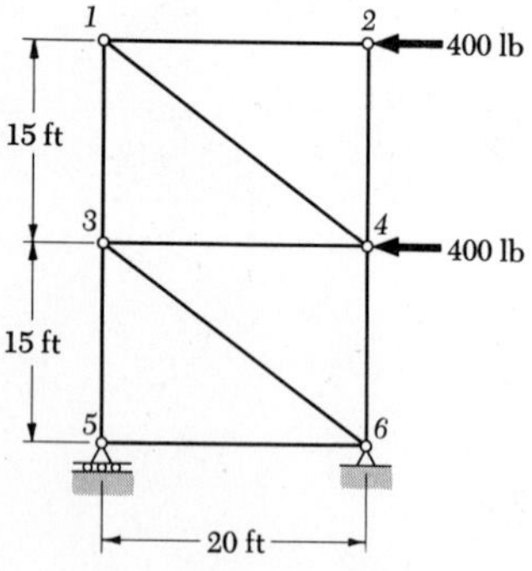

FIG. P 6.7 AND P 6.27

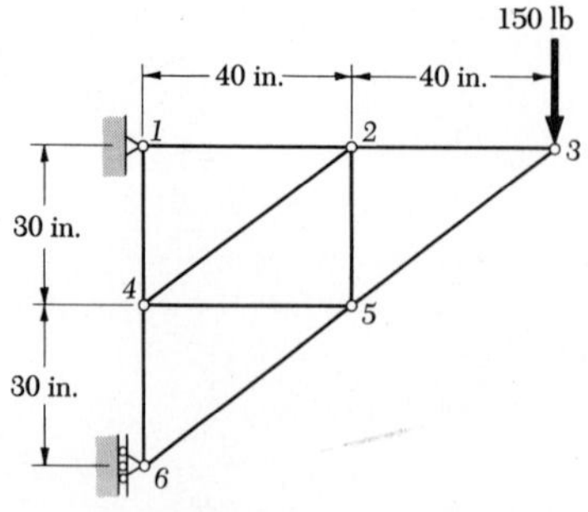

FIG. P 6.8 AND P 6.28

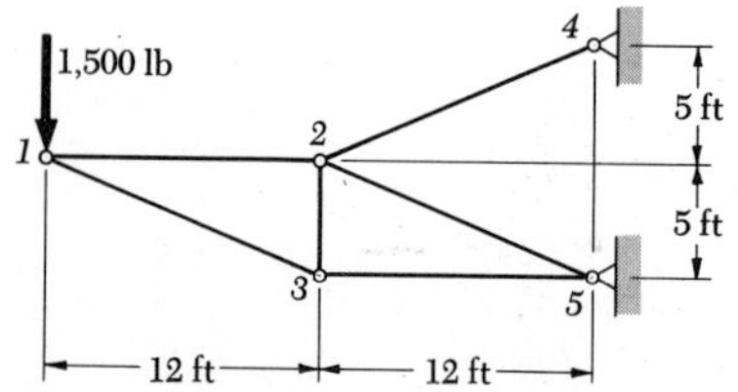

FIG. P 6.9 AND P 6.29

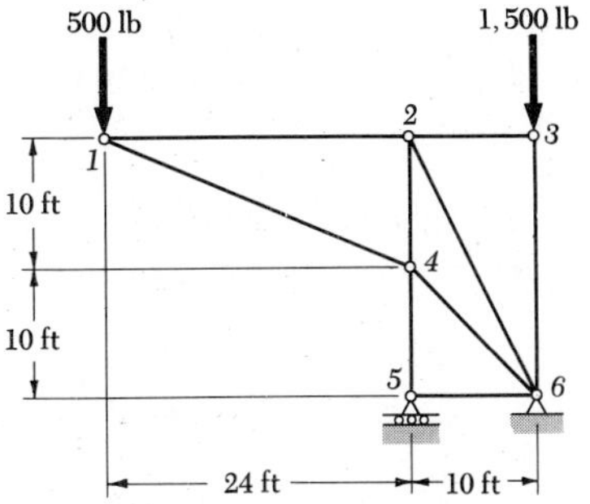

FIG. P6.10 AND P6.30

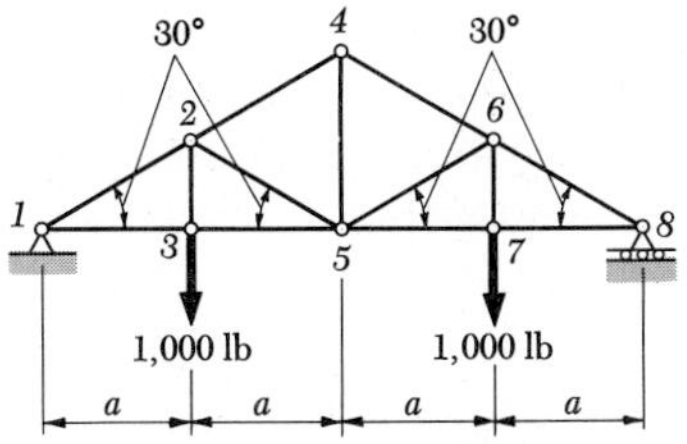

FIG. P6.11 AND P6.31

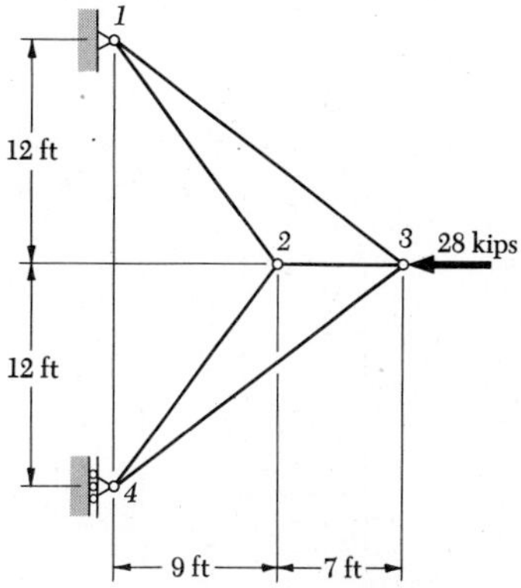

FIG. P6.12 AND P6.32

6.13 through 6.15. Determine the zero-force members in the truss shown for the given loading.

6.16. Indicate whether the trusses given in Probs. 6.4, 6.6, 6.10, 6.14, and 6.15 are simple trusses.

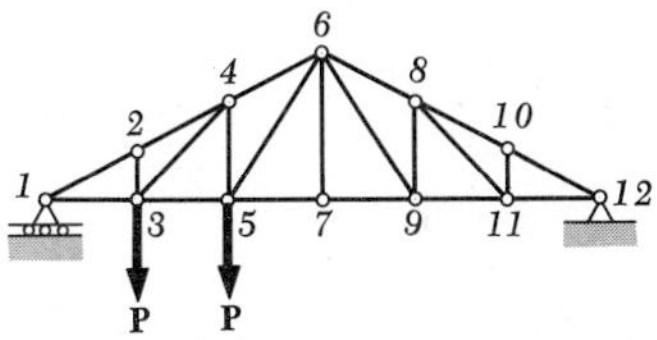

FIG. P6.13

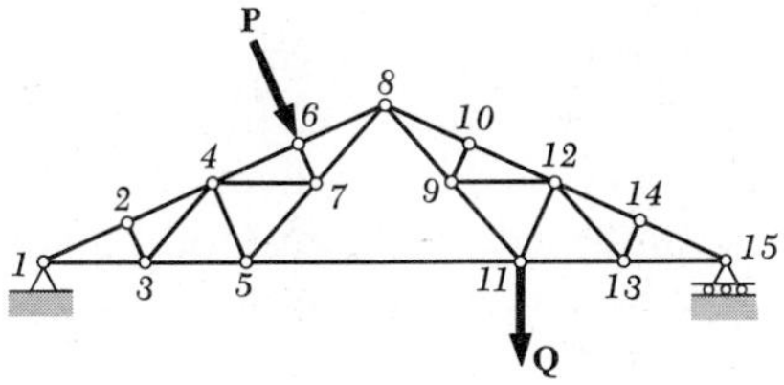

FIG. P6.14

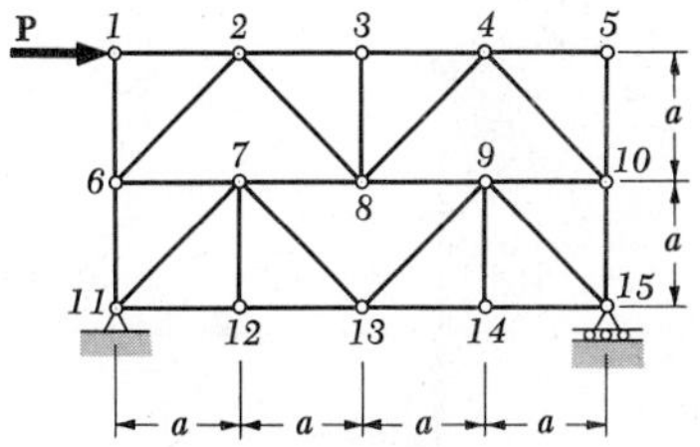

FIG. P6.15

***6.17.** Twelve members, each of length L, are connected to form a regular octahedron. Determine the force in each member if two vertical loads are applied as shown.

***6.18.** Six bars, each of length L, are connected to form a regular tetrahedron which rests on a smooth horizontal surface. Determine the force in each of the six members when a vertical force **P** is applied at A.

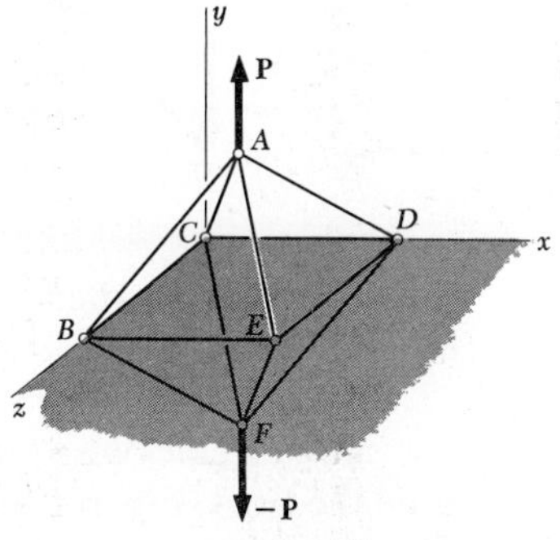

FIG. P6.17

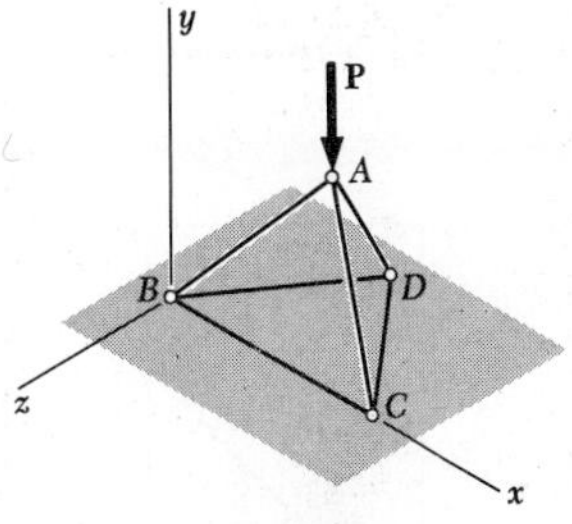

FIG. P6.18

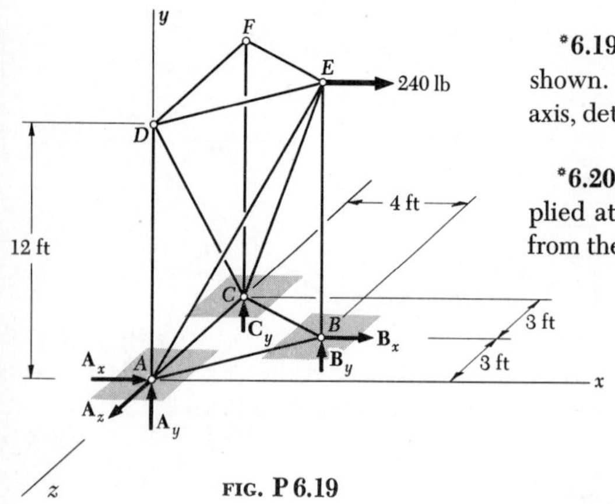

FIG. P 6.19

*6.19. The three-dimensional truss is supported by the six reactions shown. If a 240-lb load is applied at E in a direction parallel to the x axis, determine (a) the reactions, (b) the force in each member.

*6.20. Solve Prob. 6.19 assuming that the horizontal 240-lb load is applied at E in a direction parallel to member FE and is directed away from the truss.

6.7. Graphical Analysis of Trusses: Maxwell's Diagram. The method of joints may be used as the basis for a graphical analysis of trusses. We shall develop this graphical analysis by considering the truss already discussed in Sec. 6.4. This truss is shown again in Fig. 6.14a, and a force polygon has been drawn to scale for each joint in Fig. 6.14b; the force in each member may now be measured from one of these force polygons. The number of lines which have to be drawn can be greatly reduced, however, if the various force polygons are superimposed. The resulting diagram is shown in Fig. 6.14c and is known as the *Maxwell diagram* of the truss.

FIG. 6.14

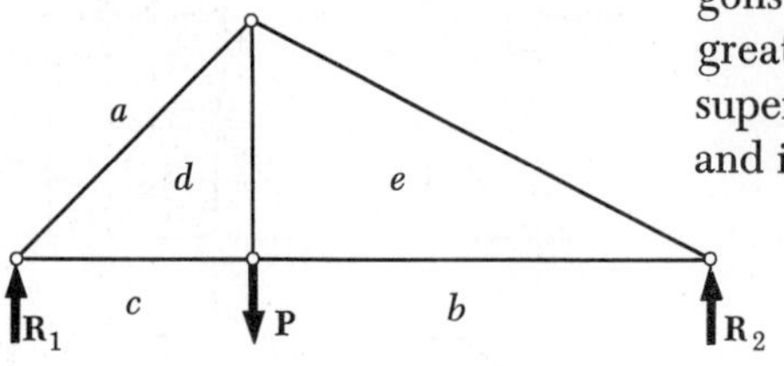

(a)

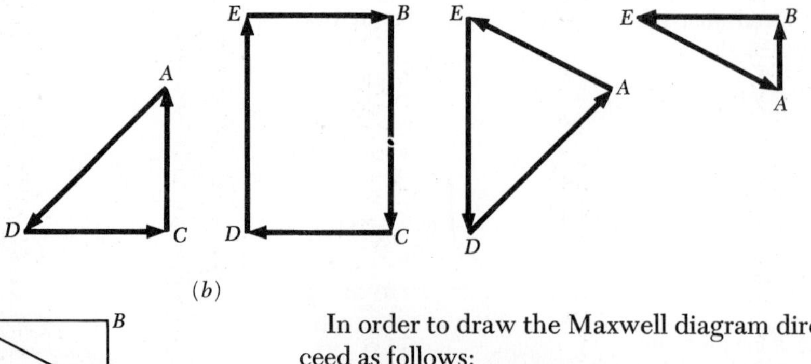

(b)

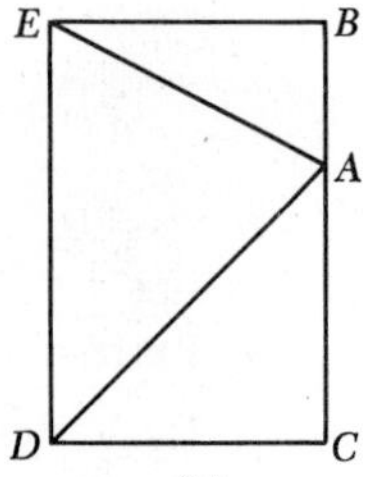

(c)

In order to draw the Maxwell diagram directly, we shall proceed as follows:

1. A lower-case letter is assigned to every region outside the truss, moving clockwise around the truss, and also to every area inside the truss (Fig. 6.14a).

2. The reactions $\mathbf{R}_1$ and $\mathbf{R}_2$ are determined. This is done either by drawing the string polygon or by solving the equations of equilibrium for the entire truss.

3. Selecting the external forces in clockwise order around the truss, we draw to scale the force polygon for the entire truss (line *ABCA* in Fig. 6.15*a*). If a joint may be found which is acted upon by only two forces, the last two steps may be omitted or at least postponed.

4. A force polygon is then drawn for each joint by treating successively joints acted upon by only two unknown forces. All lines previously drawn may be used; thus, it is necessary to draw only two additional lines to complete each new force polygon. For example, starting at joint *adc*, we draw a line parallel to *ad* through point *A* and a line parallel to *dc* through point *C*; this determines point *D* and thus completes the force triangle *ADC*, which corresponds to joint *adc* (Fig. 6.15*a*). Considering next joint *debc*, we draw a line parallel to *de* through *D* and a line parallel to *eb* through *B*; we obtain point *E* and thus complete the force polygon *DEBC*, which corresponds to joint *debc* (Fig. 6.15*b*). Next, we consider joint *aed* and draw a line parallel to *ae* through point *A* (Fig. 6.15*c*); we check that this line passes through the point *E* previously obtained. This completes the force triangle *AED* corresponding to joint *aed* and also completes the Maxwell diagram. At joint *eab*, all the forces are now known; we simply check that they form a closed triangle *EAB* (Fig. 6.15*d*).

5. The magnitude of the force in each member may now be measured on the Maxwell diagram. Thus, the magnitude of the force in member *ad* is *AD*. To determine whether a member is in tension or in compression, we shall determine whether it pulls or pushes on either of the two joints it connects. For example, consider member *ad*, which connects joints *adc* and *aed*. (*a*) We select one of these two joints, say, *adc*. (*b*) We read the names of the areas adjacent to the member in clockwise order around the joint in Fig. 6.14*a*; we read *ad*. (*c*) The direction of the force exerted on the joint is found by reading the corresponding letters of the Maxwell diagram in the same order (Fig. 6.14*c*). Since force $\overrightarrow{AD}$ is directed down and to the left, member *ad* pushes on the joint and must be in compression. The same result may be found by considering joint *aed*. The member is now read *da* and the corresponding force $\overrightarrow{DA}$. Since force $\overrightarrow{DA}$ is directed up and to the right, member *da* pushes on joint *aed* and is again found to be in compression.

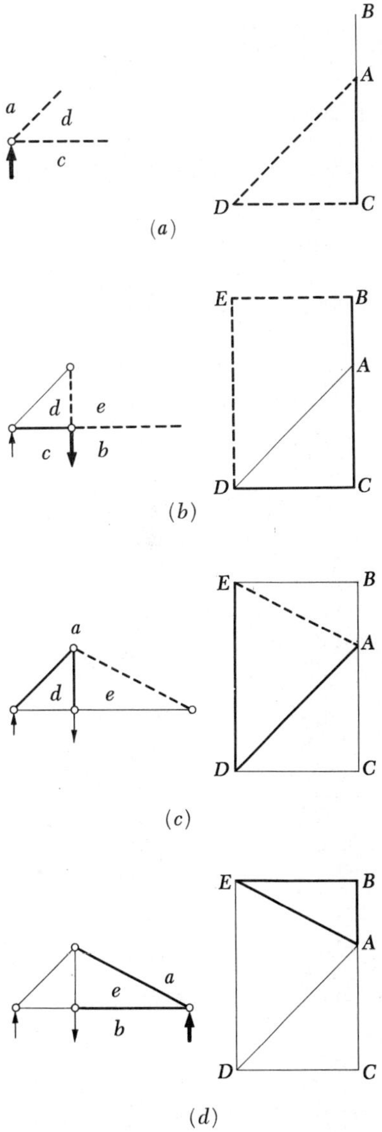

FIG. 6.15. Step-by-step construction of Maxwell's diagram

SAMPLE PROBLEM 6.2

By drawing Maxwell's diagram determine the force in each member of the truss considered in Sample Prob. 6.1.

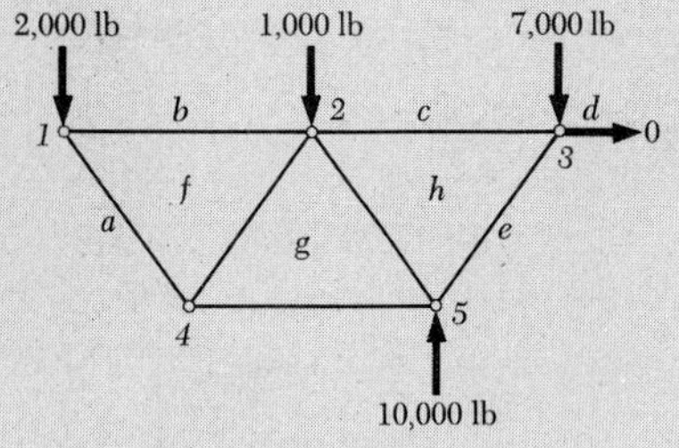

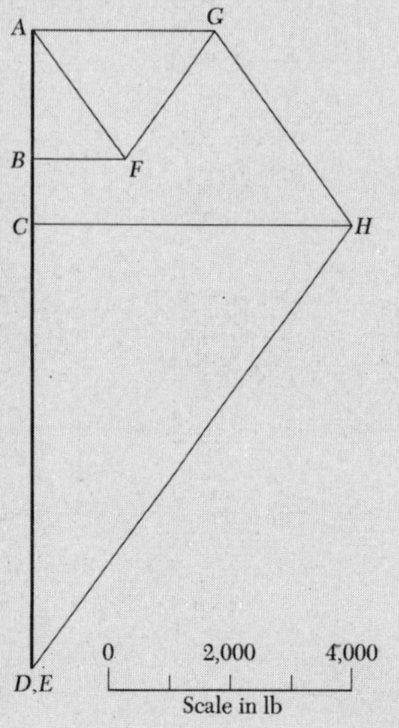

Solution. 1. The truss is drawn to scale; both the applied loads and the reactions are indicated. Using Bow's notation, a lower-case letter is assigned to each region outside the truss and to each individual area inside the truss.

2. By considering the entire truss as a free body, we compute the reactions (see Sample Prob. 6.1).

3. Selecting the external forces in clockwise order around the truss, we draw to scale the force polygon for the entire truss in tip-to-tail fashion; points *A*, *B*, *C*, *D*, and *E* are thus located on the Maxwell diagram.

4. Considering joint *1*, where only two unknown forces exist, we now locate point *F* by drawing lines *BF* and *AF*, which are parallel to members *bf* and *fa*, respectively. We next consider joint *4*, where there are now only two unknown forces and hence only one unknown point in the corresponding triangle of the Maxwell diagram. Lines *FG* and *AG* are drawn parallel to *fg* and *ga*, respectively; point *G* is located at the intersection of these lines. We next consider joint 2 and locate point *H* at the intersection of lines *CH* and *GH* which are drawn parallel to *ch* and *hg*, respectively. All the points of the Maxwell diagram have now been located. Since *HE* represents the force in member *he*, we may draw a line through point *H* parallel to member *he*; this line should pass through point *E*, which is already located. This provides a check on the accuracy of the drawing of the Maxwell diagram.

5. The magnitude and sense of the force in each member are determined from the Maxwell diagram; the magnitude is measured directly, and the sense is found as indicated in Sec. 6.7. The results are given in the table.

Member	Force
bf	1,500 lb *T*
fa	2,500 lb *C*
fg	2,500 lb *T*
ga	3,000 lb *C*
hg	3,750 lb *C*
ch	5,250 lb *T*
he	8,750 lb *C*

PROBLEMS

6.21 through 6.32. By drawing Maxwell's diagram, determine the force in each member of the truss shown. Indicate whether the member is in tension or compression. (The trusses appear on pages 200 and 201.)

6.33 through 6.37. By drawing Maxwell's diagram, determine the force in each member of the truss shown. Indicate whether the member is in tension or compression.

6.38. Solve Prob. 6.37 assuming that the truss supports vertical 10-kip loads at joints *2*, *4*, and *6*.

6.39. Solve Prob. 6.36 assuming that the 1,000-lb load supported at joint *1* is horizontal and directed to the left.

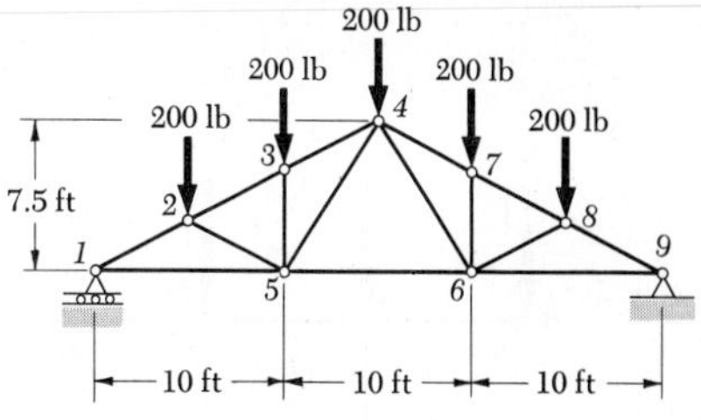

FIG. P 6.33

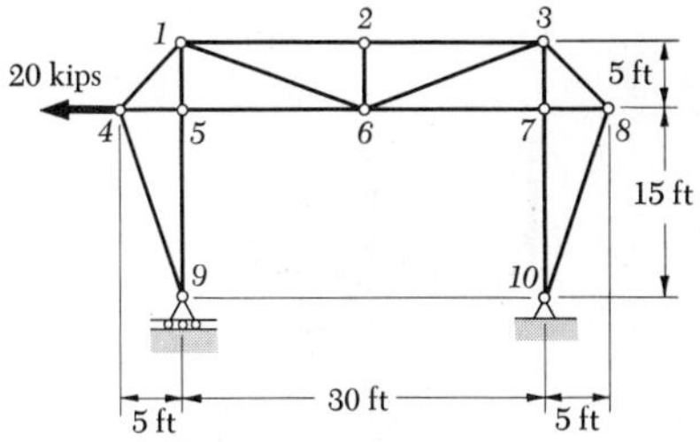

FIG. P 6.34

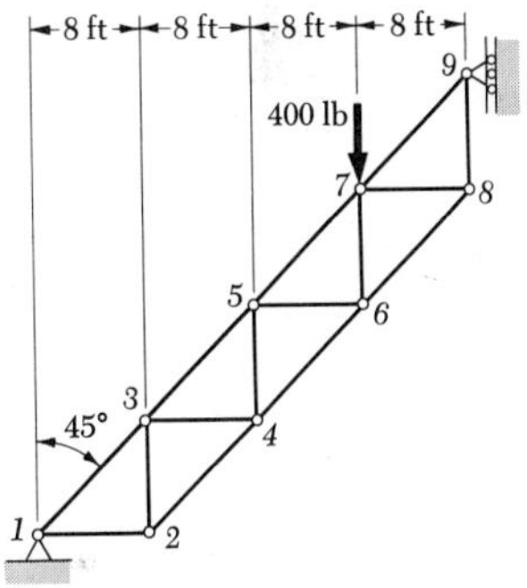

FIG. P 6.35

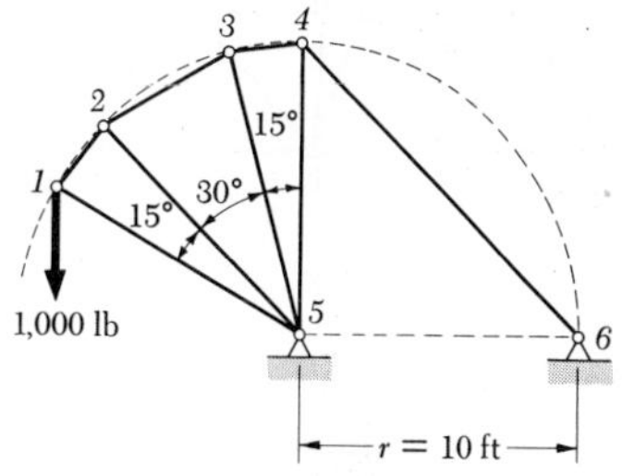

FIG. P 6.36

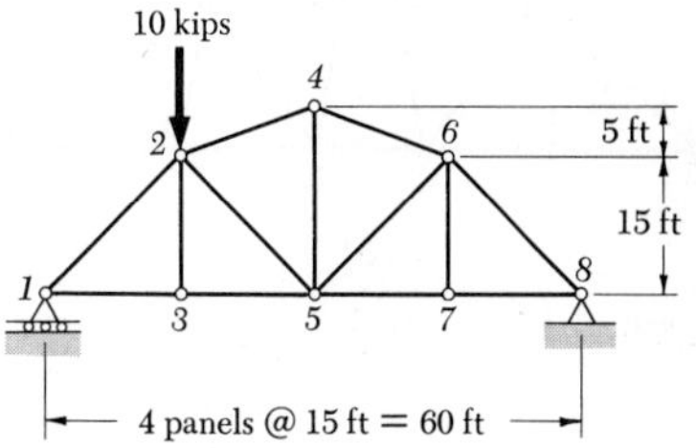

FIG. P 6.37

6.8. Analysis of Trusses by the Method of Sections.

The method of joints and Maxwell's diagram are most effective when the forces in all the members of a truss are to be determined. If, however, the force in only one member or the forces in a very few members are desired, a third method, the method of sections, will prove more efficient.

Assume, for example, that we want to determine the force in member *BD* of the truss shown in Fig. 6.16*a*. To do this, we must determine the force with which member *BD* acts on either joint *B* or joint *D*. If we were to use the method of joints, we would choose either joint *B* or joint *D* as a free body. However, we may also choose as a free body a larger portion of the truss, composed of several joints and members, provided that the desired force is one of the external forces acting on that portion. If, in addition, the portion of the truss is chosen so that there is a total of only three unknown forces acting upon it, the desired force may be obtained by solving the equations of equilibrium for this portion of the truss. In practice, the portion of the truss to be utilized is obtained by *passing a section* through three members of the truss, one of which is the desired member, i.e., by drawing a line which divides the truss into two completely separate parts but does not intersect more than three members. Either of the two portions of the truss obtained after the intersected members have been removed may then be used as a free body.†

In Fig. 6.16*a*, the section *nn* has been passed through members *BD*, *BE*, and *CE*, and the portion *ABC* of the truss is

† In the analysis of certain trusses, sections are passed which intersect more than three members; the forces in one, or possibly two, of the intersected members may be obtained if equilibrium equations can be found, each of which involves only one unknown (see Probs. 6.52 and 6.53).

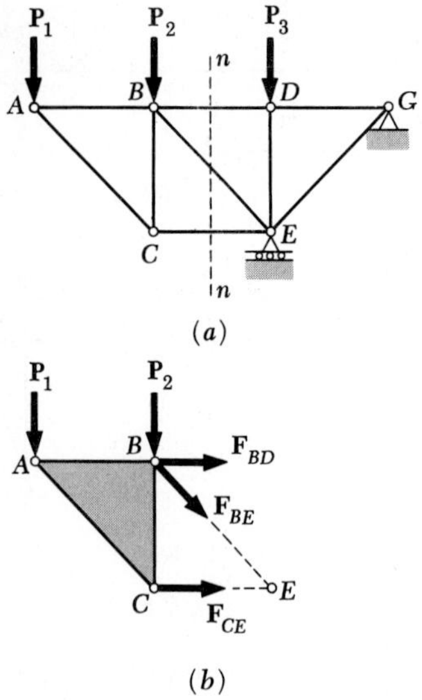

FIG. 6.16

chosen as the free body (Fig. 6.16*b*). The forces acting on the free body are the loads $\mathbf{P}_1$ and $\mathbf{P}_2$ at points A and B and the three unknown forces $\mathbf{F}_{BD}$, $\mathbf{F}_{BE}$, and $\mathbf{F}_{CE}$. Since it is not known whether the members removed were in tension or compression, the three forces have been arbitrarily drawn away from the free body as if the members were in tension.

The fact that the rigid body ABC is in equilibrium can be expressed by writing three equations which may be solved for the three unknown forces. If only the force $\mathbf{F}_{BD}$ is desired, we need write only one equation, provided that the equation does not contain the other unknowns. Thus the equation $\Sigma M_E = 0$ yields the value of the magnitude F_{BD} of the force $\mathbf{F}_{BD}$. A positive sign in the answer will indicate that our original assumption regarding the sense of $\mathbf{F}_{BD}$ was correct and that member BD is in tension; a negative sign will indicate that our assumption was incorrect and that BD is in compression.

On the other hand, if only the force $\mathbf{F}_{CE}$ is desired, an equation which does not involve $\mathbf{F}_{BD}$ or $\mathbf{F}_{BE}$ should be written; the appropriate equation is $\Sigma M_B = 0$. Again a positive sign for the magnitude F_{CE} of the desired force indicates a correct assumption, hence tension; and a negative sign indicates an incorrect assumption, hence compression.

If only the force $\mathbf{F}_{BE}$ is desired, the appropriate equation is $\Sigma F_y = 0$. Whether the member is in tension or compression is again determined from the sign of the answer.

When the force in only one member is determined, no independent check of the computation is available. However, when all the unknown forces acting on the free body are determined, the computations can be checked by writing an additional equation. For instance, if $\mathbf{F}_{BD}$, $\mathbf{F}_{BE}$, and $\mathbf{F}_{CE}$ are determined as indicated above, the computation can be checked by verifying that $\Sigma F_x = 0$.

***6.9. Trusses Made of Several Simple Trusses.** Consider two simple trusses ABC and DEF. If they are connected by three bars BD, BE, and CE as shown in Fig. 6.17*a*, they will form together a rigid truss $ABDF$. The trusses ABC and DEF can also be combined into a single rigid truss by joining joints B and D into a single joint B and by connecting joints C and E by a bar CE (Fig. 6.17*b*). The truss thus obtained is known as a Fink truss. It should be noted that the trusses of Fig. 6.17*a* and *b* are *not* simple trusses; they cannot be constructed from a triangular truss by adding successive pairs of members as prescribed in Sec. 6.3. They are rigid trusses, however, as we may check by comparing the systems of connections used to hold the simple trusses ABC and DEF together (three bars in Fig.

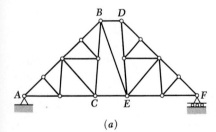

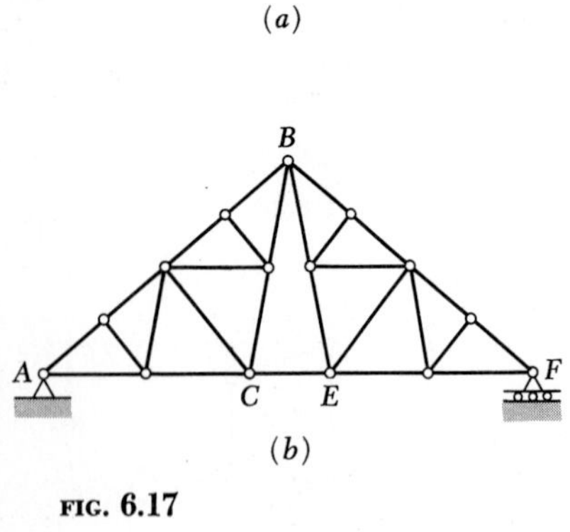

FIG. 6.17

6.17*a*, one smooth pin and one bar in Fig. 6.17*b*) with the systems of supports discussed in Secs. 4.4 and 4.5. Trusses made of several simple trusses rigidly connected are known as *compound trusses.*

It may be checked that in a compound truss the number of members m and the number of joints n are still related by the formula $m = 2n - 3$. If a compound truss is supported by a smooth pin and a roller (involving three unknown reactions), the total number of unknowns is $m + 3$ and this number is therefore equal to the number $2n$ of equations obtained by expressing that the n pins are in equilibrium. Compound trusses supported by a smooth pin and a roller, or by an equivalent system of supports, are *statically determinate, rigid,* and *completely constrained.* This means that all unknown reactions and forces in members can be determined by the methods of statics and that, all equilibrium equations being satisfied, the truss will neither collapse nor move. The forces in the members, however, cannot all be determined by the method of joints, except by solving a large number of simultaneous equations. In the case of the compound truss of Fig. 6.17*a*, for example, it will be found more expeditious to pass a section through members *BD*, *BE*, and *CE* to determine their forces.

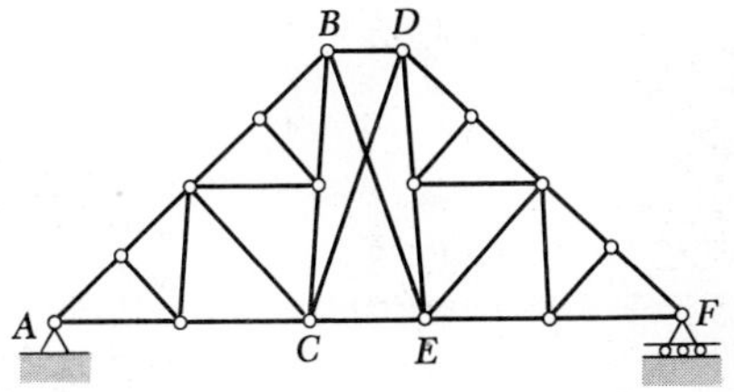

FIG. 6.18

Suppose, now, that the simple trusses *ABC* and *DEF* are connected by *four* bars *BD*, *BE*, *CD*, and *CE* (Fig. 6.18). The number of members m is now larger than $2n - 3$; the truss obtained is *overrigid,* and one of the four members *BD*, *BE*, *CD*, or *CE* is said to be *redundant.* If the truss is supported by a smooth pin at *A* and a roller at *F*, the total number of unknowns is $m + 3$. This number is now larger than the number $2n$ of available independent equations; the truss is *statically indeterminate.*

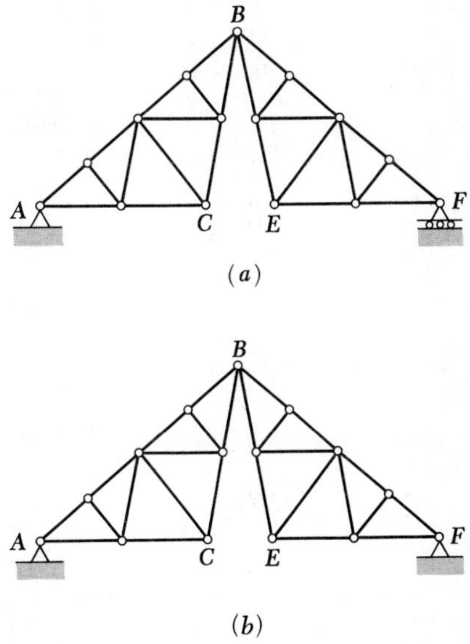

FIG. 6.19

Finally, we shall assume that the two simple trusses *ABC* and *DEF* are joined by a smooth pin as shown in Fig. 6.19*a*. The number of members m is smaller than $2n - 3$. If the truss is supported by a smooth pin at *A* and a roller at *F*, the total number of unknowns is $m + 3$. This number is now smaller than the number $2n$ of equilibrium equations which should be satisfied; the truss is *nonrigid* and will collapse under its own weight. However, if two smooth pins are used to support it, the truss becomes *rigid* and will not collapse (Fig. 6.19*b*). We note that the total number of unknowns is now $m + 4$ and is thus equal to the number of equations. While necessary, this condition, however, is not sufficient for the equilibrium of a structure which ceases to be rigid when detached from its supports (see Sec. 6.12).

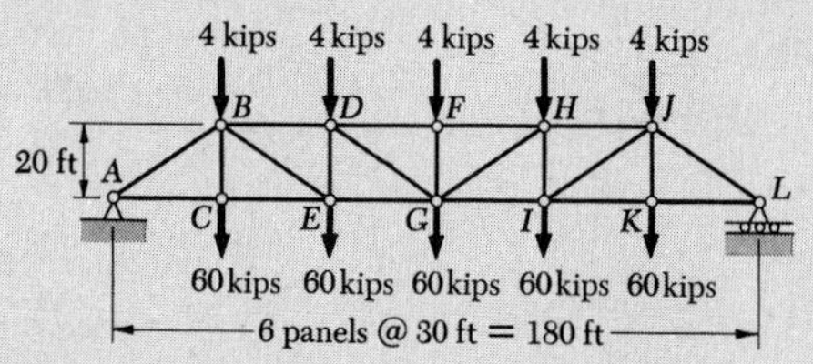

SAMPLE PROBLEM 6.3

Determine the forces in members *DE* and *HJ* of the truss shown.

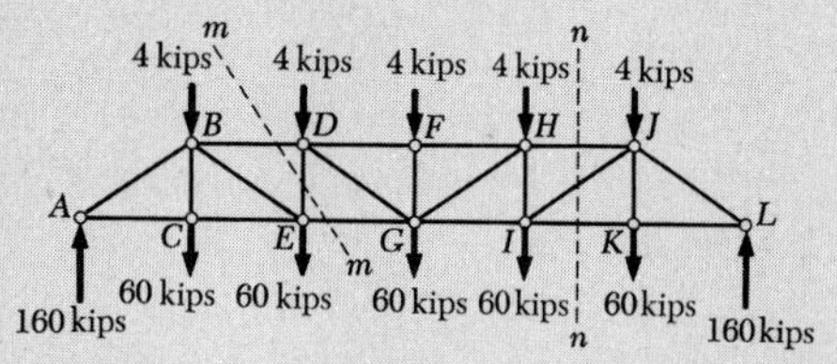

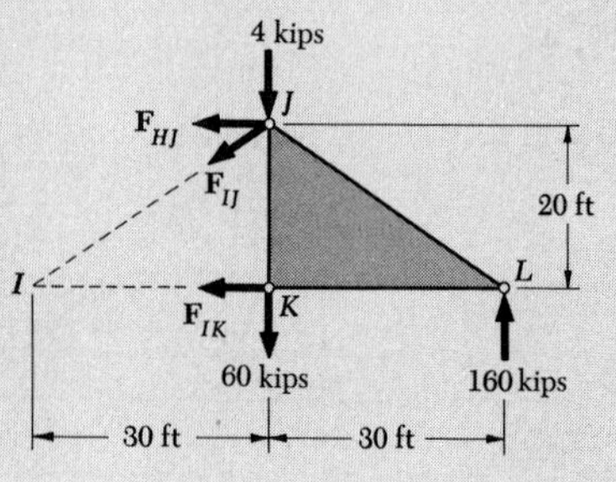

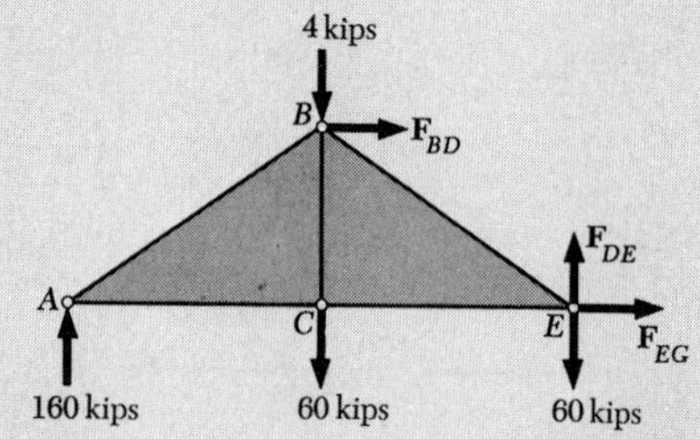

Solution. Considering the entire truss as a free body, we determine the reactions at *A* and *L*.

$$\mathbf{A} = 160 \text{ kips} \uparrow$$

$$\mathbf{L} = 160 \text{ kips} \uparrow$$

Force in Member ***HJ*****.** Section *nn* is passed through the truss so that it intersects member *HJ* and only two additional members. After the intersected members have been removed, we choose the right-hand portion of the truss as a free body. Three unknown forces are involved; to eliminate the two forces passing through point *I*, we write

$+\circlearrowleft \Sigma M_I = 0$:

$$(160 \text{ kips})(60 \text{ ft}) - (60 \text{ kips})(30 \text{ ft}) - (4 \text{ kips})(30 \text{ ft}) + F_{HJ}(20 \text{ ft}) = 0$$

$$F_{HJ} = -384 \text{ kips}$$

The sense of $\mathbf{F}_{HJ}$ was chosen assuming member *HJ* to be in tension; the negative sign obtained indicates that the member is in compression.

$$F_{HJ} = 384 \text{ kips } C \blacktriangleleft$$

Force in Member ***DE*****.** Section *mm* is passed through the truss so that it intersects member *DE* and only two additional members. After the intersected members have been removed, the left-hand portion of the truss is chosen as a free body. Three unknown forces are again involved; since the equation $\Sigma F_y = 0$ involves only F_{DE} as an unknown, we write

$+\uparrow \Sigma F_y = 0$:

$$+160 \text{ kips} - 60 \text{ kips} - 4 \text{ kips} - 60 \text{ kips} + F_{DE} = 0$$

$$F_{DE} = -36 \text{ kips} \qquad F_{DE} = 36 \text{ kips } C \blacktriangleleft$$

SAMPLE PROBLEM 6.4

Determine the forces in members *FH*, *GH*, and *GI* of the roof truss shown.

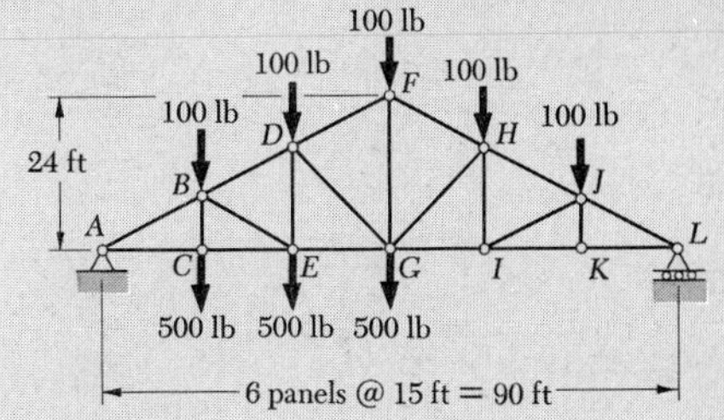

Solution. Section *nn* is passed through the truss as shown. The right-hand portion of the truss will be taken as a free body. Since the reaction at *L* acts on this free body, the value of **L** must be calculated separately, using the entire truss as a free body; the equation $\Sigma M_A = 0$ yields $\mathbf{L} = 750 \text{ lb} \uparrow$.

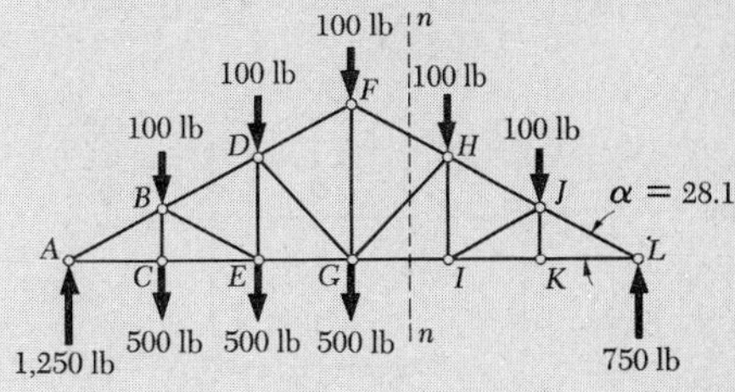

Force in Member *GI*. Using the portion *HLI* of the truss as a free body, the value of F_{GI} is obtained by writing

$$+\circlearrowleft \Sigma M_H = 0:$$
$$(750 \text{ lb})(30 \text{ ft}) - (100 \text{ lb})(15 \text{ ft}) - F_{GI}(16 \text{ ft}) = 0$$
$$F_{GI} = +1{,}313 \text{ lb} \qquad F_{GI} = 1{,}313 \text{ lb } T \blacktriangleleft$$

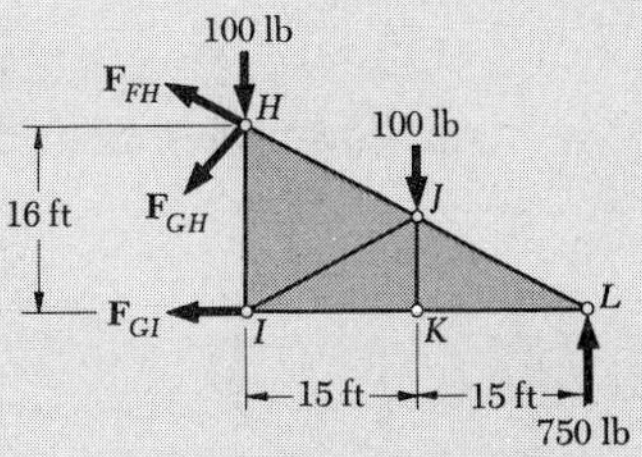

Force in Member *FH*. The value of F_{FH} is obtained from the equation $\Sigma M_G = 0$. We move $\mathbf{F}_{FH}$ along its line of action until it acts at point *F*, where it is resolved into its *x* and *y* components. The moment of $\mathbf{F}_{FH}$ with respect to point *G* is now equal to $(F_{FH} \cos \alpha)(24 \text{ ft})$.

$$+\circlearrowleft \Sigma M_G = 0:$$
$$(750 \text{ lb})(45 \text{ ft}) - (100 \text{ lb})(30 \text{ ft}) - (100 \text{ lb})(15 \text{ ft})$$
$$+ (F_{FH} \cos \alpha)(24 \text{ ft}) = 0$$
$$F_{FH} = -1{,}382 \text{ lb} \qquad F_{FH} = 1{,}382 \text{ lb } C \blacktriangleleft$$

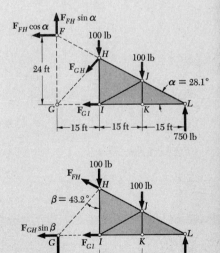

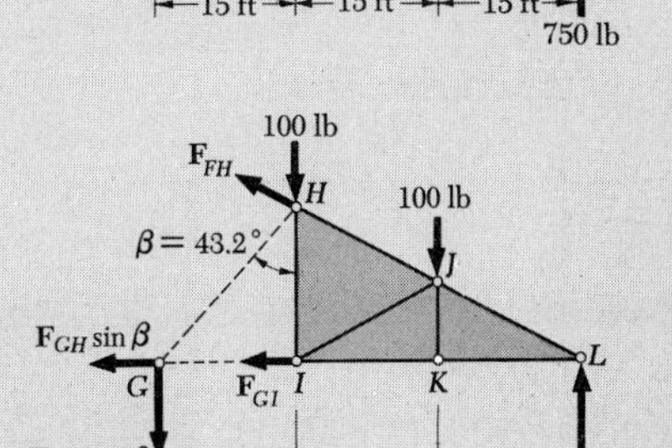

Force in Member *GH*. The value of F_{GH} is determined by first resolving the force $\mathbf{F}_{GH}$ into *x* and *y* components at point *G* and then solving the equation $\Sigma M_L = 0$.

$$+\circlearrowleft \Sigma M_L = 0:$$
$$(100 \text{ lb})(30 \text{ ft}) + (100 \text{ lb})(15 \text{ ft}) + (F_{GH} \cos \beta)(45 \text{ ft}) = 0$$
$$F_{GH} = -137.2 \text{ lb} \qquad F_{GH} = 137.2 \text{ lb } C \blacktriangleleft$$

PROBLEMS

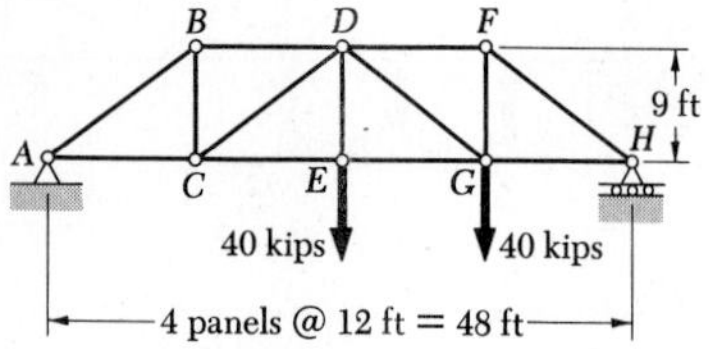

FIG. P6.40 AND P6.41

6.40. Determine the force in members *DF* and *DG* of the Howe truss shown.

6.41. Determine the force in members *FG* and *EG* of the Howe truss shown.

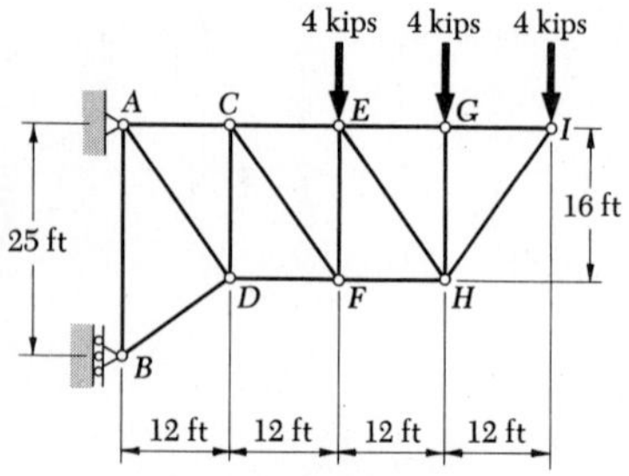

FIG. P6.42 AND P6.43

6.42. Determine the force in members *EF* and *CE* of the truss shown.

6.43. Determine the force in members *EH* and *FH* of the truss shown.

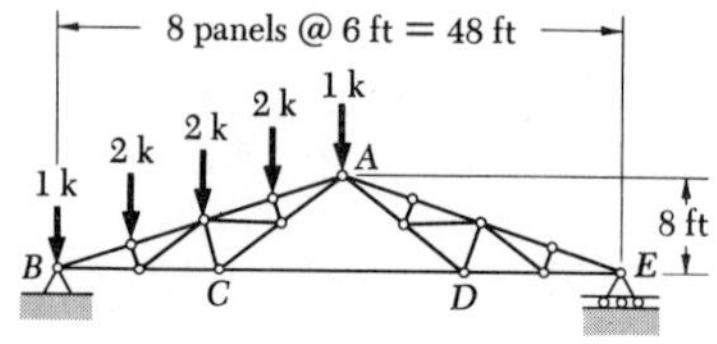

FIG. P6.44

6.44. Determine the force in member *CD* of the Fink roof truss shown.

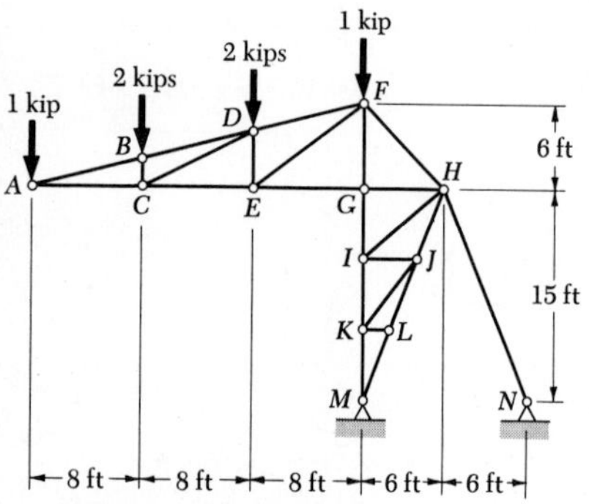

FIG. P6.45 AND P6.46

6.45. Determine the force in members *FH, GH,* and *GI* of the stadium truss shown.

6.46. Determine the force in members *DF, DE,* and *CE* of the stadium truss shown.

6.47. For the truss and loading of Sample Prob. 6.4, determine the force in members *BD, DE,* and *EG*.

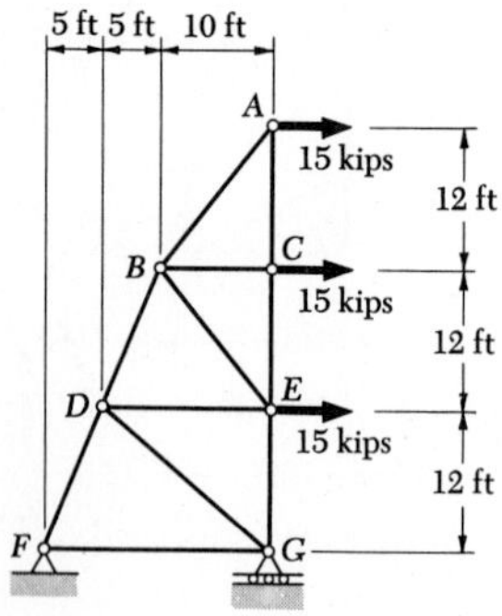

FIG. P6.48 AND P6.49

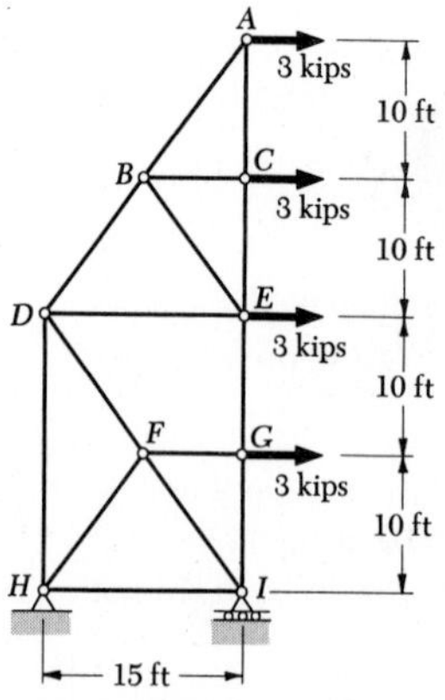

FIG. P6.50 AND P6.51

6.48. Determine the force in members *BD, BE,* and *CE* of the truss shown.

6.49. Determine the force in members *BD, DE,* and *EG* of the truss shown.

6.50. Determine the force in members *BE* and *DE* of the truss shown.

6.51. Determine the force in members *FH* and *DH* of the truss shown.

6.52. Determine the force in member EH of the K truss shown. (*Hint.* Use section aa.)

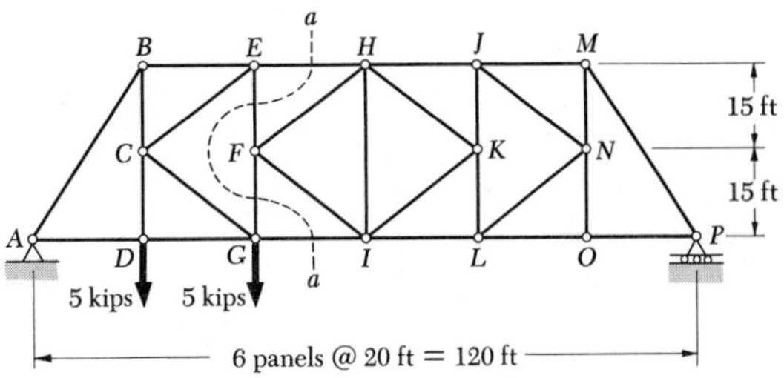

FIG. P 6.52

6.53. Determine the force in members FK and JO of the truss shown. (*Hint.* Use section aa.)

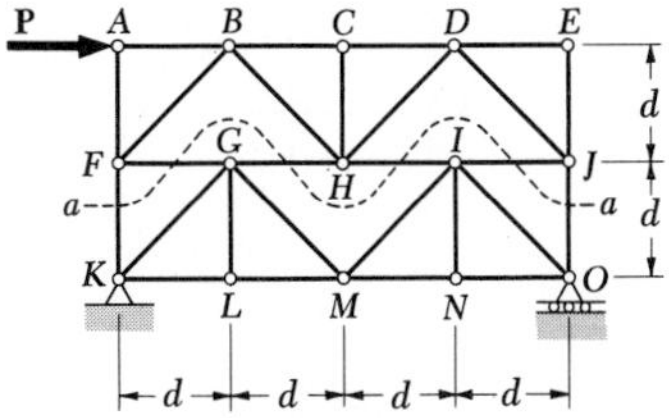

FIG. P 6.53

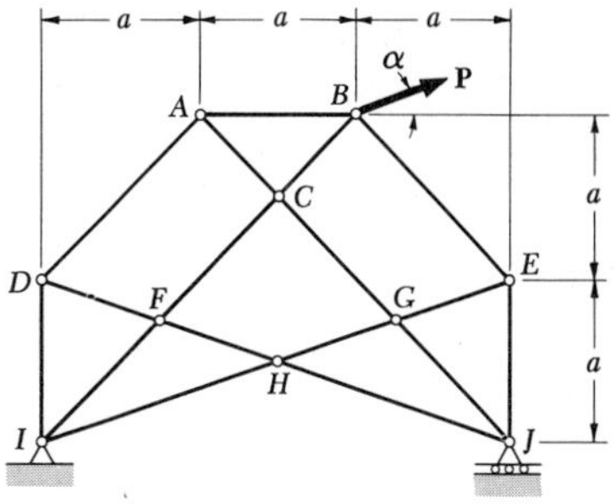

FIG. P 6.54

***6.54.** Determine the force in members AB and EJ of the truss shown, if $\alpha = 0°$. (*Hint.* Use portion IBE of the truss as a free body and apply to joints C, F, G, and H the results obtained in Sec. 6.5.)

***6.55.** Solve Prob. 6.54 assuming that $\alpha = 90°$.

***6.56.** Solve Prob. 6.54 assuming that $\mathbf{P} = 0$ and that a load $\mathbf{Q}$ is applied at joint J and is directed horizontally to the right.

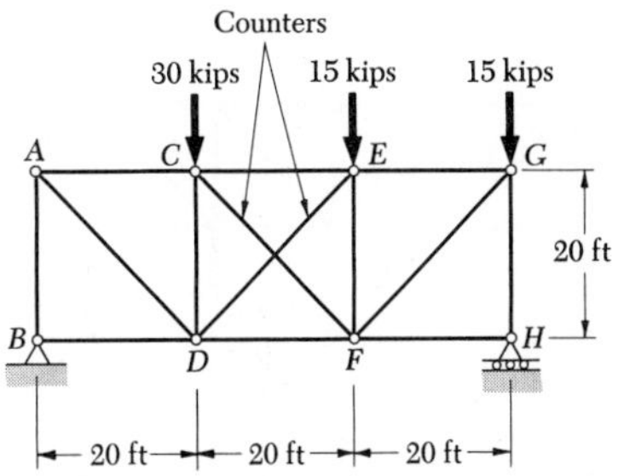

FIG. P 6.57

6.57. The diagonal members in the center panel of the truss shown are very slender and can act only in tension; such members are known as *counters*. Determine the force in members CE and DF and in the counter which is acting under the given loading.

6.58. Solve Prob. 6.57 assuming that the 30-kip load has been removed.

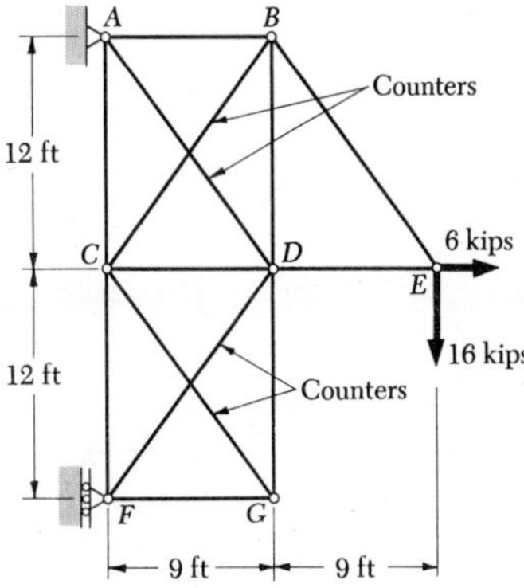

FIG. P 6.59

6.59. Determine the force in member CD and in the counters which are acting under the given loading. (See Prob. 6.57 for the definition of a counter.)

6.60. Solve Prob. 6.59 assuming that the 6-kip load has been removed.

***6.61 through 6.64.** Classify each of the given structures as completely, partially, or improperly constrained; if completely constrained, further classify as determinate or indeterminate. (All members can act both in tension and in compression.)

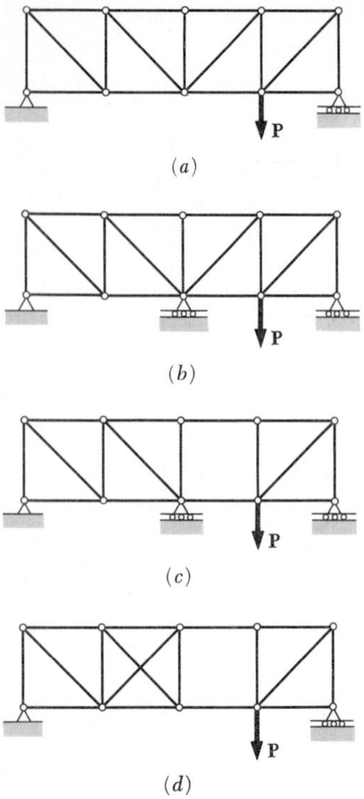

FIG. P 6.61

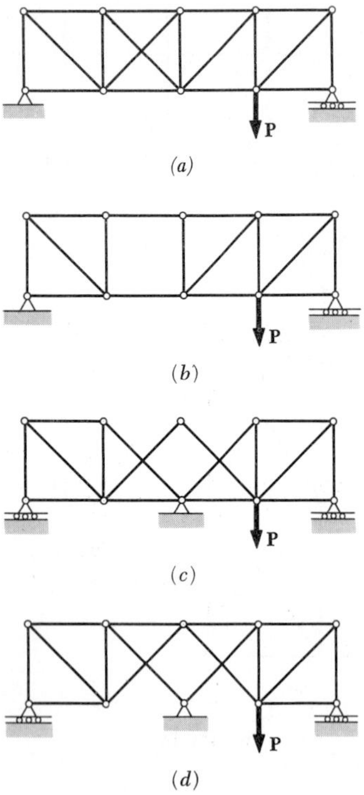

FIG. P 6.62

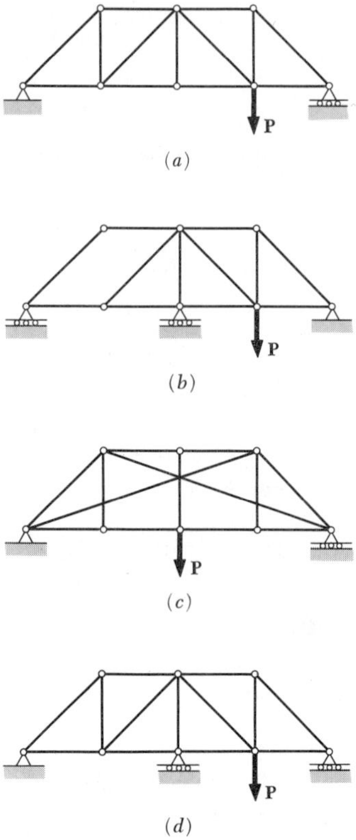

FIG. P 6.63

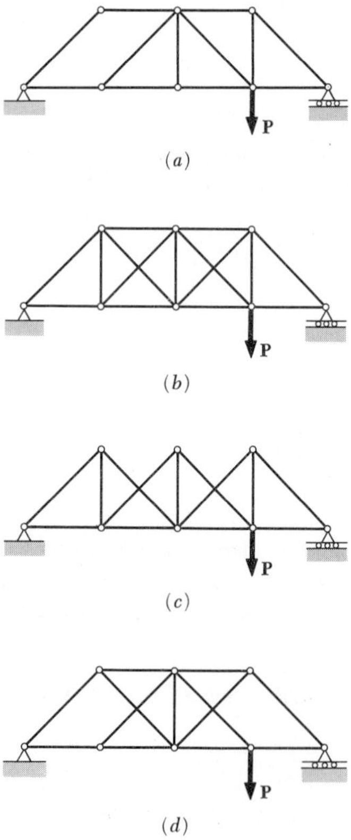

FIG. P 6.64

FRAMES AND MACHINES

6.10. Structures Containing Multiforce Members. Under Trusses, we have considered structures consisting entirely of pins and of straight two-force members. The forces acting on the two-force members were known to be directed along the members themselves. We shall now consider structures in which at least one of the members is a *multiforce* member, i.e., a member acted upon by three or more forces. These forces will generally not be directed along the members on which they act; their direction is unknown, and they should be represented therefore by two unknown components.

Frames and machines are structures containing multiforce members. *Frames* are designed to support loads and are usually stationary, fully constrained structures. *Machines* are designed to transmit and modify forces; they may or may not be stationary and will always contain moving parts.

6.11. Analysis of a Frame. As a first example of analysis of a frame, we shall consider again the crane described in Sec. 6.1, which carries a given load W (Fig. 6.20*a*). The free-body diagram of the entire frame is shown in Fig. 6.20*b*. This diagram may be used to determine the external forces acting on the frame. Summing moments about A, we first determine the force $\mathbf{T}$ exerted by the cable; summing x and y components, we then determine the components $\mathbf{A}_x$ and $\mathbf{A}_y$ of the reaction at the pin A.

In order to determine the internal forces holding the various parts of a frame together, we must dismember the frame and draw a free-body diagram for each of its component parts (Fig. 6.20*c*). First, the two-force members should be considered. In this frame, member BE is the only two-force member. The forces acting at each end of this member must have the same magnitude, same line of action, and opposite sense (Sec. 4.6). They are therefore directed along BE and will be denoted respectively by $\mathbf{F}_{BE}$ and $-\mathbf{F}_{BE}$. Their sense will be arbitrarily assumed as shown in Fig. 6.20*c*, and the correctness of this assumption will be checked later by the sign obtained for the common magnitude F_{BE} of the two forces.

Next, we consider the multiforce members, i.e., the members which are acted upon by three or more forces. According to Newton's third law, the force exerted at B by member BE on member AD must be equal and opposite to the force $\mathbf{F}_{BE}$ exerted by AD on BE. Similarly, the force exerted at E by member BE on member CF must be equal and opposite to the force $-\mathbf{F}_{BE}$ exerted by CF on BE. The forces that the two-force member BE exerts on AD and CF are therefore respectively equal to $-\mathbf{F}_{BE}$ and $\mathbf{F}_{BE}$; they have the same magnitude F_{BE} and opposite sense, and should be directed as shown in Fig. 6.20*c*.

At C two multiforce members are connected. Since neither the direction nor the magnitude of the forces acting at C is known, these forces will be represented by their x and y components. The components $\mathbf{C}_x$ and $\mathbf{C}_y$ of the force acting on member AD will be arbitrarily directed to the right and upward. Since, according to Newton's third law, the forces exerted by member CF on AD and by member AD on CF are equal and opposite, the components of the force acting on

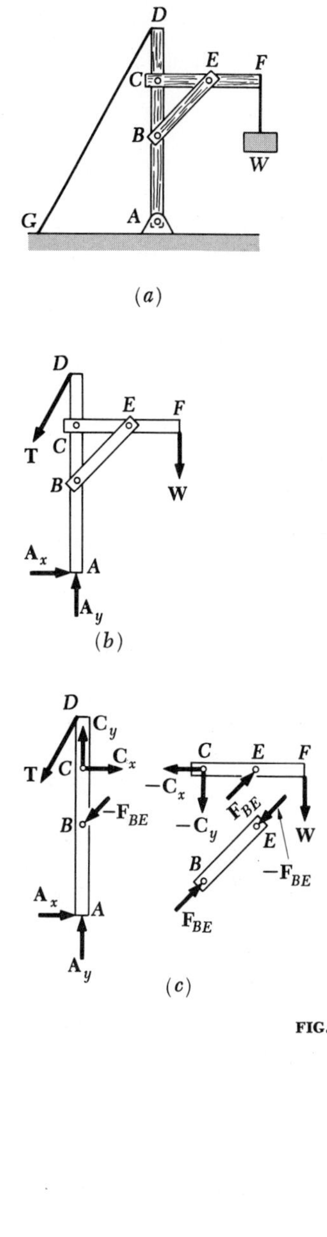

FIG. 6.20

member CF *must* be directed to the left and downward; they will be denoted, respectively, by $-\mathbf{C}_x$ and $-\mathbf{C}_y$. Whether the force $\mathbf{C}_x$ is actually directed to the right and the force $-\mathbf{C}_x$ is actually directed to the left will be determined later from the sign of their common magnitude C_x, a plus sign indicating that the assumption made was correct, and a minus sign that it was wrong. The free-body diagrams of the multiforce members are completed by showing the external forces acting at A, D, and F.†

The internal forces may now be determined by considering the free-body diagram of either of the two multiforce members. Choosing the free-body diagram of CF, for example, we write the equations $\Sigma M_C = 0$, $\Sigma M_E = 0$, and $\Sigma F_x = 0$, which yield the values of the magnitudes F_{BE}, C_y, and C_x, respectively. These values may be checked by verifying that member AD is also in equilibrium.

It should be noted that the free-body diagrams of the pins were not shown in Fig. 6.20*c*. This was because the pins were assumed to form an integral part of one of the two members they connected. This assumption can always be used to simplify the analysis of frames and machines. When a pin connects three or more members, however, or when a pin connects a support and two or more members, a clear decision must be made in choosing the member to which the pin will be assumed to belong. (If multiforce members are involved, the pin should be attached to one of these members.) The forces exerted on the pin by the other members or by the support should then be clearly identified. This is illustrated in Sample Prob. 6.7.

6.12. Frames Which Cease to Be Rigid When Detached from Their Supports. The crane analyzed in Sec. 6.11 was so constructed that it could keep the same shape without the help of its supports; it was therefore considered as a rigid body. Many frames, however, will collapse if detached from their supports; such frames cannot be considered as rigid bodies. Consider, for example, the frame shown in Fig. 6.21*a*, which consists of two members AC and CB carrying loads $\mathbf{P}$ and $\mathbf{Q}$ at their mid-points; the members are supported by pins at A and B and are connected by a pin at C. If detached from its sup-

† The use of a minus sign to distinguish the force exerted by one member on another from the equal and opposite force exerted by the second member on the first is not strictly necessary, since the two forces belong to different free-body diagrams and thus cannot easily be confused. In the Sample Problems, we shall represent by the same symbol equal and opposite forces which are applied to different free bodies.

ports, this frame will not maintain its shape; it should therefore be considered as made of *two distinct rigid parts* AC and CB.

The equations $\Sigma F_x = 0$, $\Sigma F_y = 0$, $\Sigma M = 0$ (about any given point) express the conditions for the *equilibrium of a rigid body* (Chap. 4); we should use them, therefore, in connection with the free-body diagrams of rigid bodies, namely, the free-body diagrams of members AC and CB (Fig. 6.21*b*). Since these members are multiforce members, and since pins are used at the supports and at the connection, the reactions at A and B and the forces at C will each be represented by two components. In accordance with Newton's third law, the components of the force exerted by CB on AC and the components of the force exerted by AC on CB will be represented by vectors of the same magnitude and opposite sense; thus, if the first pair of components is denoted by $\mathbf{C}_x$ and $\mathbf{C}_y$, the second pair will be denoted by $-\mathbf{C}_x$ and $-\mathbf{C}_y$. We note that four unknown force components act on free body AC, while only three independent equations may be used to express that the body is in equilibrium; similarly, four unknowns, but only three equations, are associated with CB. However, only six different unknowns are involved in the analysis of the two members, and altogether six equations are available to express that the members are in equilibrium. Writing $\Sigma M_A = 0$ for free body AC and $\Sigma M_B = 0$ for CB, we obtain two simultaneous equations which may be solved for the common magnitude C_x of the components $\mathbf{C}_x$ and $-\mathbf{C}_x$, and for the common magnitude C_y of the components $\mathbf{C}_y$ and $-\mathbf{C}_y$. Writing, then, $\Sigma F_x = 0$ and $\Sigma F_y = 0$ for each of the two free bodies, we obtain successively the magnitudes A_x, A_y, B_x, and B_y.

We shall observe, now, that, since the equations of equilibrium $\Sigma F_x = 0$, $\Sigma F_y = 0$, $\Sigma M = 0$ (about any given point) are satisfied by the forces acting on free body AC, and since they are also satisfied by the forces acting on free body CB, they must be satisfied when the forces acting on the two free bodies are considered simultaneously. Since the internal forces at C cancel each other, we find that the equations of equilibrium must be satisfied by the external forces shown on the free-body diagram of the frame ACB itself (Fig. 6.21*c*), although the frame is

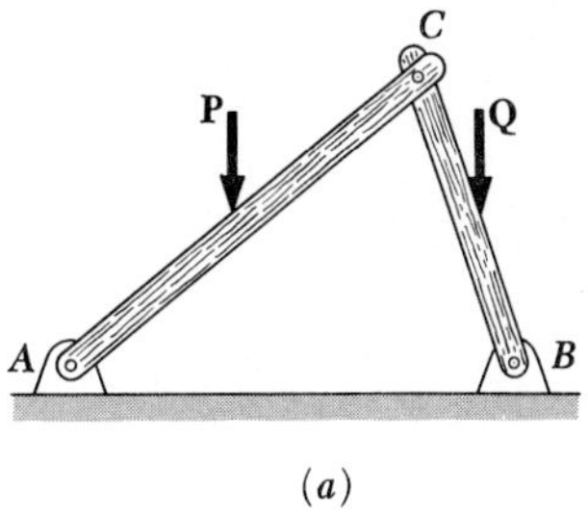

(*a*)

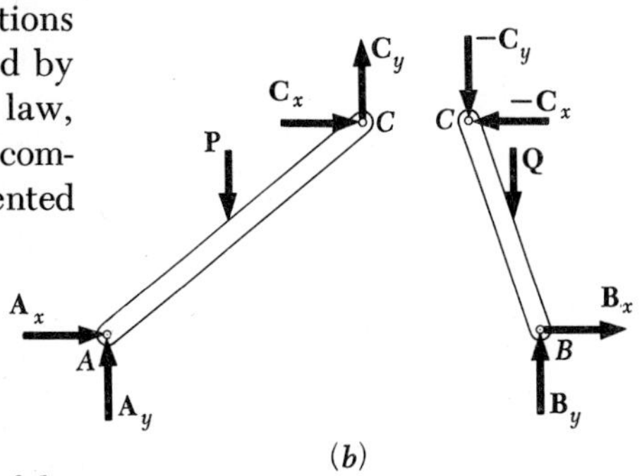

(*b*)

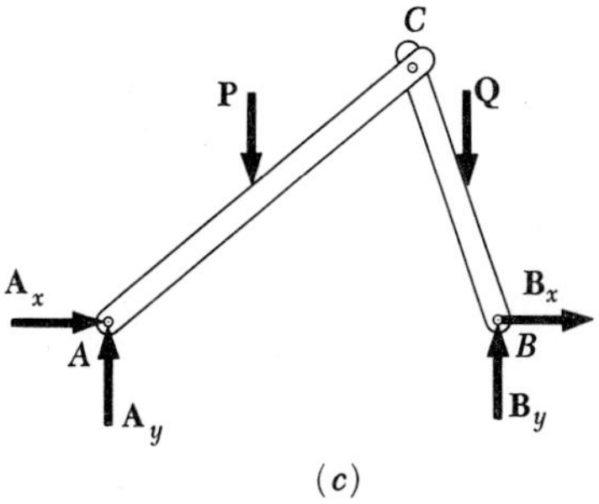

(*c*)

FIG. 6.21

not a rigid body. These equations may be used to determine some of the components of the reactions at A and B. We shall note, however, that *the reactions cannot be completely determined from the free-body diagram of the whole frame.* It is thus necessary to dismember the frame and to consider the free-body diagrams of its component parts (Fig. 6.21*b*), even when we are interested only in finding external reactions. This may be explained by the fact that the equilibrium equations obtained for free body ACB are *necessary conditions* for the equilibrium of a nonrigid structure, *but not sufficient conditions.*

The method of solution outlined in the second paragraph of this section involved simultaneous equations. We shall now discuss a more expeditious method, which utilizes the free body ACB as well as the free bodies AC and CB. Writing $\Sigma M_A = 0$ and $\Sigma M_B = 0$ for free body ACB, we obtain B_y and A_y. Writing $\Sigma M_C = 0$, $\Sigma F_x = 0$, and $\Sigma F_y = 0$ for free body AC, we obtain successively A_x, C_x, and C_y. Finally, writing $\Sigma F_x = 0$ for ACB, we obtain B_x.

We noted above that the analysis of the frame of Fig. 6.21 involves six unknown force components and six independent equilibrium equations (the equilibrium equations for the whole frame were obtained from the original six equations and, therefore, are not independent). Moreover, we checked that all unknowns could be actually determined and that all equations could be satisfied. The frame considered is *statically determinate and rigid.*† In general, to determine whether a structure is statically determinate and rigid, we should draw a free-body diagram for each of its component parts and count the reactions and internal forces involved. We should also determine the number of independent equilibrium equations (excluding equations expressing the equilibrium of the whole structure or of groups of component parts already analyzed). If there are more unknowns than equations, the structure is *statically indeterminate.* If there are fewer unknowns than equations, the structure is *nonrigid.* If there are as many unknowns as equations, *and if all unknowns may be determined and all equations satisfied* under general loading conditions, the structure is *statically determinate and rigid;* if, however, due to an *improper arrangement* of members and supports, all unknowns cannot be determined and all equations cannot be satisfied, the structure is *statically indeterminate and nonrigid.*

† The word "rigid" is used here to indicate that the frame will maintain its shape as long as it remains attached to its supports.

SAMPLE PROBLEM 6.5

In the small frame shown, members EBF and $ABCD$ are connected by a pin at B and by the cable EC. A 75-lb load is supported by a second cable which passes over a pulley at F and is attached to the vertical member at G. Determine the tension in cable EC and the components of the pin reaction at B.

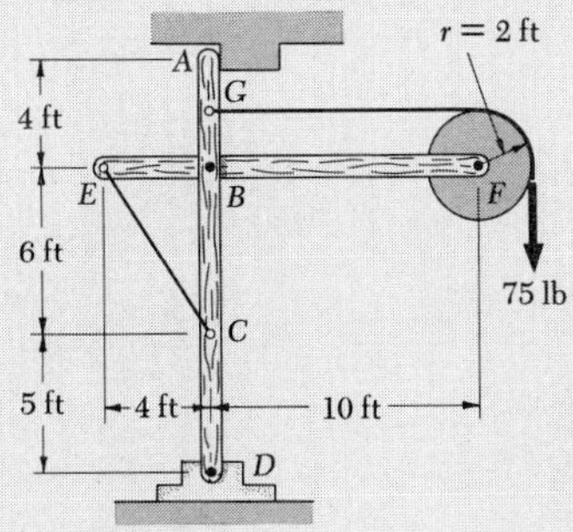

Entire Frame. The external reactions on the frame involve three unknowns; these reactions are determined by taking the entire frame as a free body.

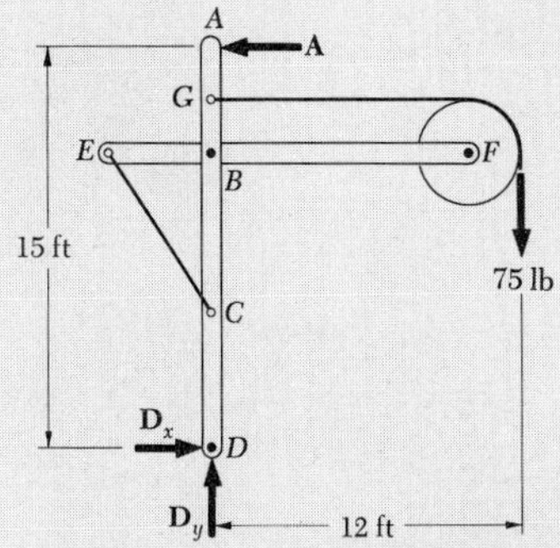

$+\uparrow \Sigma F_y = 0$: $\quad D_y - 75 \text{ lb} = 0$

$$D_y = +75 \text{ lb} \qquad \mathbf{D}_y = 75 \text{ lb} \uparrow$$

$+\circlearrowleft \Sigma M_D = 0$: $\quad -(75 \text{ lb})(12 \text{ ft}) + A(15 \text{ ft}) = 0$

$$A = +60 \text{ lb} \qquad \mathbf{A} = 60 \text{ lb} \leftarrow$$

$\xrightarrow{+} \Sigma F_x = 0$: $\quad -60 \text{ lb} + D_x = 0$

$$D_x = +60 \text{ lb} \qquad \mathbf{D}_x = 60 \text{ lb} \rightarrow$$

Since the values obtained are positive, the forces are directed as assumed in the diagram, i.e., $\mathbf{D}_x$ to the right, $\mathbf{D}_y$ up, and $\mathbf{A}$ to the left.

Members. The frame is dismembered; since only two members are connected at B, the components of the unknown forces acting on EBF and $ABCD$ at B are, respectively, equal and opposite. The forces exerted at E and C by the cable EC are equal and opposite, and their direction is known. From the free-body diagram of the pulley, it is seen that the force exerted at F by the pulley on member EBF may be resolved into two 75-lb components as shown. The cable also exerts a 75-lb force on $ABCD$ at point G.

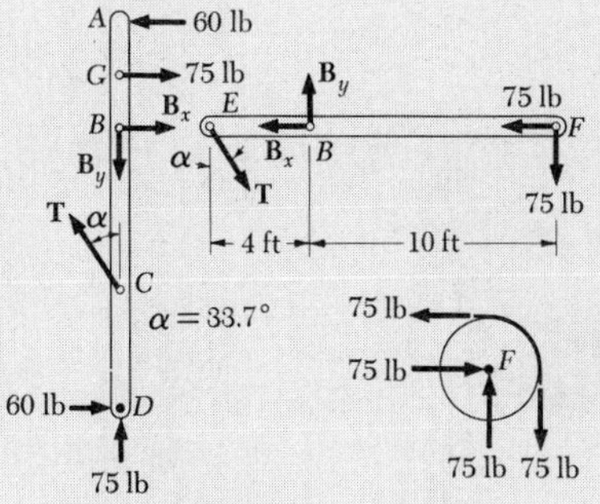

Member ***EBF.*** Using the free body EBF, we write

$+\circlearrowleft \Sigma M_E = 0$: $\quad B_y(4 \text{ ft}) - (75 \text{ lb})(14 \text{ ft}) = 0 \qquad B_y = +263 \text{ lb}$ ◄

$+\circlearrowleft \Sigma M_B = 0$: $\quad (T \cos \alpha)(4 \text{ ft}) - (75 \text{ lb})(10 \text{ ft}) = 0$

$$T = +225 \text{ lb}$$ ◄

$\xrightarrow{+} \Sigma F_x = 0$: $\quad +T \sin \alpha - B_x - 75 \text{ lb} = 0 \qquad B_x = +50.0 \text{ lb}$ ◄

Since the values obtained are positive, the forces are directed as shown on the diagram: the forces $\mathbf{B}_x$ and $\mathbf{B}_y$ acting on member $ABCD$ are directed, respectively, to the right and down, while the forces $\mathbf{B}_x$ and $\mathbf{B}_y$ acting on member EBF are directed, respectively, to the left and up.

Member ***ABCD*** **(Check).** The computations are checked by considering the free body $ABCD$. For example,

$$\xrightarrow{+} \Sigma F_x = -60 \text{ lb} + 75 \text{ lb} + B_x - T \sin \alpha + 60 \text{ lb}$$

$$= -60 \text{ lb} + 75 \text{ lb} + 50 \text{ lb} - (225 \text{ lb}) \sin 33.7° + 60 \text{ lb} = 0$$

(checks)

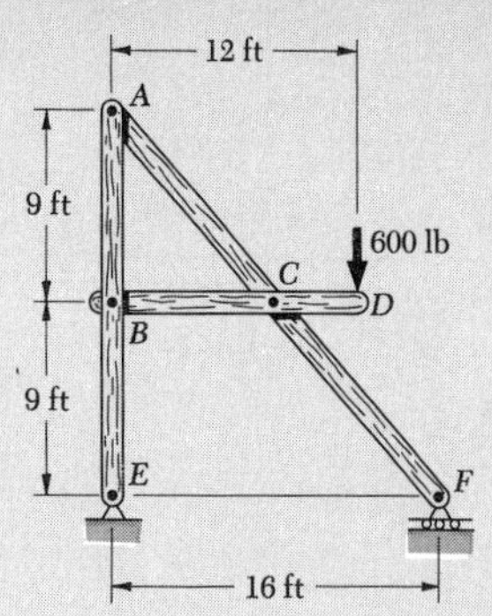

SAMPLE PROBLEM 6.6

Determine the components of the forces acting on each member of the frame shown.

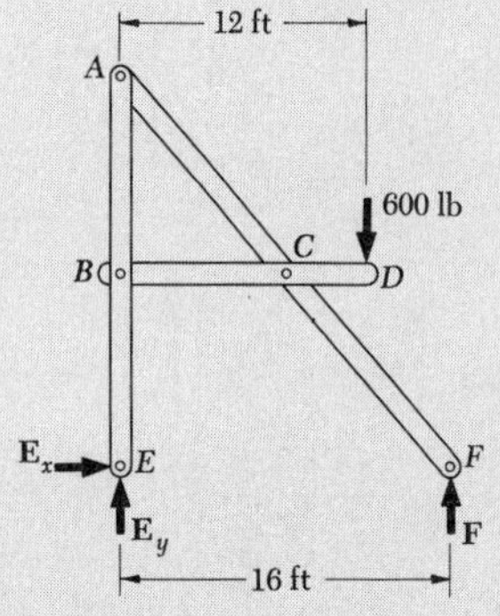

Entire Frame. Since the external reactions involve only three unknowns, we compute the reactions by considering the free-body diagram of the entire frame.

$$+\circlearrowleft \Sigma M_E = 0: \quad -(600 \text{ lb})(12 \text{ ft}) + F(16 \text{ ft}) = 0$$
$$F = +450 \text{ lb} \qquad \mathbf{F} = 450 \text{ lb}\uparrow \blacktriangleleft$$

$$+\uparrow \Sigma F_y = 0: \quad -600 \text{ lb} + 450 \text{ lb} + E_y = 0$$
$$E_y = +150 \text{ lb} \qquad \mathbf{E}_y = 150 \text{ lb}\uparrow \blacktriangleleft$$

$$\overset{+}{\rightarrow} \Sigma F_x = 0: \qquad \mathbf{E}_x = 0 \blacktriangleleft$$

The frame is now dismembered; since only two members are connected at each joint, equal and opposite components are shown on each member at each joint.

Member ***BCD***

$$+\circlearrowleft \Sigma M_B = 0: \quad -(600 \text{ lb})(12 \text{ ft}) + C_y(8 \text{ ft}) = 0 \qquad C_y = +900 \text{ lb} \blacktriangleleft$$

$$+\circlearrowleft \Sigma M_C = 0: \quad -(600 \text{ lb})(4 \text{ ft}) + B_y(8 \text{ ft}) = 0 \qquad B_y = +300 \text{ lb} \blacktriangleleft$$

$$\overset{+}{\rightarrow} \Sigma F_x = 0: \quad -B_x + C_x = 0$$

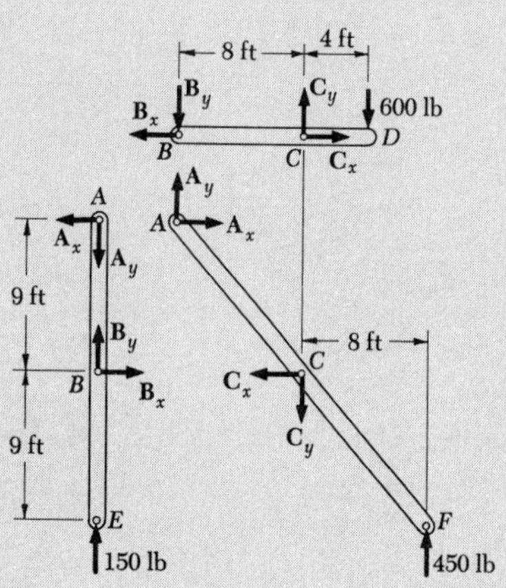

We note that neither B_x nor C_x can be obtained by considering only member *BCD*. The positive values obtained for B_y and C_y indicate that the force components $\mathbf{B}_y$ and $\mathbf{C}_y$ are directed as assumed.

Member ***ABE***

$$+\circlearrowleft \Sigma M_A = 0: \quad B_x(9 \text{ ft}) = 0 \qquad B_x = 0 \blacktriangleleft$$

$$\overset{+}{\rightarrow} \Sigma F_x = 0: \quad +B_x - A_x = 0 \qquad A_x = 0 \blacktriangleleft$$

$$+\uparrow \Sigma F_y = 0: \quad -A_y + B_y + 150 \text{ lb} = 0$$
$$-A_y + 300 \text{ lb} + 150 \text{ lb} = 0$$
$$A_y = +450 \text{ lb} \blacktriangleleft$$

Member ***BCD*****.** Returning now to member *BCD*, we write

$$\overset{+}{\rightarrow} \Sigma F_x = 0: \quad -B_x + C_x = 0 \qquad 0 + C_x = 0 \qquad C_x = 0 \blacktriangleleft$$

Member ***ACF*** **(Check).** All unknown components have now been found; to check the results, verify that member *ACF* is in equilibrium.

$$+\circlearrowleft \Sigma M_C = (450 \text{ lb})(8 \text{ ft}) - A_y(8 \text{ ft}) - A_x(9 \text{ ft})$$
$$= (450 \text{ lb})(8 \text{ ft}) - (450 \text{ lb})(8 \text{ ft}) - 0 = 0 \qquad \text{(checks)}$$

SAMPLE PROBLEM 6.7

Determine the forces acting on each member of the frame shown.

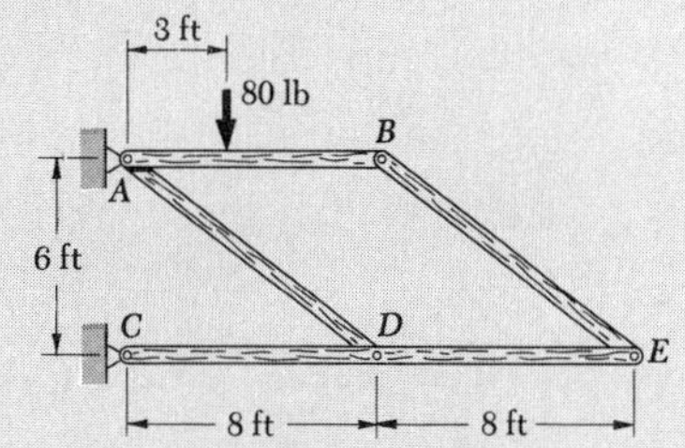

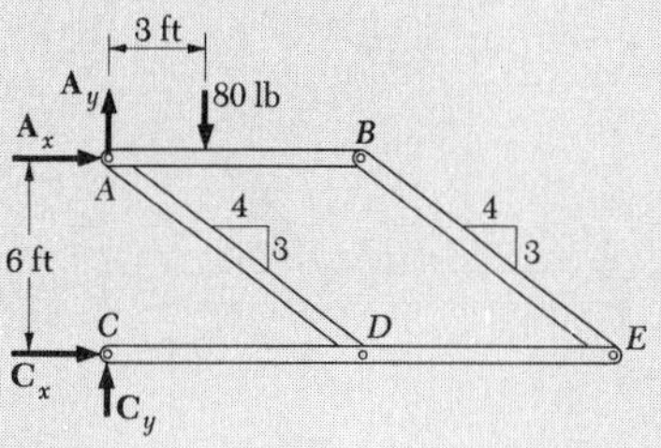

Entire Frame. The entire frame is chosen as a free body; although the reactions involve four unknowns, $\mathbf{A}_x$ and $\mathbf{C}_x$ may be determined by writing

$$+\circlearrowleft \Sigma M_A = 0: \quad -(80 \text{ lb})(3 \text{ ft}) + C_x(6 \text{ ft}) = 0$$

$$C_x = +40 \text{ lb} \qquad \mathbf{C}_x = 40 \text{ lb} \rightarrow \blacktriangleleft$$

$$\overset{+}{\rightarrow} \Sigma F_x = 0: \quad A_x + C_x = 0$$

$$A_x = -40 \text{ lb} \qquad \mathbf{A}_x = 40 \text{ lb} \leftarrow \blacktriangleleft$$

The equations of equilibrium of the entire frame are not sufficient to determine $\mathbf{A}_y$ and $\mathbf{C}_y$. The equilibrium of the various members must now be considered in order to proceed with the solution. In dismembering the frame, we have assumed that the pin at A is attached to member AB, and we have noted that both AD and BE are two-force members. The free-body diagrams of the various members are now considered separately.

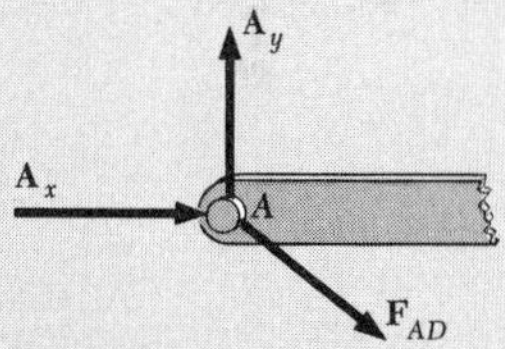

Member AB

$$+\circlearrowleft \Sigma M_A = 0: \quad -(80 \text{ lb})(3 \text{ ft}) + \tfrac{3}{5}F_{BE}(8 \text{ ft}) = 0$$

$$F_{BE} = +50 \text{ lb} \blacktriangleleft$$

Member CDE. Since the force $\mathbf{F}_{BE}$ has been determined, we may compute $\mathbf{F}_{AD}$ by writing

$$+\circlearrowleft \Sigma M_C = 0: \quad \tfrac{3}{5}F_{AD}(8 \text{ ft}) - \tfrac{3}{5}F_{BE}(16 \text{ ft}) = 0$$

$$F_{AD} = +100 \text{ lb} \blacktriangleleft$$

Using $F_{AD} = +100$ lb, we now determine $\mathbf{C}_y$ by writing

$$+\uparrow \Sigma F_y = 0: \quad C_y + \tfrac{3}{5}F_{AD} - \tfrac{3}{5}F_{BE} = 0$$

$$C_y = -30 \text{ lb} \qquad \mathbf{C}_y = 30 \text{ lb} \downarrow \blacktriangleleft$$

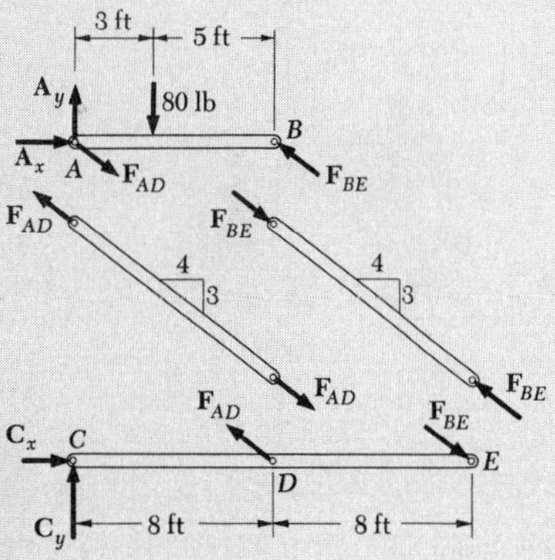

Entire Frame. Since $\mathbf{C}_y$ has been determined, we may return to the free-body diagram of the entire frame and write

$$+\uparrow \Sigma F_y = 0: \quad C_y + A_y - 80 \text{ lb} = 0$$

$$-30 \text{ lb} + A_y - 80 \text{ lb} = 0$$

$$A_y = +110 \text{ lb} \qquad \mathbf{A}_y = 110 \text{ lb} \uparrow \blacktriangleleft$$

Member AB **(Check).** We may check our computations by verifying that the equation $\Sigma F_y = 0$ is satisfied by the forces acting on member AB.

$$+\uparrow \Sigma F_y = A_y - \tfrac{3}{5}F_{AD} + \tfrac{3}{5}F_{BE} - 80 \text{ lb}$$

$$= 110 \text{ lb} - 60 \text{ lb} + 30 \text{ lb} - 80 \text{ lb} = 0 \qquad \text{(checks)}$$

PROBLEMS

6.65. Determine the tension in member BD and the reaction at C.

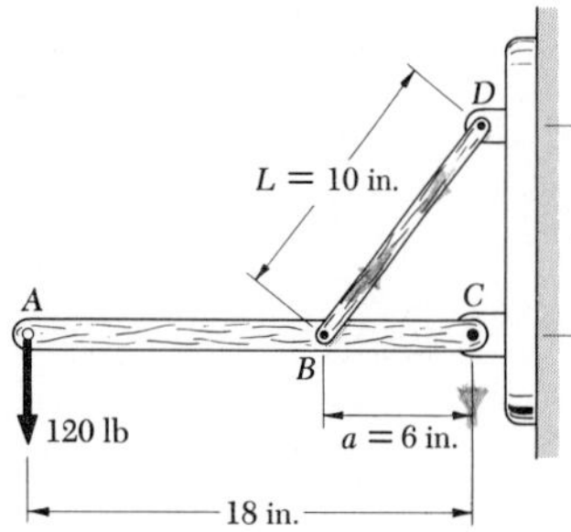

FIG. P 6.65

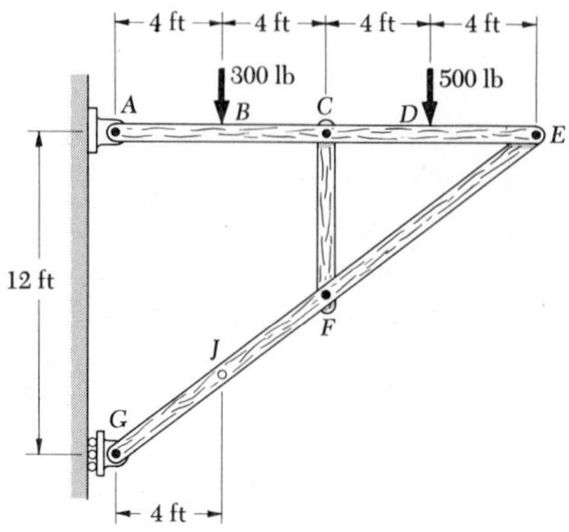

FIG. P 6.66

6.66. Determine the components of all forces acting on member AE of the frame shown.

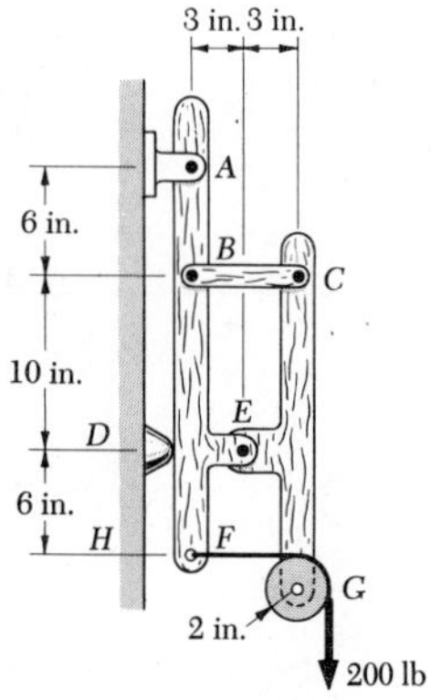

FIG. P 6.67

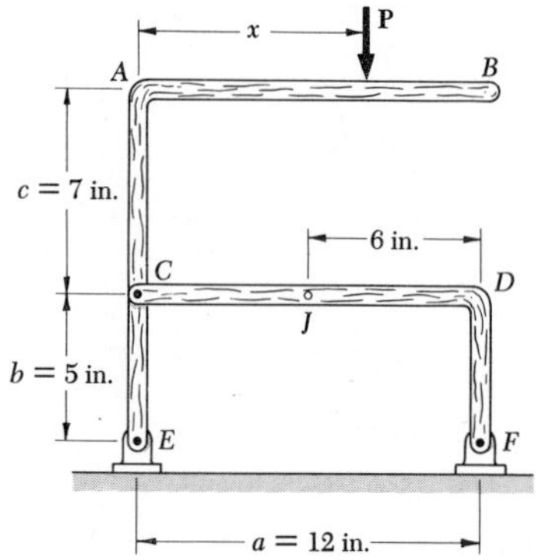

FIG. P 6.69

6.67. The assembly shown is attached to the wall by a pin at A and bears against a knob at D. A 200-lb load is supported by a cable which passes over a 2-in.-radius pulley at G and is attached to the assembly at F. Knowing that the knob at D can exert only a horizontal force, determine the components of all forces acting on member $ABEF$.

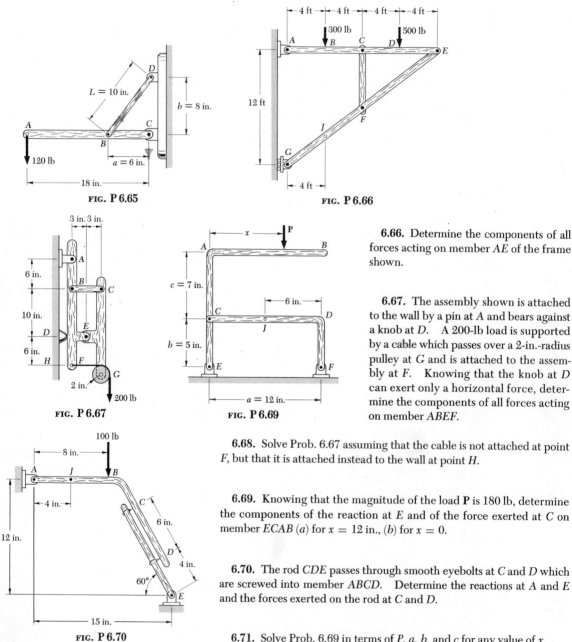

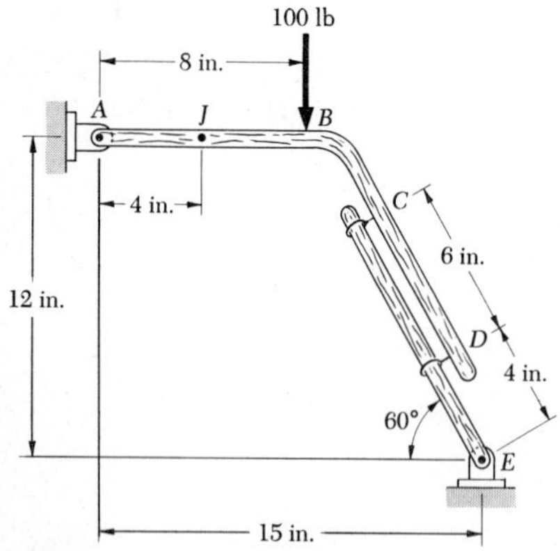

FIG. P 6.70

6.68. Solve Prob. 6.67 assuming that the cable is not attached at point F, but that it is attached instead to the wall at point H.

6.69. Knowing that the magnitude of the load **P** is 180 lb, determine the components of the reaction at E and of the force exerted at C on member $ECAB$ (*a*) for $x = 12$ in., (*b*) for $x = 0$.

6.70. The rod CDE passes through smooth eyebolts at C and D which are screwed into member $ABCD$. Determine the reactions at A and E and the forces exerted on the rod at C and D.

6.71. Solve Prob. 6.69 in terms of P, a, b, and c for any value of x.

6.72. Determine the forces exerted on member AB if the frame is loaded by a clockwise couple of moment 120 lb-in. applied (*a*) at point D, (*b*) at point E. (*c*) Determine the forces exerted on member AB if the frame is loaded by vertical forces applied at D and E which are equivalent to a 120-lb-in. clockwise couple.

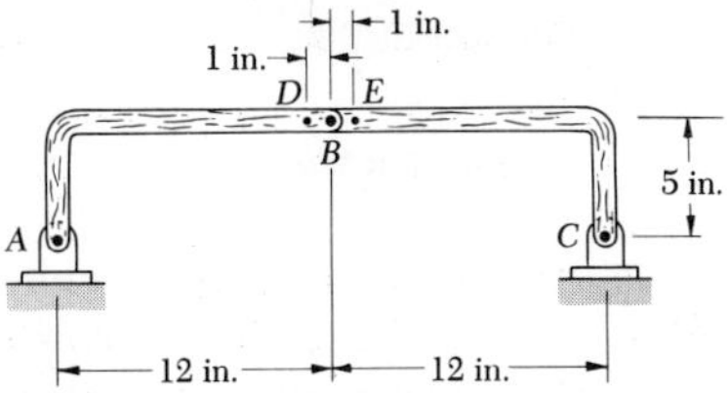

FIG. P 6.72

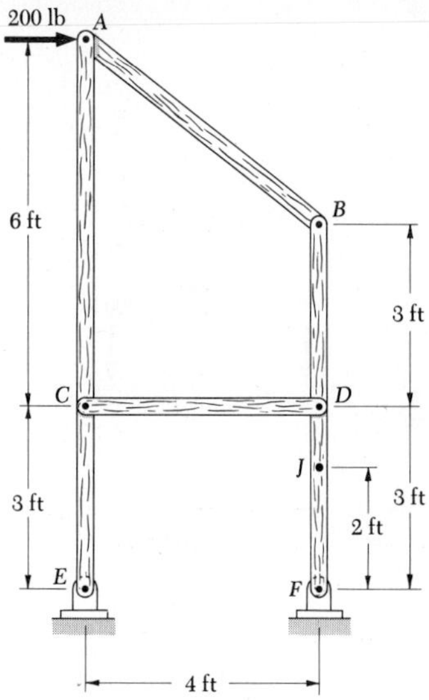

FIG. P 6.73

6.73. Determine the components of all forces acting on the two vertical members of the frame shown.

6.74. Determine the reactions at E and F and the force exerted on pin C for the frame shown.

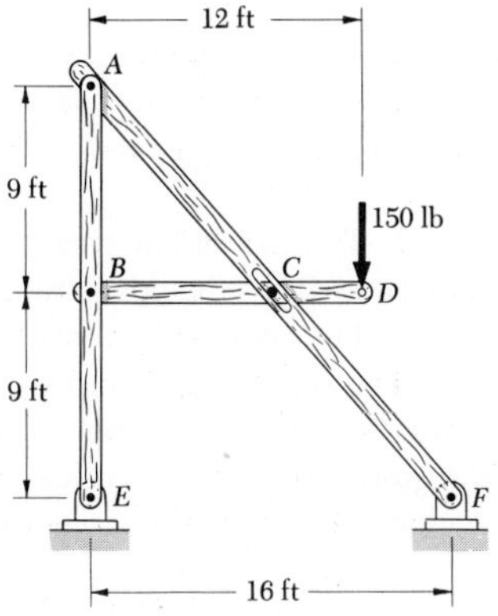

FIG. P 6.74

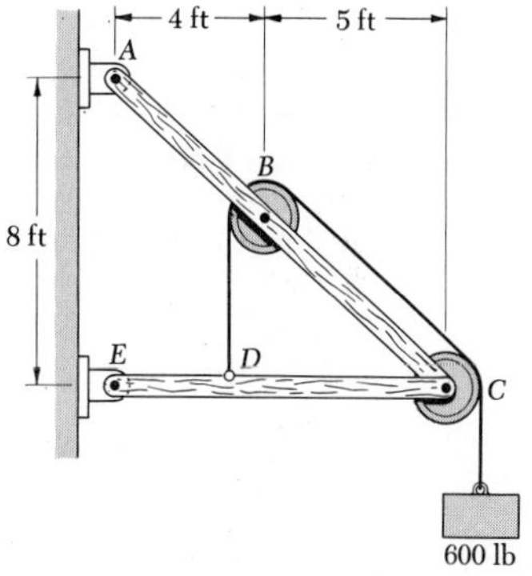

FIG. P 6.76

6.75. Determine the reactions at E and F and the force exerted on pin C for the frame of Prob. 6.74, assuming now that pin C is attached to member ACF and may slide in a horizontal slot in member BD.

6.76. Knowing that each pulley has a radius of 1 ft, determine the components of the reactions at A and E.

6.77. Determine the reactions at the supports for the beam shown.

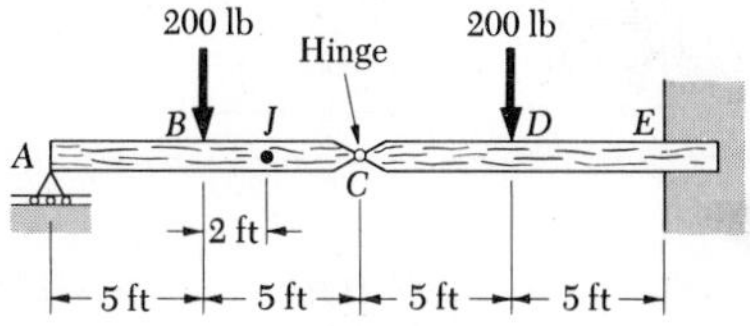

FIG. P 6.77

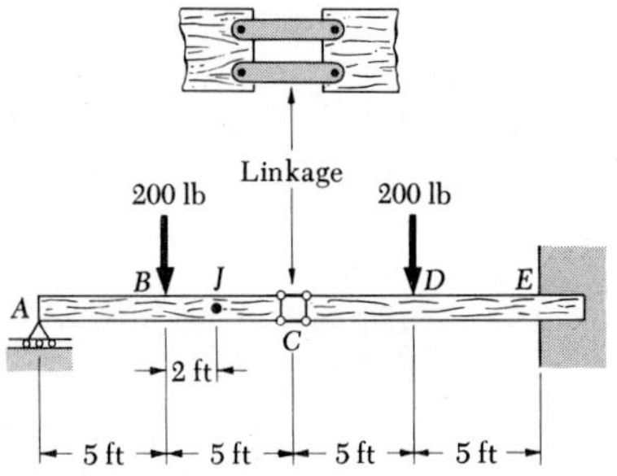

FIG. P 6.78

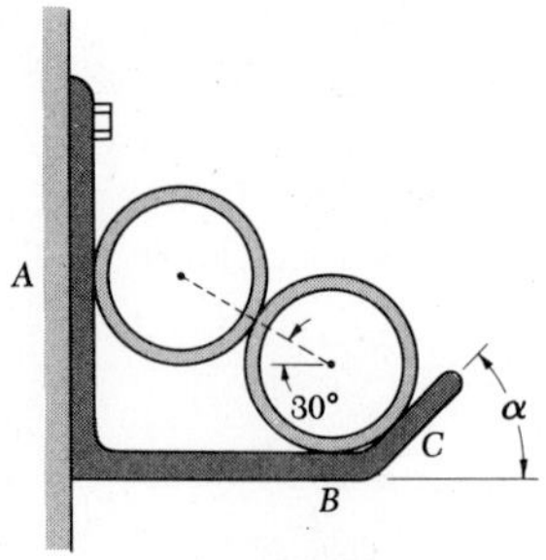

FIG. P 6.79

6.78. Determine the reactions at the supports for the beam shown.

6.79. Two equal lengths of steel tubing, of weight $2W$ each, are placed on two racks so that each rack supports half the weight of the tubing. Neglecting friction at all surfaces, determine the reactions exerted by the rack shown at A, B, and C when $\alpha = 45°$.

6.80. Determine the smallest value of the angle α for which equilibrium is possible in Prob. 6.79.

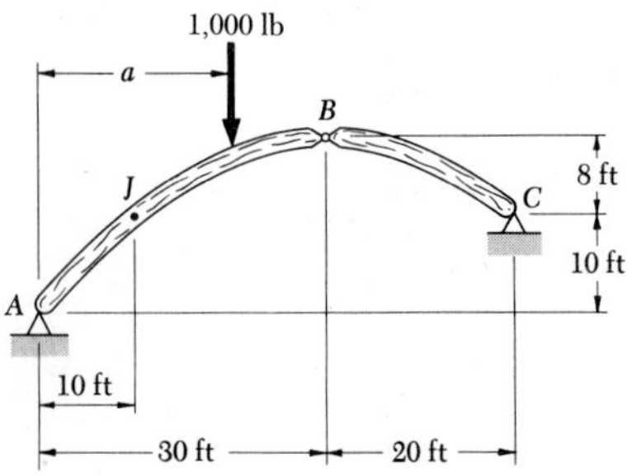

FIG. P 6.81 AND P 6.82

6.81. The axis of the three-hinged arch ABC is a parabola with its vertex at B. If $a = 25$ ft, determine the components of the reactions at A and C, and the components of the force exerted at B on segment AB.

6.82. Derive expressions for the components of the reaction at A in terms of the distance a. (*Hint.* Two expressions will be necessary for each component, one for $a < 30$ ft, the other for $a > 30$ ft.)

6.83. The tractor and scraper units shown are connected by a vertical pin located 2 ft behind the tractor wheels. The distance from C to D is 30 in. The center of gravity of the 16,000-lb tractor unit is located at G_t. The scraper unit and load together weigh 84,000 lb and have a combined center of gravity located at G_s. Knowing that the machine is at rest, with its brakes released, determine (*a*) the reactions at each of the four wheels, (*b*) the forces exerted on the tractor unit at C and D.

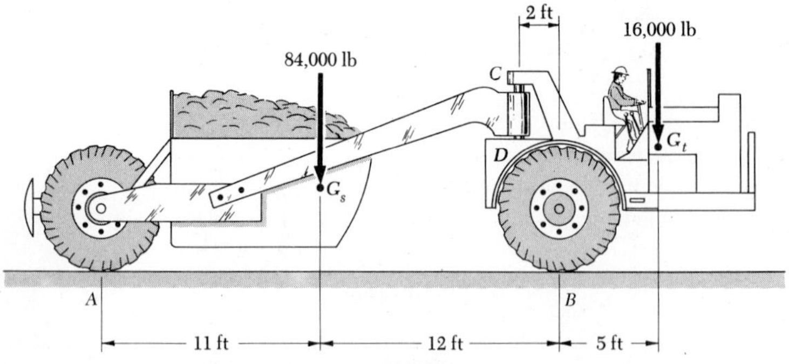

FIG. P 6.83

6.84. A trailer weighing 2,750 lb is attached to a 3,200-lb automobile by a ball-and-socket trailer hitch at D. Determine (a) the reactions at each of the six wheels when the automobile and trailer are at rest, (b) the additional load on each of the automobile wheels due to the trailer.

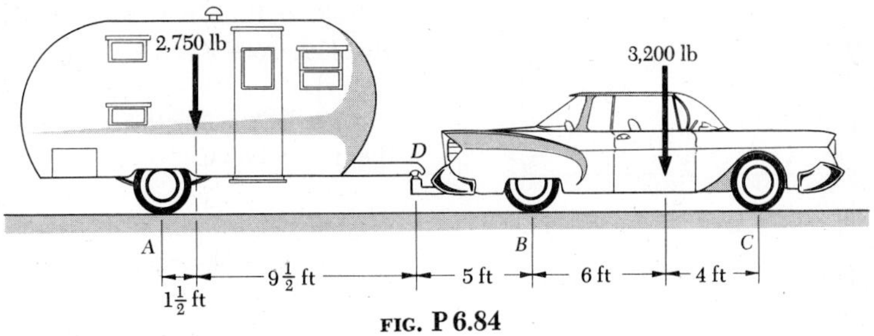

FIG. **P 6.84**

6.85. In order to obtain a better weight distribution over the four wheels of the automobile of Prob. 6.84, a compensating hitch of the type shown is used to attach the trailer to the automobile. This hitch consists of two bar springs (only one is shown in the figure) which fit into bearings inside a support rigidly attached to the automobile. The springs are also connected by chains to the trailer frame, and specially designed hooks make it possible to place both chains under a tension T. Solve Prob. 6.84 assuming that such a compensating hitch is used and that the tension T in each chain is 440 lb.

6.86. In order to obtain a better weight distribution over the wheels of the automobile of Prob. 6.84, a compensating hitch of the type described in Prob. 6.85 is used to attach the trailer to the automobile. (a) Determine the tension T required in each of the two chains if the additional load due to the trailer is to be evenly distributed over the four wheels of the automobile. (b) What are the corresponding reactions at each of the six wheels of the trailer-automobile combination?

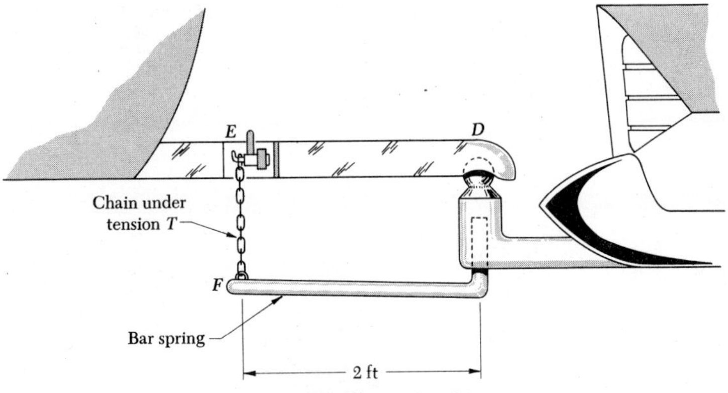

FIG. **P 6.85** AND **P 6.86**

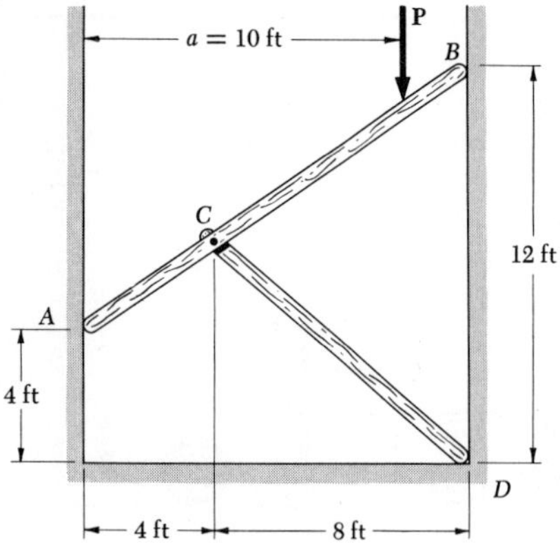

FIG. P 6.87

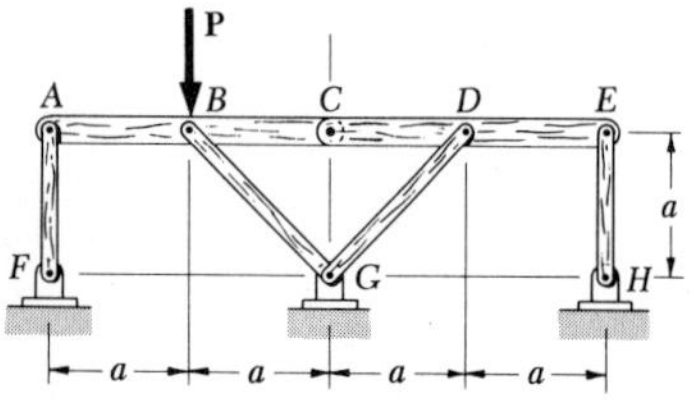

FIG. P 6.89

6.87. A load **P** of magnitude 100 lb is supported by two members *AB* and *CD* connected by a pin at *C* and placed between two smooth walls as shown. Determine the components of all forces exerted on member *AB*.

6.88. In Prob. 6.87, determine the range of values of the distance *a* for which the load **P** can be supported.

6.89. Determine the force in each of the links *AF, BG, GD,* and *EH* of the frame shown.

6.90. Solve Prob. 6.89, assuming that the force **P** is replaced by a clockwise couple of moment $\mathbf{M}_0$ applied to member *ABC* at *B*.

6.91. (*a*) Show that, when a frame supports a pulley at *A*, an equivalent loading of the frame and of each of its component parts may be obtained by removing the pulley and applying at *A* two forces equal and parallel to the forces of tension in the cable. (*b*) Further show that, if one end of the cable is attached to the frame at a point *B*, a force of magnitude equal to the tension should also be applied at *B*.

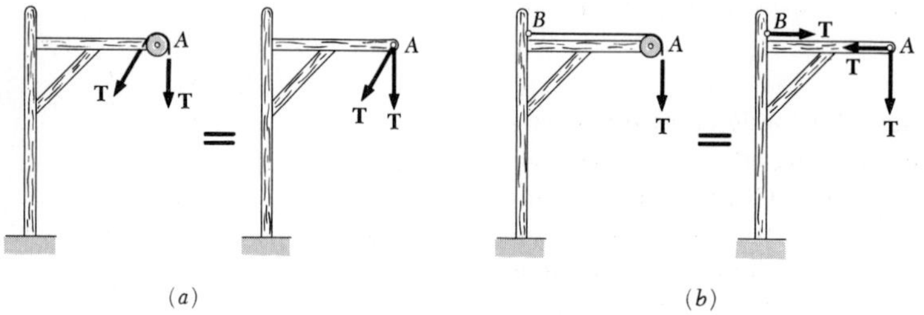

FIG. P 6.91

6.92 through 6.94. Determine the reactions at the supports for each of the trusses shown. Indicate whether the truss is rigid. The height of each truss is 12 ft; the length of each panel is 12 ft; and the magnitude of **P** is 4 kips.

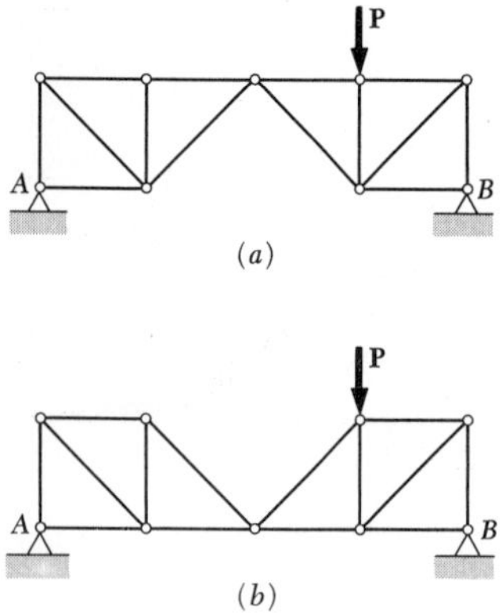

FIG. P 6.92

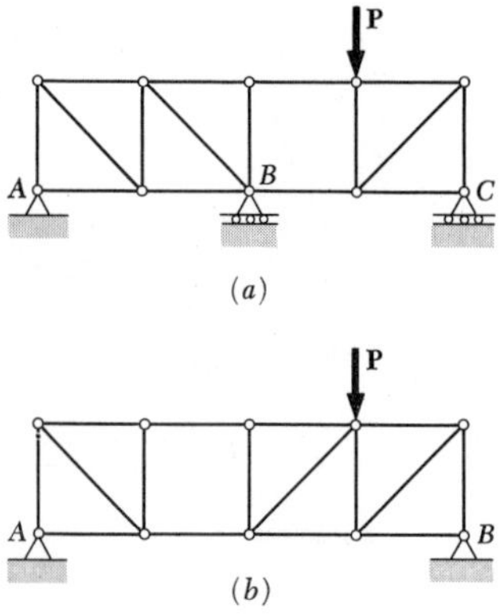

FIG. P 6.93

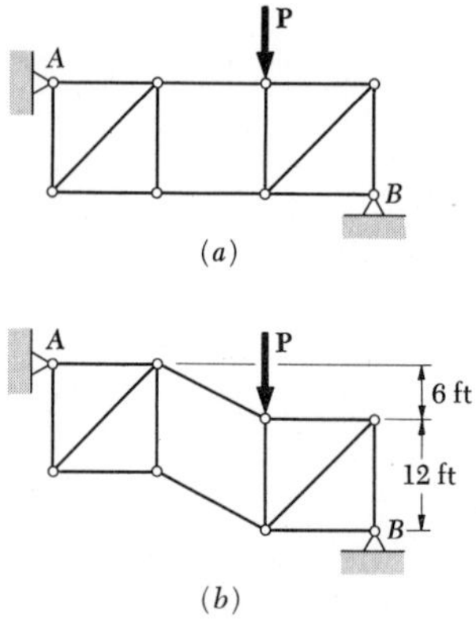

FIG. P 6.94

6.95. Determine the components of all forces acting on member *CDEF*.

6.96. Solve Prob. 6.95 assuming that the 200-lb force is attached at *B* instead of *A* and is directed horizontally to the right.

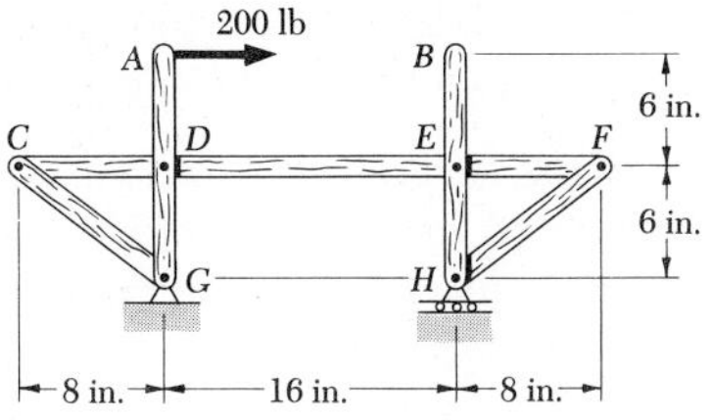

FIG. P 6.95

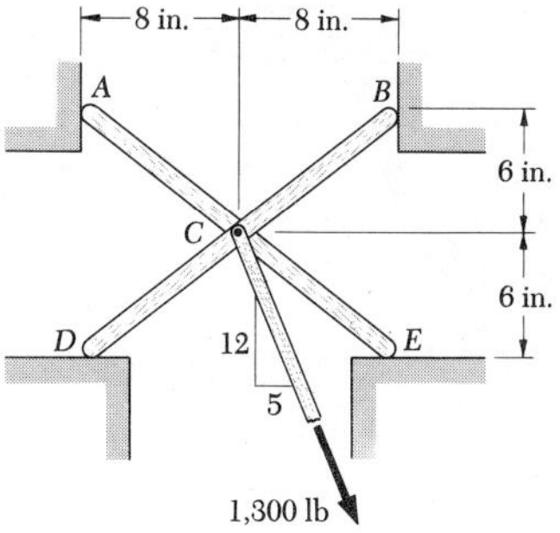

FIG. P 6.97

***6.97.** Knowing that the surfaces at *A*, *B*, *D*, and *E* are smooth, determine (*a*) the reactions, (*b*) the components of the force exerted on member *ACE* at point *C*.

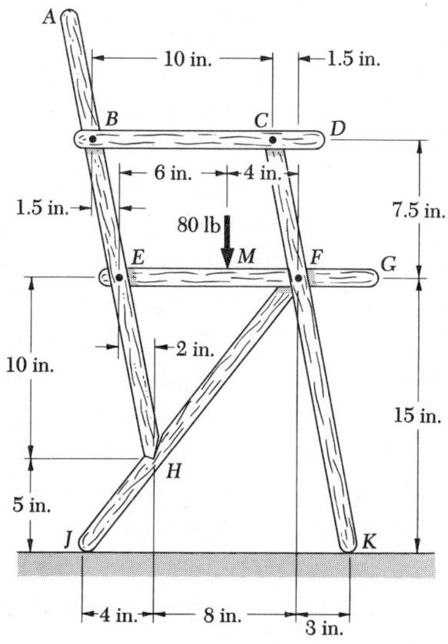

FIG. P 6.98

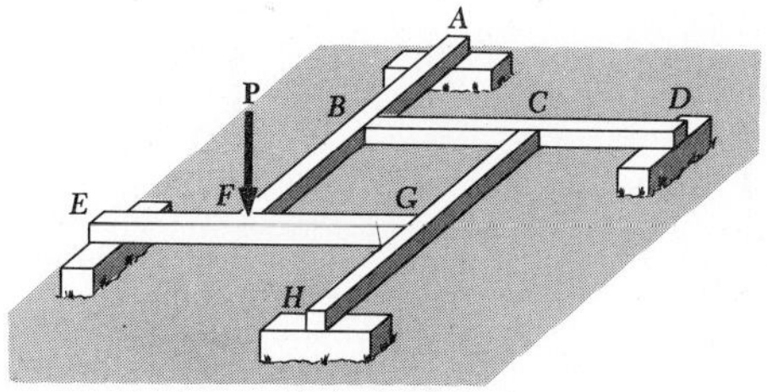

FIG. P 6.99

***6.98.** In the folding chair shown, members *ABEH* and *CFK* are parallel. Determine the components of all forces acting on member *ABEH* when a 160-lb man sits in the chair. It may be assumed that the floor is perfectly smooth and that half the man's weight is carried by each side of the chair and is applied at point *M*.

***6.99.** Four beams, each of length $2a$, are nailed together at their midpoints to form the support system shown. Assuming that only vertical forces are exerted at the connections, determine the vertical reactions at *A*, *D*, *E*, and *H*.

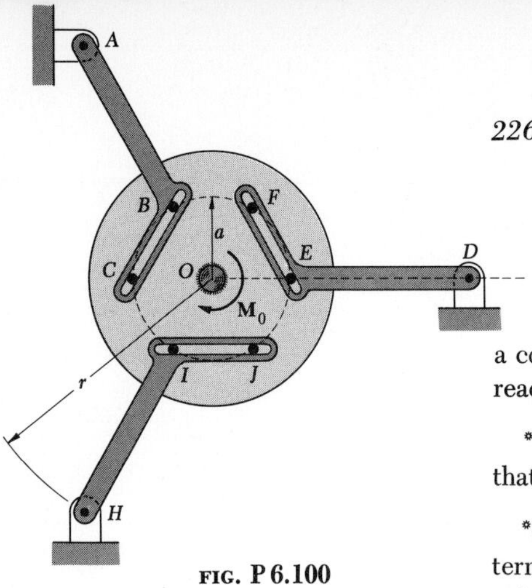

FIG. P 6.100

*6.100. Three arms are connected to a disk by six pins which are attached to the disk. The pins are equally spaced and are located at a distance a from the center of the disk. Each pin may slide freely in straight slots which are machined in the arms. If a couple of moment $\mathbf{M}_0$ is applied to the disk as shown, determine the reaction at D and the forces exerted on arm DEF at points E and F.

*6.101. Solve Prob. 6.100 assuming that the couple is removed and that a downward load $\mathbf{P}$ is applied at the center of the disk.

*6.102. In Prob. 6.65, knowing that the length BD must be 10 in., determine (a) another value of b for which the tension in BD has the same value as when $b = 8$ in., (b) the value of b for which the tension in BD is as small as possible.

6.13. Machines.

Machines are structures designed to transmit and modify forces. Whether they are simple tools or include complicated mechanisms, their main purpose is to transform *input forces* into *output forces.* Consider, for example, a pair of cutting pliers used to cut a wire (Fig. 6.22a). If we apply two equal and opposite forces $\mathbf{P}$ and $-\mathbf{P}$ on their handles, they will exert two equal and opposite forces $\mathbf{Q}$ and $-\mathbf{Q}$ on the wire (Fig. 6.22b).

To determine the magnitude Q of the output forces when the magnitude P of the input forces is known (or, conversely, to determine P when Q is known), we draw a free-body diagram of the pliers *alone,* showing the input forces $\mathbf{P}$ and $-\mathbf{P}$ and the *reactions* $-\mathbf{Q}$ and $\mathbf{Q}$ that the wire exerts on the pliers (Fig. 6.22c). However, since a pair of pliers form a nonrigid structure, we must use one of the component parts as a free body in order to determine the unknown forces. Considering Fig. 6.22d, for example, and taking moments about A, we obtain the relation $Pa = Qb$, which defines the magnitude Q in terms of P or P in terms of Q. The same free-body diagram may be used to determine the components of the internal force at A; we find $A_x = 0$ and $A_y = P + Q$.

In the case of more complicated machines, it generally will be necessary to use several free-body diagrams and, possibly, to solve simultaneous equations involving various internal forces. The free bodies should be chosen to include the input forces and the reactions to the output forces, and the total number of unknown force components involved should not exceed the number of available independent equations. While it is advisable to check whether the problem is determinate before attempting to solve it, there is no point in discussing the rigidity of a machine. A machine includes moving parts and thus must be nonrigid.

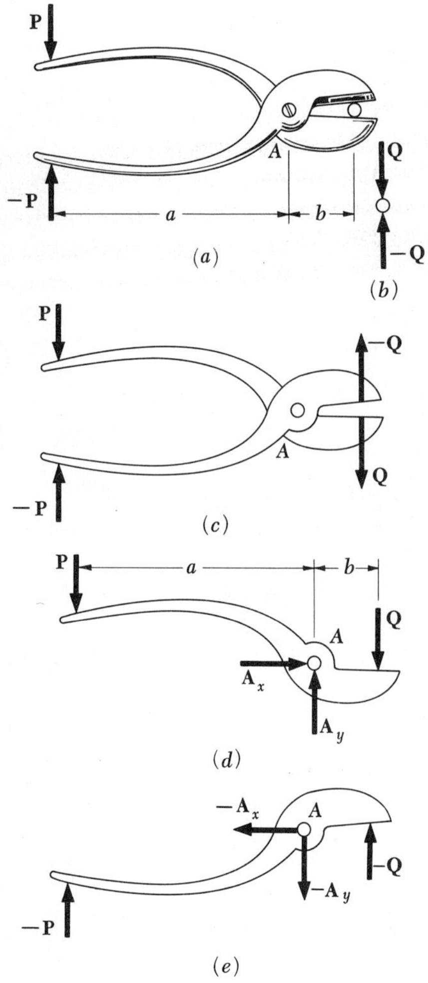

FIG. 6.22

SAMPLE PROBLEM 6.8

Determine the couple **M** which must be applied to the crank CD to hold the mechanism in equilibrium. The block at D is pinned to the crank CD and is free to slide in a slot cut in member AB.

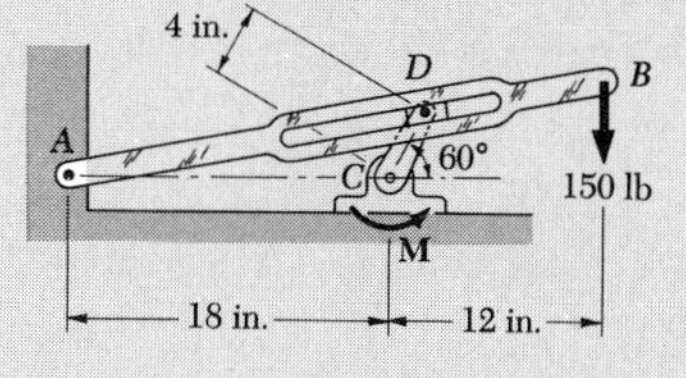

Solution. For the given position of the crank, we compute the following:

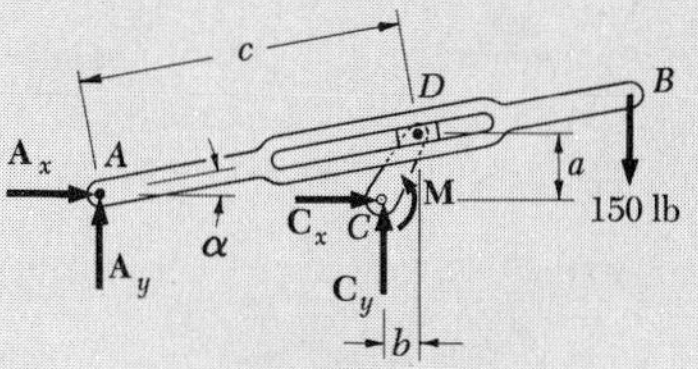

$$a = (4 \text{ in.}) \sin 60° = 3.46 \text{ in.}$$

$$b = (4 \text{ in.}) \cos 60° = 2.00 \text{ in.}$$

$$\tan\alpha = \frac{3.46}{20} \qquad \alpha = 9.8°$$

$$\sin\alpha = \frac{3.46}{c} \qquad c = 20.3 \text{ in.}$$

The mechanism is now dismembered; since the block at D slides freely along the slot, the internal force at D must be perpendicular to member AB.

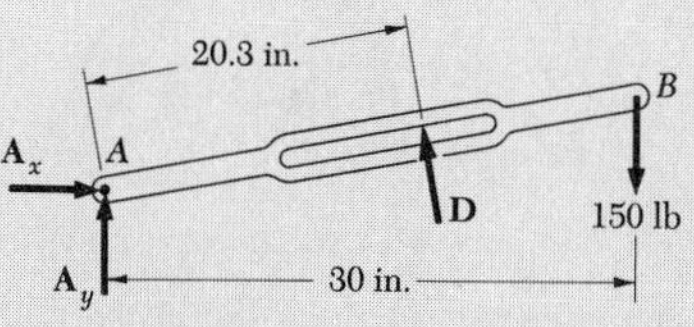

Member AB

$$+\circlearrowleft \Sigma M_A = 0: \qquad D(20.3 \text{ in.}) - (150 \text{ lb})(30 \text{ in.}) = 0$$
$$D = +222 \text{ lb}$$

Member CD. The internal force **D** is resolved into its x and y components.

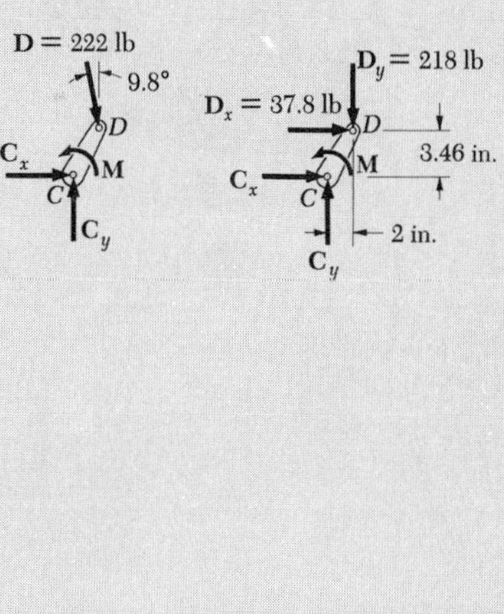

$$D_x = (222 \text{ lb}) \sin 9.8° = +37.8 \text{ lb}$$

$$D_y = -(222 \text{ lb}) \cos 9.8° = -218 \text{ lb}$$

We then write

$$+\circlearrowleft \Sigma M_C = 0: \qquad M - (218 \text{ lb})(2 \text{ in.}) - (37.8 \text{ lb})(3.46 \text{ in.}) = 0$$
$$M = +567 \text{ lb-in.} \qquad \mathbf{M} = 567 \text{ lb-in.} \circlearrowleft$$ ◄

From the free-body diagram of the crank we may also obtain $C_x = -37.8$ lb and $C_y = +218$ lb.

Entire Mechanism (Check). Considering the entire mechanism as a free body, we check that $\Sigma M_A = 0$.

$$+\circlearrowleft \Sigma M_A = M - (150 \text{ lb})(30 \text{ in.}) + C_y(18 \text{ in.})$$
$$= 567 - 4{,}500 + (218)(18) = -9$$

Although ΣM_A is equal to -9 instead of zero, it is small compared with the quantities involved (4,500) and provides a satisfactory check.

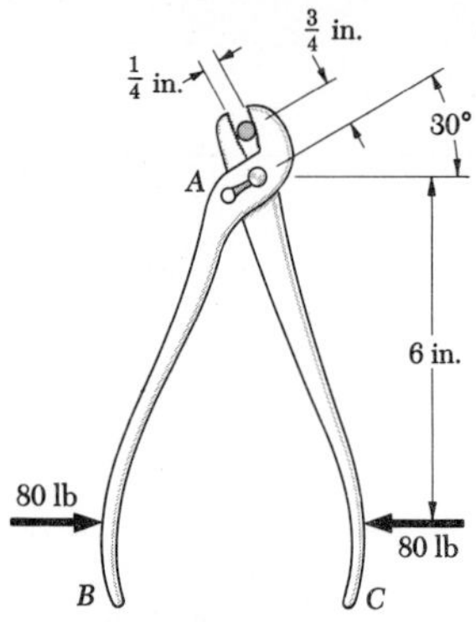

FIG. P6.103

PROBLEMS

6.103. Two 80-lb forces are applied to the handles of the pliers as shown. Determine (*a*) the magnitude of the forces exerted on the rod, (*b*) the force exerted by the pin at *A* on portion *AB* of the pliers.

6.104. Water pressure in the supply system exerts a downward force of 25 lb on the vertical plug at *A*. Determine the tension in the fusible link *DE* and the force exerted on member *BCE* at *B*.

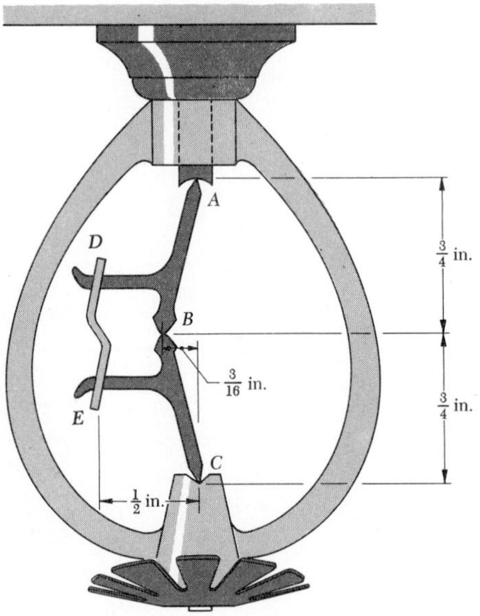

FIG. P6.104

6.105. A cylinder weighs 500 lb and is lifted by a pair of tongs as shown. Determine the forces exerted at *D* and *C* on the tong *BCD*.

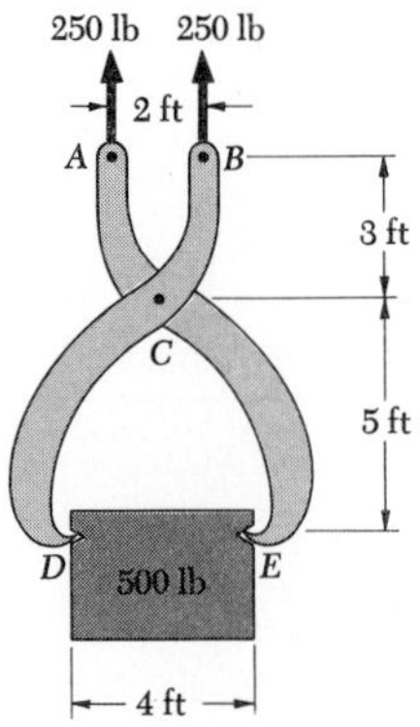

FIG. P6.105

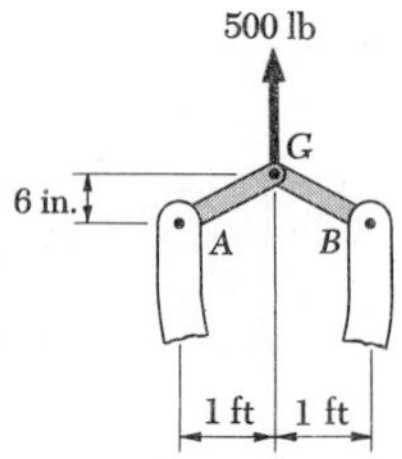

FIG. P6.106

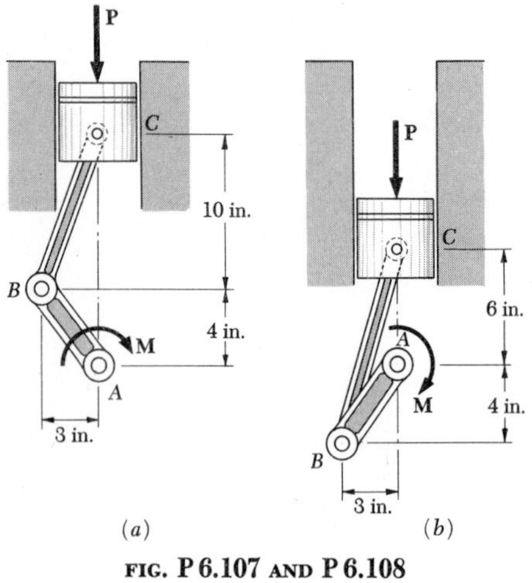

FIG. P6.107 AND P6.108

6.106. If the toggle shown is added to the tongs of Prob. 6.105 and the load is lifted by applying a single force at *G*, determine the forces exerted at *D* and *C* on the tong *BCD*.

6.107. A couple **M** of moment 210 lb-ft is applied to the crank of the engine system shown. For each of the two positions shown, determine the force **P** required to hold the system in equilibrium.

6.108. A force **P** of magnitude 500 lb is applied to the piston of the engine system shown. For each of the two positions shown, determine the couple **M** required to hold the system in equilibrium.

6.109. Two machine parts are connected by a pin at E which is attached to member CD and slides freely in a slot cut in member AB. If a couple $\mathbf{M}_D$ is applied to member CD, determine (a) the couple $\mathbf{M}_B$ required for equilibrium, (b) the reactions at B and D.

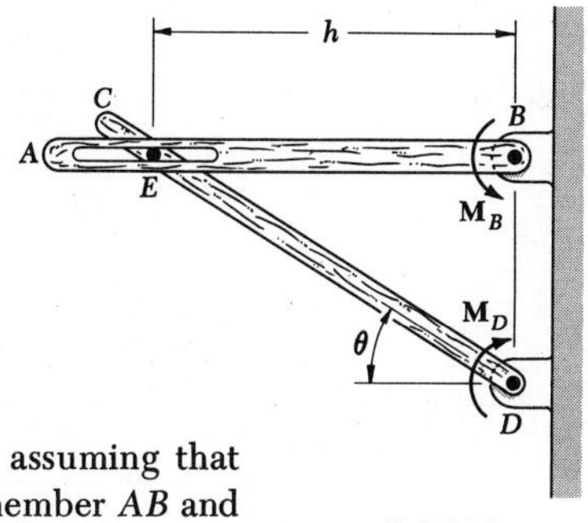

FIG. P6.109

6.110. Solve Prob. 6.109 assuming that the pin at E is attached to member AB and slides freely in a slot cut in member CD.

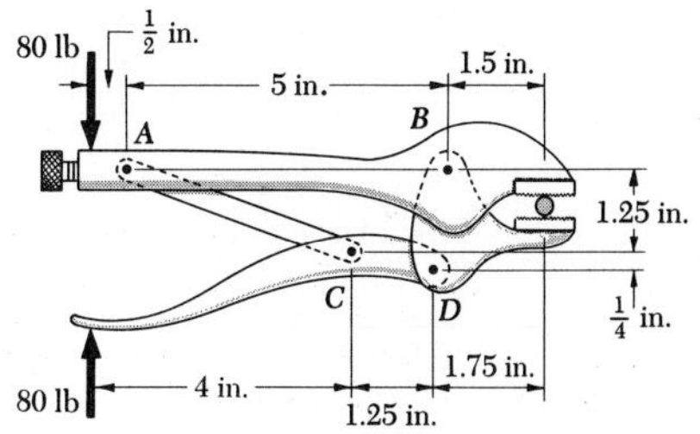

FIG. P6.111

6.111. Determine the magnitude of the gripping forces produced when two 80-lb forces are applied as shown.

6.112. In using the boltcutter shown, a man applies two 125-lb forces to the handles. Determine the magnitude of the forces exerted by the cutter on the bolt.

6.113. In the pliers shown, the clamping jaws remain parallel as objects of various sizes are held. If gripping forces of magnitude $Q = 450$ lb are desired, determine the magnitude P of the forces which must be applied. Assume that pins B and E slide freely in the slots cut in the jaws.

6.114. In Prob. 6.113, show that the magnitude P of the required forces is independent of the position of the object gripped by the jaws. (*Hint.* Determine P in terms of the distance a.)

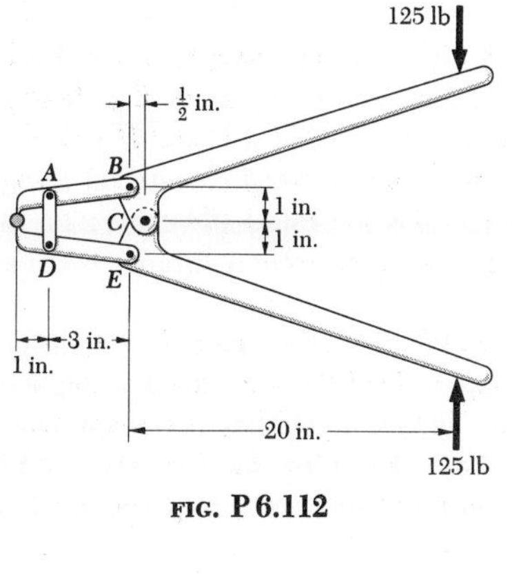

FIG. P6.112

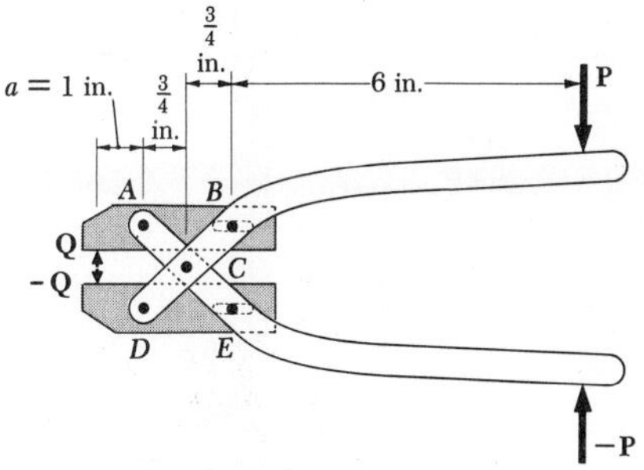

FIG. P6.113

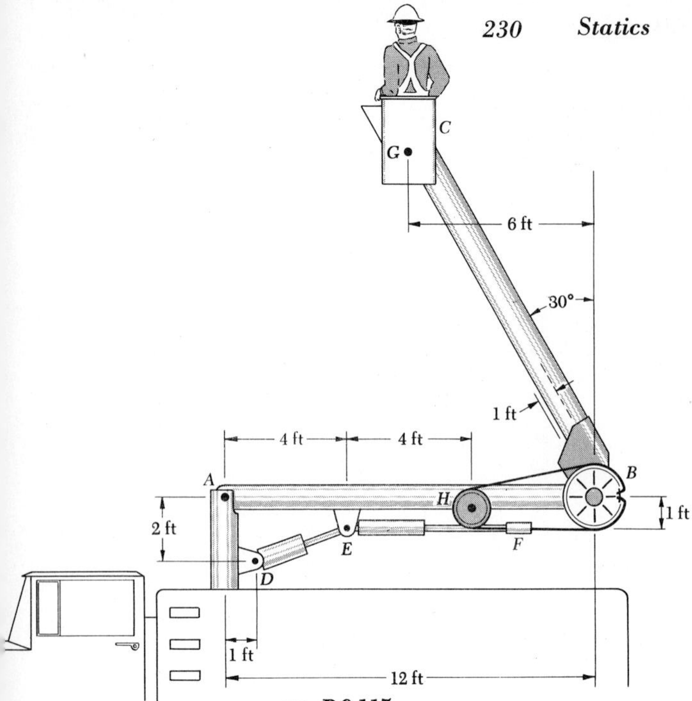

FIG. P 6.115

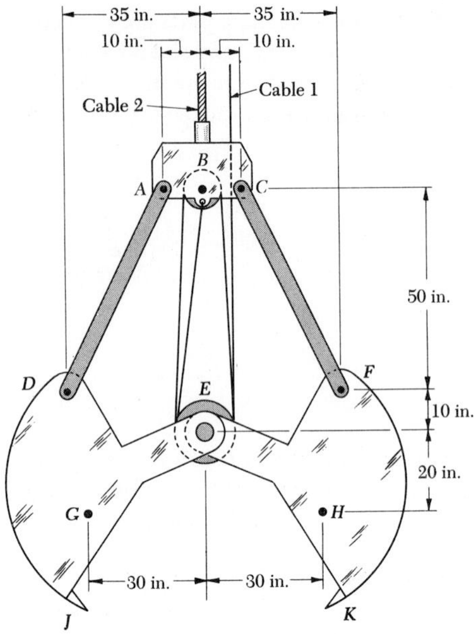

FIG. P 6.116

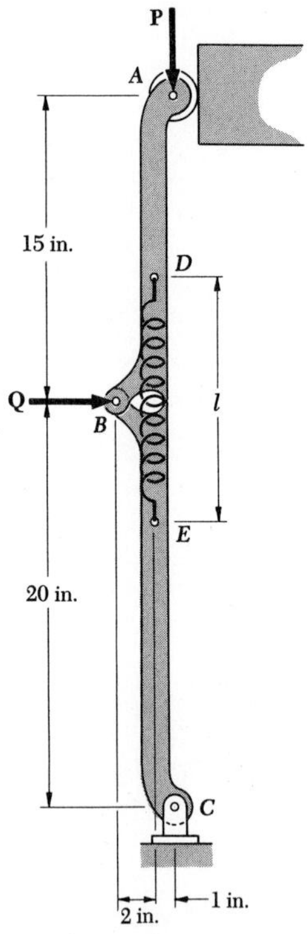

FIG. P 6.117

6.115. The truck shown is used to facilitate work on overhead wires by raising a pair of buckets to the required elevation. Two tubular members *AB* and *BC*, each of length 12 ft, form the main supporting mechanism; the position of *AB* is controlled by means of the hydraulic cylinder *DE*. Two 2-ft-diameter sheaves, one on each side, are rigidly attached to member *BC* at *B*. Cables are fastened to the sheaves, pass over pulleys at *H*, and are fastened to a common movable block at *F*. The position of block *F* is controlled by a second hydraulic cylinder *EF*. Knowing that the workmen, buckets, and equipment attached to the buckets together weigh 700 lb and have a combined center of gravity at *G*, determine the force which must be exerted by each hydraulic cylinder to maintain the position shown. Neglect the weight of the mechanism.

6.116. The total weight of the 1-yd clamshell bucket shown is 4,500 lb. The centers of gravity of sections *DEJ* and *EFK*, which weigh 2,000 lb each, are located at *G* and *H*, respectively. The double-sheave pulley *E* and a counterweight located at *E* together weigh 400 lb. Determine the tension in cable *1* and cable *2* for the position shown. (Neglect the effect of the horizontal distance between the cables.)

6.117. Since the brace shown must remain in position even when the magnitude of **P** is very small, a single safety spring is attached at *D* and *E*. The spring *DE* has a constant of 50 lb/in. and an unstretched length of 7 in. Knowing that l = 10 in. and that the magnitude of **P** is 800 lb, determine the force **Q** required to release the brace.

6.118. Members *ACE* and *DCB* are each of length 20 in. and are connected by a pin at their mid-points *C*. A load **P** of magnitude 320 lb is applied to member *DF*. If $h = 12$ in. and $a = 25$ in., determine (*a*) all forces acting on member *DCB*, (*b*) the tension in the spring *AD*, (*c*) the unstretched length of the spring knowing that the spring constant is 80 lb/in.

6.119. Show that the tension in the spring *AD* and the distance *h* are the same for any position of the load **P** on member *DF*. (*Hint*. Choose *a* as a parameter and determine the tension in *AD* in terms of *a*.)

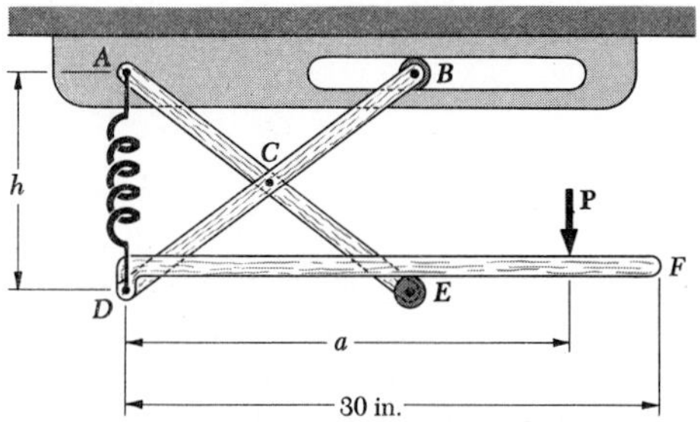

FIG. P 6.118 AND P 6.119

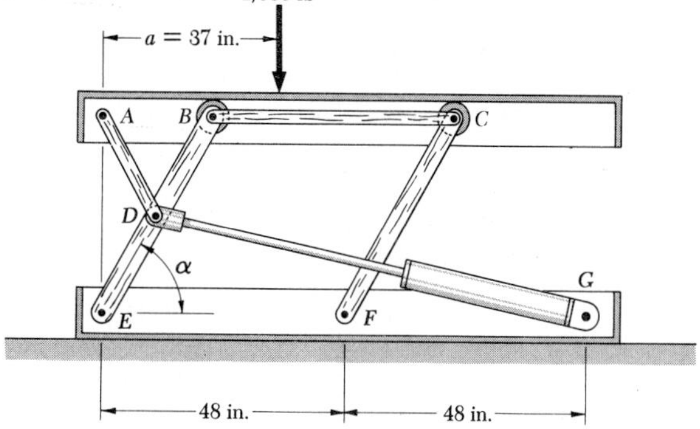

FIG. P 6.120

6.120. The top surface of the hydraulic-lift table shown is maintained at a given elevation by two identical linkage-and-hydraulic-cylinder systems; only one of the systems is shown. Members *EDB* and *CF* are each of length 42 in.; member *AD* is 21 in. long and is pinned to the mid-point *D* of member *EDB*. If a 2,000-lb load is placed on the table top so that half its weight is supported by the system shown, determine the force in members *AD* and *BC* and the force exerted by the hydraulic cylinder on point *D*. Assume $\alpha = 60°$.

***6.121.** In Prob. 6.120 show that the force exerted by the hydraulic cylinder is the same for any position of the load on the table top. Assume $\alpha = 60°$.

6.122. The two gears are rigidly attached to shafts which are held by frictionless bearings at *C*, *D*, *G*, and *H*. A couple of moment 480 lb-ft (counterclockwise when viewed from the positive *x* axis) is applied to shaft *CDE* at *E*. Assuming that the bearings cannot exert any axial thrust, determine (*a*) the couple which must be applied at *F* to maintain equilibrium, (*b*) the reaction at *B*.

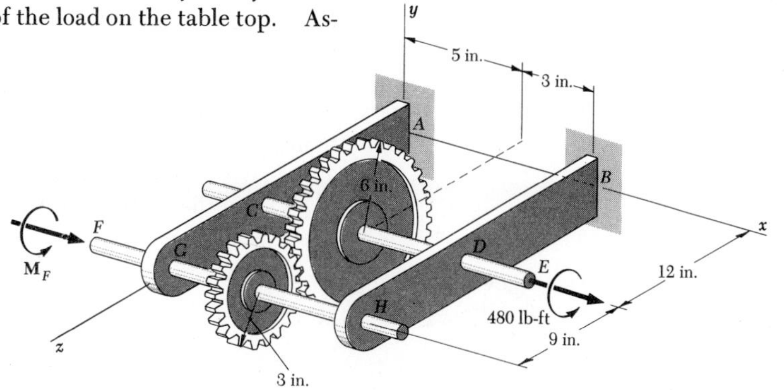

FIG. P 6.122

6.123. For the bevel-gear system shown, determine the required value of α if the ratio of M_B to M_A is to be 3.

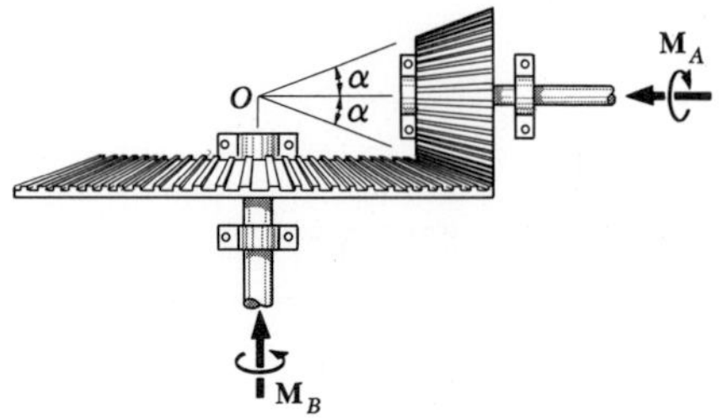

FIG. P 6.123

FIG. P 6.124 AND P 6.125

6.124. In the planetary-gear system shown, the radius of the central gear A is a, the radius of each planetary gear is b, and the radius of the outer gear E is $(a + 2b)$. In a particular gear system where $a = b = 2\frac{1}{4}$ in., a clockwise couple $\mathbf{M}_A$ is applied to gear A. If the system is to be in equilibrium, determine (*a*) the couple $\mathbf{M}_S$ which must be applied to the spider *BCD*, (*b*) the couple $\mathbf{M}_E$ which must be applied to the outer gear E.

6.125. In the planetary-gear system shown, the radius of the central gear A is a, the radius of each of the planetary gears is b, and the radius of the outer gear E is $(a + 2b)$. A clockwise couple of magnitude M_A is applied to the central gear A and a counterclockwise couple of magnitude $5M_A$ is applied to the spider *BCD*. If the system is to be in equilibrium, determine (*a*) the required ratio b/a, (*b*) the couple $\mathbf{M}_E$ which must be applied to the outer gear E.

***6.126.** Two shafts *AC* and *CF*, which lie in the vertical *xy* plane, are connected by a universal joint at *C*. The bearings at *B* and *D* do not exert any axial force. A couple of moment 500 lb-ft (clockwise when viewed from the positive *x* axis) is applied to shaft *CF* at *F*. At a time when the arm of the crosspiece attached to shaft *CF* is horizontal, determine (*a*) the moment of the couple which must be applied to shaft *AC* at *A* to maintain equilibrium, (*b*) the reactions at *B*, *D*, and *E*. (*Hint.* The sum of the couples exerted on the crosspiece must be zero.)

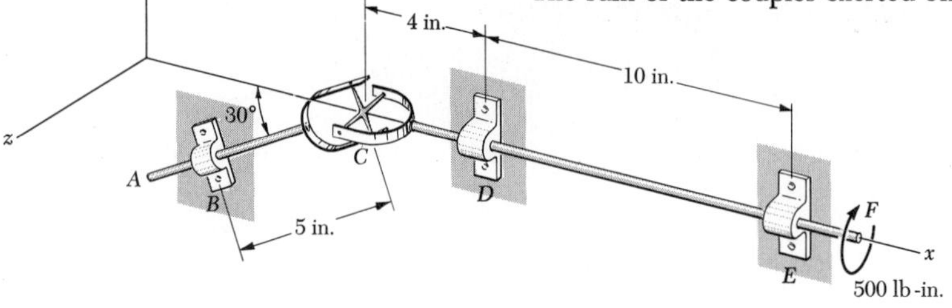

FIG. P 6.126

***6.127.** Solve Prob. 6.126 assuming that the arm of the crosspiece attached to shaft *CF* is vertical.

*6.128. The weight in ounces of letters placed on the postal scale shown is indicated on the moving dial by the stationary pointer P. The scale is shown in its unloaded position. It is known that the dial, the arm AB, and a counterweight together weigh 10 oz and have a combined center of gravity at G. The distance AG is $1\frac{1}{4}$ in., and the length of the arm AB and of the link CD is 1.00 in. At what angle θ should the 2-oz number be painted on the dial? (*Hint.* The weights of the tray, of BC, and of CD are unknown, but their effect must be considered.)

*6.129. A letter of unknown weight is placed on the postal scale of Prob. 6.128. Knowing that the dial rotates counterclockwise through 45° before coming to rest, determine the weight of the letter. (See hint of Prob. 6.128.)

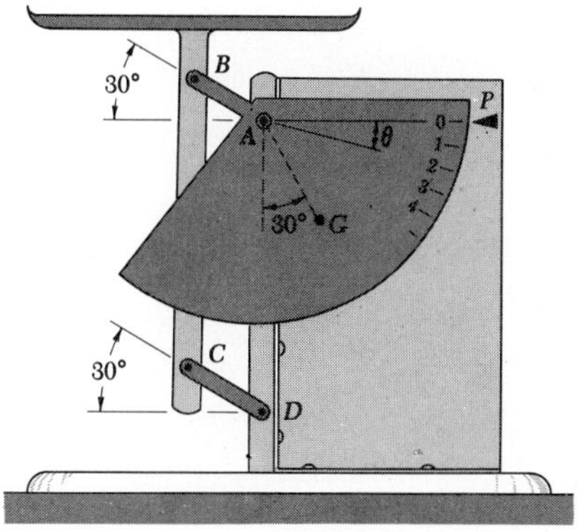

FIG. P6.128

REVIEW PROBLEMS

6.130. Determine the reaction at G and all forces acting on member $BDFH$.

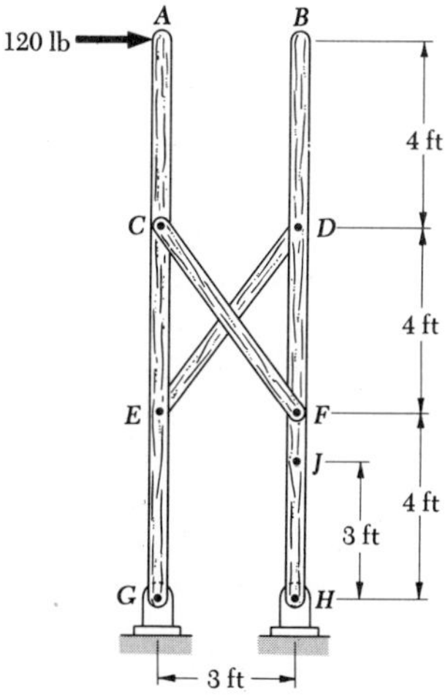

FIG. P6.130

6.131. Each of the four bars shown is of length L. Express the magnitude of the force $\mathbf{Q}$ required for equilibrium in terms of P, a, and L.

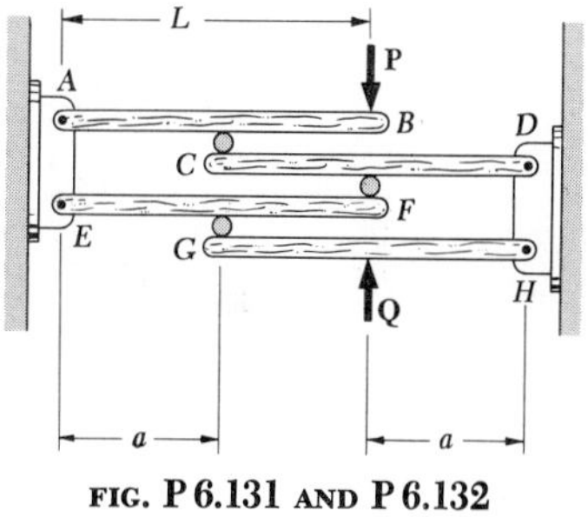

FIG. P6.131 AND P6.132

6.132. Each of the four bars shown is of length L. Knowing that the magnitude of the force $\mathbf{P}$ is 100 lb and that $a = 10$ in. and $L = 20$ in., determine the magnitude of the force $\mathbf{Q}$ required for equilibrium.

6.133. A pipe weighs 20 lb-ft and is supported every 30 ft by a small frame; a typical frame is shown. (*a*) Determine the components of the reactions and the components of the force exerted at B on member AB. (*b*) Determine the value of α for which the reactions are vertical.

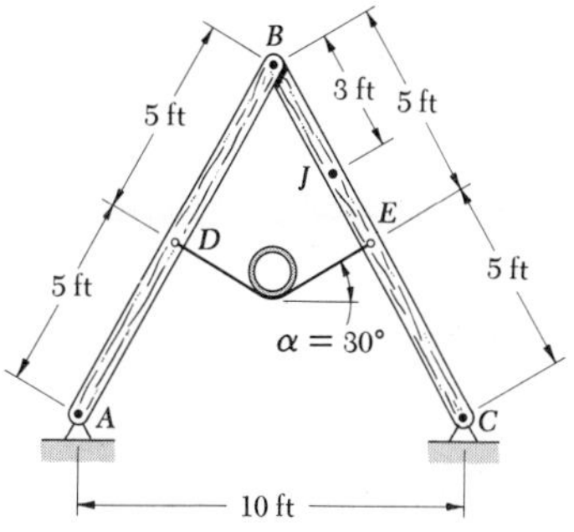

FIG. P6.133

6.134. The boom *CDE* is maintained in a horizontal position by a cable which passes over small pulleys at *A* and *F*. For the loading shown, determine the force in members *AB*, *AC*, and *GH*.

6.135. Solve Prob. 6.134 assuming that the end *E* of the boom, where the 2-kip load is applied, has been raised 6 ft.

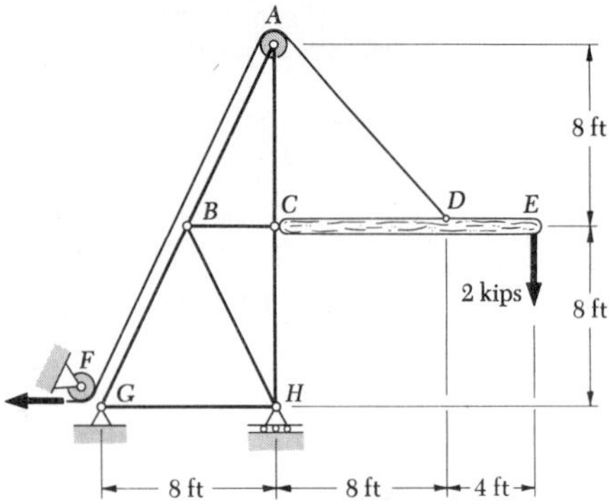

FIG. P6.134

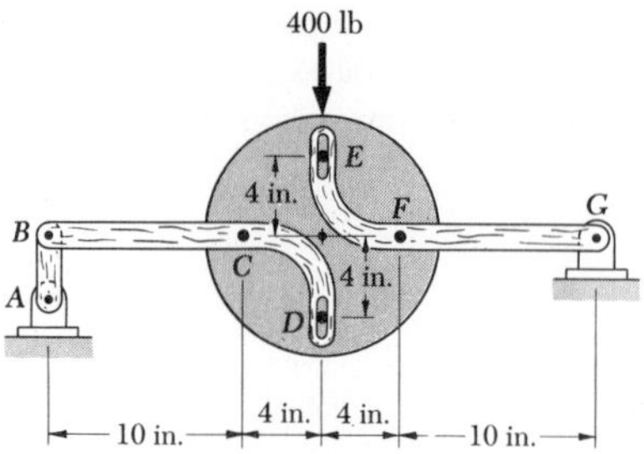

FIG. P6.136

6.136. Two arms *BCD* and *EFG* are connected to a 10-in.-diameter disk by four pins which are attached to the disk. Assuming that the pins at *D* and *E* may slide in the vertical slots, determine the components of all forces exerted on the disk when a 400-lb load is applied to the disk as shown.

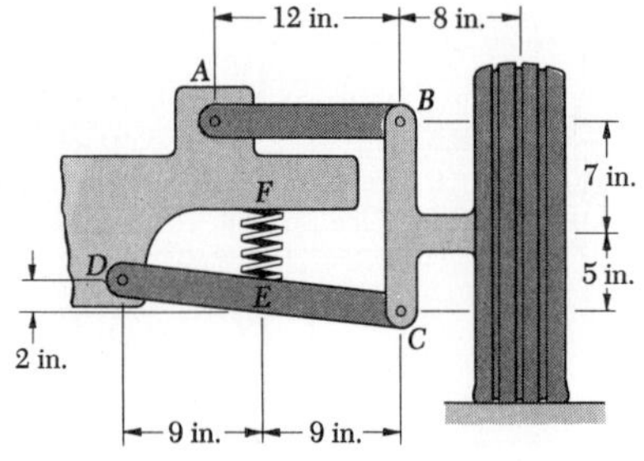

FIG. P6.138

6.137. Solve Prob. 6.136 assuming that the 400-lb load is applied to the top edge of member *EFG*.

6.138. An automobile front-wheel assembly supports 750 lb. Determine the force exerted by the spring and the components of the forces exerted on the frame at points *A* and *D*.

6.139. An 800-lb weight may be supported by a small frame in each of the four ways shown. The diameter of the pulley is 1 ft. For each case, determine the force components and the couple representing the reaction at *A* and also the force exerted at *D* on the vertical member.

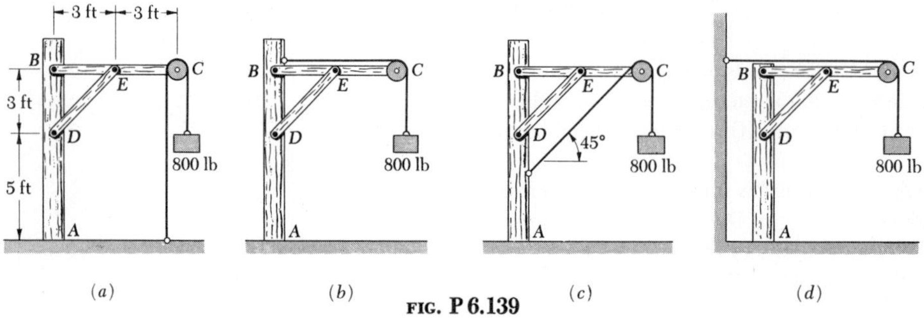

FIG. P6.139

6.140. Knowing that the forces **P** and $-$**P** are equal and opposite and have a magnitude of 2 kips, determine the force in each member of the truss shown.

6.141. Determine the magnitude of the equal and opposite forces **P** and $-$**P** for which the forces in members *2-3* and *7-8* have the same absolute value.

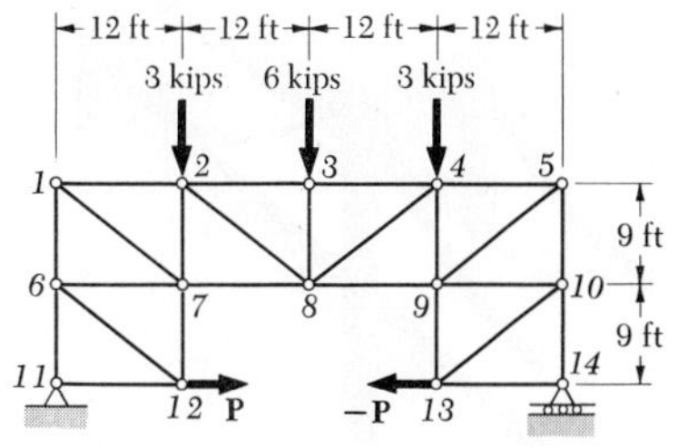

FIG. P6.140 AND P6.141

7. FORCES IN BEAMS AND CABLES

***7.1. Introduction. Internal Forces in Members.** In preceding chapters, two basic problems involving structures were considered, (1) the determination of the external forces acting on a structure (Chap. 4) and (2) the determination of the forces which hold together the various members forming a structure (Chap. 6). We shall now consider the problem of determining the internal forces which hold together the various parts of a given member.

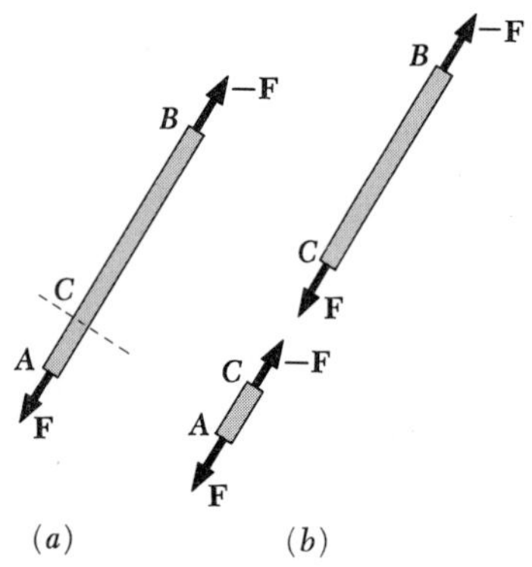

FIG. 7.1

We shall first consider a *straight two-force member AB* (Fig. 7.1*a*). From Sec. 4.6, we know that the forces **F** and $-$**F** acting at A and B respectively must be directed along AB in opposite sense and have the same magnitude F. Let us cut, now, the member at C. To maintain the equilibrium of the free bodies AC and CB thus obtained, we must apply to AC a force $-$**F** equal and opposite to **F**, and to CB a force **F** equal and opposite to $-$**F** (Fig. 7.1*b*). These new forces are directed along AB in opposite sense and have the same magnitude F. Since the two parts AC and CB were in equilibrium before the member was cut, *internal forces* equivalent to these new forces must have existed in the member itself. We see that, in the case of a straight two-force member, the internal forces acting on each part of the member are equivalent to an axial force. The magnitude F of this force does not depend upon the location of the section C and is referred to as the *force in member AB.* In the case considered, the member is in tension and will elongate under the action of the internal forces. In the case represented in Fig. 7.2, the member is in compression and will decrease in length under the action of the internal forces.

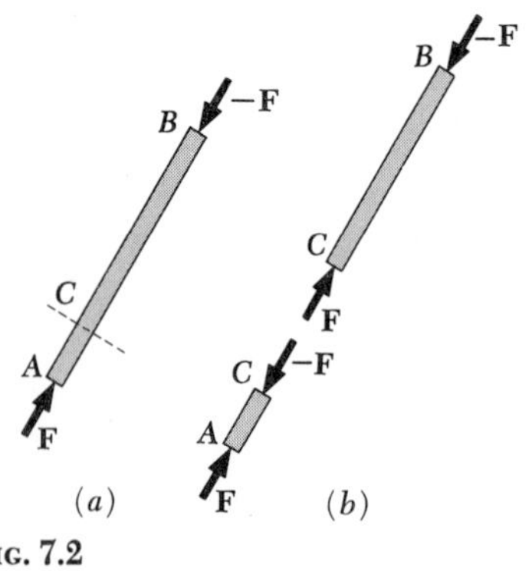

FIG. 7.2

Next we shall consider a *multiforce member.* Take, for instance, member AD of the crane analyzed in Sec. 6.11. This crane is shown again in Fig. 7.3*a*, and the free-body diagram of member AD is drawn in Fig. 7.3*b*. We now cut member AD

at J and draw a free-body diagram for each of the portions JD and AJ of the member (Fig. 7.3*c* and *d*). Considering the free body JD, we find that its equilibrium will be maintained if we apply at J a force **F** to balance the vertical component of **T**, a force **V** to balance the horizontal component of **T**, and a couple **M** to balance the moment of **T** about J. Again we conclude that internal forces must have existed at J before member AD was cut. The internal forces acting on the portion JD of member AD are equivalent to the force-couple system shown in Fig. 7.3*c*. According to Newton's third law, the internal forces acting on AJ must be equivalent to an equal and opposite force-couple system, as shown in Fig. 7.3*d*. It clearly appears that the action of the internal forces in member AD *is not limited to producing tension or compression* as in the case of straight two-force members; the internal forces *also produce shear and bending.* The force **F** is again in this case called an *axial force;* the force **V** is called a *shearing force;* and the moment **M** of the couple is known as the *bending moment* at J. We note that, when determining internal forces in a member, we should clearly indicate on which portion of the member the forces are supposed to act. The deformation which will occur in member AD is sketched in Fig. 7.3*e*. The actual analysis of such a deformation is part of the study of mechanics of materials.

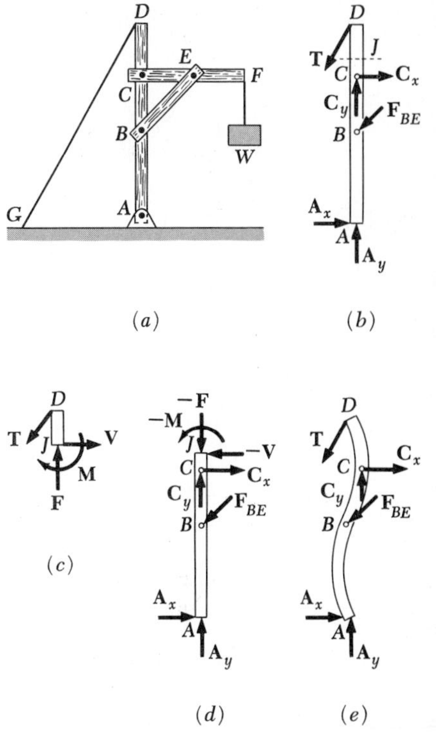

FIG. 7.3

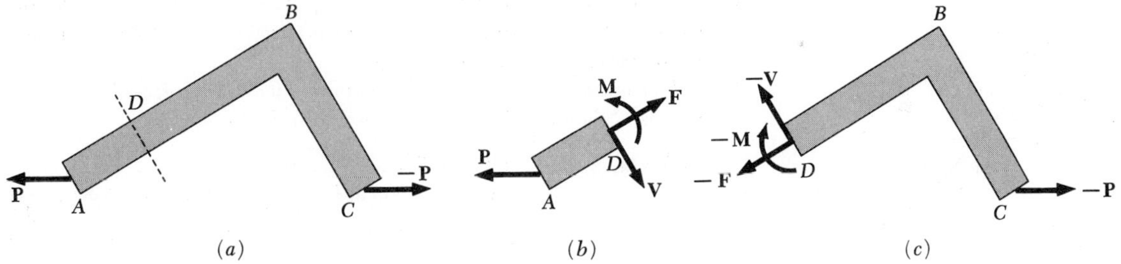

FIG. 7.4

It should be noted that, in a *two-force member which is not straight,* the internal forces are also equivalent to a force-couple system. This is shown in Fig. 7.4, where the two-force member ABC has been cut at D.

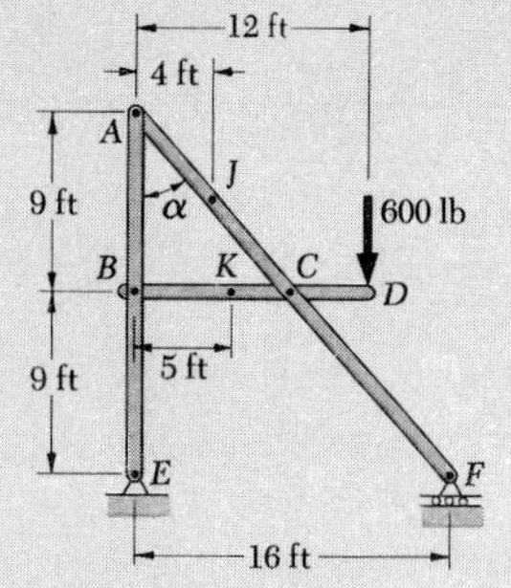

SAMPLE PROBLEM 7.1

In the frame shown, determine the internal forces (*a*) in member *ACF* at point *J* and (*b*) in member *BCD* at point *K*. This frame has been previously considered in Sample Prob. 6.6.

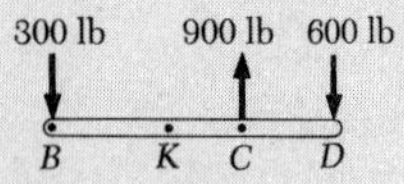

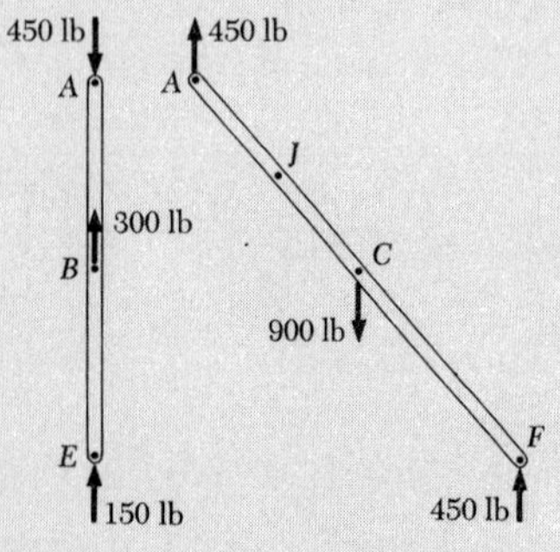

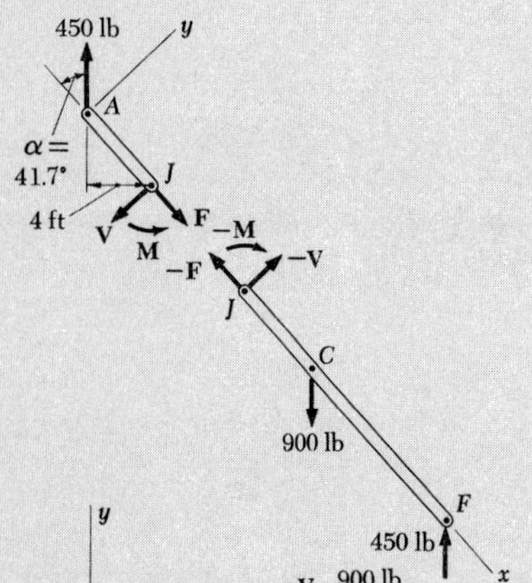

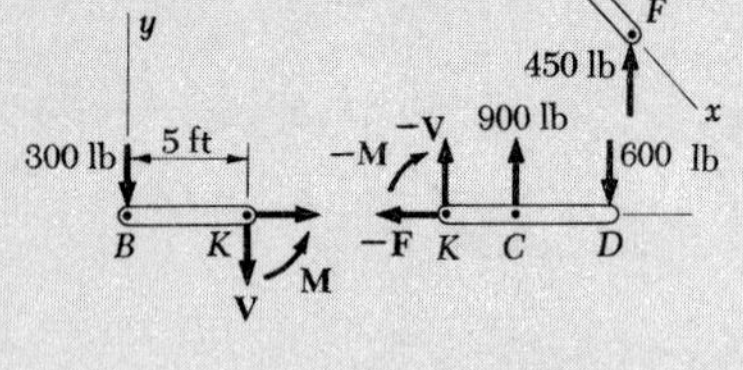

Solution. The reactions and the forces acting on each member of the frame are determined; this has been previously done in Sample Prob. 6.6, and the results are repeated here.

a. Internal Forces at J. Member *ACF* is cut at point *J*, and the two parts shown are obtained. The internal forces at *J* are represented by an equivalent force-couple system and may be determined by considering the equilibrium of either part. Considering the *free body AJ*, we write

$+\circlearrowleft \Sigma M_J = 0$: $\quad -(450 \text{ lb})(4 \text{ ft}) + M = 0$

$M = +1{,}800 \text{ lb-ft} \qquad \mathbf{M} = 1{,}800 \text{ lb-ft} \circlearrowleft$ ◄

$+\searrow \Sigma F_x = 0$: $\quad F - (450 \text{ lb}) \cos 41.7° = 0$

$F = +336 \text{ lb} \qquad \mathbf{F} = 336 \text{ lb} \searrow$ ◄

$+\nearrow \Sigma F_y = 0$: $\quad -V + (450 \text{ lb}) \sin 41.7° = 0$

$V = +299 \text{ lb} \qquad \mathbf{V} = 299 \text{ lb} \swarrow$ ◄

The internal forces at *J* are therefore equivalent to a couple **M**, an axial force **F**, and a shearing force **V**. The internal force-couple system acting on part *JCF* is equal and opposite.

b. Internal Forces at K. We cut member *BCD* at *K* and obtain the two parts shown. Considering the *free body BK*, we write

$+\circlearrowleft \Sigma M_K = 0$: $\quad (300 \text{ lb})(5 \text{ ft}) + M = 0$

$M = -1{,}500 \text{ lb-ft} \qquad \mathbf{M} = 1{,}500 \text{ lb-ft} \circlearrowright$ ◄

$\overset{+}{\rightarrow} \Sigma F_x = 0$: $\quad F = 0 \qquad \mathbf{F} = 0$ ◄

$+\uparrow \Sigma F_y = 0$: $\quad -300 \text{ lb} - V = 0$

$V = -300 \text{ lb} \qquad \mathbf{V} = 300 \text{ lb} \uparrow$ ◄

PROBLEMS

7.1 through 7.7. Determine the internal forces (axial force, shearing force, and bending moment) at point *J* of the structure indicated:

7.1. Frame and loading of Prob. 6.69.
7.2. Frame and loading of Prob. 6.66.
7.3. Frame and loading of Prob. 6.73.
7.4. Frame and loading of Prob. 6.70.
7.5. Beam and loading of Prob. 6.77.
7.6. Beam and loading of Prob. 6.78.
7.7. Arch and loading of Prob. 6.81.

7.8 and 7.9. A steel channel forms one side of a flight of stairs. If one channel weighs w lb/ft, determine the internal forces at the center of one channel due to its own weight, (*a*) in terms of w, L, and θ, (*b*) if $w = 20$ lb/ft, $l = 12$ ft, and $h = 9$ ft.

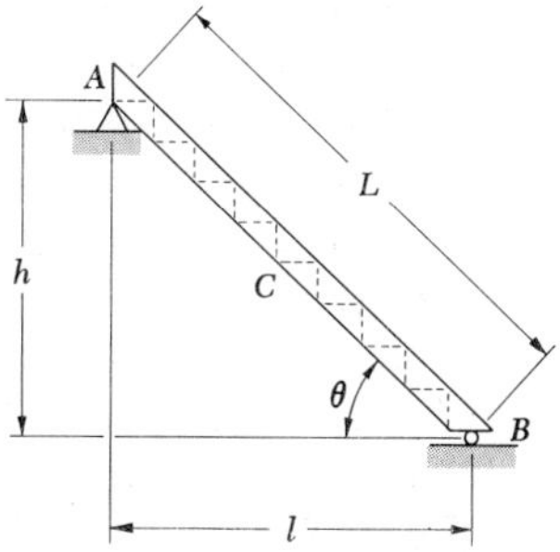

FIG. P 7.8

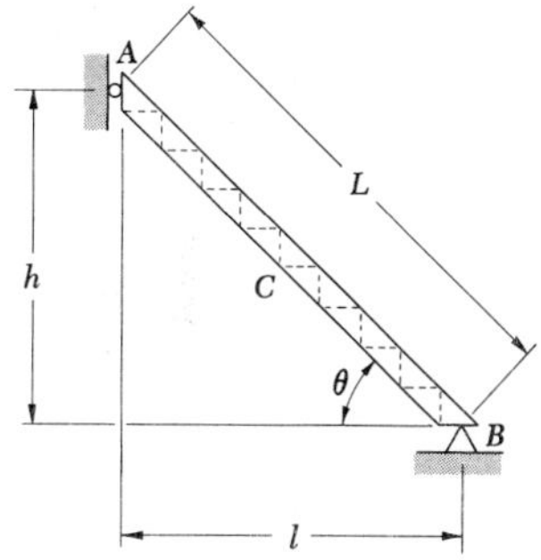

FIG. P 7.9

7.10. Determine the internal forces at points *J* and *K* of the adjustable hanger shown.

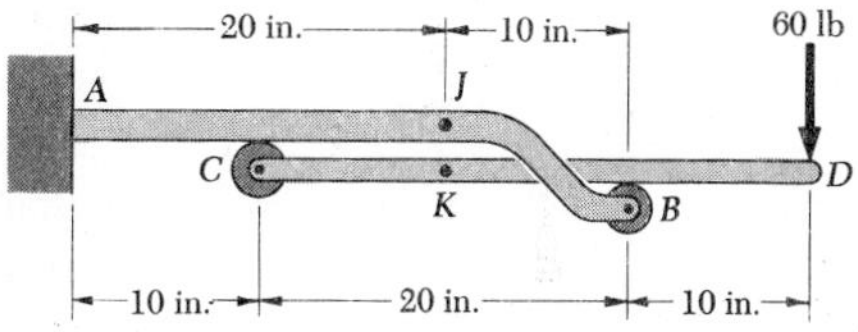

FIG. P 7.10

7.11 and 7.12. A half section of pipe, 1 ft long, rests on a smooth horizontal surface as shown. If the half section of pipe weighs 30 lb and has a diameter of 20 in., determine the bending moment at point *J* when $\theta = 90°$.

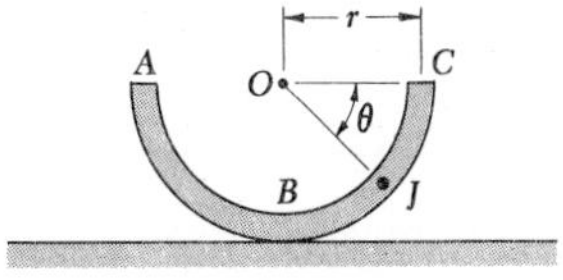

FIG. P 7.11 AND P 7.13

***7.13 and 7.14.** A half section of pipe, 1 ft long and of weight W, rests on a smooth horizontal surface. Determine the internal forces at a point *J* in terms of W, r, and θ.

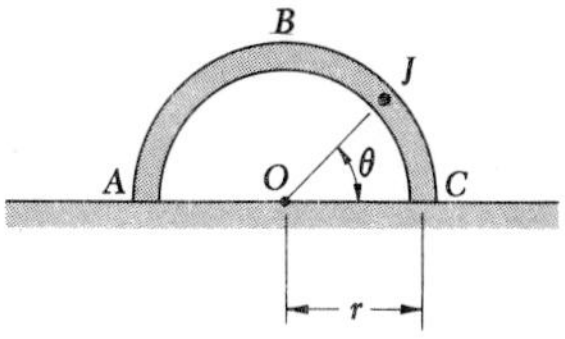

FIG. P 7.12 AND P 7.14

***7.15.** In Prob. 7.13 determine the magnitude and location of the maximum internal axial force.

BEAMS

***7.2. Various Types of Loading and Support.** A structural member designed to support loads applied at various points along the member is known as a *beam.* In most cases, the loads are perpendicular to the axis of the beam and will cause only shear and bending in the beam. When the loads are not at a right angle to the beam, they will also produce axial forces in the beam. Axial forces, however, may usually be neglected in the design of beams, since the ability of a beam to resist shear and especially bending is more critical than its ability to resist axial forces.

Beams are usually long, straight prismatic bars. Designing a beam consists essentially in selecting the cross section which will provide the most effective resistance to the shear and bending produced by the applied loads. The design of the beam, therefore, includes two distinct parts. In the first part, the shearing forces and bending moments produced by the loads are determined. The second part is concerned with the selection of the cross section best suited to resist the shearing forces and bending moments determined in the first part. This portion of the chapter, Beams, deals with the first part of the problem of beam design, namely, the determination of the shearing forces and bending moments in beams subjected to various loading conditions and supported in various ways. The second part of the problem belongs to the study of mechanics of materials.

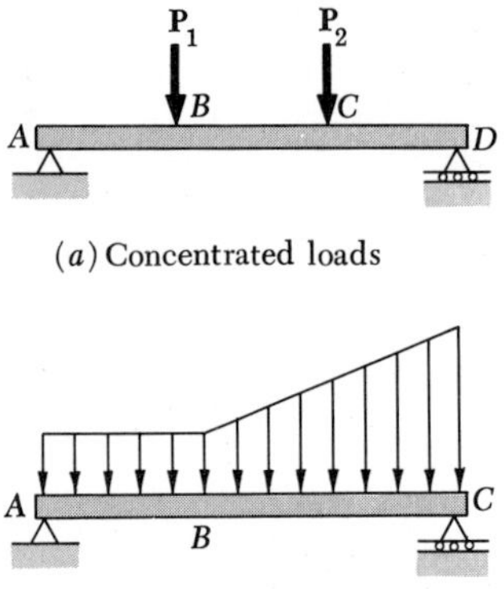

(*a*) Concentrated loads

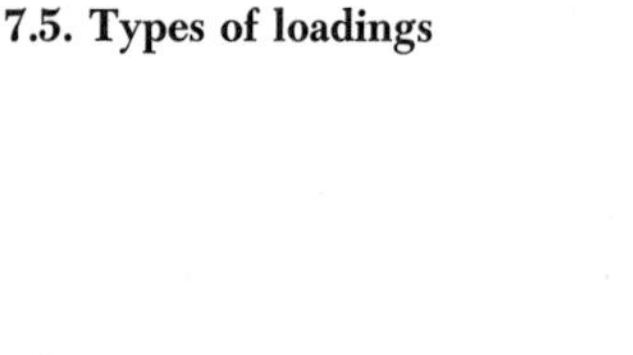

(*b*) Distributed loads

FIG. 7.5. Types of loadings

A beam may be subjected to *concentrated loads* (Fig. 7.5*a*), to *distributed loads* (Fig. 7.5*b*), or to a combination of both. When the load w per unit length has a constant value over part of the beam (as between A and B in Fig. 7.5*b*), the load is said to be *uniformly distributed* over that part of the beam. The determination of the reactions at the supports may be considerably simplified if distributed loads are replaced by equivalent concentrated loads, as explained in Sec. 5.6. This substitution, however, should not be performed, or at least should be performed with care, when internal forces are being computed (see Sample Prob. 7.3).

Beams are classified according to the way in which they are supported. Several types of beams frequently used are shown in Fig. 7.6. The distance L between supports is called the *span.* It should be noted that the reactions will be determinate if the supports involve only three unknowns. The reactions will be statically indeterminate if more unknowns are involved; the methods of statics are not sufficient then to determine the reactions, and the properties of the beam with regard to its re-

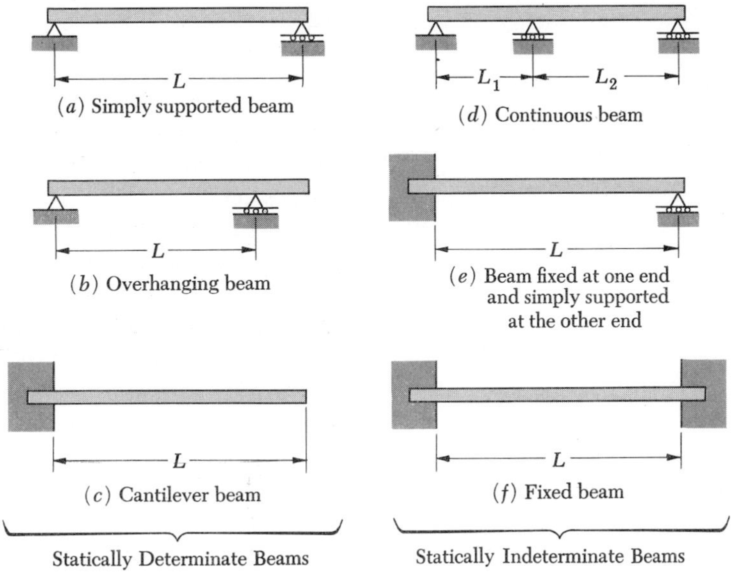

FIG. 7.6. **Types of beams**

sistance to bending must be taken into consideration. Beams supported by two rollers are not shown here; such beams are only partially constrained and will move under certain loading conditions.

Sometimes two or more beams are connected by hinges to form a single continuous structure. Two examples of beams hinged at a point H are shown in Fig. 7.7. It will be noted that the reactions at the supports involve four unknowns and cannot be determined from the free-body diagram of the two-beam system. They can be determined, however, by considering the free-body diagram of each beam separately; six unknowns are involved (including two force components at the hinge), and six equations are available.

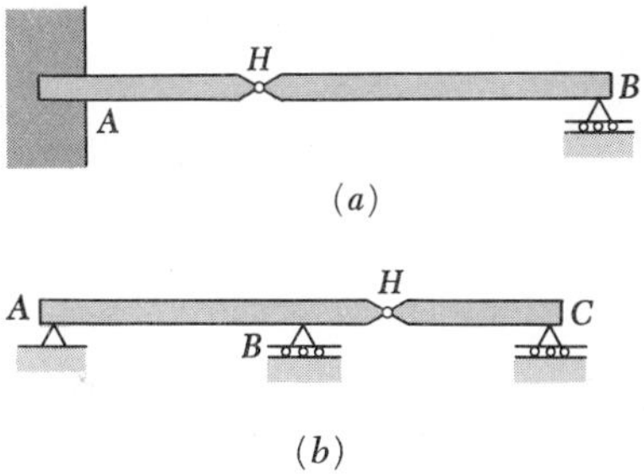

FIG. 7.7. **Combined beams**

***7.3. Shear and Bending Moment in a Beam.** Consider a beam AB subjected to various concentrated and distributed loads (Fig. 7.8a). We propose to determine the shearing force and bending moment at any point of the beam. In the example considered here, the beam is simply supported, but the method used could be applied to any type of statically determinate beam.

First we determine the reactions at A and B by choosing the entire beam as a free body (Fig. 7.8b); writing $\Sigma M_A = 0$ and $\Sigma M_B = 0$, we obtain, respectively, $\mathbf{R}_B$ and $\mathbf{R}_A$.

To determine the internal forces at C, we cut the beam at C and draw the free-body diagrams of the portions AC and CB of the beam (Fig. 7.8c). Using the free-body diagram of AC, we may determine the shearing force $\mathbf{V}$ at C by equating to zero the sum of the vertical components of all forces acting on AC. Similarly, the bending moment **M** at C may be found by equating to zero the sum of the moments about C of all forces and couples acting on AC. We could have used just as well, however, the free-body diagram of CB † and determined the shearing force **V′** and the bending moment **M′** by equating to zero the sum of the vertical components and the sum of the moments about C of all forces and couples acting on AC. While this possible choice of alternate free bodies may facilitate the computation of the numerical values of the shearing force and

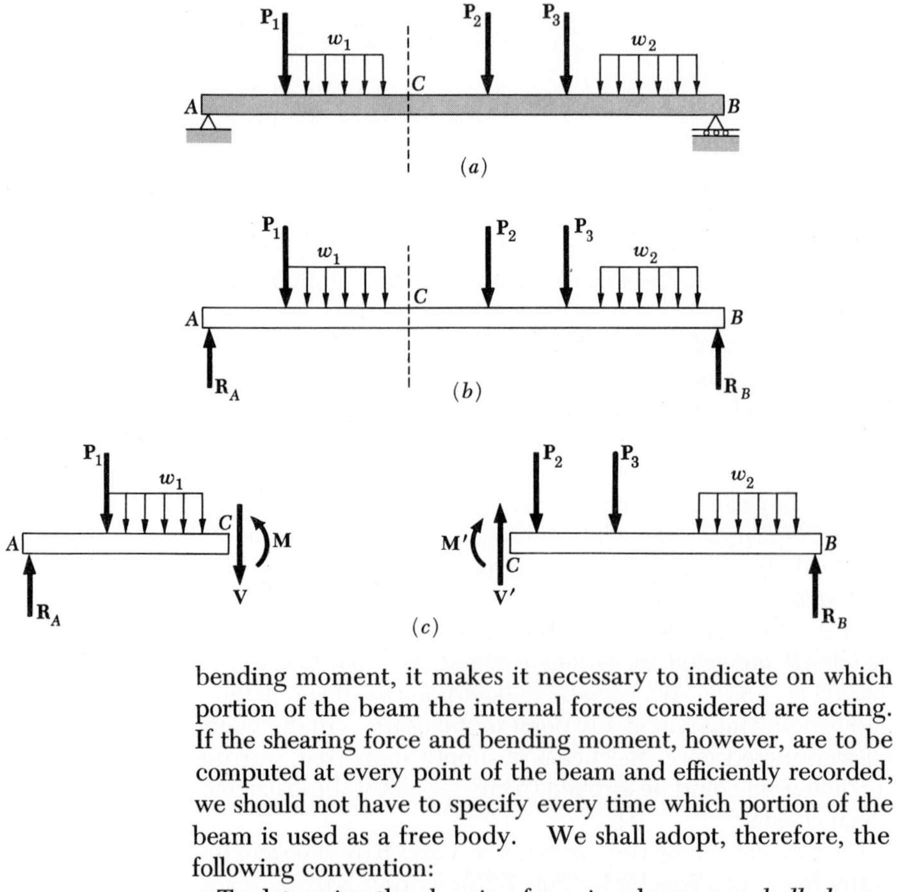

FIG. 7.8

bending moment, it makes it necessary to indicate on which portion of the beam the internal forces considered are acting. If the shearing force and bending moment, however, are to be computed at every point of the beam and efficiently recorded, we should not have to specify every time which portion of the beam is used as a free body. We shall adopt, therefore, the following convention:

To determine the shearing force in a beam, *we shall always*

† The force and couple representing the internal forces acting on CB will now be denoted by **V′** and **M′**, rather than by −**V** and −**M** as done earlier, in order to avoid confusion when applying the sign convention which we are about to introduce.

assume that the internal forces **V** and **V′** are directed as shown in Fig. 7.8*c*. A positive value obtained for their common magnitude *V* will indicate that this assumption was correct and that the shearing forces are actually directed as shown. A negative value obtained for *V* will indicate that the assumption was wrong and that the shearing forces are directed in the opposite way. Thus, only the magnitude *V*, together with a plus or minus sign, needs to be recorded to define completely the shearing forces at a given point of the beam. The scalar *V* is commonly referred to as the *shear* at the given point of the beam.

Similarly, *we shall always assume* that the internal couples **M** and **M′** are directed as shown in Fig. 7.8*c*. A positive value obtained for their magnitude *M*, commonly referred to as the bending moment, will indicate that this assumption was correct, and a negative value that it was wrong. Summarizing the sign convention we have presented, we state:

The shear V and the bending moment M at a given point of a beam are said to be positive when the internal forces and couples acting on each portion of the beam are directed as shown in Fig. 7.9a.

This convention may be more easily remembered if we note that:

1. *The shear at C is positive when the* external *forces (loads and reactions) acting on the beam tend to shear off the beam at C as indicated in Fig. 7.9b.*
2. *The bending moment at C is positive when the* external *forces acting on the beam tend to bend the beam at C as indicated in Fig. 7.9c.*

It may also help to note that the situation described in Fig. 7.9, and corresponding to positive values of the shear and of the bending moment, is precisely the situation which occurs in the left half of a simply supported beam carrying a single concentrated load at its mid-point. This particular example is fully discussed in the following section.

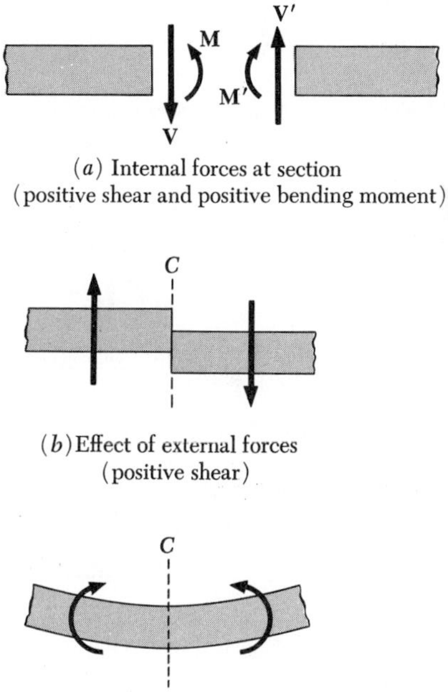

(*a*) Internal forces at section (positive shear and positive bending moment)

(*b*) Effect of external forces (positive shear)

(*c*) Effect of external forces (positive bending moment)

FIG. 7.9

***7.4. Shear and Bending-moment Diagrams.** Now that shear and bending moment have been clearly defined in sense as well as in magnitude, we may easily record their values at any point of a beam by plotting these values against the distance *x* measured from one end of the beam. The graphs obtained in this way are called, respectively, the *shear diagram* and the *bending-moment diagram*. As an example, consider a simply supported beam *AB* of span *L* subjected to a single concentrated load **P** applied at its mid-point *D* (Fig. 7.10*a*).

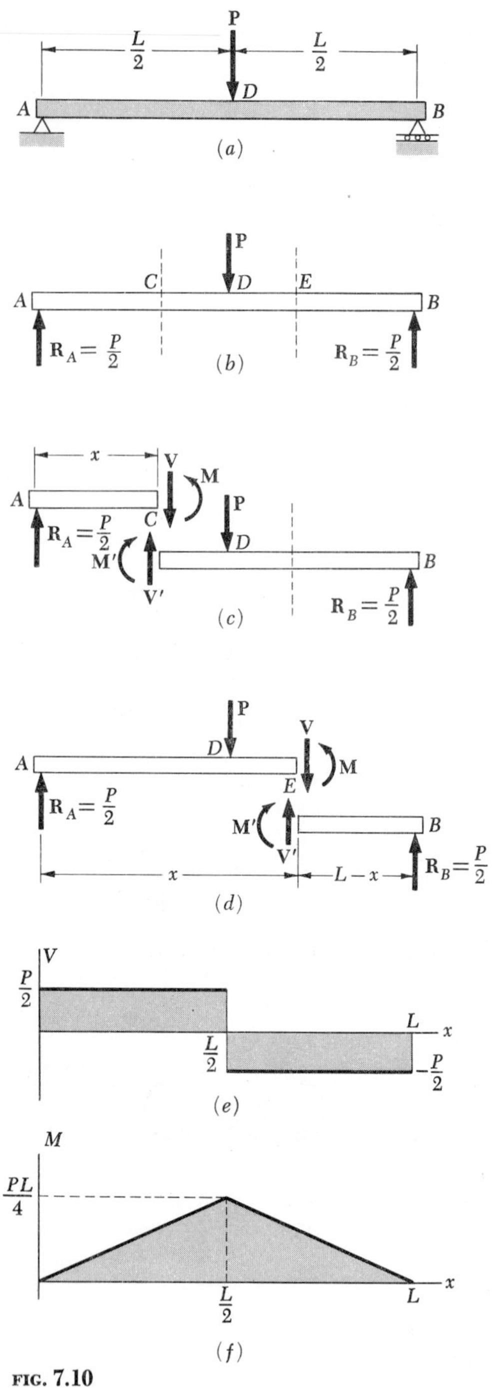

FIG. 7.10

We first determine the reactions at the supports from the free-body diagram of the entire beam (Fig. 7.10*b*); we find that the magnitude of each reaction is equal to $P/2$.

Next we cut the beam at a point C between A and D and draw the free-body diagrams of AC and CB (Fig. 7.10*c*). *Assuming that shear and bending moment are positive,* we direct the internal forces $\mathbf{V}$ and $\mathbf{V}'$ and the internal couples $\mathbf{M}$ and $\mathbf{M}'$ as indicated in Fig. 7.9*a*. Considering the free body AC and writing that the sum of the vertical components and the sum of the moments about C of the forces acting on the free body are zero, we find $V = +P/2$ and $M = +Px/2$. Both the shear and the bending moment are therefore positive; this may be checked by observing that the reaction at A tends to shear off and to bend the beam at C as indicated in Fig. 7.9*b* and *c*. We may plot V and M between A and D (Fig. 7.10*e* and *f*); the shear has a constant value $V = P/2$, while the bending moment increases linearly from $M = 0$ at $x = 0$ to $M = PL/4$ at $x = L/2$.

Cutting, now, the beam at a point E between D and B and considering the free body EB (Fig. 7.10*d*), we write that the sum of the vertical components and the sum of the moments about E of the forces acting on the free body are zero. We obtain $V = -P/2$ and $M = P(L - x)/2$. The shear is therefore negative and the bending moment positive; this may be checked by observing that the reaction at B bends the beam at E as indicated in Fig. 7.9*c* but tends to shear it off in a manner opposite to that shown in Fig. 7.9*b*. We can complete, now, the shear and bending-moment diagrams of Fig. 7.10*e* and *f*; the shear has a constant value $V = -P/2$ between D and B, while the bending moment decreases linearly from $M = PL/4$ at $x = L/2$ to $M = 0$ at $x = L$.

We shall note that, when a beam is subjected only to concentrated loads, the shear is of constant value between loads and the bending moment varies linearly between loads. On the other hand, when a beam is subjected to distributed loads, the shear and bending moment vary quite differently (see Sample Prob. 7.3).

SAMPLE PROBLEM 7.2

Draw the shear and bending-moment diagram for the beam and loading shown.

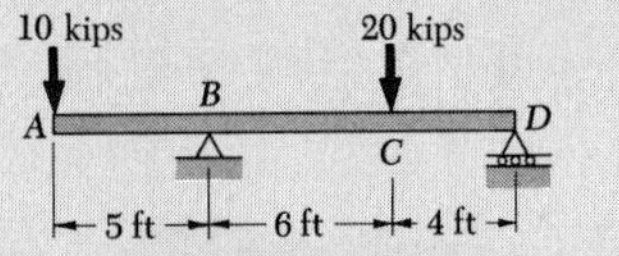

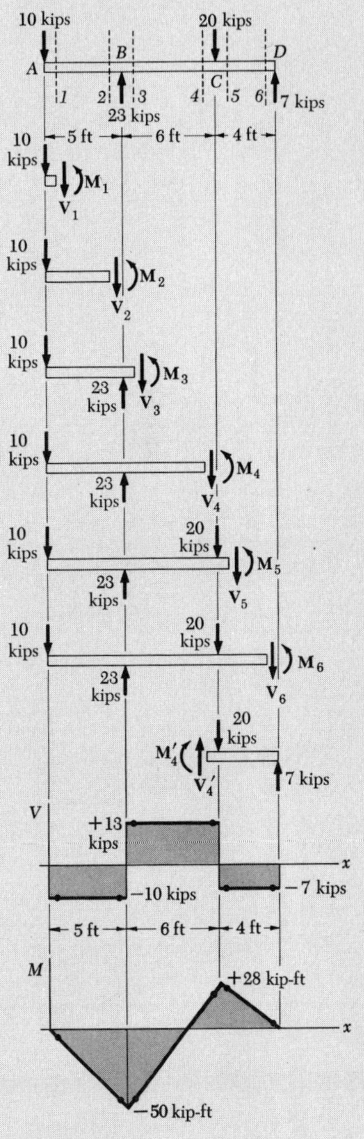

Solution. The reactions are determined by considering the entire beam as a free body; they are

$$\mathbf{R}_B = 23 \text{ kips} \uparrow \qquad \mathbf{R}_D = 7 \text{ kips} \uparrow$$

We first determine the internal forces just to the right of the 10-kip load at A. Considering the stub of beam to the left of section *1* as a free body and assuming V and M to be positive (according to the standard convention), we write

$$+\uparrow \Sigma F_y = 0: \qquad -10 \text{ kips} - V_1 = 0 \qquad V_1 = -10 \text{ kips}$$

$$+\circlearrowleft \Sigma M_1 = 0: \qquad (10 \text{ kips})(0 \text{ ft}) + M_1 = 0 \qquad M_1 = 0$$

We next consider as a free body the portion of beam to the left of section 2 and write

$$+\uparrow \Sigma F_y = 0: \qquad -10 \text{ kips} - V_2 = 0 \qquad V_2 = -10 \text{ kips}$$

$$+\circlearrowleft \Sigma M_2 = 0: \qquad (10 \text{ kips})(5 \text{ ft}) + M_2 = 0 \qquad M_2 = -50 \text{ kip-ft}$$

The shear and bending moment at sections *3*, *4*, *5*, and *6* are determined in a similar way from the free-body diagrams shown. We obtain

$$V_3 = +13 \text{ kips} \qquad M_3 = -50 \text{ kip-ft}$$

$$V_4 = +13 \text{ kips} \qquad M_4 = +28 \text{ kip-ft}$$

$$V_5 = -7 \text{ kips} \qquad M_5 = +28 \text{ kip-ft}$$

$$V_6 = -7 \text{ kips} \qquad M_6 = 0$$

For several of the latter sections, the results may be more easily obtained by considering as a free body the portion of the beam to the right of the section. For example, considering the portion of the beam to the right of section *4*, we write

$$+\uparrow \Sigma F_y = 0: \qquad V_4 - 20 \text{ kips} + 7 \text{ kips} = 0 \qquad V_4 = +13 \text{ kips}$$

$$+\circlearrowleft \Sigma M_4 = 0: \qquad -M_4 + (7 \text{ kips})(4 \text{ ft}) = 0 \qquad M_4 = +28 \text{ kip-ft}$$

We may now plot the six points shown on the shear and bending-moment diagrams. As indicated in Sec. 7.4, the shear is of constant value between concentrated loads, and the bending moment varies linearly; we obtain therefore the shear and bending-moment diagrams shown.

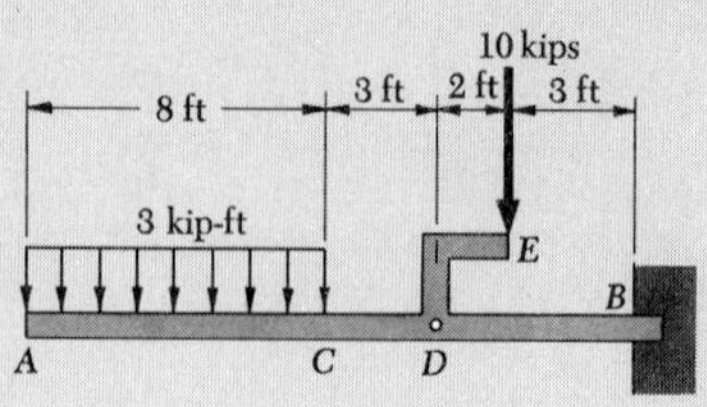

SAMPLE PROBLEM 7.3

Draw the shear and bending-moment diagrams for the cantilever beam *AB*. The distributed load of 3 kips/ft extends over 8 ft of the beam and the 10-kip load is applied at *E*.

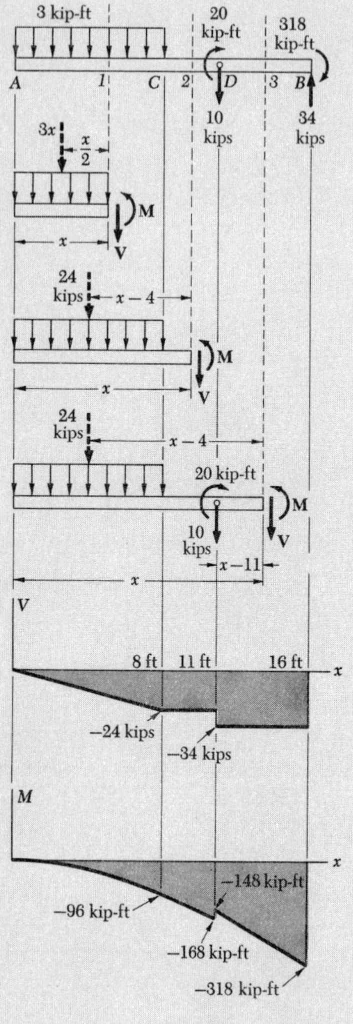

Solution. The 10-kip load is replaced by an equivalent force-couple system acting on the beam at point *D*. The reaction at *B* is determined by considering the entire beam as a free body.

From A to C. We determine the internal forces at a distance x from point *A* by considering the portion of beam to the left of section *1*. That part of the distributed load acting on the free body is replaced by its resultant, and we write

$$+\uparrow \Sigma F_y = 0: \qquad -3x - V = 0 \qquad V = -3x \text{ kips}$$

$$+\circlearrowleft \Sigma M_1 = 0: \qquad 3x(\tfrac{1}{2}x) + M = 0 \qquad M = -1.5x^2 \text{ kip-ft}$$

Since the free-body diagram shown may be used for all values of x smaller than 8 ft, the expressions obtained for V and M are valid in the region $0 < x < 8$ ft.

From C to D. Considering the portion of beam to the left of section 2 and again replacing the distributed load by its resultant, we obtain

$$+\uparrow \Sigma F_y = 0: \qquad -24 - V = 0 \qquad V = -24 \text{ kips}$$

$$+\circlearrowleft \Sigma M_2 = 0: \qquad 24(x - 4) + M = 0 \qquad M = 96 - 24x \quad \text{kip-ft}$$

These expressions are valid in the region 8 ft $< x <$ 11 ft.

From D to B. Using the portion of beam to the left of section 3, we obtain for the region 11 ft $< x <$ 16 ft

$$V = -34 \text{ kips} \qquad M = 226 - 34x \quad \text{kip-ft}$$

The shear and bending-moment diagrams for the entire beam may now be plotted. We note that the couple of moment 20 kip-ft applied at point *D* introduces a discontinuity into the bending-moment diagram.

PROBLEMS

7.16 through 7.21. Draw the shear and bending-moment diagrams for the beam and loading shown.

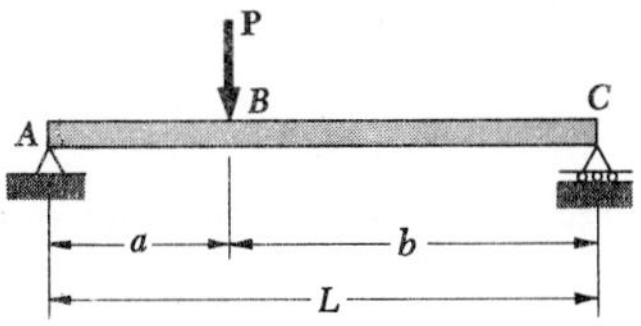

FIG. P 7.16

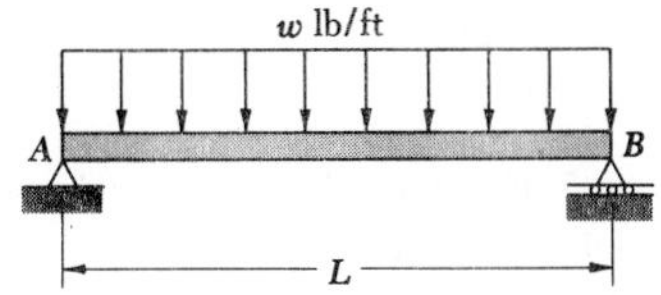

FIG. P 7.17

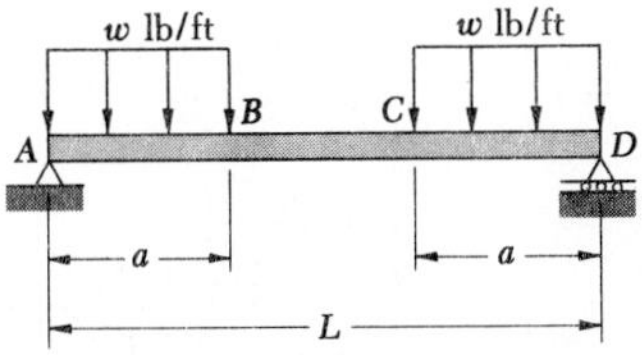

FIG. P 7.18

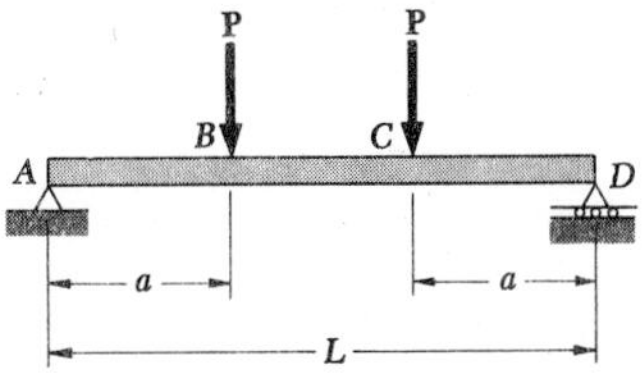

FIG. P 7.19

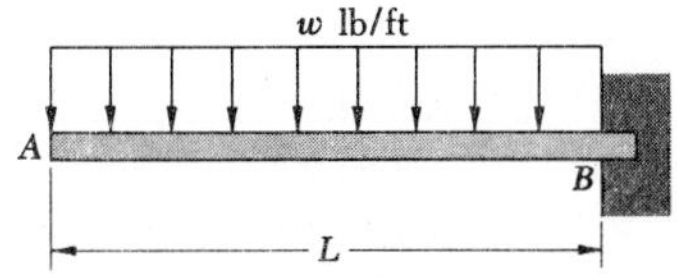

FIG. P 7.20

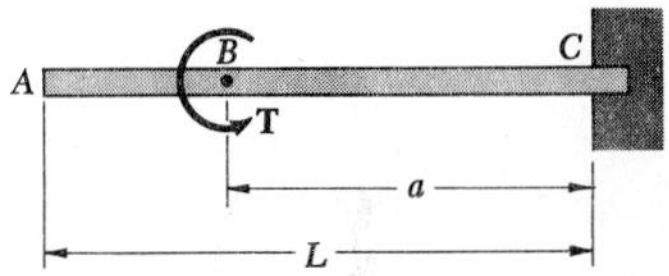

FIG. P 7.21

7.22 and 7.23. Draw the shear and bending-moment diagrams for the beam *AB*.

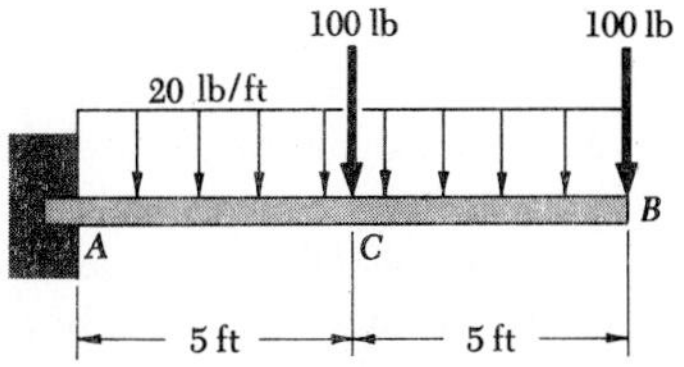

FIG. P 7.22

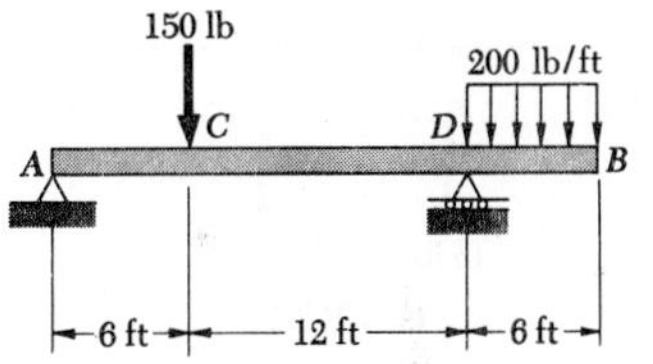

FIG. P 7.23

7.24. Draw the shear and bending-moment diagrams for the beam *AB* if $a = 6$ ft.

7.25. Draw the shear and bending-moment diagrams for the beam *AB* if the magnitude of the upward force **P** is 8 kips.

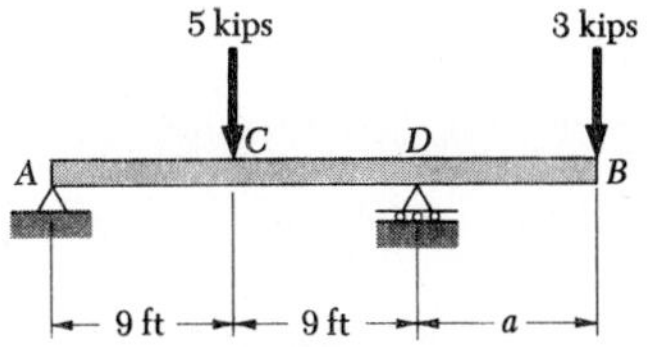

FIG. P 7.24 AND P 7.26

***7.26.** Determine the distance a for which the maximum absolute value of the bending moment in the beam is as small as possible.

***7.27.** Determine the magnitude of the upward force **P** for which the maximum absolute value of the bending moment in the beam is as small as possible.

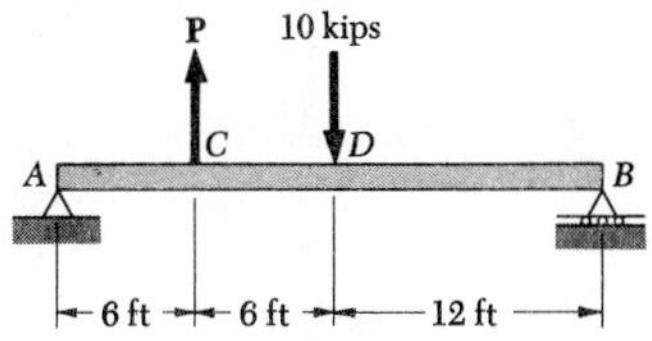

FIG. P 7.25 AND P 7.27

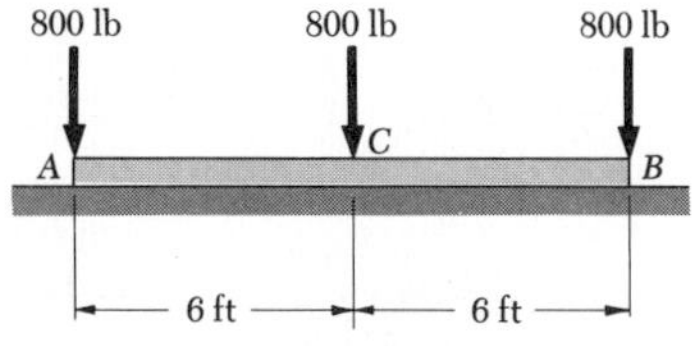

FIG. P 7.28

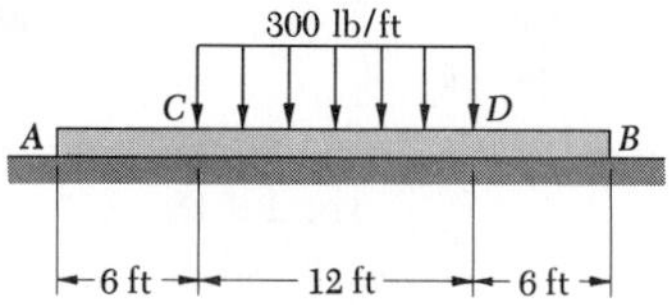

FIG. P 7.29

7.28 and 7.29. Assuming the upward reaction of the ground to be uniformly distributed, draw the shear and bending-moment diagrams for the beam *AB*.

7.30 and 7.31. Draw the shear and bending-moment diagrams for the beam *AB*.

7.32. Draw the shear and bending-moment diagrams for the beam and loading of Prob. 6.77.

7.33. Draw the shear and bending-moment diagrams for the beam and loading of Prob. 6.78.

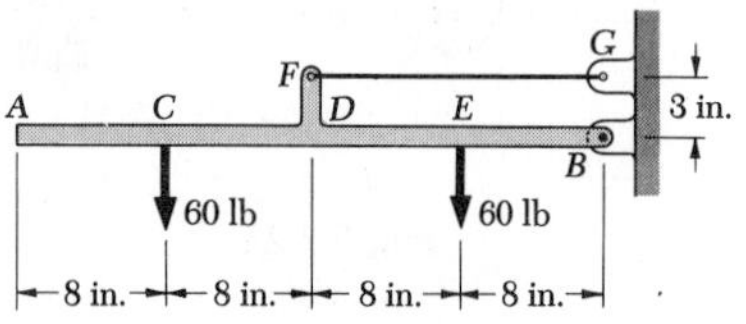

FIG. P 7.30

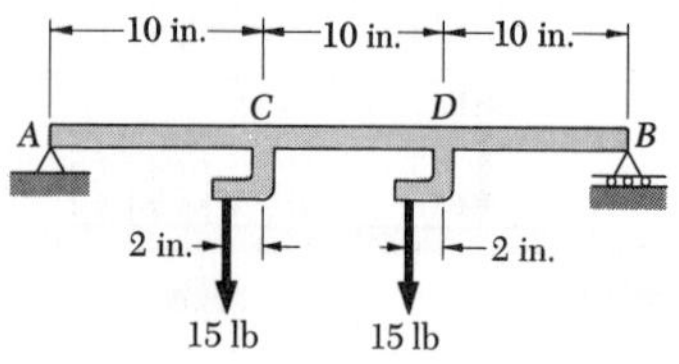

FIG. P 7.31

***7.34.** A uniform beam (w lb/ft) is to be picked up by crane cables attached at *A* and *B*. Determine the distance a from the ends of the beam to the points where the cables should be attached if the maximum absolute value of the bending moment in the beam is to be as small as possible. (*Hint.* Draw the bending-moment diagram in terms of a, L, and w, and then equate the maximum positive and negative bending moments obtained.)

***7.35.** In order to reduce the bending moment in the cantilever beam *AB*, a cable and counterweight are permanently attached at end *B*. Determine the magnitude of the counterweight for which the maximum absolute value of the bending moment in the beam is as small as possible. (*a*) Consider only the case when the force **P** is actually applied at *C*. (*b*) Consider the more general case when the force **P** may either be applied at *C* or removed.

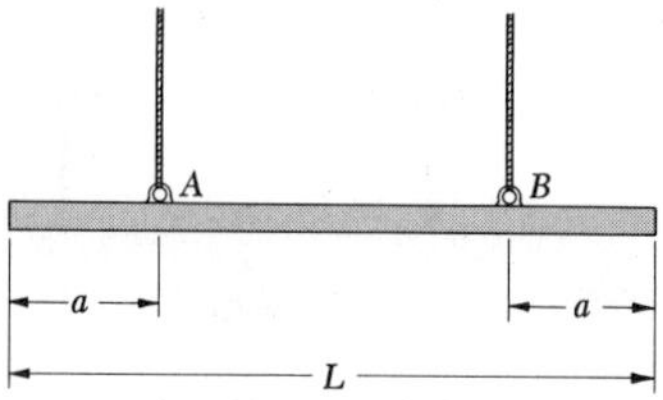

FIG. P 7.34

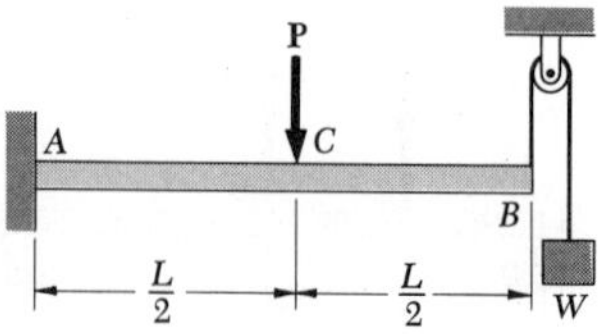

FIG. P 7.35

***7.5. Relations between Load, Shear, and Bending Moment.** When a beam carries more than two or three concentrated loads, or when it carries distributed loads, the method outlined in Sec. 7.4 for plotting shear and bending moment may prove quite cumbersome. The construction of the shear diagram and, especially, of the bending-moment diagram will be greatly facilitated if certain relations existing between load, shear, and bending moment are taken into consideration.

Let us consider a simply supported beam *AB* carrying a distributed load w per unit length (Fig. 7.11a), and let *C* and *C′* be two points of the beam at a distance Δx from each other. The shear and bending moment at *C* will be denoted by *V* and *M*, respectively, and will be assumed positive; the shear and bending moment at C' will be denoted by $V + \Delta V$ and $M + \Delta M$.

We now shall detach the portion of beam CC' and draw its free-body diagram (Fig. 7.11*b*). The forces exerted on the free body include a load of magnitude $w\,\Delta x$ and internal forces and couples at C and C'. Since shear and bending moment have been assumed positive, the forces and couples will be directed as shown in the figure.

Relations between Load and Shear. Writing that the sum of the vertical components of the forces acting on the free body CC' is zero, we obtain

$$V - (V + \Delta V) - w\,\Delta x = 0$$
$$\Delta V = -w\,\Delta x$$

Dividing both members of the equation by Δx and then letting Δx approach zero, we obtain

$$\frac{dV}{dx} = -w \qquad (7.1)$$

Formula (7.1) indicates that, for a beam loaded as shown in Fig. 7.11*a*, the slope dV/dx of the shear curve is negative; the numerical value of the slope at any point is equal to the load per unit length at that point.

Integrating (7.1) between points C and D, we obtain

$$V_D - V_C = -\int_{x_C}^{x_D} w\,dx \qquad (7.2)$$

$$V_D - V_C = -(\text{area under load curve between } C \text{ and } D) \qquad (7.2')$$

Note that this result could also have been obtained by considering the equilibrium of the portion of beam CD, since the area under the load curve represents the total load applied between C and D.

It should be observed that formula (7.1) *is not valid* at a point where a concentrated load is applied; the shear curve is discontinuous at such a point, as seen in Sec. 7.4. Similarly, formulas (7.2) and (7.2′) cease to be valid when concentrated loads are applied between C and D, since they do not take into account the sudden change in shear caused by a concentrated load. Formulas (7.2) and (7.2′), therefore, should be applied only between successive concentrated loads.

Relations between Shear and Bending Moment. Returning to the free-body diagram of Fig. 7.11*b*, and writing now that

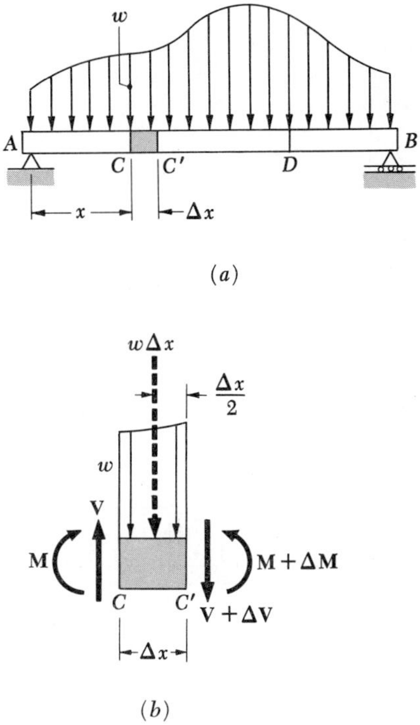

FIG. 7.11

the sum of the moments about C' is zero, we obtain

$$(M + \Delta M) - M - V\,\Delta x + w\,\Delta x\,\frac{\Delta x}{2} = 0$$

$$\Delta M = V\,\Delta x - \tfrac{1}{2}w(\Delta x)^2$$

Dividing both members of the equation by Δx and then letting Δx approach zero, we obtain

$$\frac{dM}{dx} = V \tag{7.3}$$

Formula (7.3) indicates that the slope dM/dx of the bending-moment curve is equal to the value of the shear. This is true at any point where the shear has a well-defined value, i.e., at any point where no concentrated load is applied. Formula (7.3) also shows that the shear is zero at points where the bending moment is maximum. This property facilitates the determination of the points where the beam is likely to fail under bending.

Integrating (7.3) between points C and D, we obtain

$$M_D - M_C = \int_{x_C}^{x_D} V\,dx \tag{7.4}$$

$$M_D - M_C = \text{area under shear curve between } C \text{ and } D \tag{7.4'}$$

Note that the area under the shear curve should be considered positive where the shear is positive and negative where the shear is negative. Formulas (7.4) and (7.4′) are valid even when concentrated loads are applied between C and D, as long as the shear curve has been correctly drawn. The formulas cease to be valid, however, if a *couple* is applied at a point between C and D, since they do not take into account the sudden change in bending moment caused by a couple (see Sample Prob. 7.7).

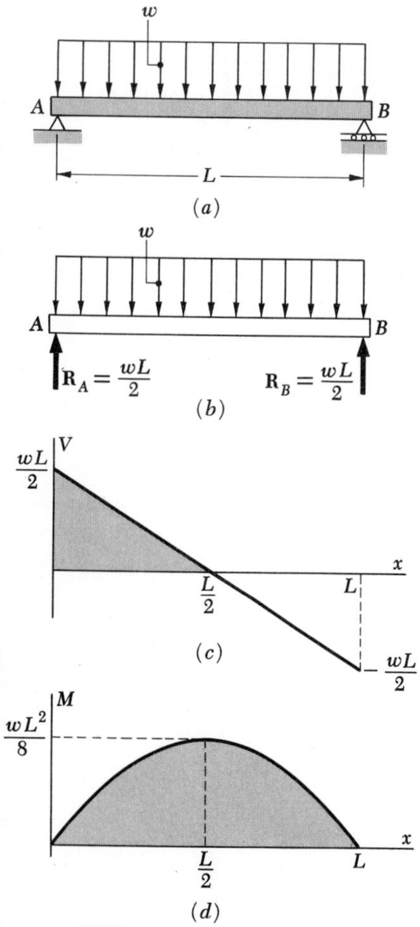

FIG. 7.12

Example. Let us consider a simply supported beam AB of span L carrying a uniformly distributed load w (Fig. 7.12*a*). From the free-body diagram of the entire beam we determine the magnitude of the reactions at the supports: $R_A = R_B = wL/2$ (Fig. 7.12*b*). Next, we draw the shear diagram. Close to the end A of the beam, the shear is equal to R_A, that is, to $wL/2$, as we may check by considering as a free body a very small portion of the beam. Using formula (7.2), we may then determine the shear V at any distance x from A; we write

$$V - V_A = -\int_0^x w\,dx = -wx$$

$$V = V_A - wx = \frac{wL}{2} - wx = w\left(\frac{L}{2} - x\right)$$

The shear curve is thus an oblique straight line which crosses the x axis at $x = L/2$ (Fig. 7.12c). Considering, now, the bending moment, we first observe that $M_A = 0$. The value M of the bending moment at any distance x from A may then be obtained from formula (7.4); we have

$$M - M_A = \int_0^x V\,dx$$

$$M = \int_0^x w\left(\frac{L}{2} - x\right)dx = \frac{w}{2}(Lx - x^2)$$

The bending-moment curve is a parabola. The maximum value of the bending moment occurs when $x = L/2$, since V (and thus dM/dx) is zero for that value of x. Substituting $x = L/2$ in the last equation, we obtain $M_{\max} = wL^2/8$.

In most engineering applications, the value of the bending moment needs to be known only at a few specific points. Once the shear diagram has been drawn, and after M has been determined at one of the ends of the beam, the value of the bending moment may then be obtained at any given point by computing the area under the shear curve and using formula (7.4′). For instance, since $M_A = 0$ for the beam of Fig. 7.12a, the maximum value of the bending moment for that beam may be obtained simply by measuring the area of the shaded triangle in the shear diagram of Fig. 7.12c. We have

$$M_{\max} = \frac{1}{2}\frac{L}{2}\frac{wL}{2} = \frac{wL^2}{8}$$

We note that, in this example, the load curve is a horizontal straight line, the shear curve an oblique straight line, and the bending-moment curve a parabola. If the load curve had been an oblique straight line (first degree), the shear curve would have been a parabola (second degree) and the bending-moment curve a cubic (third degree). The shear and bending-moment curves will always be, respectively, one and two degrees higher than the load curve. With this in mind, we should be able to sketch the shear and bending-moment diagrams without actually determining the functions $V(x)$ and $M(x)$, once a few values of the shear and bending moment have been computed. The sketches obtained will be more accurate if we make use of the fact that, at any point where the curves are continuous, the slope of the shear curve is equal to $-w$ and the slope of the bending-moment curve is equal to V.

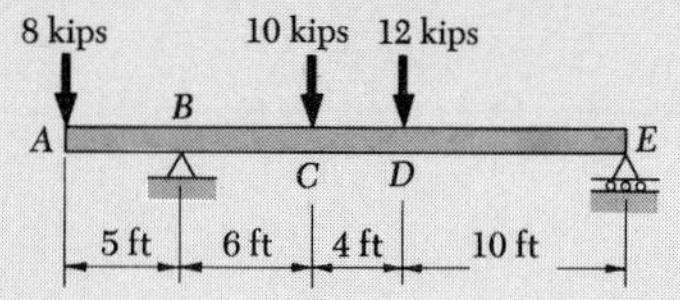

SAMPLE PROBLEM 7.4

Draw the shear and bending-moment diagrams for the beam and loading shown.

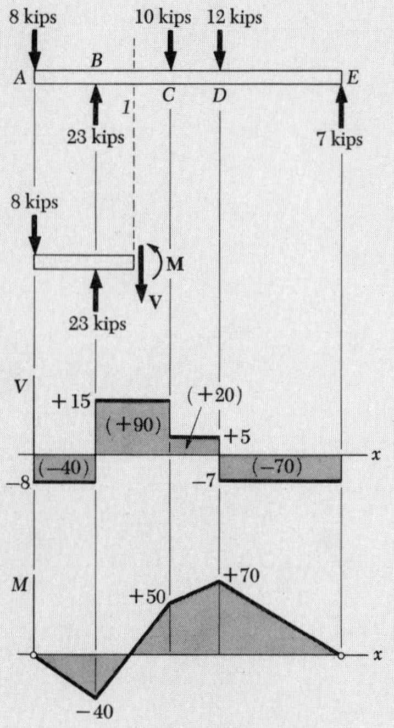

Solution. Considering the entire beam as a free body, we obtain the reactions

$$\mathbf{R}_B = 23 \text{ kips}\uparrow \qquad \mathbf{R}_E = 7 \text{ kips}\uparrow$$

We also note that at both A and E the bending moment is zero; thus two points (indicated by dots) are obtained on the bending-moment diagram.

Shear Diagram. Since $dV/dx = -w$, we find that between loads the slope of the shear diagram is zero (i.e., the shear is constant). The shear at any point is determined by dividing the beam into two parts and considering either part as a free body. For example, using the portion of beam to the left of section *1*, we obtain

$$+\uparrow\Sigma F_y = 0: \qquad -8 + 23 - V = 0 \qquad V = +15 \text{ kips}$$

Bending-moment Diagram. We recall that the area under the shear curve between two points is equal to the change in bending moment between the same two points. For convenience, the area of each portion of the shear diagram is computed and is indicated on the diagram. Since the bending moment at the free end M_A is known to be zero, we write

$$M_B - M_A = -40 \qquad M_B = -40 \text{ kip-ft}$$

$$M_C - M_B = +90 \qquad M_C = +50 \text{ kip-ft}$$

$$M_D - M_C = +20 \qquad M_D = +70 \text{ kip-ft}$$

$$M_E - M_D = -70 \qquad M_E = 0$$

Since M_E is known to be zero, a check of the computations is obtained.

The shear being constant between successive loads, the slope dM/dx is constant and the bending-moment diagram is obtained by connecting the known points with straight lines. From the V and M diagrams we note that $V_{max} = 15$ kips, and $M_{max} = 70$ kip-ft.

SAMPLE PROBLEM 7.5

Draw the shear and bending-moment diagrams for the beam and loading shown.

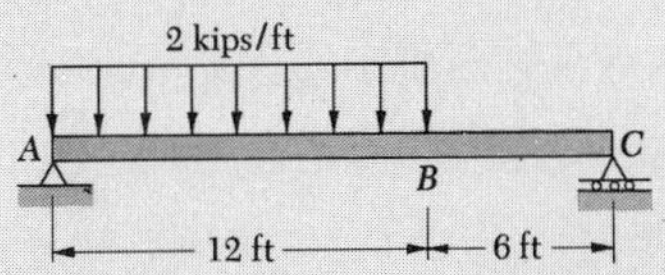

Solution. Considering the entire beam as a free body, we obtain the reactions

$$\mathbf{R}_A = 16 \text{ kips} \uparrow \qquad \mathbf{R}_C = 8 \text{ kips} \uparrow$$

Shear Diagram. The shear just to the right of A is $V_A = +16$ kips. Since the change in shear between two points is equal to *minus* the area under the load curve between the same two points, we obtain V_B by writing

$$V_B - V_A = -(2)(12) = -24$$

$$V_B = -24 + V_A = -24 + 16 = -8 \text{ kips}$$

The slope $dV/dx = -w$ being constant between A and B, the shear diagram between these two points is represented by a straight line. Between B and C, the area under the load curve is zero; therefore,

$$V_C - V_B = 0 \qquad V_C = V_B = -8 \text{ kips}$$

and the shear is constant between B and C.

Bending-moment Diagram. We note that the bending moment at each end of the beam is zero. In order to determine the maximum bending moment, we locate the section D of the beam where $V = 0$. Considering the portion of the shear diagram between A and B, we note that the triangles DAa and DBb are similar; thus,

$$\frac{x}{16 \text{ kips}} = \frac{12 - x}{8 \text{ kips}} \qquad x = 8 \text{ ft}$$

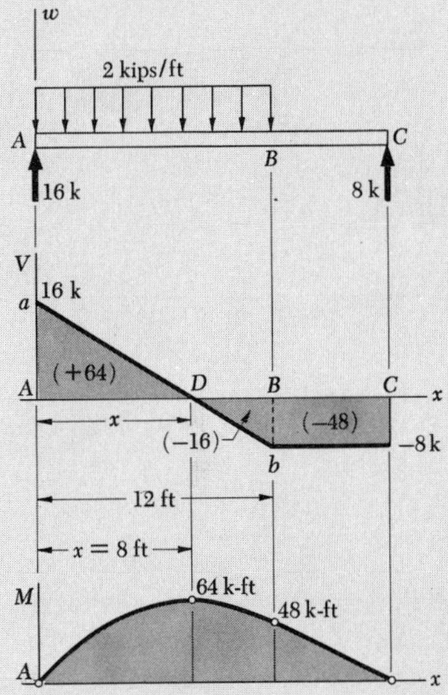

The maximum bending moment occurs at point D, where we have $dM/dx = V = 0$. The areas of the various portions of the shear diagram are computed and are given (in parentheses) on the diagram. Since the area of the shear diagram between two points is equal to the change in bending moment between the same two points, we write

$$M_D - M_A = +64 \text{ kip-ft} \qquad M_D = +64 \text{ kip-ft}$$

$$M_B - M_D = -16 \text{ kip-ft} \qquad M_B = +48 \text{ kip-ft}$$

$$M_C - M_B = -48 \text{ kip-ft} \qquad M_C = 0$$

The bending-moment diagram consists of an arc of parabola followed by a segment of straight line; the slope of the parabola at A is equal to the value of V at that point.

SAMPLE PROBLEM 7.6

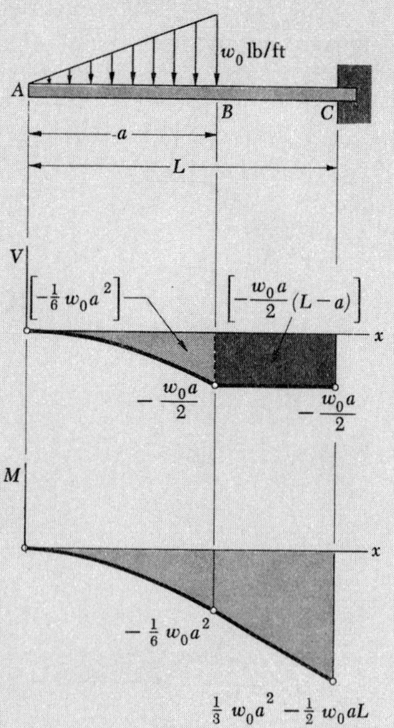

Sketch the shear and bending-moment diagrams for the cantilever beam shown.

Solution. *Shear Diagram.* At the free end of the beam, we find $V_A = 0$. Between A and B, the area under the load curve is $\frac{1}{2}w_0a$; we find V_B by writing

$$V_B - V_A = -\tfrac{1}{2}w_0a \qquad V_B = -\tfrac{1}{2}w_0a$$

Between B and C, the beam is not loaded; thus $V_C = V_B$. At A, we have $w = 0$, and therefore $dV/dx = 0$; between A and B, the loading increases linearly, and the shear diagram is parabolic. Between B and C, $w = 0$, and the shear diagram is a horizontal line.

Bending-moment Diagram. The bending moment at the free end of the beam is zero. We compute the area under the shear curve and write

$$M_B - M_A = -\tfrac{1}{6}w_0a^2 \qquad M_B = -\tfrac{1}{6}w_0a^2$$

$$M_C - M_B = -\tfrac{1}{2}w_0a(L-a)$$

$$M_C = \tfrac{1}{3}w_0a^2 - \tfrac{1}{2}w_0aL$$

The sketch of the bending-moment diagram is completed by recalling that $dM/dx = V$. We find that between A and B the diagram is represented by a cubic curve and between B and C by a straight line.

SAMPLE PROBLEM 7.7

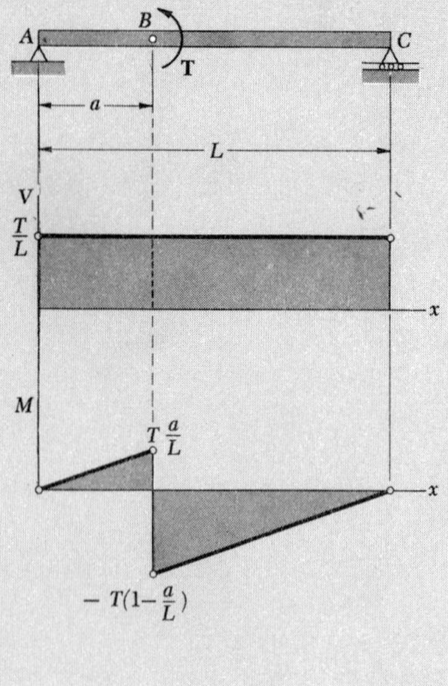

The simple beam AC is loaded by a couple of moment T applied at point B. Draw the shear and bending-moment diagrams of the beam.

Solution. The entire beam is taken as a free body, and we obtain

$$\mathbf{R}_A = \frac{T}{L}\uparrow \qquad \mathbf{R}_C = \frac{T}{L}\downarrow$$

The shear at any section is constant and equal to T/L. Since a couple is applied at B, the bending-moment diagram is discontinuous at B; the bending moment decreases suddenly by an amount equal to T.

PROBLEMS

7.36. Using the methods of Sec. 7.5, solve Prob. 7.16.
7.37. Using the methods of Sec. 7.5, solve Prob. 7.17.
7.38. Using the methods of Sec. 7.5, solve Prob. 7.18.
7.39. Using the methods of Sec. 7.5, solve Prob. 7.19.
7.40. Using the methods of Sec. 7.5, solve Prob. 7.20.
7.41. Using the methods of Sec. 7.5, solve Prob. 7.25.
7.42. Using the methods of Sec. 7.5, solve Prob. 7.22.
7.43. Using the methods of Sec. 7.5, solve Prob. 7.23.
7.44. Using the methods of Sec. 7.5, solve Prob. 7.28.
7.45. Using the methods of Sec. 7.5, solve Prob. 7.29.

7.46 through 7.49. Draw the shear and bending-moment diagrams for the beam and loading shown.

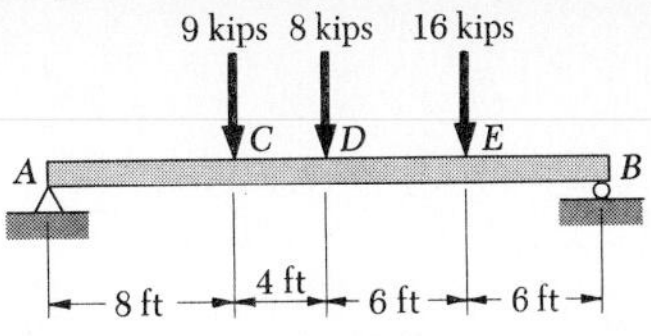

FIG. P 7.46

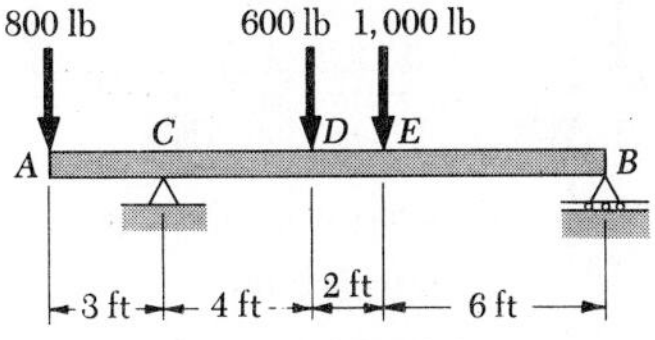

FIG. P 7.47

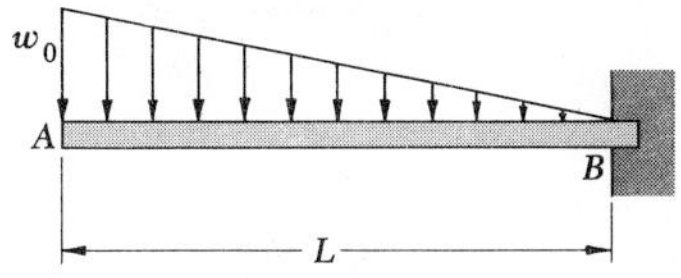

FIG. P 7.48

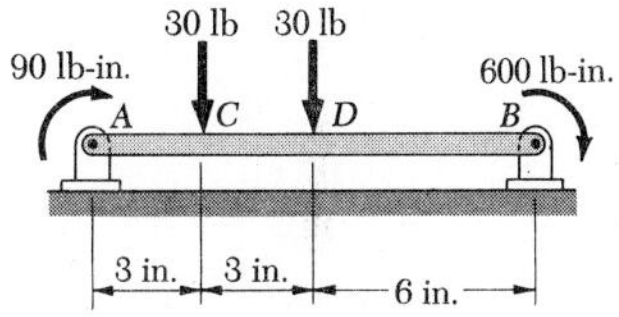

FIG. P 7.49

7.50 through 7.53. Draw the shear and bending-moment diagrams for the beam and loading shown and determine the location and magnitude of the maximum bending moment.

7.54. Determine the equations of the shear and bending-moment curves for the beam and loading of Prob. 7.20. (Place the origin at point *A*.)

7.55. Determine the equations of the shear and bending-moment curves for the beam and loading of Prob. 7.17. (Place the origin at point *A*.)

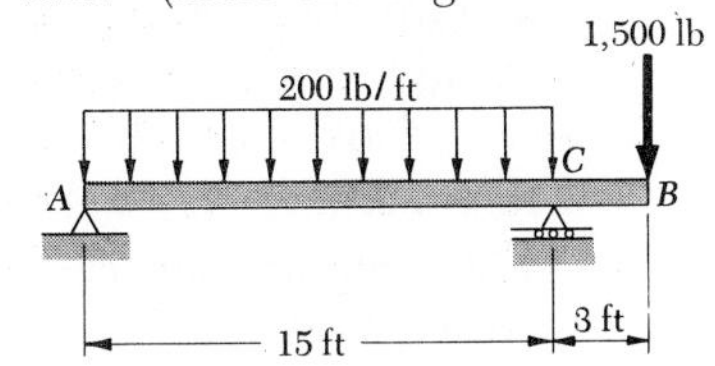

FIG. P 7.50

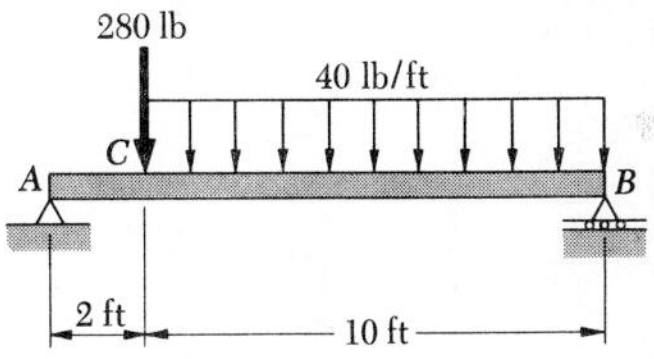

FIG. P 7.51

7.56 and 7.57. Determine the equations of the shear and bending-moment curves for the given beam and loading. Also determine the magnitude and location of the maximum bending moment in the beam.

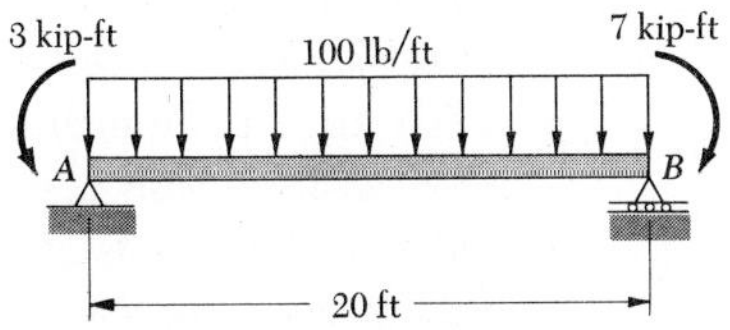

FIG. P 7.52

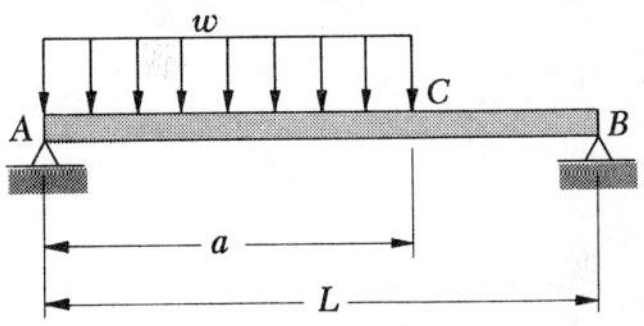

FIG. P 7.53

7.58. The rod *AB* is acted upon by a uniform downward load and by a uniformly varying upward load. Determine (*a*) the ratio w_1/w_0 required for equilibrium, (*b*) the equations of the shear and bending-moment curves, (*c*) the magnitude and location of the maximum bending moment in the rod.

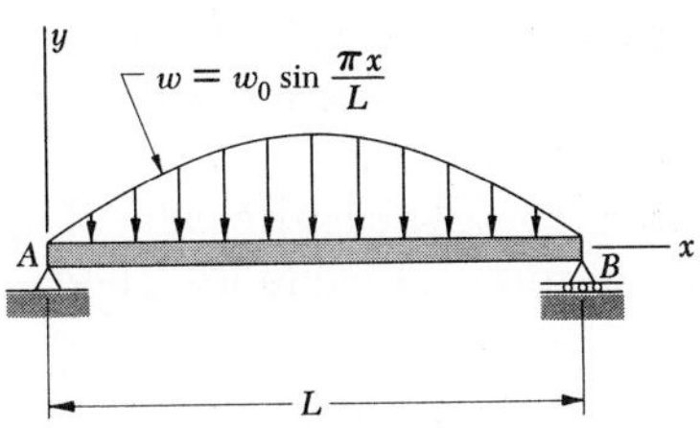

FIG. P 7.56

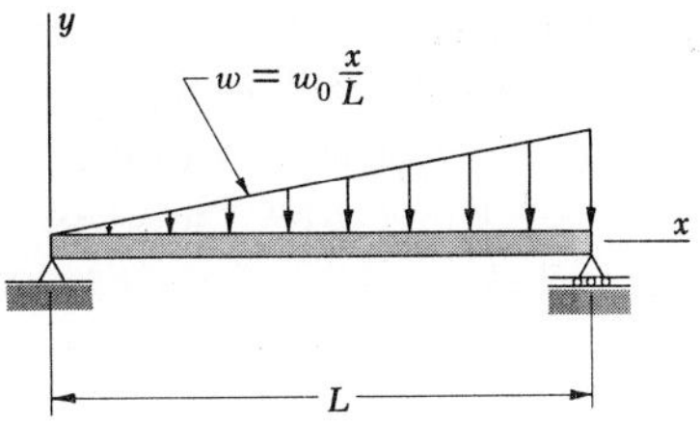

FIG. P 7.57

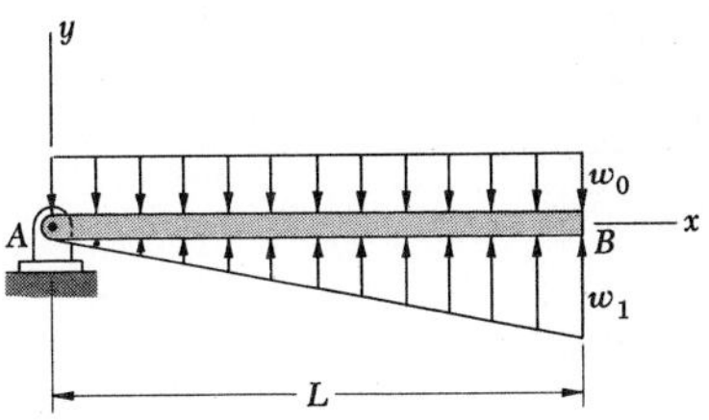

FIG. P 7.58

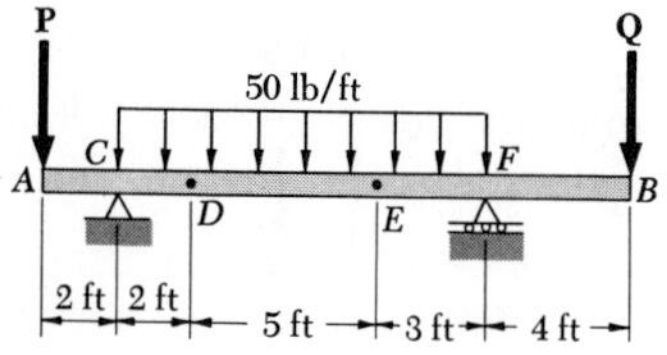

FIG. P 7.60

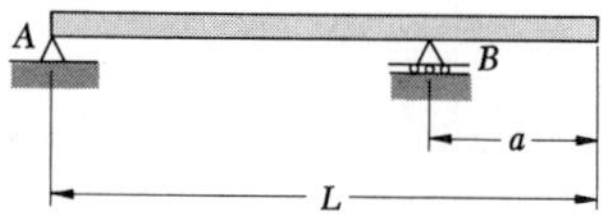

FIG. P 7.61

7.59. Solve Prob. 7.56 if the given loading is replaced by (*a*) the loading $w = w_0 \sin \dfrac{2\pi x}{L}$, (*b*) the loading $w = w_0 \sin \dfrac{n\pi x}{L}$.

***7.60.** The beam *AB* is acted upon by the uniformly distributed load of 50 lb/ft and by two forces **P** and **Q**. It has been experimentally determined that the bending moment is +200 lb-ft at point *D* and +75 lb-ft at point *E*. Draw the shear and bending-moment diagrams for the beam.

***7.61.** A uniform beam (w lb/ft) is supported as shown. Determine the distance a if the maximum absolute value of the bending moment is to be as small as possible. (See hint of Prob. 7.34.)

CABLES

***7.6. Cables with Concentrated Loads.** Cables are used in many engineering applications, such as suspension bridges, transmission lines, aerial tramways, guy wires for high towers, etc. Cables may be divided into two categories, according to their loading: (1) cables supporting concentrated loads; (2) cables supporting distributed loads. In this section, we shall examine cables of the first category.

Consider a cable attached to two fixed points *A* and *B* and supporting n given vertical concentrated loads $\mathbf{P}_1$, $\mathbf{P}_2$, . . . , $\mathbf{P}_n$ (Fig. 7.13*a*). We assume that the cable is *flexible*, i.e., that its resistance to bending is small and may be neglected. We further assume that the *weight of the cable is negligible* compared with the loads supported by the cable. Any portion of cable between successive loads may therefore be considered as a two-force member, and the internal forces at any point in the cable reduce to a *force of tension directed along the cable*.

We assume that each of the loads lies in a given vertical line, i.e., that the horizontal distance from support *A* to each of the loads is known; we also assume that the horizontal and vertical distances between the supports are known. We propose to determine the shape of the cable, i.e., the vertical distance from *A* to each of the points C_1, C_2, . . . , C_n, and also the tension T in each portion of the cable.

We first draw the free-body diagram of the entire cable (Fig. 7.13*b*). Since the slope of the portions of cable attached at

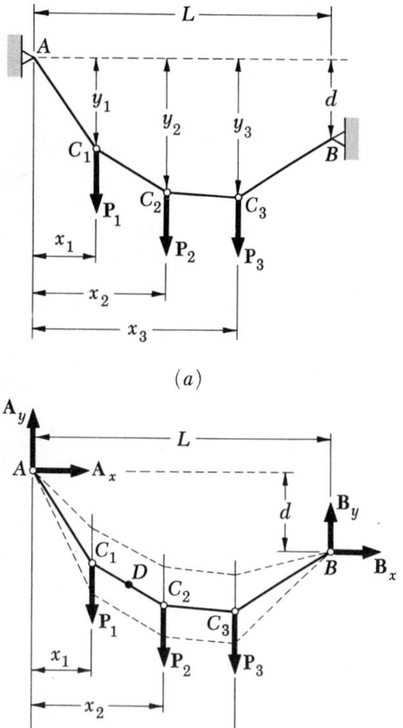

FIG. 7.13

A and B is not known, the reactions at A and B must be represented by two components each. Thus, four unknowns are involved, and the three equations of equilibrium are not sufficient to determine the reactions at A and B.† We must therefore obtain an additional equation by considering the equilibrium of a portion of the cable. This is possible if we know the coordinates x and y of a point D of the cable. Drawing the free-body diagram of the portion of cable AD (Fig. 7.14*a*) and writing $\Sigma M_D = 0$, we obtain an additional relation between the scalar components A_x and A_y and may determine the reactions at A and B. The problem would remain indeterminate, however, if we did not know the coordinates of D, unless some other relation between A_x and A_y (or between B_x and B_y) were given. The cable might hang in any of various possible ways, as indicated by the dashed lines in Fig. 7.13*b*.

Once A_x and A_y have been determined, the vertical distance from A to any point of the cable may be easily found. Considering point C_2, for example, we draw the free-body diagram of the portion of cable AC_2 (Fig. 7.14*b*). Writing $\Sigma M_{C_2} = 0$, we obtain an equation which may be solved for y_2. Writing $\Sigma F_x = 0$ and $\Sigma F_y = 0$, we obtain the components of the force $\mathbf{T}$ representing the tension in the portion of cable to the right of C_2. We observe that $T \cos \theta = A_x$; *the horizontal component of the tension force is the same at any point of the cable.* It follows that the tension T is maximum when $\cos \theta$ is minimum, i.e., in the portion of cable which has the largest angle of inclination θ. Clearly, this portion of cable must be adjacent to one of the two supports of the cable.

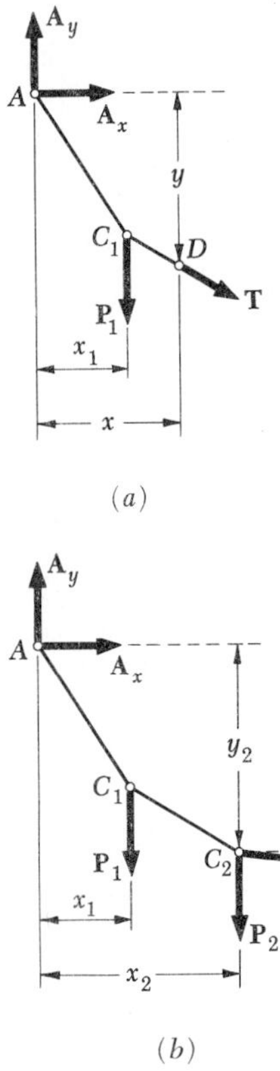

FIG. 7.14

***7.7. Cables with Distributed Loads.** Consider a cable attached to two fixed points A and B and carrying a *distributed load* (Fig. 7.15*a*). We saw in the preceding section that, for a cable supporting concentrated loads, the internal force at any point is a force of tension directed along the cable. In the case of a cable carrying a distributed load, the cable hangs in the shape of a curve, and the internal force at a point D is a force of tension $\mathbf{T}$ *directed along the tangent to the curve.* Given a certain distributed load, we propose in this section to determine the tension at any point of the cable. We shall also see in the following sections how the shape of the cable may be determined for two particular types of distributed loads.

† Clearly, the cable is not a rigid body; the equilibrium equations represent therefore *necessary but not sufficient conditions* (see Sec. 6.12).

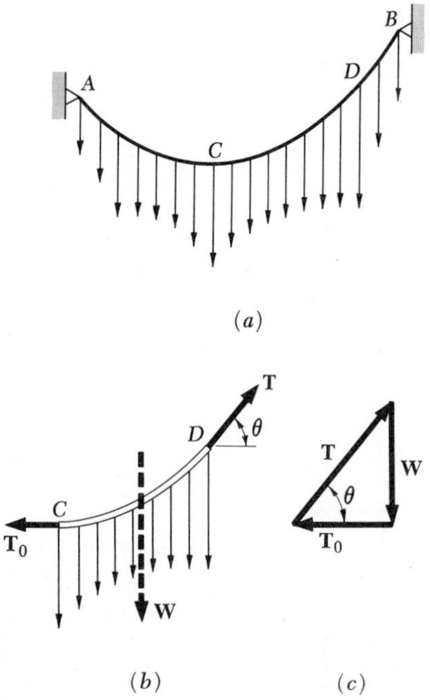

FIG. 7.15

Considering the most general case of distributed load, we draw the free-body diagram of the portion of cable extending from the lowest point C to a given point D of the cable (Fig. 7.15*b*). The forces acting on the free body are the tension force $\mathbf{T}_0$ at C, which is horizontal, the tension force $\mathbf{T}$ at D, directed along the tangent to the cable at D, and the resultant $\mathbf{W}$ of the distributed load supported by the portion of cable CD. Drawing the corresponding force triangle (Fig. 7.15*c*), we obtain the following relations:

$$T \cos \theta = T_0 \qquad T \sin \theta = W \tag{7.5}$$

$$T = \sqrt{T_0^2 + W^2} \qquad \tan \theta = \frac{W}{T_0} \tag{7.6}$$

From the relations (7.5), it appears that the horizontal component of the tension force $\mathbf{T}$ is the same at any point and that the vertical component of $\mathbf{T}$ is equal to the magnitude W of the load measured from the lowest point. Relations (7.6) show that the tension T is minimum at the lowest point and maximum at one of the two points of support.

***7.8. Parabolic Cable.** Let us assume, now, that the cable AB carries a load *uniformly distributed along the horizontal* (Fig. 7.16*a*). Cables of suspension bridges may be assumed loaded in this way, since the weight of the cables is small compared with the weight of the roadway. Denoting by w the load per unit length (*measured horizontally*) and choosing coordinate axes with origin at the lowest point C of the cable, we find that the magnitude W of the total load carried by the portion of cable extending from C to the point D of coordinates x and y is $W = wx$. The relations (7.6) defining the magnitude and direction of the tension force at D become

$$T = \sqrt{T_0^2 + w^2x^2} \qquad \tan \theta = \frac{wx}{T_0} \tag{7.7}$$

Moreover, the distance from D to the line of action of the resultant $\mathbf{W}$ is equal to half the horizontal distance from C to D (Fig. 7.16*b*). Summing moments about D, we write

$$+\circlearrowleft \Sigma M_D = 0: \qquad wx\frac{x}{2} - T_0 y = 0$$

$$y = \frac{wx^2}{2T_0} \tag{7.8}$$

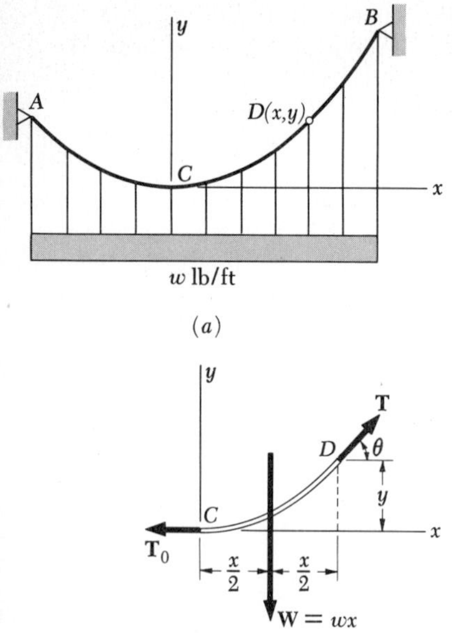

FIG. 7.16 (*b*)

This is the equation of a *parabola* with a vertical axis and its vertex at the origin of coordinates. The curve formed by cables loaded uniformly along the horizontal is thus a parabola.†

When the supports A and B of the cable have the same elevation, the distance L between the supports is called the *span* of the cable and the vertical distance h from the supports to the lowest point is called the *sag* of the cable (Fig. 7.17*a*). If the span and sag of a cable are known, and if the load w per unit horizontal length is given, the minimum tension T_0 may be found by substituting $x = L/2$ and $y = h$ in formula (7.8). Formulas (7.7) and (7.8) will then define the tension at any point and the shape of the cable.

When the supports have different elevations, the position of the lowest point of the cable is not known and the coordinates x_A, y_A and x_B, y_B of the supports must be determined. To this effect, we express that the coordinates of A and B satisfy Eq. (7.8) and that $x_B - x_A = L$, $y_B - y_A = d$, where L and d denote, respectively, the horizontal and vertical distances between the two supports (Fig. 7.17*b* and *c*).

The length of the cable from its lowest point C to its support B may be obtained from the formula

$$s_B = \int_0^{x_B} \sqrt{1 + \left(\frac{dy}{dx}\right)^2}\, dx \tag{7.9}$$

Differentiating (7.8), we obtain the derivative $dy/dx = wx/T_0$; substituting into (7.9) and using the binomial theorem to expand the radical in an infinite series, we have

$$s_B = \int_0^{x_B} \sqrt{1 + \frac{w^2x^2}{T_0^2}}\, dx$$

$$= \int_0^{x_B} \left(1 + \frac{w^2x^2}{2T_0^2} - \frac{w^4x^4}{8T_0^4} + \cdots\right) dx$$

$$= x_B \left(1 + \frac{w^2x_B^2}{6T_0^2} - \frac{w^4x_B^4}{40T_0^4} + \cdots\right)$$

and, since $wx_B^2/2T_0 = y_B$,

$$s_B = x_B \left[1 + \frac{2}{3}\left(\frac{y_B}{x_B}\right)^2 - \frac{2}{5}\left(\frac{y_B}{x_B}\right)^4 + \cdots\right] \tag{7.10}$$

The series converges for values of the ratio y_B/x_B less than 0.5; in most cases, this ratio is much smaller, and only the first two terms of the series need be computed.

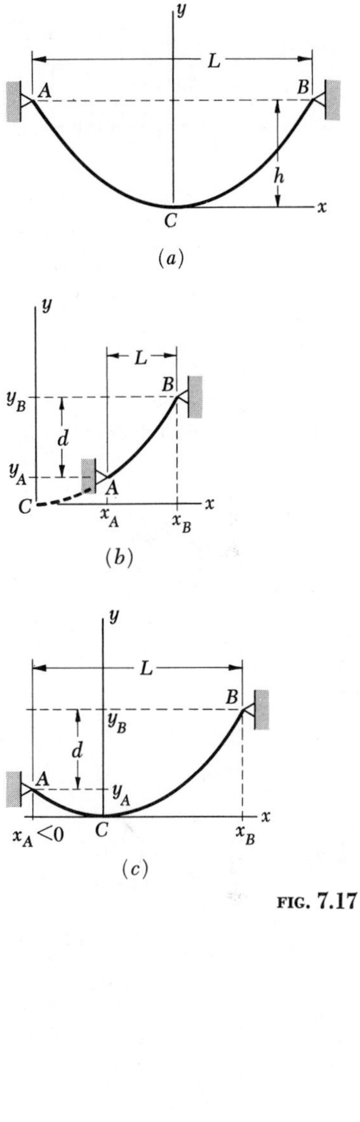

FIG. 7.17

† Cables hanging under their own weight are not loaded uniformly along the horizontal, and they do not form a parabola. The error introduced by assuming a parabolic shape for cables hanging under their own weight, however, is small when the cable is sufficiently taut. A complete discussion of cables hanging under their own weight is given in the next section.

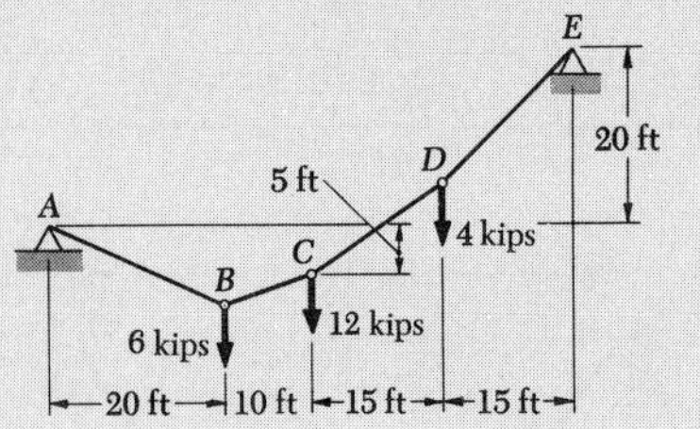

SAMPLE PROBLEM 7.8

The cable AE supports three vertical loads from the points indicated. If point C is 5 ft below the left support, determine (*a*) the elevations of points B and D, (*b*) the maximum slope and the maximum tension in the cable.

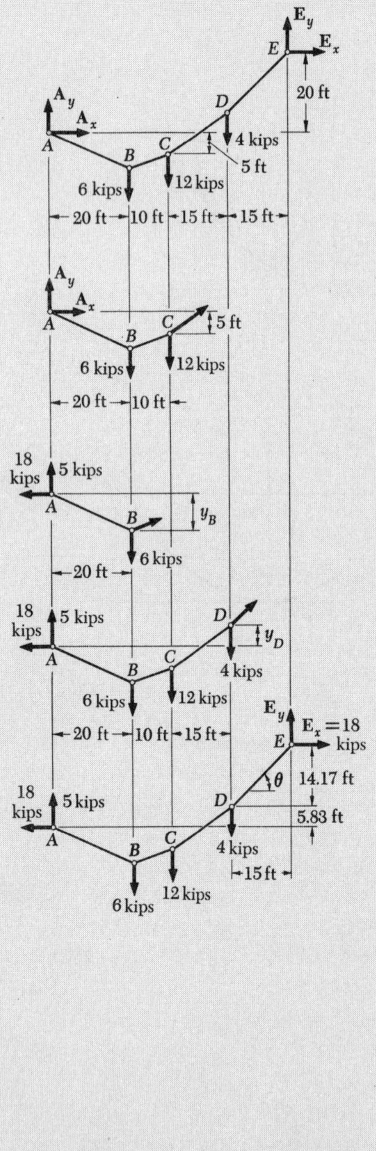

Solution. The reaction components $\mathbf{A}_x$ and $\mathbf{A}_y$ are determined as follows:

Free body: Entire cable

$+\circlearrowleft \Sigma M_E = 0$:

$$A_x(20 \text{ ft}) - A_y(60 \text{ ft}) + (6 \text{ kips})(40 \text{ ft}) + (12 \text{ kips})(30 \text{ ft}) + (4 \text{ kips})(15 \text{ ft}) = 0$$

$$20A_x - 60A_y + 660 = 0$$

Free body: ABC

$+\circlearrowleft \Sigma M_C = 0$: $\quad -A_x(5 \text{ ft}) - A_y(30 \text{ ft}) + (6 \text{ kips})(10 \text{ ft}) = 0$

$$-5A_x - 30A_y + 60 = 0$$

Solving the two equations simultaneously, we obtain

$$A_x = -18 \text{ kips} \qquad \mathbf{A}_x = 18 \text{ kips} \leftarrow$$

$$A_y = +5 \text{ kips} \qquad \mathbf{A}_y = 5 \text{ kips} \uparrow$$

a. **Elevation of Point** *B.* Considering the portion of cable AB *as a free body*, we write

$+\circlearrowleft \Sigma M_B = 0$: $\quad (18 \text{ kips})y_B - (5 \text{ kips})(20 \text{ ft}) = 0$

$$y_B = 5.56 \text{ ft} \quad \text{below } A \blacktriangleleft$$

Elevation of Point *D.* Using the portion of cable $ABCD$ *as a free body*, we write

$+\circlearrowleft \Sigma M_D = 0$:

$$-(18 \text{ kips})y_D - (5 \text{ kips})(45 \text{ ft}) + (6 \text{ kips})(25 \text{ ft}) + (12 \text{ kips})(15 \text{ ft}) = 0$$

$$y_D = 5.83 \text{ ft} \quad \text{above } A \blacktriangleleft$$

b. **Maximum Slope and Maximum Tension.** We observe that the maximum slope occurs in portion DE. Since the horizontal component of the tension is constant and equal to 18 kips, we write

$$\tan\theta = \frac{14.17 \text{ ft}}{15 \text{ ft}} \qquad \theta = 43.4° \blacktriangleleft$$

$$T_{\max} = \frac{18 \text{ kips}}{\cos\theta} \qquad T_{\max} = 24.8 \text{ kips} \blacktriangleleft$$

SAMPLE PROBLEM 7.9

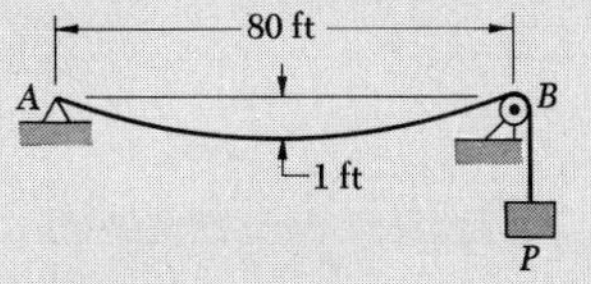

A light cable weighing 40 lb is attached to a support at A, passes over a small pulley at B, and supports a load P. Knowing that the sag of the cable is 1 ft, determine (a) the load P, (b) the slope of the cable at B, and (c) the total length of the cable from A to B. Since the ratio of the sag to the span is small, assume the cable to be parabolic. Also neglect the weight of the portion of cable from B to P.

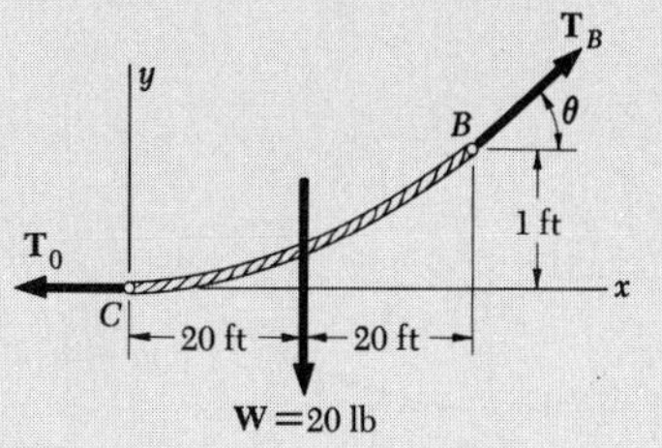

a. **Load *P*.** We denote by C the lowest point of the cable and draw the free-body diagram of the portion CB of cable. The weight $\mathbf{W}$ of the portion CB may be applied halfway between C and B since the load is assumed to be uniformly distributed along the horizontal. Summing moments about B, we write

$$+\circlearrowleft \Sigma M_B = 0: \qquad (20 \text{ lb})(20 \text{ ft}) - T_0(1 \text{ ft}) = 0 \qquad T_0 = 400 \text{ lb}$$

From the force triangle we obtain

$$T_B = \sqrt{T_0^2 + W^2}$$
$$= \sqrt{(400 \text{ lb})^2 + (20 \text{ lb})^2} = 400.5 \text{ lb}$$

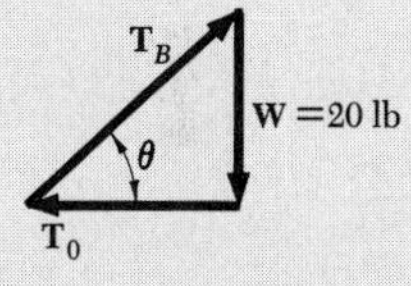

Since the tension on each side of the pulley is the same, we find

$$P = T_B = 400.5 \text{ lb} \quad ◄$$

b. **Slope of Cable at B.** We also obtain from the force triangle

$$\tan \theta = \frac{W}{T_0} = \frac{20 \text{ lb}}{400 \text{ lb}} = 0.05$$

$$\theta = 2.9° \quad ◄$$

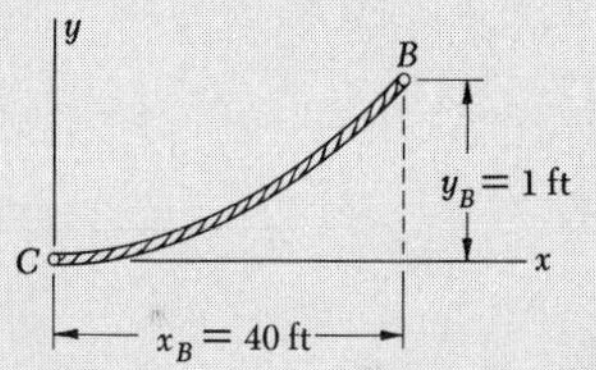

c. **Length of Cable.** Applying Eq. (7.10) between C and B, we write

$$s_B = x_B \left[1 + \frac{2}{3}\left(\frac{y_B}{x_B}\right)^2 + \cdots \right]$$
$$= 40 \left[1 + (\tfrac{2}{3})(\tfrac{1}{40})^2 + \cdots \right] = 40.0167 \text{ ft}$$

The total length of the cable between A and B is twice this value,

$$\text{Length} = 2s_B = 80.033 \text{ ft} \quad ◄$$

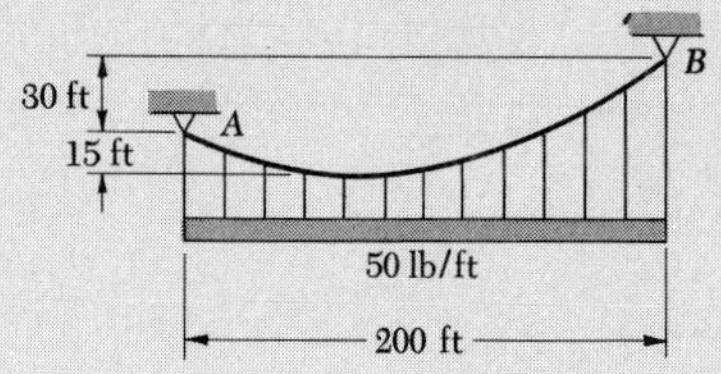

SAMPLE PROBLEM 7.10

Cable AB supports a load distributed uniformly along the horizontal as shown. The lowest point of the cable is 15 ft below the support A. Determine the maximum and minimum values of the tension in the cable.

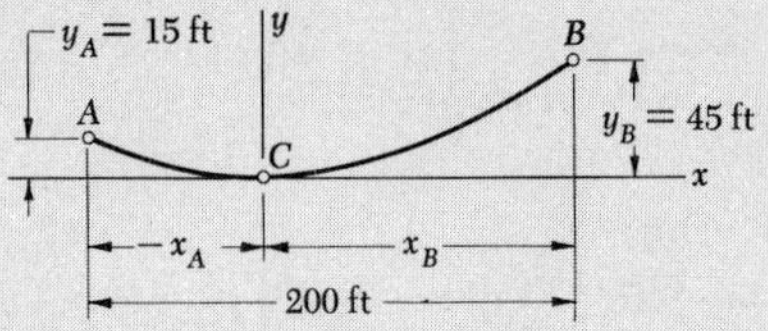

Solution. Since the load is distributed uniformly along the horizontal, the cable is parabolic; choosing the origin of coordinates at the lowest point C, the equation of the cable is given by Eq. (7.8),

$$y = \frac{wx^2}{2T_0} \qquad (1)$$

From the geometry of the sketch, we note that x_A is negative as drawn and write

$$y_A = 15 \text{ ft} \qquad y_B = 45 \text{ ft}$$

$$x_B - x_A = 200 \text{ ft} \qquad \text{or} \qquad x_A = x_B - 200 \text{ ft}$$

Substituting successively the coordinates of A and B into Eq. (1), we obtain

Point A: $$y_A = \frac{wx_A^2}{2T_0} \qquad 15 = \frac{w(x_B - 200)^2}{2T_0} \qquad (2)$$

Point B: $$y_B = \frac{wx_B^2}{2T_0} \qquad 45 = \frac{wx_B^2}{2T_0} \qquad (3)$$

Dividing (2) by (3) member by member and solving for x_B, we obtain

$$\frac{15}{45} = \frac{(x_B - 200)^2}{x_B^2}$$

$$x_B = 473 \text{ ft} \qquad \text{and} \qquad x_B = 126.8 \text{ ft}$$

The first root is discarded since it is larger than 200 ft.

Minimum Tension. The minimum tension occurs at C and equals T_0. Substituting the computed coordinates of point B into Eq. (1), we find

$$y = \frac{wx^2}{2T_0} \qquad 45 = \frac{(50)(126.8)^2}{2T_0} \qquad T_0 = 8{,}930 \text{ lb} ◄$$

Maximum Tension. Since the slope is maximum at B, the maximum tension T_{max} occurs at B. Substituting the coordinates of B into Eq. (7.7), we find

$$T_{max} = \sqrt{T_0^2 + w^2x^2} = \sqrt{(8{,}930)^2 + (50)^2(126.8)^2}$$

$$T_{max} = 10{,}950 \text{ lb} ◄$$

PROBLEMS

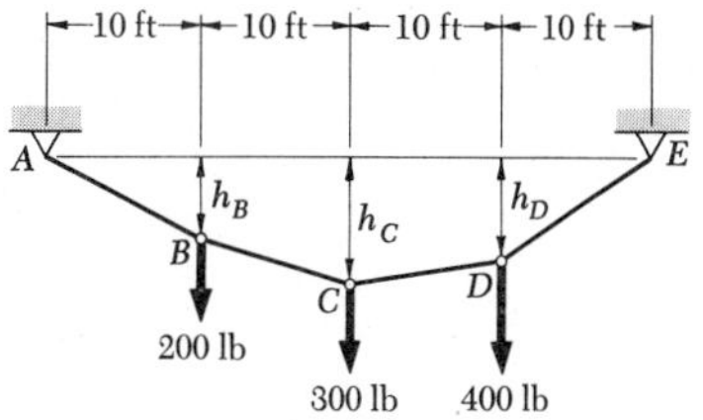

FIG. P 7.62, P 7.63, AND P 7.64

7.62. Three loads are suspended as shown from the cable. Knowing that $h_C = 6$ ft, determine (*a*) the components of the reaction at *A*, (*b*) the sag at points *B* and *D*.

7.63. Three loads are suspended as shown from the cable. Knowing that $h_C = 8$ ft, determine (*a*) the components of the reaction at *E*, (*b*) the maximum value of the tension in the cable.

7.64. Determine the sag at point *C* if the maximum tension in the cable is 1,300 lb.

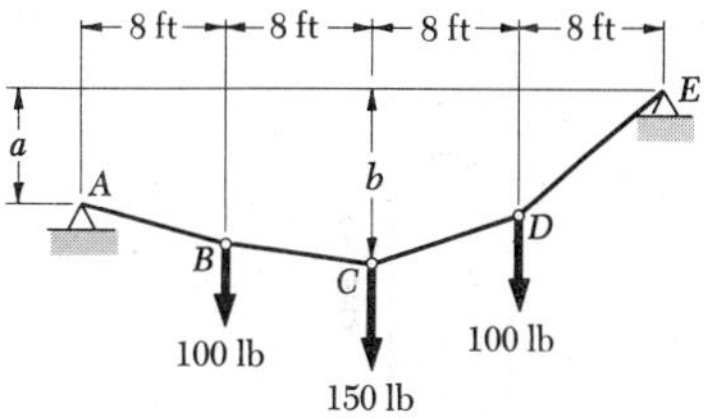

FIG. P 7.65, P 7.66, AND P 7.67

7.65. If $a = 8$ ft and $b = 9$ ft, determine the components of the reaction at *E* for the cable and loading shown.

7.66. If $a = b = 5$ ft, determine the components of the reaction at *E* and the maximum tension in the cable.

7.67. Determine the distance *a* if the portion *BC* of the cable is horizontal and if the maximum tension in the cable is 650 lb.

7.68. The center span of the George Washington Bridge, as originally constructed, consisted of a uniform roadway suspended from four cables. The uniform load supported by each cable was $w = 9.75$ kips/ft along the horizontal. Knowing that the span *L* is 3,500 ft and that the sag *h* is 316 ft, determine the maximum and minimum tension in each cable.

7.69. Determine the length of each of the cables used in the center span of the George Washington Bridge. (See Prob. 7.68 for data.)

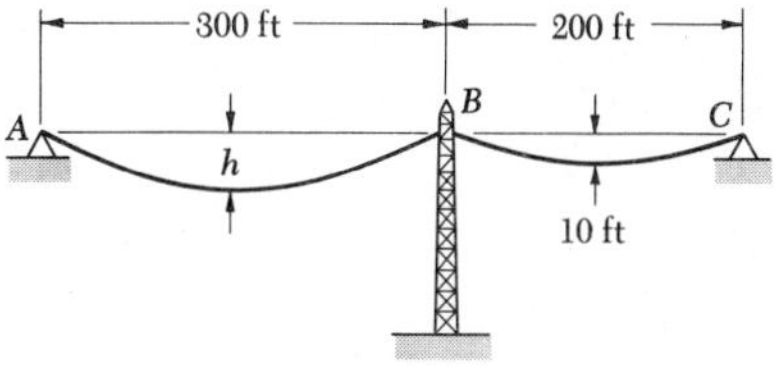

FIG. P 7.70

7.70. Two cables of the same gage are attached to a transmission tower at *B*. Since the tower is slender, the horizontal component of the resultant of the forces exerted by the cables at *B* is to be zero. Assuming the cables to be parabolic, determine the required sag *h* of cable *AB*.

7.71. An electric wire, weighing 0.20 lb/ft, is strung between two insulators at the same elevation and 100 ft apart. If the maximum tension in the wire is to be 80 lb, determine the smallest value of the sag which may be used. (Assume the wire to be parabolic.)

7.72. Knowing that a 102-ft length of wire was used in spanning a horizontal distance of 100 ft, determine the approximate sag of the wire. Assume the wire to be parabolic. (*Hint.* Use only the first two terms of Eq. 7.10.)

7.73. A cable of length $L + \Delta$ is suspended between two points which are at the same elevation and a distance L apart. (*a*) Assuming that Δ is small compared to L and that the cable is parabolic, determine the approximate sag in terms of L and Δ. (*b*) If $L = 100$ ft and $\Delta = 4$ ft, determine the approximate sag. (*Hint.* Use only the first two terms of Eq. 7.10.)

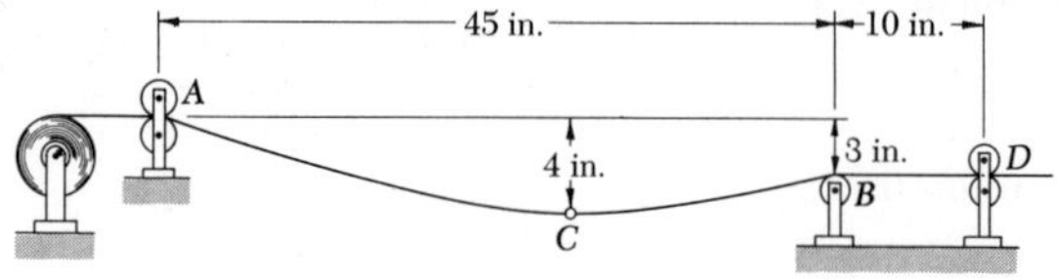

FIG. P 7.74

7.74. Before being fed into a printing press located to the right of D, a continuous sheet of paper weighing 0.20 lb/ft passes over rollers at A and B. Assuming that the curve formed by the sheet is parabolic, determine the location of the lowest point C and the maximum tension in the sheet.

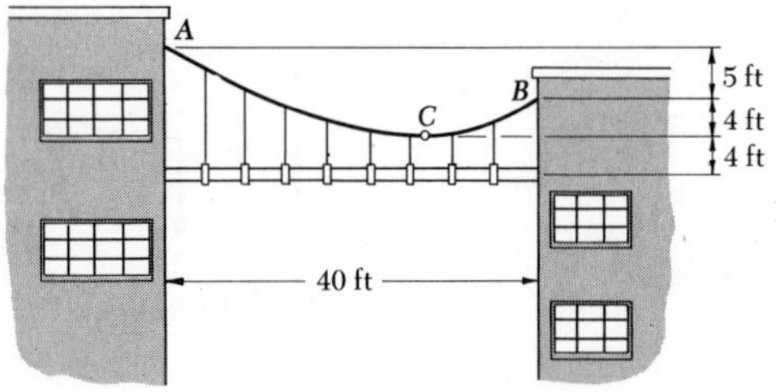

FIG. P 7.75

7.75. A steam pipe weighing 45 lb/ft, which passes between two buildings 40 ft apart, is supported by a system of cables as shown. Assuming that the weight of the cable system is equivalent to a uniformly distributed loading of 5 lb/ft, determine the location of the lowest point C of the cable and the maximum cable tension.

***7.76.** The total weight of cable AC is 60 lb. Assuming that the weight of the cable is distributed uniformly along the horizontal, determine the sag h and the slope of the cable at A and C.

7.77. The loading of a cable varies linearly from zero at the lowest point to w_0 at each support. Determine the equation of the curve assumed by each half of the cable and the tension at the center line.

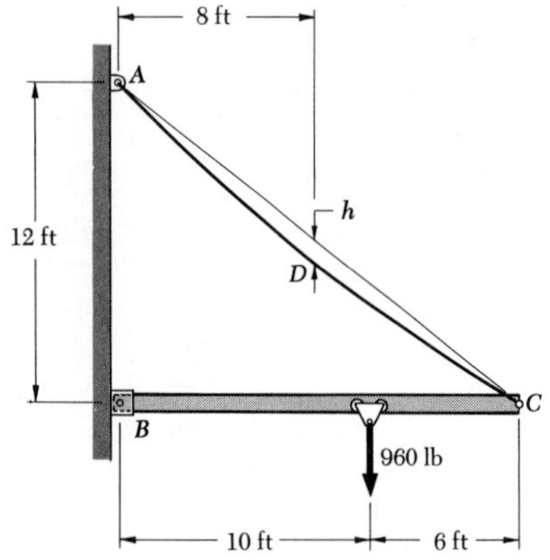

FIG. P 7.76

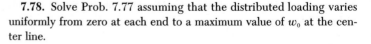

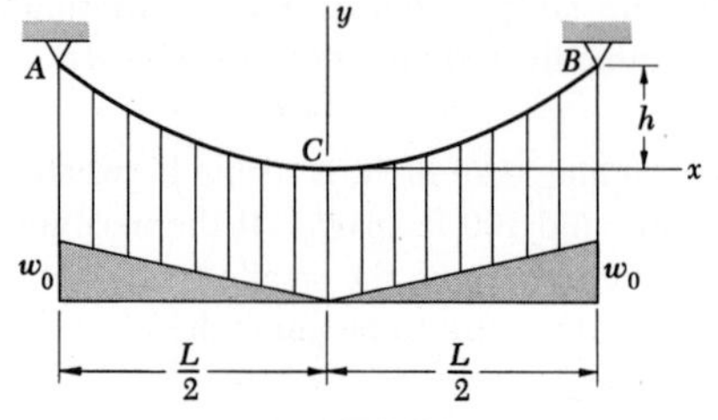

FIG. P 7.77

7.78. Solve Prob. 7.77 assuming that the distributed loading varies uniformly from zero at each end to a maximum value of w_0 at the center line.

***7.79.** A cable AB of span L and a simple beam $A'B'$ of the same span are subjected to identical vertical loadings as shown. Show that the magnitude of the bending moment at a point C' in the beam is equal to the product $T_0 h$, where T_0 is the magnitude of the horizontal component of the tension force in the cable and h is the vertical distance between point C of the cable and the chord joining the points of support A and B.

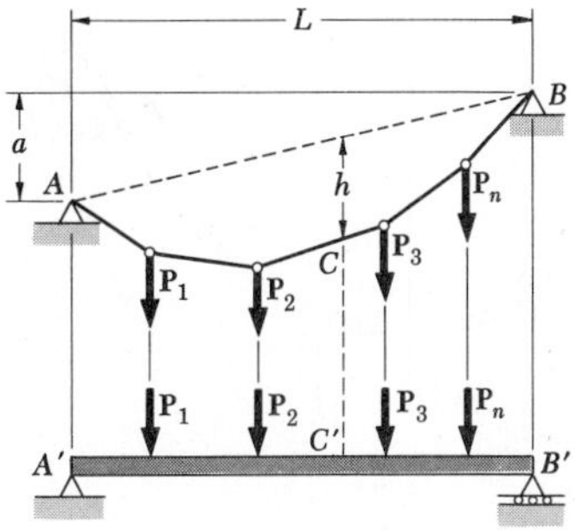

FIG. P 7.79

***7.80.** Show that the curve assumed by a cable carrying a distributed load $w(x)$ is defined by the differential equation $d^2y/dx^2 = w(x)/T_0$, where T_0 is the tension at the lowest point.

***7.81.** Using the property indicated in Prob. 7.80, determine the curve assumed by a cable of span L and sag h carrying a distributed load $w = w_0 \cos(\pi x/L)$, where x is measured from mid-span. Also determine the maximum and minimum values of the tension.

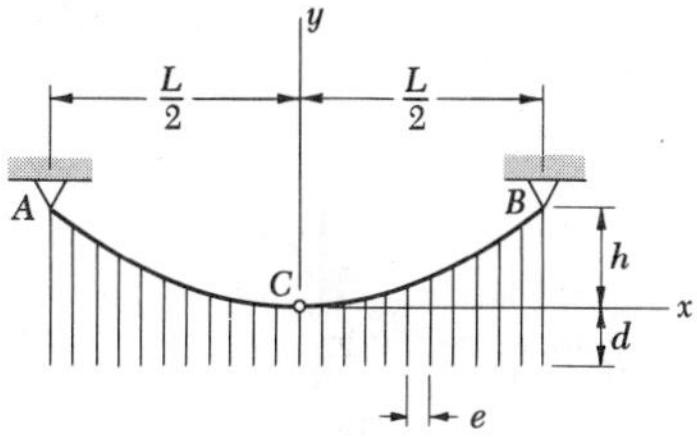

FIG. P 7.82

***7.82.** A large number of ropes are tied to a light wire which is suspended from two points A and B at the same level. Show that, if the lower ends of the ropes have been cut so that they lie in the same horizontal line, and if the ropes are kept uniformly spaced, the curve assumed by the wire ACB is

$$y + d = d \cosh\,(w_r/T_0 e)^{\frac{1}{2}}\, x$$

where w_r is the weight per unit length of the ropes, d is the length of the shortest rope, and e is the horizontal distance between adjacent ropes. (*Hint.* Use the property indicated in Prob. 7.80.)

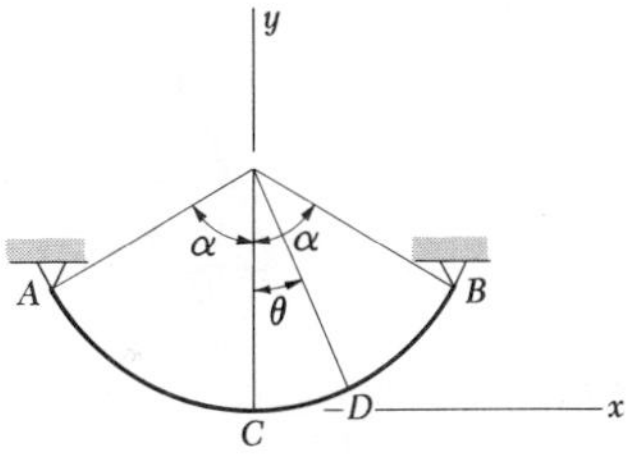

FIG. P 7.83

***7.83.** If the weight per unit length of the cable AB is $w_0/\cos^2\theta$, prove that the curve formed by the cable is a circular arc. (*Hint.* Use the property indicated in Prob. 7.80.)

***7.9. Catenary.** We shall consider now a cable AB carrying a load *uniformly distributed along the cable itself* (Fig. 7.18*a*). Cables hanging under their own weight are loaded in this way. Denoting by w the load per unit length (*measured along the cable*), we find that the magnitude W of the total load carried by a portion of cable of length s extending from the lowest point C to a point D is $W = ws$. Substituting this value for W in formula (7.6), we obtain the tension at D,

$$T = \sqrt{T_0^2 + w^2 s^2}$$

In order to simplify the subsequent computations, we shall introduce the constant $c = T_0/w$. We thus write

$$T_0 = wc \qquad W = ws \qquad T = w\sqrt{c^2 + s^2} \qquad (7.11)$$

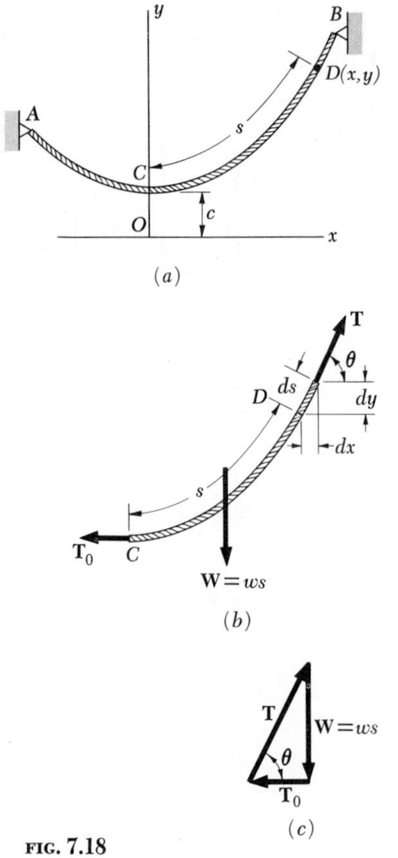

FIG. 7.18

The free-body diagram of the portion of cable CD is shown in Fig. 7.18b. This diagram, however, cannot be used to obtain directly the equation of the curve assumed by the cable, since we do not know the horizontal distance from D to the line of action of the resultant **W** of the load. To obtain this equation, we shall write first that the horizontal projection of a small element of cable of length ds is $dx = ds \cos\theta$. Observing from Fig. 7.18c that $\cos\theta = T_0/T$ and using (7.11), we write

$$dx = ds \cos\theta = \frac{T_0}{T}\,ds = \frac{wc\,ds}{w\sqrt{c^2 + s^2}} = \frac{ds}{\sqrt{1 + s^2/c^2}}$$

Selecting the origin O of the coordinates at a distance c directly below C (Fig. 7.18a) and integrating from $C(0,c)$ to $D(x,y)$, we obtain†

$$x = \int_0^s \frac{ds}{\sqrt{1 + s^2/c^2}} = c\left[\sinh^{-1}\frac{s}{c}\right]_0^s = c\sinh^{-1}\frac{s}{c}$$

This equation, which relates the length s of the portion of cable CD and the horizontal distance x, may be written in the form

$$s = c\sinh\frac{x}{c} \qquad (7.15)$$

The relation between the coordinates x and y may now be obtained by writing $dy = dx\tan\theta$. Observing from Fig. 7.18c that $\tan\theta = W/T_0$ and using (7.11) and (7.15), we write

$$dy = dx\tan\theta = \frac{W}{T_0}\,dx = \frac{s}{c}\,dx = \sinh\frac{x}{c}\,dx$$

† This integral may be found in all standard integral tables. The function

$$z = \sinh^{-1} u$$

(read "arc hyperbolic sine u") is the *inverse* of the function $u = \sinh z$ (read "hyperbolic sine z"). This function and the function $v = \cosh z$ (read "hyperbolic cosine z") are defined as follows:

$$u = \sinh z = \tfrac{1}{2}(e^z - e^{-z}) \qquad v = \cosh z = \tfrac{1}{2}(e^z + e^{-z})$$

Numerical values of these functions are found in *tables of hyperbolic functions*. The student is referred to any calculus text for a complete description of the properties of these functions. In this section, we shall make use only of the following properties, which may be easily derived from the above definitions:

$$\frac{d\sinh z}{dz} = \cosh z \qquad \frac{d\cosh z}{dz} = \sinh z \qquad (7.12)$$

$$\sinh 0 = 0 \qquad \cosh 0 = 1 \qquad (7.13)$$

$$\cosh^2 z - \sinh^2 z = 1 \qquad (7.14)$$

Integrating from $C(0,c)$ to $D(x,y)$ and using (7.12) and (7.13), we obtain

$$y - c = \int_0^x \sinh\frac{x}{c}\,dx = c\left[\cosh\frac{x}{c}\right]_0^x = c\left(\cosh\frac{x}{c} - 1\right)$$

$$y = c\cosh\frac{x}{c} \qquad (7.16)$$

This is the equation of a *catenary* with vertical axis. The ordinate c of the lowest point C is called the *parameter* of the catenary. Squaring both sides of Eqs. (7.15) and (7.16), subtracting, and taking (7.14) into account, we obtain the following relation between y and s:

$$y^2 - s^2 = c^2 \qquad (7.17)$$

Solving (7.17) for s^2 and carrying into the last of the relations (7.11), we write these relations as follows:

$$T_0 = wc \qquad W = ws \qquad T = wy \qquad (7.18)$$

The last relation indicates that the tension at any point D of the cable is proportional to the vertical distance from D to the horizontal line representing the x axis.

When the supports A and B of the cable have the same elevation, the distance L between the supports is called the *span* of the cable and the vertical distance h from the supports to the lowest point C is called the *sag* of the cable. These definitions are the same that were given in the case of parabolic cables, but it should be noted that, because of our choice of coordinate axes, the sag h is now

$$h = y_A - c \qquad (7.19)$$

It should also be observed that certain catenary problems involve transcendental equations which must be solved by successive approximations (see Sample Prob. 7.11). When the cable is fairly taut, however, the load may be assumed uniformly distributed *along the horizontal* and the catenary may be replaced by a parabola. The solution of the problem is thus greatly simplified, while the error introduced is small.

When the supports A and B have different elevations, the position of the lowest point of the cable is not known. The problem may be solved then in a manner similar to that used for parabolic cables, by expressing that the cable must pass through the supports and that $x_B - x_A = L$, $y_B - y_A = d$, where L and d denote, respectively, the horizontal and vertical distances between the two supports.

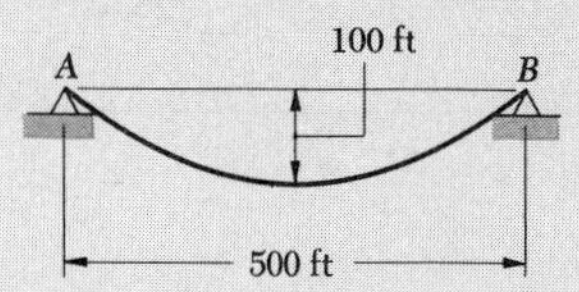

SAMPLE PROBLEM 7.11

A uniform cable weighing 3 lb/ft is suspended between two points A and B as shown. Determine (a) the maximum and minimum values of the tension in the cable, (b) the length of the cable.

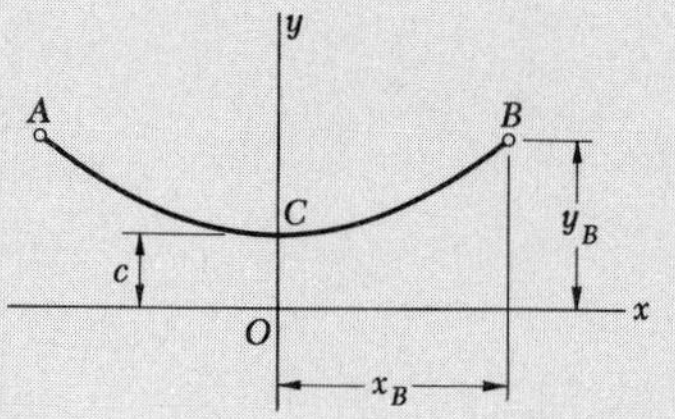

Solution. Equation of Cable. The origin of coordinates is placed at a distance c below the lowest point of the cable. The equation of the cable is given by Eq. (7.16),

$$y = c \cosh \frac{x}{c}$$

The coordinates of point B are

$$x_B = 250 \text{ ft} \qquad y_B = 100 + c$$

Substituting these coordinates into the equation of the cable, we obtain

$$100 + c = c \cosh \frac{250}{c}$$

$$\frac{100}{c} + 1 = \cosh \frac{250}{c}$$

The value of c is determined by assuming successive trial values, as shown in the following table:

c	$\frac{250}{c}$	$\frac{100}{c}$	$\frac{100}{c} + 1$	$\cosh \frac{250}{c}$
300	0.833	0.333	1.333	1.367
350	0.714	0.286	1.286	1.266
330	0.758	0.303	1.303	1.301
328	0.762	0.305	1.305	1.305

Taking $c = 328$, we have

$$y_B = 100 + c = 428 \text{ ft}$$

a. Maximum and Minimum Values of the Tension. Using Eqs. (7.18), we obtain

$$T_{min} = T_0 = wc = (3 \text{ lb/ft})(328 \text{ ft}) \qquad T_{min} = 984 \text{ lb} \blacktriangleleft$$

$$T_{max} = T_B = wy_B = (3 \text{ lb/ft})(428 \text{ ft}) \qquad T_{max} = 1{,}284 \text{ lb} \blacktriangleleft$$

b. Length of Cable. One-half the length of the cable is found by solving Eq. (7.17),

$$y_B^2 - s_{CB}^2 = c^2 \qquad s_{CB}^2 = y_B^2 - c^2 = (428)^2 - (328)^2 \qquad s_{CB} = 275 \text{ ft}$$

The total length of the cable is therefore

$$s_{AB} = 2s_{CB} = 2(275 \text{ ft}) \qquad s_{AB} = 550 \text{ ft} \blacktriangleleft$$

PROBLEMS

7.84. An aerial tramway cable of length 600 ft and weighing 3.0 lb/ft is suspended between two points at the same elevation. Knowing that the sag is 150 ft, find the horizontal distance between supports and the maximum tension.

7.85. A 100-ft rope is strung between the roofs of two buildings, each of height 30 ft. The maximum tension is found to be 50 lb and the lowest point of the cable is observed to be 10 ft above the ground. Determine the horizontal distance between the buildings and the total weight of the rope.

7.86. A 200-ft steel surveying tape weighs 4 lb. If the tape is stretched between two points at the same elevation and pulled until the tension at each end is 16 lb, determine the horizontal distance between the ends of the tape. Neglect the elongation of the tape due to the tension.

7.87. A copper transmission wire weighs 0.50 lb/ft and is attached to two insulators at the same elevation and 300 ft apart. It has been established that the horizontal component of the tension in the wire must be 175 lb if the insulators are not to be bent. Determine (*a*) the length of cable which should be used, (*b*) the resulting sag, (*c*) the resulting maximum tension.

7.88. A tramway wire rope weighing 3.4 lb/ft is suspended across a canyon; it is attached to two supports at the same elevation and 600 ft apart. Knowing that the sag is 80 ft, determine the total length of the cable and the maximum tension.

7.89. A 400-lb counterweight is attached to a cable which passes over a small pulley at *A* and is attached to a support at *B*. If the sag is 10 ft, determine (*a*) the length of the cable from *A* to *B*, (*b*) the weight per unit length of the cable. Neglect the weight of the cable from *A* to *D*.

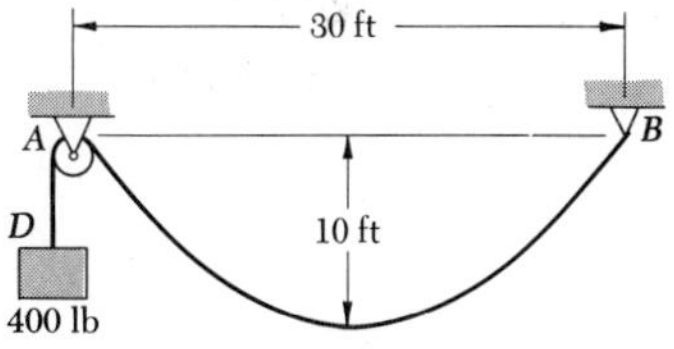

FIG. P 7.89

7.90. A chain of length 20 ft and total weight 40 lb is suspended between two points at the same elevation and 10 ft apart. Determine the sag and the maximum tension.

7.91. A 150-ft wire is suspended between two points at the same elevation and 100 ft apart. Knowing that the maximum tension is 30 lb, determine the sag and the total weight of the wire.

***7.92.** Solve Prob. 7.74 assuming that the curve formed by the sheet of paper is a catenary.

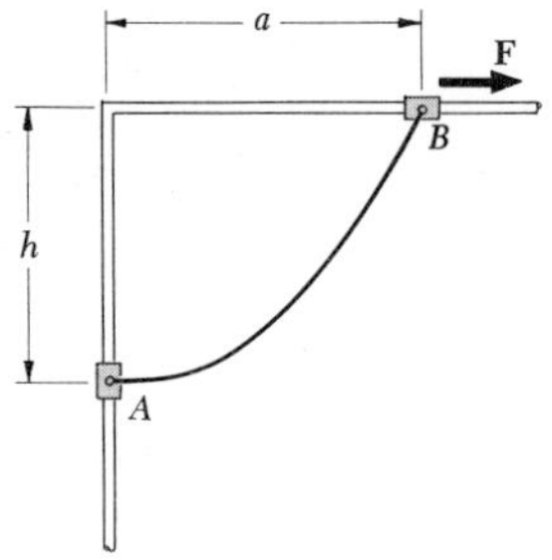

FIG. P 7.93

*7.93. The 10-ft cable AB weighs 20 lb and is attached to collars at A and B which may slide freely on the rods shown. Neglecting the weight of the collars, determine (*a*) the magnitude of the horizontal force **F** so that $h = a$, (*b*) the corresponding value of h and a, (*c*) the maximum tension in the cable.

7.94. Denoting by θ the angle formed by a uniform cable and the horizontal, show that at any point $y = c/\cos \theta$.

*7.95. (*a*) Determine the maximum allowable horizontal span for a uniform cable of weight w per unit length if the tension in the cable is not to exceed the value T_m. (*b*) Using the result of part *a*, find the maximum span of a drawn-steel wire for which $w = 0.2$ lb/ft and $T_m = 6{,}000$ lb.

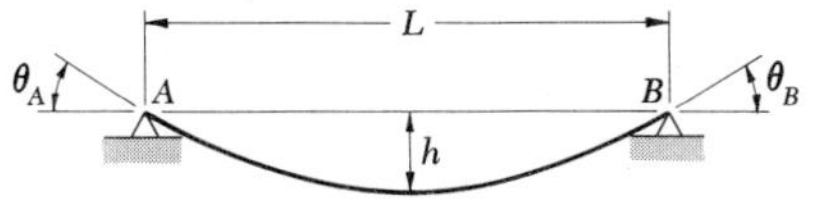

FIG. P 7.96, P 7.97, AND P 7.98

*7.96. A chain weighs 4 lb/ft and is supported as shown. Knowing that the span L is 24 ft, determine the *two* values of the sag h for which the maximum tension is 150 lb.

*7.97. Determine the sag-to-span ratio for which the maximum tension in the cable is equal to the total weight of the entire cable AB.

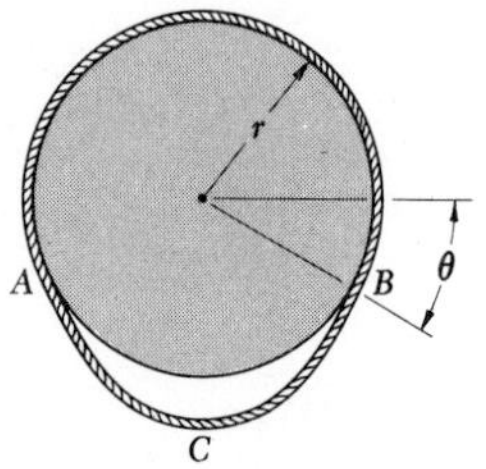

FIG. P 7.99

*7.98. A cable, of weight w per unit length, is suspended between two points at the same elevation and a distance L apart. Determine the sag-to-span ratio for which the maximum tension is as small as possible. What are the corresponding values of θ_B and T_m?

*7.99. A cable, of weight w per unit length, is looped over a cylinder and is in contact with the cylinder above points A and B. Knowing that $\theta = 30°$, determine (*a*) the length of the cable, (*b*) the tension in the cable at C. (*Hint.* Use the property indicated in Prob. 7.94.)

REVIEW PROBLEMS

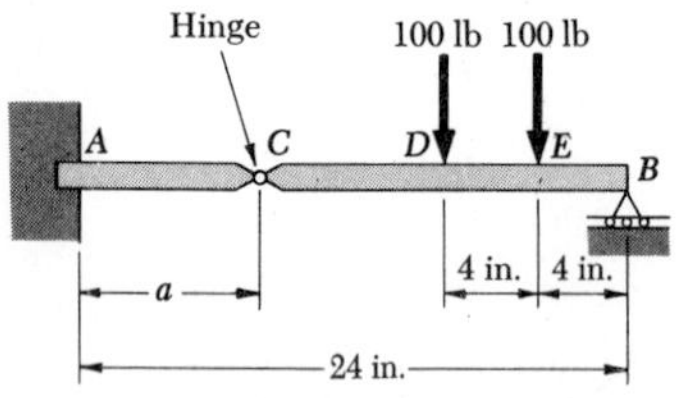

FIG. P 7.100 AND P 7.101

7.100. Draw the shear and bending-moment diagrams for the beam and loading shown when $a = 4$ in.

7.101. Determine the distance a for which the maximum absolute value of the bending moment is as small as possible.

7.102. A $\frac{1}{2}$-in.-diameter wire rope weighing 0.40 lb/ft is suspended from two supports at the same elevation and 200 ft apart. If the sag is 50 ft, determine (*a*) the total length of the cable, (*b*) the maximum tension.

7.103. Concrete piles are designed primarily to resist axial loads, and their bending resistance is relatively small. To lessen the possibility of breaking them, piles are often lifted at several points along their length. By using the arrangement shown, the concrete pile AB is lifted by four equal forces applied at points C, D, E, and F. If the total weight of the pile is 16,000 lb, draw the shear and bending-moment diagrams of the pile. Assume the weight of the pile to be uniformly distributed.

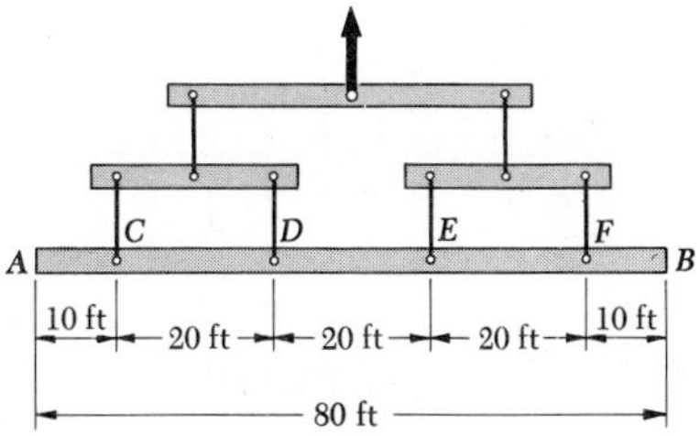

FIG. P 7.103

7.104. A heavy cable of length L weighs w lb/ft and is suspended from a support at A. Wind blowing on the cable exerts a loading of q lb/ft distributed uniformly along the vertical. Knowing that q is small compared to w, determine the equation of the curve formed by the cable.

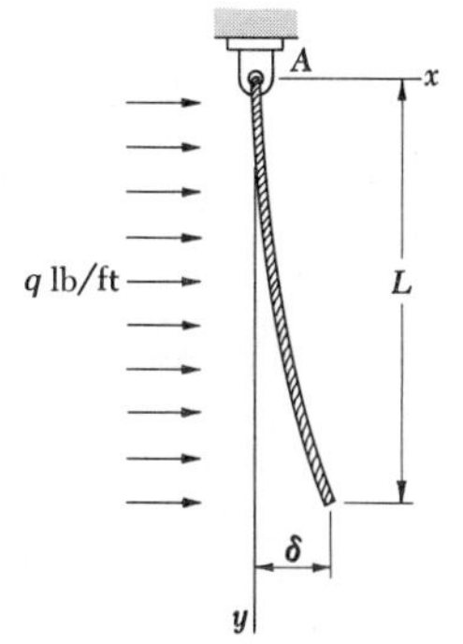

FIG. P 7.104

7.105. The axis of the curved member shown is a parabola with vertex at A. If a vertical load $\mathbf{P}$ of magnitude 600 lb is applied at A, determine the internal forces at J, when $h = 9$ in., $L = 30$ in., and $a = 20$ in.

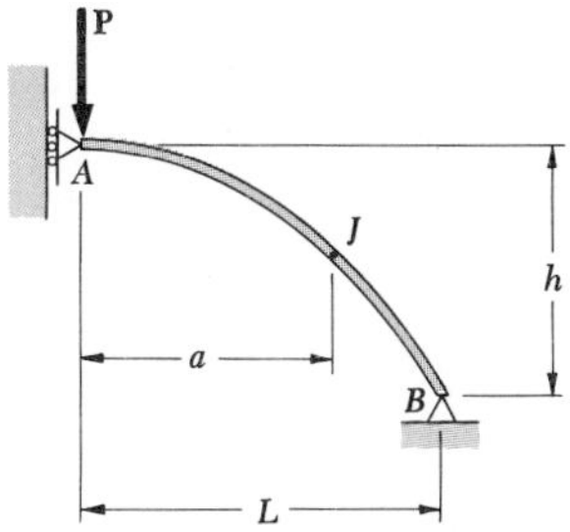

FIG. P 7.105 AND P 7.106

7.106. The axis of the curved member shown is a parabola with vertex at A. Knowing that a vertical load $\mathbf{P}$ is applied at A, determine the magnitude and location of the maximum bending moment.

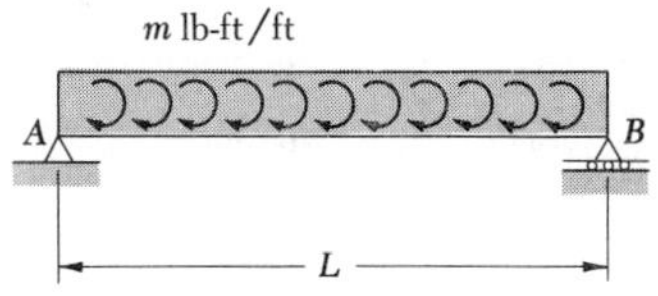

FIG. P 7.107

7.107. A beam AB is loaded by couples spaced uniformly along its length. Assuming that the couples may be represented by a uniformly distributed couple loading of m lb-ft/ft, draw the shear and bending-moment diagrams for the beam when it is supported (a) as shown, (b) as a cantilever with a fixed support at A and no support at B.

7.108. A 300-pound load is attached to a small pulley which may roll on the cable ACB. The pulley and load are held in the position shown by a second cable DE which is parallel to the portion CB of the main cable. Determine (a) the reactions at A and B, (b) the tension in cable ACB, (c) the tension in cable DE. Neglect the radius of the pulleys and the weight of the cables.

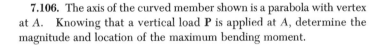

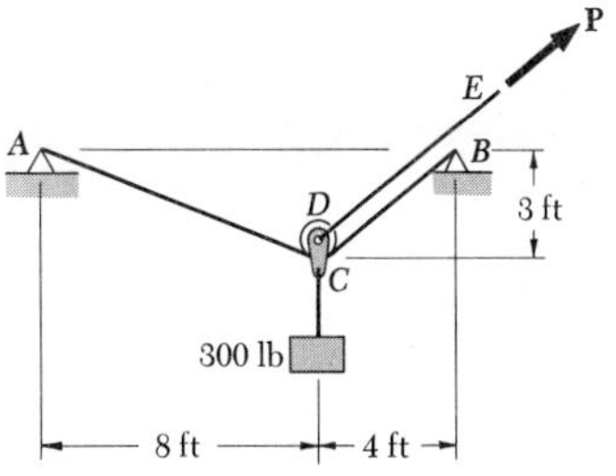

FIG. P 7.108

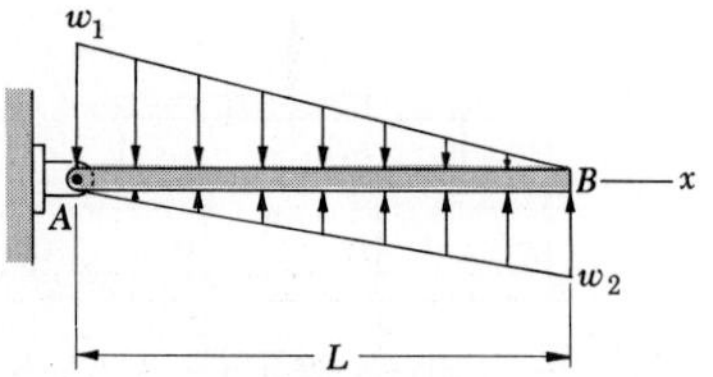

FIG. P 7.109

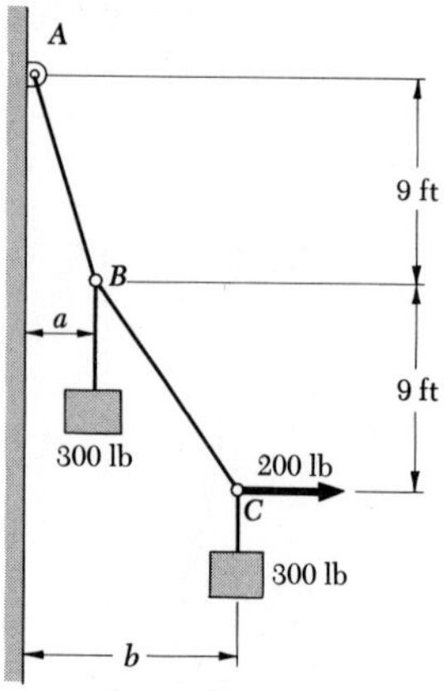

FIG. P 7.110

7.109. The rod AB is attached to a hinge at A and is free at B. Determine (*a*) the ratio of w_2 to w_1 for which the rod is in equilibrium, (*b*) the equations of the shear and bending-moment curves for the rod, (*c*) the magnitude and location of the maximum bending moment.

7.110. Cable ABC supports two 300-lb loads as shown. Determine the distances a and b when a 200-lb horizontal load is applied at C. Neglect the weight of the cable.

***7.111.** Determine the magnitude and location of the maximum bending moment for the rod of Prob. 5.23. (Choose OB as a reference axis for θ.)

8. FRICTION

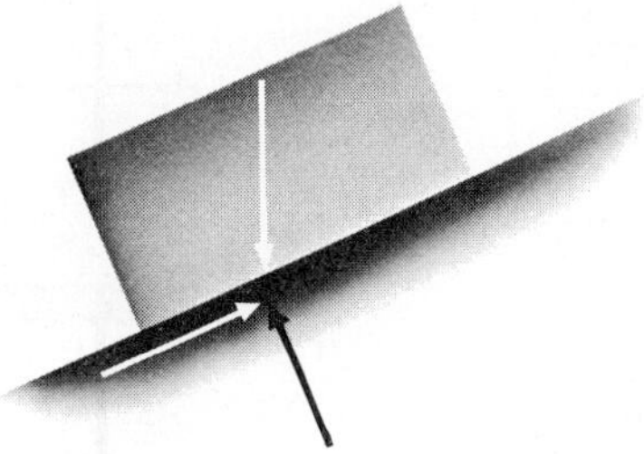

8.1. Introduction. In the preceding chapters, it was assumed that surfaces in contact were either *smooth* or *rough*. If they were smooth, it was assumed that the force each surface exerted on the other was normal to the surfaces and that the two surfaces could move freely with respect to each other. If they were rough, it was assumed that tangential forces could develop to prevent the motion of one surface with respect to the other.

This view was a simplified one. Actually, no perfectly smooth surface exists. When two surfaces are in contact, tangential forces, called *friction forces,* will always develop if one attempts to move one surface with respect to the other. On the other hand, these friction forces are limited in magnitude and will not prevent motion if sufficiently large forces are applied. The distinction between smooth and rough surfaces is thus a matter of degree. This will be seen more clearly in the present chapter, which is devoted to the study of friction and of its applications to common engineering situations.

There are two types of friction: *dry friction,* sometimes called *Coulomb friction,* and *fluid friction.* Fluid friction develops between layers of fluid moving at different velocities. Fluid friction is of great importance in problems involving the flow of fluids through pipes and orifices or dealing with bodies immersed in moving fluids. It is also basic in the analysis of the motion of *lubricated mechanisms.* Such problems are considered in texts on fluid mechanics. We shall limit our present study to dry friction, i.e., to problems involving rigid bodies which are in contact along *nonlubricated* surfaces.

8.2. The Laws of Dry Friction. Coefficients of Friction. The laws of dry friction are best understood by the following experiment. A block of weight **W** is placed on a horizontal plane surface (Fig. 8.1*a*). The forces acting on the block are

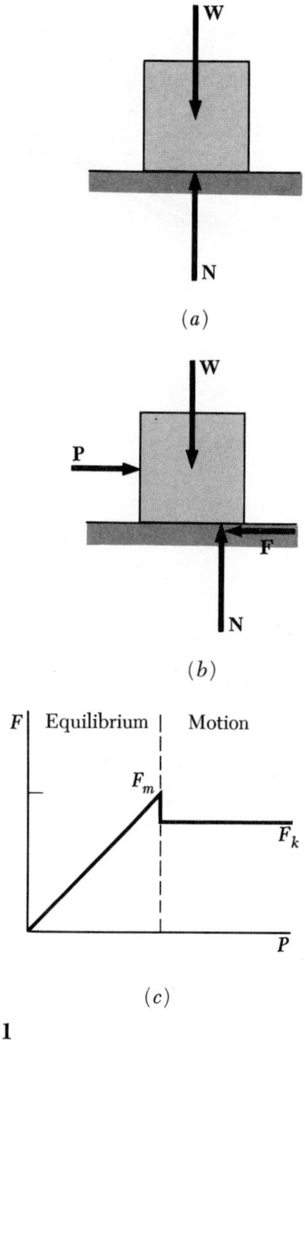

FIG. 8.1

its weight **W** and the reaction of the surface. Since the weight has no horizontal component, the reaction of the surface also has no horizontal component; the reaction is therefore *normal* to the surface and is represented by **N** in Fig. 8.1*a*. Suppose, now, that a horizontal force **P** is applied to the block (Fig. 8.1*b*). If **P** is small, the block will not move; some other horizontal force must therefore exist, which balances **P**. This other force is the *static-friction force* **F**, which is actually the resultant of a great number of forces acting over the entire surface of contact between the block and the plane. The nature of these forces is not known exactly, but it is generally assumed that these forces are due to the irregularities of the surfaces in contact and also, to a certain extent, to molecular attraction.

If the force **P** is increased, the friction force **F** also increases, continuing to oppose **P**, until its magnitude reaches a certain *maximum value* F_m (Fig. 8.1*c*). If **P** is further increased, the friction force cannot balance it any more and the block starts sliding. As soon as the block has been set in motion, the magnitude of **F** drops from F_m to a lower value F_k. This is because there is less interpenetration between the irregularities of the surfaces in contact when these surfaces move with respect to each other. From then on, the block keeps sliding with increasing velocity while the friction force, denoted by $\mathbf{F}_k$ and called the *kinetic-friction force,* remains approximately constant.

Experimental evidence shows that the maximum value F_m of the static-friction force is proportional to the normal component N of the reaction of the surface. We have

$$F_m = \mu_s N \tag{8.1}$$

where μ_s is a constant called the *coefficient of static friction.* Similarly, the magnitude F_k of the kinetic-friction force may be put in the form

$$F_k = \mu_k N \tag{8.2}$$

where μ_k is a constant called the *coefficient of kinetic friction.* The coefficients of friction μ_s and μ_k do not depend upon the area of the surfaces in contact. Both coefficients, however, depend strongly on the *nature* of the surfaces in contact. Since they also depend upon the exact condition of the surfaces, their value is seldom known with an accuracy greater than 5 per cent. Approximate values of coefficients of static friction are given in Table 8.1 for various dry surfaces. The corresponding values of the coefficient of kinetic friction would be about 25 per cent smaller.

TABLE 8.1. *Approximate Values of Coefficient of Static Friction for Dry Surfaces*

Metal on metal	0.15–0.60
Metal on wood	0.20–0.60
Metal on stone	0.30–0.70
Metal on leather	0.30–0.60
Wood on wood	0.25–0.50
Wood on leather	0.25–0.50
Stone on stone	0.40–0.70
Earth on earth	0.20–1.00
Rubber on concrete	0.60–0.90

From the description given above, it appears that four different situations may occur when a rigid body is in contact with a horizontal surface:

1. The forces applied to the body do not tend to move it along the surface of contact; there is no friction force (Fig. 8.2*a*).

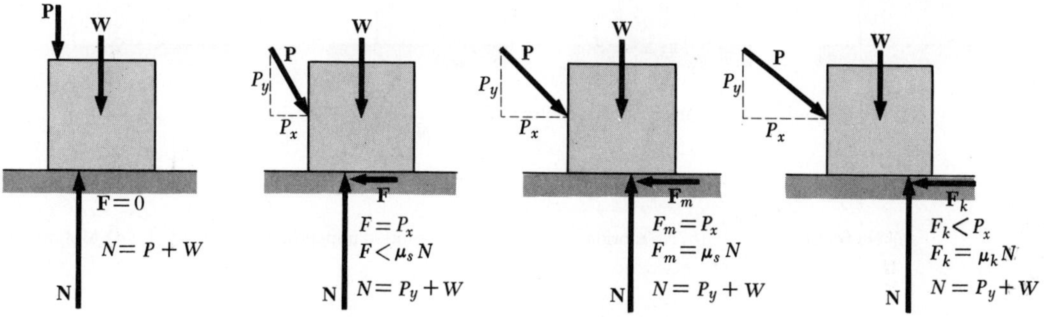

(*a*) No friction ($P_x = 0$) (*b*) No motion ($P_x < F_m$) (*c*) Motion impending → ($P_x = F_m$) (*d*) Motion → ($P_x > F_m$)

FIG. 8.2

2. The applied forces tend to move the body along the surface of contact but are not large enough to set it in motion. The friction force **F** which has developed may be found by solving the equations of equilibrium for the body. Since there is no evidence that the maximum value of the static-friction force has been reached, the equation $F_m = \mu_s N$ *cannot be used* to determine the friction force (Fig. 8.2*b*).

3. The applied forces are such that the body is just about to slide. We say that *motion is impending*. The friction force **F** has reached its maximum value F_m and, together with the normal force **N**, balances the applied forces. Both the equa-

tions of equilibrium and the equation $F_m = \mu_s N$ *may be used.* We also note that the friction force has a sense opposite to the sense of impending motion (Fig. 8.2*c*).

4. The body is sliding under the action of the applied forces, and the equations of equilibrium do not apply any more. However, **F** is now equal to the kinetic-friction force $\mathbf{F}_k$ and the equation $F_k = \mu_k N$ may be used. The sense of $\mathbf{F}_k$ is opposite to the sense of motion (Fig. 8.2*d*).

8.3. Angles of Friction. It is sometimes found convenient to replace the normal force **N** and the friction force **F** by their resultant **R**. Let us consider again a block of weight **W** resting on a horizontal plane surface. If no horizontal force is applied to the block, the resultant **R** reduces to the normal force **N** (Fig. 8.3*a*). However, if the applied force **P** has a horizon-

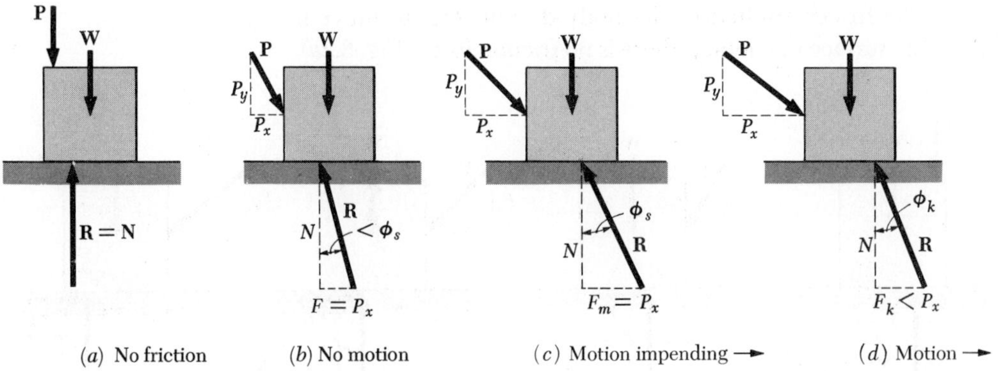

FIG. 8.3

tal component $\mathbf{P}_x$ which tends to move the block, the force **R** will have a horizontal component **F** and, thus, will form a certain angle with the vertical (Fig. 8.3*b*). If $\mathbf{P}_x$ is increased until motion becomes impending, the angle between **R** and the vertical grows and reaches a maximum value (Fig. 8.3*c*). This value is called the *angle of static friction* and is denoted by ϕ_s. From the force triangle shown in Fig. 8.3*c*, we note that

$$\tan \phi_s = \frac{F_m}{N} = \frac{\mu_s N}{N}$$

$$\tan \phi_s = \mu_s \tag{8.3}$$

If motion actually takes place, the magnitude of the friction force drops to F_k; similarly, the angle between **R** and **N** drops to a lower value ϕ_k, called the *angle of kinetic friction* (Fig. 8.3*d*). Using the force triangle of Fig. 8.3*d*, we write

$$\tan \phi_k = \frac{F_k}{N} = \frac{\mu_k N}{N}$$

$$\tan \phi_k = \mu_k \tag{8.4}$$

Another example will show how the angle of friction may be used to advantage in the analysis of certain types of problems. Consider a block resting on a board which may be given any desired inclination; the block is subjected to no other force than its weight **W** and the reaction **R** of the board. If the board is horizontal, the force **R** exerted by the board on the block is perpendicular to the board and balances the weight **W** (Fig. 8.4*a*). If the board is given a small angle of inclination θ, the force **R** will deviate from the perpendicular to the board by the angle θ and will keep balancing **W** (Fig. 8.4*b*); it will then have a normal component **N** of magnitude $N = W \cos \theta$ and a tangential component **F** of magnitude $F = W \sin \theta$.

If we keep increasing the angle of inclination, motion will soon become impending. At that time, the angle between **R** and the normal will have reached its maximum value ϕ_s (Fig. 8.4*c*). The value of the angle of inclination corresponding to impending motion is called the *angle of repose*. Clearly, the angle of repose is equal to the angle of static friction ϕ_s. If the angle of inclination θ is further increased, motion starts and the angle between **R** and the normal drops to the lower value ϕ_k (Fig. 8.4*d*). The reaction **R** is not vertical any more, and the forces acting on the block are unbalanced.

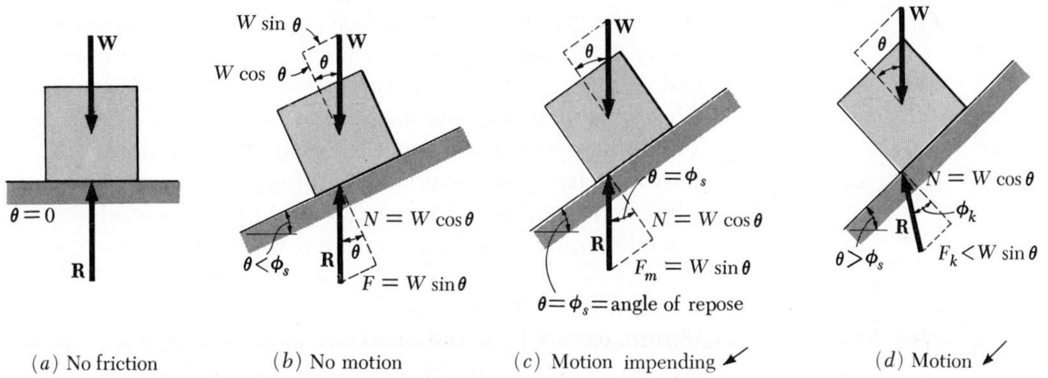

FIG. 8.4

8.4. Problems Involving Dry Friction. Problems involving dry friction are found in many engineering applications. Some deal with simple situations such as the block sliding on a plane described in the preceding sections. Others involve more complicated situations as in Sample Prob. 8.3; many deal with the stability of rigid bodies in accelerated motion and will be studied in dynamics. Also, a number of common machines and mechanisms may be analyzed by applying the laws of dry friction. These include wedges, screws, journal and thrust bearings, and belt transmissions. They will be studied in the following sections.

The *methods* which should be used to solve problems involving dry friction are the same that were used in the preceding chapters. If a problem involves only a motion of translation, with no possible rotation, the body under consideration may usually be treated as a particle and the methods of Chap. 2 may be used. If the problem involves a possible rotation, the body must be considered as a rigid body and the methods of Chap. 4 should be used. If the structure considered is made of several parts, the principle of action and reaction must be used as was done in Chap. 6.

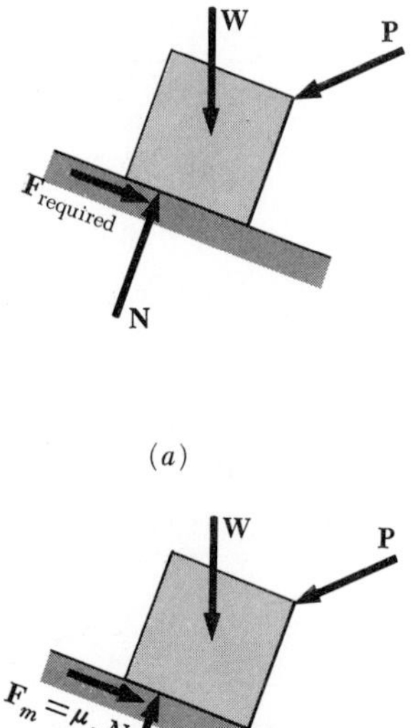

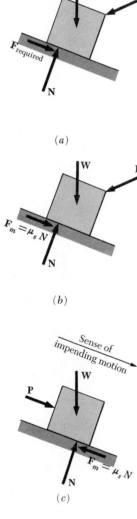

FIG. 8.5

If the body considered is acted upon by more than three forces (including the reactions at the surfaces of contact), the reaction at each surface will be represented by its components **N** and **F** and the problem will be solved from the equations of equilibrium. If only three forces act on the body under consideration, it may be found more convenient to represent each reaction by the single force **R** and to solve the problem by drawing a force triangle.

Most problems involving friction fall into one of the following *three groups:* In the *first group* of problems, all applied forces are given, and the coefficients of friction are known; we are to determine whether the body considered will remain at rest or slide. The friction force **F** *required to maintain equilibrium* is unknown (its magnitude is *not* equal to $\mu_s N$) and should be determined, together with the normal force **N**, by drawing a free-body diagram and *solving the equations of equilibrium* (Fig. 8.5*a*). The value found for the magnitude F of the friction force is then compared with the maximum value $F_m = \mu_s N$. If F is smaller than or equal to F_m, the body remains at rest. If the value found for F is larger than F_m, equilibrium cannot be maintained and motion takes place; the actual magnitude of the friction force is then $F_k = \mu_k N$.

In problems of the *second group*, all applied forces are given, and the motion is known to be impending; we are to determine the value of the coefficient of static friction. Here again, we determine the friction force and the normal force by drawing a free-body diagram and solving the equations of equilibrium (Fig. 8.5*b*). Since we know that the value found for F is the maximum value F_m, the coefficient of friction may be found by writing and solving the equation $F_m = \mu_s N$.

In problems of the *third group*, the coefficient of static friction is given, and it is known that motion is impending in a given direction; we are to determine the magnitude or the direction of one of the applied forces. The friction force should be shown in the free-body diagram with a *sense opposite to that of the impending motion* and with a magnitude $F_m = \mu_s N$ (Fig. 8.5*c*). The equations of equilibrium may then be written, and the desired force may be determined.

As noted above, it may be more convenient, when only three forces are involved, to represent the reaction of the surface by a single force **R** and to solve the problem by drawing a force triangle. Such a solution is used in Sample Prob. 8.2.

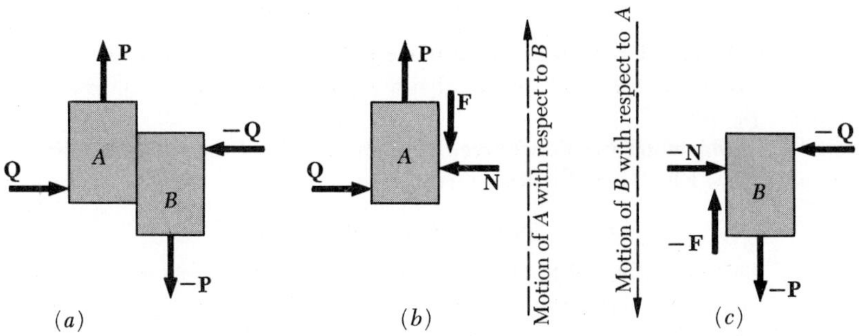

FIG. 8.6

When two bodies A and B are in contact (Fig. 8.6*a*), the forces of friction exerted, respectively, by A on B and by B on A are equal and opposite (Newton's third law). It is important, in drawing the free-body diagram of one of the bodies, to include the appropriate friction force with its correct sense. The following rule should then be observed: *The sense of the friction force acting on A is opposite to that of the motion (or impending motion) of A as observed from B* (Fig. 8.6*b*).† The sense of the friction force acting on B is determined in a similar way (Fig. 8.6*c*). Note that the motion of A as observed from B is a *relative motion*. Body A may be fixed; yet it will have a relative motion with respect to B if B itself moves. Also, A may actually move down yet be observed from B to move up if B moves down faster than A.

† It is therefore *the same as that of the motion of B as observed from A*.

SAMPLE PROBLEM 8.1

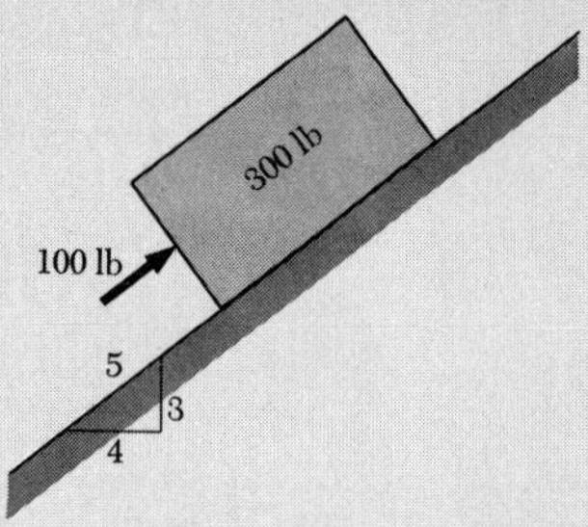

A 100-lb force acts as shown on a 300-lb block placed on an inclined plane. The coefficients of friction between the block and the plane are $\mu_s = 0.25$ and $\mu_k = 0.20$. Determine whether the block is in equilibrium, and find the value of the friction force.

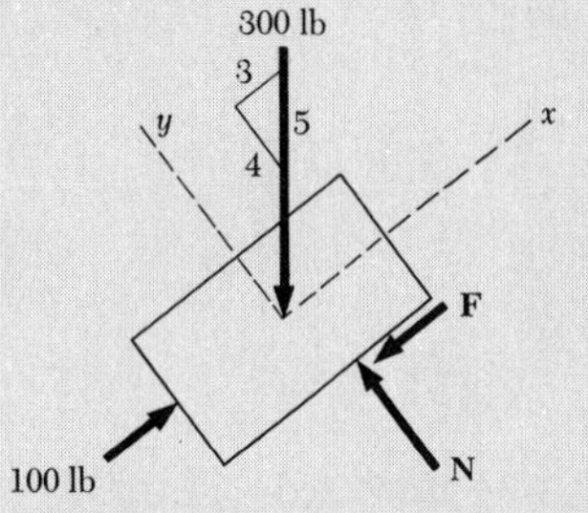

Force Required for Equilibrium. We first determine the value of the friction force *required to maintain equilibrium.* Assuming that **F** is directed down and to the left, we draw the free-body diagram of the block and write

$$+\nearrow \Sigma F_x = 0: \qquad 100 \text{ lb} - \tfrac{3}{5}(300 \text{ lb}) - F = 0$$

$$F = -80 \text{ lb} \qquad \mathbf{F} = 80 \text{ lb} \nearrow$$

$$+\nwarrow \Sigma F_y = 0: \qquad N - \tfrac{4}{5}(300 \text{ lb}) = 0$$

$$N = +240 \text{ lb} \qquad \mathbf{N} = 240 \text{ lb} \nwarrow$$

The force **F** required to maintain equilibrium is an 80-lb force directed up and to the right; the tendency of the block is thus to move down the plane.

Maximum Friction Force. The magnitude of the maximum friction force which may be developed is

$$F_{\text{max}} = \mu_s N \qquad F_{\text{max}} = 0.25(240 \text{ lb}) = 60 \text{ lb}$$

Since the value of the force required to maintain equilibrium (80 lb) is larger than the maximum value which may be obtained (60 lb), equilibrium will not be maintained and *the block will slide down the plane.*

Actual Value of Friction Force. The magnitude of the actual friction force is obtained as follows:

$$F_{\text{actual}} = F_k = \mu_k N$$
$$= 0.20(240 \text{ lb}) = 48 \text{ lb}$$

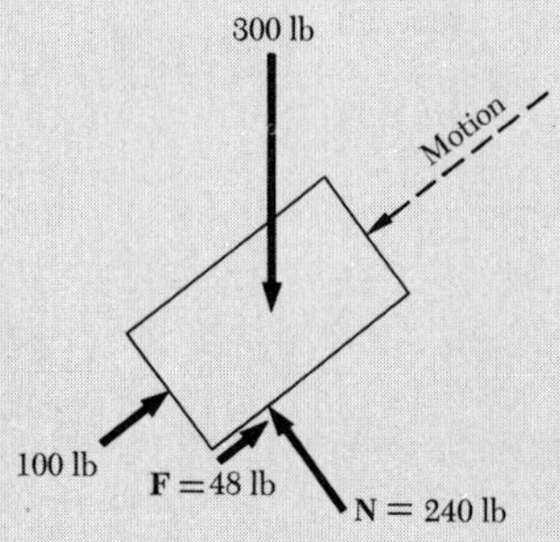

The sense of this force is opposite to the sense of motion; the force is thus directed up and to the right,

$$\mathbf{F}_{\text{actual}} = 48 \text{ lb} \nearrow \blacktriangleleft$$

It should be noted that the forces acting on the block are not balanced; the resultant is

$$\tfrac{3}{5}(300 \text{ lb}) - 100 \text{ lb} - 48 \text{ lb} = 32 \text{ lb} \swarrow$$

SAMPLE PROBLEM 8.2

A wooden sled supporting a large stone is pulled up a track inclined at 15°. The combined weight of the sled and stone is 1,500 lb, and the coefficients of friction between the sled runners and the track are $\mu_s = 0.40$ and $\mu_k = 0.30$. Determine the force **P** required (*a*) to start the sled up the track, (*b*) to keep the sled moving up after it has been started, (*c*) to keep the sled from sliding down.

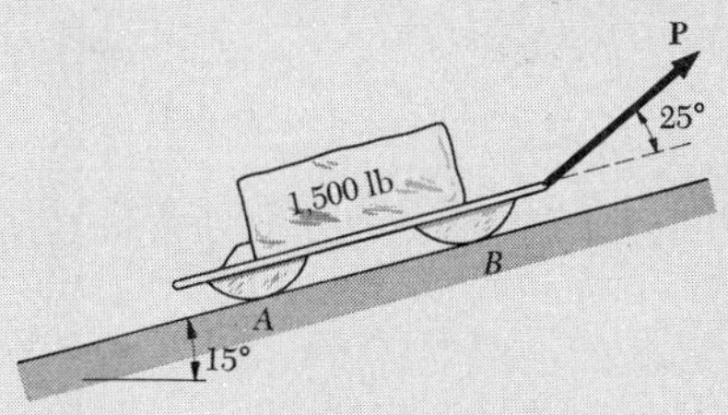

Solution. Since the normal component of the reaction of the track depends upon the unknown force **P** as well as upon the 1,500-lb weight, it would not be convenient to resolve the reactions $\mathbf{R}_A$ and $\mathbf{R}_B$ into components. Noting that $\mathbf{R}_A$ and $\mathbf{R}_B$ have the same direction (same angle of friction ϕ), we draw a force triangle including the 1,500-lb weight, the force **P**, and the sum $\mathbf{R} = \mathbf{R}_A + \mathbf{R}_B$. The direction of **R** must be redetermined in each part of the problem. The law of sines is used to determine the magnitude of **P** in each part of the problem.

a. **Force P to Start Sled Moving Up**

$$\frac{P}{\sin 36.8^\circ} = \frac{1{,}500 \text{ lb}}{\sin [180^\circ - (50^\circ + 36.8^\circ)]}$$

P = 900 lb ↗ ◄

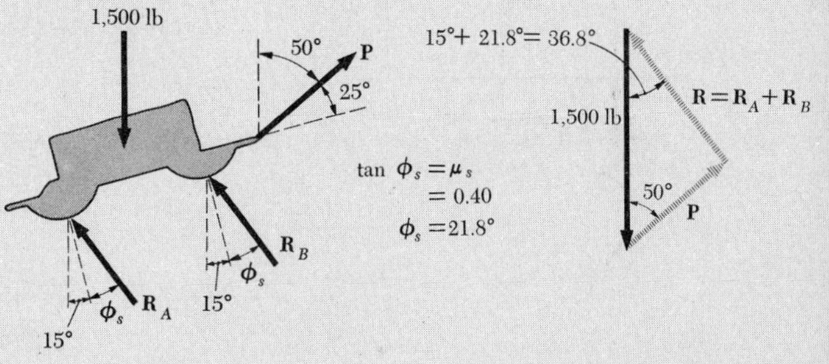

b. **Force P to Keep Sled Moving**

$$\frac{P}{\sin 31.7^\circ} = \frac{1{,}500 \text{ lb}}{\sin [180^\circ - (50^\circ + 31.7^\circ)]}$$

P = 796 lb ↗ ◄

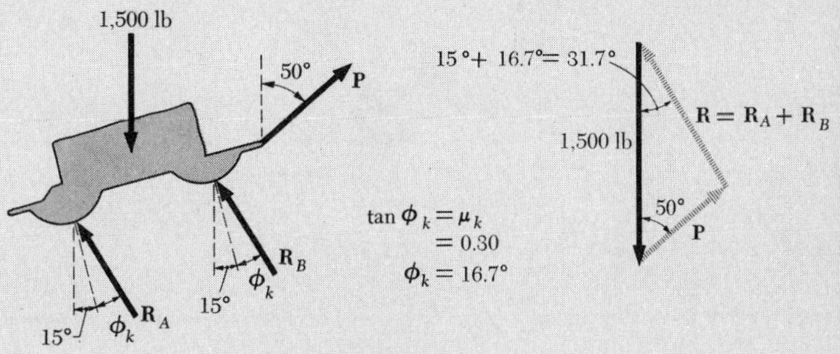

c. **Force P to Keep Sled from Sliding Down**

$$\frac{P}{\sin 6.8^\circ} = \frac{1{,}500 \text{ lb}}{\sin [180^\circ - (130^\circ + 6.8^\circ)]}$$

P = 260 lb ↙ ◄

Since the force **P** is directed downward, the sled will not slide down under its own weight.

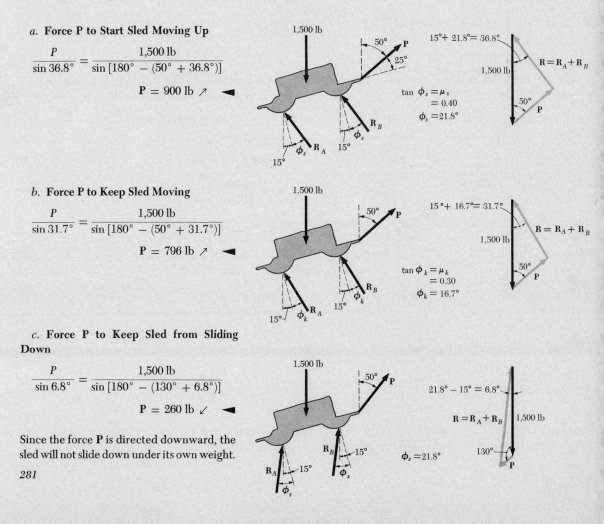

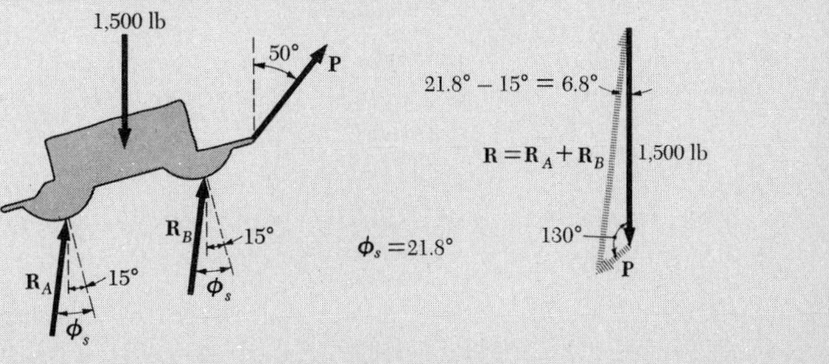

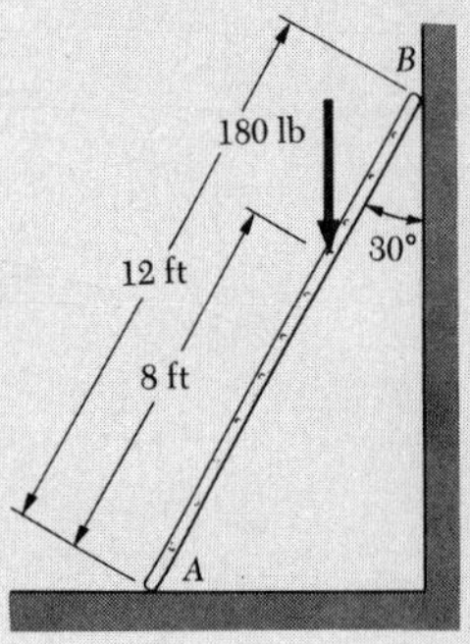

SAMPLE PROBLEM 8.3

A 12-ft ladder weighing 40 lb is placed against a vertical wall as shown. As a 180-lb man reaches a point 8 ft from the lower end A, the ladder is just about to slip. Knowing that the coefficient of static friction between the ladder and the wall is 0.20, determine the coefficient of friction μ_s between the ladder and the floor.

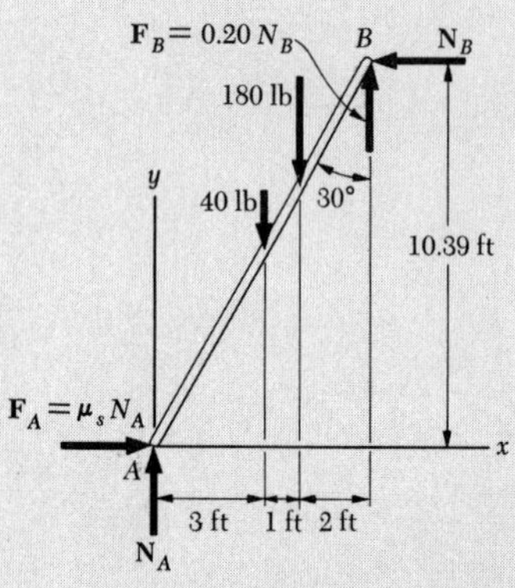

Solution. We draw the free-body diagram of the ladder. Since the ladder is about to slip, the forces of friction at A and B have reached their maximum values, equal to $\mu_s N_A$ and $0.20\ N_B$, respectively. The values of N_B, N_A, and μ_s are successively obtained from the equations of equilibrium,

$+\circlearrowleft \Sigma M_A = 0$:

$$(6\text{ ft})0.20N_B + (10.39\text{ ft})N_B - (3\text{ ft})(40\text{ lb}) - (4\text{ ft})(180\text{ lb}) = 0$$

$$N_B = 72.5\text{ lb}$$

$+\uparrow \Sigma F_y = 0$: $\quad N_A + 0.20N_B - 40\text{ lb} - 180\text{ lb} = 0$

$$N_A + 0.20(72.5\text{ lb}) - 40\text{ lb} - 180\text{ lb} = 0$$

$$N_A = 205\text{ lb}$$

$\overset{+}{\rightarrow} \Sigma F_x = 0$: $\quad \mu_s N_A - N_B = 0$

$$\mu_s(205\text{ lb}) - 72.5\text{ lb} = 0$$

$$\mu_s = \frac{72.5\text{ lb}}{205\text{ lb}} \qquad \mu_s = 0.35 \blacktriangleleft$$

PROBLEMS

8.1. A support block is acted upon by the two forces shown. Determine the magnitude of **P** required to start the block up the plane.

8.2. Determine the smallest magnitude of the force **P** which will prevent the support block from sliding down the plane.

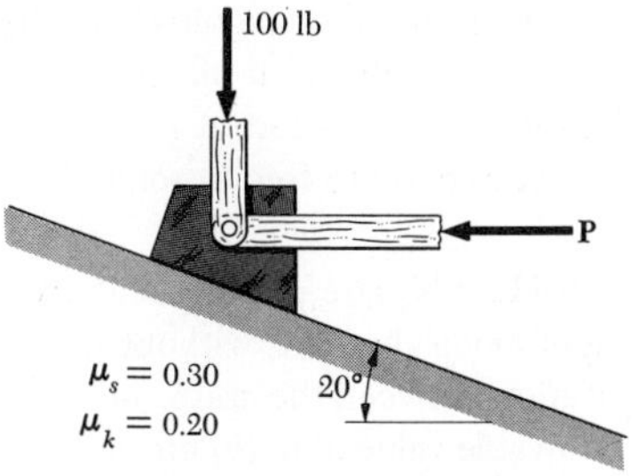

FIG. P 8.1 AND P 8.2

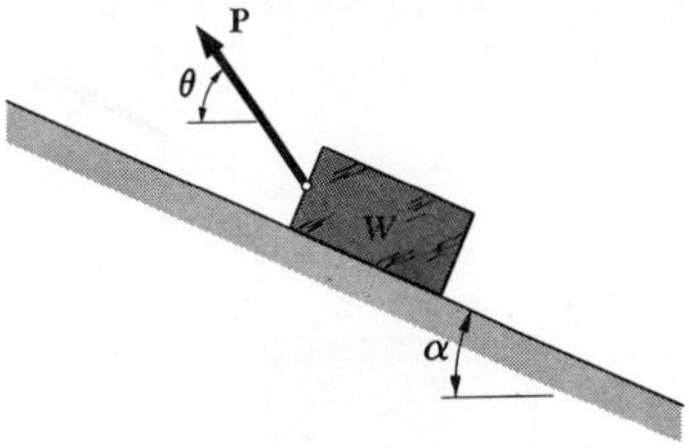

FIG. P 8.3 AND P 8.4

8.3. Denoting by ϕ_s the angle of static friction between the block and the plane, determine the magnitude and direction of the smallest force **P** which will cause the block to move up the plane.

8.4. A block of weight $W = 50$ lb rests on a rough plane as shown. Knowing that $\alpha = 20°$ and $\mu_s = 0.25$, determine the magnitude and direction of the smallest force **P** required (*a*) to start the block up the plane, (*b*) to prevent the block from moving down the plane.

8.5. Three packages *A*, *B*, and *C*, each of weight 10 lb, are placed on a conveyor belt which is at rest. Between the belt and both packages *A* and *C* the coefficients of friction are $\mu_s = 0.30$ and $\mu_k = 0.20$; between package *B* and the belt the coefficients are $\mu_s = 0.10$ and $\mu_k = 0.08$. The packages are placed on the belt so that they are in contact with each other and at rest. Determine which, if any, of the packages will move and the friction force acting on each package.

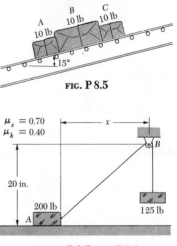

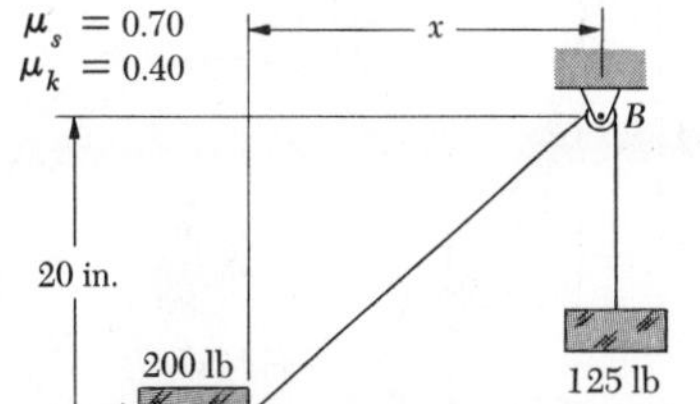

FIG. P 8.5

8.6. Solve Prob. 8.5 assuming that package *B* is placed to the right of both packages *A* and *C*.

8.7. A 200-lb block is used to secure one end of the cable shown. Determine the range of values of *x* for which the 200-lb block will not move.

8.8. Block *A* is positioned so that $x = 25$ in. Determine whether the block moves and find the value of the friction force.

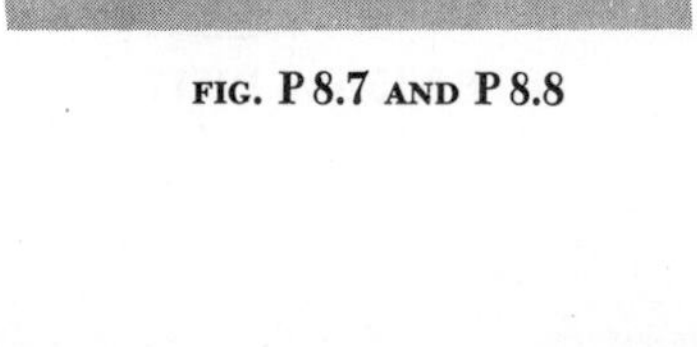

FIG. P 8.7 AND P 8.8

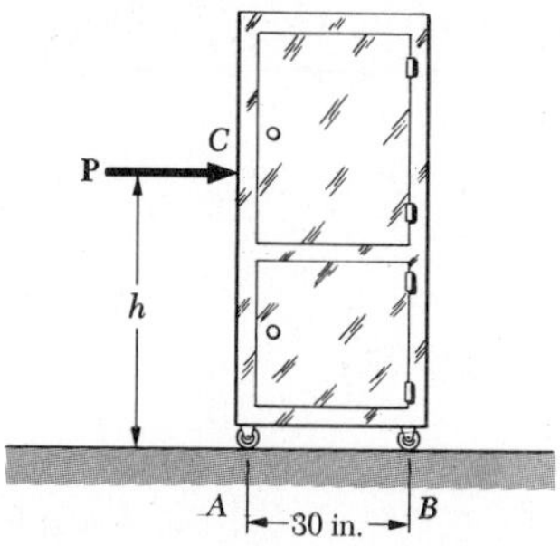

FIG. P 8.9 AND P 8.10

8.9. A 90-lb cabinet is mounted on casters which can be locked to prevent their rotation. The coefficient of friction between the floor and each caster is 0.30. Assuming that the casters at both A and B are locked, determine (a) the force **P** required to move the cabinet to the right, (b) the largest allowable value of h if the cabinet is not to tip over.

8.10. A 90-lb cabinet is mounted on casters which can be locked to prevent their rotation. The coefficient of friction is 0.30. If $h = 40$ in., determine the magnitude of the force **P** required to move the cabinet to the right (a) if all casters are locked, (b) if the casters at B are locked and the casters at A are free to rotate, (c) if casters A are locked and casters B are free to rotate.

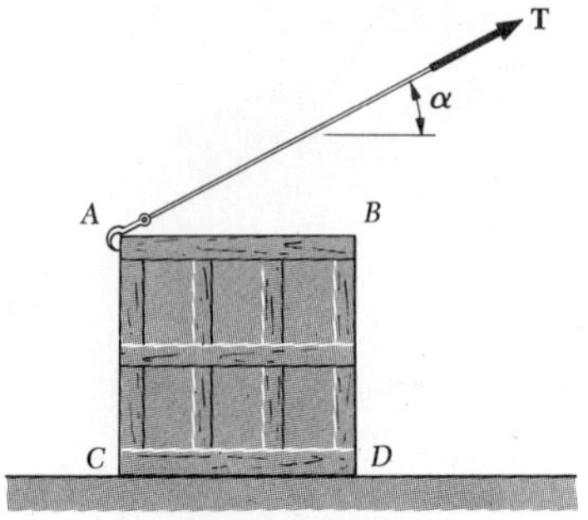

FIG. P 8.11 AND P 8.12

8.11. A square packing crate, weighing 200 lb, is to be moved to the right along the floor without tipping. Knowing that the coefficient of friction between the crate and the floor is 0.40, determine (a) the largest allowable value of α, (b) the corresponding tension T.

8.12. A square packing crate, weighing 200 lb, is pulled by a cable as shown. The coefficient of friction between the crate and the floor is 0.30. If $\alpha = 30°$, determine (a) the tension T required to move the crate, (b) whether the crate will slide or tip.

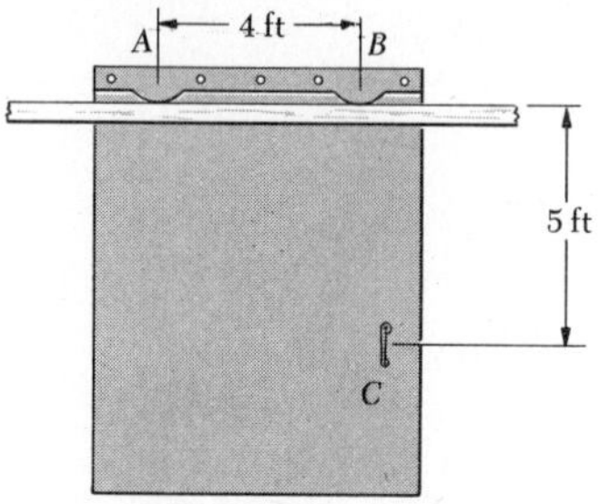

FIG. P 8.13

8.13. A 180-lb sliding door is mounted on a horizontal rail as shown. The coefficients of static friction between the rail and the door at A and B are 0.20 and 0.30, respectively. Determine the horizontal force which must be applied to the handle C in order to move the door to the right.

8.14. Solve Prob. 8.13 assuming that the door is to be moved to the left.

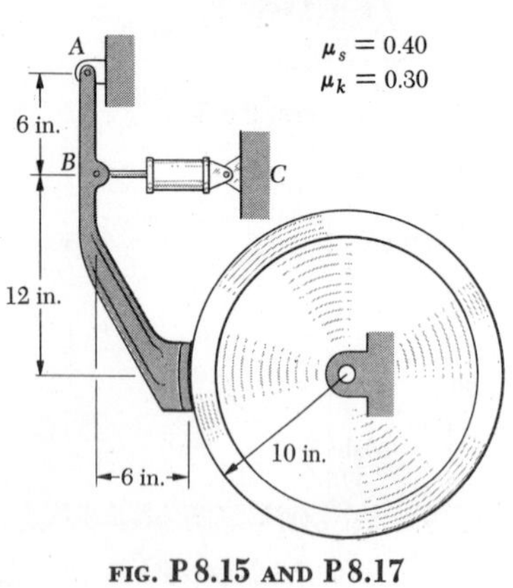

FIG. P 8.15 AND P 8.17

8.15. A clockwise couple of magnitude 60 lb-ft is applied to the drum. Determine the smallest force which must be exerted by the hydraulic cylinder if the drum is not to rotate.

8.16. Solve Prob. 8.15 assuming that a counterclockwise couple of magnitude 60 lb-ft is applied to the drum.

8.17. The hydraulic cylinder exerts on point B a force of 500 lb directed to the right. Determine the moment of the friction force about the axle of the drum if the drum is rotating (a) clockwise, (b) counterclockwise.

8.18. A large number of thin steel plates are stacked on a factory floor as shown. The coefficients of friction between two adjacent plates and between the bottom plate and the floor are 0.35 and 0.25, respectively.

All the plates are to be moved to the right, without tipping or sliding with respect to each other, by applying a horizontal force **P**. Determine the largest allowable height h at which **P** may be applied.

8.19. A large number of thin steel plates of total weight 100 lb are stacked upon each other on a factory floor. In order to move *all* the plates to the right, it is observed that a force **P** of magnitude 27.5 lb is required and that this force cannot be applied at a height h greater than 3 in. Determine the coefficient of friction (a) between the floor and the bottom plate, (b) between two adjacent plates.

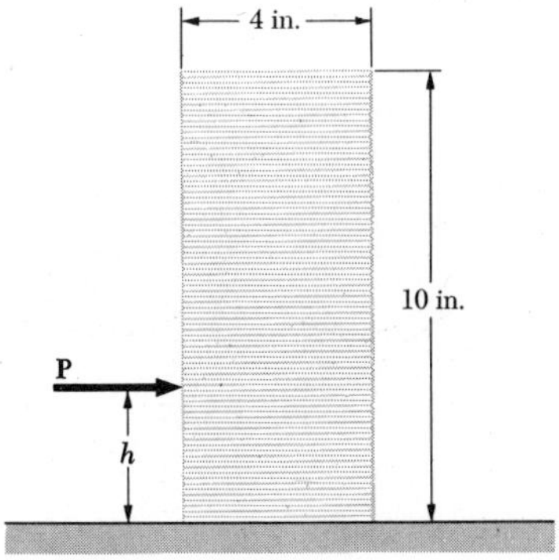

FIG. P 8.18 AND P 8.19

8.20. A 10-ft beam, weighing 1,200 lb, is to be moved to the left onto the platform. A horizontal force **P** is applied to the dolly, which is mounted on frictionless wheels. The coefficient of friction between all surfaces is 0.30. Knowing that the horizontal top surface of the dolly is slightly higher than the platform, determine the magnitude of **P** required to move the beam. (*Hint.* The beam is supported at A and D.)

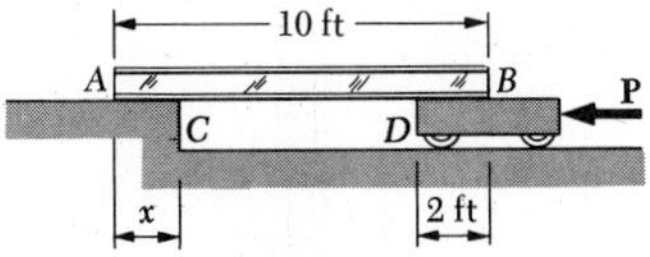

FIG. P 8.20

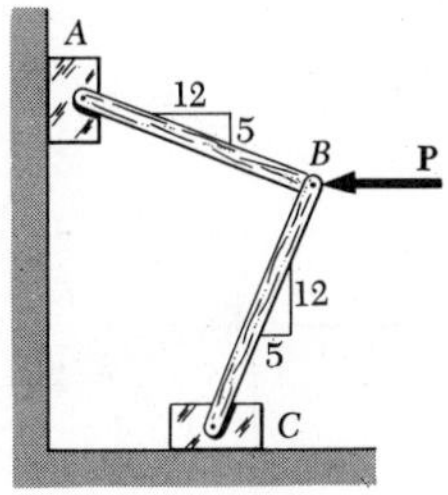

FIG. P 8.22

8.21. (a) Show that the beam of Prob. 8.20 cannot be moved if the horizontal top surface of the dolly is slightly *lower* than the platform. (b) How far can the beam be moved to the left if two 175-lb men stand on the beam at B?

8.22. Two links, of negligible weight, are connected by frictionless pins to each other and to two 10-lb blocks at A and C. The coefficient of friction is 0.30 at A and C. If neither block is to slip, determine the magnitude of the largest horizontal force **P** which can be applied at B.

8.23. In Prob. 8.22 determine the magnitude of the smallest horizontal force **P** which must be applied at B if neither block is to slip.

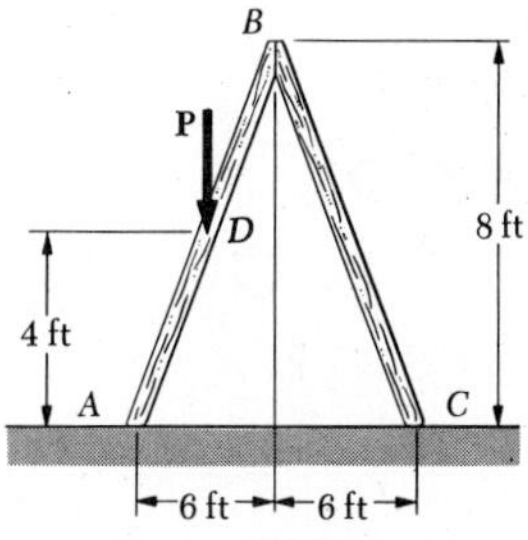

FIG. P 8.24

8.24. Two identical uniform boards, each of weight 40 lb, are temporarily leaned against each other as shown. Knowing that the coefficient of friction between all surfaces is 0.40, determine (a) the largest magnitude of the force **P** for which equilibrium will be maintained, (b) the surface at which motion will impend.

8.25. Solve Prob. 8.24 assuming that the force **P** is applied at D and is directed horizontally to the right.

8.26. The movable bracket shown may be placed at any height on the 3-in.-diameter pipe. If the coefficient of static friction between the pipe and bracket is 0.25, determine the minimum distance x at which the load W can be supported. Neglect the weight of the bracket.

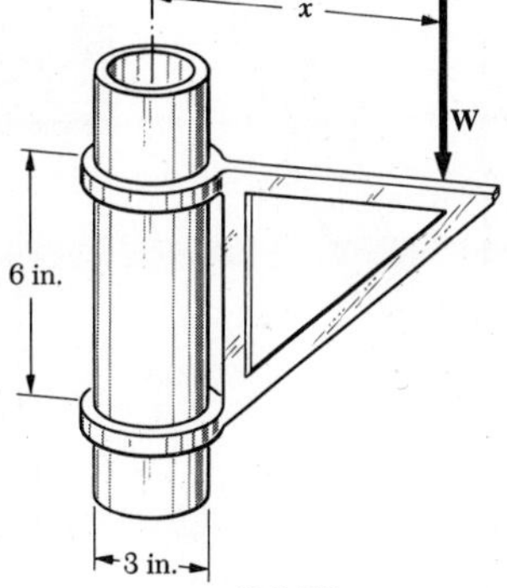

FIG. P 8.26

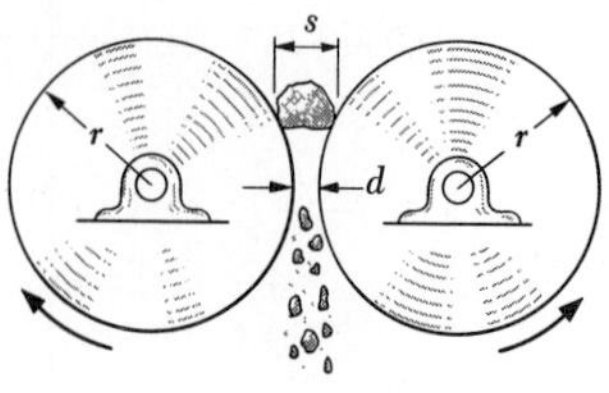

FIG. P 8.27

8.27. Two large cylinders, each of radius $r = 20$ in., rotate in opposite directions and form the main elements of a crusher for stone aggregate. The distance d is set equal to the maximum desired size of the crushed aggregate. If $d = 1$ in. and $\mu = 0.30$, determine the size s of the largest stones which will be pulled through the crusher by friction alone.

8.28. Two uniform rods, each of weight W, are held by frictionless pins A and B. It is observed that if the value of θ is greater than 10°, the rods will not remain in equilibrium. Determine the coefficient of friction at C.

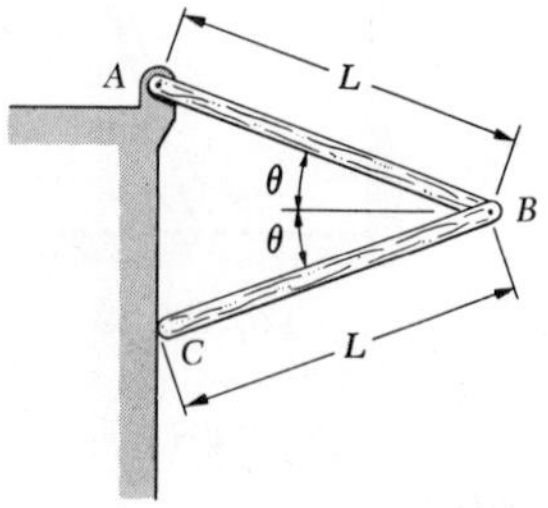

FIG. P 8.28

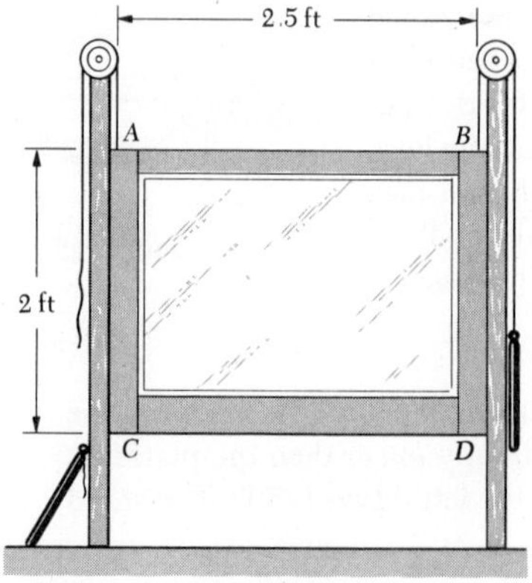

FIG. P 8.29

8.29. A window sash weighs 10 lb and is normally supported by two 5-lb sash weights. It is observed that the window remains open after one sash cord has broken. What is the smallest possible value of the coefficient of static friction? (Assume that the sash is slightly smaller than the frame and will bind only at points A and D.)

8.30. A rod DE and a small cylinder are placed between two guides as shown. The rod is not to slip downward, however large the force **W** may be; i.e., the arrangement is to be *self-locking*. Determine the minimum allowable coefficients of friction at A, B, and C.

8.31. A pipe of diameter d is gripped by the Stillson wrench shown. Portions AB and DE of the wrench are rigidly attached to each other and portion CF is connected by a pin at D. If the wrench is to grip the pipe and be self-locking, determine the required minimum coefficients of friction at A and at C, (a) in terms of the given letters, (b) if $a = \frac{1}{2}$ in., $b = 1$ in., $c = 10$ in., and $d = 1\frac{1}{4}$ in.

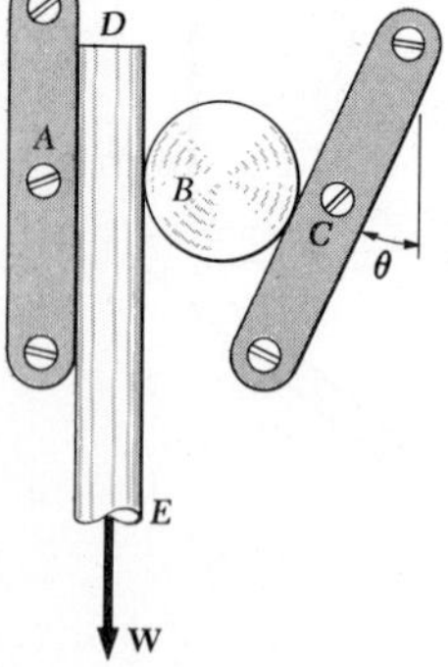

FIG. P 8.30

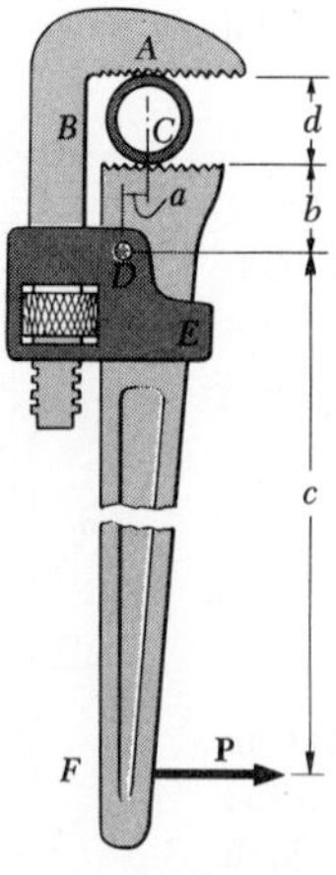

FIG. P 8.31

8.32. A block of weight W rests on an incline which forms an angle θ with the horizontal plane. A horizontal force **P**, parallel to the incline, is applied to the block. Denoting by μ the coefficient of friction, determine (*a*) the magnitude of **P** required to move the block, (*b*) the direction in which the block moves. (*c*) Obtain numerical values for parts *a* and *b*, when $\theta = 15°$, $\mu = 0.30$, and $W = 50$ lb.

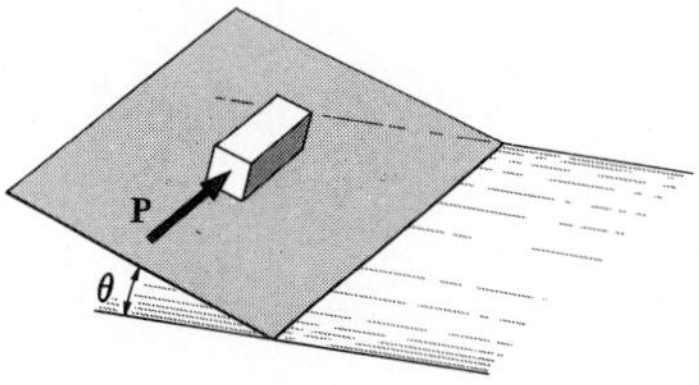

FIG. P 8.32

8.33. A uniform plank of weight $W = 60$ lb rests on two joists as shown. The coefficient of friction between the joists and the plank is $\mu = 0.40$. Determine the magnitude of the horizontal force **P** required to move the plank (*a*) when $a = 12$ ft, (*b*) when $a = 10$ ft.

8.34. Determine the smallest distance a for which the plank of Prob. 8.33 will slip at C.

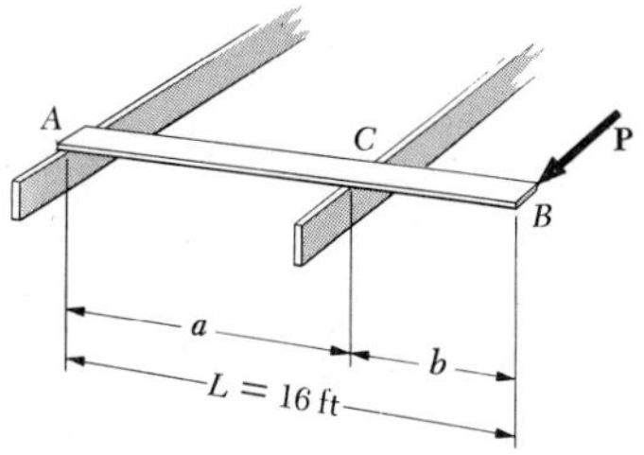

FIG. P 8.33

*8.35. A cylinder of weight W is placed in a V block as shown. Denoting by ϕ the angle of friction between the cylinder and the block and assuming $\phi < \theta$, determine (*a*) the axial force **P** required to move the cylinder, (*b*) the couple **M**, applied in the plane of the cross section of the cylinder, required to rotate the cylinder.

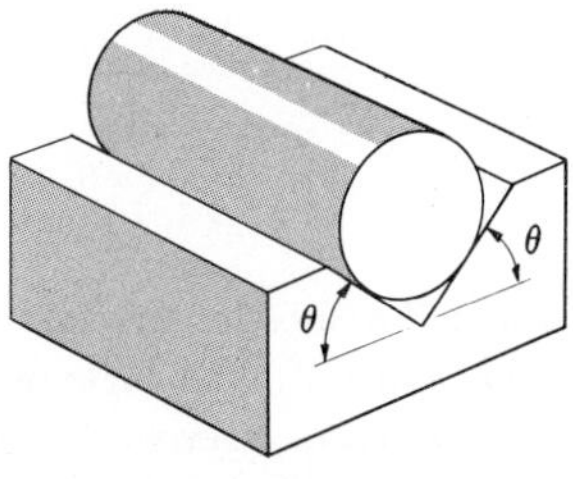

FIG. P 8.35

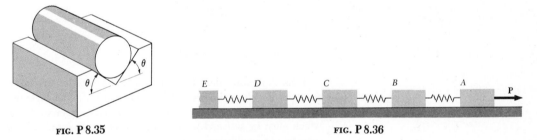

FIG. P 8.36

8.36. The mathematical model shown has been developed for the analysis of a certain structure. It consists of a large number of 1-lb blocks connected in series by springs, each of constant $k = 0.20$ lb/in. The coefficient of friction between the base and each block is 0.40. At a time when the tension in each spring is zero, the magnitude of **P** is slowly increased from zero to a maximum of 0.50 lb; the magnitude of **P** is then slowly decreased until it becomes zero again. For both the cases (1) when $P = 0.50$ lb and (2) when P is again zero, determine (*a*) the friction force acting on each block, (*b*) the tension in each spring, (*c*) the position of each block relative to its original position.

8.37. Solve Prob. 8.36 assuming that the magnitude of the force **P** increases to 1.00 lb and then decreases until it is again zero.

8.38. For the model of Prob. 8.36, construct a graph showing the magnitude of the force **P** versus the position of block A, (*a*) as P increases from zero to 1.00 lb, (*b*) as P decreases from 1.00 lb to zero.

8.39. Identical cylindrical cans, each of weight W, are raised to the top of an incline by a series of moving arms. Either one or two cans are moved by each arm. The coefficient of friction between all surfaces is $\mu = 0.20$. If $W = 2.00$ lb and $\theta = 12°$, determine the force parallel to the incline which the arm must exert on can A to move it. Does can A roll or slide?

***8.40.** Solve Prob. 8.39 considering can C instead of can A.

***8.41.** In Prob. 8.39 determine the range of values of θ for which can A will roll.

***8.42.** In Prob. 8.39 determine the range of values of θ for which can C will roll.

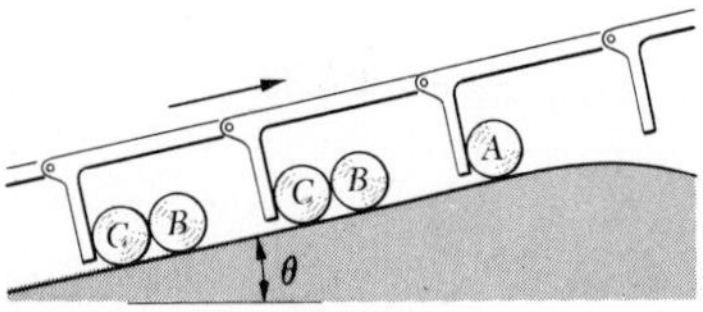

FIG. P 8.39

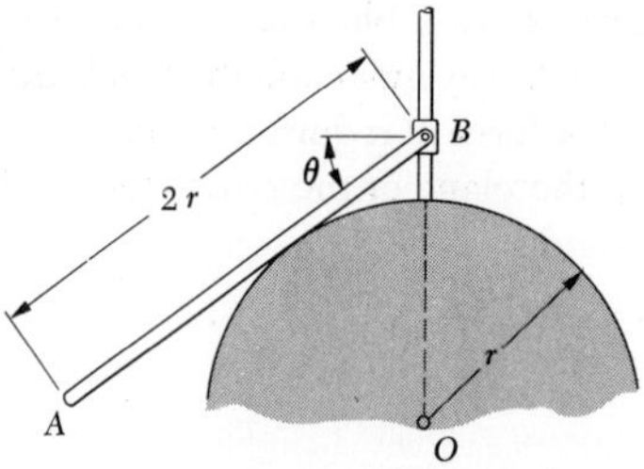

FIG. P 8.43 AND P 8.44

***8.43.** A uniform slender rod is attached to a collar at B and rests on a *smooth* circular cylindrical surface of radius r. The angle of friction between the collar and the vertical guide is ϕ. Derive the equation which must be satisfied by the largest and smallest values of θ corresponding to equilibrium.

***8.44.** A uniform slender rod is attached to a collar at B and rests on a circular cylindrical surface of radius r. The collar may slide without friction along a vertical guide. Denoting by ϕ the angle of friction between the rod and the surface, show that the largest and smallest values of θ corresponding to equilibrium must satisfy the equation

$$\tan\theta + \tan^2\theta \tan(\theta \mp \phi) = 1$$

8.5. Wedges.

Wedges are simple machines used to raise large stone blocks and other heavy loads. These loads may be raised by applying to the wedge a force usually considerably smaller than the weight of the load. Besides, because of the friction existing between the surfaces in contact, a wedge, if properly shaped, will remain in place after being forced under the load. Wedges may thus be used advantageously to make small adjustments in the position of heavy pieces of machinery.

Consider the 2,000-lb block A shown in Fig. 8.7a. This block rests against a vertical wall B and is to be raised a few inches by forcing a wedge C between block A and a second wedge D. We want to find the minimum value of the force $\mathbf{P}$ which must be applied to the wedge C to move the block.

The free-body diagrams of block A and of wedge C have been drawn in Fig. 8.7b and c. The forces acting on the block include its weight and the normal and friction forces at the surfaces of contact with wall B and wedge C. The magnitudes of the friction forces $\mathbf{F}_1$ and $\mathbf{F}_2$ are equal, respectively, to $\mu_s N_1$ and $\mu_s N_2$ since the motion of the block must be started. It is important to show the friction forces with their correct sense. Since the block will move upward, the force $\mathbf{F}_1$ exerted by the wall on the block must be directed downward. On the other hand, since the wedge C moves to the right, the relative motion of A with respect to C is to the left and the force $\mathbf{F}_2$ exerted by C on A must be directed to the right.

Considering now the free body C in Fig. 8.7c, we note that the forces acting on C include the applied force $\mathbf{P}$ and the normal and friction forces at the surfaces of contact with A and D. The weight of the wedge is small compared with the other forces involved and may be neglected. The forces acting on C are equal and opposite to the forces $\mathbf{N}_2$ and $\mathbf{F}_2$ acting on A and are denoted, respectively, by $-\mathbf{N}_2$ and $-\mathbf{F}_2$; the friction force $-\mathbf{F}_2$ must therefore be directed to the left. We check that the force $\mathbf{F}_3$ is also directed to the left.

The total number of unknowns involved in the two free-body diagrams may be reduced to four if the friction forces are expressed in terms of the normal forces. Expressing that block A and wedge C are in equilibrium will provide four equations which may be solved to obtain the magnitude of $\mathbf{P}$. It should be noted that, in the example considered here, it will be more convenient to replace each pair of normal and friction forces by their resultant. Each free body is then subjected to only three forces, and the problem may be solved by drawing the corresponding force triangles. The actual solution of the problem has been carried out in this way in Sample Prob. 8.4.

8.6. Square-threaded Screws. Square-threaded screws are frequently used in jacks, presses, and other mechanisms. Their analysis is similar to that of a block sliding along an inclined plane.

Consider the jack shown in Fig. 8.8. The screw carries a load $\mathbf{W}$ and is supported by the base of the jack. Contact be-

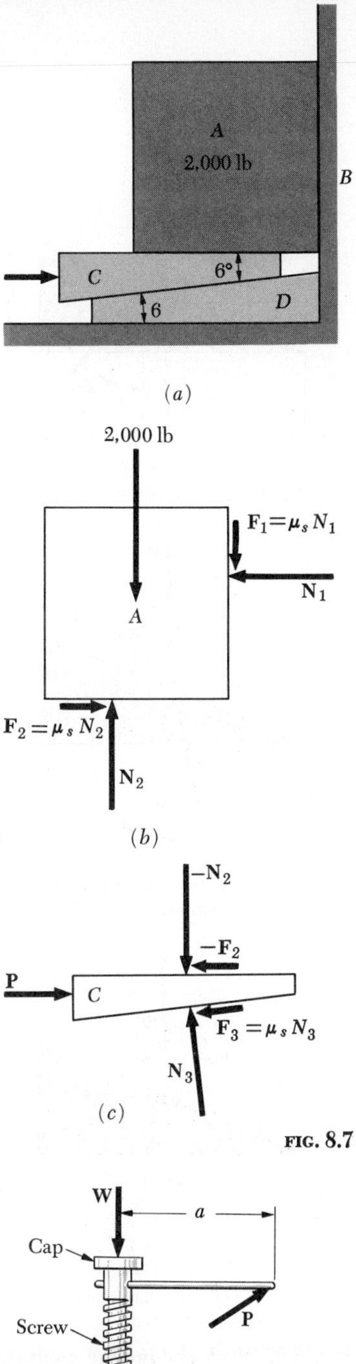

FIG. 8.7

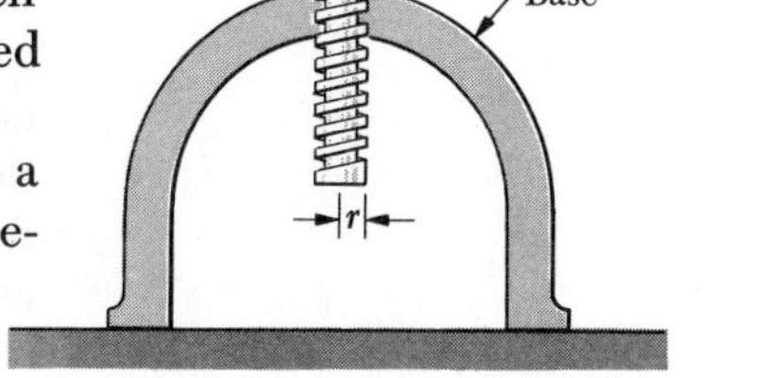

FIG. 8.8

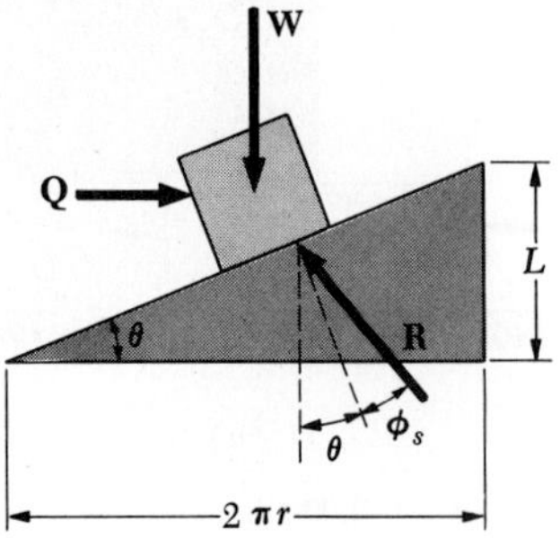

(*a*) Impending motion upward

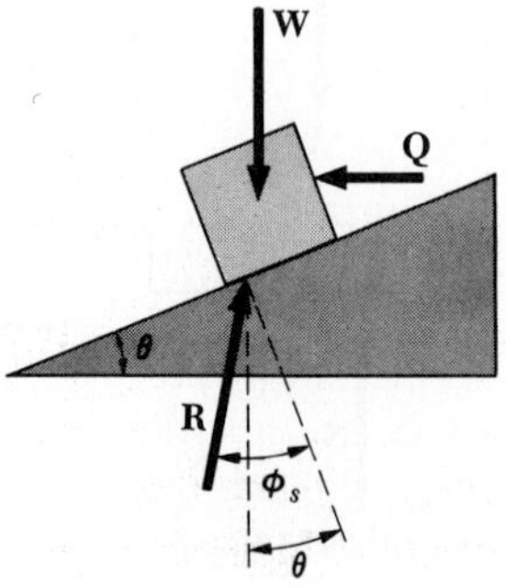

(*b*) Impending motion downward with $\phi_s > \theta$

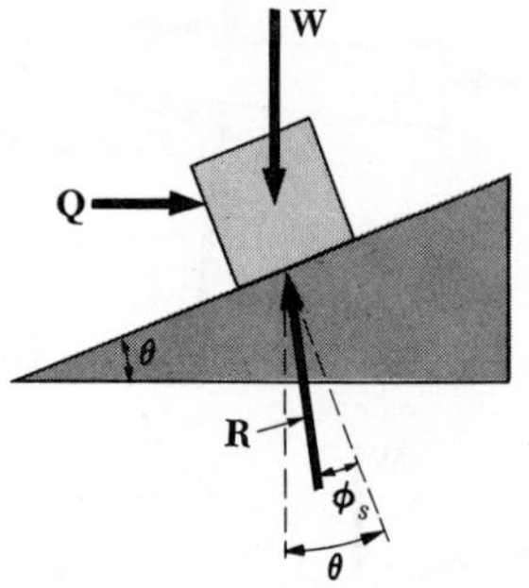

(*c*) Impending motion downward with $\phi_s < \theta$

FIG. 8.9. Block-and-incline analysis of a screw

tween screw and base takes place along a portion of their threads. By applying a force **P** on the handle, the screw may be made to turn and to raise the load **W**.

The thread of the base has been unwrapped and shown as a straight line in Fig. 8.9*a*. The correct slope was obtained by plotting horizontally the product $2\pi r$, where r is the mean radius of the thread, and vertically the *lead* L of the screw, i.e., the distance through which the screw advances in one turn. The angle θ this line forms with the horizontal is the *lead angle.* Since the force of friction between two surfaces in contact does not depend upon the area of contact, the two threads may be assumed to be in contact over a much smaller area than they actually are and the screw may be represented by the block shown in Fig. 8.9*a*. It should be noted, however, that, in this analysis of the jack, the friction between cap and screw is neglected.

The free-body diagram of the block should include the load **W**, the reaction **R** of the base thread, and a horizontal force **Q** having the same effect as the force **P** exerted on the handle. The force **Q** should have the same moment as **P** about the axis of the screw and its magnitude should thus be $Q = Pa/r$. The force **Q**, and thus the force **P** required to raise the load **W**, may be obtained from the free-body diagram shown in Fig. 8.9*a*. The friction angle is taken equal to ϕ_s since the load will presumably be raised through a succession of short strokes. In mechanisms providing for the continuous rotation of a screw, it may be desirable to distinguish between the force required to start motion (using ϕ_s) and that required to maintain motion (using ϕ_k).

If the friction angle ϕ_s is larger than the lead angle θ, the screw is said to be *self-locking;* it will remain in place under the load. To lower the load, we must then apply the force shown in Fig. 8.9*b*. If ϕ_s is smaller than θ, the screw will unwind under the load; it is then necessary to apply the force shown in Fig. 8.9*c* to maintain equilibrium.

The lead of a screw should not be confused with its *pitch.* The lead was defined as the distance through which the screw advances in one turn; the pitch is the distance measured between two consecutive threads. While lead and pitch are equal in the case of *single-threaded* screws, they are different in the case of *multiple-threaded* screws, i.e., screws having several independent threads. It is easily verified that, for double-threaded screws, the lead is twice as large as the pitch; for triple-threaded screws, it is three times as large as the pitch; etc.

SAMPLE PROBLEM 8.4

A 2,000-lb block is raised by forcing a wedge under it as shown. Determine the minimum value of the force **P** which must be applied to the wedge. The coefficient of static friction is 0.30 at all surfaces of contact.

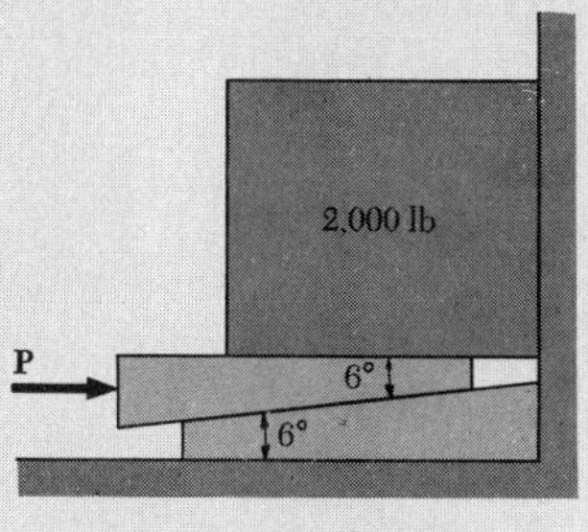

Solution. The free-body diagrams of the block and of the upper wedge are shown below; the corresponding force triangles are also shown. The sense in which friction takes place is obtained by considering the *relative motion* of the surfaces in contact (see Sec. 8.5). The force $\mathbf{R}_2$ exerted by the wedge on the block is obtained by applying the law of sines to the force triangle of the block. The force $\mathbf{R}_2$ exerted by the block on the wedge is equal and opposite; its value is used to draw the force triangle of the wedge, from which **P** is obtained.

Free Body: Block

$$\frac{R_2}{\sin 106.7°} = \frac{2{,}000 \text{ lb}}{\sin [180° - (106.7° + 16.7°)]}$$

$$R_2 = 2{,}300 \text{ lb}$$

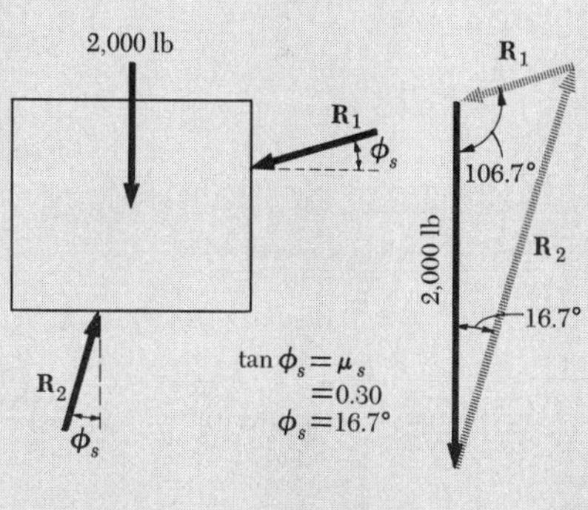

Free Body: Wedge

$$\frac{P}{\sin (16.7° + 22.7°)} = \frac{2{,}300 \text{ lb}}{\sin (90° - 22.7°)}$$

$$P = 1{,}580 \text{ lb}$$

$$\mathbf{P} = 1{,}580 \text{ lb} \rightarrow$$ ◄

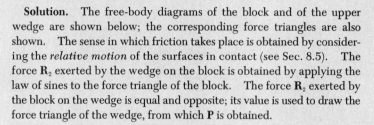

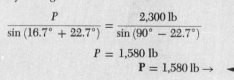

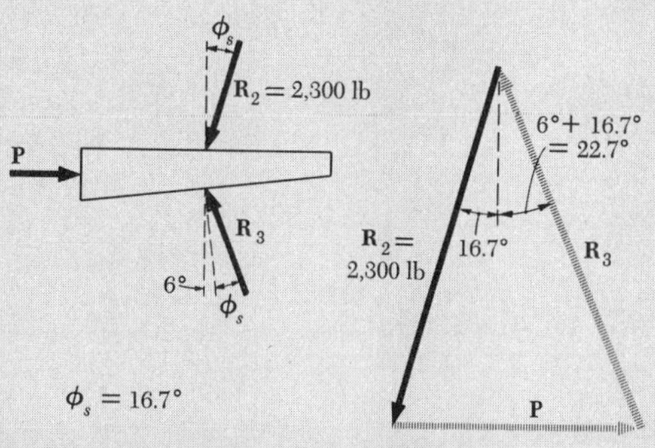

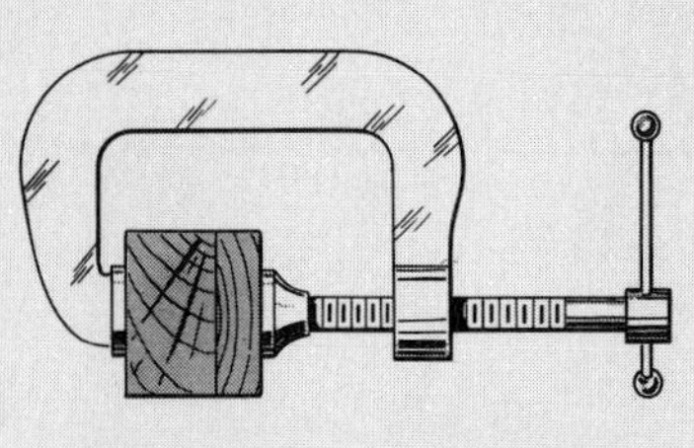

SAMPLE PROBLEM 8.5

A clamp is used to hold two pieces of wood together as shown. The clamp has a double square thread of mean diameter equal to 0.50 in. and with a pitch of 0.10 in. The coefficient of friction between threads is $\mu_s = 0.30$. If a maximum torque of 30 lb-ft is applied in tightening the clamp, determine (*a*) the force exerted on the pieces of wood, (*b*) the torque required to loosen the clamp.

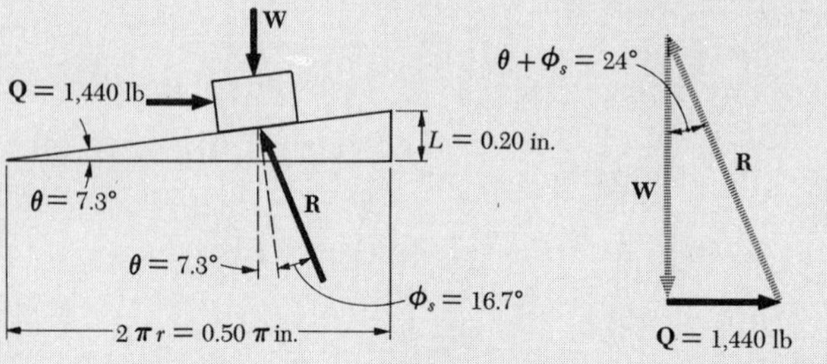

a. **Force Exerted by Clamp.** Since the screw is double-threaded, the lead L is equal to twice the pitch, i.e., to 2(0.10 in.) = 0.20 in. The lead angle θ and the friction angle ϕ_s are obtained by writing

$$\tan\theta = \frac{L}{2\pi r} = \frac{0.20 \text{ in.}}{0.50\pi \text{ in.}} = 0.1273 \qquad \theta = 7.3°$$

$$\tan\phi_s = \mu_s = 0.30 \qquad \phi_s = 16.7°$$

The force **Q** which should be applied to the block representing the screw is obtained by expressing that its moment Qr about the axis of the screw is equal to the applied torque.

$$Q(0.25 \text{ in.}) = 30 \text{ lb-ft} \qquad Q = \frac{30 \text{ lb-ft}}{0.25 \text{ in.}} = \frac{360 \text{ lb-in.}}{0.25 \text{ in.}} = 1{,}440 \text{ lb}$$

The free-body diagram and the corresponding force triangle may now be drawn for the block; the magnitude of the force **W** exerted on the pieces of wood is obtained by solving the triangle.

$$W = \frac{Q}{\tan(\theta + \phi_s)} = \frac{1{,}440 \text{ lb}}{\tan 24°}$$

$$W = 3{,}230 \text{ lb} \quad ◄$$

b. **Torque Required to Loosen Clamp.** The force **Q** required to loosen the clamp and the corresponding torque are obtained from the free-body diagram and force triangle shown.

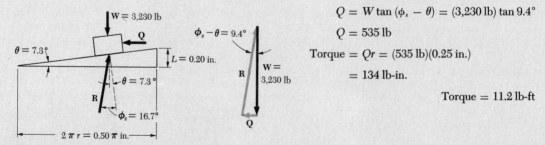

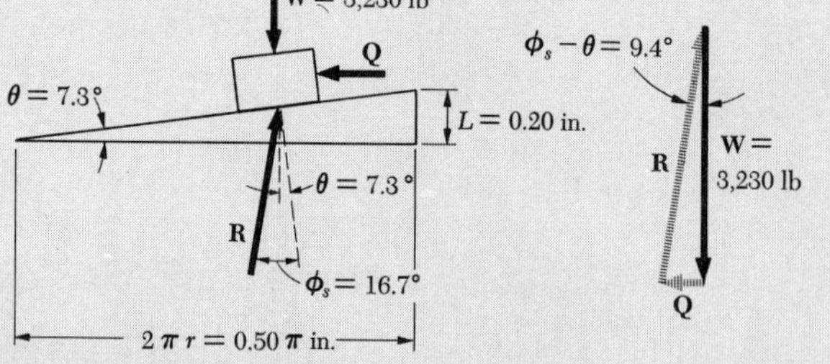

$$Q = W \tan(\phi_s - \theta) = (3{,}230 \text{ lb}) \tan 9.4°$$

$$Q = 535 \text{ lb}$$

$$\text{Torque} = Qr = (535 \text{ lb})(0.25 \text{ in.})$$

$$= 134 \text{ lb-in.}$$

$$\text{Torque} = 11.2 \text{ lb-ft} \quad ◄$$

PROBLEMS

8.45. The machine part ABC is supported by a frictionless hinge at B and by a wedge at C. Knowing that $\mu = 0.20$ at both surfaces of the wedge, determine (*a*) the force **P** required to move the wedge to the left, (*b*) the corresponding components of the reaction at B.

8.46. Solve Prob. 8.45 assuming that the wedge is to be moved to the right.

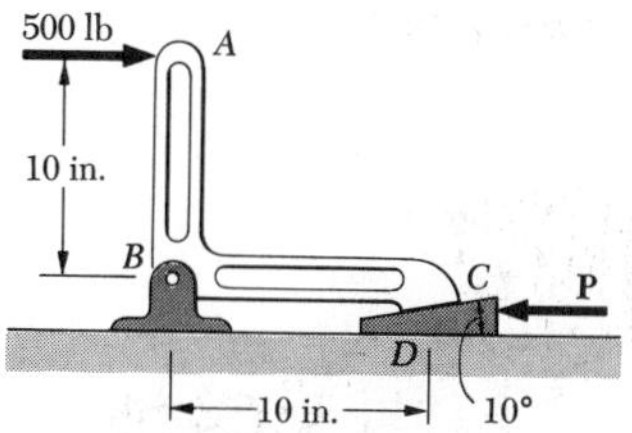

FIG. P 8.45

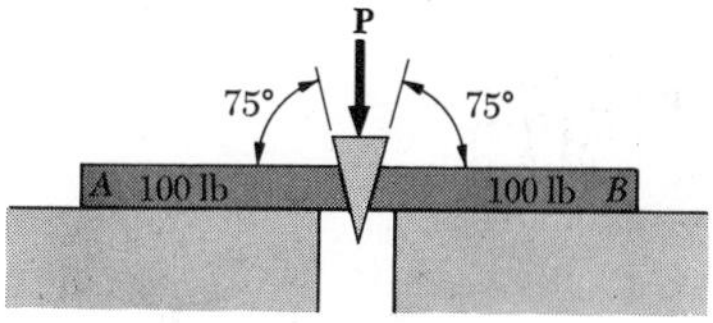

FIG. P 8.47

8.47. A wedge, of weight 4 lb, is to be driven between two plates A and B. The coefficient of static friction between all surfaces of contact is 0.35. Determine the magnitude of the force **P** required to start moving the wedge (*a*) if the plates are equally free to move, (*b*) if plate B is securely bolted to the surface.

8.48. The spring of the door latch has a constant of 1.5 lb/in. and in the position shown exerts a force of $\frac{1}{2}$ lb on the bolt. The coefficient of friction between the bolt and the guide plate is 0.40; all other surfaces are well lubricated and may be assumed to be frictionless. Determine the magnitude of the force **P** required to start closing the door.

8.49. In Prob. 8.48 determine the angle which the face of the bolt should form with the line BC if the force **P** required to close the door is to be the same for both the position shown and the position when B is almost at the guide plate.

8.50. Neglecting the weight of the wedge, determine the magnitude of the force **P** required to raise the 500-lb weight. The coefficient of friction is 0.30 at all surfaces.

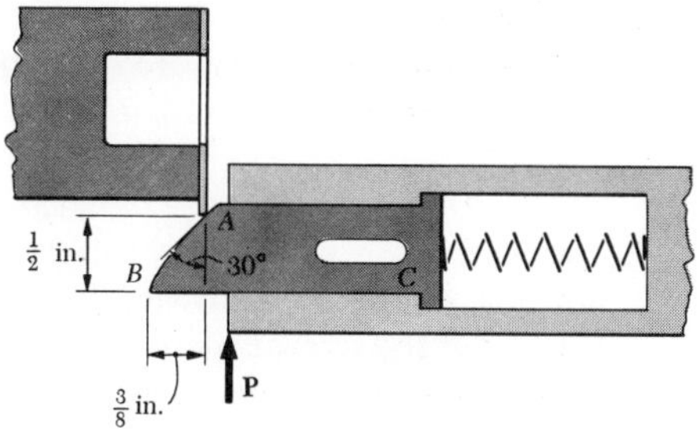

FIG. P 8.48

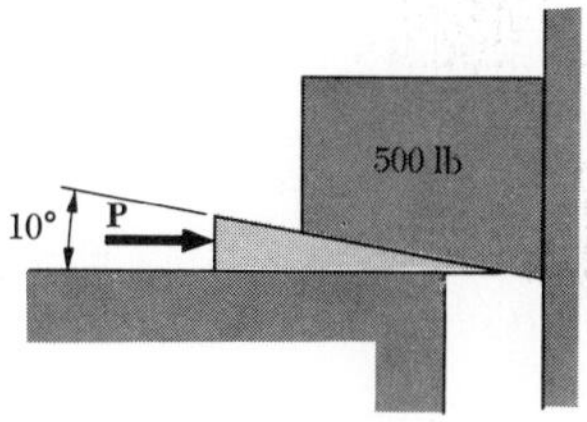

FIG. P 8.50

8.51. A 20° wedge is forced into a saw cut to prevent binding of the circular saw. The coefficient of friction between the wedge and the wood is 0.30. Knowing that a horizontal force **P** of magnitude 25 lb was required to insert the wedge, determine the magnitude of the forces exerted on the board by the wedge after it has been inserted.

8.52. A circular disk of radius $r = 2$ in. is eccentrically connected to a shaft A. A constant 10-lb force is applied to the horizontal follower BD. Knowing that $\mu = 0.20$, determine the magnitude M of the couple required to rotate the disk clockwise about A (*a*) if $\theta = 0°$, (*b*) if $\theta = 90°$.

8.53. Solve Prob. 8.52 for the case when (*a*) $\theta = 180°$, (*b*) $\theta = 270°$.

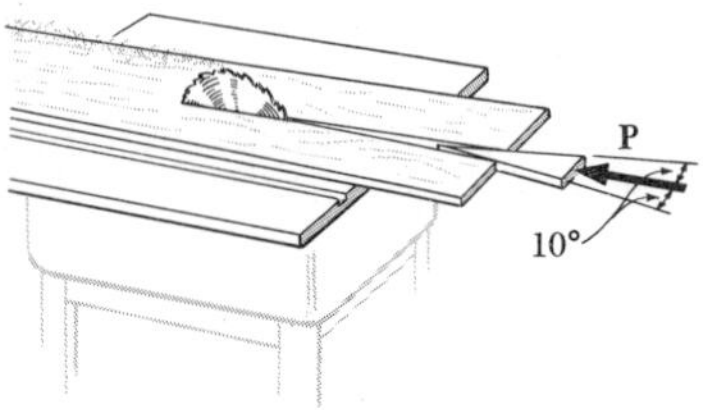

FIG. P 8.51

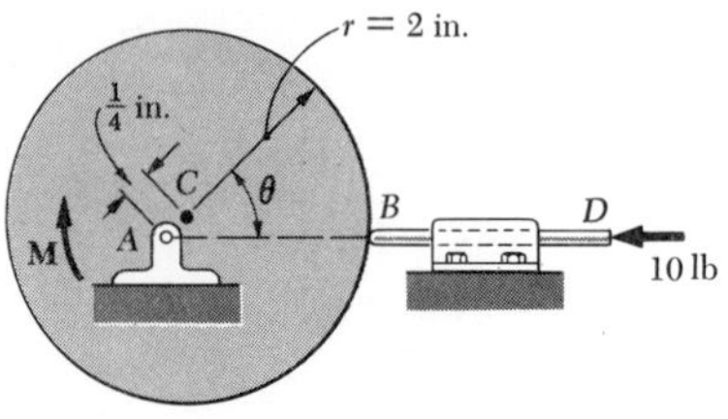

FIG. P 8.52

8.54. A 5° wedge is to be forced under a 1,400-lb machine base at A. Knowing that $\mu = 0.10$ at all surfaces, (*a*) determine the force **P** required to move the wedge, (*b*) indicate whether the machine will move.

8.55. Solve Prob. 8.54 assuming that the wedge is to be forced under the machine base at B instead of A.

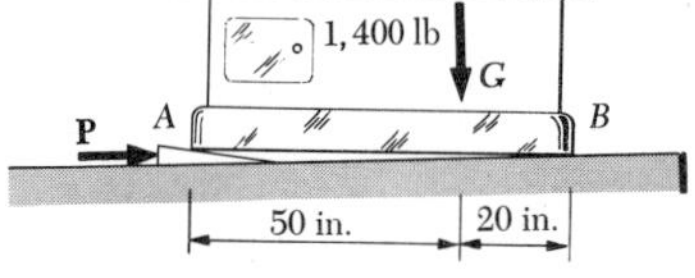

FIG. P 8.54

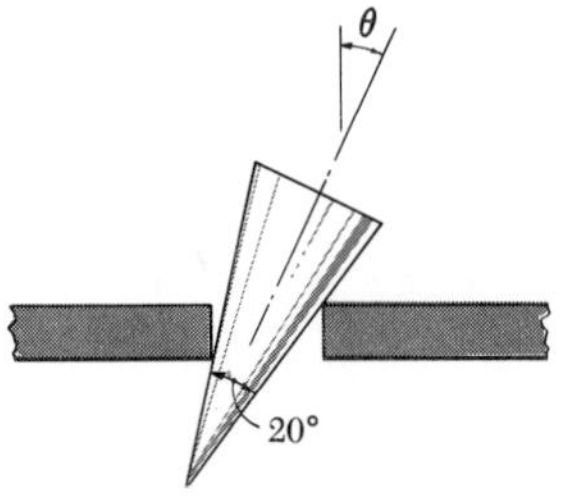

FIG. P 8.56

*8.56. A conical wedge is placed between two horizontal plates which are then slowly moved toward each other. Indicate what will happen to the wedge (*a*) if $\mu = 0.15$, (*b*) if $\mu = 0.25$.

8.57. Derive the following formulas relating the load W and the force **P** exerted on the handle of the jack discussed in Sec. 8.6: (*a*) $P = (Wr/a) \tan(\theta + \phi_s)$, to raise the load; (*b*) $P = (Wr/a) \tan(\phi_s - \theta)$, to lower the load if the screw is self-locking; (*c*) $P = (Wr/a) \tan(\theta - \phi_s)$, to hold the load if the screw is not self-locking.

8.58. High-strength bolts are now used in the construction of many buildings. For a 1-in.-nominal-diameter bolt the required minimum bolt tension is specified as 42,500 lb. It is further specified that a torque of 710 lb-ft be applied to the bolt and nut to obtain this tension. Determine the coefficient of friction for which these values are compatible. The mean diameter of the thread is 0.94 in. and the lead is 0.125 in. Neglect friction between the nut and washer, and assume the bolt to be square-threaded.

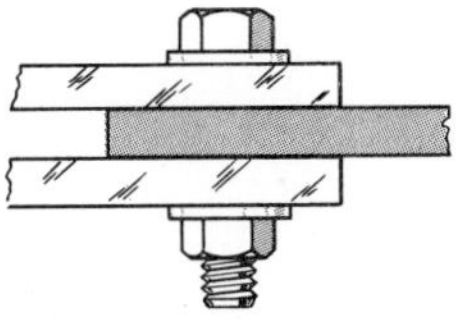

FIG. P 8.58

8.59. The square-threaded worm gear shown has a mean radius of $1\frac{1}{2}$ in. and a pitch of $\frac{3}{8}$ in. The large gear is subjected to a constant clockwise torque of 500 lb-ft. Knowing that the coefficient of friction between gear teeth is 0.10, determine the torque which must be applied to shaft *AB* in order to rotate the large gear counterclockwise. Neglect friction in the bearings at *A*, *B*, and *C*.

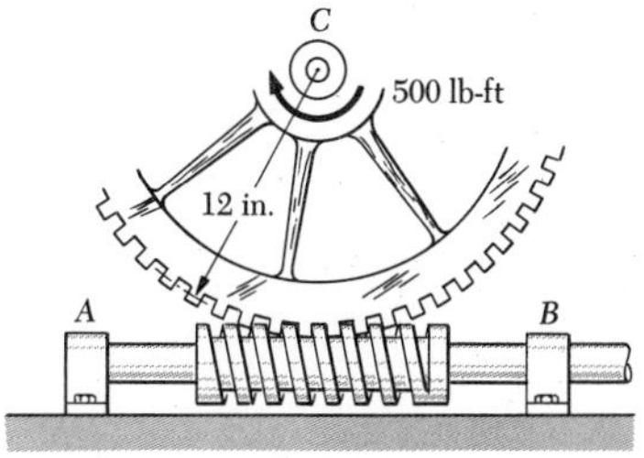

FIG. P 8.59

8.60. In Prob. 8.59 determine the torque which must be applied to shaft *AB* in order to rotate the large gear clockwise.

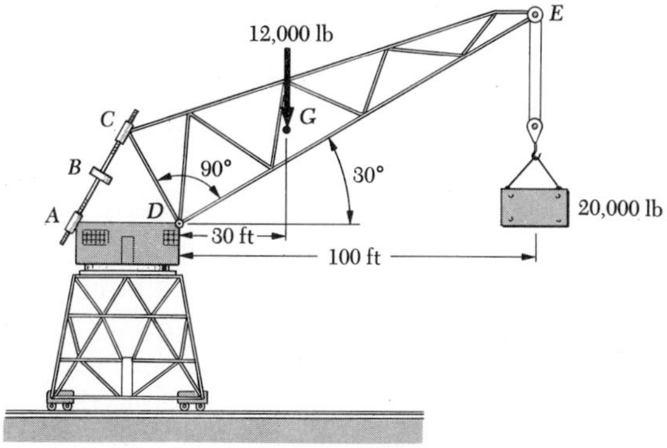

FIG. P 8.61

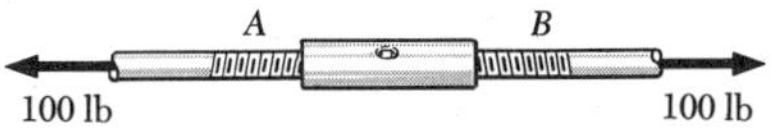

FIG. P 8.62

8.61. The main features of a screw-luffing crane are shown. Distances *AD* and *CD* are each 25 ft. The position of the boom *CDE* is controlled by the screw *ABC* which is single-threaded at each end (left-handed thread at *A*, right-handed thread at *C*). Each thread has a pitch of $1\frac{1}{4}$ in. and a mean diameter of 8 in. If $\mu = 0.08$, determine the moment of the couple which must be applied to the screw (*a*) to raise the boom, (*b*) to lower the boom.

8.62. The ends of two fixed rods *A* and *B* are each made in the form of a single-threaded screw of mean radius 0.25 in. and pitch 0.08 in. The coefficient of friction between the rods and the threaded sleeve is 0.15. Determine the moment of the couple which must be applied to the sleeve in order to draw the rods closer together. Rod *A* has a left-handed thread and rod *B* a right-handed thread.

8.63. In Prob. 8.62 a right-handed thread is used on *both* rods *A* and *B*. Determine the moment of the couple which must be applied to the sleeve in order to rotate it.

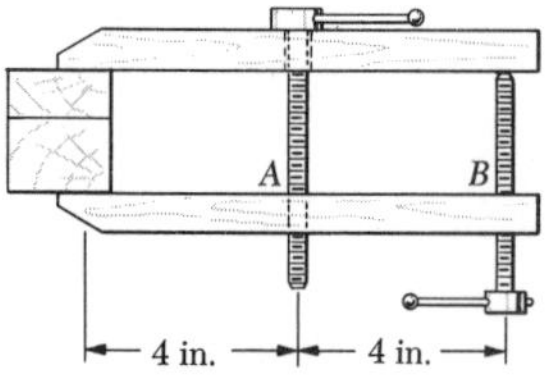

FIG. P 8.64

8.64. The vise shown consists of two members connected by two double-threaded screws of mean radius 0.20 in. and pitch 0.04 in. The lower member is threaded at *A* and *B* ($\mu_s = 0.25$), but the upper member is not threaded. It is desired to apply two equal and opposite forces of 100 lb on the blocks held between the jaws. (*a*) What screw should be adjusted first? (*b*) What is the maximum torque applied in tightening the second screw?

8.65. The vise of Prob. 8.64 has been tightened until the blocks are compressed by two equal and opposite 100-lb forces. The blocks are now to be removed from the vise. (*a*) What screw should be loosened? (*b*) What is the maximum torque applied in loosening the screw?

***8.7. Journal Bearings. Axle Friction.** Journal bearings are used to provide lateral support to rotating shafts and axles. Thrust bearings, which will be studied in the next section, are used to provide axial support to shafts and axles. If the journal bearing is fully lubricated, the frictional resistance depends upon the speed of rotation, the clearance between axle and bearing, and the viscosity of the lubricant. As indicated in Sec. 8.1, such problems are studied in fluid mechanics. The methods of this chapter, however, may be applied to the study of axle friction when the bearing is not lubricated or only partially lubricated. We may then assume that the axle and the bearing are in direct contact along a single straight line.

Consider two wheels, each of weight **W**, rigidly mounted on an axle supported symmetrically by two journal bearings (Fig. 8.10*a*). If the wheels rotate, we find that, to keep them rotating at constant speed, it is necessary to apply to each of them a couple **M**. A free-body diagram has been drawn in Fig. 8.10*c*, which represents one of the wheels and the corresponding half axle in projection on a plane perpendicular to the axle. The forces acting on the free body include the weight **W** of the wheel, the couple **M** required to maintain its motion, and a force **R** representing the reaction of the bearing. This force is vertical, equal, and opposite to **W** but does not pass through the center *O* of the axle; **R** is located to the right of *O* at a distance such that its moment about *O* balances the moment **M** of the couple. Contact between axle and bearing, there-

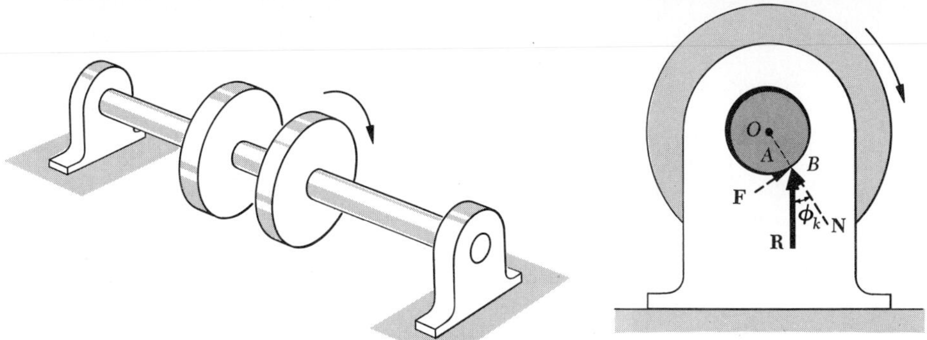

(a) (b)

fore, does not take place at the lowest point A when the axle rotates. It takes place at point B (Fig. 8.10b) or, rather, along a straight line intersecting the plane of the figure at B. Physically, this is explained by the fact that, when the wheels are set in motion, the axle "climbs" in the bearings until slippage occurs. After sliding back slightly, the axle settles more or less in the position shown. This position is such that the angle between the reaction **R** and the normal to the surface of the bearing is equal to the angle of kinetic friction ϕ_k. The distance from O to the line of action of **R** is thus $r \sin \phi_k$, where r is the radius of the axle. Writing that $\Sigma M_O = 0$ for the forces acting on the free body considered, we obtain the magnitude of the couple **M** required to overcome the frictional resistance of one of the bearings:

$$M = Rr \sin \phi_k \tag{8.5}$$

Observing that, for small values of the angle of friction, $\sin \phi_k$ may be replaced by $\tan \phi_k$, that is, by μ_k, we write the approximate formula

$$M \approx Rr\mu_k \tag{8.6}$$

In the solution of certain problems, it may be more convenient to let the line of action of **R** pass through O, as it does when the axle does not rotate. A couple $-$**M** of the same magnitude as the couple **M** must then be added to the reaction **R** (Fig. 8.10d). This couple represents the frictional resistance of the bearing.

In case a graphical solution is preferred, the line of action of **R** may be readily drawn (Fig. 8.10e) if we note that it must be tangent to a circle centered at O and of radius

$$r_f = r \sin \phi_k \approx r\mu_k \tag{8.7}$$

This circle is called the *circle of friction* of the axle and bearing and is independent of the loading conditions of the axle.

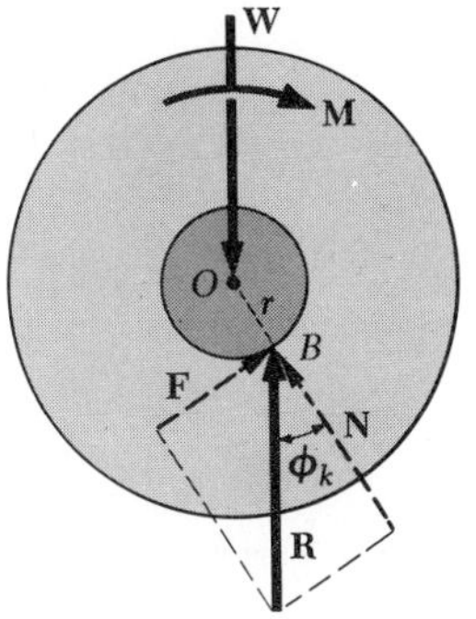

(c)

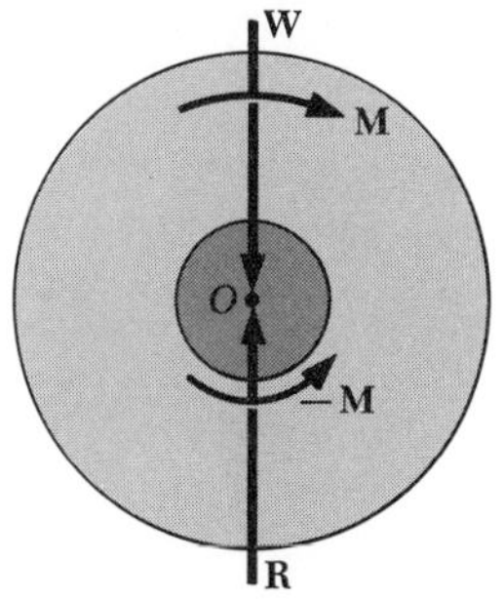

(d)

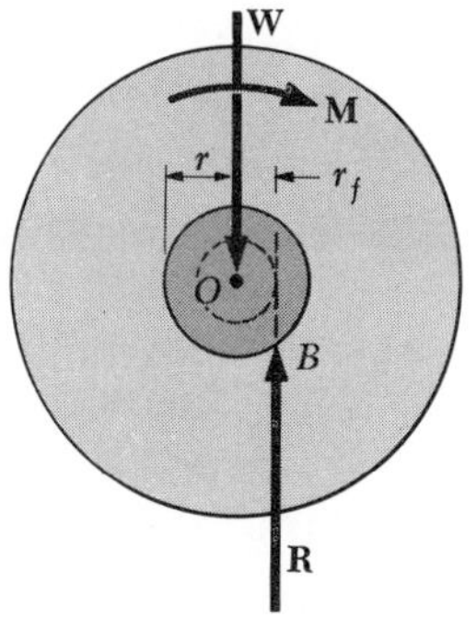

(e)

FIG. 8.10

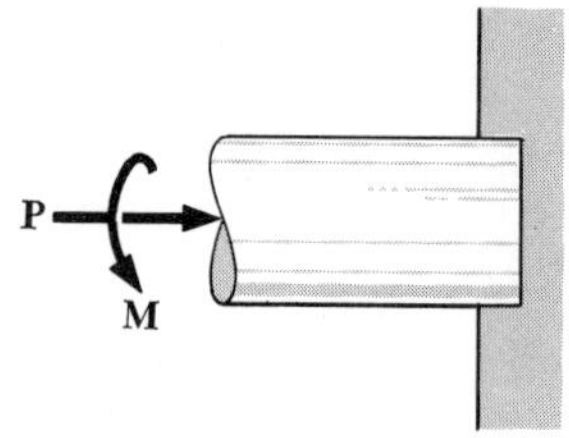

(a) End bearing

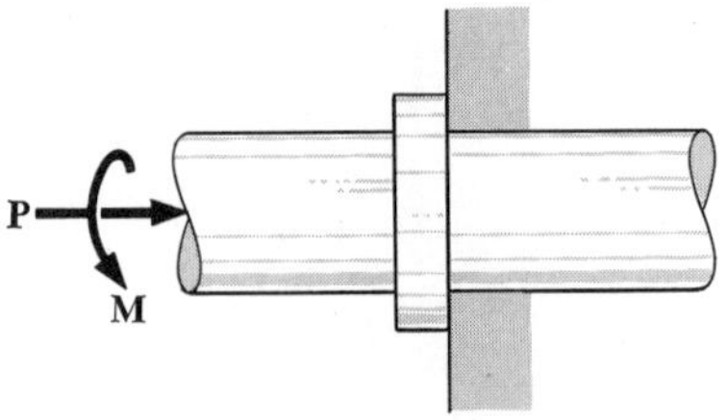

(b) Collar bearing

FIG. 8.11. **Thrust bearings**

***8.8. Thrust Bearings. Disk Friction.** Thrust bearings are used to provide axial support to rotating shafts and axles. They are of two types: (1) *end bearings* and (2) *collar bearings* (Fig. 8.11). In the case of collar bearings, friction forces develop between the two ring-shaped areas which are in contact. In the case of end bearings, friction takes place over full circular areas, or over ring-shaped areas when the end of the shaft is hollow. Friction between circular areas, called *disk friction,* also occurs in other mechanisms, such as *disk clutches.*

To obtain a formula which is valid in the most general case of disk friction, we shall consider a rotating hollow shaft. A couple **M** keeps the shaft rotating at constant speed while a force **P** maintains it in contact with a fixed bearing (Fig. 8.12). Contact between the shaft and the bearing takes place over a ring-shaped area of inner radius R_1 and outer radius R_2. Assuming that the pressure between the two surfaces in contact is uniform, we find that the magnitude of the normal force $\Delta\mathbf{N}$ exerted on an element of area ΔA is $\Delta N = P\,\Delta A/A$, where $A = \pi(R_2^2 - R_1^2)$, and that the magnitude of the friction force $\Delta\mathbf{F}$ acting on ΔA is $\Delta F = \mu_k\,\Delta N$. Denoting by r the distance from the axis of the shaft to the element of area ΔA, we express as follows the moment ΔM of $\Delta\mathbf{F}$ about the axis of the shaft:

$$\Delta M = r\,\Delta F = \frac{r\mu_k P\,\Delta A}{\pi(R_2^2 - R_1^2)}$$

The equilibrium of the shaft requires that the moment **M** of the couple applied to the shaft be equal in magnitude to the sum of the moments of the friction forces $\Delta\mathbf{F}$. Replacing ΔA by the infinitesimal element $dA = r\,d\theta\,dr$ used with polar coordinates, and integrating over the area of contact, we thus obtain the following expression for the magnitude of the couple

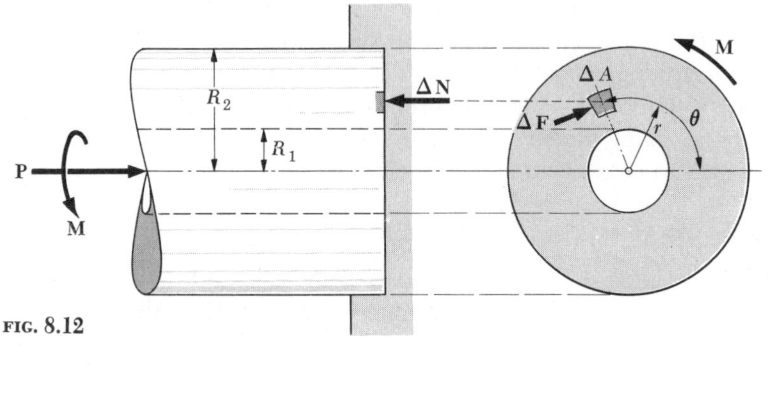

FIG. 8.12

M required to overcome the frictional resistance of the bearing:

$$M = \frac{\mu_k P}{\pi(R_2^2 - R_1^2)} \int_0^{2\pi} \int_{R_1}^{R_2} r^2 \, dr \, d\theta$$

$$= \frac{\mu_k P}{\pi(R_2^2 - R_1^2)} \int_0^{2\pi} \tfrac{1}{3} (R_2^3 - R_1^3) \, d\theta$$

$$M = \tfrac{2}{3}\mu_k P \frac{R_2^3 - R_1^3}{R_2^2 - R_1^2} \qquad (8.8)$$

When contact takes place over a full circle of radius R, formula (8.8) reduces to

$$M = \tfrac{2}{3}\mu_k PR \qquad (8.9)$$

The value of M is then the same as would be obtained if contact between shaft and bearing took place at a single point located at a distance $2R/3$ from the axis of the shaft.

The largest torque which may be transmitted by a disk clutch without causing slippage is given by a formula similar to (8.9), where μ_k has been replaced by the coefficient of static friction μ_s.

***8.9. Wheel Friction. Rolling Resistance.** The wheel is one of the most important inventions of our civilization. Its use makes it possible to move heavy loads with relatively little effort. Because the point of the wheel in contact with the ground at any given instant has no relative motion with respect to the ground, the wheel eliminates the large friction forces which would arise if the load were in direct contact with the ground. In practice, however, the wheel is not perfect, and some resistance to its motion exists. This resistance has two distinct causes. It is due (1) to a combined effect of axle friction and friction at the rim and (2) to the fact that the wheel and the ground deform, with the result that contact between wheel and ground takes place, not at a single point, but over a certain area.

To understand better the first cause of resistance to the motion of a wheel, we shall consider a railroad car supported by eight wheels mounted on axles and bearings. The car is assumed to be moving to the right at constant speed along a straight horizontal track. The free-body diagram of one of the wheels is shown in Fig. 8.13*a*. The forces acting on the free body include the load **W** supported by the wheel and the normal reaction **N** of the track. Since **W** is drawn through the center O of the axle, the frictional resistance of the bearing should be represented by a counterclockwise couple **M** (see Sec. 8.7). To keep the free body in equilibrium, we must add two equal and opposite forces **P** and **F** forming a clockwise couple of moment $-\mathbf{M}$. The force **F** is the friction force exerted by the track on the wheel, and **P** represents the force which should be applied to the wheel to keep it rolling at constant speed. Note that the forces **P** and **F** would not exist if there were no friction between wheel and track. The couple **M** representing the axle friction would then be zero; the wheel would slide on the track without turning in its bearing.

The couple **M** and the forces **P** and **F** also reduce to zero when there is no axle friction. For example, a wheel which is not held in bearings and rolls freely and at constant speed on horizontal ground (Fig. 8.13*b*) will be subjected to only two forces: its own weight **W** and the normal reaction **N** of the ground. No friction force will act on the wheel, regardless of the value of the coefficient of friction between wheel and ground. A wheel rolling freely on a horizontal ground should thus keep rolling indefinitely.

Experience, however, indicates that the wheel will slow down and eventually come to rest. This is due to the second type of resistance mentioned at the beginning of this section, known as the *rolling resistance*. Under the load **W**, both the wheel and the ground deform slightly, causing the contact between wheel and ground to take place over a certain area. Experimental evidence shows that the resultant of the forces exerted by the ground on the wheel over this area is a force **R** applied at a point *B*, which is not located directly under the center *O* of the wheel, but slightly in front of it (Fig. 8.13*c*). To balance the moment of **W** about *B* and to keep the wheel rolling at constant speed, it is necessary to apply a horizontal force **P** at the center of the wheel. Writing $\Sigma M_B = 0$, we obtain

$$Pr = Wb \tag{8.10}$$

where r = radius of wheel
b = horizontal distance between O and B

The distance b is commonly called the *coefficient of rolling resistance*. It should be noted that b is not a dimensionless coefficient since it represents a length; b is usually expressed in inches. The value of b depends upon several parameters in a manner which has not yet been clearly established. Values of the coefficient of rolling resistance vary from about 0.01 in. for a steel wheel on a steel rail to 5.0 in. for the same wheel on soft ground.

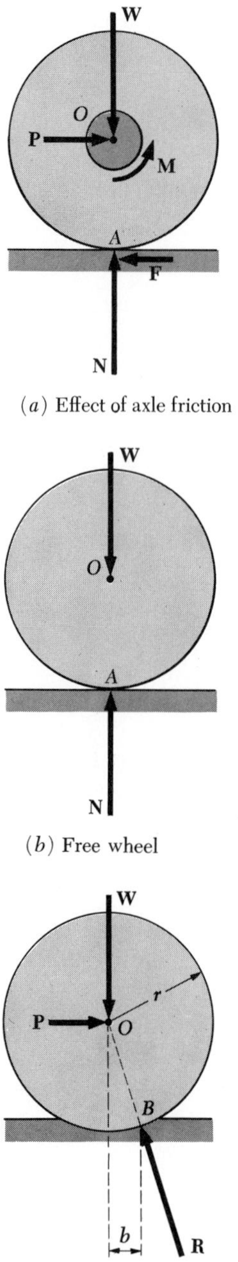

(*a*) Effect of axle friction

(*b*) Free wheel

(*c*) Rolling resistance

FIG. 8.13

SAMPLE PROBLEM 8.6

A pulley of diameter 4 in. can rotate about a fixed shaft of diameter 2 in. The coefficients of static and kinetic friction between the pulley and shaft are both assumed equal to 0.20. Determine (*a*) the smallest vertical force **P** required to raise a 500-lb load, (*b*) the smallest vertical force **P** required to hold the load, (*c*) the smallest horizontal force **P** required to raise the same load.

a. **Vertical Force P Required to Raise the Load.** When the forces in both parts of the rope are equal, contact between the pulley and shaft takes place at *A*. When **P** is increased, the pulley rolls around the shaft slightly and contact takes place at *B*. The free-body diagram of the pulley when motion is impending is drawn. The perpendicular distance from the center *O* of the pulley to the line of action of **R** is

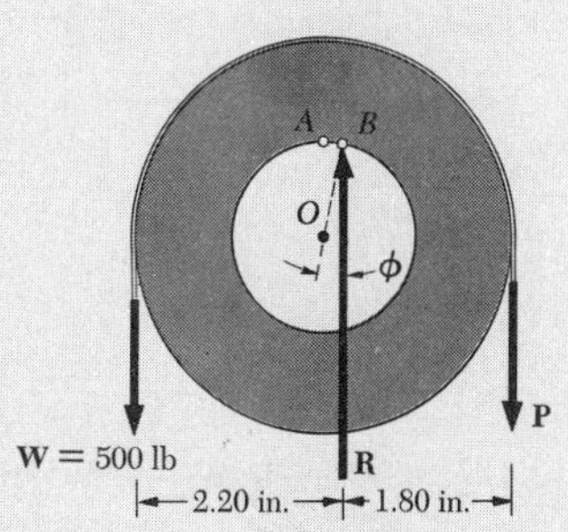

$$r_f = r \sin \phi \approx r\mu \qquad r_f \approx (1 \text{ in.})0.20 = 0.20 \text{ in.}$$

Summing moments about *B*, we write

$$+\circlearrowright \Sigma M_B = 0: \qquad (2.20 \text{ in.})(500 \text{ lb}) - (1.80 \text{ in.})P = 0$$

$$P = 611 \text{ lb} \qquad \mathbf{P} = 611 \text{ lb} \downarrow \blacktriangleleft$$

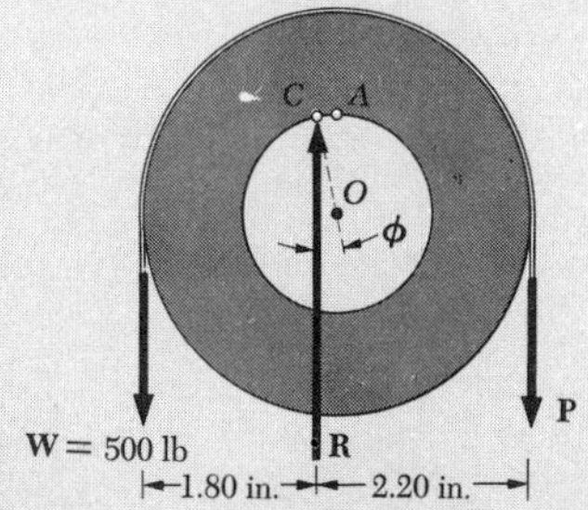

b. **Vertical Force P to Hold the Load.** As the force **P** is decreased, the pulley rolls around the shaft and contact takes place at *C*. Considering the pulley as a free body and summing moments about *C*, we write

$$+\circlearrowright \Sigma M_C = 0: \qquad (1.80 \text{ in.})(500 \text{ lb}) - (2.20 \text{ in.})P = 0$$

$$P = 409 \text{ lb} \qquad \mathbf{P} = 409 \text{ lb} \downarrow \blacktriangleleft$$

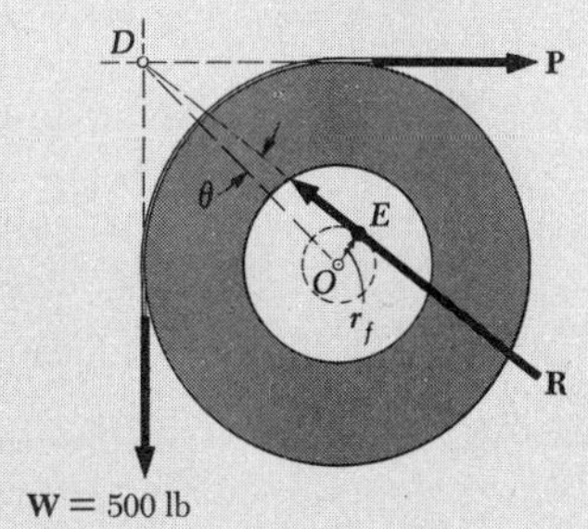

c. **Horizontal Force P to Raise the Load.** Since the three forces **W**, **P**, and **R** are not parallel, they must be concurrent. The direction of **R** is thus determined from the fact that its line of action must pass through the point of intersection *D* of **W** and **P**, and must be tangent to the circle of friction. Recalling that the radius of the circle of friction is $r_f = 0.20$ in., we write

$$\sin \theta = \frac{OE}{OD} = \frac{0.20 \text{ in.}}{(2 \text{ in.})\sqrt{2}} = 0.0707 \qquad \theta = 4.1^\circ$$

From the force triangle, we obtain

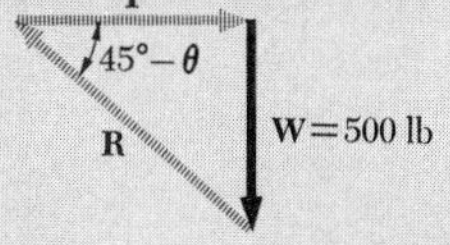

$$P = W \cot (45 \quad - \theta) = (500 \text{ lb}) \cot 40.9^\circ$$

$$P = 577 \text{ lb} \qquad \mathbf{P} = 577 \text{ lb} \rightarrow \blacktriangleleft$$

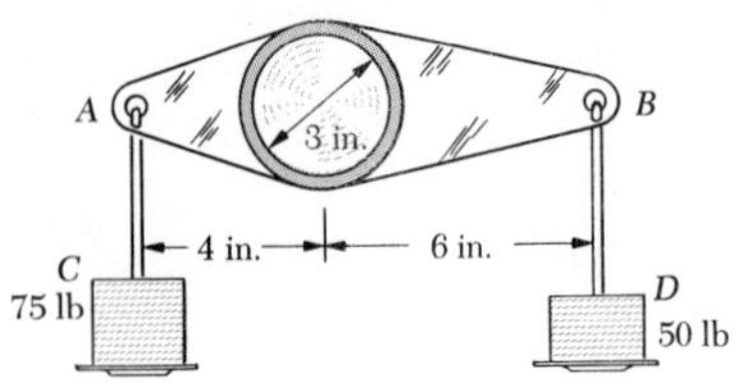

FIG. P 8.66 AND P 8.67

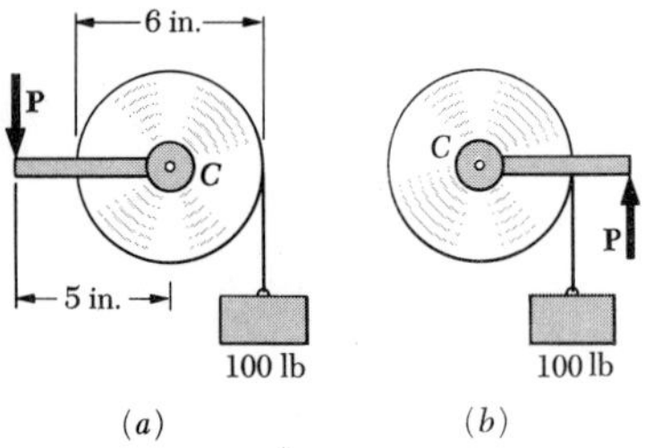

FIG. P 8.68

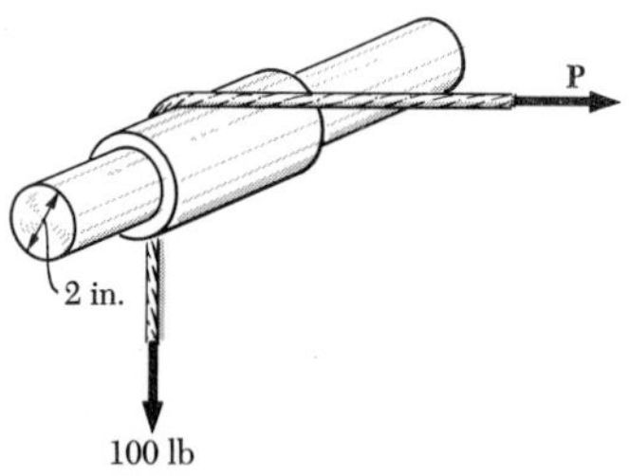

FIG. P 8.69

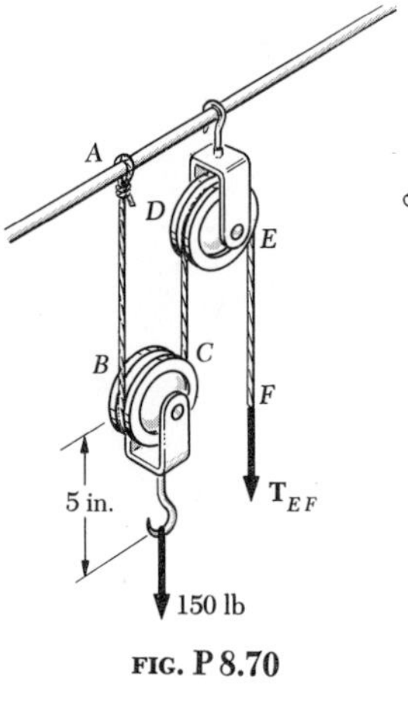

FIG. P 8.70

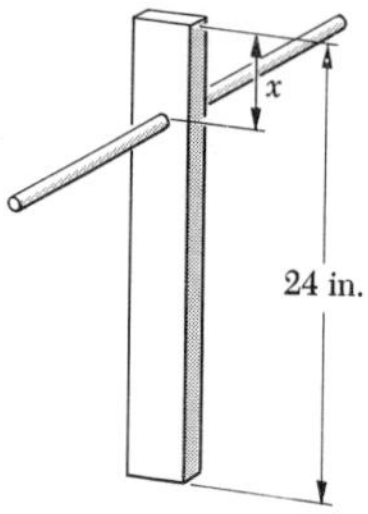

FIG. P 8.71

PROBLEMS

8.66. A lever of weight 5 lb is loosely fitted onto a 3-in.-diameter shaft and is in equilibrium under the loads shown. It is observed that the lever will just start rotating if a 4-lb weight is added at *D*. Determine the coefficient of friction between the shaft and the lever.

8.67. Determine the size of the weight which must be added at *C* to cause the lever of Prob. 8.66 to rotate counterclockwise.

8.68. A windlass, of diameter 6 in., is used to raise a 100-lb load. It is supported by two axles and bearings of diameter 2 in., poorly lubricated ($\mu = 0.40$). Determine the magnitude of the force **P** required to raise the load for each of the two positions shown.

8.69. A bushing of outside diameter 3 in. fits loosely on a horizontal 2-in.-diameter shaft. A horizontal force **P** of magnitude 110 lb is required to raise the 100-lb load attached to the rope. Determine the coefficient of friction between the shaft and the bushing. Assume that the rope does not slip on the bushing.

8.70. A 150-lb load is to be raised by the block and tackle shown. Each of the 3-in.-diameter pulleys rotates on a $\frac{1}{2}$-in.-diameter axle. Knowing that $\mu = 0.20$, determine the tension in each portion of the rope as the load is being raised.

8.71. A uniform bar of length 24 in. hangs loosely on a horizontal shaft of diameter 1 in. The shaft is slowly rotated. If the distance x is 2 in., determine the angle at which the bar initially slips. The coefficient of friction is 0.10.

8.72. Determine the minimum value of x for which the bar of Prob. 8.71 will not slip when the shaft is slowly rotated through a full turn.

8.73. A scooter is to be designed to roll down a 2 per cent slope at constant speed. Assuming that the coefficient of kinetic friction between the 1-in. axles and the bearings is 0.10, determine the required diameter of the wheels. Neglect the rolling resistance between the wheels and the ground.

8.74. A certain railroad freight car has eight steel wheels of 32-in. diameter which are supported on 5-in.-diameter axles. Assuming $\mu = 0.015$, determine the horizontal force per ton of load required to move the car at constant velocity.

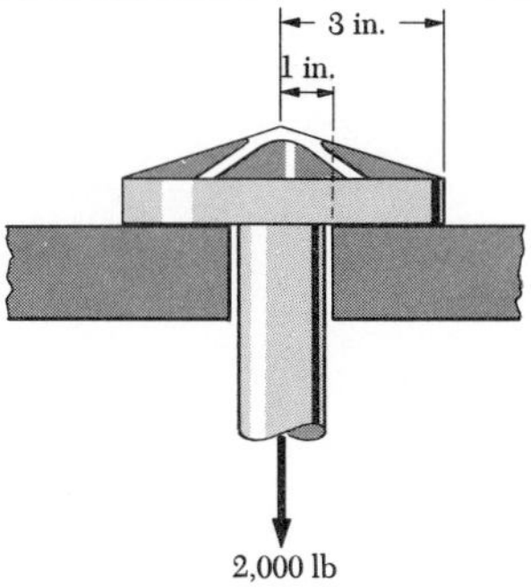

FIG. P 8.75

8.75. A couple of magnitude 60 lb-ft is required to start the vertical shaft rotating. Determine the coefficient of static friction.

8.76. A vertical force of 50 lb is applied to a 10-lb electric polisher as it is operated on a horizontal surface. Knowing that $\mu_k = 0.25$, determine the magnitude Q of the forces required to prevent rotation of the handles. Assume the force between the disk and the surface to be uniformly distributed.

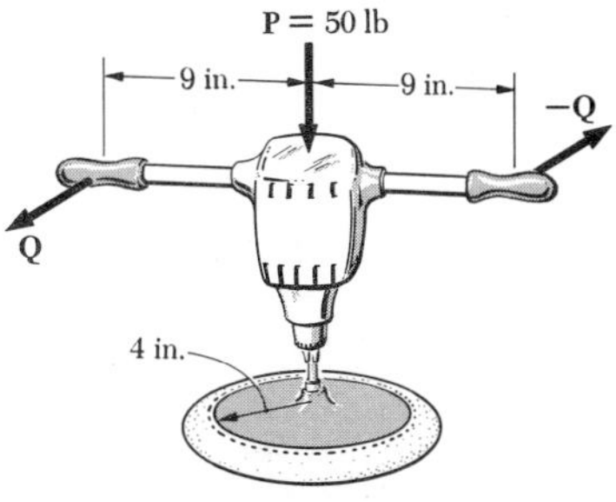

FIG. P 8.76

8.77. Four springs, each of constant 30 lb/in., are used to press plate AB against the head on the vertical rod. In the position shown each spring has been compressed 2 in. The plate AB may move vertically, but it is constrained against rotation by bolts which pass through holes cut in the plate. Knowing that $\mu = 0.30$ and $\mathbf{P} = 0$, determine the magnitude of the couple **M** required to rotate the rod.

8.78. In Prob. 8.77 determine the required magnitude of the force **P** if the rod is to just rotate when the magnitude of the couple **M** is 180 lb-in. For what magnitude of the force **P** is the rod most easily rotated?

***8.79.** Solve Prob. 8.76 assuming that between the disk and the surface the force per unit area varies uniformly from a maximum at the center to zero at the perimeter of the disk.

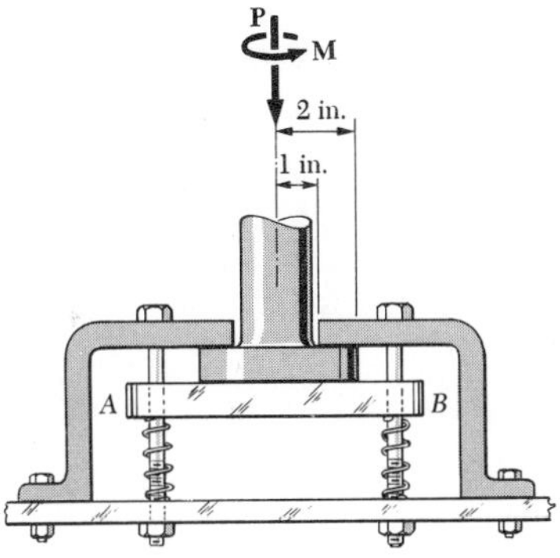

FIG. P 8.77

***8.80.** As the surfaces of shaft and bearing wear out, the frictional resistance of a thrust bearing decreases. It is generally assumed that the wear is directly proportional to the distance traveled by any given point of the shaft, and thus to the distance r from the point to the axis of the shaft. Assuming, then, that the normal force per unit area is inversely proportional to r, show that the magnitude of the couple **M** required to overcome the frictional resistance of a worn-out end bearing (with contact over the full circular area) is equal to 75 per cent of the value given by formula (8.9) for a new bearing.

***8.81.** Assuming that bearings wear out as indicated in Prob. 8.80, show that the magnitude of the couple **M** required to overcome the frictional resistance of a worn-out collar bearing is

$$M = \tfrac{1}{2}\mu_k P(R_1 + R_2)$$

where P = magnitude of the total axial force
R_1, R_2 = inner and outer radii of collar

***8.82.** Assuming that the pressure between the surfaces of contact is uniform, show that the magnitude of the couple required to overcome frictional resistance for the conical pivot shown is

$$M = \frac{2}{3}\frac{\mu_k P}{\sin\theta}\frac{R_2^3 - R_1^3}{R_2^2 - R_1^2}$$

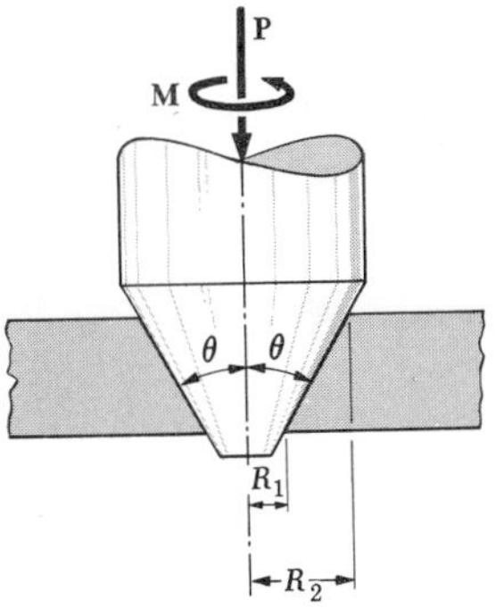

FIG. P 8.82

8.83. Determine the horizontal force required to move a 3,000-lb automobile along a horizontal road at constant velocity. Neglect all forms of friction except rolling resistance, and assume the coefficient of rolling resistance to be 0.05 in. The diameter of each tire is 24 in.

8.84. A circular disk of diameter 5 in. rolls at constant velocity down an incline which has a slope of $\frac{1}{8}$ in. per foot. Determine the coefficient of rolling resistance.

8.85. Solve Prob. 8.73 including the effect of a coefficient of rolling resistance of 0.06 in.

8.86. Solve Prob. 8.74 including the effect of a coefficient of rolling resistance of 0.02 in.

8.10. Belt Friction. Consider a flat belt passing over a fixed cylindrical drum (Fig. 8.14*a*). We propose to determine the relation existing between the values T_1 and T_2 of the tension in the two parts of the belt when the belt is just about to slide toward the right.

Let us detach from the belt a small element PP' subtending an angle $\Delta\theta$. Denoting by T the tension at P and by $T + \Delta T$ the tension at P', we draw the free-body diagram of the element of the belt (Fig. 8.14*b*). Besides the two forces of tension, the forces acting on the free body are the normal component $\Delta\mathbf{N}$ of the reaction of the drum and the friction force $\Delta\mathbf{F}$. Since motion is assumed to be impending, we have $\Delta F = \mu_s\, \Delta N$. It should be noted that if $\Delta\theta$ is made to approach zero, the magnitudes ΔN, ΔF, and the *difference* ΔT between the tension at P and the tension at P' will also approach zero; the value T of the tension at P, however, will remain unchanged. This observation helps in understanding our choice of notations.

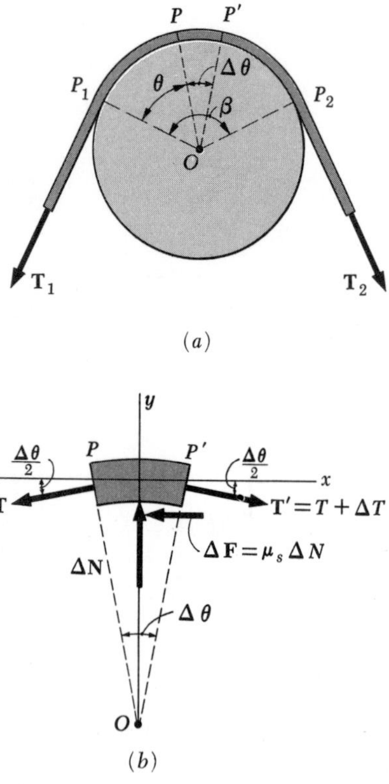

FIG. 8.14

Choosing the coordinate axes shown in Fig. 8.14*b*, we write the equations of equilibrium for the element PP':

$$\Sigma F_x = 0: \quad (T + \Delta T)\cos\frac{\Delta\theta}{2} - T\cos\frac{\Delta\theta}{2} - \mu_s\,\Delta N = 0 \qquad (8.11)$$

$$\Sigma F_y = 0: \quad \Delta N - (T + \Delta T)\sin\frac{\Delta\theta}{2} - T\sin\frac{\Delta\theta}{2} = 0 \qquad (8.12)$$

Solving Eq. (8.12) for ΔN and substituting into (8.11), we obtain after reductions

$$\Delta T\cos\frac{\Delta\theta}{2} - \mu_s(2T + \Delta T)\sin\frac{\Delta\theta}{2} = 0$$

We shall now divide both terms by $\Delta\theta$; as far as the first term is concerned, this will be simply done by dividing ΔT by $\Delta\theta$. The division of the second term is carried out by dividing the terms in the parentheses by 2 and the sine by $\Delta\theta/2$. We write

$$\frac{\Delta T}{\Delta\theta}\cos\frac{\Delta\theta}{2} - \mu_s\left(T + \frac{\Delta T}{2}\right)\frac{\sin(\Delta\theta/2)}{\Delta\theta/2} = 0$$

If we now let $\Delta\theta$ approach 0, the cosine approaches 1 and $\Delta T/2$ approaches zero as noted above. On the other hand, the quotient of sin $(\Delta\theta/2)$ over $\Delta\theta/2$ approaches 1, according to a lemma derived in all calculus textbooks. Since the limit of $\Delta T/\Delta\theta$ is by definition equal to the derivative $dT/d\theta$, we write

$$\frac{dT}{d\theta} - \mu_s T = 0 \qquad \frac{dT}{T} = \mu_s\, d\theta$$

We shall now integrate both members of the last equation obtained from P_1 to P_2 (Fig. 8.14*a*). At P_1, we have $\theta = 0$ and $T = T_1$; at P_2, we have $\theta = \beta$ and $T = T_2$. Integrating between these limits, we write

$$\int_{T_1}^{T_2}\frac{dT}{T} = \int_0^\beta \mu_s\, d\theta$$

$$\ln T_2 - \ln T_1 = \mu_s\beta$$

$$\ln\frac{T_2}{T_1} = \mu_s\beta \tag{8.13}$$

This relation may also be written in the form

$$\frac{T_2}{T_1} = e^{\mu_s\beta} \tag{8.14}$$

The formulas we have derived apply equally well to problems involving flat belts passing over fixed cylindrical drums and to problems involving ropes wrapped around a post or capstan. They may also be used to solve problems involving band brakes. In such problems, it is the drum which is about to rotate, while the band remains fixed. The formulas may also be applied to problems involving belt drives. In these problems, both the pulley and the belt rotate; our concern is then to find whether the belt will slip, i.e., whether it will move *with respect* to the pulley.

Formulas (8.13) and (8.14) should be used only if the belt, rope, or brake is *about to slip*. Formula (8.14) will be used if

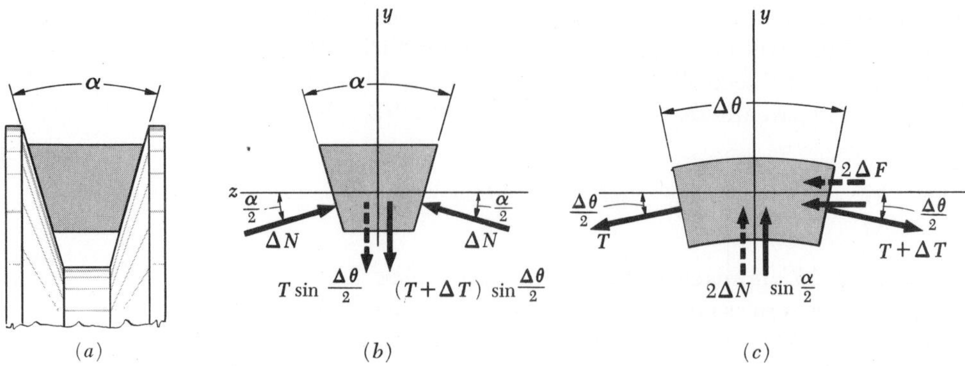

FIG. 8.15

T_1 or T_2 is desired; formula (8.13) will be preferred if either μ_s or the angle of contact β is desired.† We should note that T_2 is always larger than T_1; T_2 therefore represents the tension in that part of the belt or rope which *pulls*, while T_1 is the tension in the part which *resists*. We should also observe that the angle of contact β must be expressed in *radians*. The angle β may be larger than 2π; for example, if a rope is wrapped n times around a post, β is equal to $2\pi n$.

If the belt, rope, or brake is actually slipping, formulas similar to (8.13) and (8.14), but involving the coefficient of kinetic friction μ_k, should be used. If the belt, rope, or brake does not slip and is not about to slip, none of these formulas may be used.

The belts used in belt drives are often V-shaped. Such a belt, called a "V belt," is shown in Fig. 8.15*a*. It is seen that contact between belt and pulley takes place along the sides of the groove. The relation existing between the values T_1 and T_2 of the tension in the two parts of the belt when the belt is just about to slip may again be obtained by drawing the free-body diagram of an element of belt (Fig. 8.15*b* and *c*). Equations similar to (8.11) and (8.12) are derived, but the magnitude of the total friction force acting on the element is now $2\,\Delta F$, and the sum of the y components of the normal forces is $2\,\Delta N \sin(\alpha/2)$. Proceeding as above, we obtain

$$\frac{T_2}{T_1} = e^{\mu_s \beta / \sin(\alpha/2)} \qquad (8.15)$$

† Since the determination of a power of e and that of a logarithm to the base e (ln) involves the use of the same scales on the slide rule, there is no need for distinguishing between formulas (8.13) and (8.14) in carrying out computations on the slide rule. In every case, the product $\mu_s\beta$ should be read on the D scale and the quotient T_2/T_1 on one of the LL scales.

SAMPLE PROBLEM 8.7

A hawser thrown from a ship to a pier is wrapped two full turns around a capstan. The tension in the hawser is 1,500 lb; by exerting a force of 30 lb on its free end, a longshoreman can just keep the hawser from slipping. (*a*) Determine the coefficient of friction between the hawser and the capstan. (*b*) Determine the tension in the hawser that could be resisted by the 30-lb force if the hawser were wrapped three full turns around the capstan.

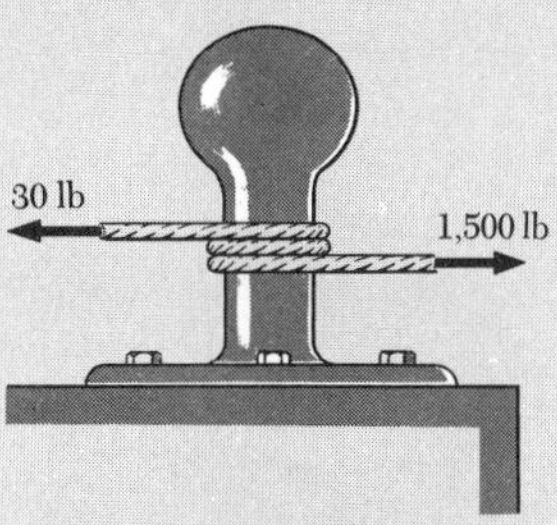

a. **Coefficient of Friction.** Since slipping of the hawser is impending, we use Eq. (8.13),

$$\ln \frac{T_2}{T_1} = \mu_s \beta$$

Since the hawser is wrapped two full turns around the capstan, we have

$$\beta = 2(2\pi \text{ radians}) = 12.6 \text{ radians}$$

$$T_1 = 30 \text{ lb} \qquad T_2 = 1{,}500 \text{ lb}$$

Therefore,

$$\mu_s \beta = \ln \frac{T_2}{T_1}$$

$$\mu_s(12.6 \text{ radians}) = \ln \frac{1{,}500 \text{ lb}}{30 \text{ lb}} = \ln 50 = 3.91$$

$$\mu_s = 0.31 \blacktriangleleft$$

b. **Hawser Wrapped Three Turns around Capstan.** Using the value of μ_s obtained in part *a*, we have now

$$\beta = 3(2\pi \text{ radians}) = 18.9 \text{ radians}$$

$$T_1 = 30 \text{ lb} \qquad \mu_s = 0.31$$

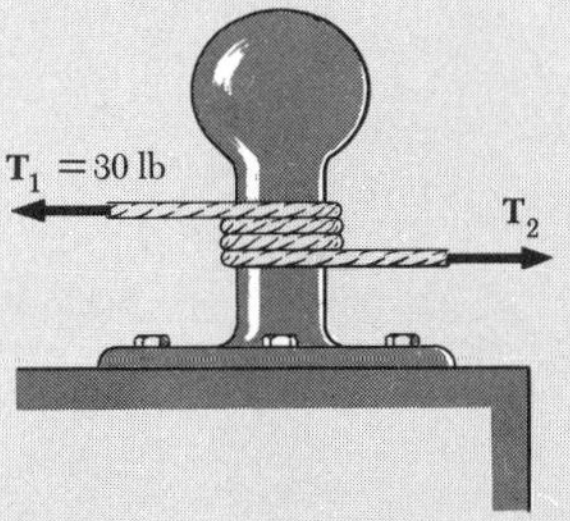

Substituting these values into Eq. (8.14), we obtain

$$\frac{T_2}{T_1} = e^{\mu_s \beta}$$

$$\frac{T_2}{30 \text{ lb}} = e^{(0.31)(18.9)} = e^{5.86} = 350$$

$$T_2 = 10{,}500 \text{ lb} \blacktriangleleft$$

Note. See the footnote on page 306 for the use of the slide rule in problems dealing with belt friction.

SAMPLE PROBLEM 8.8

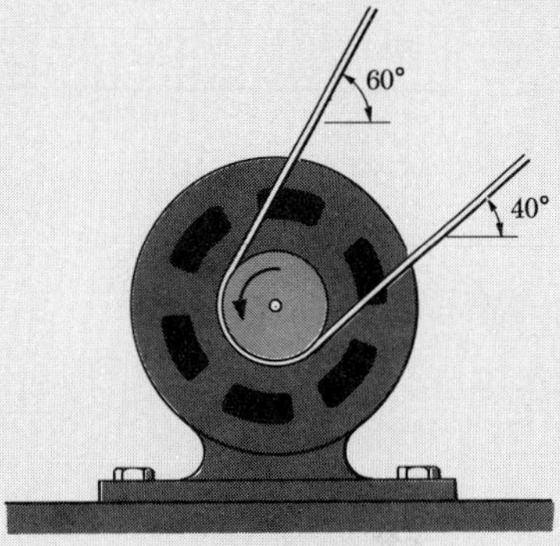

A flat belt is used to transmit the 25-lb-ft torque developed by an electric motor. The belt is in contact with a drum of diameter 6 in., as shown. The coefficient of static friction between belt and drum is 0.30. Determine the minimum values of the tension in both parts of the belt which will assure no slippage.

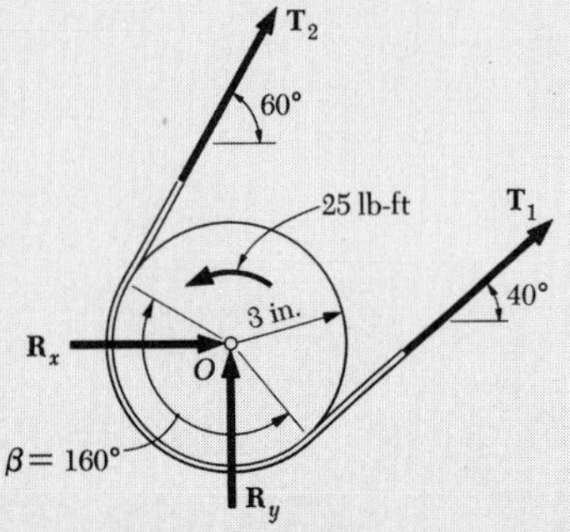

Solution. The free-body diagram of the drum is drawn. Summing moments about the center O of the drum, we write

$$+\circlearrowleft \Sigma M_O = 0: \qquad T_1(3\text{ in.}) - T_2(3\text{ in.}) + 25\text{ lb-ft} = 0$$

$$(T_2 - T_1)(3\text{ in.}) = 300\text{ lb-in.}$$

$$T_2 - T_1 = 100\text{ lb} \qquad (1)$$

The angle of contact between belt and drum is

$$\beta = 160° = 160° \frac{2\pi\text{ radians}}{360°} = 2.79\text{ radians}$$

Since the values of T_1 and T_2 corresponding to impending slippage are desired, we use Eq. (8.14).

$$\frac{T_2}{T_1} = e^{\mu_s \beta} \qquad \frac{T_2}{T_1} = e^{(0.30)(2.79)} = e^{0.837} = 2.31$$

$$T_2 = 2.31T_1 \qquad (2)$$

Substituting T_2 from Eq. (2) into Eq. (1), we obtain

$$2.31T_1 - T_1 = 100\text{ lb} \qquad T_1 = 76.4\text{ lb} ◄$$

$$T_2 = T_1 + 100\text{ lb} \qquad T_2 = 176.4\text{ lb} ◄$$

PROBLEMS

8.87. A hawser is wrapped two full turns around a capstan head. By exerting a force of 80 lb on the free end of the hawser, a seaman can resist a force of 5,000 lb on the other end of the hawser. Determine (*a*) the coefficient of friction, (*b*) the number of times the hawser should be wrapped around the capstan if a 20,000-lb force is to be resisted by the same 80-lb force.

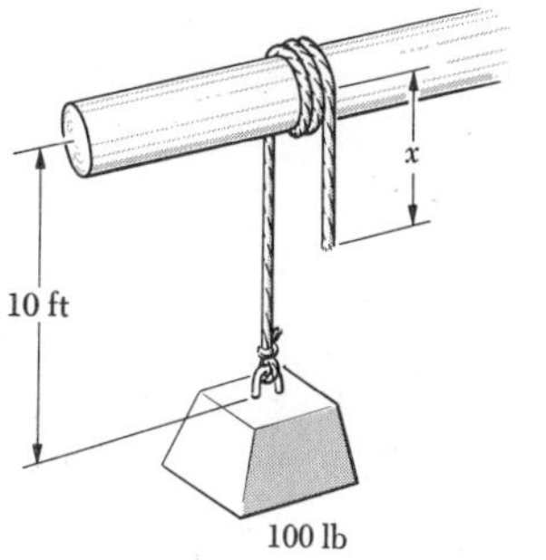

FIG. P 8.88

8.88. A rope weighing 0.5 lb/ft is wound $2\frac{1}{2}$ times around a horizontal bar. What length x of rope should be left hanging if a load of 100 lb is to be supported? The coefficient of static friction between the rope and the bar is 0.25.

8.89. Assume that the bushing of Prob. 8.69 has become frozen to the shaft and cannot rotate. Determine the coefficient of friction between the bushing and the rope if a force **P** of magnitude 120 lb is required to raise the 100-lb load.

8.90. A rope $ABCD$ is looped over two pipes as shown. Knowing that $\mu = 0.30$, determine (*a*) the smallest weight W for which equilibrium is possible, (*b*) the angle θ for which the corresponding tension in portion BC of the rope is 50 lb.

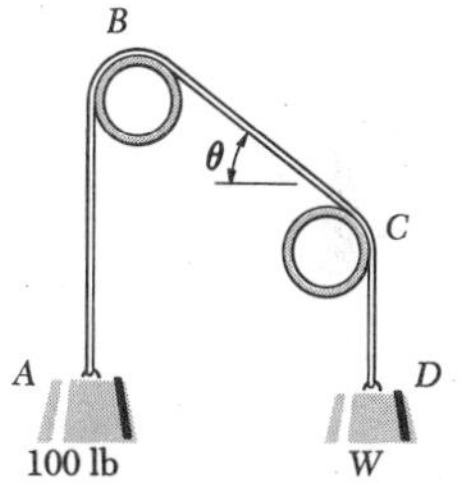

FIG. P 8.90

8.91. A flat belt is used to transmit a torque from pulley A to pulley B. The radius of each pulley is 3 in. and $\mu = 0.20$. Determine the moment of the largest torque which can be transmitted if the maximum allowable tension is 800 lb.

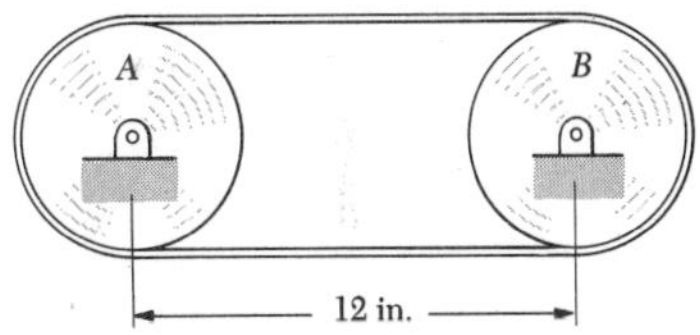

FIG. P 8.91

8.92. Solve Prob. 8.91 assuming that the belt is looped around the pulleys in a single figure 8.

8.93. A brake drum of radius $r = 5$ in. is rotating counterclockwise when a force **P** of magnitude 10 lb is applied at A. Knowing that $\mu = 0.40$, determine the moment about O of the friction forces applied to the drum when $a = 8$ in. and $b = 10$ in.

8.94. Knowing that $r = 5$ in. and $a = 8$ in., determine the maximum value of μ for which the brake is not self-locking. The brake drum revolves counterclockwise.

8.95. Knowing that $\mu = 0.40$, determine the minimum ratio of the distance a to the radius r for which the brake is not self-locking. The brake drum revolves counterclockwise and $a > r$.

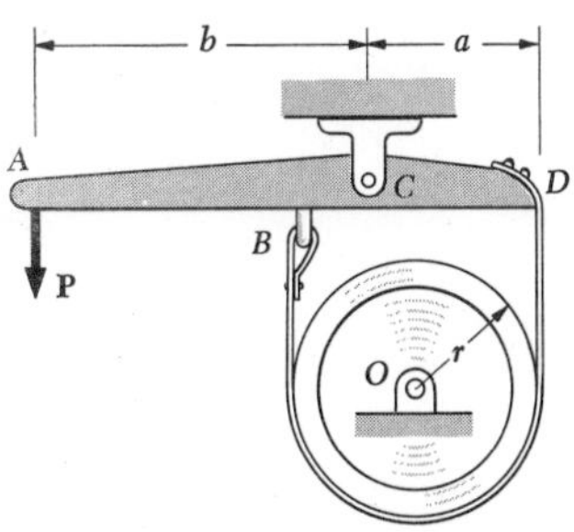

FIG. P 8.93, P 8.94, AND P 8.95

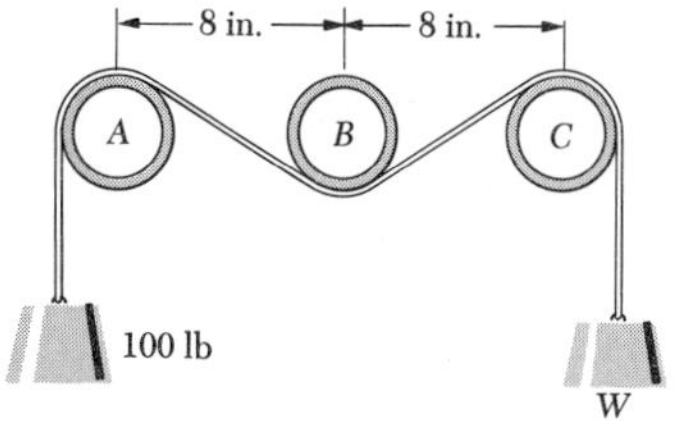

FIG. P 8.96 AND P 8.97

8.96. A cable is placed around three pipes, each of 4-in. outside diameter, located in the same horizontal plane. Two of the pipes are fixed and do not rotate; the third pipe is rotated slowly. Knowing that $\mu = 0.30$ for each pipe, determine the largest weight W which can be raised (*a*) if only pipe A is rotated, (*b*) if only pipe B is rotated, (*c*) if only pipe C is rotated.

8.97. A cable is placed around three pipes, each of 4-in. outside diameter, located in the same horizontal plane. Pipes A and C are rotated slowly clockwise while pipe B is held fixed. Knowing that $\mu = 0.30$ for each pipe, determine the largest weight W which can be raised.

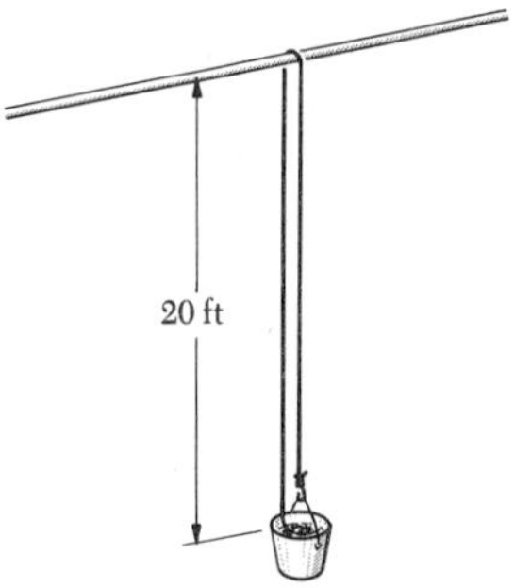

FIG. P 8.98

8.98. A 50-ft rope passes over a small horizontal shaft; one end of the rope is attached to a bucket which weighs 5 lb. The excess rope is coiled inside the bucket. The coefficient of static friction between the rope and the shaft is 0.30, and the rope weighs 0.50 lb/ft. (*a*) If the shaft is held fixed, show that the system is in equilibrium. (*b*) If the shaft is slowly rotated, how far will the bucket rise before slipping? Neglect the diameter of the shaft.

8.99. The shaft of Prob. 8.98 is slowly rotated. Determine how far the bucket can be lowered before the rope slips on the shaft.

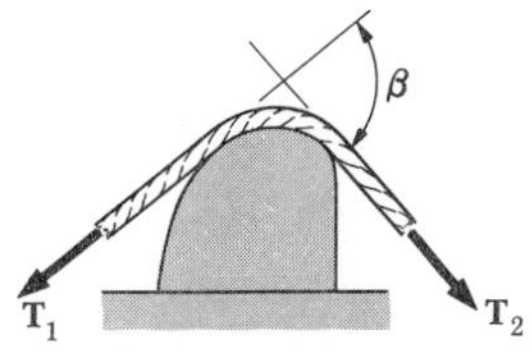

FIG. P 8.100

8.100. Prove that Eqs. (8.13) and (8.14) are valid for any shape of surface provided that the coefficient of friction is the same at all points of contact.

8.101. The axle of the pulley is frozen and cannot rotate with respect to the block. Knowing that $\mu = 0.30$ between the cable ABC and the pulley and that $\theta_1 = \theta_2 = 60°$, determine the largest value of α for which the block is in equilibrium. (Assume that the straight portions of cable meet at point D.)

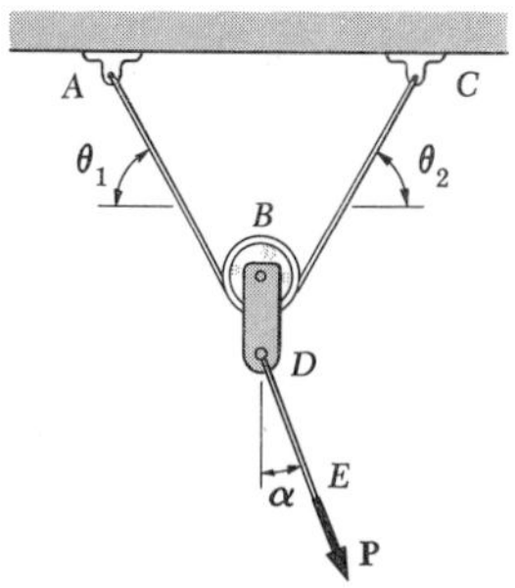

FIG. P 8.101 AND P 8.102

*8.102. The axle of the pulley is frozen and cannot rotate with respect to the block. The coefficient of friction between cable ABC and the pulley is 0.30. For the case when $\alpha = 0°$ and $\theta_1 = 60°$, determine the largest value of θ_2 for which equilibrium exists.

8.103. Complete the derivation of Eq. (8.15), which relates the tension in both parts of a V belt.

8.104. Solve Prob. 8.91 assuming that the flat belt and pulley are replaced by a V belt and V pulley with $\alpha = 28°$. (The angle α is as shown in Fig. 8.15*a*.)

REVIEW PROBLEMS

8.105. In highway bridge construction the link arrangement shown is frequently used to allow for expansion due to changes in temperature. The coefficients of friction at each of the 2-in.-diameter pins A and B is 0.20. Knowing that the vertical component of the force in beam BC is 40,000 lb, determine (a) the horizontal component of the force in beam BC required to just move the link, (b) the angle that the corresponding total force in the link forms with the vertical.

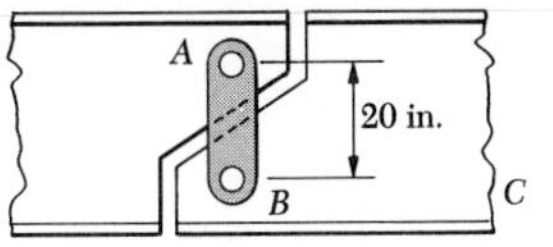

FIG. P 8.105

8.106. The arrangement shown is used to measure the power output of a small turbine. The coefficient of kinetic friction is 0.15. When the flywheel is at rest, the reading of each spring is 15 lb. What will be the reading of each spring when the flywheel is rotating clockwise? Assume that the belt is of constant length.

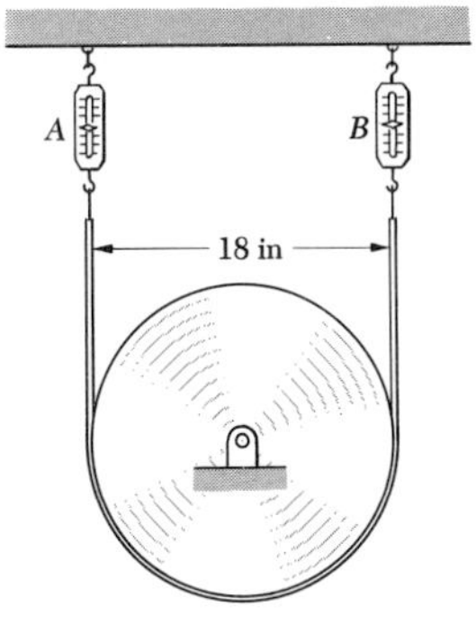

FIG. P 8.106

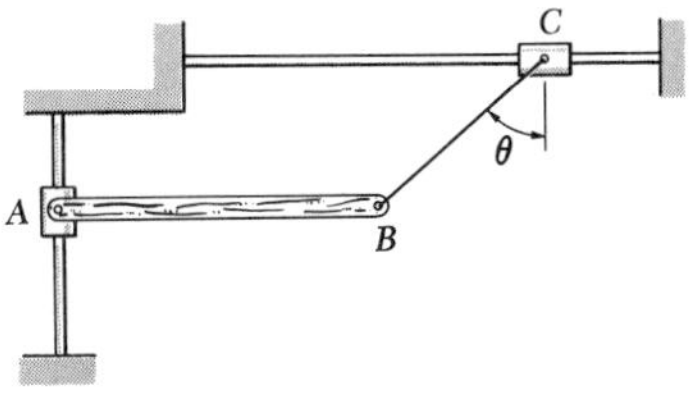

FIG. P 8.107

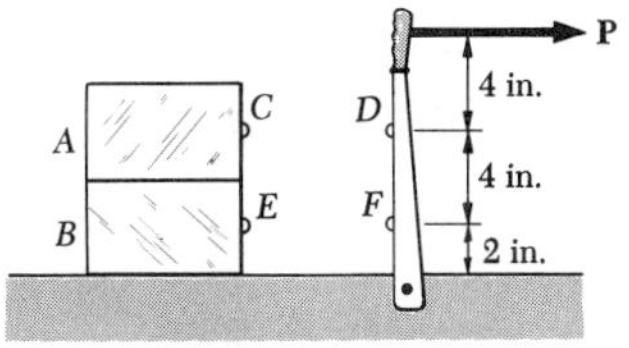

FIG. P 8.108

8.107. The uniform rod AB is connected to two collars, of negligible weight, by a pin at A and by the cord BC. The coefficient of friction between each collar and the rod upon which it may slide is denoted by μ. (a) Show that μ must be at least equal to 1.00 if the rod is to be maintained in a horizontal position. (b) If $\mu = 1.50$, determine the range of values of θ for which the rod will remain in a horizontal position.

8.108. The two 25-lb boxes A and B may be attached to the lever by means of either one or two horizontal links. The coefficient of friction between all surfaces is 0.30. Determine the magnitude of the force **P** required to move the lever (a) if a single link EF is used, (b) if a single link CD is used, (c) if two links EF and CD are used at the same time.

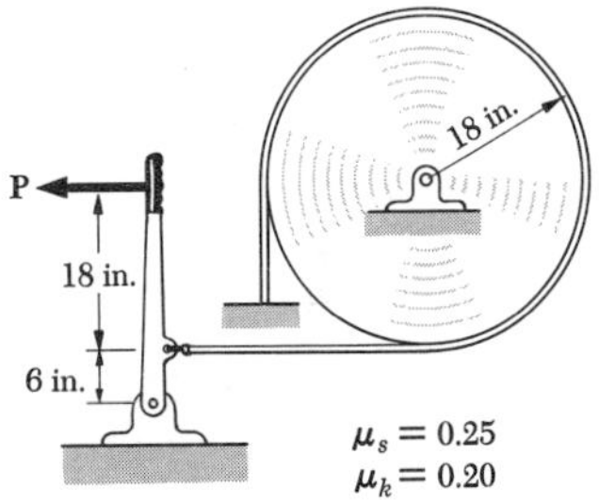

FIG. P 8.109

8.109. A band brake is used to control the speed of a flywheel as shown. What torque must be applied to the flywheel in order to keep it rotating at a constant speed, when $P = 10$ lb? Assume that the flywheel rotates clockwise.

8.110. Solve Prob. 8.109 assuming that the flywheel rotates counterclockwise.

8.111. A hot-metal ladle and its contents weigh 60 tons. Knowing that the coefficient of friction between the hooks and the pinion is 0.30, determine the tension in the cable AB required to start tipping the ladle.

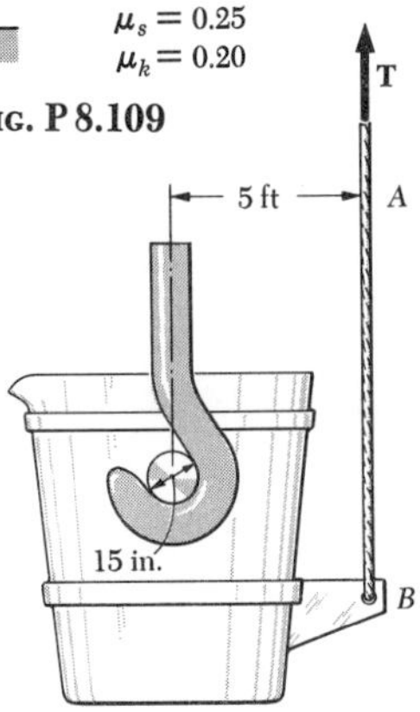

FIG. P 8.111

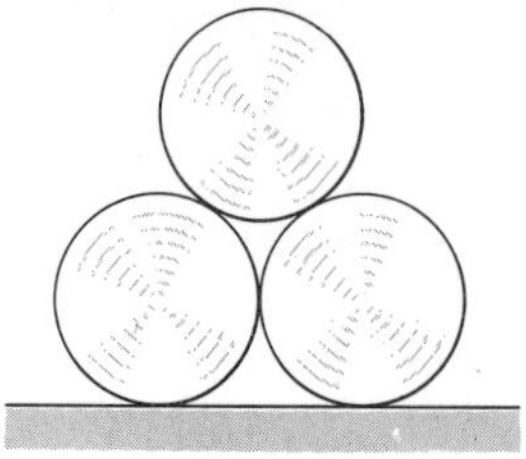

FIG. P 8.113

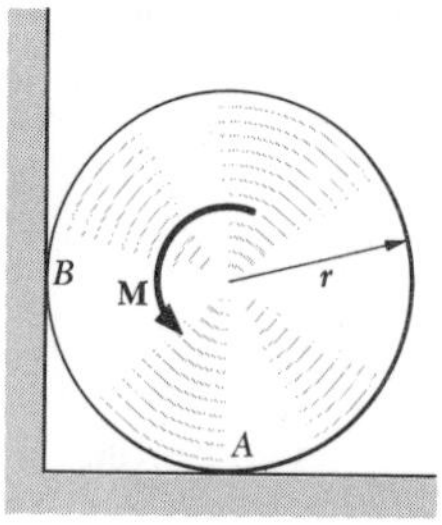

FIG. P 8.114

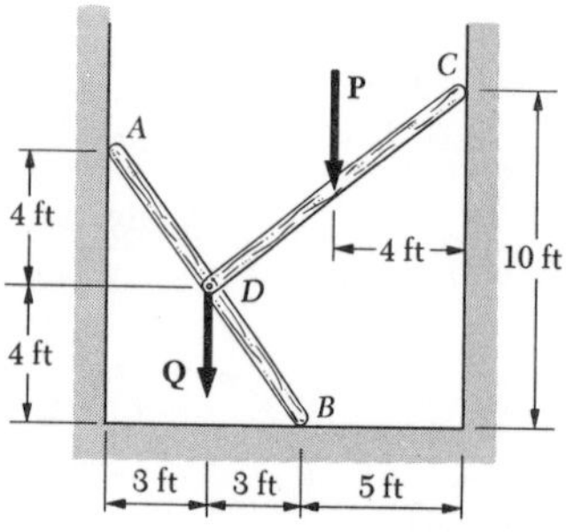

FIG. P 8.115

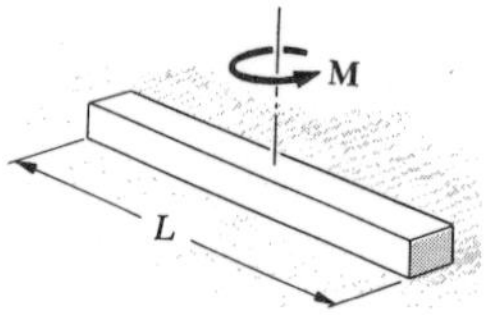

FIG. P 8.116

8.112. A rope is wrapped three complete turns around a post; the coefficient of friction is 0.30. (*a*) Determine the largest force which may be resisted at one end of the rope if a 10-lb force is applied at the other end. (*b*) How many turns will be required if the force to be resisted is doubled, while the same 10-lb force is maintained at the other end?

8.113. Determine the smallest value of the coefficient of friction for which three identical cylindrical rods may be placed as shown.

8.114. A shaft of radius r and weight W is placed as shown; the coefficient of static friction between all surfaces is μ_s. Determine the magnitude of the couple **M** required to start the shaft rotating in terms of r, W, and μ_s.

8.115. Two 10-ft beams are pin-connected at D and support two loads **P** and **Q** as shown. Knowing that the coefficient of friction is zero at A, 0.25 at B, and 0.50 at C, determine the smallest value of P for which equilibrium is maintained when $Q = 240$ lb. (*Hint.* Note that C moves up when B moves to the right.)

8.116. A thin uniform bar of length L and weight W lies on a rough horizontal surface. Denoting by μ the coefficient of friction, determine the magnitude of the couple **M** which must be applied to rotate the bar. Assume that the normal force between the surface and the bar is uniformly distributed.

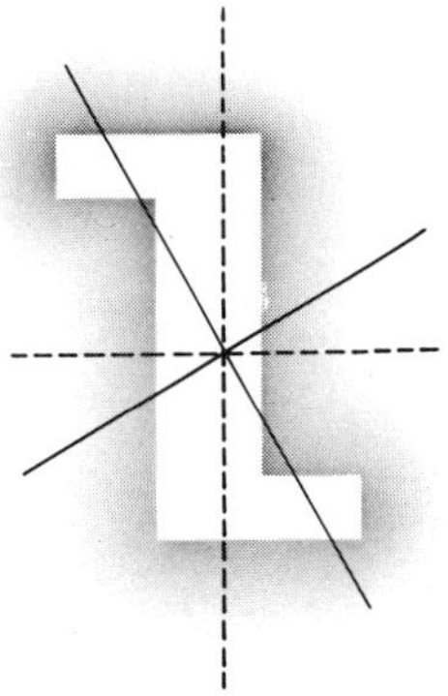

9. DISTRIBUTED FORCES: MOMENTS OF INERTIA

MOMENTS OF INERTIA OF AREAS

9.1. Second Moment, or Moment of Inertia, of an Area. In Chap. 5, we analyzed various systems of forces distributed over an area. The two main types of forces considered were (1) weights of homogeneous plates of uniform thickness (Secs. 5.2 to 5.4) and (2) distributed loads on beams and hydrostatic forces (Secs. 5.6 and 5.7). In the case of homogeneous plates, the magnitude ΔW of the weight of an element of plate was proportional to the area ΔA of the element. In the case of distributed loads on beams, the magnitude ΔW of each elementary weight was represented by an element of area $\Delta A = \Delta W$ under the load curve; in the case of hydrostatic forces on submerged rectangular surfaces, a similar procedure was followed. Thus, in all cases considered in Chap. 5, the distributed forces were proportional to the elementary areas associated with them. The resultant of these forces, therefore, could be obtained by summing the corresponding areas, and the moment of the resultant about any given axis could be determined by computing the first moments of the areas about that axis.

In this chapter, we shall consider distributed forces $\Delta \mathbf{F}$ whose magnitudes depend not only upon the element of area ΔA on which they act but also upon the distance from ΔA to some given axis. More precisely, the magnitude of the force per unit area $\Delta F/\Delta A$ will vary linearly with the distance to the axis.

Consider, for example, a beam of uniform cross section, subjected to two equal and opposite couples applied at each end of the beam. Such a beam is said to be in *pure bending*, and it is shown in mechanics of materials that the internal forces in any section of the beam are distributed forces whose magnitudes $\Delta F = ky\,\Delta A$ vary linearly with the distance y from

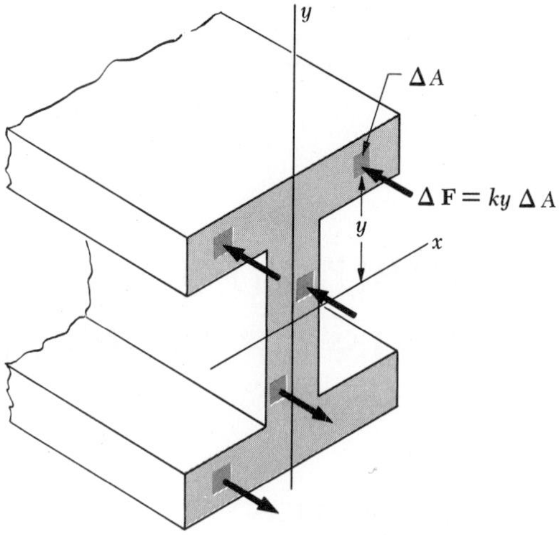

FIG. 9.1

an axis passing through the centroid of the section. This axis, represented by the x axis in Fig. 9.1, is known as the *neutral axis* of the section. The forces on one side of the neutral axis are forces of compression, and on the other side forces of tension, while on the neutral axis itself the forces are zero.

The magnitude of the resultant **R** of the elementary forces $\Delta\mathbf{F}$ over the entire section is

$$R = \int ky\, dA = k\int y\, dA$$

The last integral obtained is recognized as the *first moment* of the section about the x axis; it is equal to $\bar{y}A$ and to zero, since the centroid of the section is located on the x axis. The system of the forces $\Delta\mathbf{F}$ thus reduces to a couple. The magnitude M of this couple (bending moment) must be equal to the sum of the moments $\Delta M_x = y\,\Delta F = ky^2\,\Delta A$ of the elementary forces. Integrating over the entire section, we obtain

$$M = \int ky^2\, dA = k\int y^2\, dA$$

The last integral is known as the *second moment,* or *moment of inertia,*† of the beam section with respect to the x axis and is denoted by I_x. It is obtained by multiplying each element of area dA by the *square of its distance* from the x axis and integrating over the beam section. Since each product $y^2\, dA$ is positive, whether y is itself positive or negative (or zero if y is zero), the integral I_x will always be different from zero and positive.

† The term second moment is more proper than the term moment of inertia since, logically, the latter should be used only to denote integrals of mass (see Sec. 9.10). In common engineering practice, however, moment of inertia is used in connection with areas as well as masses.

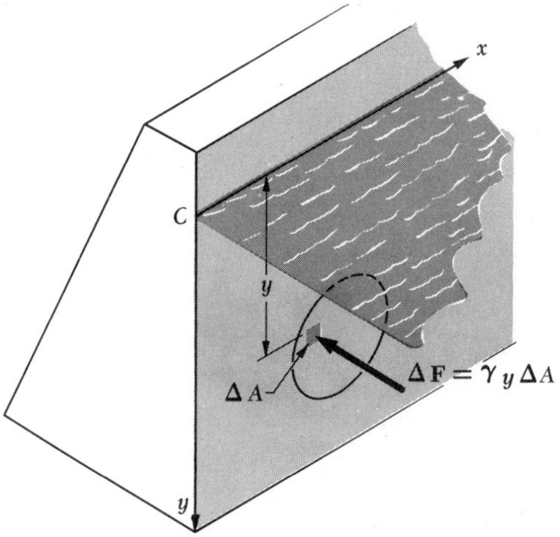

FIG. 9.2

Another example of second moment, or moment of inertia, of an area is provided by the following problem of hydrostatics: A vertical circular gate used to close the outlet of a large reservoir is submerged under water as shown in Fig. 9.2. What is the resultant of the forces exerted by the water on the gate, and what is the moment of the resultant about the line of intersection of the plane of the gate with the water surface (x axis)?

If the gate were rectangular, the resultant of the forces of pressure could be determined from the pressure curve, as was done in Sec. 5.7. Since the gate is circular, however, a more general method must be used. Denoting by y the depth of an element of area ΔA and by γ the specific weight of water, the pressure at the element is $p = \gamma y$, and the magnitude of the elementary force exerted on ΔA is $\Delta F = p\,\Delta A = \gamma y\,\Delta A$. The magnitude of the resultant of the elementary forces is thus

$$R = \int \gamma y\, dA = \gamma \int y\, dA$$

and may be obtained by computing the first moment of the area of the gate with respect to the x axis. The moment M_x of the resultant must be equal to the sum of the moments $\Delta M_x = y\,\Delta F = \gamma y^2\,\Delta A$ of the elementary forces. Integrating over the area of the gate, we have

$$M_x = \int \gamma y^2\, dA = \gamma \int y^2\, dA$$

Here again, the integral obtained represents the second moment, or moment of inertia, I_x of the area with respect to the x axis.

9.2. Determination of the Moment of Inertia of an Area by Integration. We have defined in the preceding section the second moment, or moment of inertia, of an area A with re-

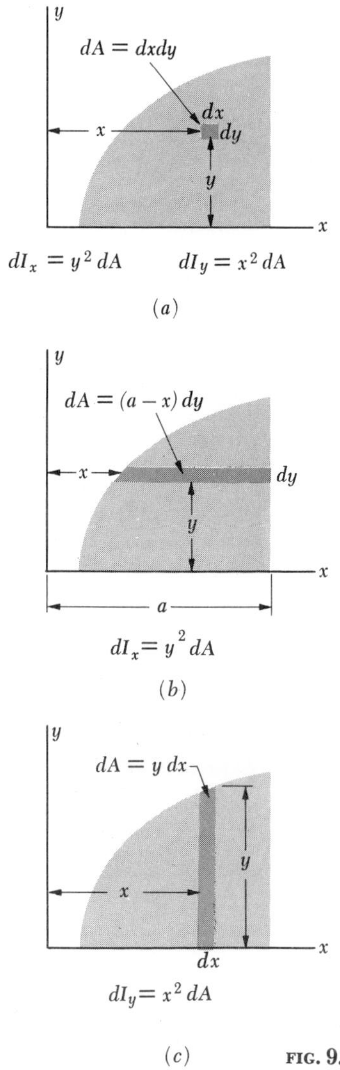

FIG. 9.3

spect to the x axis. Defining in a similar way the moment of inertia I_y of the area A with respect to the y axis, we write (Fig. 9.3a)

$$I_x = \int y^2\,dA \qquad I_y = \int x^2\,dA \tag{9.1}$$

These integrals, known as the *rectangular moments of inertia* of the area A, may be more easily computed if we choose for dA a thin strip parallel to one of the axes of coordinates. To compute I_x, the strip is chosen parallel to the x axis, so that all the points forming the strip are at the same distance y from the x axis (Fig. 9.3b); the moment of inertia dI_x of the strip is then obtained by multiplying the area dA of the strip by y^2. To compute I_y, the strip is chosen parallel to the y axis, so that all the points forming the strip are at the same distance x from the y axis (Fig. 9.3c); the moment of inertia dI_y of the strip is $x^2\,dA$.

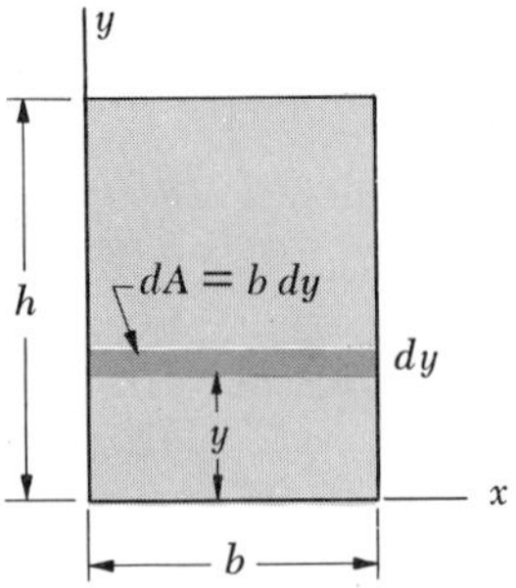

FIG. 9.4

Moment of Inertia of a Rectangular Area. As an example, we shall determine the moment of inertia of a rectangle with respect to its base (Fig. 9.4). Dividing the rectangle into strips parallel to the x axis, we obtain

$$dA = b\,dy \qquad dI_x = y^2 b\,dy \qquad I_x = \int_0^h by^2\,dy = \tfrac{1}{3}bh^3 \tag{9.2}$$

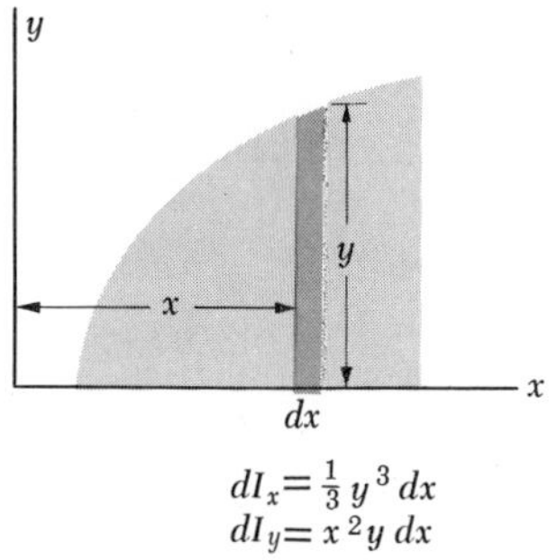

FIG. 9.5

Computing I_x and I_y from the Same Elementary Strips. The formula just derived may be used to determine the moment of inertia dI_x with respect to the x axis of a rectangular strip parallel to the y axis such as the one shown in Fig. 9.3c and reproduced in Fig. 9.5. Making $b = dx$ and $h = y$ in formula (9.2), we write

$$dI_x = \tfrac{1}{3}y^3\,dx$$

On the other hand, we have

$$dI_y = x^2\,dA = x^2 y\,dx$$

The same element may thus be used to compute the moments of inertia I_x and I_y of a given area (see Sample Prob. 9.3).

9.3. Polar Moment of Inertia. An integral of great importance in problems concerning the torsion of cylindrical shafts and in problems dealing with the rotation of slabs is

$$J_O = \int r^2\,dA \tag{9.3}$$

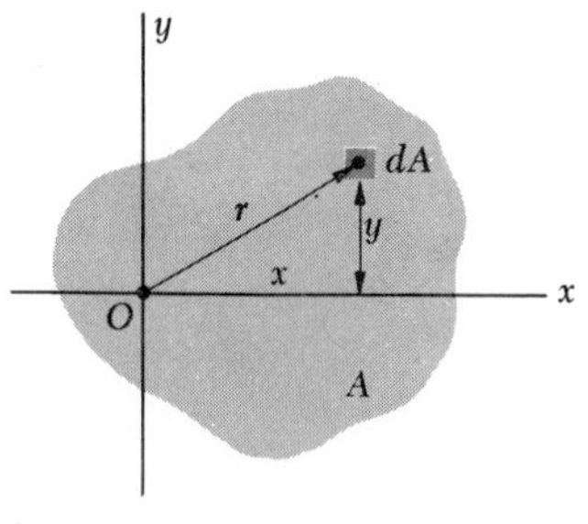

FIG. 9.6

where r is the distance from the element of area dA to the pole O (Fig. 9.6). This integral is the *polar moment of inertia* of the area A with respect to O.

The polar moment of inertia of a given area may be computed from the rectangular moments of inertia I_x and I_y of the area if these integrals are already known. Indeed, noting that $r^2 = x^2 + y^2$, we write

$$J_O = \int r^2\, dA = \int (x^2 + y^2)\, dA = \int y^2\, dA + \int x^2\, dA$$

that is,

$$J_O = I_x + I_y \tag{9.4}$$

9.4. Radius of Gyration of an Area. Consider an area A which has a moment of inertia I_x with respect to the x axis (Fig. 9.7*a*). Let us imagine that we concentrate this area into a thin strip parallel to the x axis (Fig. 9.7*b*). If the area A, thus concentrated, is to have the same moment of inertia with respect to the x axis, the strip should be placed at a distance k_x from the x axis, defined by the relation

$$I_x = k_x^2 A$$

Solving for k_x, we write

$$k_x = \sqrt{\frac{I_x}{A}} \tag{9.5}$$

The distance k_x is referred to as the *radius of gyration* of the area with respect to the x axis. We may define in a similar way the radii of gyration k_y and k_O; we write

$$I_y = k_y^2 A \qquad k_y = \sqrt{\frac{I_y}{A}} \tag{9.6}$$

$$J_O = k_O^2 A \qquad k_O = \sqrt{\frac{J_O}{A}} \tag{9.7}$$

Substituting for J_O, I_x, and I_y in terms of the radii of gyration in the relation (9.4), we observe that

$$k_O^2 = k_x^2 + k_y^2 \tag{9.8}$$

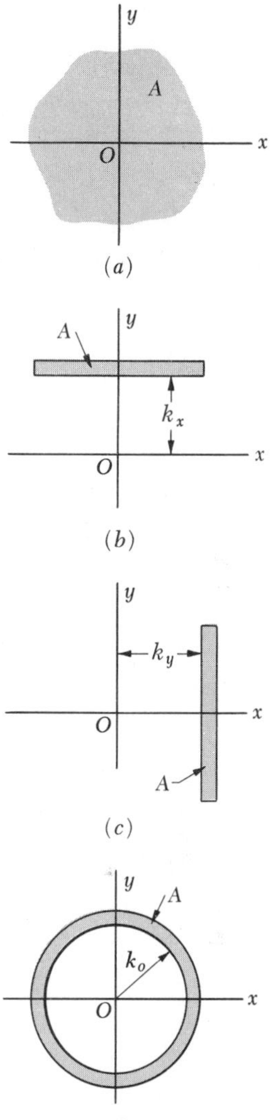

FIG. 9.7

Example. As an example, let us compute the radius of gyration k_x of the rectangle shown in Fig. 9.4. Using formulas (9.5) and (9.2), we write

$$k_x^2 = \frac{I_x}{A} = \frac{\frac{1}{3}bh^3}{bh} = \frac{h^2}{3} \qquad k_x = \frac{h}{\sqrt{3}}$$

The radius of gyration k_x of the rectangle is shown in Fig. 9.8. It should not be confused with the ordinate $\bar{y} = h/2$ of the centroid of the area. While k_x depends upon the *second moment*, or moment of inertia, of the area, the ordinate $\bar{y}$ is related to the *first moment* of the area.

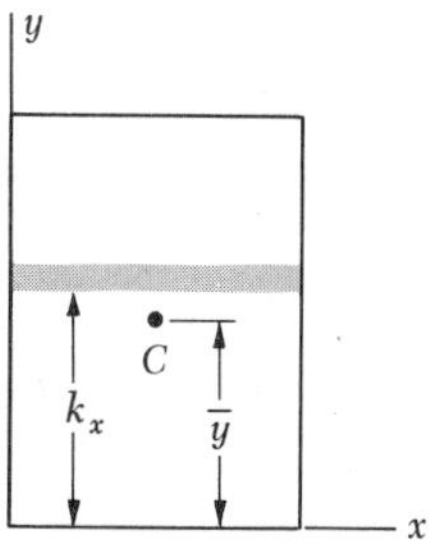

FIG. 9.8

SAMPLE PROBLEM 9.1

Determine the moment of inertia of a triangle with respect to its base.

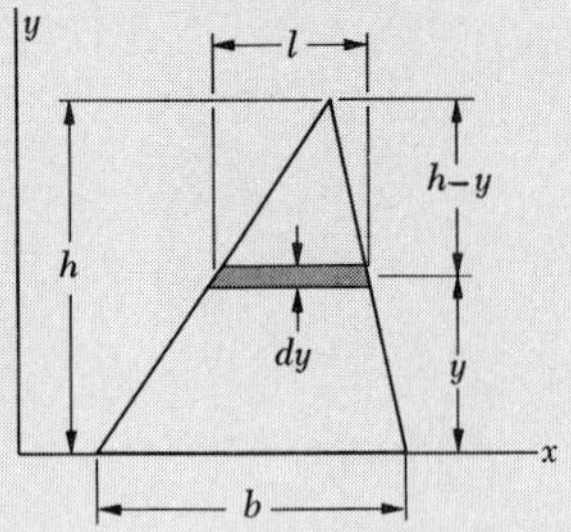

Solution. A triangle of base b and height h is drawn; the x axis is chosen to coincide with the base. A differential strip parallel to the x axis is chosen. Since all portions of the strip are at the same distance from the x axis, we write

$$dI_x = y^2\,dA \qquad dA = l\,dy$$

From the similar triangles, we have

$$\frac{l}{b} = \frac{h-y}{h} \qquad l = b\frac{h-y}{h} \qquad dA = b\frac{h-y}{h}\,dy$$

Integrating dI_x from $y = 0$ to $y = h$, we obtain

$$I_x = \int y^2\,dA = \int_0^h y^2 b\frac{h-y}{h}\,dy = \frac{b}{h}\int_0^h (hy^2 - y^3)\,dy$$

$$= \frac{b}{h}\left[h\frac{y^3}{3} - \frac{y^4}{4}\right]_0^h \qquad I_x = \frac{bh^3}{12} \blacktriangleleft$$

SAMPLE PROBLEM 9.2

(*a*) Determine the centroidal polar moment of inertia of a circular area by direct integration. (*b*) Using the result of part *a*, determine the moment of inertia of a circular area with respect to a diameter.

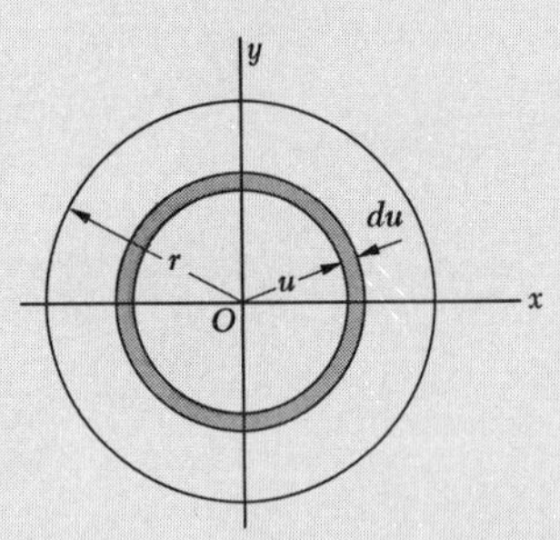

a. **Polar Moment of Inertia.** An annular differential element of area is chosen. Since all portions of this differential area are at the same distance from the origin, we write

$$dJ_O = u^2\,dA \qquad dA = 2\pi u\,du$$

$$J_O = \int dJ_O = \int_0^r u^2(2\pi u\,du) = 2\pi\int_0^r u^3\,du$$

$$J_O = \frac{\pi}{2}r^4 \blacktriangleleft$$

b. **Moment of Inertia.** Because of the symmetry of the circular area we have $I_x = I_y$. We then write

$$J_O = I_x + I_y = 2I_x \qquad \frac{\pi}{2}r^4 = 2I_x \qquad I_x = \frac{\pi}{4}r^4 \qquad I_{\text{diameter}} = \frac{\pi}{4}r^4 \blacktriangleleft$$

SAMPLE PROBLEM 9.3

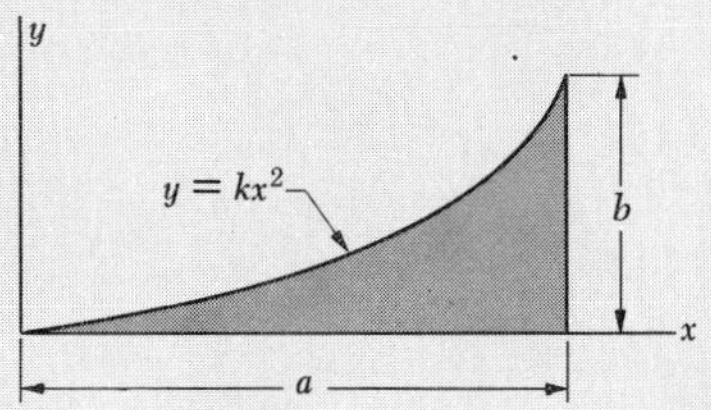

(*a*) Determine the moment of inertia of the shaded area shown with respect to each of the coordinate axes. This area has also been considered in Sample Prob. 5.4. (*b*) Using the results of part *a*, determine the radius of gyration of the shaded area with respect to each of the coordinate axes.

Solution. Referring to Sample Prob. 5.4, we obtain the following expressions for the equation of the curve and the total area:

$$y = \frac{b}{a^2}x^2 \qquad A = \tfrac{1}{3}ab$$

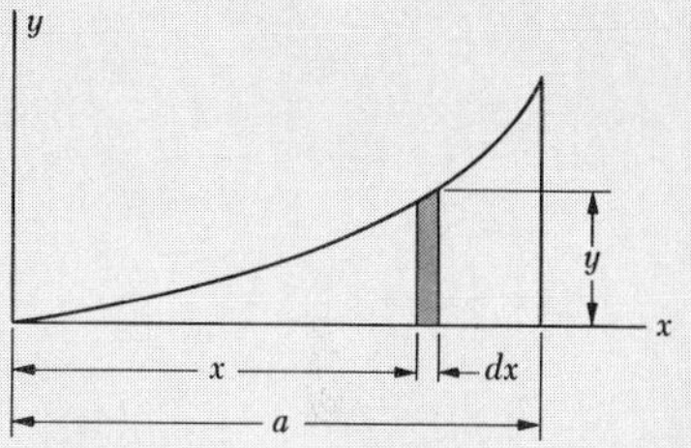

Moment of Inertia I_x. A vertical differential element of area is chosen. Since all portions of this element are *not* at the same distance from the x axis, we must treat the element as a thin rectangle. The moment of inertia of the element with respect to the x axis is

$$dI_x = \tfrac{1}{3}y^3\,dx = \frac{1}{3}\left(\frac{b}{a^2}x^2\right)^3 dx = \frac{1}{3}\frac{b^3}{a^6}x^6\,dx$$

$$I_x = \int dI_x = \int_0^a \frac{1}{3}\frac{b^3}{a^6}x^6\,dx = \left[\frac{1}{3}\frac{b^3}{a^6}\frac{x^7}{7}\right]_0^a$$

$$I_x = \frac{ab^3}{21} \quad ◀$$

Moment of Inertia I_y. The same vertical differential element of area is used. Since all portions of the element are at the same distance from the y axis, we write

$$dI_y = x^2\,dA = x^2(y\,dx) = x^2\left(\frac{b}{a^2}x^2\right)dx = \frac{b}{a^2}x^4\,dx$$

$$I_y = \int dI_y = \int_0^a \frac{b}{a^2}x^4\,dx = \left[\frac{b}{a^2}\frac{x^5}{5}\right]_0^a$$

$$I_y = \frac{a^3b}{5} \quad ◀$$

Radii of Gyration k_x and k_y

$$k_x^2 = \frac{I_x}{A} = \frac{ab^3/21}{ab/3} = \frac{b^2}{7} \qquad k_x = \sqrt{\tfrac{1}{7}}\,b \quad ◀$$

$$k_y^2 = \frac{I_y}{A} = \frac{a^3b/5}{ab/3} = \tfrac{3}{5}a^2 \qquad k_y = \sqrt{\tfrac{3}{5}}\,a \quad ◀$$

PROBLEMS

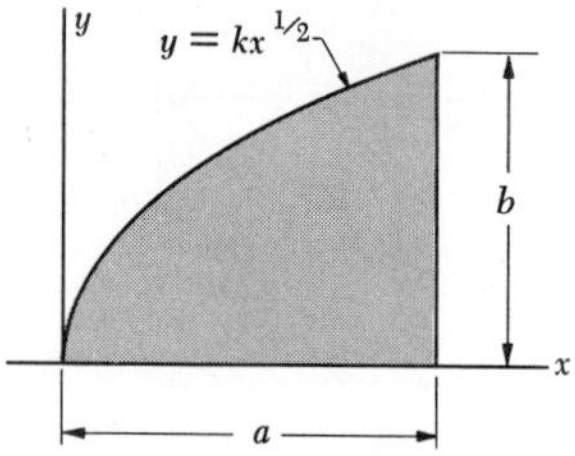

FIG. P 9.1 AND P 9.5

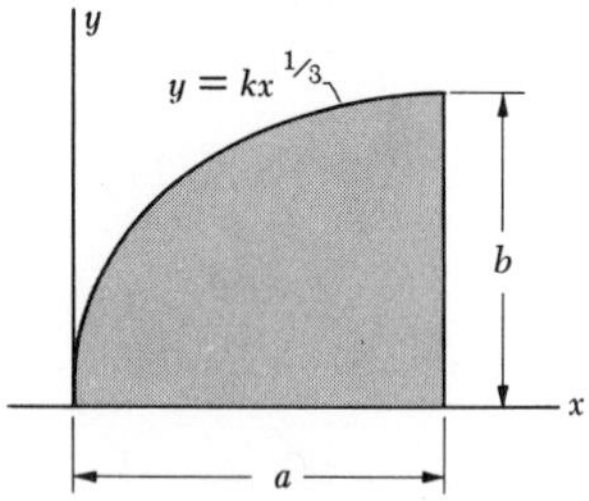

FIG. P 9.2 AND P 9.6

9.1 through 9.4. Determine by direct integration the moment of inertia of the shaded area with respect to the y axis.

9.5 through 9.8. Determine by direct integration the moment of inertia of the shaded area with respect to the x axis.

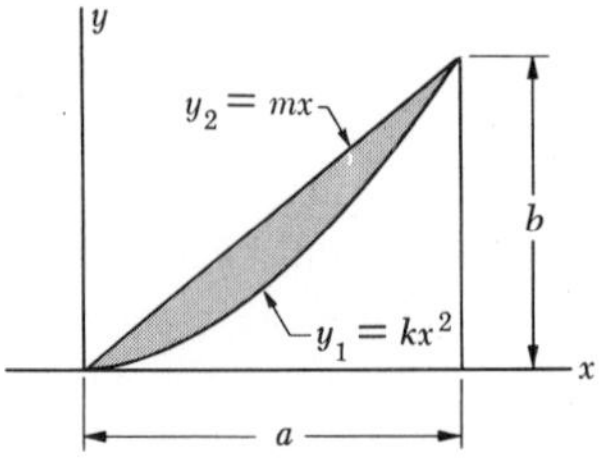

FIG. P 9.3 AND P 9.7

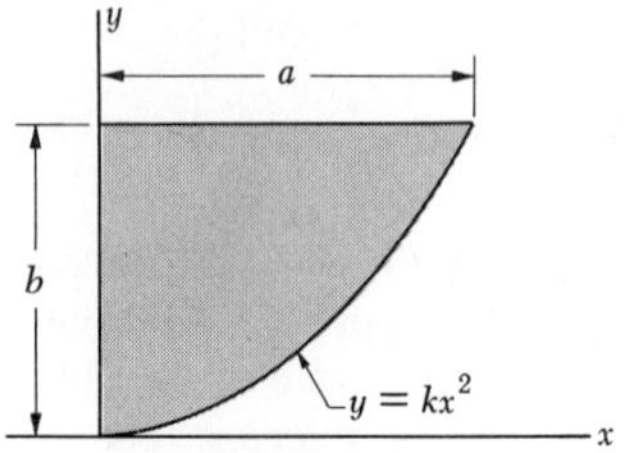

FIG. P 9.4 AND P 9.8

9.9 Determine the moment of inertia and radius of gyration of the semielliptical area shown with respect to the x axis.

9.10. Determine the moment of inertia and radius of gyration of the semielliptical area shown with respect to the y axis.

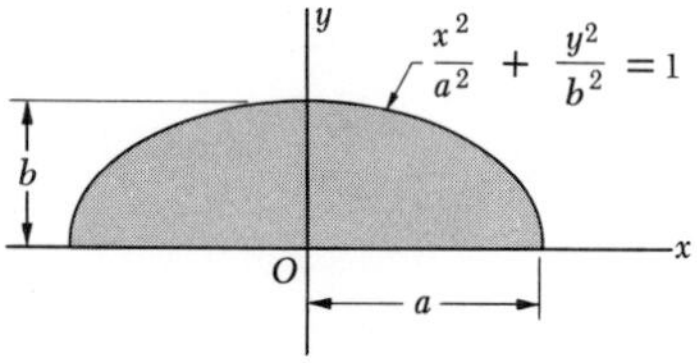

FIG. P 9.9 AND P 9.10

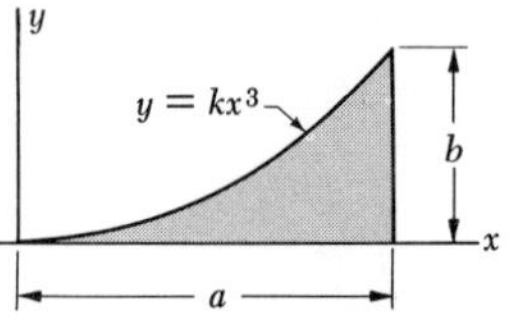

FIG. P 9.11 AND P 9.12

9.11. Determine the radius of gyration of the shaded area with respect to the x axis.

9.12. Determine the radius of gyration of the shaded area with respect to the y axis.

9.13. Determine the polar moment of inertia and the polar radius of gyration of an equilateral triangle of side a with respect to one of its vertices.

9.14. Determine the polar moment of inertia and the polar radius of gyration of a rectangle of base b and height h with respect to one of its corners.

9.15. Determine the polar moment of inertia and the polar radius of gyration of the semielliptical area of Prob. 9.9 with respect to O.

9.16. (*a*) Determine by direct integration the polar moment of inertia of the annular area shown. (*b*) Using the results of part *a*, determine the moment of inertia of the given area with respect to the x axis.

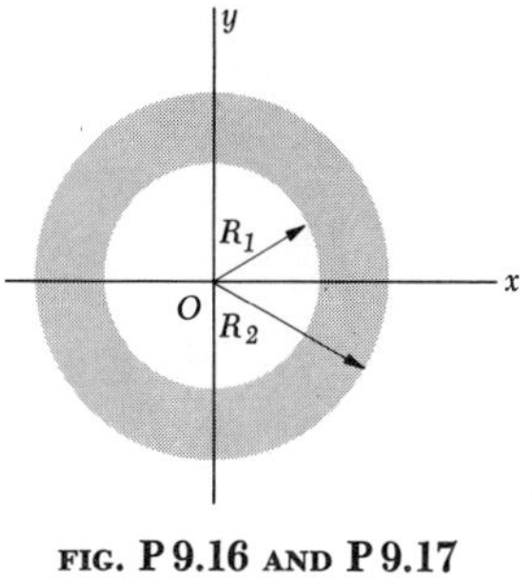

FIG. P9.16 AND P9.17

***9.17.** (*a*) Show that the polar radius of gyration k_O of the annular area shown is approximately equal to the mean radius $R_m = (R_1 + R_2)/2$ for small values of the thickness $t = R_2 - R_1$. (*b*) Determine the percentage error introduced by using R_m in place of k_O for values of t/R_m respectively equal to 1, $\frac{1}{2}$, and $\frac{1}{10}$.

***9.18.** Prove that the centroidal polar moment of inertia of a given area A cannot be smaller than $A^2/2\pi$. (*Hint.* Compare the moment of inertia of the given area with the moment of inertia of a circle of the same area and same centroid.)

***9.19.** In the plane area shown, it is desired to have I_x directly proportional to the height b. Determine the equation of the curve bounding the area on the right.

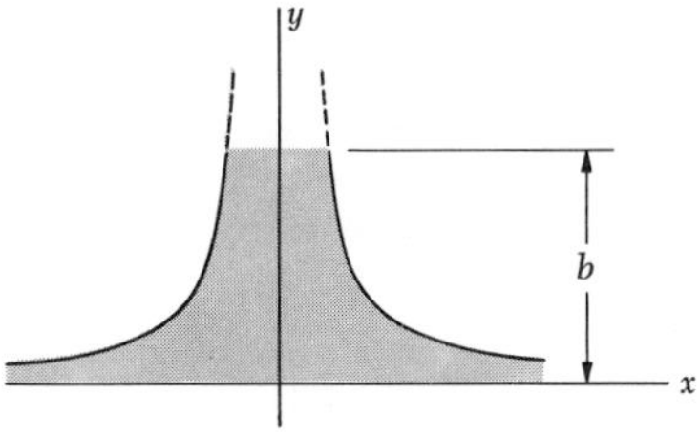

FIG. P9.19

9.5. Parallel-axis Theorem. Consider the moment of inertia I of an area A with respect to an axis AA' (Fig. 9.9). Denoting by y the distance from an element of area dA to AA', we write

$$I = \int y^2\, dA$$

Let us now draw an axis BB' parallel to AA' through the centroid C of the area; this axis is called a *centroidal axis.* Denoting by y' the distance from the element dA to BB', we write $y = y' + d$, where d is the distance between the axes AA' and BB'. Substituting for y in the integral representing I, we write

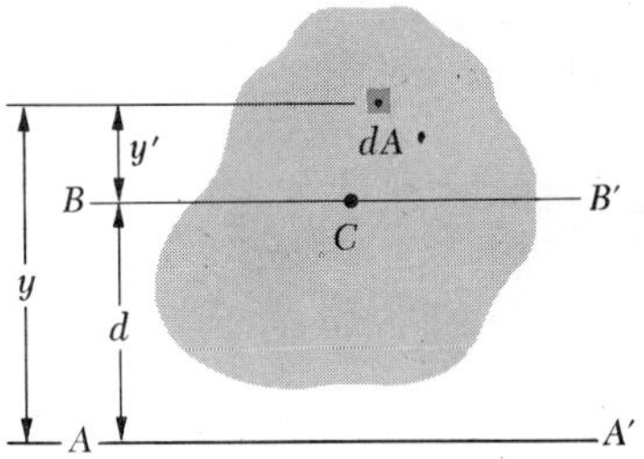

FIG. 9.9

$$I = \int y^2\, dA = \int (y' + d)^2\, dA$$
$$= \int y'^2\, dA + 2d\int y'\, dA + d^2\int dA$$

The first integral represents the moment of inertia $\bar{I}$ of the area with respect to the centroidal axis BB'. The second integral represents the first moment of the area with respect to BB'; since the centroid C of the area is located on that axis, the second integral must be zero. Finally, we observe that the last integral is equal to the total area A. We write therefore

$$I = \bar{I} + Ad^2 \tag{9.9}$$

This formula expresses that the moment of inertia I of an area with respect to any given axis AA' is equal to the moment of inertia $\bar{I}$ of the area with respect to a centroidal axis BB'

parallel to AA' *plus* the product Ad^2 of the area A and of the square of the distance d between the two axes. This theorem is known as the *parallel-axis theorem.* Substituting k^2A for I and $\bar{k}^2A$ for $\bar{I}$, the theorem may also be expressed in the following way:

$$k^2 = \bar{k}^2 + d^2 \tag{9.10}$$

A similar theorem may be used to relate the polar moment of inertia J_O of an area about a point O and the polar moment of inertia J_C of the same area about its centroid C. Denoting by d the distance between O and C, we write

$$J_O = J_C + Ad^2 \qquad \text{or} \qquad k_O^2 = k_C^2 + d^2 \tag{9.11}$$

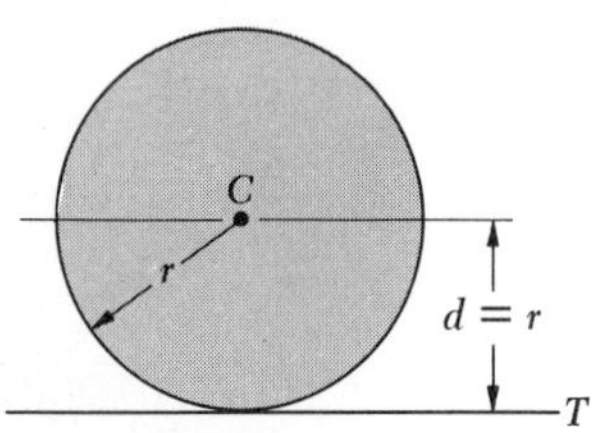

FIG. 9.10

Example 1. As an application of the parallel-axis theorem, we shall determine the moment of inertia I_T of a circular area with respect to a line tangent to the circle (Fig. 9.10). We found in Sample Prob. 9.2 that the moment of inertia of a circular area about a centroidal axis is $\bar{I} = \frac{1}{4}\pi r^4$. We may write, therefore,

$$I_T = \bar{I} + Ad^2 = \tfrac{1}{4}\pi r^4 + \pi r^2 r^2 = \tfrac{5}{4}\pi r^4$$

Example 2. The parallel-axis theorem may also be used to determine the centroidal moment of inertia of an area when the moment of inertia of this area with respect to some parallel axis is known. Consider, for instance, a triangular area (Fig. 9.11). We found in Sample Prob. 9.1 that the moment of inertia of a triangle with respect to its base AA' is equal to $\frac{1}{12}bh^3$. Using the parallel-axis theorem, we write

$$I_{AA'} = \bar{I}_{BB'} + Ad^2$$
$$\bar{I}_{BB'} = I_{AA'} - Ad^2 = \tfrac{1}{12}bh^3 - \tfrac{1}{2}bh(\tfrac{1}{3}h)^2 = \tfrac{1}{36}bh^3$$

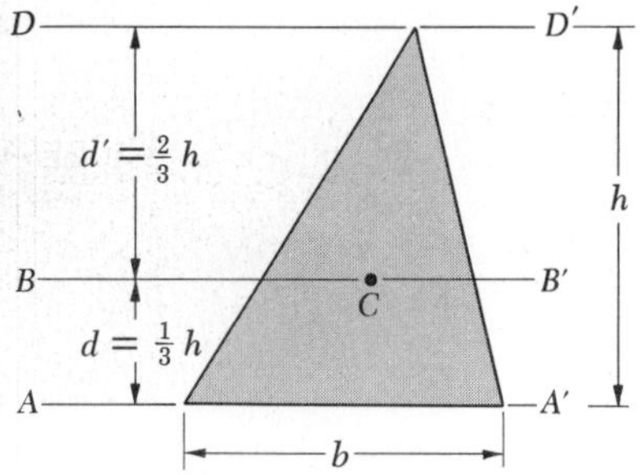

FIG. 9.11

It should be observed that the product Ad^2 was *subtracted* from the given moment of inertia in order to obtain the centroidal moment of inertia of the triangle. While this product is *added* in transferring *from* a centroidal axis to a parallel axis, it should be *subtracted* in transferring *to* a centroidal axis. In other words, the moment of inertia of an area is always smaller with respect to a centroidal axis than with respect to any other parallel axis.

Returning to Fig. 9.11, we observe that the moment of inertia of the triangle with respect to a line DD' drawn through a vertex may be obtained by writing

$$I_{DD'} = \bar{I}_{BB'} + Ad'^2 = \tfrac{1}{36}bh^3 + \tfrac{1}{2}bh(\tfrac{2}{3}h)^2 = \tfrac{1}{4}bh^3$$

Note that $I_{DD'}$ *could not* have been obtained directly from $I_{AA'}$. The parallel-axis theorem can be applied only if one of the two parallel axes passes through the centroid of the area.

9.6. Moments of Inertia of Composite Areas. Consider a composite area A made of several component areas A_1, A_2,

Rectangle	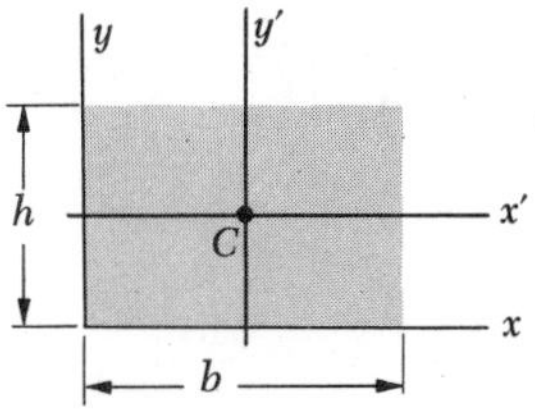	$\bar{I}_{x'} = \frac{1}{12}bh^3$ $\bar{I}_{y'} = \frac{1}{12}b^3h$ $I_x = \frac{1}{3}bh^3$ $I_y = \frac{1}{3}b^3h$ $J_C = \frac{1}{12}bh(b^2 + h^2)$
Triangle	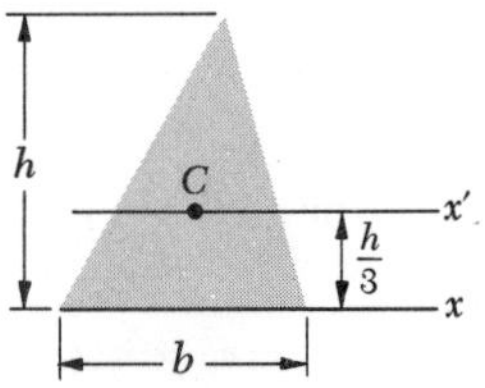	$\bar{I}_{x'} = \frac{1}{36}bh^3$ $I_x = \frac{1}{12}bh^3$
Circle	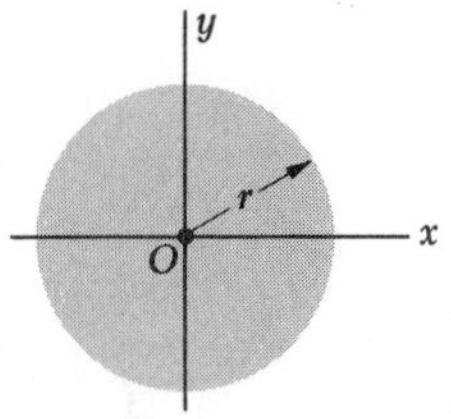	$\bar{I}_x = \bar{I}_y = \frac{1}{4}\pi r^4$ $J_O = \frac{1}{2}\pi r^4$
Semicircle	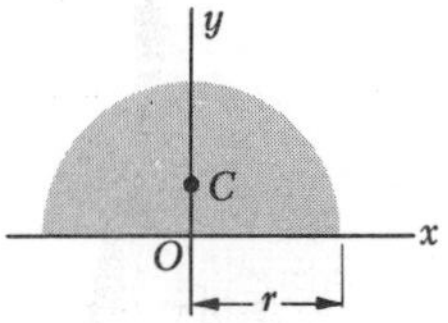	$I_x = I_y = \frac{1}{8}\pi r^4$ $J_O = \frac{1}{4}\pi r^4$
Quarter circle	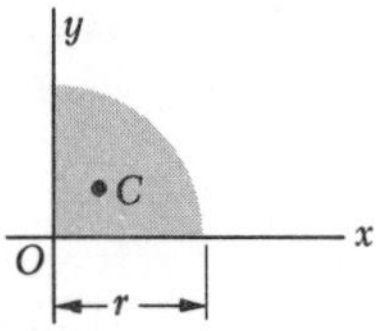	$I_x = I_y = \frac{1}{16}\pi r^4$ $J_O = \frac{1}{8}\pi r^4$
Ellipse	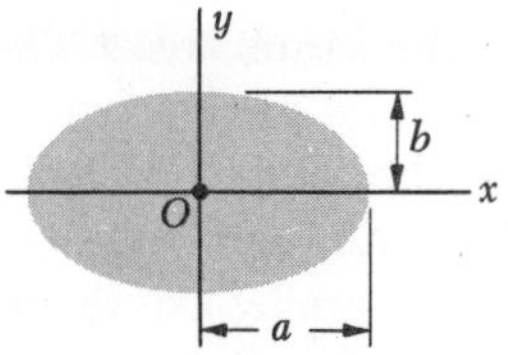	$\bar{I}_x = \frac{1}{4}\pi ab^3$ $\bar{I}_y = \frac{1}{4}\pi a^3b$ $J_O = \frac{1}{4}\pi ab(a^2 + b^2)$

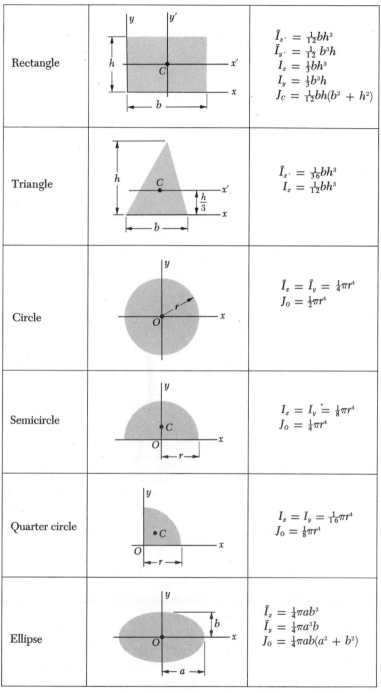

FIG. 9.12. Moments of inertia of common geometric shapes

Shape		Nominal size, in.	Wt/ft, lb
Wide-flange section	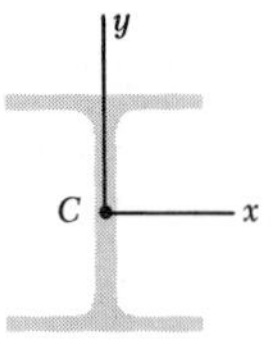	16 × $8\frac{1}{2}$† 14 × 8 8 × 8	64 43 31
American Standard beam	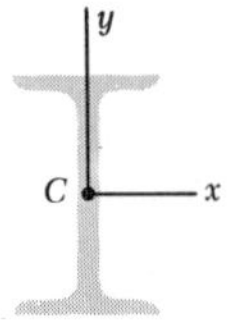	18 × 6 12 × 5 6 × $3\frac{3}{8}$	70 35 12.5
American Standard channel	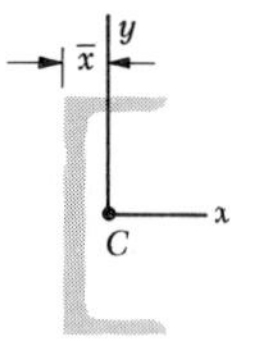	10 × $2\frac{5}{8}$ 8 × $2\frac{1}{4}$ 6 × 2	25.0 11.5 8.2
Angles	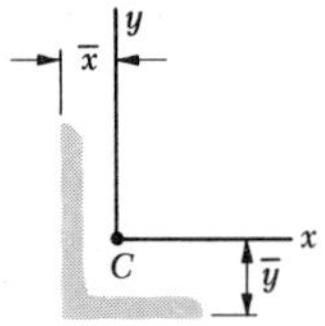	6 × 6 × 1‡ 4 × 4 × $\frac{1}{2}$ 8 × 6 × 1 5 × $3\frac{1}{2}$ × $\frac{1}{2}$	37.4 12.8 44.2 13.6

† Depth and width. ‡ The last figure represents the thickness.

FIG. 9.13. **Properties of rolled-steel**

etc. Since the integral representing the moment of inertia of A may be subdivided into integrals computed over A_1, A_2, etc., the moment of inertia of A with respect to a given axis will be obtained by adding the moments of inertia of the areas A_1, A_2, etc., with respect to the same axis. The moment of inertia of an area made of several of the common shapes shown in Fig. 9.12 may thus be obtained from the formulas given in that figure. Before adding the moments of inertia of the component areas, however, the parallel-axis theorem should be used to transfer each moment of inertia to the desired axis. This is shown in Sample Probs. 9.4 and 9.5.

Area, in.²	$\bar{I}_x$, in.⁴	$\bar{k}_x$, in.	$\bar{y}$, in.	$\bar{I}_y$, in.⁴	$\bar{k}_y$, in.	$\bar{x}$, in.
18.80	833.8	6.66	....	68.4	1.91	
12.65	429.0	5.82	....	45.1	1.89	
9.12	109.7	3.47	....	37.0	2.01	
20.46	917.5	6.70	....	24.5	1.09	
10.20	227.0	4.72	....	10.0	0.99	
3.61	21.8	2.46	....	1.8	0.72	
7.33	90.7	3.52	....	3.4	0.68	0.62
3.36	32.3	3.10	....	1.3	0.63	0.58
2.39	13.0	2.34	....	0.7	0.54	0.52
11.00	35.5	1.80	1.86	35.5	1.80	1.86
3.75	5.6	1.22	1.18	5.6	1.22	1.18
13.00	80.8	2.49	2.65	38.8	1.73	1.65
4.00	10.0	1.58	1.66	4.1	1.01	0.91

structural shapes

The properties of the cross sections of various structural shapes are given in Fig. 9.13. As noted in Sec. 9.1, the moment of inertia of a beam section about its neutral axis is closely related to the value of the internal forces. The determination of moments of inertia is thus a prerequisite to the analysis and design of structural members.

It should be noted that the radius of gyration of a composite area is *not* equal to the sum of the radii of gyration of the component areas. In order to determine the radius of gyration of a composite area, it is necessary first to compute the moment of inertia of the area.

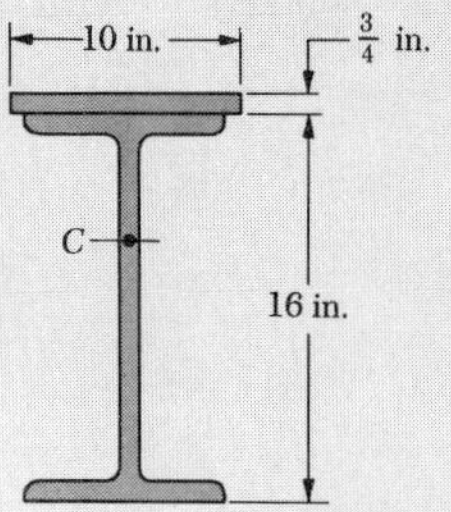

SAMPLE PROBLEM 9.4

The strength of a 16-in., 64-lb wide-flange beam is increased by attaching a 10- by $\frac{3}{4}$-in. plate to its upper flange as shown. Determine the moment of inertia and the radius of gyration of the composite section with respect to an axis through its centroid C and parallel to the plate.

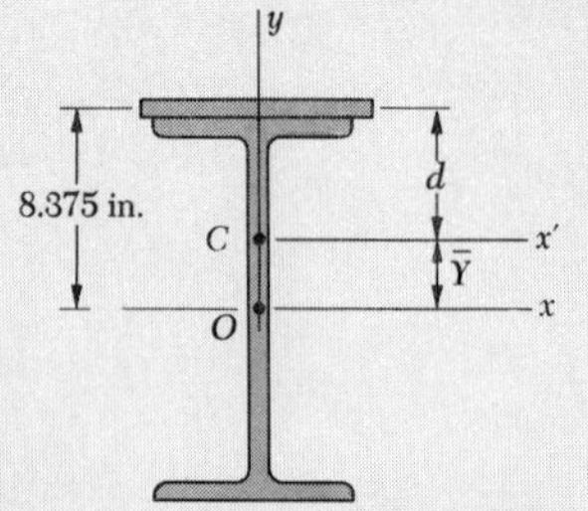

Solution. The origin of coordinates O is placed at the centroid of the wide-flange section, and the distance $\overline{Y}$ to the centroid of the composite section is computed by the methods of Chap 5. The area of the wide-flange section is found by referring to Fig. 9.13.

Section	Area	$\bar{y}$	$\bar{y}A$
Plate	7.5	8.375	62.8
Wide-flange section. . . .	18.8	0	0
	26.3	. . . .	62.8

$$\overline{Y}\Sigma A = \Sigma\bar{y}A \qquad \overline{Y}(26.3) = 62.8 \qquad \overline{Y} = 2.39 \text{ in.}$$

Moment of Inertia. The parallel-axis theorem is used to determine the moments of inertia of the wide-flange section and of the plate with respect to the x' axis. This axis is a centroidal axis for the composite section, but *not* for either of the elements considered separately. The value of $\bar{I}_x$ for the wide-flange section is obtained from Fig. 9.13.

For the wide-flange section

$$I_{x'} = \bar{I}_x + A\overline{Y}^2 = 833.8 + (18.8)(2.39)^2 = 941 \text{ in.}^4$$

For the plate

$$I_{x'} = \bar{I}_x + Ad^2 = (\tfrac{1}{12})(10)(\tfrac{3}{4})^3 + (7.5)(8.375 - 2.39)^2 = 269 \text{ in.}^4$$

For the composite area

$$I_{x'} = 941 + 269 = 1{,}210 \text{ in.}^4$$

$$I_{x'} = 1{,}210 \text{ in.}^4 \blacktriangleleft$$

Radius of Gyration

$$k_{x'}^2 = \frac{I_{x'}}{A} = \frac{1{,}210 \text{ in.}^4}{26.3 \text{ in.}^2}$$

$$k_{x'} = 6.78 \text{ in.} \blacktriangleleft$$

SAMPLE PROBLEM 9.5

Determine the moment of inertia of the shaded area with respect to the y axis.

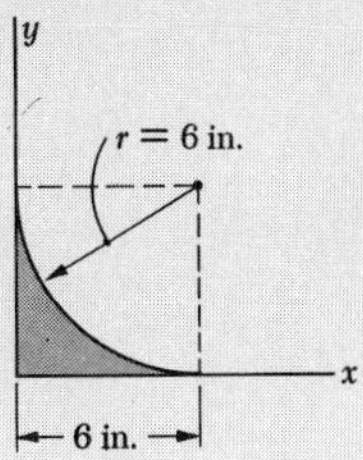

Solution. The given area may be obtained by subtracting a quarter circle from a square. The moments of inertia of the square and of the quarter circle are computed separately.

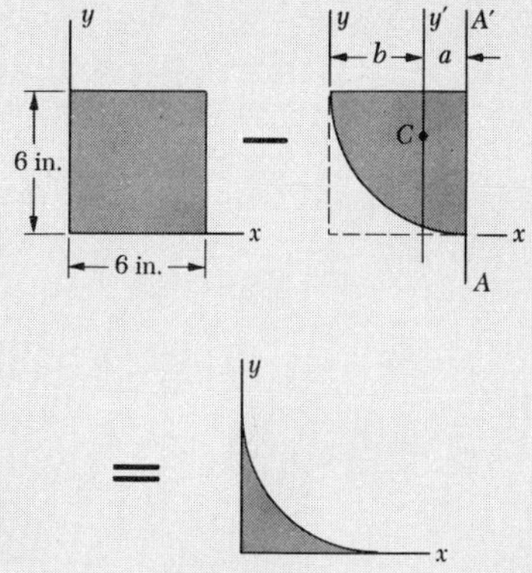

I_y for Square. Referring to Fig. 9.12, we obtain

$$I_y = \tfrac{1}{3} b^3 h = (\tfrac{1}{3})(6)^3(6) = 432 \text{ in.}^4$$

I_y for the Quarter Circle. Referring to Fig. 5.8, we locate the centroid C of the quarter circle with respect to side AA'.

$$a = \frac{4r}{3\pi} = \frac{(4)(6)}{3\pi} = 2.546 \text{ in.}$$

The distance b from the centroid C to the y axis is

$$b = 6 \text{ in.} - a = 6 \text{ in.} - 2.546 \text{ in.} = 3.454 \text{ in.}$$

Referring now to Fig. 9.12, we compute the moment of inertia of the quarter circle with respect to side AA'; we also compute the area of the quarter circle.

$$I_{AA'} = \tfrac{1}{16}\pi r^4 = \tfrac{1}{16}\pi(6)^4 = 254.5 \text{ in.}^4$$
$$A = \tfrac{1}{4}\pi r^2 = \tfrac{1}{4}\pi(6)^2 = 28.27 \text{ in.}^2$$

Using the parallel-axis theorem, we obtain the value of $\bar{I}_{y'}$,

$$I_{AA'} = \bar{I}_{y'} + Aa^2$$
$$\bar{I}_{y'} = I_{AA'} - Aa^2$$
$$= 254.5 - (28.27)(2.546)^2 = 71.2 \text{ in.}^4$$

Again using the parallel-axis theorem, we obtain the value of I_y,

$$I_y = \bar{I}_{y'} + Ab^2 = 71.2 + (28.27)(3.454)^2 = 408.5 \text{ in.}^4$$

I_y for Given Area. Subtracting the moment of inertia of the quarter circle from that of the square, we obtain

$$I_y = 432.0 \text{ in.}^4 - 408.5 \text{ in.}^4$$

$$I_y = 23.5 \text{ in.}^4 \blacktriangleleft$$

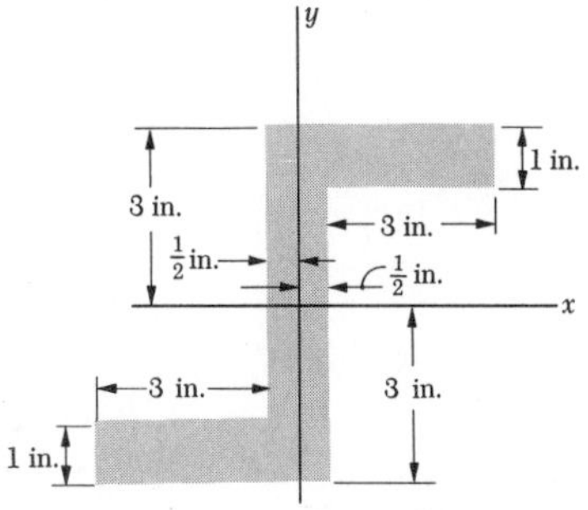

FIG. P 9.20 AND P 9.22

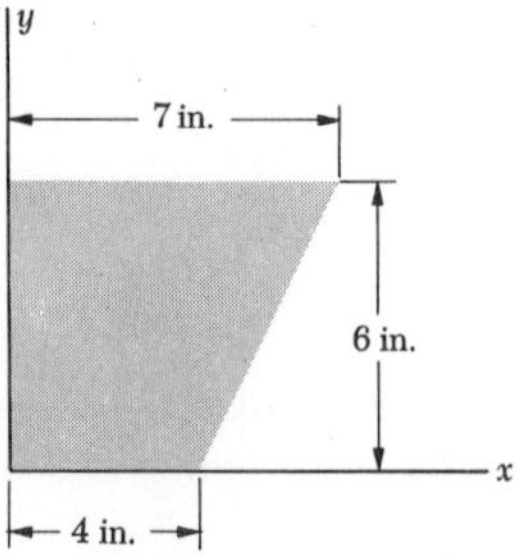

FIG. P 9.21 AND P 9.23

PROBLEMS

9.20 and 9.21. Determine the moment of inertia and the radius of gyration of the shaded area with respect to the x axis.

9.22 and 9.23. Determine the moment of inertia and the radius of gyration of the shaded area with respect to the y axis.

9.24. Knowing that the shaded area is equal to 30 in.^{2} and that its moment of inertia with respect to AA' is 1,200 in.^{4}, determine its moment of inertia with respect to BB', for $d_1 = 6$ in. and $d_2 = 2$ in.

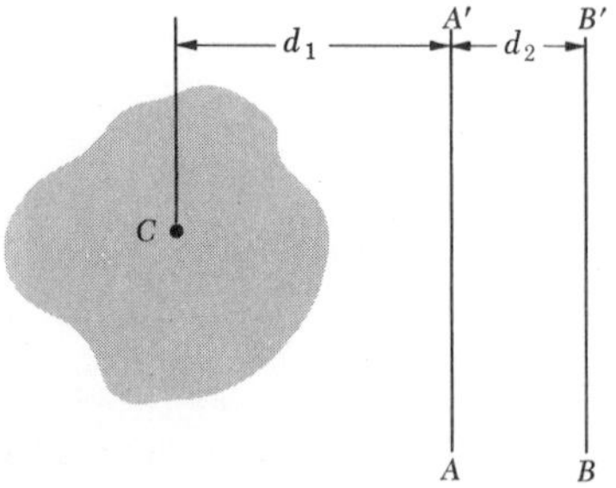

FIG. P 9.24 AND P 9.25

9.25. Determine the shaded area and its moment of inertia with respect to a centroidal axis parallel to AA', knowing that its moments of inertia with respect to AA' and BB' are respectively 1,000 in.^{4} and 2,600 in.^{4}, and that $d_1 = 6$ in. and $d_2 = 4$ in.

9.26. The polar moments of inertia of the shaded area with respect to the corners A, B, and D of a 3-in. square are respectively $J_A = 1{,}300$ in.^{4}, $J_B = 1{,}660$ in.^{4}, and $J_D = 2{,}860$ in.^{4}. Determine the shaded area, its centroidal moment of inertia J_C, and the distance d from A to C.

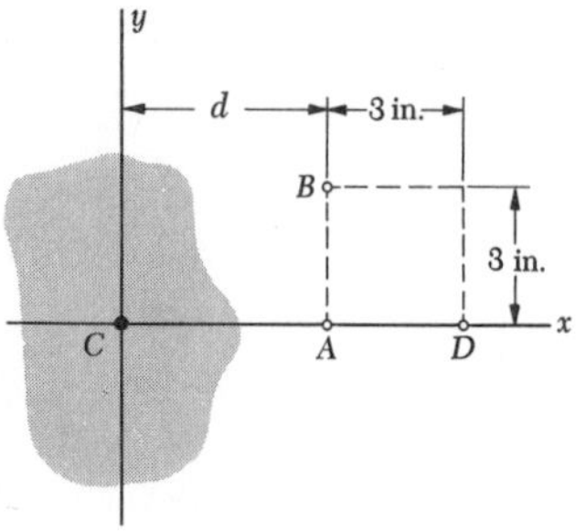

FIG. P 9.26 AND P 9.27

9.27. The shaded area is equal to 50 in.^{2}. Determine its centroidal moments of inertia $\bar{I}_x$ and $\bar{I}_y$, knowing that $\bar{I}_x = 2\bar{I}_y$, and that the polar moment of inertia of the area about point A, at the distance $d = 6$ in. from C, is $J_A = 2{,}400$ in.^{4}.

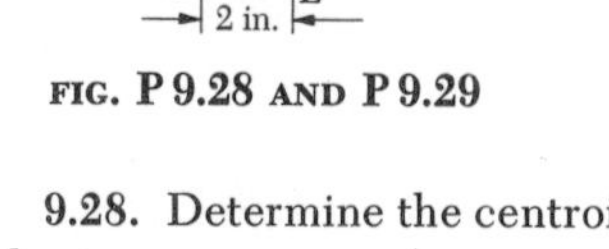

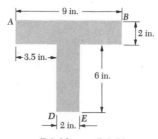

FIG. P 9.28 AND P 9.29

9.28. Determine the centroidal polar moment of inertia of the area shown.

9.29. Determine the moments of inertia $\bar{I}_x$ and $\bar{I}_y$ of the area shown with respect to centroidal axes respectively parallel and perpendicular to the side AB.

9.30. Determine the polar moment of inertia of the area shown with respect to (*a*) point *O*, (*b*) the centroid of the area.

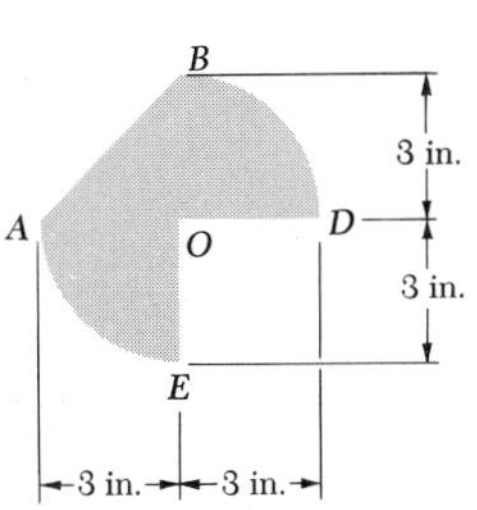

FIG. P 9.30

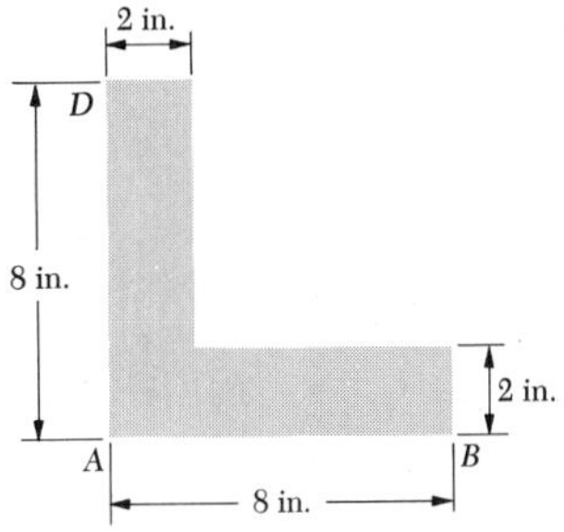

FIG. P 9.31

9.31. Determine the moments of inertia $\bar{I}_x$ and $\bar{I}_y$ of the area shown with respect to centroidal axes respectively parallel and perpendicular to the side *AB*.

9.32. A column is made of two 8-in., 11.5-lb American Standard channels welded to two 12- by $\frac{1}{4}$-in. steel plates. Determine the distance *d* for which the centroidal moments of inertia $\bar{I}_x$ and $\bar{I}_y$ of the column section are equal.

9.33. If the distance between the channels of the column of Prob. 9.32 is $d = 6$ in., determine the centroidal moments of inertia $\bar{I}_x$, $\bar{I}_y$, and J_C of the column section.

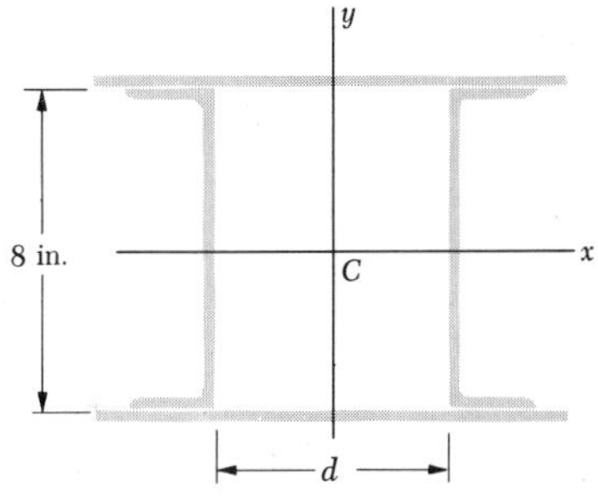

FIG. P 9.32

9.34. A steel plate, 8 by $\frac{1}{2}$ in., is welded to the flange of a 12-in., 35-lb American Standard beam as shown. Determine the moments of inertia and the radii of gyration of the combined section with respect to centroidal axes respectively parallel and perpendicular to the plate.

9.35. Three steel plates, 18 by 1 in., are riveted to four 6- by 6-in. angles, each 1 in. thick, to form the column whose cross section is shown. Determine the moments of inertia and the radii of gyration of the section with respect to centroidal axes respectively parallel and perpendicular to the flanges.

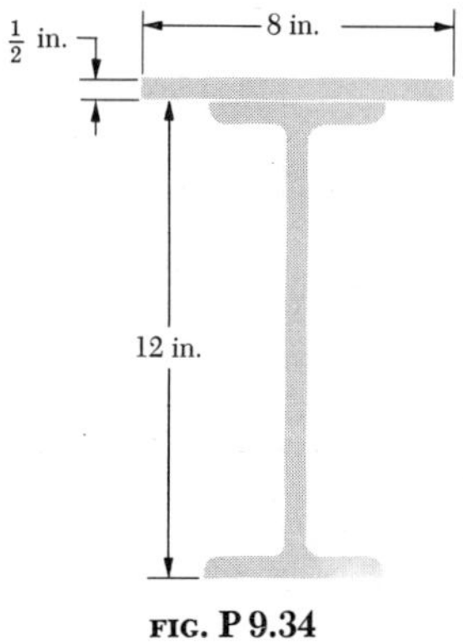

FIG. P 9.34

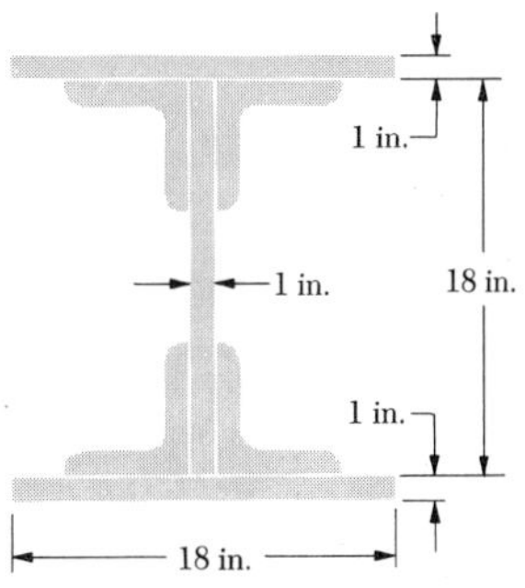

FIG. P 9.35

9.36 through 9.39. The panel shown forms the end of a trough which is filled with water to the line AA'. Referring to Sec. 9.1, determine the depth of the point of application of the resultant of the hydrostatic forces acting on the panel (center of pressure).

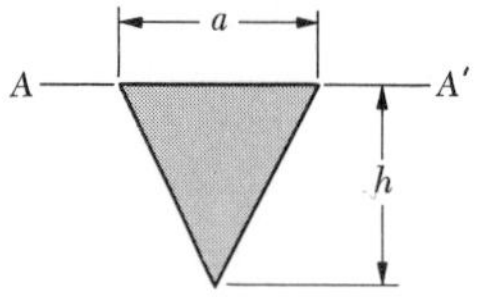

FIG. P 9.36

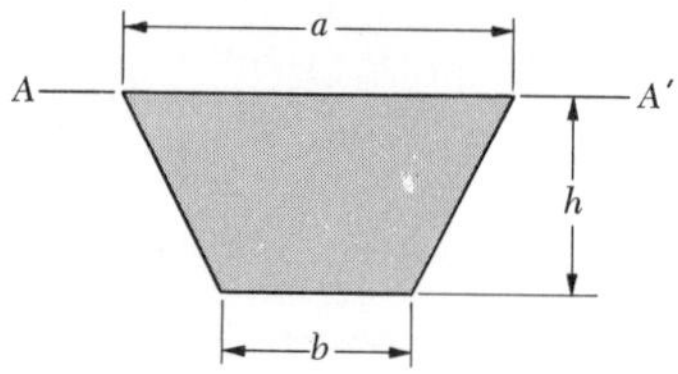

FIG. P 9.37

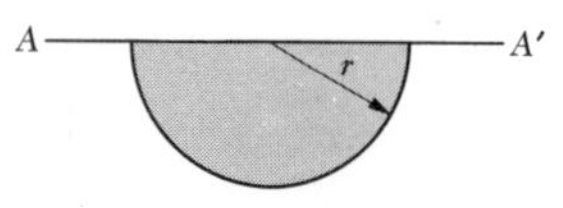

FIG. P 9.38

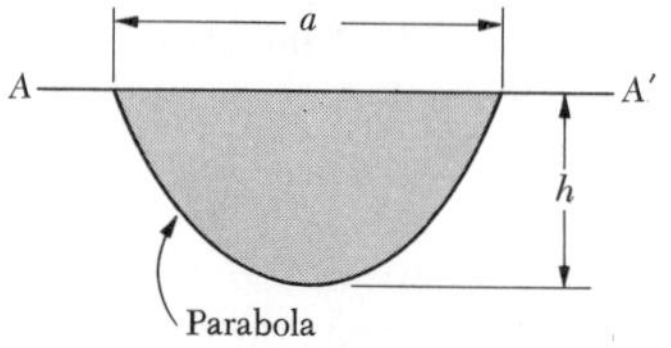

FIG. P 9.39

9.40. A vertical circular gate of radius r is completely submerged in water. If the center of the gate is at a depth h, determine the depth of the center of pressure.

9.41. Assuming that the circular gate of Prob. 9.40 is hinged about its diameter $C'C''$, and denoting the specific weight of water by γ, determine (*a*) the reaction at each hinge, (*b*) the moment of the couple required to keep the gate closed.

***9.42.** Show that the resultant of the hydrostatic forces acting on a submerged plane area A is a force **P** perpendicular to the area and of magnitude $P = \gamma A\bar{y} \sin \theta = \bar{p}A$ where γ is the specific weight of the liquid and $\bar{p}$ the pressure at the centroid C of the area. Show that **P** is applied at a point C_P, called the center of pressure, of coordinates $x_P = P_{xy}/A\bar{y}$ and $y_P = I_x/A\bar{y}$, where $P_{xy} = \int xy \, dA$ (see Sec. 9.7). Show also that the difference of ordinates $y_P - \bar{y}$ is equal to $\bar{k}_x^2/\bar{y}$ and thus depends upon the depth at which the area is submerged.

FIG. P 9.40

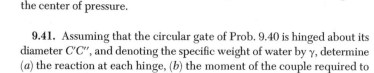

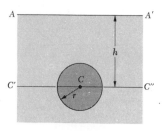

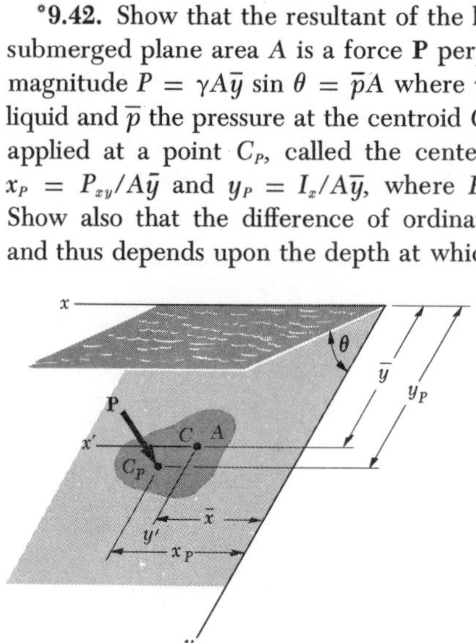

FIG. P 9.42

°**9.43.** Show that the system of hydrostatic forces acting on a submerged plane area A may be reduced to a force $\mathbf{P}$ at the centroid C of the area and two couples. The force $\mathbf{P}$ is perpendicular to the area and of magnitude $P = \gamma A\bar{y} \sin \theta$, where γ is the specific weight of the liquid, and the couples are represented by vectors directed as shown and of magnitude $M_{x'} = \gamma \bar{I}_{x'} \sin \theta$ and $M_{y'} = \gamma \bar{P}_{x'y'} \sin \theta$, where $\bar{P}_{x'y'} = \int x'\, y'\, dA$ (see Sec. 9.7). Note that the couples are independent of the depth at which the area is submerged.

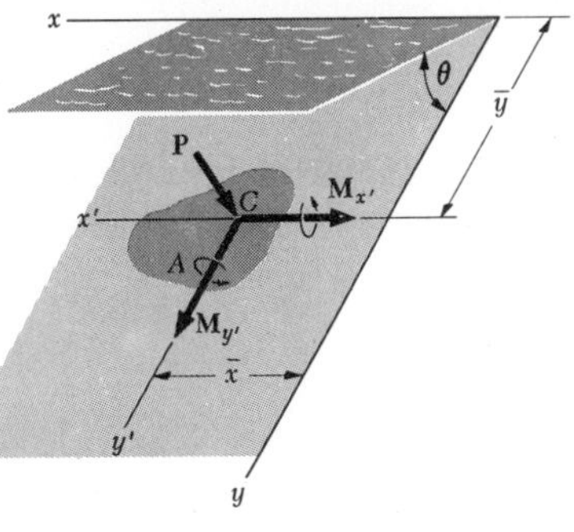

FIG. P 9.43

***9.7. Product of Inertia.** The integral

$$P_{xy} = \int xy\, dA \tag{9.12}$$

obtained by multiplying each element dA of an area A by its coordinates x and y and integrating over the area (Fig. 9.14) is known as the *product of inertia* of the area A with respect to the x and y axes. Unlike the moments of inertia I_x and I_y, the product of inertia P_{xy} may be either positive or negative.

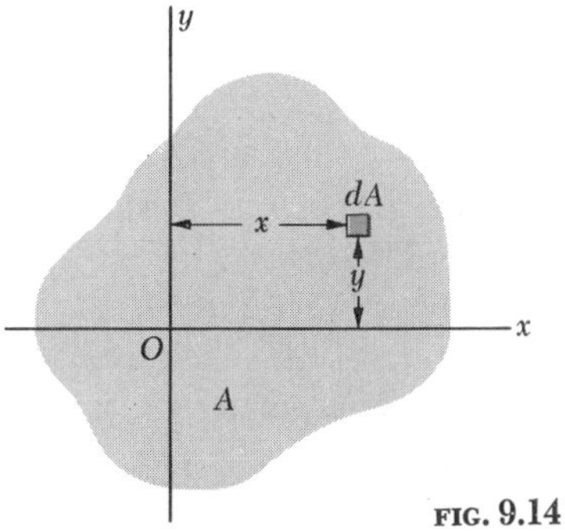

FIG. 9.14

When one or both of the x and y axes are axes of symmetry for the area A, the product of inertia P_{xy} is zero. Consider, for example, the channel section shown in Fig. 9.15. Since this section is symmetrical with respect to the x axis, we can associate to each element dA of coordinates x and y an element dA' of coordinates x and $-y$. Clearly, the contributions of any pair of elements chosen in this way cancel out, and the integral (9.12) reduces to zero.

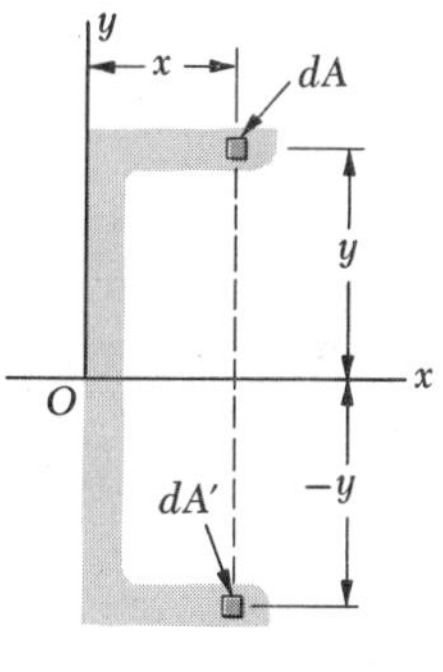

FIG. 9.15

A parallel-axis theorem similar to the one established in Sec. 9.5 for moments of inertia may be derived for products of inertia. Consider an area A and a system of rectangular coordinates x and y (Fig. 9.16). Through the centroid C of the area, of coordinates $\bar{x}$ and $\bar{y}$, we draw two *centroidal axes* x' and y' parallel, respectively, to the x and y axes. Denoting by x and y the coordinates of an element of area dA with respect to the original axes, and by x' and y' the coordinates of the same element with respect to the centroidal axes, we write $x = x' + \bar{x}$ and $y = y' + \bar{y}$. Substituting into (9.12), we obtain the following expression for the product of inertia P_{xy}:

$$\begin{aligned} P_{xy} &= \int xy\, dA = \int (x' + \bar{x})(y' + \bar{y})\, dA \\ &= \int x'y'\, dA + \bar{y}\int x'\, dA + \bar{x}\int y'\, dA + \bar{x}\bar{y}\int dA \end{aligned}$$

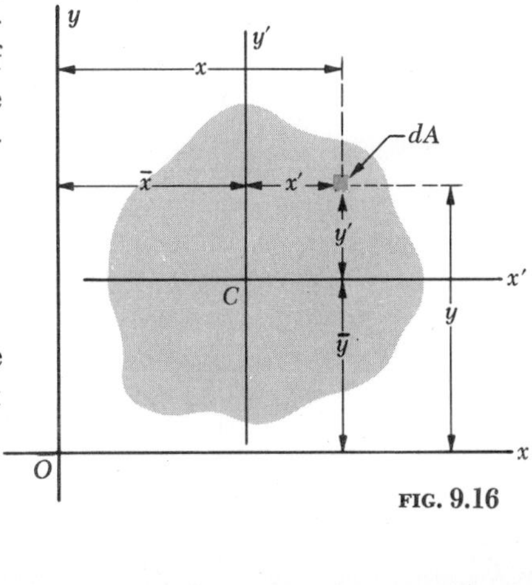

FIG. 9.16

The first integral represents the product of inertia $P_{x'y'}$ of the area A with respect to the centroidal axes x' and y'. The next two integrals represent first moments of the area with respect to the centroidal axes; they reduce to zero, since the centroid C is located on these axes. Finally, we observe that the last integral is equal to the total area A. We write therefore

$$P_{xy} = \bar{P}_{x'y'} + \bar{x}\bar{y}A \tag{9.13}$$

***9.8. Principal Axes and Principal Moments of Inertia.** Consider the area A and the coordinate axes x and y (Fig. 9.17). We assume that the moments and product of inertia

$$I_x = \int y^2\,dA \qquad I_y = \int x^2\,dA \qquad P_{xy} = \int xy\,dA \tag{9.14}$$

of the area A are known, and we propose to determine the moments and product of inertia I_u, I_v, and P_{uv} of A with respect to new axes u and v obtained by rotating the original axes about the origin through an angle θ.

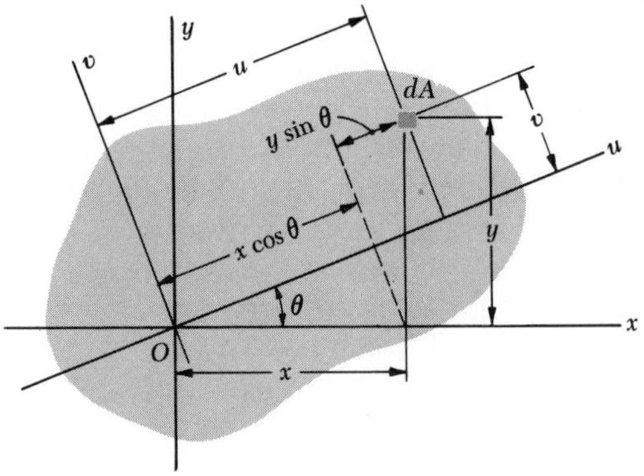

FIG. 9.17

We first note the following relations between the coordinates u, v and x, y of an element of area dA:

$$u = x\cos\theta + y\sin\theta \qquad v = y\cos\theta - x\sin\theta$$

Substituting for u and v into the expression for I_u, we write

$$\begin{aligned} I_u &= \int v^2\,dA = \int (y\cos\theta - x\sin\theta)^2\,dA \\ &= \cos^2\theta \int y^2\,dA - 2\sin\theta\cos\theta \int xy\,dA + \sin^2\theta \int x^2\,dA \end{aligned}$$

Taking the relations (9.14) into account, we write

$$I_u = I_x\cos^2\theta - 2P_{xy}\sin\theta\cos\theta + I_y\sin^2\theta \tag{9.15}$$

Similarly, we obtain for I_v and P_{uv} the expressions

$$I_v = I_x\sin^2\theta + 2P_{xy}\sin\theta\cos\theta + I_y\cos^2\theta \tag{9.16}$$

$$P_{uv} = I_x\sin\theta\cos\theta + P_{xy}(\cos^2\theta - \sin^2\theta) - I_y\sin\theta\cos\theta \tag{9.17}$$

We observe, by adding (9.15) and (9.16) member by member, that

$$I_u + I_v = I_x + I_y \tag{9.18}$$

This result could have been anticipated, since both members of (9.18) are equal to the polar moment of inertia J_O.

Using the trigonometric relations $\sin 2\theta = 2 \sin \theta \cos \theta$ and $\cos 2\theta = \cos^2 \theta - \sin^2 \theta$, we may write (9.15), (9.16), and (9.17) as follows:

$$I_u = \frac{I_x + I_y}{2} + \frac{I_x - I_y}{2} \cos 2\theta - P_{xy} \sin 2\theta \tag{9.19}$$

$$I_v = \frac{I_x + I_y}{2} - \frac{I_x - I_y}{2} \cos 2\theta + P_{xy} \sin 2\theta \tag{9.20}$$

$$P_{uv} = \frac{I_x - I_y}{2} \sin 2\theta + P_{xy} \cos 2\theta \tag{9.21}$$

Equations (9.19) and (9.21) are the parametric equations of a circle. This means that, if we choose a set of rectangular axes and plot a point M of abscissa I_u and ordinate P_{uv} for any given value of the parameter θ, all the points thus obtained will lie on a circle. To establish this property we shall eliminate θ from Eqs. (9.19) and (9.21); this is done by transposing $(I_x + I_y)/2$ in Eq. (9.19), squaring both members of Eqs. (9.19) and (9.21), and adding. We write

$$\left(I_u - \frac{I_x + I_y}{2}\right)^2 + P_{uv}^2 = \left(\frac{I_x - I_y}{2}\right)^2 + P_{xy}^2 \tag{9.22}$$

Setting

$$I_{\text{av}} = \frac{I_x + I_y}{2} \qquad \text{and} \qquad R = \sqrt{\left(\frac{I_x - I_y}{2}\right)^2 + P_{xy}^2} \tag{9.23}$$

we write the identity (9.22) in the form

$$(I_u - I_{\text{av}})^2 + P_{uv}^2 = R^2 \tag{9.24}$$

which is the equation of a circle of radius R centered at the point C of abscissa I_{av} and ordinate 0 (Fig. 9.18).

The two points A and B where the circle obtained intersects the axis of abscissas are of special interest: Point A corresponds to the maximum value of the moment of inertia I_u, while point B corresponds to its minimum value. Besides, both points correspond to a zero value of the product of inertia P_{uv}. Thus, the values θ_m of the parameter θ which correspond to the points

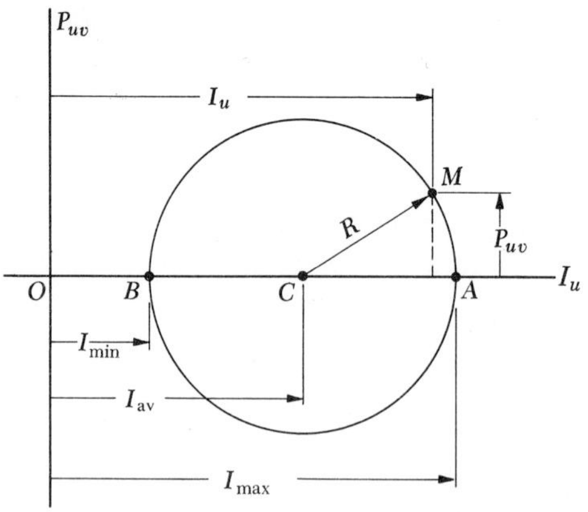

FIG. 9.18

A and B may be obtained by setting $P_{uv} = 0$ in Eq. (9.21). We obtain†

$$\tan 2\theta_m = -\frac{2P_{xy}}{I_x - I_y} \tag{9.25}$$

This equation defines two values $2\theta_m$ which are 180° apart and thus two values θ_m which are 90° apart. One of them corresponds to point A in Fig. 9.18 and to an axis through O in Fig. 9.17 with respect to which the moment of inertia of the given area is maximum; the other value corresponds to point B and an axis through O with respect to which the moment of inertia of the area is minimum. The two axes thus defined, which are perpendicular to each other, are called the *principal axes of the area about O*, and the corresponding values I_{max} and I_{min} of the moment of inertia are called the *principal moments of inertia of the area about O*. We check from Fig. 9.18 that

$$I_{max} = I_{av} + R \qquad \text{and} \qquad I_{min} = I_{av} - R \tag{9.26}$$

Substituting for I_{av} and R from formulas (9.23), we write

$$I_{max,min} = \frac{I_x + I_y}{2} \pm \sqrt{\left(\frac{I_x - I_y}{2}\right)^2 + P_{xy}^2} \tag{9.27}$$

Since the two values θ_m defined by Eq. (9.25) were obtained by setting $P_{uv} = 0$ in Eq. (9.21), it is clear that the product of inertia of the given area with respect to its principal axes is zero. Referring to Sec. 9.7, we note that, if an area possesses an axis of symmetry through a point O, this axis must be a principal axis of the area about O. On the other hand, a princi-

† This relation may also be obtained by differentiating I_u in Eq. (9.19) and setting $dI_u/d\theta = 0$.

pal axis does not need to be an axis of symmetry; whether or not an area possesses properties of symmetry, it will have two principal axes of inertia about any point O.

The properties established in this section hold for any point O located inside or outside the given area. If the point O is chosen to coincide with the centroid of the area, any axis through O is a centroidal axis; the two principal axes of the area about its centroid are referred to as the *principal centroidal axes of the area.*

***9.9. Mohr's Circle for Moments and Products of Inertia.** The circle used in the preceding section to illustrate the relations existing between the moments and products of inertia of a given area with respect to axes passing through a fixed point O was first introduced by the German engineer Otto Mohr (1835–1918) and is known as *Mohr's circle.* We shall see that, if the moments and product of inertia of an area A are known with respect to two rectangular x and y axes through a point O, Mohr's circle may be used to determine graphically (a) the principal axes and principal moments of inertia of the area about O, or (b) the moments and product of inertia of the area with respect to any other pair of rectangular axes u and v through O.

Consider a given area A and two rectangular coordinate axes x and y (Fig. 9.19a). We shall assume that the moments of inertia I_x and I_y and the product of inertia P_{xy} are known, and we shall represent them on a diagram by plotting a point

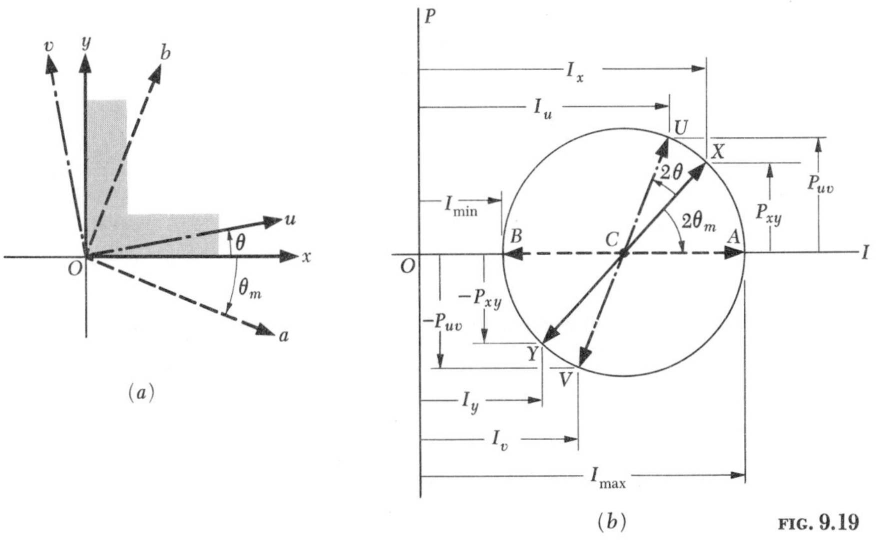

FIG. 9.19

X of coordinates I_x and P_{xy} and a point Y of coordinates I_y and $-P_{xy}$ (Fig. 9.19*b*). Joining X and Y by a straight line, we define the point C of intersection of line XY with the I axis and draw the circle of center C and diameter XY. Noting that the abscissa of C and the radius of the circle are respectively equal to the quantities I_{av} and R defined by the formulas (9.23), we conclude that the circle obtained is Mohr's circle for the given area about point O. Thus the abscissas of the points A and B where the circle intersects the I axis represent respectively the principal moments of inertia I_{max} and I_{min} of the area.

We also note that, since $\tan (XCA) = 2P_{xy}/(I_x - I_y)$, the angle XCA is equal in magnitude to one of the angles $2\theta_m$ which satisfy Eq. (9.25); thus the angle θ_m which defines in Fig. 9.19*a* the principal axis Oa corresponding to point A in Fig. 9.19*b* may be obtained by dividing in half the angle XCA measured on Mohr's circle. We further observe that, if $I_x > I_y$ and $P_{xy} > 0$, as in the case considered here, the rotation which brings CX into CA is clockwise. But, in that case, the angle θ_m obtained from Eq. (9.25) and defining the principal axis Oa in Fig. 9.19*a* is negative; thus the rotation bringing Ox into Oa is also clockwise. We conclude that the senses of rotation in both parts of Fig. 9.19 are the same; if a clockwise rotation through $2\theta_m$ is required to bring CX into CA on Mohr's circle, a clockwise rotation through θ_m will bring Ox into the corresponding principal axis Oa in Fig. 9.19*a*.

Since Mohr's circle is uniquely defined, the same circle may be obtained by considering the moments and product of inertia of the area A with respect to rectangular axes u and v (Fig. 9.19*a*). The point U of coordinates I_u and P_{uv}, and the point V of coordinates I_v and $-P_{uv}$, are therefore located on Mohr's circle, and the angle UCA in Fig. 9.19*b* must be equal to twice the angle uOa in Fig. 9.19*a*. Since, as noted above, the angle XCA is twice the angle xOa, it follows that the angle XCU in Fig. 9.19*b* is twice the angle xOu in Fig. 9.19*a*. Thus the diameter UV defining the moments and product of inertia I_u, I_v, and P_{uv} of the given area with respect to rectangular axes u and v forming an angle θ with the x and y axes may be obtained by rotating through an angle 2θ the diameter XY corresponding to the moments and product of inertia I_x, I_y, and P_{xy}. We note that the rotation which brings the diameter XY into the diameter UV in Fig. 9.19*b* has the same sense as the rotation which brings the xy axes into the uv axes in Fig. 9.19*a*.

SAMPLE PROBLEM 9.6

Determine the product of inertia of the right triangle shown (*a*) with respect to the *x* and *y* axes and (*b*) with respect to centroidal axes parallel to the *x* and *y* axes.

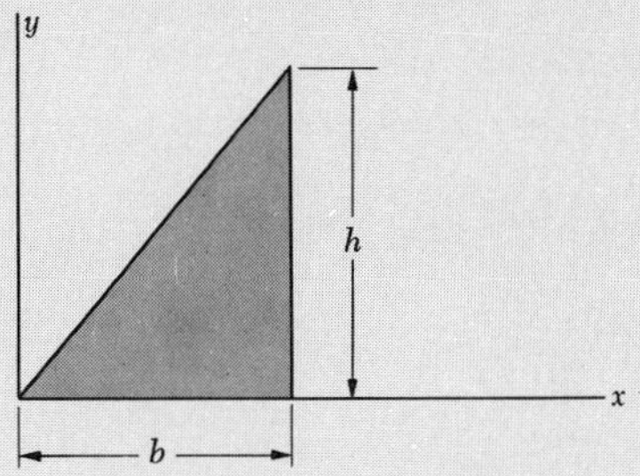

a. **Product of Inertia** P_{xy}. A vertical rectangular strip is chosen as the differential element of area. Using the parallel-axis theorem, we write

$$dP_{xy} = dP_{x'y'} + \bar{x}_{el}\bar{y}_{el}\, dA$$

Since the element is symmetrical with respect to the x' and y' axes, we note that $dP_{x'y'} = 0$. From the geometry of the triangle, we obtain

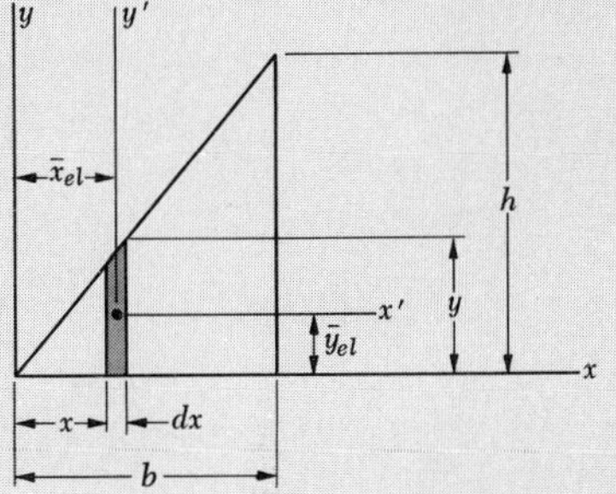

$$y = h\frac{x}{b} \qquad dA = y\,dx = h\frac{x}{b}dx$$

$$\bar{x}_{el} = x \qquad \bar{y}_{el} = \tfrac{1}{2}y = \tfrac{1}{2}h\frac{x}{b}$$

Integrating dP_{xy} from $x = 0$ to $x = b$, we obtain

$$P_{xy} = \int dP_{xy} = \int_0^b \bar{x}_{el}\bar{y}_{el}\, dA = \int_0^b x\left(\tfrac{1}{2}h\frac{x}{b}\right)h\frac{x}{b}dx$$

$$= \int_0^b \frac{h^2}{2b^2}x^3\, dx = \frac{h^2}{2b^2}\frac{b^4}{4}$$

$$P_{xy} = \tfrac{1}{8}b^2h^2 \quad ◄$$

b. **Product of Inertia** $\bar{P}_{x''y''}$. The coordinates of the centroid of the triangle are

$$\bar{x} = \tfrac{2}{3}b \qquad \bar{y} = \tfrac{1}{3}h$$

Using the expression for P_{xy} obtained in part *a*, we apply the parallel-axis theorem and write

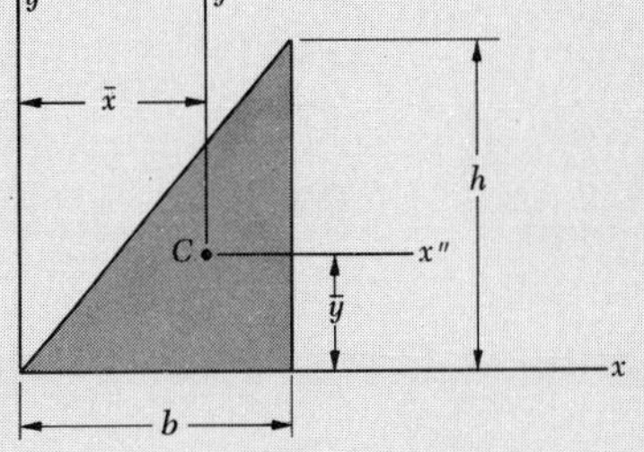

$$P_{xy} = \bar{P}_{x''y''} + \bar{x}\bar{y}A$$

$$\tfrac{1}{8}b^2h^2 = \bar{P}_{x''y''} + (\tfrac{2}{3}b)(\tfrac{1}{3}h)(\tfrac{1}{2}bh)$$

$$\bar{P}_{x''y''} = \tfrac{1}{8}b^2h^2 - \tfrac{1}{9}b^2h^2$$

$$\bar{P}_{x''y''} = \tfrac{1}{72}b^2h^2 \quad ◄$$

SAMPLE PROBLEM 9.7

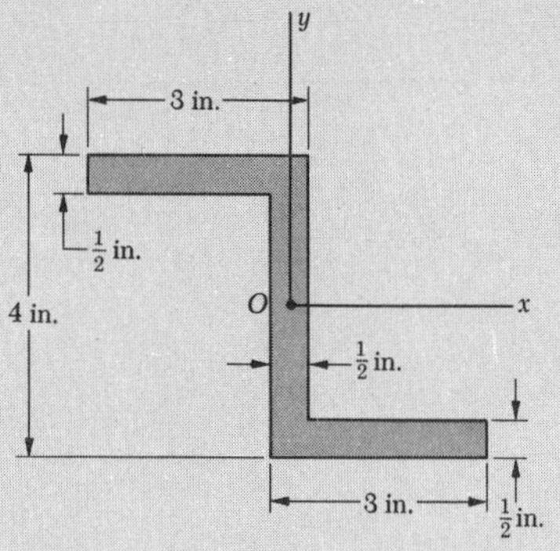

For the section shown, the moments of inertia with respect to the x and y axes have been computed and are known to be

$$I_x = 10.91 \text{ in.}^4 \qquad I_y = 6.94 \text{ in.}^4$$

Determine (*a*) the principal axes of the section about O, (*b*) the values of the principal moments of inertia of the section about O.

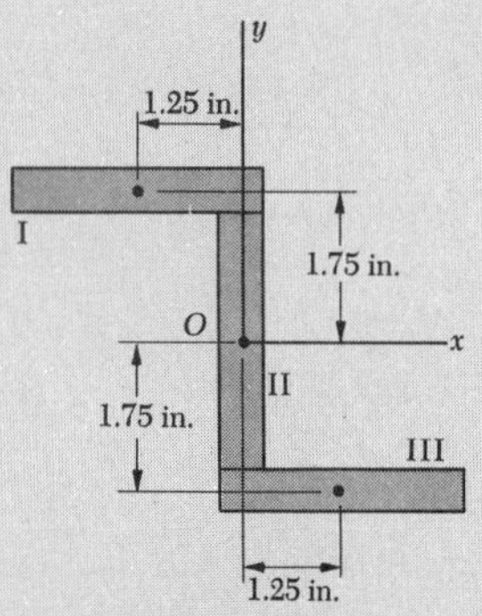

Solution. We first compute the product of inertia with respect to the x and y axes. The area is divided into three rectangles as shown. We note that the product of inertia $\bar{P}_{x'y'}$ with respect to centroidal axes parallel to the x and y axes is zero for each rectangle. Using the parallel-axis theorem $P_{xy} = \bar{P}_{x'y'} + \bar{x}\bar{y}A$, we thus find that for each rectangle P_{xy} reduces to $\bar{x}\bar{y}A$.

Rectangle	Area	$\bar{x}$	$\bar{y}$	$\bar{x}\bar{y}A$
I	1.5	−1.25	+1.75	−3.28
II	1.5	0	0	0
III	1.5	+1.25	−1.75	−3.28
				−6.56

$$P_{xy} = \Sigma\bar{x}\bar{y}A = -6.56 \text{ in.}^4$$

a. Principal Axes. Since the magnitudes of I_x, I_y, and P_{xy} are known, Eq. (9.25) is used to determine the values of θ_m,

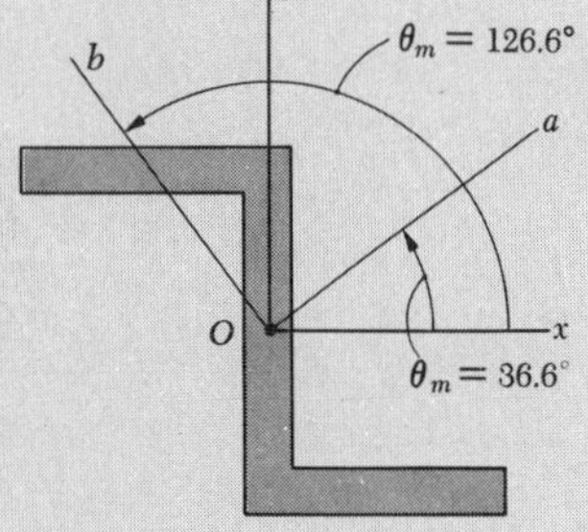

$$\tan 2\theta_m = -\frac{2P_{xy}}{I_x - I_y} = -\frac{(2)(-6.56)}{10.91 - 6.94} = +3.31$$

$$2\theta_m = 73.2° \text{ and } 253.2°$$

$$\theta_m = 36.6° \qquad \text{and} \qquad \theta_m = 126.6° \quad ◀$$

b. Principal Moments of Inertia. Using Eq. (9.27), we write

$$I_{\text{max, min}} = \frac{I_x + I_y}{2} \pm \sqrt{\left(\frac{I_x - I_y}{2}\right)^2 + P_{xy}^2}$$

$$= \frac{10.91 + 6.94}{2} \pm \sqrt{\left(\frac{10.91 - 6.94}{2}\right)^2 + (-6.56)^2}$$

$$I_{\text{max}} = 15.78 \text{ in.}^4 \qquad I_{\text{min}} = 2.07 \text{ in.}^4 \quad ◀$$

Noting that the area of the section is farther away from the a axis than from the b axis, we conclude that $I_a = I_{\text{max}} = 15.78 \text{ in.}^4$ and $I_b = I_{\text{min}} = 2.07 \text{ in.}^4$. This conclusion may be verified by substituting $\theta = 36.6°$ into Eqs. (9.19) and (9.20).

SAMPLE PROBLEM 9.8

For the section shown, the moments and product of inertia with respect to the x and y axes have been computed and are known to be

$$I_x = 10.91 \text{ in.}^4 \qquad I_y = 6.94 \text{ in.}^4 \qquad P_{xy} = -6.56 \text{ in.}^4$$

Using Mohr's circle, determine (*a*) the principal axes of the section about O, (*b*) the values of the principal moments of inertia of the section about O, (*c*) the moments and product of inertia of the section with respect to the u and v axes forming an angle of 60° with the x and y axes.

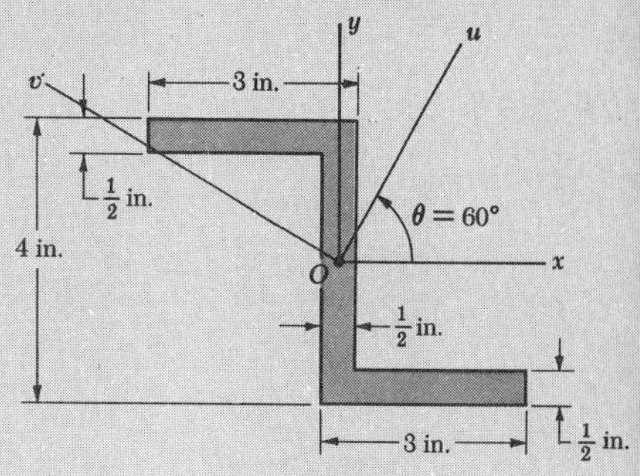

Solution. We first plot point X of coordinates $I_x = 10.91$, $P_{xy} = -6.56$, and point Y of coordinates $I_y = 6.94$, $-P_{xy} = +6.56$. Joining X and Y by a straight line, we define the center C of Mohr's circle. The abscissa of C, which represents I_{av}, and the radius R of the circle may be measured directly, or they may be determined analytically.

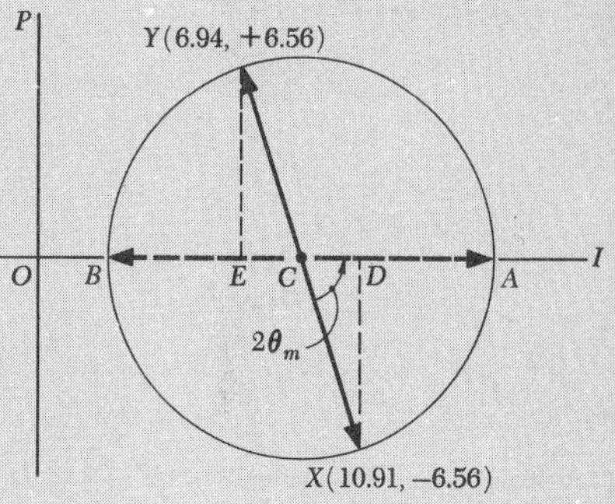

$$I_{av} = OC = \tfrac{1}{2}(I_x + I_y) = \tfrac{1}{2}(10.91 + 6.94) = 8.92 \text{ in.}^4$$

$$R = \sqrt{(CD)^2 + (DX)^2} = \sqrt{(1.98)^2 + (6.56)^2} = 6.85 \text{ in.}^4$$

a. Principal Axes. The principal axes of the section correspond to points A and B on Mohr's circle and the angle through which we should rotate CX to bring it into CA defines $2\theta_m$. We have

$$\tan 2\theta_m = \frac{DX}{CD} = \frac{6.56}{1.98} = 3.31 \qquad 2\theta_m = 73.2°\circlearrowleft \qquad \theta_m = 36.6°\circlearrowleft \quad ◀$$

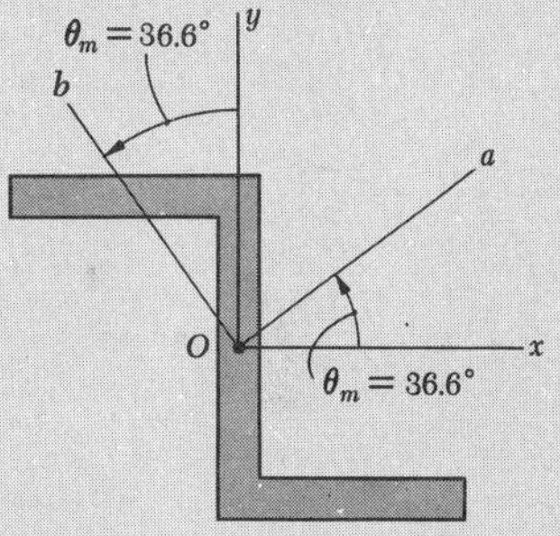

Thus the principal axis Oa corresponding to the maximum value of the moment of inertia is obtained by rotating the x axis through 36.6° counterclockwise; the principal axis corresponding to the minimum value of the moment of inertia may be obtained by rotating the y axis through the same angle.

b. Principal Moments of Inertia. The principal moments of inertia are represented by the abscissas of A and B. We have

$$I_{max} = OA = OC + CA = I_{av} + R = 8.92 + 6.85$$
$$I_{max} = 15.77 \text{ in.}^4 \quad ◀$$
$$I_{min} = OB = OC - BC = I_{av} - R = 8.92 - 6.85$$
$$I_{min} = 2.07 \text{ in.}^4 \quad ◀$$

c. Moments and Product of Inertia with Respect to uv Axes. The points U and V on Mohr's circle which correspond to the u and v axes are obtained by rotating CX and CY through an angle $2\theta = 2(60°) = 120°$ counterclockwise. The coordinates of U and V yield the desired moments and product of inertia. Noting that the angle that CU forms with the I axis is $\phi = 120° - 73.2° = 46.8°$, we write

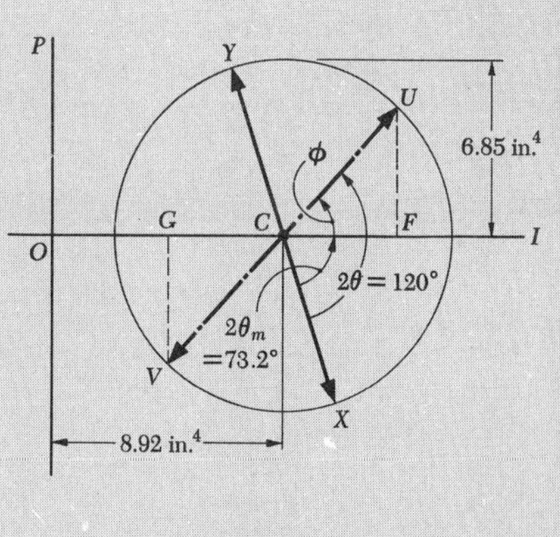

$$I_u = OF = OC + CF = 8.92 + 6.85 \cos 46.8°$$
$$I_u = 13.61 \text{ in.}^4 \quad ◀$$
$$I_v = OG = OC - GC = 8.92 - 6.85 \cos 46.8°$$
$$I_v = 4.23 \text{ in.}^4 \quad ◀$$
$$P_{uv} = FU = 6.85 \sin 46.8°$$
$$P_{uv} = +4.99 \text{ in.}^4 \quad ◀$$

PROBLEMS

9.44 through 9.47. Determine by direct integration the product of inertia of the given area with respect to the x and y axes.

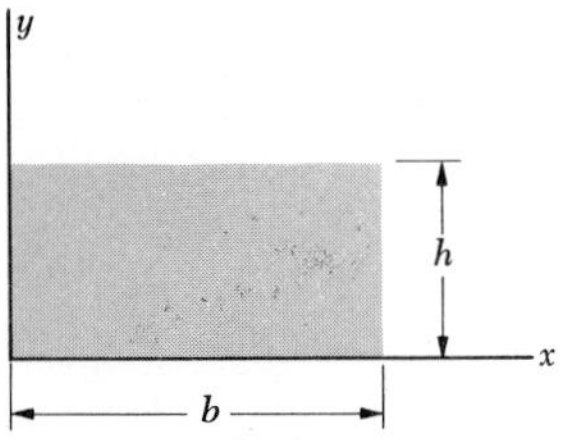

FIG. P 9.44

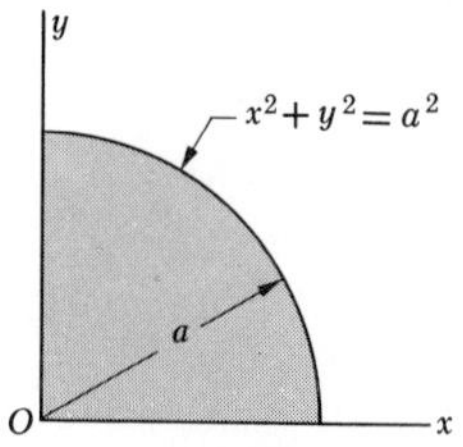

FIG. P 9.45

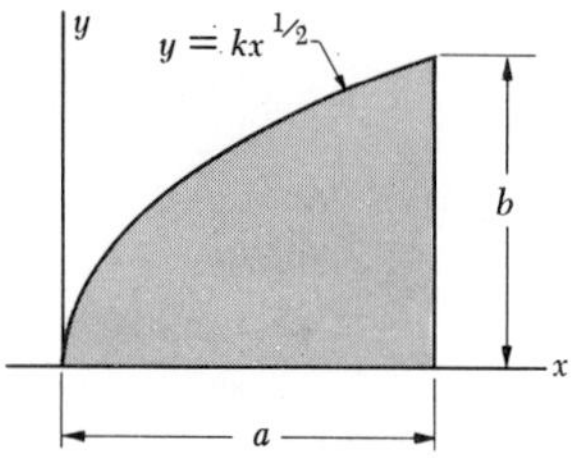

FIG. P 9.46

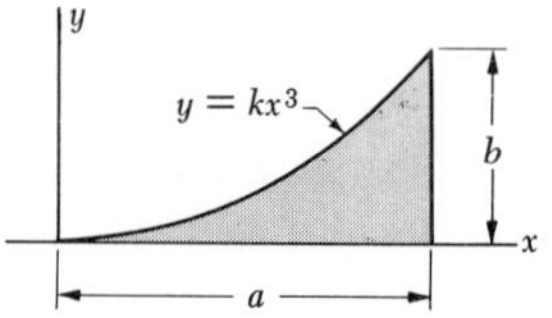

FIG. P 9.47

9.48 and 9.49. Using the parallel-axis theorem, determine the product of inertia of the area shown with respect to the centroidal x and y axes.

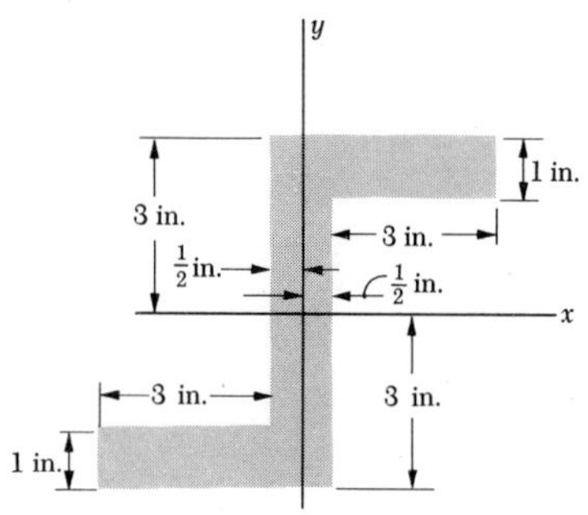

FIG. P 9.48

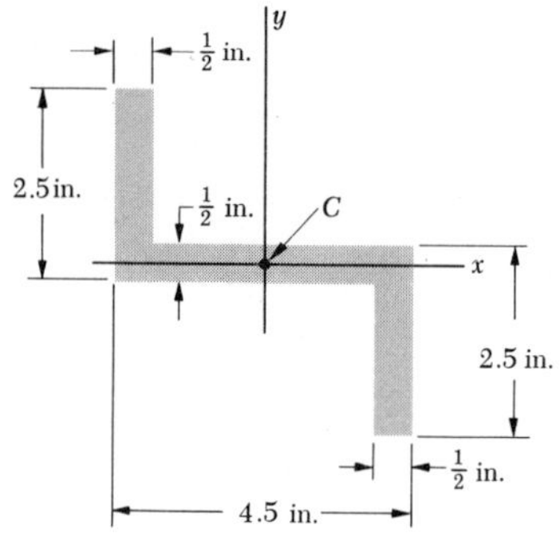

FIG. P 9.49

9.50 and 9.51. Using the parallel-axis theorem, determine the product of inertia of the angle cross section shown with respect to the centroidal x and y axes. Neglect the effect of fillets.

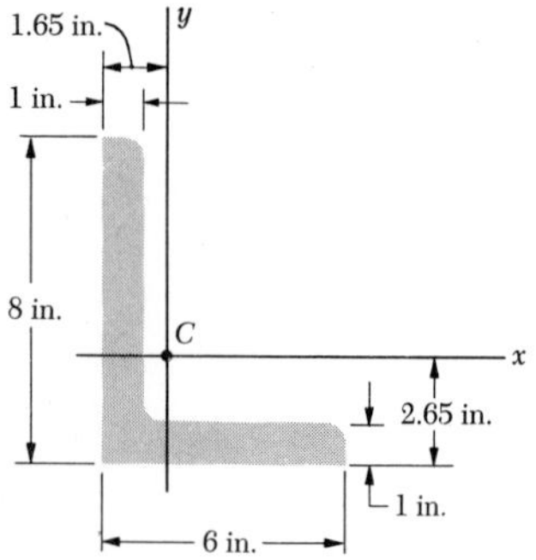

FIG. P 9.50

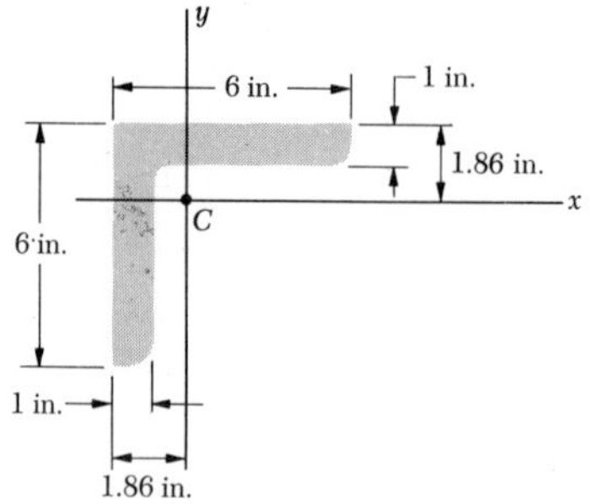

FIG. P 9.51

9.52. Determine the moments of inertia and the product of inertia of the rectangle shown with respect to the centroidal u and v axes.

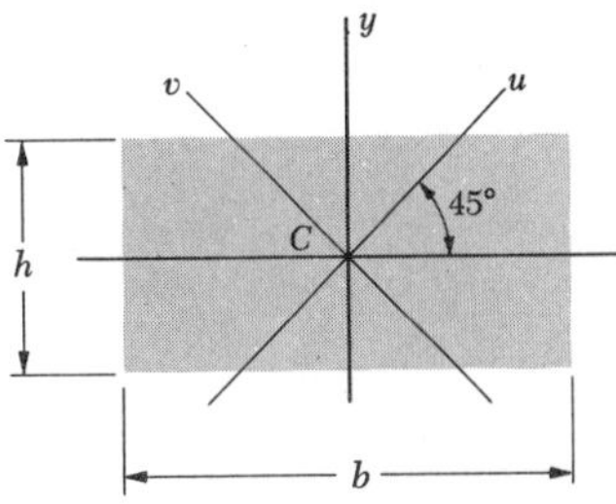

FIG. P 9.52

9.53. Determine the moments of inertia and the product of inertia of the area of Prob. 9.48 with respect to new centroidal axes obtained by rotating the x and y axes through 30° counterclockwise.

9.54. Determine the moments of inertia and the product of inertia of the quarter circle of Prob. 9.45 with respect to new axes obtained by rotating the x and y axes about O (a) through 30° counterclockwise, (b) through 45° counterclockwise.

9.55. Determine the moments of inertia and the product of inertia of the angle cross section of Prob. 9.50 with respect to new centroidal axes obtained by rotating the x and y axes through 45° clockwise. (The moments of inertia $\bar{I}_x$ and $\bar{I}_y$ of the section are given in Fig. 9.13.)

9.56. Determine the orientation of the principal axes through the centroid and the corresponding values of the moments of inertia for the area of Prob. 9.48.

9.57. Determine the orientation of the principal axes through the centroid and the corresponding values of the moment of inertia for the angle cross section shown. Neglect the effect of fillets in computing $\bar{P}_{xy}$. (The moments of inertia $\bar{I}_x$ and $\bar{I}_y$ of the section are given in Fig. 9.13.)

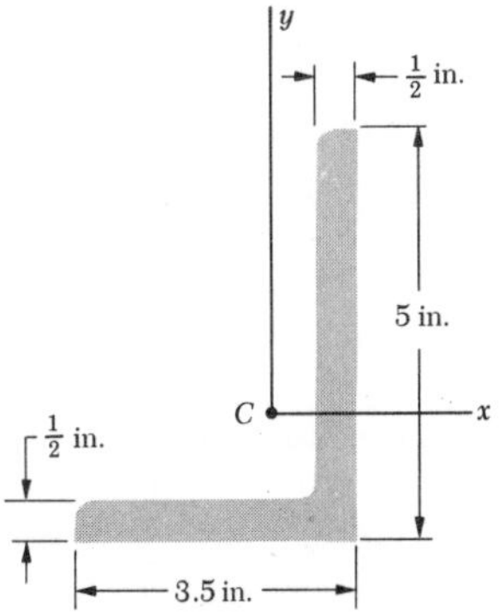

FIG. P 9.57

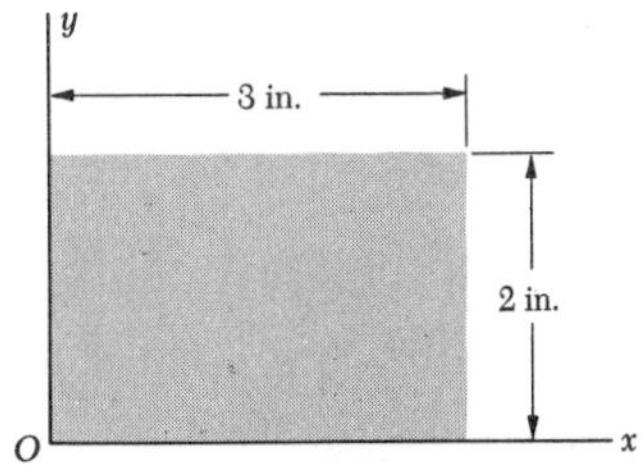

FIG. P 9.59

9.58. Determine the orientation of the principal axes through the centroid and the corresponding values of the moment of inertia for the angle cross section of Prob. 9.50. (The moments of inertia $\bar{I}_x$ and $\bar{I}_y$ of the section are given in Fig. 9.13.)

9.59. Determine the orientation of the principal axes through O and the corresponding values of the moment of inertia for the rectangle shown.

9.60. Using Mohr's circle, determine the moments of inertia and the product of inertia of the quarter circle of Prob. 9.45 with respect to new axes obtained by rotating the x and y axes about O (a) through 30° counterclockwise, (b) through 45° counterclockwise.

9.61. Using Mohr's circle, determine the moments of inertia and the product of inertia of the angle cross section of Prob. 9.50 with respect to new centroidal axes obtained by rotating the x and y axes through 45° clockwise. (The moments of inertia $\bar{I}_x$ and $\bar{I}_y$ of the section are given in Fig. 9.13.)

9.62. Solve Prob. 9.52, using Mohr's circle.

9.63. Using Mohr's circle, determine the moments of inertia and the product of inertia of the area of Prob. 9.48 with respect to new centroidal axes obtained by rotating the x and y axes through 30° counterclockwise.

9.64. Using Mohr's circle, determine the orientation of the principal axes through the centroid and the corresponding values of the moment of inertia for the angle cross section of Prob. 9.50. (The moments of inertia $\bar{I}_x$ and $\bar{I}_y$ of the section are given in Fig. 9.13.)

9.65. Solve Prob. 9.59, using Mohr's circle.

9.66. Using Mohr's circle, determine the orientation of the principal axes through the centroid and the corresponding values of the moment of inertia for the area of Prob. 9.48.

9.67. Solve Prob. 9.57, using Mohr's circle.

9.68. Using Mohr's circle, show that for any area the axes corresponding to the principal moments of inertia are 45° from the axes corresponding to the maximum product of inertia.

9.69. Using Mohr's circle, show that, for any regular polygon (such as a pentagon), (a) the moment of inertia with respect to every axis through the centroid is the same, (b) the product of inertia with respect to any pair of rectangular axes through the centroid is zero.

***9.70.** The moments and product of inertia of a given area with respect to two rectangular axes x and y through O are respectively $I_x = 48$ in.^{4}, $I_y = 32$ in.^{4}, and $P_{xy} > 0$, while the minimum value of the moment of inertia of the area with respect to any axis through O is $I_{min} = 30$ in.^{4}. Using Mohr's circle, determine the orientation of the principal axes of the area through O and the value of I_{max}.

***9.71.** Using Mohr's circle, determine the product of inertia P_{xy} of the area of Prob. 9.70 with respect to the x and y axes.

***9.72.** Prove that the expression $I_u I_v - P_{uv}^2$, where I_u, I_v, and P_{uv} represent respectively the moments and product of inertia of a given area with respect to two rectangular axes u and v through a given point O, is independent of the orientation of the u and v axes. Considering the particular case when the u and v axes correspond to the maximum value of P_{uv}, show that the given expression represents the square of the tangent drawn from the origin of the coordinates to Mohr's circle.

***9.73.** Using the invariance property established in the preceding problem, express the product of inertia P_{xy} of an area A with respect to two rectangular axes through O in terms of the moments of inertia I_x and I_y of A and of the principal moments of inertia I_{min} and I_{max} of A about O. Apply the formula obtained to calculate the product of inertia $\bar{P}_{xy}$ of the 8- by 6- by 1-in.-angle cross section shown in Fig. 9.13, knowing that its minimum moment of inertia is 21.3 in.[4].

MOMENTS OF INERTIA OF MASSES

9.10. Moment of Inertia of a Mass. Consider a small mass Δm mounted on a rod of negligible mass which may rotate freely about an axis AA' (Fig. 9.20*a*). If a couple is applied to the system, the rod and mass, assumed initially at rest, will start rotating about AA'. The details of this motion will be studied later in dynamics. At present, we wish only to indicate that the time required for the system to reach a given speed of rotation is proportional to the mass Δm and to the square of the distance r. The product $r^2\,\Delta m$ provides, therefore, a measure of the *inertia* of the system, i.e., of the resistance the system offers when we try to set it in motion. For this reason, the product $r^2\,\Delta m$ is called the *moment of inertia* of the mass Δm with respect to the axis AA'.

Consider now a body of mass m which is to be rotated about an axis AA' (Fig. 9.20*b*). Dividing the body into elements of mass Δm_1, Δm_2, etc., we find that the resistance offered by the body is measured by the sum $r_1^2\,\Delta m_1 + r_2^2\,\Delta m_2 + \cdots$. This sum defines therefore the moment of inertia of the body with respect to the axis AA'. Increasing the number of elements, we find that the moment of inertia is equal, at the limit, to the integral

$$I = \int r^2\,dm \tag{9.28}$$

The *radius of gyration* k of the body with respect to the axis AA' is defined by the relation

$$I = k^2 m \qquad \text{or} \qquad k = \sqrt{\frac{I}{m}} \tag{9.29}$$

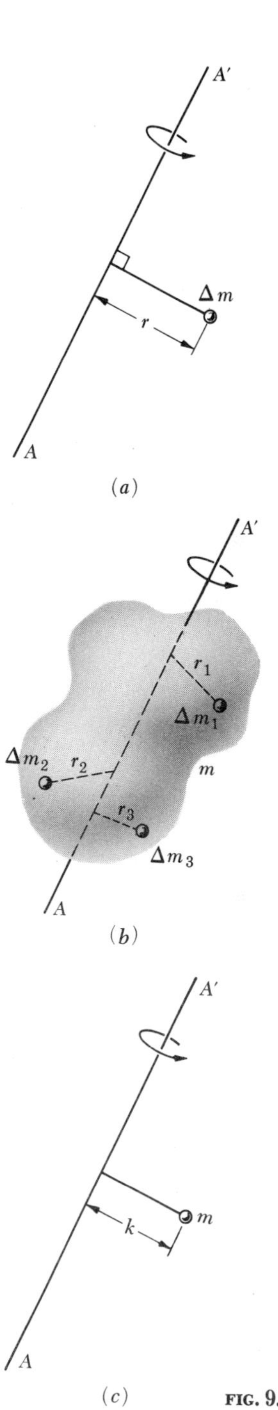

FIG. 9.20

The radius of gyration k represents, therefore, the distance at which the entire mass of the body should be concentrated if its moment of inertia with respect to AA' is to remain unchanged (Fig. 9.20*c*). Whether it is kept in its original shape (Fig. 9.20*b*) or whether it is concentrated as shown in Fig. 9.20*c*, the mass m will react in the same way to a rotation, or *gyration*, about AA'.

The radius of gyration of a mass is usually expressed in feet. Since the moment of inertia of a mass is the product of a mass (expressed in lb-sec²/ft) by a distance squared, it will generally be expressed in lb-ft-sec².

9.11. Parallel-axis Theorem. Consider a body of mass m; the moment of inertia of the body with respect to an axis AA' is $I = \int r^2\, dm$, where r is the distance from the element of mass dm to AA' (Fig. 9.21). Similarly, the moment of inertia of the body with respect to a centroidal † axis BB' parallel to the axis AA' and passing through the center of gravity G of the body is $\bar{I} = \int r'^2\, dm$, where r' is the distance from the element of mass to BB'. Choosing two systems of axes as shown in Fig. 9.21, we write

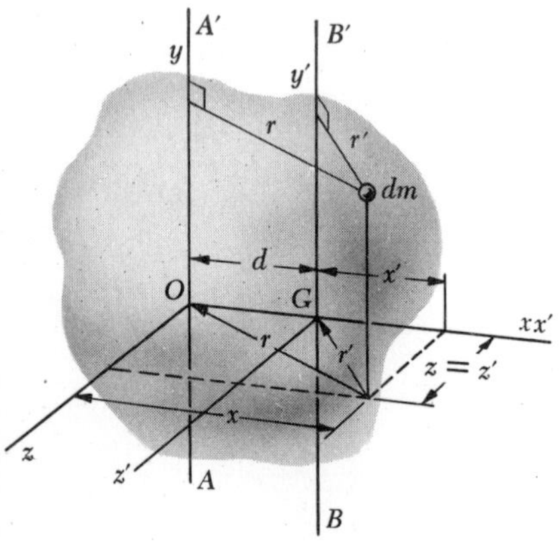

FIG. 9.21

$$r^2 = x^2 + z^2 \qquad r'^2 = x'^2 + z'^2$$

Observing that $x = x' + d$, where d is the distance between AA' and BB', and that $z = z'$, we write

$$r^2 = (x' + d)^2 + z'^2 = x'^2 + 2x'd + d^2 + z'^2$$
$$= r'^2 + 2x'd + d^2$$

Substituting for r^2 in the expression $I = \int r^2\, dm$, we write the moment of inertia of the body with respect to AA' as follows:

$$I = \int r^2\, dm = \int r'^2\, dm + 2d\int x'\, dm + d^2 \int dm$$

The first integral represents the moment of inertia $\bar{I}$ about the centroidal axis BB'; the second integral represents the first moment of the body with respect to the $y'z'$ plane and, since this plane contains G, is equal to zero; the last integral is equal to the total mass m of the body. We write, therefore,

$$I = \bar{I} + md^2 \qquad (9.30)$$

Expressing the moments of inertia in terms of the corresponding radii of gyration, we may also write

$$k^2 = \bar{k}^2 + d^2 \qquad (9.31)$$

†Note that the term centroidal is used to define an axis passing through the center of gravity G of the body, whether or not G coincides with the centroid of the volume of the body.

where k and $\bar{k}$ represent the radii of gyration about AA' and BB', respectively.

9.12. Moments of Inertia of Thin Plates. Consider a thin plate of uniform thickness t, made of a homogeneous material of density ρ (density = mass per unit volume). The mass moment of inertia of the plate with respect to an axis AA' *contained in the plane* of the plate (Fig. 9.22a) is

$$I_{AA',\text{mass}} = \int r^2\,dm$$

Since $dm = \rho t\,dA$, we write

$$I_{AA',\text{mass}} = \rho t \int r^2 dA$$

But r represents the distance of the element of area dA to the axis AA'; the integral is therefore equal to the moment of inertia of the area of the plate with respect to AA'. We have

$$I_{AA',\text{mass}} = \rho t I_{AA',\text{ area}} \tag{9.32}$$

Similarly, we have with respect to an axis BB' perpendicular to AA' (Fig. 9.22b)

$$I_{BB',\text{ mass}} = \rho t I_{BB',\text{ area}} \tag{9.33}$$

Considering now the axis CC' *perpendicular* to the plate through the point of intersection C of AA' and BB' (Fig. 9.22c), we write

$$I_{CC',\text{ mass}} = \rho t J_{C,\text{ area}} \tag{9.34}$$

where J_C is the *polar* moment of inertia of the area of the plate with respect to point C.

Recalling the relation $J_C = I_{AA'} + I_{BB'}$ existing between polar and rectangular moments of inertia of an area, we write the following relation between the mass moments of inertia of a thin plate:

$$I_{CC'} = I_{AA'} + I_{BB'} \tag{9.35}$$

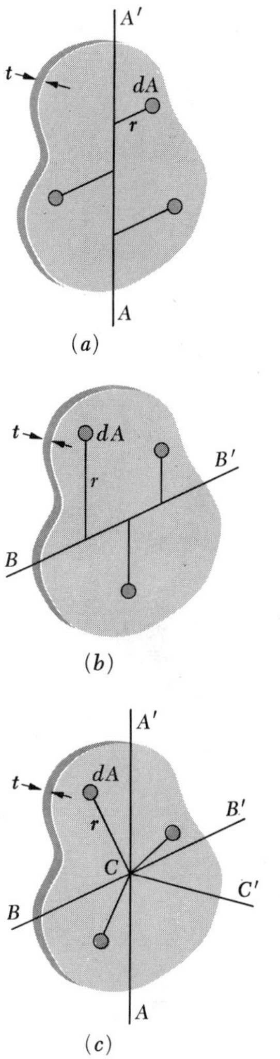

FIG. 9.22

Rectangular Plate. In the case of a rectangular plate of sides a and b (Fig. 9.23), we obtain the following mass moments of inertia with respect to axes through the center of gravity of the plate:

$$I_{AA',\text{mass}} = \rho t I_{AA',\text{area}} = \rho t(\tfrac{1}{12}a^3b)$$

$$I_{BB',\text{mass}} = \rho t I_{BB',\text{area}} = \rho t(\tfrac{1}{12}ab^3)$$

Observing that the product ρabt is equal to the mass m of the plate, we write the mass moments of inertia of a thin rectangular plate as follows:

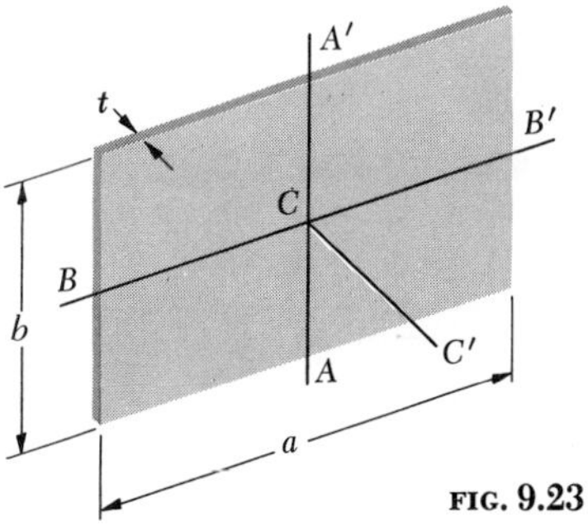

FIG. 9.23

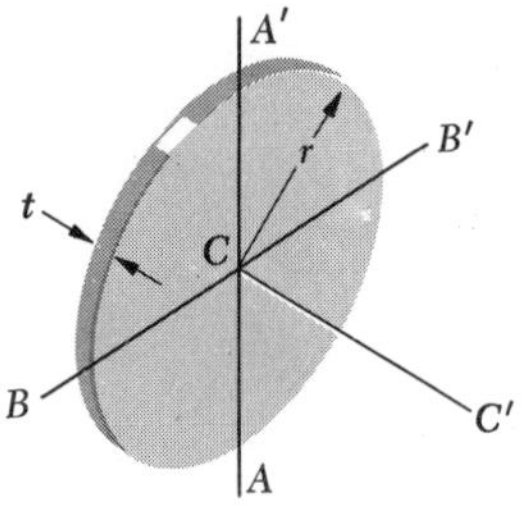

FIG. 9.24

$$I_{AA'} = \tfrac{1}{12}ma^2 \qquad I_{BB'} = \tfrac{1}{12}mb^2 \tag{9.36}$$
$$I_{CC'} = I_{AA'} + I_{BB'} = \tfrac{1}{12}m(a^2 + b^2) \tag{9.37}$$

Circular Plate. In the case of a circular plate, or disk, of radius r (Fig. 9.24), we write

$$I_{AA',\,\text{mass}} = \rho t I_{AA',\,\text{area}} = \rho t(\tfrac{1}{4}\pi r^4)$$

Observing that the product $\rho\pi r^2 t$ is equal to the mass m of the plate and that $I_{AA'} = I_{BB'}$, we write the mass moments of inertia of a circular plate as follows:

$$I_{AA'} = I_{BB'} = \tfrac{1}{4}mr^2 \tag{9.38}$$
$$I_{CC'} = I_{AA'} + I_{BB'} = \tfrac{1}{2}mr^2 \tag{9.39}$$

9.13. Determination of the Moment of Inertia of a Three-dimensional Body by Integration. The moment of inertia of a three-dimensional body is obtained by computing the integral $I = \int r^2\,dm$. If the body is made of a homogeneous material of density ρ, we have $dm = \rho\,dV$ and write $I = \rho\int r^2\,dV$. This integral depends only upon the shape of the body. In order to compute it, it will generally be necessary to perform a triple, or at least a double, integration.

However, if the body possesses two planes of symmetry, it is usually possible to determine its moment of inertia through a single integration by choosing as an element of mass dm the mass of a thin slab perpendicular to the planes of symmetry. In the case of bodies of revolution, for example, the element of mass should be a thin disk (Fig. 9.25). Using formula (9.39), the moment of inertia of the disk with respect to the axis of revolution may be readily expressed as indicated in Fig. 9.25. Its moment of inertia with respect to each of the other two axes of coordinates will be obtained by using formula (9.38) and the parallel-axis theorem. Integration of the expressions obtained will yield the desired moments of inertia of the body of revolution.

$dm = \rho\pi r^2 dx$
$dI_x = \frac{1}{2} r^2 dm$
$dI_y = dI_{y'} + x^2 dm = (\frac{1}{4}r^2 + x^2)dm$
$dI_z = dI_{z'} + x^2 dm = (\frac{1}{4}r^2 + x^2)dm$

FIG. 9.25. Determination of the moment of inertia of a body of revolution

9.14. Moments of Inertia of Composite Bodies. The moments of inertia of a few common shapes are shown in Fig. 9.26. The moment of inertia with respect to a given axis of a body made of several of these simple shapes may be obtained by computing the moments of inertia of its component parts about the desired axis and adding them together. We should note, as we already have noted in the case of areas, that the radius of gyration of a composite body *cannot* be obtained by adding the radii of gyration of its component parts.

Slender rod	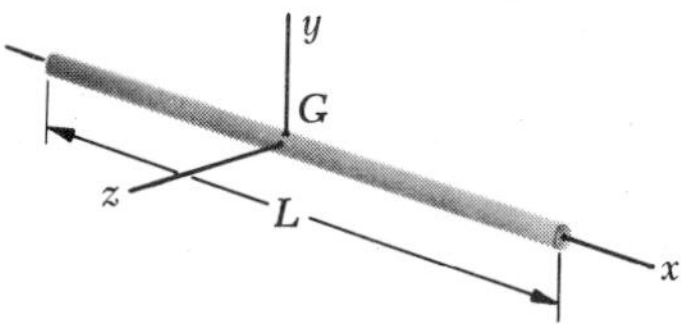	$I_y = I_z = \frac{1}{12}mL^2$
Thin rectangular plate	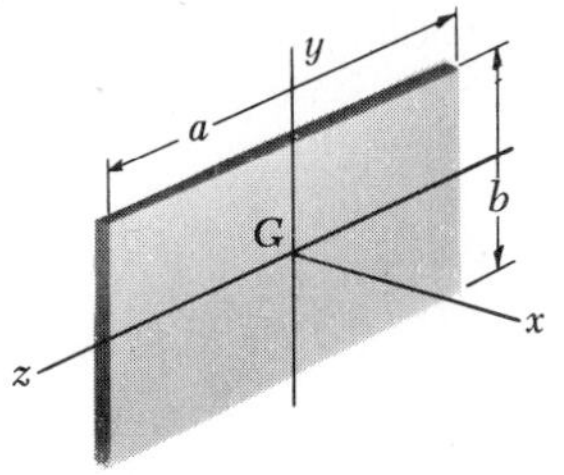	$I_x = \frac{1}{12}m(a^2 + b^2)$ $I_y = \frac{1}{12}ma^2$ $I_z = \frac{1}{12}mb^2$
Rectangular prism	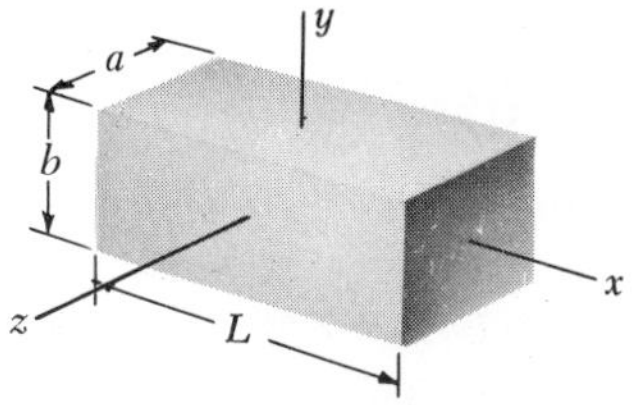	$I_x = \frac{1}{12}m(a^2 + b^2)$ $I_y = \frac{1}{12}m(a^2 + L^2)$ $I_z = \frac{1}{12}m(b^2 + L^2)$
Thin disk	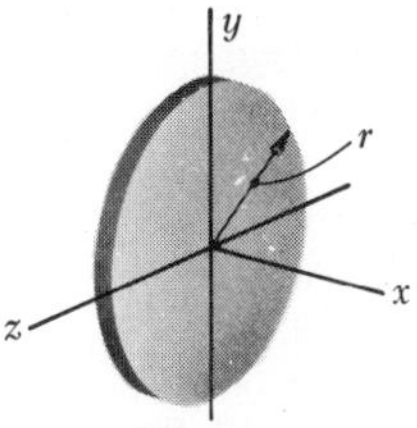	$I_x = \frac{1}{2}mr^2$ $I_y = I_z = \frac{1}{4}mr^2$
Circular cylinder	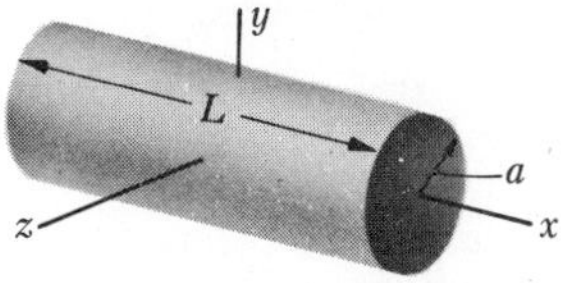	$I_x = \frac{1}{2}ma^2$ $I_y = I_z = \frac{1}{12}m(3a^2 + L^2)$
Circular cone	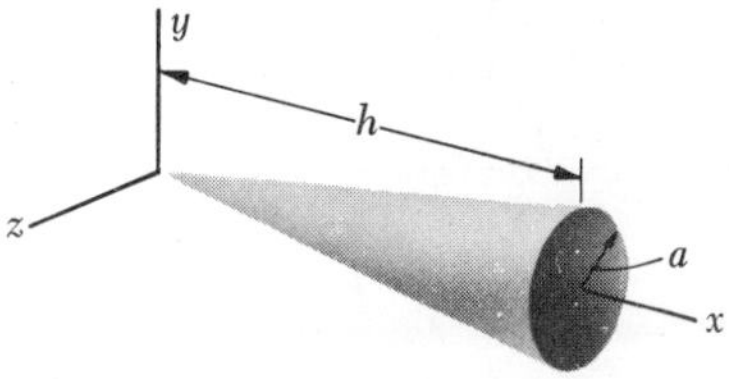	$I_x = \frac{3}{10}ma^2$ $I_y = I_z = \frac{3}{5}m(\frac{1}{4}a^2 + h^2)$
Sphere	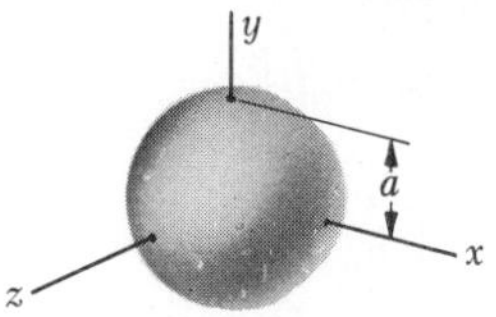	$I_x = I_y = I_z = \frac{2}{5}ma^2$

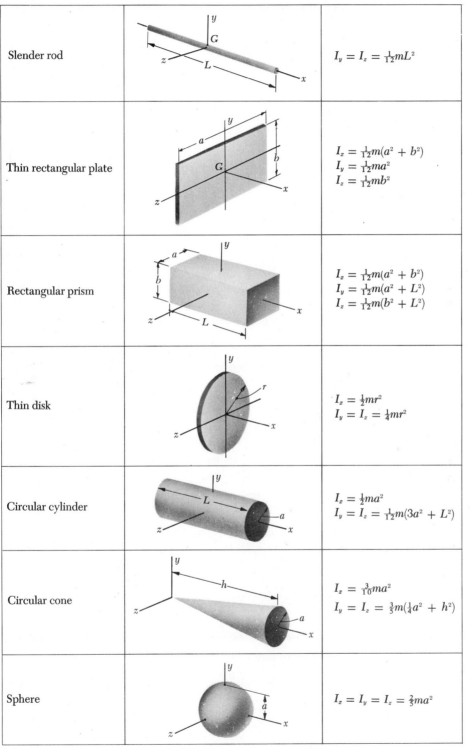

FIG. 9.26. Mass moments of inertia of common geometric shapes

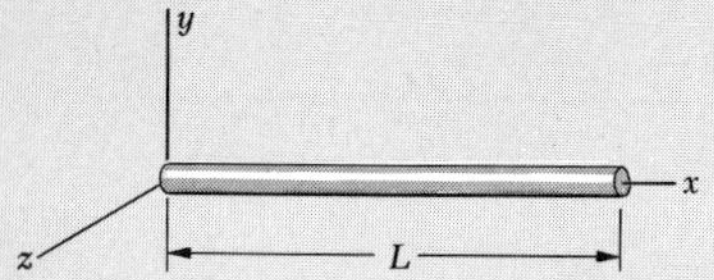

SAMPLE PROBLEM 9.9

Determine the mass moment of inertia of a slender rod of length L and mass m with respect to an axis perpendicular to the rod and passing through one end of the rod.

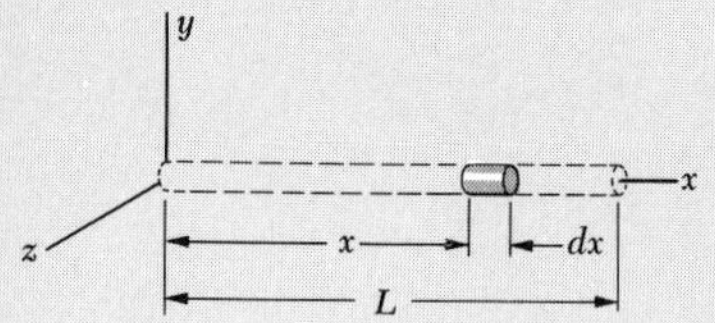

Solution. Choosing the differential element of mass shown, we write

$$dm = \frac{m}{L}\,dx$$

$$I_y = \int x^2\,dm = \int_0^L x^2 \frac{m}{L}\,dx = \left[\frac{m}{L}\frac{x^3}{3}\right]_0^L \qquad I_y = \frac{mL^2}{3} \blacktriangleleft$$

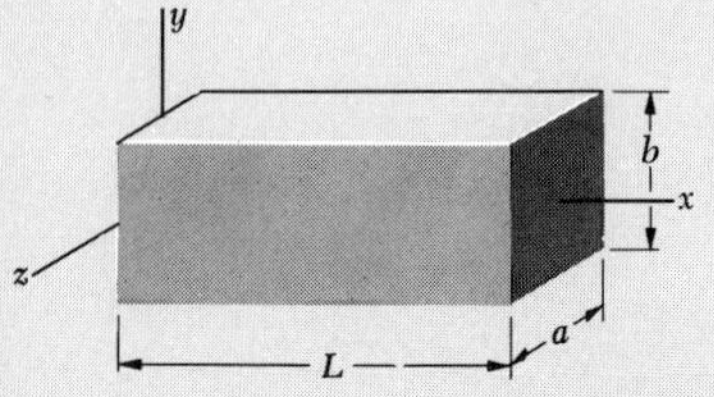

SAMPLE PROBLEM 9.10

Determine the mass moment of inertia of the homogeneous rectangular prism shown with respect to the z axis.

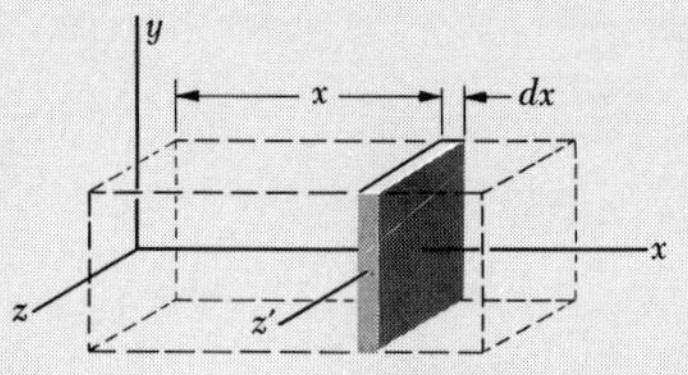

Solution. We choose as a differential element of mass the thin slab shown for which

$$dm = \rho ab\,dx$$

Referring to Sec. 9.12, we find that the moment of inertia of the element with respect to the z' axis is

$$dI_{z'} = \frac{b^2}{12}\,dm$$

Applying the parallel-axis theorem, we obtain the mass moment of inertia of the slab with respect to the z axis.

$$dI_z = dI_{z'} + x^2\,dm = \frac{b^2}{12}\,dm + x^2\,dm = \left(\frac{b^2}{12} + x^2\right)\rho ab\,dx$$

Integrating from $x = 0$ to $x = L$, we obtain

$$I_z = \int dI_z = \int_0^L \left(\frac{b^2}{12} + x^2\right)\rho ab\,dx = \rho abL\left(\frac{b^2}{12} + \frac{L^2}{3}\right)$$

Since the total mass of the prism is $m = \rho abL$, we may write

$$I_z = m\left(\frac{b^2}{12} + \frac{L^2}{3}\right) \qquad I_z = \tfrac{1}{12}m(b^2 + 4L^2) \blacktriangleleft$$

We note that if the prism is slender, b is small compared to L and the expression for I_z reduces to $mL^2/3$ (see Sample Prob. 9.9).

SAMPLE PROBLEM 9.11

Determine the mass moment of inertia of a right circular cone with respect to (*a*) its longitudinal axis, (*b*) an axis through the apex of the cone and perpendicular to its longitudinal axis, (*c*) an axis through the centroid of the cone and perpendicular to its longitudinal axis.

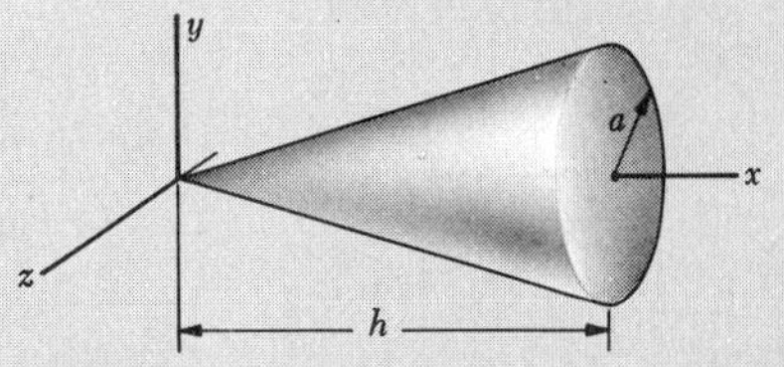

Solution. We choose the differential element of mass shown.

$$r = a\frac{x}{h} \qquad dm = \rho\pi r^2\,dx = \rho\pi\frac{a^2}{h^2}x^2\,dx$$

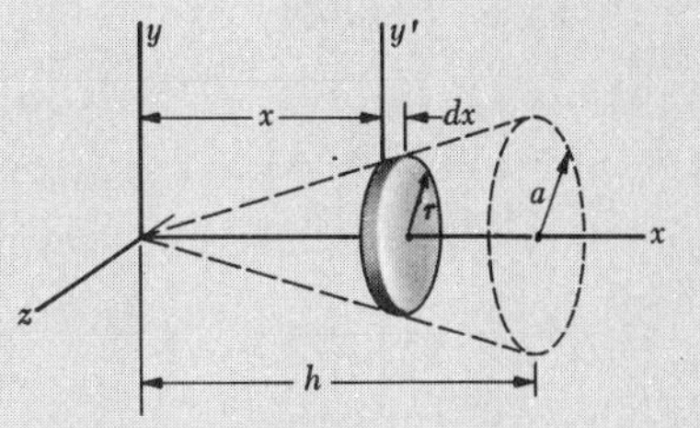

a. **Moment of Inertia I_x.** Using the expression derived in Sec. 9.12 for a thin disk, we compute the mass moment of inertia of the differential element with respect to the *x* axis.

$$dI_x = \tfrac{1}{2}r^2\,dm = \frac{1}{2}\left(a\frac{x}{h}\right)^2\left(\rho\pi\frac{a^2}{h^2}x^2\,dx\right) = \tfrac{1}{2}\rho\pi\frac{a^4}{h^4}x^4\,dx$$

Integrating from $x = 0$ to $x = h$, we obtain

$$I_x = \int dI_x = \int_0^h \tfrac{1}{2}\rho\pi\frac{a^4}{h^4}x^4\,dx = \tfrac{1}{2}\rho\pi\frac{a^4}{h^4}\frac{h^5}{5} = \tfrac{1}{10}\rho\pi a^4 h$$

Since the total mass of the cone is $m = \frac{1}{3}\rho\pi a^2 h$, we may write

$$I_x = \tfrac{1}{10}\rho\pi a^4 h = \tfrac{3}{10}a^2(\tfrac{1}{3}\rho\pi a^2 h) = \tfrac{3}{10}ma^2 \qquad I_x = \tfrac{3}{10}ma^2 \quad ◄$$

b. **Moment of Inertia I_y.** The same differential element will be used. Applying the parallel-axis theorem and using the expression derived in Sec. 9.12 for a thin disk, we write

$$dI_y = dI_{y'} + x^2\,dm = \tfrac{1}{4}r^2\,dm + x^2\,dm = (\tfrac{1}{4}r^2 + x^2)\,dm$$

Substituting the expressions for *r* and *dm*, we obtain

$$dI_y = \left(\frac{1}{4}\frac{a^2}{h^2}x^2 + x^2\right)\left(\rho\pi\frac{a^2}{h^2}x^2\,dx\right) = \rho\pi\frac{a^2}{h^2}\left(\frac{a^2}{4h^2} + 1\right)x^4\,dx$$

$$I_y = \int dI_y = \int_0^h \rho\pi\frac{a^2}{h^2}\left(\frac{a^2}{4h^2} + 1\right)x^4\,dx = \rho\pi\frac{a^2}{h^2}\left(\frac{a^2}{4h^2} + 1\right)\frac{h^5}{5}$$

Introducing the total mass of the cone *m*, we rewrite I_y as follows:

$$I_y = \tfrac{3}{5}(\tfrac{1}{4}a^2 + h^2)\tfrac{1}{3}\rho\pi a^2 h \qquad I_y = \tfrac{3}{5}m(\tfrac{1}{4}a^2 + h^2) \quad ◄$$

c. **Moment of Inertia $\bar{I}_{y''}$.** We apply the parallel-axis theorem and write

$$I_y = \bar{I}_{y''} + md^2$$

Solving for $\bar{I}_{y''}$ and recalling that $d = \frac{3}{4}h$, we have

$$\bar{I}_{y''} = I_y - md^2 = \tfrac{3}{5}m(\tfrac{1}{4}a^2 + h^2) - m(\tfrac{3}{4}h)^2$$

$$\bar{I}_{y''} = \tfrac{3}{20}m(a^2 + \tfrac{1}{4}h^2) \quad ◄$$

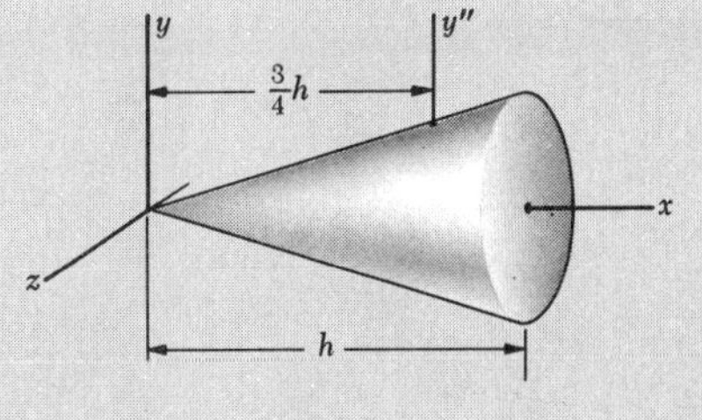

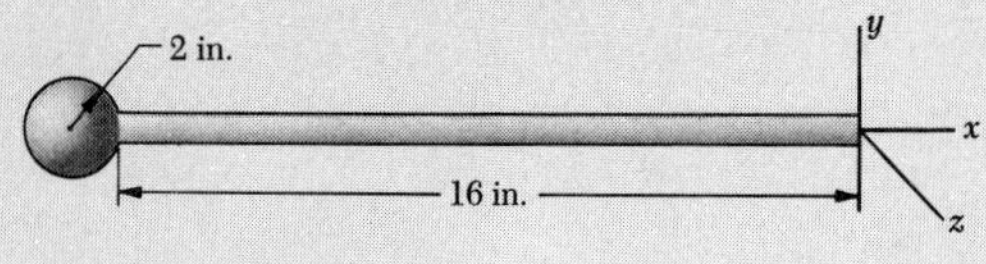

SAMPLE PROBLEM 9.12

A portion of a governor consists of a 20-lb sphere welded to a 5-lb rod as shown. Determine the mass moment of inertia and the radius of gyration of the body with respect to the y axis.

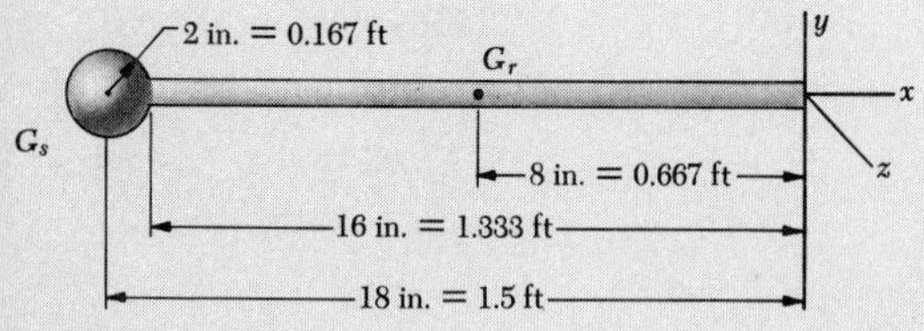

Moment of Inertia I_y. The mass moment of inertia of each component with respect to the y axis is computed in the following table. The expression for $\bar{I}_y$ of each component is obtained from Fig. 9.26, and the parallel-axis theorem is used to obtain the corresponding value of I_y. Note that all lengths should be expressed in feet.

	Weight	Mass, lb-sec²/ft	$\bar{I}_y + md^2$, lb-ft-sec²
Sphere	20 lb	$\frac{20}{32.2} = 0.621$	$\frac{2}{5}(0.621)(0.167)^2 + (0.621)(1.5)^2 = 1.404$
Rod . . .	5 lb	$\frac{5}{32.2} = 0.155$	$\frac{1}{12}(0.155)(1.333)^2 + (0.155)(0.667)^2 = 0.092$
		$m = 0.776$	$I_y = 1.496$

The moment of inertia of the composite body is

$$I_y = 1.496 \text{ lb-ft-sec}^2 \quad ◄$$

Radius of Gyration k_y

$$k_y^2 = \frac{I_y}{m} = \frac{1.496 \text{ lb-ft-sec}^2}{0.776 \text{ lb-sec}^2/\text{ft}} \qquad k_y = 1.388 \text{ ft} \quad ◄$$

PROBLEMS

9.74. Determine the mass moment of inertia of a thin elliptical plate of mass m with respect to (a) the axes AA' and BB' of the ellipse, (b) the axis CC' perpendicular to the plate.

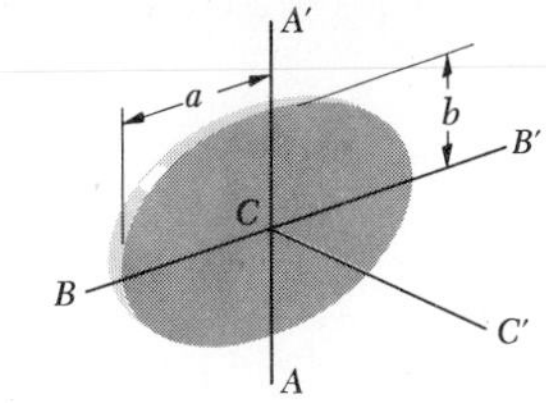

FIG. P9.74

9.75. A thin plate of mass m is cut in the shape of an isosceles triangle of base b and height h. Determine the mass moment of inertia of the plate with respect to (a) the centroidal axes AA' and BB' in the plane of the plate, (b) the centroidal axis CC' perpendicular to the plate.

9.76. Determine the mass moments of inertia of the plate of Prob. 9.75 with respect to the axes DD' and EE' parallel to the centroidal axes AA' and BB' respectively.

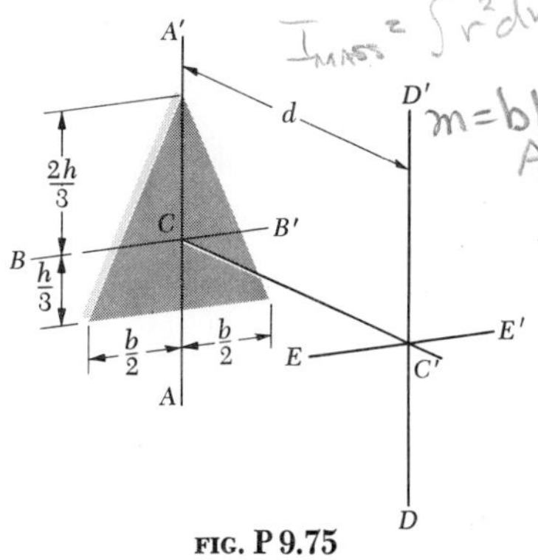

FIG. P9.75

9.77. Determine the mass moment of inertia of a ring of mass m, cut from a thin uniform plate, with respect to (a) the diameter AA' of the ring, (b) the axis CC' perpendicular to the plane of the ring.

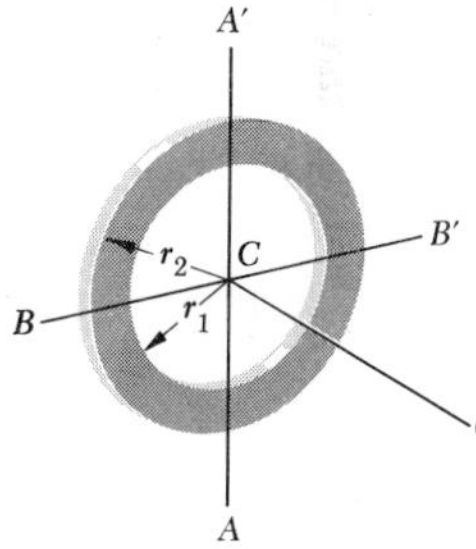

FIG. P9.77

9.78. Determine by direct integration the mass moment of inertia and the radius of gyration of a sphere of radius a and uniform density ρ with respect to a diameter.

9.79. Determine by direct integration the mass moment of inertia and the radius of gyration with respect to the x axis of the paraboloid shown, assuming a uniform density ρ.

9.80 and 9.81. The area shown is revolved about the x axis to form a homogeneous solid of revolution of mass m. Express the mass moment of inertia of the solid with respect to the x axis in terms of m and a.

9.82. Determine by direct integration the mass moment of inertia and the radius of gyration of a circular cylinder of radius a, length L, and uniform density ρ, with respect to a diameter of its base.

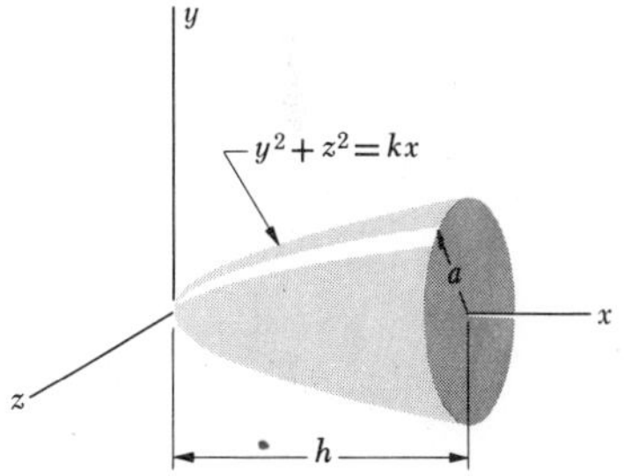

FIG. P9.79 AND P9.83

9.83. Determine by direct integration the mass moment of inertia and the radius of gyration with respect to the y axis of the paraboloid shown, assuming a uniform density ρ.

9.84 and 9.85. The area shown is revolved about the x axis to form a homogeneous solid of revolution of mass m. Express the mass moment of inertia of the solid with respect to the y axis in terms of m, a, and h.

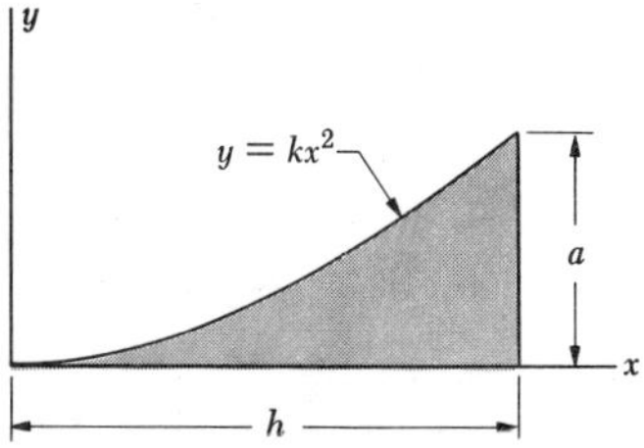

FIG. P9.80 AND P9.84

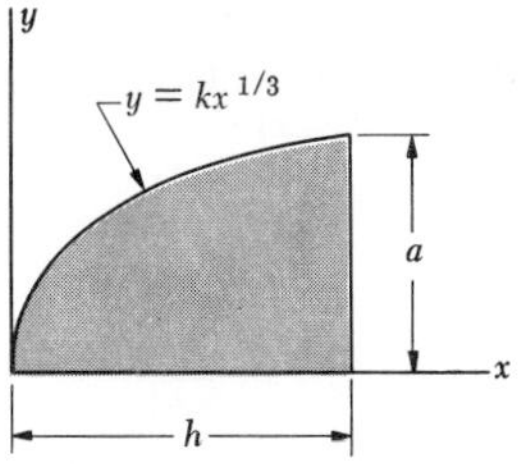

FIG. P9.81 AND P9.85

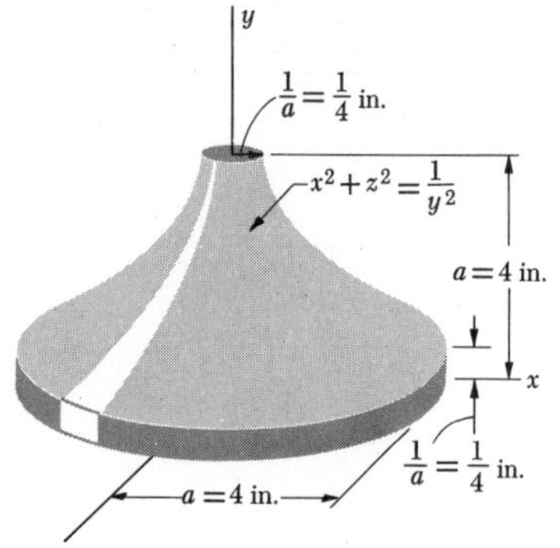

FIG. P 9.86

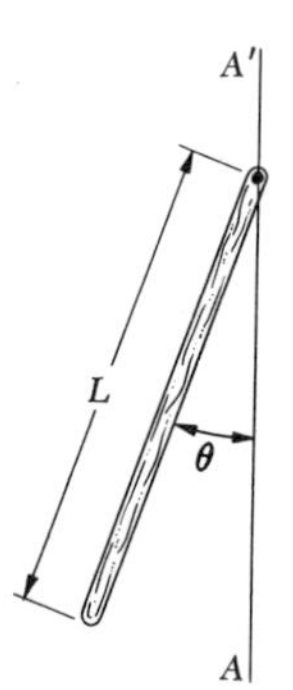

FIG. P 9.87

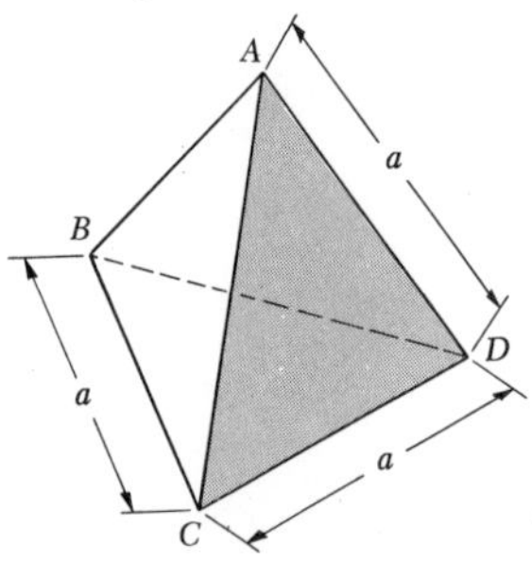

FIG. P 9.88 AND P 9.89

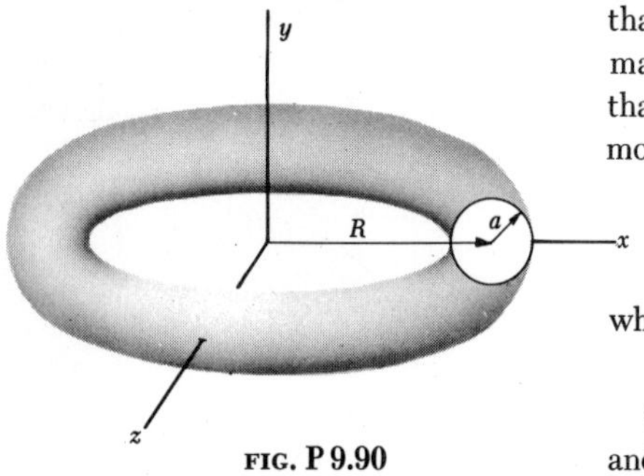

FIG. P 9.90

9.86. Determine by direct integration the mass moment of inertia and the radius of gyration of the body shown with respect to the y axis, assuming a uniform density ρ.

9.87. A slender rod of mass m and length L forms an angle θ with the vertical axis AA'. Determine the mass moment of inertia and the radius of gyration of the rod with respect to the axis AA'. Check the result obtained when $\theta = 90°$ with Sample Prob. 9.9.

***9.88.** Determine by direct integration the mass moment of inertia of the regular tetrahedron shown with respect to an axis through A perpendicular to the base BCD. Express the result in terms of a and the mass m of the body.

***9.89.** Determine by direct integration the mass moment of inertia of the regular tetrahedron shown with respect to an axis through A parallel to the base BCD. Express the result in terms of a and the mass m of the body and show that the result is independent of the orientation of the axis.

***9.90.** Determine by direct integration the mass moment of inertia of the circular ring shown (*torus*) with respect to the y axis. Express the result in terms of R, a, and the mass m of the ring.

***9.91.** Given an arbitrary solid and three rectangular axes x, y, and z, prove that the mass moment of inertia of the solid with respect to any one of the three axes cannot be larger than the sum of the moments of inertia of the solid with respect to the other two axes; i.e., prove that the inequality $I_x \leqslant I_y + I_z$ is satisfied, as well as two similar inequalities. Further prove that, if the solid is homogeneous and of revolution, and if x is the axis of revolution and y a transverse axis, then $I_y \geqslant \frac{1}{2}I_x$.

***9.92.** Given a homogeneous solid of mass m and of arbitrary shape, and three rectangular axes x, y, and z of origin O, prove that the sum $I_x + I_y + I_z$ of the mass moments of inertia of the solid cannot be smaller than the similar sum computed for a sphere of the same mass and same material centered at O. Further prove, using the result of Prob. 9.91, that, if the solid is of revolution and if x is the axis of revolution, then its moment of inertia I_y about a transverse axis y must satisfy the inequality

$$I_y \geqslant \frac{3}{10}ma^2$$

where a is the radius of the sphere of the same mass and same material.

9.93. Determine the mass moment of inertia of a sphere of radius a and mass m with respect to a line tangent to the sphere.

9.94. A homogeneous hemisphere of radius a and mass m is oriented as shown. Determine the distance y for which the moment of inertia of the hemisphere with respect to the axis AA' is twice its moment of inertia with respect to the y axis.

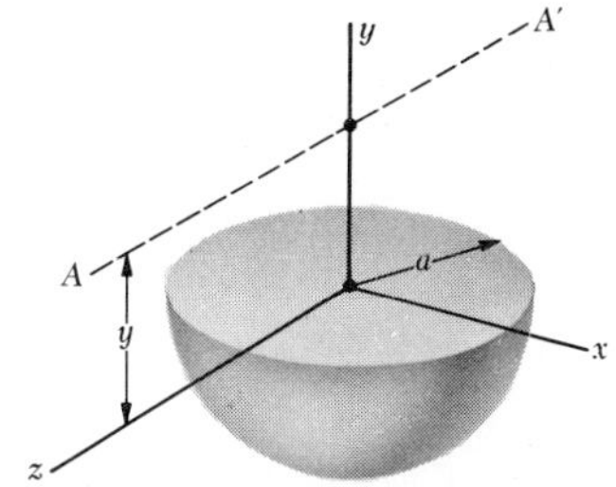

FIG. P 9.94

9.95. In using the parallel-axis theorem, the error introduced by neglecting the centroidal moment of inertia is sometimes small. For a homogeneous sphere of radius a and mass m, (a) determine the mass moment of inertia with respect to an axis AA' at a distance R from the center of the sphere, (b) express as a function of a/R the relative error introduced by neglecting the centroidal moment of inertia, (c) determine the distance R in terms of a for which the relative error is 0.4 per cent.

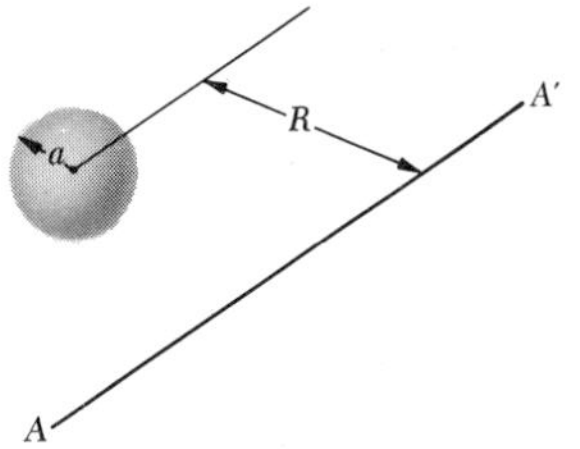

FIG. P 9.95

9.96. Determine the mass moment of inertia of a thin spherical shell of radius a and mass m with respect to one of its diameters. (*Hint.* Consider the solid bounded by spherical surfaces of radius a and $a + \varepsilon$, respectively, and let ε approach zero after the moment of inertia has been expressed in terms of a, ε, and the mass of the solid.)

9.97. Determine the radius of gyration of the homogeneous solid shown with respect to the x axis.

9.98. Determine the radius of gyration of the homogeneous solid shown with respect to the y axis.

9.99. Determine the moment of inertia of the frustum of a right circular cone of mass m with respect to its axis of symmetry.

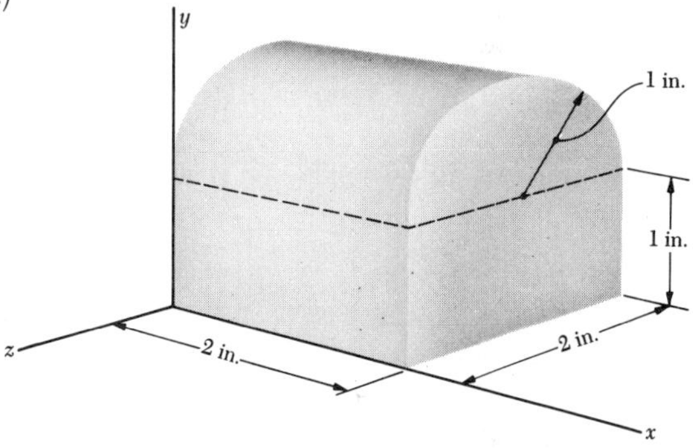

FIG. P 9.97 AND P 9.98

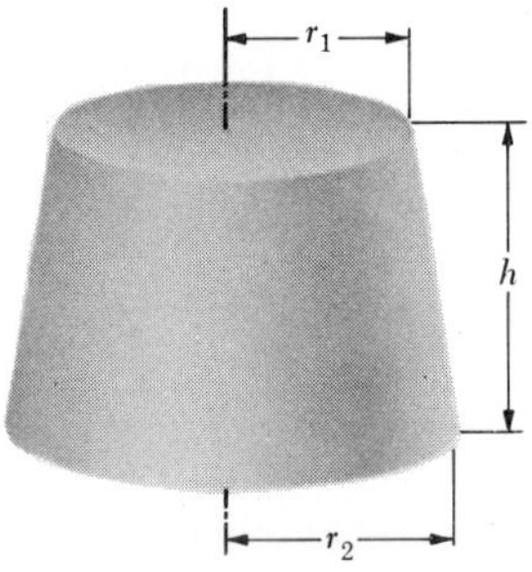

FIG. P 9.99

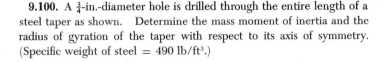

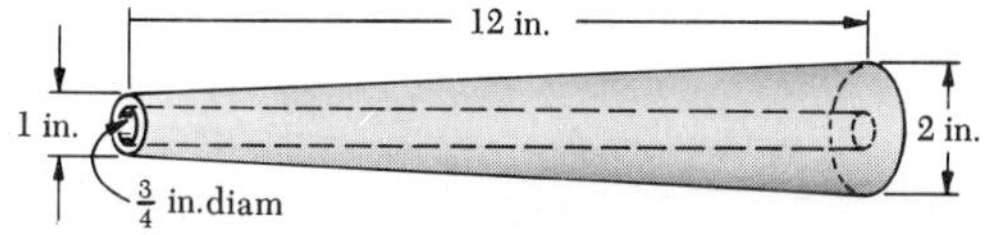

FIG. P 9.100

9.100. A $\frac{3}{4}$-in.-diameter hole is drilled through the entire length of a steel taper as shown. Determine the mass moment of inertia and the radius of gyration of the taper with respect to its axis of symmetry. (Specific weight of steel $= 490\ \text{lb/ft}^3$.)

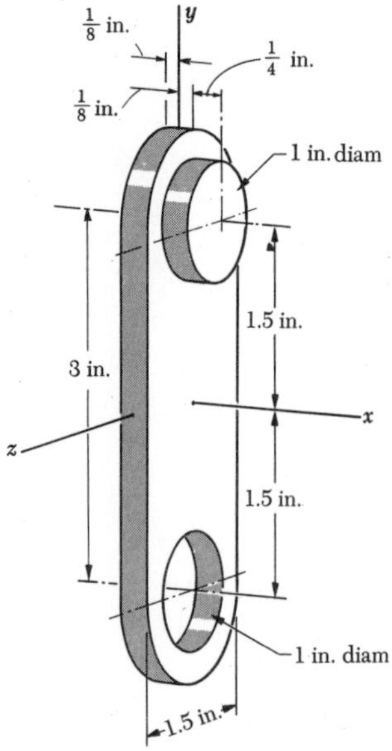

FIG. P 9.101

9.101 and 9.102. Determine the mass moment of inertia and the radius of gyration of the steel link shown with respect to the x axis. (Specific weight of steel $= 490$ lb/ft^3.)

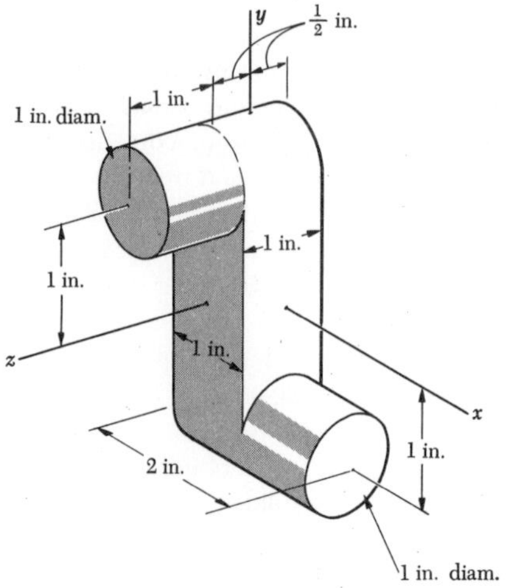

FIG. P 9.102

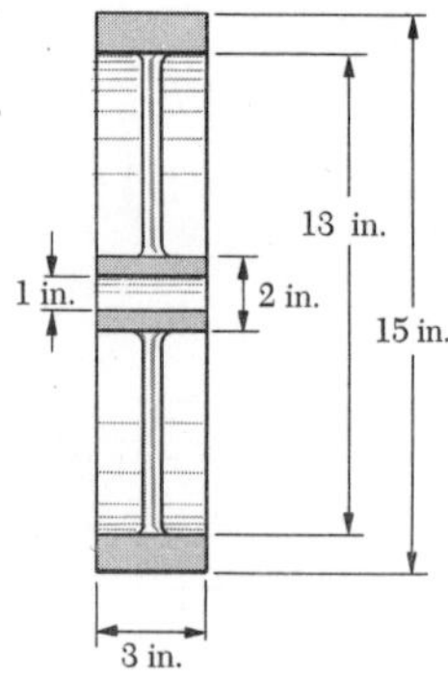

FIG. P 9.103

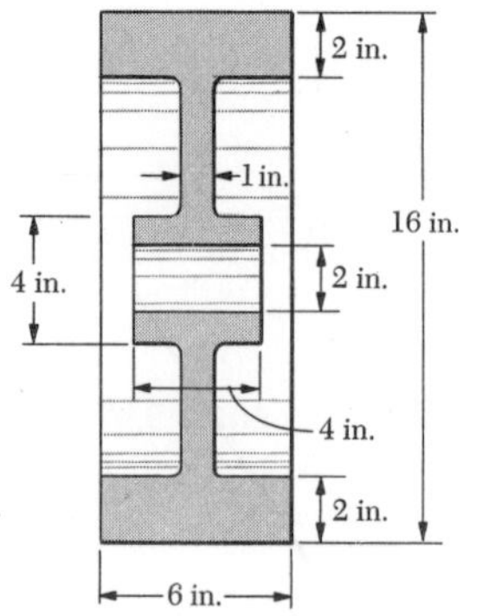

FIG. P 9.104

9.103. The cross section of a small flywheel is shown. The rim and hub are connected by eight spokes (two of which are shown in the cross section). Each spoke has a cross-sectional area of 0.1875 in.^{2}. Determine the mass moment of inertia and radius of gyration of the flywheel with respect to the axis of rotation. (Specific weight of steel $= 490$ lb/ft^3.)

9.104. Determine the mass moment of inertia and radius of gyration of the steel flywheel shown with respect to the axis of rotation. The web of the flywheel consists of a solid plate 1 in. thick. (Specific weight of steel $= 490$ lb/ft^3.)

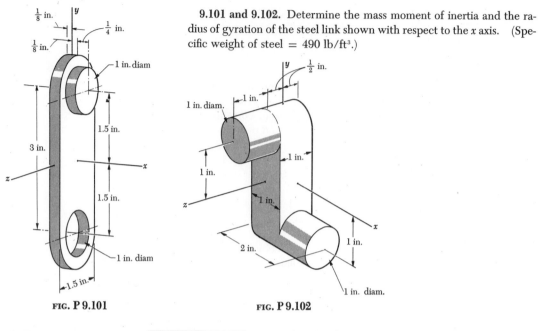

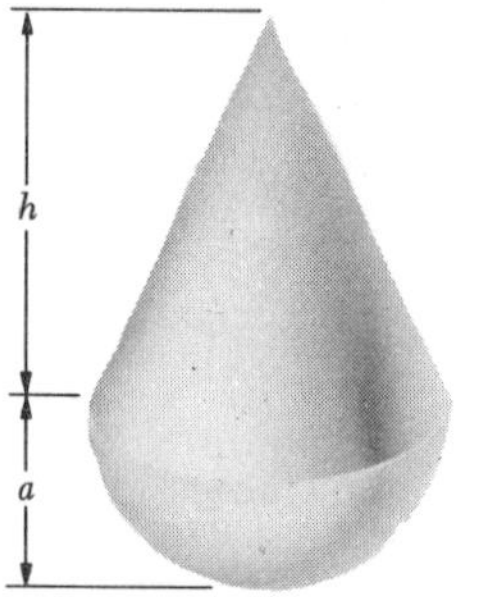

FIG. P 9.105

9.105. A hemisphere of radius a and a cone of height h, of the same density ρ, are attached as shown. (*a*) Determine the ratio h/a for which the moment of inertia of the composite body with respect to its axis of symmetry is equal to the moment of inertia of a sphere, of radius a and density ρ, with respect to one of its diameters. (*b*) Repeat the solution considering now the moment of inertia of the composite body with respect to a diameter of the base common to the cone and the hemisphere. (*Hint.* Solve the resulting cubic equation by trial and error.)

9.106. Geological evidence indicates that the earth consists of a central spherical *core* surrounded by two layers called respectively the *mantle* and the *crust.* The radii and density characterizing these three regions are as follows:

core: $0 < r < 2{,}140$ miles, density $= 10.0$
mantle: $2{,}140$ miles $< r < 3{,}940$ miles, density $= 4.7$
crust: $3{,}940$ miles $< r < 3{,}960$ miles, density $= 3.0$

Knowing that the average density of the earth is 5.51, determine the ratio of the actual moment of inertia of the earth to the moment of inertia of a sphere of radius 3,960 miles having a uniform density of 5.51.

REVIEW PROBLEMS

9.107. (*a*) Determine $\bar{I}_x$ and $\bar{I}_y$ if $b = 6$ in. (*b*) Determine the dimension b for which $\bar{I}_x = 3\bar{I}_y$.

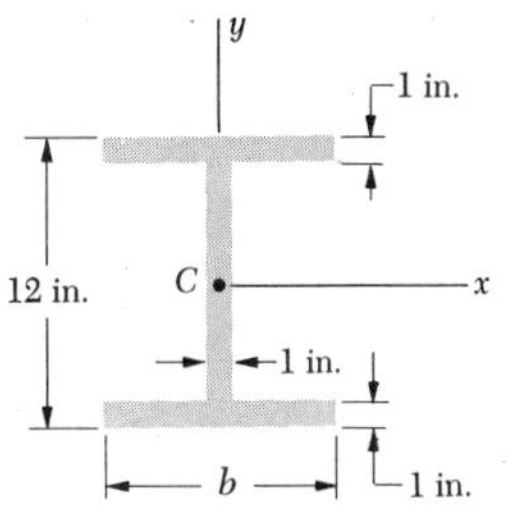

FIG. P 9.107

9.108. Determine the mass moment of inertia of the right circular cone of Sample Prob. 9.11 with respect to a diameter of its base.

9.109. Determine the radius of gyration of an equilateral triangle of side a with respect to one of its sides.

9.110. Determine the radius of gyration of the steel crankshaft shown with respect to the axis AA'.

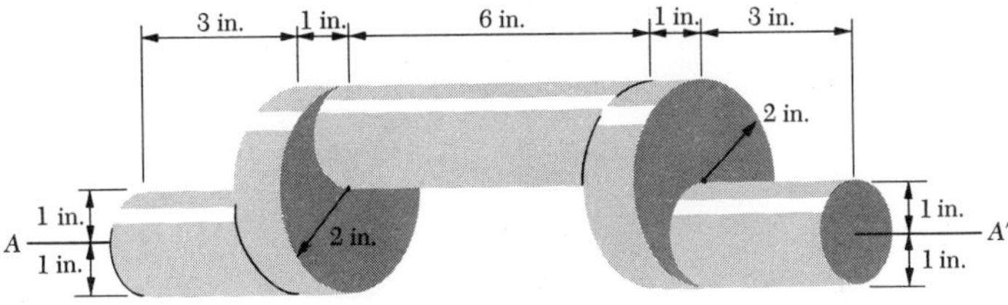

FIG. P 9.110

9.111. Determine the polar moment of inertia of the area of Prob. 5.47 with respect to the origin of coordinates.

9.112. Determine the centroidal moments of inertia $\bar{I}_x$ and $\bar{I}_y$ and the centroidal radii of gyration $\bar{k}_x$ and $\bar{k}_y$ for the structural shape shown. Neglect the effect of fillets.

9.113. Determine the orientation of the principal axes through the centroid C and the corresponding values of the moments of inertia for the structural shape shown. Neglect the effect of fillets and use the values of $\bar{I}_x$ and $\bar{I}_y$ obtained in Prob. 9.112.

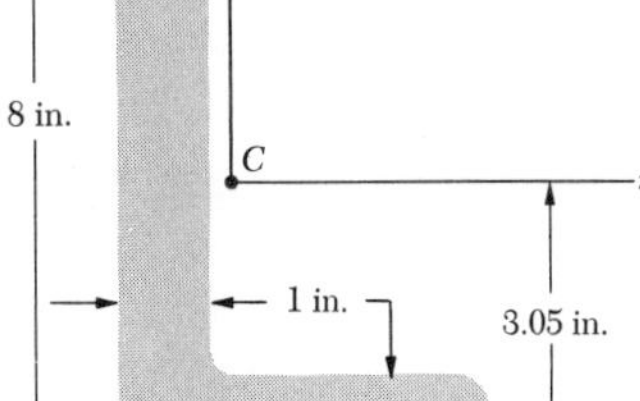

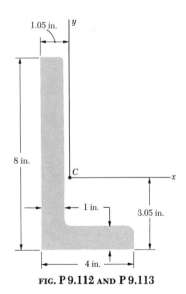

FIG. P 9.112 AND P 9.113

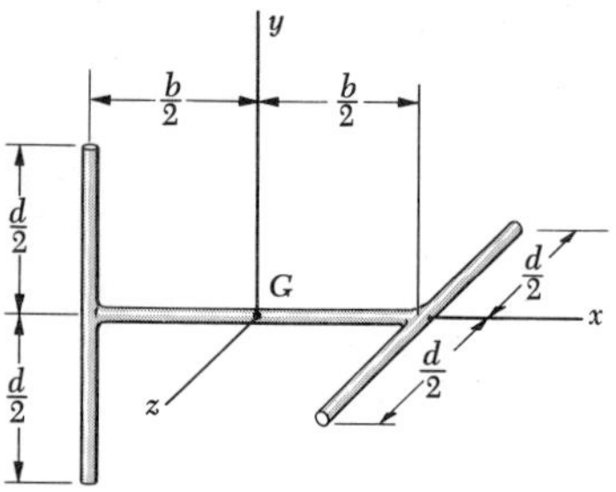

FIG. P9.114

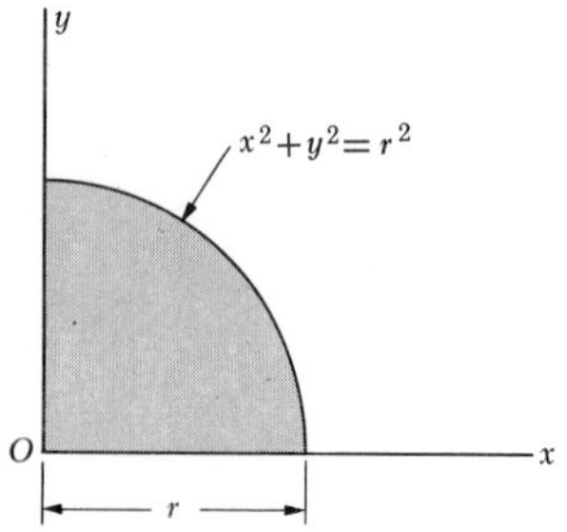

FIG. P9.116

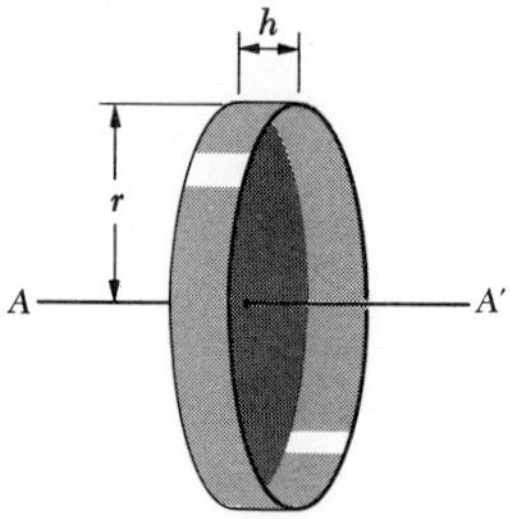

FIG. P9.118

9.114. Three slender homogeneous rods, weighing w lb/ft, are welded together as shown. If $b = d = 1$ ft and $w = 3$ lb/ft, determine the mass moment of inertia and the radius of gyration of the assembly with respect to (*a*) the x axis, (*b*) the y axis, (*c*) the z axis.

9.115. For the assembly of Prob. 9.114 determine the value of the ratio d/b for which $I_x = I_y = I_z$.

9.116. Determine the product of inertia of the quarter-circular area shown with respect to (*a*) the x and y axes, (*b*) centroidal axes, respectively parallel to the x and y axes.

9.117. Determine the orientation of the principal axes through the origin and the corresponding values of the moments of inertia for the cross-sectional area of Prob. 5.35. (*Hint.* Make use of the result of Prob. 9.116*a*.)

9.118. The rotor of an electric clock motor consists of a disk of radius r and a rim of width h; both the disk and the rim are of uniform thickness t. Determine the ratio h/r for which the radius of gyration of the rotor with respect to the axis AA' is $0.80\,r$.

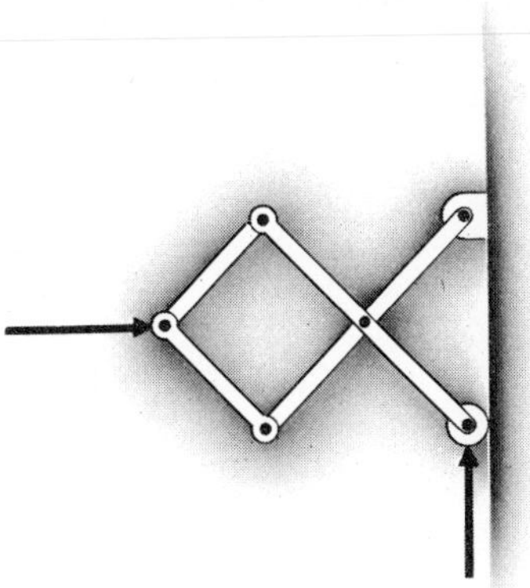

10. METHOD OF VIRTUAL WORK

***10.1. Work of a Force.** In the preceding chapters, problems involving the equilibrium of rigid bodies were solved by expressing that the external forces acting on the bodies were balanced. The equations of equilibrium $\Sigma F_x = 0$, $\Sigma F_y = 0$, $\Sigma M_A = 0$ were written and solved for the desired unknowns. We shall now consider a different method, which will prove more effective for solving certain types of equilibrium problems. This method is based on the concept of the *work of a force* and was first formally used by the Swiss mathematician Jean Bernoulli in the eighteenth century.

We shall first define the terms *displacement* and *work* as they are used in mechanics. Consider a particle which moves from a point A to a neighboring point A' (Fig. 10.1). If **r** denotes the position vector corresponding to point A, the small vector joining A and A' may be denoted by the differential $d\mathbf{r}$; the vector $d\mathbf{r}$ is called the *displacement* of the particle. Now let us assume that a force **F** is acting on the particle. The *work of the force* **F** *corresponding to the displacement* $d\mathbf{r}$ is defined as the quantity

$$dU = \mathbf{F} \cdot d\mathbf{r} \tag{10.1}$$

obtained by forming the scalar product of the force **F** and of the displacement $d\mathbf{r}$. Denoting respectively by F and ds the magnitudes of the force and of the displacement, and by α the angle formed by **F** and $d\mathbf{r}$, and recalling the definition of the scalar product of two vectors (Sec. 3.8), we write

$$dU = F\,ds\cos\alpha \tag{10.1'}$$

Being a *scalar quantity,* work has a magnitude and a sign, but no direction. We also note that work should be expressed in units such as ft-lb or in.-lb, obtained by multiplying units of length by units of force.

It follows from (10.1′) that the work dU is positive if the

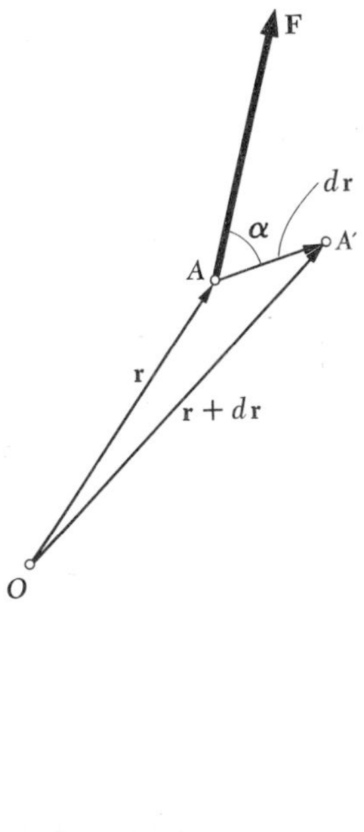

FIG. 10.1

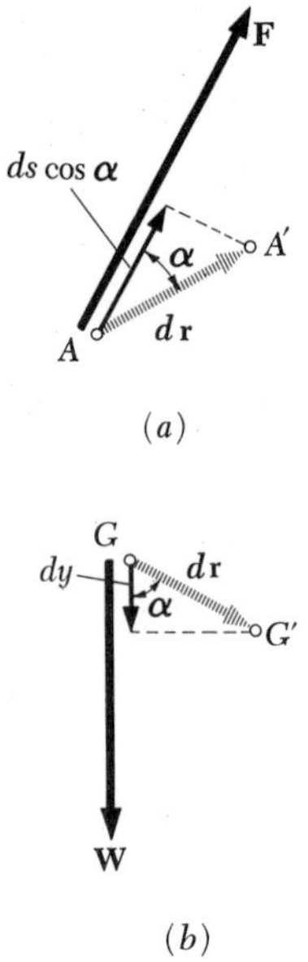

FIG. 10.2

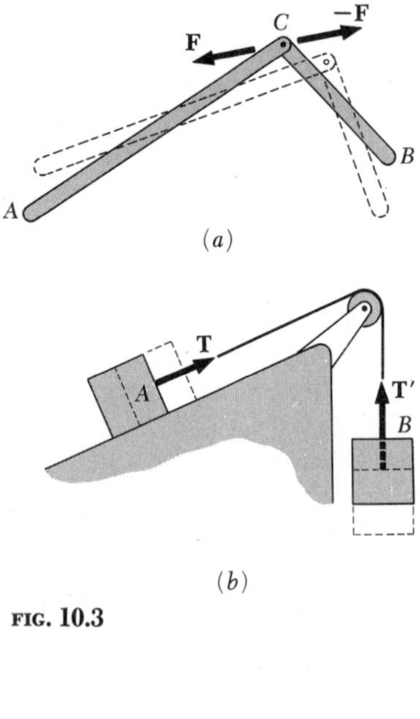

FIG. 10.3

angle α is acute, and negative if α is obtuse. Three particular cases are of special interest. If the force **F** has the same direction as $d\mathbf{r}$, the work dU reduces to $F\,ds$. If **F** has a direction opposite to that of $d\mathbf{r}$, the work is $dU = -F\,ds$. Finally, if **F** is perpendicular to $d\mathbf{r}$, the work dU is zero.

The work dU of a force **F** during a displacement $d\mathbf{r}$ may also be considered as the product of F and of the component $ds \cos \alpha$ of the displacement $d\mathbf{r}$ along **F** (Fig. 10.2*a*). This view is particularly useful in the computation of the work done by the weight **W** of a body (Fig. 10.2*b*). The work of **W** is equal to the product of W and of the vertical displacement dy of the center of gravity G of the body. If the displacement is downward, the work is positive; if it is upward, the work is negative.

A number of forces frequently encountered in statics *do no work*. They are forces applied to fixed points ($ds = 0$) or acting in a direction perpendicular to the displacement ($\cos \alpha = 0$). Among the forces which do no work are the following: the reaction at a smooth pin when the body supported rotates about the pin, the reaction at a smooth frictionless surface when the body in contact moves along the surface, the reaction at a roller moving along its track, the weight of a body when its center of gravity moves horizontally, the friction force acting on a wheel rolling without slipping (since at any instant the point of contact does not move). Examples of forces which *do work* are the weight of a body (except in the case considered above), the friction force acting on a body sliding on a rough surface, and most forces applied on a moving body.

In certain cases, the sum of the work done by several forces is zero. Consider, for example, two rigid bodies AC and BC connected at C by a *smooth pin* (Fig. 10.3*a*). Among the forces acting on AC is the force **F** exerted at C by BC. In general, the work of this force will not be zero, but it will be equal in magnitude and opposite in sign to the work of the force $-\mathbf{F}$ exerted at C by AC on BC, since these forces are equal and opposite and are applied to the same particle. Thus, when the total work done by all the forces acting on AB and BC is considered, the work of the two internal forces at C cancels out. A similar result is obtained if we consider a system consisting of two blocks connected by an *inextensible cord* AB (Fig. 10.3*b*). The work of the tension force **T** at A is equal in magnitude to the work of the tension force **T′** at B, since these forces have the same magnitude and the points A and B

move through the same distance; but in one case the work is positive, and in the other it is negative. Thus, the work of the internal forces again cancels out.

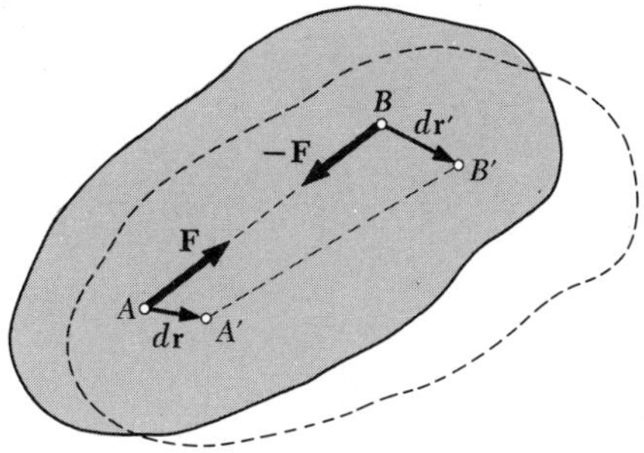

FIG. 10.4

It may be shown that the total work of the internal forces holding together the particles of a rigid body is zero. Consider two particles A and B of a rigid body and the two equal and opposite forces $\mathbf{F}$ and $-\mathbf{F}$ they exert on each other (Fig. 10.4). While, in general, the displacements $d\mathbf{r}$ and $d\mathbf{r}'$ of the two particles are different, the components of these displacements along AB must be equal; otherwise, the particles would not remain at the same distance from each other, and the body would not be rigid. Therefore, the work of $\mathbf{F}$ is equal in magnitude and opposite in sign to the work of $-\mathbf{F}$, and their sum is zero.

In computing the work of the external forces acting on a rigid body, it is often convenient to determine the work of a couple without considering separately the work of each of the two forces forming the couple. Consider the two forces $\mathbf{F}$ and $-\mathbf{F}$ forming a couple of moment $\mathbf{M}$ and acting on a rigid body (Fig. 10.5). Any small displacement of the rigid body bringing A and B, respectively, into A' and B'' may be divided into two parts, one in which points A and B undergo equal displacements $d\mathbf{r}_1$, the other in which A' remains fixed while B' moves into B'' through a displacement $d\mathbf{r}_2$ of magnitude $ds_2 = r\,d\theta$. In the first part of the motion, the work of $\mathbf{F}$ is equal in magnitude and opposite in sign to the work of $-\mathbf{F}$, and their sum is zero. In the second part of the motion, only force $\mathbf{F}$ works, and its work is $dU = F\,ds_2 = Fr\,d\theta$. But the product Fr is equal to the magnitude M of the moment of the couple. Thus, the work of a couple of moment $\mathbf{M}$ acting on a rigid body is

$$dU = M\,d\theta \tag{10.2}$$

where $d\theta$ is the small angle expressed in radians through which

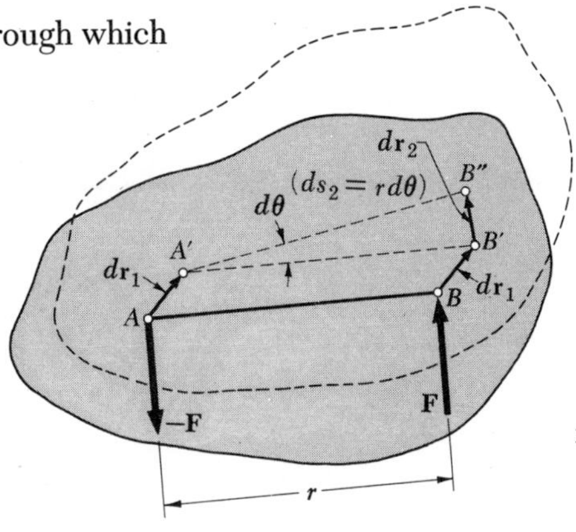

FIG. 10.5

the body rotates. We again note that work should be expressed in units obtained by multiplying units of force by units of length.

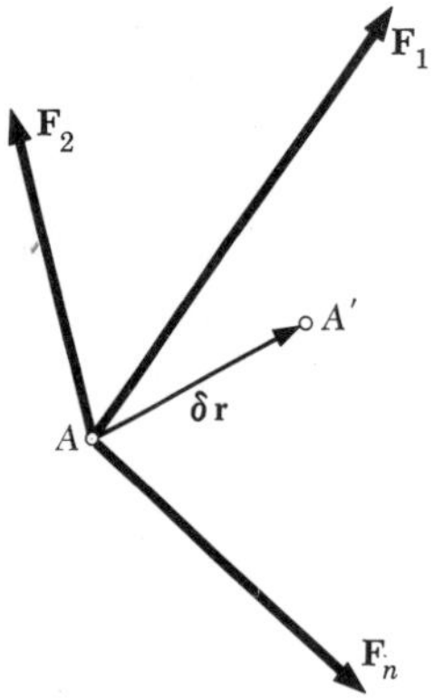

FIG. 10.6

***10.2. Principle of Virtual Work.** Consider a particle acted upon by several forces $\mathbf{F}_1, \mathbf{F}_2, \ldots \mathbf{F}_n$ (Fig. 10.6). We shall assume that the particle undergoes a small displacement from A to A'. This displacement is possible, but it will not necessarily take place. The forces may be balanced and the particle at rest, or the particle may move under the action of the given forces in a direction different from that of AA'. The displacement considered is therefore an imaginary displacement; it is called a *virtual displacement* and is denoted by $\delta\mathbf{r}$. The symbol $\delta\mathbf{r}$ represents a differential of the first order; it is used to distinguish the virtual displacement from the displacement $d\mathbf{r}$ which would take place under actual motion. As we shall see, virtual displacements may be used to determine whether the conditions of equilibrium of a particle are satisfied.

The work of each of the forces $\mathbf{F}_1, \mathbf{F}_2, \ldots, \mathbf{F}_n$ during the virtual displacement $\delta\mathbf{r}$ is called *virtual work*. The virtual work of all the forces acting on the particle of Fig. 10.6 is

$$\begin{aligned}\delta U &= \mathbf{F}_1 \cdot \delta\mathbf{r} + \mathbf{F}_2 \cdot \delta\mathbf{r} + \cdots + \mathbf{F}_n \cdot \delta\mathbf{r} \\ &= (\mathbf{F}_1 + \mathbf{F}_2 + \cdots + \mathbf{F}_n) \cdot \delta\mathbf{r} \\ &= \mathbf{R} \cdot \delta\mathbf{r} \end{aligned} \tag{10.3}$$

where $\mathbf{R}$ is the resultant of the given forces. Thus, the total virtual work of the forces $\mathbf{F}_1, \mathbf{F}_2, \ldots, \mathbf{F}_n$ is equal to the virtual work of their resultant $\mathbf{R}$.

The principle of virtual work for a particle states that, *if a particle is in equilibrium, the total virtual work of the forces acting on the particle is zero for any virtual displacement of the particle.* This condition is necessary: if the particle is in equilibrium, the resultant $\mathbf{R}$ of the forces is zero, and it follows from (10.3) that the total virtual work δU is zero. The condition is also sufficient: if the total virtual work δU is zero for any virtual displacement, the scalar product $\mathbf{R} \cdot \delta\mathbf{r}$ is zero for any $\delta\mathbf{r}$, and the resultant $\mathbf{R}$ must be zero.

In the case of a rigid body, the principle of virtual work states that, *if a rigid body is in equilibrium, the total virtual work of the external forces acting on the rigid body is zero for any virtual displacement of the body.* The condition is necessary: if the body is in equilibrium, all the particles forming the body are in equilibrium and the total virtual work of the forces acting on all the particles must be zero; but we have seen in the preceding section that the total work of the internal forces is zero; the total work of the external forces must therefore also be zero. The condition may also be proved to be sufficient.

The principle of virtual work may be extended to the case of a *system of connected rigid bodies.* If the system remains connected during the virtual displacement, *only the work of the forces external to the system need be considered,* since the total work of the internal forces at the various connections is zero.

***10.3. Applications of the Principle of Virtual Work.** The principle of virtual work is particularly effective when applied to the solution of problems involving machines or mechanisms consisting of several connected rigid bodies. Consider for instance the toggle vise ACB of Fig. 10.7*a*, used to compress a wooden block. We wish to determine the force exerted by the vise on the block when a given force **P** is applied at C, assuming that there is no friction. Denoting by **Q** the reaction of the block on the vise, we draw the free-body diagram of the vise and consider the virtual displacement obtained by giving to the angle θ a positive increment $\delta\theta$ (Fig. 10.7*b*). Choosing a system of

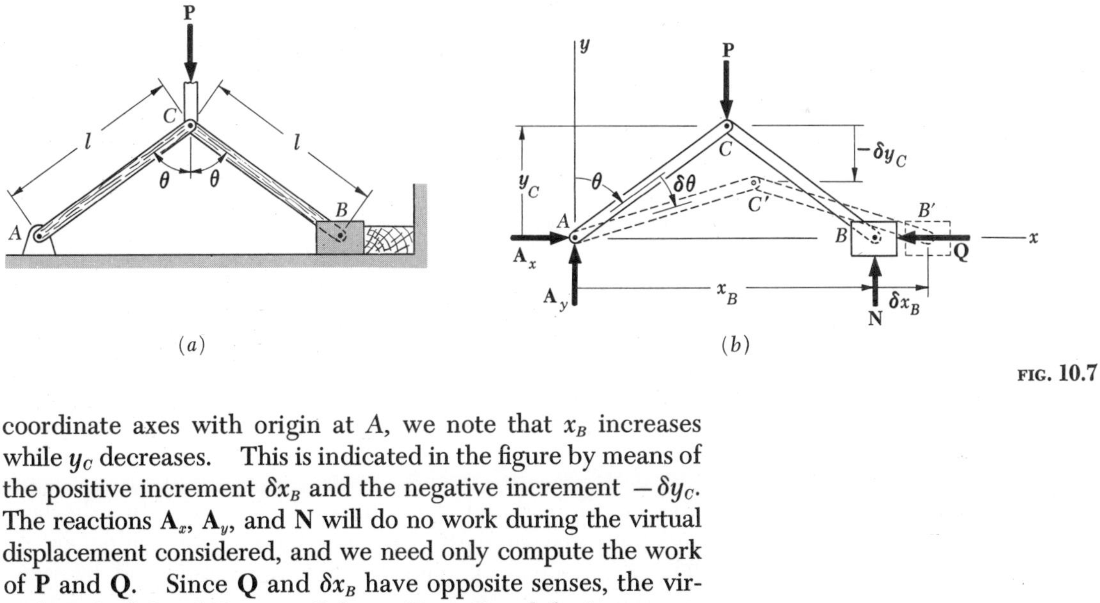

FIG. 10.7

coordinate axes with origin at A, we note that x_B increases while y_C decreases. This is indicated in the figure by means of the positive increment δx_B and the negative increment $-\delta y_C$. The reactions $\mathbf{A}_x$, $\mathbf{A}_y$, and **N** will do no work during the virtual displacement considered, and we need only compute the work of **P** and **Q**. Since **Q** and δx_B have opposite senses, the virtual work of **Q** is $\delta U_Q = -Q\,\delta x_B$. Since **P** and the increment shown $(-\delta y_C)$ have the same sense, the virtual work of **P** is $\delta U_P = +P(-\delta y_C) = -P\,\delta y_C$. The minus signs obtained could have been predicted by simply noting that the forces **Q** and **P** are directed opposite to the positive x and y axes, respectively. Expressing the coordinates x_B and y_C in terms of the angle θ and differentiating, we obtain

$$\begin{aligned} x_B &= 2l \sin\theta & y_C &= l\cos\theta \\ \delta x_B &= 2l\cos\theta\,\delta\theta & \delta y_C &= -l\sin\theta\,\delta\theta \end{aligned} \tag{10.4}$$

The total virtual work of the forces **Q** and **P** is thus

$$\begin{aligned} \delta U &= \delta U_Q + \delta U_P = -Q\,\delta x_B - P\,\delta y_C \\ &= -2Ql\cos\theta\,\delta\theta + Pl\sin\theta\,\delta\theta \end{aligned}$$

Making $\delta U = 0$, we obtain

$$2Ql\cos\theta\,\delta\theta = Pl\sin\theta\,\delta\theta \tag{10.5}$$

$$Q = \tfrac{1}{2}P\tan\theta \tag{10.6}$$

The superiority of the method of virtual work over the conventional equilibrium equations in the problem considered here is clear: by using the method of virtual work, we were able to eliminate all unknown reactions, while the equation $\Sigma M_A = 0$ would have eliminated only two of the unknown reactions. We may take advantage of this characteristic of the method of virtual work to solve many problems involving machines and mechanisms. *If the virtual displacement considered is consistent with the constraints imposed by the supports and connections, all reactions and internal forces are eliminated and only the work of the loads, applied forces, and friction forces need be considered.*

We shall observe that the method of virtual work may also be used to solve problems involving completely constrained structures, although the virtual displacements considered will never actually take place. Consider, for example, the frame ACB shown in Fig. 10.8*a*. If point A is kept fixed, while B is given a horizontal virtual displacement (Fig. 10.8*b*), we need consider only the work of **P** and $\mathbf{B}_x$. We may thus determine the reaction component $\mathbf{B}_x$ in the same way as the force **Q** of the preceding example (Fig. 10.7*b*); we have

$$B_x = -\tfrac{1}{2}P\tan\theta$$

Keeping B fixed and giving to A a horizontal virtual displacement, we may similarly determine the reaction component $\mathbf{A}_x$. The components $\mathbf{A}_y$ and $\mathbf{B}_y$ may be determined by rotating the frame ACB as a rigid body about B and A, respectively.

The method of virtual work may also be used to determine

the configuration of a system in equilibrium under given forces. For example, the value of the angle θ for which the linkage of Fig. 10.7*a* is in equilibrium under two given forces **P** and **Q** may be obtained by solving Eq. (10.6) for tan θ.

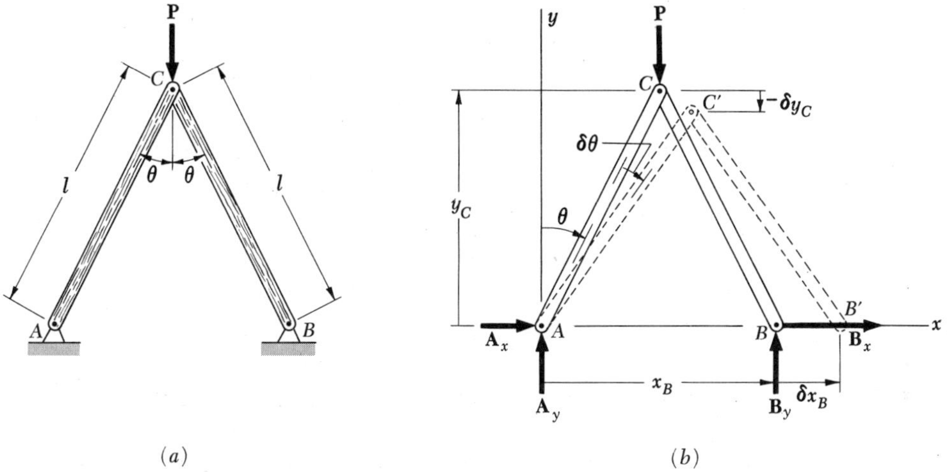

FIG. 10.8

***10.4. Real Machines. Mechanical Efficiency.** In analyzing the toggle vise in the preceding section, we assumed that no friction forces were involved. Thus, the virtual work consisted only of the work of the applied force **P** and of the reaction **Q**. But the work of the reaction **Q** is equal in magnitude and opposite in sign to the work of the force exerted by the vise on the block. Equation (10.5), therefore, expresses that the *output work* $2Ql \cos \theta \, \delta\theta$ is equal to the *input work* $Pl \sin \theta \, \delta\theta$. A machine in which input and output work are equal is said to be an "ideal" machine. In a "real" machine, friction forces will always do some work, and the output work will be smaller than the input work.

Consider, for example, the toggle vise of Fig. 10.7*a*, and assume now that a friction force **F** develops between the sliding block *B* and the horizontal plane (Fig. 10.9). Using the conventional methods of statics and summing moments about *A*, we find $N = P/2$. Denoting by μ the coefficient of friction between block *B* and the horizontal plane, we have $F = \mu N = \mu P/2$. Recalling formulas (10.4), we find that the total virtual work of the forces **Q**, **P**, and **F** during the virtual displacement shown in Fig. 10.9 is

$$\begin{aligned} \delta U &= -Q \, \delta x_B - P \, \delta y_C - F \, \delta x_B \\ &= -2Ql \cos \theta \, \delta\theta + Pl \sin \theta \, \delta\theta - \mu Pl \cos \theta \, \delta\theta \end{aligned}$$

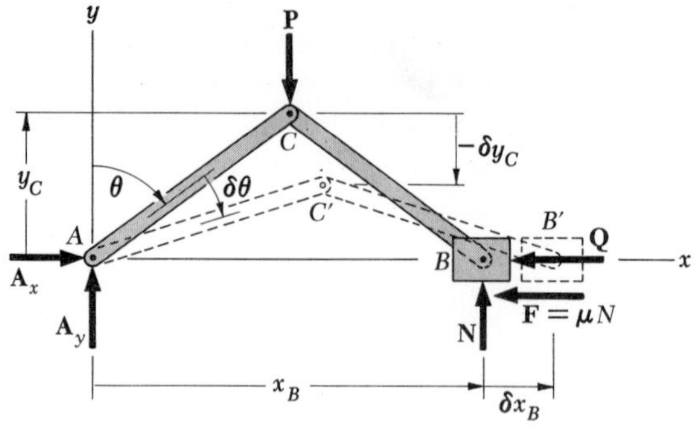

FIG. 10.9

Making $\delta U = 0$, we obtain

$$2Ql \cos \theta \; \delta\theta = Pl \sin \theta \; \delta\theta - \mu Pl \cos \theta \; \delta\theta \tag{10.7}$$

which expresses that the output work is equal to the input work minus the work of the friction force. Solving for Q, we have

$$Q = \tfrac{1}{2}P(\tan \theta - \mu) \tag{10.8}$$

We note that $Q = 0$ when $\tan \theta = \mu$, that is, when θ is equal to the angle of friction ϕ, and that $Q < 0$ when $\theta < \phi$. The toggle vise may thus be used only for values θ larger than the angle of friction.

The *mechanical efficiency* of a machine is defined as the ratio

$$\eta = \frac{\text{output work}}{\text{input work}} \tag{10.9}$$

Clearly, the mechanical efficiency of an ideal machine is $\eta = 1$, since input and output work are then equal, while the mechanical efficiency of a real machine will always be less than 1.

In the case of the toggle vise we have just analyzed, we write

$$\eta = \frac{\text{output work}}{\text{input work}} = \frac{2Ql \cos \theta \; \delta\theta}{Pl \sin \theta \; \delta\theta}$$

Substituting from (10.8) for Q, we obtain

$$\eta = \frac{P(\tan \theta - \mu)l \cos \theta \; \delta\theta}{Pl \sin \theta \; \delta\theta} = 1 - \mu \cot \theta \tag{10.10}$$

We check that, in the absence of friction forces, we would have $\mu = 0$ and $\eta = 1$. In the general case, when μ is different from zero, the efficiency η becomes zero for $\mu \cot \theta = 1$, that is, for $\tan \theta = \mu$, or $\theta = \tan^{-1} \mu = \phi$. We check again that the toggle vise may be used only for values of θ larger than the angle of friction ϕ.

SAMPLE PROBLEM 10.1

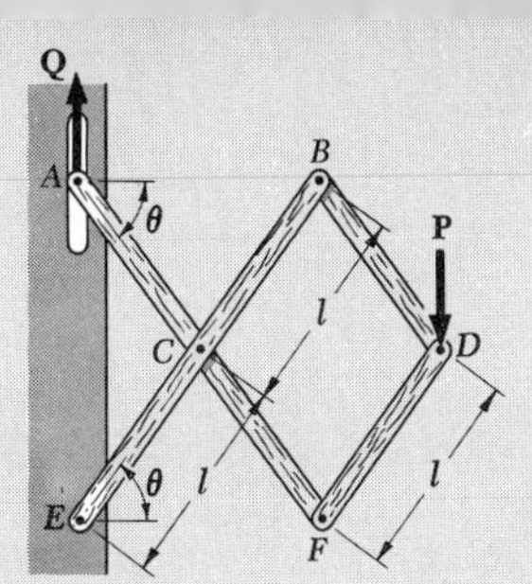

Using the method of virtual work, determine the magnitude of the force **Q** required to maintain the equilibrium of the mechanism shown.

Solution. Choosing a coordinate system with origin at E, we write

$$y_A = 2l \sin \theta \qquad y_D = l \sin \theta$$

$$\delta y_A = 2l \cos \theta \, \delta\theta \qquad \delta y_D = l \cos \theta \, \delta\theta$$

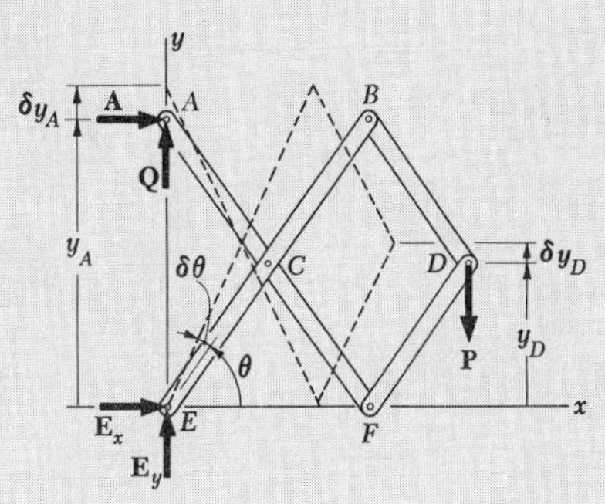

Principle of Virtual Work. Since the reactions **A**, $\mathbf{E}_x$, and $\mathbf{E}_y$ will do no work during the virtual displacement, the total virtual work done by **P** and **Q** must be zero.

$$\delta U = 0: \qquad +Q \, \delta y_A - P \, \delta y_D = 0$$

$$+Q(2l \cos \theta \, \delta\theta) - P(l \cos \theta \, \delta\theta) = 0 \qquad Q = \tfrac{1}{2}P \blacktriangleleft$$

SAMPLE PROBLEM 10.2

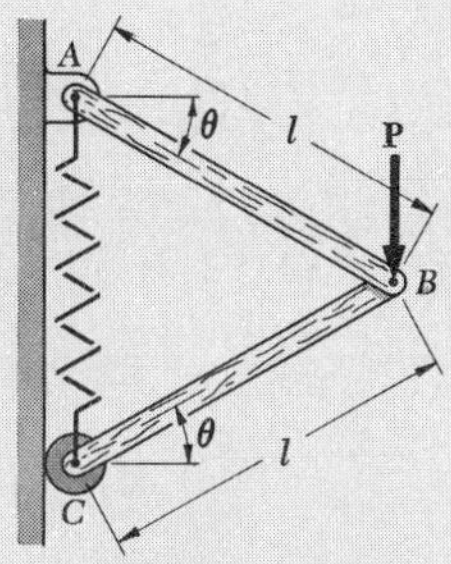

Determine the expressions for θ and for the tension in the spring which correspond to the equilibrium position of the mechanism. The unstretched length of the spring is h, and the constant of the spring is k. Neglect the weight of the mechanism.

Solution. With the coordinate system shown

$$y_B = l \sin \theta \qquad y_C = 2l \sin \theta$$

$$\delta y_B = l \cos \theta \, \delta\theta \qquad \delta y_C = 2l \cos \theta \, \delta\theta$$

The elongation of the spring is

$$s = y_C - h = 2l \sin \theta - h$$

The magnitude of the force exerted at C by the spring is

$$F = ks = k(2l \sin \theta - h) \qquad (1)$$

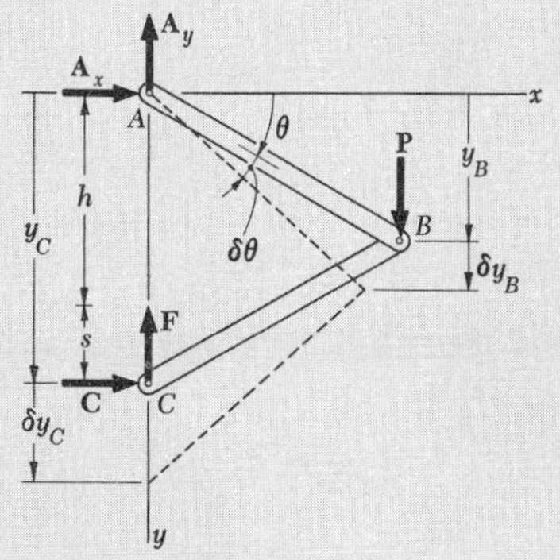

Principle of Virtual Work

$$\delta U = 0: \qquad P \, \delta y_B - F \, \delta y_C = 0$$

$$P(l \cos \theta \, \delta\theta) - k(2l \sin \theta - h)(2l \cos \theta \, \delta\theta) = 0$$

$$\sin \theta = \frac{P + 2kh}{4kl} \blacktriangleleft$$

Substituting this expression into (1), we obtain

$$F = \tfrac{1}{2}P \blacktriangleleft$$

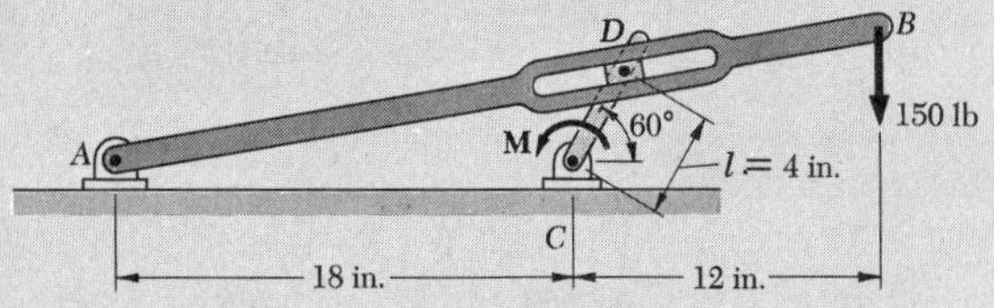

SAMPLE PROBLEM 10.3

Determine the couple **M** which must be applied to the crank CD to hold the mechanism in equilibrium. The block at D is pinned to the crank CD and is free to slide in a slot cut in member AB. This mechanism has been previously considered in Sample Prob. 6.8.

Solution. Referring to Sample Prob. 6.8, we obtain the following dimensions:

$$b = 2 \text{ in.} \qquad \alpha = 9.8°$$

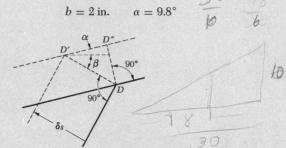

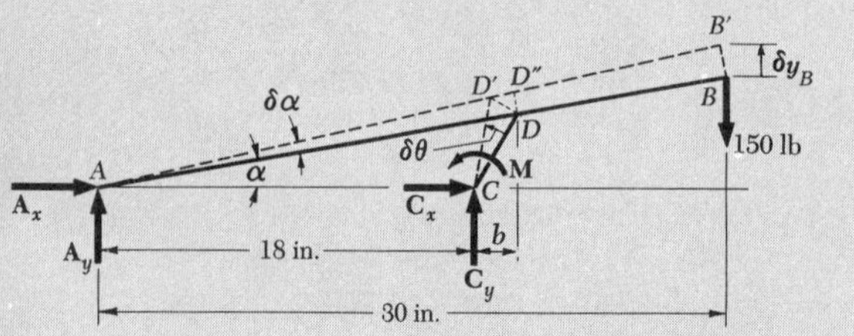

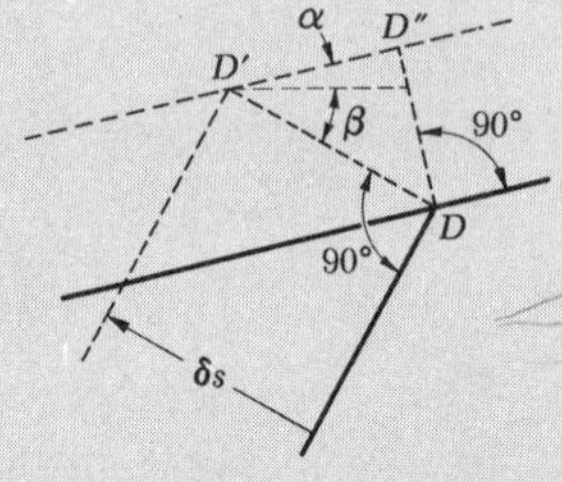

Virtual Displacement $\delta\theta$. After a virtual rotation $\delta\theta$ of the crank CD, the mechanism assumes the position indicated by the dashed lines. Member AB rotates through $\delta\alpha$ into AB', and the block D moves through δs into D'. Since the virtual rotation $\delta\theta$ represents a differential of the first order, DD' is perpendicular to CD.

$$\beta = 30° \qquad \delta s = l\,\delta\theta$$

The component of the displacement of the block perpendicular to member AB is

$$DD'' = \delta s \sin(\alpha + \beta) = (l\,\delta\theta)\sin(9.8° + 30°) = l \sin 39.8°\ \delta\theta \tag{1}$$

By similar triangles, we obtain

$$\frac{AB}{AD} = \frac{30 \text{ in.}}{18 \text{ in.} + b} \qquad \frac{AB}{AD} = \frac{30 \text{ in.}}{20 \text{ in.}} \tag{2}$$

Using the similar triangles ABB' and ADD'' together with (1) and (2), we find

$$\frac{BB'}{DD''} = \frac{AB}{AD} = \tfrac{30}{20} \qquad BB' = \tfrac{30}{20}\,DD'' = \tfrac{30}{20}\,l \sin 39.8°\ \delta\theta$$

Finally, since BB' is perpendicular to AB and $l = 4$ in., we obtain

$$\delta y_B = BB' \cos\alpha = [(\tfrac{30}{20})(4 \text{ in.}) \sin 39.8°\ \delta\theta] \cos 9.8° = (3.78 \text{ in.})\,\delta\theta$$

Principle of Virtual Work

$\delta U = 0$: $\qquad +M\,\delta\theta - (150 \text{ lb})\,\delta y_B = 0$

$$+M\,\delta\theta - (150 \text{ lb})(3.78 \text{ in.})\,\delta\theta = 0$$

$M = +567$ lb-in. $\qquad$ **M** = 567 lb-in. ↺ ◄

PROBLEMS

10.1. Determine the magnitude of the force **P** required to maintain the equilibrium of the linkage shown.

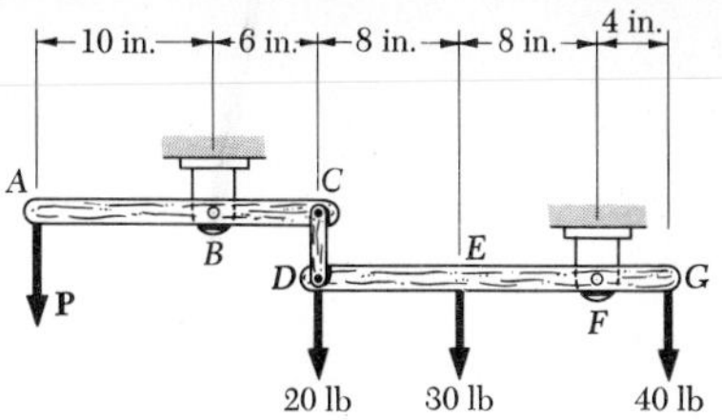

FIG. P 10.1

10.2. Using the principle of virtual work, determine the tension in the rope for each of the rope-and-pulley arrangements of Prob. 2.42.

10.3. Determine the weight W which balances the 10-lb load.

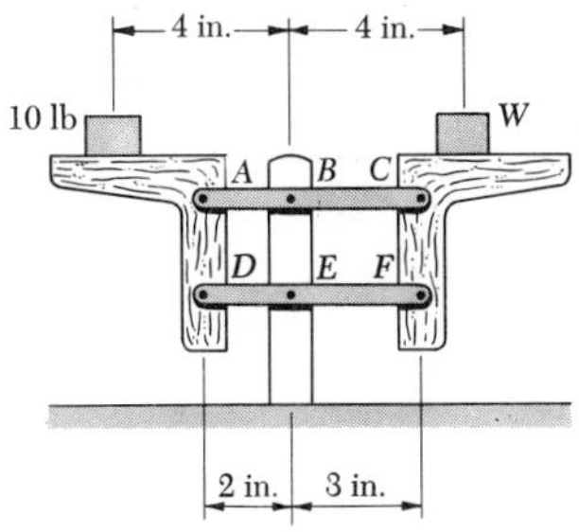

FIG. P 10.3

10.4. Determine the force **P** required to maintain the equilibrium of the linkage shown. All members are of the same length and the wheels at A and B roll freely on the horizontal rod.

10.5. Determine the vertical force **P** which must be applied at A to maintain the equilibrium of the linkage.

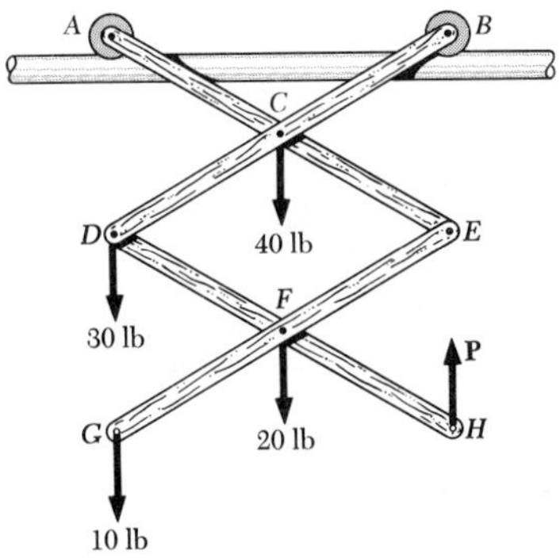

FIG. P 10.4

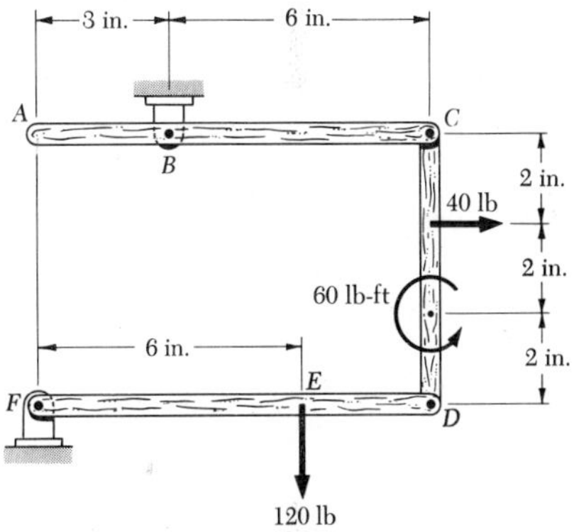

FIG. P 10.5 AND P 10.6

10.6. Determine the couple **M** which must be applied to member AC to maintain the equilibrium of the linkage.

10.7 and 10.8. The mechanism shown is acted upon by the force **P**; determine an expression for the magnitude of the force **Q** required to maintain equilibrium.

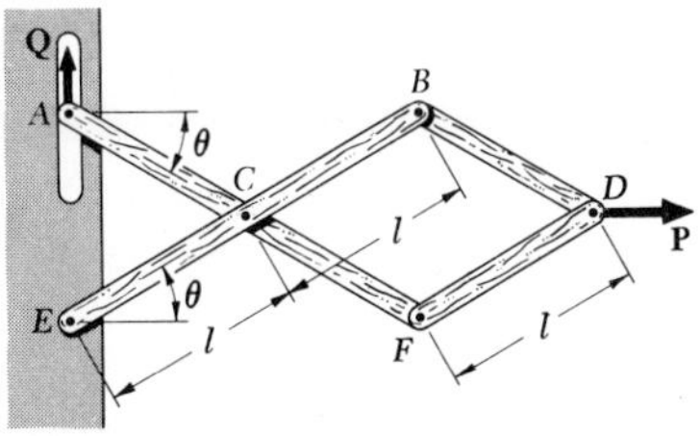

FIG. P 10.7

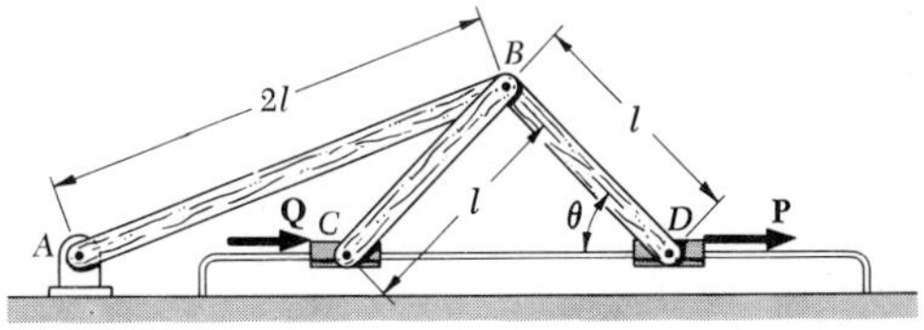

FIG. P 10.8

10.9. Three links, each of length l, are connected as shown. Knowing that the line of action of the force **Q** passes through point A, determine an expression for the magnitude of **Q** required to maintain equilibrium.

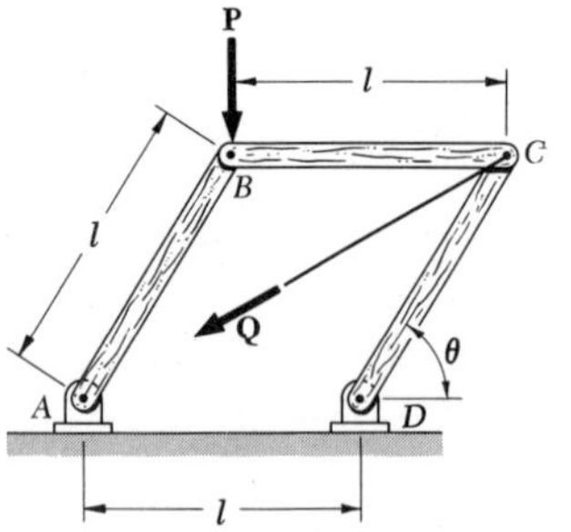

FIG. P 10.9

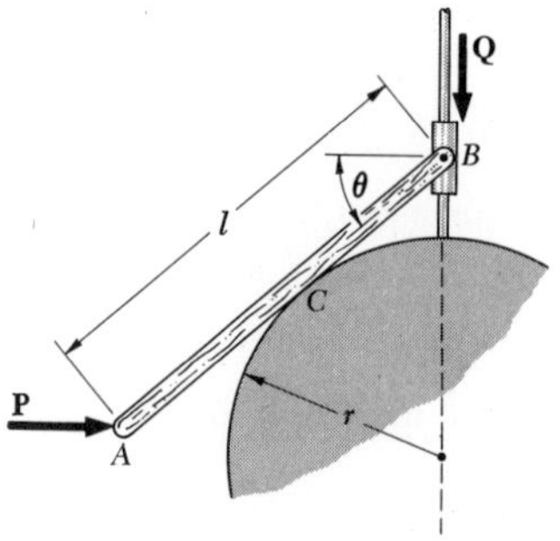

FIG. P 10.10

10.10. A slender rod of length l is attached to a collar at B and rests on a smooth circular cylinder of radius r. Knowing that the collar may slide freely along a vertical guide, determine an expression for the magnitude of the force **Q** required to maintain equilibrium.

10.11. Solve Prob. 10.10 assuming that the force **P** is removed and that a couple **M**, directed counterclockwise, is applied to rod AB.

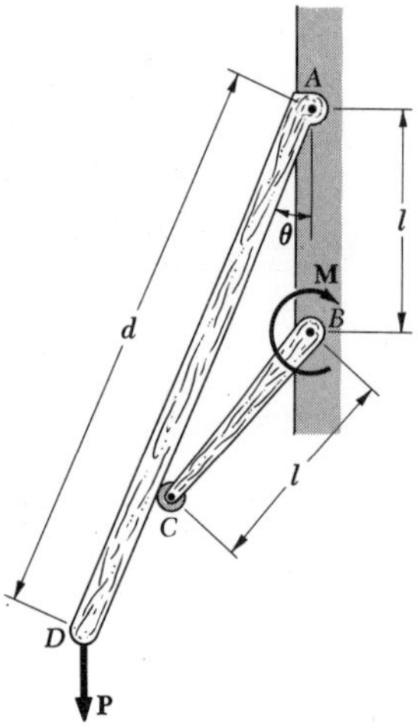

FIG. P 10.12

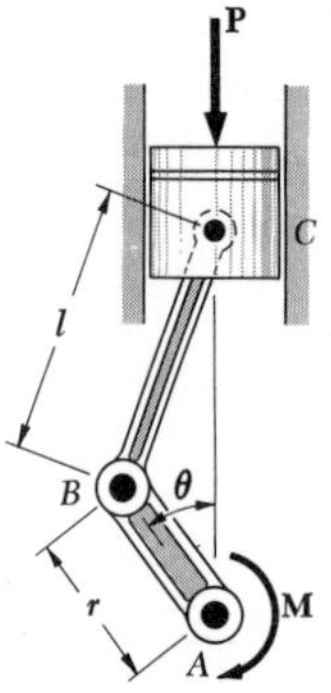

FIG. P 10.13

10.12 and 10.13. Determine an expression for the magnitude of the couple **M** required to maintain equilibrium.

10.14. Solve Prob. 10.12 assuming that the force **P** is directed horizontally to the right.

10.15. If gripping forces of magnitude $Q = 450$ lb are desired, determine the magnitude P of the forces which must be applied to the pliers of Prob. 6.113. Also show that the required magnitude P is independent of the position of the object gripped by the jaws.

10.16. In Prob. 10.7 determine the magnitude of the force **Q** required for equilibrium, when $l = 15$ in., $\theta = 30°$, and $P = 200$ lb.

10.17. In Prob. 10.9 determine the magnitude of the force **Q** required for equilibrium, when $l = 20$ in., $\theta = 45°$, and $P = 400$ lb.

10.18. In Prob. 10.13 determine the magnitude of the force **P** required for equilibrium when $r = 4$ in., $l = 8$ in., $\theta = 60°$, and $M = 4{,}000$ lb-in. clockwise.

10.19. Determine the value of θ corresponding to the equilibrium position of the mechanism of Prob. 10.7, when $P = 50$ lb and $Q = 200$ lb.

***10.20.** Determine the value of θ corresponding to the equilibrium position of the mechanism of Prob. 10.8, when $P = 100$ lb and $Q = 200$ lb.

10.21. Determine the value of θ corresponding to the equilibrium position of the mechanism of Prob. 10.9, when $P = 100$ lb and $Q = 150$ lb.

10.22. Determine the value of θ corresponding to the equilibrium position of the mechanism of Prob. 10.10, when $P = 250$ lb, $Q = 300$ lb, $r = 8$ in., and $l = 12$ in.

10.23. Two 15-in. bars AC and DE are connected by a pin at B and by a spring EC. When unstretched, the spring is 5 in. long; the constant of the spring is 15 lb/in. Determine the value of a corresponding to equilibrium.

10.24. Solve Prob. 10.23 assuming that the 20-lb force is applied at C and the 12-lb force is applied at D.

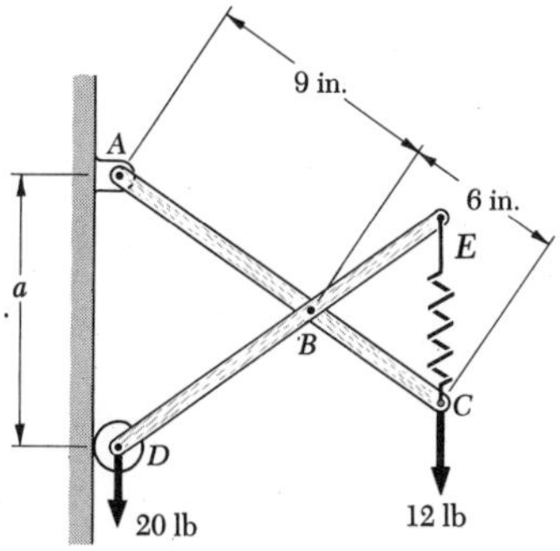

FIG. P 10.23

FIG. P 10.25 AND P 10.26

10.25. A vertical load **W** is applied to the linkage at B. The constant of the spring is k, and the spring is unstretched when AB and BC are horizontal. Neglecting the weight of the linkage, obtain an equation, in terms of θ, W, l, and k, which must be satisfied when the linkage is in equilibrium.

10.26. A load **W** of magnitude 100 lb is applied to the linkage at B. Neglecting the weight of the linkage and knowing that $l = 10$ in., determine the value of θ corresponding to equilibrium. The constant of the spring is $k = 30$ lb/in., and the spring is unstretched when AB and BC are horizontal. (*Hint.* Obtain the approximate value of θ by solving by trial and error the equation obtained.)

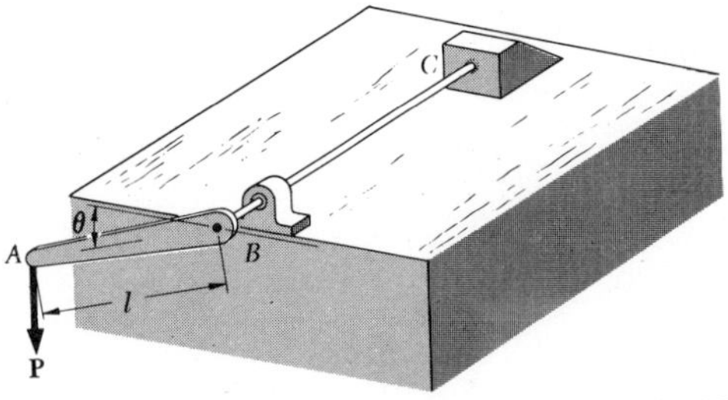

FIG. P 10.27

10.27. The lever AB is attached to the horizontal shaft BC which passes through a bearing and is welded to a fixed support at C. The torsional spring constant of the shaft BC is K; i.e., a couple of moment K is required to rotate end B through one radian. Knowing that the shaft is untwisted when AB is horizontal, determine the value of θ corresponding to the position of equilibrium, if $P = 20$ lb, $l = 10$ in., and $K = 100$ lb-in./radian.

10.28. Solve Prob. 10.27, if $P = 70$ lb, $l = 10$ in., and $K = 100$ lb-in./radian. Obtain an answer in each of the following quadrants: $0 < \theta < 90°$, $270° < \theta < 360°$, and $360° < \theta < 450°$. (It is assumed that K remains constant for the angles of twist considered.)

10.29. A block of weight W is pulled up a plane forming an angle α with the horizontal by a force **P** directed along the plane. If μ is the coefficient of friction between the block and the plane, derive an expression for the mechanical efficiency of the system. Show that the mechanical efficiency cannot exceed $\frac{1}{2}$ if the block is to remain in place when the force **P** is removed.

10.30. Derive an expression for the mechanical efficiency of the jack discussed in Sec. 8.6. Show that, if the jack is to be self-locking, the mechanical efficiency cannot exceed $\frac{1}{2}$.

10.31. In Prob. 10.7, assume that friction exists between the pin and the slot at A. Denoting by μ the coefficient of friction, determine the smallest and the largest magnitudes of the force **Q** for which equilibrium is maintained.

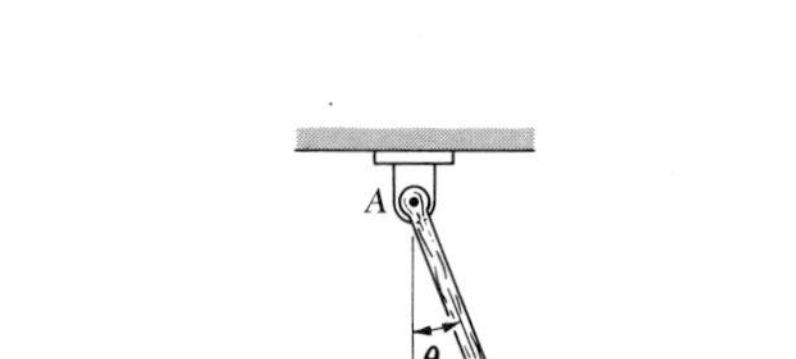

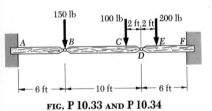

FIG. P 10.33 AND P 10.34

10.32. In Prob. 10.7, assume that the coefficient of friction between the pin and the slot at A is $\mu = 0.30$, and determine the smallest and the largest magnitudes of the force **Q** for which equilibrium is maintained when $\theta = 30°$ and $P = 200$ lb.

10.33. Using the method of virtual work, determine separately the force and the couple representing the reaction at A.

10.34. Using the method of virtual work, determine separately the force and the couple representing the reaction at F.

10.35. In Prob. 10.4 the force **P** is removed and the linkage is maintained in equilibrium by a cord which is attached to pins E and H. Determine the tension in the cord.

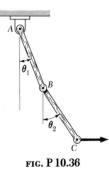

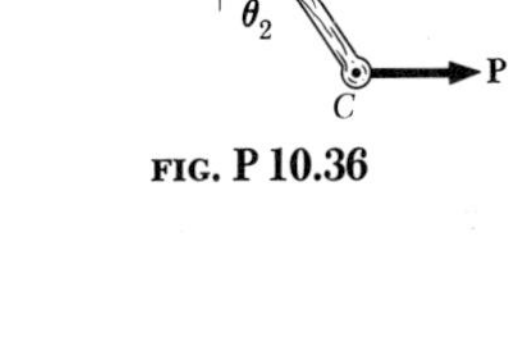

FIG. P 10.36

10.36. Two uniform rods, each of weight W and length l, are connected as shown. Using the method of virtual work, determine θ_1 and θ_2 corresponding to equilibrium.

10.37. Solve Prob. 10.36, assuming that the force **P** is replaced by a counterclockwise couple **M** applied on rod *BC*.

10.38. Determine the vertical movement of joint *G* if member *AB* is shortened 0.8 in. (*Hint.* Apply a vertical load at joint *G*, and, using the methods of Chap. 6, compute the force exerted by member *AB* on joints *A* and *B*. Then apply the method of virtual work for a virtual displacement making member *AB* shorter. This method should be used only for small changes in the length of members.)

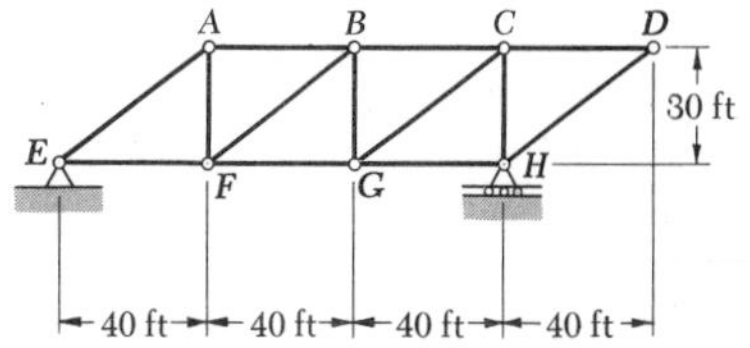

FIG. P 10.38, P 10.39, AND P 10.40

10.39. Determine the vertical movement of joint *D* if the length of member *BF* is changed to 50 ft $1\frac{1}{2}$ in. (See hint of Prob. 10.38.)

10.40. Determine the horizontal movement of joint *D* if the length of member *BF* is changed to 50 ft $1\frac{1}{2}$ in. (See hint of Prob. 10.38.)

*10.5. Work of a Force during a Finite Displacement.

Consider a force **F** acting on a particle. The work of **F** corresponding to an infinitesimal displacement $d\mathbf{r}$ of the particle was defined in Sec. 10.1 as

$$dU = \mathbf{F} \cdot d\mathbf{r} \tag{10.1}$$

The work of **F** corresponding to a finite displacement of the particle from A_1 to A_2 (Fig. 10.10*a*) is denoted by $U_{1\to 2}$ and is obtained by integrating (10.1) along the curve described by the particle:

$$U_{1\to 2} = \int_{A_1}^{A_2} \mathbf{F} \cdot d\mathbf{r} \tag{10.11}$$

Using the alternate expression

$$dU = F\, ds \cos \alpha \tag{10.1'}$$

given in Sec. 10.1 for the elementary work dU, we may also express the work $U_{1\to 2}$ as

$$U_{1\to 2} = \int_{s_1}^{s_2} (F \cos \alpha)\, ds \tag{10.11'}$$

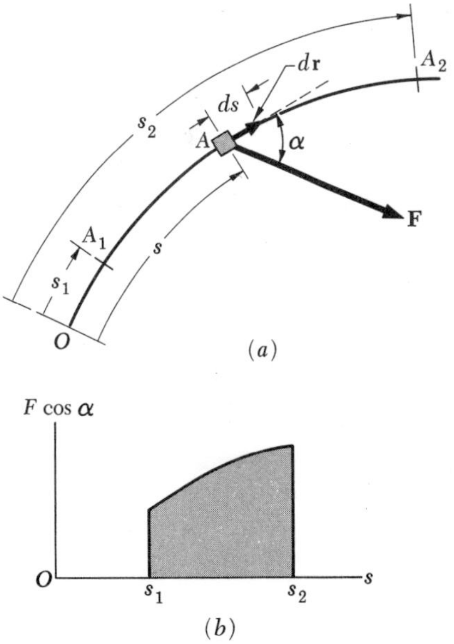

FIG. 10.10

where the variable of integration s measures the distance along the path traveled by the particle. The work $U_{1\to 2}$ is represented by the area under the curve obtained by plotting $F \cos \alpha$ against s (Fig. 10.10*b*). In the case of a force **F** of constant magnitude acting in the direction of motion, formula (10.11) yields $U_{1\to 2} = F(s_2 - s_1)$.

Recalling from Sec. 10.1 that the work of a couple of moment **M** during an infinitesimal rotation $d\theta$ of a rigid body is

$$dU = M\,d\theta \tag{10.2}$$

we express as follows the work of the couple during a finite rotation of the body:

$$U_{1\to2} = \int_{\theta_1}^{\theta_2} M\,d\theta \tag{10.12}$$

In the case of a constant couple, formula (10.12) yields

$$U_{1\to2} = M(\theta_2 - \theta_1)$$

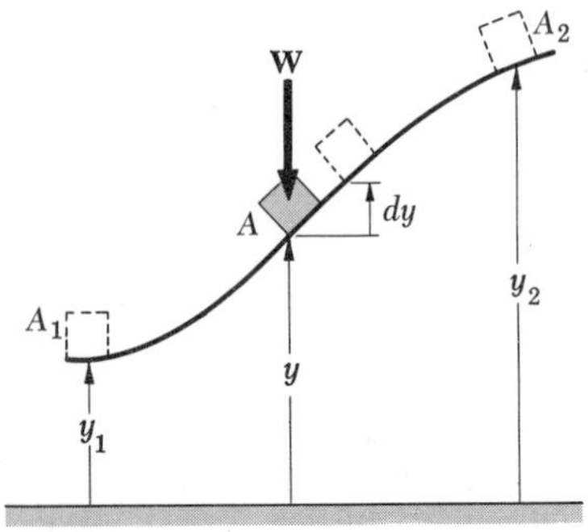

FIG. 10.11

Work of a Weight. It was stated in Sec. 10.1 that the work of the weight **W** of a body during an infinitesimal displacement of the body is equal to the product of W and of the vertical displacement of the center of gravity of the body. With the y axis pointing upward, the work of **W** during a finite displacement of the body (Fig. 10.11) is obtained by writing

$$dU = -W\,dy$$

$$U_{1\to2} = -\int_{y_1}^{y_2} W\,dy = Wy_1 - Wy_2 \tag{10.13}$$

or $$U_{1\to2} = -W(y_2 - y_1) = -W\,\Delta y \tag{10.13$'$}$$

where Δy is the vertical displacement from A_1 to A_2. The work of the weight **W** is thus equal to *the product of W and of the vertical displacement of the center of gravity of the body.* The work is *positive* when $\Delta y < 0$, that is, *when the body moves down.*

Work of the Force Exerted by a Spring. Consider a body A attached to a fixed point B by a spring; it is assumed that the spring is undeformed when the body is at A_0 (Fig. 10.12*a*). Experimental evidence shows that the magnitude of the force **F** exerted by the spring on a body A is proportional to the deflection x of the spring measured from the position A_0. We have

$$F = kx \tag{10.14}$$

where k is the *spring constant,* expressed in lb/ft or lb/in. The work of the force **F** exerted by the spring during a finite displacement of the body from $A_1(x = x_1)$ to $A_2(x = x_2)$ is obtained by writing

$$dU = -F\,dx = -kx\,dx$$

$$U_{1\to2} = -\int_{x_1}^{x_2} kx\,dx = \tfrac{1}{2}kx_1^2 - \tfrac{1}{2}kx_2^2 \tag{10.15}$$

Care should be taken to express k and x in consistent units, that is, k in lb/ft and x in feet, or k in lb/in. and x in inches; in the first case, the work is obtained in ft-lb; in the second case, in in.-lb. We note that the work of the force **F** exerted by the spring on the body is *positive* when $x_2 < x_1$, that is, *when the spring is returning to its undeformed position.*

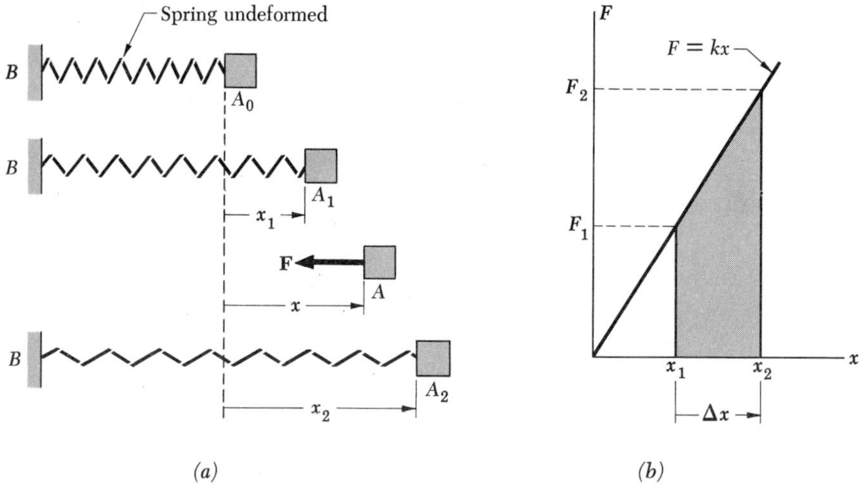

FIG. 10.12

Since Eq. (10.14) is the equation of a straight line of slope k passing through the origin, the work $U_{1\to 2}$ of **F** during the displacement from A_1 to A_2 may be obtained by evaluating the area of the trapezoid shown in Fig. 10.12*b*. This is done by computing the values F_1 and F_2 and multiplying the base Δx of the trapezoid by its mean height $\frac{1}{2}(F_1 + F_2)$. Since the work of the force **F** exerted by the spring is positive for a negative value of Δx, we write

$$U_{1\to 2} = -\tfrac{1}{2}(F_1 + F_2)\,\Delta x \tag{10.16}$$

Formula (10.16) is usually more convenient to use than (10.15) and affords fewer chances of confusing the units involved.

***10.6. Potential Energy.** Considering again the body of Fig. 10.11, we note from (10.13) that the work of the weight **W** during a finite displacement is obtained by subtracting the value of the function Wy corresponding to the second position of the body from its value corresponding to the first position. The work of **W** is thus independent of the actual path followed; it depends only upon the initial and final values of the function Wy. This function is called the *potential energy* of the body with respect to the *force of gravity* **W** and is denoted by V_g. We write

$$U_{1\to2} = (V_g)_1 - (V_g)_2 \qquad \text{with } V_g = Wy \quad (10.17)$$

We note that if $(V_g)_2 > (V_g)_1$, that is, *if the potential energy increases* during the displacement (as in the case considered here), *the work* $U_{1\to2}$ *is negative.* If, on the other hand, the work of **W** is positive, the potential energy decreases. Therefore, the potential energy V_g of the body provides a measure of *the work which may be done* by its weight **W**. Since only the *change* in potential energy, and not the actual value of V_g, is involved in formula (10.17), an arbitrary constant may be added to the expression obtained for V_g. In other words, the level from which the elevation y is measured may be chosen arbitrarily. Note that potential energy is expressed in the same units as work, i.e., in ft-lb or in in.-lb.

Considering now the body of Fig. 10.12*a*, we note from formula (10.15) that the work of the elastic force **F** is obtained by subtracting the value of the function $\frac{1}{2}kx^2$ corresponding to the second position of the body from its value corresponding to the first position. This function is denoted by V_e and is called the *potential energy* of the body with respect to the *elastic force* **F**. We write

$$U_{1\to2} = (V_e)_1 - (V_e)_2 \qquad \text{with } V_e = \tfrac{1}{2}kx^2 \quad (10.18)$$

and observe that, during the displacement considered, the work of the force **F** exerted by the spring on the body is negative and the potential energy V_e increases. We should note that the expression obtained for V_e is valid only if the deflection of the spring is measured from its undeformed position.

The concept of potential energy may be used when forces other than gravity forces and elastic forces are involved. It remains valid as long as the elementary work dU of the force considered is an *exact differential.* It is then possible to find a function V, called potential energy, such that

$$dU = -dV \qquad (10.19)$$

Integrating (10.19) over a finite displacement, we obtain the general formula

$$U_{1\to2} = V_1 - V_2 \qquad (10.20)$$

which expresses that *the work of the force is independent of the path followed and is equal to minus the change in potential energy.* A force which satisfies Eq. (10.20) is said to be a *conservative force.*†

† A detailed discussion of conservative forces is given in Sec. 13.6.

***10.7. Potential Energy and Equilibrium.** The application of the principle of virtual work is considerably simplified when the potential energy of a system is known. In the case of a virtual displacement, formula (10.19) becomes $\delta U = -\delta V$. Besides, if the position of the system is defined by a single independent variable θ we may write $\delta V = (dV/d\theta)\delta\theta$. Since $\delta\theta$ must be different from zero, the condition $\delta U = 0$ for the equilibrium of the system becomes

$$\frac{dV}{d\theta} = 0 \tag{10.21}$$

In terms of potential energy, the principle of virtual work states therefore that, *if a system is in equilibrium, the derivative of its total potential energy is zero.* If the position of the system depends upon several independent variables (the system is then said to possess *several degrees of freedom*), the partial derivatives of V with respect to each of the independent variables must be zero.

Consider, for example, a structure made of two members AC and CB and carrying a load $\mathbf{W}$ at C. The structure is supported by a pin at A and a roller at B, and a spring BD connects B to a fixed point D (Fig. 10.13a). The constant of the spring

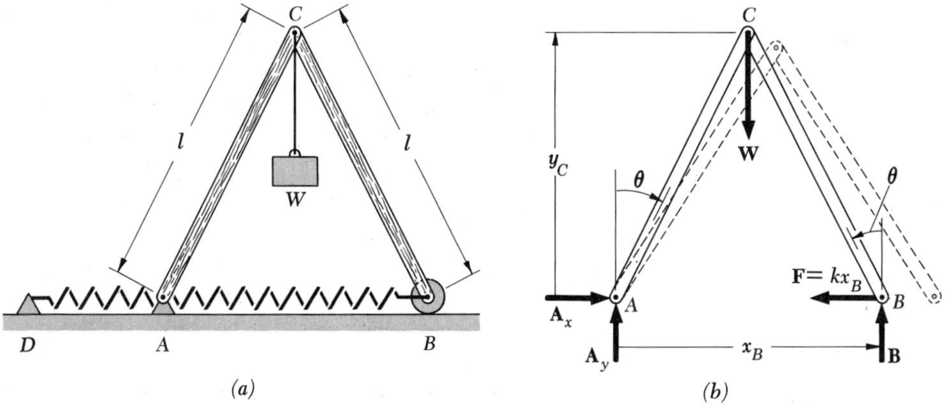

FIG. 10.13

is k, and it is assumed that the natural length of the spring is equal to AD, and thus that the spring is undeformed when B coincides with A. Neglecting the friction forces and the weight of the members, we find that the only forces which work during a displacement of the structure are the weight $\mathbf{W}$ and the force $\mathbf{F}$ exerted by the spring at point B. The total potential energy of the system will thus be obtained by adding the potential energy V_g corresponding to the gravity force **W** and the potential energy V_e corresponding to the elastic force **F**.

Choosing a coordinate system with origin at A and noting that the deflection of the spring, measured from its undeformed position, is $AB = x_B$, we write

$$V_e = \tfrac{1}{2}kx_B^2 \qquad V_g = Wy_C$$

Expressing the coordinates x_B and y_C in terms of the angle θ, we have

$$x_B = 2l \sin \theta \qquad y_C = l \cos \theta$$
$$V_e = \tfrac{1}{2}k(2l \sin \theta)^2 \qquad V_g = W(l \cos \theta)$$
$$V = V_e + V_g = 2kl^2 \sin^2 \theta + Wl \cos \theta \qquad (10.22)$$

The positions of equilibrium of the system are obtained by equating to zero the derivative of the potential energy V,

$$\frac{dV}{d\theta} = 4kl^2 \sin \theta \cos \theta - Wl \sin \theta = 0$$

$$\sin \theta = 0 \qquad 4kl \cos \theta - W = 0$$

There are therefore two positions of equilibrium, corresponding to the values $\theta = 0$ and $\theta = \cos^{-1}(W/4kl)$.†

***10.8. Stability of Equilibrium.** Consider the three uniform rods of length $2a$ and weight **W** shown in Fig. 10.14. While each rod is in equilibrium, there is an important difference between the three cases considered. Suppose that each rod is slightly disturbed from its position of equilibrium and then released: rod a will move back toward its original position, rod b will keep moving away from its original position, and rod c will remain in its new position. In case a, the equilibrium of the rod is said to be *stable;* in case b, the equilibrium is said to be *unstable;* and, in case c, to be *neutral.*

Recalling from Sec. 10.6 that the potential energy V_g with respect to gravity is equal to Wy, where y is the elevation of the point of application of **W** measured from an arbitrary level, we observe that the potential energy of rod a is minimum in the position of equilibrium considered, that the potential energy of rod b is maximum, and that the potential energy of rod c is constant. Equilibrium is thus *stable, unstable,* or *neutral* according to whether the potential energy is *minimum, maximum,* or *constant.*

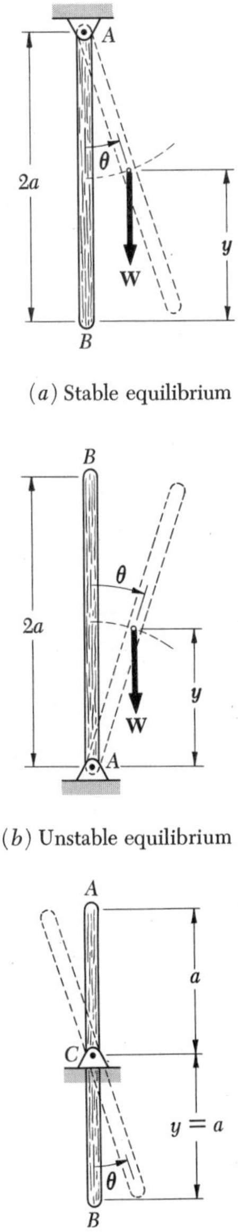

(a) Stable equilibrium

(b) Unstable equilibrium

(c) Neutral equilibrium

FIG. 10.14

† The second position does not exist if $W > 4kl$ (see Prob. 10.51 for a further discussion of the equilibrium of this system).

That the result obtained is quite general may be seen as follows: We first observe that a force always tends to do positive work and thus to decrease the potential energy of the system on which it is applied. Therefore, when a system is disturbed from its position of equilibrium, the forces acting on the system will tend to bring it back to its original position if V is minimum (Fig. 10.15*a*) and to move it farther away if V is maximum (Fig. 10.15*b*). If V is constant (Fig. 10.15*c*), the forces will not tend to move the system either way.

Recalling from calculus that a function is minimum or maximum according to whether its second derivative is positive or negative, we may summarize as follows the conditions for the equilibrium of a system with one degree of freedom (i.e., a system the position of which is defined by a single independent variable θ):

$$\frac{dV}{d\theta} = 0 \qquad \frac{d^2V}{d\theta^2} > 0: \quad \text{Stable equilibrium}$$

$$\frac{dV}{d\theta} = 0 \qquad \frac{d^2V}{d\theta^2} < 0: \quad \text{Unstable equilibrium} \tag{10.23}$$

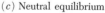

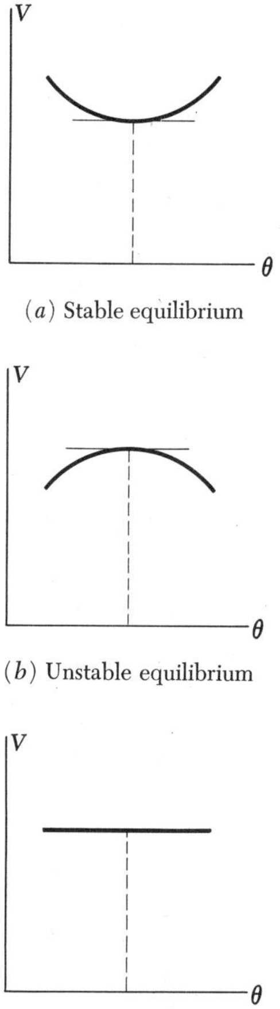

(*a*) Stable equilibrium

(*b*) Unstable equilibrium

(*c*) Neutral equilibrium

FIG. 10.15

If both the first and the second derivatives of V are zero, it is necessary to examine derivatives of a higher order to determine whether the equilibrium is stable, unstable, or neutral. The equilibrium will be neutral if all derivatives are zero, since the potential energy V is then a constant. The equilibrium will be stable if the first derivative found to be different from zero is of even order, and if that derivative is positive. In all other cases the equilibrium will be unstable.

If the system considered possesses *several degrees of freedom*, the potential energy V depends upon several variables and it is thus necessary to apply the theory of functions of several variables to determine whether V is minimum. It may be verified that a system with two degrees of freedom will be stable, and the corresponding potential energy $V(\theta_1, \theta_2)$ will be minimum, if the following relations are satisfied simultaneously:

$$\frac{\partial V}{\partial \theta_1} = \frac{\partial V}{\partial \theta_2} = 0$$

$$\left(\frac{\partial^2 V}{\partial \theta_1 \, \partial \theta_2}\right)^2 - \frac{\partial^2 V}{\partial \theta_1^2} \frac{\partial^2 V}{\partial \theta_2^2} < 0 \tag{10.24}$$

$$\frac{\partial^2 V}{\partial \theta_1^2} > 0 \qquad \text{or} \qquad \frac{\partial^2 V}{\partial \theta_2^2} > 0$$

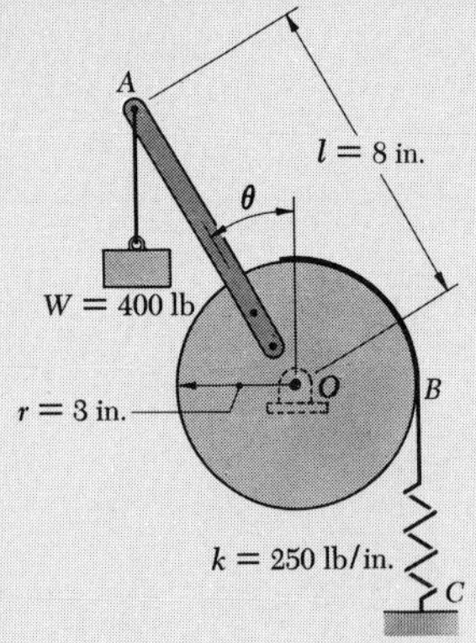

SAMPLE PROBLEM 10.4

A 400-lb weight is attached to the lever AO as shown. The constant of the spring BC is $k = 250$ lb/in., and the spring is unstretched when $\theta = 0$. Determine the position or positions of equilibrium, and state in each case whether the equilibrium is stable, unstable, or neutral.

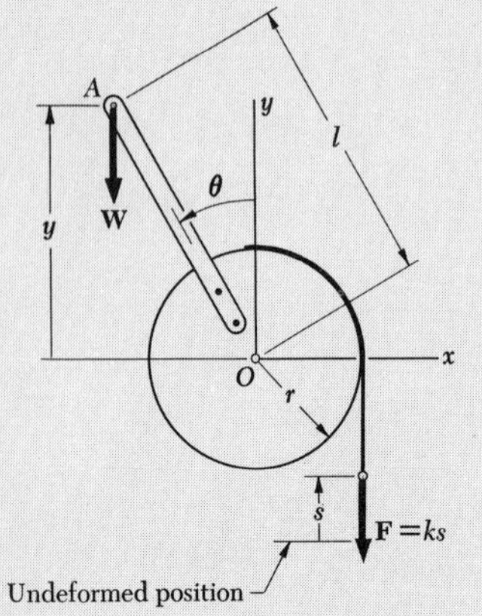

Potential Energy. Denoting by s the deflection of the spring from its undeformed position and placing the origin of coordinates at O, the potential energy of the system is

$$V_e = \tfrac{1}{2}ks^2 \qquad V_g = Wy$$

Measuring θ in radians, we have

$$s = r\theta \qquad y = l\cos\theta$$
$$V_e = \tfrac{1}{2}kr^2\theta^2 \qquad V_g = Wl\cos\theta$$
$$V = V_e + V_g = \tfrac{1}{2}kr^2\theta^2 + Wl\cos\theta$$

Positions of Equilibrium. Setting $dV/d\theta = 0$, we write

$$\frac{dV}{d\theta} = kr^2\theta - Wl\sin\theta = 0$$

$$\sin\theta = \frac{kr^2}{Wl}\theta$$

Substituting the given data, we obtain

$$\sin\theta = \frac{(250\text{ lb/in.})(3\text{ in.})^2}{(400\text{ lb})(8\text{ in.})}\theta \qquad \sin\theta = 0.703\theta$$

Solving by trial and error for θ, we find

$$\theta = 0 \qquad \text{and} \qquad \theta = 80.4° \quad ◀$$

Stability of Equilibrium. The second derivative of the potential energy V with respect to θ is

$$\frac{d^2V}{d\theta^2} = kr^2 - Wl\cos\theta = (250\text{ lb/in.})(3\text{ in.})^2 - (400\text{ lb})(8\text{ in.})\cos\theta$$

$$= 2{,}250 - 3{,}200\cos\theta$$

For $\theta = 0$: $\qquad \dfrac{d^2V}{d\theta^2} = 2{,}250 - 3{,}200\cos 0° = -950 < 0$

The equilibrium is unstable for $\theta = 0°$. ◀

For $\theta = 80.4°$: $\qquad \dfrac{d^2V}{d\theta^2} = 2{,}250 - 3{,}200\cos 80.4° = +1{,}716 > 0$

The equilibrium is stable for $\theta = 80.4°$. ◀

PROBLEMS

10.41. Show that the position of equilibrium is neutral in Probs. 10.1 and 10.3.

10.42. Show that the position of equilibrium is neutral in Prob. 10.4.

10.43. Two uniform rods, each of weight W, are attached to gears of equal radii as shown. Determine the positions of equilibrium of the system and state in each case whether the equilibrium is stable, unstable, or neutral.

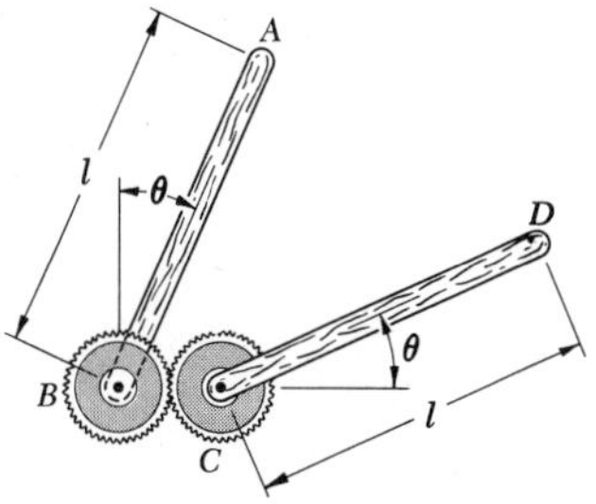

FIG. P 10.43 AND P 10.44

10.44. A vertical force $\mathbf{P}$ of magnitude 10 lb is applied to rod CD at D. Knowing that the uniform rods AB and CD weigh 5 lb each, determine the positions of equilibrium of the system and state in each case whether the equilibrium is stable, unstable, or neutral.

10.45. Using the method of Sec. 10.7, solve Prob. 10.27. Determine whether the equilibrium is stable, unstable, or neutral. (*Hint.* The potential energy corresponding to the couple exerted by a torsion spring is $\frac{1}{2}K\theta^2$, where K is the torsional spring constant and θ is the angle of twist.)

10.46. In Prob. 10.28 determine whether each of the positions of equilibrium is stable, unstable, or neutral. (See hint of Prob. 10.45.)

10.47. Using the method of Sec. 10.7, solve Prob. 10.26. Determine whether the equilibrium is stable, unstable, or neutral.

10.48. (*a*) Obtain an equation defining the angle θ corresponding to the equilibrium position. (*b*) Determine the angle θ corresponding to the equilibrium position if $W = P$.

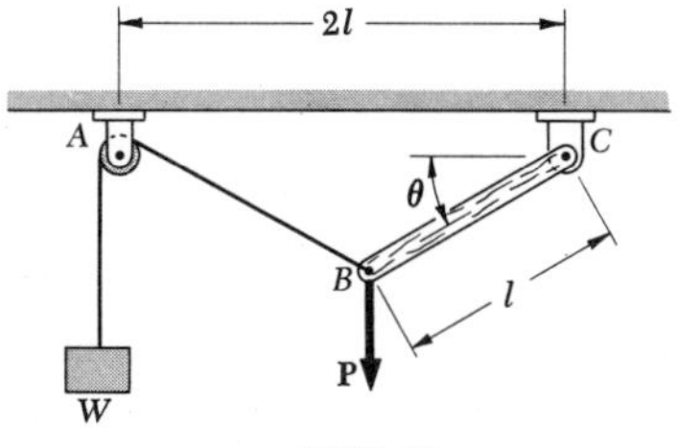

FIG. P 10.48

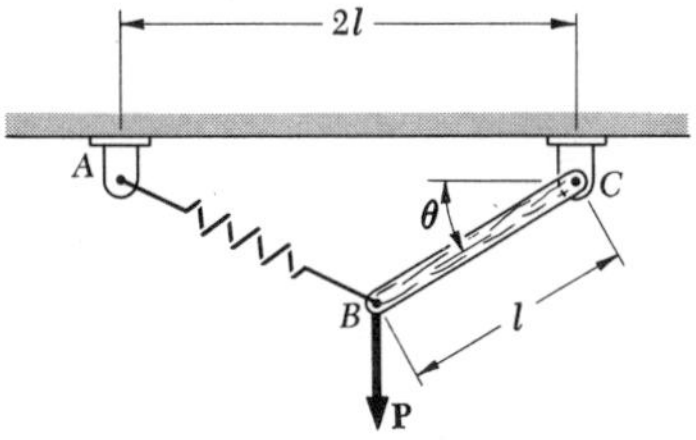

FIG. P 10.49

10.49. Knowing that the spring AB is of constant k and is unstretched when $\theta = 0$, (*a*) obtain an equation defining the angle θ corresponding to the equilibrium position, (*b*) determine the value of θ corresponding to the equilibrium position if $P = kl$.

10.50. For the mechanism considered in Prob. 10.25, show that for any finite values of W and k there is only one equilibrium position. Further show that the equilibrium position is stable.

10.51. In Sec. 10.7, two positions of equilibrium were obtained for the system shown in Fig. 10.13, namely, $\theta = 0$ and $\theta = \cos^{-1}(W/4kl)$. Show that (*a*) if $W < 4kl$ the equilibrium is stable in the first position ($\theta = 0$) and unstable in the second, (*b*) if $W = 4kl$, the two positions coincide and the equilibrium is unstable, (*c*) if $W > 4kl$, the equilibrium is unstable in the first position ($\theta = 0$) and the second position does not exist. (*Note.* It is assumed that the system must deform as shown and that the system cannot rotate as a single rigid body about A when A and B coincide.)

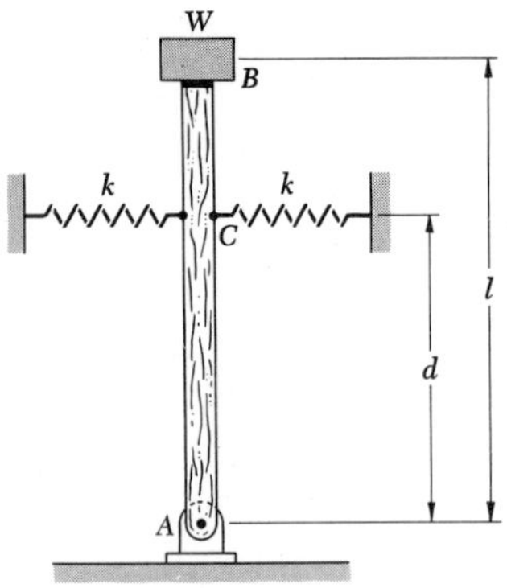

FIG. P 10.53, P 10.54, AND P 10.55

10.52. For the mechanism of Sample Prob. 10.4, determine the largest vertical load W for which stable equilibrium exists when lever AO is vertical. Express the result in terms of l, r, and k.

10.53. The rod AB is attached to a hinge at A and to two springs each of constant k. If $l = 20$ in., $d = 15$ in., and $W = 750$ lb, determine the smallest value of k for which the equilibrium of rod AB is stable in the position shown. Each spring can act in either tension or compression.

10.54. If $W = 100$ lb, $l = 30$ in., and the constant of each spring is $k = 12$ lb/in., determine the smallest distance d for which the equilibrium of the rod AB is stable in the position shown. Each spring can act in either tension or compression.

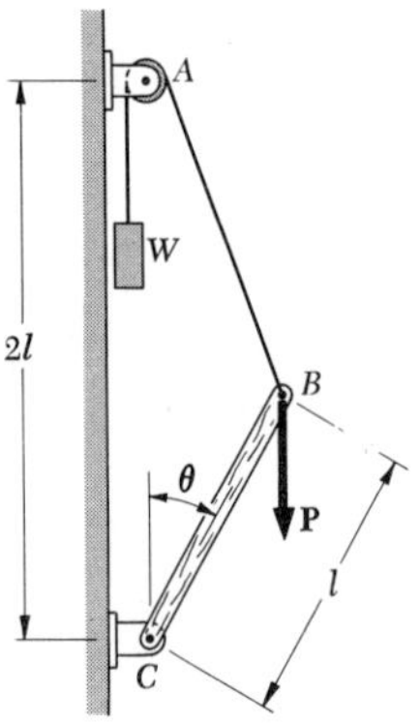

FIG. P 10.56

10.55. If $d = 16$ in., $l = 24$ in., and the constant of each spring is $k = 50$ lb/in., determine the largest load W for which the equilibrium of the rod AB is stable in the position shown. Each spring can act in either tension or compression.

***10.56.** Determine (*a*) the largest ratio P/W for which $\theta = 0$ is a stable position of equilibrium, (*b*) the smallest ratio P/W for which $\theta = 180°$ is a stable position of equilibrium, (*c*) the range of values of P/W for which both $\theta = 0$ and $\theta = 180°$ are stable positions of equilibrium.

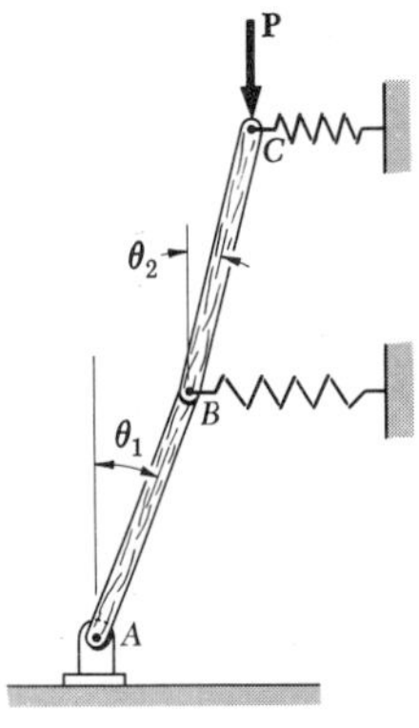

FIG. P 10.58

***10.57.** In Prob. 10.56 show that the value of θ defined by the equation $(5 - 4\cos\theta)^{1/2} = 2W/P$ corresponds to a position of equilibrium. Further show that this position of equilibrium is always unstable.

***10.58.** Two bars AB and BC, each of length l and of negligible weight, are attached to springs each of constant k. The springs are undeformed and the system is in equilibrium when $\theta_1 = \theta_2 = 0$. Determine the largest value of the force **P** for which this equilibrium position is stable.

*10.59. Two rods, of negligible weight, are attached to drums of radius r which are connected by a belt and a spring of constant k. The spring is undeformed when $\theta_1 = \theta_2 = 0$. Determine the largest value of the force **P** for which the equilibrium position $\theta_1 = \theta_2 = 0$ is stable.

*10.60. Solve Prob. 10.59 knowing that $k = 20$ lb/in., $r = 3$ in., $l = 6$ in., and $W = 10$ lb.

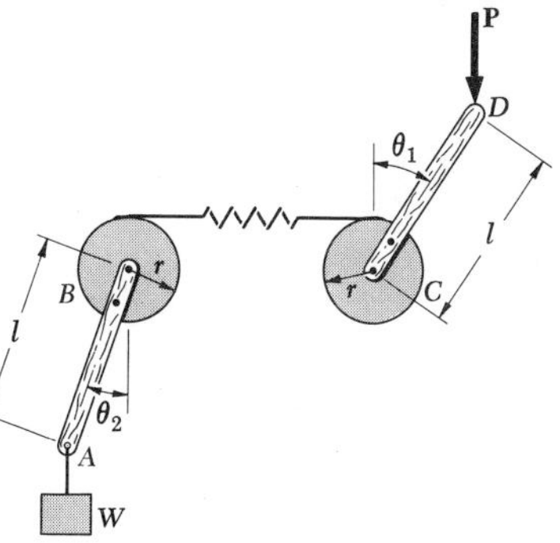

FIG. P 10.59

REVIEW PROBLEMS

10.61. Two bars AB and BC are attached to a single spring of constant k which is unstretched when the bars are vertical. Determine the largest value of the force **P** for which the equilibrium of the system is stable in the position shown.

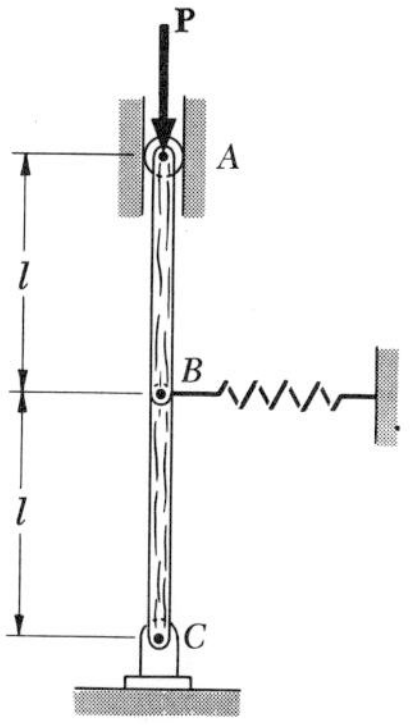

FIG. P 10.61

10.62. Solve parts b and c of Prob. 6.118 by the method of virtual work.

10.63. Collar B may slide along rod OC and is attached by a pin to a block which may slide in the vertical slot. Derive an expression for the magnitude of the couple **M** required to maintain equilibrium.

10.64. Determine the value of θ corresponding to the equilibrium position of rod OC when $R = 10$ in., $P = 50$ lb, and $M = 2{,}000$ lb-in.

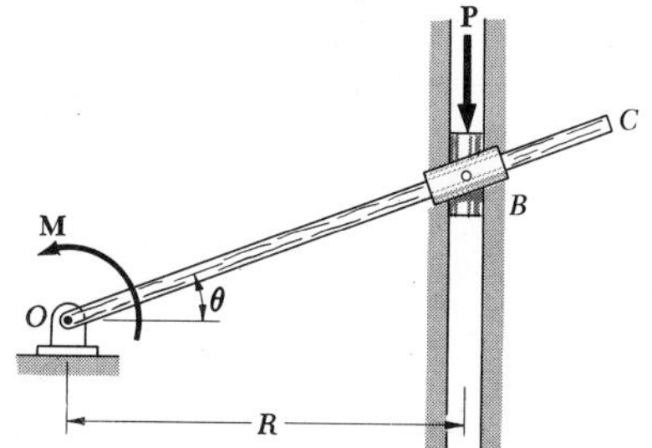

FIG. P 10.63 AND P 10.64

10.65. A spring AB of constant k is attached to two identical gears as shown. A uniform bar CD of weight W is supported by cords wrapped around drums of radius b which are attached to the gears. If the spring is undeformed when $\theta = 0$, obtain an equation defining the angle θ corresponding to the equilibrium position.

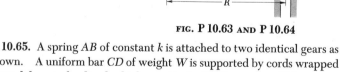

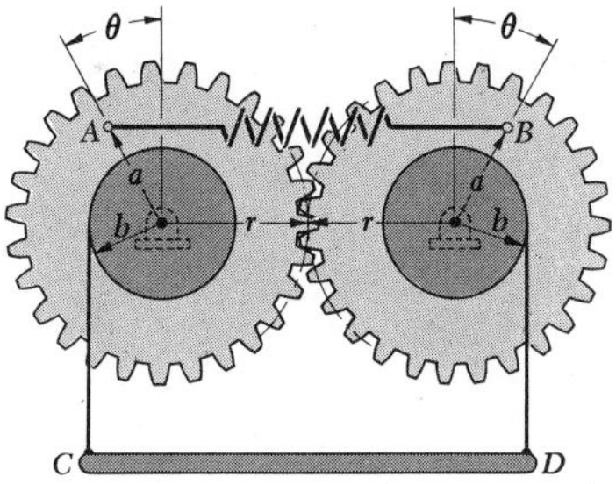

FIG. P 10.65

10.66. For the mechanism of Prob. 10.65 the following numerical values are given: $k = 50$ lb/in., $a = 4$ in., $b = 3$ in., $r = 6$ in., and $W = 200$ lb. Determine the values of θ corresponding to equilibrium positions and state in each case whether the equilibrium is stable, unstable, or neutral.

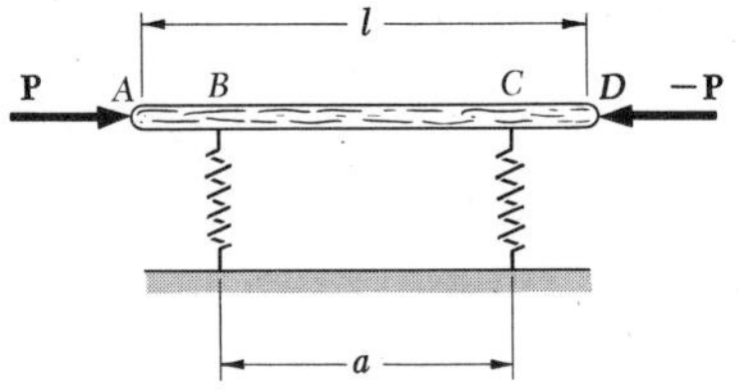

FIG. P 10.68

10.67. Solve Prob. 6.132 by the method of virtual work.

10.68. The horizontal bar AD is attached to two springs of constant k and is in equilibrium in the position shown. Knowing that the springs are equidistant from the center of the bar, determine the largest value of the magnitude P of the two equal and opposite *horizontal* forces **P** and −**P** for which the equilibrium position shown is stable.

10.69. Solve Prob. 10.68 assuming that the distance AB is twice as large as the distance CD.

10.70. Solve Prob. 6.77 by the method of virtual work.

10.71. Derive an expression for the magnitude P of the two equal and opposite forces **P** and −**P** required to maintain the equilibrium of the mechanism shown.

10.72. Determine the value of θ corresponding to the equilibrium position of the mechanism shown when $P = W$.

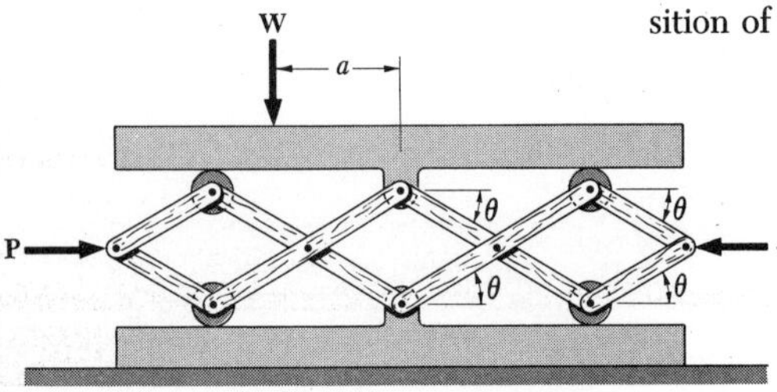

FIG. P 10.71 AND P 10.72

DYNAMICS

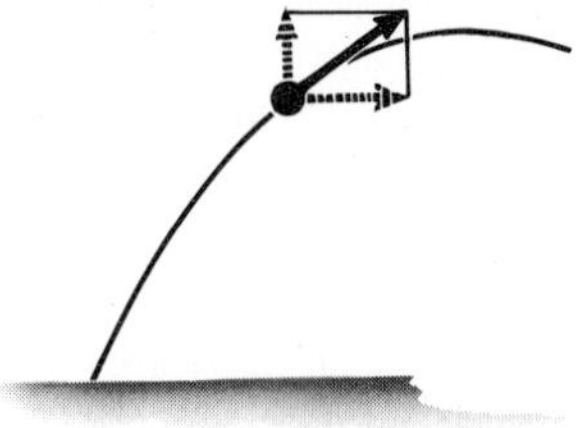

11. KINEMATICS OF PARTICLES

11.1. Introduction to Dynamics. Chapters 1 to 10 were devoted to *statics,* i.e., to the analysis of bodies at rest. We shall now begin the study of *dynamics,* which is the part of mechanics dealing with the analysis of bodies in motion.

While the study of statics goes back to the time of the Greek philosophers, the first significant contribution to dynamics was made by Galileo (1564–1642). His experiments on uniformly accelerated bodies led Newton (1642–1727) to formulate his fundamental laws of motion.

Dynamics is divided into two parts: (1) *Kinematics,* which is the study of the geometry of motion; kinematics is used to relate displacement, velocity, acceleration, and time, without reference to the cause of the motion. (2) *Kinetics,* which is the study of the relation existing between the forces acting on a body, the mass of the body, and the motion of the body; kinetics is used to predict the motion caused by given forces or to determine the forces required to produce a given motion.

Chapters 11 to 14 are devoted to the *dynamics of particles,* and Chap. 11 more particularly to the *kinematics of particles.* The use of the word particles does not imply that we shall restrict our study to that of small corpuscles; it rather indicates that in these first chapters we shall study the motion of bodies—possibly as large as cars, rockets, or airplanes—without regard to their size. By saying that the bodies are analyzed as particles, we mean that only their motion as an entire unit will be considered; any rotation about their own mass center will be neglected. There are cases, however, when such a rotation is not negligible; the bodies, then, may not be considered as particles. The analysis of such motions will be carried out in later chapters dealing with the *dynamics of rigid bodies.*

RECTILINEAR MOTION OF PARTICLES

11.2. Position, Velocity, and Acceleration. A particle moving along a straight line is said to be in *rectilinear motion.* At any given instant t, the particle will occupy a certain position on the straight line. To define the position P of the particle, we choose a fixed origin O on the straight line and a positive direction along the line. We measure the distance s from O to P and record it with a plus or minus sign, according to whether P is reached from O by moving along the line in the positive or the negative direction. The distance s, with the appropriate sign, completely defines the position of the particle; it is called the *position coordinate* of the particle considered. For example, the position coordinate corresponding to P in Fig. 11.1*a* is $s = +5$ ft, while the coordinate corresponding to P' in Fig. 11.1*b* is $s' = -2$ ft.

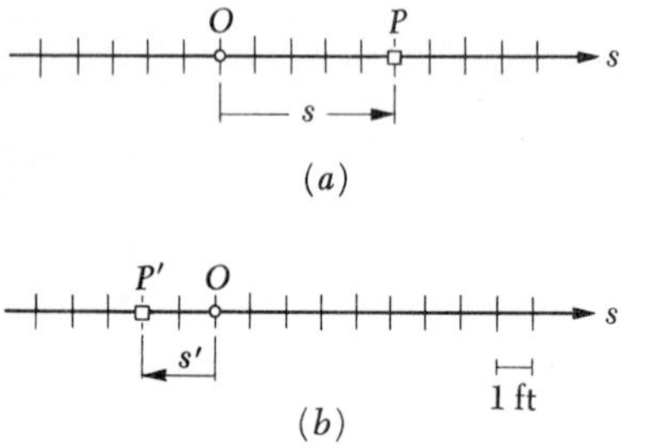

FIG. 11.1

When the position coordinate s of a particle is known for every value of the time t, we say that the motion of the particle is known. The "timetable" of the motion may be given in the form of an equation in s and t, such as $s = 6t^2 - t^3$, or in the form of a graph of s vs. t as shown in Fig. 11.6. The units most generally used to measure s and t are, respectively, feet and seconds.

Consider the position P occupied by the particle at time t and the corresponding coordinate s (Fig. 11.2). Consider also the position P' occupied by the particle at a later time $t + \Delta t$; the position coordinate of P' may be obtained by adding to the coordinate s of P the small displacement Δs, which will be positive or negative according to whether P' is to the right or to the left of P. The *average velocity* of the particle over the time interval Δt is defined as the quotient of the displacement Δs and the time interval Δt,

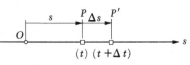

FIG. 11.2

$$\text{Average velocity} = \frac{\Delta s}{\Delta t}$$

If Δs is expressed in feet and Δt in seconds, the average velocity will be expressed in ft/sec.

The *instantaneous velocity* v of the particle at the instant t is obtained from the average velocity by choosing shorter and shorter time intervals Δt and displacements Δs,

$$\text{Instantaneous velocity} = v = \lim_{\Delta t \to 0} \frac{\Delta s}{\Delta t}$$

The instantaneous velocity will also be expressed in ft/sec. Observing that the limit of the quotient is equal, by definition, to the derivative of s with respect to t, we write

$$v = \frac{ds}{dt} \tag{11.1}$$

The velocity v is represented by an algebraic number which may be positive or negative.† A positive value of v indicates that s increases, i.e., that the particle moves in the positive direction (Fig. 11.3*a*); a negative value of v indicates that s decreases, i.e., that the particle moves in the negative direction (Fig. 11.3*b*). The magnitude of v is known as the *speed* of the particle.

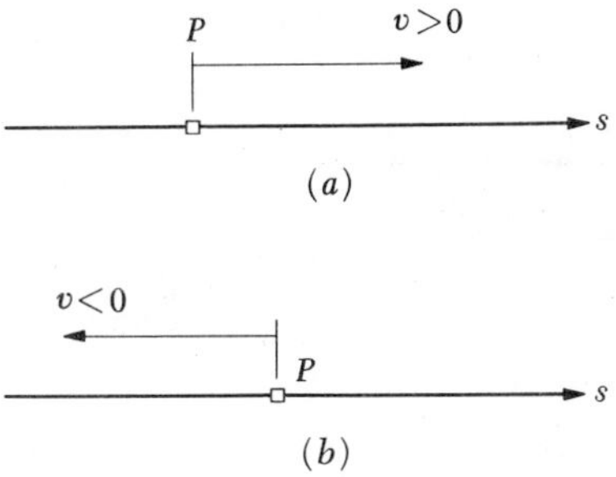

FIG. 11.3

Consider the velocity v of the particle at time t and also its velocity $v + \Delta v$ at a later time $t + \Delta t$ (Fig. 11.4). The *average acceleration* of the particle over the time interval Δt is defined as the quotient of Δv and Δt,

$$\text{Average acceleration} = \frac{\Delta v}{\Delta t}$$

If Δv is expressed in ft/sec and Δt in seconds, the average acceleration will be expressed in ft/sec^2.

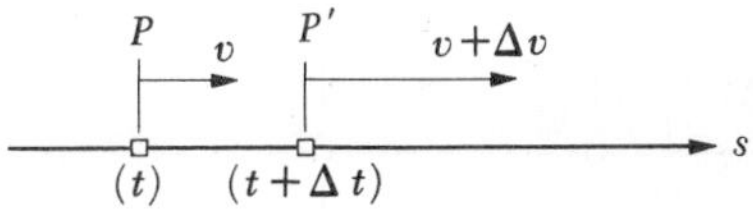

FIG. 11.4

The *instantaneous acceleration* a of the particle at the instant t is obtained from the average acceleration by choosing smaller and smaller values for Δt and Δv,

$$\text{Instantaneous acceleration} = a = \lim_{\Delta t \to 0} \frac{\Delta v}{\Delta t}$$

The instantaneous acceleration will also be expressed in ft/sec^2. The limit of the quotient is by definition the derivative of v with respect to t and measures the rate of change of the velocity. We write

$$a = \frac{dv}{dt} \tag{11.2}$$

or, substituting for v from (11.1),

$$a = \frac{d^2s}{dt^2} \tag{11.3}$$

The acceleration a is represented by an algebraic number which

† As we shall see in Sec. 11.9, the velocity is actually a vector quantity. However, since we are considering here the rectilinear motion of a particle, where the velocity of the particle has a known and fixed direction, we need only specify the sense and magnitude of the velocity; this may be conveniently done by using a scalar quantity with a plus or minus sign. The same remark will apply to the acceleration of a particle in rectilinear motion.

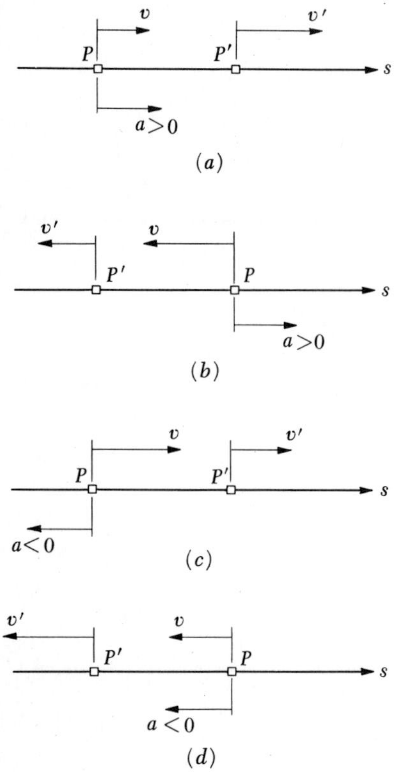

FIG. 11.5

may be positive or negative.† A positive value of a indicates that the velocity (i.e., the algebraic number v) increases. This may mean that the particle is moving faster in the positive direction (Fig. 11.5*a*) or that it is moving more slowly in the negative direction (Fig. 11.5*b*); in both cases, Δv is positive. A negative value of a indicates that the velocity decreases; either the particle is moving more slowly in the positive direction (Fig. 11.5*c*), or it is moving faster in the negative direction (Fig. 11.5*d*).

The term *deceleration* is sometimes used to refer to a when the speed of the particle (i.e., the magnitude of v) decreases; the particle is then moving more slowly. For example, the particle of Fig. 11.5 is decelerated in parts b and c, while it is truly accelerated (i.e., moves faster) in parts a and d.

Another expression may be obtained for the acceleration by eliminating the differential dt in Eqs. (11.1) and (11.2). Solving (11.1) for dt, we obtain $dt = ds/v$; carrying into (11.2), we write

$$a = v\frac{dv}{ds} \tag{11.4}$$

Example. Consider a particle moving in a straight line, and assume that its position is defined by the equation

$$s = 6t^2 - t^3$$

where t is expressed in seconds and s in feet. The velocity v at any time t is obtained by differentiating s with respect to t,

$$v = \frac{ds}{dt} = 12t - 3t^2$$

The acceleration a is obtained by differentiating again with respect to t,

$$a = \frac{dv}{dt} = 12 - 6t$$

The position coordinate, the velocity, and the acceleration have been plotted against t in Fig. 11.6. The curves obtained are known as *motion curves.* It should be kept in mind, however, that the particle does not move along any of these curves; the particle moves in a straight line. Since the derivative of a function measures the slope of the corresponding curve, the slope of the s–t curve at any given time is equal to the value of v at that time and the slope of the v–t curve is equal to the value of a. Since $a = 0$ at $t = 2$ sec, the slope of the v–t curve must be zero at $t = 2$ sec; the velocity reaches a maximum at this in-

† See footnote, page 387.

stant. Also, since $v = 0$ at $t = 0$ and at $t = 4$ sec, the tangent to the s–t curve must be horizontal for both of these values of t.

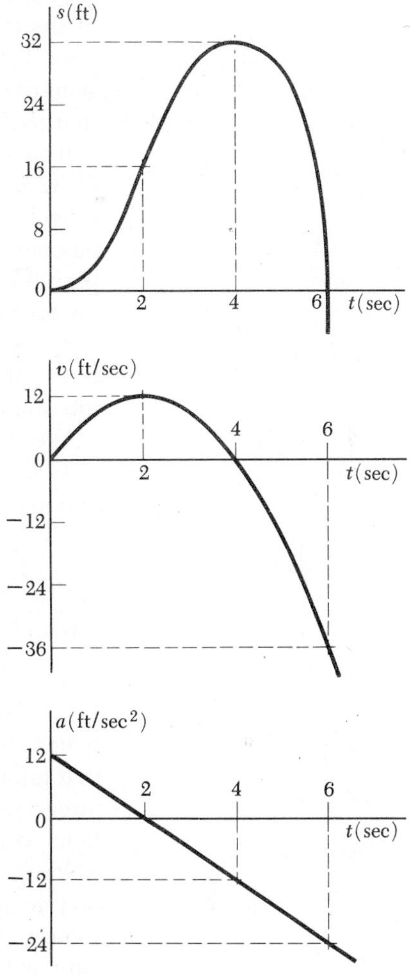

FIG. 11.6

A study of the three motion curves of Fig. 11.6 shows that the motion of the particle from $t = 0$ to $t = \infty$ may be divided into four phases:

1. The particle starts from the origin, $s = 0$, with no velocity but with a positive acceleration. Under this acceleration, the particle gains a positive velocity and moves in the positive direction. From $t = 0$ to $t = 2$ sec, s, v, and a are all positive.

2. At $t = 2$ sec, the acceleration is zero; the velocity has reached its maximum value. From $t = 2$ sec to $t = 4$ sec, v is positive, but a is negative; the particle still moves in the positive direction but more and more slowly; the particle is decelerated.

3. At $t = 4$ sec, the velocity is zero; the position coordinate s has reached its maximum value. From then on, both v and a are negative; the particle is accelerated and moves in the negative direction with increasing speed.

4. At $t = 6$ sec, the particle passes through the origin; its coordinate s is then zero, while the total distance traveled since the beginning of the motion is 64 ft. For values of t larger than 6 sec, s, v, and a will all be negative. The particle keeps moving in the negative direction, away from O, faster and faster.

11.3. Determination of the Motion of a Particle. We saw in the preceding section that the motion of a particle is said to be known if the position of the particle is known for every value of the time t. In practice, however, a motion is seldom defined by a relation between s and t. More often, the conditions of the motion will be specified by the type of acceleration that the particle possesses. For example, a freely falling body will have a constant acceleration, directed downward and equal to 32.2 ft/sec^2; a mass attached to a spring which has been stretched will have an acceleration proportional to the instantaneous elongation of the spring measured from the equilibrium position; etc. In general, the acceleration of the particle may be expressed as a function of one or several of the variables s, v, and t. In order to determine the position coordinate s in terms of t, it will thus be necessary to perform two successive integrations.

We shall consider three common classes of motion:

1. $a = f(t)$. *The Acceleration Is a Given Function of t.* Solving (11.2) for dv and substituting $f(t)$ for a, we write

$$dv = a\,dt$$
$$dv = f(t)\,dt$$

Integrating both members, we obtain the equation

$$\int dv = \int f(t)\,dt$$

which defines v in terms of t. It should be noted, however, that an arbitrary constant will be introduced as a result of the integration. This is due to the fact that there are many motions which correspond to the given acceleration $a = f(t)$. In order to uniquely define the motion of the particle, it is necessary to specify the *initial conditions* of the motion, i.e., the value v_0 of the velocity and the value s_0 of the position coordinate at $t = 0$. Replacing the indefinite integrals by *definite integrals* with lower limits corresponding to the initial conditions $t = 0$ and $v = v_0$ and upper limits corresponding to $t = t$ and $v = v$, we write

$$\int_{v_0}^{v} dv = \int_0^t f(t)\,dt$$

$$v - v_0 = \int_0^t f(t)\,dt$$

which yields v in terms of t.

We shall now solve (11.1) for ds,

$$ds = v\,dt$$

and substitute for v the expression just obtained. Both members are then integrated, the left-hand member with respect to s from $s = s_0$ to $s = s$, and the right-hand member with respect to t from $t = 0$ to $t = t$. The position coordinate s is thus obtained in terms of t; the motion is completely determined.

Two important particular cases will be studied in greater detail in Secs. 11.4 and 11.5, the case when $a = 0$, corresponding to a *uniform motion*, and the case when $a =$ constant, corresponding to a *uniformly accelerated motion.*

2. $a = f(s)$. *The Acceleration Is a Given Function of s.* Rearranging Eq. (11.4) and substituting $f(s)$ for a, we write

$$v\,dv = a\,ds$$
$$v\,dv = f(s)\,ds$$

Since each member contains only one variable, we may integrate the equation. Denoting again by v_0 and s_0, respectively, the initial values of the velocity and of the position coordinate, we obtain

$$\int_{v_0}^{v} v\,dv = \int_{s_0}^{s} f(s)\,ds$$
$$\tfrac{1}{2}v^2 - \tfrac{1}{2}v_0^2 = \int_{s_0}^{s} f(s)\,ds$$

which yields v in terms of s. We now solve (11.1) for dt,

$$dt = \frac{ds}{v}$$

and substitute for v the expression just obtained. Both members may be integrated, and the desired relation between s and t is obtained.

3. $a = f(v)$. *The Acceleration Is a Given Function of v.* We may then substitute $f(v)$ for a either in (11.2) or in (11.4) to obtain either of the following relations:

$$f(v) = \frac{dv}{dt} \qquad\qquad f(v) = v\frac{dv}{ds}$$
$$dt = \frac{dv}{f(v)} \qquad\qquad ds = \frac{v\,dv}{f(v)}$$

Integration of the first equation will yield a relation between v and t; integration of the second equation will yield a relation between v and s. Either of these relations may be used in conjunction with Eq. (11.1) to obtain the relation between s and t which characterizes the motion of the particle.

SAMPLE PROBLEM 11.1

The position of a particle which moves along a straight line is defined by the relation $s = t^3 - 6t^2 - 15t + 40$, where s is expressed in feet and t in seconds. Determine (*a*) the time at which the velocity will be zero, (*b*) the position and distance traveled by the particle at that time, (*c*) the acceleration of the particle at that time, (*d*) the distance traveled by the particle from $t = 4$ sec to $t = 6$ sec.

Solution. The equations of motion are

$$s = t^3 - 6t^2 - 15t + 40 \tag{1}$$

$$v = \frac{ds}{dt} = 3t^2 - 12t - 15 \tag{2}$$

$$a = \frac{dv}{dt} = 6t - 12 \tag{3}$$

a. **Time at Which $v = 0$.** We make $v = 0$ in (2),

$$3t^2 - 12t - 15 = 0 \qquad t = -1 \text{ sec} \qquad \text{and} \qquad t = +5 \text{ sec} \blacktriangleleft$$

Only the root $t = +5$ sec corresponds to a time after the motion has begun. For $t < 5$ sec, $v < 0$, the particle moves in the negative direction; for $t > 5$ sec, $v > 0$, the particle moves in the positive direction.

b. **Position and Distance Traveled When $v = 0$.** Carrying $t = +5$ sec into (1), we have

$$s_5 = (5)^3 - (6)(5)^2 - (15)(5) + 40 \qquad s_5 = -60 \text{ ft} \blacktriangleleft$$

The initial position at $t = 0$ was $s_0 = +40$ ft. Since $v \neq 0$ during the interval $t = 0$ to $t = 5$ sec, we have

$$\text{Distance traveled} = s_5 - s_0 = -60 \text{ ft} - 40 \text{ ft} = -100 \text{ ft}$$
$$= 100 \text{ ft in the negative direction} \blacktriangleleft$$

c. **Acceleration When $v = 0$.** We carry $t = +5$ sec into (3):

$$a_5 = (6)(5) - 12 \qquad a_5 = +18 \text{ ft/sec}^2 \blacktriangleleft$$

d. **Distance Traveled from $t = 4$ sec to $t = 6$ sec.** Since the particle moves in the negative direction from $t = 4$ sec to $t = 5$ sec and in the positive direction from $t = 5$ sec to $t = 6$ sec, we shall compute separately the distance traveled during each of these time intervals.

From $t = 4$ sec to $t = 5$ sec: $\quad s_5 = -60$ ft

$$s_4 = (4)^3 - (6)(4)^2 - (15)(4) + 40 = -52 \text{ ft}$$

$$\text{Distance traveled} = s_5 - s_4 = -60 \text{ ft} - (-52 \text{ ft}) = -8 \text{ ft}$$
$$= 8 \text{ ft in the negative direction}$$

From $t = 5$ sec to $t = 6$ sec: $\quad s_5 = -60$ ft

$$s_6 = (6)^3 - (6)(6)^2 - (15)(6) + 40 = -50 \text{ ft}$$

$$\text{Distance traveled} = s_6 - s_5 = -50 \text{ ft} - (-60 \text{ ft}) = +10 \text{ ft}$$
$$= 10 \text{ ft in the positive direction}$$

Total distance traveled from $t = 4$ sec to $t = 6$ sec is

$$8 \text{ ft} + 10 \text{ ft} = 18 \text{ ft} \blacktriangleleft$$

SAMPLE PROBLEM 11.2

A ball is thrown from the top of a tower 60 ft high, with a velocity of 40 ft/sec directed vertically upward. Knowing that the acceleration of the ball is constant and equal to 32.2 ft/sec^2 downward, determine (*a*) the velocity and elevation of the ball above the ground at any time t, (*b*) the highest elevation reached by the ball and the corresponding value of t, (*c*) the time when the ball will hit the ground and the corresponding velocity. Draw the v–t and s–t curves.

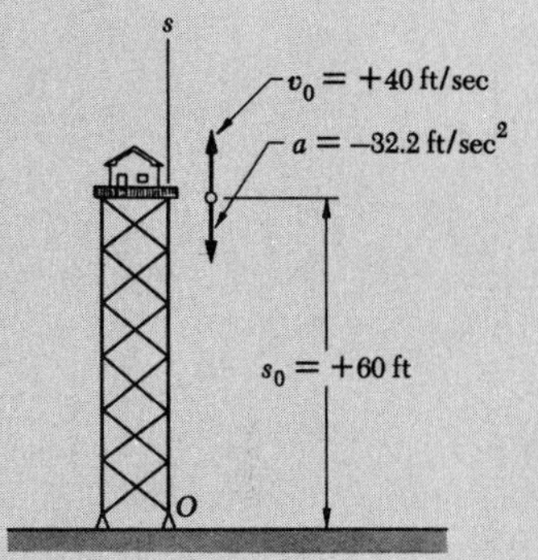

a. **Velocity and Elevation.** The s axis measuring the position coordinate (or elevation) is chosen with its origin O on the ground and its positive sense upward. The value of the acceleration and the initial values of v and s are as indicated. Substituting for a in $a = dv/dt$ and noting that, at $t = 0$, $v_0 = +40$ ft/sec, we have

$$\frac{dv}{dt} = a = -32.2$$

$$\int_{v_0=40}^{v} dv = -\int_0^t 32.2\, dt$$

$$[v]_{40}^{v} = -[32.2t]_0^t$$

$$v - 40 = -32.2t$$

$$v = 40 - 32.2t \quad (1)$$ ◄

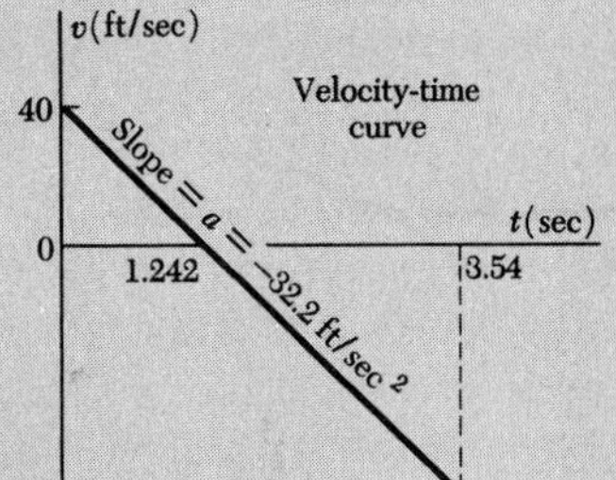

Substituting for v in $v = ds/dt$ and noting that, at $t = 0$, $s_0 = 60$ ft, we have

$$\frac{ds}{dt} = v = 40 - 32.2t$$

$$\int_{s_0=60}^{s} ds = \int_0^t (40 - 32.2t)\, dt$$

$$[s]_{60}^{s} = [40t - 16.1t^2]_0^t$$

$$s - 60 = 40t - 16.1t^2$$

$$s = 60 + 40t - 16.1t^2 \quad (2)$$ ◄

b. **Highest Elevation.** When the ball reaches its highest elevation, we have $v = 0$. Substituting into (1), we obtain

$$40 - 32.2t = 0 \qquad t = 1.242 \text{ sec}$$ ◄

Carrying $t = 1.242$ sec into (2), we have

$$s = 60 + (40)(1.242) - (16.1)(1.242)^2 \qquad s = 84.8 \text{ ft}$$ ◄

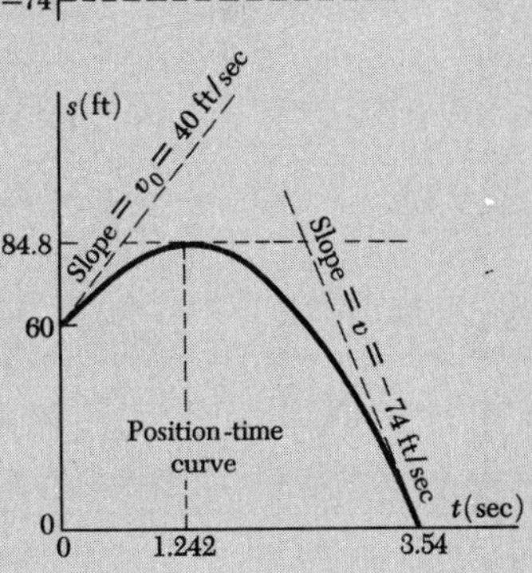

c. **Ball Hits the Ground.** When the ball hits the ground, we have $s = 0$. Substituting into (2), we obtain

$$60 + 40t - 16.1t^2 = 0 \qquad t = -1.06 \text{ sec} \quad \text{and} \quad t = +3.54 \text{ sec}$$ ◄

Only the root $t = +3.54$ sec corresponds to a time after the motion has begun. Carrying this value of t into (1), we have

$$v = 40 - (32.2)(3.54) = -74.0 \text{ ft/sec}$$

$$v = 74.0 \text{ ft/sec} \downarrow$$ ◄

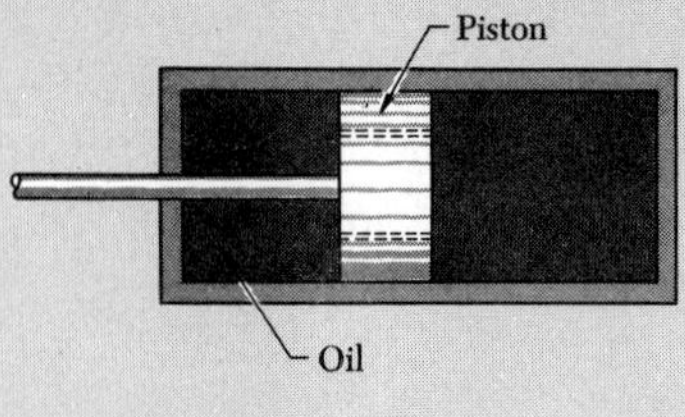

SAMPLE PROBLEM 11.3

The brake mechanism used to reduce recoil in certain types of guns consists essentially of a piston which is attached to the barrel and may move in a fixed cylinder filled with oil. As the barrel recoils with an initial velocity v_0, the piston moves and oil is forced through orifices in the piston, causing the piston and the barrel to decelerate at a rate proportional to their velocity, i.e., $a = -kv$. Express (*a*) v in terms of t, (*b*) s in terms of t, (*c*) v in terms of s. Draw the corresponding motion curves.

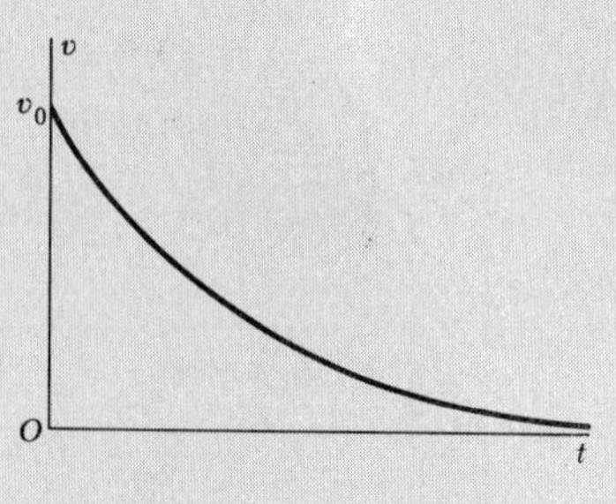

a. **v in Terms of t.** Substituting $-kv$ for a in the fundamental formula defining acceleration, $a = dv/dt$, we write

$$-kv = \frac{dv}{dt} \qquad \frac{dv}{v} = -k\,dt \qquad \int_{v_0}^{v} \frac{dv}{v} = -k \int_0^t dt$$

$$\ln \frac{v}{v_0} = -kt \qquad\qquad v = v_0 e^{-kt} \blacktriangleleft$$

b. **s in Terms of t.** Substituting the expression just obtained for v into $v = ds/dt$, we write

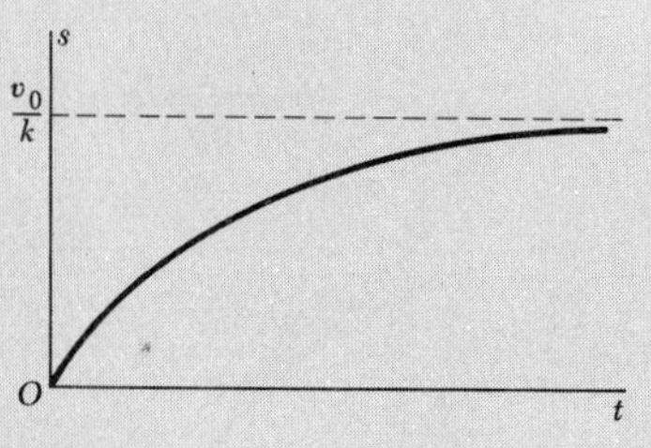

$$v_0 e^{-kt} = \frac{ds}{dt}$$

$$\int_0^s ds = v_0 \int_0^t e^{-kt}\,dt$$

$$s = -\frac{v_0}{k}\Big[e^{-kt}\Big]_0^t = -\frac{v_0}{k}\left(e^{-kt} - 1\right)$$

$$s = \frac{v_0}{k}\left(1 - e^{-kt}\right) \blacktriangleleft$$

c. **v in Terms of s.** Substituting $-kv$ for a in $a = v\,dv/ds$, we write

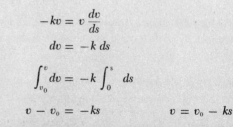

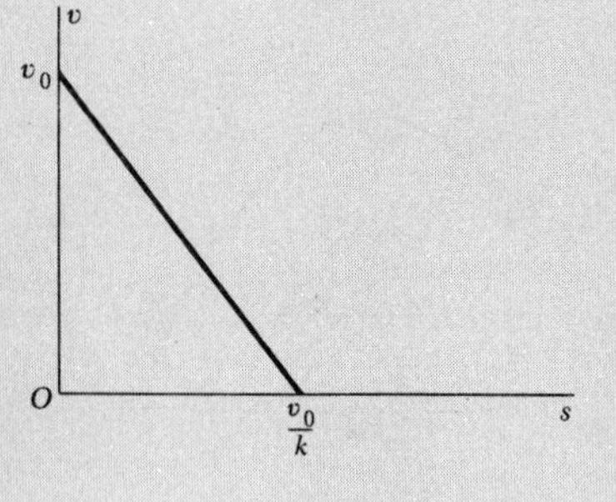

$$-kv = v\frac{dv}{ds}$$

$$dv = -k\,ds$$

$$\int_{v_0}^{v} dv = -k \int_0^s ds$$

$$v - v_0 = -ks \qquad\qquad v = v_0 - ks \blacktriangleleft$$

Check. Part *c* could have been solved by eliminating t from the answers obtained for parts *a* and *b*. This alternate method may be used as a check. From part *a* we obtain $e^{-kt} = v/v_0$; substituting in the answer of part *b*, we obtain

$$s = \frac{v_0}{k}(1 - e^{-kt}) = \frac{v_0}{k}\left(1 - \frac{v}{v_0}\right) \qquad v = v_0 - ks \qquad \text{(checks)}$$

PROBLEMS

11.1. The motion of a particle is defined by the relation $s = 2t^3 - 15t^2 + 36t - 10$, where s is expressed in inches and t in seconds. Determine the position, velocity, and acceleration when $t = 4$ sec.

11.2. The motion of a particle is defined by the relation $s = 2t^3 - 15t^2 + 36t - 27$, where s is expressed in inches and t in seconds. Determine the time, position, and acceleration when $v = 0$.

11.3. The motion of a particle is defined by the relation $s = t^3 - 9t^2 + 15t + 5$, where s is expressed in feet and t in seconds. Determine (*a*) when the velocity is zero, (*b*) the position and the total distance traveled when the acceleration is zero.

11.4. In Prob. 11.3 we have $v = +15$ ft/sec when $t = 0$. Determine the time, position, and total distance traveled when the velocity of the particle is again equal to $+15$ ft/sec.

11.5. The acceleration of a particle is defined by the relation $a = -5$ ft/sec^2. If $v = +20$ ft/sec and $s = 0$ when $t = 0$, determine the velocity, position, and total distance traveled when $t = 6$ sec.

11.6. The acceleration of a particle is directly proportional to the time t. At $t = 0$, the velocity of the particle is $v = -9$ ft/sec. Knowing that both the velocity and the position coordinate are zero when $t = 3$ sec, write the equations of motion for the particle.

11.7. The acceleration of a particle is defined by the relation $a = kt^2$. (*a*) Knowing that $v = -32$ ft/sec when $t = 0$ and that $v = +32$ ft/sec when $t = 4$ sec, determine the constant k. (*b*) Write the equations of motion knowing also that $s = 0$ when $t = 4$ sec.

11.8. The acceleration of a particle is defined by the relation $a = 9 - 3t^2$. The particle starts at $t = 0$ with $v = 0$ and $s = -3$ ft. Determine (*a*) the time when the velocity is again zero, (*b*) the position and velocity when $t = 4$ sec, (*c*) the total distance traveled by the particle from $t = 0$ to $t = 4$ sec.

11.9. The acceleration of an oscillating particle is defined by the relation $a = -ks$. Find the value of k such that $v = 15$ in./sec when $s = 0$ and $s = 3$ in. when $v = 0$.

11.10. The acceleration of a particle is defined by the relation $a = 25 - 3s^2$, where a is expressed in ft/sec^2 and s in feet. The particle starts with no initial velocity at the position $s = 0$. Determine (*a*) the velocity when $s = 2$ ft, (*b*) the position where the velocity is again zero, (*c*) the position where the velocity is maximum.

11.11. The acceleration of a particle moving in a straight line is directed toward a fixed point O and is inversely proportional to the distance of the particle from O. At $t = 0$, the particle is 2 ft to the right of O, has a velocity of 4 ft/sec to the right, and has an acceleration of 3 ft/sec^2 to the left. Determine (*a*) the velocity of the particle when it is 3 ft away from O, (*b*) the position of the particle at which its velocity is zero.

11.12. The acceleration of a particle is defined by the relation $a = -ks^{-2}$. The particle starts with no initial velocity at $s = 10$ in., and it is observed that its velocity is 4 in./sec when $s = 5$ in. Determine (*a*) the value of k, (*b*) the velocity of the particle when $s = 1$ in.

11.13. The acceleration of a particle is defined by the relation $a = -0.002v^2$, where a is the acceleration in ft/sec^2 and v is the velocity in ft/sec. If the particle is given an initial velocity v_0, find the distance it will travel (*a*) before its velocity drops to half the initial value, (*b*) before it comes to rest.

11.14. The acceleration of a particle is defined by the relation $a = -20v$, where a is expressed in ft/sec^2 and v in ft/sec. Knowing that at $t = 0$ the velocity is 200 ft/sec, determine (*a*) the distance the particle will travel before coming to rest, (*b*) the time required for the particle to come to rest, (*c*) the time required for the velocity of the particle to be reduced to 1 per cent of its initial value.

11.15. The acceleration of a particle is defined by the relation $a = -kv^{1.5}$. The particle starts at $t = 0$ and $s = 0$ with an initial velocity v_0. (*a*) Show that the velocity and position coordinate at any time t are related by the equation $s/t = \sqrt{v_0 v}$. (*b*) Determine the value of k, knowing that for $v_0 = 100$ ft/sec the particle comes to rest after traveling 5 ft.

11.16. The acceleration of a particle falling through the atmosphere is defined by the relation $a = g(1 - k^2v^2)$. Knowing that the particle starts at $t = 0$ and $s = 0$ with no initial velocity, (*a*) show that the velocity at any time t is $v = (1/k) \tanh kgt$, (*b*) write an equation defining the velocity for any value of s. (*c*) Why is $v_t = 1/k$ called the terminal velocity?

11.17. The position of an oscillating particle is defined by the relation $s = A \sin (pt + \phi)$. Denoting the velocity and position coordinate when $t = 0$ by v_0 and s_0 respectively, show (*a*) that $\tan \phi = s_0 p/v_0$, (*b*) that the maximum value of the position coordinate is

$$A = \sqrt{s_0^2 + (v_0/p)^2}$$

11.18. The acceleration of a particle is defined by the relation $a = k \sin \pi t/T$. Knowing that both the velocity and the position coordinate of the particle are zero when $t = 0$, determine (*a*) the equations of motion, (*b*) the maximum velocity, (*c*) the position at $t = 2T$, (*d*) the average velocity during the interval $t = 0$ to $t = 2T$.

11.19. The acceleration due to gravity of a particle falling toward the earth is $a = -gR^2/r^2$, where r is the distance from the *center* of the earth to the particle, R is the radius of the earth, and g is the acceleration due to gravity at the surface of the earth. Derive an expression for the *escape velocity*, i.e., for the minimum velocity with which a particle should be projected vertically upward from the surface of the earth if it is not to return to the earth. (*Hint.* $v = 0$ for $r = \infty$.)

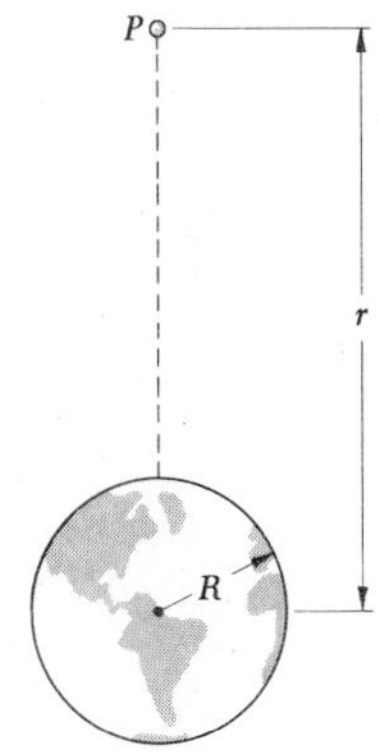

FIG. P 11.19

11.20. A more accurate expression for the acceleration due to gravity is

$$g = \frac{32.2}{\left(1 + \dfrac{y}{20.9 \times 10^6}\right)^2}$$

where g is expressed in ft/sec² and y is the altitude in feet. Using this value of g, compute the height reached by a bullet fired vertically upward with the following initial velocities: (*a*) 1,000 ft/sec, (*b*) 10,000 ft/sec, (*c*) 36,700 ft/sec.

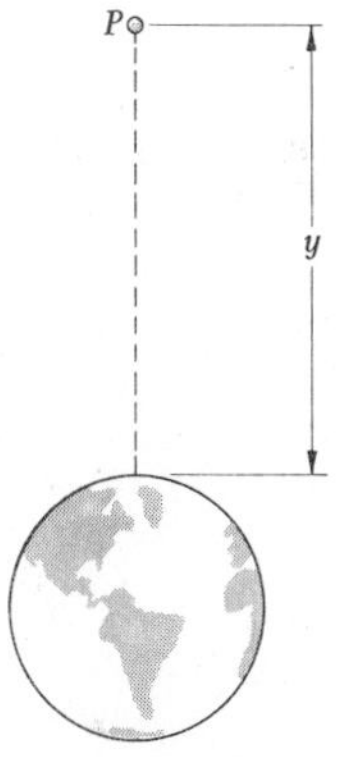

FIG. P 11.20

*11.21. When a package is dropped on a rigid surface, the acceleration of its cushioned contents may be defined by the relation $a = -k \tan \pi s/2L$, where L is the distance through which the cushioning material can be compressed. Denoting by v_0 the velocity when $s = 0$, show that $v^2 = v_0^2 + (4kL/\pi) \ln \cos \pi s/2L$. If $k = 1{,}000$ ft/sec² and $L = 12$ in., compute the initial velocity v_0 for which the maximum value of the position coordinate s is (*a*) 6 in., (*b*) 12 in.

*11.22. A particle is released from rest at a distance R above the surface of the earth. Using the expression for the acceleration due to gravity given in Prob. 11.19, determine (*a*) the velocity of the particle as it strikes the earth, (*b*) the time required for it to fall to the surface of the earth. (Radius of earth $= R = 3{,}960$ miles, $g = 32.2$ ft/sec².)

*11.23. Using the expression for the acceleration due to gravity given in Prob. 11.19, derive an expression for the time required for a particle to reach the surface of the earth if it is released with no velocity at a distance r_0 from the center of the earth.

11.4. Uniform Rectilinear Motion. This is a type of straight-line motion which is frequently encountered in practical applications. In this motion, the acceleration a of the particle is zero for every value of t. The velocity v is therefore constant, and Eq. (11.1) becomes

$$\frac{ds}{dt} = v = \text{constant}$$

The position coordinate s is obtained by integrating this equation. Denoting by s_0 the initial value of s, we write

$$\int_{s_0}^{s} ds = v \int_0^t dt$$

$$s - s_0 = vt$$

$$s = s_0 + vt \tag{11.5}$$

This equation may be used *only if the velocity of the particle is known to be constant.*

11.5. Uniformly Accelerated Rectilinear Motion. This is another common type of motion. In this motion, the acceleration a of the particle is constant, and Eq. (11.2) becomes

$$\frac{dv}{dt} = a = \text{constant}$$

The velocity v of the particle is obtained by integrating this equation,

$$\int_{v_0}^{v} dv = a \int_0^t dt$$

$$v - v_0 = at$$

$$v = v_0 + at \tag{11.6}$$

where v_0 is the initial velocity. Substituting for v into (11.1), we write

$$\frac{ds}{dt} = v_0 + at$$

Denoting by s_0 the initial value of s and integrating, we have

$$\int_{s_0}^{s} ds = \int_0^t (v_0 + at)\, dt$$

$$s - s_0 = v_0 t + \tfrac{1}{2}at^2$$

$$s = s_0 + v_0 t + \tfrac{1}{2}at^2 \tag{11.7}$$

We may also use Eq. (11.4) and write

$$v\frac{dv}{ds} = a = \text{constant}$$

$$v\, dv = a\, ds$$

Integrating both sides, we obtain

$$\int_{v_0}^{v} v\, dv = a \int_{s_0}^{s} ds$$

$$\tfrac{1}{2}(v^2 - v_0^2) = a(s - s_0)$$

$$v^2 = v_0^2 + 2a(s - s_0) \tag{11.8}$$

The three equations we have derived provide useful relations between position coordinate, velocity, and time in the case of a uniformly accelerated motion, as soon as appropriate values have been substituted for a, v_0, and s_0. The origin O of the s axis should first be defined and a positive direction chosen along the axis; this direction will be used to determine the signs of a, v_0, and s_0. Equation (11.6) relates v and t and should be used when the value of v corresponding to a given value of t is desired, or inversely. Equation (11.7) relates s and t; Eq. (11.8) relates v and s. An important application of uniformly accelerated motion is the motion of a *freely falling body*. The acceleration of a freely falling body (usually denoted by g) is equal to 32.2 ft/sec^2.

It is important to keep in mind that the three equations above may be used *only when the acceleration of the particle is known to be constant*. If the acceleration of the particle is variable, its motion should be determined from the fundamental equations (11.1) to (11.4), according to the methods outlined in Sec. 11.3.

11.6. Motion of Several Particles. When several particles move independently along the same line, independent equations of motion may be written for each particle. Whenever possible, time should be recorded from the same initial instant for all particles, and displacements should be measured from the same origin and in the same direction. In other words, a single clock and a single measuring tape should be used.

Relative Motion of Two Particles. Consider two particles A and B moving along the same straight line (Fig. 11.7). If the position coordinates s_A and s_B are measured from the same origin, the difference $s_B - s_A$ defines the *relative position coordinate of B with respect to* A and is denoted by $s_{B/A}$. We write

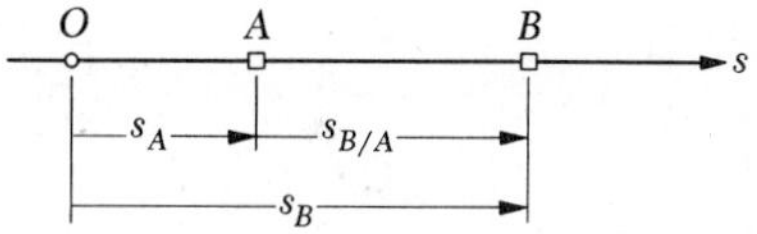

FIG. 11.7

$$s_{B/A} = s_B - s_A \qquad \text{or} \qquad s_B = s_A + s_{B/A} \qquad (11.9)$$

A positive sign for $s_{B/A}$ means that B is to the right of A, a negative sign that B is to the left of A, regardless of the position of A and B with respect to the origin.

The rate of change of $s_{B/A}$ is known as the *relative velocity of B with respect to* A and is denoted by $v_{B/A}$. Differentiating (11.9) we write

$$v_{B/A} = v_B - v_A \qquad \text{or} \qquad v_B = v_A + v_{B/A} \qquad (11.10)$$

A positive sign for $v_{B/A}$ means that B is *observed from* A to move in the positive direction; a negative sign, that it is observed to move in the negative direction.

The rate of change of $v_{B/A}$ is known as the *relative acceleration of B with respect to A* and is denoted by $a_{B/A}$. Differentiating (11.10), we obtain

$$a_{B/A} = a_B - a_A \qquad \text{or} \qquad a_B = a_A + a_{B/A} \qquad (11.11)$$

Dependent Motions. Sometimes, the position of a particle will depend upon the position of another or of several other particles. The motions are then said to be dependent. For example, the position of block B in Fig. 11.8 depends upon the position of block A. Since the rope $ACDEFG$ is of constant length, and since the lengths of the portions of rope CD and EF wrapped around the pulleys remain constant, it follows that the sum of the lengths of the segments AC, DE, and FG is constant. Observing that the length of the segment AC differs from s_A only by a constant, and that, similarly, the lengths of the segments DE and FG differ from s_B only by a constant, we write

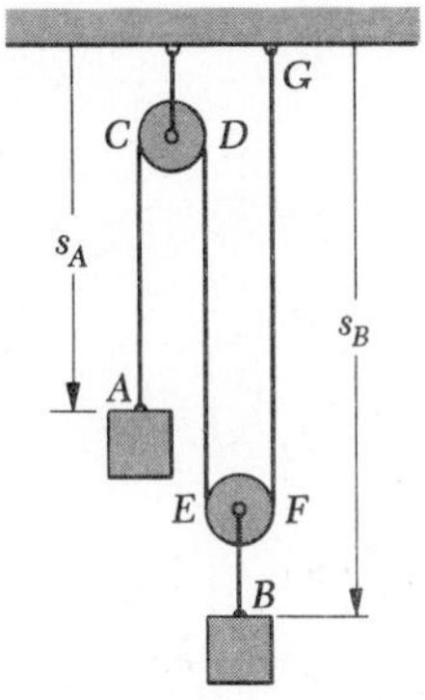

FIG. 11.8

$$s_A + 2s_B = \text{constant}$$

Since only one of the two coordinates s_A and s_B may be chosen arbitrarily, we say that the system shown in Fig. 11.8 has *one degree of freedom.* From the relation between the position coordinates s_A and s_B, it follows that if s_A is given an increment Δs_A, i.e., if block A is lowered by an amount Δs_A, the coordinate s_B will receive an increment $\Delta s_B = -\frac{1}{2}\Delta s_A$, i.e., block B will rise by half the same amount; this may easily be checked directly from Fig. 11.8.

In the case of the three blocks of Fig. 11.9, we may again observe that the length of the rope which passes over the pulleys is constant, and thus that the following relation must be satisfied by the position coordinates of the three blocks:

$$2s_A + 2s_B + s_C = \text{constant}$$

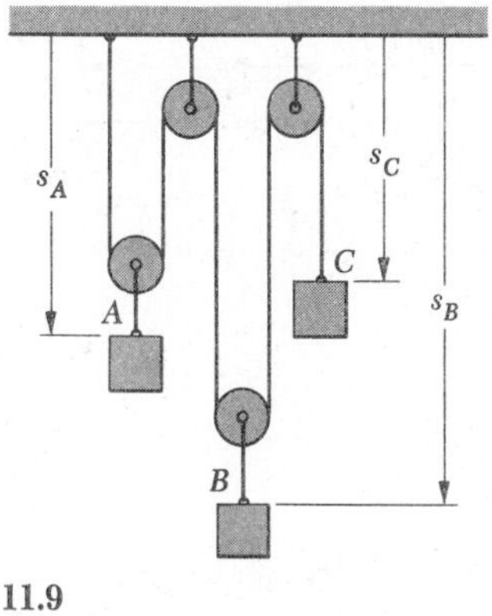

FIG. 11.9

Since two of the coordinates may be chosen arbitrarily, we say that the system shown in Fig. 11.9 has *two degrees of freedom.*

When the relation existing between the position coordinates of several particles is *linear,* a similar relation holds between the velocities and between the accelerations of the particles. In the case of the blocks of Fig. 11.9, for instance, we differentiate twice the equation obtained and write

$$2\frac{ds_A}{dt} + 2\frac{ds_B}{dt} + \frac{ds_C}{dt} = 0 \qquad \text{or} \qquad 2v_A + 2v_B + v_C = 0$$

$$2\frac{dv_A}{dt} + 2\frac{dv_B}{dt} + \frac{dv_C}{dt} = 0 \qquad \text{or} \qquad 2a_A + 2a_B + a_C = 0$$

SAMPLE PROBLEM 11.4

A ball is thrown vertically upward from the 40-ft level in an elevator shaft, with an initial velocity of 50 ft/sec. At the same instant an open-platform elevator passes the 10-ft level, moving upward with a constant velocity of 5 ft/sec. Determine (*a*) when and where the ball will hit the elevator, (*b*) the relative velocity of the ball with respect to the elevator when the ball hits the elevator.

Motion of Ball. Since the ball has a constant acceleration, its motion is *uniformly accelerated.* Placing the origin *O* at the ground level and choosing arbitrarily the positive direction upward, we find that the initial position is $s_0 = +40$ ft, the initial velocity is $v_0 = +50$ ft/sec, and the acceleration is $a = -32.2$ ft/sec². Substituting these values in the equations for uniformly accelerated motion, we write

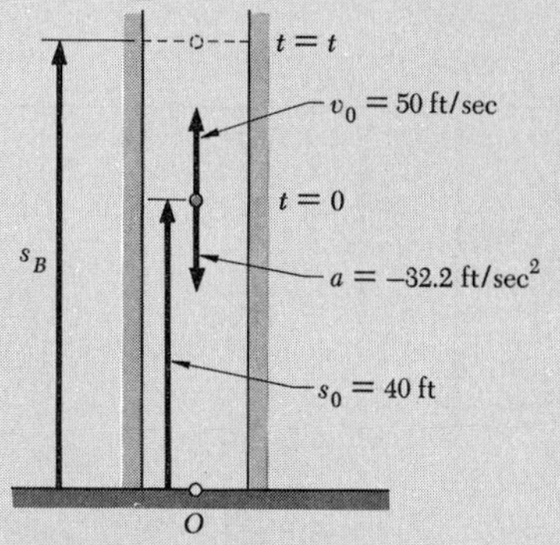

$$v_B = v_0 + at \qquad v_B = 50 - 32.2t \qquad (1)$$
$$s_B = s_0 + v_0 t + \tfrac{1}{2}at^2 \qquad s_B = 40 + 50t - 16.1t^2 \qquad (2)$$

Motion of Elevator. Since the elevator has a constant velocity, its motion is *uniform.* Again placing the origin *O* at the ground level and choosing the positive direction upward, we note that $s_0 = +10$ ft and write

$$v_E = +5 \text{ ft/sec} \qquad (3)$$
$$s_E = s_0 + v_E t \qquad s_E = 10 + 5t \qquad (4)$$

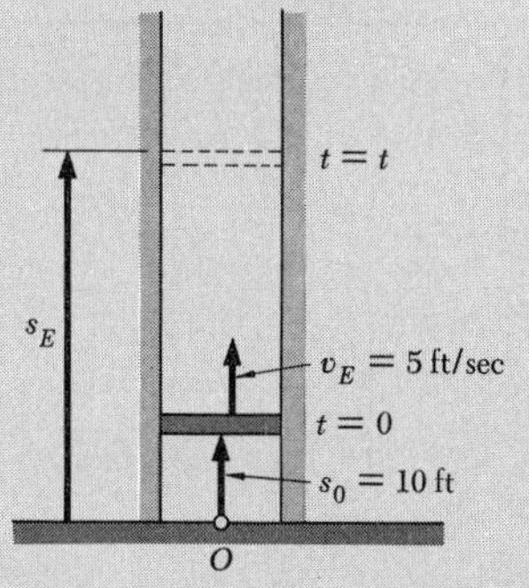

Ball Hits Elevator. We first note that the same time *t* and the same origin *O* were used in writing the equations of motion of both the ball and the elevator. We see from the figure that, when the ball hits the elevator,

$$s_E = s_B \qquad (5)$$

Substituting for s_E and s_B from (2) and (4) into (5), we have

$$10 + 5t = 40 + 50t - 16.1t^2$$
$$t = -0.56 \text{ sec} \qquad \text{and} \qquad t = +3.35 \text{ sec} \blacktriangleleft$$

Only the root $t = 3.35$ sec corresponds to a time after the motion has begun. Substituting this value into (4), we have

$$s_E = 10 + (5)(3.35) = 26.7 \text{ ft}$$

Elevation from ground = 26.7 ft ◀

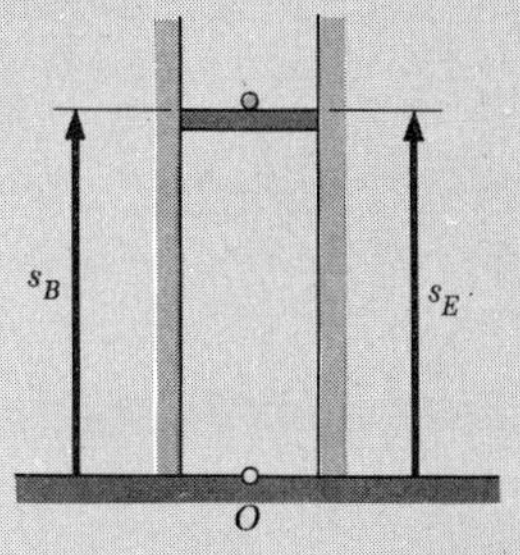

The relative velocity of the ball with respect to the elevator is

$$v_{B/E} = v_B - v_E = (50 - 32.2t) - 5 = 45 - 32.2t$$

When the ball hits the elevator at time $t = 3.35$ sec, we have

$$v_{B/E} = 45 - (32.2)(3.35) \qquad v_{B/E} = -62.9 \text{ ft/sec} \blacktriangleleft$$

The negative sign means that the ball is observed from the elevator to be moving in the negative sense (downward).

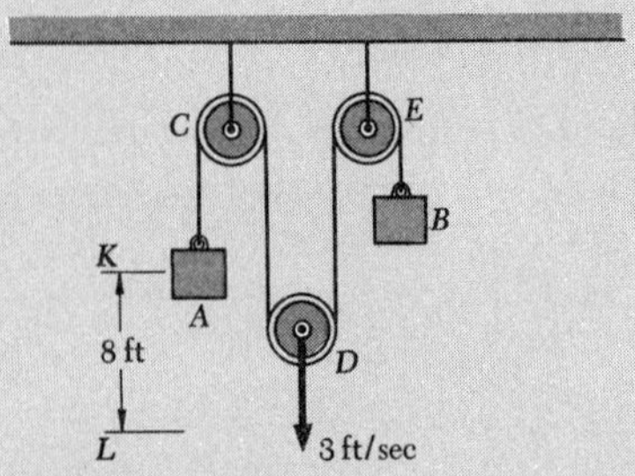

SAMPLE PROBLEM 11.5

Two blocks A and B are connected by a cord passing over three pulleys C, D, and E as shown. Pulleys C and E are fixed, while D is pulled downward with a constant velocity of 3 ft/sec. At $t = 0$, block A starts moving downward from the position K with a constant acceleration and no initial velocity. Knowing that the velocity of block A is 12 ft/sec as it passes through point L, determine the change in elevation, the velocity, and the acceleration of block B when A passes through L.

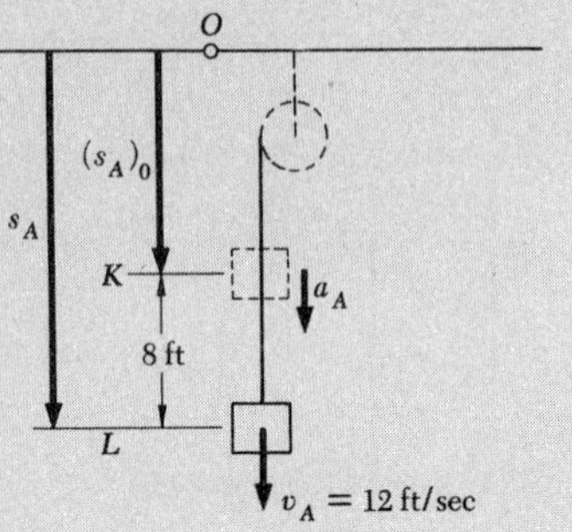

Motion of Block A. We place the origin O at the horizontal surface and choose the positive direction downward. We observe that when $t = 0$, block A is at position K and $(v_A)_0 = 0$. Since $v_A = 12$ ft/sec and $s_A - (s_A)_0 = 8$ ft when the block passes through L, we write

$$v_A^2 = (v_A)_0^2 + 2a_A[s_A - (s_A)_0] \qquad (12)^2 = 0 + 2a_A(8)$$
$$a_A = 9 \text{ ft/sec}^2$$

The time at which block A reaches point L is obtained by writing

$$v_A = (v_A)_0 + a_A t \qquad 12 = 0 + 9t \qquad t = 1.333 \text{ sec}$$

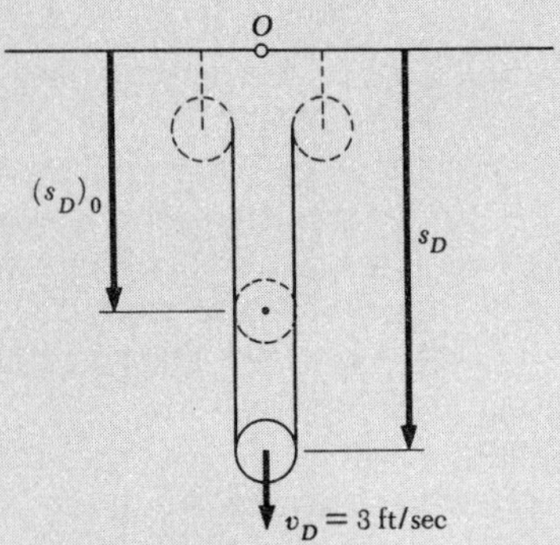

Motion of Pulley D. Recalling that the positive direction is downward, we write

$$a_D = 0 \qquad v_D = 3 \text{ ft/sec} \qquad s_D = (s_D)_0 + v_D t = (s_D)_0 + 3t$$

When block A reaches L, at $t = 1.333$ sec, we have

$$s_D = (s_D)_0 + (3)(1.333) = (s_D)_0 + 4$$

Thus, $$s_D - (s_D)_0 = 4 \text{ ft}$$

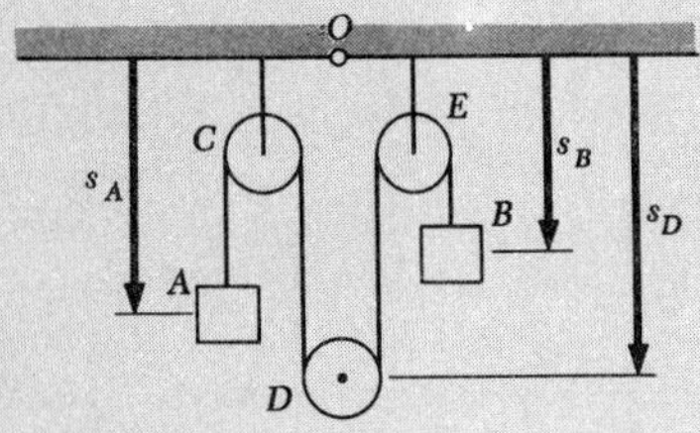

Motion of Block B. We note that the total length of cord $ACDEB$ differs from the quantity $(s_A + 2s_D + s_B)$ only by a constant. Since the cord length is constant during the motion, this quantity must also remain constant. Thus considering the times $t = 0$ and $t = 1.333$ sec, we write

$$s_A + 2s_D + s_B = (s_A)_0 + 2(s_D)_0 + (s_B)_0 \qquad (1)$$
$$[s_A - (s_A)_0] + 2[s_D - (s_D)_0] + [s_B - (s_B)_0] = 0 \qquad (2)$$

But we know that $s_A - (s_A)_0 = 8$ ft and $s_D - (s_D)_0 = 4$ ft; substituting these values in (2), we find

$$8 + 2(4) + [s_B - (s_B)_0] = 0 \qquad s_B - (s_B)_0 = -16 \text{ ft}$$

Thus the change in elevation of B is 16 ft ↑ ◄

Differentiating (1) twice, we obtain equations relating the velocities and the accelerations of A, B, and D. Substituting for the velocities and accelerations of A and D at $t = 1.333$ sec, we have

$v_A + 2v_D + v_B = 0$: $\quad 12 + 2(3) + v_B = 0$

$v_B = -18$ ft/sec $\qquad v_B = 18$ ft/sec ↑ ◄

$a_A + 2a_D + a_B = 0$: $\quad 9 + 2(0) + a_B = 0$

$a_B = -9$ ft/sec² $\qquad a_B = 9$ ft/sec² ↑ ◄

PROBLEMS

11.24. An automobile travels 600 ft in 20 sec while being accelerated at a constant rate of 1.5 ft/sec². Determine (*a*) its initial velocity, (*b*) its final velocity, (*c*) the distance traveled during the first 10 sec.

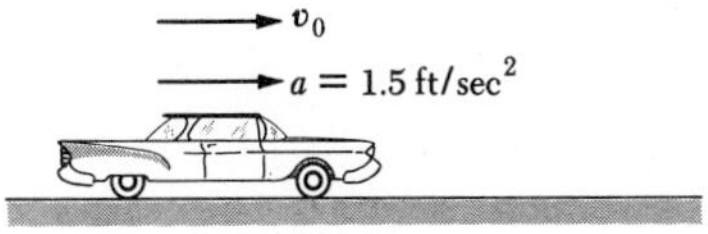

FIG. P 11.24

11.25. A stone is released from an elevator moving up at a speed of 15 ft/sec and reaches the bottom of the shaft in 3 sec. (*a*) How high was the elevator when the stone was released? (*b*) With what speed does the stone strike the bottom of the shaft?

11.26. A man jumps from a 20-ft cliff with no initial velocity. (*a*) How long does it take him to reach the ground, and with what velocity does he hit the ground? (*b*) If this were to happen on the moon, where $g = 5.31$ ft/sec², what would be the values obtained for the time and velocity? (*c*) If a motion picture were taken on the earth, but if the scene were supposed to take place on the moon, how many frames per second should be used so that the scene would appear realistic when projected at the standard speed of 24 frames per second?

11.27. A motorist is traveling at 50 mph when he observes that a traffic light 800 ft ahead of him turns red. The traffic light is timed to stay red for 15 sec. If the motorist wishes to pass the light without stopping just as it turns green again, determine (*a*) the required uniform deceleration of the car, (*b*) the speed of the car as it passes the light.

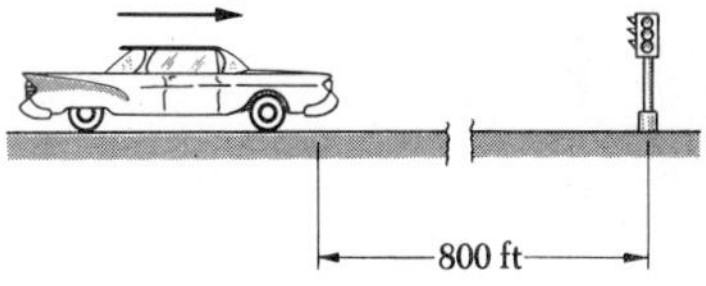

FIG. P 11.27

11.28. (*a*) A stone is dropped with no initial velocity into a well. The sound of the stone hitting the water is heard 4.7 sec later. Knowing that the speed of sound is 1,100 ft/sec, determine the vertical distance from the top of the well to the water surface. (*b*) A second stone is thrown downward into the well with an initial velocity v_0. If the sound of the second stone hitting the water is heard in 4.3 sec, determine the initial velocity of the second stone.

11.29. An open-platform elevator is moving down a mine shaft at a constant velocity v_e when the elevator platform hits and dislodges a stone. Assuming that the stone starts falling with no initial velocity, (*a*) show that the stone will hit the platform with a relative velocity of magnitude v_e. (*b*) If $v_e = 15$ ft/sec, determine when and where the stone will hit the elevator platform.

11.30. Two automobiles *A* and *B* traveling in the same direction in adjacent lanes are stopped at a highway traffic signal. As the signal turns green, automobile *A* accelerates at the constant rate of 3 ft/sec². Two seconds later automobile *B* starts and accelerates at the constant rate of 4 ft/sec². Determine (*a*) when and where *B* will overtake *A*, (*b*) the speed of each automobile at that time.

11.31. Drops of water are observed to drip from a faucet at uniform intervals of time. As any drop B begins to fall freely, the preceding drop A has already fallen 1 ft. Determine the distance drop A will have fallen by the time the distance between A and B will have increased to 3 ft.

***11.32.** Drops of water fall down a mine shaft at the uniform rate of one drop per second. A mine elevator moving up the shaft at 30 ft/sec is struck by a drop of water when it is 300 ft below ground level. When and where will the next drop of water strike the elevator?

***11.33.** Solve Prob. 11.32 assuming that the elevator is moving *down* the shaft at 30 ft/sec.

11.34. The elevator shown in the figure moves upward at the constant velocity of 12 ft/sec. Determine (*a*) the velocity of the cable C, (*b*) the velocity of the counterweight W, (*c*) the relative velocity of the cable C with respect to the elevator, (*d*) the relative velocity of the counterweight W with respect to the elevator.

11.35. The elevator shown starts from rest and moves upward with a constant acceleration. If the counterweight W moves through 30 ft in 5 sec, determine (*a*) the accelerations of the elevator and the cable C, (*b*) the velocity of the elevator after 5 sec.

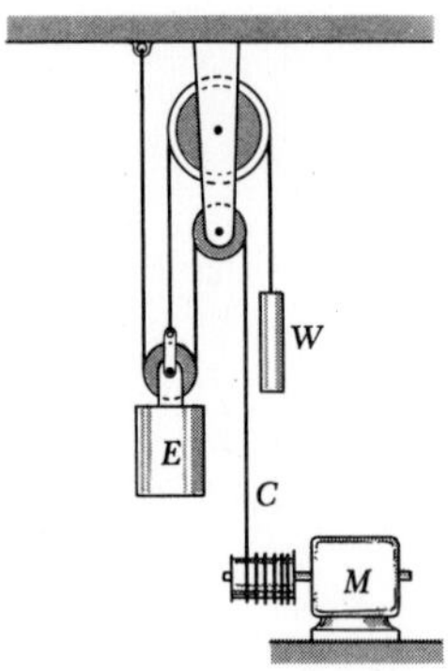

FIG. P 11.34 AND P 11.35

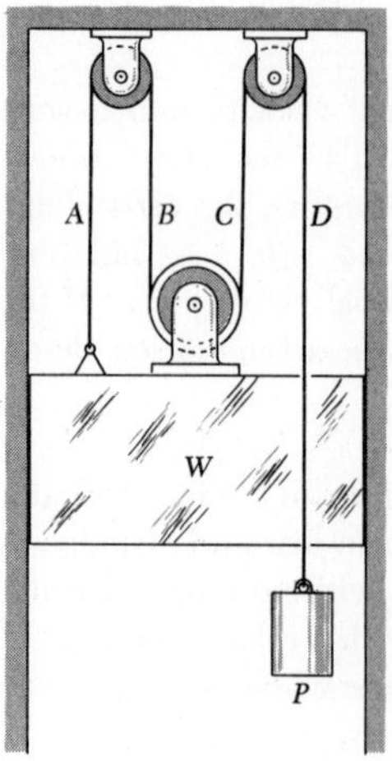

FIG. P 11.36 AND P 11.37

11.36. The slider block W moves downward at a constant velocity of 12 in./sec. Find (*a*) the velocities of portions A, B, C, and D of the cable, (*b*) the relative velocity of P with respect to the weight W, (*c*) the relative velocity of portion B of the cable with respect to portion C.

11.37. The slider block W starts from rest and moves downward with a constant acceleration. If after 5 sec the relative velocity of P with respect to W is 30 in./sec, determine (*a*) the accelerations of W and P, (*b*) the velocity and position of W after 4 sec.

11.38. Blocks A and B start from rest and move to the right with the following accelerations: $a_A = 3$ in./sec² and $a_B = 2t$ in./sec². Determine (*a*) when the velocity of C will again be zero, (*b*) the corresponding position of each block.

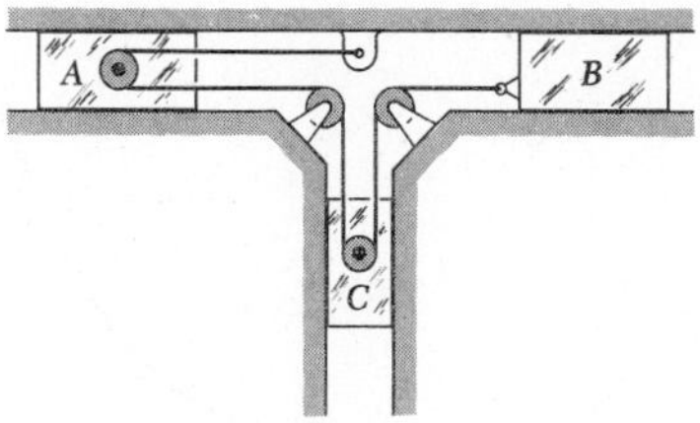

FIG. P 11.38 AND P 11.40

11.39. (*a*) Choosing the positive sense downward for each block, express the velocity of C in terms of the velocities of A and B. (*b*) Knowing that both blocks B and C start from rest and move downward with the respective accelerations $a_B = 4$ in./sec² and $a_C = 3$ in./sec², determine the position and velocity of A after 2 sec.

11.40. The three blocks shown move with constant velocities. Find the velocities of A and B, knowing that C moves downward with a velocity of 10 in./sec and that B is observed from A to move to the right with a relative velocity of 4 in./sec.

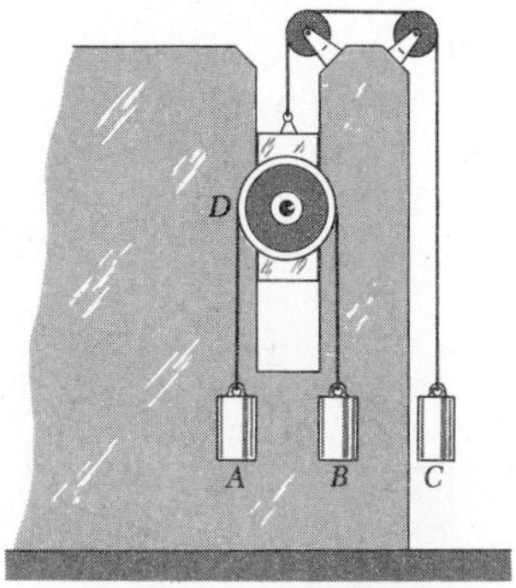

FIG. P 11.39 AND P 11.41

11.41. The three blocks shown move with constant velocities. Find the velocity of each block, knowing that the relative velocity of A with respect to C is 12 in./sec downward and that the relative velocity of B with respect to C is 4 in./sec upward.

11.42. The three blocks of Fig. 11.9 move with constant velocities. Find the velocity of each block, knowing that C is observed from B to move upward with a relative velocity of 7 ft/sec and A is observed from B to move downward with a relative velocity of 6 ft/sec.

***11.7. Graphical Solution of Rectilinear-motion Problems.** It was observed in Sec. 11.2 that the fundamental formulas

$$v = \frac{ds}{dt} \qquad \text{and} \qquad a = \frac{dv}{dt}$$

have a geometrical significance. The first formula expresses that the velocity at any instant is equal to the slope of the s–t curve at the same instant (Fig. 11.10). The second formula expresses that the acceleration is equal to the slope of the v–t curve. These two properties may be used to derive graphically the v–t and a–t curves of a motion when the s–t curve is known.

Integrating the two fundamental formulas from a time t_1 to a time t_2, we write

$$s_2 - s_1 = \int_{t_1}^{t_2} v\,dt \qquad \text{and} \qquad v_2 - v_1 = \int_{t_1}^{t_2} a\,dt \qquad (11.12)$$

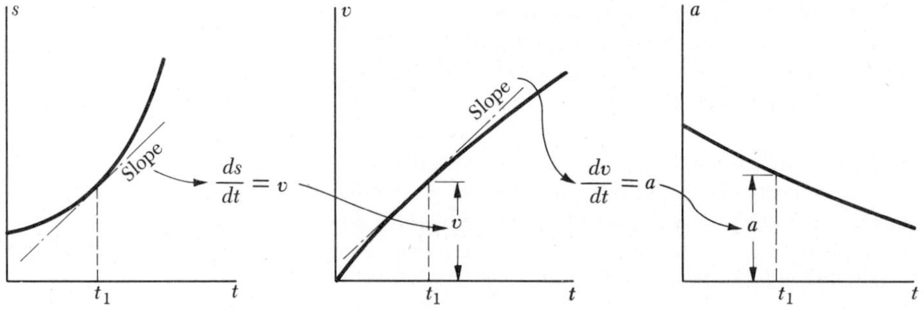

FIG. 11.10

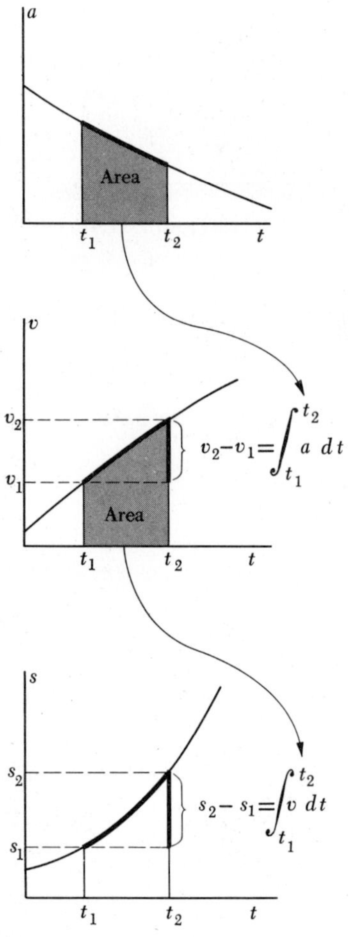

FIG. 11.11

The first formula expresses that the area measured under the v–t curve from t_1 to t_2 is equal to the change in s during that time interval (Fig. 11.11). The second formula expresses similarly that the area measured under the a–t curve from t_1 to t_2 is equal to the change in v during that time interval. These two properties may be used to determine graphically the s–t curve of a motion when its v–t curve or its a–t curve is known (see Sample Prob. 11.6).

Graphical solutions are particularly useful when the motion considered is defined from experimental data and when s, v, and a are not analytical functions of t. They may also be used to advantage when the motion consists of distinct parts and when its analysis requires writing a different equation for each of its parts. When using a graphical solution, however, one should be careful to note (1) that the area under the v-t curve measures the *change in s*, not s itself, and, similarly, that the area under the a-t curve measures the change in v; (2) that, while an area above the t axis corresponds to an increase in s or v, an area located below the t axis measures a decrease in s or v.

It will be useful to remember, in drawing motion curves, that, if the velocity is constant, it will be represented by a horizontal straight line; the position coordinate s will then be a linear function of t and will be represented by an oblique straight line. If the acceleration is constant and different from zero, it will be represented by a horizontal straight line; v will then be a linear function of t, represented by an oblique straight line; and s will be expressed as a second-degree polynomial in t, represented by a parabola. If the acceleration is a linear function of t, the velocity and the position coordinate will be equal, respectively, to second-degree and third-degree polynomials; a is then represented by an oblique straight line, v by a parabola, and s by a cubic. In general, if the acceleration is a polynomial of degree n in t, the velocity will be a polynomial of degree $n + 1$ and the position coordinate a polynomial of degree $n + 2$; these polynomials are represented by motion curves of a corresponding degree.

***11.8. Other Graphical Methods.** An alternate graphical solution may be used to determine directly from the a–t curve the position of a particle at a given instant. Denoting respectively by s_0 and v_0 the values of s and v at $t = 0$, by s_1 and v_1 their values at $t = t_1$, and observing that the area under the v–t curve may be divided into a rectangle of area $v_0 t_1$ and horizontal differential elements of area $(t_1 - t)\,dv$ (Fig. 11.12a), we write

$$s_1 - s_0 = \text{area under } v\text{–}t \text{ curve} = v_0 t_1 + \int_{v_0}^{v_1} (t_1 - t)\,dv$$

Substituting $dv = a\,dt$ in the integral, we obtain

$$s_1 - s_0 = v_0 t_1 + \int_0^{t_1} (t_1 - t) a\,dt$$

Referring to Fig. 11.12b, we note that the integral represents the first moment of the area under the a–t curve with respect to the line $t = t_1$ bounding the area on the right. This method of solution is known, therefore, as the *moment-area method*. If the abscissa $\bar{t}$ of the centroid C of the area is known, the position coordinate s_1 may be obtained by writing

$$s_1 = s_0 + v_0 t_1 + (\text{area under } a\text{–}t \text{ curve})(t_1 - \bar{t}) \qquad (11.13)$$

If the area under the a–t curve is a composite area, the last term in (11.13) may be obtained by multiplying each component area by the distance from its centroid to the line $t = t_1$. Areas above the t axis should be considered as positive and areas below the t axis as negative.

Another type of motion curve, the v–s curve, is sometimes used. If such a curve has been plotted (Fig. 11.13), the acceleration a may be obtained at any time by drawing the normal to the curve and *measuring the subnormal BC*. Indeed, observing that the angle between AC and AB is equal to the angle θ between the horizontal and the tangent at A (the slope of which is $\tan\theta = dv/ds$), we write

$$BC = AB \tan\theta = v\frac{dv}{ds}$$

and thus, recalling formula (11.4),

$$BC = a$$

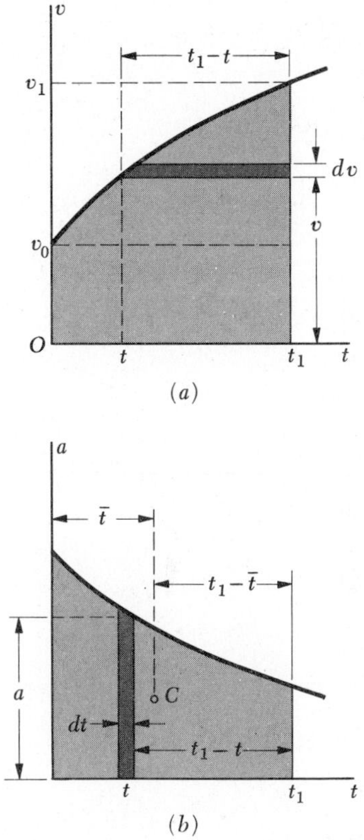

FIG. 11.12

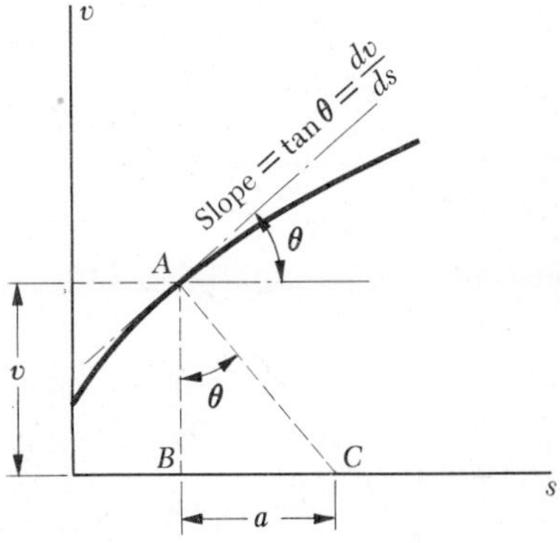

FIG. 11.13

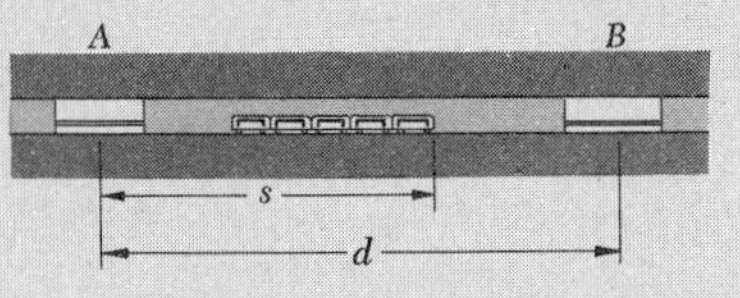

SAMPLE PROBLEM 11.6

A subway train leaves station A; it gains speed at the rate of 4 ft/sec² for 6 sec, and then at the rate of 6 ft/sec² until it has reached the speed of 48 ft/sec. The train maintains the same speed until it approaches station B; brakes are then applied, giving the train a constant deceleration and bringing it to a stop in 6 sec. The total running time from A to B is 40 sec. Draw the a–t, v–t, and s–t curves, and determine the distance between stations A and B.

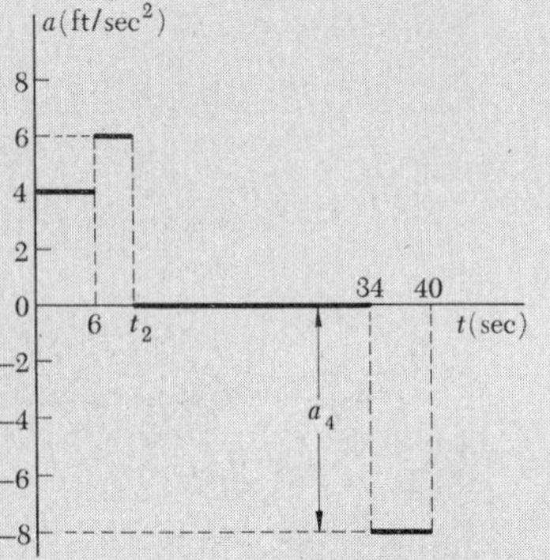

Acceleration-Time Curve. Since the acceleration is either constant or zero, the a–t curve is made of horizontal straight-line segments. The values of t_2 and a_4 are determined as follows:

$0 < t < 6$:

$$\text{Change in } v = \text{area under } a\text{–}t \text{ curve}$$
$$v_6 - 0 = (6 \text{ sec})(4 \text{ ft/sec}^2) = 24 \text{ ft/sec}$$

$6 < t < t_2$: Since the velocity increases from 24 to 48 ft/sec,

$$\text{Change in } v = \text{area under } a\text{–}t \text{ curve}$$
$$48 - 24 = (t_2 - 6)(6 \text{ ft/sec}^2) \qquad t_2 = 10 \text{ sec}$$

$t_2 < t < 34$: Since the velocity is constant, the acceleration is zero.

$34 < t < 40$:

$$\text{Change in } v = \text{area under } a\text{–}t \text{ curve}$$
$$0 - 48 = (6 \text{ sec})a_4 \qquad a_4 = -8 \text{ ft/sec}^2$$

The acceleration being negative, the corresponding area is below the t axis; this area represents a decrease in velocity.

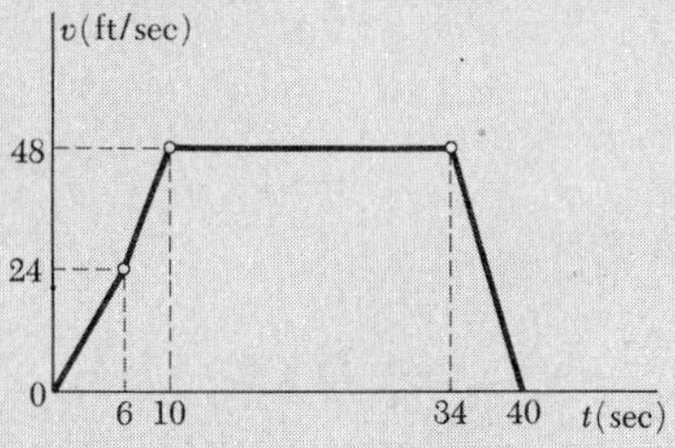

Velocity-Time Curve. Since the acceleration is either constant or zero, the v–t curve is made of segments of straight line connecting the points determined above.

$$\text{Change in } s = \text{area under } v\text{–}t \text{ curve}$$

$0 < t < 6$: $\quad s_6 - 0 = \frac{1}{2}(6)(24) = 72 \text{ ft}$

$6 < t < 10$: $\quad s_{10} - s_6 = \frac{1}{2}(4)(24 + 48) = 144 \text{ ft}$

$10 < t < 34$: $\quad s_{34} - s_{10} = (24)(48) = 1{,}152 \text{ ft}$

$34 < t < 40$: $\quad s_{40} - s_{34} = \frac{1}{2}(6)(48) = 144 \text{ ft}$

Adding the changes in s, we obtain the distance from A to B:

$$d = s_{40} - 0 = 1{,}512 \text{ ft}$$

$$d = 1{,}512 \text{ ft} \blacktriangleleft$$

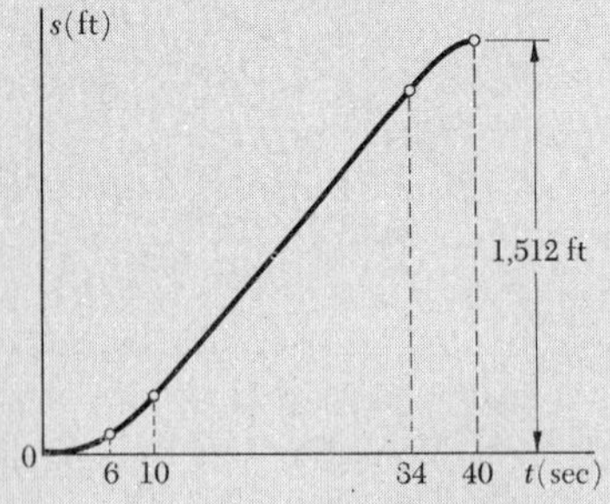

Position-Time Curve. The points determined above should be joined by three arcs of parabola and one segment of straight line. The construction of the s–t curve will be performed more easily and more accurately if we keep in mind that for any value of t the slope of the tangent to the s–t curve is equal to the value of v at that instant.

PROBLEMS

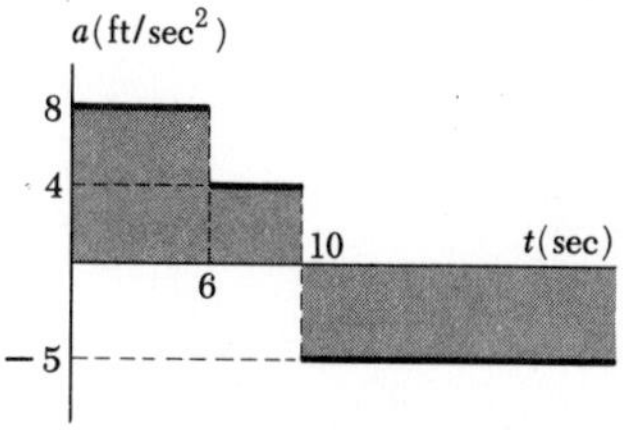

FIG. P 11.43

11.43. A particle moves in a straight line with the acceleration shown in the figure. Knowing that it starts from the origin with $v_0 = -24$ ft/sec, (*a*) plot the v–t and s–t curves for $0 < t < 20$ sec, (*b*) determine its velocity, its position, and the total distance traveled after 14 sec.

11.44. For the particle and motion of Prob. 11.43, plot the v–t and s–t curves for $0 < t < 20$ sec and determine (*a*) the maximum value of the velocity of the particle, (*b*) the maximum value of its position coordinate.

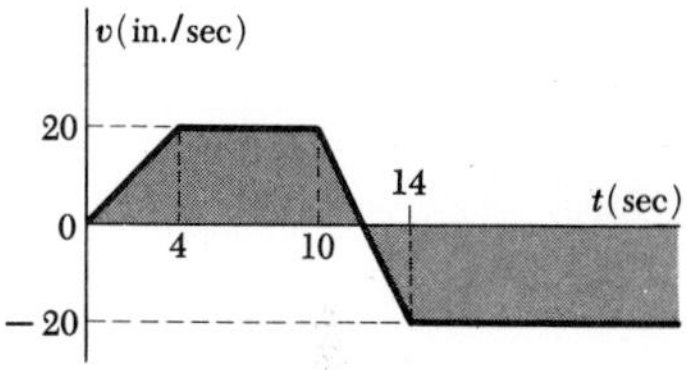

FIG. P 11.45

11.45. A particle moves in a straight line with the velocity shown in the figure. Knowing $s = -60$ in. at $t = 0$, draw the a–t and s–t curves for $0 < t < 20$ sec and determine (*a*) the total distance traveled by the particle after 16 sec, (*b*) the two values of t at which the particle passes through the origin.

11.46. For the particle and motion of Prob. 11.45, plot the a–t and s–t curves for $0 < t < 20$ sec and determine (*a*) the maximum value of the position coordinate of the particle, (*b*) the values of t for which the particle is at a distance of 60 in. from the origin.

11.47. The firing of a howitzer causes the barrel to recoil 40 in. before a braking mechanism brings it to rest. From a high-speed photographic record, it is found that the maximum value of the recoil velocity is 270 in./sec and that this is reached 0.02 sec after firing. Assuming that the recoil period consists of two phases during which the acceleration has, respectively, a constant positive value a_1 and a constant negative value a_2, determine (*a*) the values of a_1 and a_2, (*b*) the position of the barrel 0.02 sec after firing, (*c*) the time at which the velocity of the barrel is zero.

11.48. A motorist is traveling at 50 mph when he observes that a traffic signal 800 ft ahead of him turns red. He knows that the signal is timed to stay red for 15 sec. What should he do to pass the signal at 50 mph just as it turns green again? Draw the v–t curve, selecting the solution which calls for the smallest possible deceleration and acceleration, and determine (*a*) the common value of the deceleration and acceleration in ft/sec^2, (*b*) the minimum speed reached in mph.

11.49. A series of city traffic signals are timed so that an automobile traveling at a constant speed of 25 mph will reach each signal just as it turns green. A motorist misses a signal and is stopped at signal A. Knowing that the next signal B is 600 ft ahead and that the maximum acceleration of his automobile is 5 ft/sec^2, determine what the motorist should do to keep his maximum speed as small as possible, yet reach signal B just as it turns green. What is the maximum speed reached?

11.50. During a finishing operation the bed of an industrial planer moves alternately 16 ft to the right and 16 ft to the left. The velocity of the bed is limited to a maximum value of 2 ft/sec to the right and 4 ft/sec to the left; the acceleration is successively equal to 2 ft/sec² to the right, zero, 2 ft/sec² to the left, zero, etc. Determine the time required for the bed to complete a full cycle, and draw the v–t and s–t curves.

11.51. A policeman on a motorcycle is escorting a motorcade which is traveling at 30 mph. The policeman suddenly decides to take a new position in the motorcade, 200 ft ahead. Assuming that he accelerates and decelerates at the rate of 11 ft/sec² and that he does not exceed at any time a speed of 45 mph, draw the a–t and v–t curves for his motion and determine (*a*) the shortest time in which he can occupy his new position in the motorcade, (*b*) the distance he will travel in that time.

11.52. A fighter plane flying horizontally in a straight line at 800 ft/sec is overtaking a bomber flying in the same straight line at 600 ft/sec. The pilot of the fighter plane fires an air-to-air missile at the bomber when his plane is 1,900 ft behind the bomber. The missile accelerates at a constant rate of 1,000 ft/sec² for 1 sec and then travels at a constant speed. (*a*) How many seconds after firing will the missile reach the bomber? (*b*) If both planes continue at constant speeds, what will be the distance between the planes when the missile strikes the bomber?

11.53. A car and a truck are both traveling at the constant speed of 35 mph; the car is 30 ft behind the truck. The driver of the car wants to pass the truck, i.e., he wishes to place his car at *B*, 30 ft in front of the truck, and then resume the speed of 35 mph. The maximum acceleration of the car is 5 ft/sec² and the maximum deceleration obtained by applying the brakes is 20 ft/sec². What is the shortest time in which the driver of the car can complete the passing operation if he does not at any time exceed the speed limit of 50 mph? Draw the v–t curve.

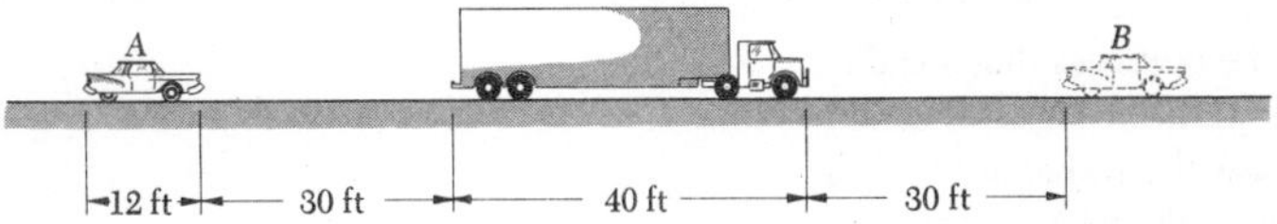

FIG. P 11.53 AND P 11.55

11.54. Solve Prob. 11.53 assuming that the driver of the car does not pay any attention to the speed limit while passing and concentrates on reaching position *B* and resuming a speed of 35 mph in the shortest possible time. What is the maximum speed reached? Draw the v–t curve.

11.55. A car and a truck are both traveling at the constant speed of 50 mph; the car is 30 ft behind the truck. The truck driver suddenly applies his brakes, causing the truck to decelerate at the constant rate of 9 ft/sec². Two seconds later the driver of the car applies his brakes and just manages to avoid a rear-end collision. Determine the constant rate at which the car decelerated.

11.56. Solve Prob. 11.55 assuming that the truck and the car are traveling at 80 mph.

11.57. An express subway train and a train making local stops run on parallel tracks between stations A and E, which are 3,200 ft apart. The local train makes stops of 30-sec duration at each of the stations B, C, and D; the express train proceeds to station E without any intermediate stop. Each train accelerates at a rate of 4 ft/sec^2 until it reaches a speed of 40 ft/sec; it then proceeds at that constant speed. As the train approaches its next stop, the brakes are applied, providing a constant deceleration of 5 ft/sec^2. If the express train leaves station A four minutes after the local train has left A, determine (a) which of the two trains will arrive at station E first, (b) when the other train will arrive at station E.

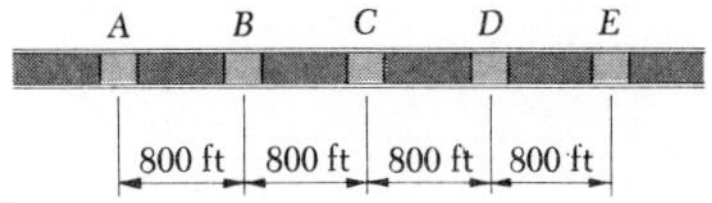

FIG. P 11.57

11.58. A police officer observes a car approaching at the unlawful speed of 60 mph. He gets on his motorcycle and starts chasing the car, just as it passes in front of him. After accelerating for 10 sec at a constant rate, the officer reaches his top speed of 75 mph. How long does it take him to overtake the car from the time he started? Draw the v–t and s–t curves for the car and the motorcycle.

11.59. A train starts at a station and accelerates uniformly at a rate of 1 ft/sec^2 until it reaches a speed of 20 ft/sec; it then proceeds at the constant speed of 20 ft/sec. Determine the time and the distance traveled if its *average* velocity is (a) 12 ft/sec, (b) 18 ft/sec.

11.60. The acceleration of a particle varies uniformly from $a = 90$ in./sec^2 at $t = 0$, to $a = -90$ in./sec^2 at $t = 6$ sec. Knowing that $s = 0$ and $v = 0$ when $t = 0$, determine (a) the maximum velocity of the particle, (b) its position at $t = 6$ sec, (c) its *average* velocity over the interval $0 < t < 6$ sec. Draw the a–t, v–t, and s–t curves for the motion.

11.61. The rate of change of acceleration is known as the *jerk;* large or abrupt rates of change of acceleration cause discomfort to elevator passengers. If the jerk, or rate of change of the acceleration, of an elevator is limited to ± 1.5 ft/sec^2 per second, determine the shortest time required for an elevator, starting from rest, to rise 24 ft and stop.

11.62. In order to maintain passenger comfort, the acceleration of an elevator is limited to 3 ft/sec^2 and the jerk, or rate of change of acceleration, is limited to ± 1.5 ft/sec^2 per second. If the elevator starts from rest, determine (a) the shortest time required for it to attain a constant velocity of 18 ft/sec, (b) the distance traveled in that time.

11.63. A training airplane lands on an aircraft carrier and is brought to rest in 3.0 sec by the arresting gear of the carrier. An accelerometer attached to the airplane provides the acceleration record shown. Determine by approximate means (*a*) the initial velocity of the airplane relative to the deck, (*b*) the distance the airplane travels along the deck before coming to rest.

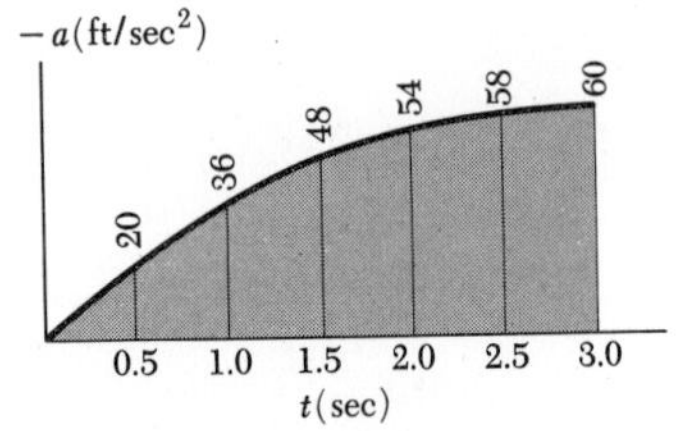

FIG. P 11.63

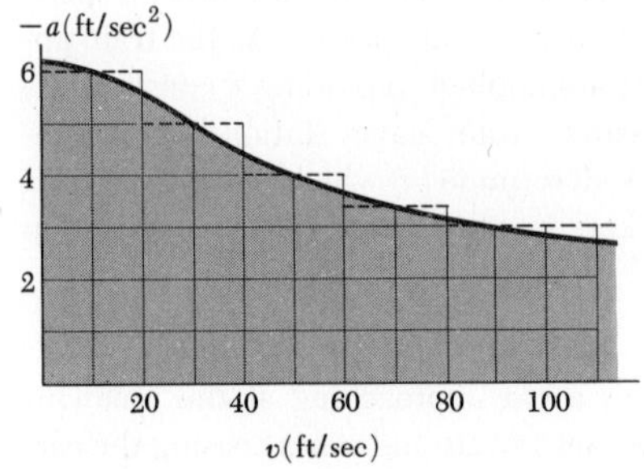

FIG. P 11.64

11.64. The maximum possible deceleration of a freight train under emergency conditions was determined experimentally; the results are shown (solid curve) in the figure. If the brakes are applied when the train is traveling at 40 mph, determine by approximate means (*a*) the time required for the train to come to rest, (*b*) the distance traveled in that time.

11.65. Solve Prob. 11.64 assuming that the train is traveling at 70 mph when the brakes are applied.

11.66. The v–s curve shown was obtained experimentally during the recoil of a gun. Determine by approximate means the acceleration (*a*) when $s = 3$ in., (*b*) when $v = 40$ in./sec.

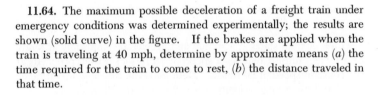

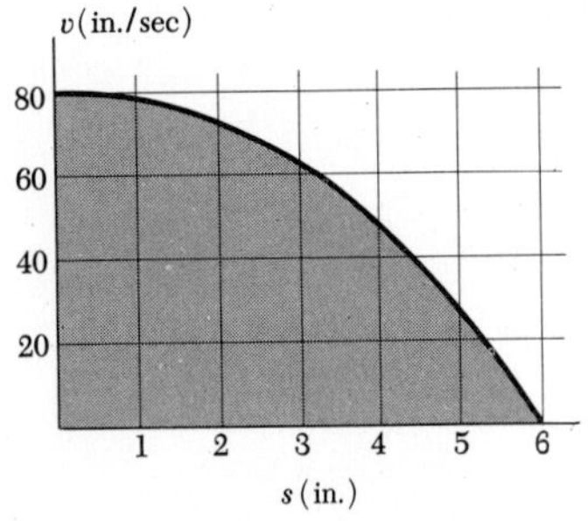

FIG. P 11.66

11.67. Using the method of Sec. 11.8, determine the position of the particle of Prob. 11.43 when $t = 12$ sec.

11.68. Using the method of Sec. 11.8, determine the maximum value of the position coordinate of the particle of Prob. 11.43.

11.69. For the particle of Prob. 11.45, draw the a–t curve and, using the method of Sec. 11.8, determine the position of the particle when (*a*) $t = 10$ sec, (*b*) $t = 14$ sec.

11.70. For the particle of Prob. 11.45, draw the a–t curve and, using the method of Sec. 11.8, determine (*a*) the position of the particle when $t = 8$ sec, (*b*) the maximum value of its position coordinate.

11.71. The acceleration of an object subjected to the blast of a large bomb is defined approximately by the curve shown. The object is initially at rest and is again at rest at time t_1. Using the method of Sec. 11.8, determine the distance through which the object is moved by the blast.

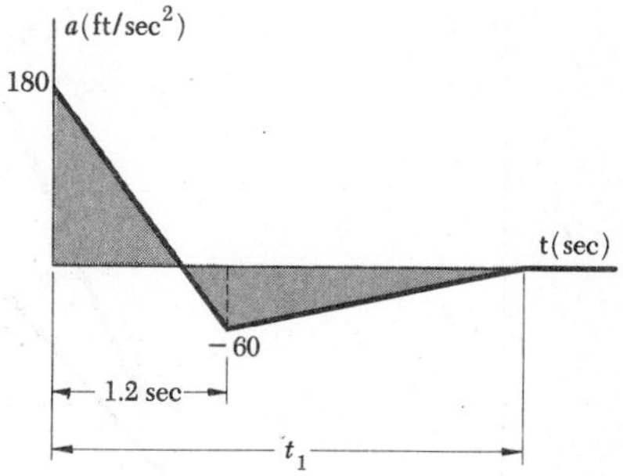

FIG. P 11.71

11.72. Using the method of Sec. 11.8, derive the formula $s = s_0 + v_0t + \frac{1}{2}at^2$, for the position coordinate of a particle in uniformly accelerated rectilinear motion.

CURVILINEAR MOTION OF PARTICLES

11.9. Position Vector, Velocity, and Acceleration. When a particle moves along a curve other than a straight line, we say that the particle is in *curvilinear motion.* To define the position P occupied by the particle at a given time t, we select a fixed reference system, such as the x, y, z axes shown in Fig. 11.14*a*, and draw the vector **r** joining the origin O and the point P. Since the vector **r** is characterized by its magnitude r and its direction with respect to the reference axes, it completely defines the position of the particle with respect to those axes; the vector **r** is referred to as the *position vector* of the particle at time t.

Consider now the vector **r**′ defining the position P' occupied by the same particle at a later time $t + \Delta t$. The vector Δ**r** joining P and P' represents the change in the position vector during the time interval Δt since, as we may easily check from Fig. 11.14*a*, the vector **r**′ is obtained by adding the vectors **r** and Δ**r** according to the triangle rule. We note that Δ**r** represents a change in *direction* as well as a change in *magnitude* of the position vector **r**. The *average velocity* of the particle over the time interval Δt is defined as the quotient of Δ**r** and Δt. Since Δ**r** is a vector and Δt a scalar, the quotient $\Delta\mathbf{r}/\Delta t$ is a vector attached at P, of the same direction as Δ**r**, and of magnitude equal to the magnitude of Δ**r** divided by Δt (Fig. 11.14*b*).

The *instantaneous velocity* of the particle at time t is obtained by choosing shorter and shorter time intervals Δt and, correspondingly, shorter and shorter vector increments Δ**r**. The instantaneous velocity is thus represented by the vector

$$\mathbf{v} = \lim_{\Delta t \to 0} \frac{\Delta \mathbf{r}}{\Delta t} \tag{11.14}$$

As Δt and Δ**r** become shorter, the points P and P' get closer; the vector **v** obtained at the limit must therefore be tangent to the path of the particle (Fig. 11.14*c*).

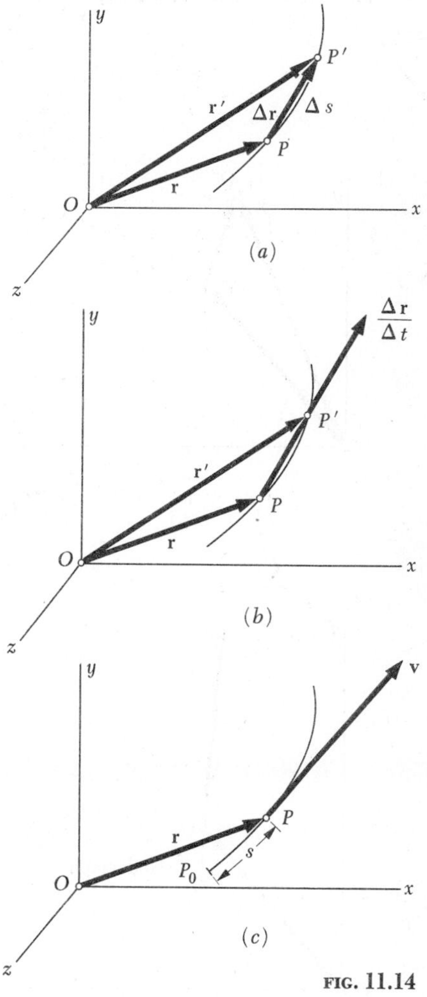

FIG. 11.14

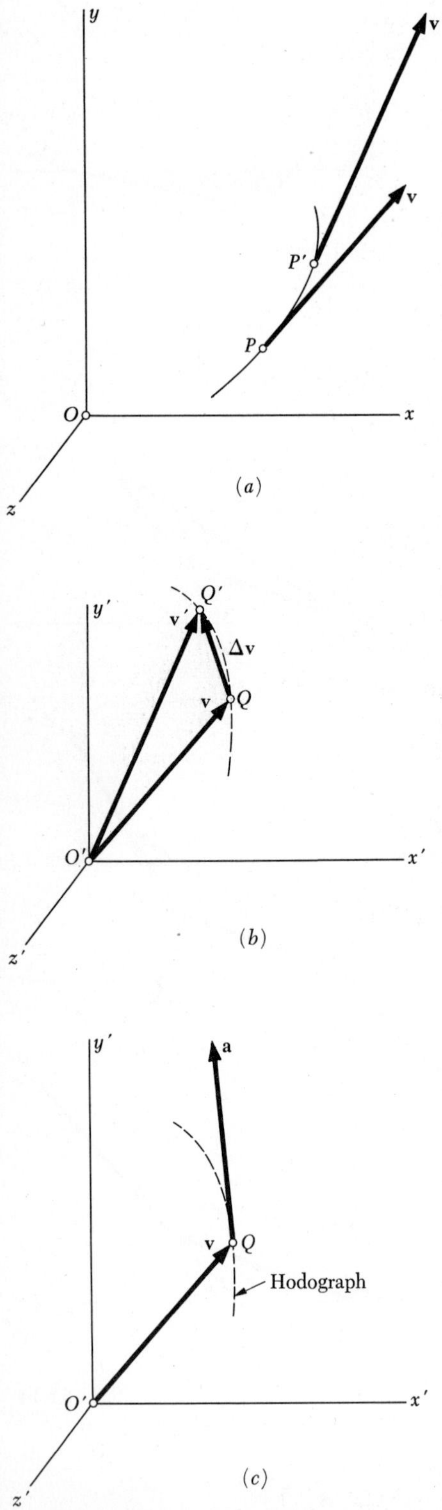

Since the position vector **r** depends upon the time t, we may refer to it as a *vector function* of the scalar variable t and denote it by $\mathbf{r}(t)$. Extending the concept of derivative of a scalar function introduced in elementary calculus, we shall refer to the limit of the quotient $\Delta\mathbf{r}/\Delta t$ as the *derivative* of the vector function $\mathbf{r}(t)$. We write

$$\mathbf{v} = \frac{d\mathbf{r}}{dt} \tag{11.15}$$

The magnitude v of the vector **v** is called the *speed* of the particle. It may be obtained by substituting for the vector $\Delta\mathbf{r}$ in formula (11.14) its magnitude represented by the straight-line segment PP'. But the length of the segment PP' approaches the length Δs of the arc PP' as Δt decreases (Fig. 11.14*a*), and we may write

$$v = \lim_{\Delta t \to 0} \frac{PP'}{\Delta t} = \lim_{\Delta t \to 0} \frac{\Delta s}{\Delta t}$$

$$v = \frac{ds}{dt} \tag{11.16}$$

The speed v may thus be obtained by differentiating with respect to t the length s of the arc described by the particle.

Consider the velocity **v** of the particle at time t and also its velocity $\mathbf{v}'$ at a later time $t + \Delta t$ (Fig. 11.15*a*). Let us draw both vectors **v** and $\mathbf{v}'$ from the same origin O' (Fig. 11.15*b*). The vector $\Delta\mathbf{v}$ joining Q and Q' represents the change in the velocity of the particle during the time interval Δt, since the vector $\mathbf{v}'$ may be obtained by adding the vectors **v** and $\Delta\mathbf{v}$. We should note that $\Delta\mathbf{v}$ represents a change in the *direction* of the velocity as well as a change in *speed*. The *average acceleration* of the particle over the time interval Δt is defined as the quotient of $\Delta\mathbf{v}$ and Δt. Since $\Delta\mathbf{v}$ is a vector and Δt a scalar, the quotient $\Delta\mathbf{v}/\Delta t$ is a vector of the same direction as $\Delta\mathbf{v}$.

The *instantaneous acceleration* of the particle at time t is ob-

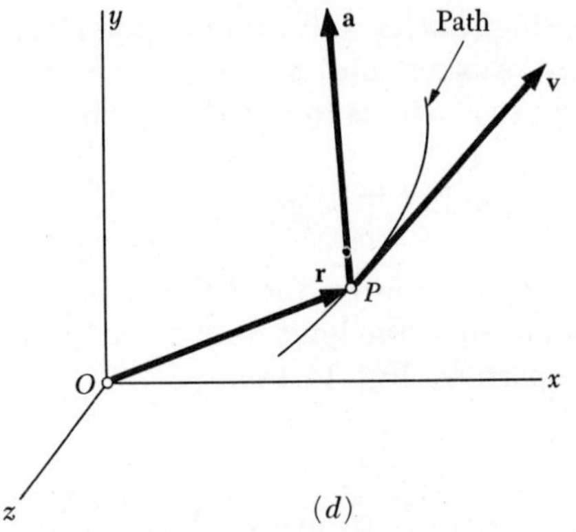

FIG. 11.15

tained by choosing smaller and smaller values for Δt and $\Delta \mathbf{v}$. The instantaneous acceleration is thus represented by the vector

$$\mathbf{a} = \lim_{\Delta t \to 0} \frac{\Delta \mathbf{v}}{\Delta t} \tag{11.17}$$

Noting that the velocity $\mathbf{v}$ is a vector function $\mathbf{v}(t)$ of the time t, we may refer to the limit of the quotient $\Delta \mathbf{v}/\Delta t$ as the derivative of $\mathbf{v}$ with respect to t. We write

$$\mathbf{a} = \frac{d\mathbf{v}}{dt} \tag{11.18}$$

We observe that the acceleration $\mathbf{a}$ is tangent to the curve described by the tip Q of the vector $\mathbf{v}$ when the latter is drawn from a fixed origin O' (Fig. 11.15*c*) and that, in general, the acceleration is *not* tangent to the path of the particle (Fig. 11.15*d*). The curve described by the tip of $\mathbf{v}$ and shown in Fig. 11.15*c* is called the *hodograph* of the motion.

11.10. Derivatives of Vector Functions. We saw in the preceding section that the velocity $\mathbf{v}$ of a particle in curvilinear motion may be represented by the derivative of the vector function $\mathbf{r}(t)$ characterizing the position of the particle. Similarly, the acceleration $\mathbf{a}$ of the particle may be represented by the derivative of the vector function $\mathbf{v}(t)$. In this section, we shall give a formal definition of the derivative of a vector function and establish a few rules governing the differentiation of sums and products of vector functions.

Let $\mathbf{P}(u)$ be a vector function of the scalar variable u. By that we mean that the scalar u completely defines the magnitude and direction of the vector $\mathbf{P}$. If the vector $\mathbf{P}$ is drawn from a fixed origin O and the scalar u is allowed to vary, the tip of $\mathbf{P}$ will describe a given curve in space. Consider the vectors $\mathbf{P}$ corresponding respectively to the values u and $u + \Delta u$ of the scalar variable (Fig. 11.16*a*). Let $\Delta\mathbf{P}$ be the vector joining the tips of the two given vectors; we write

$$\Delta\mathbf{P} = \mathbf{P}(u + \Delta u) - \mathbf{P}(u)$$

Dividing through by Δu and letting Δu approach zero, *we define the derivative of the vector function* $\mathbf{P}(u)$:

$$\frac{d\mathbf{P}}{du} = \lim_{\Delta u \to 0} \frac{\Delta\mathbf{P}}{\Delta u} = \lim_{\Delta u \to 0} \frac{\mathbf{P}(u + \Delta u) - \mathbf{P}(u)}{\Delta u} \tag{11.19}$$

As Δu approaches zero, the line of action of $\Delta\mathbf{P}$ becomes tangent to the curve of Fig. 11.16*a*. Thus, the derivative $d\mathbf{P}/du$ of the

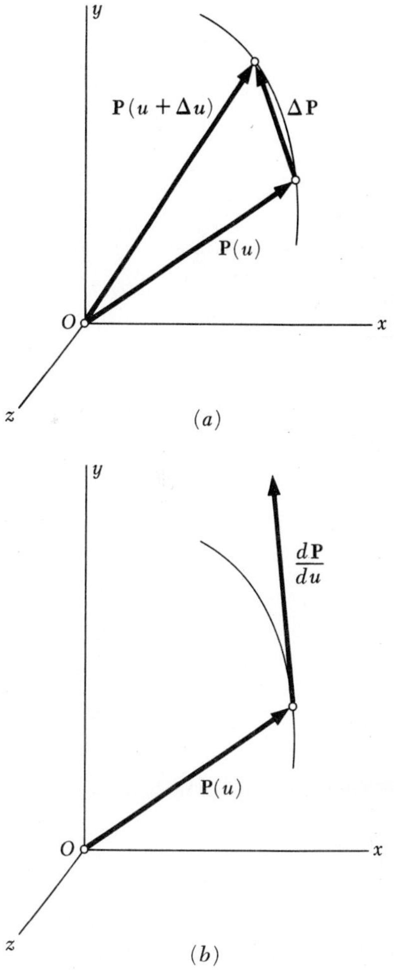

FIG. 11.16

vector function $\mathbf{P}(u)$ *is tangent to the curve described by the tip of* $\mathbf{P}(u)$ (Fig. 11.16*b*).

We shall now show that the standard rules for the differentiation of the sums and products of scalar functions may be extended to vector functions. Consider first the *sum of two vector functions* $\mathbf{P}(u)$ and $\mathbf{Q}(u)$ of the same scalar variable u. According to the definition given in (11.19), the derivative of the vector $\mathbf{P} + \mathbf{Q}$ is

$$\frac{d(\mathbf{P} + \mathbf{Q})}{du} = \lim_{\Delta u \to 0} \frac{\Delta(\mathbf{P} + \mathbf{Q})}{\Delta u} = \lim_{\Delta u \to 0} \left(\frac{\Delta \mathbf{P}}{\Delta u} + \frac{\Delta \mathbf{Q}}{\Delta u} \right)$$

or, since the limit of a sum is equal to the sum of the limits of its terms,

$$\frac{d(\mathbf{P} + \mathbf{Q})}{du} = \lim_{\Delta u \to 0} \frac{\Delta \mathbf{P}}{\Delta u} + \lim_{\Delta u \to 0} \frac{\Delta \mathbf{Q}}{\Delta u}$$

$$\frac{d(\mathbf{P} + \mathbf{Q})}{du} = \frac{d\mathbf{P}}{du} + \frac{d\mathbf{Q}}{du} \tag{11.20}$$

Next, we shall consider the *product of a scalar function* $f(u)$ *and of a vector function* $\mathbf{P}(u)$ of the same scalar variable u. The derivative of the vector $f\mathbf{P}$ is

$$\frac{d(f\mathbf{P})}{du} = \lim_{\Delta u \to 0} \frac{(f + \Delta f)(\mathbf{P} + \Delta \mathbf{P}) - f\mathbf{P}}{\Delta u}$$

$$= \lim_{\Delta u \to 0} \left(\frac{\Delta f}{\Delta u} \mathbf{P} + f \frac{\Delta \mathbf{P}}{\Delta u} \right)$$

or, recalling the properties of the limits of sums and products,

$$\frac{d(f\mathbf{P})}{du} = \frac{df}{du} \mathbf{P} + f \frac{d\mathbf{P}}{du} \tag{11.21}$$

The derivatives of the *scalar product* and of the *vector product* of two vector functions $\mathbf{P}(u)$ and $\mathbf{Q}(u)$ may be obtained in a similar way. We have

$$\frac{d(\mathbf{P} \cdot \mathbf{Q})}{du} = \frac{d\mathbf{P}}{du} \cdot \mathbf{Q} + \mathbf{P} \cdot \frac{d\mathbf{Q}}{du} \tag{11.22}$$

$$\frac{d(\mathbf{P} \times \mathbf{Q})}{du} = \frac{d\mathbf{P}}{du} \times \mathbf{Q} + \mathbf{P} \times \frac{d\mathbf{Q}}{du} \tag{11.23†}$$

† Since the vector product is not commutative (Sec. 3.3), the order of the factors in (11.23) must be maintained.

We shall use the properties established above to determine the *rectangular components of the derivative of a vector function* $\mathbf{P}(u)$. Resolving $\mathbf{P}$ into components along fixed rectangular axes x, y, z, we write

$$\mathbf{P} = P_x\mathbf{i} + P_y\mathbf{j} + P_z\mathbf{k} \tag{11.24}$$

where P_x, P_y, P_z are the rectangular scalar components of the vector $\mathbf{P}$, and $\mathbf{i}$, $\mathbf{j}$, $\mathbf{k}$ the unit vectors corresponding respectively to the x, y, and z axes (Sec. 2.11). By (11.20), the derivative of $\mathbf{P}$ is equal to the sum of the derivatives of the terms in the right-hand member. Since each of these terms is the product of a scalar and a vector function, we should use (11.21). But the unit vectors $\mathbf{i}$, $\mathbf{j}$, $\mathbf{k}$ have a constant magnitude (equal to 1) and fixed directions. Their derivatives are therefore zero, and we write

$$\frac{d\mathbf{P}}{du} = \frac{dP_x}{du}\mathbf{i} + \frac{dP_y}{du}\mathbf{j} + \frac{dP_z}{du}\mathbf{k} \tag{11.25}$$

Noting that the coefficients of the unit vectors are, by definition, the scalar components of the vector $d\mathbf{P}/du$, we conclude that *the rectangular scalar components of the derivative* $d\mathbf{P}/du$ *of the vector function* $\mathbf{P}(u)$ *are obtained by differentiating the corresponding scalar components of* $\mathbf{P}$.

Rate of Change of a Vector. When the vector $\mathbf{P}$ is a function of the time t, its derivative $d\mathbf{P}/dt$ represents the *rate of change* of $\mathbf{P}$ with respect to the frame $Oxyz$. Resolving $\mathbf{P}$ into rectangular components, we have, by (11.25),

$$\frac{d\mathbf{P}}{dt} = \frac{dP_x}{dt}\mathbf{i} + \frac{dP_y}{dt}\mathbf{j} + \frac{dP_z}{dt}\mathbf{k} \tag{11.25$'$}$$

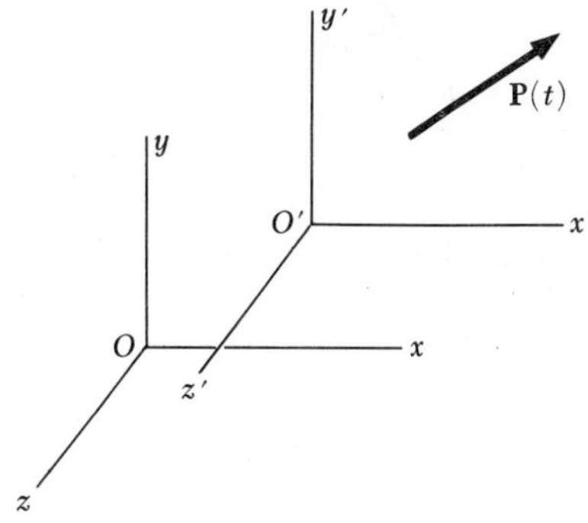

FIG. 11.17

As we shall see in Sec. 15.12, the rate of change of a vector $\mathbf{P}$, as observed from a *moving frame of reference*, is, in general, different from its rate of change as observed from a fixed frame of reference. However, if the moving frame $O'x'y'z'$ is in *translation*, i.e., if its axes remain parallel to the corresponding axes of the fixed frame $Oxyz$ (Fig. 11.17), the same unit vectors $\mathbf{i}$, $\mathbf{j}$, $\mathbf{k}$ are used in both frames, and the vector $\mathbf{P}$ has, at any given instant, the same components P_x, P_y, P_z in both frames. It follows from (11.25′) that the rate of change $d\mathbf{P}/dt$ is the same with respect to the frames $Oxyz$ and $O'x'y'z'$. We state, therefore: *The rate of change of a vector is the same with respect to a fixed frame and with respect to a frame in translation.* This property will greatly simplify our work, since we shall deal mainly with frames in translation.

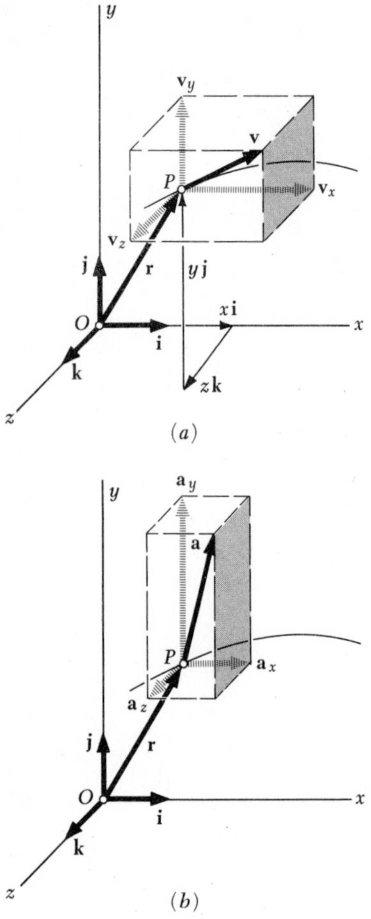

FIG. 11.18

11.11. Rectangular Components of Velocity and Acceleration. When the position of a particle P is defined at any instant by its rectangular coordinates x, y, and z, it is convenient to resolve the velocity **v** and the acceleration **a** of the particle into rectangular components (Fig. 11.18).

Resolving the position vector **r** of the particle into rectangular components, we write

$$\mathbf{r} = x\mathbf{i} + y\mathbf{j} + z\mathbf{k} \tag{11.26}$$

where the coordinates x, y, z are functions of t. Differentiating twice, we obtain

$$\mathbf{v} = \frac{d\mathbf{r}}{dt} = \dot{x}\mathbf{i} + \dot{y}\mathbf{j} + \dot{z}\mathbf{k} \tag{11.27}$$

$$\mathbf{a} = \frac{d\mathbf{v}}{dt} = \ddot{x}\mathbf{i} + \ddot{y}\mathbf{j} + \ddot{z}\mathbf{k} \tag{11.28}$$

where $\dot{x}$, $\dot{y}$, $\dot{z}$ and $\ddot{x}$, $\ddot{y}$, $\ddot{z}$ represent, respectively, the first and second derivatives of x, y, and z with respect to t. It follows from (11.27) and (11.28) that the scalar components of the velocity and acceleration are

$$v_x = \dot{x} \qquad v_y = \dot{y} \qquad v_z = \dot{z} \tag{11.29}$$

$$a_x = \ddot{x} \qquad a_y = \ddot{y} \qquad a_z = \ddot{z} \tag{11.30}$$

A positive value for v_x indicates that the vector component $\mathbf{v}_x$ is directed to the right, a negative value that it is directed to the left; the sense of each of the other vector components may be determined in a similar way from the sign of the corresponding scalar component. If desired, the magnitudes and directions of the velocity and acceleration may be obtained from their scalar components by the methods of Secs. 2.6 and 2.11.

The use of rectangular components to describe the position, the velocity, and the acceleration of a particle is particularly effective when the component a_x of the acceleration depends only upon t, x, and/or v_x, and when, similarly, a_y depends only upon t, y, and/or v_y, and a_z upon t, z, and/or v_z. Equations (11.30) may then be integrated independently, and so may Eqs. (11.29). In other words, the motion of the particle in the x direction, its motion in the y direction, and its motion in the z direction may be considered separately.

In the case of the *motion of a projectile*, for example, it may be shown (see Sec. 12.7) that the components of the acceleration are

$$a_x = \ddot{x} = 0 \qquad a_y = \ddot{y} = -g \qquad a_z = \ddot{z} = 0$$

if the resistance of the air is neglected. Denoting by x_0, y_0, z_0

the coordinates of the gun, and by $(v_x)_0$, $(v_y)_0$, $(v_z)_0$ the components of the initial velocity $\mathbf{v}_0$ of the projectile, we integrate twice in t and obtain

$$v_x = \dot{x} = (v_x)_0 \qquad v_y = \dot{y} = (v_y)_0 - gt \qquad v_z = \dot{z} = (v_z)_0$$
$$x = x_0 + (v_x)_0 t \qquad y = y_0 + (v_y)_0 t - \tfrac{1}{2}gt^2 \qquad z = z_0 + (v_z)_0 t$$

If the projectile is fired in the xy plane from the origin O, we have $x_0 = y_0 = z_0 = 0$ and $(v_z)_0 = 0$, and the equations of motion reduce to

$$v_x = (v_x)_0 \qquad v_y = (v_y)_0 - gt \qquad v_z = 0$$
$$x = (v_x)_0 t \qquad y = (v_y)_0 t - \tfrac{1}{2}gt^2 \qquad z = 0$$

These equations show that the projectile remains in the xy plane and that its motion in the horizontal direction is uniform, while its motion in the vertical direction is uniformly accelerated. The motion of a projectile may thus be replaced by two independent rectilinear motions, which are easily visualized if we assume that the projectile is fired vertically with an initial velocity $(\mathbf{v}_y)_0$ from a platform moving with a constant horizontal velocity $(\mathbf{v}_x)_0$ (Fig. 11.19). The coordinate x of the projectile is equal at any instant to the distance traveled by the platform, while its coordinate y may be computed as if the projectile were moving along a vertical line.

It may be observed that the equations defining the coordinates x and y of a projectile at any instant are the parametric equations of a parabola. Thus, the trajectory of a projectile is *parabolic.* This result, however, ceases to be valid when the resistance of the air or the variation of g with altitude is taken into account.

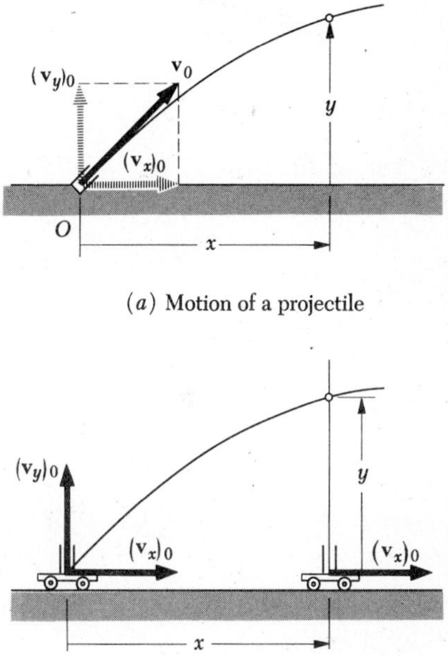

(*a*) Motion of a projectile

(*b*) Equivalent rectilinear motions

FIG. 11.19

11.12. Motion Relative to a Frame in Translation. In the preceding section, a single frame of reference was used to describe the motion of a particle. In most cases this frame was attached to the earth and was considered as fixed. We shall now analyze situations in which it is convenient to use simultaneously several frames of reference. If one of the frames is attached to the earth, we shall call it a *fixed frame of reference* and the other frames will be referred to as *moving frames of reference.* It should be understood, however, that the selection of a fixed frame of reference is purely arbitrary. Any frame may be designated as "fixed"; all other frames not rigidly attached to this frame will then be described as "moving."

Consider two particles A and B moving in space (Fig. 11.20); the vectors $\mathbf{r}_A$ and $\mathbf{r}_B$ define their positions at any given instant with respect to the fixed frame of reference $Oxyz$. Consider now a system of axes x', y', z' centered at A and parallel to the

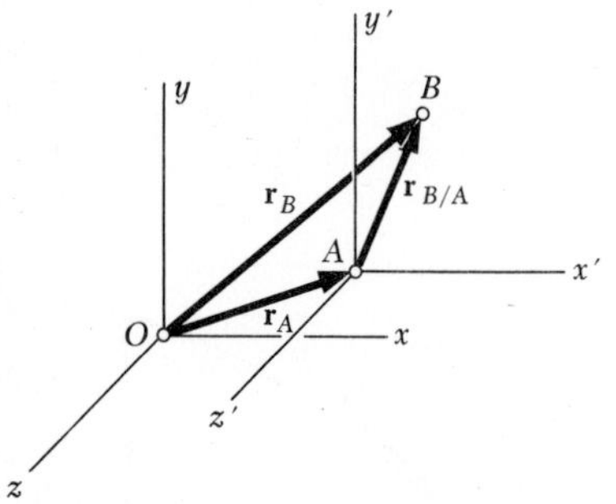

FIG. 11.20

x, y, z axes. While the origin of these axes moves, their orientation remains the same; the frame of reference $Ax'y'z'$ is in *translation* with respect to $Oxyz$. The vector $\mathbf{r}_{B/A}$ joining A and B defines *the position of B relative to the moving frame* $Ax'y'z'$ (or, for short, *the position of B relative to* A).

We note from Fig. 11.20 that the position vector $\mathbf{r}_B$ of particle B is the sum of the position vector $\mathbf{r}_A$ of particle A and of the position vector $\mathbf{r}_{B/A}$ of B relative to A; we write

$$\mathbf{r}_B = \mathbf{r}_A + \mathbf{r}_{B/A} \tag{11.31}$$

Differentiating (11.31) with respect to t within the fixed frame of reference, we have

$$\frac{d\mathbf{r}_B}{dt} = \frac{d\mathbf{r}_A}{dt} + \frac{d\mathbf{r}_{B/A}}{dt} \tag{11.32}$$

The derivatives $d\mathbf{r}_A/dt$ and $d\mathbf{r}_B/dt$ represent, respectively, the velocities $\mathbf{v}_A$ and $\mathbf{v}_B$ of the particles A and B. The derivative $d\mathbf{r}_{B/A}/dt$ represents the rate of change of $\mathbf{r}_{B/A}$ with respect to the frame $Ax'y'z'$, as well as with respect to the fixed frame, since $Ax'y'z'$ is in translation (Sec. 11.10). This derivative, therefore, defines *the velocity* $\mathbf{v}_{B/A}$ *of B relative to the frame* $Ax'y'z'$ (or, for short, *the velocity* $\mathbf{v}_{B/A}$ *of B relative to* A). We write

$$\mathbf{v}_B = \mathbf{v}_A + \mathbf{v}_{B/A} \tag{11.33}$$

Differentiating Eq. (11.33) with respect to t, and using the derivative $d\mathbf{v}_{B/A}/dt$ to define *the acceleration* $\mathbf{a}_{B/A}$ *of B relative to the frame* $Ax'y'z'$ (or, for short, *the acceleration of* $\mathbf{a}_{B/A}$ *of B relative to* A), we write

$$\mathbf{a}_B = \mathbf{a}_A + \mathbf{a}_{B/A} \tag{11.34}$$

The motion of B with respect to the fixed frame $Oxyz$ is referred to as the *absolute motion of B*. The equations derived in this section show that *the absolute motion of B may be obtained by combining the motion of A and the relative motion of B with respect to the moving frame attached to A.* Equation (11.33), for example, expresses that the absolute velocity $\mathbf{v}_B$ of particle B may be obtained by adding vectorially the velocity of A and the velocity of B relative to the frame $Ax'y'z'$. Equation (11.34) expresses a similar property in terms of the accelerations. We should keep in mind, however, that *the frame* $Ax'y'z'$ *is in translation*, i.e., that, while it moves with A, it maintains the same orientation. As we shall see later (Sec. 15.13), different relations must be used in the case of a rotating frame of reference.

SAMPLE PROBLEM 11.7

A projectile is fired from the edge of a 500-ft cliff with an initial velocity of 600 ft/sec, at an angle of 30° with the horizontal. Neglecting air resistance, find (*a*) the horizontal distance from the gun to the point where the projectile strikes the ground, (*b*) the greatest elevation above the ground reached by the projectile.

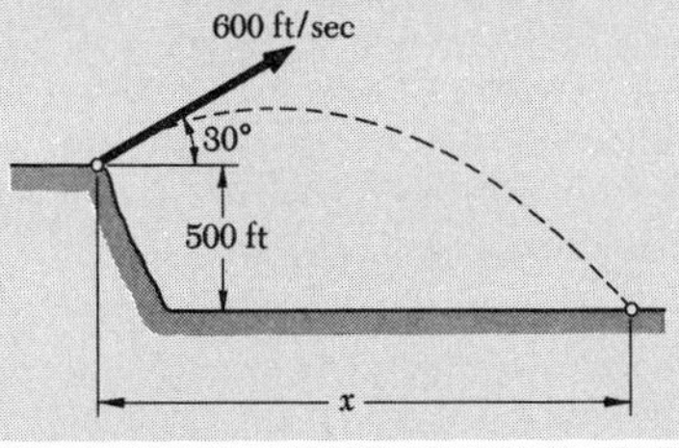

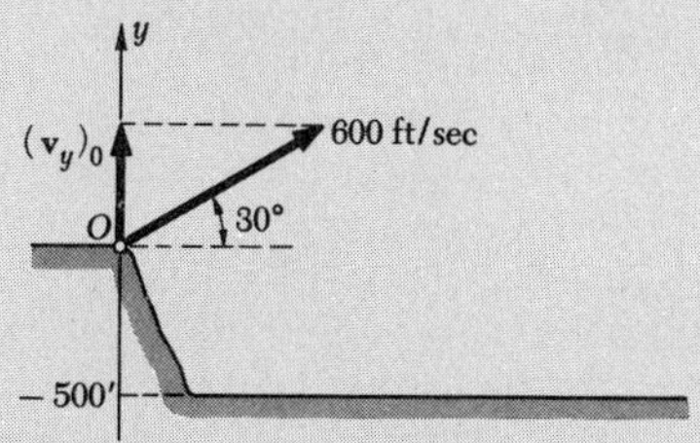

Vertical Motion. Uniformly accelerated motion. Choosing the positive sense of the y axis upward and placing the origin O at the gun, we have

$$(v_y)_0 = 600 \sin 30° = +300 \text{ ft/sec}$$
$$a = -32.2 \text{ ft/sec}^2$$

Substituting into the equations of uniformly accelerated motion, we have

$$v_y = (v_y)_0 + at \qquad v_y = 300 - 32.2t \qquad (1)$$
$$y = (v_y)_0 t + \tfrac{1}{2}at^2 \qquad y = 300t - 16.1t^2 \qquad (2)$$
$$v_y^2 = (v_y)_0^2 + 2ay \qquad v_y^2 = 90{,}000 - 64.4y \qquad (3)$$

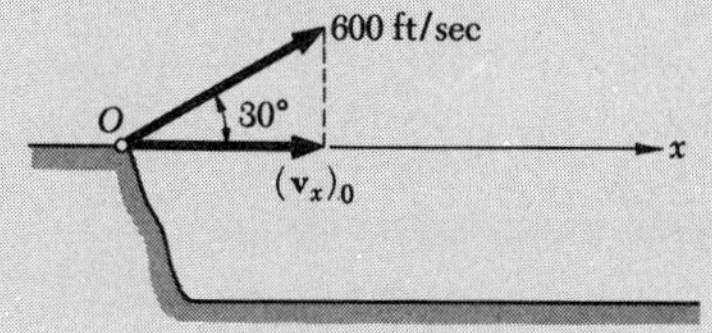

Horizontal Motion. Uniform motion. Choosing the positive sense of the x axis to the right, we have

$$(v_x)_0 = 600 \cos 30° = +520 \text{ ft/sec}$$

Substituting into the equation of uniform motion, we obtain

$$x = (v_x)_0 t \qquad x = 520t \qquad (4)$$

a. **Horizontal Distance.** When the projectile strikes the ground, we have

$$y = -500 \text{ ft}$$

Carrying this value into Eq. (2) for the vertical motion, we write

$$-500 = 300t - 16.1t^2 \qquad t^2 - 18.6t - 31.1 = 0 \qquad t = 20.1 \text{ sec}$$

Carrying $t = 20.1$ sec into Eq. (4) for the horizontal motion, we obtain

$$x = (520)(20.1) \qquad x = 10{,}450 \text{ ft} \quad ◄$$

b. **Greatest Elevation.** When the projectile reaches its greatest elevation, we have $v_y = 0$; carrying this value into Eq. (3) for the vertical motion, we write

$$0 = 90{,}000 - 64.4y \qquad y = 1{,}398 \text{ ft}$$

Greatest elevation above ground = 500 ft + 1,398 ft
= 1,898 ft ◄

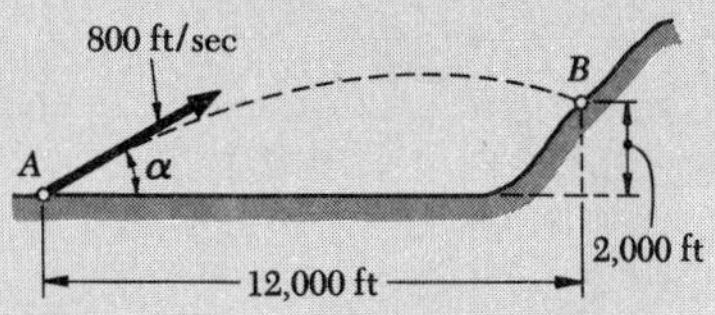

SAMPLE PROBLEM 11.8

A projectile is fired with an initial velocity of 800 ft/sec at a target B located 2,000 ft above the gun A and at a horizontal distance of 12,000 ft. Neglecting air resistance, determine the value of the firing angle α.

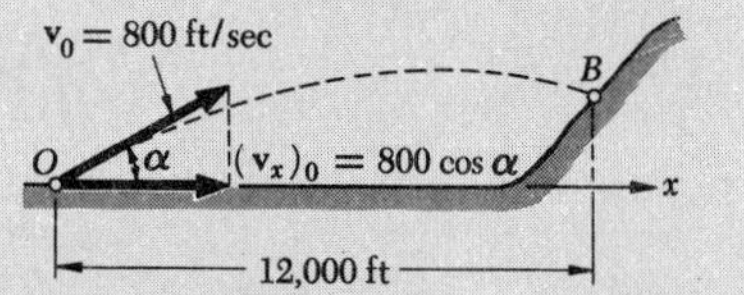

Horizontal Motion. Placing the origin of coordinates at the gun, we have

$$(v_x)_0 = 800 \cos \alpha$$

Substituting into the equation of uniform horizontal motion, we obtain

$$x = (v_x)_0 t \qquad x = (800 \cos \alpha)t$$

The time required for the projectile to move through a horizontal distance of 12,000 ft is obtained by making x equal to 12,000 ft.

$$12{,}000 = (800 \cos \alpha)t$$

$$t = \frac{12{,}000}{800 \cos \alpha} = \frac{15}{\cos \alpha}$$

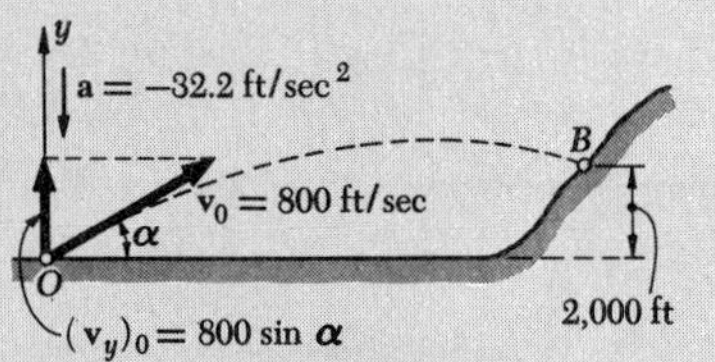

Vertical Motion

$$(v_y)_0 = 800 \sin \alpha \qquad a = -32.2 \text{ ft/sec}^2$$

Substituting into the equation of uniformly accelerated vertical motion, we obtain

$$y = (v_y)_0 t + \tfrac{1}{2}at^2 \qquad y = (800 \sin \alpha)t - 16.1t^2$$

When $x = 12{,}000$ ft, we must have $y = 2{,}000$ ft if the projectile is to hit the target. Substituting for y and making t equal to the value found above, we write

$$2{,}000 = 800 \sin \alpha \frac{15}{\cos \alpha} - 16.1\left(\frac{15}{\cos \alpha}\right)^2$$

Since $1/\cos^2 \alpha = \sec^2 \alpha = 1 + \tan^2 \alpha$, we have

$$2{,}000 = (800)(15) \tan \alpha - (16.1)(15^2)(1 + \tan^2 \alpha)$$

$$3{,}622 \tan^2 \alpha - 12{,}000 \tan \alpha + 5{,}622 = 0$$

Solving this quadratic equation for $\tan \alpha$, we have

$$\tan \alpha = 0.565 \qquad \text{and} \qquad \tan \alpha = 2.75$$

$$\alpha = 29.5° \qquad \text{and} \qquad \alpha = 70.0° \quad ◄$$

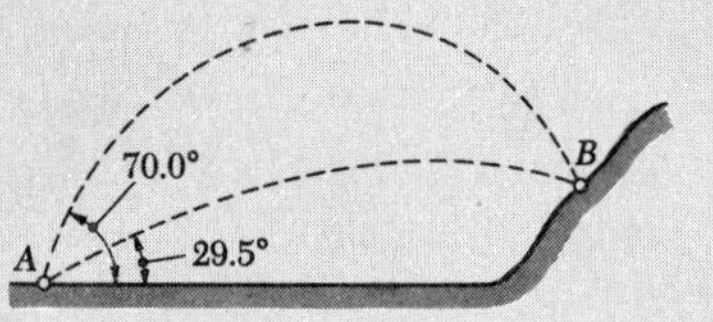

The target will be hit if either of these two firing angles is used (see figure).

SAMPLE PROBLEM 11.9

Automobile A is traveling east at the constant speed of 15 mph. As automobile A crosses the intersection shown, automobile B starts from rest 90 ft north of the intersection and moves south with a constant acceleration of 4 ft/sec². Determine the position, velocity, and acceleration of B relative to A five sec after A crosses the intersection.

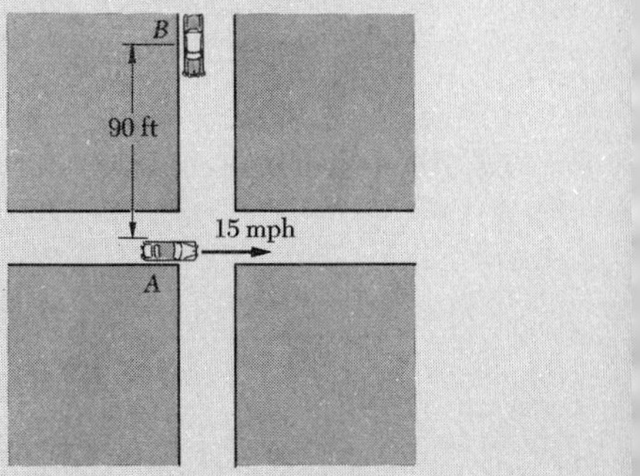

Solution. We choose x and y axes with origin at the intersection of the two streets and with positive senses directed respectively east and north.

Motion of Automobile A. First the speed is expressed in ft/sec.

$$15 \text{ mph} = \left(15 \frac{\text{miles}}{\text{hr}}\right)\left(\frac{5{,}280 \text{ ft}}{1 \text{ mile}}\right)\left(\frac{1 \text{ hr}}{3{,}600 \text{ sec}}\right) = 22 \text{ ft/sec}$$

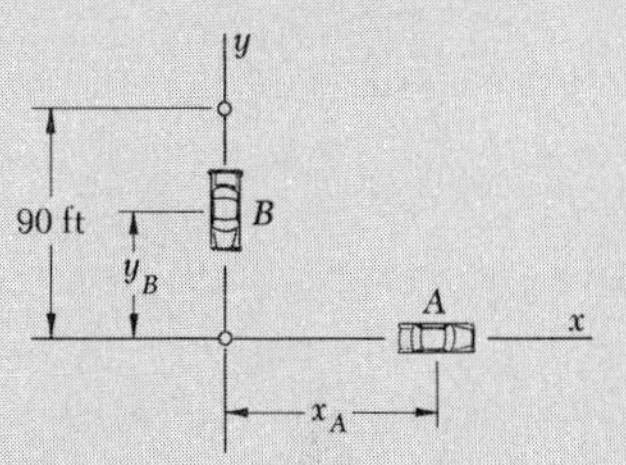

Noting that the motion of A is uniform, we write, for any time t,

$$a_A = 0$$
$$v_A = +22 \text{ ft/sec}$$
$$x_A = (x_A)_0 + v_A t = 0 + 22t$$

For $t = 5$ sec, we have

$$a_A = 0 \qquad \mathbf{a}_A = 0$$
$$v_A = +22 \text{ ft/sec} \qquad \mathbf{v}_A = 22 \text{ ft/sec} \rightarrow$$
$$x_A = +(22)(5) = +110 \text{ ft} \qquad \mathbf{r}_A = 110 \text{ ft} \rightarrow$$

Motion of Automobile B. We note that the motion of B is uniformly accelerated, and write

$$a_B = -4 \text{ ft/sec}^2$$
$$v_B = (v_B)_0 + at = 0 - 4t$$
$$y_B = (y_B)_0 + (v_B)_0 t + \tfrac{1}{2}a_B t^2 = 90 + 0 - \tfrac{1}{2}(4)t^2$$

For $t = 5$ sec, we have

$$a_B = -4 \text{ ft/sec}^2 \qquad \mathbf{a}_B = 4 \text{ ft/sec}^2 \downarrow$$
$$v_B = -(4)(5) = -20 \text{ ft/sec} \qquad \mathbf{v}_B = 20 \text{ ft/sec} \downarrow$$
$$y_B = 90 - \tfrac{1}{2}(4)(5)^2 = +40 \text{ ft} \qquad \mathbf{r}_B = 40 \text{ ft} \uparrow$$

Motion of B **Relative to** A. We draw the triangle corresponding to the vector equation $\mathbf{r}_B = \mathbf{r}_A + \mathbf{r}_{B/A}$ and obtain the magnitude and direction of the position vector of B relative to A.

$$r_{B/A} = 117.1 \text{ ft} \qquad \alpha = 20.0°$$
$$\mathbf{r}_{B/A} = 117.1 \text{ ft} \measuredangle 20.0° \blacktriangleleft$$

Proceeding in a similar fashion, we find the velocity and acceleration of B relative to A.

$$\mathbf{v}_B = \mathbf{v}_A + \mathbf{v}_{B/A}$$
$$v_{B/A} = 29.7 \text{ ft/sec} \qquad \beta = 42.3°$$
$$\mathbf{v}_{B/A} = 29.7 \text{ ft/sec} \measuredangle 42.3° \blacktriangleleft$$

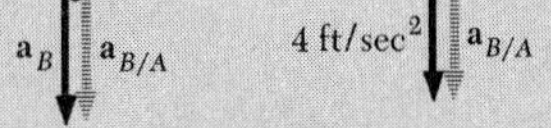

$$\mathbf{a}_B = \mathbf{a}_A + \mathbf{a}_{B/A}$$
$$\mathbf{a}_{B/A} = 4 \text{ ft/sec}^2 \downarrow \blacktriangleleft$$

PROBLEMS

Note. Neglect air resistance in problems concerning projectiles.

11.73. The motion of a particle is defined by the equations $x = 2t^2 - 4t$ and $y = 2(t - 1)^2 - 4(t - 1)$, where x and y are expressed in feet and t in seconds. Determine the velocity and acceleration when (*a*) $t = 1$ sec, (*b*) $t = 3$ sec.

11.74. Determine the magnitude of the smallest velocity reached by the particle of Prob. 11.73. Determine also the corresponding time, position, and direction of the velocity.

11.75. The motion of a particle is defined by the equations $x = (t + 1)^2$ and $y = (t + 1)^{-2}$, where x and y are expressed in feet and t in seconds. Show that the path of the particle is a rectangular hyperbola and determine the velocity and acceleration when (*a*) $t = 0$, (*b*) $t = \frac{1}{2}$ sec.

11.76. The motion of a particle is defined by the equations $x = 10(1 - e^{-t})$ and $y = 10t/(t + 1)$, where x and y are expressed in inches and t in seconds. Determine the position, velocity, and acceleration when (*a*) $t = 0$, (*b*) $t = 1$ sec.

11.77. The motion of a vibrating particle is defined by the position vector $\mathbf{r} = (4 \sin \pi t)\mathbf{i} + (\cos 2\pi t)\mathbf{j}$, where r is expressed in inches and t in seconds. (*a*) Determine the velocity and acceleration when $t = 1$ sec. (*b*) Show that the path of the particle is parabolic.

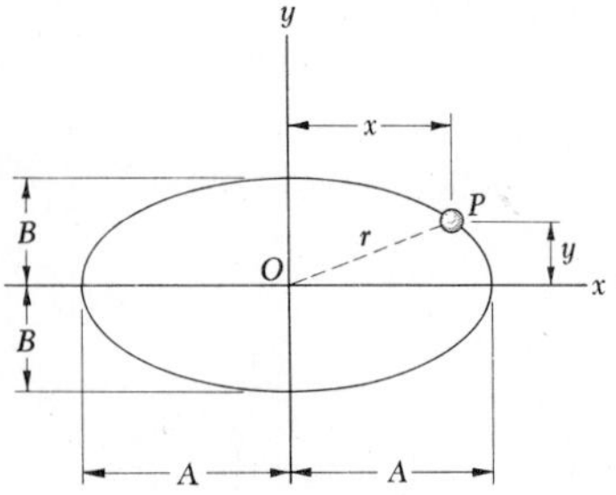

FIG. P11.78

11.78. A particle moves in an elliptic path defined by the position vector $\mathbf{r} = (A \cos pt)\mathbf{i} + (B \sin pt)\mathbf{j}$. Show that the acceleration (*a*) is directed toward the origin, (*b*) is proportional to the distance from the origin to the particle.

11.79. The three-dimensional motion of a particle is defined by the position vector $\mathbf{r} = t\mathbf{i} + t^2\mathbf{j} + t^3\mathbf{k}$, where r is expressed in feet and t in seconds. Determine the magnitudes of the velocity and acceleration when (*a*) $t = 0$, (*b*) $t = 1$ sec.

11.80. The three-dimensional motion of a particle is defined by the position vector $\mathbf{r} = ct\mathbf{i} + (R \sin pt)\mathbf{j} + (R \cos pt)\mathbf{k}$. Determine the magnitudes of the velocity and acceleration of the particle. (The space curve described by the particle is a helix.)

11.81. A man standing on the edge of a 60-ft cliff throws a stone in a horizontal direction, straight ahead of him. Knowing that the stone hits the ground 80 ft from the bottom of the cliff, determine (*a*) the initial velocity of the stone, (*b*) the distance at which a stone would hit the ground if it were thrown horizontally with the same velocity from a cliff 120 ft high.

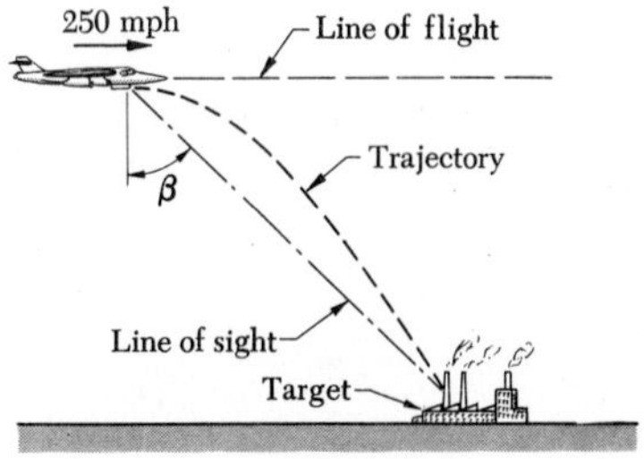

FIG. P 11.82

11.82. A bomber is flying horizontally in a straight line at 250 mph at an altitude $h = 10{,}000$ ft. (*a*) Find the angle β that the line of sight from the bomber to the target should form with the vertical when the bombs are released. (*b*) Where will the bomber be when the bombs strike the target?

11.83. In Prob. 11.82, determine the altitude h for which the angle β is 45°.

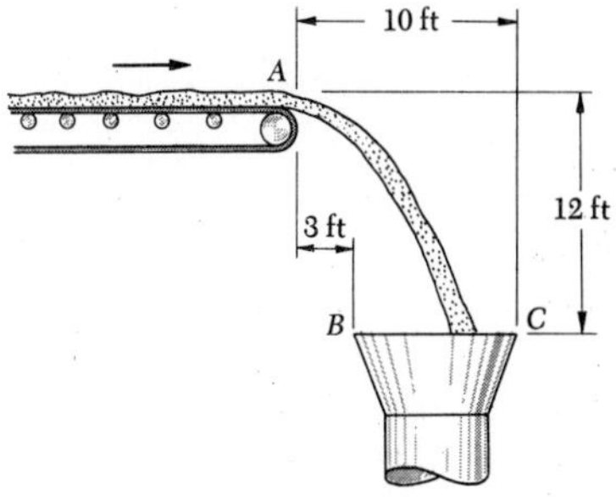

FIG. P 11.84

11.84. Sand is discharged at A from a horizontal conveyor belt into a hopper as shown. For what range of speeds of the belt will the sand enter the hopper BC?

11.85. Standing on the side of a hill, an archer shoots an arrow with an initial velocity of 200 ft/sec at an angle $\alpha = 15°$ with the horizontal. Determine the horizontal distance d traveled by the arrow before it strikes the ground at B.

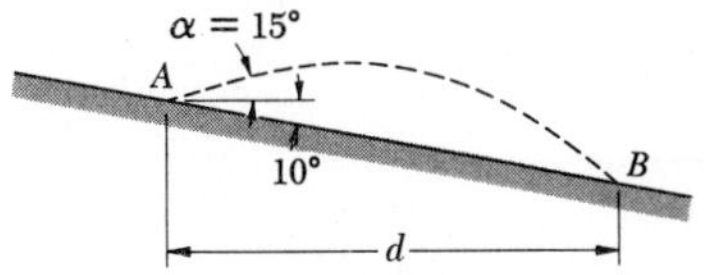

FIG. P 11.85

11.86. A man wants to throw a ball onto the flat roof of a building 37 ft high. Standing 30 ft from the wall, he throws the ball with a velocity of 55.8 ft/sec at an angle of 60° with the horizontal, releasing it 4.8 ft from the ground. How far from the edge of the roof will the ball fall? Check that the ball will clear the edge of the roof.

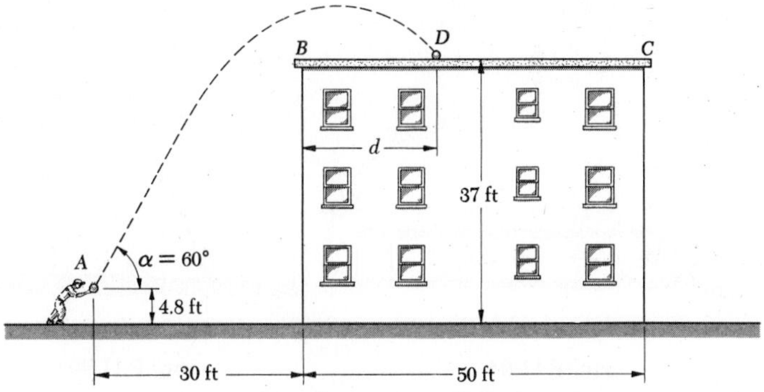

FIG. P 11.86 AND P 11.88

11.87. In Prob. 11.86, determine the largest and smallest values of the initial velocity for which the ball will fall on the roof.

11.88. A man throws a ball from A in the direction shown. Determine the portion of the roof on which the ball cannot land.

11.89. A projectile is fired with an initial velocity of 700 ft/sec. Find the angle at which it should be fired if it is to hit a target located at a distance of 12,000 ft on the same level.

11.90. Solve Sample Prob. 11.8 assuming that the projectile is fired from B and that the target is at A.

11.91. A projectile is fired with an initial velocity $\mathbf{v}_0$ at an angle α with the horizontal. Determine (*a*) the maximum height h reached by the projectile, (*b*) the horizontal range R of the projectile.

11.92. Find the maximum horizontal range R of a projectile fired with an initial velocity of magnitude v_0, and determine the corresponding firing angle α.

11.93. A boy can throw a baseball a maximum distance of 90 ft in New York, where $g = 32.2$ ft/sec². How far could he throw the baseball (*a*) in Singapore, where $g = 32.1$ ft/sec²? (*b*) on the moon, where $g = 5.31$ ft/sec²?

11.94. A nozzle discharges a stream of water with an initial velocity $\mathbf{v}_0$ of 40 ft/sec into the end of a horizontal pipe of inside diameter $d = 4$ ft. Determine the largest distance x that the stream can reach.

11.95. If the maximum horizontal range of a given gun is R, determine the firing angle which should be used to hit a target located at a distance $\frac{1}{2}R$ on the same level.

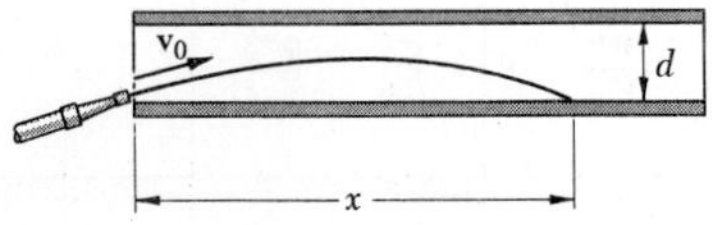

FIG. P11.94

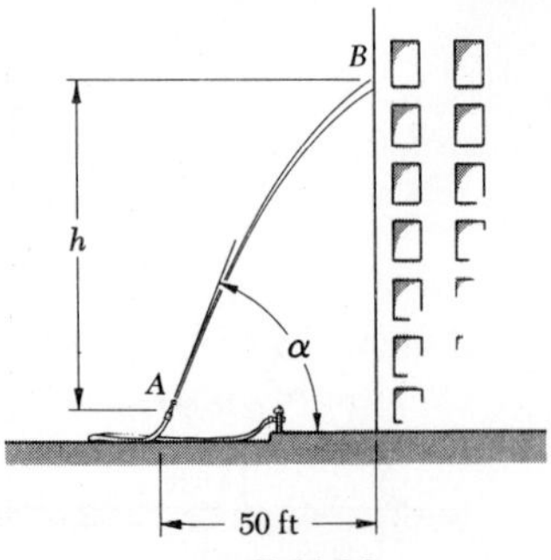

FIG. P11.96

11.96. A fire nozzle discharges water with an initial velocity $\mathbf{v}_0$ of 80 ft/sec. Knowing that the nozzle is located 50 ft from a building, determine (*a*) the maximum height h that can be reached by the water, (*b*) the corresponding angle α.

11.97. Solve Prob. 11.96 assuming that the nozzle is located 100 ft from the building.

11.98. Show that the trajectory of a projectile is a parabola if air resistance is neglected.

11.99. Determine the equation of the path of the projectile of Sample Prob. 11.7 in terms of the coordinates x and y.

***11.100.** A conveyor belt AB of length 20 ft is attached to a hinge at A and may be set at any slope as shown. Sand is discharged by the belt at B and falls freely until it reaches the ground at point C. Knowing that the belt moves with a constant velocity $\mathbf{v}_0$ of 10 ft/sec, determine (*a*) the largest possible distance d between A and C, (*b*) the corresponding angle α.

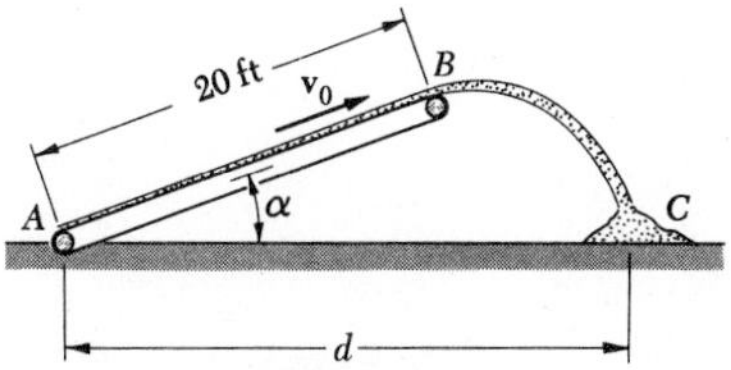

FIG. P 11.100

11.101. Ship A travels due south at 18 knots, while ship B travels toward the southeast at 15 knots. Determine the velocity (*a*) of ship B relative to ship A, (*b*) of ship A relative to ship B.

11.102. As observed from a ship moving due east at 8 mph, the wind appears to blow from the southwest at 12 mph. Determine the magnitude and direction of the true wind velocity.

11.103. Two airplanes A and B are each flying at a constant altitude of 3,000 ft. Plane A is flying due east at a constant speed of 300 mph while plane B is flying southwest at a constant speed of 450 mph. Determine the change in position of plane B relative to plane A which takes place during a 2-min interval.

11.104. The truck A and the automobile B travel at the constant speeds shown. Five seconds after the automobile crosses the overpass, the truck goes under the same overpass. Determine (*a*) the velocity of the automobile relative to the truck, (*b*) the change in position of the automobile relative to the truck during a 10-sec interval, (*c*) the distance between the automobile and the truck 10 sec after the truck has gone under the overpass.

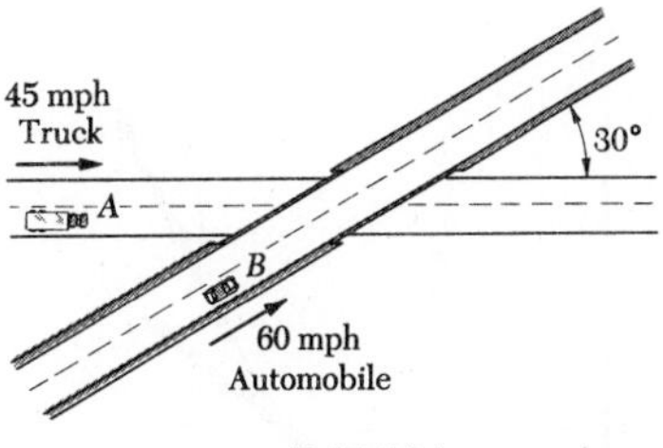

FIG. P 11.104

11.105. As he passes a pole, a man riding in a truck tries to hit the pole by throwing a stone with a horizontal velocity of 75 ft/sec relative to the truck. Knowing that the speed of the truck is 30 mph, determine (*a*) the direction in which he must throw the stone, (*b*) the horizontal velocity of the stone with respect to the ground.

11.106. During a rainstorm the paths of the raindrops appear to form an angle of 30° with the vertical when observed from a side window of a train moving at a speed of 10 mph. A short time later, after the speed of the train has increased to 20 mph, the angle between the vertical and the paths of the drops appears to be 45°. If the train were stopped, at what angle and with what velocity would the drops be observed to fall?

11.107. As the speed of the train of Prob. 11.106 increases, the angle between the vertical and the paths of the drops becomes equal to 60°. Determine the speed of the train at that time.

11.108. An antiaircraft gun fires a shell as a plane passes directly over the position of the gun at an altitude of 6,000 ft. The muzzle velocity of the shell is 1,500 ft/sec. Knowing that the plane is flying horizontally at 450 mph, determine (*a*) the required firing angle if the shell is to hit the plane, (*b*) the velocity and acceleration of the shell relative to the plane at the time of impact.

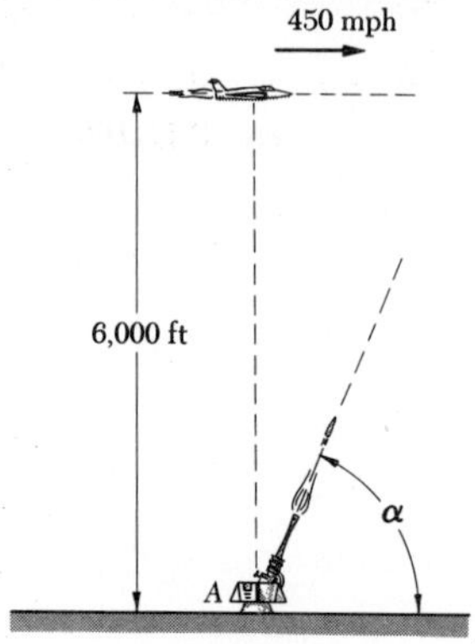

FIG. P11.108

11.109. The conveyor belt *A* moves at a constant velocity and discharges sand onto belt *B* as shown. Knowing that the velocity of belt *B* is 8 ft/sec, determine the velocity of the sand relative to belt *B* as it lands on belt *B*.

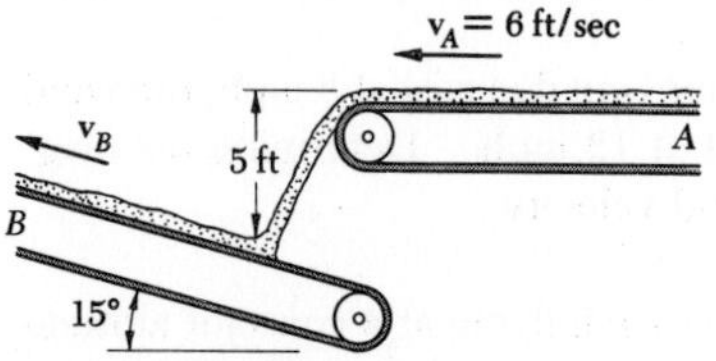

FIG. P11.109 AND P11.110

11.110. Determine the required velocity of belt *B* if the relative velocity with which the sand hits belt *B* is to be (*a*) vertical, (*b*) as small as possible.

11.13. Tangential and Normal Components. We saw in Sec. 11.9 that the velocity of a particle is a vector tangent to the path of the particle but that, in general, the acceleration is not tangent to the path. It is sometimes convenient to resolve the acceleration into components directed, respectively, along the tangent and the normal to the path of the particle.

Plane Motion of a Particle. We shall first consider a particle which moves along a curve contained in the plane of the figure. Let *P* be the position of the particle at a given instant. We attach at *P* a unit vector $\mathbf{i}_t$ tangent to the path of the particle and pointing toward the direction of motion (Fig. 11.21*a*). Let $\mathbf{i}'_t$ be the unit vector corresponding to the position *P'* of the particle at a later instant. Drawing both vectors from the same origin *O'*, we define the vector $\Delta\mathbf{i}_t = \mathbf{i}'_t - \mathbf{i}_t$ (Fig. 11.21*b*). Since $\mathbf{i}_t$ and $\mathbf{i}'_t$ are of unit length, their tips lie on a circle of radius 1. Denoting by $\Delta\theta$ the angle formed by $\mathbf{i}_t$ and $\mathbf{i}'_t$, we find that the magnitude of $\Delta\mathbf{i}_t$ is $2 \sin (\Delta\theta/2)$. Considering now the vector $\Delta\mathbf{i}_t/\Delta\theta$, we note that, as $\Delta\theta$ approaches zero, this vector becomes tangent to the unit circle of Fig. 11.21*b*, i.e., perpendic-

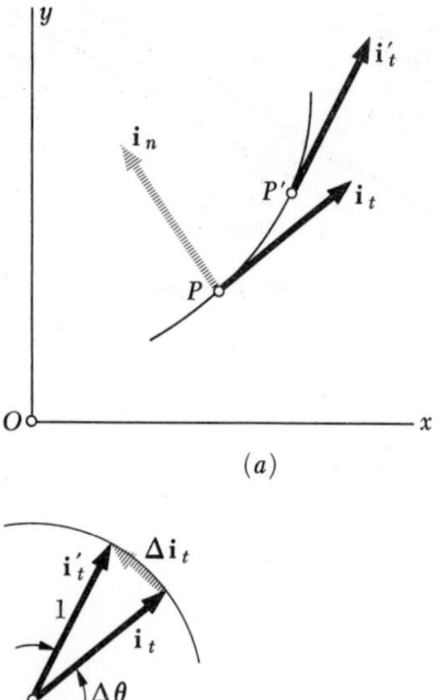

FIG. 11.21

ular to $\mathbf{i}_t$, and that its magnitude approaches

$$\lim_{\Delta\theta\to 0} \frac{2\sin(\Delta\theta/2)}{\Delta\theta} = \lim_{\Delta\theta\to 0} \frac{\sin(\Delta\theta/2)}{\Delta\theta/2} = 1$$

Thus, the vector obtained at the limit is a unit vector along the normal to the path of the particle, in the direction toward which $\mathbf{i}_t$ turns. Denoting this vector by $\mathbf{i}_n$, we write

$$\mathbf{i}_n = \lim_{\Delta\theta\to 0} \frac{\Delta \mathbf{i}_t}{\Delta\theta}$$

$$\mathbf{i}_n = \frac{d\mathbf{i}_t}{d\theta} \tag{11.35}$$

Since the velocity $\mathbf{v}$ of the particle is tangent to the path, we may express it as the product of the scalar v and the unit vector $\mathbf{i}_t$. We have

$$\mathbf{v} = v\mathbf{i}_t \tag{11.36}$$

To obtain the acceleration of the particle, we shall differentiate (11.36) with respect to t. Applying the rule for the differentiation of the product of a scalar and a vector function (Sec. 11.10), we write

$$\mathbf{a} = \frac{d\mathbf{v}}{dt} = \frac{dv}{dt}\mathbf{i}_t + v\frac{d\mathbf{i}_t}{dt} \tag{11.37}$$

But

$$\frac{d\mathbf{i}_t}{dt} = \frac{d\mathbf{i}_t}{d\theta}\frac{d\theta}{ds}\frac{ds}{dt}$$

Recalling from (11.16) that $ds/dt = v$, from (11.35) that $d\mathbf{i}_t/d\theta = \mathbf{i}_n$, and from elementary calculus that $d\theta/ds$ is equal to $1/\rho$, where ρ is the radius of curvature of the path at P (Fig. 11.22), we have

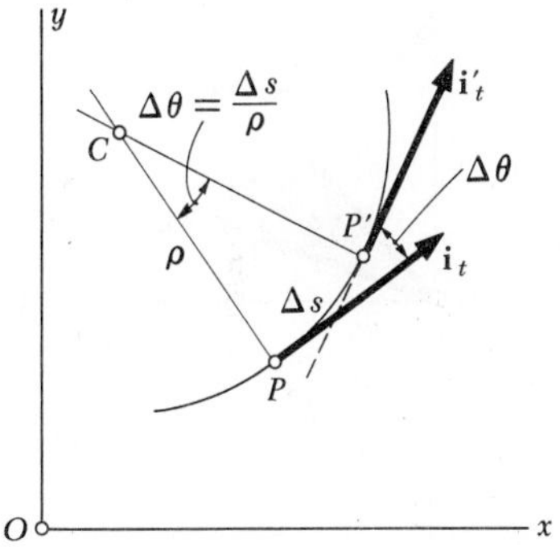

FIG. 11.22

$$\frac{d\mathbf{i}_t}{dt} = \frac{v}{\rho}\mathbf{i}_n \tag{11.38}$$

Substituting into (11.37), we obtain

$$\mathbf{a} = \frac{dv}{dt}\mathbf{i}_t + \frac{v^2}{\rho}\mathbf{i}_n \tag{11.39}$$

Thus, the scalar components of the acceleration are

$$a_t = \frac{dv}{dt} \qquad a_n = \frac{v^2}{\rho} \tag{11.40}$$

The relations obtained express that the *tangential component*

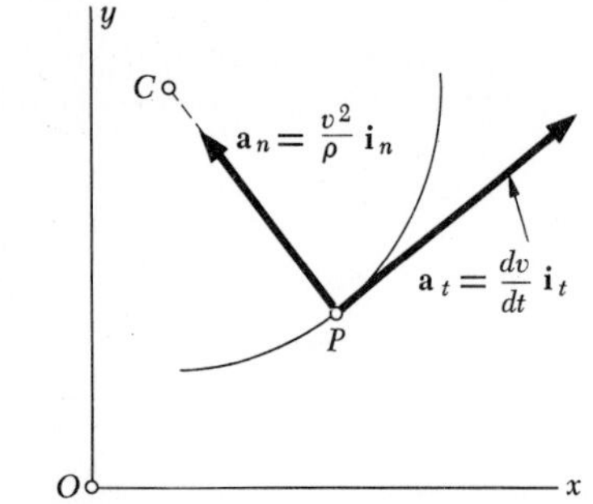

FIG. 11.23

of the acceleration is equal to the *rate of change of the speed of the particle*, while the *normal component* is equal to the *square of the speed divided by the radius of curvature of the path at P*. Depending upon whether the speed of the particle increases or decreases, a_t is positive or negative, and the vector component $\mathbf{a}_t$ points in the direction of motion or against the direction of motion. The vector component $\mathbf{a}_n$, on the other hand, *is always directed toward the center of curvature C of the path* (Fig. 11.23).

It appears from the above that the tangential component of the acceleration reflects a change in the speed of the particle, while its normal component reflects a change in the direction of motion of the particle. The acceleration of a particle will be zero only if both its components are zero. Thus, the acceleration of a particle moving with constant speed along a curve will not be zero, unless the particle happens to pass through a point of inflection of the curve (where the radius of curvature is infinite) or unless the curve is a straight line.

The fact that the normal component of the acceleration depends upon the radius of curvature of the path followed by the particle is taken into account in the design of structures or mechanisms as widely different as airplane wings, railroad tracks, and cams. In order to avoid sudden changes in the acceleration of the air particles flowing past a wing, wing profiles are designed without any sudden change in curvature. Similar care is taken in designing railroad curves, to avoid sudden changes in the acceleration of the cars (which would be hard on the equipment and unpleasant for the passengers). A straight section of track, for instance, is never directly followed by a circular section. Special transition sections are used, to help pass smoothly from the infinite radius of curvature of the straight section to the finite radius of the circular track. Likewise, in the design of high-speed cams, abrupt changes in acceleration are avoided by using transition curves which produce a continuous change in acceleration.

Motion of a Particle in Space. The relations (11.39) and (11.40) still hold in the case of a particle moving along a space curve. However, since there is an infinite number of straight lines which are perpendicular to the tangent at a given point P of a space curve, it is then necessary to define more precisely the direction of the unit vector $\mathbf{i}_n$.

Let us consider again the unit vectors $\mathbf{i}_t$ and $\mathbf{i}'_t$ tangent to the path of the particle at two neighboring points P and P' (Fig. 11.24*a*) and the vector $\Delta\mathbf{i}_t$ representing the difference between

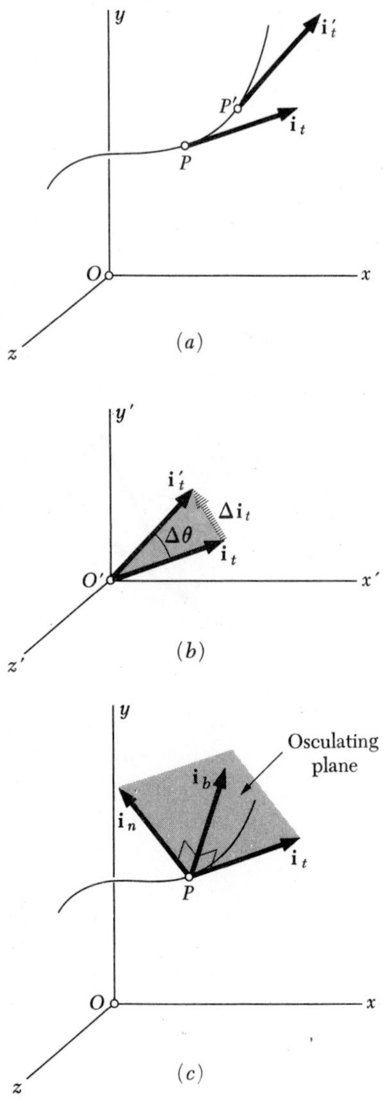

FIG. 11.24

$\mathbf{i}_t$ and $\mathbf{i}_t'$ (Fig. 11.24*b*). Let us now imagine a plane through P (Fig. 11.24*a*), parallel to the plane defined by the vectors $\mathbf{i}_t$, $\mathbf{i}_t'$, and $\Delta\mathbf{i}_t$ (Fig. 11.24*b*). This plane contains the tangent to the curve at P and is parallel to the tangent at P'. If we let P' approach P, we obtain at the limit the plane which fits the curve most closely in the neighborhood of P. This plane is called the *osculating plane* at P.† It follows from this definition that the osculating plane contains the unit vector $\mathbf{i}_n$, since this vector represents the limit of the vector $\Delta\mathbf{i}_t/\Delta\theta$. The normal defined by $\mathbf{i}_n$ is thus contained in the osculating plane; it is called the *principal normal* at P. The unit vector $\mathbf{i}_b = \mathbf{i}_t \times \mathbf{i}_n$ which completes the right-handed triad $\mathbf{i}_t$, $\mathbf{i}_n$, $\mathbf{i}_b$ (Fig. 11.24*c*) defines the *binormal* at P. The binormal is thus perpendicular to the osculating plane. We conclude that, as stated in (11.39), the acceleration of the particle at P may be resolved into two components, one along the tangent, the other along the principal normal at P. The acceleration has no component along the binormal.

11.14. Radial and Transverse Components. In certain problems of plane motion, the position of the particle P is defined by its polar coordinates r and θ (Fig. 11.25*a*). It is then convenient to resolve the velocity and acceleration of the particle into components parallel and perpendicular, respectively, to the line OP. These components are called *radial* and *transverse components*.

We attach at P two unit vectors, $\mathbf{i}_r$ and $\mathbf{i}_\theta$ (Fig. 11.25*b*). The vector $\mathbf{i}_r$ is directed along OP and the vector $\mathbf{i}_\theta$ is obtained by rotating $\mathbf{i}_r$ through 90° counterclockwise. The unit vector $\mathbf{i}_r$ defines the *radial* direction, i.e., the direction in which P would move if r were increased and θ kept constant; the unit vector $\mathbf{i}_\theta$ defines the *transverse* direction, i.e., the direction in which P would move if θ were increased and r kept constant. A derivation similar to the one we used in Sec. 11.13 to determine the derivative of the unit vector $\mathbf{i}_t$ leads to the relations

$$\frac{d\mathbf{i}_r}{d\theta} = \mathbf{i}_\theta \qquad \frac{d\mathbf{i}_\theta}{d\theta} = -\mathbf{i}_r \tag{11.41}$$

where $-\mathbf{i}_r$ denotes a unit vector of sense opposite to that of $\mathbf{i}_r$ (Fig. 11.25*c*).

Expressing the position vector of $\mathbf{r}$ of the particle P as the product of the scalar r and the unit vector $\mathbf{i}_r$, and differentiating with respect to t, we write

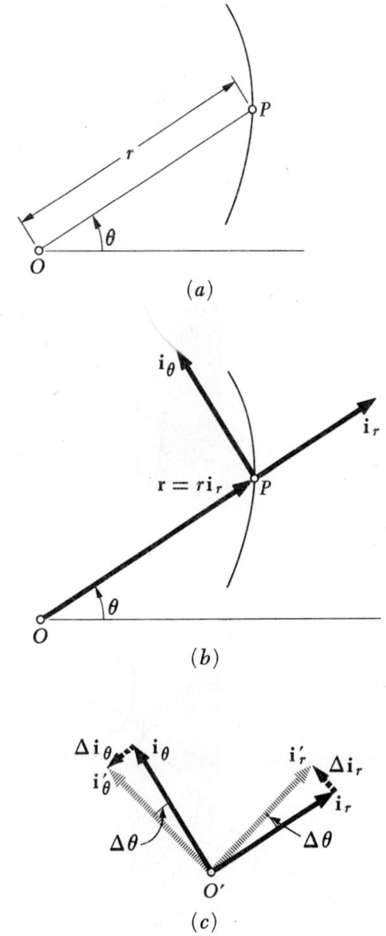

FIG. 11.25

† From the Latin *osculari*, to embrace.

$$\mathbf{r} = r\mathbf{i}_r \tag{11.42}$$

$$\mathbf{v} = \frac{d\mathbf{r}}{dt} = \frac{dr}{dt}\mathbf{i}_r + r\frac{d\mathbf{i}_r}{dt}$$

$$= \frac{dr}{dt}\mathbf{i}_r + r\frac{d\theta}{dt}\frac{d\mathbf{i}_r}{d\theta}$$

Recalling the first of the relations (11.41), and using dots to indicate time derivatives, we have

$$\mathbf{v} = \dot{r}\mathbf{i}_r + r\dot{\theta}\mathbf{i}_\theta \tag{11.43}$$

Differentiating again with respect to t, we write

$$\mathbf{a} = \frac{d\mathbf{v}}{dt} = \ddot{r}\mathbf{i}_r + \dot{r}\frac{d\mathbf{i}_r}{dt} + \dot{r}\dot{\theta}\mathbf{i}_\theta + r\ddot{\theta}\mathbf{i}_\theta + r\dot{\theta}\frac{d\mathbf{i}_\theta}{dt}$$

or, since $d\mathbf{i}_r/dt = \dot{\theta}\mathbf{i}_\theta$ and $d\mathbf{i}_\theta/dt = -\dot{\theta}\mathbf{i}_r$,

$$\mathbf{a} = (\ddot{r} - r\dot{\theta}^2)\mathbf{i}_r + (r\ddot{\theta} + 2\dot{r}\dot{\theta})\mathbf{i}_\theta \tag{11.44}$$

The scalar components of the velocity and acceleration in the radial and transverse directions are therefore

$$v_r = \dot{r} \qquad v_\theta = r\dot{\theta} \tag{11.45}$$

$$a_r = \ddot{r} - r\dot{\theta}^2 \qquad a_\theta = r\ddot{\theta} + 2\dot{r}\dot{\theta} \tag{11.46}$$

In the case of a particle moving along a circle of center O, we have $r =$ constant, $\dot{r} = \ddot{r} = 0$, and the formulas (11.43) and (11.44) reduce, respectively, to

$$\mathbf{v} = r\dot{\theta}\mathbf{i}_\theta \qquad \mathbf{a} = -r\dot{\theta}^2\mathbf{i}_r + r\ddot{\theta}\mathbf{i}_\theta \tag{11.47}$$

Extension to the Motion of a Particle in Space: Cylindrical Coordinates. The position of a particle P in space is sometimes defined by its cylindrical coordinates R, θ, and z (Fig. 11.26*a*). It is then convenient to use the unit vectors $\mathbf{i}_R$, $\mathbf{i}_\theta$, and $\mathbf{k}$ shown in Fig. 11.26*b*. Resolving the position vector $\mathbf{r}$ of the particle P into components along the unit vectors, we write

$$\mathbf{r} = R\mathbf{i}_R + z\mathbf{k} \tag{11.48}$$

Observing that $\mathbf{i}_R$ and $\mathbf{i}_\theta$ define, respectively, the radial and transverse direction in the horizontal xy plane, and that the vector $\mathbf{k}$, which defines the *axial* direction, is constant in direction as well as in magnitude, we easily verify that

$$\mathbf{v} = \frac{d\mathbf{r}}{dt} = \dot{R}\mathbf{i}_R + R\dot{\theta}\mathbf{i}_\theta + \dot{z}\mathbf{k} \tag{11.49}$$

$$\mathbf{a} = \frac{d\mathbf{v}}{dt} = (\ddot{R} - R\dot{\theta}^2)\mathbf{i}_R + (R\ddot{\theta} + 2\dot{R}\dot{\theta})\mathbf{i}_\theta + \ddot{z}\mathbf{k} \tag{11.50}$$

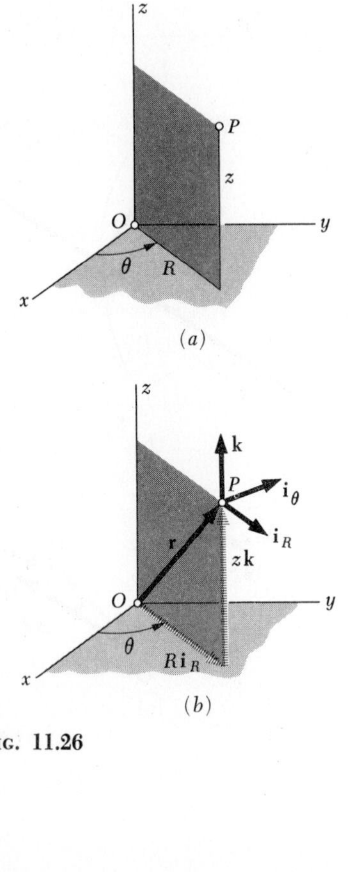

FIG. 11.26

SAMPLE PROBLEM 11.10

A train is traveling on a curved section of track of radius 3,000 ft at the speed of 90 mph. The brakes are suddenly applied, causing the train to slow down at a constant rate; after 6 sec, the speed has been reduced to 60 mph. Determine the acceleration of a car immediately after the brakes have been applied.

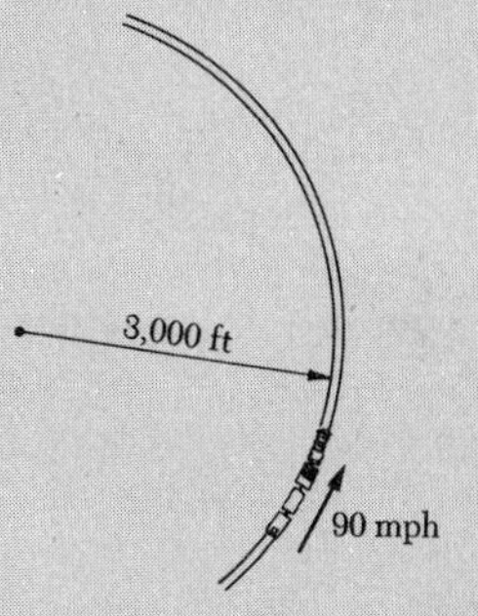

Tangential Component of Acceleration. First the speeds are expressed in ft/sec.

$$90 \text{ mph} = 90 \frac{\text{miles}}{\text{hr}} \frac{5{,}280 \text{ ft}}{1 \text{ mile}} \frac{1 \text{ hr}}{3{,}600 \text{ sec}} = 132 \text{ ft/sec}$$

$$60 \text{ mph} = 88 \text{ ft/sec}$$

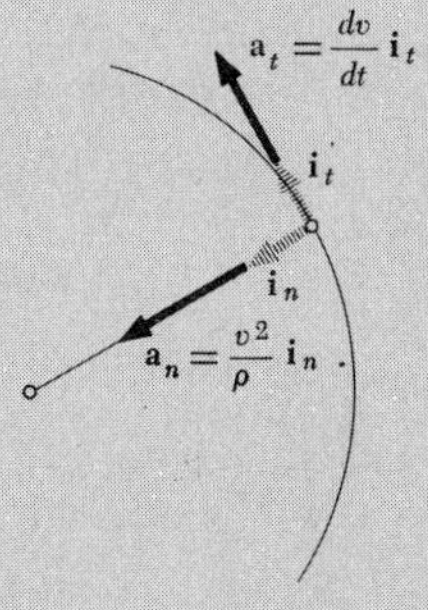

Since the train slows down at a constant rate, we have

$$a_t = \text{average } a_t = \frac{\Delta v}{\Delta t} = \frac{88 \text{ ft/sec} - 132 \text{ ft/sec}}{6 \text{ sec}} = -7.33 \text{ ft/sec}^2$$

Normal Component of Acceleration. Immediately after the brakes have been applied, the speed is still 132 ft/sec, and we have

$$a_n = \frac{v^2}{\rho} = \frac{(132 \text{ ft/sec})^2}{3{,}000 \text{ ft}} = 5.81 \text{ ft/sec}^2$$

Magnitude and Direction of Acceleration. The magnitude and direction of the resultant **a** of the components $\mathbf{a}_n$ and $\mathbf{a}_t$ are determined as follows:

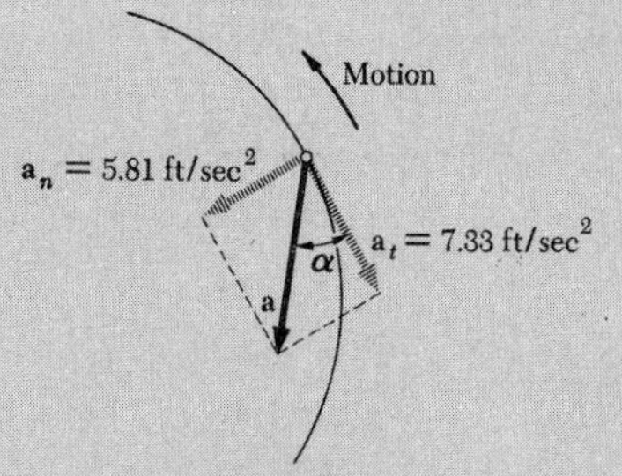

$$\tan \alpha = \frac{a_n}{a_t} = \frac{5.81 \text{ ft/sec}^2}{7.33 \text{ ft/sec}^2} \qquad \alpha = 38.4° \quad ◄$$

$$a = \frac{a_n}{\sin \alpha} = \frac{5.81 \text{ ft/sec}^2}{\sin 38.4°} \qquad a = 9.35 \text{ ft/sec}^2 \quad ◄$$

SAMPLE PROBLEM 11.11

Determine the minimum radius of curvature of the trajectory described by the projectile considered in Sample Prob. 11.7.

Solution. Since $a_n = v^2/\rho$, we have $\rho = v^2/a_n$. The radius will be small when v is small or when a_n is large. The speed v is minimum at the top of the trajectory, since $v_y = 0$ at that point; a_n is maximum at that same point, since the direction of the vertical coincides with the direction of the normal. Therefore, the minimum radius of curvature occurs at the top of the trajectory. At this point, we have

$$v = v_x = 520 \text{ ft/sec} \qquad a_n = a = 32.2 \text{ ft/sec}^2$$

$$\rho = \frac{v^2}{a_n} = \frac{(520 \text{ ft/sec})^2}{32.2 \text{ ft/sec}^2} \qquad \rho = 8{,}400 \text{ ft} \quad ◄$$

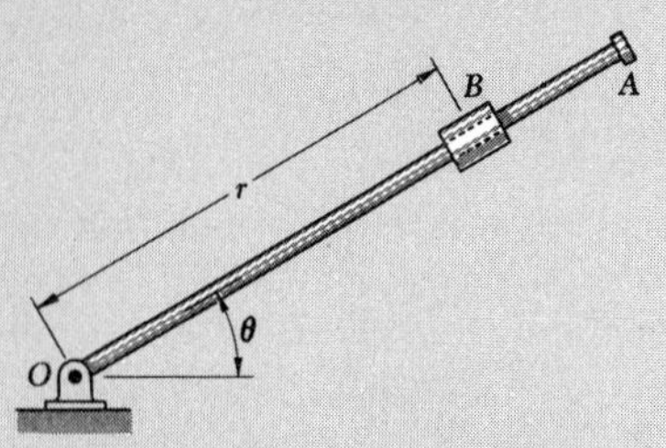

SAMPLE PROBLEM 11.12

The rotation of the 3-ft arm OA about O is defined by the relation $\theta = 0.15t^2$, where θ is expressed in radians and t in seconds. Block B slides along the arm in such a way that its distance from O is $r = 3 - 0.40t^2$, where r is expressed in feet and t in seconds. Determine the total velocity and the total acceleration of block B after the arm OA has rotated through 30°.

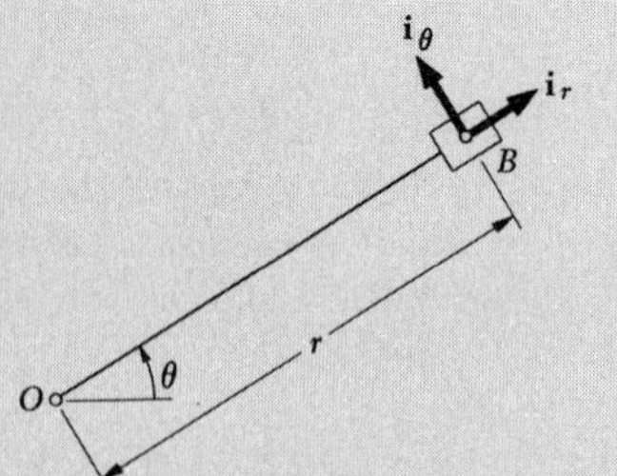

$\mathbf{v} = v_r \mathbf{i}_r + v_\theta \mathbf{i}_\theta$

$\mathbf{a} = a_r \mathbf{i}_r + a_\theta \mathbf{i}_\theta$

Time When $\theta = 30°$. Substituting $\theta = 30° = 0.524$ radian into the expression for θ, we obtain

$$\theta = 0.15t^2 \qquad 0.524 = 0.15t^2 \qquad t = 1.869 \text{ sec}$$

Equations of Motion. Substituting $t = 1.869$ sec in the expressions for r, θ, and their first and second derivatives, we have

$$r = 3 - 0.40t^2 = 1.603 \text{ ft} \qquad \theta = 0.15t^2 = 0.524 \text{ radian}$$

$$\frac{dr}{dt} = -0.80t = -1.495 \text{ ft/sec} \qquad \frac{d\theta}{dt} = 0.30t = 0.561 \text{ radian/sec}$$

$$\frac{d^2r}{dt^2} = -0.80 = -0.800 \text{ ft/sec}^2 \qquad \frac{d^2\theta}{dt^2} = 0.30 = 0.300 \text{ radian/sec}^2$$

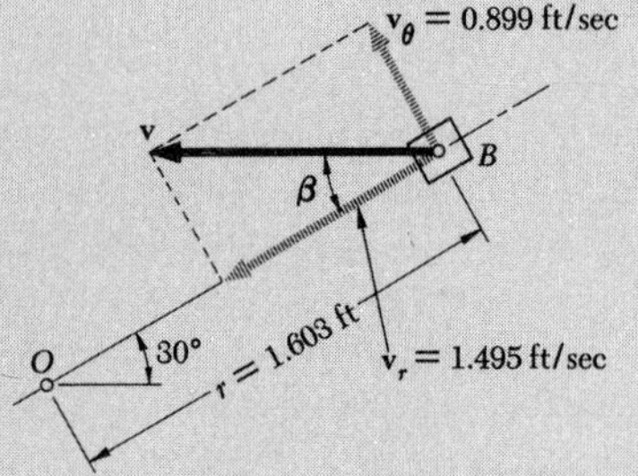

Velocity of B. Using Eqs. (11.45), we obtain the values of v_r and v_θ when $t = 1.869$ sec.

$$v_r = \frac{dr}{dt} = -1.495 \text{ ft/sec}$$

$$v_\theta = r\frac{d\theta}{dt} = (1.603)(0.561) = 0.899 \text{ ft/sec}$$

Solving the right triangle shown, we obtain the magnitude and direction of the velocity,

$$v = 1.745 \text{ ft/sec} \qquad \beta = 31.0° \blacktriangleleft$$

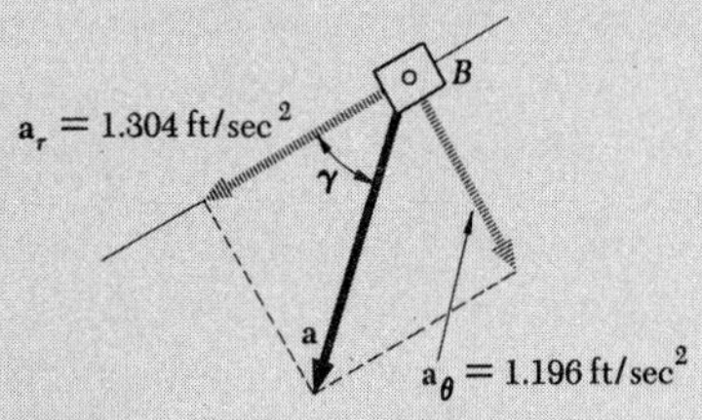

Acceleration of B. Using Eqs. (11.46), we obtain

$$a_r = \frac{d^2r}{dt^2} - r\left(\frac{d\theta}{dt}\right)^2$$

$$= -0.800 - (1.603)(0.561)^2 = -1.304 \text{ ft/sec}^2$$

$$a_\theta = r\frac{d^2\theta}{dt^2} + 2\frac{dr}{dt}\frac{d\theta}{dt}$$

$$= (1.603)(0.300) + (2)(-1.495)(0.561) = -1.196 \text{ ft/sec}^2$$

$$a = 1.770 \text{ ft/sec} \qquad \gamma = 42.5° \blacktriangleleft$$

PROBLEMS

11.111. What is the smallest radius which should be used for a highway curve if the normal component of the acceleration of a car traveling at 70 mph is not to exceed 3 ft/sec^2?

11.112. A car goes around a highway curve of 900-ft radius at a speed of 45 mph. (*a*) What is the normal component of its acceleration? (*b*) At what speed is the normal component of the acceleration twice as large as that found in part *a*?

11.113. During the test of an airplane it is desired that the normal component of the acceleration be equal to 6g. Determine the radius of the circle along which the pilot should fly if the speed of the airplane is 1,500 mph.

11.114. The peripheral speed of the edge of a 22-in.-radius turbine disk is 740 ft/sec. Determine the normal component of the acceleration of a point *P* on the edge of the disk.

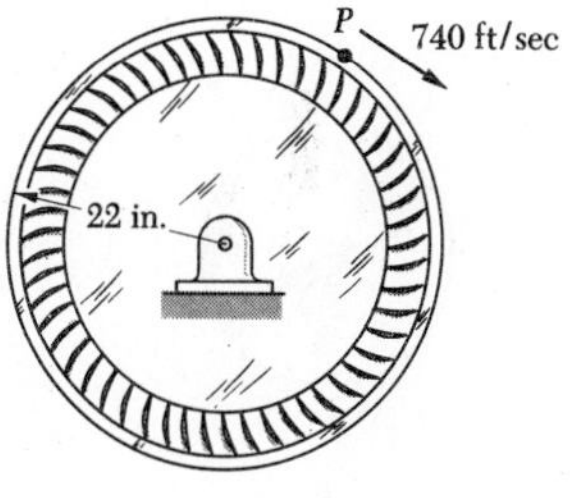

FIG. P 11.114

11.115. A motorist enters a curve of 500-ft radius at a speed of 45 mph. As he applies his brakes, he decreases his speed at a constant rate of 5 ft/sec^2. Determine the magnitude of the total acceleration of the automobile when its speed is 40 mph.

11.116. A motorist starts from rest on a curve of 400-ft radius and accelerates at the uniform rate $a_t = 3$ ft/sec^2. Determine the distance that his automobile will travel before the magnitude of its total acceleration is 6 ft/sec^2.

11.117. The speed of a car is increased at a constant rate from 45 mph to 60 mph over a distance of 500 ft along a curve of 600-ft radius. Determine the magnitude of the total acceleration of the car after it has traveled 300 ft along the curve.

11.118. As a train enters a curve of radius 4,000 ft at a speed of 60 mph, the brakes are applied sufficiently to cause the magnitude of the *total* acceleration of the train to be 2.5 ft/sec^2. After 10 sec the brakes are more fully applied so that the magnitude of the total acceleration is again 2.5 ft/sec^2. If this second brake setting is then maintained, how many seconds are required to bring the train to a stop?

11.119. A nozzle discharges a stream of water horizontally with an initial velocity of 60 ft/sec. Determine the radius of curvature of the stream (*a*) as it leaves the nozzle, (*b*) as it strikes the wall at *B*.

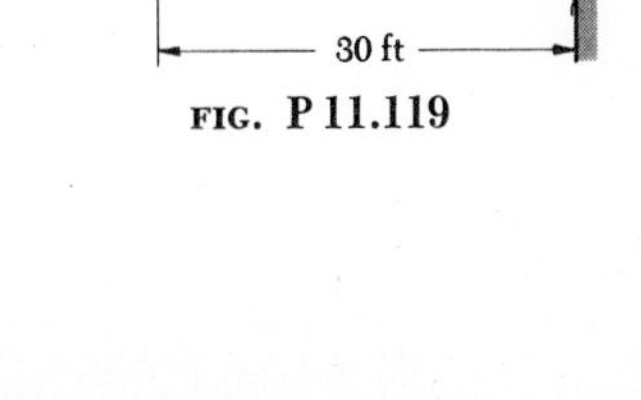

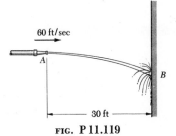

FIG. P 11.119

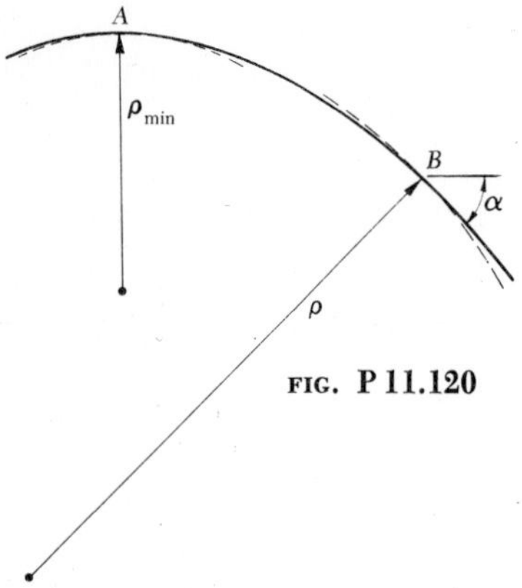

FIG. P 11.120

11.120. (*a*) Show that the radius of curvature of the trajectory of a projectile reaches its minimum value at the highest point A of the trajectory. (*b*) Denoting by α the angle formed by the trajectory and the horizontal at a given point B, show that the radius of curvature of the trajectory at B is $\rho = \rho_{min}/\cos^3\alpha$.

***11.121.** Determine the radius of curvature of the path described by the particle of Prob. 11.79 when (*a*) $t = 0$, (*b*) $t = 1$ sec.

***11.122.** Determine the radius of curvature of the helix of Prob. 11.80.

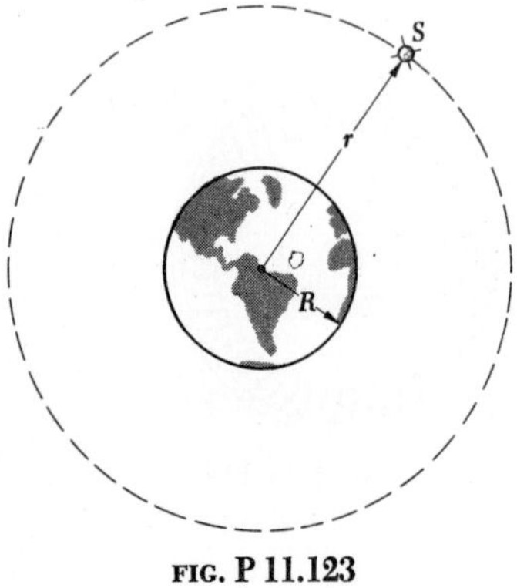

FIG. P 11.123

11.123. A satellite will travel indefinitely in a circular orbit around the earth if the normal component of its acceleration is equal to $g(R/r)^2$, where $g = 32.2$ ft/sec², R = radius of the earth = 3,960 miles, and r = distance from the center of the earth to the satellite. Determine the height above the surface of the earth at which a satellite will travel indefinitely around the earth at a speed of 15,000 mph.

11.124. Determine the speed of an earth satellite traveling in a circular orbit 300 miles above the surface of the earth. (See information given in Prob. 11.123.)

11.125. Assuming the orbit of the moon to be a circle of radius 239,000 miles, determine the speed of the moon relative to the earth. (See information given in Prob. 11.123.)

11.126. Show that the speed of an earth satellite traveling in a circular orbit is inversely proportional to the square root of the radius of its orbit. Also, determine the minimum time in which a satellite can circle the earth. (See information given in Prob. 11.123.)

11.127. The two-dimensional motion of a particle is defined by the relations $r = t^3 - 2t^2$ and $\theta = t^3 - 4t$, where r is expressed in inches, t in seconds, and θ in radians. Determine the position, velocity, and acceleration of the particle when (*a*) $t = 0$, (*b*) $t = 1$ sec.

11.128. The particle of Prob. 11.127 is at the origin at $t = 0$. Determine its velocity and acceleration as it passes again through the origin.

11.129. The two-dimensional motion of a particle is defined by the relations $r = 2k \cos t$ and $\theta = t$. Determine (*a*) the path of the particle, (*b*) the velocity and acceleration of the particle at any time t.

11.130. The two-dimensional motion of a particle is defined by the relations $r = k(1 + \cos \frac{1}{2}\pi t)$ and $\theta = \frac{1}{2}\pi t$. Determine the velocity and acceleration of the particle when (*a*) $t = 1$, (*b*) $t = 2$.

11.131. A rocket is fired vertically from a launching pad at B. Its flight is tracked by radar from point A. Determine the velocity of the rocket in terms of d, θ, and $d\theta/dt$.

11.132. Determine the acceleration of the rocket of Prob. 11.131 in terms of d, θ, $d\theta/dt$, and $d^2\theta/dt^2$.

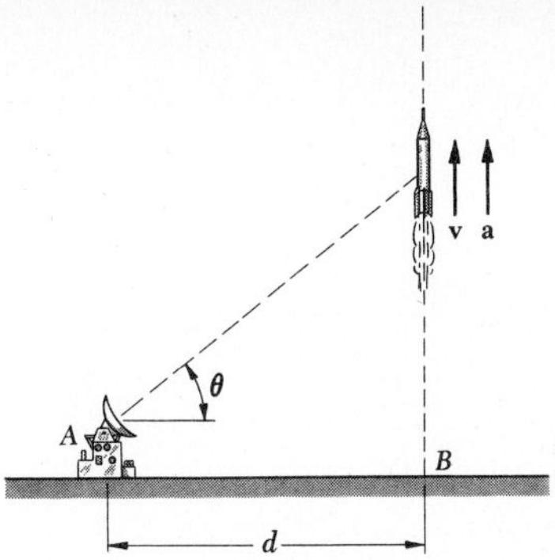

FIG. P 11.131

11.133. An airplane passes over a radar tracking station at A and continues to fly due east. When the airplane is at P, the distance and angle of elevation of the plane are, respectively, $r = 11{,}200$ ft and $\theta = 26.5°$. Two seconds later the radar station sights the plane at $r = 12{,}300$ ft and $\theta = 23.3°$. Determine approximately the speed and the angle of dive α of the plane during the 2-sec interval.

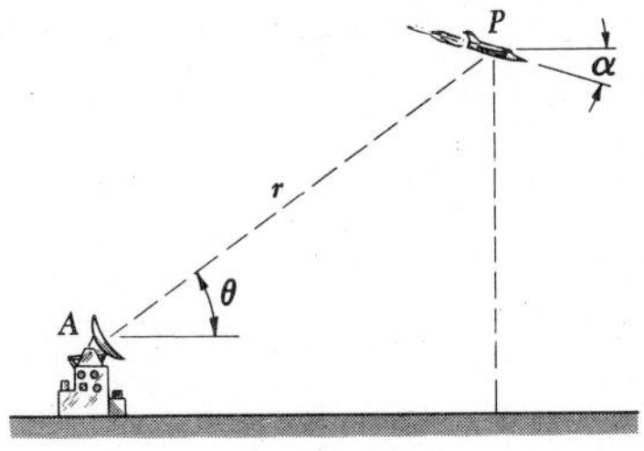

FIG. P 11.133

11.134 through 11.136. A particle moves along the spiral shown. (*a*) Determine the magnitude of the velocity of the particle in terms of b, θ, and $d\theta/dt$. (*b*) Knowing that $d\theta/dt$ is constant and denoting this constant by ω, determine the magnitude of the acceleration in terms of b, θ, and ω.

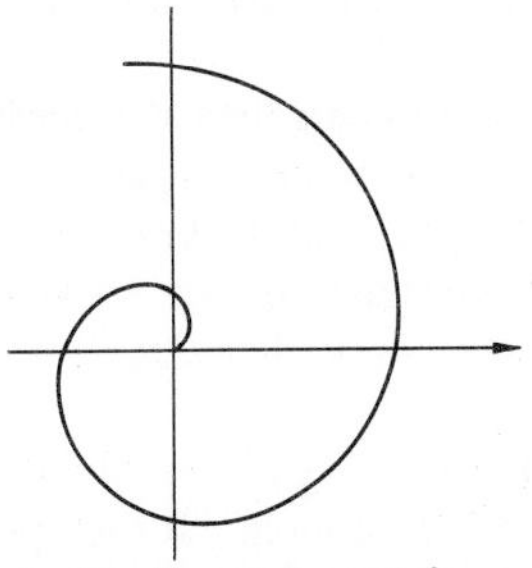

Archimedian spiral $r = b\,\theta$

FIG. P 11.134

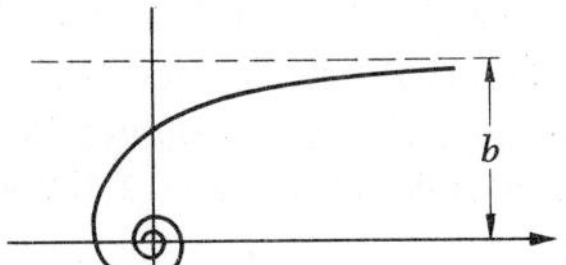

Hyperbolic spiral $r\,\theta = b$

FIG. P 11.135

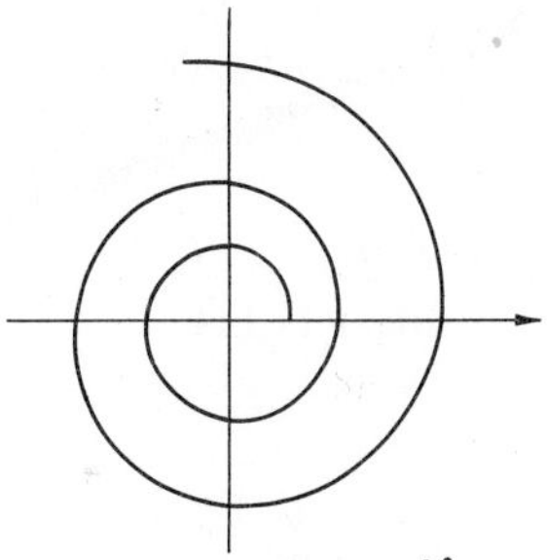

Logarithmic spiral $r = e^{b\theta}$

FIG. P 11.136

11.137. The pin at B is free to slide along the circular slot and along the rotating rod OC. If pin B slides counterclockwise around the circular slot at a constant speed v_0, determine the rate $d\theta/dt$ at which rod OC rotates and the radial component v_r of the velocity of the pin B (*a*) when $\phi = 0°$, (*b*) when $\phi = 90°$.

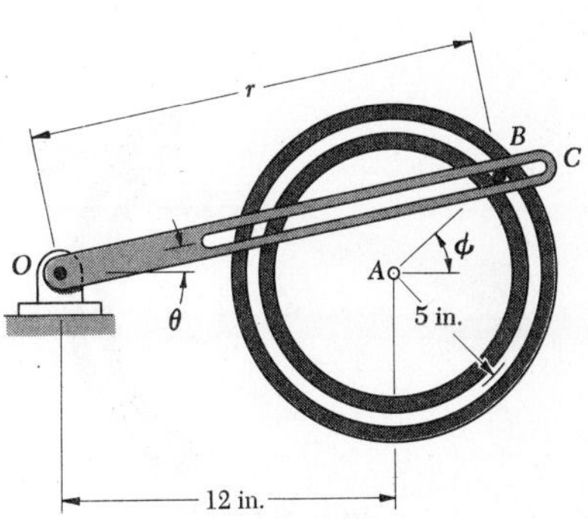

FIG. P 11.137

11.138. The three-dimensional motion of a particle is defined by the relations $R = 2k \cos t$, $\theta = t$, and $z = pt$. Determine (*a*) the path of the particle, (*b*) the magnitudes of the velocity and acceleration at any time t, (*c*) the radius of curvature of the path at any time t.

11.139. The three-dimensional motion of a particle is defined by the relations $R = A(1 - e^{-t})$, $\theta = 2\pi t$, and $z = B(1 - e^{-t})$. Determine the magnitudes of the velocity and acceleration when (*a*) $t = 0$, (*b*) $t = \infty$.

11.140. The motion of a particle on the surface of a right circular cylinder is defined by the relations $R = A$, $\theta = 2\pi t$, and $z = B \sin 2\pi nt$, where A and B are constants and n is an integer. Determine the magnitudes of the velocity and acceleration of the particle at any time t.

11.141. For the case when $n = 1$ in Prob. 11.140, (*a*) show that the path of the particle is contained in a plane, (*b*) determine the maximum and minimum radii of curvature of the path.

***11.142.** For the helix of Prob. 11.80, determine the angle that the osculating plane forms with the x axis.

***11.143.** Determine the binormal of the path described by the particle of Prob. 11.79 when (*a*) $t = 0$, (*b*) $t = 1$ sec.

REVIEW PROBLEMS

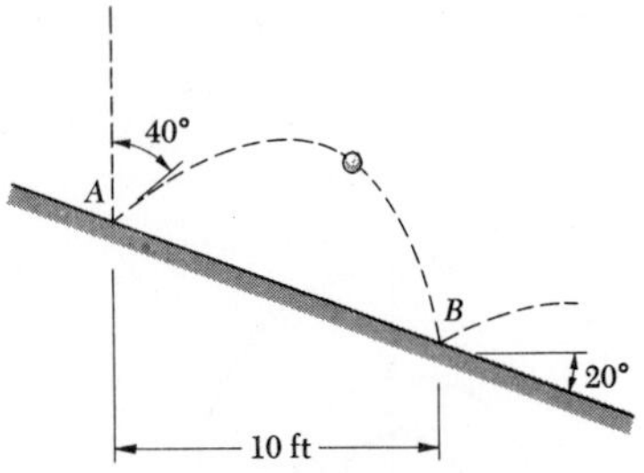

FIG. P11.144

11.144. A ball is dropped vertically onto a 20° incline at A; the direction of rebound forms an angle of 40° with the vertical. Knowing that the ball next strikes the incline at B, determine (*a*) the velocity of rebound at A, (*b*) the time required for the ball to travel from A to B.

11.145. A battleship moving at 30 knots fires at a stationary target and hits it. Find the direction in which the guns are aimed, knowing that the muzzle velocity is 2,000 ft/sec, that the firing angle is 20°, and that the target is sighted 25° off the ship's course. (1 knot = 1 nautical mile per hour = 1.152 statute miles per hour.)

11.146. A car starts from rest at point A and accelerates at the rate of 3 ft/sec² until it reaches a speed of 45 mph. It then proceeds at 45 mph until the brakes are applied; it comes to a stop at point B, 198 ft beyond the point where the brakes were applied. Knowing that the *average* speed of the car is 30 mph, determine (*a*) the time required for the car to travel from A to B, (*b*) the distance from A to B.

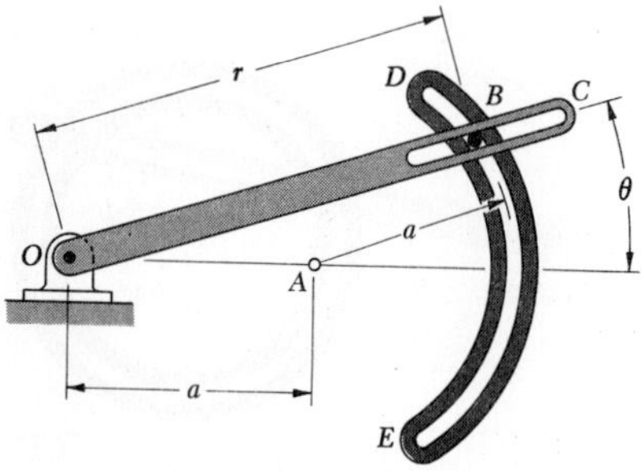

FIG. P11.147

11.147. The pin at B is free to slide along the circular slot DE and along the rotating rod OC. Assuming that the rod OC rotates at a constant rate $d\theta/dt$, show that the acceleration of pin B is of constant magnitude. Also determine the direction of the acceleration of pin B.

11.148. In Prob. 11.60, the average velocity of the particle during the interval $t = 0$ to $t = t$ varies. Determine (*a*) the time t when the average velocity is maximum, (*b*) the magnitude of the maximum average velocity.

11.149. Determine the speed of an earth satellite which travels in a circular orbit at an altitude of 4,000 miles. (See information given in Prob. 11.123.)

11.150. An enemy ship is observed from a shore battery 12°30′ east of north, at a distance of 6 nautical miles, steaming due west at a speed of 25 knots. The battery guns are immediately trained 0° north, ready to be fired when the ship crosses the line of sight. Knowing that the battery is located 60 ft above water level and that the muzzle velocity of its guns is 2,400 ft/sec, determine the firing angle α and the direction of the line of sight (angle β). (1 nautical mile = 1.152 statute miles, and 1 knot = 1 nautical mile per hour.)

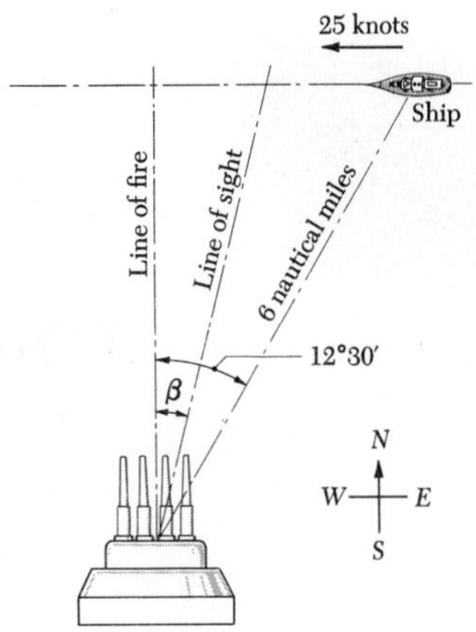

FIG. **P 11.150**

11.151. An experimental ion-propulsion engine is capable of giving a space vehicle a constant acceleration of 0.01 ft/sec^2. If the engine is placed in operation when the speed of the vehicle is 18,000 mph, determine the time required to bring the speed of the vehicle to 20,000 mph. Assume that the vehicle is moving in a straight line, far from the sun or any planet.

11.152. For each of the two firing angles obtained in Sample Prob. 11.8, determine the radius of curvature of the trajectory described by the projectile as it leaves the gun.

11.153. The magnitude in ft/sec^2 of the deceleration due to air resistance of the nose cone of a small experimental rocket is known to be $0.0002\, v^2$, where v is expressed in ft/sec. If the nose cone is projected vertically from the ground with an initial velocity of 300 ft/sec, determine the maximum height that it will reach.

11.154. Determine the velocity of the nose cone of Prob. 11.153 when it returns to the ground.

11.155. Determine the time required for the nose cone of Prob. 11.153 to reach its maximum elevation.

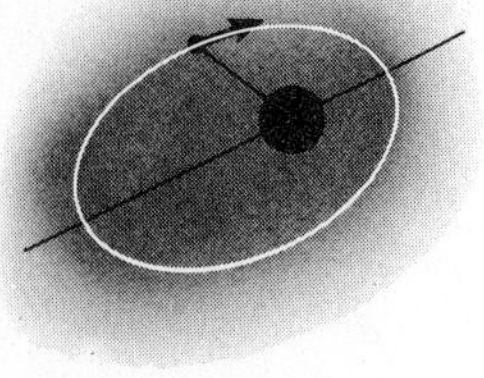

12. KINETICS OF PARTICLES: FORCE, MASS, AND ACCELERATION

12.1. Newton's Second Law of Motion. Newton's first and third laws of motion were used extensively in statics to study bodies at rest and the forces acting upon them. These two laws are also used in dynamics; in fact, they are sufficient for the study of the motion of bodies which have no acceleration. However, when bodies are accelerated, i.e., when the magnitude or the direction of their velocity changes, it is necessary to use the second law of motion in order to relate the motion of the body with the forces acting on it. This law may be stated as follows:

If the resultant force acting on a particle is not zero, the particle will have an acceleration proportional to the magnitude of the resultant and in the direction of this resultant force.

Newton's second law of motion may best be understood if we imagine the following experiment: A particle is subjected to a force $\mathbf{F}_1$ of constant direction and constant magnitude F_1. Under the action of that force, the particle will be observed to move in a straight line and *in the direction of the force* (Fig. 12.1*a*). By determining the position of the particle at various instants, we find that its acceleration has a constant magnitude a_1. If the experiment is repeated with forces $\mathbf{F}_2$, $\mathbf{F}_3$, etc., of different magnitude or direction (Fig. 12.1*b* and *c*), we find each time that the particle moves in the direction of the force acting on it and that the magnitudes a_1, a_2, a_3, etc., of the accelerations are proportional to the magnitudes F_1, F_2, F_3, etc., of the corresponding forces,

$$\frac{F_1}{a_1} = \frac{F_2}{a_2} = \frac{F_3}{a_3} = \cdots = \text{constant}$$

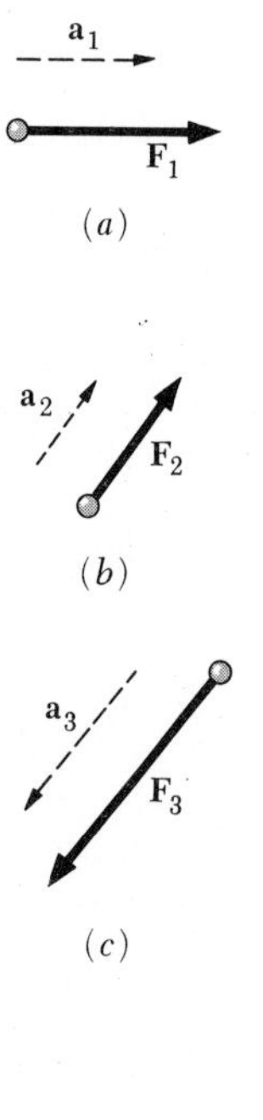

FIG. 12.1

The constant value obtained for the ratio of the magnitudes of the forces and accelerations is a characteristic of the particle under consideration. It is called the *mass* of the particle and is denoted by m. When a particle of mass m is acted upon by a force **F**, the force **F** and the acceleration **a** of the particle must therefore satisfy the relation

$$\mathbf{F} = m\mathbf{a} \tag{12.1}$$

This relation provides a complete formulation of Newton's second law; it expresses not only that the magnitudes of **F** and **a** are proportional, but also (since m is a positive scalar) that the vectors **F** and **a** have the same direction (Fig. 12.2). We should note that, when **F** is not constant but varies with t, the acceleration **a** will also vary with t; however, Eq. (12.1) will still hold at any given instant.

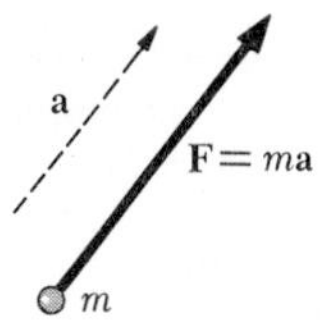

FIG. 12.2

When a particle is subjected simultaneously to several forces, Eq. (12.1) should be replaced by

$$\Sigma\mathbf{F} = m\mathbf{a} \tag{12.2}$$

where $\Sigma\mathbf{F}$ represents the sum, or resultant, of all the forces acting on the particle.

It should be noted that the system of axes with respect to which the acceleration **a** is determined is not arbitrary. These axes must have a constant orientation with respect to the stars, and their origin must either be attached to the sun† or move with a constant velocity with respect to the sun. Such a system of axes is called a *newtonian frame of reference.*‡ A system of axes attached to the earth does *not* constitute a newtonian frame of reference, since the earth rotates with respect to the stars and is accelerated with respect to the sun. However, in most engineering applications, the acceleration **a** may be determined with respect to axes attached to the earth and Eqs. (12.1) and (12.2) used without any appreciable error. On the other hand, these equations do not hold if **a** represents a relative acceleration measured with respect to moving axes, such as axes attached to an accelerated car or to a rotating piece of machinery.

12.2. Systems of Units. In using the fundamental equation $\mathbf{F} = m\mathbf{a}$, the units of force, mass, length, and time cannot be chosen arbitrarily. If they were, the magnitude of the force **F** required to give an acceleration **a** to the mass m would *not* be numerically equal to the product ma; it would only be proportional to this product. Thus, we may choose three of the

† More accurately, to the mass center of the solar system.

‡ Since the stars are not actually fixed, a more rigorous definition of a newtonian frame of reference (also called *inertial system*) is *one with respect to which Eq. (12.2) holds.*

four units arbitrarily but must choose the fourth unit so that the equation $\mathbf{F} = ma$ is satisfied. The units are then said to form a consistent system of kinetic units.

Five consistent systems of kinetic units are shown in Table 12.1. Consider, for instance, the mks system, generally used

TABLE 12.1
Systems of Units

Dimensions	British systems	Metric systems	
	Absolute:	Absolute (mks):	Absolute (cgs):
Length	Foot (ft)	Meter (m)	Centimeter (cm)
Mass	Pound (lb)	Kilogram (kg)	Gram (g)
Time	Second (sec)	Second (sec)	Second (sec)
Force, from $F = ma$	Poundal (lb-ft/sec^2)	Newton (kg-m/sec^2)	Dyne (g-cm/sec^2)
	Gravitational:	Gravitational:	
Length	Foot (ft)	Meter (m)	
Force	Pound (lb)	Kilogram (kg)	
Time	Second (sec)	Second (sec)	
Mass, from $F = ma$	Slug (lb-sec^2/ft)	Kg-sec^2/m	

by physicists. The units of length, mass, and time are, respectively, the *meter* (m), the *kilogram* (kg), and the *second* (sec). All three are arbitrarily defined. The second, which represents the 1/86,400 part of the mean solar day, is officially defined as the 1/31,556,925.9747 part of the tropical year 1900. The meter, originally intended to represent 1 ten-millionth of the distance from the equator to the pole, is now defined as 1,650,763.73 wavelengths of the orange-red line of krypton-86. The kilogram, which is approximately equal to the mass of 0.001 cubic meter of water, is actually defined as the mass of a platinum standard kept at the International Bureau of Weights and Measures at Sèvres, near Paris, France. The unit of force, called the *newton*, is not arbitrary. It is defined as the force which gives an acceleration of 1 m/sec^2 to a mass of 1 kg. From (12.1), we write

$$1 \text{ newton} = (1 \text{ kg})(1 \text{ m/sec}^2)$$

The mks system is said to be an *absolute* system of units. This means that the three fundamental units chosen (meter, kilogram, second) are independent of the location where measurements are made. The meter, the kilogram, and the second may be used anywhere on the earth; they might even be used on another planet. They will always have the same significance.

Other absolute systems of units are the cgs system and the British absolute sytem. In the cgs system, the units of length, mass, and time are, respectively, the *centimeter* (cm), the *gram* (g), and the *second.* The centimeter is defined as 0.01 m and the gram as 0.001 kg. The unit of force is the *dyne,* defined as the force which gives an acceleration of 1 cm/sec^2 to a mass of 1 g. In the British absolute system, the units of length, mass, and time are, respectively, the *foot,* the *pound,* and the *second.* The foot is equal to 0.304800 m, and the pound is equal to 0.45359243 kg. Both units are represented by standards kept at the National Bureau of Standards in Washington. The unit of force in this system is the *poundal,* defined as the force which gives an acceleration of 1 ft/sec^2 to a mass of 1 lb.

Engineers do not use absolute systems of units. They prefer to choose as fundamental units the units of *length, force,* and *time.* Such a system of units is called a *gravitational* system of units. In English-speaking countries, engineers use the British gravitational system of units, based on the foot, the pound, and the second. It should be noted that in this system the pound is used, not as a unit of mass, but as a *unit of force.* This force is defined as the *weight* of a mass of 1 lb (i.e., the force exerted by the earth on a mass of 1 lb) at sea level and at the latitude of 45°. Since at such a location the acceleration of freely falling bodies is 32.2 ft/sec^2, we see that a force of 1 lb gives an acceleration of 32.2 ft/sec^2 to a mass of 1 lb (Fig. 12.3*a*). The foot, the pound force, the second, and the pound mass, therefore, do not form a consistent system of units. The unit of mass consistent with the foot, the pound force, and the second must be a mass which receives an acceleration of 1 ft/sec^2 when a force of 1 lb is applied to it (Fig. 12.3*b*). This unit, sometimes called a *slug,* is obtained by solving the equation $F = ma$ for m and substituting 1 lb and 1 ft/sec^2 for F and a, respectively:

$$m = \frac{F}{a} \qquad 1 \text{ slug} = \frac{1 \text{ lb}}{1 \text{ ft/sec}^2} = 1 \text{ lb-sec}^2\text{/ft}$$

From the definition of the pound force and of the slug (or

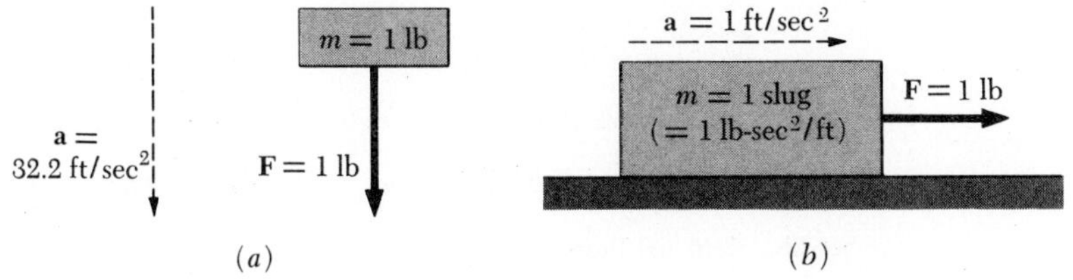

FIG. 12.3

lb-sec^2/ft), it appears (Fig. 12.3) that

$$1 \text{ slug} = 1 \text{ lb-sec}^2/\text{ft} = 32.2 \text{ lb mass}$$

The mass m (in slugs) of a body whose weight is known to have a magnitude W (in lb) may therefore be expressed as

$$m = \frac{W}{g}$$

where g is the acceleration of gravity ($g = 32.2$ ft/sec^2).

Gravitational units are preferred to absolute units in engineering because forces are more frequently used than masses; it is thus more natural to use the pound as a unit of force than as a unit of mass. These units, however, would present difficulties if very precise measurements were needed (which is usually not the case in engineering) or if experiments were to be conducted on another planet (which engineers have not done yet). Since the force of attraction exerted by the earth on a given object varies with the altitude and latitude of the object,† the weight of the standard kept at the National Bureau of Standards will not be exactly 1 lb at altitudes other than sea level or at latitudes other than 45°, and the weight of the standard pound will obviously be very different if it is measured on the moon, where gravitational forces are much smaller than on the earth. Clearly, the units used by engineers *are not absolute;* and because they depend upon the effects of gravitation, they are said to form a gravitational system of units. However, variations in gravitation may usually be neglected in studying the motion of engineering structures on the surface of the earth.

12.3. Equations of Motion. Dynamic Equilibrium. Consider a particle of mass m acted upon by several forces. Newton's second law of motion states that the resultant of these forces must be equal to the vector $m\mathbf{a}$ obtained by multiplying the acceleration $\mathbf{a}$ of the particle by its mass m (Fig. 12.4a),

$$\Sigma\mathbf{F} = m\mathbf{a} \tag{12.2}$$

Resolving each force $\mathbf{F}$ and the acceleration $\mathbf{a}$ into rectangular components, we write

$$\Sigma(F_x\mathbf{i} + F_y\mathbf{j} + F_z\mathbf{k}) = m(a_x\mathbf{i} + a_y\mathbf{j} + a_z\mathbf{k})$$

from which it follows that

$$\Sigma F_x = ma_x \qquad \Sigma F_y = ma_y \qquad \Sigma F_z = ma_z \tag{12.2'}$$

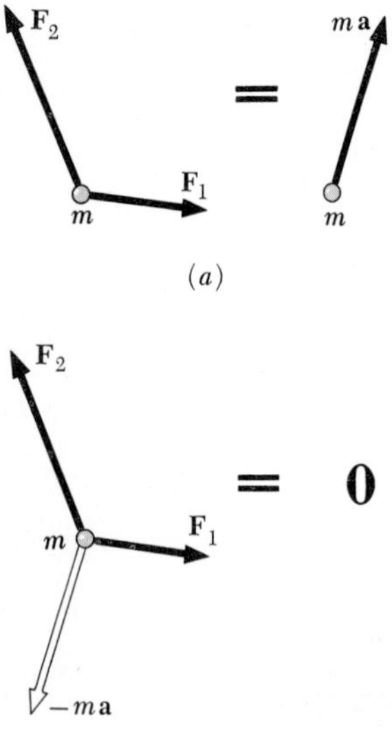

FIG. 12.4 (b)

† See Sec. 12.10 and Prob. 12.1.

Transposing the right-hand member in Eq. (12.2), we have

$$\Sigma \mathbf{F} - m\mathbf{a} = 0 \tag{12.3}$$

Written in this form, Newton's second law expresses that, if the vector $-m\mathbf{a}$ is added to the forces acting on the particle, *we obtain a system of vectors equivalent to zero* (Fig. 12.4*b*). The vector $-m\mathbf{a}$, of magnitude ma and of *sense opposite* to that of the acceleration, is called an *inertia vector*. The particle may thus be considered to be in equilibrium under the given forces and the inertia vector. The particle is said to be in *dynamic equilibrium*, and the problem under consideration may be solved by using the methods developed earlier in statics. We may, for instance, write that the sums of the components of the vectors shown in Fig. 12.4*b*, *including the inertia vector*, are zero,

$$\Sigma F_x = 0 \quad \Sigma F_y = 0 \quad \Sigma F_z = 0 \quad \text{including inertia vector} \tag{12.3'}$$

or, if the forces are coplanar, we may draw all vectors tip to tail, including again the inertia vector, to form a closed vector polygon.

The inertia vector measures the resistance the particle offers when we try to set it in motion or when we try to change the conditions of its motion. For this reason, it is often called an *inertia force*. The inertia force, however, is not a force like the forces found in statics, which are either contact forces or gravitational forces (weights). Many people, therefore, object to the use of the word force when referring to the vector $-m\mathbf{a}$ or even avoid altogether the concept of dynamic equilibrium. Others point out that inertia forces and actual forces such as gravitational forces affect our senses in the same way and cannot be distinguished by physical measurements. A man riding in an elevator which is accelerated upward will have the feeling that his weight has suddenly increased; and no measurement made within the elevator could establish whether the elevator is truly accelerated or whether the force of attraction exerted by the earth has suddenly increased.

Our main interest in this text, however, is not the philosophical interpretation of physical concepts but rather the application of these concepts to the solution of engineering problems. From this viewpoint, it makes little difference whether we use Eq. (12.2) or Eq. (12.3) to express the conditions of motion of a particle. In order to distinguish the vector $-m\mathbf{a}$ from actual forces, however, we shall call it an inertia vector throughout this text, rather than an inertia force.

12.4. Systems of Particles. D'Alembert's Principle. When a problem involves the motion of several particles, the equations of motion (12.2′) or (12.3′) may be written for each particle considered separately. However, in the case of a system involving a large number of particles, such as a rigid body, it will generally be more convenient to consider the system as a whole. In that case, we should note that the forces acting on a given particle of the system consist (1) of *external forces* exerted by bodies outside the system (such as the weight of the particle, which is exerted by the earth) and (2) of *internal forces* exerted by the other particles of the system. According to Newton's second law, the resultant of the external and internal forces acting on the particle considered is equal to the vector $m\mathbf{a}$ obtained by multiplying the acceleration $\mathbf{a}$ of the particle by its mass m. This vector is generally known as the *effective force* of the particle.

We now consider simultaneously all the particles of the system (Fig. 12.5). Since the relation we have established holds for any particle, it follows that the resultant of all the external and internal forces acting on the particles of the system is equal to the resultant of the effective forces of all the particles. But, according to Newton's third law, the internal forces occur by pairs of equal and opposite forces having the same line of action, and the system of the internal forces therefore reduces to zero. We thus conclude that *the external forces acting on the system of particles are equivalent to the effective forces of the various particles of the system.*

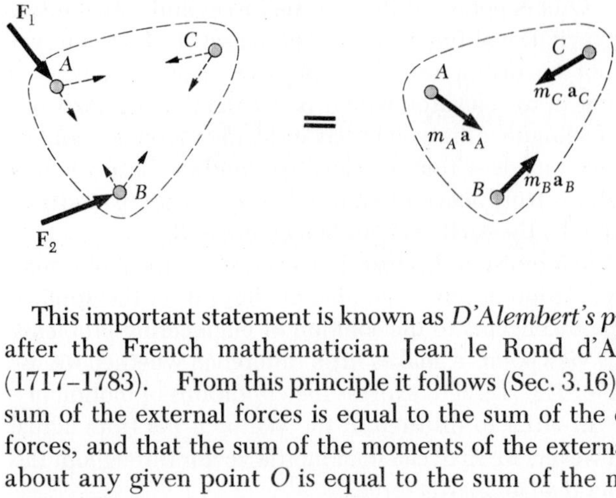

FIG. 12.5

This important statement is known as *D'Alembert's principle*, after the French mathematician Jean le Rond d'Alembert (1717–1783). From this principle it follows (Sec. 3.16) that the sum of the external forces is equal to the sum of the effective forces, and that the sum of the moments of the external forces about any given point O is equal to the sum of the moments of the effective forces about the same point O. Denoting by

r the position vector of a given particle, we write

$$\Sigma \mathbf{F}_{\text{ext}} = \Sigma m\mathbf{a} \qquad \Sigma(\mathbf{M}_O)_{\text{ext}} = \Sigma(\mathbf{r} \times m\mathbf{a}) \tag{12.4}$$

D'Alembert's principle may be presented in an alternate form if we consider the inertia vectors $-m\mathbf{a}$. Adding these vectors, also called *reversed effective forces*, to the external forces, we obtain a system equivalent to zero (Fig. 12.6).

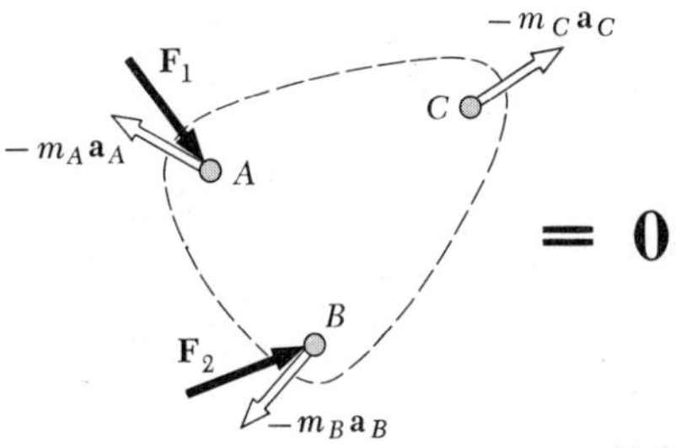

FIG. 12.6

12.5. Motion of the Mass Center of a System of Particles. The first of the equations (12.4) may be written in a modified form if the *mass center* of the system of particles is considered. The mass center of the system is the point G defined by the position vector $\bar{\mathbf{r}}$ which satisfies the relation

$$(\Sigma m)\bar{\mathbf{r}} = \Sigma m\mathbf{r} \tag{12.5}$$

Resolving the position vectors $\mathbf{r}$ and $\bar{\mathbf{r}}$ into rectangular components, we obtain the following three scalar equations, which may be used to determine the coordinates $\bar{x}$, $\bar{y}$, $\bar{z}$ of the mass center:

$$(\Sigma m)\bar{x} = \Sigma mx \qquad (\Sigma m)\bar{y} = \Sigma my \qquad (\Sigma m)\bar{z} = \Sigma mz \tag{12.5'}$$

Since $W = mg$, we note that G is also the center of gravity of the system. However, in order to avoid any confusion, we shall call G the *mass center* of the system of particles when discussing properties of the system associated with the *mass* of the particles, and we shall refer to it as the *center of gravity* of the system when considering properties associated with the *weight* of the particles. Particles located outside the gravitational field of the earth, for example, have a mass but no weight. We may then properly refer to their mass center, but obviously not to their center of gravity.†

Differentiating relation (12.5) with respect to t, we write

$$(\Sigma m)\frac{d\bar{\mathbf{r}}}{dt} = \Sigma m \frac{d\mathbf{r}}{dt}$$

or, observing that $d\bar{\mathbf{r}}/dt$ represents the velocity $\bar{\mathbf{v}}$ of the mass center G of the system of particles,

$$(\Sigma m)\bar{\mathbf{v}} = \Sigma m\mathbf{v} \tag{12.6}$$

Differentiating again, and denoting by $\bar{\mathbf{a}}$ the acceleration of the mass center G, we have

† It may also be pointed out that the mass center and the center of gravity of a system of particles do not exactly coincide, since the weights of the particles are directed toward the center of the earth and thus do not truly form a system of parallel forces.

$$(\Sigma m)\frac{d\bar{\mathbf{v}}}{dt} = \Sigma m \frac{d\mathbf{v}}{dt}$$

$$(\Sigma m)\bar{\mathbf{a}} = \Sigma m\mathbf{a} \tag{12.7}$$

Eliminating $\Sigma m\mathbf{a}$ from (12.7) and the first of the relations (12.4), we write the equation

$$\Sigma\mathbf{F}_{\text{ext}} = (\Sigma m)\bar{\mathbf{a}} \tag{12.8}$$

which defines the motion of the mass center of the system. We note that Eq. (12.8) is identical with the equation we would obtain for a particle of mass Σm, acted upon by all the external forces. We state therefore: *The mass center of a system of particles moves as if the entire mass of the system and all the external forces were concentrated at that point.*

This principle is best illustrated by the motion of an exploding shell. We know that, if the resistance of the air is neglected, a shell may be assumed to travel along a parabolic path. After the shell has exploded, the mass center G of the fragments of shell will continue to travel along the same path. Indeed, point G must move as if the mass and the weight of all fragments were concentrated at G; it must move, therefore, as if the shell had not exploded.

The principle we have established shows that we may replace a rigid body by a particle of the same mass if we are interested in the motion of the mass center of the body, and not in the motion of the body about its mass center. We should keep in mind, however, that Eqs. (12.7) and (12.8) *do not relate* the moments of the forces and vectors involved. For example, Eq. (12.7) *does not express* that the effective forces of the particles of the system are equivalent to a vector $(\Sigma m)\bar{\mathbf{a}}$ attached at the mass center G. As we shall see in Chap. 16, the resultant of the effective forces and, thus, the resultant of the external forces do not in general pass through the mass center of the system of particles.

12.6. Rectilinear Motion of a Particle. Consider a particle of mass m moving in a straight line under the action of coplanar forces $\mathbf{F}_1$, $\mathbf{F}_2$, $\mathbf{F}_3$, etc. The conditions of motion of the particle are expressed by Eq. (12.2). Since the particle moves in a straight line, its acceleration $\mathbf{a}$ must be directed along that line. Choosing the x axis in the same direction and the y axis in the plane of the forces (Fig. 12.7), we have $a_x = a$, $a_y = 0$ and write

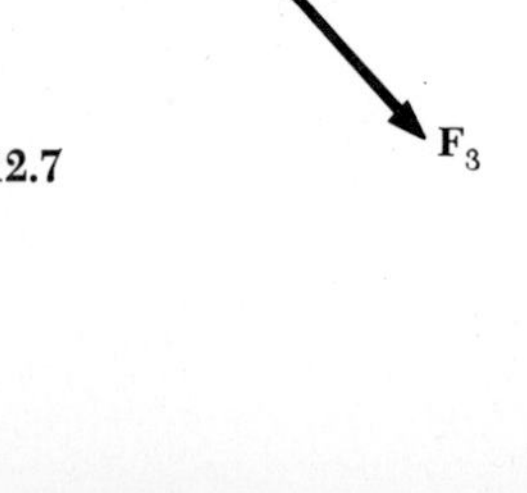

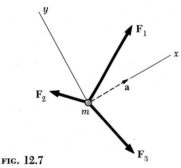

FIG. 12.7

$$\Sigma F_x = ma \qquad \Sigma F_y = 0 \tag{12.9}$$

The equations obtained may be solved for two unknowns.

SAMPLE PROBLEM 12.1

A 200-lb block rests on a horizontal plane. Find the magnitude of the force **P** required to give the block an acceleration of 10 ft/sec² to the right. The coefficient of friction between the block and the plane is $\mu = 0.25$.

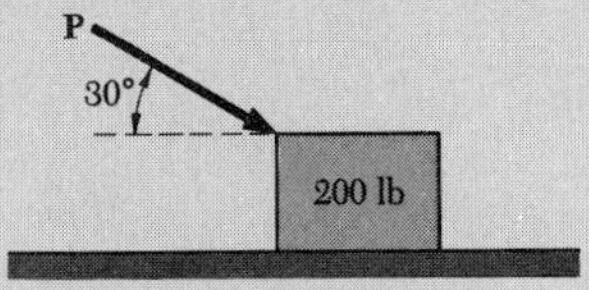

Solution. The mass of the block is

$$m = \frac{W}{g} = \frac{200 \text{ lb}}{32.2 \text{ ft/sec}^2} = 6.21 \text{ lb-sec}^2\text{/ft}$$

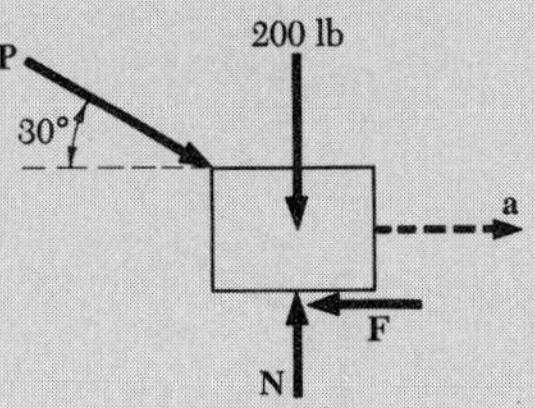

We note that $F = \mu N = 0.25N$ and that $a = 10 \text{ ft/sec}^2$. Expressing that the forces acting on the block are equivalent to the vector $m\mathbf{a}$, we write

$$\overset{+}{\rightarrow} \Sigma F_x = ma: \quad P \cos 30° - 0.25N = (6.21)(10) \quad (1)$$
$$+\uparrow \Sigma F_y = 0: \quad N - P \sin 30° - 200 = 0 \quad (2)$$

Solving (2) for N and carrying the result into (1), we obtain

$$N = P \sin 30° + 200$$
$$P \cos 30° - 0.25(P \sin 30° + 200) = 62.1$$
$$P = 151 \text{ lb} \blacktriangleleft$$

SAMPLE PROBLEM 12.2

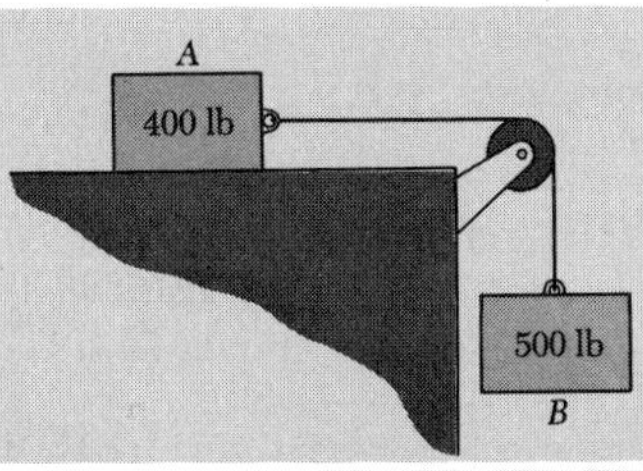

The two blocks shown start from rest; block A moves on a horizontal frictionless plane. Determine the acceleration of block A and the tension in the cord.

Solution. We note that the accelerations of blocks A and B have the same magnitude a. Applying Newton's second law to each of the blocks, we write the following:

Block A:

$$m_A = \frac{400 \text{ lb}}{32.2 \text{ ft/sec}^2} = 12.42 \text{ lb-sec}^2\text{/ft}$$

$$\overset{+}{\rightarrow} \Sigma F_x = m_A a: \quad T = 12.42a \quad (1)$$

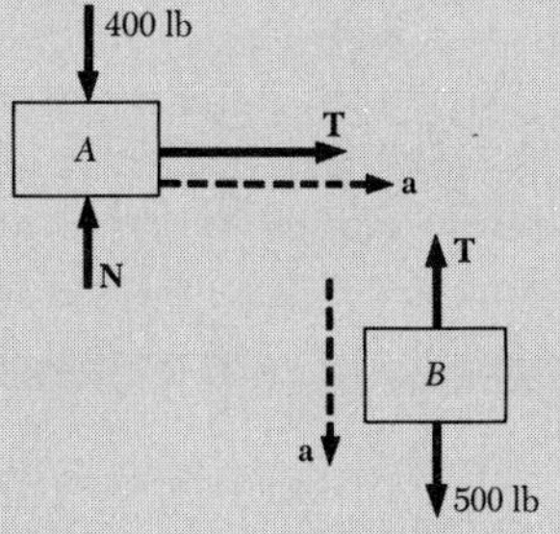

Block B:

$$m_B = \frac{500 \text{ lb}}{32.2 \text{ ft/sec}^2} = 15.53 \text{ lb-sec}^2\text{/ft}$$

$$+\downarrow \Sigma F_y = m_B a: \quad 500 - T = 15.53a \quad (2)$$

Solving Eqs. (1) and (2) simultaneously, we obtain

$$a = 17.89 \text{ ft/sec}^2 \qquad T = 222 \text{ lb} \blacktriangleleft$$

We should note that the tension in the cord does *not* equal the weight of block B.

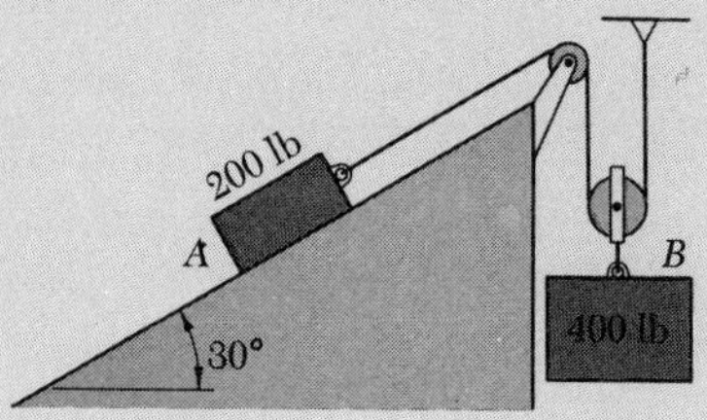

SAMPLE PROBLEM 12.3

The two blocks shown start from rest. The coefficient of friction between block A and the incline is 0.25, and the pulleys are weightless and frictionless. Determine the acceleration of each block and the tension in each cord.

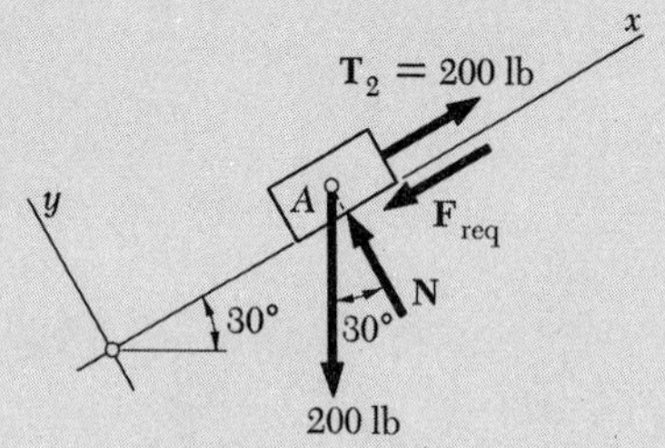

Sense of Motion. When friction is involved, the sense of motion should be determined at the outset by finding what friction force would be *required* to keep the system from moving. This part of the solution may be carried out by the methods of statics with the system at rest and with no acceleration. We first find that the tension in the cable attached to block A is $T_2 = 200$ lb. *Note that this will not be the tension when the blocks are moving.*

$$+\nearrow \Sigma F_x = 0: \qquad 200 - 200 \sin 30° - F_{req} = 0$$

$$F_{req} = +100 \text{ lb} \qquad \mathbf{F}_{req} = 100 \text{ lb} \swarrow$$

$$+\nwarrow \Sigma F_y = 0: \qquad N - 200 \cos 30° = 0 \qquad N = 173 \text{ lb}$$

$$F_m = \mu N \qquad F_m = (0.25)(173) = 43.3 \text{ lb} \qquad \mathbf{F}_m = 43.3 \text{ lb} \swarrow$$

Since the force of friction required to keep the blocks from moving is larger than the maximum friction force $\mathbf{F}_m$ and is directed to the left, block A will *move to the right.*

Accelerations and Tensions. Since the system has only one degree of freedom, the magnitudes of the accelerations of blocks A and B may be expressed in terms of the single unknown a_A.

Block B. The acceleration of B is directed downward and is of magnitude $a_B = \frac{1}{2}a_A$. The mass of B is

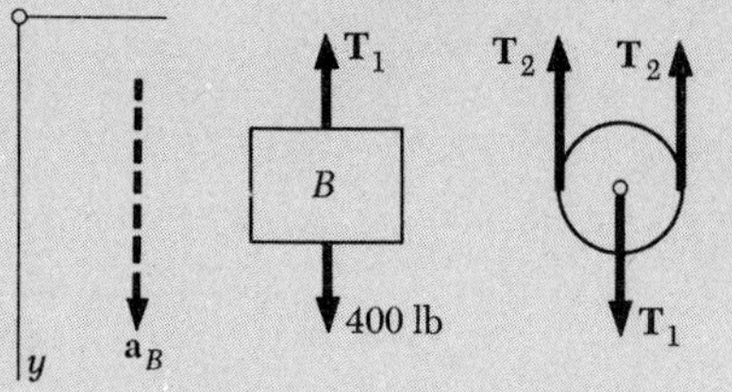

$$m_B = (400 \text{ lb})/(32.2 \text{ ft/sec}^2) = 12.42 \text{ lb-sec}^2/\text{ft}$$

$$+\downarrow \Sigma F_y = m_B a_B: \qquad 400 - T_1 = (12.42)(\tfrac{1}{2}a_A) \tag{1}$$

Pulley. Since the mass of the pulley is assumed to be zero, we have

$$+\downarrow \Sigma F_y = 0: \qquad T_1 - 2T_2 = 0 \tag{2}$$

Block A. The mass of block A is

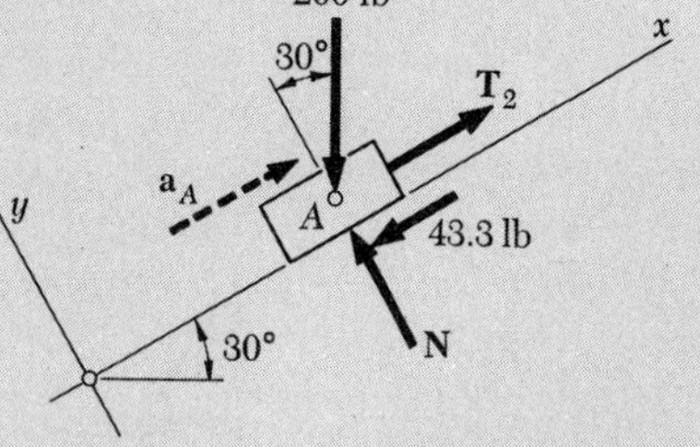

$$m_A = (200 \text{ lb})/(32.2 \text{ ft/sec}^2) = 6.21 \text{ lb-sec}^2/\text{ft}$$

The friction force was found above:

$$\mathbf{F}_m = 43.3 \text{ lb} \swarrow$$

$$+\nearrow \Sigma F_x = m_A a_A: \qquad T_2 - 200 \sin 30° - 43.3 = 6.21 a_A \tag{3}$$

Solving Eqs. (1), (2), and (3) simultaneously, we obtain

$$a_A = +6.09 \text{ ft/sec}^2 \qquad \mathbf{a}_A = 6.09 \text{ ft/sec}^2 \nearrow \blacktriangleleft$$

$$T_1 = 362 \text{ lb} \qquad T_2 = 181 \text{ lb} \blacktriangleleft$$

Since $a_B = \frac{1}{2}a_A$,

$$a_B = (\tfrac{1}{2})(6.09) = +3.05 \text{ ft/sec}^2 \qquad \mathbf{a}_B = 3.05 \text{ ft/sec}^2 \downarrow \blacktriangleleft$$

PROBLEMS

12.1. The value of g at any latitude ϕ may be obtained from the formula

$$g = 32.09(1 + 0.0053 \sin^2 \phi) \text{ ft/sec}^2$$

Determine with four significant figures the weight in pounds, the mass in pounds, and the mass in lb-sec²/ft, at the latitudes of 0°, 45°, and 90°, of a silver bar whose mass is officially defined as 100.00 lb.

12.2. The acceleration due to gravity on the moon is 5.31 ft/sec². Determine the weight in pounds, the mass in pounds, and the mass in lb-sec²/ft, on the moon, of a silver bar whose mass is officially defined as 100.00 lb.

12.3. Two boxes are weighed on the scales shown: scale *a* is a lever scale, scale *b* is a spring scale. The scales are attached to the roof of an elevator. When the elevator is at rest, each scale indicates a load of 25 lb. Determine the load which each scale will indicate when the elevator is accelerated upward at the rate of 6.44 ft/sec².

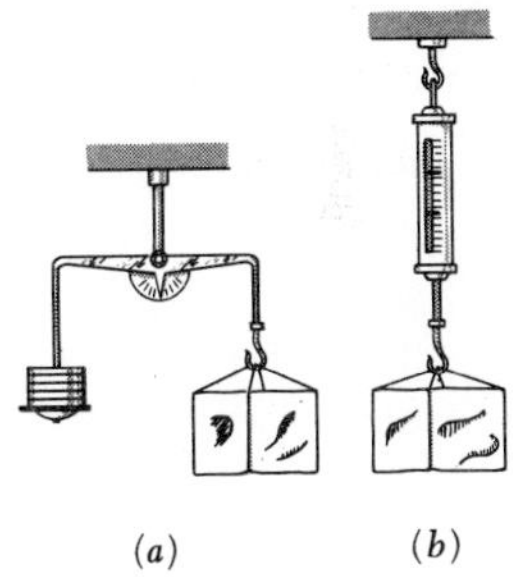

FIG. P 12.3

12.4. If the spring scale of Prob. 12.3 indicates a load of 22 lb, determine the acceleration of the elevator and the load indicated by the lever scale.

12.5. A motorist traveling at a speed of 30 mph suddenly applies his brakes and comes to a stop after skidding 60 ft. Determine (*a*) the time required for the car to stop, (*b*) the coefficient of friction between the tires and the pavement.

12.6. (*a*) Determine the smallest distance in which a car traveling at 60 mph can be stopped on a dry road where the coefficient of friction between the tires and the road is 0.80. (*b*) Determine the maximum allowable speed of a car if it is to stop in the same distance on an icy road where $\mu = 0.08$.

12.7. A truck is proceeding up a long 3 per cent grade at a constant speed of 35 mph. If the driver does not change the setting of his throttle or shift gears, what will be the acceleration of the truck as it starts moving on the level section of the road?

FIG. P 12.7

12.8. A package is projected up a 20° incline with an initial velocity of 25 ft/sec. The package moves up the incline to point *B* and then slides back toward point *A*. Knowing that the distance *d* between *A* and *B* is 20 ft, determine (*a*) the coefficient of friction between the package and the incline, (*b*) the velocity of the package as it returns to point *A*.

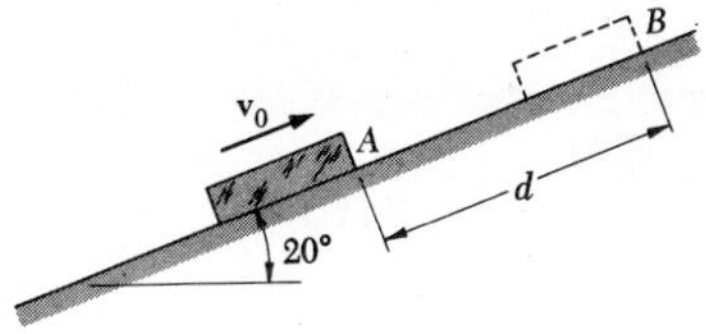

FIG. P 12.8

12.9. A package is projected up a 20° incline with an initial velocity $\mathbf{v}_0$; the package comes to rest at point B and then slides back to point A. Knowing that the package reaches B in 2.4 sec and returns to A in an additional 4.5 sec, determine (*a*) the coefficient of friction between the package and the incline, (*b*) the distance d from A to B, (*c*) the initial and final values of the velocity of the package at point A.

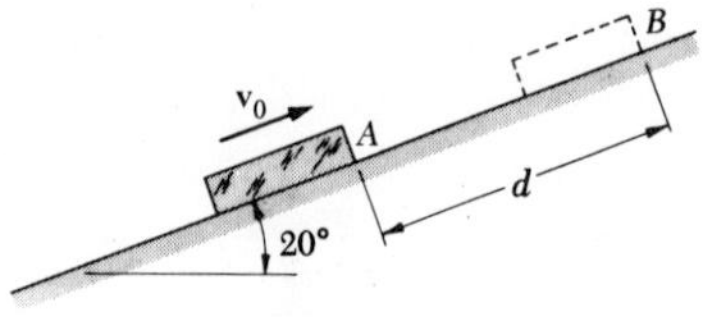

FIG. P 12.9

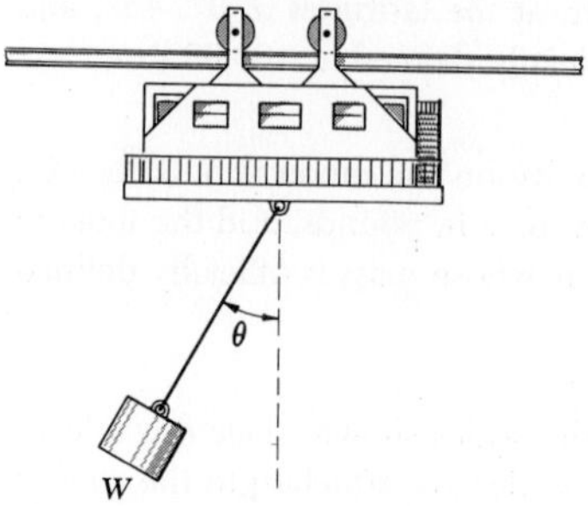

FIG. P 12.10 AND P 12.11

12.10. A load hangs from an overhead crane as shown. Determine the angle θ that the cables supporting the load form with the vertical when the crane moves with an acceleration of 2.5 ft/sec² to the right.

12.11. If the overhead crane shown moves to the left and if the angle θ is equal to 8°, find the acceleration or deceleration of the crane.

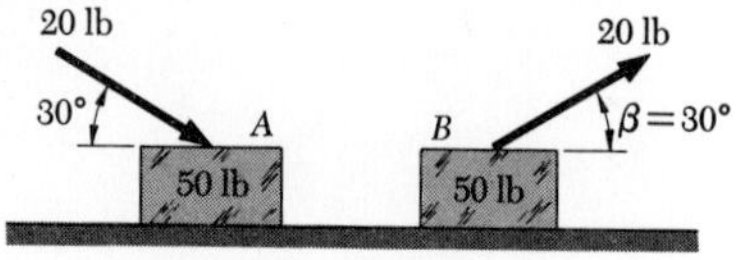

FIG. P 12.12

12.12. Each of the 50-lb blocks is initially at rest and is acted upon by a 20-lb force as shown. Assuming the coefficient of friction $\mu = 0.20$, determine for each block (*a*) the acceleration, (*b*) the velocity after 10 sec, (*c*) the velocity after it has moved 50 ft.

12.13. Assuming that block A and block B of Prob. 12.12 are connected by a horizontal inextensible cable, determine the acceleration of the blocks and the tension in the cable.

12.14. For block B of Prob. 12.12 determine (*a*) the angle β for which the acceleration is as large as possible, (*b*) the corresponding value of the acceleration.

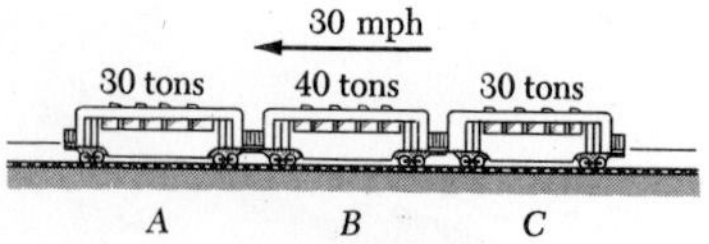

FIG. P 12.15

12.15. The subway train shown travels at a speed of 30 mph. Determine the force in each coupling when the brakes are applied, knowing that the braking force is 5,000 lb on each car.

12.16. Solve Prob. 12.15 assuming that the brakes on car C fail to operate.

12.17. Each of the systems shown is initially at rest. Assuming the pulleys to be weightless and neglecting axle friction, determine for each system (*a*) the acceleration of block *A*, (*b*) the velocity of block *A* after 4 sec, (*c*) the velocity of block *A* after it has moved 10 ft.

12.18. How much weight should be added to or taken away from block *A* in each system if the acceleration of block *A* is to be $\frac{1}{4}g$ downward?

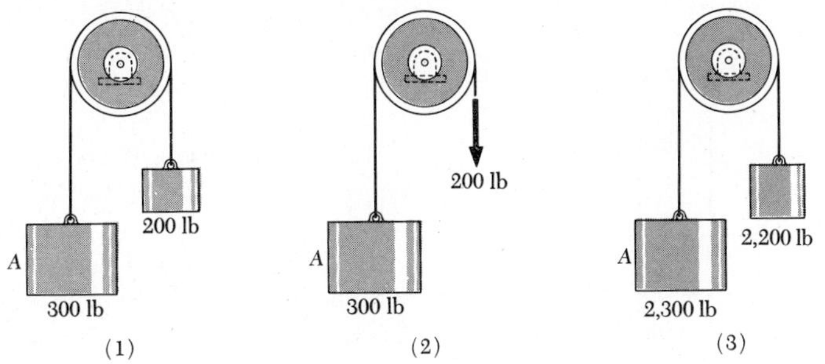

FIG. **P 12.17** AND **P 12.18**

12.19. It is assumed that friction exists between block *A* and the horizontal plane in Sample Prob. 12.2. If block *B* is observed to move 30 ft in 2 sec after starting from rest, determine the coefficient of friction between block *A* and the horizontal plane.

12.20. The Atwood machine sketched was used by physicists to determine the value of *g*. The two weights were released from rest, and their speed *v* was measured after they had moved through a distance *h*. Assuming the pulley weightless and frictionless, derive the formula expressing *g* in terms of m_1, m_2, *v*, and *h*.

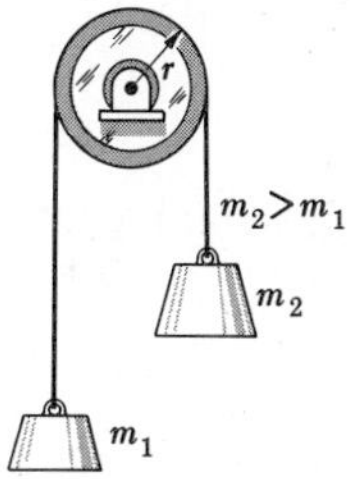

FIG. **P 12.20**

12.21 and 12.22. The 100-lb slider block *A* is attached to a block *B* of weight 40 lb by the cable arrangement shown. Knowing that the system is released from rest and neglecting friction, determine (*a*) the velocity of block *A* after 5 sec, (*b*) the distance traveled by block *A* when its speed has reached 8 ft/sec.

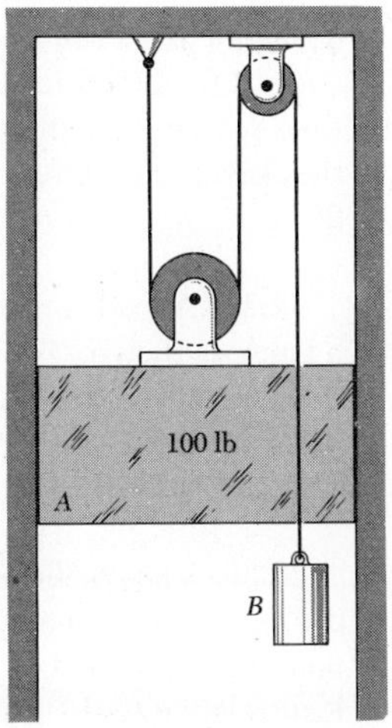

FIG. **P 12.21** AND **P 12.23**

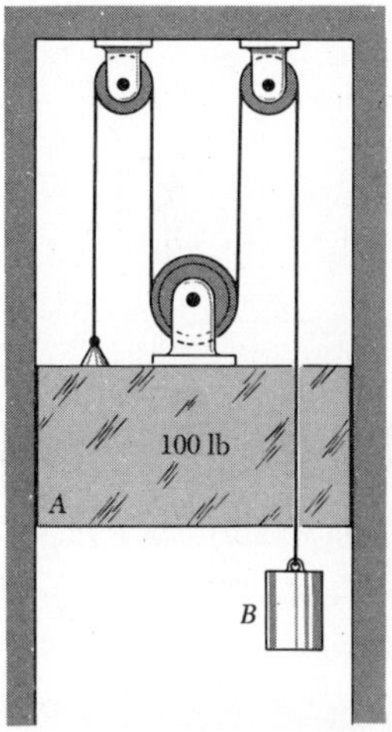

FIG. **P 12.22** AND **P 12.24**

12.23 and 12.24. (*a*) Determine the weight of block *B* knowing that the acceleration of block *A* is 4 ft/sec² directed upward. (*b*) Attempt to solve part *a* assuming the acceleration of *A* to be 18 ft/sec² upward; explain the difficulties encountered.

12.25. The cage of an elevator, of weight W_1, is attached to two cables, which connect it, respectively, to the motor and to a counterweight of weight W_2. Determine the tension in each cable while the cage is brought to a stop after moving down. The deceleration of the cage while it slows down is denoted by a.

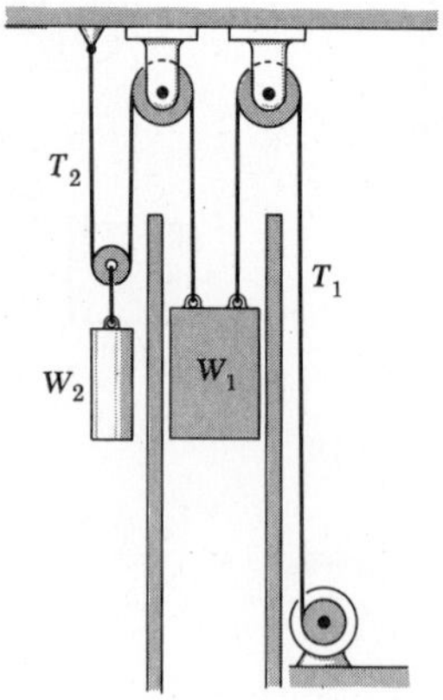

FIG. P 12.25 AND P 12.27

12.26. Solve Prob. 12.25 when $W_1 = 500$ lb, $W_2 = 100$ lb, and the deceleration of W_1 is $g/10$.

12.27. In the system shown, $W_1 = 500$ lb and $W_2 = 600$ lb. Determine the acceleration of W_1 and W_2 (*a*) when $T_1 = 300$ lb, (*b*) when $T_1 = 800$ lb.

12.28. The *rimpull* of a truck is defined as the tractive force between the rubber tires of the driving wheels and the ground. For a truck used to haul earth at a construction site, the rimpull actually utilized by the average driver in each of the first five forward gears and the maximum speed attained in each gear are as follows:

Gear	Max v (mph)	Average rimpull (lb)
1st	3	6,000
2d	6	3,800
3d	9	2,800
4th	15	2,000
5th	27	1,500

Knowing that a truck (and load) weighs 44,000 lb and has a rolling resistance of 60 lb/ton for the unpaved surface encountered, determine the time required for the truck to attain a speed of 27 mph. Assume that the driver can perform all the required gear shifting in a total time of 20 sec.

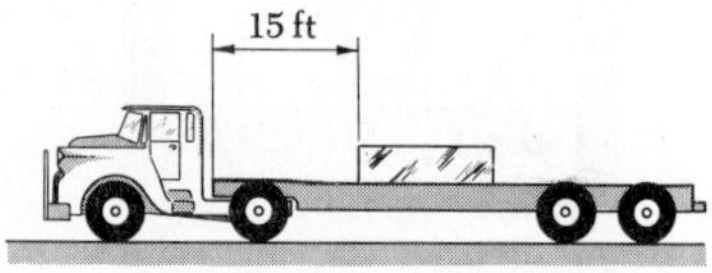

FIG. P 12.29 AND P 12.30

12.29. A load is placed 15 ft from the forward edge of the trailer of a truck as shown. The coefficient of friction between the load and the trailer is 0.30. Knowing that the forward speed of the truck is 30 mph, determine the shortest distance in which the truck can be brought to a stop if the load is not to shift.

12.30. The coefficient of friction between the load and the trailer is 0.30. While traveling at 60 mph, the driver makes an emergency stop and the truck skids to rest in 250 ft. Determine the velocity of the load relative to the trailer as it reaches the forward edge of the trailer.

***12.31.** In Prob. 12.30, determine the shortest distance in which the truck can be stopped without having the load slide beyond the forward edge of the trailer. (*Note.* As the truck comes to a stop, the load is still moving relative to the trailer.)

12.32. A 200-lb crate rests on a 100-lb cart; the coefficient of static friction between the crate and the cart is 0.25. If the crate is not to slip with respect to the cart, determine (*a*) the maximum allowable magnitude of **P**, (*b*) the corresponding acceleration of the cart.

12.33. Solve Prob. 12.32 assuming that the force **P** is applied to the 200-lb crate.

12.34. The coefficients of friction between the 200-lb crate and the 100-lb cart are $\mu_s = 0.25$ and $\mu_k = 0.15$. If a force **P** of magnitude 80 lb is applied to the cart, determine the acceleration (*a*) of the cart, (*b*) of the crate, (*c*) of the cart with respect to the crate.

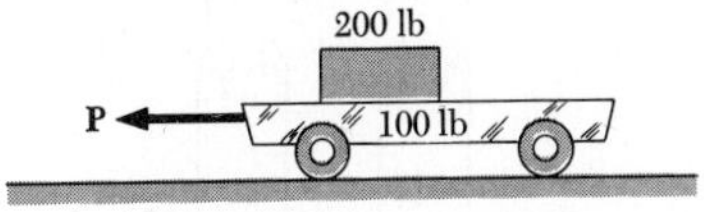

FIG. P 12.32 AND P 12.34

12.35. Solve Prob. 12.34 assuming that the force **P** is applied to the 200-lb crate.

12.36. The force exerted by a magnet on a small steel block varies inversely as the square of the distance between the block and the magnet. When the block is 10 in. from the magnet, the magnetic force is 5 oz. If the block is released from the position shown, determine its velocity when it is 4 in. from the magnet. Assume no friction.

12.37. Solve Prob. 12.36 assuming that the coefficient of friction between the steel block and the horizontal surface is 0.50.

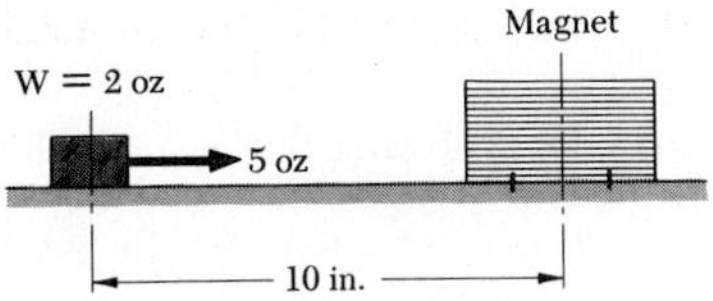

FIG. P 12.36

12.38. The propellers of a ship can produce a propulsive force $\mathbf{F}_0$; they produce a force of the same magnitude but of opposite direction when the engines are reversed. Knowing that the ship was proceeding forward at its maximum speed v_0 when the engines were put into reverse, determine the distance the ship travels before coming to a stop. Assume that the frictional resistance of the water varies directly with the square of the velocity.

12.39. A spring *AB* of constant *k* is attached to a support at *A* and to a collar of weight *W*. The unstretched length of the spring is *l*. Neglecting friction between the collar and the horizontal rod, express the acceleration of the collar as a function of the distance *x*.

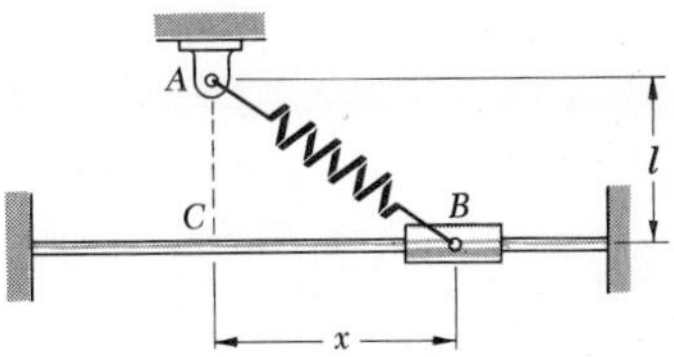

FIG. P 12.39

***12.40.** The collar of Prob. 12.39 is released from rest at $x = x_0$. Determine the velocity of the collar as it passes through point *C*.

12.41. Knowing that blocks B and C strike the ground simultaneously and exactly 1 sec after the system is released from rest, determine W_B and W_C in terms of W_A.

12.42. Determine the acceleration of each block when $W_A = 10$ lb, $W_B = 30$ lb, and $W_C = 20$ lb. Which block strikes the ground first?

12.43. In the system shown, $W_A = 10$ lb and $W_C = 20$ lb. Determine the required weight W_B if block B is not to move when the system is released from rest.

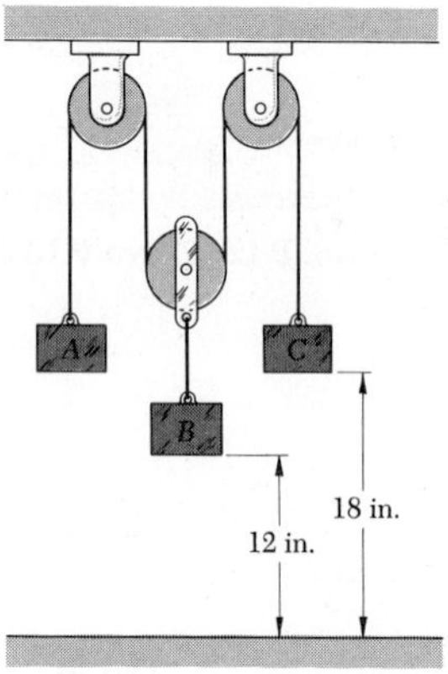

FIG. P 12.41, P 12.42, AND P 12.43

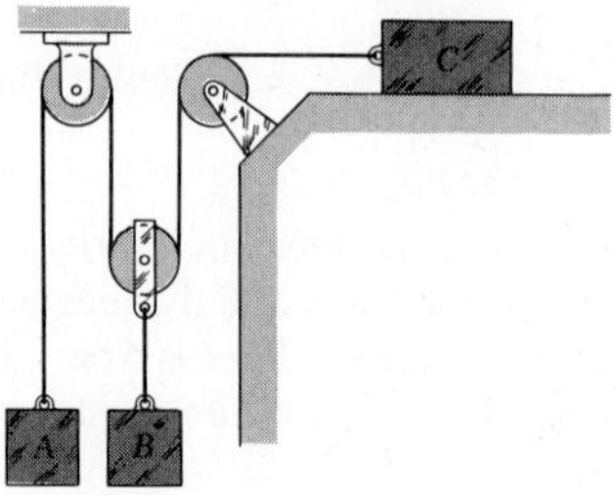

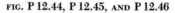

FIG. P 12.44, P 12.45, AND P 12.46

12.44. Knowing that $\mu = 0.30$ and $W_C = 10$ lb, determine W_A and W_B if the acceleration of both A and B is to be $g/5$ directed downward.

12.45. Knowing that $\mu = 0.30$, determine the acceleration of each block when $W_A = W_B = W_C$.

12.46. Knowing that $\mu = 0.50$, determine the acceleration of each block when $W_A = 10$ lb, $W_B = 40$ lb, and $W_C = 30$ lb.

12.7. Curvilinear Motion of a Particle. We saw in Chap. 11 that the acceleration of a particle P moving along a curved path may be resolved into rectangular components, into tangential and normal components, or into radial and transverse components. We may therefore use any one of these methods of representation to express Newton's second law of motion.

Rectangular Components. We saw in Sec. 12.3 that, if each of the forces **F** acting on the particle P and the acceleration **a** of the particle are resolved into rectangular components, Newton's second law may be expressed by the scalar equations

$$\Sigma F_x = ma_x \qquad \Sigma F_y = ma_y \qquad \Sigma F_z = ma_z \qquad (12.2')$$

Recalling from Sec. (11.11) that the components of the acceleration are equal to the second derivatives of the coordinates of P, we have

$$\Sigma F_x = m\ddot{x} \qquad \Sigma F_y = m\ddot{y} \qquad \Sigma F_z = m\ddot{z} \qquad (12.10)$$

Consider, as an example, the motion of a projectile. If the resistance of the air is neglected, the only force acting on the projectile after it has been fired is its weight $\mathbf{W} = -W\mathbf{j}$. The equations defining the motion of the projectile are therefore

$$m\ddot{x} = 0 \qquad m\ddot{y} = -W \qquad m\ddot{z} = 0$$

and the components of the acceleration of the projectile are

$$\ddot{x} = 0 \qquad \ddot{y} = -\frac{W}{m} = -g \qquad \ddot{z} = 0$$

where $g = 32.2$ ft/sec². The equations obtained may be integrated independently, as was shown in Sec. 11.11, to determine the velocity and position of the projectile at any instant.

Tangential and Normal Components. Resolving the forces and the acceleration of the particle into components along the unit vectors $\mathbf{i}_t$ and $\mathbf{i}_n$ (Sec. 11.13), we obtain the two scalar equations

$$\Sigma F_t = ma_t \qquad \Sigma F_n = ma_n \qquad (12.11)$$

Substituting for a_t and a_n from 11.40, we have

$$\Sigma F_t = m\frac{dv}{dt} \qquad \Sigma F_n = m\frac{v^2}{\rho} \qquad (12.12)$$

The equations obtained may be solved for two unknowns.

Dynamic Equilibrium. As an alternate method of solution, we may add the inertia vector $-m\mathbf{a}$ to the forces acting on the particle and express that the system obtained is balanced. In practice, it is found convenient to resolve the inertia vector into two components. Resolving, for example, the inertia vector into its tangential and normal components, we obtain the system of vectors shown in Fig. 12.8. The tangential component of the inertia vector provides a measure of the resistance the particle offers to a change in speed, while its normal component (also called *centrifugal force*) represents the tendency of the particle to leave its curved path. We should note that either of these two components may be zero under special conditions: (1) if the particle starts from rest, its initial velocity is zero and the normal component of the inertia vector is zero at $t = 0$; (2) if the particle moves at constant speed along its path, the tangential component of the inertia vector is zero and only its normal component needs to be considered.

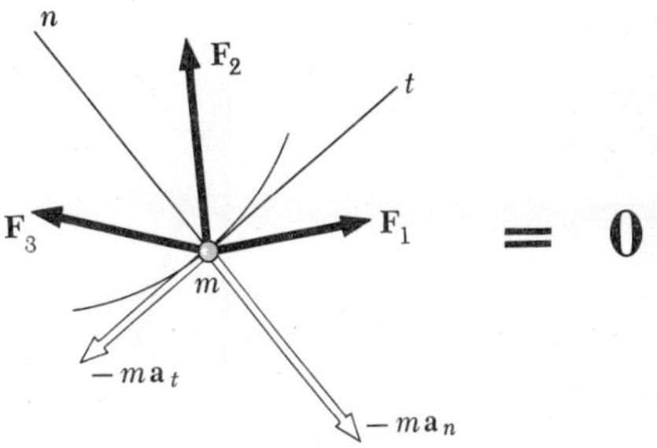

FIG. 12.8

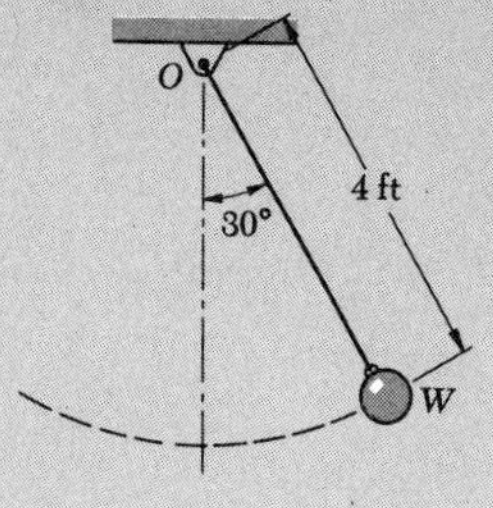

SAMPLE PROBLEM 12.4

The bob of a 4-ft pendulum describes an arc of circle in a vertical plane. If the tension in the cord is 2.5 times the weight of the bob for the position shown, find the velocity and acceleration of the bob in that position.

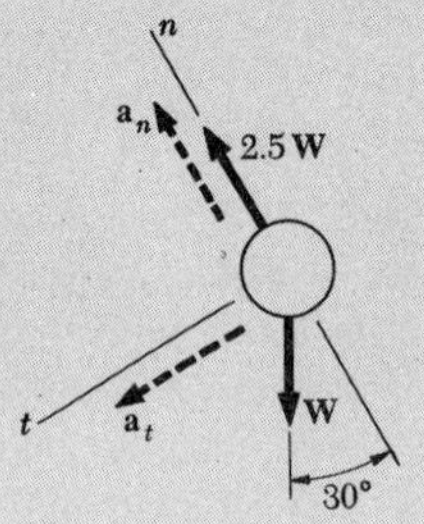

Solution. The mass of the bob is $m = W/g$. Recalling that $\mathbf{a}_n$ is directed toward O and assuming $\mathbf{a}_t$ as shown, we apply Newton's second law and obtain

$$+\swarrow \Sigma F_t = ma_t: \qquad W \sin 30° = \frac{W}{g} a_t$$

$$a_t = g \sin 30° = +16.1 \text{ ft/sec}^2 \qquad \mathbf{a}_t = 16.1 \text{ ft/sec}^2 \swarrow \blacktriangleleft$$

$$+\nwarrow \Sigma F_n = ma_n: \qquad 2.5W - W \cos 30° = \frac{W}{g} a_n$$

$$a_n = (1.633)g = +52.6 \text{ ft/sec}^2 \qquad \mathbf{a}_n = 52.6 \text{ ft/sec}^2 \nwarrow \blacktriangleleft$$

Since $a_n = v^2/\rho$, we write $52.6 = v^2/4$ and obtain

$$v = \pm 14.50 \text{ ft/sec} \qquad \mathbf{v} = 14.50 \text{ ft/sec} \swarrow\!\!\nearrow \text{ (up or down)} \blacktriangleleft$$

SAMPLE PROBLEM 12.5

Determine the rated speed of a highway curve of radius $\rho = 400$ ft banked through an angle $\theta = 18°$. The rated speed of a banked curved road is the speed at which a car should travel if no lateral friction force is to be exerted on its wheels.

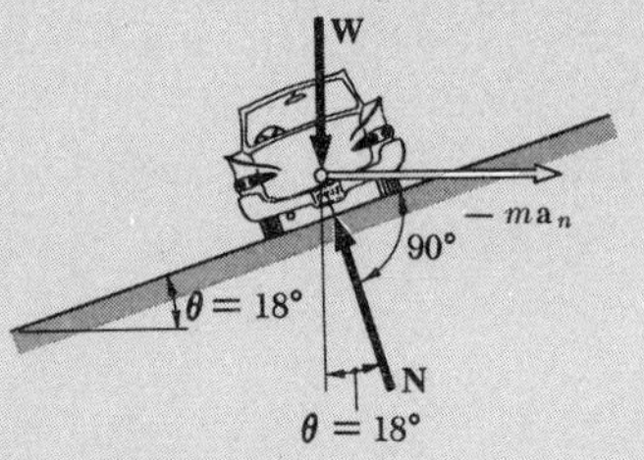

Solution. The car travels in a *horizontal* circular path of radius ρ. The normal component $\mathbf{a}_n$ of the acceleration is directed toward the center of the path; its magnitude is $a_n = v^2/\rho$ where v is the speed of the car in ft/sec. The mass m of the car is W/g, where W is the weight of the car. Since no lateral friction force is to be exerted on the car, the reaction of the road reduces to its normal component **N**.

The car is in *dynamic equilibrium* under the action of **W**, the force **N** exerted by the road, and the inertia vector $-m\mathbf{a}_n$ directed opposite to $\mathbf{a}_n$, i.e., away from the center of the path. We solve the vector triangle shown for the magnitude of the inertia vector and obtain

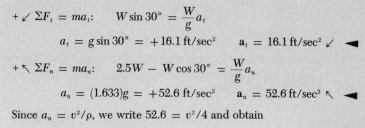

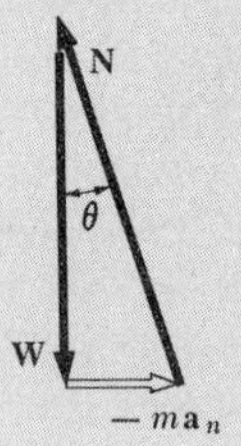

$$ma_n = W \tan \theta \tag{1}$$

Substituting $a_n = v^2/\rho$ into (1), we write

$$\frac{W}{g}\frac{v^2}{\rho} = W \tan \theta \qquad v^2 = g\rho \tan \theta$$

Substituting the given data, $\rho = 400$ ft and $\theta = 18°$, into this equation, we obtain

$$v^2 = (32.2)(400) \tan 18° \qquad v = 64.7 \text{ ft/sec} \qquad v = 44.1 \text{ mph} \blacktriangleleft$$

PROBLEMS

12.47. A small ball of weight $W = 5$ lb is attached to a cord of length $L = 6$ ft and is made to revolve in a horizontal circle at a constant speed v_0. Knowing that the cord forms an angle $\theta = 30°$ with the vertical, determine (*a*) the tension in the cord, (*b*) the speed v_0 of the ball.

12.48. A small ball of weight $W = 5$ lb is made to revolve in a horizontal circle as shown. Knowing that the maximum allowable tension in the cord is 15 lb, determine (*a*) the maximum allowable velocity if $L = 6$ ft, (*b*) the minimum allowable length of the cord if the velocity of the ball is 15 ft/sec.

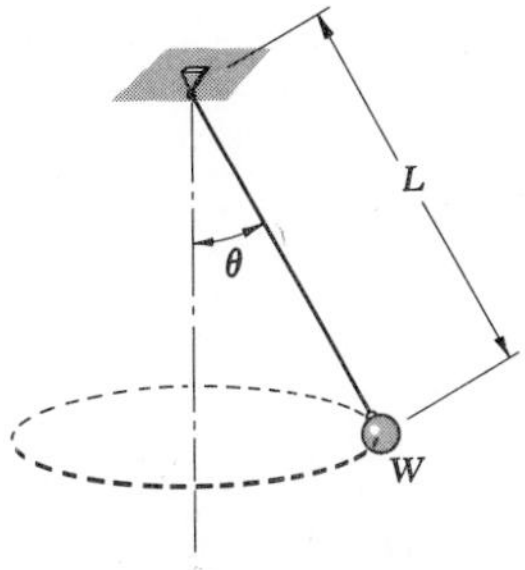

FIG. P 12.47 AND P 12.48

12.49. Two wires AC and BC are each tied to a weight at C. The weight is made to revolve in a horizontal circle at a constant speed v. Determine the range of values of the speed v for which *both* wires are taut.

12.50. A single wire ACB passes through a small pulley at C and is attached to supports at A and B. A weight W is attached to the pulley and is made to revolve in a horizontal circle at a constant speed v. Determine the speed v for which the wires will form the angles shown with the horizontal and vertical.

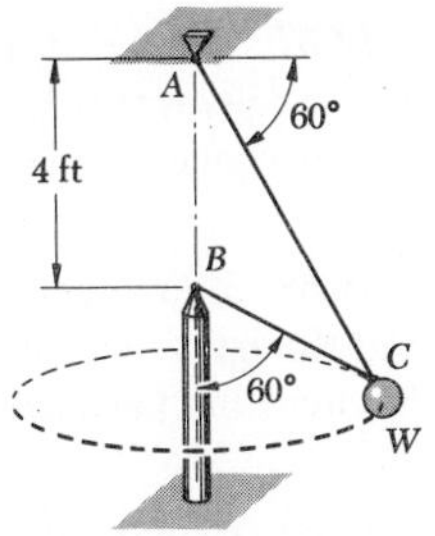

FIG. P 12.49 AND P 12.50

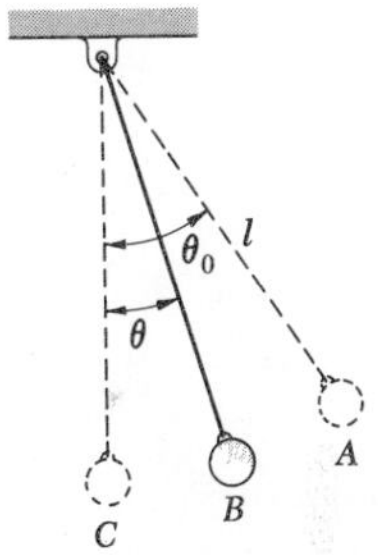

FIG. P 12.51, P 12.52, AND P 12.53

12.51. A 3-lb ball is swung in a vertical circle at the end of a cord of length $l = 18$ in. Find the tangential component of its acceleration when (*a*) $\theta = 90°$, (*b*) $\theta = 30°$, (*c*) $\theta = 0$.

12.52. A 3-lb ball is swung in a vertical circle at the end of a cord of length $l = 18$ in. Find the tension in the cord when $\theta = 60°$, knowing that the velocity is then 6 ft/sec.

12.53. A ball of weight W is released with no velocity from position A and oscillates in a vertical plane at the end of a cord of length l. Determine (*a*) the tangential component of the acceleration in position B in terms of the angle θ, (*b*) the velocity in position B in terms of θ, θ_0, and l, (*c*) the tension in the cord in terms of W and θ_0 when the ball passes through its lowest position C, (*d*) the value of θ_0 if the tension in the cord is $T = 2W$ when the ball passes through position C.

12.54. A small sphere of weight W is attached to the ceiling by means of two wires AB and CD. Wire AB is then cut. Determine (*a*) the tension in wire CD before AB was cut, (*b*) the tension in wire CD and the acceleration of the weight just after AB has been cut.

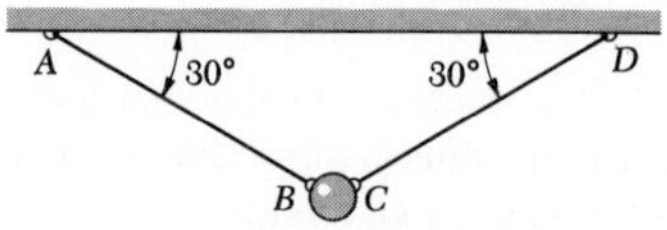

FIG. P 12.54

12.55. A 175-lb pilot flies a small plane in a vertical loop of 300-ft radius. Determine the speed of the plane at points A and C, knowing that at point A the pilot experiences weightlessness and that at point C the pilot's apparent weight is 600 lb.

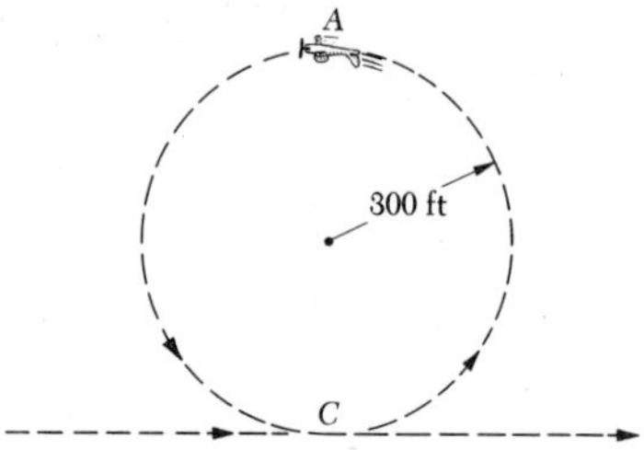

FIG. P 12.55

12.56. At the bottom of a vertical curve, a 175-lb man driving a car seems to weigh 200 lb. (*a*) If the speed of his car is 45 mph, determine the radius of the curve. (*b*) What would the man seem to weigh if the speed of his car was 60 mph?

12.57. A series of small packages, each weighing 10 oz, are discharged from a conveyor belt as shown. Determine the force exerted by the belt on a package just after the package has passed point A.

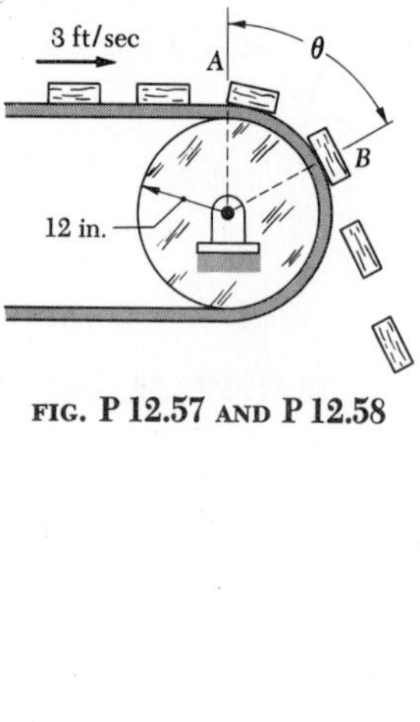

FIG. P 12.57 AND P 12.58

12.58. Knowing that the coefficient of friction between each package and the conveyor belt is 0.50, determine the angle θ defining the point B where the packages first *slip* relative to the belt.

12.59. Express the rated speed of a banked road in terms of the radius r of the curve and the banking angle θ (see Sample Prob. 12.5 for the definition of the rated speed).

12.60. Express the minimum and maximum safe speeds, with respect to skidding, of a car traveling on a banked road, in terms of the radius r of the curve, the banking angle θ, and the friction angle ϕ between the tires and the pavement.

12.61. A man on a motorcycle takes a turn on a flat unbanked road at 45 mph. If the radius of the turn is 100 ft, determine the minimum value of the coefficient of friction between the tires and the road which will ensure no skidding.

12.62. What angle of banking should be given to the road in Prob. 12.61 if the man on the motorcycle is to be able to take the turn at 45 mph with a coefficient of friction $\mu = 0.40$?

12.63. A small ball rolls at a speed v_0 along a horizontal circle inside a bowl as shown. The inside surface of the bowl is a surface of revolution obtained by rotating the curve OA about the y axis. Determine the required equation of the curve OA if the speed v_0 of the ball is to be proportional to the distance x from the y axis to the ball.

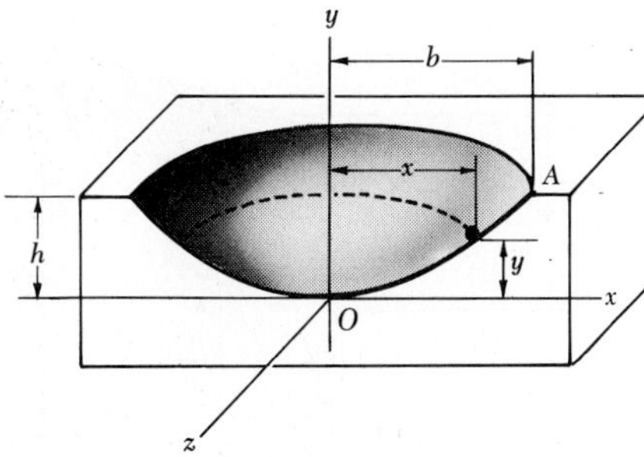

FIG. P 12.63

12.64. Solve Prob. 12.63 assuming that the speed v_0 of the ball is to be proportional to the height y of the ball above the bottom of the bowl.

12.65. A circular curve in an automobile racing track is banked as shown in the cross section. A driver follows a path which is at a constant distance $d = 25$ ft from the inside railing at A. (*a*) At what speed will the lateral friction force exerted on the wheels be zero? (*b*) What is the maximum safe speed of the car with respect to skidding if $\mu = 0.60$?

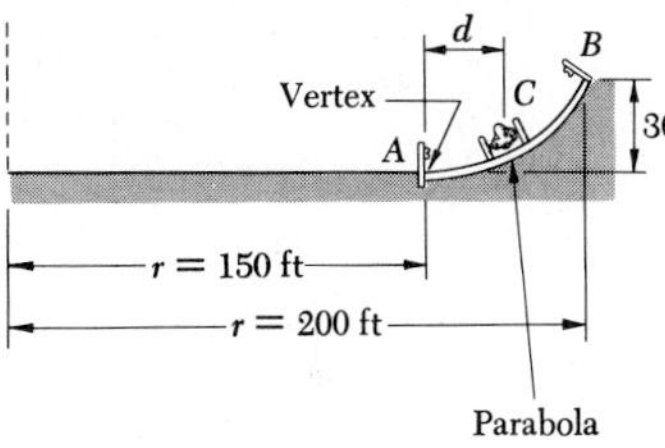

FIG. P 12.65

12.66. Solve Prob. 12.65 assuming that the driver follows the top railing at B, where $d = 50$ ft.

12.67. A bucket is attached to a rope of length $L = 4$ ft and is made to revolve in a horizontal circle. Drops of water leaking from the bucket fall and strike the floor along the perimeter of a circle of radius a. Determine the radius a when $\theta = 30°$.

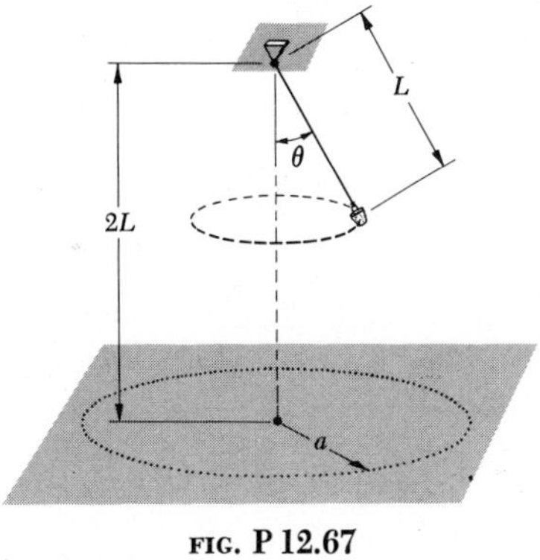

FIG. P 12.67

12.68. Solve Prob. 12.67 assuming that the speed of the bucket is 15 ft/sec. (The angle θ is not 30° in this case.)

12.69. In the cathode-ray tube shown, electrons emitted by the cathode and attracted by the anode pass through a small hole in the anode and keep traveling in a straight line with a speed v_0 until they strike the screen at A. However, if a difference of potential V is established between the two parallel plates, each electron will be subjected to a force $\mathbf{F}$ perpendicular to the plates while it travels between the plates and will strike the screen at point B at a distance δ from A. The magnitude of the force $\mathbf{F}$ is $F = eV/d$, where $-e$ is the charge of the electron and d is the distance between the plates. Derive an expression for the deflection δ in terms of V, v_0, the charge $-e$ of the electron, its mass m, and the dimensions d, l, and L.

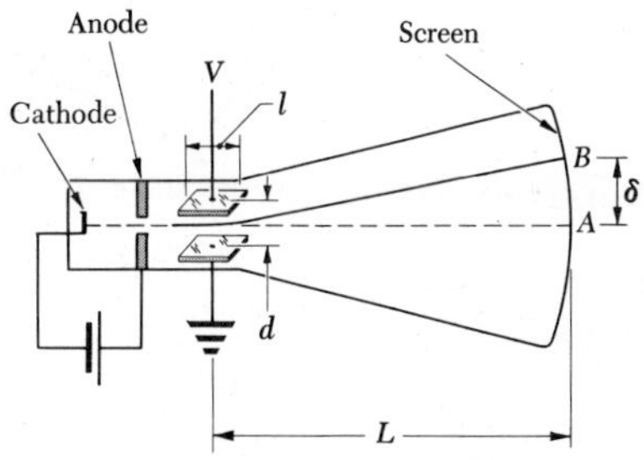

FIG. P 12.69 AND P 12.70

12.70. A manufacturer wishes to design a new cathode-ray tube which will be only half as long as his current model. If the size of the screen is to remain the same, how should the length l of the plates be modified if all the other characteristics of the circuit are to remain unchanged?

12.71. In Prob. 12.69, determine the smallest allowable value of the ratio d/l in terms of e, m, v_0, and V if the electrons are not to strike the positive plate.

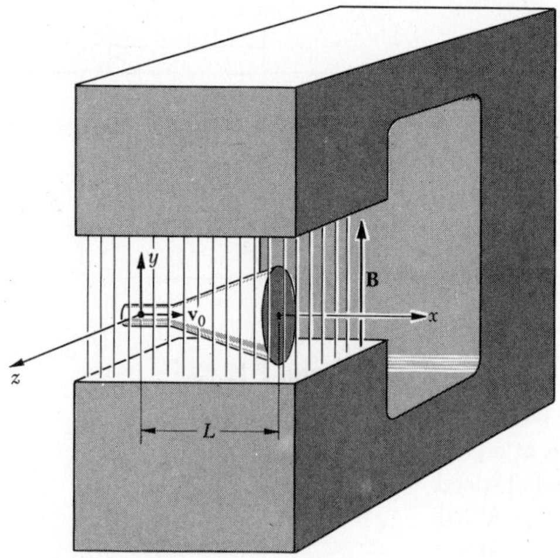

FIG. P 12.72

12.72. A cathode-ray tube emitting electrons with a velocity $\mathbf{v}_0$ is placed as shown between the poles of a large electromagnet which creates a uniform magnetic field of strength **B**. Determine the coordinates of the point where the electron beam strikes the tube screen when no difference of potential exists between the plates. It is known that an electron (mass m and charge $-e$) traveling with a velocity **v** at a right angle to the lines of force of a magnetic field of strength **B** is subjected to a force $\mathbf{F} = e\mathbf{B} \times \mathbf{v}$.

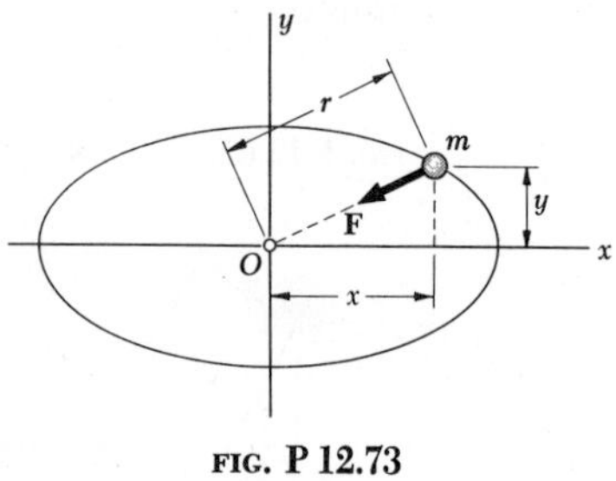

FIG. P 12.73

12.73. A particle of mass m is acted upon by a force **F** of magnitude $F = kr$ directed toward the origin O and proportional to the distance r from O to the particle. If, at $t = 0$, the coordinates of the particle are $x = x_0$, $y = 0$ and the components of its velocity are $v_x = 0$, $v_y = v_0$, show (*a*) that the path of the particle is an ellipse of semiaxes x_0 and $v_0\sqrt{m/k}$, (*b*) that the radius of curvature of the path when $t = 0$ is mv_0^2/kx_0.

***12.8. Curvilinear Motion of a Particle. Radial and Transverse Components.** Consider a particle P, of polar coordinates r and θ, which moves in a plane along a curved path (Fig. 12.9). Resolving each of the forces **F** acting on P and the acceleration **a** of the particle into components along the unit vectors $\mathbf{i}_r$ and $\mathbf{i}_\theta$ (Sec. 11.14), we check that Newton's second law of motion may be expressed by the two scalar equations

$$\Sigma F_r = ma_r \qquad \Sigma F_\theta = ma_\theta \tag{12.13}$$

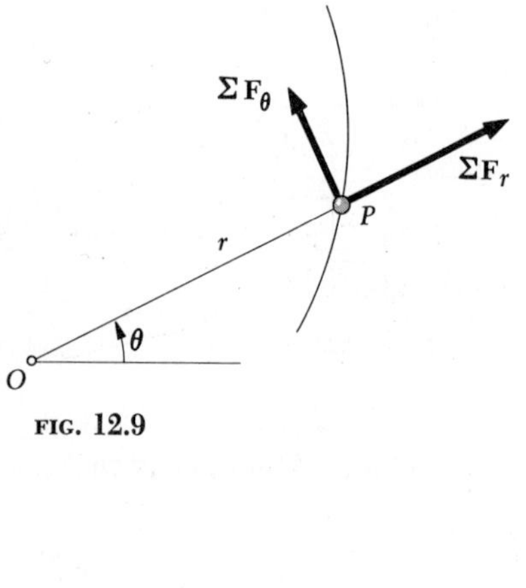

FIG. 12.9

Substituting for a_r and a_θ from (11.46), we have

$$\Sigma F_r = m\left[\frac{d^2r}{dt^2} - r\left(\frac{d\theta}{dt}\right)^2\right]$$
$$\Sigma F_\theta = m\left(r\frac{d^2\theta}{dt^2} + 2\frac{dr}{dt}\frac{d\theta}{dt}\right) \tag{12.14}$$

The equations obtained may be solved for two unknowns.

***12.9. Motion under a Central Force.** When the only force acting on a particle is a force **F** directed toward the origin O or away from the origin O, the particle is said to be moving *under a central force* (Fig. 12.10). Since the transverse component of **F** is zero, the second of Eqs. (12.14) yields

$$r\frac{d^2\theta}{dt^2} + 2\frac{dr}{dt}\frac{d\theta}{dt} = 0 \qquad \text{or} \qquad \frac{1}{r}\frac{d}{dt}\left(r^2\frac{d\theta}{dt}\right) = 0$$

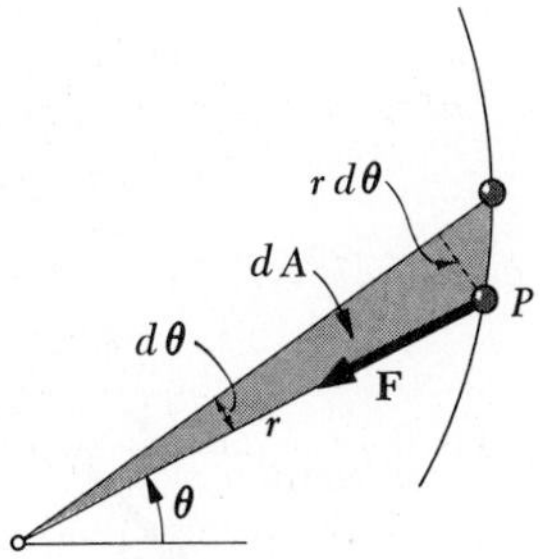

FIG. 12.10

It follows that, for any finite value of r, we must have

$$r^2\frac{d\theta}{dt} = h \tag{12.15}$$

where h is a constant. We may observe from Fig. 12.10 that the radius vector OP sweeps an infinitesimal area $dA = \frac{1}{2}r^2\,d\theta$ as it rotates through an angle $d\theta$. Defining the *areal velocity* of the particle as the quotient dA/dt, we note that the left-hand member of Eq. (12.15) represents twice the areal velocity of the particle. We conclude therefore that, *when a particle moves under a central force, its areal velocity is constant.*

Equation (12.15) may be used to eliminate t from the first of Eqs. (12.14). Noting that $d\theta/dt = h/r^2$, we write

$$\frac{dr}{dt} = \frac{dr}{d\theta}\frac{d\theta}{dt} = \frac{h}{r^2}\frac{dr}{d\theta} = -h\frac{d}{d\theta}\left(\frac{1}{r}\right)$$

$$\frac{d^2r}{dt^2} = \frac{d}{dt}\left(\frac{dr}{dt}\right) = \frac{d}{d\theta}\left(\frac{dr}{dt}\right)\frac{d\theta}{dt}$$

$$= \frac{h}{r^2}\frac{d}{d\theta}\left(\frac{dr}{dt}\right) = \frac{h}{r^2}\frac{d}{d\theta}\left[-h\frac{d}{d\theta}\left(\frac{1}{r}\right)\right]$$

$$\frac{d^2r}{dt^2} = -\frac{h^2}{r^2}\frac{d^2}{d\theta^2}\left(\frac{1}{r}\right) \tag{12.16}$$

Substituting for $d\theta/dt$ and d^2r/dt^2 from (12.15) and (12.16), respectively, into the first of Eqs. (12.14), setting $\Sigma F_r = -F$, and introducing the function $u = 1/r$, we obtain after reductions

$$\frac{d^2u}{d\theta^2} + u = \frac{F}{mh^2u^2} \tag{12.17}$$

In deriving Eq. (12.17), the force **F** was assumed directed toward O. The magnitude F should therefore be positive if **F** is actually directed toward O (attractive force) and negative if **F** is directed away from O (repulsive force). If F is a known function of r and thus of u, Eq. (12.17) is a differential equation in u and θ. This differential equation defines the path followed by the particle under the central force **F**.

12.10. Newton's Law of Gravitation. In his *law of universal gravitation*, Newton states that two particles at distance r from each other and, respectively, of mass M and m attract each other with equal and opposite forces **F** and $-\mathbf{F}$ directed along the line joining the particles (Fig. 12.11). The common magnitude F of the two forces is

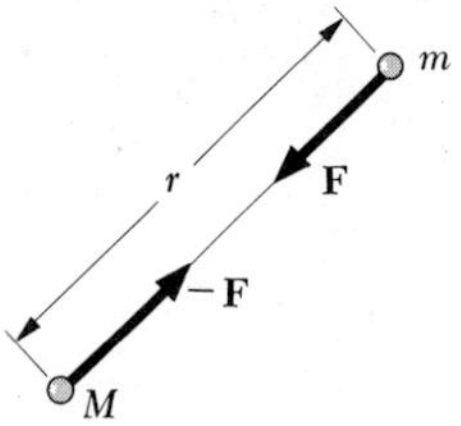

FIG. 12.11

$$F = G\frac{Mm}{r^2} \tag{12.18}$$

where G is a universal constant, called the *constant of gravitation*. Recent experiments show that the value of G is $(6.673 \pm 0.003) \times 10^{-8}$ cm^3/g-sec^2 in the cgs system, or approximately 3.44×10^{-8} ft^4/lb-sec^4 in the British gravitational system of units. While gravitational forces exist between any pair of bodies, their effect is appreciable only when one of the bodies has a very large mass. The effect of gravitational forces is apparent in the case of the motion of a planet about the sun, of satellites orbiting about the earth, or of bodies falling on the surface of the earth.

Since the force exerted by the earth on a body of mass m located on or near its surface is defined as the weight **W** of the body, we may substitute the magnitude $W = mg$ of the weight for F, and the radius R of the earth for r, in Eq. (12.18). We obtain

$$W = mg = \frac{GM}{R^2}m \qquad \text{or} \qquad g = \frac{GM}{R^2} \tag{12.19}$$

where M is the mass of the earth. Since the earth is not truly spherical, the distance R from the center of the earth depends upon the point selected on its surface, and the values of W and g will thus vary with the altitude and latitude of the point considered. Another reason for the variation of W and g with the latitude is that a system of axes attached to the earth does not constitute a newtonian frame of reference (see Sec. 12.1). A more accurate definition of the weight of a body should therefore include a component representing the centrifugal force due to the rotation of the earth. Values of g at sea level vary from 32.09 ft/sec^2 at the equator to 32.26 ft/sec^2 at the poles.†

The discovery of the law of universal gravitation has often

† A formula expressing g in terms of the latitude ϕ was given in Prob. 12.1.

been attributed to the fact that Newton, after observing an apple falling from a tree, had reflected that the earth must attract an apple and the moon in much the same way. While it is doubtful that this incident actually took place, it may be said that Newton would not have formulated his law if he had not first perceived that the acceleration of a falling body must have the same cause as the acceleration which keeps the moon in its orbit. This basic concept of continuity of the gravitational attraction is more easily understood now, when the gap between the apple and the moon is being filled with long-range ballistic missiles and artificial earth satellites.

***12.11. Application to Space Mechanics.** After the last stage of their launching rockets has burned out, earth satellites and other space vehicles are subjected only to the gravitational pull of the earth. Their motion may therefore be determined from Eqs. (12.15) and (12.17), which govern the motion of a body under a central force, after F has been replaced by the expression obtained for the force of gravitational attraction.† Setting in Eq. (12.17)

$$F = \frac{GMm}{r^2} = GMmu^2$$

where M = mass of the earth
m = mass of the space vehicle
r = distance from center of the earth to vehicle
$u = 1/r$

we obtain the differential equation

$$\frac{d^2u}{d\theta^2} + u = \frac{GM}{h^2} \tag{12.20}$$

where the right-hand member is observed to be a constant.

The solution of the differential equation (12.20) is obtained by adding the particular solution $u = GM/h^2$ to the general solution $u = C \cos (\theta - \theta_0)$ of the corresponding homogeneous equation (i.e., the equation obtained by setting the right-hand member equal to zero). Choosing the polar axis so that $\theta_0 = 0$, we write

$$\frac{1}{r} = u = \frac{GM}{h^2} + C \cos \theta \tag{12.21}$$

† It is assumed that the space vehicles considered here are attracted only by the earth, and that their mass is negligible compared to the mass of the earth. If a vehicle moves very far from the earth, its path may be affected by the attraction of the sun, the moon, or another planet.

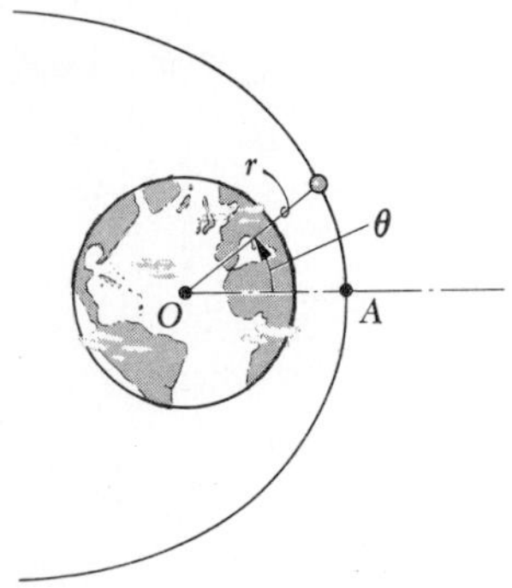

FIG. 12.12

Equation (12.21) is the equation of a *conic section* (ellipse, parabola, or hyperbola) in the polar coordinates r and θ. The origin O of the coordinates, which is located at the center of the earth, is a *focus* of this conic section, and the polar axis is one of its axes of symmetry (Fig. 12.12).

The ratio of the constants C and GM/h^2 defines the *eccentricity* ε of the conic section; we write

$$\varepsilon = \frac{C}{GM/h^2} = \frac{Ch^2}{GM} \tag{12.22}$$

Three cases may be distinguished:

1. $\varepsilon > 1$, or $C > GM/h^2$: There are two values θ_1 and $-\theta_1$ of the polar angle, defined by $\cos\theta_1 = -GM/Ch^2$, for which the right-hand member of Eq. (12.21) becomes zero. For both of these values, the radius vector r becomes infinite; the conic section is a *hyperbola* (Fig. 12.13).

2. $\varepsilon = 1$, or $C = GM/h^2$: The radius vector becomes infinite for $\theta = 180°$; the conic section is a *parabola*.

3. $\varepsilon < 1$, or $C < GM/h^2$: The radius vector remains finite for every value of θ; the conic section is an *ellipse*. In the particular case when $\varepsilon = C = 0$, the length of the radius vector is constant; the conic section is a circle.

We shall see now how the constants C and GM/h^2 which characterize the trajectory of a space vehicle may be determined from the position and the velocity of the space vehicle at the beginning of its free flight. We shall assume, as it is generally the case, that the powered phase of its flight has been programmed in such a way that, as the last stage of the launching rocket burns out, the vehicle has a velocity parallel to the surface of the earth (Fig. 12.14). In other words, we shall assume that the space vehicle begins its free flight at the vertex A of its trajectory.†

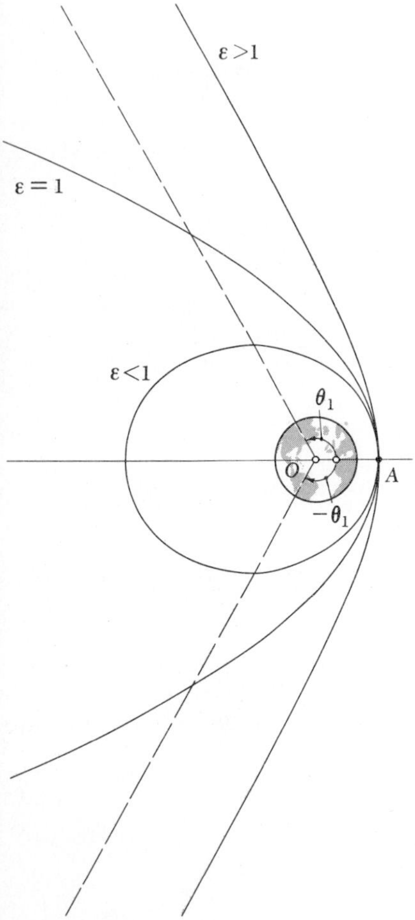

FIG. 12.13

Denoting respectively by r_0 and v_0 the radius vector and speed of the vehicle at the beginning of its free flight, we observe, since the radial component of the velocity is zero, that $v_0 = r_0(d\theta/dt)_0$. Recalling the definition of h given in (12.15), we write

$$h = r_0^2\left(\frac{d\theta}{dt}\right)_0 = r_0 v_0 \tag{12.23}$$

The value obtained for h may be used to determine the constant GM/h^2. We should also note that the computation of this con-

† Problems involving oblique launchings will be considered in Sec. 14.13.

stant will be simplified if we use the second of the relations (12.19) and write

$$GM = gR^2 \tag{12.24}$$

where R is the radius of the earth ($R = 3{,}960$ mi.) and g the acceleration of gravity at the surface of the earth.

The constant C will be determined by setting $\theta = 0$, $r = r_0$ in Eq. (12.21); we obtain

$$C = \frac{1}{r_0} - \frac{GM}{h^2} \tag{12.25}$$

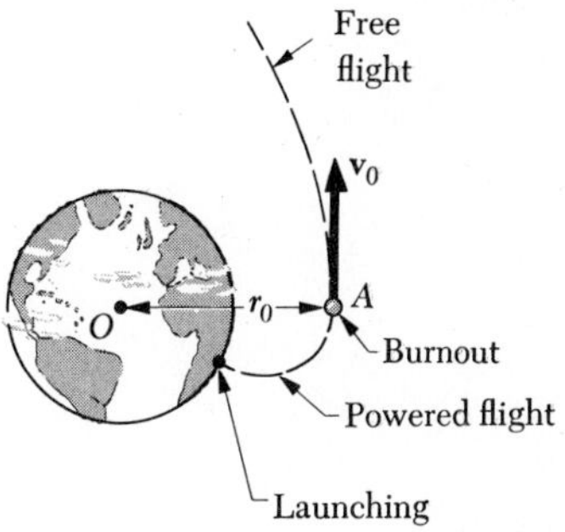

FIG. 12.14

Substituting for h from (12.23), we may then easily express C in terms of r_0 and v_0.

Let us now determine the initial conditions corresponding to each of the three fundamental trajectories indicated above. Considering first the parabolic trajectory, we set C equal to GM/h^2 in Eq. (12.25) and eliminate h between Eqs. (12.23) and (12.25). Solving for v_0, we obtain

$$v_0 = \sqrt{2GM/r_0}$$

We may easily check that a larger value of the initial velocity corresponds to a hyperbolic trajectory, and a smaller value to an elliptic orbit. Since the value of v_0 obtained for the parabolic trajectory is the smallest value for which the space vehicle does not return to its starting point, it is called the *escape velocity*. We write therefore

$$v_{esc} = \sqrt{2GM/r_0} \qquad \text{or} \qquad v_{esc} = \sqrt{2gR^2/r_0} \tag{12.26}$$

if we make use of Eq. (12.24). We note that the trajectory will be (1) hyperbolic if $v_0 > v_{esc}$; (2) parabolic if $v_0 = v_{esc}$; (3) elliptic if $v_0 < v_{esc}$.

Among the various possible elliptic orbits, one is of special interest, the *circular orbit*, which is obtained when $C = 0$. The value of the initial velocity corresponding to a circular orbit is easily found to be

$$v_{circ} = \sqrt{GM/r_0} \qquad \text{or} \qquad v_{circ} = \sqrt{gR^2/r_0} \tag{12.27}$$

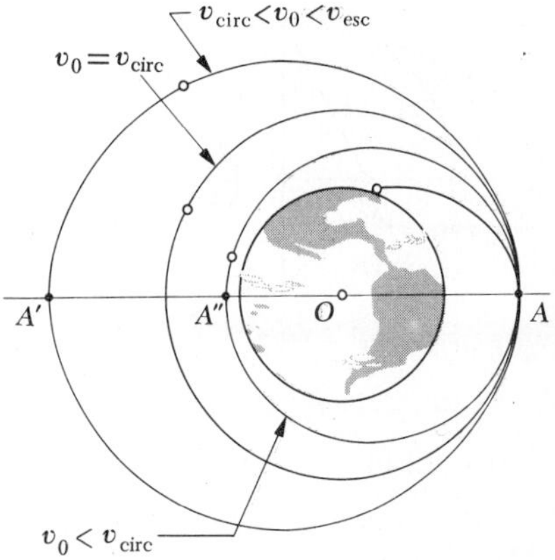

FIG. 12.15

if Eq. (12.24) is taken into account. We may note from Fig. 12.15 that, for values of v_0 comprised between v_{circ} and v_{esc}, point A where free flight begins is the point of the orbit closest to the earth; this point is called the *perigee*, while point A', which is farthest away from the earth, is known as the *apogee*. For values of v_0 smaller than v_{circ}, point A becomes the apogee, while point A'', on the other side of the orbit, becomes the perigee. For values of v_0 much smaller than v_{circ}, the trajectory of the space vehicle intersects the surface of the earth; in such a case, the vehicle does not go into orbit.

Ballistic missiles, which are designed to hit the surface of the earth, also travel along elliptic trajectories. In fact, we should now realize that any object projected in vacuum with an initial velocity v_0 smaller than v_{esc} will move along an elliptic path. It is only when the distances involved are small that the gravitational field of the earth may be assumed uniform, and that the elliptic path may be approximated by a parabolic path, as was done earlier (Sec. 11.11) in the case of conventional projectiles.

Periodic Time. An important characteristic of the motion of an earth satellite is the time required by the satellite to describe its orbit. This time is known as the *periodic time* of the satellite and is denoted by τ. We first observe, in view of the definition of the areal velocity (Sec. 12.9), that τ may be obtained by dividing the area inside the orbit by the areal velocity. Since the area of an ellipse is equal to πab, where a and b denote, respectively, the semimajor and semiminor axes, and since the areal velocity is equal to $h/2$, we write

$$\tau = \frac{2\pi ab}{h} \tag{12.28}$$

While h may be readily determined from r_0 and v_0 in the case of a satellite launched in a direction parallel to the surface of the earth, the semiaxes a and b are not directly related to the initial conditions. Since, on the other hand, the values r_0 and r_1 of r corresponding to the perigee and apogee of the orbit may easily be determined from Eq. (12.21), we shall express the semiaxes a and b in terms of r_0 and r_1.

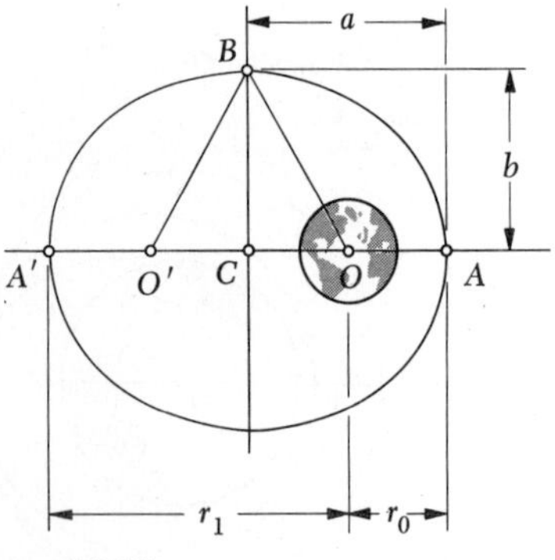

FIG. 12.16

Consider the elliptic orbit shown in Fig. 12.16. The earth's center is located at O and coincides with one of the two foci of the ellipse, while the points A and A' represent, respectively, the perigee and apogee of the orbit. We easily check that

$$r_0 + r_1 = 2a$$

and thus

$$a = \tfrac{1}{2}(r_0 + r_1) \tag{12.29}$$

Recalling that the sum of the distances from each of the foci to any point of the ellipse is constant, we write

$$O'B + BO = O'A + OA = 2a \qquad \text{or} \qquad BO = a$$

On the other hand, we have $CO = a - r_0$. We may therefore write

$$b^2 = (BC)^2 = (BO)^2 - (CO)^2 = a^2 - (a - r_0)^2$$
$$b^2 = r_0(2a - r_0) = r_0 r_1$$

and thus

$$b = \sqrt{r_0 r_1} \tag{12.30}$$

Formulas (12.29) and (12.30) indicate that the semimajor and semiminor axes of the orbit are respectively equal to the arithmetic and geometric means of the maximum and minimum values of the radius vector. Once r_0 and r_1 have been determined, the lengths of the semiaxes may thus be easily computed and substituted for a and b in formula (12.28).

***12.12. Kepler's Laws of Planetary Motion.** The equations governing the motion of an earth satellite may be used to describe the motion of the moon around the earth. In that case, however, the mass of the moon is not negligible compared to the mass of the earth, and the results obtained are not entirely accurate.

The theory developed in the preceding sections may also be applied to the study of the motion of the planets around the sun. While another error is introduced by neglecting the forces exerted by the planets on each other, the approximation obtained is excellent. Indeed, the properties expressed by Eq. (12.21), where M now represents the mass of the sun, and by Eq. (12.15) had been discovered by the German astronomer Johann Kepler (1571–1630) from astronomical observations of the motion of the planets, even before Newton had formulated his fundamental theory.

Kepler's three *laws of planetary motion* may be stated as follows:

1. Each planet describes an ellipse with the sun located at one of its foci.
2. The radius vector drawn from the sun to a planet sweeps equal areas in equal times.
3. The squares of the periodic times of the planets are proportional to the cubes of the semimajor axes of their orbits.

The first law states a particular case of the result established in Sec. 12.11, while the second law expresses that the areal velocity of each planet is constant (see Sec. 12.9). Kepler's third law may also be derived from the results obtained in Sec. 12.11.†

† See Prob. 12.97.

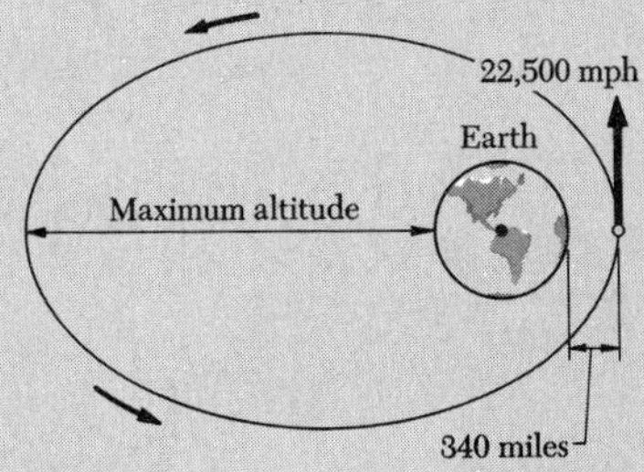

SAMPLE PROBLEM 12.6

A satellite is launched in a direction parallel to the surface of the earth with a velocity of 22,500 mph from an altitude of 340 miles. Determine (*a*) the maximum altitude reached by the satellite, (*b*) the periodic time of the satellite.

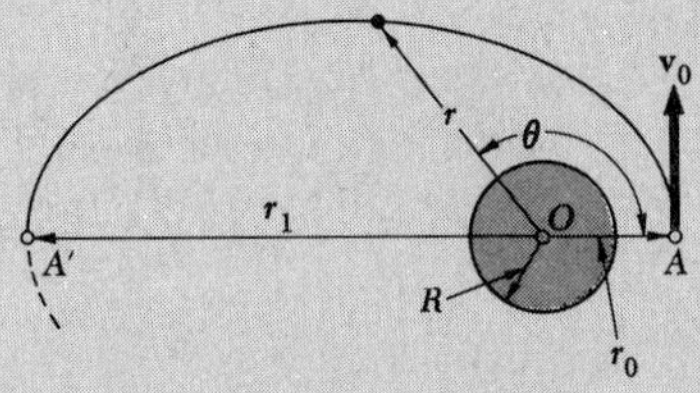

a. **Maximum Altitude.** After launching, the satellite is subjected only to the gravitational attraction of the earth; its motion is thus governed by Eq. (12.21).

$$\frac{1}{r} = \frac{GM}{h^2} + C\cos\theta \tag{1}$$

Since the radial component of the velocity is zero at the point of launching A, we have $h = r_0 v_0$. Recalling that the radius of the earth is $R = 3{,}960$ miles, we compute

$$r_0 = 3{,}960 + 340 = 4{,}300 \text{ miles} = 22.7 \times 10^6 \text{ ft}$$
$$v_0 = 22{,}500 \text{ mph} = 33{,}000 \text{ ft/sec}$$

$$h = r_0 v_0 = (22.7 \times 10^6)(33{,}000) = 0.7492 \times 10^{12} \text{ ft}^2\text{/sec}$$
$$h^2 = 0.5613 \times 10^{24} \text{ ft}^4\text{/sec}^2$$

Since $GM = gR^2$, where R is the radius of the earth, we have

$$GM = gR^2 = (32.2)(3{,}960 \times 5{,}280)^2 = 1.408 \times 10^{16} \text{ ft}^3\text{/sec}^2$$

$$\frac{GM}{h^2} = \frac{1.408 \times 10^{16}}{0.5613 \times 10^{24}} = 2.508 \times 10^{-8} \text{ ft}^{-1}$$

Substituting this value into (1), we obtain

$$\frac{1}{r} = 2.508 \times 10^{-8} + C\cos\theta \tag{2}$$

Noting that at point A we have $\theta = 0$ and $r = r_0 = 4{,}300$ miles, we compute the constant C.

$$\frac{1}{(4{,}300)(5{,}280)} = 2.508 \times 10^{-8} + C(\cos 0°) \qquad C = 1.896 \times 10^{-8} \text{ ft}^{-1}$$

At A', the point on the orbit farthest from the earth, we have $\theta = 180°$. Using (2), we compute the corresponding distance r_1.

$$\frac{1}{r_1} = 2.508 \times 10^{-8} + (1.896 \times 10^{-8})(\cos 180°)$$
$$r_1 = 1.634 \times 10^8 \text{ ft} = 30{,}950 \text{ miles}$$

Maximum altitude = 30,950 − 3,960 = 26,990 miles ◀

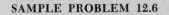

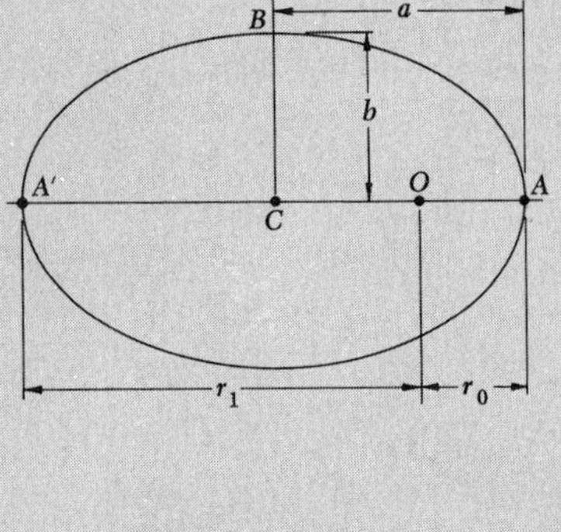

b. **Periodic Time.** Since A and A' are the perigee and apogee, respectively, of the elliptic orbit, we use Eqs. (12.29) and (12.30) and compute the semimajor and semiminor axes of the orbit.

$$a = \tfrac{1}{2}(r_0 + r_1) = \tfrac{1}{2}(22.7 + 163.4)10^6 = 93.05 \times 10^6 \text{ ft}$$
$$b = \sqrt{r_0 r_1} = \sqrt{(22.7)(163.4)}\, 10^6 = 60.9 \times 10^6 \text{ ft}$$
$$\tau = \frac{2\pi ab}{h} = \frac{2\pi(93.05 \times 10^6)(60.9 \times 10^6)}{0.7493 \times 10^{12}}$$
$$\tau = 47{,}500 \text{ sec} = 792 \text{ min} = 13 \text{ hr } 12 \text{ min} \quad ◀$$

PROBLEMS

12.74. The two-dimensional motion of a particle is defined by the relations $r = t^3 - 2t^2$ and $\theta = t^3 - 4t$, where r is expressed in feet, t in seconds, and θ in radians. If the particle weighs 10 lb and moves in a horizontal plane, determine the radial and transverse components of the force acting on the particle when (*a*) $t = 0$, (*b*) $t = 1$ sec.

12.75. For the motion defined in Prob. 12.74, determine the radial and transverse components of the force acting on the 10-lb particle when it passes through the origin at $t = 2$ sec.

12.76. The two-dimensional motion of a particle is defined by the relations $r = 10(1 + \cos \frac{1}{2}\pi t)$ and $\theta = \frac{1}{2}\pi t$, where r is expressed in feet, t in seconds, and θ in radians. If the particle weighs 2 lb and moves in a horizontal plane, determine the radial and transverse components of the force acting on the particle when (*a*) $t = 0$, (*b*) $t = 1$ sec.

12.77. For the motion defined in Sample Prob. 11.12, determine the force exerted by the arm *OA* on block *B* and the radial force which must act on the block (*a*) when $\theta = 0°$ and (*b*) when $\theta = 30°$. Assume that block *B* weighs 2 lb and that the arm rotates in a vertical plane.

12.78. A particle moves under a central force in a path defined by the equation $r = r_0/\cos n\theta$, where n is a positive constant. Using Eq. (12.15), show that the radial and transverse components of the velocity are $v_r = nv_0 \sin n\theta$ and $v_\theta = v_0 \cos n\theta$, where v_0 is the velocity of the particle for $\theta = 0$. What is the motion of the particle when $n = 0$ and when $n = 1$?

12.79. A particle moves under a central force in a circular path of diameter r_0 which passes through the center of force *O*. Show that its speed is $v = v_0/\cos^2 \theta$, where v_0 is the speed of the particle at point P_0 directly across the circle from *O*. [*Hint.* Use Eq. (12.15) with $r = r_0 \cos \theta$.]

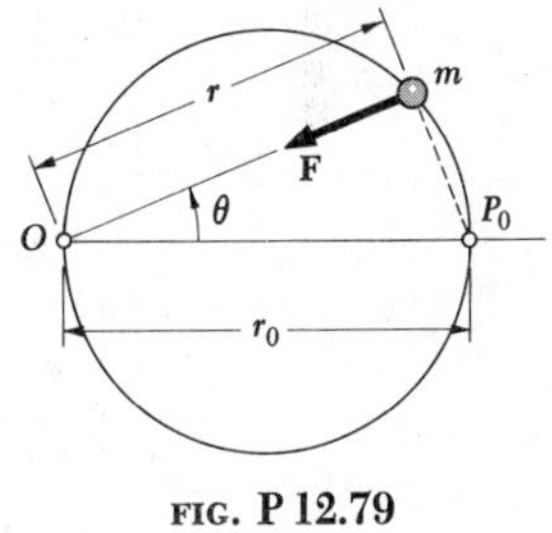

FIG. P 12.79

12.80. Determine the mass of the earth from Newton's law of gravitation, knowing that the radius of the earth is 3,960 miles and that the acceleration of gravity is $g = 32.2$ ft/sec^2 at the surface of the earth.

12.81. Determine the acceleration of gravity at the surface of the planet Mars, knowing that the radius of that planet is 2,110 miles and that its mass is 0.108 times the mass of the earth.

12.82. Determine the acceleration of gravity at the surface of the moon, knowing that the radius of the moon is 1,080 miles and that its mass is 81.3 times smaller than the mass of the earth.

12.83. Show that the radius r of the moon's orbit may be determined from the radius R of the earth, the acceleration of gravity g at the surface of the earth, and the time τ required by the moon to revolve once around the earth. Compute r knowing that $\tau = 27.3$ days.

12.84. A satellite is launched in a direction parallel to the earth's surface from an altitude of 400 miles. (*a*) Determine the required initial velocity if the satellite is to describe a circular orbit. (*b*) What is the allowable percentage of error in the initial velocity if the satellite is not to come closer than 200 miles from the surface of the earth?

12.85. A capsule is to be returned to the earth from a satellite describing a circular orbit at an altitude of 6,000 miles. (*a*) With what absolute velocity $\mathbf{v}_0$, tangential to the orbit, should the capsule leave the satellite if it is to land tangentially to the surface of the earth? (*b*) With what relative velocity does the capsule leave the satellite in part *a*?

12.86. The maximum altitude of an Explorer satellite, as it orbits around the earth, is observed to be 26,000 miles above the earth's surface, and its minimum altitude 400 miles. Determine the maximum and minimum values of its velocity.

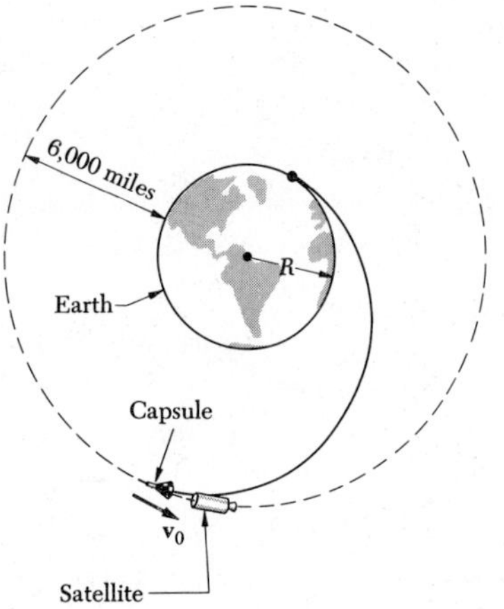

FIG. P 12.85

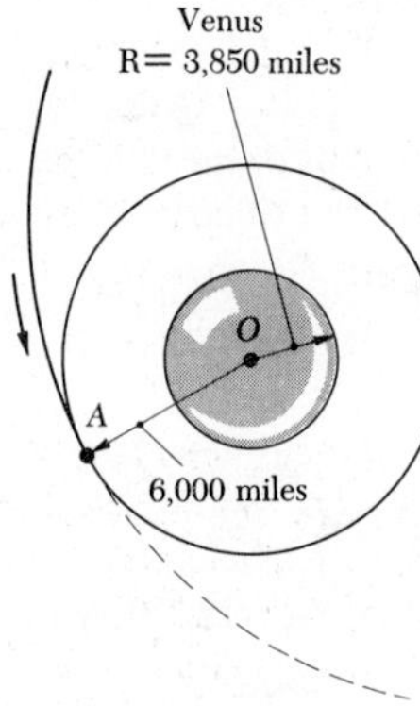

FIG. P 12.87

12.87. A space vehicle approaches the planet Venus along a hyperbolic trajectory of eccentricity $\varepsilon = 2$. As the vehicle reaches point A, which is the point of the trajectory closest to the planet, retrorockets are fired to slow the vehicle and place it in a circular orbit. Knowing that the distance from the center O of the planet to A is 6,000 miles, and that the mass of Venus is 0.82 times the mass of the earth, determine the velocity of the vehicle (*a*) as it approaches A, (*b*) after the retrorockets have been fired.

12.88. A space vehicle approaches the planet Mars along a parabolic trajectory. As the vehicle reaches point A, which is the point of the trajectory closest to the planet, retrorockets are fired to slow the vehicle and place it in an elliptic path which will bring it to a tangential landing at B. Knowing that the distance from the center O of the planet to A is 8,000 miles, that the radius of the planet is 2,110 miles, and that its mass is 0.108 times the mass of the earth, determine the velocity of the vehicle (a) as it approaches A, (b) after the retrorockets have been fired, (c) as it lands at B.

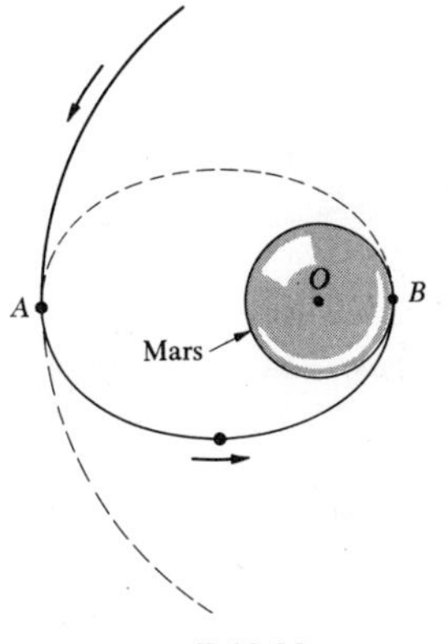

FIG. P 12.88

12.89. In order to place a satellite in a circular orbit of 20,000-mile radius around the earth, the satellite is first projected horizontally from A at an altitude of 300 miles into an elliptic path whose apogee A' is at a distance of 20,000 miles from the center of the earth. Auxiliary rockets are fired as the satellite reaches A' in order to place it in its final orbit. Determine (a) the initial velocity of the satellite at A, (b) the increase in velocity resulting from the firing of the rockets at A'.

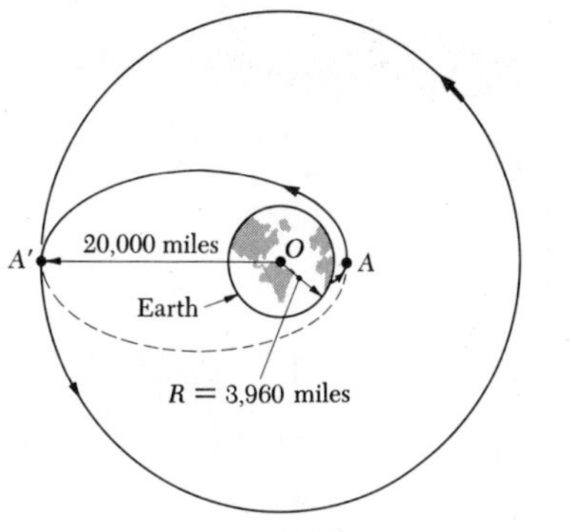

FIG. P 12.89

12.90. Determine the periodic time of the Explorer satellite of Prob. 12.86.

12.91. Determine the periodic time of the space vehicle of Prob. 12.87 after it has been placed in a circular orbit around the planet Venus.

12.92. Determine the time required for the space vehicle of Prob. 12.88 to land on the planet Mars after the retrorockets have been fired.

12.93. Referring to Prob. 12.89, determine the time elapsed between the end of the launching of the satellite at A and the firing of the auxiliary rockets at A' which will place the satellite in its final orbit.

12.94. A satellite is describing a circular orbit of radius r_0 around the earth when auxiliary rockets are fired to increase its velocity by $33\frac{1}{3}$ per cent. Determine (a) the maximum distance from the center of the earth reached by the satellite on its new orbit, (b) the quotient of the periodic times corresponding respectively to the new and the old orbits of the satellite.

12.95. Two space stations S_1 and S_2 are describing coplanar circular counterclockwise orbits of radius r_0 and $8r_0$, respectively, around the earth. It is desired to send a vehicle from S_1 to S_2. The vehicle is to be launched in a direction tangent to the orbit of S_1 and is to reach S_2 with a velocity tangent to the orbit of S_2. After a short powered phase, the vehicle will travel in free flight from S_1 to S_2. (a) Determine the launching velocity (velocity of the vehicle relative to S_1) in terms of the velocity v_0 of S_1. (b) Briefly describe the landing operation on S_2. (c) Determine the angle θ defining the required position of S_2 relative to S_1 at the time of the launching.

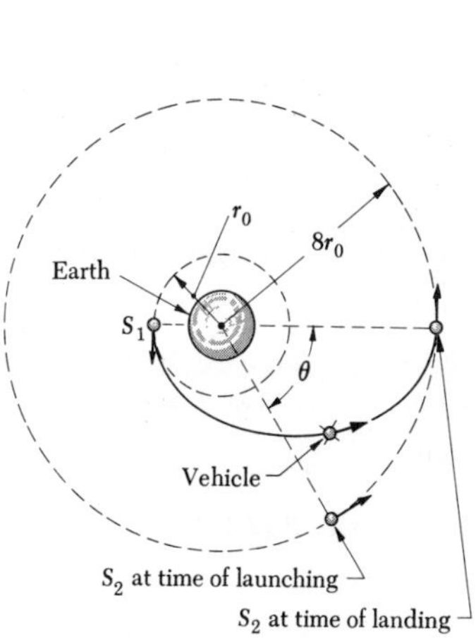

FIG. P 12.95

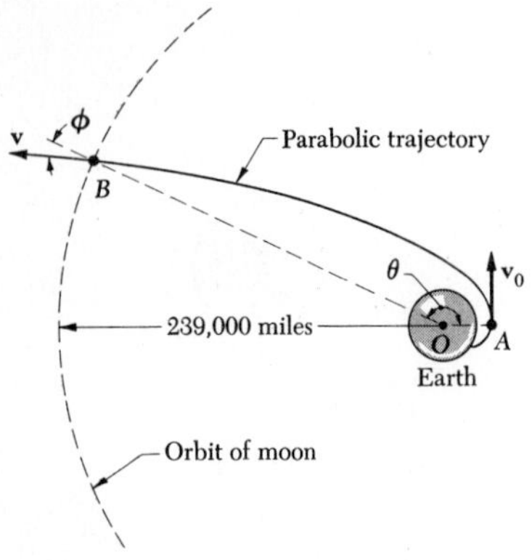

FIG. P 12.96

*12.96. A space vehicle is launched in a direction parallel to the earth's surface from point A at an altitude of 340 miles. Knowing that the trajectory of the space vehicle is parabolic, determine (*a*) the launching velocity $\mathbf{v}_0$ of the vehicle, (*b*) the angle θ described by the vehicle as it crosses the orbit of the moon at point B, 239,000 miles away from the center of the earth, (*c*) the velocity of the vehicle at B (magnitude and angle ϕ), (*d*) the time elapsed as the vehicle travels from A to B.

12.97. Derive Kepler's third law of planetary motion from Eqs. (12.21) and (12.28).

REVIEW PROBLEMS

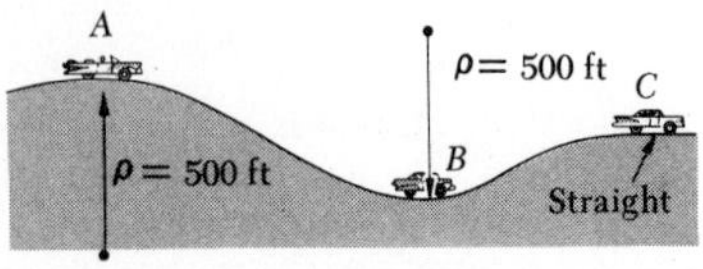

FIG. P 12.98

12.98. Three automobiles are proceeding at a speed of 50 mph along the road shown. Knowing that the coefficient of friction between the tires and the road is 0.60, determine the tangential deceleration of each automobile if its brakes are suddenly applied and the wheels skid.

12.99. A man swings a bucket full of water in a vertical plane in a circle of radius 3 ft. What is the smallest velocity that the bucket should have at the top of the circle if no water is to be spilled?

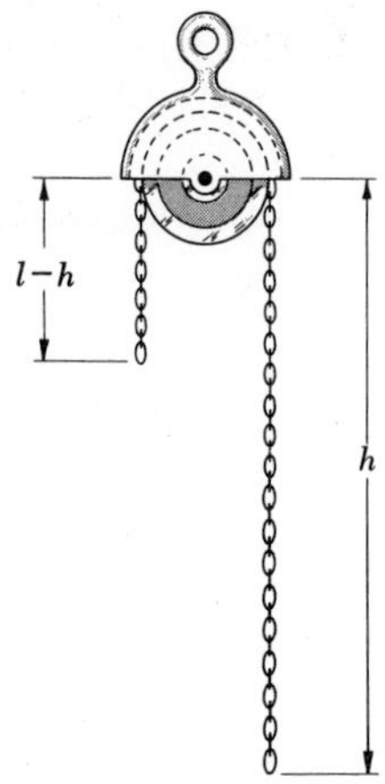

FIG. P 12.100

12.100. A chain weighing w lb/ft and of length l ft rests over a small pulley of negligible mass. If the chain is released in the position shown ($h > \frac{1}{2}l$), determine the velocity of the chain when the end of the chain leaves the pulley. Also determine the maximum possible final velocity by letting h approach $\frac{1}{2}l$.

12.101. A bomber flying horizontally in a straight line at a constant speed v_0 releases a powered missile which will fly ahead of the bomber in a parallel horizontal path. The missile engine, which is started at the time of release, provides a constant thrust T, while the atmosphere produces a drag equal to kv^2, where v is the speed of the missile. Neglecting any change in the mass of the missile, express the acceleration of the missile as a function of the distance traveled in free flight. It is assumed that $v_0 < \sqrt{T/k}$.

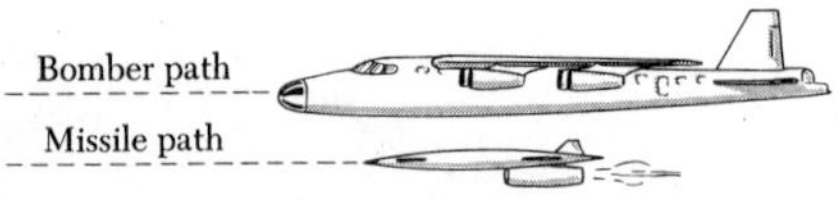

FIG. P 12.101

12.102. In problem 12.101 determine the time t required for the missile to reach a given speed v. Explain why v cannot exceed $\sqrt{T/k}$.

12.103. At what distance from the center of the earth will an object directly in line with the earth and the moon be attracted equally by these two bodies? The mass of the moon is 81.3 times smaller than the mass of the earth, and the distance from the earth to the moon is 239,000 miles.

12.104. A constant force **P** is applied to a piston and rod of total mass m in order to make them move in a cylinder filled with oil. As the piston moves, the oil is forced through orifices in the piston and exerts on the piston an additional force of magnitude kv, proportional to the speed v of the piston and in a direction opposite to its motion. Express the acceleration of the piston as a function of the time t, assuming that the piston starts from rest at time $t = 0$.

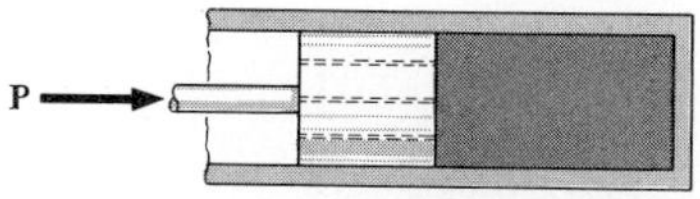

FIG. P 12.104

12.105. What should be the weight of block B of Sample Prob. 12.3 if block A is to move downward with an acceleration of 5 ft/sec²?

12.106. A daredevil rides a small automobile on the vertical wall of a circular pit of radius 40 ft at a speed of 30 mph. Knowing that this is the lowest speed at which he can perform this stunt, determine the coefficient of friction between the tires and the wall.

12.107. The edge AB of the plate is cut to form a parabola with vertex at A. As the frame and plate are accelerated to the left, the sphere is observed to remain at a distance x from the edge of the frame. Express the horizontal acceleration of the frame in terms of x, L, and h.

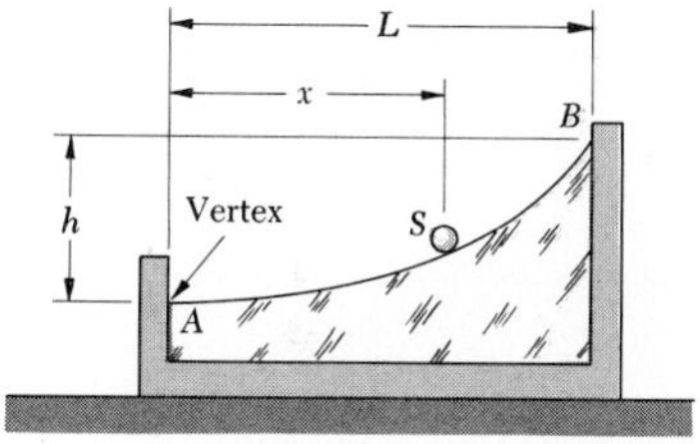

FIG. P 12.107

12.108. A satellite is to be placed in a circular equatorial orbit around the earth. At what distance from the center of the earth should it be placed if it is to remain in the same position relative to the earth?

12.109. A ship of total weight W is anchored in the middle of a river which is flowing with a constant velocity $\mathbf{v}_0$. The horizontal component of the force exerted on the ship by the anchor chain is $\mathbf{T}_0$. If the anchor chain suddenly breaks, determine the time required for the ship to attain a velocity equal to $\frac{1}{2}\mathbf{v}_0$. Assume that the frictional resistance of the water is proportional to the velocity of the ship relative to the water.

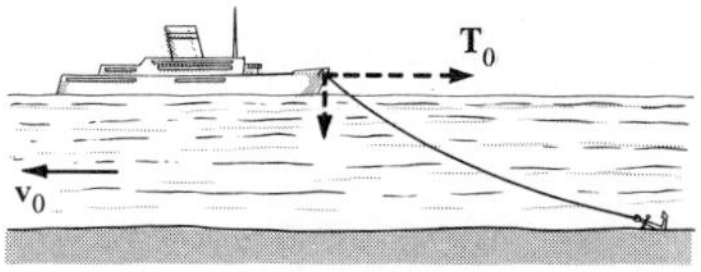

FIG. P 12.109

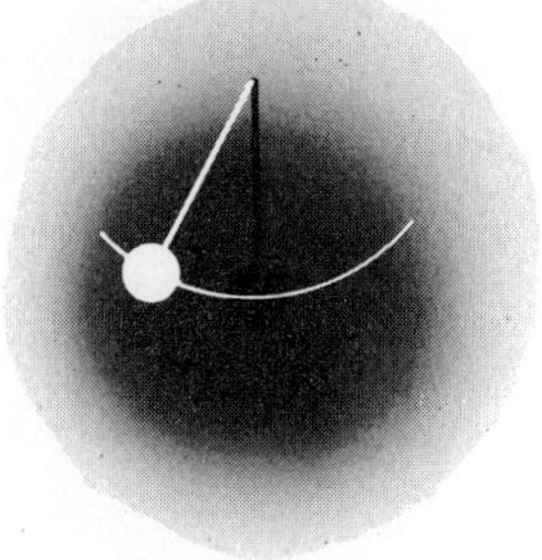

13. KINETICS OF PARTICLES: WORK AND ENERGY

13.1. Introduction. In the preceding chapter, problems dealing with the motion of particles were solved through the use of the fundamental equation of motion $\mathbf{F} = m\mathbf{a}$. Given a particle acted upon by a force $\mathbf{F}$, we could solve this equation for the acceleration $\mathbf{a}$; then, by applying the principles of kinematics, we could determine from $\mathbf{a}$ the velocity and position of the particle at any time.

If the equation $\mathbf{F} = m\mathbf{a}$ and the principles of kinematics are combined, two additional methods of analysis may be obtained, the *method of work and energy* and the *method of impulse and momentum.* The advantage of these methods lies in the fact that they make the determination of the acceleration unnecessary. Indeed, the method of work and energy relates directly force, mass, velocity, and displacement, while the method of impulse and momentum relates force, mass, velocity, and time.

The method of work and energy is treated in the present chapter. It is based on two important concepts, the concept of the *work of a force* and the concept of the *kinetic energy of a particle.* These concepts are defined in the following sections.

13.2. Work of a Force. We shall first define the terms *displacement* and *work* as they are used in mechanics.† Consider a particle which moves from a point A to a neighboring point A' (Fig. 13.1). If $\mathbf{r}$ denotes the position vector corresponding to point A, the small vector joining A and A' may be denoted by the differential $d\mathbf{r}$; the vector $d\mathbf{r}$ is called the *displacement* of the particle. Now, let us assume that a force $\mathbf{F}$ is acting on the particle. The *work of the force* $\mathbf{F}$ *corresponding to the displacement* $d\mathbf{r}$ is defined as the quantity

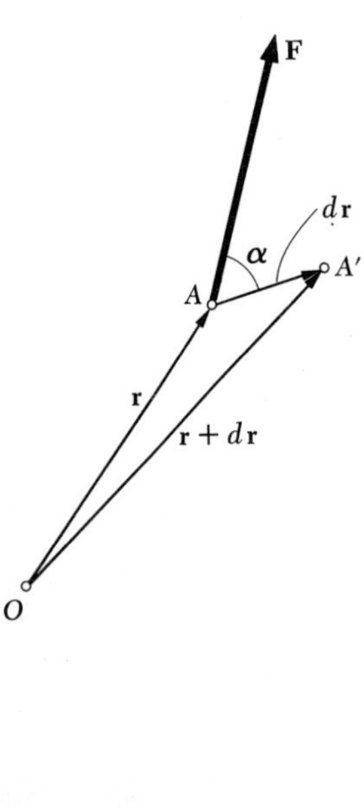

FIG. 13.1

† The definition of work was given in Sec. 10.1, and the basic properties of the work of a force were outlined in Secs. 10.1 and 10.5. For convenience, we repeat here the portions of this material which relate to the kinetics of particles.

$$dU = \mathbf{F} \cdot d\mathbf{r} \tag{13.1}$$

obtained by forming the scalar product of the force **F** and of the displacement $d\mathbf{r}$. Denoting respectively by F and ds the magnitudes of the force and of the displacement, and by α the angle formed by **F** and $d\mathbf{r}$, and recalling the definition of the scalar product of two vectors (Sec. 3.8), we write

$$dU = F\,ds \cos\alpha \tag{13.1$'$}$$

Using formula (3.27), we may also express the work dU in terms of the rectangular components of the force and of the displacement:

$$dU = F_x\,dx + F_y\,dy + F_z\,dz \tag{13.1$''$}$$

Being a *scalar quantity,* work has a magnitude and a sign, but no direction. We also note that work should be expressed in units such as ft-lb or in.-lb, obtained by multiplying units of length by units of force.

It follows from (13.1′) that the work dU is positive if the angle α is acute, and negative if α is obtuse. Three particular cases are of special interest. If the force **F** has the same direction as $d\mathbf{r}$, the work dU reduces to $F\,ds$. If **F** has a direction opposite to that of $d\mathbf{r}$, the work is $dU = -F\,ds$. Finally, if **F** is perpendicular to $d\mathbf{r}$, the work dU is zero.

The work of **F** during a *finite* displacement of the particle from A_1 to A_2 (Fig. 13.2*a*) is obtained by integrating Eq. (13.1) along the path described by the particle. This work, denoted by $U_{1\to2}$, is

$$U_{1\to2} = \int_{A_1}^{A_2} \mathbf{F} \cdot d\mathbf{r} \tag{13.2}$$

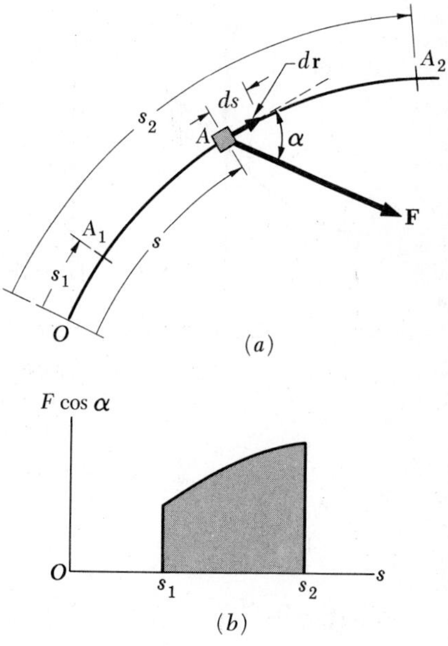

FIG. 13.2

Using the alternate expression (13.1′) for the elementary work dU, and observing that $F\cos\alpha$ represents the tangential component F_t of the force, we may also express the work $U_{1\to2}$ as

$$U_{1\to2} = \int_{s_1}^{s_2} (F\cos\alpha)\,ds = \int_{s_1}^{s_2} F_t\,ds \tag{13.2$'$}$$

where the variable of integration s measures the distance traveled by the particle along the path. The work $U_{1\to2}$ is represented by the area under the curve obtained by plotting $F_t = F\cos\alpha$ against s (Fig. 13.2*b*).

When the force **F** is defined by its rectangular components, the expression (13.1″) may be used for the elementary work. We write then

$$U_{1\to2} = \int_{A_1}^{A_2} (F_x\,dx + F_y\,dy + F_z\,dz) \tag{13.2$''$}$$

where the integration is to be performed along the path described by the particle.

Work of a Constant Force in Rectilinear Motion. When a particle moving in a straight line is acted upon by a force **F** of constant magnitude and of constant direction (Fig. 13.3), formula (13.2′) yields

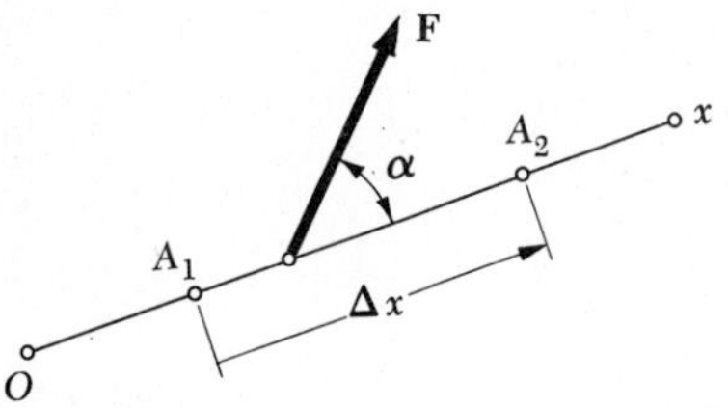

FIG. 13.3

$$U_{1\to2} = (F\cos\alpha)\,\Delta x \tag{13.3}$$

where α = angle the force forms with direction of motion
Δx = displacement from A_1 to A_2

Work of a Weight. The work of the weight **W** of a body is obtained by substituting the components of **W** into (13.1″) and (13.2″). With the y axis chosen upward (Fig. 13.4), we have $F_x = 0$, $F_y = -W$, $F_z = 0$, and we write

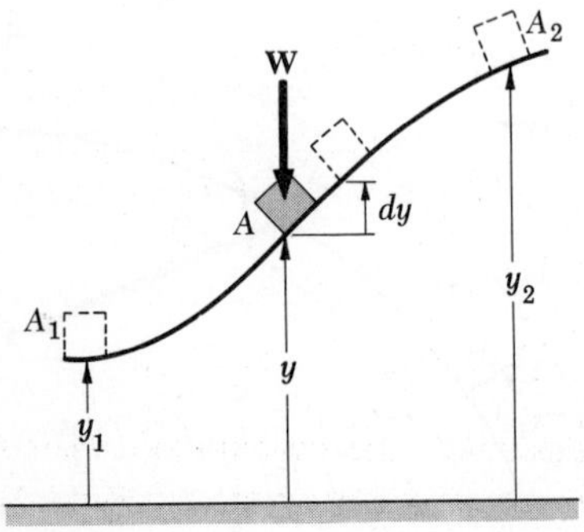

FIG. 13.4

$$dU = -W\,dy$$

$$U_{1\to2} = -\int_{y_1}^{y_2} W\,dy = Wy_1 - Wy_2 \tag{13.4}$$

or

$$U_{1\to2} = -W(y_2 - y_1) = -W\,\Delta y \tag{13.4'}$$

where Δy is the vertical displacement from A_1 to A_2. The work of the weight **W** is thus equal to *the product of W and of the vertical displacement of the center of gravity of the body.* The work is *positive* when $\Delta y < 0$, that is, *when the body moves down.*

Work of the Force Exerted by a Spring. Consider a body A attached to a fixed point B by a spring; it is assumed that the spring is undeformed when the body is at A_0 (Fig. 13.5*a*). Experimental evidence shows that the magnitude of the force **F** exerted by the spring on body A is proportional to the deflection x of the spring measured from the position A_0. We have

$$F = kx \tag{13.5}$$

where k is the *spring constant,* expressed in lb/ft or lb/in.† The work of the force **F** exerted by the spring during a finite displacement of the body from $A_1(x = x_1)$ to $A_2(x = x_2)$ is obtained by writing

$$dU = -F\,dx = -kx\,dx$$

$$U_{1\to2} = -\int_{x_1}^{x_2} kx\,dx = \tfrac{1}{2}kx_1^2 - \tfrac{1}{2}kx_2^2 \tag{13.6}$$

† The relation $F = kx$ is correct under static conditions only. Under dynamic conditions, formula (13.5) should be modified to take the inertia of the spring into account. However, the error introduced by using the relation $F = kx$ in the solution of kinetics problems is small if the mass of the spring is small compared with the other masses in motion.

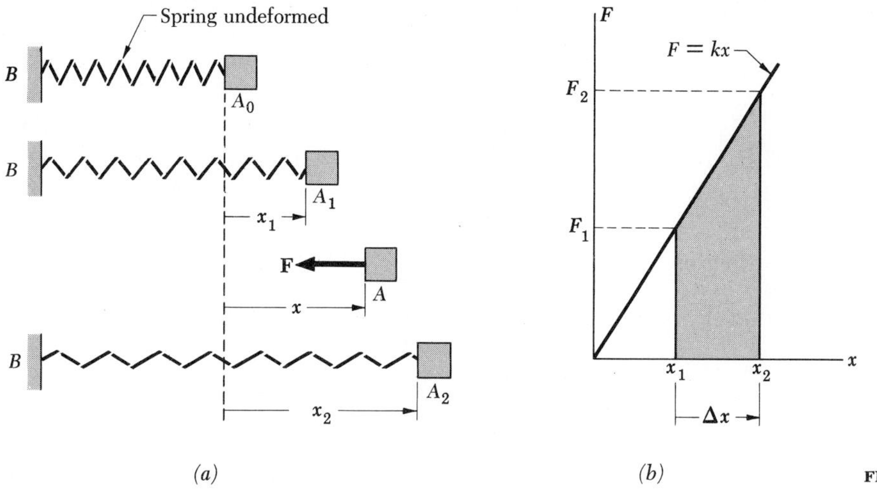

FIG. 13.5

Care should be taken to express k and x in consistent units, that is, k in lb/ft and x in feet, or k in lb/in. and x in inches; in the first case, the work is obtained in ft-lb, in the second case, in in.-lb. We note that the work of the force **F** exerted by the spring on the body is *positive* when $x_2 < x_1$, i.e., *when the spring is returning to its undeformed position.*

Since Eq. (13.5) is the equation of a straight line of slope k passing through the origin, the work $U_{1\rightarrow 2}$ of **F** during the displacement from A_1 to A_2 may be obtained by evaluating the area of the trapezoid shown in Fig. 13.5*b*. This is done by computing F_1 and F_2 and multiplying the base Δx of the trapezoid by its mean height $\frac{1}{2}(F_1 + F_2)$. Since the work of the force **F** exerted by the spring is positive for a negative value of Δx, we write

$$U_{1\rightarrow 2} = -\tfrac{1}{2}(F_1 + F_2)\,\Delta x \qquad (13.6')$$

Formula (13.6′) is usually more convenient to use than (13.6) and affords fewer chances of confusing the units involved.

Work of a Gravitational Force. We saw in Sec. 12.10 that two particles at distance r from each other and, respectively, of mass M and m attract each other with equal and opposite forces **F** and $-$**F** directed along the line joining the particles, and of magnitude

$$F = G\frac{Mm}{r^2}$$

Let us assume that the particle M occupies a fixed position O while the particle m moves along the path shown in Fig. 13.6. The work of the force **F** exerted on the particle m during an

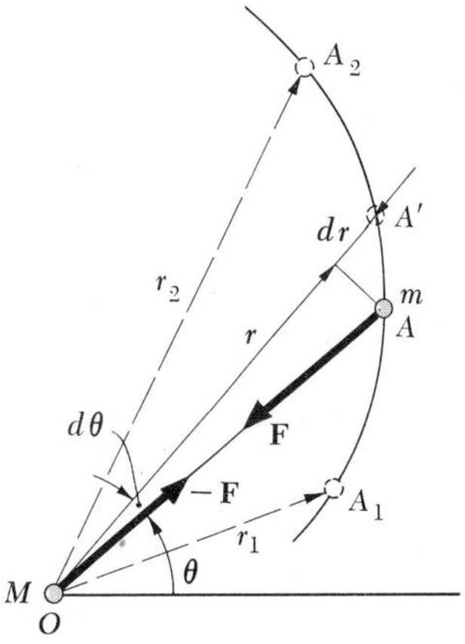

FIG. 13.6

infinitesimal displacement of the particle from A to A' may be obtained by multiplying the magnitude F of the force by the radial component dr of the displacement. Since **F** is directed toward O, the work is negative and we write

$$dU = -F dr = -G\frac{Mm}{r^2}dr$$

The work of the gravitational force **F** during a finite displacement from $A_1(r = r_1)$ to $A_2(r = r_2)$ is therefore

$$U_{1\to2} = -\int_{r_1}^{r_2}\frac{GMm}{r^2}dr = \frac{GMm}{r_2} - \frac{GMm}{r_1} \tag{13.7}$$

The formula obtained may be used to determine the work of the force exerted by the earth on a body of mass m at a distance r from the center of the earth, when r is larger than the radius R of the earth. The letter M represents then the mass of the earth; recalling the first of the relations (12.19), we may thus replace the product GMm in Eq. (13.7) by WR^2, where R is the radius of the earth ($R = 3{,}960$ miles) and W the value of the weight of the body at the surface of the earth.

A number of forces frequently encountered in problems of kinetics *do no work*. They are forces applied to fixed points ($ds = 0$) or acting in a direction perpendicular to the displacement ($\cos\alpha = 0$). Among the forces which do no work are the following: the reaction at a smooth pin when the body supported rotates about the pin, the reaction at a smooth frictionless surface when the body in contact moves along the surface, the reaction at a roller moving along its track, and the weight of a body when its center of gravity moves horizontally.

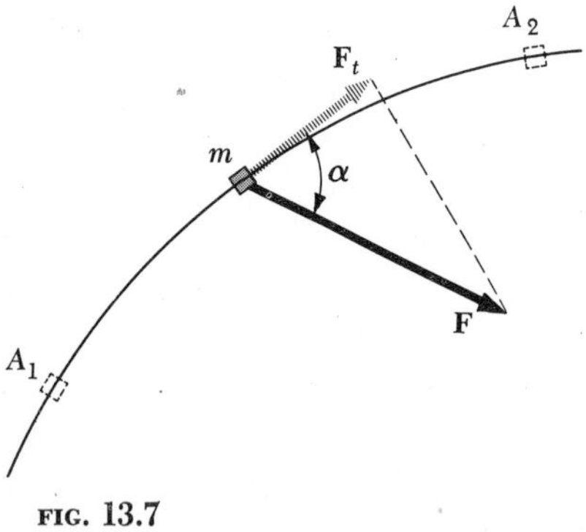

FIG. 13.7

13.3. Kinetic Energy of a Particle. Principle of Work and Energy. Consider a particle of mass m acted upon by a force **F** and moving along a path which is either rectilinear or curved (Fig. 13.7). Expressing Newton's second law in terms of the tangential components of the force and of the acceleration (see Sec. 12.7), we write

$$F_t = ma_t \qquad \text{or} \qquad F_t = m\frac{dv}{dt}$$

where v is the speed of the particle. Recalling from Sec. 11.9 that $v = ds/dt$, we obtain

$$F_t = m\frac{dv}{ds}\frac{ds}{dt} = mv\frac{dv}{ds}$$

$$F_t\,ds = mv\,dv$$

Integrating from A_1, where $s = s_1$ and $v = v_1$, to A_2, where

$s = s_2$ and $v = v_2$, we write

$$\int_{s_1}^{s_2} F_t\,ds = m\int_{v_1}^{v_2} v\,dv = \tfrac{1}{2}mv_2^2 - \tfrac{1}{2}mv_1^2 \qquad (13.8)$$

The left-hand member of Eq. (13.8) represents the work $U_{1\to2}$ of the force **F** exerted on the particle during the displacement from A_1 to A_2; as indicated in Sec. 13.2, the work $U_{1\to2}$ is a scalar quantity. The expression $\frac{1}{2}mv^2$ is also a scalar quantity; it is defined as the kinetic energy of the particle and is denoted by T. We write

$$T = \tfrac{1}{2}mv^2 \qquad (13.9)$$

Substituting into (13.8), we have

$$U_{1\to2} = T_2 - T_1 \qquad (13.10)$$

which expresses that, when a particle moves from A_1 to A_2 under the action of a force **F**, *the work of the force* **F** *is equal to the change in kinetic energy of the particle.* This is known as the *principle of work and energy.* Rearranging the terms in (13.10), we write

$$T_1 + U_{1\to2} = T_2 \qquad (13.11)$$

Thus, *the kinetic energy of the particle at A_2 may be obtained by adding to its kinetic energy at A_1 the work done during the displacement from A_1 to A_2 by the force* **F** *exerted on the particle.* As Newton's second law from which it is derived, the principle of work and energy applies only with respect to a newtonian frame of reference (Sec. 12.1). The speed v used to determine the kinetic energy T should therefore be measured with respect to a newtonian frame of reference.

Since both work and kinetic energy are scalar quantities, their sum may be computed as an ordinary algebraic sum, the work $U_{1\to2}$ being considered as positive or negative according to the direction of **F**. When several forces act on the particle, the expression $U_{1\to2}$ represents the total work of the forces acting on the particle; it is obtained by adding algebraically the work of the various forces.

As noted above, the kinetic energy of a particle is a scalar quantity. It further appears from the definition $T = \frac{1}{2}mv^2$ that the kinetic energy is always positive, regardless of the direction of motion of the particle. Considering the particular case when $v_1 = 0$, $v_2 = v$, and substituting $T_1 = 0$, $T_2 = T$ into (13.12), we observe that the work done by the forces acting on the particle is equal to T. Thus, the kinetic energy of a particle moving with a speed v represents the work which must be done to bring the particle from rest to the speed v. Substituting $T_1 = T$ and $T_2 = 0$ into (13.12), we also note that, when a particle moving with a speed v is brought to rest, the work done by the forces acting on the particle is $-T$. Assuming that no energy is dissipated into heat, we conclude that the work done by the forces exerted *by the particle* on the bodies which cause it to come to rest is equal to T. Thus, the kinetic energy of a particle also represents *the capacity to do work associated with the speed of the particle.*

The kinetic energy is measured in the same units as work. For example, if length, force, and time are measured, respectively, in feet, pounds, and seconds, the kinetic energy should be expressed in ft-lb. We check from formula (13.11) that

$$T = \tfrac{1}{2}mv^2 = \frac{\text{lb-sec}^2}{\text{ft}}\,\frac{\text{ft}^2}{\text{sec}^2} = \text{ft-lb}$$

13.4. Applications of the Principle of Work and Energy. The application of the principle of work and energy greatly simplifies the solution of many problems involving forces, displacements, and velocities. Consider, for example, a pendulum consisting of a bob of weight W attached to a cord of length l (Fig. 13.8*a*). The pendulum is released with no initial velocity from a horizontal position OA_1 and allowed to swing in a vertical plane. We wish to determine the speed of the bob as it passes through A_2, directly under O.

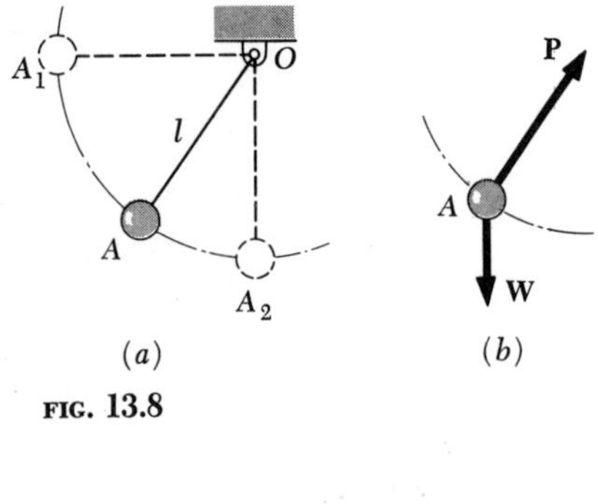

FIG. 13.8

We first determine the work done during the displacement from A_1 to A_2 by the forces acting on the bob. We draw a free-body diagram of the bob, showing all the *actual* forces acting on it, i.e., the weight **W** and the force **P** exerted by the cord (Fig. 13.8*b*). The inertia vector is not an actual force and *should not* be included in the free-body diagram. We note that the force **P** does no work, since it is normal to the path; the only force which does work is thus the weight **W**. The work of **W** is obtained by multiplying its magnitude W by the vertical displacement l (Sec. 13.2); since the displacement is downward, the work is positive. We write therefore $U_{1\to2} = Wl$.

Considering, now, the kinetic energy of the bob, we find $T_1 = 0$ at A_1 and $T_2 = \tfrac{1}{2}(W/g)v_2^2$ at A_2. We may now apply the principle of work and energy; recalling formula (13.11), we write

$$T_1 + U_{1\to2} = T_2 \qquad 0 + Wl = \frac{1}{2}\frac{W}{g}v_2^2$$

Solving for v_2, we find $v_2 = \sqrt{2gl}$. We note that the speed obtained is that of a body falling freely from a height l.

The example we have considered illustrates the following advantages of the method of work and energy:

1. In order to find the speed at A_2, there is no need to determine the acceleration in an intermediate position A and to integrate the expression obtained from A_1 to A_2.
2. All quantities involved are scalars and may be added directly, without using x and y components.
3. Forces which do no work are eliminated from the solution of the problem.

What is an advantage in one problem, however, may become a disadvantage in another. It is evident, for instance, that the method of work and energy cannot be used to determine directly an acceleration. We also note that it should be supplemented by the direct application of Newton's second law in order to determine a force which is normal to the path of the particles, since such a force does no work. Suppose, for example, that we wish to determine the tension in the cord of the pendulum of Fig. 13.8*a* as the bob passes through A_2. We draw a free-body diagram of the bob in that position (Fig. 13.9) and express Newton's second law in terms of tangential and normal components.† The equations $\Sigma F_t = ma_t$ and $\Sigma F_n = ma_n$ yield, respectively, $a_t = 0$ and

$$P = W + \frac{W}{g}a_n = W + \frac{W}{g}\frac{v^2}{l}$$

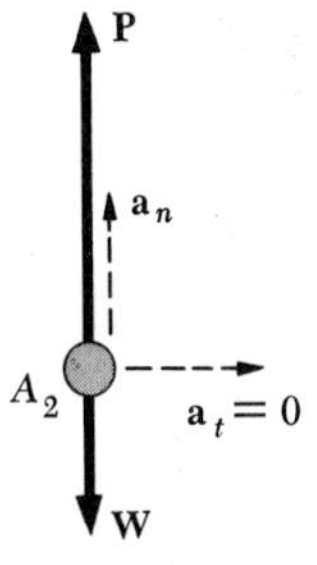

FIG. 13.9

But the speed at A_2 was determined earlier by the method of work and energy. Substituting $v^2 = 2gl$, we write

$$P = W + \frac{W}{g}\frac{2gl}{l} = 3W$$

13.5. Systems of Particles. When a problem involves several particles, each particle may be considered separately and the principle of work and energy may be applied to each particle. Adding the kinetic energies of all the particles, and considering the work of all the forces involved, we may also write the equation of work and energy for the entire system. We have

$$T_1 + U_{1\to 2} = T_2 \qquad (13.11)$$

where T represents the arithmetic sum of the kinetic energies of the particles forming the system (all terms are positive) and $U_{1\to 2}$ the work of all the forces acting on the various particles,

† We may also use the method of dynamic equilibrium.

whether these forces are *internal* or *external* from the point of view of the system as a whole.

The method of work and energy is particularly useful in solving problems involving a system of bodies connected by *inextensible cords or links.* In this case, the internal forces occur by pairs of equal and opposite forces, and the points of application of the forces in each pair *move through equal distances.* As a result, the work of the internal forces is zero and $U_{1\to2}$ reduces to the work of the *external forces only* (see Sample Prob. 13.2).

Using a Centroidal Frame of Reference. It is often convenient, when computing the kinetic energy of a system comprising a large number of particles (as in the case of a rigid body), to consider separately the motion of the mass center G of the system and the motion of the system relative to a moving frame of reference attached to G.

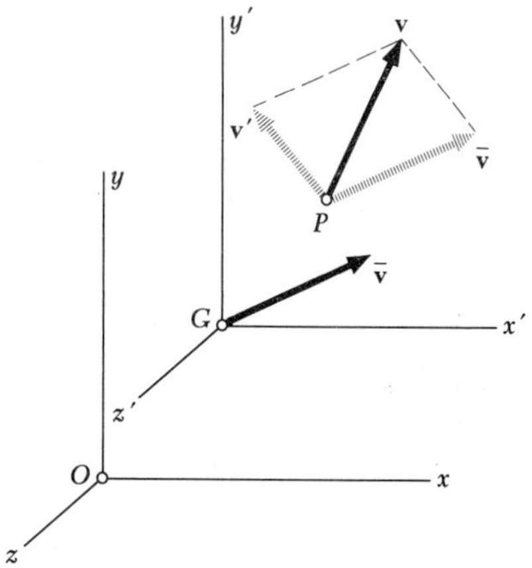

FIG. 13.10

Let P be a particle of the system, $\mathbf{v}$ its velocity relative to the newtonian frame of reference $Oxyz$, and $\mathbf{v}'$ its velocity relative to the moving frame $Gx'y'z'$ which is in translation with respect to $Oxyz$ (Fig. 13.10). Referring to Sec. 11.12, we write

$$\mathbf{v} = \bar{\mathbf{v}} + \mathbf{v}' \tag{13.12}$$

where $\bar{\mathbf{v}}$ denotes the velocity of the mass center G relative to the newtonian frame $Oxyz$. Observing that v^2 is equal to the scalar product $\mathbf{v} \cdot \mathbf{v}$, we express as follows the kinetic energy T of the system relative to the newtonian frame $Oxyz$:

$$T = \tfrac{1}{2}\Sigma m v^2 = \tfrac{1}{2}\Sigma(m\mathbf{v} \cdot \mathbf{v})$$

or, substituting for $\mathbf{v}$ from (13.12),

$$\begin{aligned} T &= \tfrac{1}{2}\Sigma\,[m(\bar{\mathbf{v}} + \mathbf{v}')\cdot(\bar{\mathbf{v}} + \mathbf{v}')] \\ &= \tfrac{1}{2}(\Sigma m)\bar{v}^2 + \bar{\mathbf{v}}\cdot\Sigma m\mathbf{v}' + \tfrac{1}{2}\Sigma m v'^2 \end{aligned}$$

Referring to the relation (12.6) of Sec. 12.5, we note that

$$\Sigma m\mathbf{v}' = (\Sigma m)\bar{\mathbf{v}}' = 0$$

since $\bar{\mathbf{v}}'$, which represents the velocity of G relative to the frame $Gx'y'z'$, is clearly zero. We write therefore

$$T = \tfrac{1}{2}(\Sigma m)\bar{v}^2 + \tfrac{1}{2}\Sigma m v'^2 \tag{13.13}$$

This equation shows that the kinetic energy T of a system of particles may be obtained *by adding the kinetic energy of the mass center G* (assuming the entire mass concentrated at G) *and the kinetic energy of the system in its motion relative to the frame Gx′y′z′.*

SAMPLE PROBLEM 13.1

A railroad car weighing 80,000 lb is initially at rest on a 2° incline. A force of constant magnitude 4,000 lb is then applied as shown. Neglecting friction, determine how far the car will have moved when its velocity is 10 mph.

Solution. *Kinetic Energy*

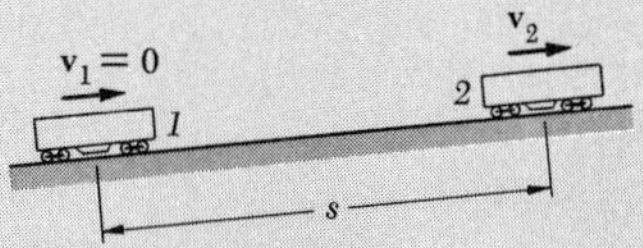

Position *1*: $v_1 = 0 \qquad T_1 = 0$

Position 2: $v_2 = 10 \dfrac{\text{miles}}{\text{hr}} \dfrac{5{,}280 \text{ ft}}{1 \text{ mile}} \dfrac{1 \text{ hr}}{3{,}600 \text{ sec}} = 14.67 \text{ ft/sec}$

$$T_2 = \tfrac{1}{2} m v_2^2 = \frac{1}{2} \frac{80{,}000}{32.2} (14.67)^2 = 267{,}000 \text{ ft-lb}$$

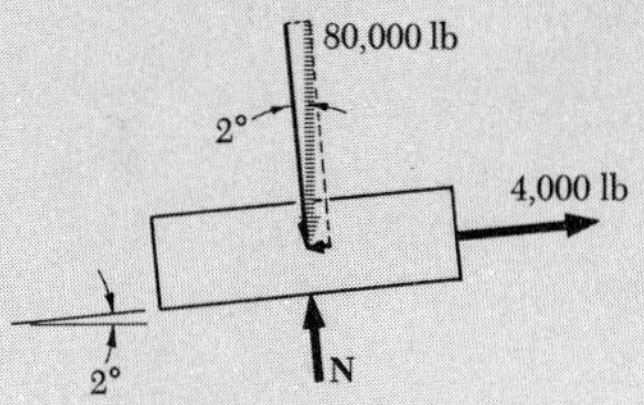

Work
$$U_{1 \to 2} = 4{,}000s - (80{,}000 \sin 2°)s$$
$$= 4{,}000s - 2{,}790s = 1{,}210s$$

Principle of Work and Energy

$$T_1 + U_{1 \to 2} = T_2$$
$$0 + 1{,}210s = 267{,}000 \qquad\qquad s = 221 \text{ ft} \blacktriangleleft$$

SAMPLE PROBLEM 13.2

Two blocks are joined by an inextensible cable as shown. If the system is released from rest, determine the velocity of block *A* after it has moved 5 ft. Assume that μ equals 0.25 between block *A* and the plane and that the pulley is weightless and frictionless.

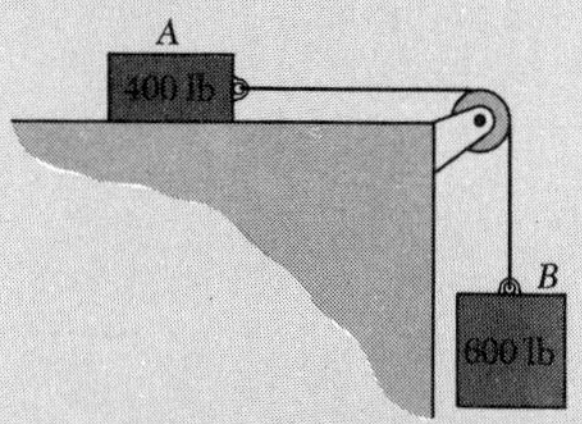

Solution. Since the cable is inextensible, the work done by the forces exerted by the cable will cancel if we consider the two blocks as a single system.

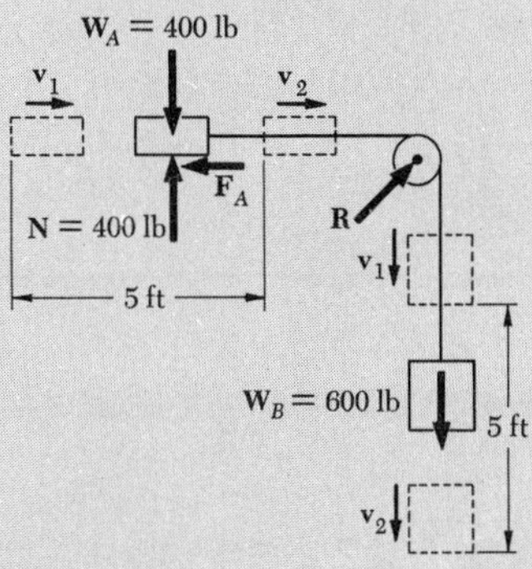

Kinetic Energy

Position *1*: $v_1 = 0 \qquad T_1 = 0$

Position 2: $v_2 = v \qquad T_2 = \tfrac{1}{2} m_A v^2 + \tfrac{1}{2} m_B v^2$

$$T_2 = \frac{1}{2} \frac{400}{g} v^2 + \frac{1}{2} \frac{600}{g} v^2 = \frac{500}{g} v^2$$

Work. During the motion, only $\mathbf{W}_B$ and $\mathbf{F}_A$ do work. Since $W_B = 600$ lb and $F_A = \mu N_A$, we have

$$U_{1 \to 2} = W_B(5 \text{ ft}) - F_A(5 \text{ ft})$$
$$= (600)(5) - (0.25)(400)(5) = 2{,}500 \text{ ft-lb}$$

Principle of Work and Energy

$$T_1 + U_{1 \to 2} = T_2$$
$$0 + 2{,}500 = \frac{500}{g} v^2 \qquad\qquad v = 12.69 \text{ ft/sec} \blacktriangleleft$$

SAMPLE PROBLEM 13.3

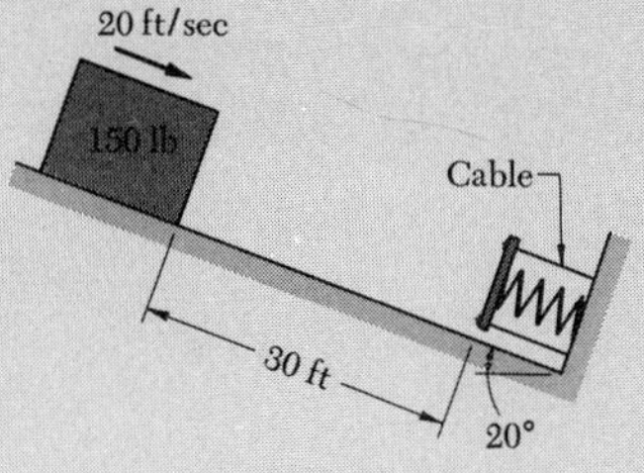

A spring is used to stop a 150-lb package which is moving down a 20° incline. The spring has a constant $k = 150$ lb/in. and is held by cables so that it is initially compressed 4 in. If the velocity of the package is 20 ft/sec when it is 30 ft from the spring, determine the maximum additional deformation of the spring in bringing the package to rest. Assume $\mu = 0.20$.

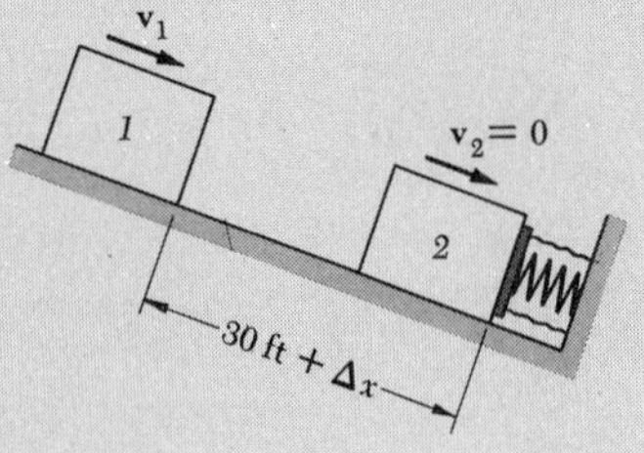

Kinetic Energy

Position *1*: $\quad v_1 = 20$ ft/sec

$$T_1 = \tfrac{1}{2}mv_1^2 = \frac{1}{2}\frac{150}{32.2}(20)^2 = 932 \text{ ft-lb}$$

Position 2 (maximum spring deformation):

$$v_2 = 0 \qquad T_2 = 0$$

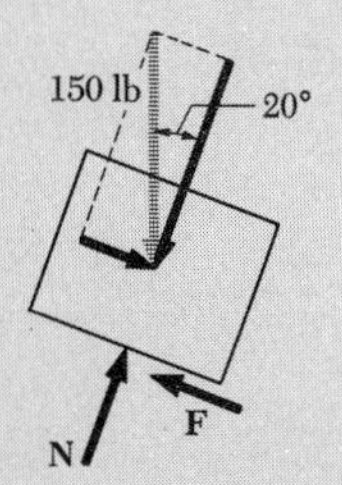

Work. We assume that when the package is brought to rest the additional deflection of the spring is Δx. The component of the weight parallel to the plane and the friction force act through the entire displacement, i.e., through 30 ft + Δx. The work done by these forces is

$$\begin{aligned} U_{1\to 2} &= W_t(30 + \Delta x) - F(30 + \Delta x) \\ &= (150 \sin 20°)(30 + \Delta x) - 0.20(150 \cos 20°)(30 + \Delta x) \\ &= 23.1(30 + \Delta x) \end{aligned}$$

In addition, during the compression of the spring, the variable force **P** exerted by the spring does an amount of negative work equal to the area under the force-deflection curve of the spring force.

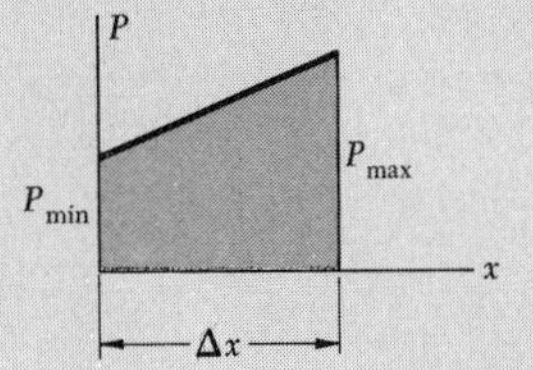

$$\begin{aligned} P_{min} &= (4 \text{ in.})(150 \text{ lb/in.}) = 600 \text{ lb} \\ P_{max} &= 600 + k\,\Delta x \\ &= 600 + (150 \text{ lb/in.})(12 \text{ in./ft})\,\Delta x \\ &= 600 + 1{,}800\,\Delta x \\ U_{1\to 2} &= -\tfrac{1}{2}(P_{min} + P_{max})\,\Delta x = -600\,\Delta x - 900(\Delta x)^2 \end{aligned}$$

The total work is thus

$$U_{1\to 2} = 23.1(30 + \Delta x) - 600\,\Delta x - 900(\Delta x)^2$$

Principle of Work and Energy

$$T_1 + U_{1\to 2} = T_2$$

$$932 + 23.1(30 + \Delta x) - 600\,\Delta x - 900(\Delta x)^2 = 0$$

$$\Delta x = 1.06 \text{ ft} \quad ◄$$

SAMPLE PROBLEM 13.4

A 2,000-lb car starts from rest at point *1* and moves without friction down the track shown. (*a*) Determine the force exerted by the track on the car at point 2, where the radius of curvature of the track is 20 ft. (*b*) Determine the minimum safe value of the radius of curvature at point 3.

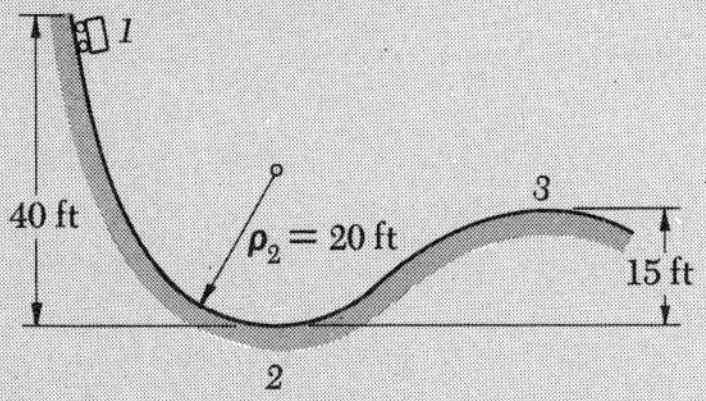

a. **Force Exerted by the Track at Point** 2. The principle of work and energy is used to determine the velocity of the car as it passes through point 2.

Kinetic Energy

$$T_1 = 0 \qquad T_2 = \tfrac{1}{2}mv_2^2 = \frac{1}{2}\frac{W}{g}v_2^2$$

Work. The only force which does work is the weight **W**. Since the vertical displacement from point *1* to point *2* is 40 ft downward, the work of the weight is

$$U_{1\to2} = +W(40\text{ ft})$$

Principle of Work and Energy

$$T_1 + U_{1\to2} = T_2 \qquad 0 + W(40) = \frac{1}{2}\frac{W}{g}v_2^2$$

$$v_2^2 = 80g \qquad v_2 = 50.8\text{ ft/sec}$$

Newton's Second Law at Point 2. The acceleration $\mathbf{a}_n$ of the car at point 2 has a magnitude $a_n = v_2^2/\rho$ and is directed upward. Since the external forces acting on the car are **W** and **N**, we write

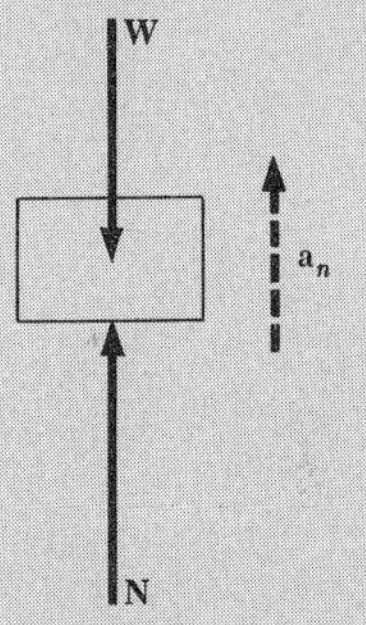

$$+\uparrow \Sigma F_n = ma_n: \qquad -W + N = ma_n$$

$$-W + N = \frac{W}{g}\frac{v_2^2}{\rho}$$

$$-W + N = \frac{W}{g}\frac{80g}{20}$$

$$N = 5W \qquad \mathbf{N} = 10{,}000\text{ lb}\uparrow \blacktriangleleft$$

b. **Minimum Value of** ρ **at Point** 3. *Principle of Work and Energy.* Applying the principle of work and energy between point *1* and point 3, we obtain

$$T_1 + U_{1\to3} = T_3 \qquad 0 + W(25) = \frac{1}{2}\frac{W}{g}v_3^2$$

$$v_3^2 = 50g \qquad v_3 = 40.1\text{ ft/sec}$$

Newton's Second Law at Point 3. The minimum safe value of ρ occurs when $N = 0$. In this case, the acceleration $\mathbf{a}_n$, of magnitude $a_n = v_3^2/\rho$, is directed downward, and we write

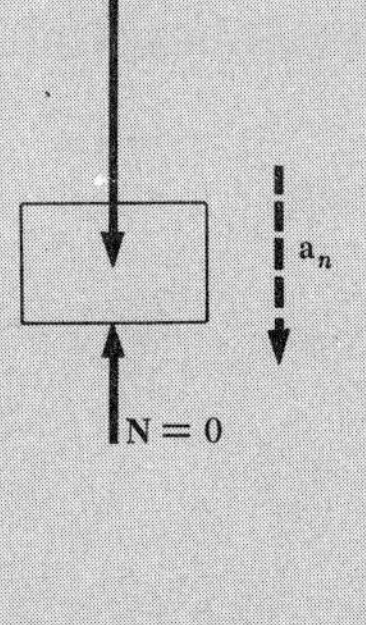

$$+\downarrow \Sigma F_n = ma_n: \qquad W = \frac{W}{g}\frac{v_3^2}{\rho}$$

$$W = \frac{W}{g}\frac{50g}{\rho}$$

$$\rho = 50\text{ ft} \blacktriangleleft$$

PROBLEMS

13.1. A stone which weighs 5 lb is dropped from a height h and strikes the ground with a velocity of 90 ft/sec. (*a*) Find the kinetic energy of the stone as it strikes the ground and the height h from which it was dropped. (*b*) Solve part *a* assuming that the same stone is dropped on the moon. (Acceleration of gravity on the moon = 5.31 ft/sec^2.)

13.2. A 50-lb satellite was placed in a circular orbit 1,548 miles above the surface of the earth. At this elevation the acceleration of gravity is 16.7 ft/sec^2. Determine the kinetic energy of the satellite, knowing that its orbital speed is 15,000 mph.

13.3. Knowing that the coefficient of friction between rubber tires and concrete is approximately 0.80, determine the length of skid marks which would indicate that an automobile was traveling at 60 mph or faster when the brakes were applied. Assume that all wheels of the car produce skid marks.

13.4. A railroad car weighing 40 tons rolls 500 ft down a 2 per cent incline and then rolls 333 ft up a 2 per cent incline before coming to a stop. Determine the average rolling resistance of the car.

13.5. Packages are thrown down a chute at A with a velocity of 4 ft/sec. Knowing that $\mu = 0.25$, determine the distance d if the packages are to arrive at point C with a velocity of 8 ft/sec.

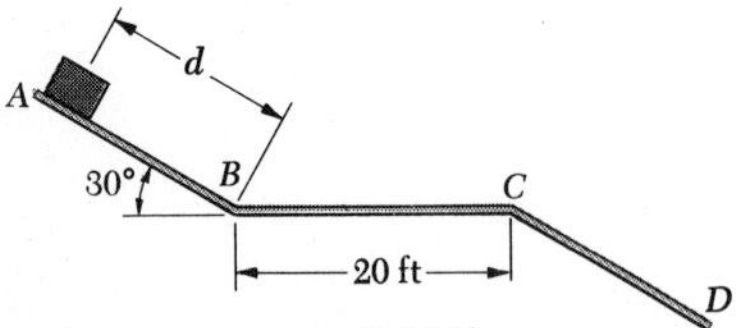

FIG. P 13.5

13.6. Using the method of work and energy, solve Prob. 12.8.

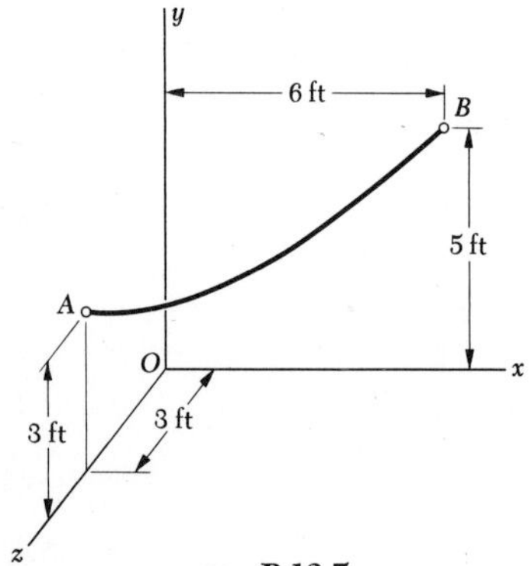

FIG. P 13.7

13.7. A 10-lb block moves without friction from A to B along the curved path shown. During the motion the block is acted upon by the force $\mathbf{P} = 2x^2\mathbf{i} + 3y^2\mathbf{j} + z^2\mathbf{k}$ (lb). Knowing that the speed of the block at point A is 20 ft/sec, determine the speed of the block as it reaches point B. Show that the result obtained is independent of the shape of the path.

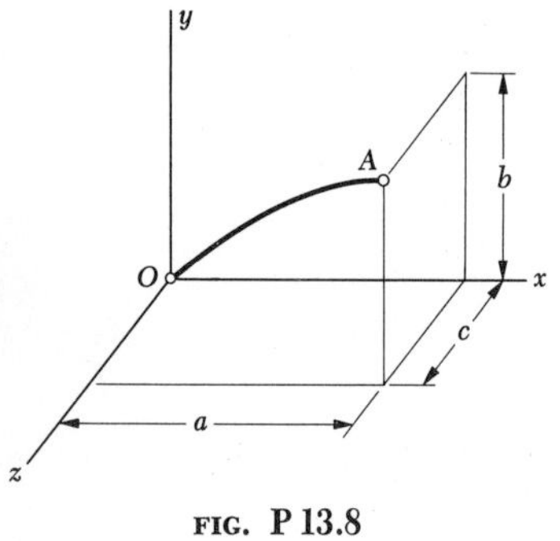

FIG. P 13.8

13.8. A particle of mass m starts from rest at the origin of coordinates O and moves without friction along the path OA. During the motion the particle is acted upon by the force $\mathbf{P} = P_1 \cos(\pi x/2a)\ \mathbf{i} + P_2 \cos(\pi y/2b)\ \mathbf{j} + P_3 \cos(\pi z/2c)\ \mathbf{k}$. Determine the speed of the particle at point A. Show that the result obtained is independent of the shape of the path.

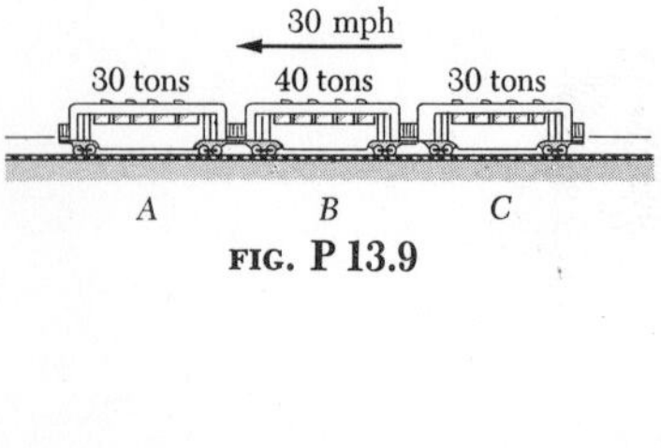

FIG. P 13.9

13.9. The subway train shown travels at a speed of 30 mph. Knowing that $\mu = 0.30$, determine the distance required to stop the train and the force in each coupling if the brakes are fully applied on car A but are not applied on cars B and C.

13.10. Solve Prob. 13.9 assuming that the brakes are fully applied on cars *B* and *C* but are not applied on car *A*.

13.11. The system shown is released from rest. Determine the velocity of the block *A* after it has moved 6 ft.

13.12. The system shown is released from rest. After moving a distance *d*, block *B* strikes the ground and the cable becomes slack. Determine the required distance *d* if block *A* is to come to rest after moving a total distance of 10 ft.

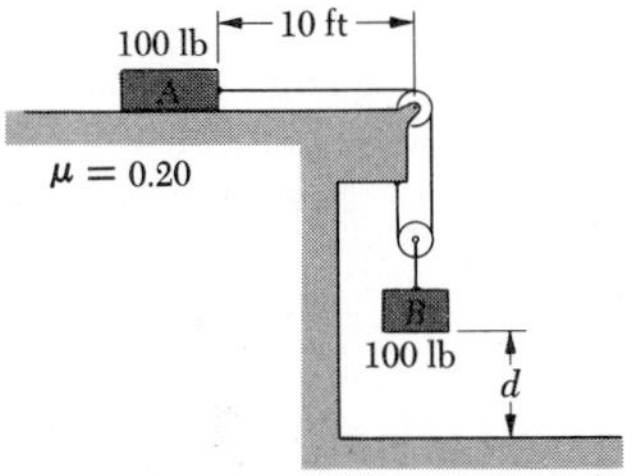

FIG. P 13.11 AND P 13.12

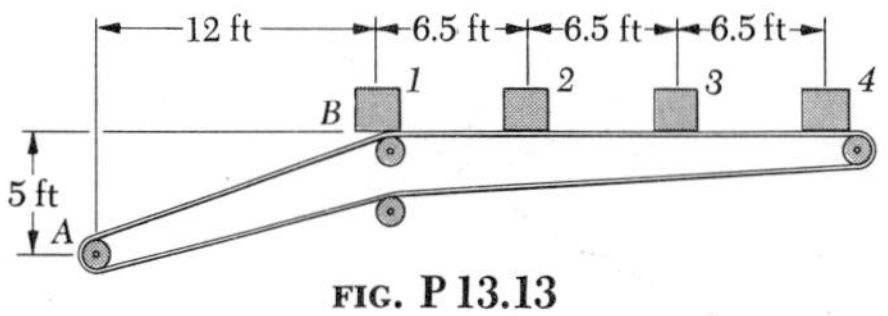

FIG. P 13.13

13.13. Four packages weighing 125 lb each are placed as shown on a conveyor belt which is disengaged from its drive motor. Package *1* is just to the left of the horizontal portion of the belt. If the system is released from rest, determine the velocity of package *1* as it falls off the belt at point *A*. Assume that the weight of the belt and rollers is small compared to the weight of the packages.

13.14. In Prob. 13.13, determine the velocity of package *2* as it falls from the belt at *A*.

13.15. Two blocks *A* and *B*, weighing 9 lb and 10 lb, respectively, are connected by a cord which passes over pulleys as shown. A collar *C* is placed on block *A* and the system is released from rest. After the blocks have moved 3 ft, the collar *C* is removed and the blocks continue to move. Knowing that collar *C* weighs 5 lb, determine the speed of block *A* just before it strikes the ground.

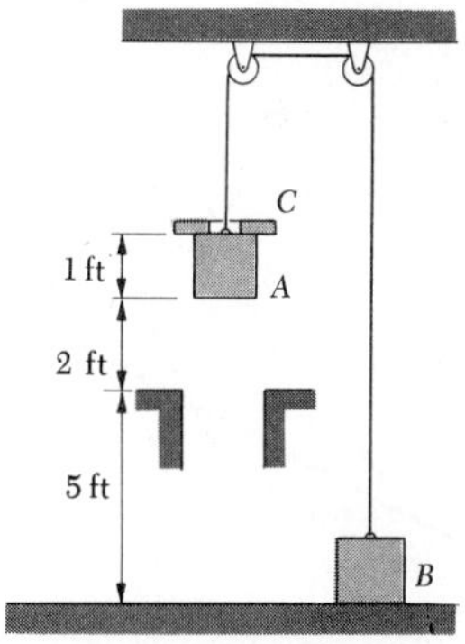

FIG. P 13.15

13.16. In Prob. 13.15, determine the smallest weight of the collar *C* for which block *A* will reach the ground.

13.17. Using the method of work and energy, solve Prob. 12.17*c*.

13.18. Using the method of work and energy, solve Prob. 12.20.

13.19. Using the method of work and energy, solve Prob. 12.21*b*.

13.20. Using the method of work and energy, solve Prob. 12.22*b*.

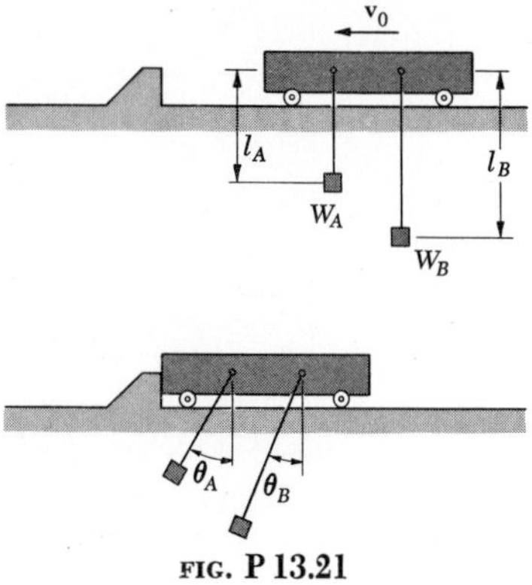

FIG. P 13.21

13.21. The load W_A is suspended from the car by a cable of length l_A. Initially, the car and load are moving at a constant velocity v_0. After the car is stopped by the bumper, the load swings forward. (*a*) What is the maximum angle θ_A through which the load will swing? (*b*) If the maximum angle through which the load swings is 30°, what was the initial velocity of the car, assuming $l_A = 10$ ft?

13.22. When the car of Prob. 13.21 is stopped by the bumper, the maximum angle through which the load W_A swings is observed to be $\theta_A = 30°$. Knowing that $l_A = 10$ ft and $l_B = 20$ ft, determine the maximum angle θ_B through which the load W_B will swing.

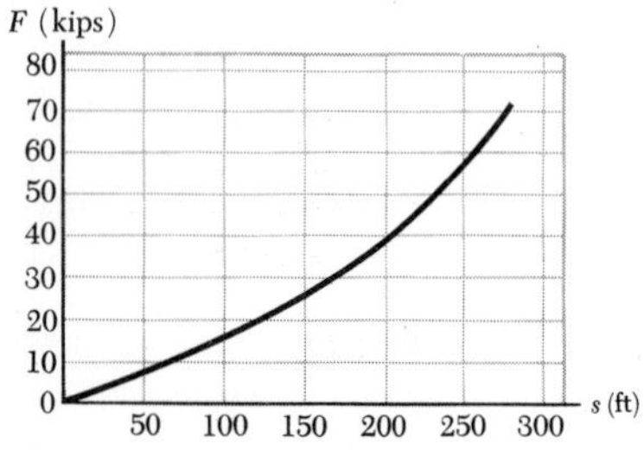

FIG. P 13.23

13.23. An airplane weighing 12,000 lb lands on an aircraft carrier and is caught by an arresting cable which is characterized by the force-deflection diagram shown. Knowing that the landing speed of the plane is 100 mph, determine (*a*) the distance required for the plane to come to rest, (*b*) the maximum rate of deceleration of the plane.

13.24. In Prob. 13.23, determine the landing speed of an 18,000-lb airplane if it is brought to rest by the arresting cable in 200 ft.

13.25. Two types of energy-absorbing fenders designed to be used on a pier are statically loaded. The force-deflection curve for each type of fender is given in the graph. Determine the maximum deflection of each fender when a 100-ton ship moving at 1 mph strikes the fender and is brought to rest.

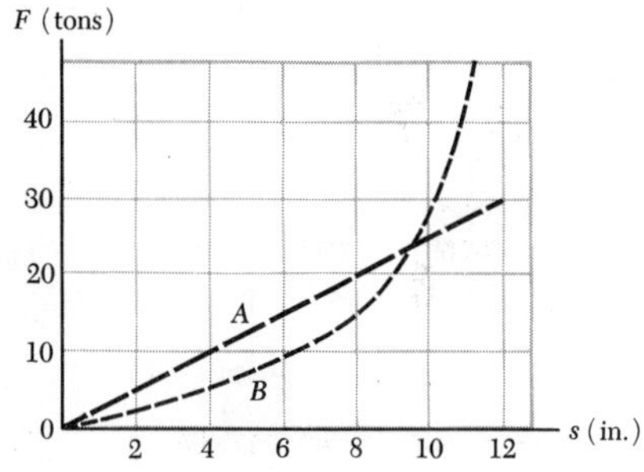

FIG. P 13.25

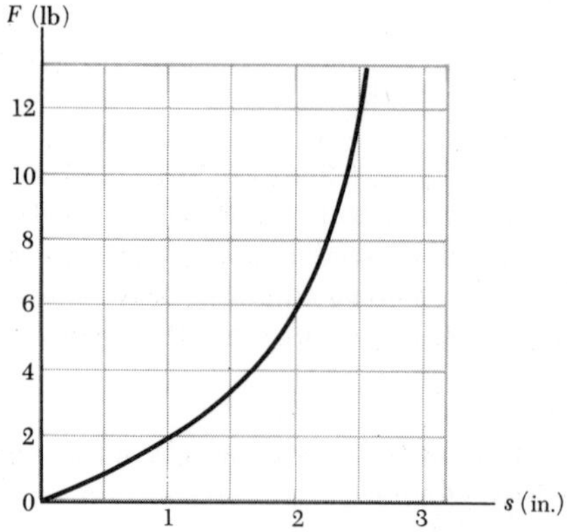

FIG. P 13.26

13.26. In order to protect it during shipping, a delicate instrument weighing 4 oz is packed in excelsior. From the static test of similar excelsior, the force-deflection curve shown was obtained. Determine the maximum height from which the package may be dropped if the force exerted on the instrument is not to exceed 12 lb.

13.27. A railroad car weighing 50,000 lb starts from rest and coasts down a 1 per cent incline for a distance of 50 ft. It is stopped by a bumper having a spring constant of 8,000 lb/in. (*a*) What is the velocity of the car at the bottom of the incline? (*b*) How many inches will the spring be compressed?

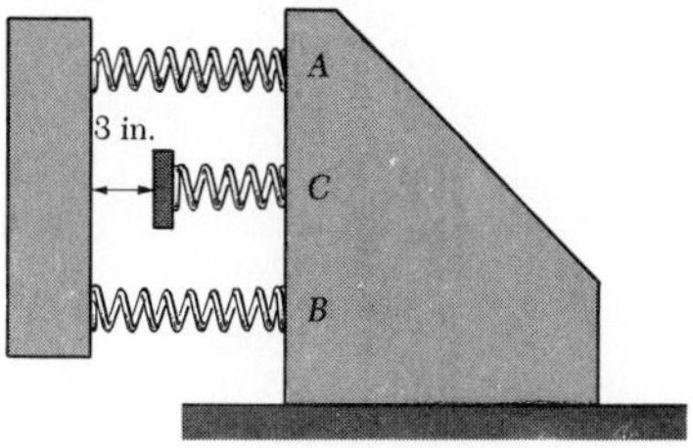

FIG. P 13.28

13.28. The bumper shown is used to stop the railroad car of Prob. 13.27. Knowing that $k_A = k_B = 4{,}000$ lb/in., determine the required value of k_C if the maximum deflection of the bumper is to be 8 in.

13.29. A weight W is dropped from a height h onto a spring of constant k. Determine (*a*) the maximum deflection of the spring, (*b*) the maximum velocity attained by the weight. (*c*) Solve parts *a* and *b* for $h = 0$.

PE $\frac{1}{2}ks^2$
IN SPRING

ENERGY LOST BY W = W(h + s)

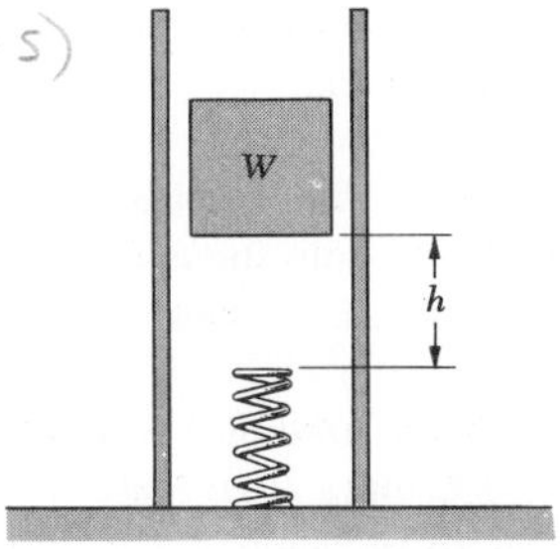

FIG. P 13.29 AND P 13.30

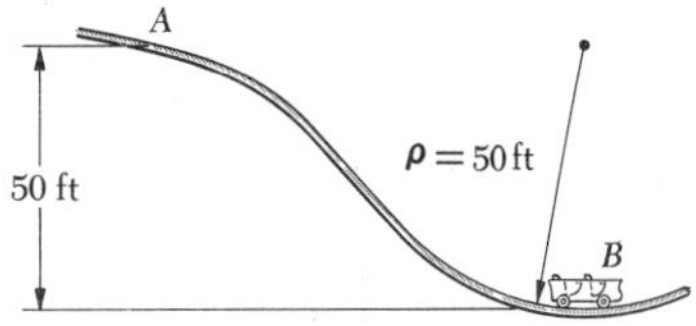

FIG. P 13.31

13.30. A 10-lb weight is released from rest at a distance h above the top of an undeformed spring of constant $k = 5$ lb/in. Determine h if the maximum force exerted on the weight by the spring is to be (*a*) 40 lb, (*b*) 20 lb, (*c*) 15 lb.

13.31. A roller coaster is released with no velocity at A and rolls down the track shown. The brakes are suddenly applied as the car passes through point B, causing the wheels of the car to slide on the track ($\mu = 1/3$). Assuming no energy loss between A and B and knowing that the radius of curvature of the track at B is 50 ft, determine the normal and tangential components of the acceleration of the car just after the brakes have been applied.

13.32. A small package of weight W is projected into a vertical return loop at A with a velocity v_0. The package travels without friction along a circle of radius r and is deposited on a horizontal surface at C. For each of the two loops shown, determine (*a*) the smallest velocity v_0 for which the package will reach the horizontal surface at C, (*b*) the corresponding force exerted by the loop on the package as it passes point B.

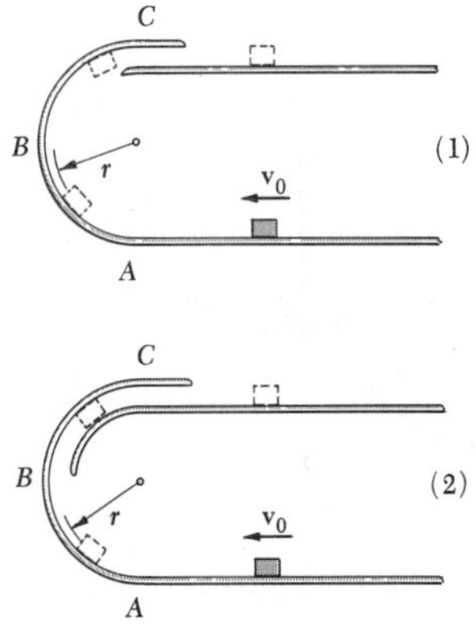

FIG. P 13.32

13.33. In Prob. 13.32, it is desired to have the package deposited on the horizontal surface at C with a speed of 6 ft/sec. Knowing that $r = 24$ in., (a) show that this requirement cannot be fulfilled by the first loop, (b) determine the required initial velocity $\mathbf{v}_0$ when the second loop is used.

13.34. Using the method of work and energy, solve Prob. 12.36.

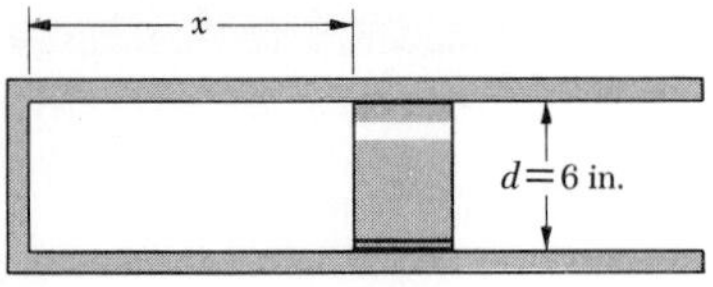

FIG. P 13.35

13.35. A 6-in.-diameter piston weighing 8 lb slides without friction in a cylinder. When the piston is at a distance $x = 10$ in. from the end of the cylinder, the pressure in the cylinder is atmospheric ($p_a = 14.7$ lb/in.^{2}). If the pressure varies inversely as the volume, find the work done in moving the piston until $x = 4$ in.

13.36. The piston of Prob. 13.35 is moved to the left and released with no velocity when $x = 4$ in. Neglecting friction, determine (a) the maximum velocity attained by the piston, (b) the maximum value of the coordinate x.

13.37. An object is released with no initial velocity at a very great distance from the earth. With what velocity will it strike the earth? (Neglect air resistance.)

13.38. An object is dropped with no initial velocity from an altitude of 400 miles. (a) With what velocity does it strike the earth? (Neglect air resistance.) (b) What relative error is introduced by assuming a uniform gravitational field?

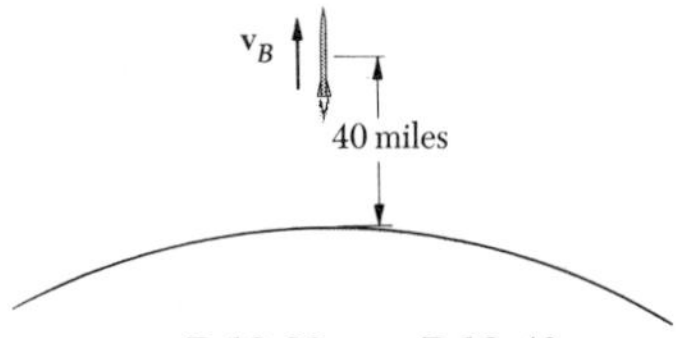

FIG. P 13.39 AND P 13.40

13.39. A rocket is fired vertically from the ground. Knowing that at burnout the rocket is 40 miles above the ground and has a velocity of 15,000 ft/sec, determine the highest altitude it will reach.

13.40. A rocket is fired vertically from the ground. What should be its velocity $\mathbf{v}_B$ at burnout, 40 miles above the ground, if it is to reach an altitude of 600 miles?

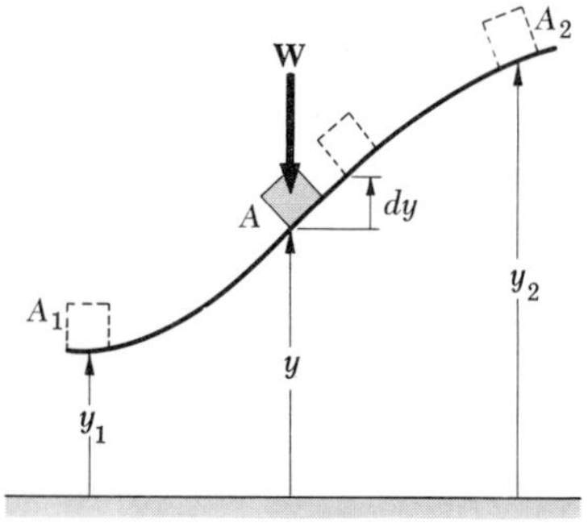

FIG. 13.4 (*repeated*)

13.6. Potential Energy. Conservative Forces. Let us consider again a body of weight $\mathbf{W}$ which moves along a curved path from a point A_1 of elevation y_1 to a point A_2 of elevation y_2 (Fig. 13.4). We recall from Sec. 13.2 that the work of the weight $\mathbf{W}$ during this displacement is

$$U_{1\to 2} = Wy_1 - Wy_2 \tag{13.4}$$

The work of **W** may thus be obtained by subtracting the value of the function Wy corresponding to the second position of the body from its value corresponding to the first position. The work of **W** is independent of the actual path followed; it depends only upon the initial and final values of the function Wy. This function is called the *potential energy* of the body with respect to the *force of gravity* **W** and is denoted by V_g. We write

$$U_{1\to2} = (V_g)_1 - (V_g)_2 \qquad \text{with } V_g = Wy \qquad (13.14)$$

We note that if $(V_g)_2 > (V_g)_1$, i.e., *if the potential energy increases* during the displacement (as in the case considered here), *the work* $U_{1\to2}$ *is negative.* If, on the other hand, the work of **W** is positive, the potential energy decreases. Therefore, the potential energy V_g of the body provides a measure of the work which may be done by its weight **W**. Since only the *change* in potential energy, and not the actual value of V_g, is involved in formula (13.14), an arbitrary constant may be added to the expression obtained for V_g. In other words, the level, or datum, from which the elevation y is measured may be chosen arbitrarily. Note that potential energy is expressed in the same units as work, i.e., in ft-lb or in in.-lb.

It should be noted that the expression just obtained for the potential energy of a body with respect to gravity is valid only as long as the weight **W** of the body may be assumed to remain constant, i.e., as long as the displacements of the body are small compared to the radius of the earth. In the case of a space vehicle, however, we should take into consideration the variation of the force of gravity with the distance r from the center of the earth. Using the expression obtained in Sec. 13.2 for the work of a gravitational force, we write (Fig. 13.6)

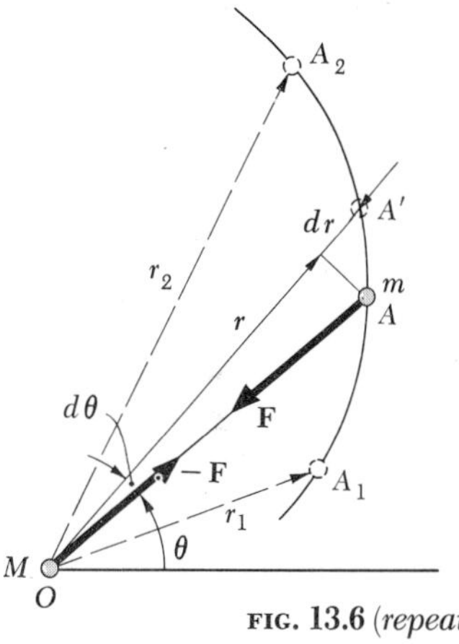

FIG. 13.6 (*repeated*)

$$U_{1\to2} = \frac{GMm}{r_2} - \frac{GMm}{r_1} \qquad (13.7)$$

The work of the force of gravity may therefore be obtained by subtracting the value of the function $-GMm/r$ corresponding to the second position of the body from its value corresponding to the first position. Thus, the expression which should be used for the potential energy V_g when the variation in the force of gravity cannot be neglected is

$$V_g = -\frac{GMm}{r} \qquad (13.15)$$

Taking the first of the relations (12.19) into account, we write V_g in the alternate form

$$V_g = -\frac{WR^2}{r} \qquad (13.15')$$

where R is the radius of the earth (R = 3,960 miles) and W the value of the weight of the body at the surface of the earth. When either of the relations (13.15) and (13.15′) is used to express V_g, the distance r should, of course, be measured from the center of the earth.† Note that V_g is always negative and that it approaches zero for very large values of r.

Consider, now, a body attached to a spring and moving from a position A_1, corresponding to a deflection x_1 of the spring, to a position A_2, corresponding to a deflection x_2 (Fig. 13.5).

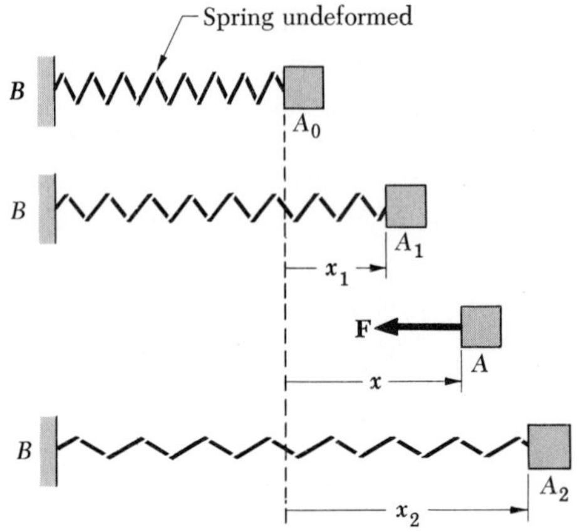

FIG. 13.5 *(repeated)*

We recall from Sec. 13.2 that the work of the force **F** exerted by the spring on the body is

$$U_{1\to 2} = \tfrac{1}{2}kx_1^2 - \tfrac{1}{2}kx_2^2 \qquad (13.6)$$

The work of the elastic force is thus obtained by subtracting the value of the function $\frac{1}{2}kx^2$ corresponding to the second position of the body from its value corresponding to the first position. This function is denoted by V_e and is called the *potential energy* of the body with respect to the *elastic force* **F**. We write

$$U_{1\to 2} = (V_e)_1 - (V_e)_2 \qquad \text{with } V_e = \tfrac{1}{2}kx^2 \qquad (13.16)$$

† The expressions given for V_g in (13.15) and (13.15′) are valid only when $r \geqq R$, i.e., when the body considered is above the surface of the earth.

and observe that, during the displacement considered, the work of the force **F** exerted by the spring on the body is negative and the potential energy V_e increases. We should note that the expression obtained for V_e is valid only if the deflection of the spring is measured from its undeformed position. On the other hand, formula (13.16) may be used even when the spring is rotated about its fixed end (Fig. 13.11*a*). The work of the elastic force depends only upon the initial and final deflections of the spring (Fig. 13.11*b*).

The concept of potential energy may be used when forces other than gravity forces and elastic forces are involved. Indeed, it remains valid as long *as the work* $U_{1\to2}$ *of the force* **F** *is independent of the path followed by the particle from* A_1 *to* A_2 (Fig. 13.12*a*). The force **F** is then said to be a *conservative force* and we may write

$$U_{1\to2} = V(x_1,y_1,z_1) - V(x_2,y_2,z_2) \qquad (13.17)$$

or, for short,

$$U_{1\to2} = V_1 - V_2 \qquad (13.17')$$

The function $V(x,y,z)$ is called the potential energy, or *potential function* of **F**.

We note that, if A_2 is chosen to coincide with A_1, i.e., if the particle describes a closed path (Fig. 13.12*b*), we have $V_1 = V_2$ and the work is zero. We may thus write for any conservative force **F**

$$\oint \mathbf{F}\cdot d\mathbf{r} = 0 \qquad (13.18)$$

where the circle on the integral sign indicates that the path is closed.

Let us now apply (13.17) between two neighboring points $A(x,y,z)$ and $A'(x + dx,y + dy,z + dz)$. The elementary work dU corresponding to the displacement $d\mathbf{r}$ from A to A' is

$$dU = V(x,y,z) - V(x + dx,y + dy,z + dz)$$

or,

$$dU = -dV(x,y,z) \qquad (13.19)$$

Thus, the elementary work of a conservative force is an *exact differential.*

Substituting for dU in (13.19) the expression obtained in (13.1″), and recalling the definition of the differential of a function of several variables, we write

$$F_x\,dx + F_y\,dy + F_z\,dz = -\left(\frac{\partial V}{\partial x}dx + \frac{\partial V}{\partial y}dy + \frac{\partial V}{\partial z}dz\right)$$

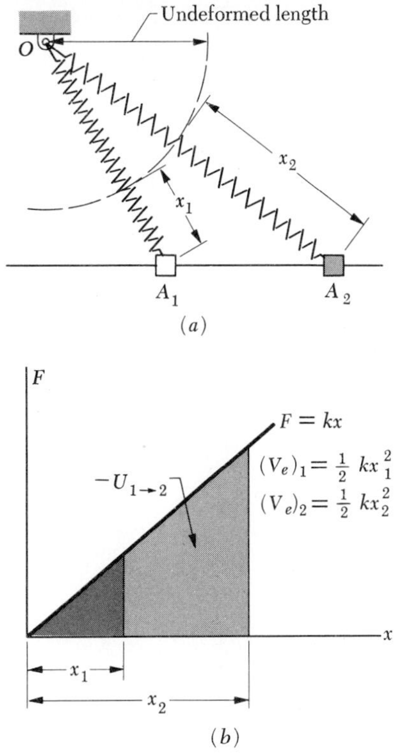

FIG. 13.11

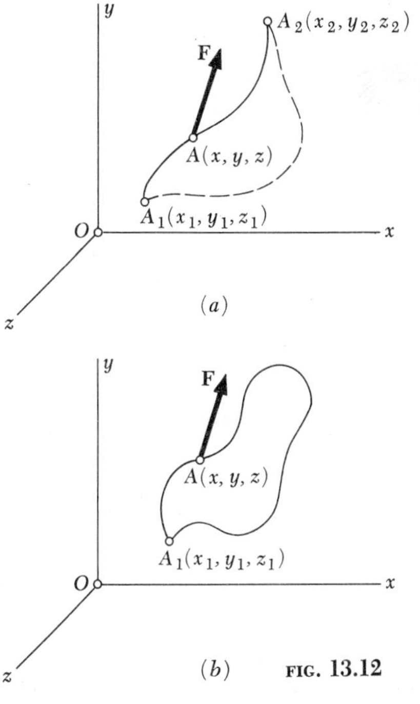

FIG. 13.12

from which it follows that

$$F_x = -\frac{\partial V}{\partial x} \qquad F_y = -\frac{\partial V}{\partial y} \qquad F_z = -\frac{\partial V}{\partial z} \tag{13.20}$$

It is clear that the components of **F** must be functions of the coordinates x, y, z. Thus, a *necessary* condition for a conservative force is that it depend only upon the position of its point of application. The relations (13.20) may be expressed more concisely if we write

$$\mathbf{F} = F_x\mathbf{i} + F_y\mathbf{j} + F_z\mathbf{k} = -\left(\frac{\partial V}{\partial x}\mathbf{i} + \frac{\partial V}{\partial y}\mathbf{j} + \frac{\partial V}{\partial z}\mathbf{k}\right)$$

The vector in parentheses is known as the *gradient of the scalar function* V and is denoted by **grad** V. We thus write for any conservative force

$$\mathbf{F} = -\mathbf{grad}\, V \tag{13.21}$$

The relations (13.17) to (13.21) were shown to be satisfied by any conservative force. It may also be shown that if a force **F** satisfies one of these relations, **F** must be a conservative force.

13.7. Conservation of Energy. We saw in the preceding section that the work of a conservative force, such as the weight of a particle or the force exerted by a spring, may be expressed as a change in potential energy. When a particle, or a system of particles, moves under the action of conservative forces, the principle of work and energy stated in Sec. 13.3 may be expressed in a modified form. Substituting for $U_{1\to2}$ from (13.17′) into (13.10), we write

$$V_1 - V_2 = T_2 - T_1$$

$$T_1 + V_1 = T_2 + V_2 \tag{13.22}$$

Formula (13.22) indicates that, when a system of particles moves under the action of conservative forces, *the sum of the kinetic energy and of the potential energy of the system remains constant.*† The sum $T + V$ is called the *total mechanical energy* of the system and is denoted by E.

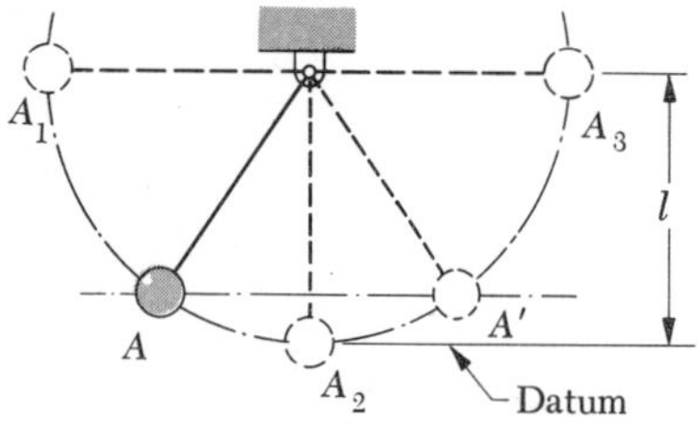

FIG. 13.13

Consider, for example, the pendulum analyzed in Sec. 13.4, which is released with no velocity from A_1 and allowed to swing in a vertical plane (Fig. 13.13). Measuring the potential energy from the level of A_2, we have, at A_1,

† When the particles of a system move with respect to each other under the action of internal forces, the potential energy of the system must include the potential energy corresponding to the internal forces.

$$T_1 = 0 \qquad V_1 = Wl \qquad T_1 + V_1 = Wl$$

Recalling that, at A_2, the speed of the pendulum is $v_2 = \sqrt{2gl}$, we have

$$T_2 = \frac{1}{2}\frac{W}{g}v_2^2 = Wl \qquad V_2 = 0 \qquad T_2 + V_2 = Wl$$

We thus check that the total mechanical energy $E = T + V$ of the pendulum is the same at A_1 and A_2. While the energy is entirely potential at A_1, it becomes entirely kinetic at A_2, and, as the pendulum keeps swinging to the right, the kinetic energy is transformed back into potential energy. At A_3, we shall have $T_3 = 0$ and $V_3 = Wl$.

Since the total mechanical energy of the pendulum remains constant and since its potential energy depends only upon its elevation, the kinetic energy of the pendulum will have the same value at any two points located on the same level. Thus, the speed of the pendulum is the same at A and at A' (Fig. 13.13). This result may be extended to the case of a particle moving along any given path, regardless of the shape of the path, as long as the only forces acting on the particle are its weight and the normal reaction of the path. The particle of Fig. 13.14, for example, which slides in a vertical plane along a frictionless track, will have the same speed at A, A', and A''.

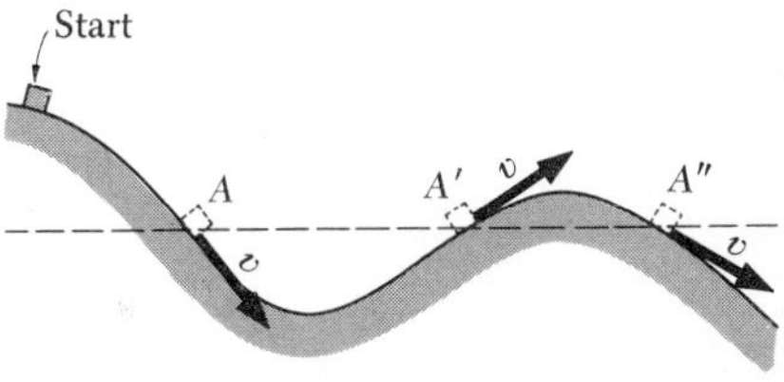

FIG. 13.14

While the weight of a particle and the force exerted by a spring are conservative forces, *friction forces are nonconservative forces*. In other words, *the work of a friction force cannot be expressed as a change in potential energy*. The work of a friction force depends upon the path followed by its point of application; and while the work $U_{1\to2}$ defined by (13.17) is positive or negative according to the sense of motion, *the work of a friction force is always negative*. It follows that, when a system involves friction, its total mechanical energy does not remain constant but decreases. The mechanical energy of the system, however, is not lost; it is transformed into heat, and the sum of the *mechanical energy* and of the *thermal energy* of the system remains constant.

Other forms of energy may also be involved in a system. For instance, a generator converts mechanical energy into *electrical energy;* a gasoline engine converts *chemical energy* into mechanical energy; a nuclear reactor converts *mass* into thermal energy. If all forms of energy are considered, the energy of any system may be considered as constant and the principle of conservation of energy remains valid under all conditions.

SAMPLE PROBLEM 13.5

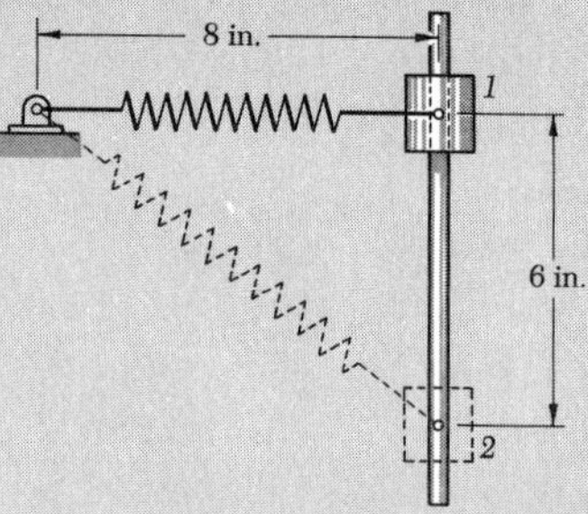

A 20-lb collar slides without friction along a vertical rod as shown. The spring attached to the collar has an undeformed length of 4 in. and a constant of 3 lb/in. If the collar is released from rest in position *1*, determine its velocity after it has moved 6 in. to position 2.

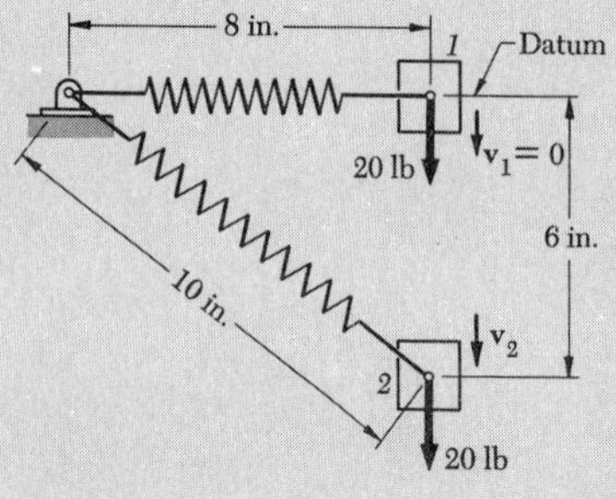

Position *1*. *Potential Energy.* The elongation of the spring is $x_1 = 8 \text{ in.} - 4 \text{ in.} = 4 \text{ in.}$, and we have

$$V_e = \tfrac{1}{2}kx_1^2 = \tfrac{1}{2}(3 \text{ lb/in.})(4 \text{ in.})^2 = 24 \text{ in.-lb}$$

Choosing the datum as shown, we have $V_g = 0$. Therefore,

$$V_1 = V_e + V_g = 24 \text{ in.-lb} = 2 \text{ ft-lb}$$

Kinetic Energy. Since the velocity in position *1* is zero, $T_1 = 0$.

Position 2. *Potential Energy.* The elongation of the spring is $x_2 = 10 \text{ in.} - 4 \text{ in.} = 6 \text{ in.}$, and we have

$$V_e = \tfrac{1}{2}kx_2^2 = \tfrac{1}{2}(3 \text{ lb/in.})(6 \text{ in.})^2 = 54 \text{ in.-lb}$$
$$V_g = Wy = (20 \text{ lb})(-6 \text{ in.}) = -120 \text{ in.-lb}$$

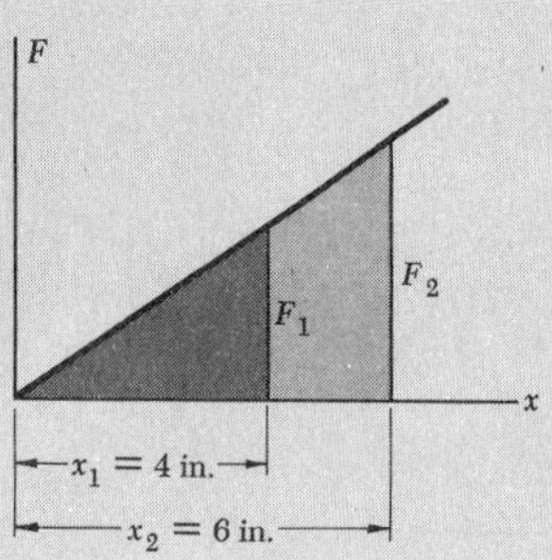

Therefore,

$$V_2 = V_e + V_g = 54 - 120 = -66 \text{ in.-lb} = -5.5 \text{ ft-lb}$$

Kinetic Energy

$$T_2 = \tfrac{1}{2}mv_2^2 = \frac{1}{2}\frac{20}{32.2}v_2^2 = 0.311v_2^2$$

Conservation of Energy. Applying the principle of conservation of energy between positions *1* and 2, we write

$$T_1 + V_1 = T_2 + V_2$$
$$0 + 2 \text{ ft-lb} = 0.311v_2^2 - 5.5 \text{ ft-lb}$$

$$v_2 = \pm 4.92 \text{ ft/sec} \qquad \mathbf{v}_2 = 4.92 \text{ ft/sec} \downarrow$$ ◀

SAMPLE PROBLEM 13.6

The $\frac{1}{2}$-lb pellet is released from rest at A when the spring is compressed 3 in. and travels around the loop $ABCDE$. Determine the smallest value of the spring constant for which the pellet will travel around the loop and will at all times remain in contact with the loop.

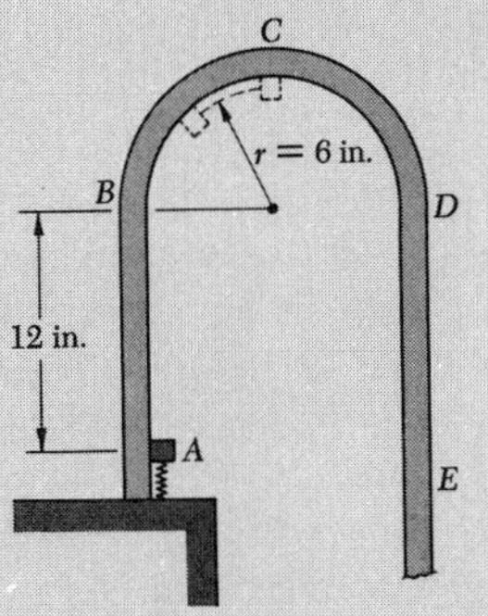

Required Speed at Point C. As the pellet passes through the highest point C, its potential energy with respect to gravity is maximum; thus, at the same point its kinetic energy and its speed are minimum. Since the pellet must remain in contact with the loop, the force **N** exerted on the pellet by the loop must be equal to, or greater than, zero. Setting **N** $= 0$, we compute the smallest possible speed v_C.

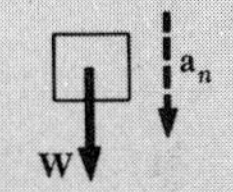

$$+\downarrow \Sigma F_n = ma_n: \quad W = \frac{W}{g} a_n = \frac{W}{g}\frac{v_C^2}{r}$$

$$v_C^2 = gr = g(\tfrac{6}{12}\text{ ft}) = \tfrac{1}{2}g$$

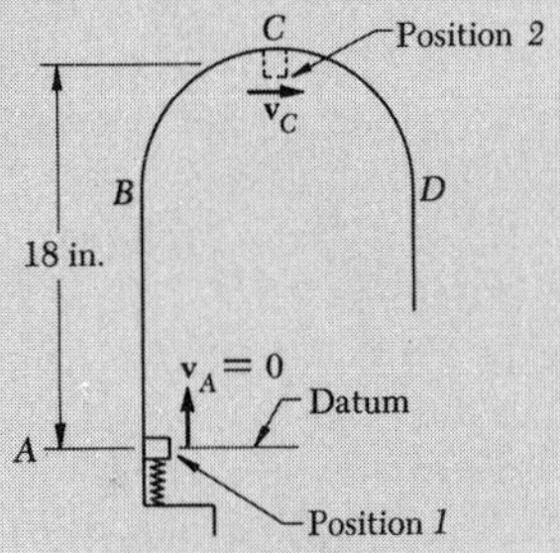

Position *1*. *Potential Energy.* Since the spring is compressed 3 in. from its undeformed position, we have

$$V_e = \tfrac{1}{2}kx^2 = \tfrac{1}{2}k(\tfrac{3}{12}\text{ ft})^2 = \tfrac{1}{32}k$$

Choosing the datum at A, we have $V_g = 0$; therefore,

$$V_1 = V_e + V_g = \tfrac{1}{32}k$$

Kinetic Energy. Since the pellet is released from rest, $v_A = 0$ and we have $T_1 = 0$.

Position *2*. *Potential Energy.* The spring is now undeformed; thus $V_e = 0$. Since the pellet is 18 in. above the datum,

$$V_g = Wy = (\tfrac{1}{2}\text{ lb})(\tfrac{18}{12}\text{ ft}) = 0.75\text{ ft-lb}$$
$$V_2 = V_e + V_g = 0.75\text{ ft-lb}$$

Kinetic Energy. Using the value of v_C^2 obtained above, we write

$$T_2 = \frac{1}{2}\frac{W}{g}v_C^2 = \frac{1}{2}\frac{0.50}{g}(\tfrac{1}{2}g) = 0.125\text{ ft-lb}$$

Conservation of Energy. Applying the principle of conservation of energy between positions *1* and *2*, we write

$$T_1 + V_1 = T_2 + V_2$$
$$0 + \tfrac{1}{32}k = 0.125 + 0.75$$
$$k = (0.875)(32) = 28\text{ lb/ft}$$

The required minimum value of k is therefore

$$k = 28\text{ lb/ft} = 2.33\text{ lb/in.} \blacktriangleleft$$

PROBLEMS

13.41. Knowing that the relation between the force and deflection of a given nonlinear spring is $F = kx(1 + cx^2)$, (*a*) derive an expression for the potential energy of the spring, (*b*) compute the values of k and c, if $F = 11$ lb when $x = 1$ in., and $F = 28$ lb when $x = 2$ in.

13.42. A ball of weight W is attached to the spring AB and to the rod BC. The spring has a constant k and is undeformed when $\theta = 0$. Express the potential energy of the ball with respect (*a*) to the spring, (*b*) to gravity (place datum at C).

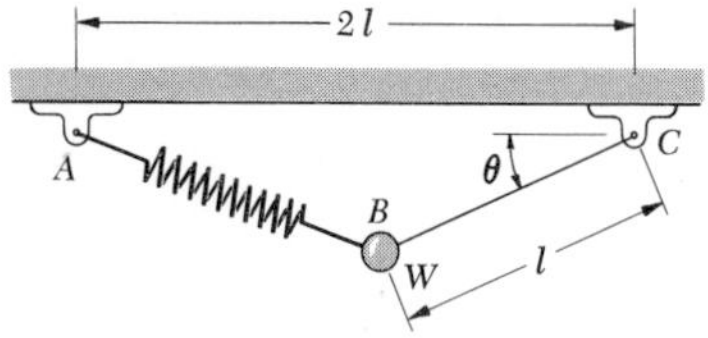

FIG. P 13.42

13.43. Prove that a force $\mathbf{F}(x,y,z)$ is conservative if, and only if, the following relations are satisfied:

$$\frac{\partial F_x}{\partial y} = \frac{\partial F_y}{\partial x} \qquad \frac{\partial F_y}{\partial z} = \frac{\partial F_z}{\partial y} \qquad \frac{\partial F_z}{\partial x} = \frac{\partial F_x}{\partial z}$$

13.44. The force $\mathbf{F} = (x\mathbf{i} + y\mathbf{j})/(x^2 + y^2)$ acts on the particle $P(x,y)$ which moves in the xy plane. (*a*) Using the first of the relations derived in Prob. 13.43, prove that $\mathbf{F}$ is a conservative force. (*b*) Determine the potential function $V(x,y)$ associated with $\mathbf{F}$.

13.45. The force $\mathbf{F} = (x\mathbf{i} + y\mathbf{j} + z\mathbf{k})/(x^2 + y^2 + z^2)^{3/2}$ acts on the particle $P(x,y,z)$ which moves in space. (*a*) Using the relations derived in Prob. 13.43, prove that $\mathbf{F}$ is a conservative force. (*b*) Determine the potential function $V(x,y,z)$ associated with $\mathbf{F}$.

13.46. The force $\mathbf{F} = (x^2\mathbf{i} + y^2\mathbf{j} + z^2\mathbf{k})/(x^3 + y^3 + z^3)$ acts on the particle $P(x,y,z)$ which moves in space. (*a*) Using the relations derived in Prob. 13.43, prove that $\mathbf{F}$ is a conservative force. (*b*) Determine the potential function $V(x,y,z)$ associated with $\mathbf{F}$.

13.47. The force $\mathbf{F} = ky\mathbf{i}$ acts on the particle $P(x,y)$ which moves in the xy plane. Prove that $\mathbf{F}$ is a nonconservative force and determine the work of $\mathbf{F}$ when P describes in counterclockwise sense the square of vertices A, B, C, and D.

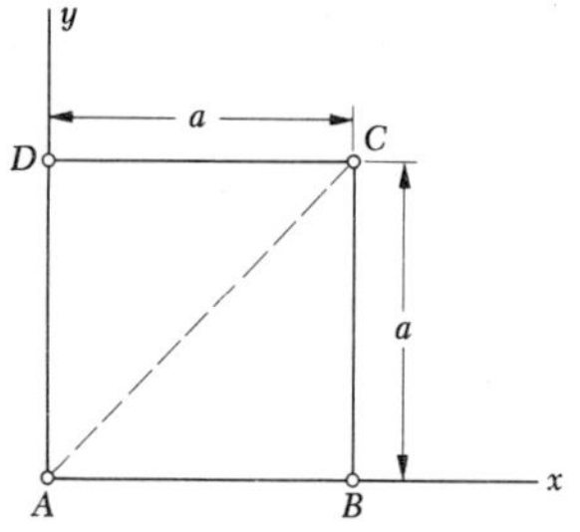

FIG. P 13.47 AND P 13.48

13.48. The force $\mathbf{F} = x^2y\mathbf{i} + xy^2\mathbf{j}$ acts on the particle $P(x,y)$ which moves in the xy plane. Prove that $\mathbf{F}$ is a nonconservative force and determine the work of $\mathbf{F}$ as it moves from A to C along each of the paths ABC, ADC, and AC.

13.49. Two blocks A and B connected by a cord are released from rest in the position shown. Neglecting the effect of friction, determine the maximum velocity attained by block B.

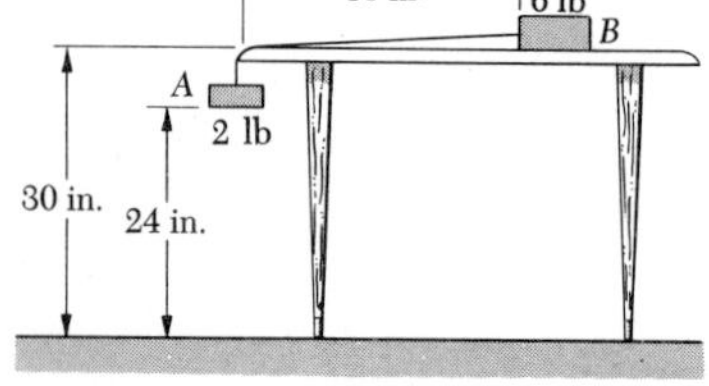

FIG. P 13.49

13.50. In Prob. 13.49, determine the position of block A when the velocity of block B is 4 ft/sec to the left.

13.51. A collar of weight W slides without friction between two springs. If the collar is pushed until spring A is compressed 3 in. and released, determine the distance the collar will travel before coming to rest (a) if $W = 2$ lb, (b) if $W = 5$ lb.

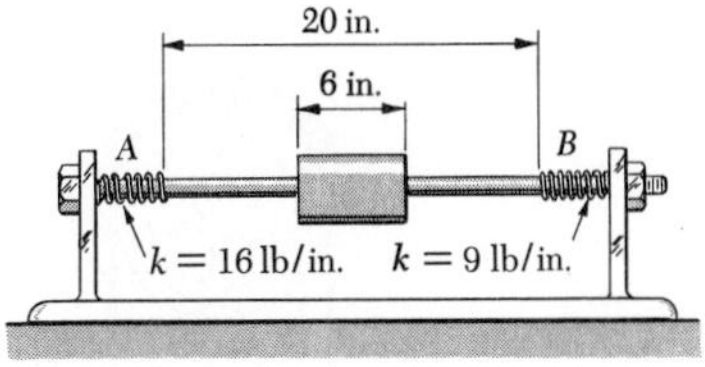

FIG. P 13.51

13.52. Solve Prob. 13.51 assuming that the frame is placed in a vertical position with spring B at the top.

13.53. A collar of weight $W = 2$ lb is attached to a spring and slides without friction along a circular rod which lies in a *horizontal* plane. The spring has a constant $k = 3$ lb/in. and is undeformed when the collar is at B. If the collar is released from rest at C, determine the speed of the collar as it passes through point B.

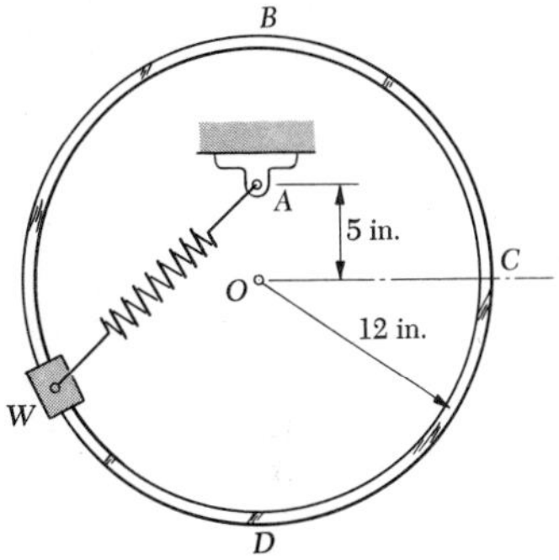

FIG. P 13.53

13.54. It is possible for the collar of Prob. 13.53 to have a continuous, although nonuniform, motion along the rod. If the speed of the collar at B is to be twice the speed of the collar at D, determine (a) the required speed at D, (b) the corresponding speed at C.

13.55. Assuming that the circular rod of Prob. 13.53 lies in a *vertical* plane with point B directly above point D, determine (a) the value of the spring constant k for which the speed at B and at D is 8 ft/sec, (b) the corresponding speed at C.

13.56. The 2-lb collar slides without friction along the horizontal rod. Knowing that the spring has a constant $k = 3$ lb/in. and is unstretched in the position shown, determine the required speed v_0 if it is to reach point C.

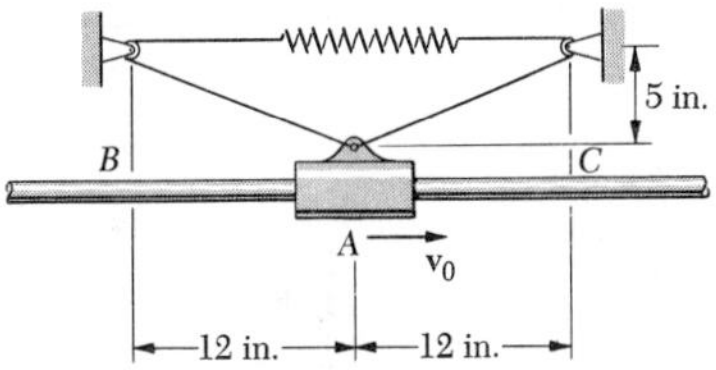

FIG. P 13.56 AND P 13.57

13.57. The 2-lb collar slides without friction along the horizontal rod. Knowing that the constant of the spring is 3 lb/in. and that $v_0 = 12$ ft/sec, determine the required spring tension in the position shown if the speed of the collar is to be 8 ft/sec at point C.

13.58. The ball of Prob. 13.42 is released from rest when $\theta = 0$. If $W = kl$, determine the velocity of the ball when $\theta = 45°$.

13.59. A particle is released from rest at A on the surface of a smooth circular cylinder of radius r. The particle slides to a point B where it leaves the surface of the cylinder. Derive an expression relating the angles θ_0 and θ_1.

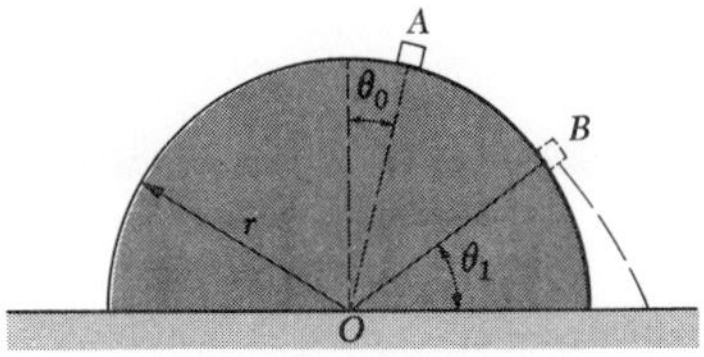

FIG. P 13.59

13.60. The particle of Prob. 13.59 is released from the position $\theta_0 = 0$. Determine (a) the value of θ_1 defining the point B where the particle leaves the cylinder, (b) the distance from the center of the cylinder O to the point where the particle strikes the floor, knowing that $r = 3$ ft.

13.61. In Prob. 13.53, determine the force exerted on the collar as it passes through point B.

13.62. The collar of Prob. 13.53 is released from rest at point D. Determine the horizontal component of the force exerted by the rod on the collar as the collar passes through point C. Show that the force is independent of the weight of the collar.

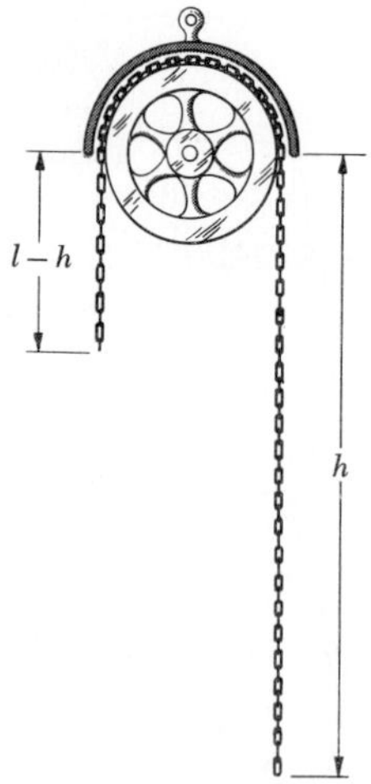

FIG. P 13.63

13.63. A chain weighing w lb/ft and of length l ft rests over a small pulley of negligible mass. If the chain is released in the position shown ($h > \frac{1}{2}l$), determine the velocity of the chain when the end of the chain leaves the pulley. Also determine the maximum possible final velocity by letting h approach $\frac{1}{2}l$.

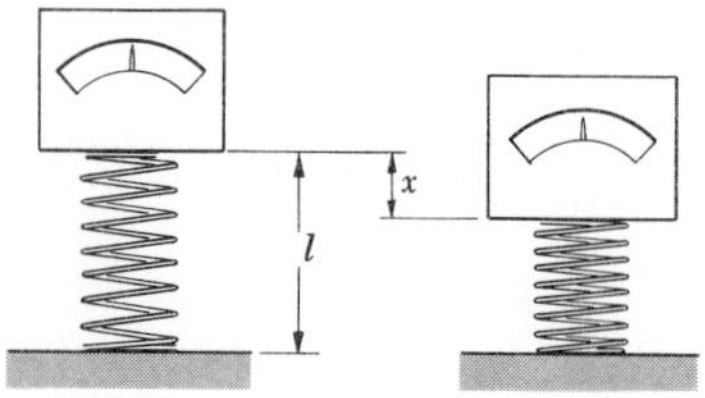

FIG. P 13.64

13.64. A delicate instrument weighing 8 lb is placed on a spring of length l so that its base is just touching the undeformed spring. The instrument is then inadvertently released from that position. Determine the maximum deflection x of the spring and the maximum force exerted by the spring if the constant of the spring is $k = 10$ lb/in.

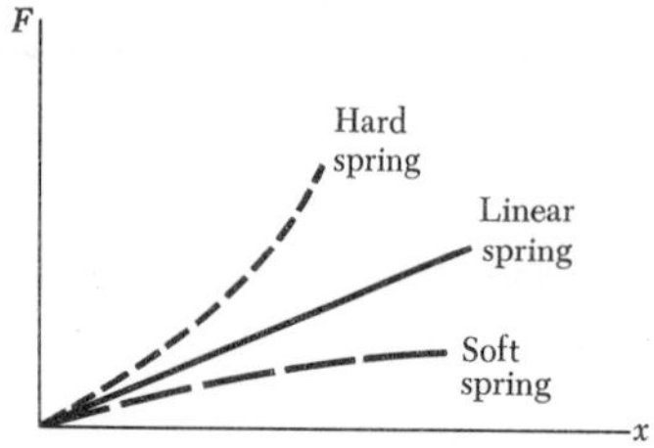

FIG. P 13.65

13.65. Nonlinear springs are classified as hard or soft, depending upon the curvature of their force-deflection curves (see figure). Solve Prob. 13.64 assuming (*a*) that a hard spring is used, for which $F = 10x(1 + 0.1x^2)$, (*b*) that a soft spring is used, for which $F = 10x(1 - 0.1x^2)$.

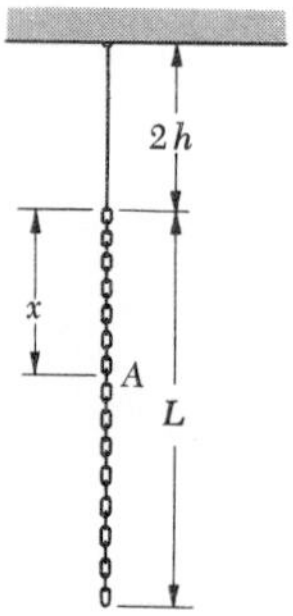

FIG. P 13.66

13.66. A chain of length L is suspended from a strip of rubber, of natural length h, and is in equilibrium in the position shown. The chain is then cut at point A. Determine the length x, knowing that the remaining portion of the chain will rise sufficiently (*a*) to allow the rubber strip to become slack, (*b*) to touch the ceiling.

13.67. Show, by setting $r = R + y$ in formula (13.15′) and expanding in a power series in y/R, that the expression obtained in (13.14) for the potential energy V_g due to gravity is a first-order approximation for the expression given in (13.15′). Using the same expansion, derive a second-order approximation for V_g.

13.68. Determine the escape velocity of a missile, i.e., the velocity with which it should be fired from the surface of the earth if it is to reach an infinite distance from the earth. Show that the result obtained is independent of the firing angle.

13.69. How much energy should be imparted to a 5-ton satellite in order to place it in a circular orbit at an altitude of (*a*) 300 miles, (*b*) 3,000 miles?

13.70. Determine the minimum amount of energy which should be imparted to a space vehicle of mass m (*a*) to place it in a low-level circular orbit around the earth, (*b*) to send it to another planet. Why would it be more convenient to originate space trips from a station circling the earth?

13.71. A satellite of mass m describes a circular orbit around the earth. Express (*a*) its potential energy, (*b*) its kinetic energy, and (*c*) its total energy as a function of the radius r of the orbit, assuming that both its potential and its kinetic energies had a value equal to zero when the satellite was on its launching pad. Plot the kinetic, potential, and total energies against r.

***13.72.** Knowing that the satellite of Prob. 12.89 weighs 500 lb, determine (*a*) the energy imparted to the satellite during the original launching operation, (*b*) the additional energy imparted to the satellite in placing it in its final circular orbit.

13.73. Show that the ratio of the potential and kinetic energies of an electron, as it enters the plates of the cathode-ray tube of Prob. 12.69, is equal to $d\delta/lL$. (Place the datum at the surface of the positive plate.)

13.8. Power and Efficiency. *Power* is defined as the time rate at which work is done. In the selection of a motor or engine, power is a much more important criterion than the actual amount of work to be performed. A small motor or a large power plant may both be used to do a given amount of work; but the small motor may require a month to do the work done by the power plant in a matter of minutes. If ΔU is the work done during the time interval Δt, then the average power during this time interval is

$$\text{Average power} = \frac{\Delta U}{\Delta t}$$

Letting Δt approach zero, we obtain at the limit

$$\text{Power} = \frac{dU}{dt} \tag{13.23}$$

Substituting the scalar product $\mathbf{F} \cdot d\mathbf{r}$ for dU, we may also write

$$\text{Power} = \frac{dU}{dt} = \frac{\mathbf{F} \cdot d\mathbf{r}}{dt}$$

and, recalling that $d\mathbf{r}/dt$ represents the velocity $\mathbf{v}$ of the point of application of $\mathbf{F}$,

$$\text{Power} = \mathbf{F} \cdot \mathbf{v} \tag{13.24}$$

Several units are used to measure power; mechanical power

is usually measured in *horsepower* (hp) and electrical power in *watts* or *kilowatts* (kw). These units are defined as follows:

$$\begin{aligned} 1 \text{ hp} &= 550 \text{ ft-lb/sec} = 33{,}000 \text{ ft-lb/min} \\ 1 \text{ watt} &= 1 \text{ joule/sec} = 1 \text{ newton-m/sec} \\ 1 \text{ kw} &= 1{,}000 \text{ watts} \end{aligned}$$

We may check the following relations:

$$\begin{aligned} 1 \text{ hp} &= 746 \text{ watts} = 0.746 \text{ kw} \\ 1 \text{ kw} &= 737 \text{ ft-lb/sec} \end{aligned}$$

Although many specific formulas exist, from which the horsepower or kilowatt requirements may be computed for given applications, it is advisable to compute the power directly from its definition. For instance, when work is done at a constant rate, we may determine the work done during a given time interval and note that each 550 ft-lb of work done per second is equivalent to 1 hp.

The *mechanical efficiency* of a machine was defined in Sec. 10.4 as the ratio of the output work to the input work:

$$\eta = \frac{\text{output work}}{\text{input work}} \tag{13.25}$$

This definition is based on the assumption that work is done at a constant rate. The ratio of the output to the input work is therefore equal to the ratio of the rates at which output and input work are done, and we have

$$\eta = \frac{\text{power output}}{\text{power input}} \tag{13.26}$$

Because of energy losses due to friction, the output work is always smaller than the input work, and, consequently, the power output is always smaller than the power input. The mechanical efficiency of a machine, therefore, is always less than 1.

When a machine is used to transform mechanical energy into electrical energy, or thermal energy into mechanical energy, its *over-all efficiency* may be obtained from formula (13.26). The over-all efficiency of a machine is always less than 1; it provides a measure of all the various energy losses involved (losses of electrical or thermal energy as well as frictional losses). We should note that it is necessary, before using formula (13.26), to express the power output and the power input in the same units.

SAMPLE PROBLEM 13.7

A train of total weight 800 tons starts from rest and accelerates uniformly to a speed of 30 mph in 25 sec. After reaching this speed, the train travels with constant velocity. During the entire motion the train is traveling up a 3 per cent grade, and the rolling resistance is 15 lb/ton. Determine the horsepower required as a function of time.

Solution. The two types of motion will be treated separately: for $t < 25$ sec, uniformly accelerated motion; for $t > 25$ sec, uniform motion.

Uniformly Accelerated Motion ($t < 25$ sec). *Velocity.* Since the velocity is known, we write, at $t = 0$, $v_0 = 0$; at $t = 25$ sec, $v = 30$ mph $= 44$ ft/sec.

$$v = v_0 + at \qquad 44 \text{ ft/sec} = 0 + a(25 \text{ sec}) \qquad a = 1.76 \text{ ft/sec}^2$$
$$v = +1.76t$$

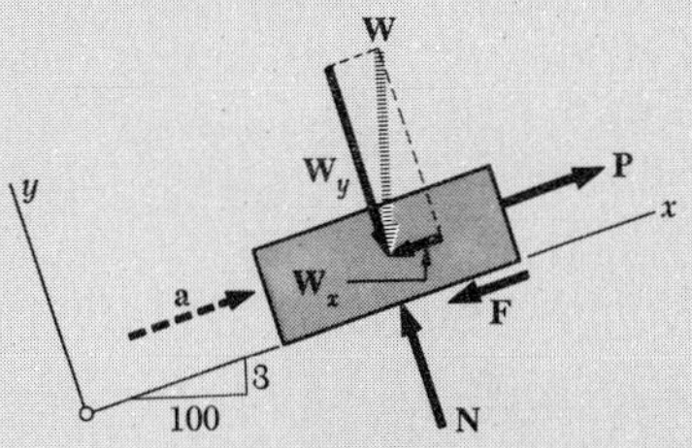

Engine Force. The magnitude of the engine force **P** may be calculated by choosing the x axis parallel to the tracks and writing $+\nearrow \Sigma F_x = ma$. The x component of the weight is

$$\mathbf{W}_x \approx \tfrac{3}{100}(800 \text{ tons})\frac{2{,}000 \text{ lb}}{1 \text{ ton}} = 48{,}000 \text{ lb} \swarrow$$

The friction force due to rolling resistance is

$$\mathbf{F} = (15 \text{ lb/ton})\,(800 \text{ tons}) = 12{,}000 \text{ lb} \swarrow$$

$$+\nearrow \Sigma F_x = ma: \qquad P - W_x - F = ma$$

$$P - 48{,}000 - 12{,}000 = \frac{(800)\,(2{,}000)}{32.2}(1.76)$$

$$P = +147{,}500 \text{ lb}$$

Horsepower. Since the power is equal to the product of the magnitudes of the force and velocity, we write

$$\text{Power} = Pv = (147{,}500)\,(1.76t)$$

$$\text{Horsepower} = \frac{Pv}{550} = \frac{(147{,}500)\,(1.76t)}{550} = 472t$$

Uniform Motion ($t > 25$ sec). *Velocity.* We have $v = 30$ mph $=$ 44 ft/sec.

Engine Force. Since v is constant, we have $a = 0$ and write

$$+\nearrow \Sigma F_x = 0: \qquad P - W_x - F = 0$$

$$P - 48{,}000 - 12{,}000 = 0 \qquad P = +60{,}000 \text{ lb}$$

$$\textit{Horsepower} = \frac{Pv}{550} = \frac{(60{,}000 \text{ lb})\,(44 \text{ ft/sec})}{550} = 4{,}800$$

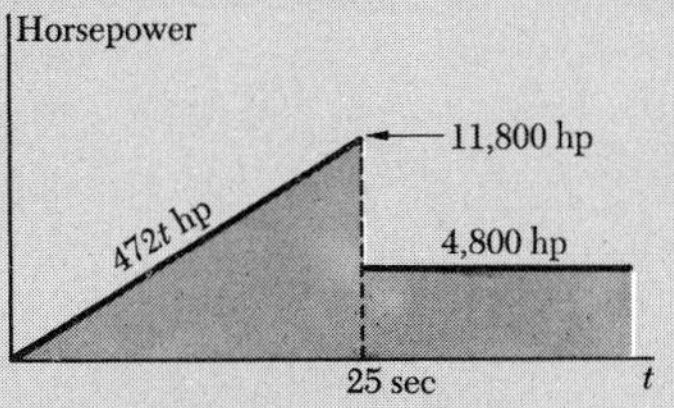

Horsepower Required vs. Time. For $t < 25$ sec, the horsepower required increases linearly with t, reaching, at $t = 25$ sec, a maximum value.

For $t > 25$ sec, the train is no longer accelerated, and the horsepower required is constant.

PROBLEMS

13.74. A 150-lb man and a 175-lb man run up a flight of stairs in 4 sec. If the flight of stairs is 12 ft high, determine the average horsepower required by each man.

13.75. A utility hoist can lift its maximum allowable load of 7,000 lb at the rate of 65 ft/min. Knowing that the hoist is run by a 20-hp engine, determine the over-all efficiency of the hoist.

13.76. Starting from rest, a 3,000-lb automobile is accelerated at a constant rate of 4 ft/sec^2 until it reaches a speed of 40 mph and then travels at a constant speed. During the entire motion, the automobile is traveling on a horizontal road, and the rolling resistance is equal to 1.8 per cent of the weight of the automobile. Determine the power required as a function of time.

13.77. Solve Prob. 13.76 assuming that the automobile travels down a 2 per cent grade.

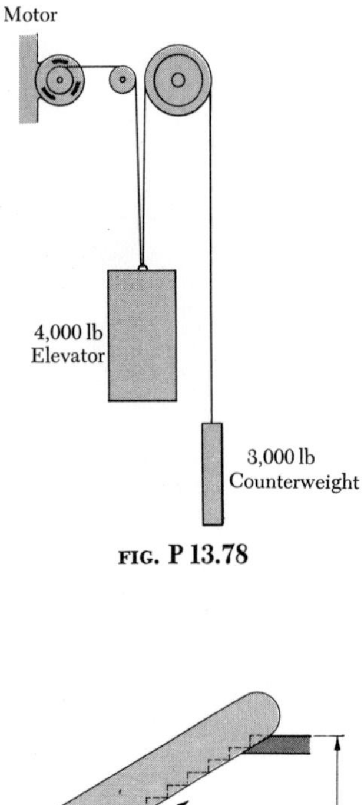

FIG. P 13.78

13.78. Determine the power required when the elevator shown (*a*) is moving upward at a constant speed of 20 ft/sec, (*b*) has an instantaneous velocity of 20 ft/sec upward and an upward acceleration of 3 ft/sec^2.

13.79. Solve Prob. 13.78 assuming that the weight of the elevator and the counterweight have both been increased by 1,000 lb.

13.80. The escalator shown is designed to transport 8,000 persons per hour at a constant speed of 90 ft/min. Assuming an average weight of 150 lb per person, determine (*a*) the average power required, (*b*) the required capacity of the motor if the mechanical efficiency is 85 per cent and if a 300 per cent overload is to be allowed.

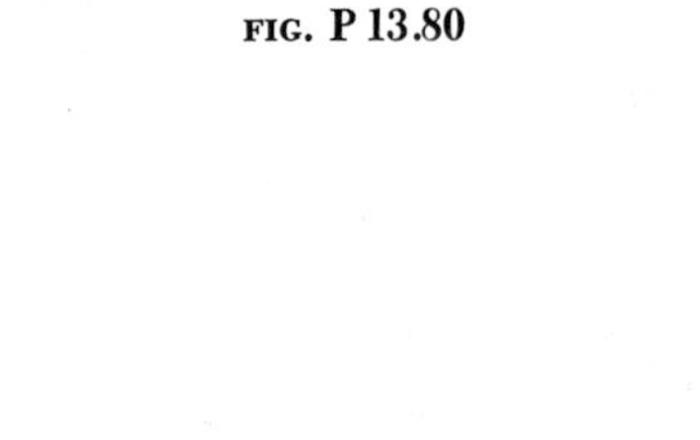

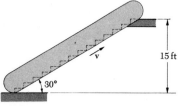

FIG. P 13.80

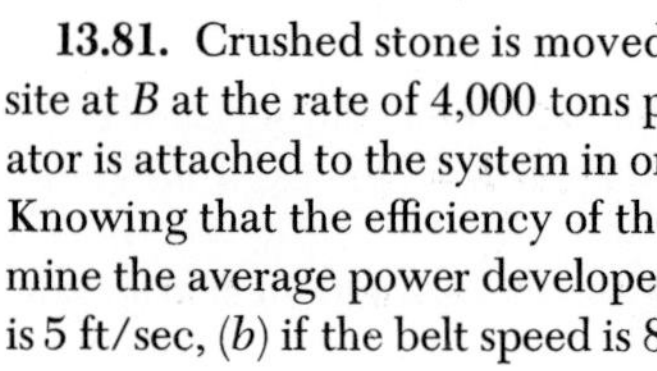

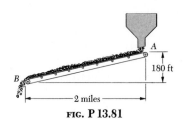

FIG. P 13.81

13.81. Crushed stone is moved from a quarry at *A* to a construction site at *B* at the rate of 4,000 tons per 8-hour period. An electric generator is attached to the system in order to maintain a constant belt speed. Knowing that the efficiency of the belt-generator system is 0.65, determine the average power developed by the generator (*a*) if the belt speed is 5 ft/sec, (*b*) if the belt speed is 8 ft/sec.

13.82. The engine of the rocket shown provides a constant vertical thrust of 60,000 lb. The rocket and fuel weigh 20,000 lb at the time of firing, and the rocket has attained a speed of 4,500 mph when the engine is cut off, after burning 12,000 lb of fuel. Determine the horsepower actually used to propel the rocket (*a*) just after firing, (*b*) just before the engine is cut off.

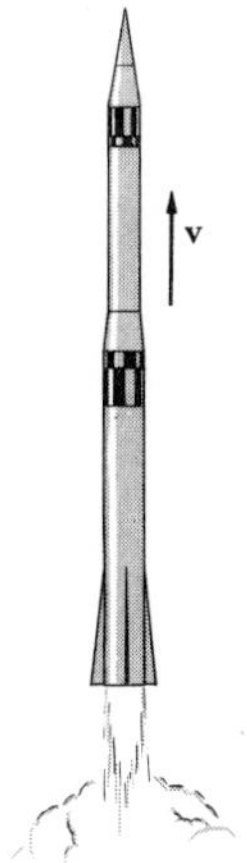

FIG. P 13.82

***13.83.** The fluid transmission of a truck of weight W permits the engine to deliver an essentially constant power P to the driving wheels. Determine the time elapsed and the distance traveled as the speed is increased from v_0 to v_1.

***13.84.** The fluid transmission of a 15-ton truck permits the engine to deliver an essentially constant power of 75 hp to the driving wheels. Determine the time required and the distance traveled as the speed of the truck is increased from 30 mph to 45 mph.

***13.85.** Determine the time required for the truck of Prob. 13.84 to increase its speed from 30 to 45 mph assuming that the truck has a rolling resistance of 20 lb/ton.

***13.86.** The frictional resistance F of a ship of weight W is known to vary as the square of the speed v of the ship and is expressed as $F = kv^2$. (*a*) Show that the power P_0 required to maintain a constant speed v_0 is $P_0 = kv_0^3$. (*b*) If the power delivered by the engine is suddenly increased to P_2 and then held constant, determine the distance that the ship will travel before reaching a given speed v_1. (The speed v_1 is chosen smaller than the constant speed v_2 which can be maintained with the power P_2.)

13.87. A $\frac{1}{2}$-oz bullet leaves a fixed rifle barrel 0.002 sec after it is fired. Knowing that the muzzle velocity is 2,800 ft/sec, determine the average power developed by the rifle. Neglect the effect of friction.

REVIEW PROBLEMS

13.88. An elevator travels upward at a constant speed of 5 ft/sec. A boy riding the elevator throws a 2-lb stone upward with a speed of 10 ft/sec *relative* to the elevator. Determine (*a*) the work done by the boy in throwing the stone, (*b*) the difference in the values of the kinetic energy of the stone before and after it was thrown. (*c*) Why are the values obtained in parts *a* and *b* not the same?

13.89. The weight C and the block A are both moving to the left with a velocity $\mathbf{v}_0$ when the block is suddenly stopped by the wall. Determine the smallest velocity $\mathbf{v}_0$ for which the weight C will swing in a full circle about the pivot B (*a*) if BC is a slender rod of negligible weight, (*b*) if BC is a cord.

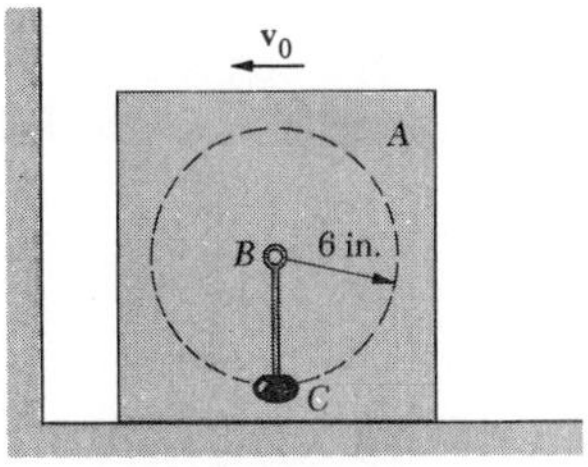

FIG. P 13.89

13.90. The frictional resistance of a ship is known to vary directly as the 1.8 power of the speed v of the ship. A single tugboat can tow the ship at a constant speed of 4 mph by exerting a constant force of 50,000 lb. (*a*) Determine the horsepower delivered by the single tugboat. (*b*) Three tugboats are then used to tow the same ship. If each tugboat exerts a towing force of 50,000 lb, determine the resulting speed and the horsepower delivered by each tugboat. (*c*) If each of the three tugboats can deliver only the horsepower delivered by the single tugboat of part *a*, determine the resulting speed and the force exerted by each tugboat.

13.91. As the bracket *ABC* is slowly rotated, the 12-lb block starts to slide toward the spring when $\theta = 15°$. The maximum deflection of the spring is observed to be 2 in. Determine the values of the coefficients of static and kinetic friction.

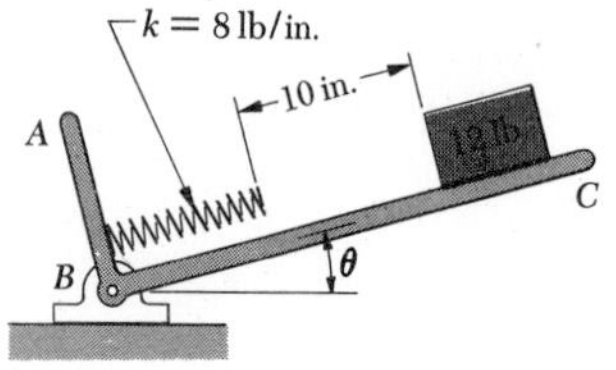

FIG. P 13.91

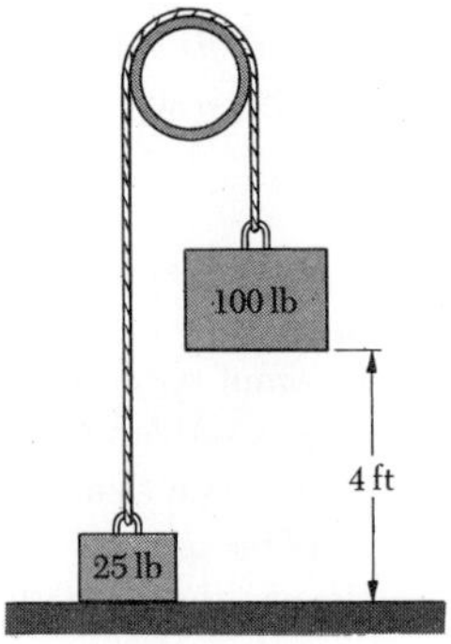

FIG. P 13.93

13.92. Using the methods of Chap. 13, solve Prob. 12.40.

13.93. Two weights are attached to a rope which passes over a fixed pipe as shown. The coefficient of friction between the rope and the pipe is 0.30. Knowing that the system is released from rest in the position shown, determine the velocity of the 100-lb weight as it strikes the floor.

13.94. Determine the energy which must be imparted to a missile of mass m (*a*) to shoot it vertically to a height equal to the radius R of the earth, (*b*) to place it in a circular orbit of radius $2R$.

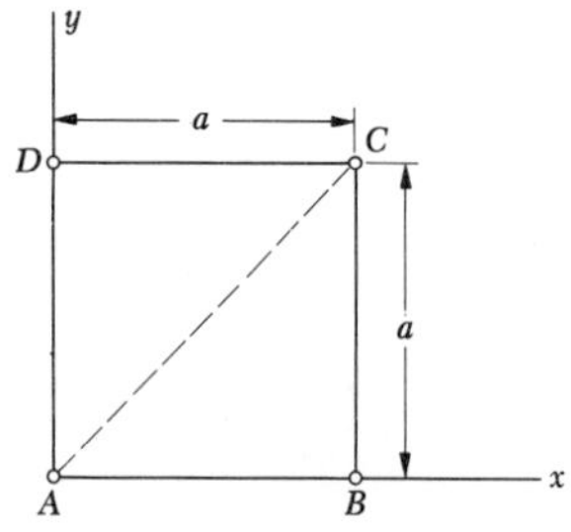

FIG. P 13.95

13.95. The force $\mathbf{F} = (y + 2)\mathbf{i} + (2x - 2)\mathbf{j}$ acts on the particle $P(x,y)$ which moves in the xy plane. Determine the work of **F** knowing that P is initially at point A and moves along (*a*) the path *ABC*, (*b*) the path *AC*, (*c*) the path *ADC*.

13.96. Two portions AB and BC of the same elastic cord are connected as shown. The portion of cord BC supports a load W while, initially, the portion AB is under no tension. Determine the maximum tension which will develop in the entire cord after the stick DE suddenly breaks. (Assume that the tensions in AB and BC are instantaneously equalized after the stick breaks and that the elongation of the cord is small compared to L.)

13.97. A toy spring gun is used to shoot 1-oz bullets vertically upward. The undeformed length of the spring is 5 in.; it is compressed to a length of 1 in. when the gun is ready to be shot and expands to a length of 3 in. as the bullet leaves the gun. A force of 8 lb is required to maintain the spring in firing position when the length of the spring is 1 in. Determine (a) the velocity of the bullet as it leaves the gun, (b) the maximum height reached by the bullet.

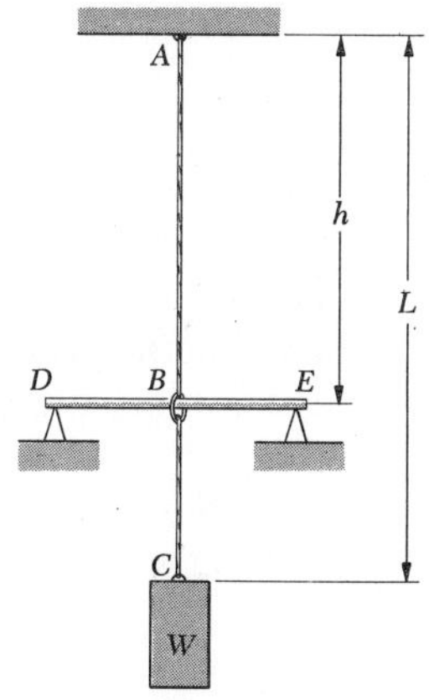

FIG. P 13.96

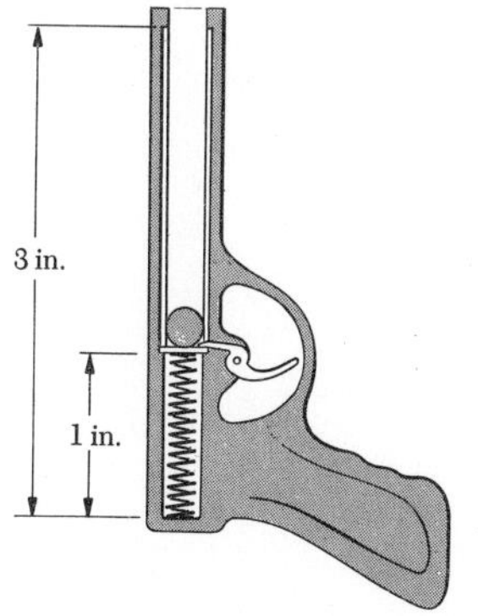

FIG. P 13.97

13.98. A 45-lb package is projected up a 15° incline with an initial speed of 40 ft/sec. Knowing that the package returns to its original position with a speed of 20 ft/sec, determine (a) the distance the package moved up the incline, (b) the coefficient of friction between the package and the incline.

13.99. A package of weight W is released from rest at A and swings in a vertical plane at the end of a 12-ft rope. The rope will break when the tension in the rope is equal to twice the weight of the package. (a) Determine the difference in elevation h between point A and point B where the rope will break. (b) How far from the vertical wall will the package strike the floor?

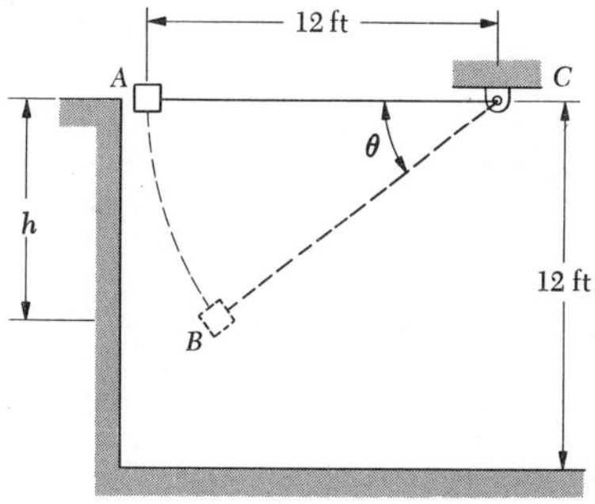

FIG. P 13.99

14. KINETICS OF PARTICLES: IMPULSE AND MOMENTUM

14.1. Principle of Impulse and Momentum. A third basic method for the solution of problems dealing with the motion of particles will be considered in this chapter. This method is based on the principle of impulse and momentum and is of particular interest in problems involving force, mass, velocity, and time.

Consider a particle of mass m acted upon by a force $\mathbf{F}$. Substituting $\mathbf{a} = d\mathbf{v}/dt$ in Newton's second law $\mathbf{F} = m\mathbf{a}$, we write

$$\mathbf{F} = m\frac{d\mathbf{v}}{dt}$$

or, since the mass m of the particle is constant,

$$\mathbf{F} = \frac{d}{dt}(m\mathbf{v}) \tag{14.1}$$

The vector $m\mathbf{v}$ is called the *linear momentum*, or simply the *momentum*, of the particle. It has the same direction as the velocity of the particle and its magnitude is expressed in lb-sec; we check that

$$mv = \frac{\text{lb-sec}^2}{\text{ft}}\,\frac{\text{ft}}{\text{sec}} = \text{lb-sec}$$

Equation (14.1) expresses that *the force* $\mathbf{F}$ *acting on the particle is equal to the rate of change of the momentum of the particle.* It is in this form that the second law of motion was originally stated by Newton.

Multiplying both sides of Eq. (14.1) by dt and integrating from a time t_1 to a time t_2, we write

$$\mathbf{F}\,dt = d(m\mathbf{v})$$

$$\int_{t_1}^{t_2} \mathbf{F}\,dt = m\mathbf{v}_2 - m\mathbf{v}_1$$

or, transposing the last term,

$$m\mathbf{v}_1 + \int_{t_1}^{t_2} \mathbf{F}\,dt = m\mathbf{v}_2 \tag{14.2}$$

The integral in Eq. (14.2) is a vector known as the *linear impulse*, or simply the *impulse*, of the force **F** during the interval of time considered. Resolving **F** into rectangular components, we write

$$\mathbf{Imp}_{1\to 2} = \int_{t_1}^{t_2} \mathbf{F}\,dt$$

$$= \mathbf{i}\int_{t_1}^{t_2} F_x\,dt + \mathbf{j}\int_{t_1}^{t_2} F_y\,dt + \mathbf{k}\int_{t_1}^{t_2} F_z\,dt \tag{14.3}$$

and note that the components of the impulse of the force **F** are, respectively, equal to the areas under the curves obtained by plotting the components F_x, F_y, and F_z against t (Fig. 14.1). In the case of a force **F** of constant magnitude and direction, the impulse is represented by the vector $\mathbf{F}(t_2 - t_1)$, which has the same direction as **F**. We easily check that the magnitude of the impulse of a force is expressed in lb-sec.

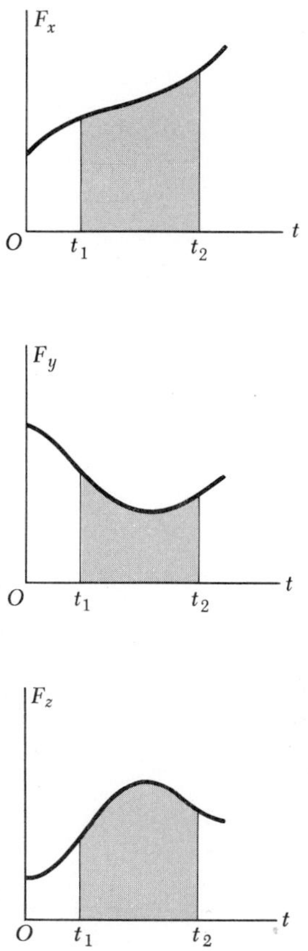

FIG. 14.1

Equation (14.2) expresses that, when a particle is acted upon by a force **F** during a given time interval, *the final momentum* $m\mathbf{v}_2$ *of the particle may be obtained by adding vectorially its initial momentum* $m\mathbf{v}_1$ *and the impulse of the force* **F** *during the time interval considered* (Fig. 14.2). We write

$$m\mathbf{v}_1 + \mathbf{Imp}_{1\to 2} = m\mathbf{v}_2 \tag{14.4}$$

We note that, while kinetic energy and work are scalar quantities, momentum and impulse are vector quantities. To obtain

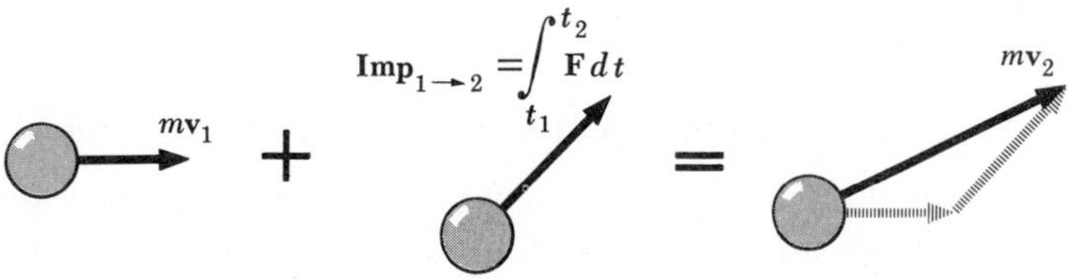

FIG. 14.2

an analytic solution, it is thus necessary to replace Eq. (14.4) by the equivalent component equations

$$\begin{aligned}(mv_x)_1 + \int_{t_1}^{t_2} F_x\,dt &= (mv_x)_2\\ (mv_y)_1 + \int_{t_1}^{t_2} F_y\,dt &= (mv_y)_2\\ (mv_z)_1 + \int_{t_1}^{t_2} F_z\,dt &= (mv_z)_2\end{aligned} \tag{14.5}$$

When several forces act on a particle, the impulse of each of the forces must be considered. We have

$$m\mathbf{v}_1 + \Sigma\,\mathbf{Imp}_{1\to2} = m\mathbf{v}_2 \tag{14.6}$$

Again, the equation obtained represents a relation between vector quantities; in the actual solution of a problem, it should be replaced by the corresponding component equations.

14.2. Systems of Particles. When a problem involves the motion of several particles, each particle may be considered separately and Eq. (14.6) may be written for each particle. We may also add vectorially the momenta of all the particles and the impulses of all the forces involved. We write then

$$\Sigma m\mathbf{v}_1 + \Sigma\,\mathbf{Imp}_{1\to2} = \Sigma m\mathbf{v}_2 \tag{14.7}$$

But since the internal forces occur by pairs of equal and opposite forces having the same line of action, their sum is zero and we need consider only the impulses of the external forces. We have

$$\Sigma m\mathbf{v}_1 + \Sigma \int_{t_1}^{t_2} \mathbf{F}_{\text{ext}}\,dt = \Sigma m\mathbf{v}_2 \tag{14.8}$$

or

$$\Sigma m\mathbf{v}_1 + \Sigma\,\mathbf{Ext\ Imp}_{1\to2} = \Sigma m\mathbf{v}_2 \tag{14.9}$$

Equation (14.9) may be written in a modified form if the mass center G of the system of particles is considered. Recalling from Sec. 12.5 the relation (12.6), we write

$$\Sigma m\mathbf{v} = (\Sigma m)\bar{\mathbf{v}} \tag{14.10}$$

where $\bar{\mathbf{v}}$ is the velocity of G. Substituting into (14.9), we obtain

$$(\Sigma m)\bar{\mathbf{v}}_1 + \Sigma\,\mathbf{Ext\ Imp}_{1\to2} = (\Sigma m)\bar{\mathbf{v}}_2 \tag{14.11}$$

We note that Eq. (14.11) is identical with the equation we would obtain for a particle of mass Σm acted upon by all the external forces. We thus check that the mass center of a system of particles moves as if the entire mass of the system and all the external forces were concentrated at that point. We should keep in mind, however, that Eqs. (14.10) and (14.11) *do not relate* the moments of the impulses and momenta involved. Therefore, Eq. (14.10) *does not express* that the momenta of the particles of the system are equivalent to a vector $(\Sigma m)\bar{\mathbf{v}}$ attached at the mass center G. Indeed, as we shall see in Chap. 17, the resultant of the momenta of the particles of a system does not in general pass through the mass center of the system.

SAMPLE PROBLEM 14.1

A 40-ton railroad car is moving down a 2° incline with a speed of 4 ft/sec. The rolling resistance of the car is 15 lb/ton. If a force **P** of magnitude 4,000 lb is applied as shown, determine the time required to stop the car.

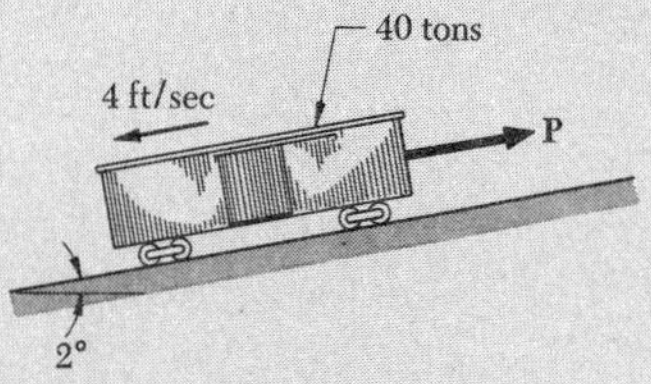

Solution. The rolling resistance of the car is equivalent to a force **F** of magnitude

$$F = (15\text{ lb/ton})(40\text{ tons}) = 600\text{ lb}$$

The forces acting on the car are its weight **W**, the applied force **P**, the normal reaction **N**, and the rolling resistance **F**. Since the magnitude and direction of each force are constant, the impulse of each force is equal to the product of the force and the time interval t.

Principle of Impulse and Momentum. The momentum at $t_1 = 0$ is shown in the first sketch, the impulses of the forces during the time interval t are shown in the second sketch, and the momentum at $t_2 = t$ is shown in the third sketch.

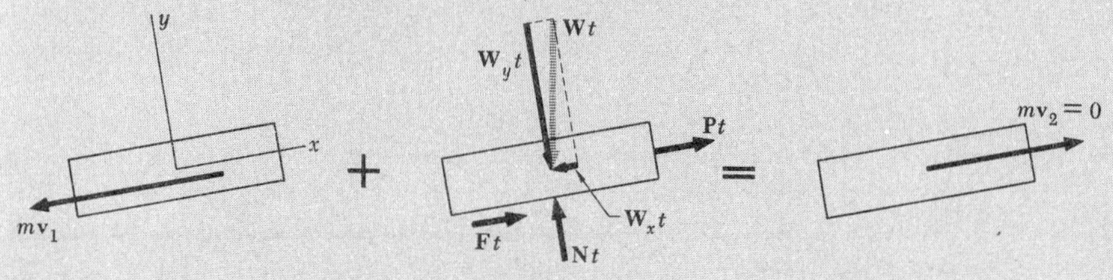

Applying the principle of impulse and momentum, we write

$$m\mathbf{v}_1 + \Sigma\, \mathbf{Imp}_{1\to 2} = m\mathbf{v}_2$$

$+\nearrow x$ components: $\quad -mv_1 - W_x t + Pt + Ft = 0$

$$-\frac{80{,}000}{32.2}(4\text{ ft/sec}) - 80{,}000\,(\sin 2°)t + 4{,}000t + 600t = 0$$

$$t = 5.50\text{ sec} \blacktriangleleft$$

PROBLEMS

14.1. A stone weighing 5 lb is dropped from rest and strikes the ground with a velocity of 90 ft/sec. (*a*) Determine the momentum of the stone as it strikes the ground and the time of fall. (*b*) Solve part *a* assuming that the same stone is dropped on the moon. (Acceleration of gravity on the moon = 5.31 ft/sec^2.)

14.2. A 50-lb satellite has been placed in a circular orbit 1,548 miles above the surface of the earth. The acceleration of gravity at this elevation is 16.7 ft/sec^2. Determine the momentum of the satellite, knowing that its orbital speed is 15,000 mph.

14.3. A 2,800-lb automobile is moving at a speed of 45 mph when the brakes are fully applied, causing all four wheels to skid. Determine the time required to stop the automobile (*a*) on concrete ($\mu = 0.80$), (*b*) on ice ($\mu = 0.10$).

PAGE 510

$\int F\,dt = mv_2 - mv_1$

14.4. A tugboat exerts a constant force of 15 tons on a 50,000-ton ocean liner. Neglecting the frictional resistance of the water, determine the time required to increase the speed of the liner (*a*) from 1 mph to 2 mph, (*b*) from 2 mph to 3 mph.

14.5. A 10-lb particle is acted upon by the force $\mathbf{F} = 2t\mathbf{i} + (3 - t)\mathbf{j} + t^3\mathbf{k}$ (lb). Knowing that the velocity of the particle at $t = 0$ is $\mathbf{v} = -24\mathbf{i} + 15\mathbf{j} - 60\mathbf{k}$ (ft/sec), determine the velocity of the particle at $t = 4$ sec.

14.6. A 2-lb particle is acted upon by a force $\mathbf{F}$ of magnitude $F = 14t^2$ (lb) which acts in the direction of the unit vector $\boldsymbol{\lambda} = \frac{2}{7}\mathbf{i} + \frac{3}{7}\mathbf{j} + \frac{6}{7}\mathbf{k}$. Knowing that the velocity of the particle at $t = 0$ is $\mathbf{v} = 180\mathbf{i} + 540\mathbf{j}$ (ft/sec), determine the velocity when $t = 3$ sec.

14.7. A 5-lb particle is acted upon by the force $\mathbf{F} = (4 - 3t)\mathbf{i} + (2 - t^2)\mathbf{j} + (2 + t)\mathbf{k}$ (lb). Knowing that at $t = 0$ the velocity of the particle is $\mathbf{v} = 150\mathbf{i} + 100\mathbf{j} - 250\mathbf{k}$ (ft/sec), determine (*a*) the time at which the velocity of the particle is parallel to the *yz* plane, (*b*) the corresponding velocity of the particle.

14.8. A particle of mass *m* is acted upon by the force $\mathbf{F} = F_1 \cos \pi t\,\mathbf{i} + F_2 \cos \pi t\,\mathbf{j} + F_3 \cos \pi t\,\mathbf{k}$. Knowing that the particle starts from rest at $t = 0$, determine the velocity of the particle when (*a*) $t = \frac{1}{2}$ sec, (*b*) $t = 1$ sec.

14.9. A light train made of two cars travels at 60 mph. The first car weighs 15 tons, and the second car weighs 20 tons. When the brakes are applied, a constant braking force of 5,000 lb is applied to each car. Determine (*a*) the time required for the train to stop after the brakes are applied, (*b*) the force in the coupling between the cars while the train is slowing down.

14.10. At a time $t = 0$ when the velocity of the 50-lb counterweight is 10 ft/sec downward, a force **T** of magnitude 80 lb is applied as shown. Determine the time t at which the 50-lb counterweight has (*a*) no velocity, (*b*) a velocity of 10 ft/sec upward.

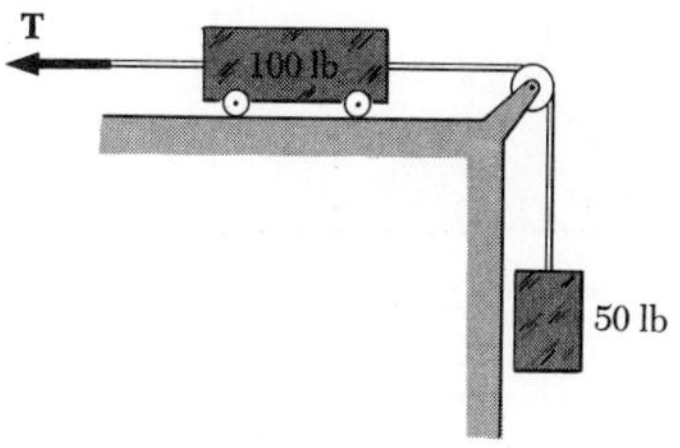

FIG. **P 14.10**

14.11. Solve Prob. 14.10 assuming that the wheels of the 100-lb car are locked and skid along the horizontal surface ($\mu = 0.20$).

14.12. Using the principle of impulse and momentum, solve Prob. 12.17*b*.

14.13. Using the principle of impulse and momentum, solve Prob. 12.21*a*.

14.14. Using the principle of impulse and momentum, solve Prob. 12.22*a*.

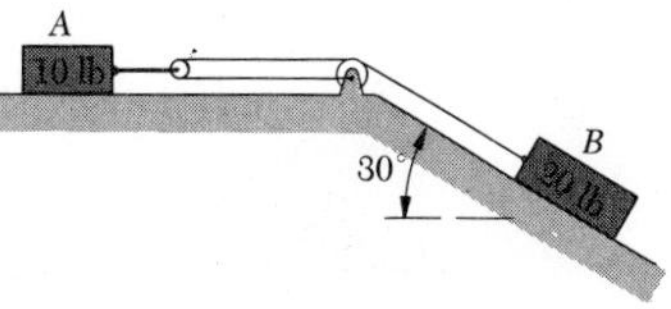

FIG. **P 14.15**

14.15. Blocks *A* and *B* slide on lubricated surfaces for which μ may be assumed equal to 0.10. Knowing that the system is released from rest, determine the velocity of block *B* after 5 sec.

14.16. Solve Prob. 14.15 assuming that block *A* weighs 20 lb and block *B* weighs 10 lb.

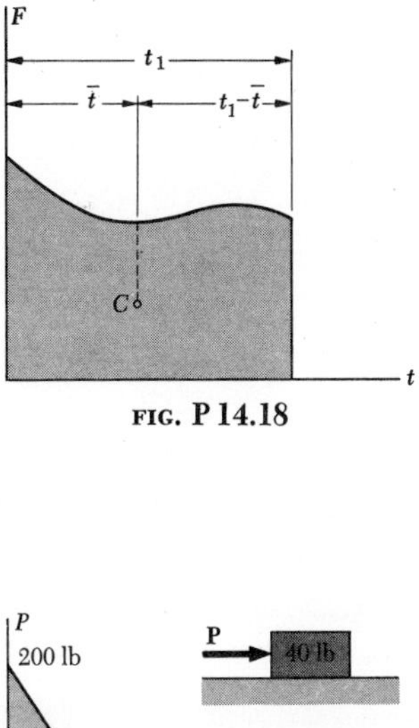

FIG. **P 14.18**

***14.17.** A grain of sand of mass m is released from rest in water. It is acted upon by a constant force of magnitude Q (equal to its submerged weight) and by a frictional force of magnitude kv, where k is a constant and v is the speed of the particle. Using the principle of impulse and momentum ($F\,dt = m\,dv$), show that, if at $t = 0$, $v_0 = 0$, the speed at any time t is $v = (Q/k)(1 - e^{-(k/m)t})$. Further show that the resultant of the forces acting on the grain at any time t is $Qe^{-(k/m)t}$.

***14.18.** A particle of mass m moves in a straight line under the action of a force of magnitude F which varies with respect to the time t as shown. Derive the following expressions for the motion of the particle: $v_1 = v_0 + A/m$; $s_1 = s_0 + v_0 t_1 + (t_1 - \bar{t})A/m$, where A is the area under the F–t curve between $t = 0$ and $t = t_1$ and C is the centroid of the same area.

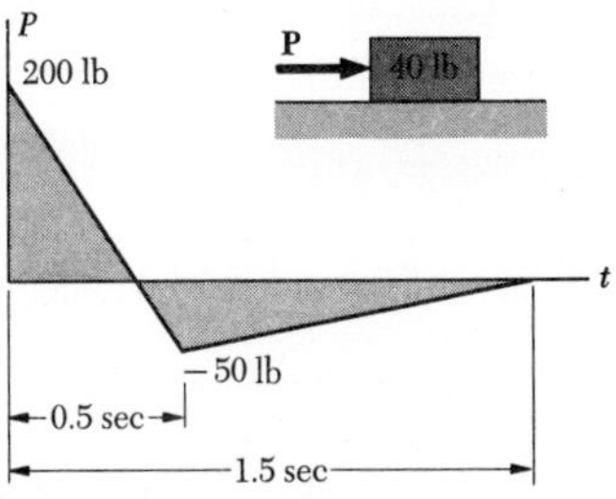

FIG. **P 14.19**

14.19. A block weighing 40 lb is initially at rest and is subjected to a force **P** which varies as shown. Neglecting the effect of friction, determine (*a*) the maximum speed attained by the block, (*b*) the speed of the block at $t = 1.5$ sec.

14.20. Solve Prob. 14.19 assuming that $\mu = 0.25$ between the block and the surface.

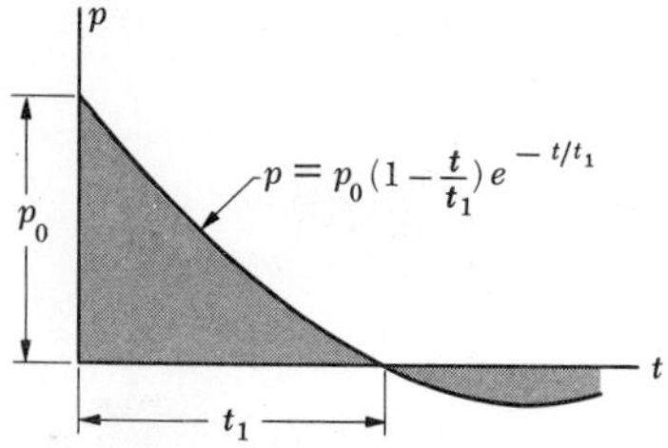

FIG. P 14.21

*14.21. The explosion of a bomb creates a pressure wave which travels in all directions from the point of explosion. The graph shown represents the pressure-time curve at a large distance from the point of explosion of an atomic bomb. Show that the total positive impulse per unit area is p_0t_1/e and that the total impulse per unit area from $t = 0$ to $t = \infty$ is zero. (*Hint.* $\lim_{t\to\infty} te^{-t} = 0$.)

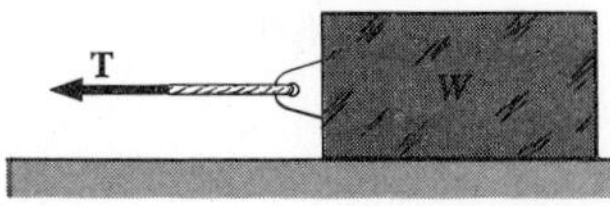

*14.22. An object of mass m and effective area A, initially at rest, is subjected to the pressure p defined in Prob. 14.21. Show that (*a*) at $t = t_1$, $v_1 = v_{\max} = \dfrac{p_0t_1}{e}\dfrac{A}{m}$, (*b*) at $t = t_1$, $s_1 = p_0t_1^2(1 - 2/e)(A/m)$, (*c*) the final displacement of the object is $s = p_0t_1^2\,(A/m)$.

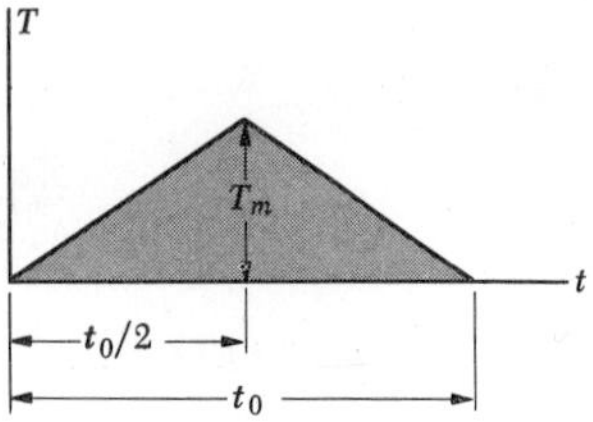

FIG. P 14.23

*14.23. A block of weight W is at rest on a rough surface when a force **T** is applied to the cable. The magnitude T of the force varies with time as shown in the graph. Denoting by μ the coefficient of friction between the block and the surface, determine (*a*) the value of T_m for which the block will move and will again be at rest when $t = t_0$, (*b*) the corresponding maximum velocity attained by the block.

14.3. Impulsive Forces. In some problems, a very large force may act during a very short time interval on a particle and produce a definite change in momentum. Such a force is called an *impulsive force*. For example, when a baseball is struck, the contact between bat and ball takes place during a very short time interval Δt. But the average value of the force **F** exerted by the bat on the ball is very large, and the resulting impulse $\mathbf{F}\,\Delta t$ is large enough to change the sense of motion of the ball (Fig. 14.3).

When impulsive forces act on a particle, Eq. (14.6) becomes

$$m\mathbf{v}_1 + \Sigma\mathbf{F}\,\Delta t = m\mathbf{v}_2 \tag{14.12}$$

Any force which is not an impulsive force may be neglected, since the corresponding impulse $\mathbf{F}\,\Delta t$ is very small. *Nonimpulsive forces* include the weight of the body, the force exerted by a spring, or any other force which is *known* to be small compared with an impulsive force. Unknown reactions may or may not be impulsive; their impulse should therefore be included in Eq. (14.12) as long as it has not been proved negligible. The impulse of the weight of the baseball considered above, for example, may be neglected. If the motion of the bat is analyzed,

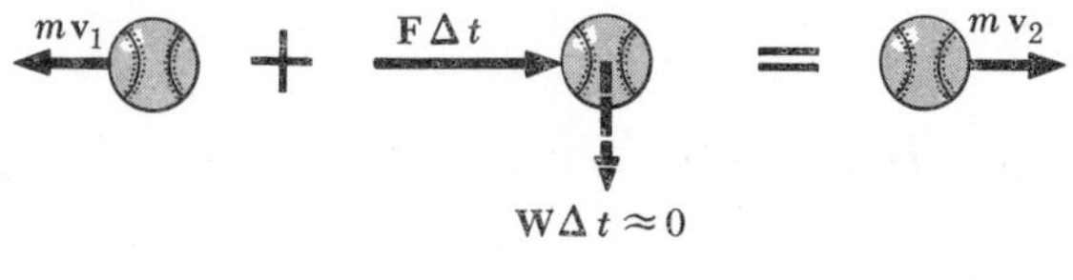

FIG. 14.3

the impulse of the weight of the bat may also be neglected. The impulses of the reactions of the player's hands on the bat, however, should be included; these impulses will not be negligible if the ball is incorrectly hit.

14.4. Conservation of Momentum. We saw in Sec. 14.2 that, when a system of particles moves under the action of various forces, the following relation must hold between the initial momenta of the particles, the final momenta of the particles, and the impulses of the external forces:

$$\Sigma m\mathbf{v}_1 + \Sigma \textbf{ Ext Imp}_{1\to 2} = \Sigma m\mathbf{v}_2 \tag{14.9}$$

Let us now consider the case when the sum of the impulses of the external forces is zero. Equation (14.9) reduces then to

$$\Sigma m\mathbf{v}_1 = \Sigma m\mathbf{v}_2 \tag{14.13}$$

Thus, *when the sum of the impulses of the external forces acting on a system of particles is zero, the total momentum of the system remains constant.*

Introducing again the mass center G of the system, and using the relation (14.10), Eq. (14.13) reduces to

$$\overline{\mathbf{v}}_1 = \overline{\mathbf{v}}_2 \tag{14.14}$$

Thus, when the sum of the impulses of the external forces acting on a system of particles is zero, *the mass center of the system moves with a constant velocity.*

Two distinct cases of conservation of momentum are frequently encountered:

1. *The external forces acting on the system during the interval of time considered are balanced.* No matter how long the time interval is, we have Σ **Ext Imp**$_{1\to 2} = 0$ and formula (14.13) applies. Consider, for example, two boats, of mass m_A and m_B, initially at rest, which are being pulled together (Fig. 14.4). If the resistance of the water is neglected, the only external forces acting on the boats are their weights and the buoyant forces exerted on them. Since these forces are balanced, we write

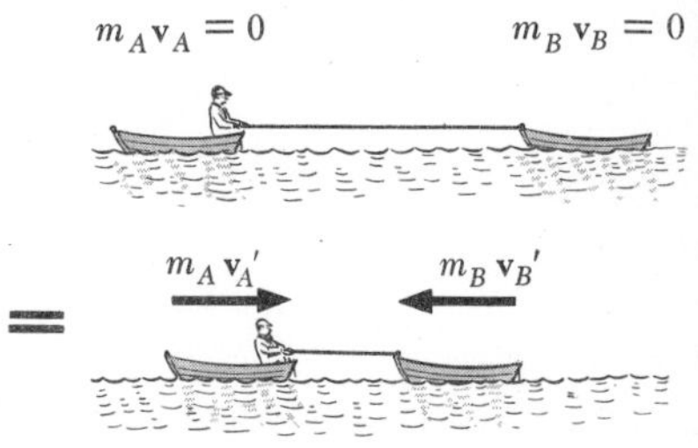

FIG. 14.4

$$\Sigma m\mathbf{v}_1 = \Sigma m\mathbf{v}_2$$
$$0 = m_A\mathbf{v}_A' + m_B\mathbf{v}_B'$$

where $\mathbf{v}_A'$ and $\mathbf{v}_B'$ represent the velocities of the boats after a finite interval of time. The equation obtained indicates that the boats move in opposite directions (toward each other) with velocities inversely proportional to their masses. We also note that the mass center of the two boats, which was initially at rest, remains in the same position.

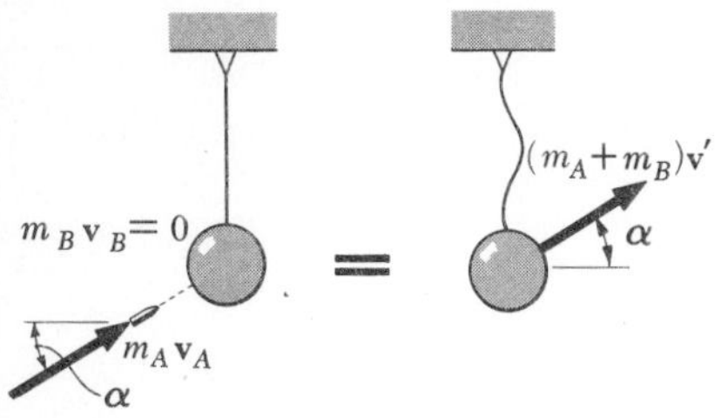

FIG. 14.5

2. *The interval of time considered is very short, and all the external forces are nonimpulsive.* Again we have Σ **Ext Imp** $_{1 \to 2} = 0$, and formula (14.13) applies. Consider, for example, a bullet of mass m_A fired with a velocity $\mathbf{v}_A$ into a wooden sphere of mass m_B suspended from an inextensible wire and initially at rest (Fig. 14.5). The bullet penetrates the sphere and imparts to it a velocity $\mathbf{v}'$, which we propose to determine. After the sphere has been hit, the tension in the wire becomes zero and the combined weight of the sphere and bullet is unbalanced. But the impulse of the weight may be neglected since the time interval is very short. Thus, we write

$$\Sigma m\mathbf{v}_1 = \Sigma m\mathbf{v}_2$$
$$m_A\mathbf{v}_A + 0 = (m_A + m_B)\mathbf{v}'$$

The equation obtained may be solved for $\mathbf{v}'$; we note that $\mathbf{v}'$ will have the same direction as $\mathbf{v}_A$.

Let us now consider the case when the bullet is fired downward into the sphere (Fig. 14.6). Since the wire is inextensi-

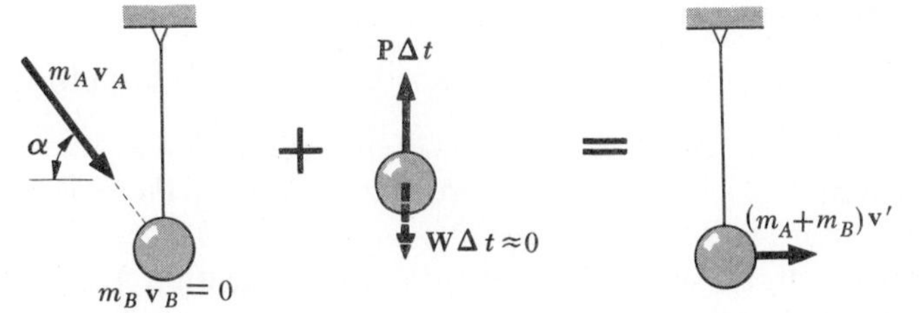

FIG. 14.6

ble, it will prevent any downward motion of the sphere and exert on it a reaction **P**. This reaction is unknown and should therefore be assumed impulsive until proved to the contrary. Writing the general formula (14.9) in terms of horizontal and vertical components, and observing again that the impulse of the weight is negligible, we have

$$\Sigma m\mathbf{v}_1 + \Sigma \textbf{ Ext Imp}_{1 \to 2} = \Sigma m\mathbf{v}_2$$

$\xrightarrow{+} x$ components: $\quad m_A v_A \cos\alpha + 0 = (m_A + m_B)v'$

$+\uparrow y$ components: $\quad -m_A v_A \sin\alpha + P\,\Delta t = 0$

The first equation expresses that *the x component of the momentum is conserved;* it may be used to determine v'. The second equation indicates that *the y component of the linear momentum is not conserved;* this equation may be used to determine the magnitude $P\,\Delta t$ of the impulse of the force exerted by the wire. Thus, the momentum of the system considered is not conserved, and Eq. (14.13) holds only in the x direction.

SAMPLE PROBLEM 14.2

An old 4,000-lb gun fires a 20-lb shell with an initial velocity of 2,000 ft/sec at an angle of 30°. The gun rests on a horizontal surface and is free to move horizontally. Assuming that the barrel of the gun is rigidly attached to the frame (no recoil mechanism) and that the shell leaves the barrel 0.006 sec after firing, determine the recoil velocity of the gun and the resultant **R** of the vertical impulsive forces exerted by the ground on the gun.

Solution. We apply the principle of impulse and momentum to the system consisting of the gun and the shell. Since the time interval $\Delta t = 0.006$ sec is very short, we neglect all nonimpulsive forces and consider only the impulse $\mathbf{R}\,\Delta t$.

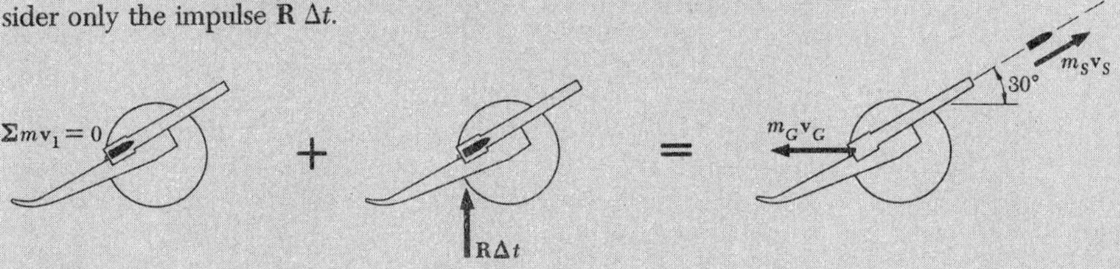

$$\Sigma m\mathbf{v}_1 + \Sigma\ \mathbf{Ext\ Imp}_{1\to2} = \Sigma m\mathbf{v}_2$$

$\xrightarrow{+}$ x components: $\quad 0 + 0 = -m_G v_G + m_S v_S \cos 30°$

$$0 = -\frac{4{,}000}{32.2} v_G + \frac{20}{32.2}(2{,}000)(0.866)$$

$$v_G = +8.66 \text{ ft/sec}$$

$$\mathbf{v}_G = 8.66 \text{ ft/sec} \leftarrow \blacktriangleleft$$

$+\uparrow$ y components: $\quad 0 + R\,\Delta t = m_S v_S \sin 30°$

$$R(0.006) = \frac{20}{32.2}(2{,}000)(0.500)$$

$$R = +103{,}500 \text{ lb}$$

$$\mathbf{R} = 103{,}500 \text{ lb} \uparrow \blacktriangleleft$$

The total force exerted by the ground on the gun during the time interval Δt should include the static reaction due to the weight of the gun as well as the impulsive reaction **R**. Since the gun weighs 4,000 lb, the magnitude of this total force is 103,500 + 4,000 = 107,500 lb.

The high value obtained for the magnitude of **R** clearly indicates the need in modern guns for a recoil mechanism which will allow the barrel to move and will bring it to rest over a period of time substantially longer than Δt. Although the total vertical impulse must remain constant, the longer time interval will result in a smaller value for the magnitude of the reaction **R**.

PROBLEMS

14.24. A 1-oz rifle bullet is fired with an initial velocity of 2,200 ft/sec into a block of wood rigidly attached to the ground. If the bullet is brought to rest in 0.001 sec, determine the average impulsive force exerted by the bullet on the block.

14.25. A 12,000-lb plane lands on the deck of an aircraft carrier at a speed of 120 mph relative to the carrier and is brought to a stop in 3.0 sec. Determine the average impulsive force exerted by the carrier on the plane (*a*) if the carrier is at rest, (*b*) if the carrier is steaming at a speed of 15 knots in the same direction as the airplane. (1 knot = 1.152 mph.)

14.26. A 4-oz baseball is pitched with a velocity of 60 ft/sec toward a batter. After the ball is hit by the bat *B*, it has a velocity of 120 ft/sec in the direction shown. If the bat and ball are in contact 0.03 sec, determine the average impulsive force exerted on the ball during the impact.

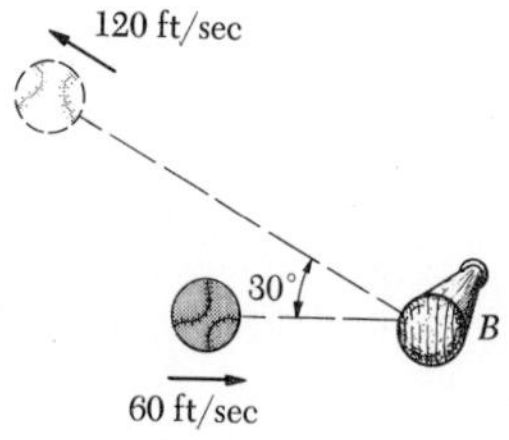

FIG. P 14.26

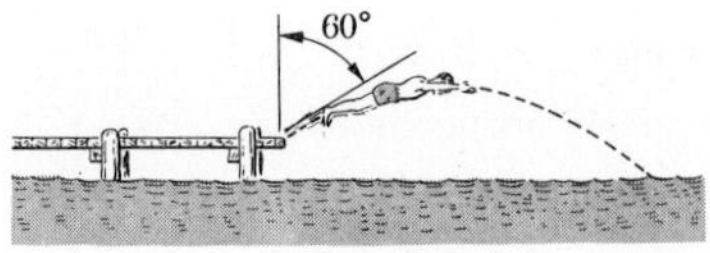

FIG. P 14.27

14.27. A 175-lb man dives off the end of a pier with an initial velocity of 8 ft/sec in the direction shown. Determine the horizontal and vertical components of the force exerted on the pier during the 0.75 sec that the man takes to leave the pier.

14.28. Determine the initial recoil velocity of a 9-lb rifle which fires a $\frac{3}{4}$-oz bullet with a velocity of 2,000 ft/sec.

14.29. A 2-oz bullet is fired horizontally into an 8-lb block which can move freely in the horizontal direction. The horizontal velocity of the block after the bullet has embedded itself is 20 ft/sec. Determine the initial velocity of the bullet.

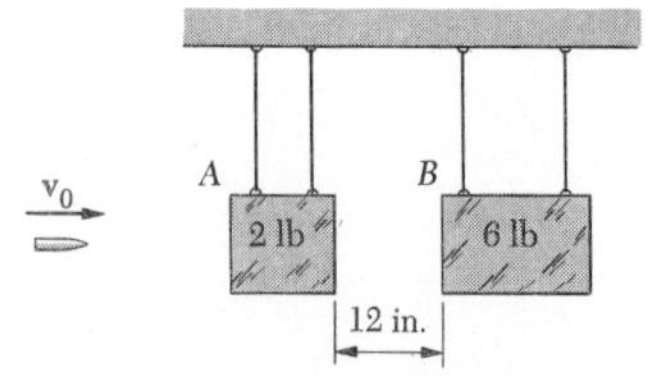

FIG. P 14.30

14.30. A $\frac{3}{4}$-oz bullet is fired in a horizontal direction through block *A* and becomes embedded in block *B*. The bullet causes *A* and *B* to start moving with velocities of 15 ft/sec and 12 ft/sec respectively. Determine (*a*) the initial velocity $\mathbf{v}_0$ of the bullet, (*b*) the velocity of the bullet as it travels from block *A* to block *B*.

14.31. A barge is initially at rest and carries a 1,000-lb crate. The barge weighs 3 tons and is equipped with a winch which is used to move the crate along the deck. Neglecting any friction between the crate and the barge, determine (*a*) the velocity of both the barge and the crate when the winch is drawing in rope at the rate of 9 ft/sec, (*b*) the final position of the barge after 30 ft of rope has been drawn in by the winch. (*c*) Solve parts *a* and *b* assuming that $\mu = 0.25$ between the crate and the barge.

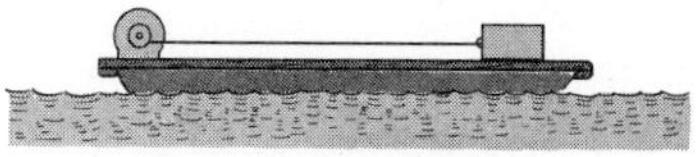

FIG. P 14.31

14.32. A 40-ton railroad car is to be coupled to a second car which weighs 60 tons. If initially the speed of the 40-ton car is 1 mph and the 60-ton car is at rest, determine the final speed of the coupled cars and the average impulsive force acting on each car if the coupling is completed in 0.3 sec.

14.33. Solve Prob. 14.32 assuming that, initially, the 40-ton car is at rest and the 60-ton car has a speed of 1 mph.

14.34. An airline employee tosses a 30-lb suitcase with a horizontal velocity of 10 ft/sec onto a 70-lb baggage carrier. Knowing that the carrier can roll freely and is initially at rest, determine the final velocity of the carrier (*a*) if the suitcase slides to a relative stop on the carrier, (*b*) if the suitcase is stopped by end *A* of the carrier.

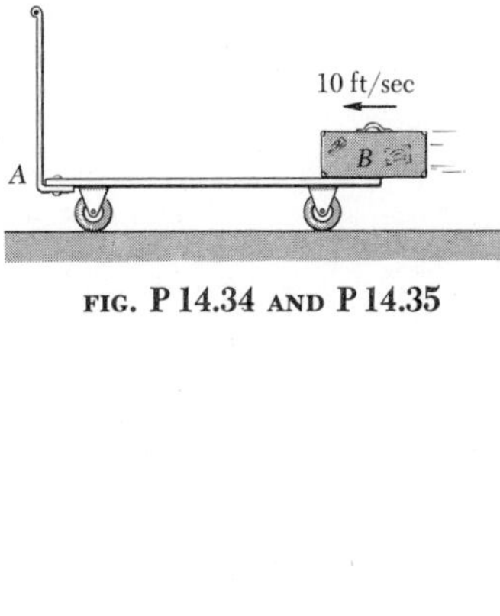

FIG. P 14.34 AND P 14.35

14.35. An employee tosses suitcases with a horizontal velocity of 10 ft/sec relative to the ground onto a carrier. Determine the final velocity of the 70-lb carrier after the employee has tossed (*a*) one 30-lb suitcase, (*b*) two 15-lb suitcases. In the latter case the first 15-lb suitcase comes to a relative stop on the carrier before the second suitcase reaches the carrier.

14.36. A 150-lb man dives horizontally off the end of a 300-lb boat, which is initially at rest. During the dive, the relative horizontal velocity of the man with respect to the boat is 12 ft/sec to the right. (*a*) Determine the resulting velocity of the boat. (*b*) If the man leaves the boat in 0.75 sec, determine the average impulsive force that he exerted on the boat.

14.37. Two men dive horizontally off the end of a 300-lb boat. The boat is initially at rest, and each man weighs 150 lb. If each man dives so that his relative horizontal velocity with respect to the boat is 12 ft/sec to the right, determine (*a*) the velocity of the boat after the men dive simultaneously, (*b*) the velocity of the boat after one man dives and the velocity of the boat after the second man dives.

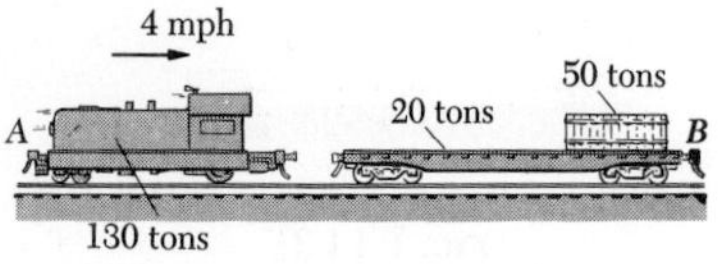

FIG. P 14.38

14.38. A 130-ton engine coasting at 4 mph strikes, and is automatically coupled with, a 20-ton flat car which carries a 50-ton load. The load is *not* securely fastened to the car but may slide along the floor ($\mu = 0.20$). Knowing that the car was at rest with its brakes released, determine the velocity of the engine *immediately* after the coupling, assuming that the coupling takes place (*a*) instantaneously, (*b*) in a period of 0.40 sec. (*c*) Determine the final velocity of the engine after the load has slid to a stop relative to the car.

14.39. A rifle is rigidly attached to a test stand when a $\frac{1}{2}$-oz bullet is fired. Knowing that the muzzle velocity of the bullet is 2,800 ft/sec, determine the total horizontal impulse exerted on the rifle by the stand. A second bullet weighing $\frac{3}{4}$ oz is then fired using the same size of powder charge. Assuming that the kinetic energy of the second bullet is the same as that of the first bullet, determine again the total impulse exerted on the rifle.

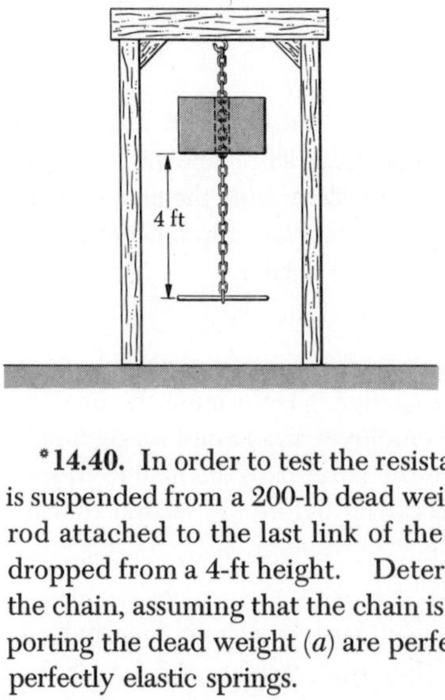

FIG. P 14.40

***14.40.** In order to test the resistance of a chain to impact, the chain is suspended from a 200-lb dead weight supported by two columns. A rod attached to the last link of the chain is then hit by a 50-lb block dropped from a 4-ft height. Determine the initial impulse exerted on the chain, assuming that the chain is inelastic and that the columns supporting the dead weight (*a*) are perfectly rigid, (*b*) are equivalent to two perfectly elastic springs.

***14.41.** A machine part is forged in a small drop forge. The hammer weighs 400 lb and is dropped from a height of 5 ft. Determine the initial impulse exerted on the machine part, assuming that the 1,000-lb anvil (*a*) is resting directly on hard ground, (*b*) is supported by springs.

14.5. Impact. A collision between two bodies which occurs in a very small interval of time, and during which the two bodies exert on each other relatively large forces, is called an *impact*. The common normal to the surfaces in contact during the impact is called the *line of impact*. If the mass centers of the two colliding bodies are located on this line, the impact is a *central impact*. Otherwise, the impact is said to be *eccentric*. We shall limit our present study to that of the central impact of two particles and postpone until later the analysis of the eccentric impact of two rigid bodies (Sec. 17.12).

If the velocities of the two particles are directed along the line of impact, the impact is said to be a *direct impact* (Fig. 14.7*a*). If, on the other hand, either or both particles move along a line other than the line of impact, the impact is said to be an *oblique impact* (Fig. 14.7*b*).

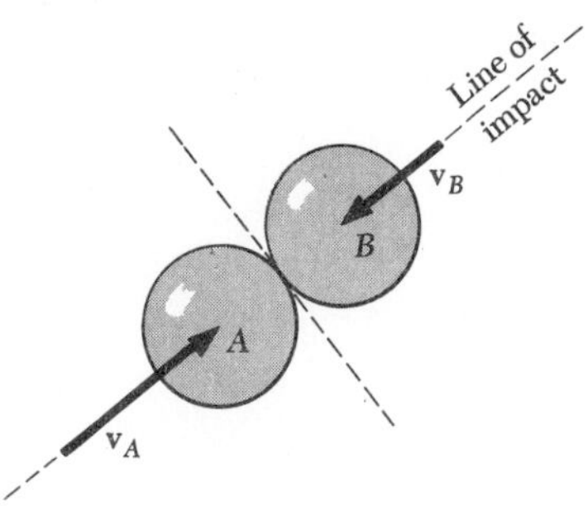

(*a*) Direct central impact

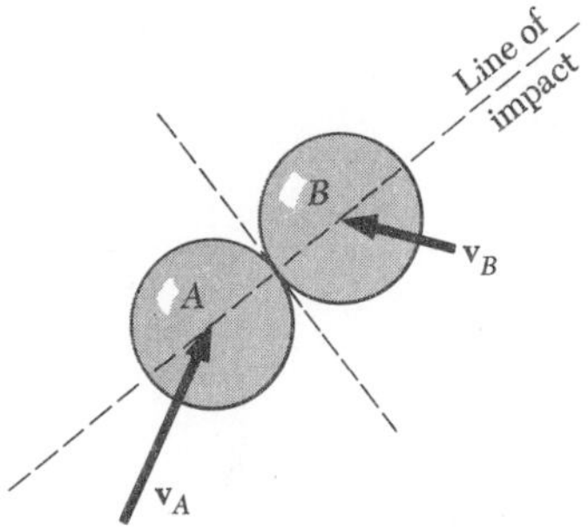

(*b*) Oblique central impact

FIG. 14.7

14.6. Direct Central Impact. Consider two particles A and B, of mass m_A and m_B, which are moving in the same straight line and to the right with known velocities $\mathbf{v}_A$ and $\mathbf{v}_B$ (Fig. 14.8*a*). If $\mathbf{v}_A$ is larger than $\mathbf{v}_B$, particle A will eventually strike particle B. Under the impact, the two particles will *deform* and, at the end of the period of deformation, they will have the same velocity $\mathbf{u}$ (Fig. 14.8*b*). A period of *restitution* will then take place, at the end of which, depending upon the magnitude of the impact forces and upon the materials involved, the two particles either will have regained their original shape or will stay permanently deformed. Our purpose here is to determine the velocities $\mathbf{v}'_A$ and $\mathbf{v}'_B$ of the particles at the end of the period of restitution (Fig. 14.8*c*).

Considering first the system of the two particles as a whole, we note that the only impulsive forces acting during the impact are internal forces. Thus, *the momentum of the system is conserved*, and we write

$$m_A\mathbf{v}_A + m_B\mathbf{v}_B = m_A\mathbf{v}'_A + m_B\mathbf{v}'_B$$

Since all the velocities considered are directed along the same axis, we may replace the equation obtained by the following relation involving only scalar components:

$$m_A v_A + m_B v_B = m_A v'_A + m_B v'_B \qquad (14.15)$$

A positive value for any of the scalar quantities v_A, v_B, v'_A, or v'_B means that the corresponding vector is directed to the right; a negative value indicates that the corresponding vector is directed to the left.

To obtain the velocities $\mathbf{v}'_A$ and $\mathbf{v}'_B$, it is necessary to establish a second relation between the scalars v'_A and v'_B. For this purpose, we shall consider now the motion of particle A during the period of deformation and apply the principle of im-

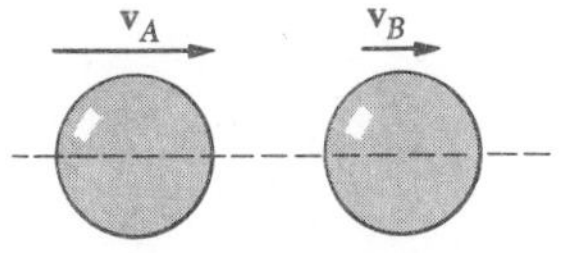

(*a*) Before impact

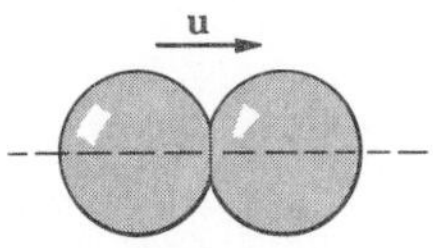

(*b*) At maximum deformation

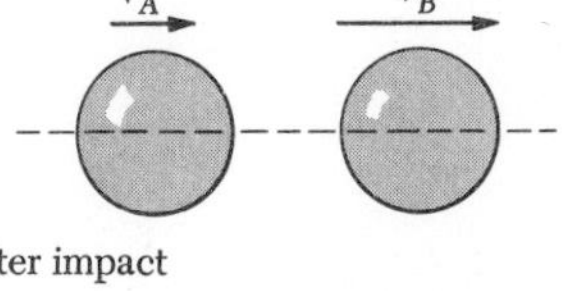

(*c*) After impact

FIG. 14.8

pulse and momentum. Since the only impulsive force acting on A during this period is the force $\mathbf{P}$ exerted by B (Fig. 14.9*a*), we write, using again scalar components,

$$m_A v_A - \int P\,dt = m_A u \tag{14.16}$$

where the integral extends over the period of deformation. Considering now the motion of A during the period of restitution, and denoting by $\mathbf{R}$ the force exerted by B on A during this period (Fig. 14.9*b*), we write

$$m_A u - \int R\,dt = m_A v'_A \tag{14.17}$$

where the integral extends over the period of restitution.

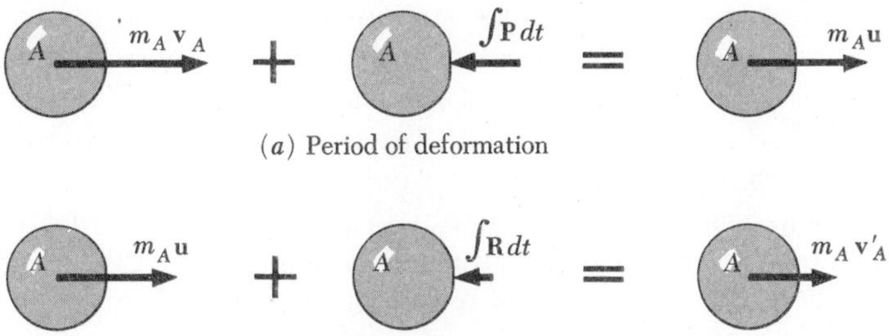

(*a*) Period of deformation

FIG. 14.9 (*b*) Period of restitution

In general, the force $\mathbf{R}$ exerted on A during the period of restitution differs from the force $\mathbf{P}$ exerted during the period of deformation, and the magnitude $\int R dt$ of its impulse is smaller than the magnitude $\int P dt$ of the impulse of $\mathbf{P}$. The ratio of the magnitudes of the impulses corresponding respectively to the period of restitution and to the period of deformation is called the *coefficient of restitution* and is denoted by e. We write

$$e = \frac{\int R\,dt}{\int P\,dt} \tag{14.18}$$

The value of the coefficient e is always between 0 and 1 and depends to a large extent on the two materials involved. However, it also varies considerably with the impact velocity and the shape and size of the two colliding bodies.

Solving Eqs. (14.16) and (14.17) for the two impulses and substituting into (14.18), we write

$$e = \frac{u - v'_A}{v_A - u} \tag{14.19}$$

A similar analysis of particle B leads to the relation

$$e = \frac{v'_B - u}{u - v_B} \tag{14.20}$$

Since the quotients in (14.19) and (14.20) are equal, they are also equal to the quotient obtained by adding, respectively, their numerators and their denominators. We have, therefore,

$$e = \frac{(u - v'_A) + (v'_B - u)}{(v_A - u) + (u - v_B)} = \frac{v'_B - v'_A}{v_A - v_B}$$

and

$$v'_B - v'_A = e(v_A - v_B) \tag{14.21}$$

Since $v'_B - v'_A$ represents the relative velocity of the two particles after impact and $v_A - v_B$ their relative velocity before impact, formula (14.21) expresses that *the relative velocity of the two particles after impact may be obtained by multiplying their relative velocity before impact by the coefficient of restitution.* This property is used to determine experimentally the value of the coefficient of restitution of two given materials.

The velocities of the two particles after impact may now be obtained by solving Eqs. (14.15) and (14.21) simultaneously for v'_A and v'_B, i.e., by using the principle of conservation of momentum and the concept of coefficient of restitution. It is recalled that the derivation of Eqs. (14.15) and (14.21) was based on the assumption that particle B is located to the right of A, and that both particles are initially moving to the right. If particle B is initially moving to the left, the scalar v_B should be considered negative. The same sign convention holds for the velocities after impact: a positive sign for v'_A will indicate that particle A moves to the right after impact, and a negative sign that it moves to the left.

Two particular cases of impact are of special interest:

1. $e = 0$, *Perfectly Plastic Impact.* When $e = 0$, Eq. (14.21) yields $v'_B = v'_A$. There is no period of restitution, and both particles stay together after impact. Substituting $v'_B = v'_A = v'$ into Eq. (14.15), which expresses that the momentum of the system is conserved, we write

$$m_A v_A + m_B v_B = (m_A + m_B)v' \tag{14.22}$$

This equation may be solved for the common velocity v' of the two particles after impact.

2. $e = 1$, *Perfectly Elastic Impact.* When $e = 1$, Eq. (14.21) reduces to

$$v'_B - v'_A = v_A - v_B \tag{14.23}$$

which expresses that the relative velocities before and after impact are equal. The impulses received by each particle during the period of deformation and during the period of restitution are equal. The particles move away from each other after impact with the same velocity with which they approached each other before impact. The velocities v'_A and v'_B may be obtained by solving Eqs. (14.15) and (14.23) simultaneously.

It is worth noting that, *in the case of a perfectly elastic impact, the energy of the system,* as well as its momentum, *is conserved.* Equations (14.15) and (14.23) may be written as follows:

$$m_A(v_A - v'_A) = m_B(v'_B - v_B) \tag{14.15'}$$

$$v_A + v'_A = v_B + v'_B \tag{14.23'}$$

Multiplying (14.15′) and (14.23′) member by member, we have

$$m_A(v_A - v'_A)(v_A + v'_A) = m_B(v'_B - v_B)(v'_B + v_B)$$

$$m_A v_A^2 - m_A(v'_A)^2 = m_B(v'_B)^2 - m_B v_B^2$$

Rearranging the terms in the equation obtained, and multiplying by $\frac{1}{2}$, we write

$$\tfrac{1}{2}m_A v_A^2 + \tfrac{1}{2}m_B v_B^2 = \tfrac{1}{2}m_A(v'_A)^2 + \tfrac{1}{2}m_B(v'_B)^2$$

which expresses that the kinetic energy of the system is conserved. It should be noted, however, that *in the general case of impact,* i.e., when e is not equal to 1, *the energy of the system is not conserved.* This may be shown in any given case by comparing the kinetic energies before and after impact. The lost kinetic energy is in part transformed into heat and in part spent in generating elastic waves within the two colliding bodies.

14.7. Oblique Central Impact. Let us now consider the case when the velocities of the two colliding particles are *not* directed along the line of impact (Fig. 14.10). As indicated in Sec. 14.5, the impact is said to be *oblique.* Since the velocities $\mathbf{v}'_A$ and $\mathbf{v}'_B$ of the particles after impact are unknown in direction as well as in magnitude, their determination will require the use of four independent equations.

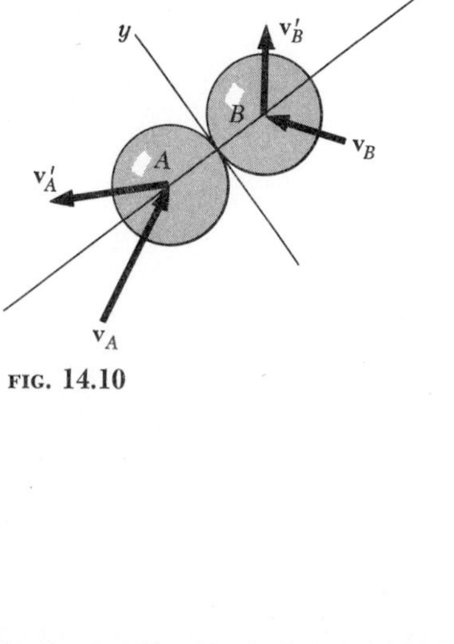

FIG. 14.10

We choose x and y axes, respectively, along the line of impact and along the common tangent to the surfaces in contact. Assuming that the particles are perfectly *smooth and frictionless,* we observe that the only impulsive forces acting on the particles during the impact are internal forces directed along the x axis. We may therefore express that:

1. The y component of the momentum of particle A is conserved.
2. The y component of the momentum of particle B is conserved.
3. The x component of the total momentum of the system is conserved.
4. The x component of the relative velocity of the two particles after impact is obtained by multiplying the x component of their relative velocity before impact by the coefficient of restitution.

We thus obtain four independent equations which may be solved for the components of the velocities of A and B after impact. This method of solution is illustrated in Sample Prob. 14.5.

14.8. Problems Involving Energy and Momentum. We have now at our disposal three different methods for the solution of kinetics problems: the application of the fundamental equation $\Sigma \mathbf{F} = m\mathbf{a}$, the method of work and energy, and the method of impulse and momentum. To derive the maximum benefit from these three methods, we should be able to choose the method best suited for the solution of a given problem. We should also be prepared to use different methods for solving the various parts of a problem when such a procedure seems advisable.

We have already seen that the method of work and energy is in many cases more expeditious than the direct application of the equation $\Sigma \mathbf{F} = m\mathbf{a}$. As indicated in Sec. 13.4, however, the method of work and energy has limitations, and it must sometimes be supplemented by the use of $\Sigma \mathbf{F} = m\mathbf{a}$. This is the case, for example, when we wish to determine an acceleration or a normal force.

There is generally no great advantage in using the method of impulse and momentum for the solution of problems involving no impulsive forces. It will usually be found that the equation $\Sigma \mathbf{F} = m\mathbf{a}$ yields a solution just as fast and that the method of work and energy, if it applies, is more rapid and more convenient. However, the method of impulse and momentum is the only practicable method in problems of impact. A solution based on the direct application of $\Sigma \mathbf{F} = m\mathbf{a}$ would be unwieldy, and the method of work and energy cannot be used since impact (unless perfectly elastic) involves a loss of mechanical energy.

Many problems involve only conservative forces, except for a short impact phase during which impulsive forces act. The solution of such problems may be divided into several parts. While the part corresponding to the impact phase calls for the application of the method of impulse and momentum and the use of the coefficient of restitution, the other parts may usually be solved by the method of work and energy. The use of the equation $\Sigma\mathbf{F} = m\mathbf{a}$ will be necessary, however, if the problem involves the determination of a normal force.

Consider, for example, a pendulum A, of weight $\mathbf{W}_A$ and length l, which is released with no velocity from a position A_1 (Fig. 14.11a). The pendulum swings freely in a vertical plane and hits a second pendulum B, of weight $\mathbf{W}_B$ and same length l, which is initially at rest. Under the impact (with coefficient of restitution e), pendulum B swings through an angle θ that we wish to determine.

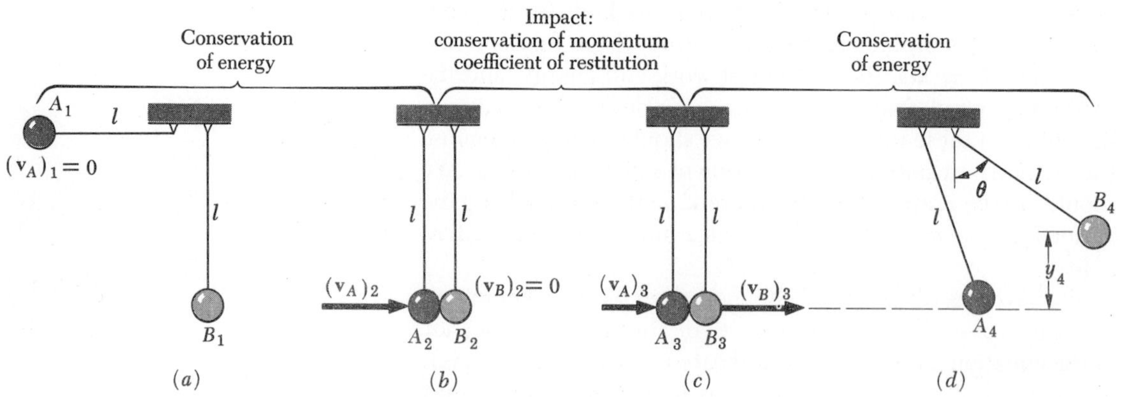

FIG. 14.11

The solution of the problem may be divided into three parts:

1. *Pendulum A Swings from A_1 to A_2.* The principle of conservation of energy may be used to determine the velocity $(\mathbf{v}_A)_2$ of the pendulum at A_2 (Fig. 14.11b).

2. *Pendulum A Hits Pendulum B.* Using the principle of conservation of momentum and the coefficient of restitution e, we determine the velocities $(\mathbf{v}_A)_3$ and $(\mathbf{v}_B)_3$ of the two pendulums after impact (Fig. 14.11c).

3. *Pendulum B Swings from B_3 to B_4.* Applying the principle of conservation of energy, we determine the maximum elevation y_4 reached by pendulum B (Fig. 14.11d). The angle θ may then be determined by trigonometry.

We note that the method of solution just described should be supplemented by the use of $\Sigma\mathbf{F} = m\mathbf{a}$ if the tensions in the cords holding the pendulums are to be determined.

SAMPLE PROBLEM 14.3

A 40,000-lb railroad car moving at a speed of 2 ft/sec to the right collides with a 70,000-lb car which is at rest. If after the collision the 70,000-lb car is observed to move to the right at a speed of 1.2 ft/sec, determine the coefficient of restitution between the two cars.

Solution. We consider the system consisting of the two cars and apply the principle of conservation of momentum.

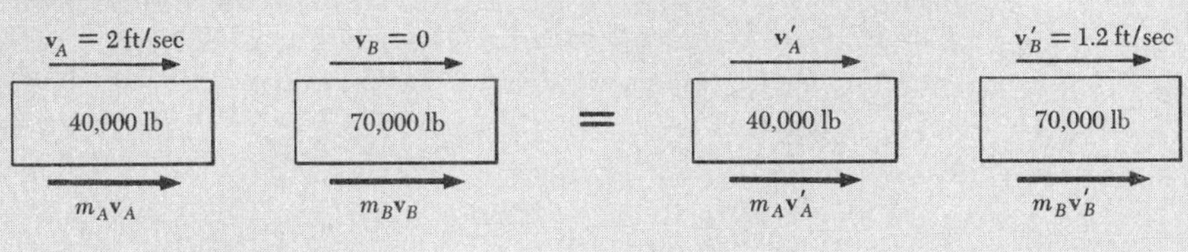

$$m_A \mathbf{v}_A + m_B \mathbf{v}_B = m_A \mathbf{v}'_A + m_B \mathbf{v}'_B$$

$$\frac{40{,}000}{32.2}(+2) + \frac{70{,}000}{32.2}(0) = \frac{40{,}000}{32.2} v'_A + \frac{70{,}000}{32.2}(+1.2)$$

$$v'_A = -0.1 \text{ ft/sec} \qquad \mathbf{v}'_A = 0.1 \text{ ft/sec} \leftarrow$$

The coefficient of restitution is obtained by writing

$$e = \frac{v'_B - v'_A}{v_A - v_B} \qquad e = \frac{+1.2 - (-0.1)}{+2.0 - 0} = \frac{1.3}{2.0} \qquad e = 0.65 \blacktriangleleft$$

SAMPLE PROBLEM 14.4

A ball is thrown against a smooth vertical wall. Immediately before the ball strikes the wall, its velocity has a magnitude v and forms an angle of 30° with the horizontal. Knowing that $e = 0.90$, determine the magnitude and direction of the velocity of the ball as it rebounds from the wall.

Solution. We resolve the initial velocity of the ball into components

$$v_x = v \cos 30° = 0.866v \qquad v_y = v \sin 30° = 0.500v$$

Vertical Motion. Since the wall is smooth, no vertical impulsive force acts on the ball during the time it is in contact with the wall. The vertical component of the momentum, and hence the vertical component of the velocity, of the ball is thus unchanged:

$$\mathbf{v}'_y = \mathbf{v}_y = 0.500v \uparrow$$

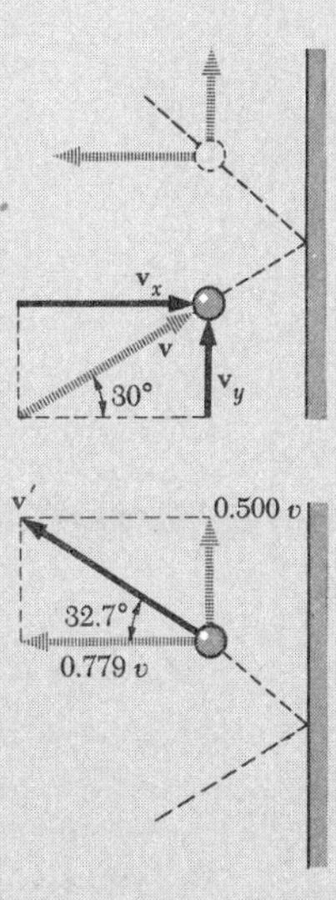

Horizontal Motion. Since the mass of the wall (and earth) is essentially infinite, there is no point in expressing that the momentum of the ball-wall system is conserved. Using the coefficient of restitution, we write

$$0 - v'_x = e(v_x - 0)$$

$$v'_x = -(0.90)(0.866v) = -0.779v \qquad \mathbf{v}'_x = 0.779v \leftarrow$$

Resultant Motion. Adding vectorially the components $\mathbf{v}'_x$ and $\mathbf{v}'_y$,

$$\mathbf{v}' = 0.925v \;\measuredangle\; 32.7° \blacktriangleleft$$

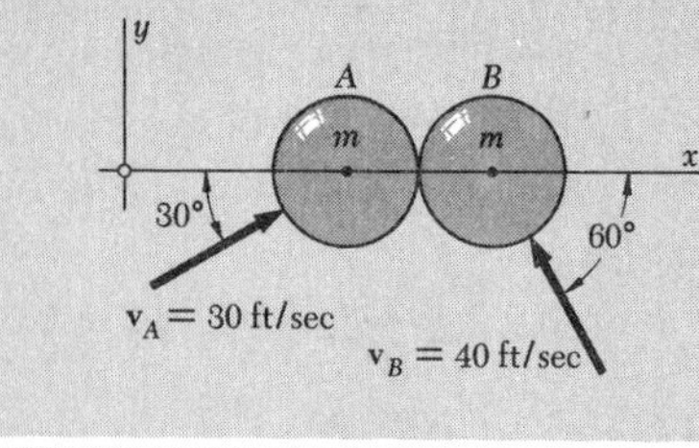

SAMPLE PROBLEM 14.5

The magnitude and direction of the velocities of two identical smooth balls before they strike each other are as shown. Assuming $e = 0.90$, determine the magnitude and direction of the velocity of each ball after the impact.

Solution. The impulsive forces acting between the balls during the impact are directed along a line joining the centers of the balls called the *line of impact*. Choosing x and y axes, respectively, parallel and perpendicular to the line of impact and directed as shown, we write

$$\begin{aligned}(v_A)_x &= v_A \cos 30^\circ &= +26.0 \text{ ft/sec}\\ (v_A)_y &= v_A \sin 30^\circ &= +15.0 \text{ ft/sec}\\ (v_B)_x &= v_B \cos 60^\circ &= -20.0 \text{ ft/sec}\\ (v_B)_y &= v_B \sin 60^\circ &= +34.6 \text{ ft/sec}\end{aligned}$$

Principle of Impulse and Momentum. In the following sketches we show in turn the initial momenta, the impulsive reactions, and the final momenta.

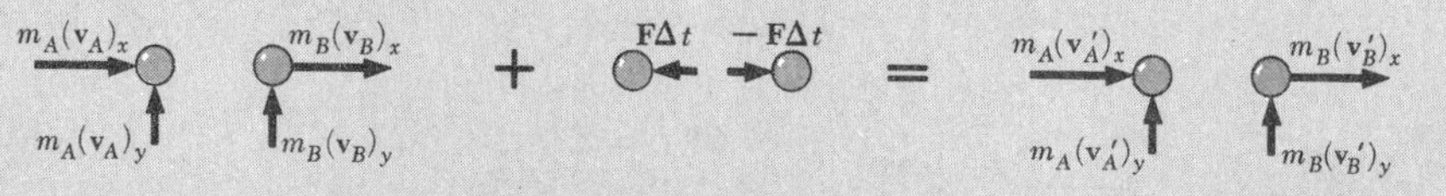

Motion Perpendicular to the Line of Impact. Considering only the y components, we apply the principle of impulse and momentum to each ball *separately*. Since no vertical impulsive force acts during the impact, the vertical component of the momentum, and hence the vertical component of the velocity, of each ball is unchanged.

$$(\mathbf{v}'_A)_y = 15.0 \text{ ft/sec} \uparrow \qquad (\mathbf{v}'_B)_y = 34.6 \text{ ft/sec} \uparrow$$

Motion Parallel to the Line of Impact. In the x direction, we consider the two balls as a *single* system and note that, by Newton's third law, the internal impulses are respectively $\mathbf{F}\,\Delta t$ and $-\mathbf{F}\,\Delta t$ and cancel. Applying the principle of conservation of momentum, we write

$$m_A(v_A)_x + m_B(v_B)_x = m_A(v'_A)_x + m_B(v'_B)_x$$
$$m(26.0) + m(-20.0) = m(v'_A)_x + m(v'_B)_x \qquad (v'_A)_x + (v'_B)_x = 6.0 \quad (1)$$

Using the coefficient of restitution, we write

$$(v'_B)_x - (v'_A)_x = e[(v_A)_x - (v_B)_x]$$
$$(v'_B)_x - (v'_A)_x = (0.90)\,[26.0 - (-20.0)] \qquad (v'_B)_x - (v'_A)_x = 41.4 \quad (2)$$

Solving Eqs. (1) and (2) simultaneously, we obtain

$$(v'_A)_x = -17.7 \qquad (v'_B)_x = +23.7$$
$$(\mathbf{v}'_A)_x = 17.7 \text{ ft/sec} \leftarrow \qquad (\mathbf{v}'_B)_x = 23.7 \text{ ft/sec} \rightarrow$$

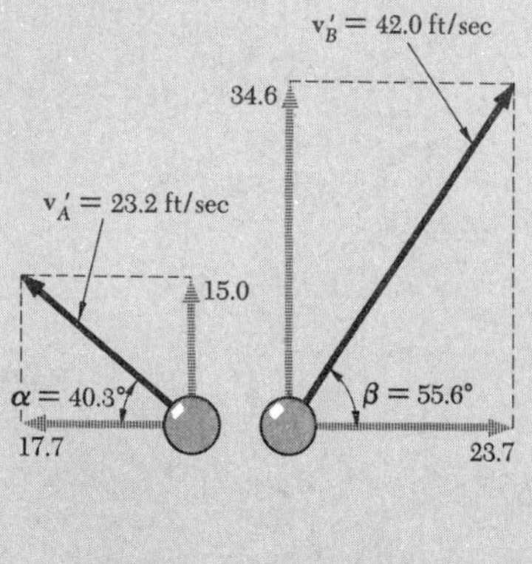

Resultant Motion. Adding vectorially the velocity components of each ball, we obtain

$$\mathbf{v}'_A = 23.2 \text{ ft/sec} \measuredangle\, 40.3^\circ \qquad \mathbf{v}'_B = 42.0 \text{ ft/sec} \measuredangle\, 55.6^\circ \blacktriangleleft$$

SAMPLE PROBLEM 14.6

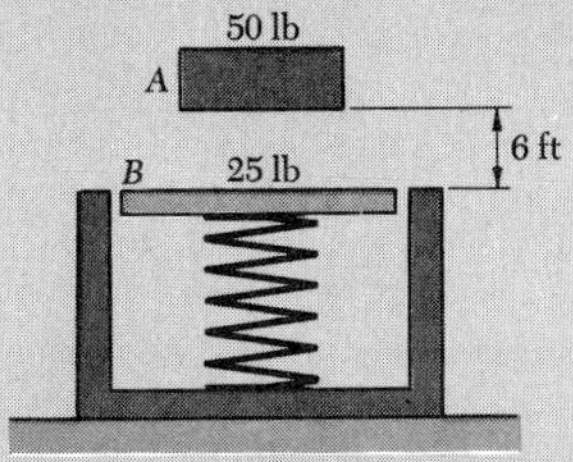

A 50-lb block is dropped from a height of 6 ft onto the 25-lb pan of a spring scale. Assuming the impact to be perfectly plastic, determine the maximum deflection of the pan. The constant of the spring is $k = 100$ lb/in.

Solution. The impact between the block and the pan *must* be treated separately; therefore we divide the solution into three parts.

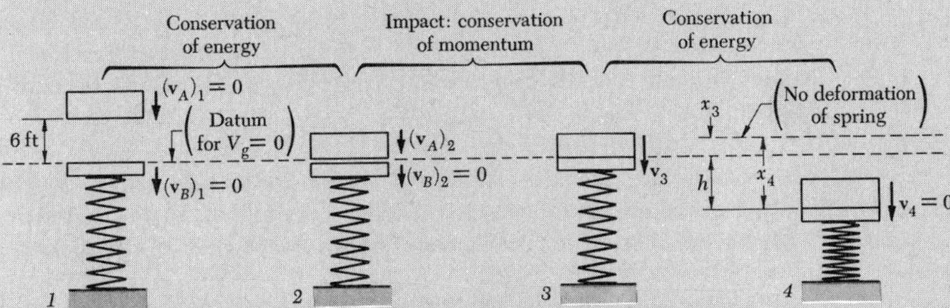

Conservation of Energy

$$T_1 = \tfrac{1}{2}m_A(v_A)_1^2 = 0 \qquad V_1 = Wy = (50 \text{ lb})(6 \text{ ft}) = 300 \text{ ft-lb}$$

$$T_2 = \tfrac{1}{2}m_A(v_A)_2^2 \qquad \frac{1}{2}\frac{50}{32.2}(v_A)_2^2 = 0.776(v_A)_2^2 \qquad V_2 = 0$$

$$T_1 + V_1 = T_2 + V_2 \qquad 0 + 300 = 0.776(v_A)_2^2 + 0$$

$$(v_A)_2 = +19.66 \text{ ft/sec} \qquad (\mathbf{v}_A)_2 = 19.66 \text{ ft/sec} \downarrow$$

Impact: Conservation of Momentum. Since the impact is perfectly plastic, $e = 0$; the block and pan move together with a velocity $\mathbf{v}_3$ after the impact.

$$m_A(v_A)_2 + m_B(v_B)_2 = (m_A + m_B)v_3$$

$$\frac{50}{32.2}(19.66) + 0 = \frac{50 + 25}{32.2}v_3$$

$$v_3 = +13.11 \text{ ft/sec} \qquad \mathbf{v}_3 = 13.11 \text{ ft/sec} \downarrow$$

Conservation of Energy. Initially the spring supports the 25-lb pan; thus the initial deflection of the spring is $x_3 = \frac{1}{4}$ in. Denoting by x_4 the total maximum deflection of the spring, we write

$$T_3 = \tfrac{1}{2}(m_A + m_B)v_3^2 = \frac{1}{2}\frac{50 + 25}{32.2}(13.11)^2 = 200 \text{ ft-lb} = 2{,}400 \text{ in.-lb}$$

$$V_3 = V_g + V_e = 0 + \tfrac{1}{2}kx_3^2 = \tfrac{1}{2}(100 \text{ lb/in.})(\tfrac{1}{4} \text{ in.})^2 = 3.12 \text{ in.-lb}$$

$$T_4 = 0$$

$$V_4 = V_g + V_e = (W_A + W_B)(-h) + \tfrac{1}{2}kx_4^2 = -75h + (\tfrac{1}{2})(100)x_4^2$$

Noting that the displacement of the pan is $h = x_4 - x_3 = x_4 - \frac{1}{4}$ in., we write

$$T_3 + V_3 = T_4 + V_4 \qquad 2{,}400 + 3.12 = 0 - 75(x_4 - \tfrac{1}{4}) + (\tfrac{1}{2})(100)x_4^2$$

$$x_4 = 7.70 \text{ in.} \qquad h = x_4 - x_3 = 7.70 \text{ in.} - 0.25 \text{ in.}$$

$$h = 7.45 \text{ in.} \blacktriangleleft$$

PROBLEMS

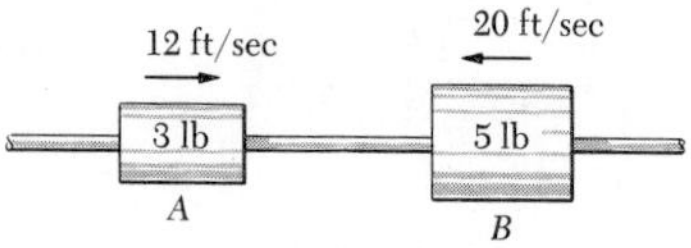

FIG. P 14.42, P 14.44, AND P 14.45

14.42. The coefficient of restitution between the two collars is known to be 0.75; determine (*a*) their velocities after impact, (*b*) the energy loss during the impact.

14.43. Solve Prob. 14.42 assuming that the velocity of collar *A* is 12 ft/sec to the left.

14.44. Knowing that $e = 0.75$, determine how much additional weight should be attached to collar *B* if its velocity after impact is to be zero.

14.45. The velocities of the two collars before impact are as shown. If after the impact the velocity of collar *B* is observed to be 2 ft/sec to the left, determine the coefficient of restitution between the two collars.

14.46. Several identical steel balls *B*, *C*, and *D* are at rest when ball *B* is struck by a ball *A* of the same weight, moving with an initial velocity $\mathbf{v}_A$. This causes a series of collisions between the various balls. Determine the final velocity of ball *D* in terms of the initial velocity $\mathbf{v}_A$ and the coefficient of restitution *e*.

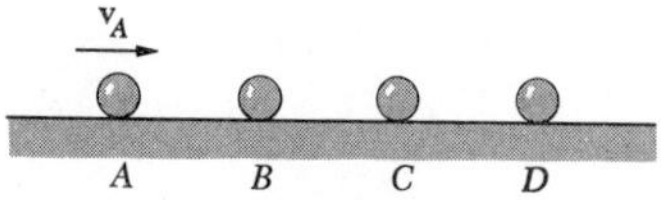

FIG. P 14.46

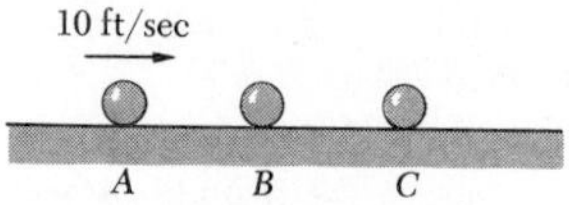

FIG. P 14.47

14.47. Two identical balls *B* and *C* are at rest when ball *B* is struck by a ball *A* of the same weight, moving with a velocity of 10 ft/sec. This causes a series of collisions between the various balls. Knowing that $e = 0.40$, determine the velocity of each ball after *all* collisions have taken place.

14.48. The official weights of various United States coins are: silver dollar, 412.5 grains; half dollar, 192.9 grains; quarter dollar, 96.45 grains; dime, 38.58 grains. Determine the velocity imparted to a quarter dollar which is at rest on a smooth surface when it is struck squarely by each of the following coins moving with a velocity $\mathbf{v}_1$: (*a*) a silver dollar, (*b*) a half dollar, (*c*) a dime. Assume the impact to be perfectly elastic.

14.49. A dime which is at rest on a *rough* surface is struck squarely by a half dollar moving to the right. After the impact, each coin slides and comes to rest; the dime slides 22.6 in. to the right, and the half dollar slides 4.2 in. to the right. Assuming the coefficient of friction is the same for each coin, determine the value of the coefficient of restitution between the coins. (See Prob. 14.48 for the weight of United States coins.)

14.50. Two identical billiard balls A and B of radius r may move freely on a horizontal table. If B is at rest and A has an initial velocity of components $v_x = v$ and $v_y = 0$, determine the distance a so that the y component of the velocity of B after impact is maximum. Also determine the corresponding resultant velocity of B and the direction in which B will move. Assume $e = 1$.

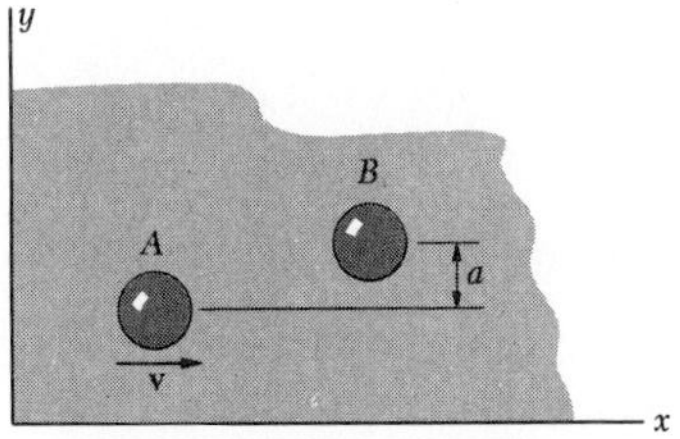

FIG. P 14.50 AND P 14.51

14.51. Ball B weighs 2 lb and is initially at rest. Ball A weighs 4 lb and has an initial velocity of 8 ft/sec to the right. It is desired to have ball B, after the impact, move to the right in a direction forming an angle of 30° with the x axis. (a) Knowing that the diameter of each ball is 2 in., determine the required distance a. (b) Assuming $e = 0.80$, determine the final velocity of each ball.

14.52. In Sample Prob. 14.5, determine the required value of the coefficient of restitution if the angles α and β between the horizontal and the respective directions of the final velocities are to be equal.

*14.53. Three identical balls A, B, and C may roll freely on a horizontal surface. Balls B and C are at rest and in contact when struck by ball A, which was moving to the right with a velocity $\mathbf{v}_A$. Determine the final velocity of each ball assuming (a) that the path of A is perfectly centered and that A strikes B and C simultaneously, (b) that the path of A is not perfectly centered and that A strikes B slightly before it strikes C. Assume perfectly elastic impact and conservation of energy.

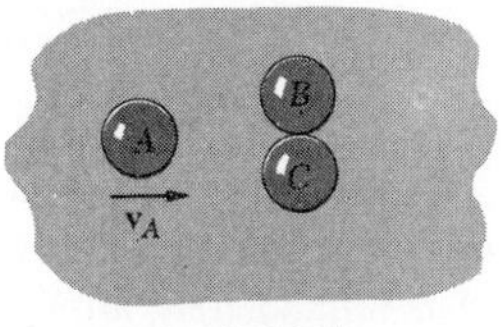

FIG. P 14.53

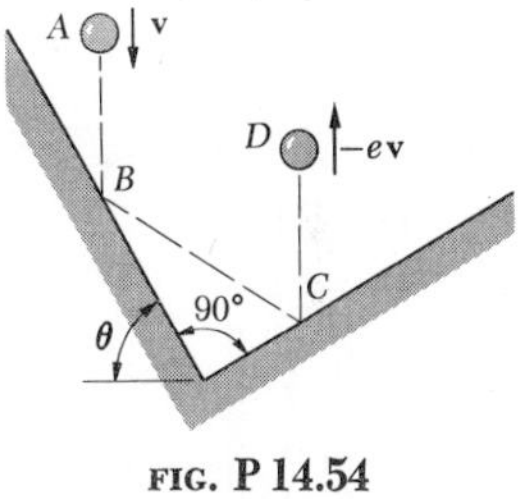

FIG. P 14.54

14.54. A steel ball strikes a 90° corner at B, is deflected, and again strikes the corner at C. The coefficient of restitution is denoted by e. If the ball strikes B with a velocity of magnitude v, show (a) that the magnitude of its final velocity after striking C is ev and (b) that the initial and final paths AB and CD are parallel. Assume that v is large and that the short intermediate path BC is a straight line.

14.55. In Prob. 14.54, derive an expression for θ, knowing that path BC is to be perpendicular to paths AB and CD.

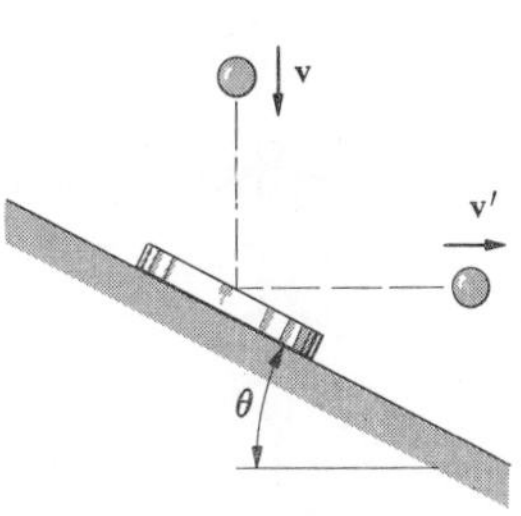

FIG. P 14.56

14.56. A steel ball falling vertically strikes a rigid plate and rebounds horizontally as shown. Denoting by e the coefficient of restitution, determine (a) the required angle θ, (b) the magnitude of the velocity $\mathbf{v}'$.

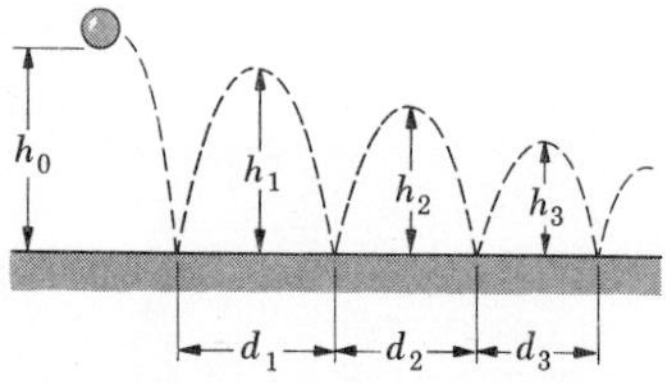

FIG. P 14.57, P 14.58, AND P 14.59

14.57. A ball is dropped from a height $h_0 = 36$ in. onto a smooth floor. Knowing that the height of the first bounce is $h_1 = 32$ in., determine (*a*) the coefficient of restitution, (*b*) the expected height h_2 of the second bounce.

14.58. A ball is dropped onto a smooth floor and bounces as shown. The lengths of the first two bounces are measured and found to be $d_1 = 14.5$ in. and $d_2 = 13.7$ in. Determine (*a*) the coefficient of restitution, (*b*) the expected length d_3 of the third bounce.

14.59. A ball is dropped onto a smooth floor and allowed to bounce several times as shown. Derive an expression for the coefficient of restitution in terms of (*a*) the height of two successive bounces h_n and h_{n+1}, (*b*) the length of two successive bounces d_n and d_{n+1}, (*c*) the duration of two successive bounces t_n and t_{n+1}.

14.60. A ball is dropped from a height h above the landing and bounces down a flight of stairs. Determine the value of h for which the ball will bounce to the same height above each step.

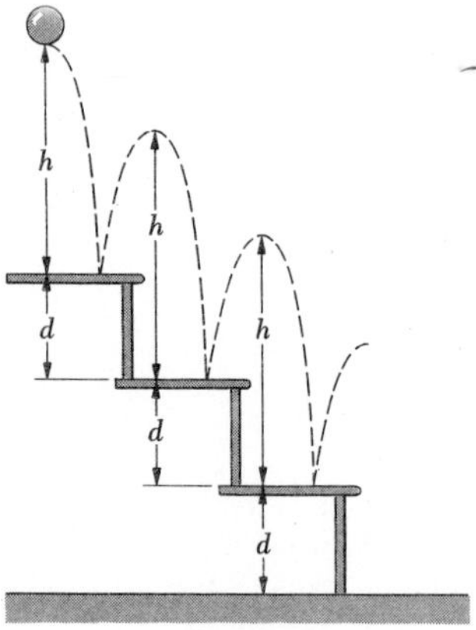

FIG. P 14.60

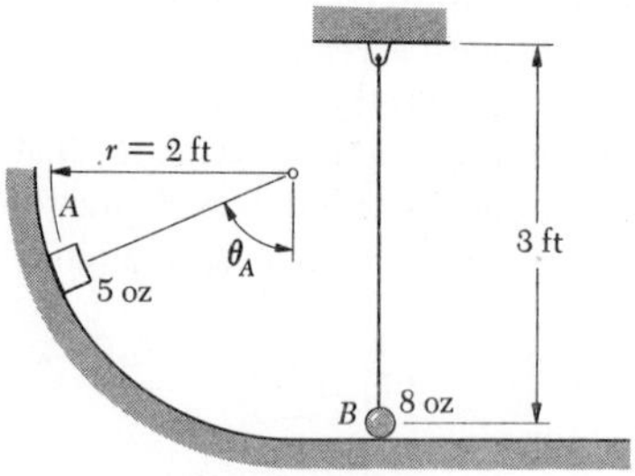

FIG. P 14.61

14.61. Block *A* is released when $\theta_A = 90°$ and slides without friction until it strikes ball *B*. Knowing that $e = 0.90$, determine (*a*) the velocity of *B* immediately after impact, (*b*) the maximum tension in the cord holding *B*, (*c*) the maximum height to which ball *B* will rise.

14.62. What should be the value of the angle θ_A in Prob. 14.61 if the maximum angle between the cord holding ball *B* and the vertical is to be 45°?

14.63. The 1,500-lb hammer of a drop-hammer pile driver falls from a height of 4 ft onto the top of a 400-lb pile. The pile is driven 8 in. into the ground. Assuming perfectly plastic impact, determine the average resistance of the ground to penetration.

14.64. If the average resistance of the ground to the penetration of a 400-lb pile is 2 tons, determine the height h of drop required by a 1,500-lb hammer to drive the pile 9 in. into the ground. Assume that the impact is perfectly plastic.

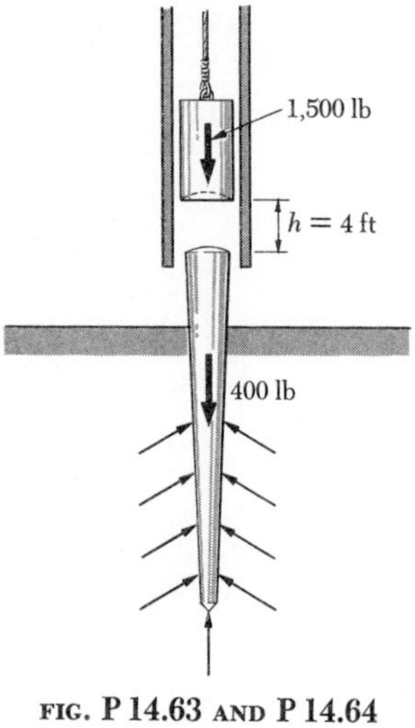

FIG. P 14.63 AND P 14.64

14.65. A $\frac{3}{4}$-oz bullet is fired with a velocity of 1,800 ft/sec into a 10-lb block. Knowing that the coefficient of friction between the block and the floor is 0.30, determine (*a*) through what distance the block will slide, (*b*) the percentage of the initial kinetic energy lost in friction between the block and the floor.

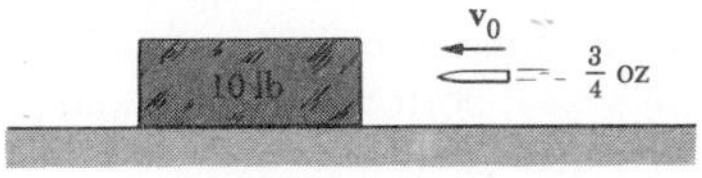

FIG. P 14.65

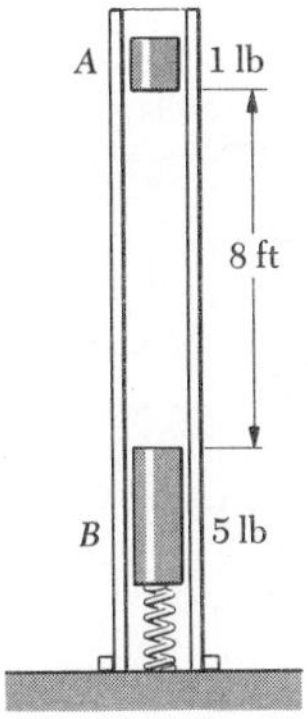

FIG. P 14.66

14.66. Cylinder *A* is dropped 8 ft onto cylinder *B*, which is resting on a spring of constant $k = 10$ lb/in. Assuming a perfectly plastic impact, determine (*a*) the maximum deflection of cylinder *B*, (*b*) the energy loss during the impact.

14.67. Collars *A* and *B* of weight $W_A = 2$ lb and $W_B = 3$ lb, respectively, may slide without friction on the horizontal rod shown. Collar *A* is released from rest when spring *C* is compressed 6 in.; it slides and strikes collar *B*. Assuming $e = 0.80$, determine the maximum deflection of spring *D*.

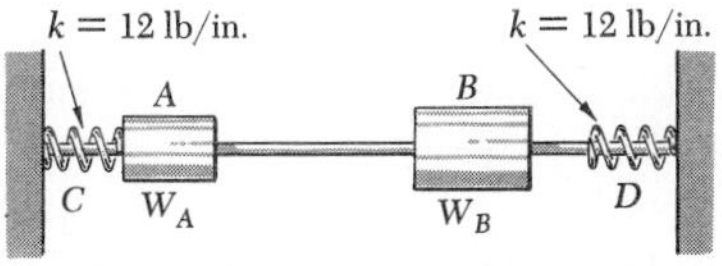

FIG. P 14.67 AND P 14.68

14.68. Block *A* is released when spring *C* is compressed a distance δ; it slides without friction and strikes collar *B*. The coefficient of restitution between the collars is denoted by *e*. What should be the weight of collar *A* if the velocity of collar *B* immediately after impact is to be as large as possible?

14.69. Three steel rods of uniform cross section may slide without friction on a horizontal surface. Rods *B* and *C* are at rest when *B* is struck by rod *A*, which was moving with a velocity $\mathbf{v}_0$. (*a*) Denoting by *e* the coefficient of restitution of the rods, determine the length *x* of rod *B* for which we obtain the maximum velocity of rod *C* after it has been struck by *B* for the first time. (*b*) Using the value of *x* found in part *a*, determine the kinetic energy of *C* after impact as a fraction of the initial kinetic energy of *A*.

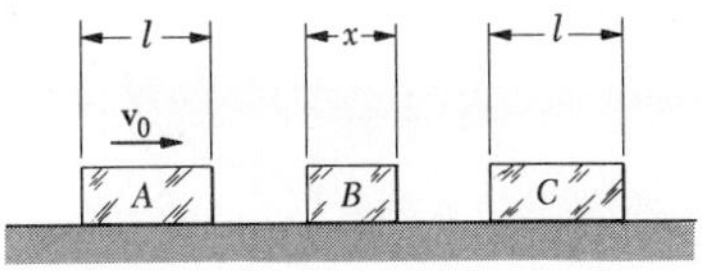

FIG. 14.69

***14.70.** Determine the energy absorbed by the chain of Prob. 14.40 under each condition of support. Assume perfectly plastic impact.

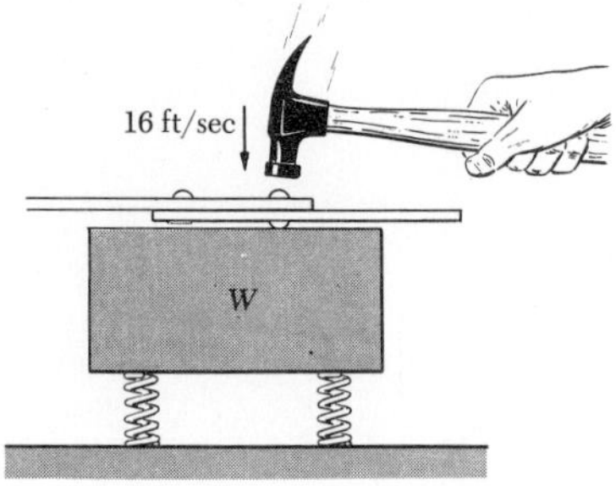

FIG. P 14.72

*14.71. Determine the energy absorbed by the machine part of Prob. 14.41 under each condition of support. Assume perfectly plastic impact.

*14.72. A small rivet connecting two pieces of sheet metal is being clinched by hammering. Determine the energy absorbed by the rivet under each blow, knowing that the head of the hammer weighs 1 lb and that it strikes the rivet with a velocity of 16 ft/sec. Assume that the anvil is supported by springs and (*a*) is infinite in weight (rigid support), (*b*) weighs 10 lb.

*14.73. In Prob. 14.72, determine the weight of the hammer required to deliver to the rivet an amount of energy equal to 5-ft-lb per blow if the hammer strikes the rivet with a velocity of 16 ft/sec. Consider both types of support.

*14.74. In Prob. 14.66, determine the maximum deflection of cylinder *B* and the height to which cylinder *A* will rebound, assuming that $e = 0.75$ between the two cylinders.

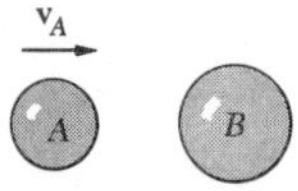

FIG. P 14.75

*14.75. A mass m_A moving to the right with a velocity $\mathbf{v}_A$ strikes a second mass m_B which is at rest. Derive an expression for the kinetic-energy loss during the impact of the two masses. Assume that the balls strike each other squarely, and denote the coefficient of restitution by *e*.

14.9. Angular Momentum of a Particle. Consider a particle *P* of mass *m* moving with respect to a newtonian frame of reference *Oxyz*. As we saw in Sec. 14.1, the momentum of the particle at a given instant is defined as the vector $m\mathbf{v}$ obtained by multiplying the velocity $\mathbf{v}$ of the particle by its mass *m*. The moment about *O* of the vector $m\mathbf{v}$ is called the *moment of momentum*, or the *angular momentum*, of the particle about *O* at that instant and is denoted by $\mathbf{h}_O$. Recalling the definition of the moment of a vector (Sec. 3.5), and denoting by $\mathbf{r}$ the position vector of *P*, we write

$$\mathbf{h}_O = \mathbf{r} \times m\mathbf{v} \tag{14.24}$$

and note that $\mathbf{h}_O$ is a vector perpendicular to the plane containing $\mathbf{r}$ and $m\mathbf{v}$, and of magnitude

$$h_O = rmv \sin \phi \tag{14.25}$$

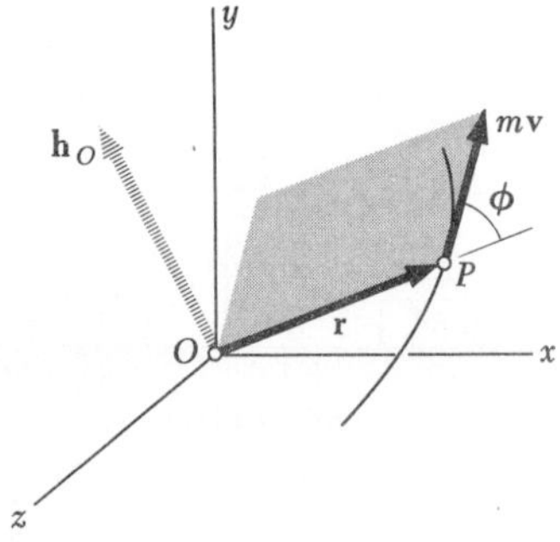

FIG. 14.12

where ϕ is the angle between $\mathbf{r}$ and $m\mathbf{v}$ (Fig. 14.12). The sense of $\mathbf{h}_O$ may be determined from the sense of $m\mathbf{v}$ by applying the right-hand rule.

Resolving the vectors **r** and $m\mathbf{v}$ into components, and applying formula (3.10), we write

$$\mathbf{h}_O = \begin{vmatrix} \mathbf{i} & \mathbf{j} & \mathbf{k} \\ x & y & z \\ mv_x & mv_y & mv_z \end{vmatrix} \tag{14.26}$$

The components of $\mathbf{h}_O$, which also represent the moments of the linear momentum $m\mathbf{v}$ about the coordinate axes, may be obtained by expanding the determinant in (14.26). We have

$$\begin{aligned} h_x &= m(yv_z - zv_y) \\ h_y &= m(zv_x - xv_z) \\ h_z &= m(xv_y - yv_x) \end{aligned} \tag{14.27}$$

In the case of a particle moving in the xy plane, we have $z = v_z = 0$ and the components h_x and h_y reduce to zero. The angular momentum is thus perpendicular to the xy plane; it is then completely defined by the scalar

$$h_O = h_z = m(xv_y - yv_x) \tag{14.28}$$

which will be positive or negative, according to the sense in which the particle is observed to move from O.

We shall now compute the derivative with respect to t of the angular momentum $\mathbf{h}_O$ of a particle moving in space. Differentiating both members of (14.24), and recalling the rule for the differentiation of a vector product (Sec. 11.10), we write

$$\frac{d\mathbf{h}_O}{dt} = \frac{d\mathbf{r}}{dt} \times m\mathbf{v} + \mathbf{r} \times m\frac{d\mathbf{v}}{dt} = \mathbf{v} \times m\mathbf{v} + \mathbf{r} \times m\mathbf{a}$$

Since the vectors **v** and $m\mathbf{v}$ are collinear, the first term of the expression obtained is zero; and, by Newton's second law, $m\mathbf{a}$ is equal to the force **F** acting on the particle. Thus, the right-hand member reduces to the moment $\mathbf{M}_O$ of **F** about O and we write

$$\mathbf{M}_O = \frac{d\mathbf{h}_O}{dt} \tag{14.29}$$

Equation (14.29) expresses that *the moment about O of the force* **F** *acting on the particle is equal to the rate of change of the moment of momentum, or angular momentum, of the particle about O.*

14.10. Angular Momentum of a System of Particles. The moment of momentum, or angular momentum, $\mathbf{h}_O$ of a system of particles about O is defined as the sum of the moments about O of the momenta of the various particles of the system; we write

$$\mathbf{h}_O = \Sigma(\mathbf{r} \times m\mathbf{v}) \tag{14.30}$$

Differentiating both members of (14.30), we have

$$\frac{d\mathbf{h}_O}{dt} = \sum\left(\frac{d\mathbf{r}}{dt} \times m\mathbf{v}\right) + \sum\left(\mathbf{r} \times m\frac{d\mathbf{v}}{dt}\right)$$
$$= \Sigma(\mathbf{v} \times m\mathbf{v}) + \Sigma(\mathbf{r} \times m\mathbf{a}) = \Sigma(\mathbf{r} \times m\mathbf{a})$$

since the vectors $\mathbf{v}$ and $m\mathbf{v}$ are collinear. But, by Newton's second law, $m\mathbf{a} = \mathbf{F}$; the expression obtained represents therefore the sum of the moments about O of the forces acting on the various particles of the system. Since the internal forces occur by pairs of equal and opposite forces having the same line of action, the sum of their moments is zero and we need consider only the sum of the moments of the external forces. We thus write

$$\Sigma(\mathbf{M}_O)_{\text{ext}} = \frac{d\mathbf{h}_O}{dt} \tag{14.31}$$

Note that, while the origin O may be chosen arbitrarily, the frame $Oxyz$ must be a newtonian frame of reference.

Angular Momentum about the Mass Center. In some applications (for example, in the analysis of the motion of a rigid body) it is convenient to consider the motion of the particles of the system with respect to a centroidal frame of reference $Gx'y'z'$ which translates with respect to the newtonian frame $Oxyz$ (Fig. 14.13). While such a frame is not, in general, a newtonian frame of reference, we shall see that the fundamental relation (14.31) still holds when the frame $Oxyz$ is replaced by $Gx'y'z'$.

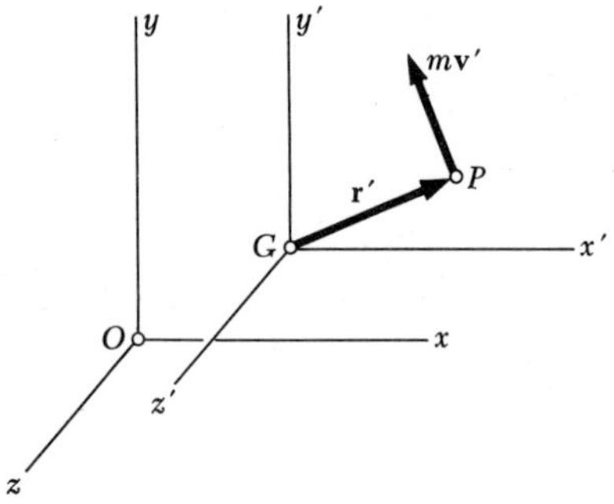

FIG. 14.13

Denoting respectively by $\mathbf{r}'$ and $\mathbf{v}'$ the position vector and the velocity of a particle P relative to the moving frame of reference $Gx'y'z'$, we define the *angular momentum* $\mathbf{h}'_G$ of the system of particles *about the mass center G*:

$$\mathbf{h}'_G = \Sigma(\mathbf{r}' \times m\mathbf{v}') \tag{14.32}$$

We now differentiate both members of (14.32); this operation being similar to that performed on (14.30), we write immediately

$$\frac{d\mathbf{h}'_G}{dt} = \Sigma(\mathbf{r}' \times m\mathbf{a}') \tag{14.33}$$

where $\mathbf{a}'$ denotes the acceleration of the particle P relative to the moving frame of reference. Substituting into (14.33) $\mathbf{a}' = \mathbf{a} - \bar{\mathbf{a}}$, where $\mathbf{a}$ and $\bar{\mathbf{a}}$ denote, respectively, the accelerations of P and G relative to the frame $Oxyz$, we write

$$\frac{d\mathbf{h}'_G}{dt} = \Sigma(\mathbf{r}' \times m\mathbf{a}) - (\Sigma m\mathbf{r}') \times \bar{\mathbf{a}}$$

But, by (12.5), the sum $\Sigma m\mathbf{r}'$ is equal to $(\Sigma m)\bar{\mathbf{r}}'$ and, thus, to zero, since the position vector $\bar{\mathbf{r}}'$ of G relative to the frame $Gx'y'z'$ is clearly zero. On the other hand, since $\mathbf{a}$ denotes the acceleration of P relative to a newtonian frame, we may substitute $\mathbf{F}$ for $m\mathbf{a}$; the expression obtained represents therefore the sum of the moments about G of the forces acting on the various particles of the system. Recalling that the internal forces cancel out, we write

$$\Sigma(\mathbf{M}_G)_{\text{ext}} = \frac{d\mathbf{h}'_G}{dt} \tag{14.34}$$

14.11. Generalized Principle of Impulse and Momentum. We have defined in Sec. 14.1 the linear impulse of a force $\mathbf{F}$ over a given time interval. We shall now define the *angular impulse about O* of a force $\mathbf{F}$ over a time interval from t_1 to t_2 as the integral from t_1 to t_2 of the moment of the force $\mathbf{F}$ about O:

$$\textbf{Ang Imp}_{1\to 2} = \int_{t_1}^{t_2} \mathbf{M}_O\, dt = \int_{t_1}^{t_2} (\mathbf{r} \times \mathbf{F})\, dt \tag{14.35}$$

This new concept, as we shall see presently, will enable us to express in a more general form the principle of impulse and momentum for a system of particles.

Consider a system of particles and the *external forces* acting on the various particles. We shall draw three separate sketches (Fig. 14.14). The first and third sketches will show the momenta of the particles at a time t_1 and a time t_2, respectively. The second sketch will show a vector attached at O, equal to the sum of the linear impulses of the external forces, and a couple of moment equal to the sum of the angular impulses about O of the external forces. For simplicity, the particles

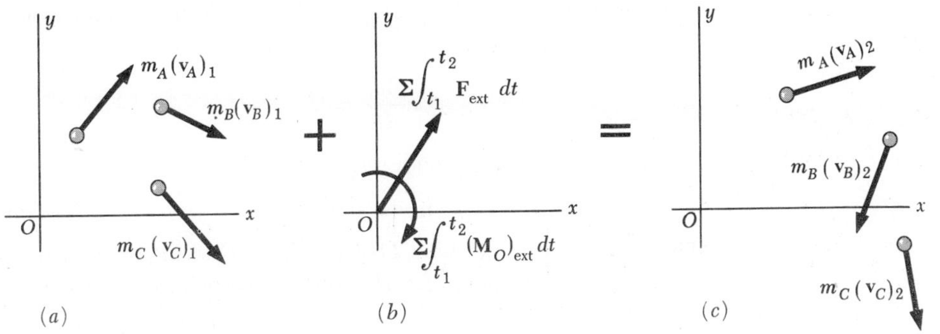

FIG. 14.14

shown in Fig. 14.14 have been assumed to move in the plane of the figure, but the present discussion remains valid in the case of particles moving in space. Recalling Eq. (14.8) of Sec. 14.2, we write

$$\Sigma m\mathbf{v}_1 + \Sigma \int_{t_1}^{t_2} \mathbf{F}_{\text{ext}}\, dt = \Sigma m\mathbf{v}_2 \tag{14.8}$$

We now return to Eq. (14.31), which was derived in Sec. 14.10, and integrate both members over the time interval from t_1 to t_2. We have

$$(\mathbf{h}_O)_1 + \Sigma \int_{t_1}^{t_2} (\mathbf{M}_O)_{\text{ext}}\, dt = (\mathbf{h}_O)_2 \tag{14.36}$$

Equation (14.8) states that the sum of the vectors shown in parts *a* and *b* of Fig. 14.14 is equal to the sum of the vectors shown in part *c* of the same figure. Equation (14.36) expresses similarly that the sum of the moments about *O* of the vectors in parts *a* and *b* of Fig. 14.14 is equal to the sum of the moments of the vectors in part *c*. Together, Eqs. (14.8) and (14.36) express therefore that the vectors in parts *a* and *b* of the figure and the vectors in part *c* form *two equivalent vector systems*. We write

$$\blacktriangleright \textbf{Syst Momenta}_1 + \textbf{Syst Ext Imp}_{1\to 2} = \textbf{Syst Momenta}_2 \tag{14.37}$$

This more general statement of the principle of impulse and momentum for a system of particles will prove particularly useful in the study of the plane motion of rigid bodies (Chap. 17). Note that, in general, six scalar equations are required to express this statement (three component equations and three moment equations). However, in the case of the plane motion of a system of particles, only three equations are required. The first two are obtained by considering respectively the *x* and *y* components of the vectors shown in Fig. 14.14, while the third equation is obtained by summing their moments about *O*.

14.12. Conservation of Angular Momentum. We saw in Sec. 14.9 that the rate of change of the angular momentum of a particle about a point *O* is equal to the moment $\mathbf{M}_O$ about *O* of the force **F** acting on the particle. If $\mathbf{M}_O$ is zero for every value of *t*, (Eq. 14.29) yields

$$\frac{d\mathbf{h}_O}{dt} = 0$$

for any *t* or, integrating with respect to *t*,

$$\mathbf{h}_O = \text{constant} \tag{14.38}$$

Thus, if the moment about *O* of the force **F** acting on a particle is zero for every value of *t*, *the angular momentum of the particle about O is conserved.*

Clearly, the angular momentum of a particle about a fixed point O will be conserved if the resultant of the forces acting on the particle is zero. But the angular momentum of the particle about O will also be conserved when the particle is acted upon by an unbalanced force $\mathbf{F}$ *if the force* $\mathbf{F}$ *is a central force whose line of action passes through the fixed point* O (Fig. 14.15).

Recalling the definition (14.24) of the angular momentum $\mathbf{h}_O$, we write for any particle moving under a central force

$$\mathbf{h}_O = \mathbf{r} \times m\mathbf{v} = \text{constant}$$

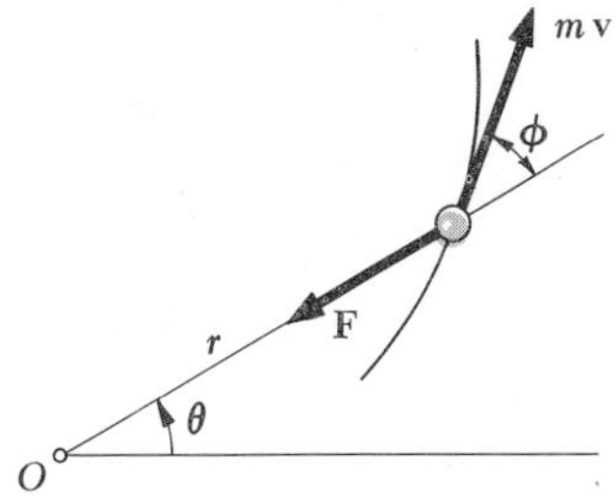

FIG. 14.15

It follows from this relation that the position vector $\mathbf{r}$ of the particle must be perpendicular to the constant vector $\mathbf{h}_O$. Thus, a particle under a central force moves in a fixed plane perpendicular to $\mathbf{h}_O$. The vector $\mathbf{h}_O$ and the fixed plane are defined by the initial position vector $\mathbf{r}_0$ and the initial velocity $\mathbf{v}_0$ of the particle. For convenience, we shall assume in the following analysis that the plane of the figure coincides with the fixed plane of motion (Fig. 14.15).

Denoting by ϕ the angle between the radius vector and the tangent to the path of the particle, we write that the magnitude h_O of the angular momentum is constant:

$$h_O = r(mv \sin \phi) = \text{constant} \tag{14.39}$$

Observing that $v \sin \phi$ represents the transverse component v_θ of the velocity, which is equal to $r d\theta/dt$ (Sec. 11.14), we may also write

$$h_O = mr^2 \frac{d\theta}{dt} = \text{constant} \tag{14.40}$$

Comparing Eq. (14.40) and Eq. (12.15), we note that

$$h_O = mh = 2m \frac{dA}{dt}$$

where h is the constant introduced in Sec. 12.9, and dA/dt the areal velocity of the particle. Thus, stating that a particle moves in a plane with a constant areal velocity is equivalent to stating that the angular momentum of the particle is conserved.

14.13. Application to Space Mechanics. The principles of conservation of energy and of conservation of angular momentum may be used to solve many problems concerning the motion of earth satellites and other space vehicles.

Consider a space vehicle which begins its free flight at point

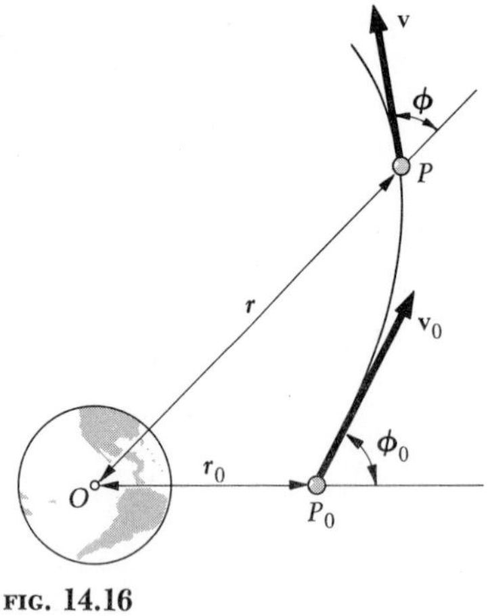

FIG. 14.16

P_0, at a distance r_0 from the center of the earth, with a velocity $\mathbf{v}_0$, forming an angle ϕ_0 with the radius vector OP_0 (Fig. 14.16). Let P be a point of the trajectory described by the vehicle; we denote by r the distance from O to P, by $\mathbf{v}$ the velocity of the vehicle at P, and by ϕ the angle formed by $\mathbf{v}$ and the radius vector OP.

Recalling from Sec. 13.6 that the potential energy due to the force of gravity is

$$V = -\frac{GMm}{r}$$

where M is the mass of the earth, we apply the principle of conservation of energy between P_0 and P and write

$$T_0 + V_0 = T + V$$

$$\tfrac{1}{2}mv_0^2 - \frac{GMm}{r_0} = \tfrac{1}{2}mv^2 - \frac{GMm}{r} \tag{14.41}$$

Since the force of gravity acting on the space vehicle is directed toward the center O of the earth, the angular momentum of the vehicle about O is conserved. Using the expression (14.39), we write

$$r_0 m v_0 \sin\phi_0 = rmv \sin\phi \tag{14.42}$$

Equation (14.41) may be solved for the magnitude v of the velocity of the vehicle at P when the distance r from O to P is known; Eq. (14.42) may then be used to determine the angle ϕ that the velocity forms with the radius vector OP.

Equations (14.41) and (14.42) may also be used to determine the maximum and minimum values of r in the case of a satellite launched from P_0 in a direction forming an angle ϕ_0 with the vertical OP_0 (Fig. 14.17). The desired values of r are obtained by making $\phi = 90°$ in (14.42) and eliminating v between Eqs. (14.41) and (14.42).

It should be noted that the application of the principles of conservation of energy and of conservation of angular momentum leads to a more fundamental formulation of the problems of space mechanics than the method indicated in Sec. 12.11. In all cases involving oblique launchings, it will also result in much simpler computations. And while the method of Sec. 12.11 must be used when the actual trajectory or the periodic time of a space vehicle is to be determined, the calculations will be simplified if the conservation principles are first used to compute the maximum and minimum values of the radius vector r.

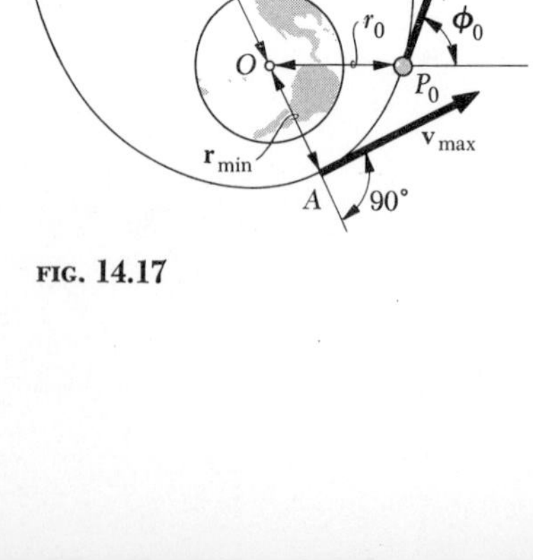

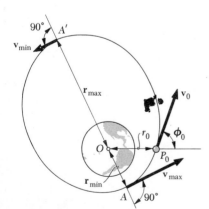

FIG. 14.17

SAMPLE PROBLEM 14.7

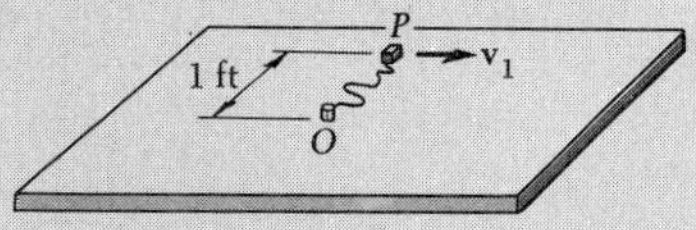

A 2-lb block P rests on a smooth horizontal table at a distance of 1 ft from a fixed pin O. The block is attached to pin O by an elastic cord of constant $k = 2$ lb/in. and of undeformed length 2 ft. If the block is set in motion to the right as shown, determine (*a*) the speed v_1 for which the distance from O to the block P will reach a maximum value of 3 ft, (*b*) the speed v_2 when $OP = 3$ ft, (*c*) the radius of curvature of the path of the block when $OP = 3$ ft.

Principle of Impulse and Momentum. We note that the force **T** exerted on P by the cord passes through the fixed point O and that the velocity $\mathbf{v}_2$ is perpendicular to OP when OP has reached its maximum value of 3 ft.

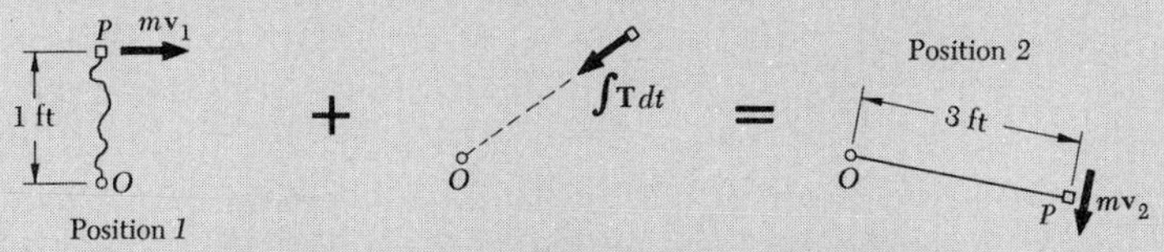

$$\text{Momentum}_1 + \text{Impulse}_{1\to 2} = \text{Momentum}_2$$

$+\circlearrowright$ moments about O: $\quad -(mv_1)(1\text{ ft}) + 0 = -(mv_2)(3\text{ ft})$

$$v_1 = 3v_2 \qquad (1)$$

Conservation of Energy. *Kinetic Energy*

$$T_1 = \tfrac{1}{2}mv_1^2 = \frac{1}{2}\frac{W}{g}v_1^2 = \frac{1}{2}\frac{2}{g}v_1^2 \qquad T_2 = \frac{1}{2}\frac{2}{g}v_2^2$$

Potential Energy. Since the cord is unstretched in position *1*, $V_1 = 0$. In position *2* the elongation of the cord is $x = 3\text{ ft} - 2\text{ ft} = 1$ ft. Recalling that $k = 2$ lb/in. $= 24$ lb/ft, we have

$$V_2 = \tfrac{1}{2}kx^2 = \tfrac{1}{2}(24\text{ lb/ft})(1\text{ ft})^2 = 12\text{ ft-lb}$$

Applying the principle of conservation of energy, we write

$$T_1 + V_1 = T_2 + V_2 \qquad \frac{1}{2}\frac{2}{g}v_1^2 + 0 = \frac{1}{2}\frac{2}{g}v_2^2 + 12 \qquad (2)$$

Substituting $v_1 = 3v_2$ from (1) into (2), we find

$$\frac{(3v_2)^2}{g} = \frac{v_2^2}{g} + 12 \qquad v_2^2 = \frac{12g}{8} = 48.3 \qquad v_2 = 6.95\text{ ft/sec} \blacktriangleleft$$

$$v_1 = 3v_2 = 3(6.95) \qquad v_1 = 20.85\text{ ft/sec} \blacktriangleleft$$

Radius of Curvature. When the block is 3 ft from O, we have $v_2 = 6.95$ ft/sec and the tension in the cord is

$$T = kx = (24\text{ lb/ft})(1\text{ ft}) = 24\text{ lb}$$

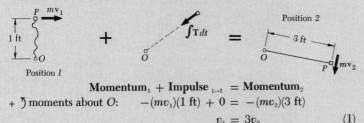

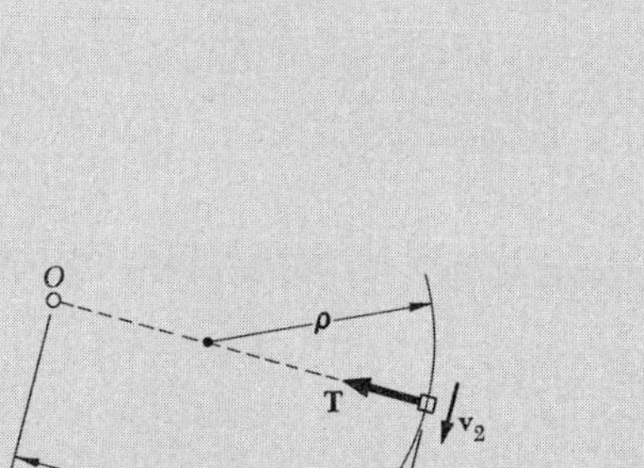

Since the acceleration of the block is directed toward O, we write

$$\mathbf{F} = m\mathbf{a}_n\text{:} \qquad T = \frac{W}{g}\frac{v_2^2}{\rho} \qquad 24 = \frac{2}{g}\frac{(48.3)}{\rho}$$

$$\rho = 0.1250\text{ ft} = 1.500\text{ in.} \blacktriangleleft$$

SAMPLE PROBLEM 14.8

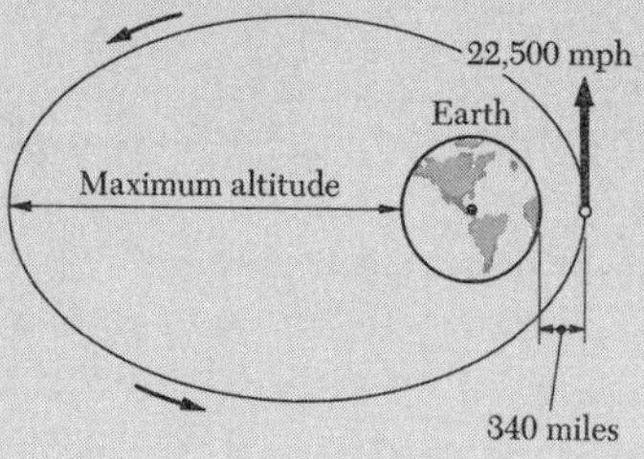

A satellite is launched in a direction parallel to the surface of the earth with a velocity of 22,500 mph from an altitude of 340 miles. Determine (*a*) the maximum altitude reached by the satellite, (*b*) the maximum allowable error in the direction of launching if the satellite is to go into orbit and to come not closer than 140 miles to the surface of the earth.

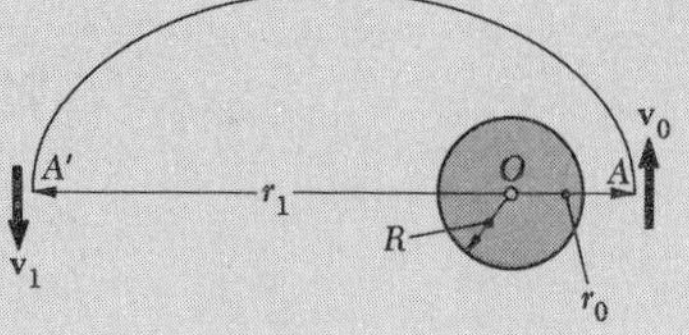

a. **Maximum Altitude.** We denote by A' the point of the orbit farthest from the earth and by r_1 the corresponding distance from the center of the earth. Since the satellite is in free flight between A and A', we apply the principle of conservation of energy.

$$T_A + V_A = T_{A'} + V_{A'}$$

$$\tfrac{1}{2}mv_0^2 - \frac{GMm}{r_0} = \tfrac{1}{2}mv_1^2 - \frac{GMm}{r_1} \tag{1}$$

Since the only force acting on the satellite is the force of gravity, which is a central force, the angular momentum of the satellite about O is conserved. Considering points A and A', we write

$$mr_0v_0 = mr_1v_1 \qquad v_1 = v_0\frac{r_0}{r_1} \tag{2}$$

Substituting this expression for v_1 into Eq. (1) and dividing each term by the mass m, we obtain, after rearranging the terms,

$$\tfrac{1}{2}v_0^2\left(1 - \frac{r_0^2}{r_1^2}\right) = \frac{GM}{r_0}\left(1 - \frac{r_0}{r_1}\right) \qquad 1 + \frac{r_0}{r_1} = \frac{2GM}{r_0v_0^2} \tag{3}$$

Recalling that the radius R of the earth is 3,960 miles, we compute

$$r_0 = 3{,}960 + 340 = 4{,}300 \text{ miles} = 22.7 \times 10^6 \text{ ft}$$
$$v_0 = 22{,}500 \text{ mph} = 33{,}000 \text{ ft/sec}$$
$$GM = gR^2 = (32.2)(3{,}960 \times 5{,}280)^2 = 1.408 \times 10^{16}$$

Substituting these values into (3), we obtain $r_1 = 30{,}940$ miles.

Maximum altitude = 30,940 − 3,960 = 26,980 miles ◄

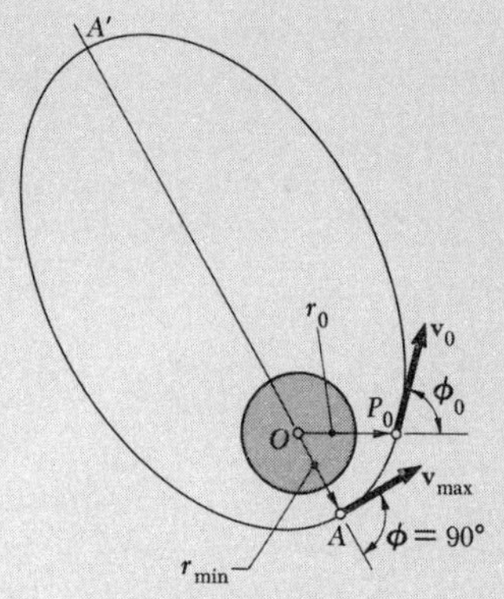

b. **Allowable Error in Direction of Launching.** The satellite is launched from P_0 in a direction forming an angle ϕ_0 with the vertical OP_0. The value of ϕ_0 corresponding to $r_{min} = 3{,}960 + 140 = 4{,}100$ miles is obtained by applying the principles of conservation of energy and of conservation of momentum between P_0 and the perigee A.

$$\tfrac{1}{2}mv_0^2 - \frac{GMm}{r_0} = \tfrac{1}{2}mv_{max}^2 - \frac{GMm}{r_{min}} \tag{4}$$

$$mr_0v_0 \sin\phi_0 = mr_{min}v_{max} \tag{5}$$

Solving (5) for v_{max} and then substituting for v_{max} into (4), we may solve (4) for $\sin\phi_0$. Using the values of v_0 and GM computed in part *a* and noting that $r_0/r_{min} = 4{,}300/4{,}100 = 1.0488$, we find

$$\sin\phi_0 = 0.9796 \qquad \phi_0 = 90° \pm 11.6°$$

Allowable error = ±11.6° ◄

PROBLEMS

14.76. A heavy ball is mounted on a horizontal rod which rotates freely about a vertical shaft. In the position shown, the speed of the ball is $v_1 = 50$ in./sec and the ball is held by a cord attached to the shaft. The cord is suddenly cut and the ball moves to position A' as the rod rotates. Neglecting the mass of the rod, determine (*a*) the speed of the ball in position A', (*b*) the change in the kinetic energy of the system, (*c*) the path (on the xz plane) of the ball as it moves from A to A'.

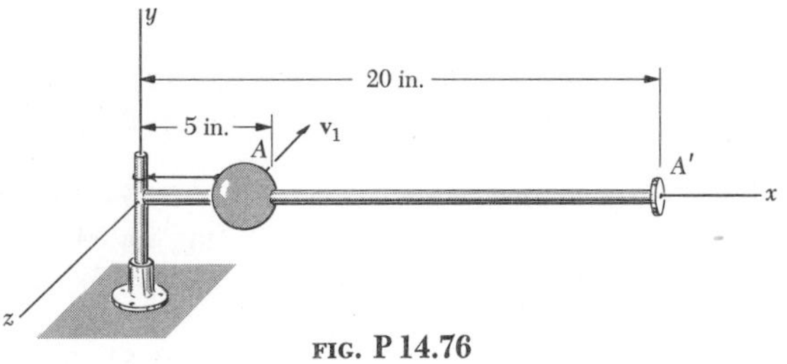

FIG. P 14.76

14.77. A particle is set in motion in a hemispherical cup by projecting it horizontally along the inside of the rim with an arbitrary initial velocity $\mathbf{v}_0$. If the particle slides without friction, show that its path will never pass through the base of the cup.

14.78. A ball of mass m slides on a smooth horizontal table at the end of a string which passes through a small hole in the table at O. When the length of string above the table is r_1, the speed of the ball is v_1. If the string is drawn in until the length of string above the table is $r_2 = \frac{1}{2}r_1$, determine (*a*) the speed v_2, (*b*) the per cent change in the magnitude of the linear momentum of the ball, (*c*) the per cent change in the angular momentum of the ball with respect to O, (*d*) the per cent change in the kinetic energy of the ball.

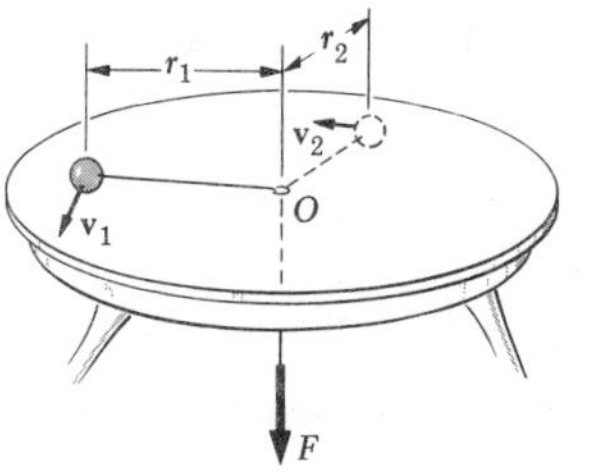

FIG. P 14.78

14.79. Solve Prob. 14.78 assuming that the string wraps around a rod at O of very small diameter instead of being drawn through a hole at O. (*Hint.* No work is done by the forces acting on the system.)

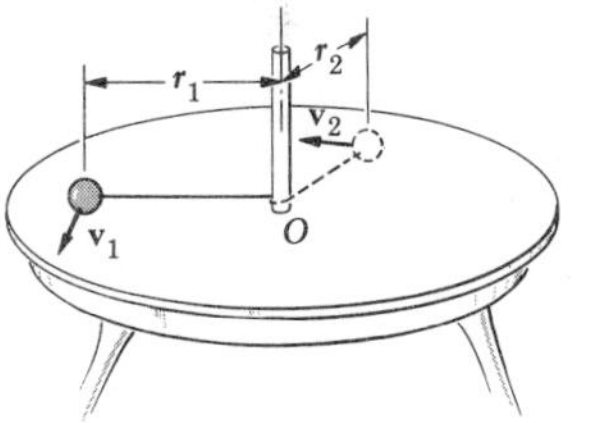

FIG. P 14.79

14.80. A $\frac{1}{2}$-lb ball is attached to a fixed point O by means of an elastic cord of constant $k = 10$ lb/ft and of undeformed length 2 ft. The ball slides on a smooth horizontal surface. When the ball is in position *1*, the length of the cord is 3 ft and the velocity of the ball is 10 ft/sec, directed as shown. Determine (*a*) the speed of the ball after the cord has become slack, (*b*) the distance d when the ball is closest to point O.

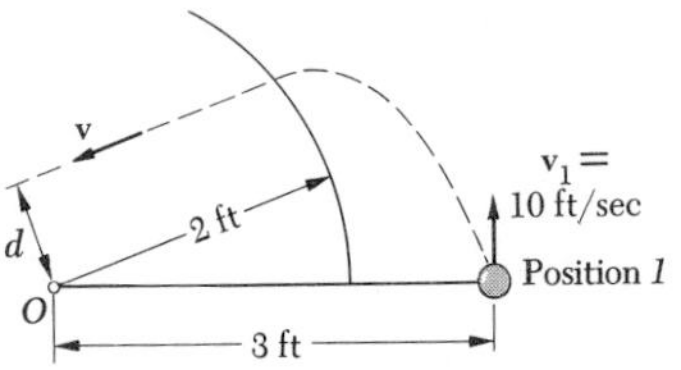

FIG. P 14.80

14.81. In Prob. 14.80, determine the required magnitude of $\mathbf{v}_1$ if the ball is to pass at a distance $d = 4$ in. from point O. The direction of $\mathbf{v}_1$ is not changed.

14.82. In Prob. 14.80, determine the smallest magnitude of $\mathbf{v}_1$ for which the elastic cord will remain taut at all times.

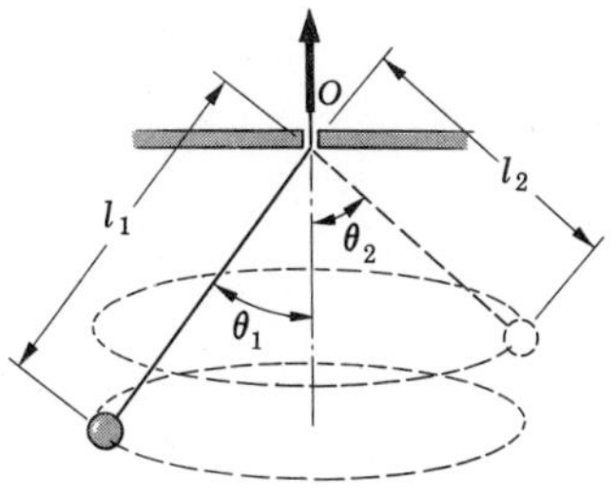

FIG. P 14.83

14.83. A small ball swings in a horizontal circle at the end of a cord of length l_1 which forms an angle θ_1 with the vertical. If the cord is slowly drawn through the support at O until the free length is l_2, derive a relation between l_1, l_2, θ_1, and θ_2.

14.84. The ball of Prob. 14.83 is set in motion so that, initially, $l_1 = 20$ in. and $\theta_1 = 30°$. Determine the length l_2 for which $\theta_2 = 60°$.

14.85. The ball of Prob. 14.83 is set in motion so that, initially, $l_1 = 20$ in. and $\theta_1 = 30°$. Determine the angle θ_2 when $l_2 = 15$ in.

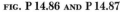

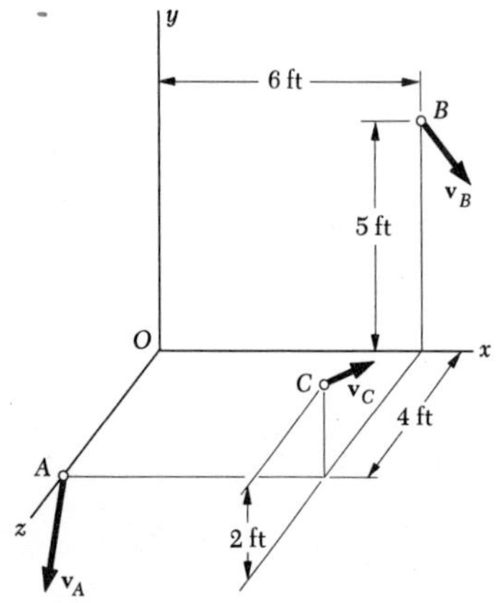

FIG. P 14.86 AND P 14.87

14.86. Determine the angular momentum $\mathbf{h}_O$ of (*a*) particle *A*, knowing that $W_A = 2$ lb and $\mathbf{v}_A = -10\mathbf{j} + 5\mathbf{k}$ (ft/sec), (*b*) particle *B*, knowing that $W_B = 3$ lb and $\mathbf{v}_B = 8\mathbf{i} - 6\mathbf{j} + 4\mathbf{k}$ (ft/sec).

14.87. In the position shown the velocity of particle *C* is $\mathbf{v}_C = v_x\mathbf{i} + v_y\mathbf{j} + 10\mathbf{k}$ (ft/sec). Knowing that $W_C = 4$ lb, determine the values of v_x and v_y for which the total angular momentum about *O* of particles *A*, *B*, and *C* is parallel to the *z* axis. (See Prob. 14.86 for data concerning particles *A* and *B*.)

14.88. Show that the angular momentum $\mathbf{h}'_G$ of a system of particles defined in (14.32) is identically equal to the angular momentum

$$\mathbf{h}_G = \Sigma(\mathbf{r}' \times m\mathbf{v})$$

obtained by adding the moments about *G* of the linear momenta $m\mathbf{v}$ relative to the newtonian frame *Oxyz*.

14.89. Derive the relation

$$\mathbf{h}_O = \bar{\mathbf{r}} \times (\Sigma m)\bar{\mathbf{v}} + \mathbf{h}'_G$$

between the angular momenta $\mathbf{h}_O$ and $\mathbf{h}'_G$ defined in (14.30) and (14.32). The vectors $\bar{\mathbf{r}}$ and $\bar{\mathbf{v}}$ define respectively the position and the velocity of the mass center *G* of the system of particles relative to the newtonian frame of reference *Oxyz*.

14.90. Show that formula (14.34) may be derived directly from (14.31) by substituting for $\mathbf{h}_O$ the expression given in Prob. 14.89.

***14.91.** Show that the relation

$$\Sigma(\mathbf{M}_A)_{\text{ext}} = \frac{d\mathbf{h}'_A}{dt}$$

based on a moving frame of reference $Ax'y'z'$ which translates with respect to the newtonian frame *Oxyz* is valid if, and only if, one of the following conditions is satisfied: (*a*) the frame $Ax'y'z'$ is itself a newtonian frame of reference, (*b*) *A* coincides with the mass center *G*, (*c*) the acceleration $\mathbf{a}_A$ of *A* relative to *Oxyz* is directed along the line *AG*.

14.92 through 14.95. Using the principles of conservation of energy and of conservation of angular momentum, solve the following problems:

14.92. Prob. 12.84.
14.93. Prob. 12.85.
14.94. Prob. 12.86.
14.95. Prob. 12.89.

14.96. A satellite is describing a circular orbit of radius r_0 around the earth. By firing auxiliary rockets, its kinetic energy is suddenly increased by 50 per cent. Determine the maximum distance from the center of the earth reached by the satellite in its new orbit.

14.97. A satellite is describing a circular orbit of radius r_0 around the earth. (*a*) How much should the kinetic energy of the satellite be increased to place it in an elliptic orbit with apogee A' at a distance $2r_0$ from the center of the earth? (*b*) What further increase in energy would be required to place the satellite in a circular orbit of radius $2r_0$?

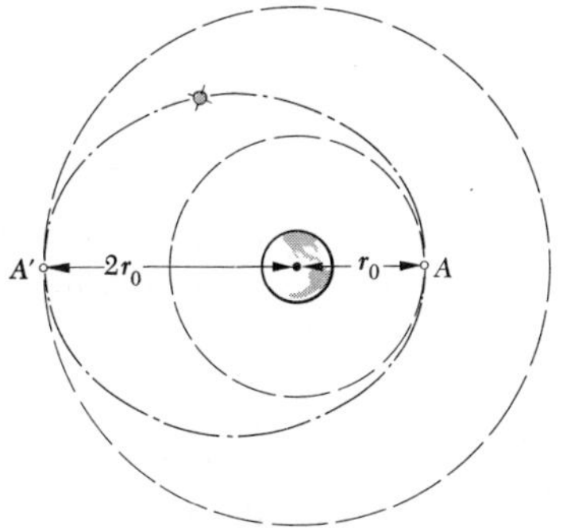

FIG. **P 14.97**

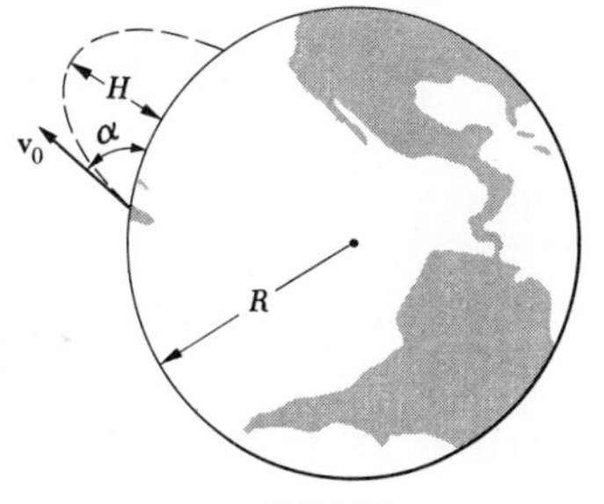

FIG. **P 14.98**

14.98. A missile is fired from the ground with an initial velocity of magnitude $v_0 = \sqrt{gR}$, where R is the radius of the earth. Determine the firing angle α if the missile is to reach a maximum height H equal to half the radius of the earth.

14.99. An artificial satellite is projected into space with a velocity $\mathbf{v}_0$ at a distance r_0 from the center of the earth by the last stage of its launching rocket. The initial velocity $\mathbf{v}_0$ was designed to send the satellite into a circular orbit around the earth. However, owing to a malfunction of control, the satellite is not projected horizontally but at an angle α with the horizontal and, as a result, is propelled into an elliptic orbit. Determine the maximum and minimum values of the distance from the center of the earth to the satellite.

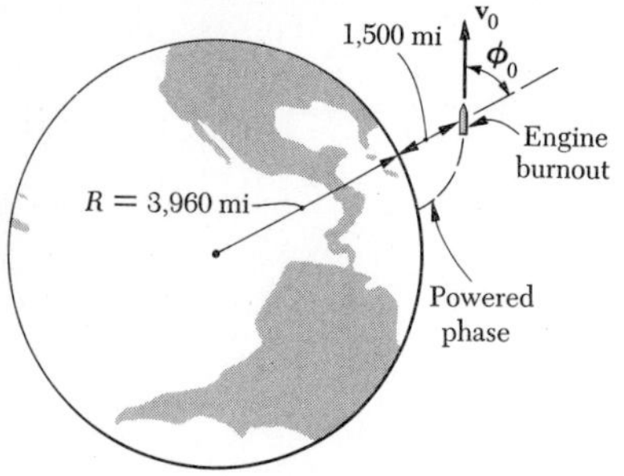

FIG. P 14.100 AND P 14.101

14.100. At engine burnout a satellite has reached an altitude of 1,500 miles and has a velocity $\mathbf{v}_0$ of 26,700 ft/sec forming an angle $\phi_0 = 76°$ with the vertical. Determine the maximum and minimum heights reached by the satellite.

14.101. At engine burnout a satellite has reached an altitude of 1,500 miles and has a velocity $\mathbf{v}_0$ of magnitude 26,700 ft/sec. For what range of values of the angle ϕ_0, formed by $\mathbf{v}_0$ and the vertical, will the satellite go into a permanent orbit? (Assume that if the satellite gets closer than 200 miles from the earth's surface, it will soon burn up.)

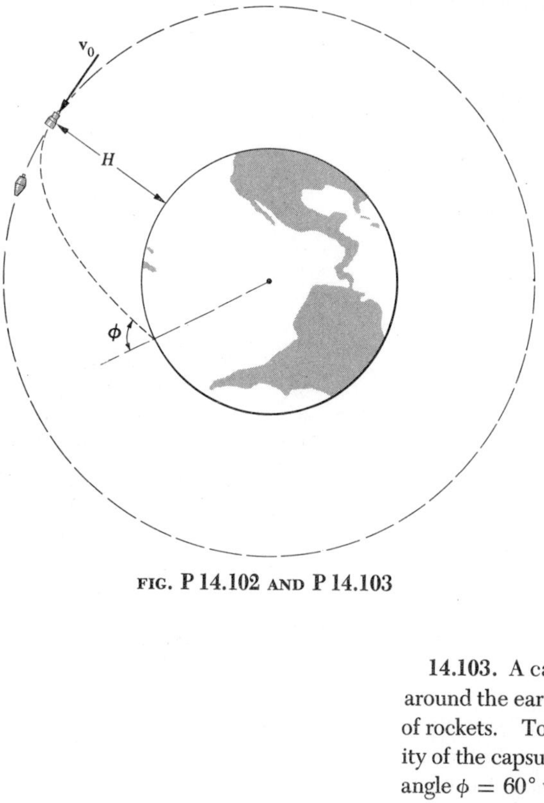

FIG. P 14.102 AND P 14.103

14.102. A satellite describing a circular orbit around the earth at an altitude $H = 4{,}000$ miles ejects a capsule. If the speed of the capsule is reduced to $v_0 = 6{,}000$ ft/sec by means of rockets, determine the speed with which the capsule will reach the earth's surface and the angle of impact ϕ with the vertical. (Neglect the effect of the atmosphere.)

14.103. A capsule is ejected from a satellite describing a circular orbit around the earth at an altitude $H = 1{,}000$ miles and is slowed by means of rockets. To what value v_0 should the magnitude of the absolute velocity of the capsule be reduced by the rockets if it is to strike the earth at an angle $\phi = 60°$ with the vertical? (Neglect the effect of the atmosphere.)

14.104. A missile fired from the ground with an initial velocity of magnitude v_0 is to reach a maximum altitude equal to the radius of the earth. (*a*) Show that the required firing angle α is defined by the relation

$$\cos \alpha = 2\sqrt{1 - \tfrac{1}{2}(v_{esc}/v_0)^2}$$

where v_{esc} is the escape velocity. (*b*) Determine the maximum and minimum allowable values of v_0.

***14.105.** Solve Prob. 12.95.

***14.14. Variable Systems of Particles.** All the systems of particles considered so far consisted of well-defined particles. These systems did not gain or lose any particles during their motion. In a large number of engineering applications, however, it is necessary to consider *variable systems of particles,* i.e., systems which are continuously gaining or losing particles, or doing both at the same time. Consider, for example, a hydraulic turbine. Its analysis involves the determination of the forces exerted by a stream of water on rotating blades, and we note that the particles of water in contact with the blades form an ever-changing system which continuously acquires and loses particles. Rockets furnish another example of variable systems, since their propulsion depends upon the continuous ejection of fuel particles.

We recall that all the kinetics principles established so far were derived for constant systems of particles, which neither gain nor lose particles. We must therefore find a way to reduce the analysis of a variable system of particles to that of an auxiliary constant system. The procedure to follow is indicated in Secs. 14.15 and 14.16 for two broad categories of applications.

***14.15. Steady Stream of Particles.** Consider a steady stream of particles, such as a stream of water diverted by a fixed vane or a flow of air through a duct or through a blower. In order to determine the resultant of the forces exerted on the particles in contact with the vane, duct, or blower, we isolate these particles and denote by S the system thus defined (Fig. 14.18). We observe that S is a variable system of particles, since it continuously gains particles flowing in and loses an equal number of particles flowing out. Therefore, the kinetics principles that have been established so far cannot be directly applied to S.

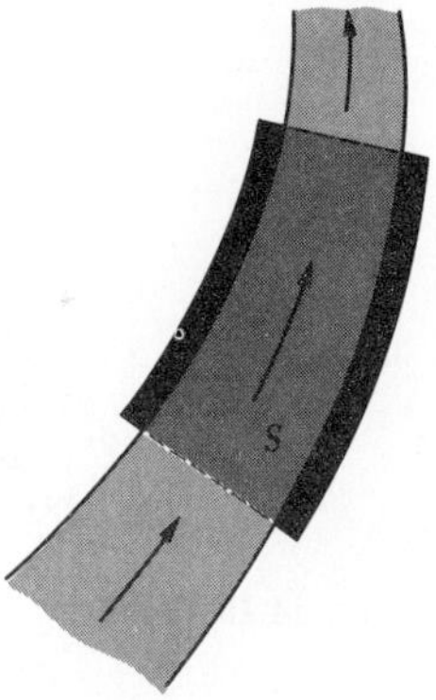

FIG. 14.18

However, we may easily define an auxiliary system of particles which does remain constant for a short interval of time Δt. Consider at time t the system S *plus* the particles which will enter S during the interval of time Δt (Fig. 14.19a). Next, consider at time $t + \Delta t$ the system S *plus* the particles which have left S during the interval Δt (Fig. 14.19c). Clearly, *the same particles are involved in both cases*, and we may apply to these particles the principle of impulse and momentum. Since the total mass m of the system S remains constant, the particles entering the system and those leaving the system in the time Δt must have the same mass Δm. Denoting by $\mathbf{v}_1$ and $\mathbf{v}_2$, respectively, the velocities of the particles entering and leaving

S and by $\Sigma m\mathbf{v}$ the sum of the momenta of the particles of S, we express the principle of impulse and momentum as follows:

$$(\Delta m)\mathbf{v}_1 + \Sigma m\mathbf{v} + \Sigma\mathbf{F}\,\Delta t = \Sigma m\mathbf{v} + (\Delta m)\mathbf{v}_2$$

or, canceling the term $\Sigma m\mathbf{v}$ which appears in both members,

$$(\Delta m)\mathbf{v}_1 + \Sigma\mathbf{F}\,\Delta t = (\Delta m)\mathbf{v}_2 \qquad (14.43)$$

This equation expresses that *the momentum of the particles leaving S in the time Δt may be obtained by adding vectorially the momentum of the particles entering S in the time Δt and the impulses of the forces exerted on S during the same time interval.* Dividing all terms of (14.43) by Δt and letting Δt approach zero, we obtain at the limit

$$\Sigma\mathbf{F} = \frac{dm}{dt}(\mathbf{v}_2 - \mathbf{v}_1) \qquad (14.44)$$

where $\mathbf{v}_2 - \mathbf{v}_1$ represents the difference between the vectors $\mathbf{v}_2$ and $\mathbf{v}_1$.

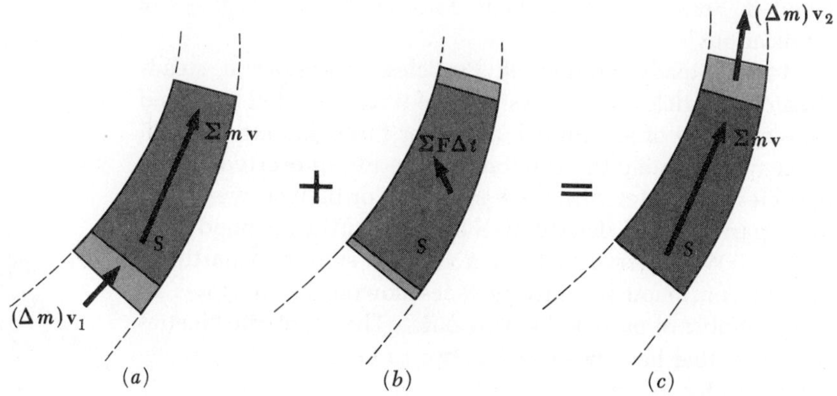

FIG. 14.19

The principle we have just established may be used to analyze a large number of engineering applications. Some of the most common are indicated below.

Fluid Stream Diverted by a Vane. If the vane is fixed, the method of analysis given above may be applied directly to find the force $\mathbf{F}$ exerted by the vane on the stream. We note that $\mathbf{F}$ is the only force which needs to be considered since the pressure in the stream is constant (atmospheric pressure). The force exerted by the stream on the vane will be equal and opposite to $\mathbf{F}$. If the vane moves with a constant velocity, the stream is not steady. However, it will appear steady to an observer moving with the vane. We should therefore choose a system of axes moving with the vane. Since this system of axes is not accelerated, Eq. (14.43) may still be used, but $\mathbf{v}_1$ and $\mathbf{v}_2$ must be replaced by the *relative velocities* of the stream with respect to the vane (see Sample Prob. 14.9).

Fluid Flowing through a Pipe. The force exerted by the fluid on a pipe transition such as a bend or a contraction may be determined by considering the system of particles S in contact with the transition. Since, in general, the pressure in the flow will vary, we should also consider the forces exerted on S by the adjoining portions of the fluid.

Jet Engine. In a jet engine, air enters with no velocity through the front of the engine and leaves through the rear with a high velocity. The energy required to accelerate the air particles is obtained by burning fuel. While the exhaust gases contain burned fuel, the mass of the fuel is small compared with the mass of the air flowing through the engine and usually may be neglected. Thus, the analysis of a jet engine reduces to that of an air stream. This stream may be considered as a steady stream if all velocities are measured with respect to the airplane. The air stream should be assumed, therefore, to enter the engine with a velocity $\mathbf{v}$ of magnitude equal to the speed of the airplane and to leave with a velocity $\mathbf{u}$ equal to the relative velocity of the exhaust gases (Fig. 14.20). Since the intake and exhaust pressures are nearly atmospheric, the only external force which needs to be considered is the force exerted by the engine on the air stream. This force is equal and opposite to the thrust.

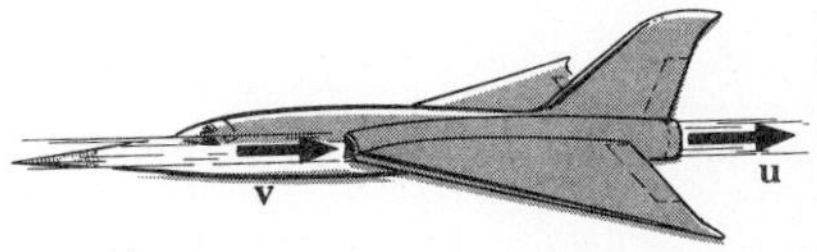

FIG. 14.20

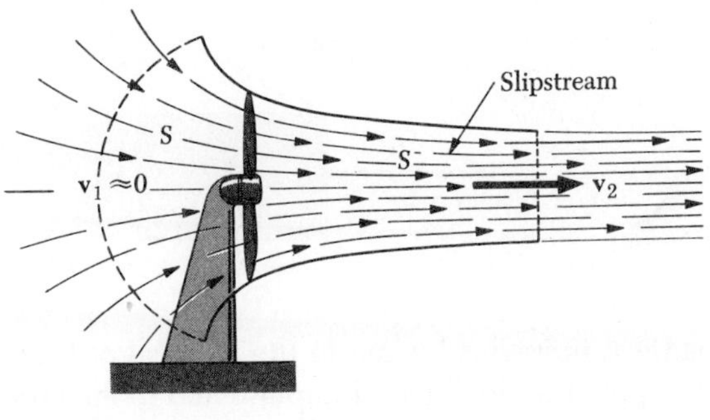

FIG. 14.21

Fan. We consider the system of particles S shown in Fig. 14.21. The velocity $\mathbf{v}_1$ of the particles entering the system is assumed equal to zero, and the velocity $\mathbf{v}_2$ of the particles leaving the system is the velocity of the *slipstream.* The rate of flow may be obtained by multiplying v_2 by the cross-sectional area of the slipstream. Since the pressure all around S is atmospheric, the only external force acting on S is the thrust of the fan.

Airplane Propeller. In order to obtain a steady stream of air, velocities should be measured with respect to the airplane. Thus, the air particles should be assumed to enter the system with a velocity **v** of magnitude equal to the speed of the airplane and to leave with a velocity **u** equal to the relative velocity of the slipstream.

***14.16. Systems Gaining or Losing Mass.** We shall now analyze a different type of variable system of particles, namely, a system which gains mass by continuously absorbing particles or loses mass by continually expelling particles. Consider the system S shown in Fig. 14.22. Its mass, equal to m at the instant t, increases by Δm in the interval of time Δt. In order to apply the principle of impulse and momentum to the analysis of this system, we must consider at time t the system S *plus* the particles of mass Δm which S absorbs during the time interval Δt. The velocity of S at time t is denoted by v, and its velocity at time $t + \Delta t$ is denoted by $\mathbf{v} + \Delta\mathbf{v}$, while the absolute velocity of the particles which are absorbed is denoted by $\mathbf{v}_a$.

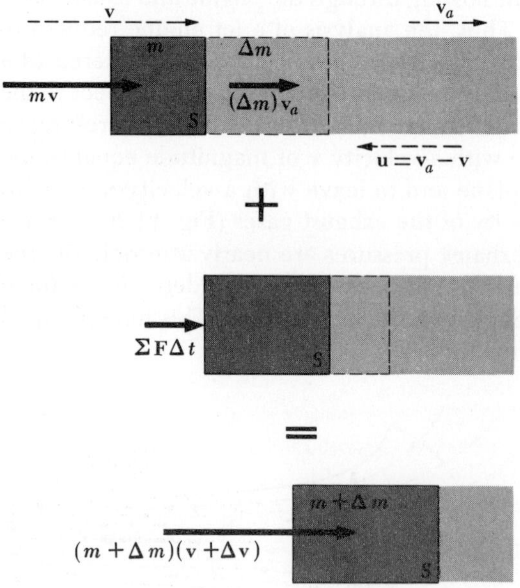

FIG. 14.22

Applying the principle of impulse and momentum, we write

$$m\mathbf{v} + (\Delta m)\mathbf{v}_a + \Sigma\mathbf{F}\,\Delta t = (m + \Delta m)(\mathbf{v} + \Delta\mathbf{v})$$

Solving for the sum $\Sigma\mathbf{F}\,\Delta t$ of the impulses of the external forces acting on S (excluding the forces exerted by the particles being absorbed), we have

$$\Sigma\mathbf{F}\,\Delta t = m\,\Delta\mathbf{v} + \Delta m(\mathbf{v} - \mathbf{v}_a) + (\Delta m)(\Delta\mathbf{v}) \qquad (14.45)$$

Introducing the *relative velocity* $\mathbf{u}$ with respect to S of the particles which are absorbed, we write $\mathbf{u} = \mathbf{v}_a - \mathbf{v}$ and note, since $v_a < v$, that the relative velocity $\mathbf{u}$ is directed to the left, as shown in Fig. 14.22. Neglecting the last term in Eq. (14.45), which is of the second order, we write

$$\Sigma\mathbf{F}\,\Delta t = m\,\Delta\mathbf{v} - (\Delta m)\mathbf{u}$$

Dividing through by Δt and letting Δt approach zero, we have at the limit†

$$\Sigma\mathbf{F} = m\frac{d\mathbf{v}}{dt} - \frac{dm}{dt}\mathbf{u} \qquad (14.46)$$

Rearranging the terms, we obtain the equation

$$\Sigma\mathbf{F} + \frac{dm}{dt}\mathbf{u} = m\frac{d\mathbf{v}}{dt} \qquad (14.47)$$

which shows that the action on S of the particles being absorbed is equivalent to a thrust of magnitude $(dm/dt)u$ which tends to slow down the motion of S, since the relative velocity $\mathbf{u}$ of the particles is directed to the left.

The equations obtained may also be used to determine the motion of a system S losing mass. In this case, the rate of change of mass is negative, and the action on S of the particles being expelled is equivalent to a thrust in the direction of $-\mathbf{u}$, i.e., in the direction opposite to that in which the particles are being expelled. A *rocket* represents a typical case of a system continuously losing mass (see Sample Prob. 14.10).

† When the absolute velocity $\mathbf{v}_a$ of the particles absorbed is zero, we have $\mathbf{u} = -\mathbf{v}$, and formula (14.46) becomes

$$\Sigma\mathbf{F} = \frac{d}{dt}(m\mathbf{v})$$

Comparing the formula obtained to Eq. (14.1) of Sec. 14.1, we observe that Newton's second law may be applied to a system gaining mass, *provided that the particles absorbed are initially at rest.* It may also be applied to a system losing mass, *provided that the velocity of the particles expelled is zero* with respect to the frame of reference selected.

SAMPLE PROBLEM 14.9

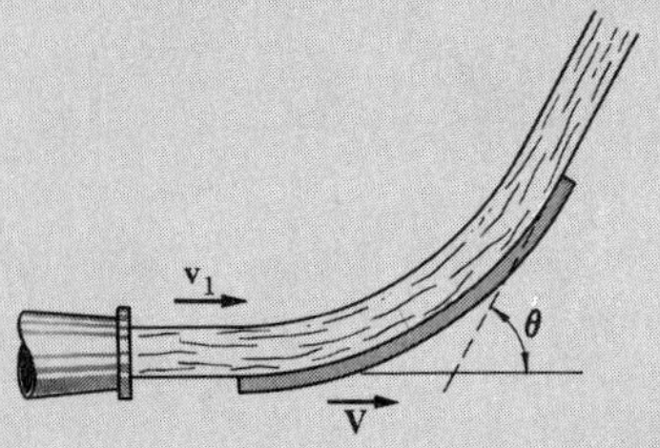

A nozzle discharges a stream of water of cross-sectional area A with a velocity $\mathbf{v}_1$. The stream is deflected by a *single* blade which moves to the right with a constant velocity $\mathbf{V}$. Assuming that the water moves along the blade at constant speed, determine (*a*) the components of the force $\mathbf{F}$ exerted by the blade on the stream, (*b*) the velocity $\mathbf{V}$ for which maximum power is developed.

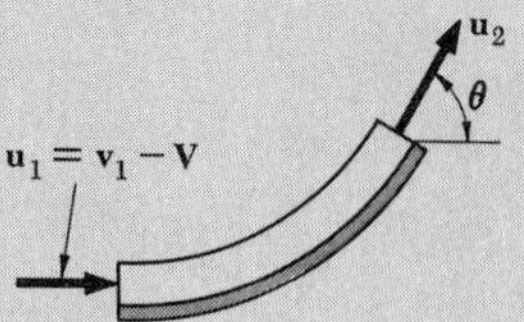

a. **Components of Force Exerted on Stream.** We choose a coordinate system which moves with the blade at a constant velocity $\mathbf{V}$. The particles of water strike the blade with a relative velocity $\mathbf{u}_1 = \mathbf{v}_1 - \mathbf{V}$ and leave the blade with a relative velocity $\mathbf{u}_2$. Since the particles move along the blade at a constant speed, the relative velocities $\mathbf{u}_1$ and $\mathbf{u}_2$ have the same magnitude u. Denoting the density of water by ρ, the mass of the particles striking the blade during the time interval Δt is $\Delta m = A\rho(v_1 - V)\,\Delta t$; an equal mass of particles leaves the blade during Δt. Since the momentum of the particles leaving the blade is equal to the momentum of the particles striking the blade plus the impulses of the forces exerted by the blade, we write

$$(\Delta m)\mathbf{u}_1 + \Sigma\mathbf{F}\,\Delta t = (\Delta m)\mathbf{u}_2$$

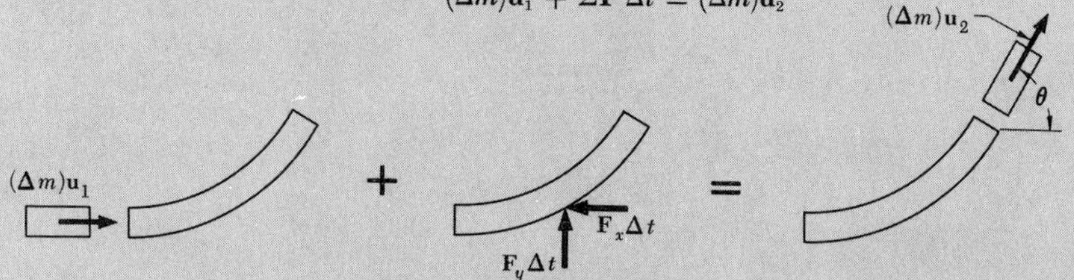

Recalling that $\mathbf{u}_1$ and $\mathbf{u}_2$ have the same magnitude u, we write

$\xrightarrow{+}$ x components: $\quad (\Delta m)u - F_x\,\Delta t = (\Delta m)u\cos\theta$

$+\uparrow$ y components: $\quad +F_y\,\Delta t = (\Delta m)u\sin\theta$

Substituting $\Delta m = A\rho(v_1 - V)\,\Delta t$ and $u = v_1 - V$, we obtain

$$\mathbf{F}_x = A\rho(v_1 - V)^2(1 - \cos\theta)\leftarrow \qquad \mathbf{F}_y = A\rho(v_1 - V)^2\sin\theta\uparrow \quad ◄$$

b. **Velocity of Blade for Maximum Power.** The power is obtained by multiplying the velocity V of the blade by the component $-F_x$ of the force exerted by the stream on the blade.

$$\text{Power} = -F_xV = A\rho(v_1 - V)^2(1 - \cos\theta)V$$

Differentiating the power with respect to V and setting the derivative equal to zero, we obtain

$$\frac{d(\text{power})}{dV} = A\rho(v_1^2 - 4v_1V + 3V^2)(1 - \cos\theta) = 0$$

$$V = v_1 \qquad V = \tfrac{1}{3}v_1 \qquad \text{For maximum power } \mathbf{V} = \tfrac{1}{3}v_1 \rightarrow \quad ◄$$

Note. These results are valid only when a *single* blade deflects the stream. Different results are obtained when a series of blades deflects the stream, as in a Pelton-wheel turbine. (See Prob. 14.144.)

SAMPLE PROBLEM 14.10

A rocket of initial mass m_0 (including shell and fuel) is fired vertically at time $t = 0$. The fuel is consumed at a constant rate $q = dm/dt$ and is expelled at a constant speed u relative to the rocket. Derive an expression for the velocity of the rocket at time t, neglecting the resistance of the air.

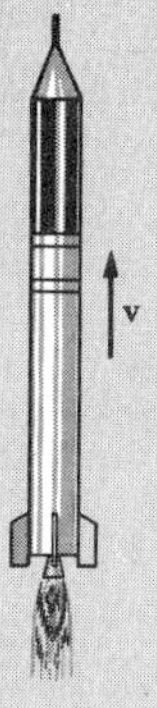

Solution. At time t, the mass of the rocket shell and remaining fuel is $m = m_0 - qt$, and the velocity is $\mathbf{v}$. During the time interval Δt, a mass of fuel $\Delta m = q\,\Delta t$ is expelled with a speed u relative to the rocket. Denoting by $\mathbf{v}_e$ the absolute velocity of the expelled fuel, we apply the principle of impulse and momentum between time t and time $t + \Delta t$.

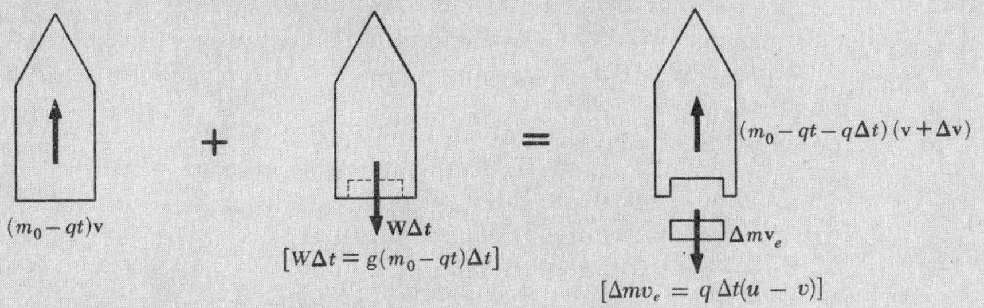

$$(m_0 - qt)v - g(m_0 - qt)\,\Delta t$$
$$= (m_0 - qt - q\,\Delta t)(v + \Delta v) - q\,\Delta t(u - v)$$

Dividing through by Δt, and letting Δt approach zero, we obtain

$$-g(m_0 - qt) = (m_0 - qt)\frac{dv}{dt} - qu$$

Separating variables and integrating from $t = 0$, $v = 0$ to $t = t$, $v = v$,

$$dv = \left(\frac{qu}{m_0 - qt} - g\right)dt \qquad \int_0^v dv = \int_0^t \left(\frac{qu}{m_0 - qt} - g\right)dt$$

$$v = [-u \ln(m_0 - qt) - gt]_0^t \qquad v = u \ln \frac{m_0}{m_0 - qt} - gt \quad ◄$$

Remark. The mass remaining at time t_f, after all of the fuel has been expended, is equal to the mass of the rocket shell $m_s = m_0 - qt_f$, and the maximum velocity attained by the rocket is $v_m = u \ln(m_0/m_s) - gt_f$. Assuming that the fuel is expelled in a relatively short period of time, the term gt_f is small and we have $v_m \approx u \ln(m_0/m_s)$. In order to escape the gravitational field of the earth, a rocket must reach a velocity of 36,700 ft/sec. Assuming $u = 7{,}000$ ft/sec and $v_m = 36{,}700$ ft/sec, we obtain $m_0/m_s = 188$. Thus, to project each pound of the rocket shell into space, it is necessary to consume more than 188 lb of fuel if a propellant yielding $u = 7{,}000$ ft/sec is used.

PROBLEMS

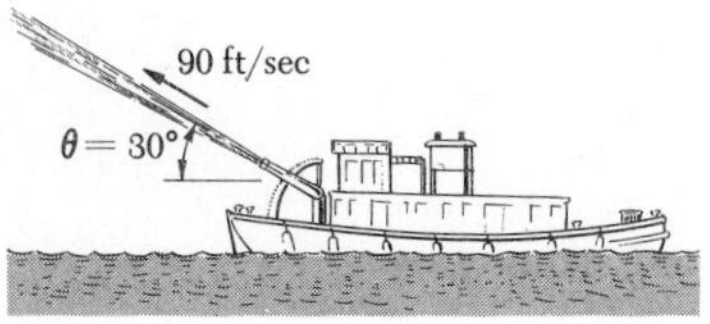

FIG. P 14.106

14.106. A hose discharges 2,000 gal/min from the stern of a 20-ton fireboat. If the velocity of the water stream is 90 ft/sec, determine the reaction on the boat.

14.107. A 15-lb machine gun fires 600 bullets per minute. Knowing that each bullet weighs 1.5 oz and that the muzzle velocity is 2,400 ft/sec, determine the magnitude of the average force required to hold the gun motionless.

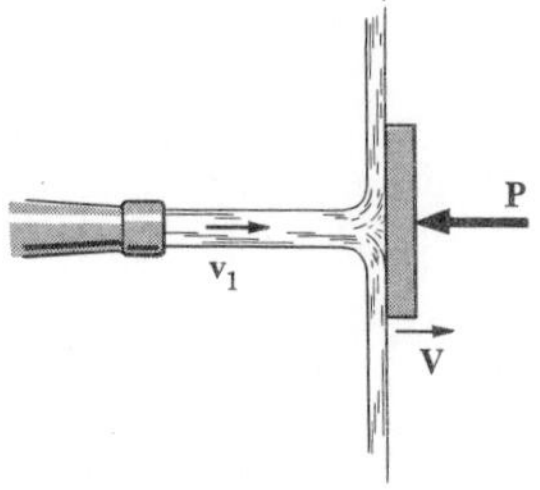

FIG. P 14.108 AND P 14.109

14.108. A fire nozzle discharges water with an initial velocity $\mathbf{v}_1$. If the cross-sectional area of the stream is A, derive an expression for the magnitude of the force **P** required to hold the plate motionless. Determine the numerical value of P, if $A = 3$ in.², $v_1 = 90$ ft/sec, and $V = 0$.

14.109. A fire nozzle discharges water with an initial velocity $\mathbf{v}_1$. If the cross-sectional area of the stream is A, derive an expression for the magnitude of the force **P** required to hold the plate when the velocity of the plate is **V** directed to the right.

14.110. Water flows in a continuous sheet from between two plates A and B with a velocity **v**. The stream is split into two equal streams *1* and *2* by a vane attached to plate C. Denoting the total rate of flow by Q, determine the force exerted by the stream on plate C.

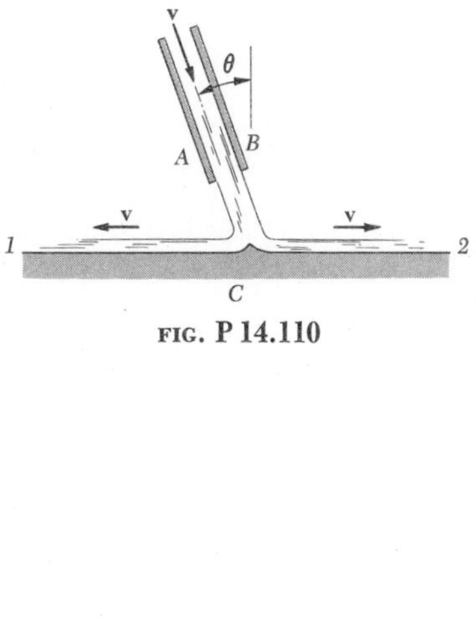

FIG. P 14.110

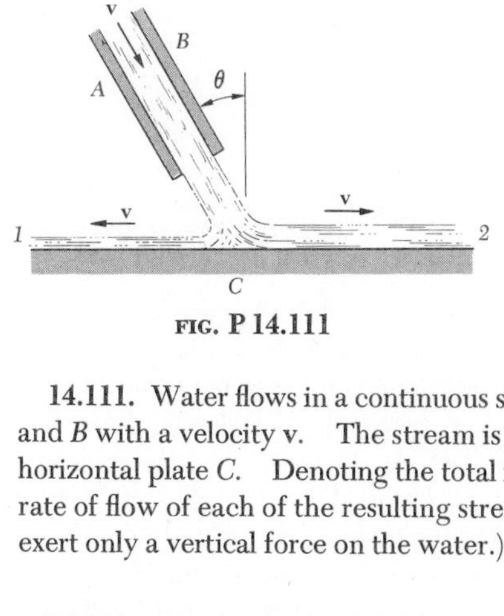

FIG. P 14.111

14.111. Water flows in a continuous sheet from between two plates A and B with a velocity **v**. The stream is split into two parts by a smooth horizontal plate C. Denoting the total rate of flow by Q, determine the rate of flow of each of the resulting streams. (*Hint.* The plate C can exert only a vertical force on the water.)

14.112. A jet airplane scoops in air at the rate of 190 lb/sec and discharges it with a velocity of 2,200 ft/sec relative to the airplane. If the speed of the airplane is 650 mph, determine (*a*) the propulsive force developed, (*b*) the horsepower developed by the engine, (*c*) the horsepower actually used to propel the airplane.

14.113. The total drag due to air friction of a jet airplane traveling at 600 mph is 3,500 lb. Knowing that the exhaust velocity is 2,000 ft/sec relative to the airplane, determine the weight of air which must pass through the engine per second to maintain the speed of 600 mph in level flight.

14.114. A jet airplane weighing 15,000 lb scoops in air at the rate of 200 lb/sec and discharges it with a velocity of 2,000 ft/sec relative to the airplane. If the total drag due to air friction is 5,000 lb, determine the angle of climb α at which the airplane can maintain a constant speed of 600 mph.

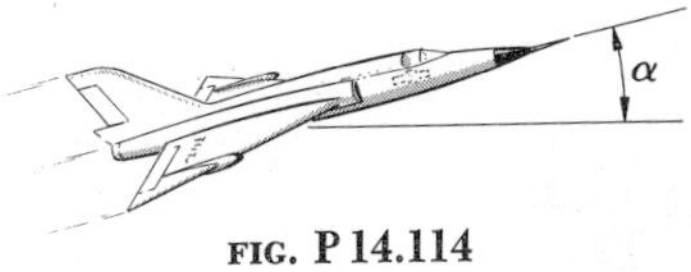

FIG. P 14.114

14.115. If the jet airplane of Prob. 14.114 climbs at an angle $\alpha = 4°$, determine (*a*) the acceleration of the airplane when its speed is 600 mph, (*b*) the maximum speed possible, assuming that the drag due to air friction increases 150 lb for each additional 10 mph in the speed of the airplane. (*Note.* Drag is 5,000 lb at 600 mph.)

14.116. A jet airplane scoops in w lb of air per second and discharges it with a speed u relative to the airplane. (*a*) Denoting the speed of the airplane by v, derive an expression for the thrust provided by the jet engine. (*b*) Using the results of part *a*, show that the speed v of the airplane must be less than the relative speed u.

14.117. The maximum speed of a jet airliner is known to be 600 mph. Each of the four engines discharges air with a velocity of 2,000 ft/sec relative to the plane. Assuming that the drag due to air resistance is proportional to the square of the speed, determine the maximum cruising speed of the airliner when only two of the engines are in operation.

14.118. A rotary power plow is used to remove snow from a level section of railroad track. The plow car is placed ahead of an engine which propels it at a constant speed of 15 mph. The plow clears 180 tons of snow per minute, projecting it in the direction shown with a velocity of 40 ft/sec relative to the plow car. Neglecting rolling friction, determine (*a*) the magnitude of the force **P** exerted by the engine on the plow car, (*b*) the lateral force exerted on the plow car by the track.

FIG. P 14.118

14.119. In Prob. 14.118, what angle should the discharge duct form with the z axis, if, at the speed considered, the force **P** exerted by the engine on the plow car is to be zero?

14.120. The slipstream of a fan has an area A and a speed v. Derive an expression (*a*) for the magnitude of the force $\mathbf{F}$ required to hold the fan motionless, (*b*) for the kinetic energy imparted per second to the air of the slipstream.

14.121. The propeller of an airplane produces a thrust of 800 lb when the airplane is at rest on the ground and has a slipstream of 6-ft diameter. Assuming that air weighs 0.076 lb/ft^3, determine (*a*) the speed of the air in the slipstream, (*b*) the volume of air passing through the propeller per second, (*c*) the kinetic energy imparted per second to the air of the slipstream.

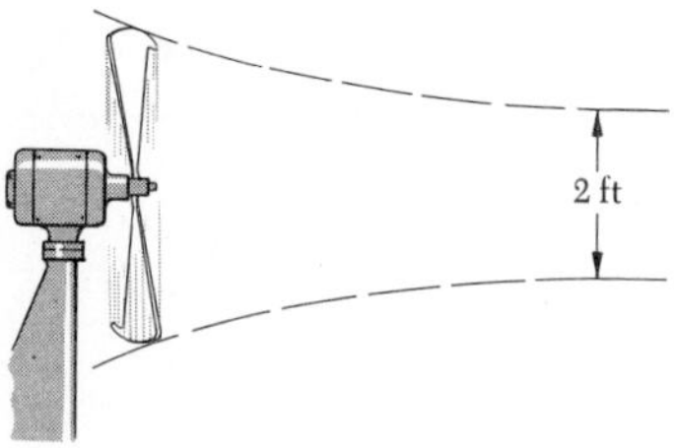

FIG. P 14.122

14.122. The slipstream of a fan has a diameter of 2 ft and a velocity of 40 ft/sec relative to the fan. Assuming air weighs 0.076 lb/ft^3 and neglecting the velocity of approach of the air, determine the force required to hold the fan motionless.

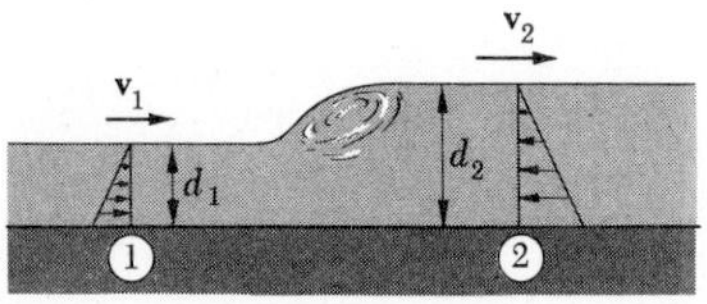

FIG. P 14.123

***14.123.** The depth of water flowing in a rectangular channel of width b at a speed v_1 and depth d_1 increases to a depth d_2 at a *hydraulic jump*. Determine the relation between the depth d_1 and the depth d_2 for a given total flow Q.

14.124. Determine the rate of flow of water in the channel of Prob. 14.123, knowing that $d_1 = 2$ ft, $d_2 = 4$ ft, and that the rectangular channel is 10 ft wide.

14.125. A circular reentrant orifice (also called Borda's mouthpiece) of diameter D is placed at a depth h below the surface of a tank. Knowing that the speed of the issuing stream is $v = \sqrt{2gh}$ and assuming that the speed of approach v_1 is zero, show that the diameter of the stream is $d = D/\sqrt{2}$. (*Hint.* Consider the section of water indicated, and note that P is equal to the pressure at a depth h multiplied by the area of the orifice.)

14.126. A helicopter of gross weight 1,500 lb produces a slipstream of 22-ft diameter. Assuming that air weighs 0.076 lb/ft^3, determine the vertical component of the velocity of the air in the slipstream when the helicopter is hovering in mid-air.

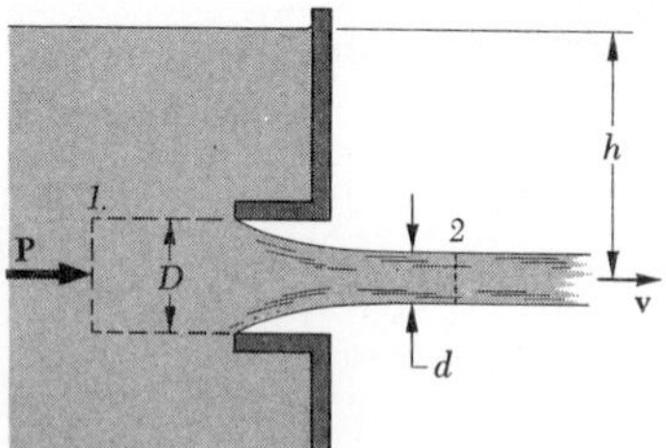

FIG. P 14.125

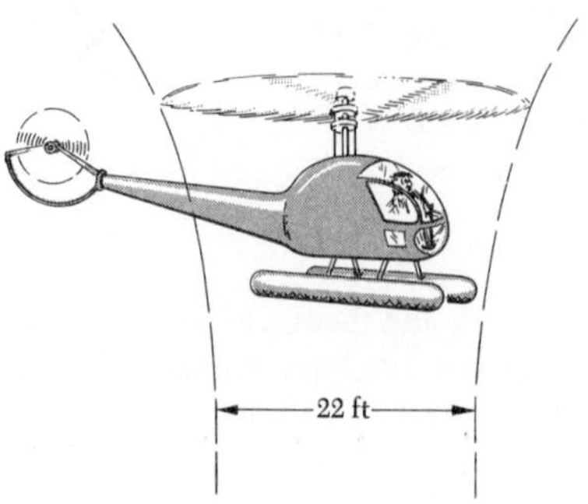

FIG. P 14.126 AND P 14.127

14.127. Knowing that the helicopter shown weighs 1,500 lb and can produce a maximum downward air speed of 160 ft/sec in the 22-ft-diameter slipstream, determine the maximum load which the helicopter can carry while hovering in mid-air. Air weighs 0.076 lb/ft^3.

14.128. On some long-distance runs, steam locomotives used to scoop up water from long troughs placed between the rails. Assuming that a locomotive scoops up water at the rate of 4,000 gal/min while traveling at a constant speed of 45 mph, determine (*a*) the magnitude of the additional force **P** which must be exerted by the locomotive to maintain the constant speed, (*b*) the additional power required to maintain the constant speed. Neglect the drag on the scoop and the change in potential energy of the water as it is raised into the tender of the locomotive.

14.129. Because of the play existing in the couplings of railroad freight cars, a long train may be started by successively setting each car in motion. If the engine moves at a constant speed v, (*a*) show that the magnitude of the constant force required to set the cars in motion is $F = v(dm/dt)$, where dm/dt is the rate at which the mass of the cars is set in motion. (*b*) Show that the work done in setting each car in motion is m_0v^2, where m_0 is the mass of a car. (*Note.* Although only half the work done is used to increase the kinetic energy of the train, this method of starting long trains is frequently used in order to overcome static friction.)

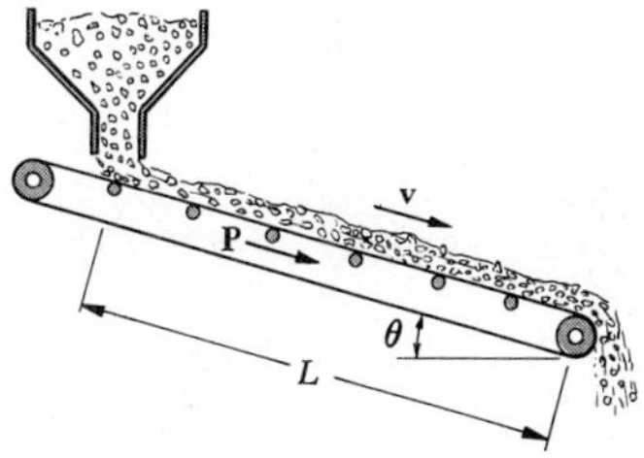

FIG. P 14.130 AND P 14.131

14.130. Coal falls onto a conveyor belt at the constant rate of w lb/sec. (*a*) Determine the magnitude of the force **P** required to maintain a constant belt speed v, when $\theta = 0$. (*b*) Solve part *a* when $w = 50$ lb/sec and $v = 6$ ft/sec.

14.131. Coal falls onto a conveyor belt at the constant rate of w lb/sec. A force **P** is applied to the belt to maintain a constant speed v. Derive an expression for the angle θ for which the force **P** is zero.

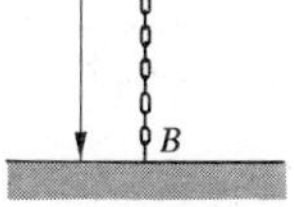

FIG. P 14.132

14.132. A chain of weight w lb/ft and total length l is held at end A by a force **P**. If end B of the chain is just in contact with the floor at time $t = 0$ and the velocity of the chain is **v** directed downward, determine (*a*) the magnitude of the force **P** required to lower the chain with the constant velocity **v**, (*b*) the magnitude of the upward force exerted by the floor as the chain is lowered.

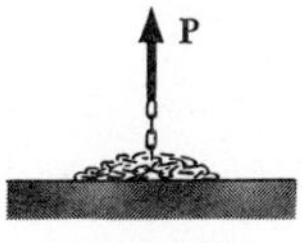

FIG. P 14.133

14.133. A chain of weight w lb/ft and total length l lies in a pile on the floor. At time $t = 0$ a force **P** is applied and the chain is raised with a constant velocity **v**. Determine (*a*) the required magnitude of the force **P**, (*b*) the magnitude of the upward force exerted by the floor as the chain is raised.

14.134. The *specific impulse* of a rocket fuel is defined as the propulsive thrust produced by burning the fuel at the rate of 1 lb per second. Determine the specific impulse of a fuel which is consumed and expelled at a constant speed u relative to the rocket.

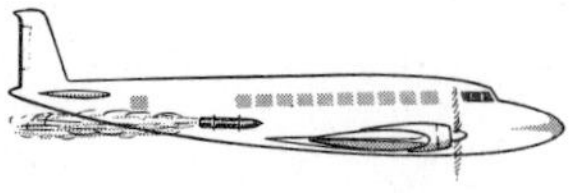

FIG. P 14.135

14.135. A booster rocket is attached to the fuselage of an airplane weighing 40,000 lb. The rocket fuel is consumed at the rate of 20 lb/sec and is ejected with a relative velocity of 5,000 ft/sec. Determine the additional propulsive thrust available while the rocket is being fired (*a*) if the speed of the airplane is 500 mph, (*b*) if the airplane is at rest on the ground.

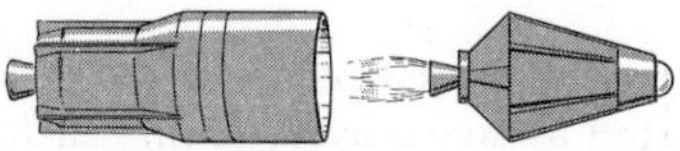

FIG. P 14.136

14.136. A space vehicle describing a circular orbit at a speed of 15,000 mph releases a capsule which has a gross weight of 1,000 lb, including 750 lb of fuel. If the fuel is consumed at the constant rate of 30 lb/sec and is ejected with a relative velocity of 6,000 ft/sec, determine the tangential acceleration of the capsule (*a*) as the engine is fired, (*b*) as the last particle of fuel is being consumed.

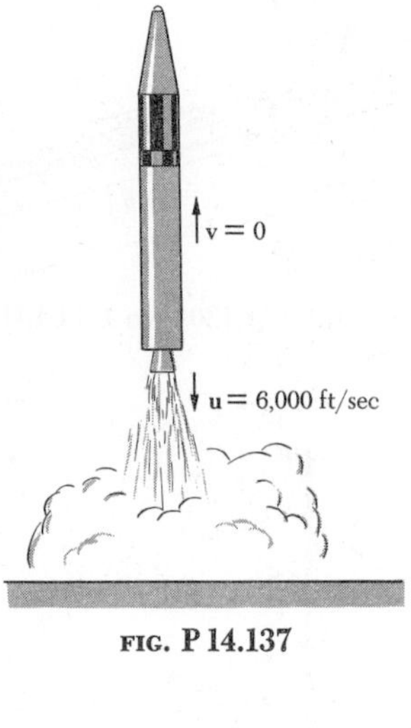

FIG. P 14.137

14.137. A test rocket is designed to hover motionless above the ground. The shell of the rocket weighs 2,000 lb, and the initial fuel load is 8,000 lb. The fuel is burned and ejected with a velocity of 6,000 ft/sec. Determine the required rate of fuel consumption (*a*) when the rocket is fired, (*b*) as the last particle of fuel is being consumed.

14.138. A test rocket consists of a shell weighing 50 lb and 450 lb of fuel. The fuel is consumed at a rate of 10 lb/sec and is ejected with a relative velocity of 5,000 ft/sec. Determine the maximum speed attained by the rocket when it is fired vertically. Neglect the effect of air friction.

14.139. A multiple-stage rocket is more efficient than a rocket consisting of a single shell because expendable mass such as emptied fuel tanks can be discarded when no longer required. Assume that the rocket of Sample Prob. 14.10 is the second stage of a two-stage rocket and that, as the first section of the rocket is discarded, the velocity of the second section is v_0 directed vertically upward. Taking $t = 0$ when the second stage begins, derive an expression for the velocity of the rocket at any time t.

14.140. Two rockets A and B similar to the rocket of Prob. 14.138 are used to form a two-stage rocket which is fired vertically. When rocket A expels its last particle of fuel, its shell is released and rocket B is fired. Determine (*a*) the speed when rocket A is released, (*b*) the maximum speed attained by rocket B.

FIG. P 14.140

14.141. A space vehicle equipped with a retrorocket, which may expel fuel with a relative velocity $\mathbf{u}$, is moving with a velocity $\mathbf{v}_0$. Denoting by m_s the net mass of the vehicle and by m_f the mass of the unexpended fuel, determine the minimum ratio m_f/m_s for which the velocity of the vehicle can be reduced to zero.

14.142. In Prob. 14.136, determine the final velocity of the capsule after all its fuel has been expended, assuming (*a*) that the capsule is ejected forward, (*b*) that the capsule is ejected to the rear.

14.143. The kinetic energy available per second from the stream of Sample Prob. 14.9 is $\frac{1}{2}Q\rho v_1^2$, where Q is the flow of water per second, $Q = Av_1$. Derive an expression for the mechanical efficiency of the single blade, and determine the maximum possible value of the efficiency.

14.144. In a Pelton-wheel turbine, a stream of water is deflected by a series of blades so that the rate at which water is deflected by the blades is equal to the rate at which water issues from the nozzle ($\Delta m/\Delta t = A\rho v_1$). Using the same notation as in Sample Prob. 14.9, (*a*) determine the velocity $\mathbf{V}$ of the blades for which maximum power is developed, (*b*) derive an expression for the maximum power, (*c*) derive an expression for the mechanical efficiency.

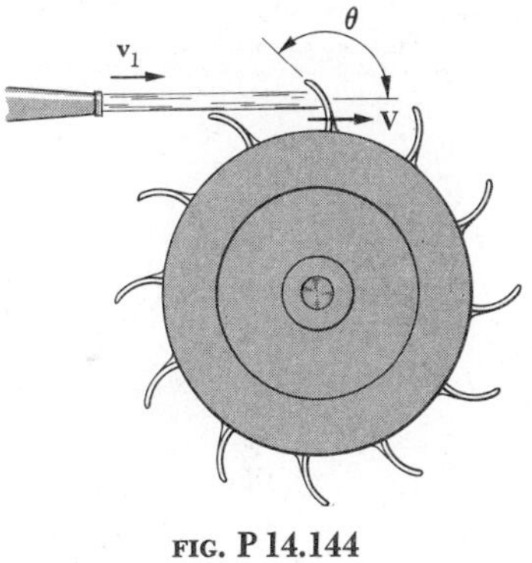

FIG. P 14.144

***14.145.** For the rocket of Sample Prob. 14.10 derive an expression for the height of the rocket as a function of the time t.

***14.146.** Determine the distance between the capsule and the space vehicle of Prob. 14.136 as the last particle of fuel is being ejected by the rocket of the capsule. Both the capsule and the space vehicle may be considered to move in a straight line during the time interval considered.

***14.147.** In a jet airplane, the kinetic energy imparted to the exhaust gases is wasted as far as propelling the airplane is concerned. The useful power is equal to the product of the force available to propel the airplane and the speed of the airplane. If v is the speed of the airplane and u is the relative speed of the expelled gases, show that the efficiency is $\eta = 2v/(u + v)$. Explain why $\eta = 1$ when $u = v$.

***14.148.** In a rocket, the kinetic energy imparted to the consumed and ejected fuel is wasted as far as propelling the rocket is concerned. The useful power is equal to the product of the force available to propel the rocket and the speed of the rocket. If v is the speed of the rocket and u is the relative speed of the expelled fuel, show that the efficiency is $\eta = 2uv/(u^2 + v^2)$. Explain why $\eta = 1$ when $u = v$.

REVIEW PROBLEMS

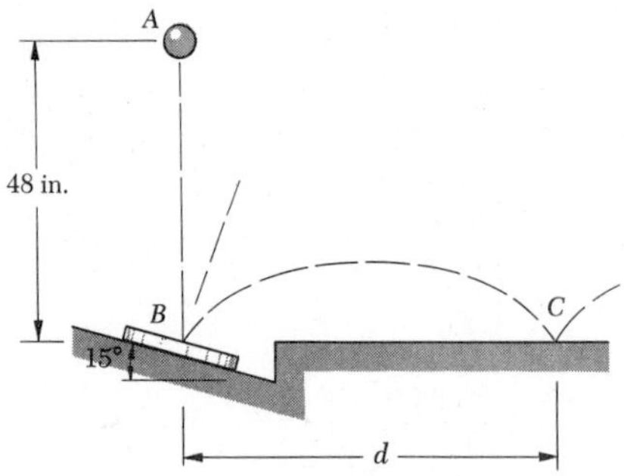

FIG. P 14.149

14.149. A steel ball dropped from A strikes a rigid steel plate at B and bounces to point C. Knowing that the distance d is 4.80 ft, determine the coefficient of restitution between the ball and the plate.

14.150. A conveyor belt moves with a constant velocity **v** under the action of a force **P**. If coal falls vertically onto the belt at the rate dm/dt, show that the kinetic energy acquired by the coal in a given time interval is equal to one-half of the work done in that interval by the force **P**. Explain what happens to the other half of the work done by **P**.

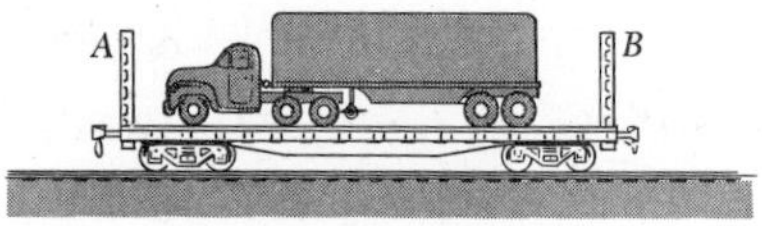

FIG. P 14.151

14.151. The 20-ton truck and the 40-ton railroad flatcar are both at rest with their brakes released. An engine bumps the flatcar and causes the flatcar alone to start moving with a velocity of 3 ft/sec to the right. Assuming $e = 1$ between the truck and the ends of the flatcar, determine the velocities of the truck and of the flatcar after end A strikes the truck. Describe the subsequent motion of the system. Neglect the effect of friction.

14.152. A steel ball A weighing 2 oz hits squarely a larger steel ball which is at rest. If ball A bounces back with half its initial speed, determine (a) the weight of ball B, (b) the percentage of the initial kinetic energy acquired by ball B. ($e = 1$.)

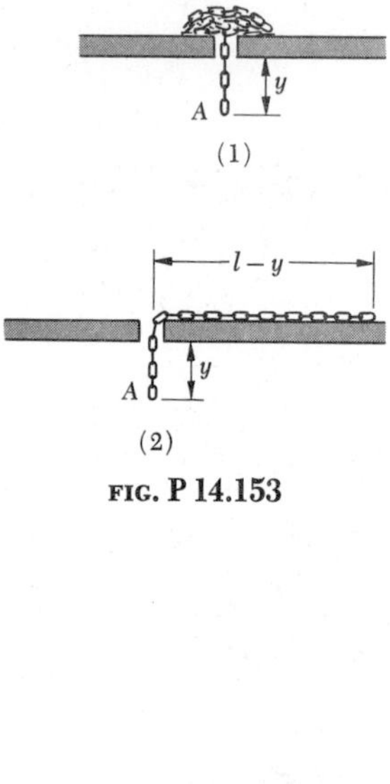

FIG. P 14.153

***14.153.** A chain of weight w lb/ft and length l falls through a small hole in a plate. Initially, when y is very small, the chain is at rest. In each case shown, determine (a) the acceleration of the first link A as a function of y, (b) the velocity of the chain as the last link passes through the hole. In case *1* assume that the individual links are at rest until they fall through the hole; in case 2 assume that at any instant all links have the same speed. Ignore the effect of friction.

14.154. An air-to-air missile is test-fired horizontally from a stationary support. The fuel is consumed at a constant rate q and is ejected with a relative velocity of constant magnitude u. Knowing that the atmospheric drag on the missile may be represented by a force of magnitude kv^2, show that the maximum speed v_m attained by the missile is defined by the formula

$$\frac{c + v_m}{c - v_m} = \left(\frac{m_0}{m_s}\right)^{2u/c}$$

where m_0 is the initial gross mass of the missile, m_s the mass of the shell, and $c^2 = qu/k$.

14.155. Derive an expression for the maximum speed attained by the missile of Prob. 14.154 if it is fired horizontally from a plane traveling horizontally at a speed v_0.

14.156. The ends of a chain of weight w lb/ft lie in piles at A and at C; when released, the chain moves over the pulley at B. Determine the required initial speed v for which the chain will move at constant speed. Neglect the effect of friction.

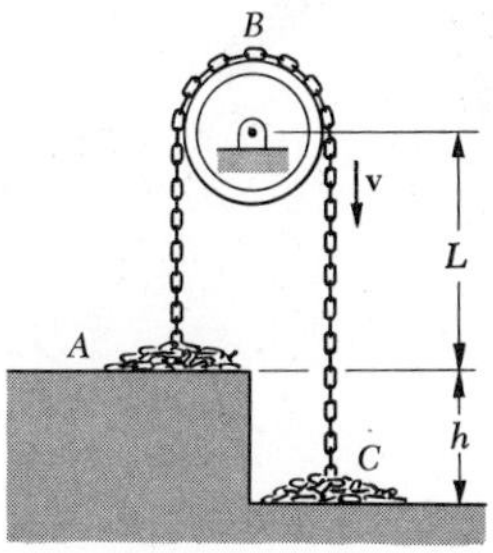

FIG. P 14.156

14.157. Two railroad freight cars move with a velocity $\mathbf{v}$ through a switchyard. Car B hits a third car C, which was at rest with its brakes released, and it automatically couples with C. Knowing that all three cars have the same weight, determine their common velocity after they are all coupled together, as well as the percentage of their total initial kinetic energy which is absorbed by each coupling mechanism, assuming (*a*) that cars A and B were originally coupled, (*b*) that cars A and B were moving a few feet apart and that the coupling operation between B and C is completed before A hits B and becomes coupled with it.

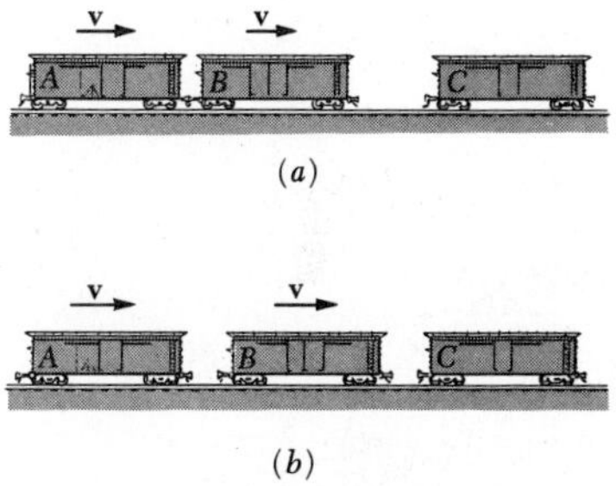

FIG. P 14.157

14.158. A large number of small blocks of total weight W are at rest on a smooth table when a constant force of magnitude P is applied to block A. Knowing that the blocks are in contact with each other but are not connected, determine the speed of block A after half the blocks have been pushed off the table.

14.159. Solve Prob. 14.158 assuming that the coefficient of friction between the blocks and the horizontal table is μ.

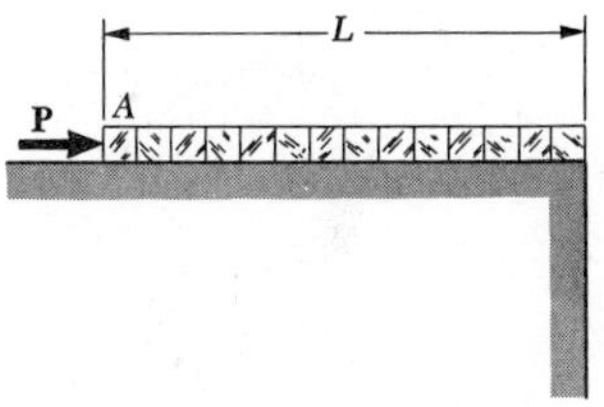

FIG. P 14.158

14.160. A series of 10 castings, each of weight 25 lb, is at rest on an assembly-line belt. Knowing that the tension T in the belt must not exceed 60 lb, determine the time t_1 required for the belt to acquire a speed of 2 ft/sec (*a*) if the T–t curve is parabolic, (*b*) if the T–t curve is triangular. Ignore the effect of friction.

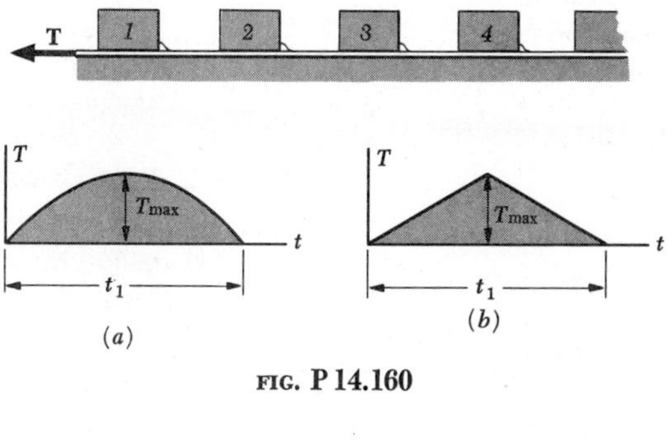

FIG. P 14.160

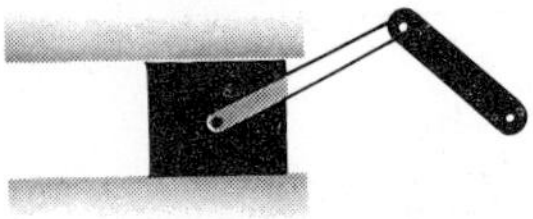

15. KINEMATICS OF RIGID BODIES

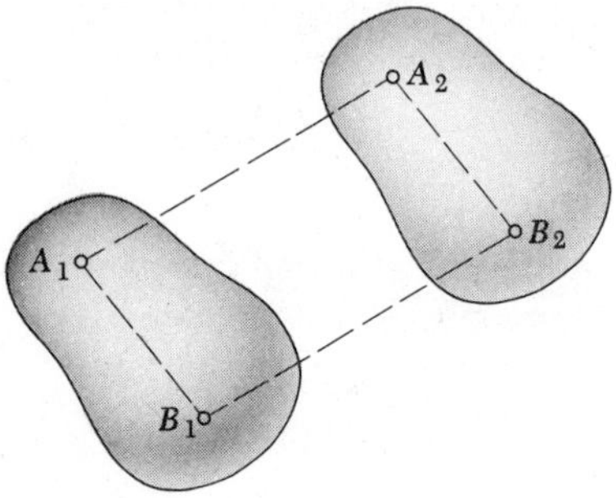

FIG. 15.1

15.1. Introduction. In this chapter, we shall study the kinematics of *rigid bodies*. We shall investigate the relations existing between the time, the positions, the velocities, and the accelerations of the various particles forming a rigid body. As we shall see, the various types of rigid-body motion may be conveniently grouped as follows:

1. *Translation.* A motion is said to be a translation if any straight line inside the body keeps the same direction during the motion. It may also be observed that in a translation all the particles forming the body move along parallel paths. If these paths are straight lines, the motion is said to be a *rectilinear translation* (Fig. 15.1); if the paths are curved lines, the motion is a *curvilinear translation* (Fig. 15.2).

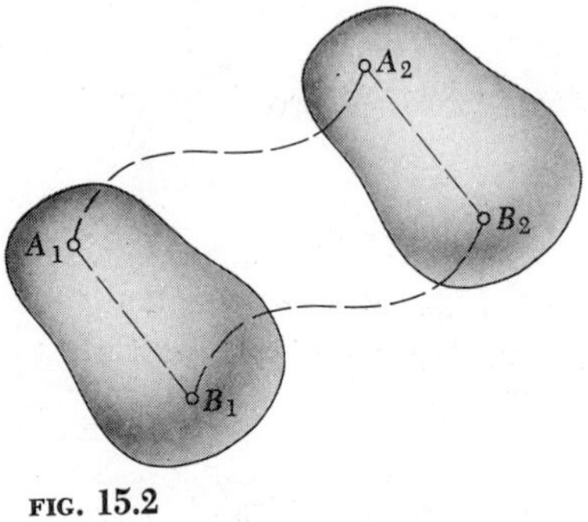

FIG. 15.2

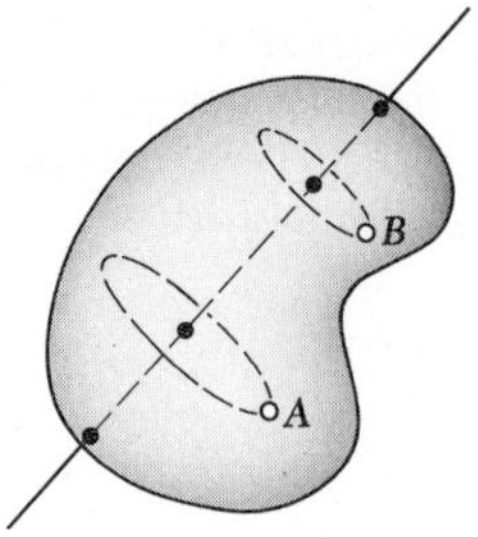

FIG. 15.3

2. *Rotation about a Fixed Axis.* In this motion, the particles forming the rigid body move in parallel planes along circles centered on the same fixed axis (Fig. 15.3). If this axis, called the *axis of rotation*, intersects the rigid body, the particles located on the axis have zero velocity and zero acceleration.

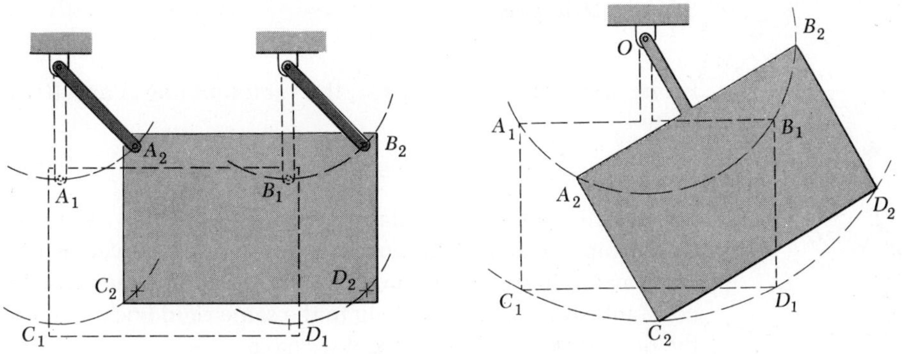

(*a*) Curvilinear translation

(*b*) Rotation

FIG. 15.4

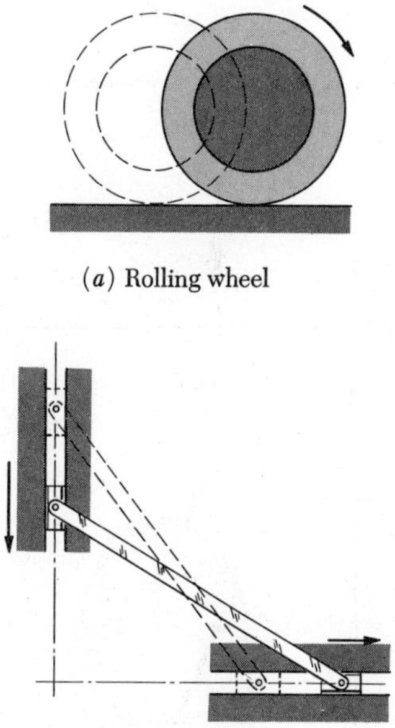

(*a*) Rolling wheel

(*b*) Sliding rod

FIG. 15.5. Examples of general plane motion

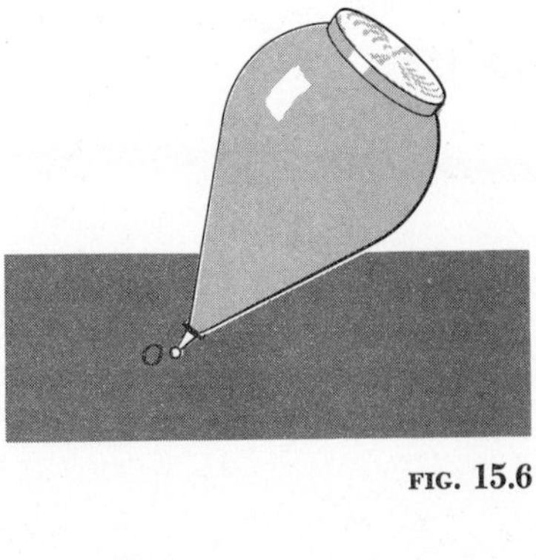

FIG. 15.6

Rotation should not be confused with certain types of curvilinear translation. For example, the plate shown in Fig. 15.4*a* is in curvilinear translation, with all its particles moving along *parallel* circles, while the plate shown in Fig. 15.4*b* is in rotation, with all its particles moving along *concentric* circles. In the first case, any given straight line drawn on the plate will maintain the same direction, while, in the second case, point O remains fixed.

Because each particle moves in a given plane, the rotation of a body about a fixed axis is said to be a *plane motion.*

3. *General Plane Motion.* There are many other types of plane motion, i.e., motions in which all the particles of the body move in parallel planes. Any plane motion which is neither a rotation nor a translation is referred to as a general plane motion. Two examples of general plane motion are given in Fig. 15.5.

4. *Motion about a Fixed Point.* This is the three-dimensional motion of a rigid body attached at a fixed point O. An example of motion about a fixed point is provided by the motion of a top on a rough floor (Fig. 15.6).

5. *General Motion.* Any motion of a rigid body which does not fall in any of the above categories is referred to as a general motion.

15.2. Translation. Consider a rigid body in translation (either rectilinear or curvilinear translation), and let A and B be any two of its particles (Fig. 15.7*a*). Denoting respectively by $\mathbf{r}_A$ and $\mathbf{r}_B$ the position vectors of A and B with respect to a fixed

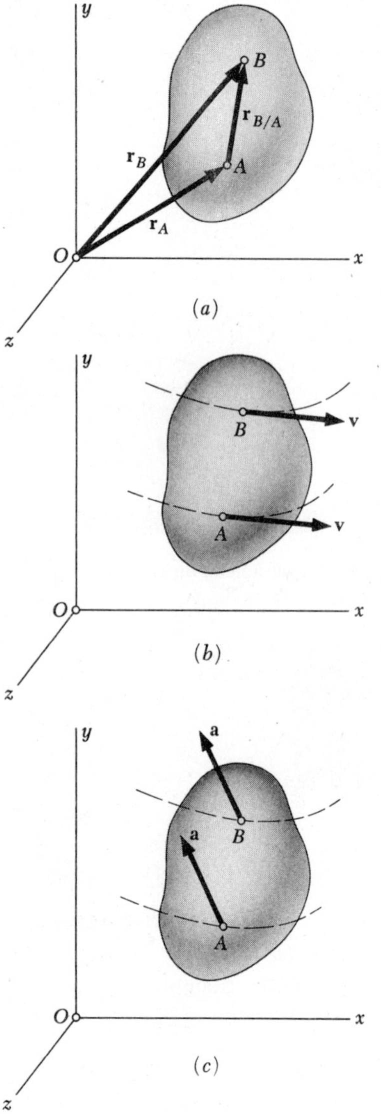

FIG. 15.7

frame of reference, and by $\mathbf{r}_{B/A}$ the vector joining A and B, we write

$$\mathbf{r}_B = \mathbf{r}_A + \mathbf{r}_{B/A} \tag{15.1}$$

Let us differentiate this relation with respect to t. We note that, from the very definition of a translation, the vector $\mathbf{r}_{B/A}$ must maintain a constant direction; its magnitude must also be constant, since A and B belong to the same rigid body. Thus, the derivative of $\mathbf{r}_{B/A}$ is zero and we have

$$\mathbf{v}_B = \mathbf{v}_A \tag{15.2}$$

Differentiating once more, we write

$$\mathbf{a}_B = \mathbf{a}_A \tag{15.3}$$

Thus, *when a rigid body is in translation, all the points of the body have the same velocity and the same acceleration at any given instant* (Fig. 15.7*b* and *c*). In the case of curvilinear translation, the velocity and acceleration change in direction as well as in magnitude at every instant. In the case of rectilinear translation, all particles of the body move along parallel straight lines, and their velocity and acceleration keep the same direction during the entire motion.

15.3. Rotation about a Fixed Axis. Consider a rigid body which rotates about a fixed axis AA'. Let P be a point of the body and $\mathbf{r}$ its position vector with respect to a fixed frame of reference. For convenience, we shall assume that the frame is centered at point O on AA' and that the z axis coincides with AA' (Fig. 15.8). Let B be the projection of P on AA'; since P must remain at a constant distance from B, it will describe a circle of center B and of radius $r \sin \phi$, where ϕ denotes the angle formed by $\mathbf{r}$ and AA'.

The position of P and of the entire body is completely defined by the angle θ the line BP forms with the xz plane. The angle θ is known as the *angular coordinate* of the body. The angular coordinate is defined as positive when counterclockwise as viewed from A' and will be expressed in radians or, occasionally, in degrees (°) or revolutions (rev). We recall that

$$1 \text{ rev} = 2\pi \text{ radians} = 360°$$

We recall from Sec. 11.9 that the velocity $\mathbf{v} = d\mathbf{r}/dt$ of a particle P is a vector tangent to the path of P and of magnitude $v = ds/dt$. Observing that the length Δs of the arc described by P when the body rotates through $\Delta\theta$ is

$$\Delta s = (BP)\Delta\theta = (r \sin \phi)\Delta\theta$$

and dividing both members by Δt, we obtain at the limit, as Δt approaches zero,

$$v = \frac{ds}{dt} = r\dot{\theta} \sin \phi \tag{15.4}$$

where $\dot{\theta}$ denotes the time derivative of θ. (Note that, while the angle θ depends upon the position of P within the body, the rate of change $\dot{\theta}$ is itself independent of P.) We conclude that the velocity $\mathbf{v}$ of P is a vector perpendicular to the plane containing AA' and $\mathbf{r}$, and of magnitude v defined by (15.4). But this is precisely the result we would obtain if we drew along AA' a vector $\boldsymbol{\omega} = \dot{\theta}\mathbf{k}$ and formed the vector product $\boldsymbol{\omega} \times \mathbf{r}$ (Fig. 15.9). We thus write

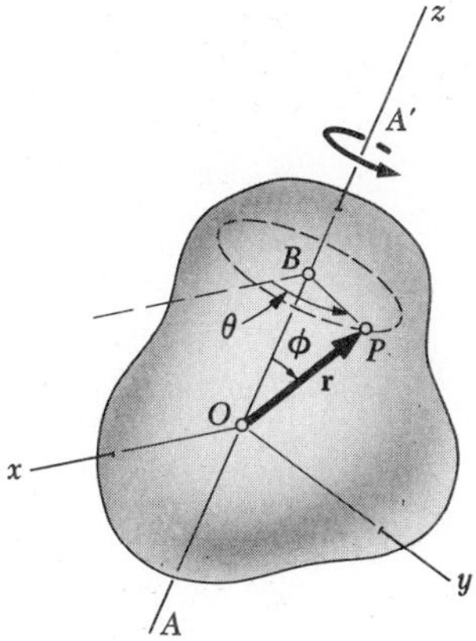

FIG. 15.8

$$\mathbf{v} = \frac{d\mathbf{r}}{dt} = \boldsymbol{\omega} \times \mathbf{r} \tag{15.5}$$

The vector

$$\boldsymbol{\omega} = \omega\mathbf{k} = \dot{\theta}\mathbf{k} \tag{15.6}$$

is called the *angular velocity* of the body. It is directed along the axis of rotation, it is equal in magnitude to the rate of change $\dot{\theta}$ of the angular coordinate, and its sense may be obtained by the right-hand rule (Sec. 3.5) from the sense of rotation of the body.†

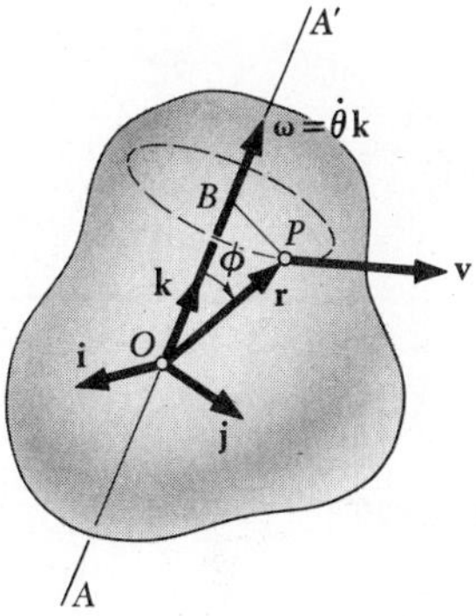

FIG. 15.9

We shall now determine the acceleration $\mathbf{a}$ of the particle P. Differentiating (15.5) and recalling the rule for the differentiation of a vector product (Sec. 11.10), we write

$$\mathbf{a} = \frac{d\mathbf{v}}{dt} = \frac{d}{dt}(\boldsymbol{\omega} \times \mathbf{r})$$

$$= \frac{d\boldsymbol{\omega}}{dt} \times \mathbf{r} + \boldsymbol{\omega} \times \frac{d\mathbf{r}}{dt}$$

$$\mathbf{a} = \frac{d\boldsymbol{\omega}}{dt} \times \mathbf{r} + \boldsymbol{\omega} \times \mathbf{v} \tag{15.7}$$

The vector $d\boldsymbol{\omega}/dt$ is denoted by $\boldsymbol{\alpha}$ and called the *angular acceleration* of the body. Substituting also for $\mathbf{v}$ from (15.5), we have

$$\mathbf{a} = \boldsymbol{\alpha} \times \mathbf{r} + \boldsymbol{\omega} \times (\boldsymbol{\omega} \times \mathbf{r}) \tag{15.8}$$

Differentiating (15.6), and recalling that $\mathbf{k}$ is constant in magni-

† It will be shown in Sec. 15.10 in the more general case of a rigid body rotating simultaneously about axes having different directions, that angular velocities obey the parallelogram law of addition and, thus, are actually vector quantities.

tude and direction, we have

$$\boldsymbol{\alpha} = \alpha\mathbf{k} = \dot{\omega}\mathbf{k} = \ddot{\theta}\mathbf{k} \tag{15.9}$$

Thus, the angular acceleration of a body rotating about a fixed axis is a vector directed along the axis of rotation, and equal in magnitude to the rate of change $\dot{\omega}$ of the angular velocity. Returning to (15.8), we note that the acceleration of P is the sum of two vectors. The first vector is equal to the vector product $\boldsymbol{\alpha} \times \mathbf{r}$; it is tangent to the circle described by P and represents, therefore, the tangential component of the acceleration. The second vector is equal to the *vector triple product* $\boldsymbol{\omega} \times (\boldsymbol{\omega} \times \mathbf{r})$ obtained by forming the vector product of $\boldsymbol{\omega}$ and $\boldsymbol{\omega} \times \mathbf{r}$; since $\boldsymbol{\omega} \times \mathbf{r}$ is tangent to the circle described by P, the vector triple product is directed toward the center B of the circle and represents, therefore, the normal component of the acceleration.

Rotation of a Representative Slab. The rotation of a rigid body about a fixed axis may be defined by the motion of a representative slab in a reference plane perpendicular to the axis of rotation. Let us choose the xy plane as the reference plane and assume that it coincides with the plane of the figure, with the z axis pointing out of the paper (Fig. 15.10). We note that a positive value of the scalar ω corresponds to a counterclockwise rotation of the representative slab, and a negative value to a clockwise rotation. Since the vector $\mathbf{r}$ defining the position of a particle P of the slab is perpendicular to the axis of rotation, the angle ϕ in (15.4) is equal to 90° and we have

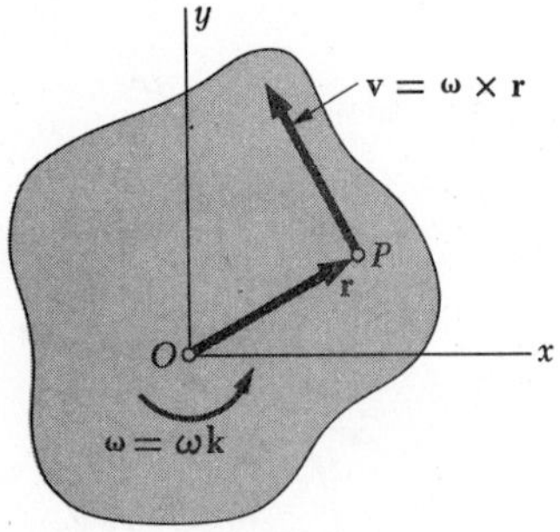

FIG. 15.10

$$\mathbf{v} = \boldsymbol{\omega} \times \mathbf{r} \qquad v = r\omega \tag{15.10}$$

for any point of the representative slab. We observe that cross-multiplying $\mathbf{r}$ by $\boldsymbol{\omega}$ results in rotating $\mathbf{r}$ through 90° in the sense of rotation of the slab, and in multiplying its magnitude by the scalar ω. Thus, cross-multiplying twice by $\boldsymbol{\omega}$ produces a 180° rotation and Eq. (15.8) reduces to

$$\mathbf{a} = \boldsymbol{\alpha} \times \mathbf{r} - \omega^2\mathbf{r} \tag{15.11}$$

for any point of the representative slab. Resolving the acceleration into tangential and normal components (Fig. 15.11), we may also write

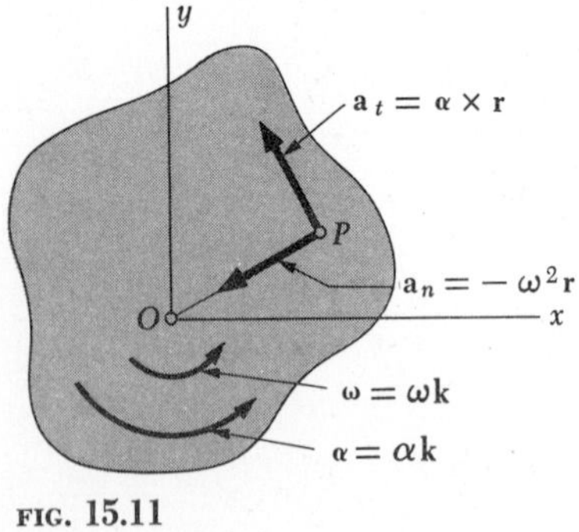

FIG. 15.11

$$\mathbf{a}_t = \boldsymbol{\alpha} \times \mathbf{r} \qquad a_t = r\alpha$$
$$\mathbf{a}_n = -\omega^2\mathbf{r} \qquad a_n = r\omega^2 \tag{15.11'}$$

The tangential component $\mathbf{a}_t$ points in the counterclockwise direction if the scalar α is positive, and in the clockwise direction if α is negative. The normal component $\mathbf{a}_n$ always points in the direction opposite to that of $\mathbf{r}$, i.e., toward O.

15.4. Equations Defining the Rotation of a Rigid Body about a Fixed Axis. The motion of a rigid body rotating about a fixed axis AA' is said to be *known* when its angular coordinate θ may be expressed as a known function of t. In practice, however, the rotation of a rigid body is seldom defined by a relation between θ and t. More often, the conditions of motion will be specified by the type of angular acceleration that the body possesses. For example, α may be given as a function of t, or as a function of θ, or as a function of ω. Recalling the relations (15.6) and (15.9), we write

$$\omega = \frac{d\theta}{dt} \tag{15.12}$$

$$\alpha = \frac{d\omega}{dt} = \frac{d^2\theta}{dt^2} \tag{15.13}$$

or, solving (15.12) for dt and substituting into (15.13),

$$\alpha = \omega \frac{d\omega}{d\theta} \tag{15.14}$$

Since these equations are similar to those obtained in Chap. 11 for the rectilinear motion of a particle, their integration may be performed by following the procedure outlined in Sec. 11.3.

Two particular cases of rotation are frequently encountered:

1. *Uniform Rotation.* This case is characterized by the fact that the angular acceleration is zero. The angular velocity is thus constant, and the angular coordinate is given by the formula

$$\theta = \theta_0 + \omega t \tag{15.15}$$

2. *Uniformly Accelerated Rotation.* In this case, the angular acceleration is constant. The following formulas relating angular velocity, angular coordinate, and time may then be derived in a manner similar to that described in Sec. 11.5. The similitude between the formulas derived here and those obtained for the rectilinear uniformly accelerated motion of a particle is easily noted.

$$\begin{aligned} \omega &= \omega_0 + \alpha t \\ \theta &= \theta_0 + \omega_0 t + \tfrac{1}{2}\alpha t^2 \\ \omega^2 &= \omega_0^2 + 2\alpha(\theta - \theta_0) \end{aligned} \tag{15.16}$$

It should be emphasized that formula (15.15) may be used only when $\alpha = 0$, and formulas (15.16) only when $\alpha =$ constant. In any other case, the general formulas (15.12) to (15.14) should be used.

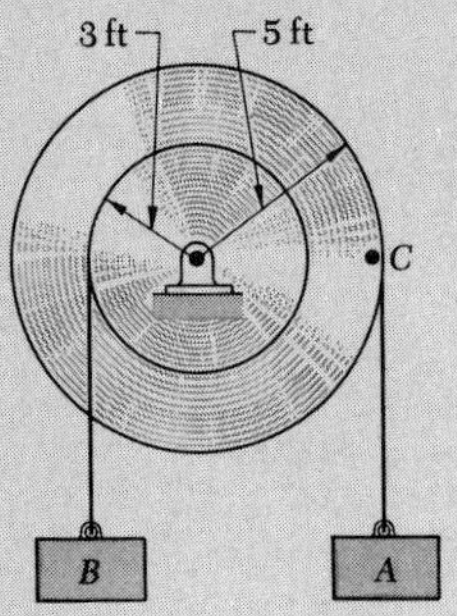

SAMPLE PROBLEM 15.1

A pulley and two loads are connected by inextensible cords as shown. Load A has a constant acceleration of 10 ft/sec² and an initial velocity of 15 ft/sec, both directed upward. Determine (*a*) the number of revolutions executed by the pulley in 3 sec, (*b*) the velocity and position of load B after 3 sec, (*c*) the acceleration of point C on the rim of the pulley at $t = 0$.

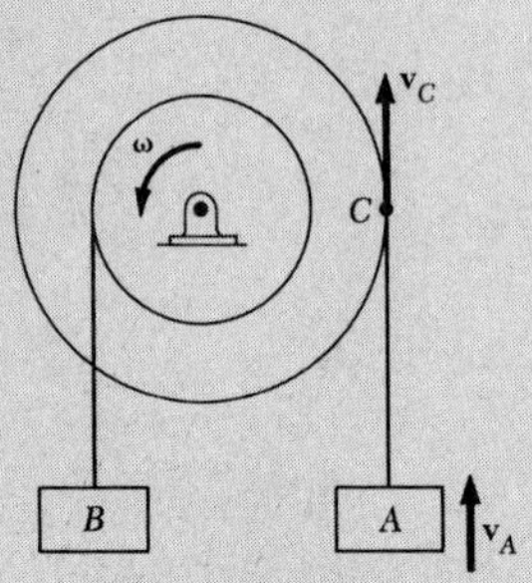

a. **Motion of Pulley.** Since the cord connecting the pulley to load A is inextensible, the velocity of C is equal to the velocity of A and the tangential component of the acceleration of C is equal to the acceleration of A.

$$(\mathbf{v}_C)_0 = (\mathbf{v}_A)_0 = 15\text{ ft/sec}\uparrow \qquad (\mathbf{a}_C)_t = \mathbf{a}_A = 10\text{ ft/sec}^2\uparrow$$

Noting that the distance from C to the center of the pulley is 5 ft, we write

$$(v_C)_0 = r\omega_0 \qquad 15\text{ ft/sec} = (5\text{ ft})\omega_0 \qquad \omega_0 = 3\text{ radians/sec} \circlearrowleft$$
$$(a_C)_t = r\alpha \qquad 10\text{ ft/sec}^2 = (5\text{ ft})\alpha \qquad \alpha = 2\text{ radians/sec}^2 \circlearrowleft$$

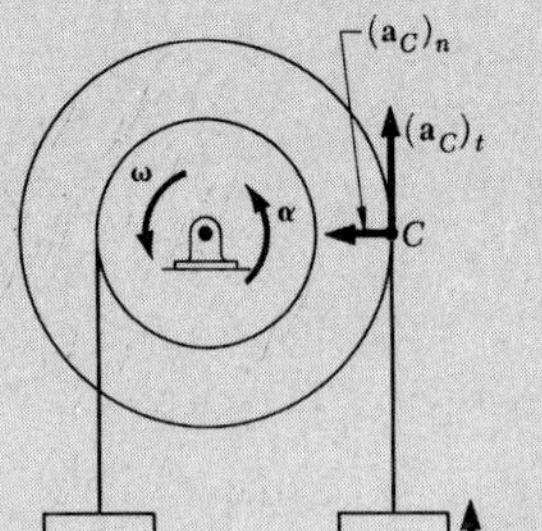

From the equations for uniformly accelerated motion, we obtain, for $t = 3$ sec,

$$\omega = \omega_0 + \alpha t = 3\text{ radians/sec} + (2\text{ radians/sec}^2)(3\text{ sec}) = 9\text{ radians/sec}$$
$$\omega = 9\text{ radians/sec} \circlearrowleft$$
$$\theta = \omega_0 t + \tfrac{1}{2}\alpha t^2 = (3\text{ radians/sec})(3\text{ sec}) + \tfrac{1}{2}(2\text{ radians/sec}^2)(3\text{ sec})^2$$
$$\theta = 18\text{ radians}$$

$$\text{Number of revolutions} = (18\text{ radians})\frac{1\text{ rev}}{2\pi\text{ radians}} = 2.86\text{ rev} \blacktriangleleft$$

b. **Motion of Load** B. Using the following relations between the linear and angular motion, with $r = 3$ ft, we write

$$v_B = r\omega = (3\text{ ft})(9\text{ radians/sec}) \qquad \mathbf{v}_B = 27\text{ ft/sec}\downarrow \blacktriangleleft$$
$$s_B = r\theta = (3\text{ ft})(18\text{ radians}) \qquad \mathbf{s}_B = 54\text{ ft}\downarrow \blacktriangleleft$$

c. **Acceleration of Point** C **at** $t = 0$. The tangential component of the acceleration is

$$(\mathbf{a}_C)_t = \mathbf{a}_A = 10\text{ ft/sec}^2\uparrow$$

Since, at $t = 0$, $\omega_0 = 3$ radians/sec, the normal component of the acceleration is

$$(a_C)_n = r_C\omega_0^2 = (5\text{ ft})(3\text{ radians/sec})^2 \qquad (\mathbf{a}_C)_n = 45\text{ ft/sec}^2\leftarrow$$

The magnitude and direction of the total acceleration are obtained by writing

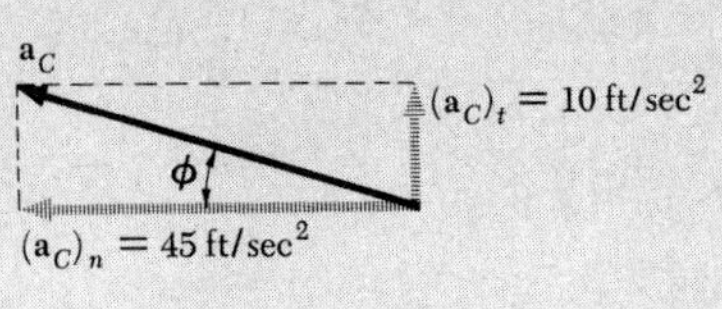

$$(45\text{ ft/sec}^2)\tan\phi = 10\text{ ft/sec}^2 \qquad \phi = 12.5°$$
$$a_C \sin 12.5° = 10\text{ ft/sec}^2 \qquad a_C = 46.1\text{ ft/sec}^2$$
$$\mathbf{a}_C = 46.1\text{ ft/sec}^2 \measuredangle 12.5° \blacktriangleleft$$

PROBLEMS

15.1. The motion of an oscillating crank is defined by the relation $\theta = \theta_0 \sin(2\pi t/T)$, where θ is expressed in radians and t in seconds. Knowing that $\theta_0 = 0.60$ radians and $T = 0.50$ sec, determine the maximum angular velocity and the maximum angular acceleration of the crank.

15.2. The motion of a disk rotating in an oil bath is defined by the relation $\theta = \theta_0(1 - e^{-t/4})$, where θ is expressed in radians and t in seconds. Knowing that $\theta_0 = 0.80$ radians, determine the angular coordinate, velocity, and acceleration of the disk when (*a*) $t = 0$, (*b*) $t = 4$ sec, (*c*) $t = \infty$.

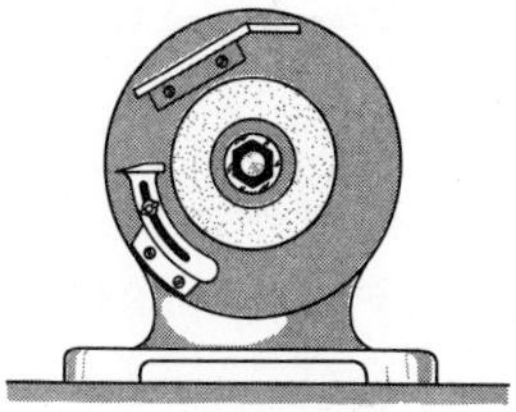

FIG. P 15.3

15.3. A small grinding wheel is attached to the shaft of an electric motor which has a rated speed of 3,600 rpm. When the power is turned on, the unit reaches its rated speed in 5 sec, and when the power is turned off, the unit coasts to rest in 70 sec. Assuming uniformly accelerated motion, determine the number of revolutions that the motor executes (*a*) in reaching its rated speed, (*b*) in coasting to rest.

15.4. As steam is slowly injected into a turbine, the angular acceleration of the rotor is observed to increase linearly with the time t. Knowing that the rotor starts from rest at $t = 0$ and that after 10 sec the rotor has completed 20 revolutions, write the equations of motion for the rotor and determine (*a*) the angular velocity at $t = 20$ sec, (*b*) the time required for the rotor to complete its first 40 revolutions.

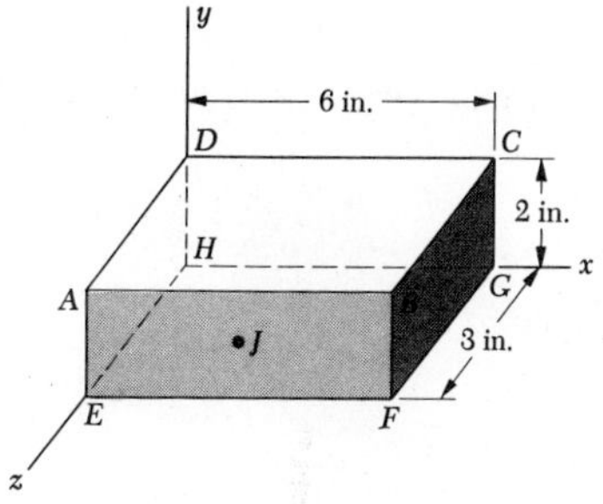

FIG. P 15.5

15.5. The rectangular box shown rotates about its diagonal *HB* with a constant angular velocity of 14 radians/sec. Knowing that the angular velocity is counterclockwise when viewed from end *B* of the diagonal, determine the velocity and acceleration of the midpoint *J* of face *ABFE*.

15.6. The rod *ABCD* has been bent as shown and is supported by bearings at *A* and *D*. The rod rotates about the line joining points *A* and *D* with a constant angular velocity of 3 radians/sec. Knowing that, at the instant considered, the vertical component of the velocity of corner *B* is downward, determine the velocity and acceleration of corner *C*.

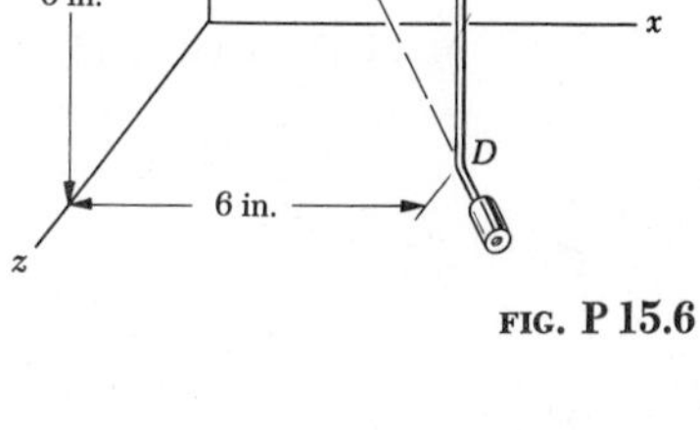

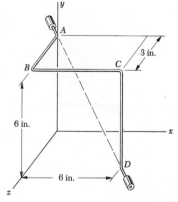

FIG. P 15.6

15.7. Solve Prob. 15.5 assuming that the angular velocity of 14 radians/sec about the diagonal *HB* is being increased at the rate of 70 radians/sec^2.

15.8. Solve Prob. 15.6 assuming that the angular velocity of 3 radians/sec about the line joining points *A* and *D* is being decreased at the rate of 6 radians/sec^2.

15.9. The earth makes one complete revolution on its axis in 23.93 hr. Knowing that the mean radius of the earth is 3,960 miles, determine the linear velocity and acceleration of a point on the surface of the earth (*a*) at the equator, (*b*) at Philadelphia, latitude 40° north, (*c*) at the north pole.

15.10. The earth makes one complete revolution about the sun in 365.24 days. Assuming that the orbit of the earth is circular and has a radius of 93,000,000 miles, determine the velocity and acceleration of the earth.

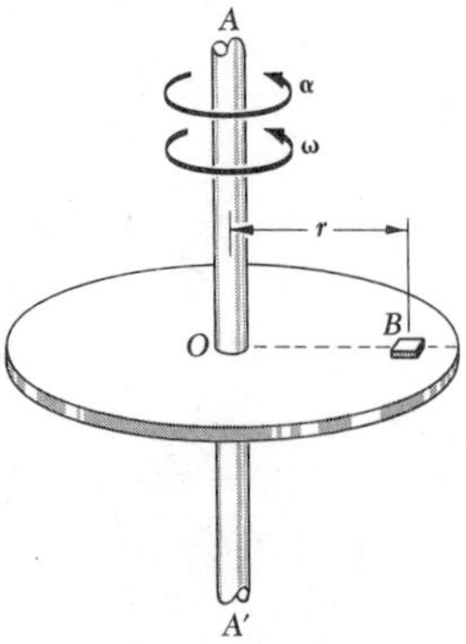

FIG. P 15.11 AND P 15.12

15.11. A small block *B* rests on a horizontal plate which can rotate about a fixed vertical axis *AA'*. If the plate is initially at rest at $t = 0$ and is accelerated at the constant rate of α radians/sec^2, derive an expression (*a*) for the total acceleration of the block at time *t*, (*b*) for the angle between the total acceleration and the radius *OB* at time *t*.

15.12. It is known that the static-friction force between block *B* and the plate will be exceeded and that the block will start sliding on the plate when the total acceleration of the block reaches 15 ft/sec^2. If the plate starts from rest at $t = 0$ and is accelerated at the constant rate of 4 radians/sec^2, determine the time *t* and the angular velocity of the plate when the block starts sliding, assuming $r = 6$ in.

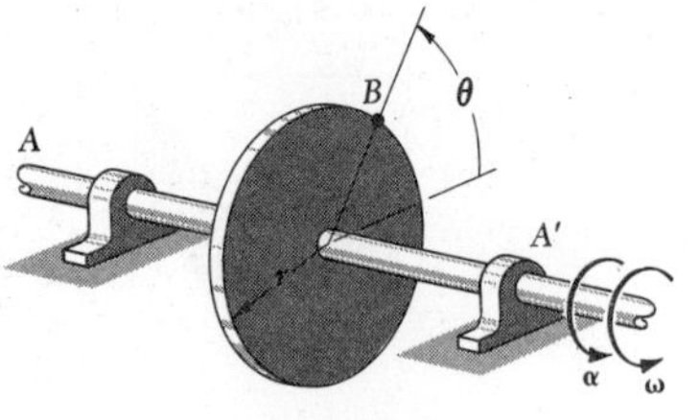

FIG. P 15.14

15.13. In Prob. 15.12, determine the constant value α of the angular acceleration for which the block will start sliding when the angle between the total acceleration of the block and the radius *OB* is 45°. What is the value of the angular velocity when the block starts sliding?

15.14. The angular acceleration of the circular plate is defined by the relation $\alpha = \alpha_0 e^{-t}$. The plate has a radius of 2 ft and starts from rest at $t = 0$. Knowing that $\alpha_0 = 10$ radians/sec^2, determine the total acceleration of point *B* when (*a*) $t = 0$, (*b*) $t = 1$ sec, (*c*) $t = \infty$.

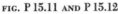

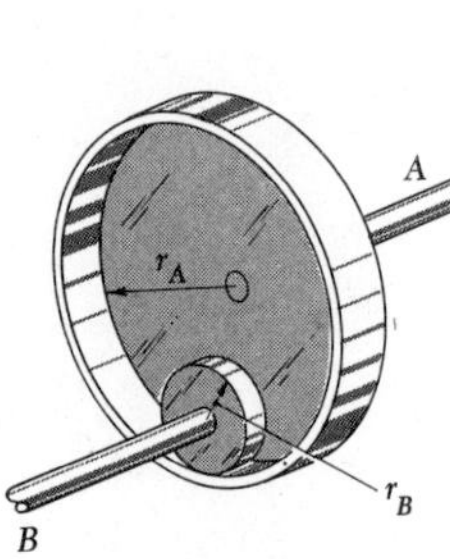

FIG. P 15.15 AND P 15.16

15.15. The friction wheel *B* rolls without slipping on the inside rim of wheel A. Knowing that shaft *B* rotates at a constant angular velocity ω_B, determine (*a*) the angular velocity of shaft A, (*b*) the linear acceleration of a point on the inside rim of wheel A.

15.16. The angular velocity of wheel *B* increases uniformly from 200 rpm to 500 rpm over a 10-sec interval. Knowing that $r_A = 6$ in. and $r_B = 2$ in., determine (*a*) the angular acceleration of wheel A, (*b*) the number of revolutions executed by wheel A during the 10-sec interval.

15.17. When released from rest at $t = 0$, the load is observed to fall 48 ft in 4 sec. Assuming uniformly accelerated motion, determine (*a*) the angular acceleration of the drum, (*b*) the angular velocity of the drum at $t = 3$ sec.

15.18. The hoisting drum shown has an angular velocity of 120 rpm when the power is suddenly cut off. Knowing that the load rises through 60 more feet before coming to rest, determine (*a*) the angular acceleration of the drum, (*b*) the time required for the drum to come to rest.

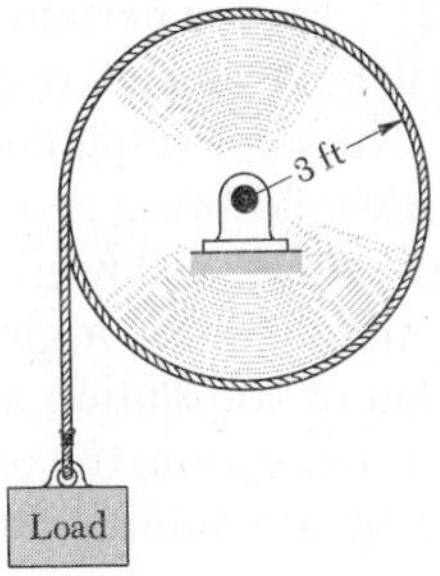

FIG. P 15.17 AND P 15.18

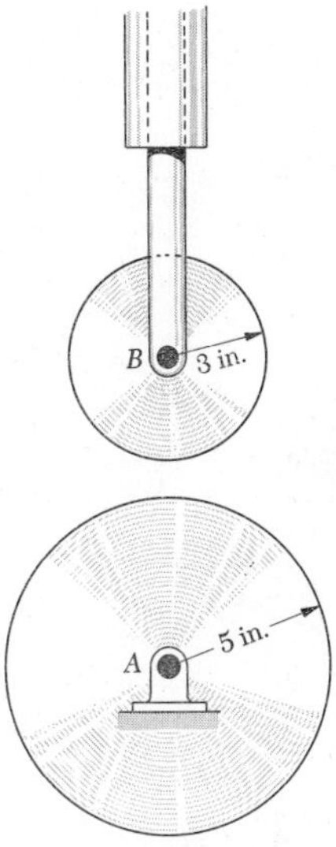

FIG. P 15.19 AND P 15.20

15.19. The two friction wheels *A* and *B* are to be brought together. Wheel *A* has an initial angular velocity of 600 rpm clockwise and will coast to rest in 40 sec, while wheel *B* is initially at rest and is given a constant counterclockwise angular acceleration of 2 radians/sec^2. Determine (*a*) at what time the wheels may be brought together if they are not to slip, (*b*) the angular velocity of each wheel as contact is made.

15.20. Two friction wheels *A* and *B* are both rotating freely at 300 rpm clockwise when they are brought into contact. After 3 sec of slippage, during which each wheel has a constant angular acceleration, wheel *A* reaches a final angular velocity of 60 rpm clockwise. Determine (*a*) the angular acceleration of each wheel during the period of slippage, (*b*) the time at which the angular velocity of wheel *B* is equal to zero.

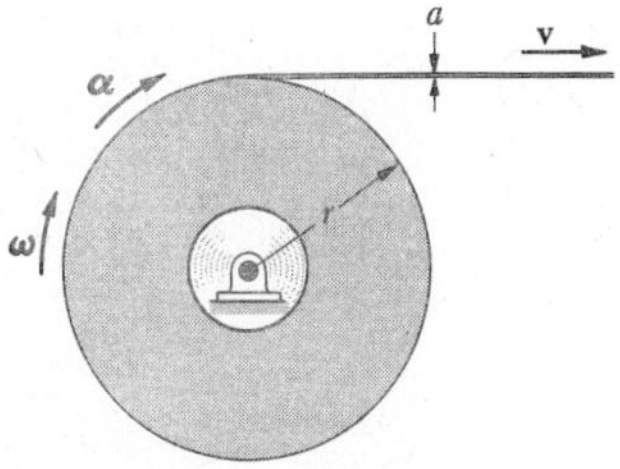

FIG. P 15.21

***15.21.** In a continuous printing process, paper is drawn into the presses at a constant speed v. Denoting by r the radius of paper on the roll at any given time and by a the thickness of the paper, derive an expression for the angular acceleration of the paper roll.

***15.22.** The motion of the circular plate of Fig. P 15.14 is defined by the relation $\theta = \theta_0 \sin(2\pi t/T)$, where θ is expressed in radians and t in seconds. Derive expressions (*a*) for the magnitude of the total acceleration of point *B* on the rim of the plate, (*b*) for the values of θ at which the total acceleration of point *B* reaches its maximum and minimum values, and for the corresponding values of the total acceleration of point *B*.

15.5. General Plane Motion. As indicated in Sec. 15.1, we understand by general plane motion a plane motion which is neither a translation nor a rotation. As we shall presently see, however, *a general plane motion may always be considered as the sum of a translation and a rotation.*

Consider, for example, a wheel rolling on a straight track (Fig. 15.12). Over a certain interval of time, two given points A and B will have moved, respectively, from A_1 to A_2 and from B_1 to B_2. The same result could be obtained through a translation which would bring A and B into A_2 and B_1' (the line AB remaining vertical), followed by a rotation about A bringing B into B_2. Although the original rolling motion differs from the combination of translation and rotation when these motions are taken in succession, the original motion may be completely duplicated by a combination of simultaneous translation and rotation.

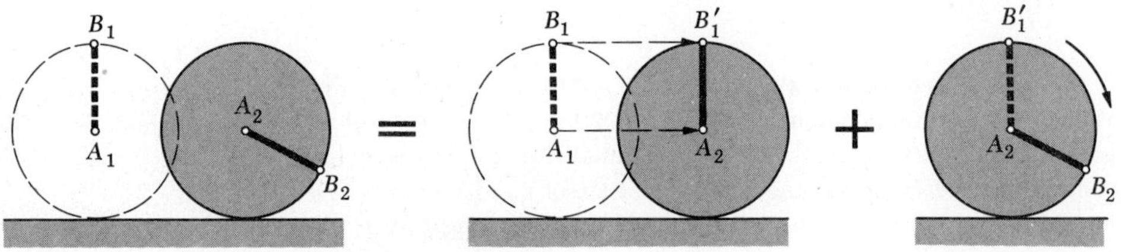

FIG. 15.12 Plane motion = Translation with A + Rotation about A

Another example of plane motion is given in Fig. 15.13, which represents a rod whose extremities slide, respectively, along a horizontal and a vertical track. This motion may be replaced by a translation in a horizontal direction and a rotation about A (Fig. 15.13*a*) or by a translation in a vertical direction and a rotation about B (Fig. 15.13*b*).

In general, we shall consider a small displacement which brings two particles A and B of a representative slab, respectively, from A_1 and B_1 into A_2 and B_2 (Fig. 15.14). This displacement may be divided into two parts, one in which the particles move into A_2 and B_1' while the line AB maintains the same direction, the other in which B moves into B_2 while A remains fixed. Clearly, the first part of the motion is a translation, and the second part a rotation about A.

Recalling from Sec. 11.12 the definition of the "relative motion" of a particle with respect to a moving frame of reference—as opposed to its "absolute motion" with respect to a fixed frame of reference—we may restate as follows the result ob-

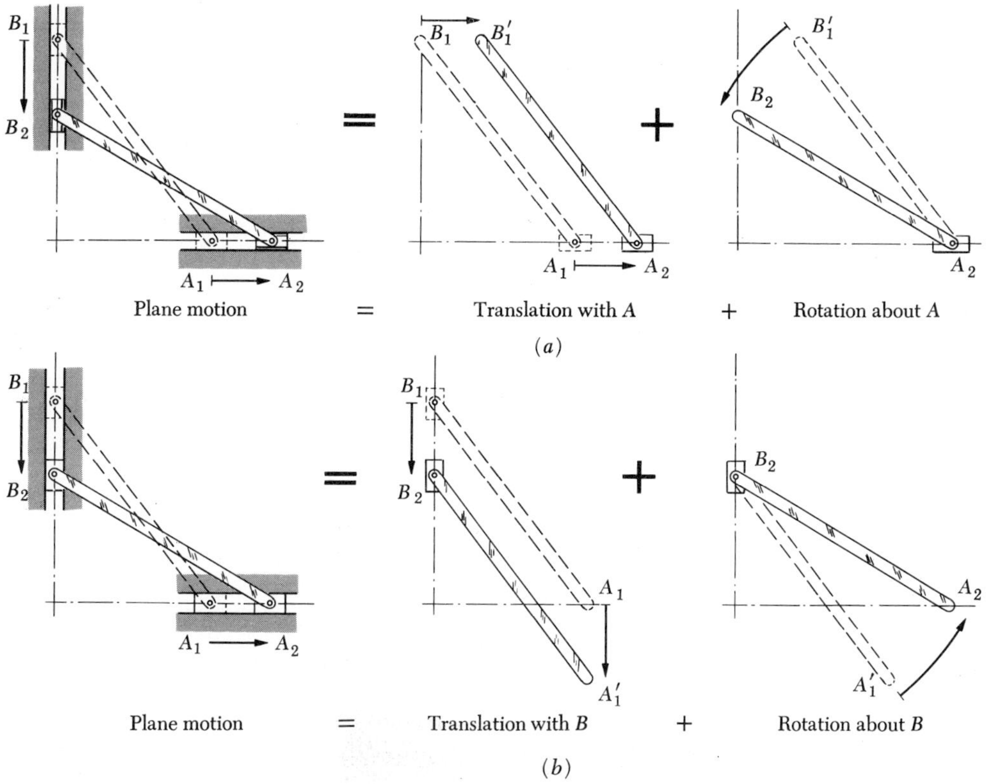

FIG. 15.13

tained above: Given two particles A and B of a rigid slab in plane motion, the relative motion of B with respect to a frame attached to A and of fixed orientation is a rotation. To an observer moving with A, but not rotating, particle B will appear to describe an arc of circle centered at A.

15.6. Absolute and Relative Velocity in Plane Motion. We saw in the preceding section that any plane motion of a slab may be replaced by a translation defined by the motion of an arbitrary reference point A, and by a rotation about A. The absolute velocity $\mathbf{v}_B$ of a particle B of the slab is obtained from the relative-velocity formula derived in Sec. 11.12,

$$\mathbf{v}_B = \mathbf{v}_A + \mathbf{v}_{B/A} \tag{15.17}$$

where the right-hand member represents a vector sum. The velocity $\mathbf{v}_A$ corresponds to the translation of the slab with A, while the relative velocity $\mathbf{v}_{B/A}$ is associated with the rotation of the slab about A and is measured with respect to axes centered at A and of fixed orientation (Fig. 15.15). Denoting by $\mathbf{r}_{B/A}$ the position vector of B relative to A, and by ω the angular

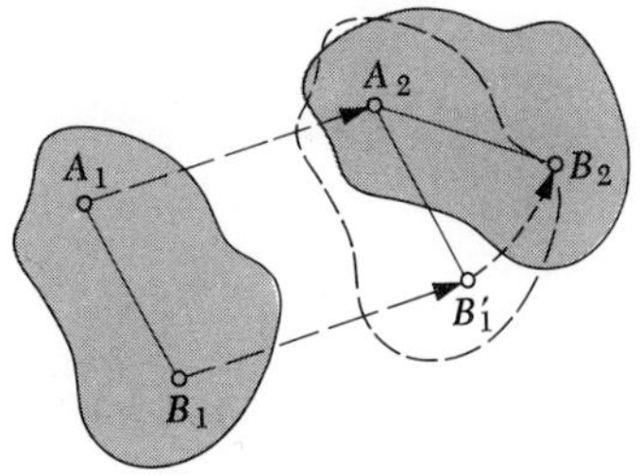

FIG. 15.14

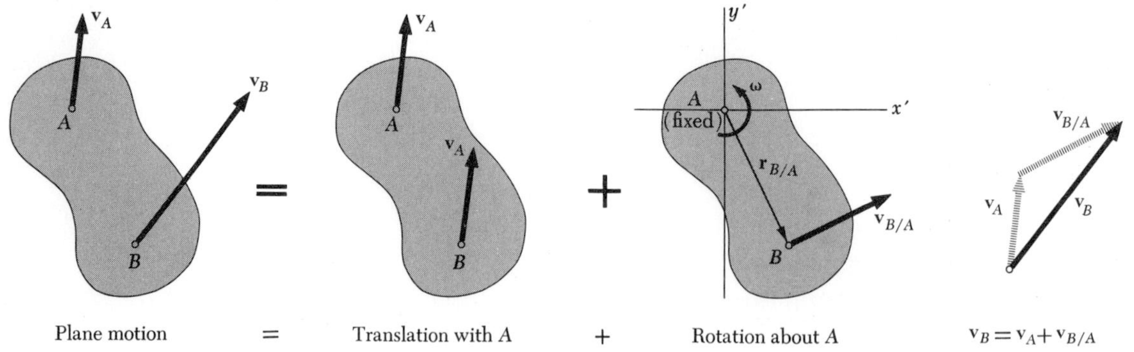

FIG. 15.15

velocity of the slab with respect to axes of fixed orientation, we have from (15.10)

$$\mathbf{v}_{B/A} = \boldsymbol{\omega} \times \mathbf{r}_{B/A} \qquad v_{B/A} = r\omega \tag{15.18}$$

where r is the distance from A to B.

As an example, we shall consider again the rod AB of Fig. 15.13. Assuming that the velocity $\mathbf{v}_A$ of end A is known, we propose to find the velocity $\mathbf{v}_B$ of end B and the angular velocity $\boldsymbol{\omega}$ of the rod, in terms of the velocity $\mathbf{v}_A$, the length l, and the angle θ. Choosing A as reference point, we express that the given motion is equivalent to a translation with A and a rotation about A (Fig. 15.16). The absolute velocity of B must therefore be equal to the vector sum

$$\mathbf{v}_B = \mathbf{v}_A + \mathbf{v}_{B/A} \tag{15.17}$$

We note that, while the direction of $\mathbf{v}_{B/A}$ is known, its magnitude $l\omega$ is unknown. However, this is compensated by the fact that the direction of $\mathbf{v}_B$ is known. We may therefore complete the diagram of Fig. 15.16. Solving for the magnitudes v_B and ω, we write

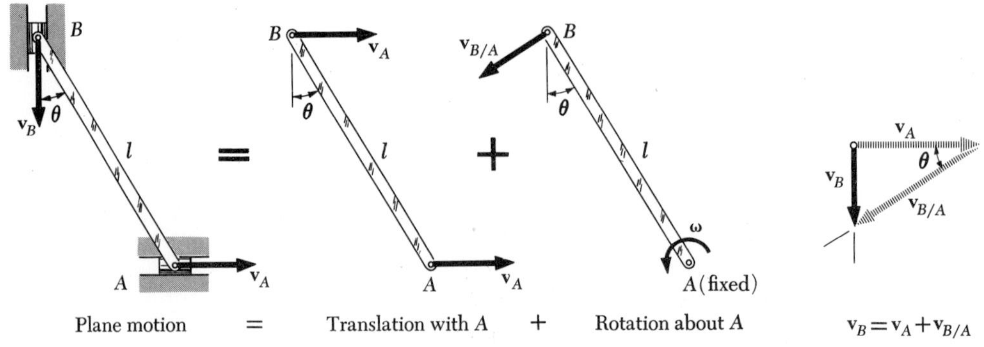

FIG. 15.16

$$v_B = v_A \tan\theta \qquad \omega = \frac{v_{B/A}}{l} = \frac{v_A}{l\cos\theta} \tag{15.19}$$

The same result may be obtained by using B as a point of reference. Resolving the given motion into a translation with B and a rotation about B (Fig. 15.17), we write the equation

$$\mathbf{v}_A = \mathbf{v}_B + \mathbf{v}_{A/B} \tag{15.20}$$

which is represented graphically in Fig. 15.17. We note that $\mathbf{v}_{A/B}$ and $\mathbf{v}_{B/A}$ have the same magnitude $l\omega$ but opposite sense. The sense of the relative velocity depends, therefore, upon the point of reference which has been selected and should be carefully ascertained from the appropriate diagram (Fig. 15.16 or 15.17).

Finally, we observe that the angular velocity ω of the rod in its rotation about B is the same as in its rotation about A. It is measured in both cases by the rate of change of the angle θ. This result is quite general; we should therefore bear in mind that *the angular velocity ω of a rigid body in plane motion is independent of the reference point.*

Most mechanisms consist, not of one, but of *several* moving parts. When the various parts of a mechanism are pin-connected, its analysis may be carried out by considering each part as a rigid body, while keeping in mind that the points where two parts are connected must have the same absolute velocity (see Sample Prob. 15.3). A similar analysis may be used when gears are involved, since the teeth in contact must also have the same absolute velocity. However, when a mechanism contains parts which slide on each other, the relative velocity of the parts in contact must be taken into account (see Secs. 15.13 and 15.14).

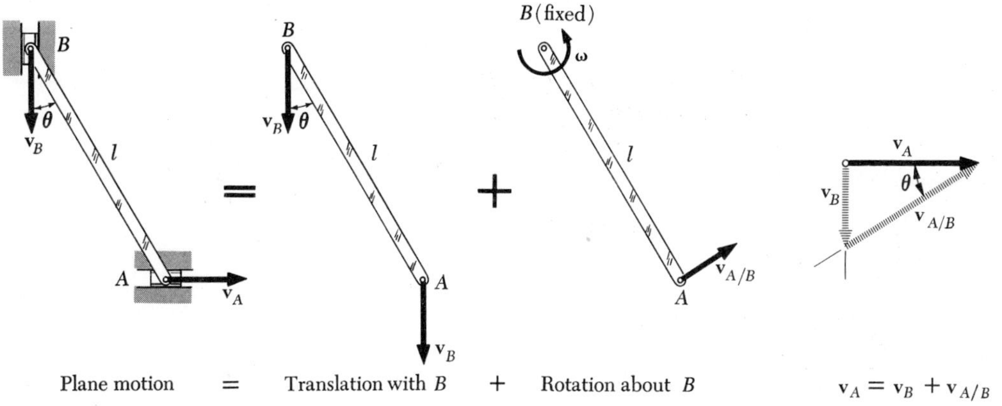

FIG. 15.17

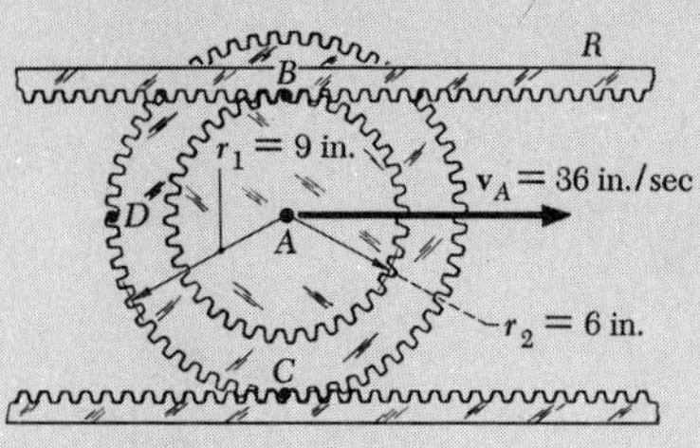

SAMPLE PROBLEM 15.2

The double gear shown rolls on the stationary lower rack; the velocity of its center A is 36 in./sec directed to the right. Determine (a) the angular velocity of the gear, (b) the velocities of the upper rack R and of points C and D of the gear.

a. **Angular Velocity of the Gear.** Since the gear rolls on the lower rack, its center A moves through a distance equal to the outer circumference $2\pi r_1$ for each full revolution of the gear. Noting that 1 rev = 2π radians, we obtain the coordinate s_A in terms of the corresponding angular coordinate θ (in radians) of the gear by a proportion,

$$\frac{s_A}{2\pi r_1} = \frac{\theta}{2\pi} \qquad s_A = r_1\theta$$

Differentiating with respect to the time t and substituting the known values $v_A = 36$ in./sec and $r_1 = 9$ in., we obtain

$$v_A = r_1\omega \qquad 36 \text{ in./sec} = (9 \text{ in.})\omega \qquad \omega = 4 \text{ radians/sec}$$

$$\boldsymbol{\omega} = 4 \text{ radians/sec} \curvearrowright = -4\mathbf{k} \text{ radians/sec} \blacktriangleleft$$

where $\mathbf{k}$ is a unit vector pointing out of the paper.

b. **Velocities.** The rolling motion is resolved into two component motions: a translation with the center A and a rotation about the center A. In the translation, all points of the gear move with the same velocity $\mathbf{v}_A$. In the rotation, each point P of the gear moves about A with a relative velocity $\mathbf{v}_{P/A} = \boldsymbol{\omega} \times \mathbf{r}_{P/A}$, where $\mathbf{r}_{P/A}$ is the position vector of P relative to A.

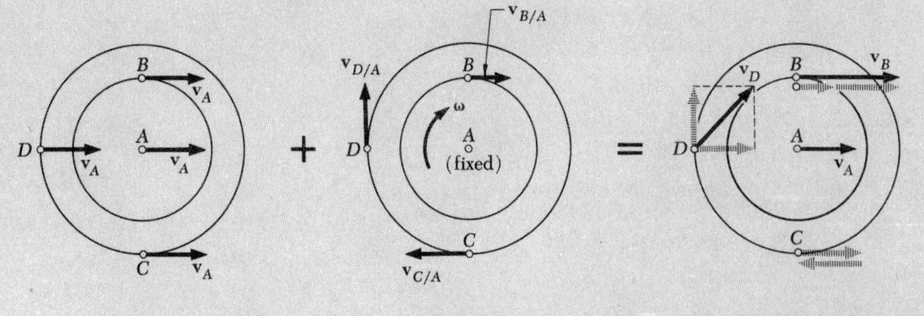

Translation + Rotation = Rolling motion

Velocity of Upper Rack. The velocity of the upper rack is equal to the velocity of point B; we write

$$\mathbf{v}_R = \mathbf{v}_B = \mathbf{v}_A + \mathbf{v}_{B/A} = \mathbf{v}_A + \boldsymbol{\omega} \times \mathbf{r}_{B/A}$$
$$= 36\mathbf{i} - 4\mathbf{k} \times 6\mathbf{j} = 36\mathbf{i} + 24\mathbf{i} = 60\mathbf{i}$$
$$\mathbf{v}_R = 60 \text{ in./sec} \rightarrow \blacktriangleleft$$

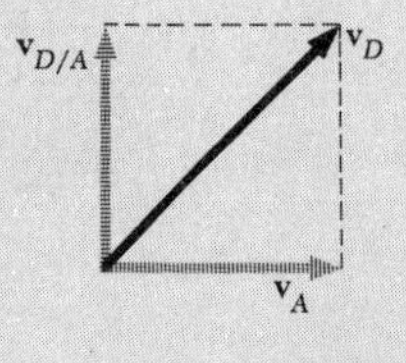

Velocity of Point C:

$$\mathbf{v}_C = \mathbf{v}_A + \mathbf{v}_{C/A} = \mathbf{v}_A + \boldsymbol{\omega} \times \mathbf{r}_{C/A}$$
$$= 36\mathbf{i} - 4\mathbf{k} \times (-9\mathbf{j}) = 36\mathbf{i} - 36\mathbf{i} = 0$$
$$\mathbf{v}_C = 0 \blacktriangleleft$$

Velocity of Point D:

$$\mathbf{v}_D = \mathbf{v}_A + \mathbf{v}_{D/A} = \mathbf{v}_A + \boldsymbol{\omega} \times \mathbf{r}_{D/A}$$
$$= 36\mathbf{i} - 4\mathbf{k} \times (-9\mathbf{i}) = 36\mathbf{i} + 36\mathbf{j}$$
$$\mathbf{v}_D = 50.9 \text{ in./sec} \angle 45° \blacktriangleleft$$

SAMPLE PROBLEM 15.3

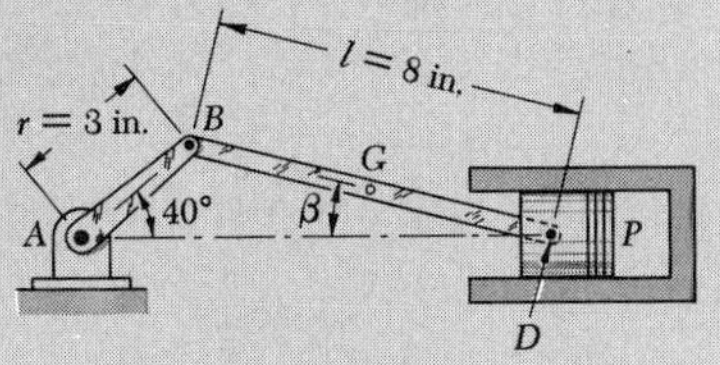

In the engine system shown, the crank AB has a constant clockwise angular velocity of 2,000 rpm. For the crank position indicated, determine (a) the angular velocity of the connecting rod BD, (b) the velocity of the piston P.

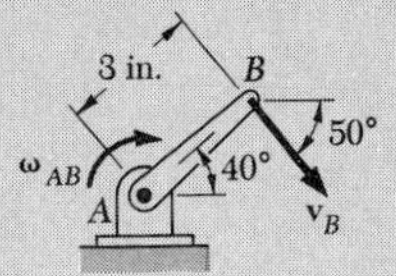

Motion of Crank AB. The crank AB rotates about point A. Expressing ω_{AB} in radians/sec and writing $v_B = r\omega_{AB}$, we obtain

$$\omega_{AB} = \left(2{,}000 \frac{\text{rev}}{\text{min}}\right)\left(\frac{1 \text{ min}}{60 \text{ sec}}\right)\left(\frac{2\pi \text{ radians}}{1 \text{ rev}}\right) = 209 \text{ radians/sec}$$

$$v_B = (AB)\omega_{AB} = (3 \text{ in.})(209 \text{ radians/sec}) = 627 \text{ in./sec}$$
$$\mathbf{v}_B = 627 \text{ in./sec} \measuredangle 50°$$

Motion of Connecting Rod BD. We consider this motion as a general plane motion. Using the law of sines, we compute the angle β between the connecting rod and the horizontal,

$$\frac{\sin 40°}{8 \text{ in.}} = \frac{\sin \beta}{3 \text{ in.}} \qquad \beta = 13.9°$$

The velocity $\mathbf{v}_D$ of the point D where the rod is attached to the piston must be horizontal, while the velocity of point B is equal to the velocity $\mathbf{v}_B$ obtained above. Resolving the motion of BD into a translation with B and a rotation about B, we obtain

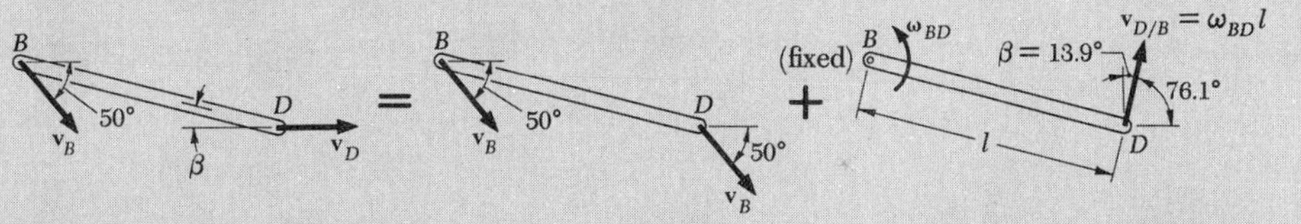

Plane motion = Translation + Rotation

Expressing the relation between the velocities $\mathbf{v}_D$, $\mathbf{v}_B$, and $\mathbf{v}_{D/B}$, we write

$$\mathbf{v}_D = \mathbf{v}_B + \mathbf{v}_{D/B}$$

We draw the vector diagram corresponding to this equation. Recalling that $\beta = 13.9°$, we determine the angles of the triangle and write

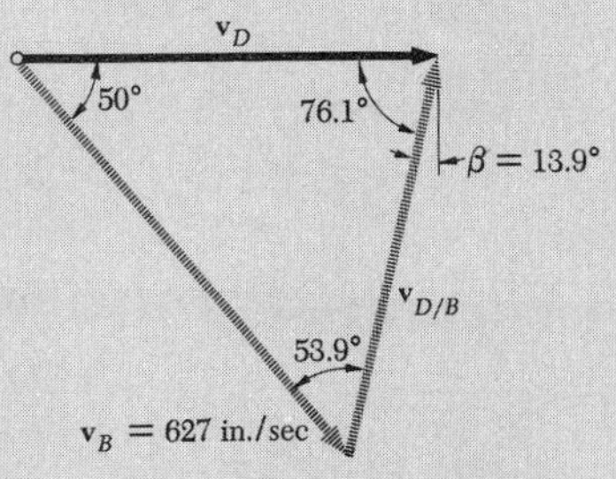

$$\frac{v_D}{\sin 53.9°} = \frac{v_{D/B}}{\sin 50°} = \frac{627 \text{ in./sec}}{\sin 76.1°}$$

$$v_{D/B} = 495 \text{ in./sec} \qquad \mathbf{v}_{D/B} = 495 \text{ in./sec} \measuredangle 76.1°$$
$$v_D = 522 \text{ in./sec} = 43.5 \text{ ft/sec} \qquad \mathbf{v}_D = 43.5 \text{ ft/sec} \rightarrow$$
$$\mathbf{v}_P = \mathbf{v}_D = 43.5 \text{ ft/sec} \rightarrow \blacktriangleleft$$

Since $v_{D/B} = l\omega_{BD}$, we have

$$495 \text{ in./sec} = (8 \text{ in.})\omega_{BD} \qquad \omega_{BD} = 61.9 \text{ radians/sec} \circlearrowleft \blacktriangleleft$$

PROBLEMS

15.23. An automobile travels to the right at a constant speed of 60 mph. If the diameter of a wheel is 26 in., determine the velocities of points *B, C, D,* and *E* on the rim of the wheel.

15.24. Solve Prob. 15.23 assuming that the diameter of the wheel is reduced to 24 in.

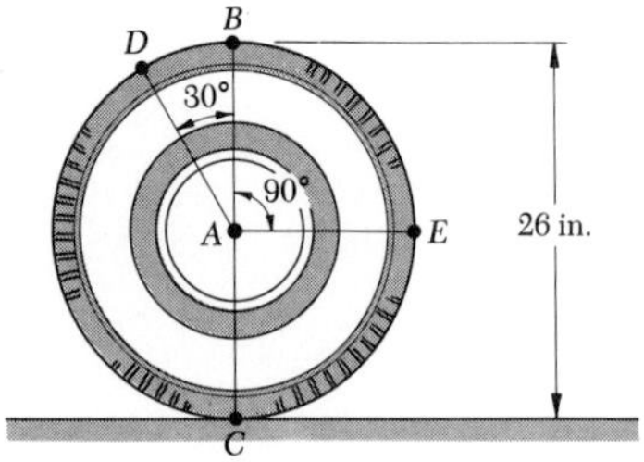

FIG. **P 15.23**

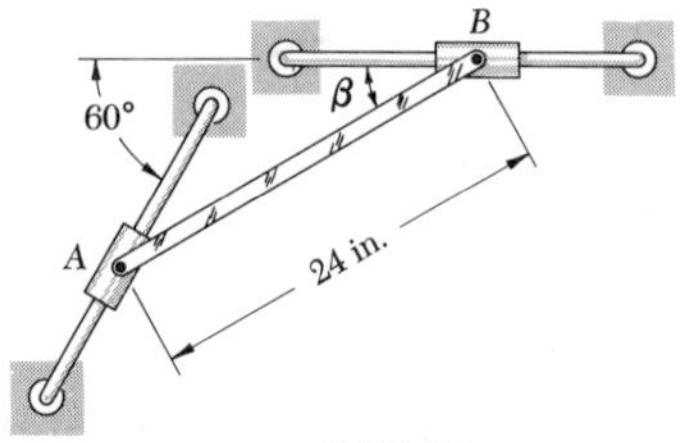

FIG. **P 15.25**

15.25. Collar *B* moves with a constant velocity of 30 in./sec to the left. At the instant when $\beta = 30°$, determine (*a*) the angular velocity of rod *AB*, (*b*) the velocity of collar *A*.

15.26. Solve Prob. 15.25 assuming that $\beta = 45°$.

15.27. The rigid slab shown moves in the *xy* plane. Knowing that $(v_A)_x = 4$ in./sec, $(v_B)_y = -3$ in./sec, and $(v_C)_x = 16$ in./sec, determine the angular velocity of the slab and the velocity of point *A*.

15.28. In Prob. 15.27 determine the equation of the locus of points of the slab for which the magnitude of the velocity is 8 in./sec.

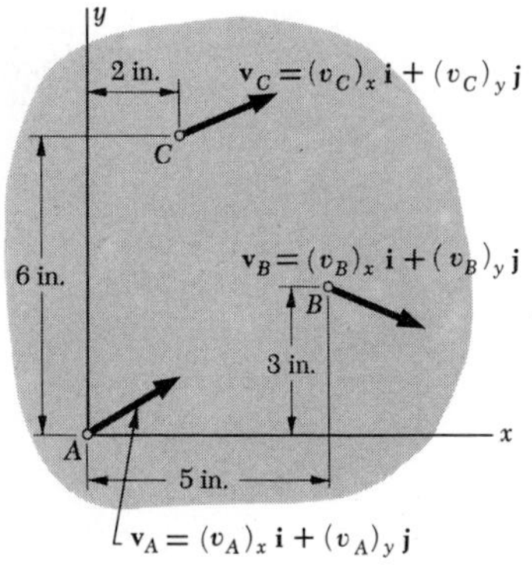

FIG. **P 15.27**

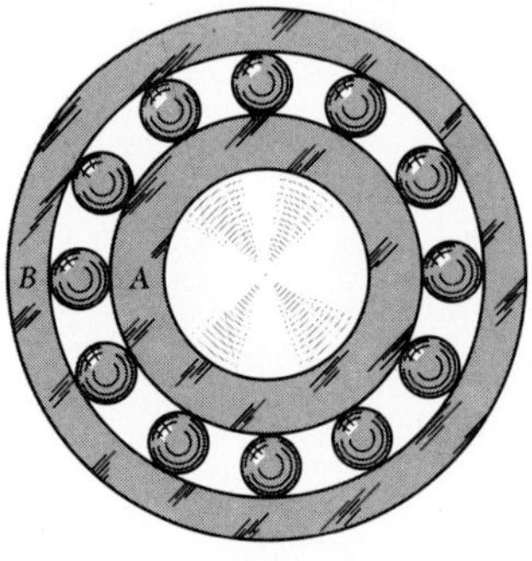

FIG. **P 15.29**

15.29. In the simplified sketch of a ball bearing shown, the diameter of the inner race *A* is 2.5 in. and the diameter of each ball is 0.5 in. The outer race *B* is stationary while the inner race has an angular velocity of 3,600 rpm. Determine (*a*) the linear velocity of the center of each ball, (*b*) the angular velocity of each ball, (*c*) the number of times per minute each ball describes a complete circle.

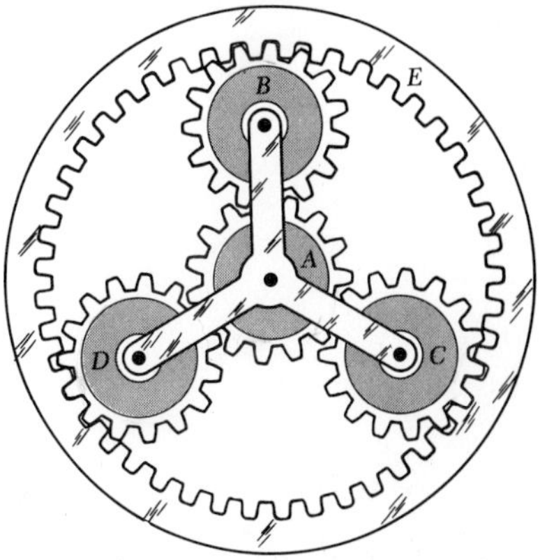

FIG. P 15.30 AND P 15.31

15.30. In the planetary gear system shown, the radius of the central gear A is a, the radius of each planetary gear is b, and the radius of the outer gear E is $a + 2b$. In a particular gear system where $a = b = 2\frac{1}{4}$ in., the angular velocity of gear A is ω_A clockwise. Knowing that the outer gear is stationary, determine (a) the angular velocity of the spider connecting the planetary gears, (b) the angular velocity of each planetary gear.

15.31. In the planetary gear system shown, the radius of the central gear A is a, the radius of each of the planetary gears is b, and the radius of the outer gear E is $a + 2b$. The angular velocity of gear A is ω_A clockwise and the outer gear is stationary. If the angular velocity of the spider BCD is to be $\omega_A/5$, determine (a) the required value of the ratio b/a, (b) the corresponding angular velocity of each planetary gear.

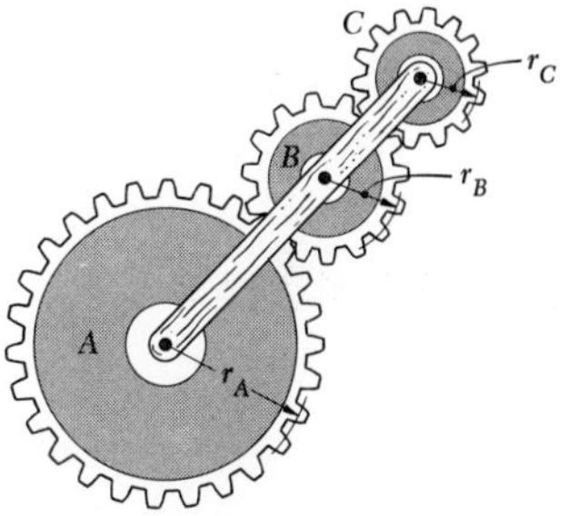

FIG. P 15.32

15.32. Three gears A, B, and C are pinned at their centers to rod ABC. Knowing that $r_A = 3r_B = 3r_C$ and that gear A does not rotate, determine the angular velocity of gears B and C when the rod ABC rotates clockwise with an angular velocity of 10 rpm.

15.33. Crank AB has a constant angular velocity of 200 rpm counterclockwise. Determine the angular velocity of rod BD and the velocity of collar D when (a) $\theta = 0$, (b) $\theta = 90°$, (c) $\theta = 180°$.

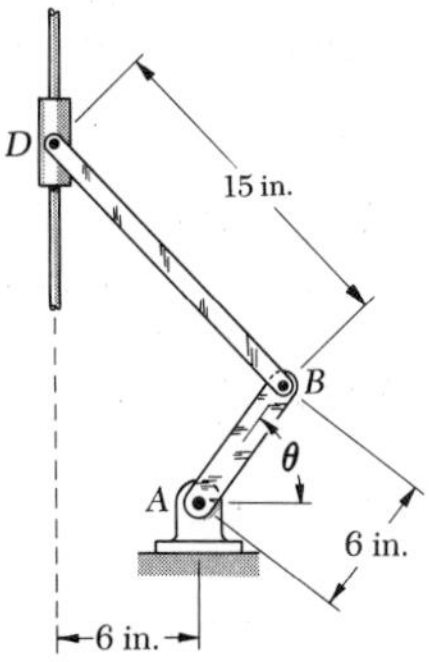

FIG. P 15.33

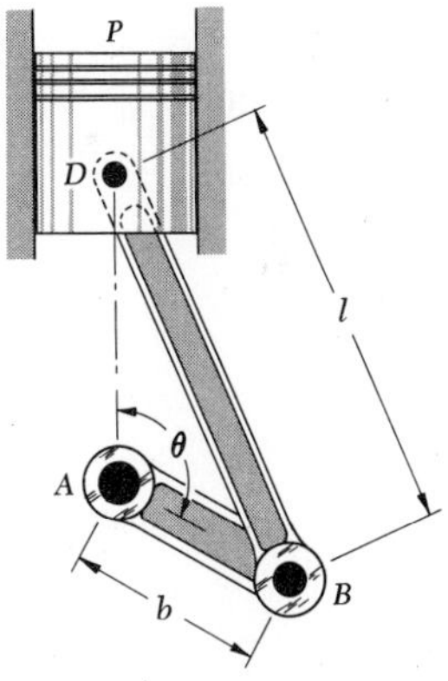

FIG. P 15.34

15.34. In the engine system shown, $l = 8$ in. and $b = 2$ in.; the crank AB rotates with a constant angular velocity of 1,000 rpm clockwise. Determine the velocity of the piston P and the angular velocity of the connecting rod for the position corresponding to (a) $\theta = 0$, (b) $\theta = 90°$, (c) $\theta = 180°$.

15.35. Solve Prob. 15.33 for the position corresponding to $\theta = 30°$.

15.36. Solve Prob. 15.34 for the position corresponding to $\theta = 60°$.

15.37 through 15.40. In the position shown, bar AB has a constant angular velocity of 4 radians/sec counterclockwise. Determine the angular velocity of bars BD and DE.

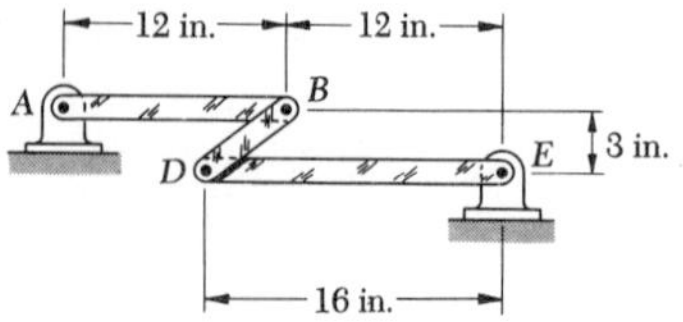

FIG. P 15.37

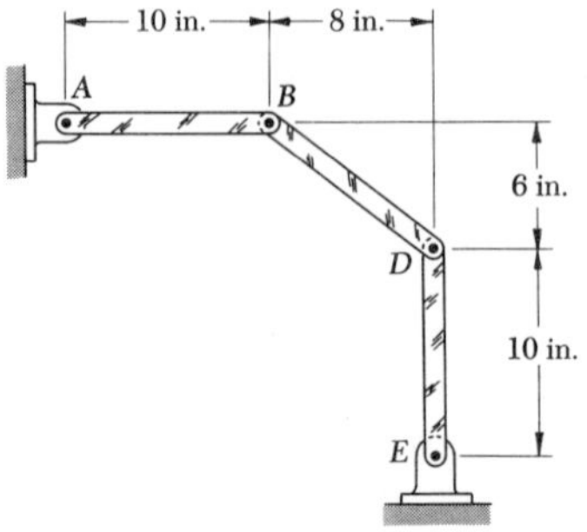

FIG. P 15.38

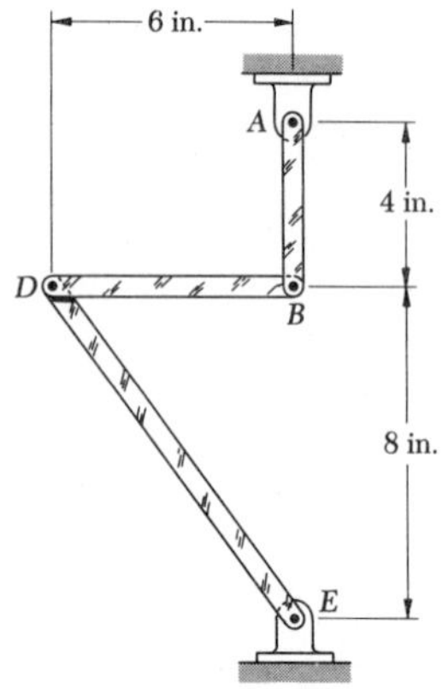

FIG. P 15.39

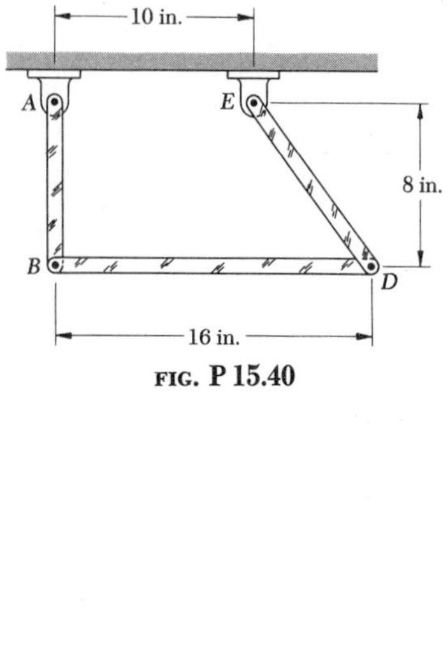

FIG. P 15.40

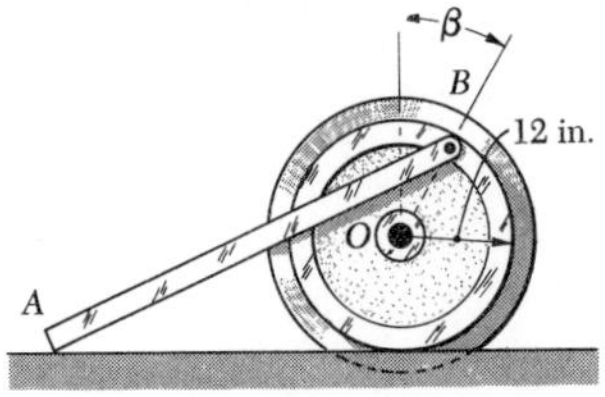

FIG. P 15.41

15.41. The flanged wheel rolls to the right with a constant velocity of 4 ft/sec. The rod AB is 48 in. long and is attached to the wheel at B. Determine the angular velocity of AB and the linear velocity of A (*a*) when $\beta = 0$, (*b*) when $\beta = 90°$.

15.42. Solve Prob. 15.41 assuming (*a*) $\beta = 180°$, (*b*) $\beta = 60°$.

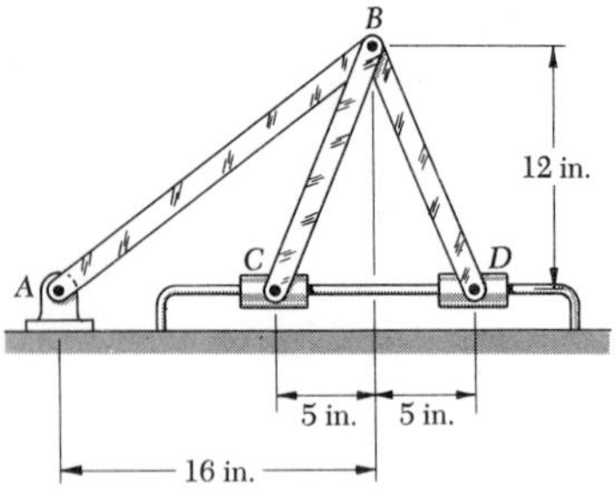

FIG. P 15.43

15.43. Two collars C and D move along the horizontal rod shown. Knowing that the velocity of collar D is 42 in./sec to the left, determine (*a*) the velocity of collar C, (*b*) the angular velocity of member AB.

***15.44.** Prove for any given position of the mechanism of Prob. 15.43 that the ratio of the magnitudes of the velocities of collars C and D is equal to the ratio of the distances AC and AD.

***15.45.** Derive an expression for the angular velocity ω_C of gear C of the system of Prob. 15.32 and show that ω_C is independent of the radius of gear B. Assume that point A is fixed and denote the angular velocities of rod ABC and gear A by ω_{ABC} and ω_A respectively.

*15.46. Assuming that the crank AB of Prob. 15.34 rotates with a constant clockwise angular velocity ω and that $\theta = 0$ at $t = 0$, derive an expression for the velocity of the piston P in terms of the time t.

15.7. Instantaneous Center of Rotation in Plane Motion. Consider the general plane motion of a slab. We shall show that at any given instant the velocities of the various particles of the slab are the same as if the slab were rotating about a certain axis perpendicular to the plane of the slab, called the *instantaneous axis of rotation.* This axis intersects the plane of the slab at a point C, called the *instantaneous center of rotation* of the slab.

To prove our statement, we first recall that the plane motion of a slab may always be replaced by a translation defined by the motion of an arbitrary reference point A, and by a rotation about A. As far as the velocities are concerned, the translation is characterized by the velocity $\mathbf{v}_A$ of the reference point A and the rotation is characterized by the angular velocity ω of the slab (which is independent of the choice of A). Thus, the velocity $\mathbf{v}_A$ of point A and the angular velocity ω of the slab define completely the velocities of all the other particles of the slab (Fig. 15.18*a*). Now let us assume that $\mathbf{v}_A$ and ω are known and that they are both different from zero. (If $\mathbf{v}_A = 0$, point A is itself the instantaneous center of rotation, and if $\omega = 0$, the slab is in translation.) These velocities could be obtained by letting the slab rotate with the angular velocity ω about a point C located on the perpendicular to $\mathbf{v}_A$ at a distance $r = v_A/\omega$ from A as shown in Fig. 15.18*b*. We check that the velocity of A would be perpendicular to AC and that its magnitude would be $r\omega = (v_A/\omega)\omega = v_A$. Thus the velocities of all the other particles of the slab would be the same as originally defined. Therefore, *as far as the velocities are concerned, the slab seems to rotate about the instantaneous center C at the instant considered.*

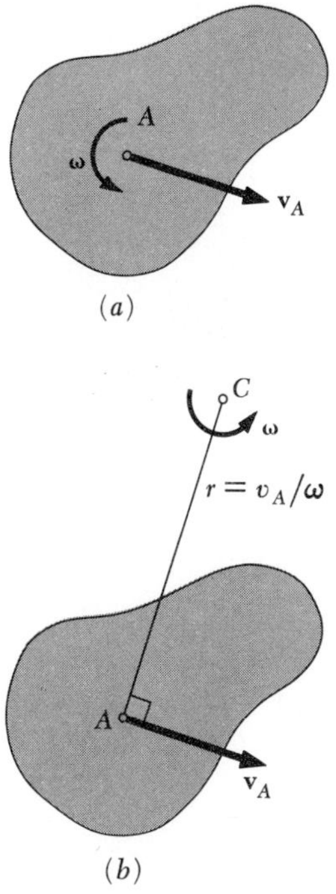

FIG. 15.18

The position of the instantaneous center may be defined in two other ways. If the directions of the velocities of two particles A and B of the slab are known, and if they are different, the instantaneous center C is obtained by drawing the perpendicular to $\mathbf{v}_A$ through A and the perpendicular to $\mathbf{v}_B$ through B and determining the point in which these two lines intersect (Fig. 15.19*a*). If the velocities $\mathbf{v}_A$ and $\mathbf{v}_B$ of two particles A and B are perpendicular to the line AB, and if their magnitudes are known, the instantaneous center may be found by intersecting the line AB with the line joining the extremities of the vectors

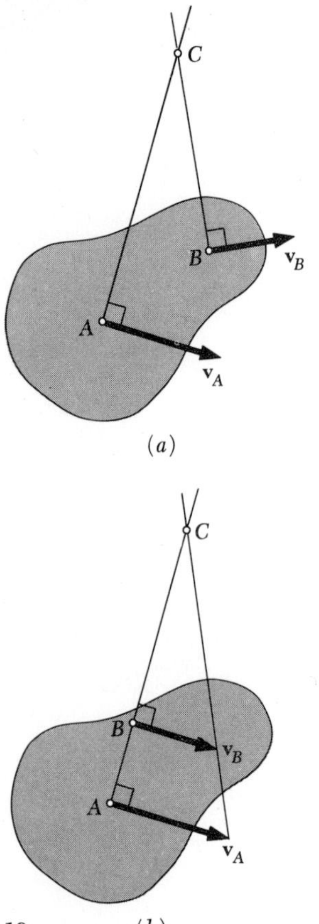

FIG. 15.19

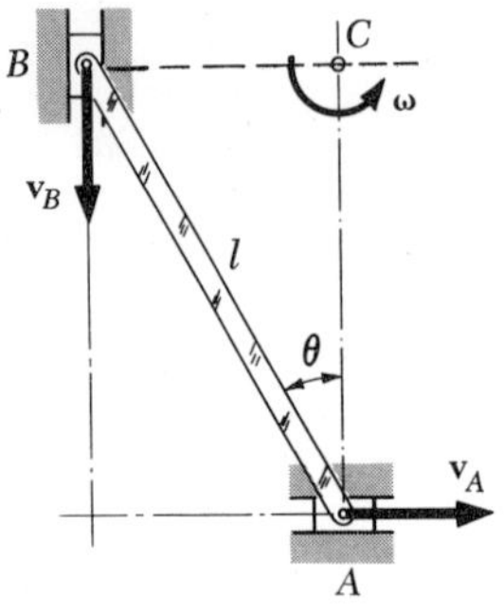

FIG. 15.20

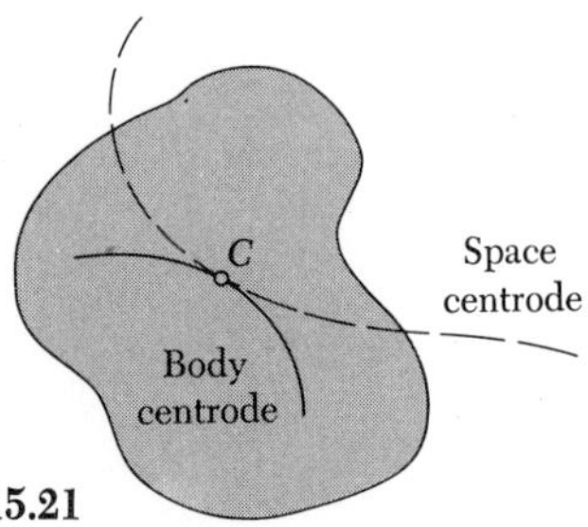

FIG. 15.21

$\mathbf{v}_A$ and $\mathbf{v}_B$ (Fig. 15.19*b*). Note that, if $\mathbf{v}_A$ and $\mathbf{v}_B$ were parallel in Fig. 15.19*a*, or if $\mathbf{v}_A$ and $\mathbf{v}_B$ had the same magnitude in Fig. 15.19*b*, the instantaneous center C would be at an infinite distance and ω would be zero; the slab would be in translation.

To see how the concept of instantaneous center of rotation may be put to use, let us consider again the rod of Sec. 15.6. Drawing the perpendicular to $\mathbf{v}_A$ through A and the perpendicular to $\mathbf{v}_B$ through B (Fig. 15.20), we obtain the instantaneous center C. At the instant considered, the velocities of all the particles of the rod are thus the same as if the rod rotated about C. Now, if the magnitude v_A of the velocity of A is known, the magnitude ω of the angular velocity of the rod may be obtained by writing

$$\omega = \frac{v_A}{AC} = \frac{v_A}{l \cos \theta}$$

The magnitude of the velocity of B may then be obtained by writing

$$v_B = (BC)\omega = l \sin \theta \frac{v_A}{l \cos \theta} = v_A \tan \theta$$

Note that only *absolute* velocities are involved in the computation.

The instantaneous center of a slab in plane motion may be located either on the slab or outside the slab. If it is located on the slab, the particle C coinciding with the instantaneous center at a given instant t must have zero velocity at that instant. However, it should be noted that the instantaneous center of rotation is valid only at a given instant. Thus, the particle C of the slab which coincides with the instantaneous center at time t will generally not coincide with the instantaneous center at time $t + \Delta t$; while its velocity is zero at time t, it will probably be different from zero at time $t + \Delta t$. This means that, in general, the particle C *does not have zero acceleration*, and therefore that the *accelerations* of the various particles of the slab *cannot* be determined as if the slab were rotating about C.

As the motion of the slab proceeds, the instantaneous center moves in space. But it was just pointed out that the position of the instantaneous center on the slab keeps changing. Thus, the instantaneous center describes one curve in space, called the *space centrode*, and another curve on the slab, called the *body centrode* (Fig. 15.21). It may be shown that, at any instant, these two curves are tangent at C and that, as the slab moves, the body centrode appears to *roll* on the space centrode.

SAMPLE PROBLEM 15.4

Solve Sample Prob. 15.2, using the method of the instantaneous center of rotation.

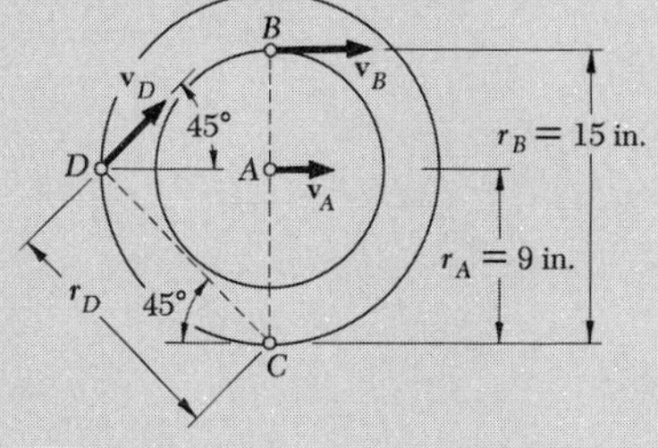

Solution *a.* **Angular Velocity of the Gear.** Since the gear rolls on the stationary lower rack, the point of contact C of the gear with the rack has no velocity; point C is therefore the instantaneous center of rotation. We write

$$v_A = r_A\omega \qquad 36 \text{ in./sec} = (9 \text{ in.})\omega \qquad \omega = 4 \text{ radians/sec} \circlearrowright$$ ◀

b. **Velocities.** All points of the gear seem to rotate about the instantaneous center as far as velocities are concerned.

Velocity of Upper Rack. Recalling that $v_R = v_B$, we write

$$v_R = v_B = r_B\omega \qquad v_R = (15 \text{ in.})(4 \text{ radians/sec}) = 60 \text{ in./sec}$$

$$\mathbf{v}_R = 60 \text{ in./sec} \rightarrow$$ ◀

Velocity of Point D. Since $r_D = (9 \text{ in.})\sqrt{2} = 12.72$ in., we write

$$v_D = r_D\omega \qquad v_D = (12.72 \text{ in.})(4 \text{ radians/sec}) = 50.9 \text{ in./sec}$$

$$\mathbf{v}_D = 50.9 \text{ in./sec} \measuredangle 45°$$ ◀

SAMPLE PROBLEM 15.5

Solve Sample Prob. 15.3, using the method of the instantaneous center of rotation.

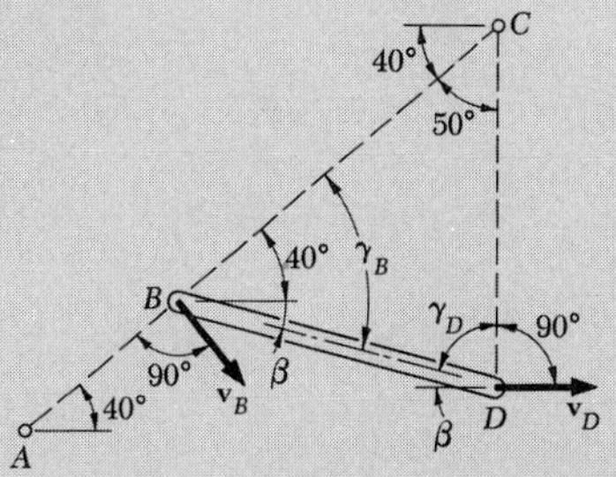

Solution. Motion of Crank ***AB*****.** Referring to Sample Prob. 15.3, we obtain the velocity of point B; $\mathbf{v}_B = 627$ in./sec $\measuredangle$ 50°.

Motion of the Connecting Rod ***BD*****.** We first locate the instantaneous center C by drawing lines perpendicular to the absolute velocities $\mathbf{v}_B$ and $\mathbf{v}_D$. Recalling from Sample Prob. 15.3 that $\beta = 13.9°$ and that $BD = 8$ in., we solve the triangle BCD.

$$\gamma_B = 40° + \beta = 53.9° \qquad \gamma_D = 90° - \beta = 76.1°$$

$$\frac{BC}{\sin 76.1°} = \frac{CD}{\sin 53.9°} = \frac{8 \text{ in.}}{\sin 50°}$$

$$BC = 10.14 \text{ in.} \qquad CD = 8.44 \text{ in.}$$

Since the connecting rod BD seems to rotate about point C, we write

$$v_B = (BC)\omega_{BD}$$

$$627 \text{ in./sec} = (10.14 \text{ in.})\omega_{BD}$$

$$\omega_{BD} = 61.9 \text{ radians/sec} \circlearrowleft$$ ◀

$$v_D = (CD)\omega_{BD} = (8.44 \text{ in.})(61.9 \text{ radians/sec})$$
$$= 522 \text{ in./sec} = 43.5 \text{ ft/sec}$$

$$\mathbf{v}_P = \mathbf{v}_D = 43.5 \text{ ft/sec} \rightarrow$$ ◀

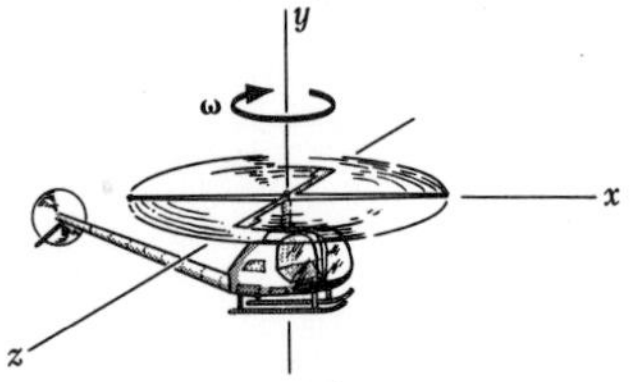

FIG. P 15.49

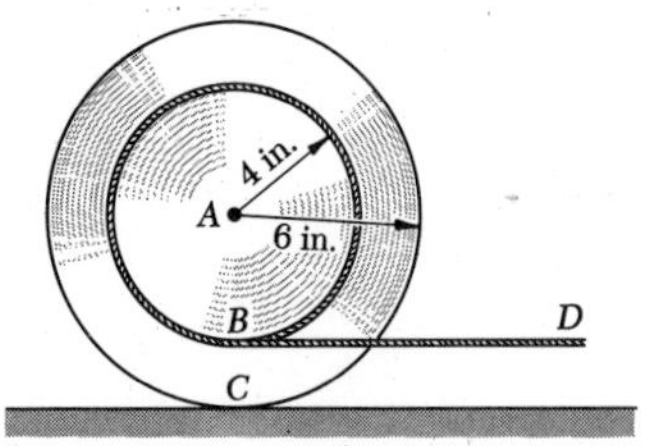

FIG. P 15.50

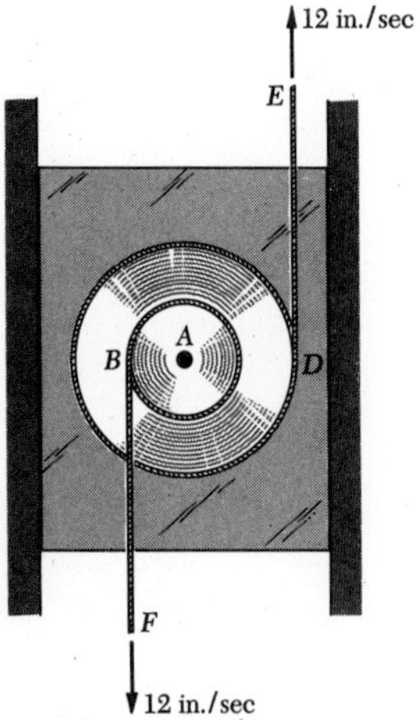

FIG. P 15.51

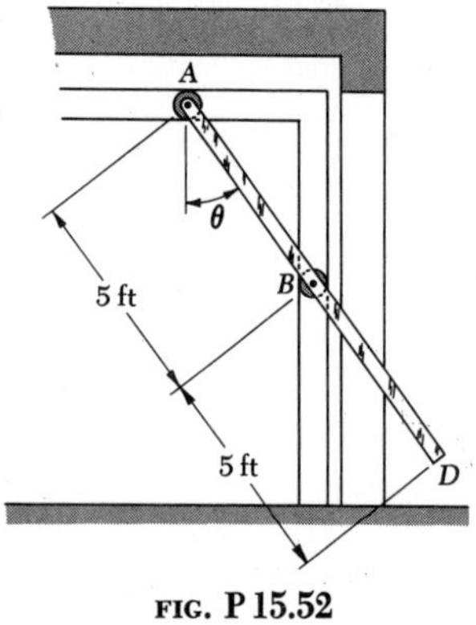

FIG. P 15.52

PROBLEMS

15.47. Denoting by $\mathbf{r}_A$ the position vector of a point A of a rigid slab which moves in plane motion, show that the position vector $\mathbf{r}_C$ of the instantaneous center of rotation is

$$\mathbf{r}_C = \mathbf{r}_A + \frac{\boldsymbol{\omega} \times \mathbf{v}_A}{\omega^2}$$

where $\boldsymbol{\omega}$ is the angular velocity of the slab and $\mathbf{v}_A$ the velocity of point A.

15.48. A disk of radius 5 in. rolls and slides on a smooth horizontal surface. Knowing that the center of the disk has a constant velocity of 16 in./sec to the right and that the disk rotates counterclockwise at a constant angular velocity of 8 radians/sec, (*a*) locate the instantaneous center of rotation, (*b*) determine the velocity of the point of the disk that is in contact with the surface.

15.49. A helicopter moves horizontally in the x direction at a speed of 45 mph. Knowing that the main blades rotate clockwise at an angular velocity of 120 rpm, determine the instantaneous axis of rotation of the main blades.

15.50. A drum, of radius 4 in., is mounted on a cylinder of radius 6 in. A cord is wound around the drum, and its extremity D is pulled to the right at a constant velocity of 5 in./sec, causing the cylinder to roll without sliding. Determine (*a*) the angular velocity of the cylinder, (*b*) the velocity of the center of the cylinder, (*c*) the number of inches of cord which are wound or unwound per second.

15.51. A double pulley is attached to a slider block by a pin at A. The 2-in.-radius inner pulley is rigidly attached to the 4-in.-radius outer pulley. Knowing that each of the two cords is pulled at a constant speed of 12 in./sec as shown, determine (*a*) the instantaneous center of rotation of the double pulley, (*b*) the velocity of the slider block, (*c*) the number of inches of cord wrapped or unwrapped on each pulley per second.

15.52. A 10-ft channel, used to form one edge of an overhead door, is guided by wheels at A and B which roll in horizontal and vertical tracks as shown. Knowing that $\theta = 30°$ and the velocity of B is 2 ft/sec upward, determine the angular velocity of the door and the velocity of D.

15.53. Knowing that at the instant shown the velocity of collar D is 12 in./sec upward, determine (*a*) the instantaneous center of rotation of link BD, (*b*) the angular velocities of crank AB and link BD, (*c*) the velocity of the mid-point of link BD.

15.54. Knowing that at the instant shown the angular velocity of crank AB is 3 radians/sec clockwise, determine (*a*) the angular velocity of link BD, (*b*) the velocity of collar D, (*c*) the velocity of the mid-point of link BD.

15.55. Two rods AB and BD are connected to three collars as shown. Knowing that collar A moves downward with a constant velocity of 6 in./sec, determine (*a*) the angular velocity of each rod, (*b*) the velocity of collar D.

15.56. Two links AB and BD, each of length l, are connected to three collars as shown. Collar A moves downward at a constant speed v_A. Show that $\omega_{AB} \sin \beta = \omega_{BD} \sin \gamma$ and that $v_A \tan \beta = v_D \tan \gamma$.

15.57. In the position shown, the piston A has a velocity of 3 ft/sec upward. Determine the instantaneous center of rotation and the angular velocity (*a*) of gear D, (*b*) of the connecting rod AB.

15.58. In the position shown, the velocity of the center of gear D is 24 in./sec to the left. Determine (*a*) the angular velocity of the connecting rod AB, (*b*) the velocity of the piston A.

15.59. Describe the space centrode and the body centrode of gear D of Prob. 15.57 as the gear rolls on the horizontal rack.

15.60. Describe the space centrode and the body centrode of link AB of Prob. 15.56 as point B moves to the right. (*Note.* The body centrode need not lie on a physical portion of the link.)

15.61. Using the method of Sec. 15.7, solve Prob. 15.37.

15.62. Using the method of Sec. 15.7, solve Prob. 15.38.

15.63. Using the method of Sec. 15.7, solve Prob. 15.39.

15.64. Using the method of Sec. 15.7, solve Prob. 15.40.

15.65. Using the method of Sec. 15.7, solve Prob. 15.41.

15.66. Using the method of Sec. 15.7, solve Prob. 15.43.

15.67. Using the method of Sec. 15.7, solve Prob. 15.33.

15.68. Using the method of Sec. 15.7, solve Prob. 15.30.

15.69. Using the method of Sec. 15.7, solve Prob. 15.31.

15.70. Using the method of Sec. 15.7, solve Prob. 15.32.

15.71. Using the method of Sec. 15.7, solve Prob. 15.29.

15.8. Absolute and Relative Acceleration in Plane Motion. We saw in Sec. 15.5 that any plane motion may be replaced by a translation defined by the motion of an arbitrary reference point A, and by a rotation about A. This property was used in Sec. 15.6 to determine the velocity of the various points of a

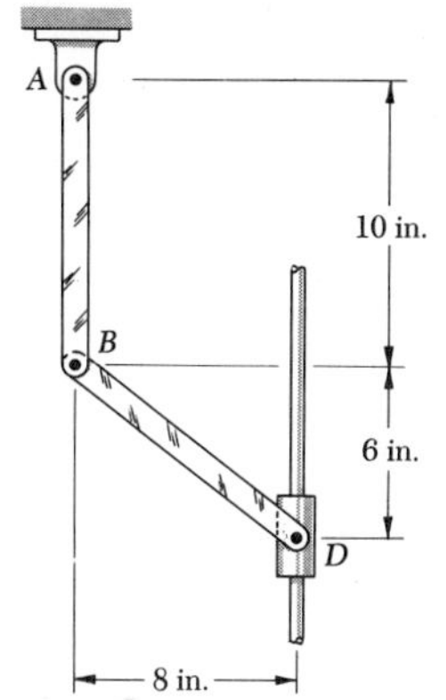

FIG. P 15.53 AND P 15.54

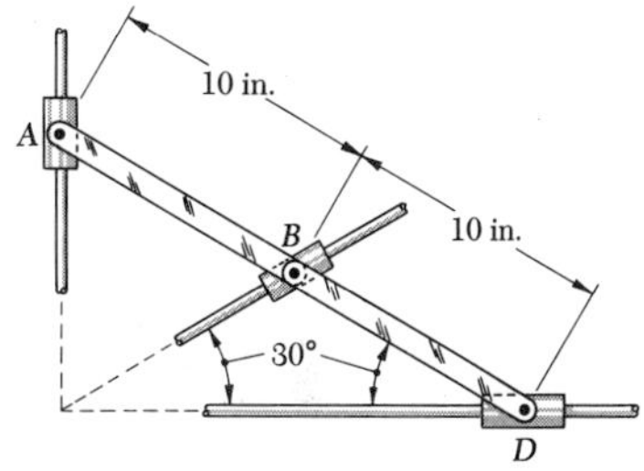

FIG. P 15.55

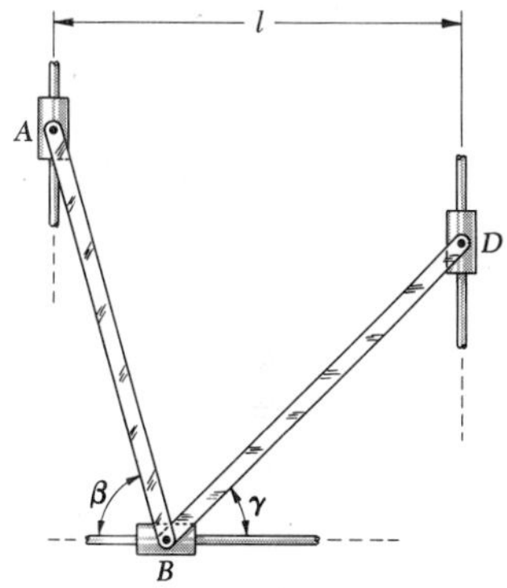

FIG. P 15.56

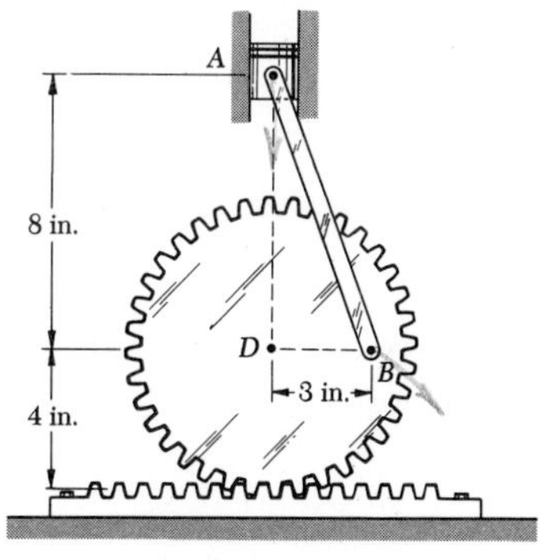

FIG. P 15.57 AND P 15.58

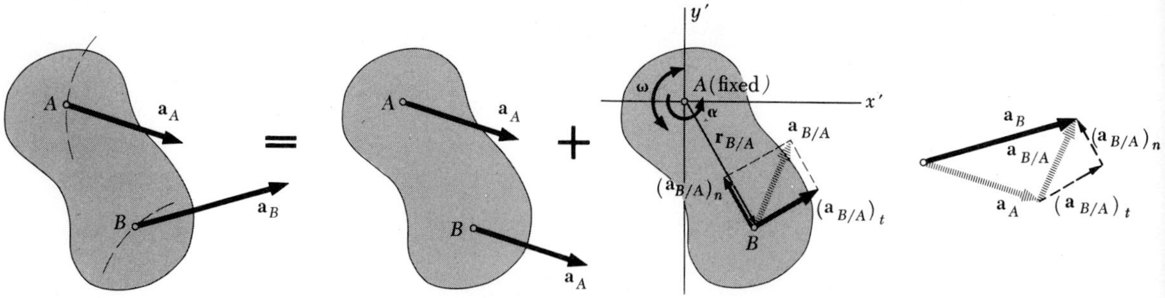

Plane motion = Translation with A + Rotation about A

FIG. 15.22

moving slab. We shall now use the same property to determine the acceleration of the points of the slab.

We first recall that the absolute acceleration $\mathbf{a}_B$ of a particle of the slab may be obtained from the relative-acceleration formula derived in Sec. 11.12,

$$\mathbf{a}_B = \mathbf{a}_A + \mathbf{a}_{B/A} \tag{15.21}$$

where the right-hand member represents a vector sum. The acceleration $\mathbf{a}_A$ corresponds to the translation of the slab with A, while the relative acceleration $\mathbf{a}_{B/A}$ is associated with the rotation of the slab about A and is measured with respect to axes centered at A and of fixed orientation (Fig. 15.22). We recall from Sec. 15.3 that the relative acceleration $\mathbf{a}_{B/A}$ may be resolved into two components, a *tangential component* $(\mathbf{a}_{B/A})_t$ perpendicular to the line AB, and a *normal component* $(\mathbf{a}_{B/A})_n$ directed toward A. Denoting by $\mathbf{r}_{B/A}$ the position vector of B relative to A and, respectively, by $\boldsymbol{\omega}$ and $\boldsymbol{\alpha}$ the angular velocity and angular acceleration of the slab with respect to axes of fixed orientation, we have

$$\begin{aligned} (\mathbf{a}_{B/A})_t &= \boldsymbol{\alpha} \times \mathbf{r}_{B/A} & (a_{B/A})_t &= r\alpha \\ (\mathbf{a}_{B/A})_n &= -\omega^2 \mathbf{r}_{B/A} & (a_{B/A})_n &= r\omega^2 \end{aligned} \tag{15.22}$$

where r is the distance from A to B.

As an example, we shall consider again the rod AB whose extremities slide, respectively, along a horizontal and a vertical track (Fig. 15.23). Assuming that the velocity $\mathbf{v}_A$ and the

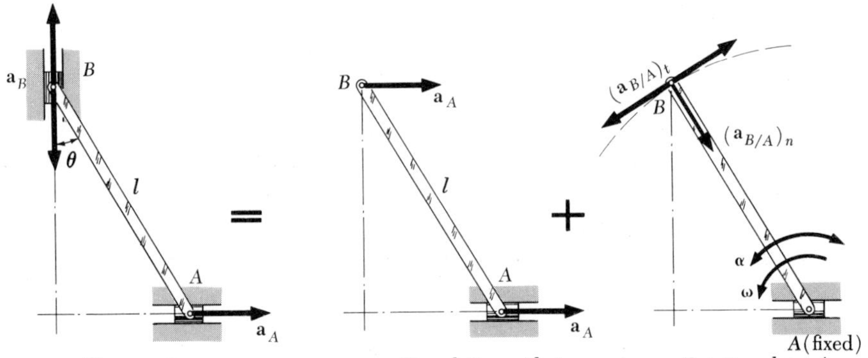

FIG. 15.23 Plane motion = Translation with A + Rotation about A

acceleration $\mathbf{a}_A$ of A are known, we propose to determine the acceleration $\mathbf{a}_B$ of B and the angular acceleration α of the rod. Choosing A as a reference point, we express that the given motion is equivalent to a translation with A and a rotation about A. The absolute acceleration of B must be equal to the sum

$$\begin{aligned}\mathbf{a}_B &= \mathbf{a}_A + \mathbf{a}_{B/A} \\ &= \mathbf{a}_A + (\mathbf{a}_{B/A})_n + (\mathbf{a}_{B/A})_t \qquad (15.23)\end{aligned}$$

where $(\mathbf{a}_{B/A})_n$ has the magnitude $l\omega^2$ and is *directed toward A*, while $(\mathbf{a}_{B/A})_t$ has the magnitude $l\alpha$ and is perpendicular to AB. There is no way of telling at the present time whether the tangential component $(\mathbf{a}_{B/A})_t$ is directed to the left or to the right, and the student should not rely on his "intuition" in this matter. We shall therefore indicate both possible directions for this component in Fig. 15.23. Similarly, we indicate both possible senses for $\mathbf{a}_B$, since we do not know whether point B is accelerated upward or downward.

Equation (15.23) has been expressed geometrically in Fig. 15.24. Four different vector polygons may be obtained, depending upon the sense of $\mathbf{a}_A$ and the relative magnitude of a_A and $(a_{B/A})_n$. If we are to determine a_B and α from one of these diagrams, we must know not only a_A and θ but also ω. The angular velocity of the rod, therefore, should be separately determined by one of the methods indicated in Secs. 15.6 and 15.7. The values of a_B and α may then be obtained by considering successively the x and y components of the vectors shown in Fig. 15.24. In the case of polygon a, for example, we write the equations

$\overset{+}{\rightarrow}$ x components: $\quad 0 = a_A + l\omega^2 \sin\theta - l\alpha\cos\theta$

$+\uparrow$ y components: $\quad -a_B = -l\omega^2\cos\theta - l\alpha\sin\theta$

which may be solved for a_B and α. The two unknowns may also be obtained by direct measurement on the vector polygon. In that case, care should be taken to draw first the known vectors $\mathbf{a}_A$ and $(\mathbf{a}_{B/A})_n$.

It is quite evident that the determination of accelerations is considerably more involved than the determination of velocities. Yet, in the example considered here, the extremities A and B of the rod were moving along straight tracks, and the diagrams drawn were relatively simple. If A and B had moved along curved tracks, the accelerations $\mathbf{a}_A$ and $\mathbf{a}_B$ should have been resolved into normal and tangential components and the solution of the problem would have involved six different vectors.

When a mechanism consists of several moving parts which

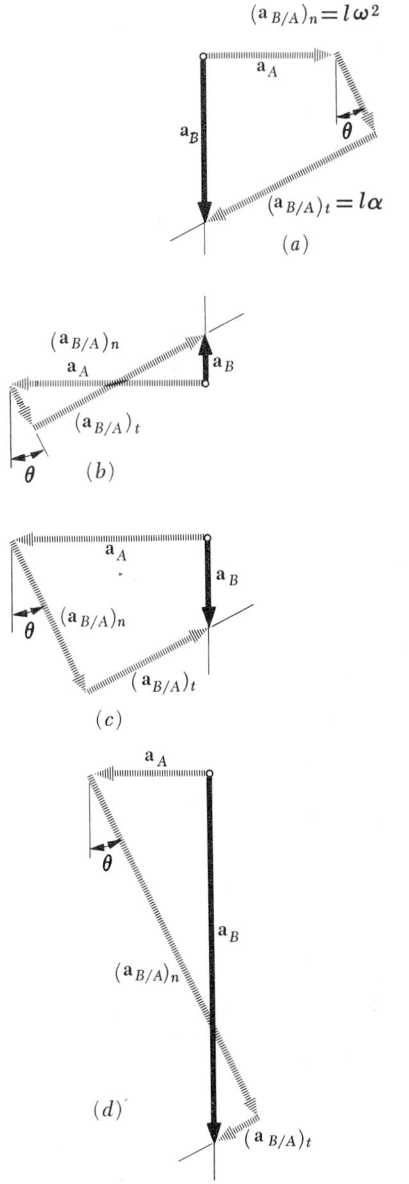

FIG. 15.24

are pin-connected, its analysis may be carried out by considering each part as a rigid body, while keeping in mind that the points where two parts are connected must have the same absolute acceleration (see Sample Prob. 15.7). In the case of meshed gears, the tangential components of the accelerations of the teeth in contact are equal, but their normal components are different.

***15.9. Analysis of Plane Motion in Terms of a Parameter.** In the case of certain mechanisms, it is possible to express the coordinates x and y of all the significant points of the mechanism by means of simple analytic expressions containing a single parameter. It may be advantageous in such a case to determine directly the absolute velocity and the absolute acceleration of the various points of the mechanism, since the components of the velocity and of the acceleration of a given point may be obtained by differentiating the coordinates x and y of that point.

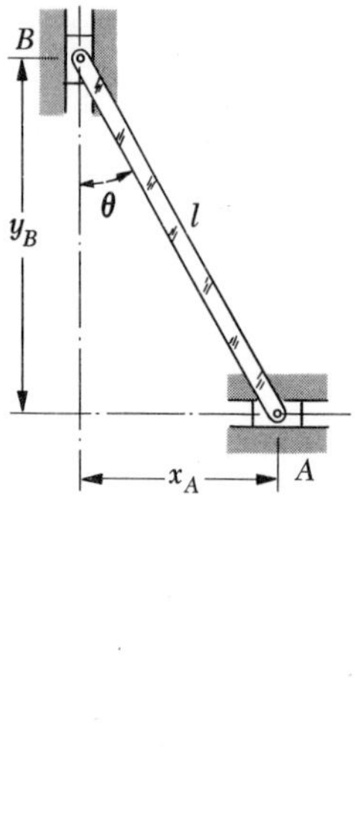

FIG. 15.25

Let us consider again the rod AB whose extremities slide, respectively, in a horizontal and a vertical track (Fig. 15.25). The coordinates x_A and y_B of the extremities of the rod may be expressed in terms of the angle θ the rod forms with the vertical,

$$x_A = l \sin\theta \qquad y_B = l \cos\theta \tag{15.24}$$

Differentiating Eqs. (15.24) twice, we write

$$v_A = \frac{dx_A}{dt} = l\cos\theta\,\frac{d\theta}{dt} \qquad v_B = \frac{dy_B}{dt} = -l\sin\theta\,\frac{d\theta}{dt}$$

$$a_A = \frac{d^2x_A}{dt^2} = -l\sin\theta\left(\frac{d\theta}{dt}\right)^2 + l\cos\theta\,\frac{d^2\theta}{dt^2}$$

$$a_B = \frac{d^2y_B}{dt^2} = -l\cos\theta\left(\frac{d\theta}{dt}\right)^2 - l\sin\theta\,\frac{d^2\theta}{dt^2}$$

Recalling that $d\theta/dt = \omega$ and $d^2\theta/dt^2 = \alpha$, we obtain

$$v_A = l\omega\cos\theta \qquad v_B = -l\omega\sin\theta \tag{15.25}$$

$$a_A = -l\omega^2\sin\theta + l\alpha\cos\theta \qquad a_B = -l\omega^2\cos\theta - l\alpha\sin\theta \tag{15.26}$$

We note that a positive sign for v_A or a_A indicates that the velocity $\mathbf{v}_A$ or the acceleration $\mathbf{a}_A$ is directed to the right; a positive sign for v_B or a_B indicates that $\mathbf{v}_B$ or $\mathbf{a}_B$ is directed upward. Equations (15.25) may be used, for example, to determine v_B and ω when v_A and θ are known. Substituting for ω in (15.26), we may then determine a_B and α if a_A is known.

SAMPLE PROBLEM 15.6

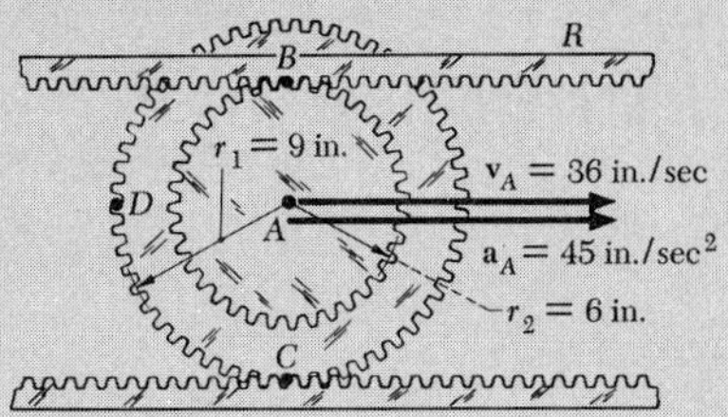

The center of the double gear of Sample Prob. 15.2 has a velocity of 36 in./sec to the right and an acceleration of 45 in./sec² to the right. Determine (*a*) the angular acceleration of the gear, (*b*) the accelerations of points *B*, *C*, and *D* of the gear.

a. **Angular Acceleration of the Gear.** In Sample Prob. 15.2, we found that $s_A = r_1\theta$ and $v_A = r_1\omega$. Differentiating the latter with respect to time, we obtain $a_A = r_1\alpha$.

$$v_A = r_1\omega \qquad 36 \text{ in./sec} = (9 \text{ in.})\omega \qquad \omega = -4\mathbf{k} \text{ radians/sec}$$

$$a_A = r_1\alpha \qquad 45 \text{ in./sec}^2 = (9 \text{ in.})\alpha \qquad \alpha = -5\mathbf{k} \text{ radians/sec}^2 \quad \blacktriangleleft$$

b. **Accelerations.** The rolling motion of the gear is resolved into a translation with *A* and a rotation about *A*.

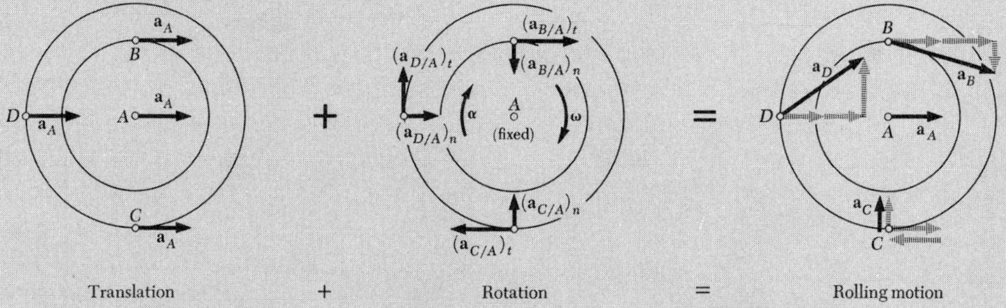

Acceleration of Point B. Adding vectorially the accelerations corresponding to the translation and to the rotation, we obtain

$$\mathbf{a}_B = \mathbf{a}_A + \mathbf{a}_{B/A} = \mathbf{a}_A + (\mathbf{a}_{B/A})_t + (\mathbf{a}_{B/A})_n$$
$$= \mathbf{a}_A + \boldsymbol{\alpha} \times \mathbf{r}_{B/A} - \omega^2\mathbf{r}_{B/A}$$
$$= 45\mathbf{i} - 5\mathbf{k} \times 6\mathbf{j} - (4)^2(6\mathbf{j}) = 45\mathbf{i} + 30\mathbf{i} - 96\mathbf{j}$$
$$\mathbf{a}_B = 75\mathbf{i} - 96\mathbf{j} \qquad a_B = 121.8 \text{ in./sec}^2 \searrow 52.0° \quad \blacktriangleleft$$

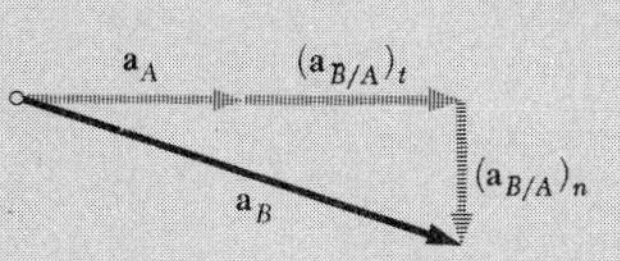

Acceleration of Point C

$$\mathbf{a}_C = \mathbf{a}_A + \mathbf{a}_{C/A} = \mathbf{a}_A + \boldsymbol{\alpha} \times \mathbf{r}_{C/A} - \omega^2\mathbf{r}_{C/A}$$
$$= 45\mathbf{i} - 5\mathbf{k} \times (-9\mathbf{j}) - (4)^2(-9\mathbf{j}) = 45\mathbf{i} - 45\mathbf{i} + 144\mathbf{j}$$
$$\mathbf{a}_C = 144\mathbf{j} \qquad a_C = 144 \text{ in./sec}^2 \uparrow \quad \blacktriangleleft$$

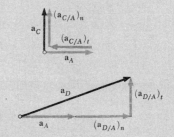

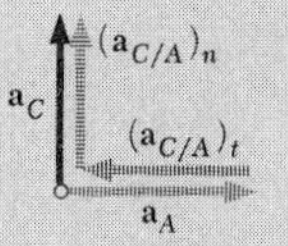

Acceleration of Point D

$$\mathbf{a}_D = \mathbf{a}_A + \mathbf{a}_{D/A} = \mathbf{a}_A + \boldsymbol{\alpha} \times \mathbf{r}_{D/A} - \omega^2\mathbf{r}_{D/A}$$
$$= 45\mathbf{i} - 5\mathbf{k} \times (-9\mathbf{i}) - (4)^2(-9\mathbf{i}) = 45\mathbf{i} + 45\mathbf{j} + 144\mathbf{i}$$
$$\mathbf{a}_D = 189\mathbf{i} + 45\mathbf{j} \qquad a_D = 194 \text{ in./sec}^2 \angle 13.4° \quad \blacktriangleleft$$

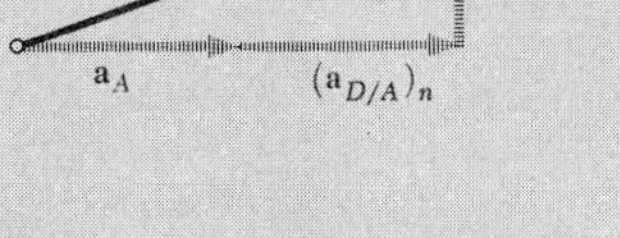

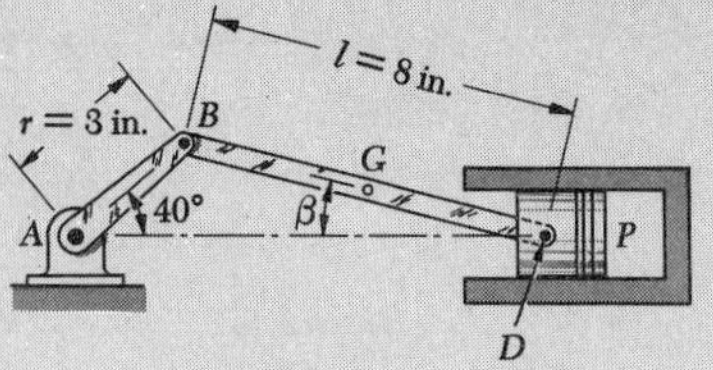

SAMPLE PROBLEM 15.7

Crank AB of the engine system of Sample Prob. 15.3 has a constant clockwise angular velocity of 2,000 rpm. For the crank position shown, determine the angular acceleration of the connecting rod BD and the acceleration of point D.

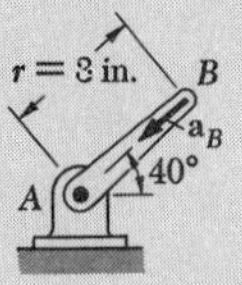

Motion of Crank AB. Since the crank rotates about A with constant $\omega_{AB} = 2{,}000$ rpm $= 209$ radians/sec, we have $\alpha_{AB} = 0$. The acceleration of B is therefore directed toward A and has a magnitude

$$a_B = r\omega_{AB}^2 = (\tfrac{3}{12}\text{ ft})(209)^2 = 10{,}920\text{ ft/sec}^2$$
$$\mathbf{a}_B = 10{,}920\text{ ft/sec} \measuredangle\ 40°$$

Motion of the Connecting Rod BD. The angular velocity ω_{BD} and the value of β were obtained in Sample Prob. 15.3.

$$\omega_{BD} = 61.9\text{ radians/sec} \circlearrowleft \qquad \beta = 13.9°$$

The motion of BD is resolved into a translation with B and a rotation about B. The relative acceleration $\mathbf{a}_{D/B}$ is resolved into normal and tangential components.

$$(a_{D/B})_n = (BD)\omega_{BD}^2 = (\tfrac{8}{12})(61.9)^2 = 2{,}560\text{ ft/sec}^2$$
$$(\mathbf{a}_{D/B})_n = 2{,}560\text{ ft/sec}^2 \measuredangle\ 13.9°$$
$$(a_{D/B})_t = (BD)\alpha_{BD} = (\tfrac{8}{12})\alpha_{BD} = 0.667\alpha_{BD}$$
$$(\mathbf{a}_{D/B})_t = 0.667\alpha_{BD} \measuredangle\ 76.1°$$

While $(\mathbf{a}_{B/D})_t$ must be perpendicular to BD, its sense is not known.

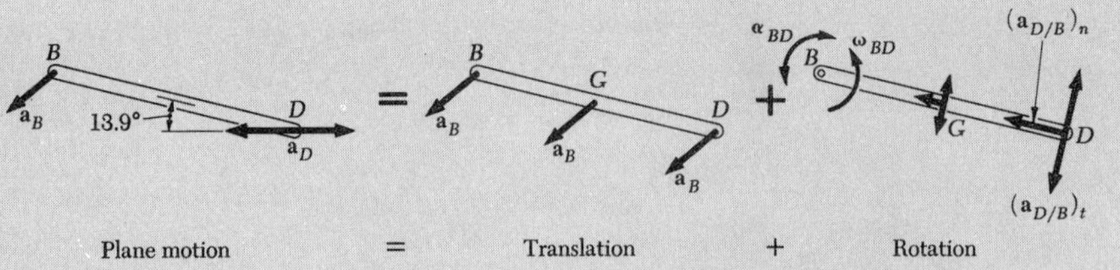

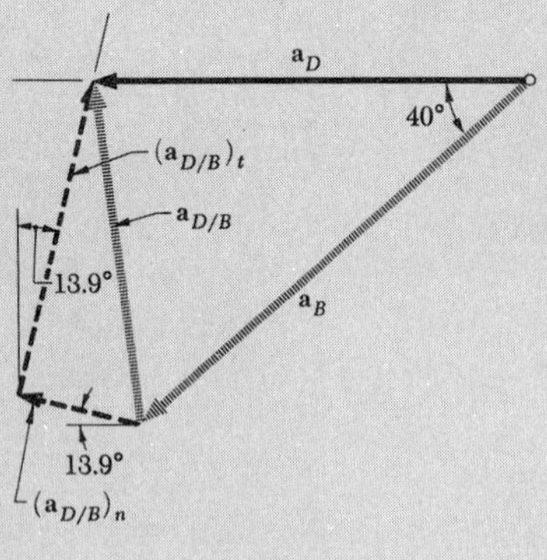

Noting that the acceleration $\mathbf{a}_D$ must be horizontal, we write

$$\mathbf{a}_D = \mathbf{a}_B + \mathbf{a}_{D/B} = \mathbf{a}_B + (\mathbf{a}_{D/B})_n + (\mathbf{a}_{D/B})_t$$
$$[a_D \leftrightarrow] = [10{,}920 \measuredangle\ 40°] + [2{,}560 \measuredangle\ 13.9°] + [0.667\alpha_{BD} \measuredangle\ 76.1°]$$

Equating x and y components, we obtain the following scalar equations:

$\xrightarrow{+}$ x components:

$$-a_D = -10{,}920\cos 40° - 2{,}560\cos 13.9° + 0.667\alpha_{BD}\sin 13.9°$$

$+\uparrow$ y components:

$$0 = -10{,}920\sin 40° + 2{,}560\sin 13.9° + 0.667\alpha_{BD}\cos 13.9°$$

Solving the equations simultaneously, we obtain $\alpha_{BD} = +9{,}900$ radians/sec² and $a_D = +9{,}260$ ft/sec². The positive signs indicate that the senses shown on the vector polygon are correct; we write

$$\alpha_{BD} = 9{,}900\text{ radians/sec}^2 \circlearrowleft \blacktriangleleft$$
$$\mathbf{a}_D = 9{,}260\text{ ft/sec}^2 \leftarrow \blacktriangleleft$$

SAMPLE PROBLEM 15.8

The linkage $ABDE$ moves in the vertical plane. Knowing that in the position shown crank AB has a constant angular velocity ω_1 of 20 radians/sec counterclockwise, determine the angular velocities and angular accelerations of the connecting rod BD and of the crank DE.

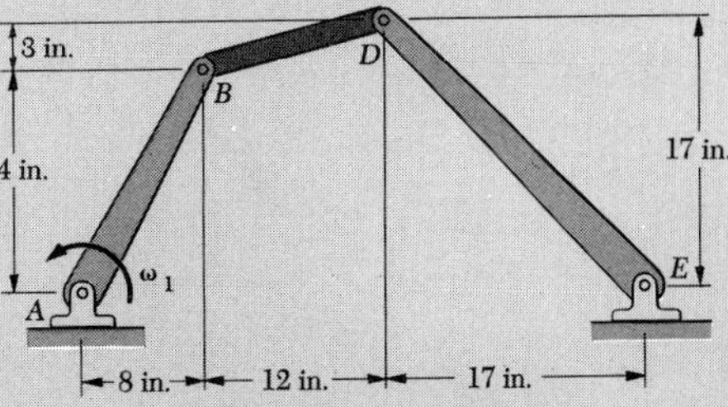

Solution. While this problem could be solved by the method used in Sample Prob. 15.7, we shall make full use of the vector approach in the present case. The position vectors $\mathbf{r}_B$, $\mathbf{r}_D$, and $\mathbf{r}_{D/B}$ are chosen as shown in the sketch.

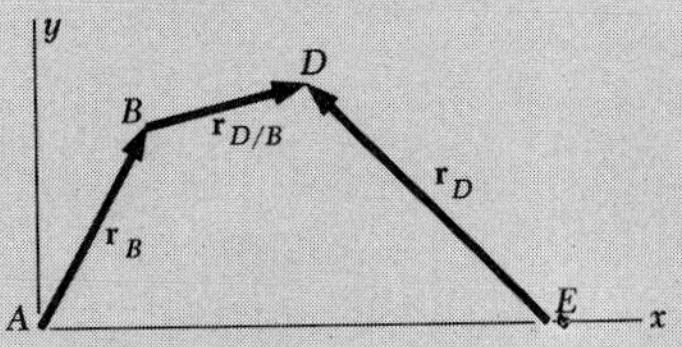

$\mathbf{r}_B = 8\mathbf{i} + 14\mathbf{j}$
$\mathbf{r}_D = -17\mathbf{i} + 17\mathbf{j}$
$\mathbf{r}_{D/B} = 12\mathbf{i} + 3\mathbf{j}$

Velocities. Since the motion of each element of the linkage is contained in the plane of the figure, we have

$$\boldsymbol{\omega}_{AB} = (20 \text{ radians/sec})\mathbf{k} \qquad \boldsymbol{\omega}_{BD} = \omega_{BD}\mathbf{k} \qquad \boldsymbol{\omega}_{DE} = \omega_{DE}\mathbf{k}$$

where $\mathbf{k}$ is a unit vector pointing out of the paper. We now write

$$\mathbf{v}_D = \mathbf{v}_B + \mathbf{v}_{D/B}$$
$$\boldsymbol{\omega}_{DE} \times \mathbf{r}_D = \boldsymbol{\omega}_{AB} \times \mathbf{r}_B + \boldsymbol{\omega}_{BD} \times \mathbf{r}_{D/B}$$
$$\omega_{DE}\mathbf{k} \times (-17\mathbf{i} + 17\mathbf{j}) = 20\mathbf{k} \times (8\mathbf{i} + 14\mathbf{j}) + \omega_{BD}\mathbf{k} \times (12\mathbf{i} + 3\mathbf{j})$$
$$-17\omega_{DE}\mathbf{j} - 17\omega_{DE}\mathbf{i} = 160\mathbf{j} - 280\mathbf{i} + 12\omega_{BD}\mathbf{j} - 3\omega_{BD}\mathbf{i}$$

Equating the coefficients of the unit vectors $\mathbf{i}$ and $\mathbf{j}$, we obtain the following two scalar equations:

$$-17\omega_{DE} = -280 - 3\omega_{BD}$$
$$-17\omega_{DE} = +160 + 12\omega_{BD}$$

$$\omega_{BD} = 29.3 \text{ radians/sec} \circlearrowright \qquad \omega_{DE} = 11.29 \text{ radians/sec} \circlearrowleft \blacktriangleleft$$

Accelerations. Noting that at the instant considered crank AB has a constant angular velocity, we write

$$\boldsymbol{\alpha}_{AB} = 0 \qquad \boldsymbol{\alpha}_{BD} = \alpha_{BD}\mathbf{k} \qquad \boldsymbol{\alpha}_{DE} = \alpha_{DE}\mathbf{k}$$
$$\mathbf{a}_D = \mathbf{a}_B + \mathbf{a}_{D/B} \qquad (1)$$

Each term of Eq. (1) is evaluated separately:

$$\mathbf{a}_D = \boldsymbol{\alpha}_{DE} \times \mathbf{r}_D - \omega_{DE}^2\mathbf{r}_D$$
$$= \alpha_{DE}\mathbf{k} \times (-17\mathbf{i} + 17\mathbf{j}) - (11.29)^2(-17\mathbf{i} + 17\mathbf{j})$$
$$= -17\alpha_{DE}\mathbf{j} - 17\alpha_{DE}\mathbf{i} + 2{,}170\mathbf{i} - 2{,}170\mathbf{j}$$
$$\mathbf{a}_B = \boldsymbol{\alpha}_{AB} \times \mathbf{r}_B - \omega_{AB}^2\mathbf{r}_B = 0 - (20)^2(8\mathbf{i} + 14\mathbf{j})$$
$$= -3{,}200\mathbf{i} - 5{,}600\mathbf{j}$$
$$\mathbf{a}_{D/B} = \boldsymbol{\alpha}_{BD} \times \mathbf{r}_{D/B} - \omega_{BD}^2\mathbf{r}_{D/B}$$
$$= \alpha_{BD}\mathbf{k} \times (12\mathbf{i} + 3\mathbf{j}) - (29.3)^2(12\mathbf{i} + 3\mathbf{j})$$
$$= 12\alpha_{BD}\mathbf{j} - 3\alpha_{BD}\mathbf{i} - 10{,}320\mathbf{i} - 2{,}580\mathbf{j}$$

Substituting into Eq. (1) and equating the coefficients of $\mathbf{i}$ and $\mathbf{j}$, we obtain

$$-17\alpha_{DE} + 3\alpha_{BD} = -15{,}690$$
$$-17\alpha_{DE} - 12\alpha_{BD} = -6{,}010$$

$$\alpha_{BD} = 645 \text{ radians/sec}^2 \circlearrowright \qquad \alpha_{DE} = 809 \text{ radians/sec}^2 \circlearrowleft \blacktriangleleft$$

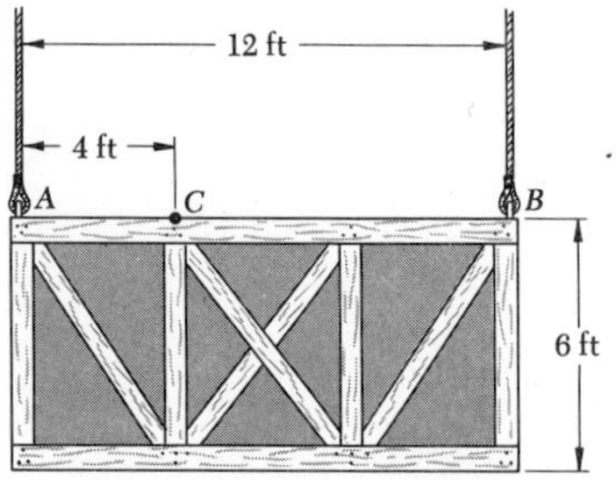

FIG. P 15.72 AND P 15.73

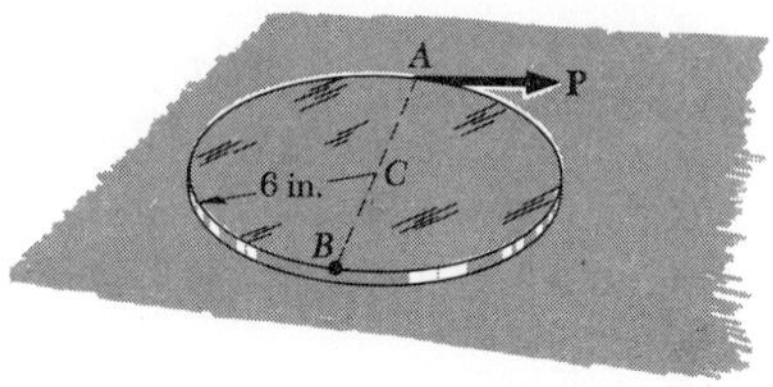

FIG. P 15.74

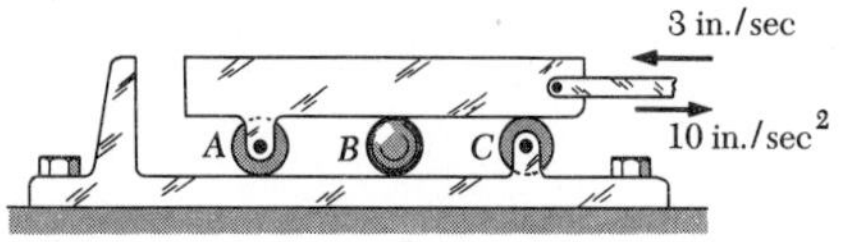

FIG. P 15.79

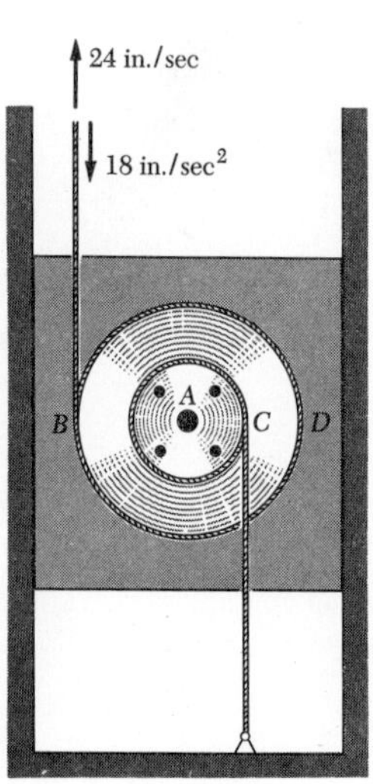

FIG. P 15.80

PROBLEMS

15.72. The crate shown is lowered by means of two cables unwinding at the same speed from overhead cranes. As the crate approaches the ground, the crane operators apply brakes to slow down the unwinding motion. The deceleration of the cable attached at A is 10 ft/sec^2, while that of the cable attached at B is 16 ft/sec^2. Determine the acceleration of point C and the angular acceleration of the crate at that instant.

15.73. The acceleration of point C is 5 ft/sec^2 upward and the angular acceleration of the crate is 2 radians/sec^2 clockwise. Knowing that the angular velocity of the crate is zero at the instant considered, determine the acceleration of each cable.

15.74. A 12-in.-diameter plate rests on a smooth horizontal table. A force **P** applied as shown produces the following accelerations: $\mathbf{a}_A = 36$ in./sec^2 to the right, $\alpha = 4$ radians/sec^2 clockwise as viewed from above. Determine the acceleration (*a*) of point B, (*b*) of point C.

15.75. In Prob. 15.74, determine the point of the plate which (*a*) has no acceleration, (*b*) has an acceleration of 18 in./sec^2 to the right.

15.76. Determine the accelerations of points C and D of the wheel of Prob. 15.23, knowing that the automobile moves at a constant speed of 60 mph.

15.77. Determine the accelerations of points B and E of the wheel of Prob. 15.23, knowing that the automobile moves at a constant speed of 60 mph.

15.78. In Prob. 15.50, the extremity of the cord D has a velocity of 5 in./sec and an acceleration of 2 in./sec^2, both directed to the right. Assuming that the cylinder rolls without slipping, determine the accelerations of points A, B, and C of the cylinder.

15.79. The moving carriage is supported by two casters A and C, each of $\frac{1}{2}$-in. diameter, and by a $\frac{1}{2}$-in.-diameter ball B. If at a given instant the velocity and acceleration of the carriage are as shown, determine (*a*) the angular velocities and angular accelerations of the ball and of each caster, (*b*) the velocities and accelerations of the center of the ball and of each caster.

15.80. A double pulley is attached to a slider block by a pin at A. The 2-in.-radius inner pulley is rigidly attached to the 4-in.-radius outer pulley. Determine the accelerations of points A and B of the pulley at the instant shown.

15.81. In Prob. 15.80 determine the accelerations of points C and D of the pulley.

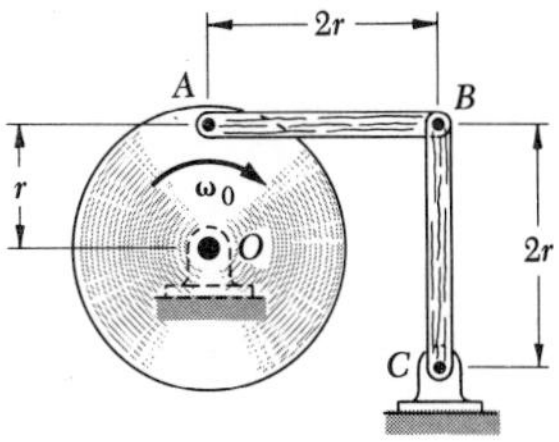

FIG. P 15.82

15.82 and 15.83. At the instant shown, the disk rotates with a constant angular velocity ω_0 clockwise. Determine the angular velocities and the angular accelerations of the rods AB and BC.

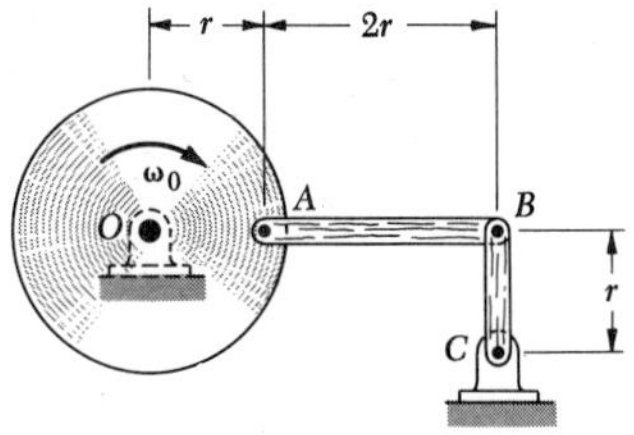

FIG. P 15.83

15.84. Crank AB rotates about A with a constant angular velocity of 600 rpm clockwise. Determine the acceleration of the piston P when (*a*) $\theta = 0$, (*b*) $\theta = 90°$.

15.85. Solve Prob. 15.84 when (*a*) $\theta = 180°$, (*b*) $\theta = 270°$.

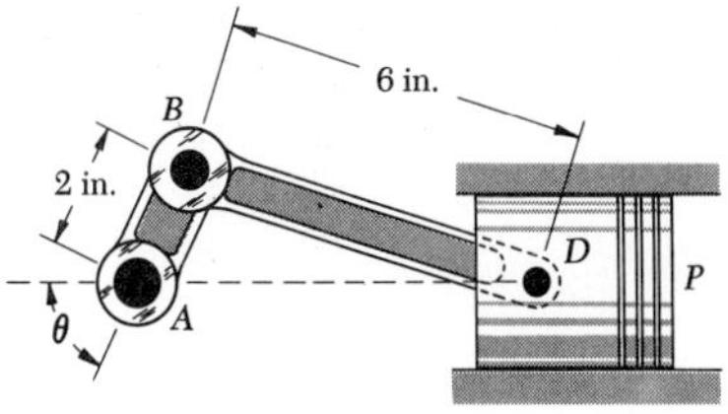

FIG. P 15.84

15.86. Two rollers A and B each of radius 2 in. are connected by a link AB and roll along a horizontal surface. A drum of radius 4 in. is placed on the rollers as shown. If the link moves to the right with a constant velocity of 12 in./sec, determine the accelerations of points D, E, and F on the drum.

15.87. In Prob. 15.86, determine the accelerations of the point of the drum and of the point of roller A which are in contact with each other.

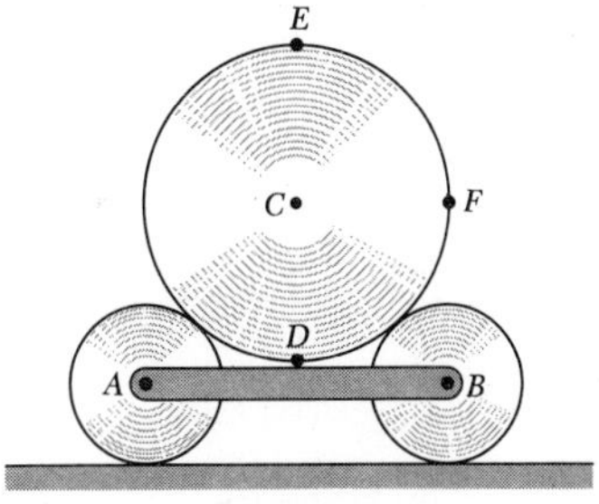

FIG. P 15.86

15.88 and 15.89. For the linkage indicated, determine the angular acceleration (*a*) of bar BD, (*b*) of bar DE.

15.88. Linkage of Prob. 15.38.

15.89. Linkage of Prob. 15.37.

15.90 and 15.91. For the linkage indicated, determine (*a*) the angular acceleration of bar BD, (*b*) the horizontal and vertical components of the acceleration of the mid-point of bar BD.

15.90. Linkage of Prob. 15.40.

15.91. Linkage of Prob. 15.39.

15.92 and 15.93. The disk shown has a constant angular velocity of 8 radians/sec clockwise. For the position shown, determine (*a*) the angular acceleration of each rod, (*b*) the accelerations of points C and D.

15.94 and 15.95. In the position shown, the disk has an instantaneous angular velocity of 8 radians/sec clockwise and an angular acceleration of 30 radians/sec² counterclockwise. Determine (*a*) the angular acceleration of each rod, (*b*) the accelerations of points C and D.

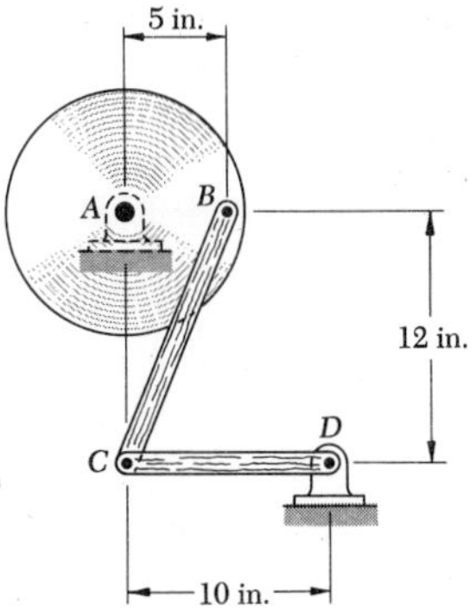

FIG. P 15.92 AND P 15.94

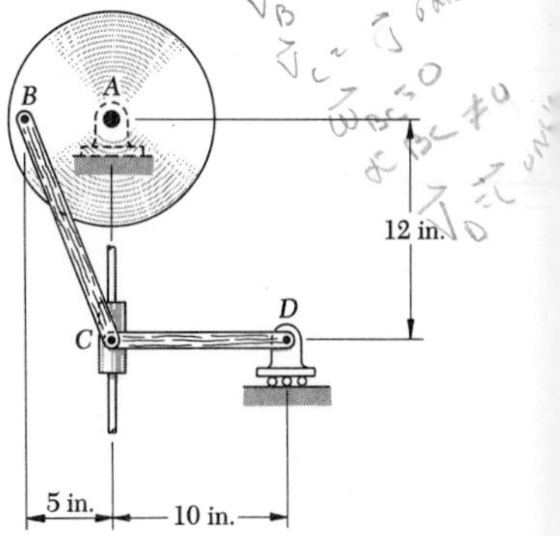

FIG. P 15.93 AND P 15.95

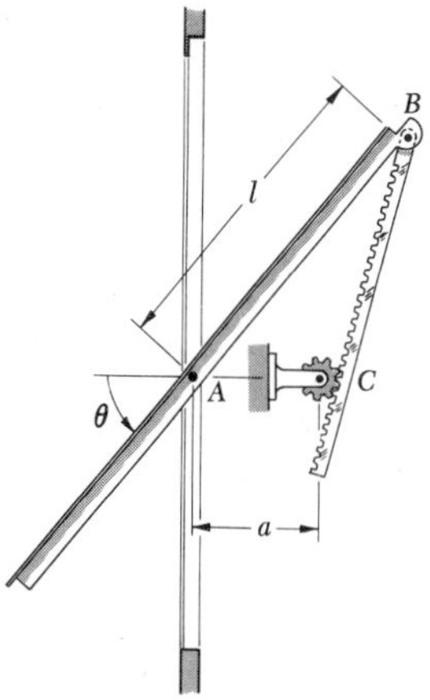

FIG. P 15.97

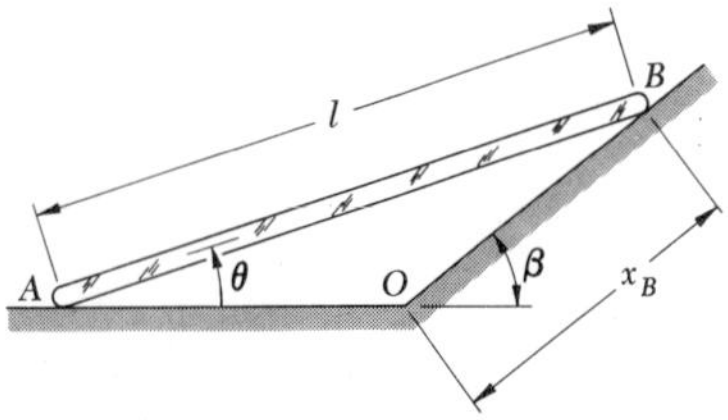

FIG. P 15.98 AND P 15.99

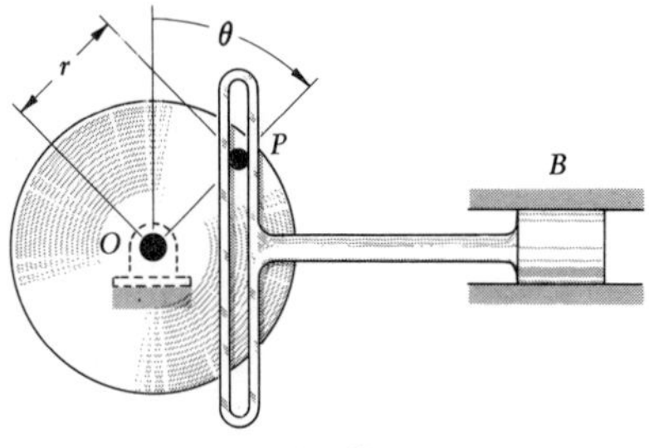

FIG. P 15.100

15.96. Show that the acceleration of the instantaneous center of rotation of the slab of Prob. 15.47 is zero, if, and only if,

$$\mathbf{a}_A = \frac{\alpha}{\omega}\mathbf{v}_A + \boldsymbol{\omega} \times \mathbf{v}_A$$

where $\boldsymbol{\alpha} = \alpha\mathbf{k}$ is the angular acceleration of the slab.

***15.97.** The position of a factory window is controlled by the rack and pinion shown. Knowing that the pinion C has a radius r and rotates counterclockwise at a constant rate ω, derive an expression for the angular velocity of the window.

***15.98.** Rod AB slides with its ends in contact with the floor and the inclined plane. Using the method of Sec. 15.9, derive an expression for the angular velocity of the rod in terms of v_B, θ, l, and β.

***15.99.** Derive an expression for the angular acceleration of the rod AB in terms of v_B, θ, l, and β, knowing that the acceleration of point B is zero.

***15.100.** The drive disk of the Scotch crosshead mechanism shown has an angular velocity $\boldsymbol{\omega}$ and an angular acceleration $\boldsymbol{\alpha}$, both directed clockwise. Using the method of Sec. 15.9, derive an expression (*a*) for the velocity of block B, (*b*) for the acceleration of block B.

***15.101.** Collar B slides along rod OC and is attached to a sliding block which moves upward with a constant velocity $\mathbf{v}$ in a vertical slot. Using the method of Sec. 15.9, derive an expression (*a*) for the angular velocity of rod OC, (*b*) for the angular acceleration of rod OC.

***15.102.** Collar B slides along rod OC and is attached to a sliding block which moves in a vertical slot. Knowing that rod OC rotates with an angular velocity $\boldsymbol{\omega}$ and with an angular acceleration $\boldsymbol{\alpha}$, both counterclockwise, derive expressions for the velocity and acceleration of collar B.

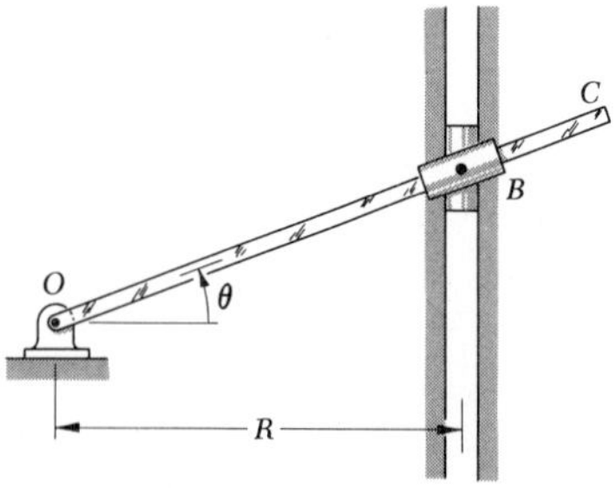

FIG. P 15.101 AND P 15.102

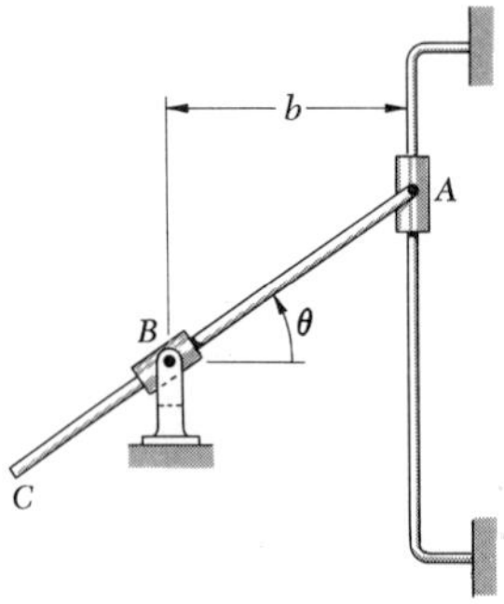

FIG. P 15.103

***15.103.** Rod AC of length $2b$ is attached to a collar at A and passes through a pivoted collar at B. Knowing that the collar A moves upward with a constant velocity $\mathbf{v}_A$, derive an expression for (*a*) the angular velocity of rod AC, (*b*) the velocity of the point of the rod in contact with the pivoted collar B.

***15.104.** In Prob. 15.103, derive an expression for the angular acceleration of rod AC.

*15.105. A disk of radius r rolls without slipping along the inside of a fixed cylinder of radius R. The angular velocity ω of the disk is constant. Denoting by P the point of the disk in contact with the cylinder at $t = 0$, derive expressions for the horizontal and vertical components of the velocity of P at any time t. (The curve described by point P is called a *hypocycloid.*)

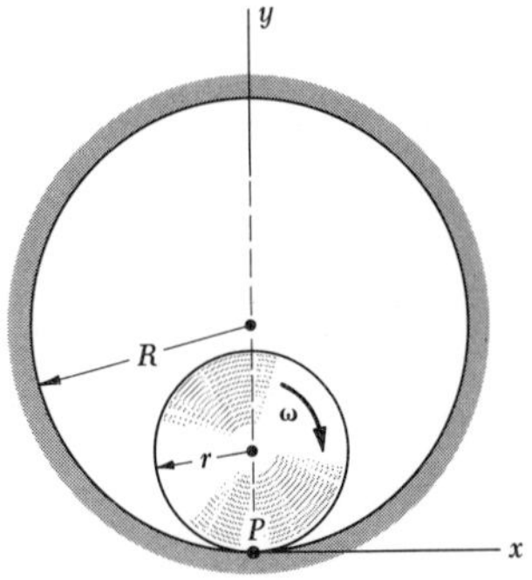

FIG. P 15.105

*15.106. In Prob. 15.105, show that the path of P is a vertical straight line when $r = \frac{1}{2}R$. Derive expressions for the corresponding velocity and acceleration of P at any time t.

*15.107. The crank AB of Prob. 15.34 rotates with a constant clockwise angular velocity ω, and $\theta = 0$ at $t = 0$. Using the method of Sec. 15.9, derive an expression for the velocity of the piston P in terms of the time t.

15.10. Motion about a Fixed Point.

We have studied in Sec. 15.3 the motion of a rigid body constrained to rotate about a fixed axis. We shall now consider the more general case of the motion of a rigid body which has a fixed point O.

First, we shall prove that *the most general displacement of a rigid body with a fixed point O is equivalent to a rotation of the body about an axis through O.*† Instead of considering the rigid body itself, we may detach a sphere of center O from the body and analyze the motion of that sphere. Clearly, the motion of the sphere completely characterizes the motion of the given body. Since three points define the position of a solid in space, the center O and two points A and B on the surface of the sphere will define the position of the sphere and, thus, the position of the body. Let A_1 and B_1 characterize the position of the sphere at one instant, and A_2 and B_2 its position at a later instant (Fig. 15.26a). Since the sphere is rigid, the lengths of the arcs of great circle A_1B_1 and A_2B_2 must be equal, but, except for this requirement, the positions of A_1, A_2, B_1, and B_2 are arbitrary. We propose to prove that the points A and B may be brought, respectively, from A_1 and B_1 into A_2 and B_2 by a single rotation of the sphere about an axis.

For convenience, and without loss of generality, we may select point B so that its initial position coincides with the final position of A; thus, $B_1 = A_2$ (Fig. 15.26b). We draw the arcs

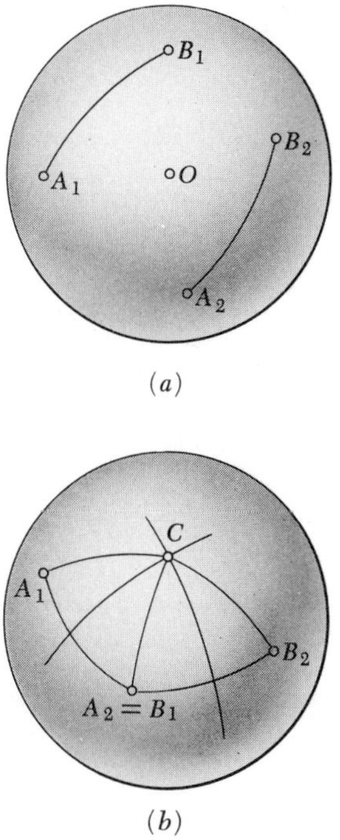

FIG. 15.26

† This is known as Euler's theorem.

of great circle A_1A_2, A_2B_2 and the arcs bisecting, respectively, A_1A_2 and A_2B_2. Let C be the point of intersection of these last two arcs; we complete the construction by drawing A_1C, A_2C, and B_2C. As pointed out above, $A_1B_1 = A_2B_2$ on account of the rigidity of the sphere; on the other hand, since C is by construction equidistant from A_1, A_2, and B_2, we have $A_1C = A_2C = B_2C$. As a result, the spherical triangles A_1CA_2 and B_1CB_2 are congruent and the angles A_1CA_2 and B_1CB_2 are equal. Denoting by θ the common value of these angles, we conclude that the sphere may be brought from its initial position into its final position by a single rotation through θ about the axis OC.

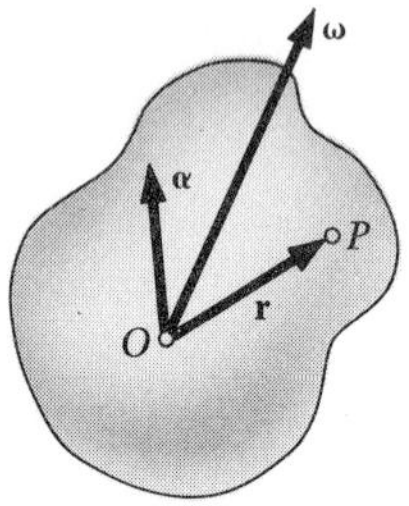

FIG. 15.27

It follows that the motion during a time interval Δt of a rigid body with a fixed point O may be considered as a rotation through $\Delta\theta$ about a certain axis. Drawing along that axis a vector of magnitude $\Delta\theta/\Delta t$ and letting Δt approach zero, we obtain at the limit the *instantaneous axis of rotation* and the angular velocity $\boldsymbol{\omega}$ of the body at the instant considered (Fig. 15.27). The velocity of a particle P of the body may then be obtained, as in Sec. 15.3, by forming the vector product of $\boldsymbol{\omega}$ and of the position vector $\mathbf{r}$ of the particle:

$$\mathbf{v} = \frac{d\mathbf{r}}{dt} = \boldsymbol{\omega} \times \mathbf{r} \qquad (15.27)$$

The acceleration of the particle is obtained by differentiating (15.27) with respect to t. As in Sec. 15.3 we have

$$\mathbf{a} = \boldsymbol{\alpha} \times \mathbf{r} + \boldsymbol{\omega} \times (\boldsymbol{\omega} \times \mathbf{r}) \qquad (15.28)$$

where $\boldsymbol{\alpha}$ represents the rate of change $d\boldsymbol{\omega}/dt$ of the angular velocity $\boldsymbol{\omega}$.

In the case of the motion of a rigid body with a fixed point, the direction of $\boldsymbol{\omega}$ and of the instantaneous axis of rotation changes from one instant to the next. The angular acceleration $\boldsymbol{\alpha}$, therefore, reflects the change in direction of $\boldsymbol{\omega}$ as well as its change in magnitude and, in general, *is not directed along the instantaneous axis of rotation.* While the particles of the body located on the instantaneous axis of rotation have zero velocity at the instant considered, they do not have zero acceleration. Also, the accelerations of the various particles of the body *cannot* be determined as if the body were rotating permanently about the instantaneous axis.

The direction of the vector $\boldsymbol{\alpha}$ may be determined by considering the curve described in space by the tip of the vector $\boldsymbol{\omega}$. Since $\boldsymbol{\alpha}$ represents the rate of change of $\boldsymbol{\omega}$, its direction must be that of the tangent to the curve thus described. We also note that the vector ω moves within the body, as well as in space. It thus generates two cones, respectively called the *body cone* and the *space cone* (Fig. 15.28).† It may be shown that, at any given instant, the two cones are tangent along the instantaneous axis of rotation and that, as the body moves, the body cone appears to *roll* on the space cone.

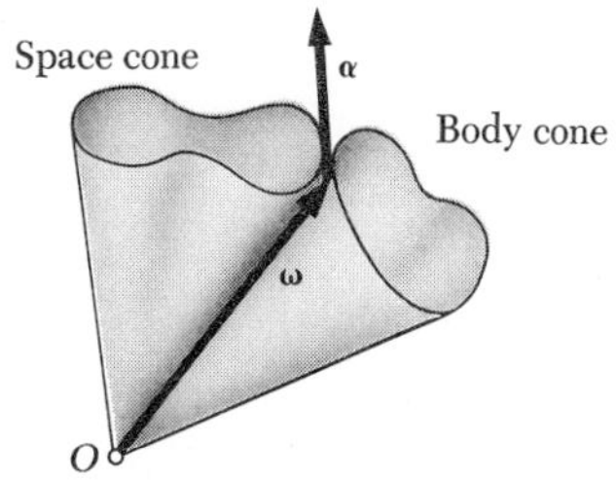

FIG. 15.28

Before concluding our analysis of the motion of a rigid body with a fixed point, we should prove that angular velocities are actually vectors. As it was indicated in Sec. 2.2, some quantities, such as the *finite rotations* of a rigid body, have magnitude and direction, but do not obey the parallelogram law of addition; these quantities cannot be considered as vectors. We shall see presently that angular velocities (and also *infinitesimal rotations*) *do obey* the parallelogram law and, thus, are truly vector quantities.

Consider a rigid body with a fixed point O which, at a given instant, rotates simultaneously about the axes OA and OB with angular velocities ω_1 and ω_2 (Fig. 15.29*a*). We know that this motion must be equivalent at the instant considered to a single rotation of angular velocity ω. We propose to show that

$$\omega = \omega_1 + \omega_2 \tag{15.29}$$

i.e., that the resulting angular velocity may be obtained by adding ω_1 and ω_2 by the parallelogram law (Fig. 15.29*b*).

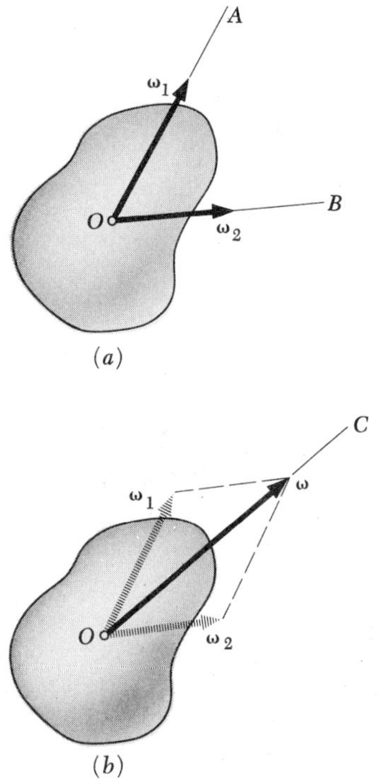

FIG. 15.29

Consider a particle P of the body, defined by the position vector $\mathbf{r}$. Denoting respectively by $\mathbf{v}_1$, $\mathbf{v}_2$, and $\mathbf{v}$ the velocity of P when the body rotates about OA only, about OB only, and about both axes simultaneously, we write

$$\mathbf{v} = \omega \times \mathbf{r} \qquad \mathbf{v}_1 = \omega_1 \times \mathbf{r} \qquad \mathbf{v}_2 = \omega_2 \times \mathbf{r} \tag{15.30}$$

But the vectorial character of *linear* velocities is well established (since they represent the derivatives of position vectors). We have therefore

$$\mathbf{v} = \mathbf{v}_1 + \mathbf{v}_2$$

where the plus sign indicates vector addition. Substituting from (15.30), we write

$$\omega \times \mathbf{r} = \omega_1 \times \mathbf{r} + \omega_2 \times \mathbf{r}$$
$$\omega \times \mathbf{r} = (\omega_1 + \omega_2) \times \mathbf{r}$$

where the plus sign still indicates vector addition. Since the

† It is recalled that a *cone* is, by definition, a surface generated by a straight line passing through a fixed point. In general, the cones considered here *will not be circular cones*.

relation obtained holds for an arbitrary **r**, we conclude that (15.29) must be true.

15.11. General Motion. We shall now consider the most general motion of a rigid body in space. Let A and B be two particles of the body. We recall from Sec. 11.12 that the velocity of B with respect to the fixed frame of reference $Oxyz$ may be expressed as

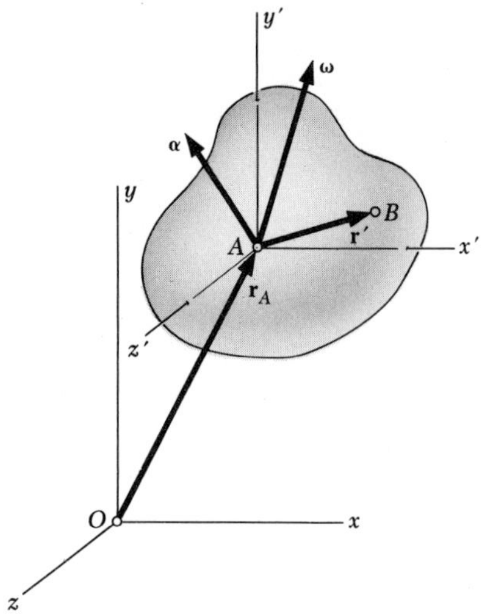

FIG. 15.30

$$\mathbf{v}_B = \mathbf{v}_A + \mathbf{v}_{B/A} \tag{15.30}$$

where $\mathbf{v}_{B/A}$ is the velocity of B relative to a frame $Ax'y'z'$ attached to A and of fixed orientation (Fig. 15.30). Since A is fixed in this frame, the motion of the body relative to $Ax'y'z'$ is the motion of a body with a fixed point. Therefore, the relative velocity $\mathbf{v}_{B/A}$ may be obtained from (15.27), after **r** has been replaced by the position vector $\mathbf{r}'$ of B relative to A. Substituting for $\mathbf{v}_{B/A}$ into (15.30), we write

$$\mathbf{v}_B = \mathbf{v}_A + \boldsymbol{\omega} \times \mathbf{r}' \tag{15.31}$$

where $\boldsymbol{\omega}$ is the angular velocity of the body at the instant considered.

The acceleration of B is obtained by a similar reasoning. We first write

$$\mathbf{a}_B = \mathbf{a}_A + \mathbf{a}_{B/A}$$

and, recalling Eq. (15.28),

$$\mathbf{a}_B = \mathbf{a}_A + \boldsymbol{\alpha} \times \mathbf{r}' + \boldsymbol{\omega} \times (\boldsymbol{\omega} \times \mathbf{r}') \tag{15.32}$$

where $\boldsymbol{\alpha}$ is the angular acceleration of the body at the instant considered.

Equations (15.31) and (15.32) show that *the most general motion of a rigid body is equivalent, at any given instant, to the sum of a translation,* in which all the particles of the body have the same velocity and acceleration as a reference particle A, *and of a rotation about an instantaneous axis through A.*† It may easily be shown, by solving (15.31) and (15.32) for $\mathbf{v}_A$ and $\mathbf{a}_A$, that the motion of the body with respect to a frame attached to B would be characterized by the same vectors $\boldsymbol{\omega}$ and $\boldsymbol{\alpha}$ as its motion relative to $Ax'y'z'$. Thus, the angular velocity and angular acceleration of a rigid body at a given instant are independent of the choice of the reference point.

† It is recalled from Sec. 15.10 that, in general, the vectors $\boldsymbol{\omega}$ and $\boldsymbol{\alpha}$ are not collinear, and that the accelerations of the particles of the body in their motion relative to the frame $Ax'y'z'$ cannot be determined as if the body were rotating permanently about the instantaneous axis through A.

SAMPLE PROBLEM 15.9

The crane shown rotates with a constant angular velocity ω_1 of 0.30 radian/sec. Simultaneously, the boom is being raised with a constant angular velocity ω_2 of 0.50 radian/sec relative to the cab. Knowing that the length of the boom OP is $l = 40$ ft, determine (*a*) the angular velocity $\boldsymbol{\omega}$ of the boom, (*b*) the angular acceleration $\boldsymbol{\alpha}$ of the boom, (*c*) the velocity $\mathbf{v}$ of the tip of the boom, (*d*) the acceleration $\mathbf{a}$ of the tip of the boom.

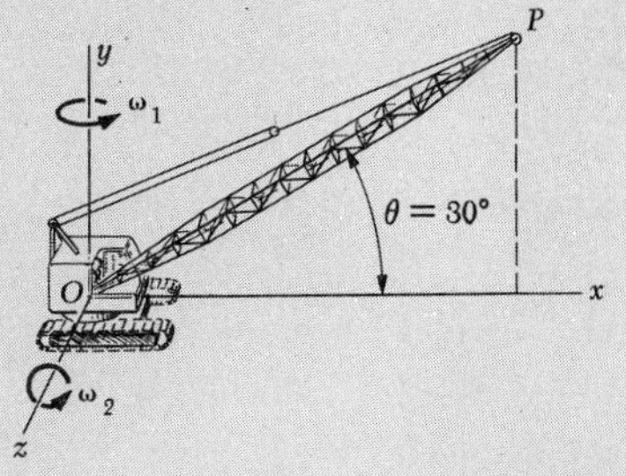

a. **Angular Velocity of Boom.** Adding the angular velocity $\boldsymbol{\omega}_1$ of the cab and the angular velocity $\boldsymbol{\omega}_2$ of the boom relative to the cab, we obtain the angular velocity $\boldsymbol{\omega}$ of the boom:

$$\boldsymbol{\omega} = \boldsymbol{\omega}_1 + \boldsymbol{\omega}_2 \qquad \boldsymbol{\omega} = 0.30\mathbf{j} + 0.50\mathbf{k} \quad \text{(radian/sec)} \blacktriangleleft$$

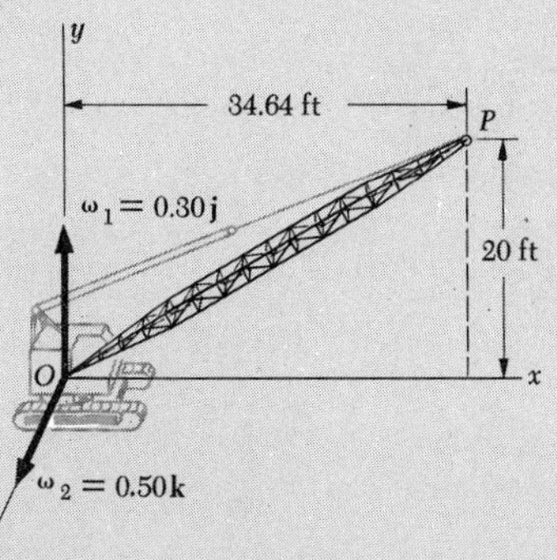

b. **Angular Acceleration of Boom.** Since the vector $\boldsymbol{\omega}_1$ is constant in magnitude and direction, the angular acceleration $\boldsymbol{\alpha}$ of the boom reduces to the derivative $d\boldsymbol{\omega}_2/dt$, which represents the velocity of the tip of the vector $\boldsymbol{\omega}_2$. Observing that $\boldsymbol{\omega}_2$ rotates with the cab (i.e., with the angular velocity $\boldsymbol{\omega}_1$), we write

$$\boldsymbol{\alpha} = \frac{d\boldsymbol{\omega}_2}{dt} = \boldsymbol{\omega}_1 \times \boldsymbol{\omega}_2 = 0.30\mathbf{j} \times 0.50\mathbf{k}$$

$$\boldsymbol{\alpha} = 0.15\mathbf{i} \quad \text{(radian/sec}^2\text{)} \blacktriangleleft$$

c. **Velocity of Tip of Boom.** Noting that the position vector of point P is $\mathbf{r} = 34.64\mathbf{i} + 20\mathbf{j}$ and using the expression found for $\boldsymbol{\omega}$ in part *a*, we write

$$\mathbf{v} = \boldsymbol{\omega} \times \mathbf{r} = \begin{vmatrix} \mathbf{i} & \mathbf{j} & \mathbf{k} \\ 0 & 0.30 & 0.50 \\ 34.64 & 20 & 0 \end{vmatrix}$$

$$\mathbf{v} = -10\mathbf{i} + 17.32\mathbf{j} - 10.39\mathbf{k} \quad \text{(ft/sec)} \blacktriangleleft$$

d. **Acceleration of Tip Boom.** Recalling that $\mathbf{v} = \boldsymbol{\omega} \times \mathbf{r}$, we write

$$\mathbf{a} = \boldsymbol{\alpha} \times \mathbf{r} + \boldsymbol{\omega} \times (\boldsymbol{\omega} \times \mathbf{r}) = \boldsymbol{\alpha} \times \mathbf{r} + \boldsymbol{\omega} \times \mathbf{v}$$

$$\mathbf{a} = \begin{vmatrix} \mathbf{i} & \mathbf{j} & \mathbf{k} \\ 0.15 & 0 & 0 \\ 34.64 & 20 & 0 \end{vmatrix} + \begin{vmatrix} \mathbf{i} & \mathbf{j} & \mathbf{k} \\ 0 & 0.30 & 0.50 \\ -10 & 17.32 & -10.39 \end{vmatrix}$$

$$= 3\mathbf{k} - 3.12\mathbf{i} - 8.66\mathbf{i} - 5\mathbf{j} + 3\mathbf{k}$$

$$\mathbf{a} = -11.78\mathbf{i} - 5\mathbf{j} + 6\mathbf{k} \quad \text{(ft/sec}^2\text{)} \blacktriangleleft$$

SAMPLE PROBLEM 15.10

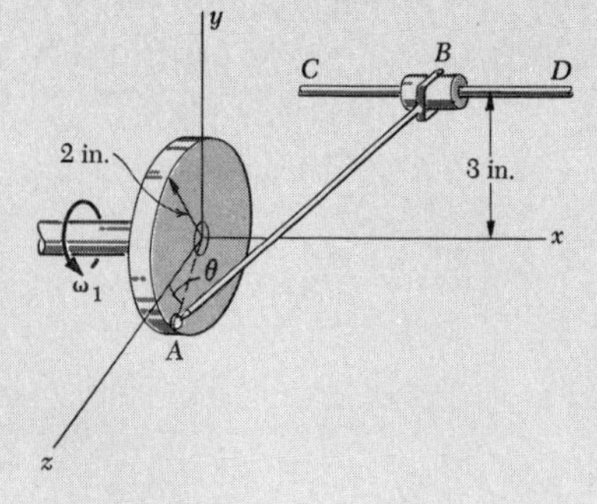

The rod AB, of length 7 in., is attached to the disk by a ball-and-socket connection and to the collar B by a clevis. The disk rotates in the yz plane at a constant rate $\omega_1 = 12$ radians/sec, while the collar is free to slide along the horizontal rod CD. For the position $\theta = 0$, determine (*a*) the velocity of the collar, (*b*) the angular velocity of the rod.

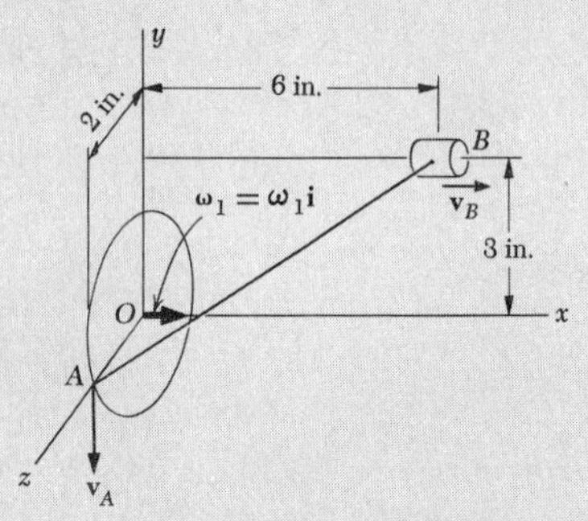

$\boldsymbol{\omega}_1 = 12\mathbf{i}$
$\mathbf{r}_A = 2\mathbf{k}$
$\mathbf{r}_B = 6\mathbf{i} + 3\mathbf{j}$
$\mathbf{r}_{B/A} = 6\mathbf{i} + 3\mathbf{j} - 2\mathbf{k}$

Solution. Since point A is attached to the disk and since collar B moves parallel to the x axis, we have

$$\mathbf{v}_A = \boldsymbol{\omega}_1 \times \mathbf{r}_A = 12\mathbf{i} \times 2\mathbf{k} = -24\mathbf{j} \qquad \mathbf{v}_B = v_B\mathbf{i}$$

Denoting by $\boldsymbol{\omega}$ the angular velocity of the rod, we write

$$\mathbf{v}_B = \mathbf{v}_A + \mathbf{v}_{B/A} = \mathbf{v}_A + \boldsymbol{\omega} \times \mathbf{r}_{B/A}$$

$$v_B\mathbf{i} = -24\mathbf{j} + \begin{vmatrix} \mathbf{i} & \mathbf{j} & \mathbf{k} \\ \omega_x & \omega_y & \omega_z \\ 6 & 3 & -2 \end{vmatrix}$$

$$v_B\mathbf{i} = -24\mathbf{j} + (-2\omega_y - 3\omega_z)\mathbf{i} + (6\omega_z + 2\omega_x)\mathbf{j} + (3\omega_x - 6\omega_y)\mathbf{k}$$

Equating the coefficients of the unit vectors, we obtain

$$v_B = \quad -2\omega_y \quad -3\omega_z \tag{1}$$
$$24 = 2\omega_x \quad +6\omega_z \tag{2}$$
$$0 = 3\omega_x \quad -6\omega_y \tag{3}$$

We eliminate ω_z by multiplying Eq. (2) by $\frac{1}{2}$ and adding to Eq. (1):

$$v_B + 12 = \omega_x - 2\omega_y$$

Noting from Eq. (3) that $\omega_x - 2\omega_y = 0$, we write

$$v_B + 12 = 0 \qquad v_B = -12 \qquad \mathbf{v}_B = -12\mathbf{i} \text{ (in./sec)} \blacktriangleleft$$

Angular Velocity $\boldsymbol{\omega}$ of Rod AB. We note that the angular velocity cannot be determined from Eqs. (1), (2), and (3), since the determinant formed by the coefficients of ω_x, ω_y, and ω_z is zero. We must therefore obtain an additional equation by considering the constraint imposed by the clevis at B.

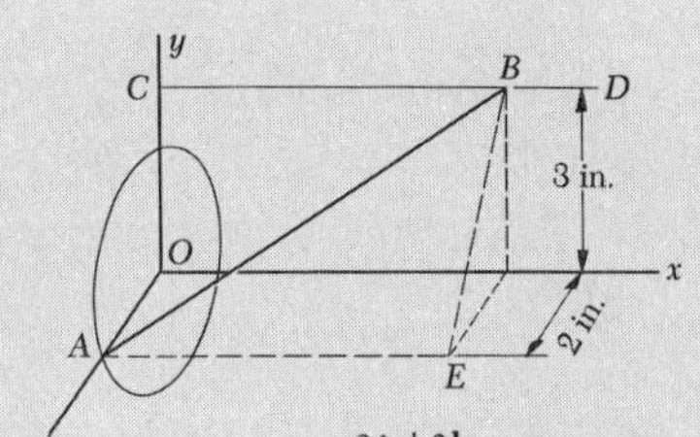

$\mathbf{r}_{E/B} = -3\mathbf{j} + 2\mathbf{k}$

The collar-clevis connection at B permits rotation of AB about the rod CD and also about an axis perpendicular to the plane containing AB and CD. It prevents rotation of AB about the axis EB, which is perpendicular to CD and lies in the plane containing AB and CD. Thus the projection of $\boldsymbol{\omega}$ on $\mathbf{r}_{E/B}$ must be zero and we write†

$$\boldsymbol{\omega} \cdot \mathbf{r}_{E/B} = 0 \qquad (\omega_x\mathbf{i} + \omega_y\mathbf{j} + \omega_z\mathbf{k}) \cdot (-3\mathbf{j} + 2\mathbf{k}) = 0$$
$$-3\omega_y + 2\omega_z = 0 \tag{4}$$

Solving Eqs. (1) through (4) simultaneously, we obtain

$$v_B = -12 \qquad \omega_x = 3.69 \qquad \omega_y = 1.846 \qquad \omega_z = 2.77$$
$$\boldsymbol{\omega} = 3.69\mathbf{i} + 1.846\mathbf{j} + 2.77\mathbf{k} \text{ (radians/sec)} \blacktriangleleft$$

† We could also note that the direction of EB is that of the vector triple product $\mathbf{r}_{B/C} \times (\mathbf{r}_{B/C} \times \mathbf{r}_{B/A})$ and write $\boldsymbol{\omega} \cdot [\mathbf{r}_{B/C} \times (\mathbf{r}_{B/C} \times \mathbf{r}_{B/A})] = 0$. This formulation would be particularly useful if the rod CD were skew.

PROBLEMS

15.108. The rigid body shown rotates about the origin of coordinates with an angular velocity ω. Denoting the velocity of point A by $\mathbf{v}_A = (v_A)_x\mathbf{i} + (v_A)_y\mathbf{j} + (v_A)_z\mathbf{k}$, and knowing that $(v_A)_y = 9$ in./sec and $(v_A)_z = -22$ in./sec, determine the velocity component $(v_A)_x$.

15.109. The rigid body shown rotates about the origin of coordinates with an angular velocity $\omega = \omega_x\mathbf{i} + \omega_y\mathbf{j} + \omega_z\mathbf{k}$. Knowing that $(v_A)_y = 15$ in./sec, $(v_B)_y = 9$ in./sec, and $\omega_y = 0$, determine (*a*) the angular velocity of the body, (*b*) the velocities of points A and B.

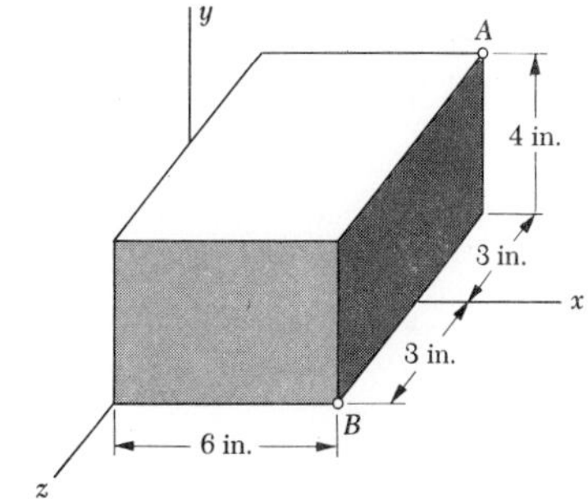

FIG. P 15.108 AND P 15.109

15.110. A rigid body rotates about the origin of coordinates with an angular velocity $\omega = \omega_x\mathbf{i} + \omega_y\mathbf{j} + \omega_z\mathbf{k}$. Determine the velocity components v_x, v_y, and v_z of the point $P(x,y,z)$.

15.111. A rigid body rotates about the origin of coordinates with an angular velocity $\omega = \omega_x\mathbf{i} + \omega_y\mathbf{j} + \omega_z\mathbf{k}$. Show that $v_x + v_y + v_z = 0$ for a point P located on the line $x = y = z$; that is, show that the algebraic sum of the scalar components of the velocity of P is zero.

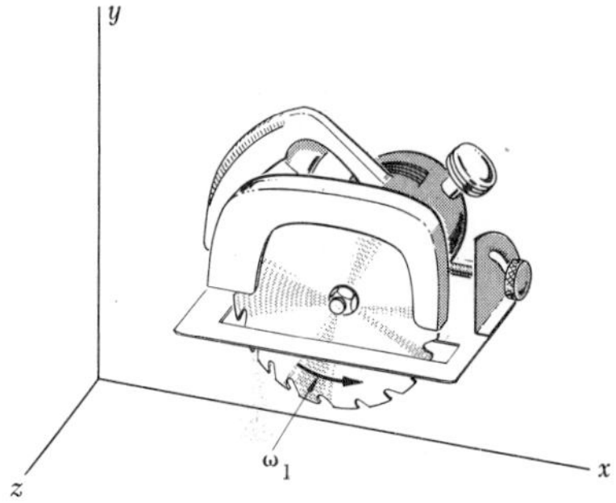

FIG. P 15.112

15.112. The blade of a portable saw rotates at a constant rate $\omega_1 = 1{,}800$ rpm as shown. Determine the angular acceleration of the blade as a man rotates the saw about the y axis with an angular velocity of 2 radians/sec and an angular acceleration of 3 radians/sec^2, both clockwise when viewed from above.

FIG. P 15.113

15.113. Knowing that the turbine rotor shown rotates at a constant rate $\omega_1 = 10{,}000$ rpm, determine the angular acceleration of the rotor if the turbine housing has a constant angular velocity of 3 radians/sec clockwise as viewed from (*a*) the positive y axis, (*b*) the positive z axis.

15.114. In the portion of a differential gear system shown, gears A and B are free to rotate about the rod AB, while the rod itself is free to rotate in the xz plane about its mid-point. Assuming that gear D is fixed and that gear C rotates with a constant angular velocity ω_1, determine (*a*) the angular velocity of gear B, (*b*) the angular acceleration of gear B.

15.115. Solve Prob. 15.114 assuming that gears C and D rotate with constant angular velocities ω_1 and ω_2, respectively, both counterclockwise as viewed from the positive y axis.

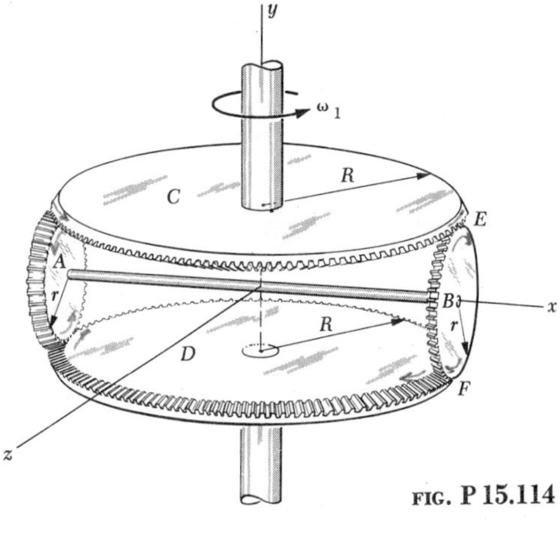

FIG. P 15.114

15.116. Two shafts AC and CF, which lie in the vertical xy plane, are connected by a universal joint at C. Shaft CF rotates at a constant angular velocity ω_1 as shown. At a time when the arm of the crosspiece attached to shaft CF is horizontal, determine the angular velocity of shaft AC.

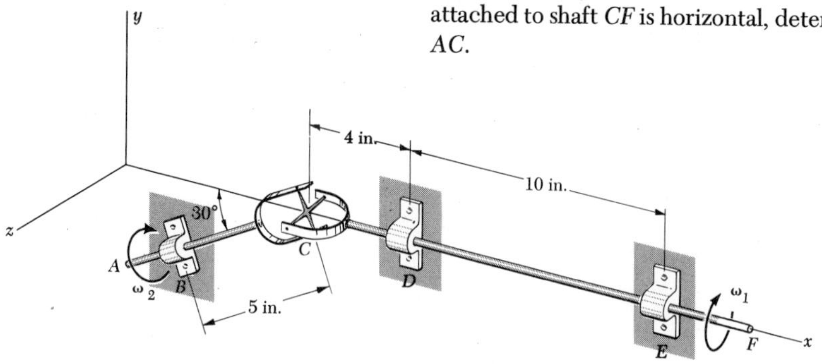

FIG. P 15.116

15.117. Solve Prob. 15.116 assuming that the arm of the crosspiece attached to shaft CF is vertical.

15.118. The cone shown rolls on the zx plane with its apex at the origin of coordinates. Denoting by ω_1 the constant angular velocity of the axis OB of the cone about the y axis, determine (a) the rate of spin of the cone about the axis OB, (b) the total angular velocity of the cone, (c) the angular acceleration of the cone.

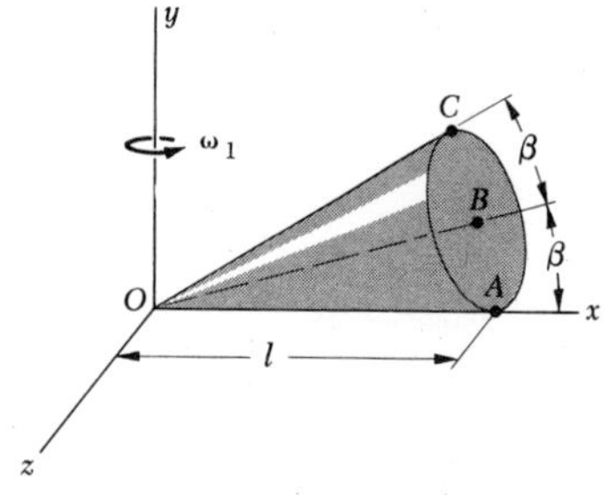

FIG. P 15.118

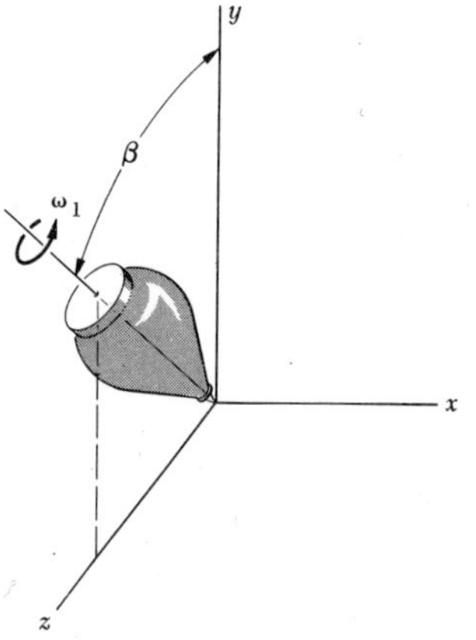

FIG. P 15.119

15.119. A top spins about its geometric axis at a constant rate ω_1 and its axis precesses about the y axis at a constant rate ω_2, counterclockwise as viewed from above. Knowing that β is constant, determine the angular acceleration of the top for the position shown, if (a) $\beta = 30°$, (b) $\beta = 60°$.

15.120. A gun barrel of length $OP = 12$ ft is mounted on a turret as shown. To keep it aimed at a moving target the azimuth angle β is being increased at the rate $d\beta/dt = 30°/\text{sec}$ and the elevation angle γ is being increased at the rate $d\gamma/dt = 10°/\text{sec}$. For the position $\beta = 90°$ and $\gamma = 30°$, determine (*a*) the angular velocity of the barrel, (*b*) the angular acceleration of the barrel, (*c*) the velocity and acceleration of point *P*.

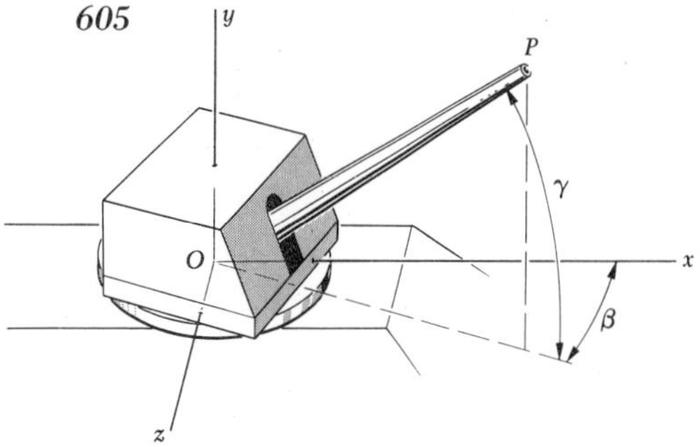

FIG. P 15.120

15.121. Solve Problem 15.120 for the position $\beta = 30°$ and $\gamma = 45°$.

15.122. In the planetary gear system shown gears *A* and *B* are rigidly connected to each other and rotate as a unit about the inclined shaft. Gears *C* and *D* rotate with constant angular velocities of 20 radians/sec and 30 radians/sec respectively (both counterclockwise when viewed from the right). Choosing the *x* axis to the right, the *y* axis upward, and the *z* axis pointing out of the plane of the figure, determine (*a*) the common angular velocity of gears *A* and *B*, (*b*) the angular velocity of shaft *FH*, which is rigidly attached to the inclined shaft.

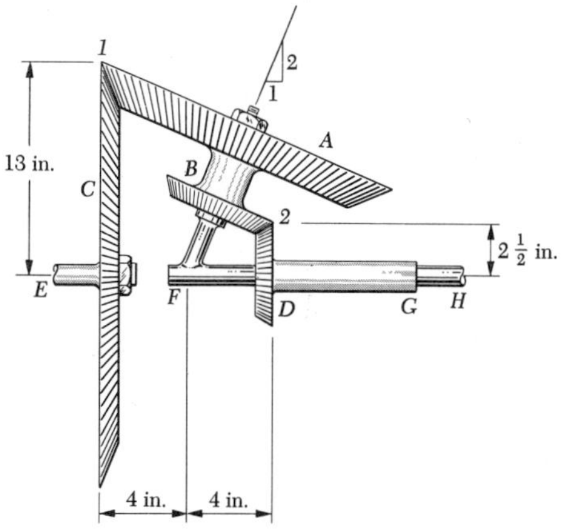

FIG. P 15.122

15.123. In Prob. 15.122, determine (*a*) the common angular acceleration of gears *A* and *B*, (*b*) the accelerations of the two gear teeth which are in contact at point *1*.

15.124. The bent rod *AOB* is attached to a fixed ball-and-socket joint at *O*. Portion *OA* of the rod slides in a straight inclined slot at *D* while portion *OB* slides on a horizontal surface. In the position shown, portion *OB* is guided by a plate which moves with a constant velocity $\mathbf{v}_1 = (112 \text{ in./sec})\mathbf{k}$. Determine (*a*) the angular velocity of the rod, (*b*) the angular acceleration of the rod, (*c*) the velocity and acceleration of end *A* of the rod.

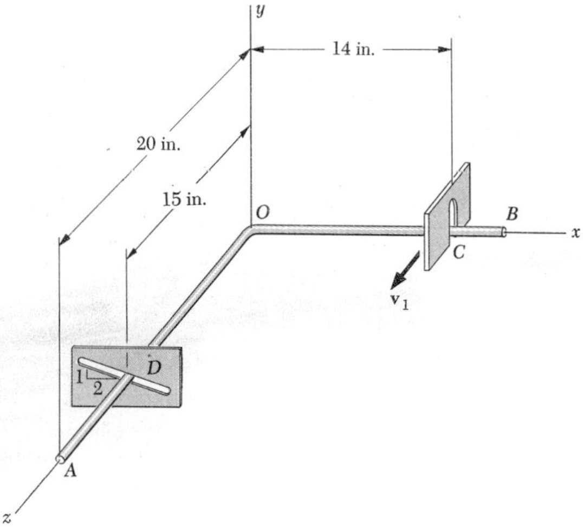

FIG. P 15.124

15.125. Solve Prob. 15.124 assuming that the plate guiding portion *OB* of the rod has a velocity $\mathbf{v}_1 = (112 \text{ in./sec})\mathbf{k}$ and an acceleration $\mathbf{a}_1 = (-224 \text{ in./sec}^2)\mathbf{k}$.

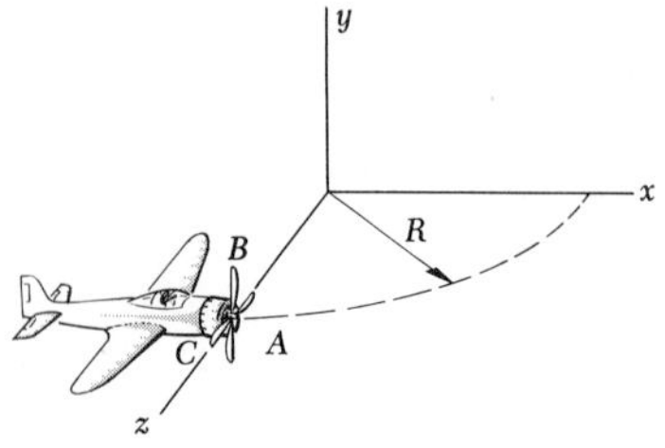

FIG. P 15.126

15.126. An airplane is flying in a horizontal circle of radius R at a constant speed v_0. The propeller rotates at a constant rate ω_0, clockwise as viewed by the pilot. Denoting by r the radius of the propeller, determine (*a*) the angular velocity and angular acceleration of the propeller, (*b*) the velocity and acceleration of the propeller tip B.

15.127. In Prob. 15.126, determine the velocity and acceleration of the propeller tip C.

***15.128.** A disk of radius r rotates at a constant rate ω_3 about a pin D which is held by a shaft CD which itself rotates at a constant rate ω_1. Knowing that the entire assembly rotates about the y axis at a constant rate ω_2, determine (*a*) the angular velocity and angular acceleration of the disk, (*b*) the velocity and acceleration of point E on the rim of the disk.

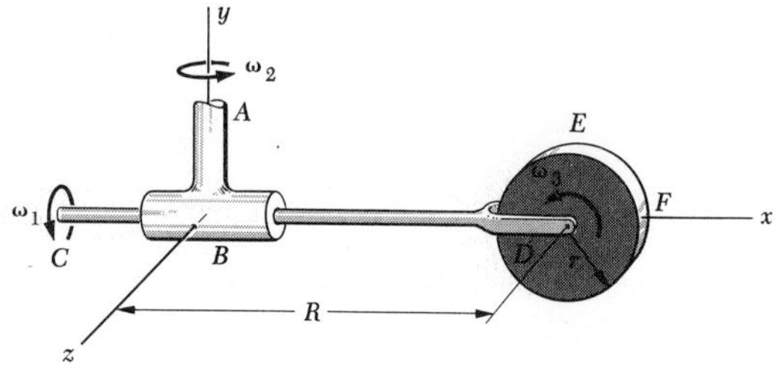

FIG. P 15.128

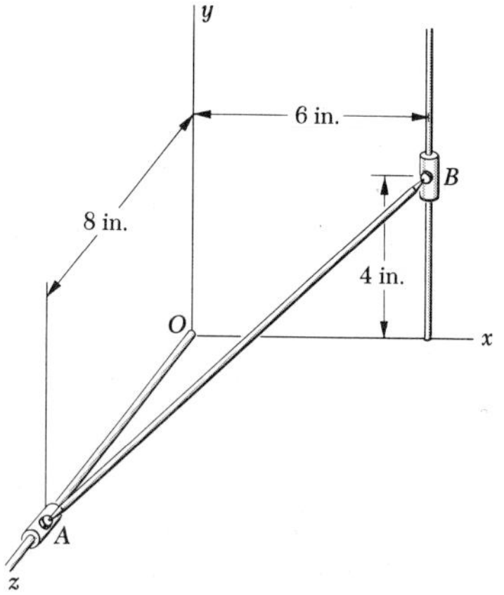

FIG. P 15.130

15.129. In Prob. 15.128, determine the velocity and acceleration of point F on the rim of the disk.

15.130. Rod AB is connected by ball-and-socket joints to collars A and B, which slide along the two rods shown. Knowing that collar A moves toward the origin of coordinates with a constant speed of 10 in./sec, determine the velocity of collar B.

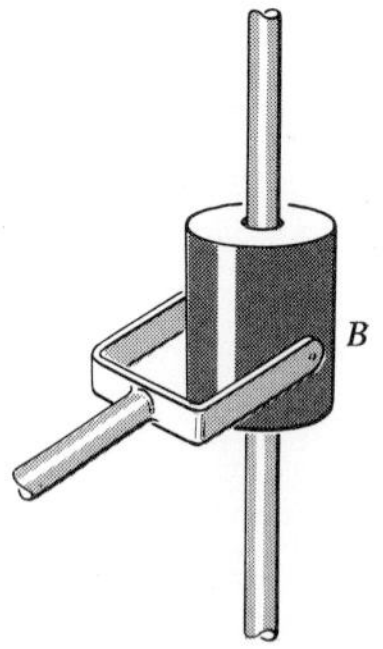

FIG. P 15.131

15.131. In Prob. 15.130, the ball-and-socket joint between the rod and collar B is replaced by the clevis connection shown. Determine (*a*) the angular velocity of the rod, (*b*) the velocity of collar B. (*Hint.* The collar and the clevis connection at B permit rotation about the vertical rod and about an axis perpendicular to the plane which contains the vertical rod and the rod AB; they prevent rotation about the horizontal axis through B contained in the vertical plane which passes through A and B).

15.132. Two rods are welded together to form a T-shaped machine element which bears against a smooth vertical surface at *D* and is guided by pins sliding in the horizontal slots shown. Knowing that in the position shown point *A* moves to the right with a constant velocity of 16 in./sec, determine (*a*) the angular velocity of the element, (*b*) the velocities of points *B* and *D*.

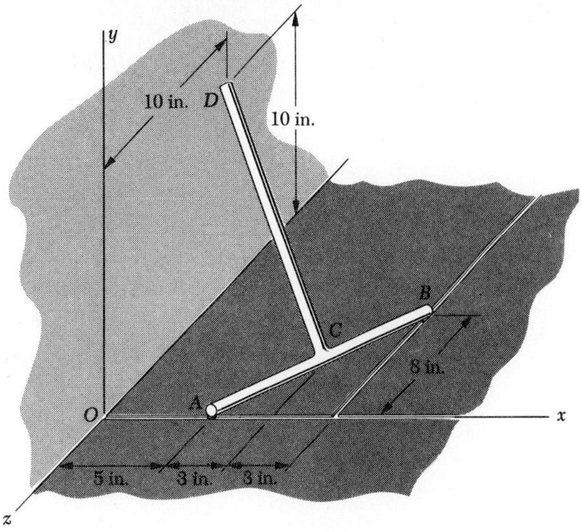

FIG. P 15.132

15.133. In the linkage shown, crank *BC* rotates in the *yz* plane while crank *ED* rotates in a plane parallel to the *xy* plane. Knowing that crank *BC* has an angular velocity ω_1 of 10 radians/sec and no angular acceleration, determine the corresponding angular velocity ω_2 of crank *ED*.

***15.134.** In Prob. 15.130, determine the acceleration of collar *B*.

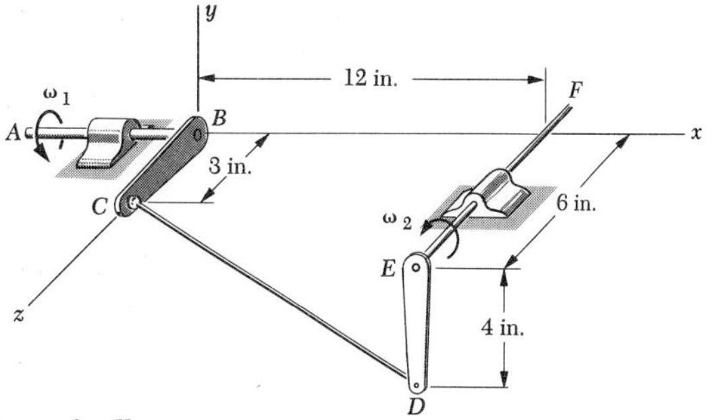

FIG. P 15.133

***15.135.** In Sample Prob. 15.10, determine the acceleration of collar *B*.

***15.136.** In Prob. 15.132, determine (*a*) the angular acceleration of the element, (*b*) the accelerations of points *B* and *D*.

***15.137.** In Prob. 15.133, determine the angular acceleration of crank *ED*.

***15.12. Rate of Change of a Vector with Respect to a Rotating Frame.** We saw in Sec. 11.10 that the rate of change of a vector **P** is the same with respect to a fixed frame and with respect to a frame in translation. In this section, we shall compare the rates of change of a vector **P** with respect to a fixed frame and with respect to a rotating frame of reference.† We shall also learn to determine the rate of change of **P** with respect to one frame of reference when **P** is defined by its components in another frame.

† It is recalled that the selection of a fixed frame of reference is arbitrary. Any frame may be designated as "fixed"; all others will then be considered as moving.

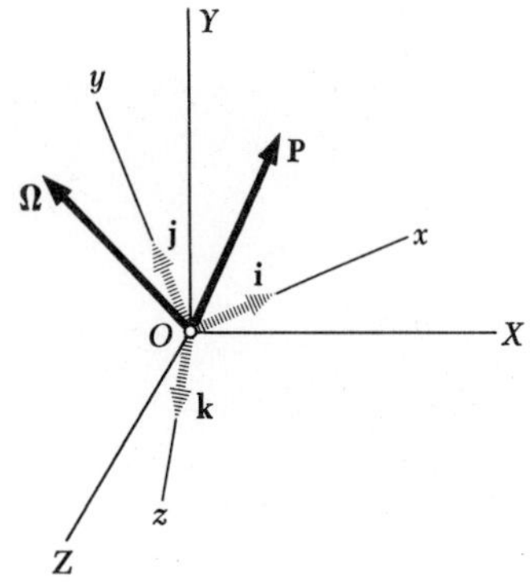

FIG. 15.31

Consider two frames of reference centered at O, a fixed frame $OXYZ$ and a rotating frame $Oxyz$; let $\mathbf{\Omega}$ denote the angular velocity of the frame $Oxyz$ at a given instant (Fig. 15.31). Consider now a vector function $\mathbf{P}(t)$ represented by the vector $\mathbf{P}$ attached at O; as the time t varies, both the direction and the magnitude of $\mathbf{P}$ change. Since the variation of $\mathbf{P}$ is viewed differently by an observer using $OXYZ$ as a frame of reference and by an observer using $Oxyz$, we should expect the rate of change of $\mathbf{P}$ to depend upon the frame of reference which has been selected. Therefore, we shall denote by $d\mathbf{P}/dt$ the rate of change of $\mathbf{P}$ with respect to the fixed frame $OXYZ$, and by $\delta\mathbf{P}/\delta t$ its rate of change with respect to the rotating frame $Oxyz$. We propose to determine the relationship existing between these two rates of change.

Let us first resolve the vector $\mathbf{P}$ into components along the x, y, and z axes of the rotating frame. Denoting by $\mathbf{i}$, $\mathbf{j}$, and $\mathbf{k}$ the corresponding unit vectors, we write

$$\mathbf{P} = P_x\mathbf{i} + P_y\mathbf{j} + P_z\mathbf{k} \tag{15.33}$$

Differentiating (15.33) with respect to t and considering the unit vectors $\mathbf{i}$, $\mathbf{j}$, $\mathbf{k}$ as fixed, we obtain the rate of change $\delta\mathbf{P}/\delta t$ of $\mathbf{P}$ *with respect to the rotating frame:*

$$\frac{\delta\mathbf{P}}{\delta t} = \frac{dP_x}{dt}\mathbf{i} + \frac{dP_y}{dt}\mathbf{j} + \frac{dP_z}{dt}\mathbf{k} \tag{15.34}$$

To obtain the rate of change $d\mathbf{P}/dt$ of $\mathbf{P}$ *with respect to the fixed frame,* we must consider the unit vectors $\mathbf{i}$, $\mathbf{j}$, $\mathbf{k}$ as variable when differentiating (15.33). We write therefore

$$\frac{d\mathbf{P}}{dt} = \frac{dP_x}{dt}\mathbf{i} + \frac{dP_y}{dt}\mathbf{j} + \frac{dP_z}{dt}\mathbf{k} + P_x\frac{d\mathbf{i}}{dt} + P_y\frac{d\mathbf{j}}{dt} + P_z\frac{d\mathbf{k}}{dt} \tag{15.35}$$

Recalling (15.34), we observe that the sum of the first three terms in the right-hand member of (15.35) represents the rate of change $\delta\mathbf{P}/\delta t$. We note, on the other hand, that the rate of change $d\mathbf{P}/dt$ would reduce to the last three terms in (15.35) if the vector $\mathbf{P}$ were fixed within the frame $Oxyz$, since $\delta\mathbf{P}/\delta t$ would then be zero. But, in that case, $d\mathbf{P}/dt$ would represent the velocity of a particle located at the tip of $\mathbf{P}$ and belonging to a body rigidly attached to the frame $Oxyz$. Thus, the last three terms in (15.35) represent the velocity of that particle; since the frame $Oxyz$ has an angular velocity $\mathbf{\Omega}$ at the instant considered, we write, by (15.27),

$$P_x \frac{d\mathbf{i}}{dt} + P_y \frac{d\mathbf{j}}{dt} + P_z \frac{d\mathbf{k}}{dt} = \boldsymbol{\Omega} \times \mathbf{P} \tag{15.36}$$

Substituting from (15.34) and (15.36) into (15.35), we obtain the fundamental relation

$$\frac{d\mathbf{P}}{dt} = \frac{\delta \mathbf{P}}{\delta t} + \boldsymbol{\Omega} \times \mathbf{P} \tag{15.37}$$

We conclude that the rate of change $d\mathbf{P}/dt$ of the vector $\mathbf{P}$ with respect to the fixed frame $OXYZ$ is made of two parts: The first part, $\delta\mathbf{P}/\delta t$, is the rate of change of $\mathbf{P}$ with respect to the rotating frame $Oxyz$; the second part, $\boldsymbol{\Omega} \times \mathbf{P}$, is induced by the rotation of the frame $Oxyz$.

The use of the relation (15.37) greatly simplifies the determination of the rate of change $d\mathbf{P}/dt$ of a vector $\mathbf{P}$ defined by its components along the axes of a rotating frame, since the rate of change $\delta\mathbf{P}/\delta t$ of such a vector may be readily obtained from (15.34).

***15.13. Motion of a Particle Relative to a Rotating Frame. Coriolis Acceleration.** Consider two frames of reference centered at O, a fixed frame $OXYZ$, and a rotating frame $Oxyz$ (Fig. 15.32). Let P be a particle moving in space. While the position vector $\mathbf{r}$ of P is the same in both frames, its rate of change depends upon the frame of reference which has been selected.

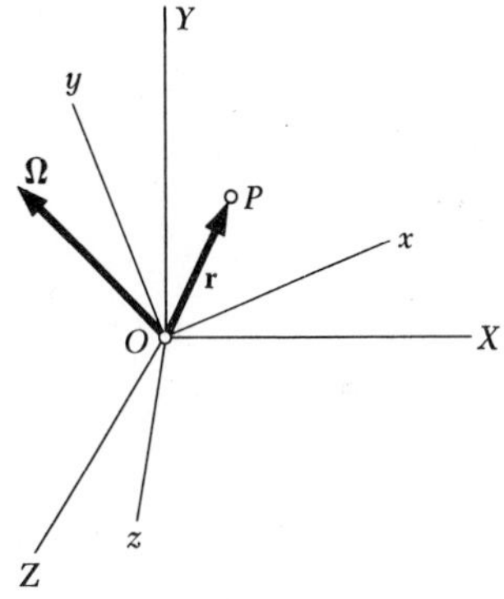

FIG. 15.32

The absolute velocity $\mathbf{v}_P$ of the particle is defined as the rate of change $d\mathbf{r}/dt$ of $\mathbf{r}$ with respect to the fixed frame $OXYZ$. We may, however, express $\mathbf{v}_P$ in terms of the rate of change $\delta\mathbf{r}/\delta t$ observed from the rotating frame if we make use of (15.37). Denoting by $\boldsymbol{\Omega}$ the angular velocity of the frame $Oxyz$ at the instant considered, we write

$$\mathbf{v}_P = \frac{d\mathbf{r}}{dt} = \boldsymbol{\Omega} \times \mathbf{r} + \frac{\delta \mathbf{r}}{\delta t} \tag{15.38}$$

But $\delta\mathbf{r}/\delta t$ defines the velocity of the particle P relative to the frame $Oxyz$. Besides, if we regard the rotating frame as a rigid body, the term $\boldsymbol{\Omega} \times \mathbf{r}$ in (15.38) represents the velocity of the point of the rotating frame which coincides with P at the instant considered. Thus, we have

$$\mathbf{v}_P = \mathbf{v}_{P'} + \mathbf{v}_{P/\mathcal{F}} \tag{15.39}$$

where $\mathbf{v}_P$ = absolute velocity of particle P
$\mathbf{v}_{P'}$ = velocity of point of moving frame coinciding with P
$\mathbf{v}_{P/\mathcal{F}}$ = velocity of P relative to moving frame

The absolute acceleration $\mathbf{a}_P$ of the particle is defined as the rate of change of $\mathbf{v}_P$ with respect to $OXYZ$. Substituting for $\mathbf{v}_P$ from (15.38), we write

$$\mathbf{a}_P = \frac{d\mathbf{v}_P}{dt} = \frac{d\mathbf{\Omega}}{dt} \times \mathbf{r} + \mathbf{\Omega} \times \frac{d\mathbf{r}}{dt} + \frac{d}{dt}\left(\frac{\delta \mathbf{r}}{\delta t}\right)$$

Substituting for $d\mathbf{r}/dt$ from (15.38), and observing from (15.37) that

$$\frac{d}{dt}\left(\frac{\delta \mathbf{r}}{\delta t}\right) = \mathbf{\Omega} \times \frac{\delta \mathbf{r}}{\delta t} + \frac{\delta^2 \mathbf{r}}{\delta t^2}$$

we have

$$\mathbf{a}_P = \frac{d\mathbf{\Omega}}{dt} \times \mathbf{r} + \mathbf{\Omega} \times (\mathbf{\Omega} \times \mathbf{r}) + 2\mathbf{\Omega} \times \frac{\delta \mathbf{r}}{\delta t} + \frac{\delta^2 \mathbf{r}}{\delta t^2} \qquad (15.40)$$

Referring to the expression (15.28) obtained in Sec. 15.10 for the acceleration of a particle in a rigid body with a fixed point, we note that the sum of the first two terms represents the acceleration $\mathbf{a}_F$ of the point of the rotating frame which coincides with P at the instant considered. On the other hand, the last term defines the acceleration $\mathbf{a}_{P/F}$ of P relative to the rotating frame. If it were not for the third term, which has not been accounted for, a relation similar to (15.39) could be written for the accelerations, and $\mathbf{a}_P$ could be expressed as the sum of $\mathbf{a}_F$ and $\mathbf{a}_{P/F}$. However, it is clear that *such a relation would be incorrect* and that we must include the additional term. This term, which we shall denote by $\mathbf{a}_c$, is called the *complementary acceleration*, or *Coriolis acceleration*, after the French mathematician De Coriolis (1792–1843). We write

$$\mathbf{a}_P = \mathbf{a}_F + \mathbf{a}_{P/F} + \mathbf{a}_c \qquad (15.41)$$

where $\mathbf{a}_P$ = absolute acceleration of particle P
$\mathbf{a}_F$ = acceleration of point of moving frame coinciding with P
$\mathbf{a}_{P/F}$ = acceleration of P relative to moving frame
$\mathbf{a}_c = 2\mathbf{\Omega} \times \dfrac{\delta \mathbf{r}}{\delta t} = 2\mathbf{\Omega} \times \mathbf{v}_{P/F}$
= complementary, or Coriolis, acceleration

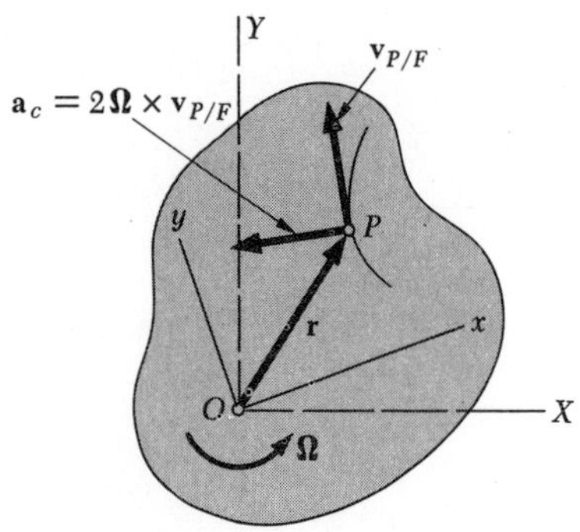

FIG. 15.33

We note that the Coriolis acceleration is perpendicular to the vectors $\mathbf{\Omega}$ and $\mathbf{v}_{P/F}$, and that it reduces to zero when these vectors are parallel, or when either of them is zero.

Coriolis Acceleration in Plane Motion. In the particular case of the plane motion of a particle, the vector $\mathbf{\Omega}$ is perpendicular to the plane of motion and, thus, to $\mathbf{v}_{P/F}$. The magnitude of $\mathbf{a}_c$ is then equal to $2\Omega v_{P/F}$, and its direction may be obtained by rotating the vector $\mathbf{v}_{P/F}$ through 90° in the sense of rotation of the moving frame. This has been shown in Fig. 15.33, where the particle P describes a path on a slab which rotates about O with the frame Oxy.

The following example will help in understanding the physical meaning of the Coriolis acceleration. Consider a collar P which is made to slide at a constant relative speed u along a rod OB rotating at a constant angular velocity ω about O (Fig. 15.34*a*). If we attach the rotating frame of reference to the rod, we find that, according to (15.41), the absolute acceleration of P may be obtained by adding vectorially the acceleration $\mathbf{a}_A$ of the point A of the rod coinciding with P, the relative acceleration $\mathbf{a}_{P/OB}$ of P with respect to the rod, and the Coriolis acceleration $\mathbf{a}_c$. Since the angular velocity ω of the rod is constant, $\mathbf{a}_A$ reduces to its normal component $(\mathbf{a}_A)_n$ of magnitude $r\omega^2$; and since u is constant, the relative acceleration $\mathbf{a}_{P/OB}$ is zero. According to the definition given above, the Coriolis acceleration is a vector perpendicular to OB, of magnitude $2\omega u$, and directed as shown in the figure. The acceleration of the collar P consists, therefore, of the two vectors shown in Fig. 15.34*a*. Note that the result obtained may be checked by applying the relation (11.44).

To understand better the significance of the Coriolis acceleration, we shall consider the absolute velocity of P at time t and at time $t + \Delta t$ (Fig. 15.34*b*). At time t, the velocity may be resolved into its components $\mathbf{u}$ and $\mathbf{v}_A$, and at time $t + \Delta t$ into its components $\mathbf{u}'$ and $\mathbf{v}_{A'}$. Drawing these components from the same origin (Fig. 15.34*c*), we note that the change in velocity during the time Δt may be represented by the sum of three vectors $\overrightarrow{RR'}$, $\overrightarrow{TT''}$, and $\overrightarrow{T''T'}$. The vector $\overrightarrow{TT''}$ measures the change in direction of the velocity $\mathbf{v}_A$, and the quotient $\overrightarrow{TT''}/\Delta t$ represents the acceleration $\mathbf{a}_A$ when Δt approaches zero. We check that the direction of $\overrightarrow{TT''}$ is that of $\mathbf{a}_A$ when Δt approaches zero and that

$$\lim_{\Delta t \to 0} \frac{TT''}{\Delta t} = \lim_{\Delta t \to 0} v_A \frac{\Delta \theta}{\Delta t} = r\omega\omega = r\omega^2 = a_A$$

The vector $\overrightarrow{RR'}$ measures the change in direction of $\mathbf{u}$ due to the rotation of the rod; the vector $\overrightarrow{T''T'}$ measures the change in magnitude of $\mathbf{v}_A$ due to the motion of P on the rod. The vectors $\overrightarrow{RR'}$ and $\overrightarrow{T''T'}$ result from the *combined effect* of the relative motion of P and of the rotation of the rod; they would

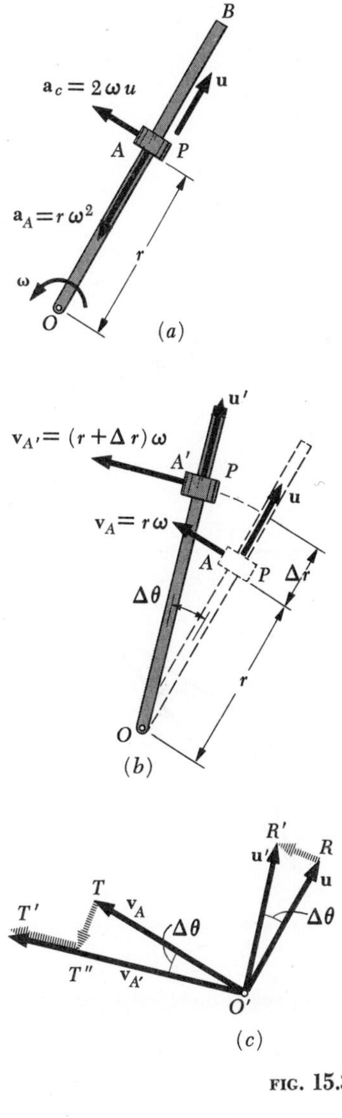

FIG. 15.34

vanish if *either* of these two motions were stopped. We may easily verify that the sum of these two vectors defines the Coriolis acceleration. Their direction is that of $\mathbf{a}_c$ when Δt approaches zero and, since $RR' = u\Delta\theta$ and $T''T' = v_{A'} - v_A = (r + \Delta r)\omega - r\omega = \omega\Delta r$, we check that

$$\lim_{\Delta t\to 0}\left(\frac{RR'}{\Delta t} + \frac{T''T'}{\Delta t}\right) = \lim_{\Delta t\to 0}\left(u\frac{\Delta\theta}{\Delta t} + \omega\frac{\Delta r}{\Delta t}\right)$$

$$= u\omega + \omega u = 2\omega u = a_c$$

Formulas (15.39) and (15.41) may be used to analyze the motion of mechanisms which contain parts sliding on each other. They make it possible, for example, to relate the absolute and relative motions of sliding pins and collars (see Sample Probs. 15.11 and 15.12). The concept of Coriolis acceleration is also very useful in the study of long-range projectiles and of other bodies whose motions are appreciably affected by the rotation of the earth. As was pointed out in Sec. 12.1, a system of axes attached to the earth does not truly constitute a newtonian frame of reference; such a system of axes should actually be considered as rotating. The formulas derived in this section will therefore facilitate the study of the motion of bodies with respect to axes attached to the earth.

***15.14. Frame of Reference in General Motion.** Consider a fixed frame of reference $OXYZ$ and a frame $Axyz$ which moves in a known, but arbitrary, fashion with respect to $OXYZ$ (Fig. 15.35). Let P be a particle moving in space. The position of P is defined at any instant by the vector $\mathbf{r}$ in the fixed frame, and by the vector $\mathbf{r}'$ in the moving frame. Denoting by $\mathbf{r}_A$ the position vector of A in the fixed frame, we have

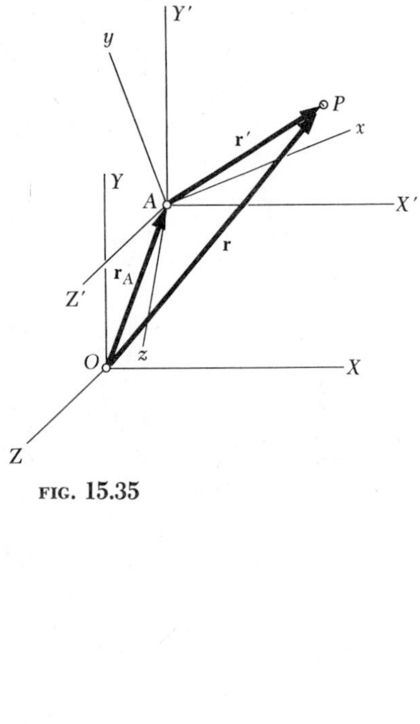

FIG. 15.35

$$\mathbf{r} = \mathbf{r}_A + \mathbf{r}' \qquad (15.42)$$

The absolute velocity $\mathbf{v}_P$ of the particle is obtained by writing

$$\mathbf{v}_P = \frac{d\mathbf{r}}{dt} = \frac{d\mathbf{r}_A}{dt} + \frac{d\mathbf{r}'}{dt} \qquad (15.43)$$

where the derivatives are defined with respect to the fixed frame. Thus, the first term in the right-hand member of (15.43) represents the velocity $\mathbf{v}_A$ of the origin of the moving axes. On the other hand, since the rate of change of a vector is the same with respect to a fixed frame and with respect to a frame in translation (Sec. 11.10), the second term may be regarded as the velocity of P relative to the frame $AX'Y'Z'$ of same orientation as $OXYZ$ and same origin as $Axyz$. This velocity may be obtained from (15.38) after $\mathbf{r}'$ has been substituted for $\mathbf{r}$. We write therefore

$$\mathbf{v}_P = \mathbf{v}_A + \mathbf{\Omega} \times \mathbf{r}' + \frac{\delta \mathbf{r}'}{\delta t} \tag{15.44}$$

where $\mathbf{\Omega}$ is the angular velocity of the frame $Axyz$ at the instant considered.

The absolute acceleration $\mathbf{a}_P$ of the particle is obtained by writing

$$\mathbf{a}_P = \frac{d\mathbf{v}_P}{dt} = \frac{d\mathbf{v}_A}{dt} + \frac{d}{dt}\left(\mathbf{\Omega} \times \mathbf{r}' + \frac{\delta \mathbf{r}'}{\delta t}\right) \tag{15.45}$$

But the first term in the right-hand member of (15.45) represents the acceleration $\mathbf{a}_A$ of the origin of the moving axes, and the second term may be obtained from (15.40) after $\mathbf{r}'$ has been substituted for $\mathbf{r}$. Thus, we have

$$\mathbf{a}_P = \mathbf{a}_A + \frac{d\mathbf{\Omega}}{dt} \times \mathbf{r}' + \mathbf{\Omega} \times (\mathbf{\Omega} \times \mathbf{r}') + 2\mathbf{\Omega} \times \frac{\delta \mathbf{r}'}{\delta t} + \frac{\delta^2 \mathbf{r}'}{\delta t^2} \tag{15.46}$$

Formulas (15.44) and (15.46) make it possible to determine the velocity and acceleration of a given particle with respect to a fixed frame of reference, when the motion of the particle is known with respect to a moving frame. These formulas become more significant, and considerably easier to remember, if we note that the sum of the first two terms in (15.44) represents the velocity of the point of the moving frame which coincides with P at the instant considered, and that the sum of the first three terms in (15.46) represents the acceleration of the same point. Thus, the relations (15.39) and (15.41) of the preceding section are still valid in the case of a reference frame in general motion, and we write

$$\mathbf{v}_P = \mathbf{v}_{\mathcal{F}} + \mathbf{v}_{P/\mathcal{F}} \tag{15.39}$$

$$\mathbf{a}_P = \mathbf{a}_{\mathcal{F}} + \mathbf{a}_{P/\mathcal{F}} + \mathbf{a}_c \tag{15.41}$$

where the various vectors involved have been defined in Sec. 15.13.

We may note that, if the reference frame $Oxyz$ is in translation, the velocity and acceleration of the point of the frame which coincides with P become respectively equal to the velocity and acceleration of the origin A of the frame. On the other hand, since the frame maintains a fixed orientation, $\mathbf{a}_c$ is zero, and the relations (15.39) and (15.41) reduce, respectively, to the relations (11.33) and (11.34) derived in Sec. 11.12.

SAMPLE PROBLEM 15.11

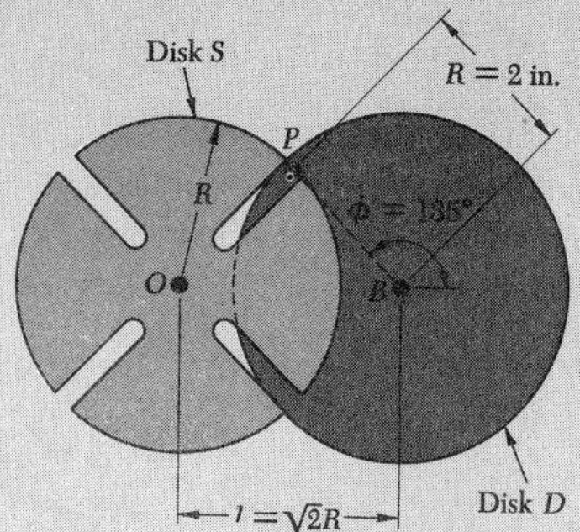

The Geneva mechanism shown is used in many counting instruments and in other applications where an intermittent rotary motion is required. Disk D rotates with a constant counterclockwise angular velocity ω_D of 10 radians/sec. A pin P is attached to disk D and slides along one of several slots cut in disk S. It is desirable that the angular velocity of disk S be zero as the pin enters and leaves each slot; in the case of four slots, this will occur if the distance between the centers of the disks is $l = \sqrt{2}\,R$.

At the instant when $\phi = 150°$, determine (*a*) the angular velocity of disk S, (*b*) the velocity of pin P relative to disk S.

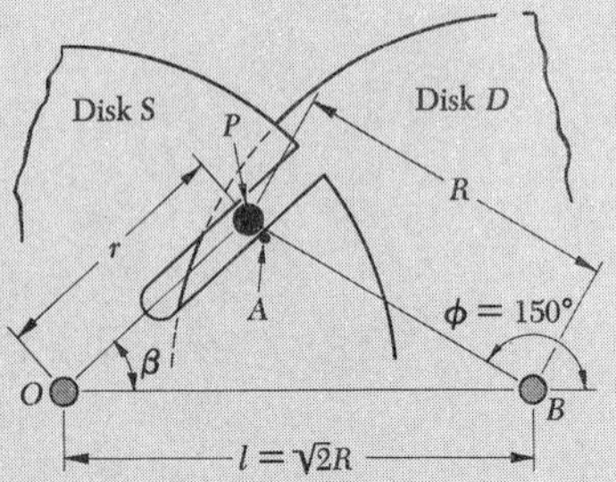

Solution. We solve triangle OPB, which corresponds to the position $\phi = 150°$, and obtain

$$\beta = 42.4° \qquad r = 0.742R = 1.484 \text{ in.}$$

Since pin P is attached to disk D, and since disk D rotates about point B, the magnitude of the absolute velocity of P is

$$v_P = R\omega_D = (2 \text{ in.})(10 \text{ radians/sec}) = 20 \text{ in./sec}$$

$$\mathbf{v}_P = 20 \text{ in./sec} \angle 60°$$

We consider now the motion of pin P along the slot in disk S. Denoting by A the point of disk S which coincides with P at the instant considered, we write

$$\mathbf{v}_P = \mathbf{v}_A + \mathbf{v}_{P/S}$$

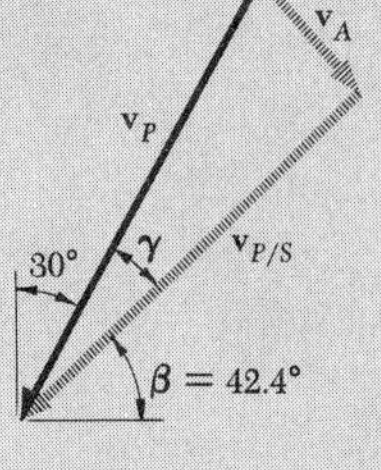

Noting that $\mathbf{v}_A$ is perpendicular to the radius OA and that $\mathbf{v}_{P/S}$ is directed along the slot, we draw the velocity triangle corresponding to the above equation. From the triangle, we compute

$$\gamma = 90° - 42.4° - 30° = 17.6°$$

$$v_A = v_P \sin\gamma = (20 \text{ in./sec}) \sin 17.6°$$

$$\mathbf{v}_A = 6.05 \text{ in./sec} \searrow 42.4°$$

$$v_{P/S} = v_P \cos\gamma = (20 \text{ in./sec}) \cos 17.6°$$

$$\mathbf{v}_{P/S} = 19.06 \text{ in./sec} \angle 42.4° \quad ◄$$

Since $\mathbf{v}_A$ is perpendicular to the radius OA, we write

$$v_A = r\omega_S \qquad 6.05 \text{ in./sec} = (1.484 \text{ in.})\,\omega_S$$

$$\omega_S = 4.07 \text{ radians/sec} \circlearrowright \quad ◄$$

SAMPLE PROBLEM 15.12

In the Geneva mechanism of Sample Prob. 15.11, disk D rotates with a constant counterclockwise angular velocity ω_D of 10 radians/sec. At the instant when $\phi = 150°$, determine the angular acceleration of disk S.

Solution. Referring to Sample Prob. 15.11, we obtain the angular velocity of disk S and the velocity of the pin relative to disk S.

$$\omega_S = 4.07 \text{ radians/sec} \circlearrowright$$

$$\beta = 42.4° \qquad \mathbf{v}_{P/S} = 19.06 \text{ in./sec} \measuredangle 42.4°$$

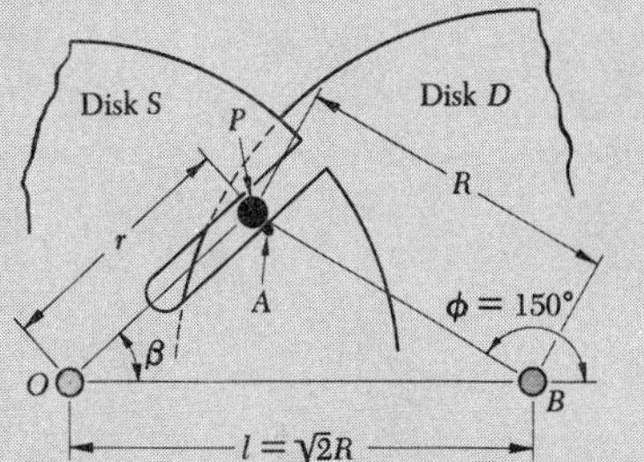

Since pin P moves with respect to the rotating disk S, we write

$$\mathbf{a}_P = \mathbf{a}_A + \mathbf{a}_{P/S} + \mathbf{a}_c \tag{1}$$

Each term of this vector equation is investigated separately.

Absolute Acceleration $\mathbf{a}_P$. Since disk D rotates with constant ω, the absolute acceleration $\mathbf{a}_P$ is directed toward B.

$$a_P = R\omega_D^2 = (2 \text{ in.})(10 \text{ radians/sec})^2 = 200 \text{ in./sec}^2$$

$$\mathbf{a}_P = 200 \text{ in./sec}^2 ⦩ 30°$$

Acceleration $\mathbf{a}_A$ *of the Coinciding Point A.* The acceleration $\mathbf{a}_A$ of the point A of disk S which coincides with P at the instant considered is resolved into normal and tangential components. (We recall from Sample Prob. 15.11 that $r = 1.484$ in.)

$$(a_A)_n = r\omega_S^2 = (1.484)(4.07)^2 = 24.6 \text{ in./sec}^2$$

$$(\mathbf{a}_A)_n = 24.6 \text{ in./sec}^2 \measuredangle 42.4°$$

$$(a_A)_t = r\alpha_S = 1.484\alpha_S \qquad (\mathbf{a}_A)_t = 1.484\alpha_S ⦫ 42.4°$$

Relative Acceleration $\mathbf{a}_{P/S}$. Since the pin P moves in a straight slot cut in disk S, the relative acceleration $\mathbf{a}_{P/S}$ must be parallel to the slot, i.e., its direction must be ∡ 42.4°.

Coriolis Acceleration $\mathbf{a}_c$. Rotating the relative velocity $\mathbf{v}_{P/S}$ through 90° in the sense of ω_S, we obtain the direction of the Coriolis component of the acceleration.

$$a_c = 2\omega_S v_{P/S} = (2)(4.07 \text{ radians/sec})(19.06 \text{ in./sec}) = 155.1 \text{ in./sec}^2$$

$$\mathbf{a}_c = 155.1 \text{ in./sec}^2 ⦪ 42.4°$$

We rewrite Eq. (1) and substitute the accelerations found above.

$$\mathbf{a}_P = (\mathbf{a}_A)_n + (\mathbf{a}_A)_t + \mathbf{a}_{P/S} + \mathbf{a}_c$$

$$[200 ⦩ 30°] = [24.6 \measuredangle 42.4°] + [1.484\alpha_S ⦫ 42.4°] + [a_{P/S} ∡ 42.4°] + [155.1 ⦪ 42.4°]$$

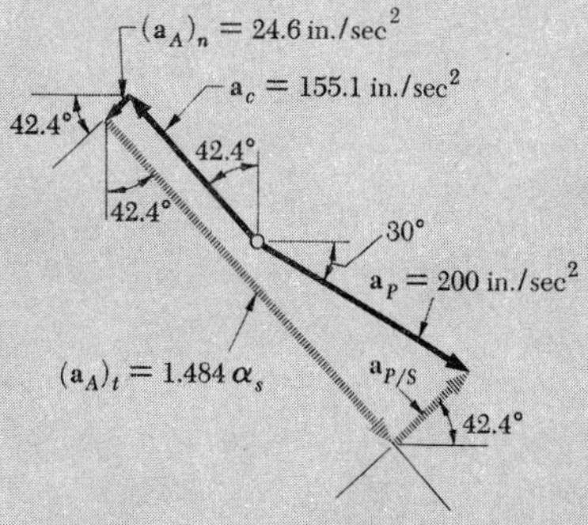

Solving this equation analytically or graphically, we obtain

$$1.484\alpha_S = 346 \text{ in./sec}^2$$

$$\alpha_S = 233 \text{ radians/sec}^2 \circlearrowright$$

SAMPLE PROBLEM 15.13

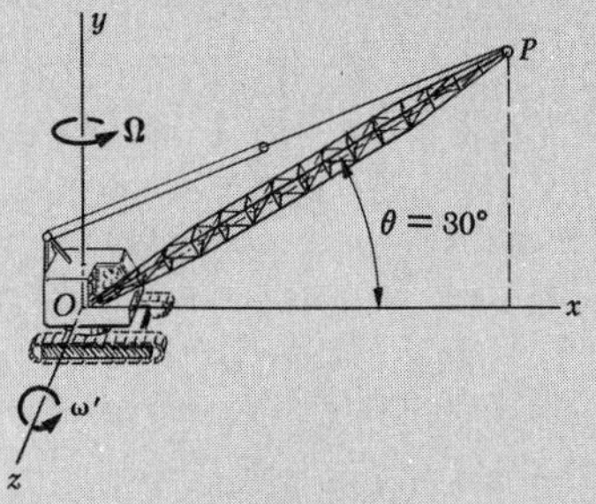

The crane shown rotates with a constant angular velocity $\boldsymbol{\Omega}$ of 0.30 radian/sec. Simultaneously, the boom is being raised with a constant angular velocity ω' of 0.50 radian/sec relative to the cab. Knowing that the length of the boom OP is $l = 40$ ft, determine (*a*) the velocity and acceleration of the tip P of the boom, (*b*) the angular velocity and angular acceleration of the boom.

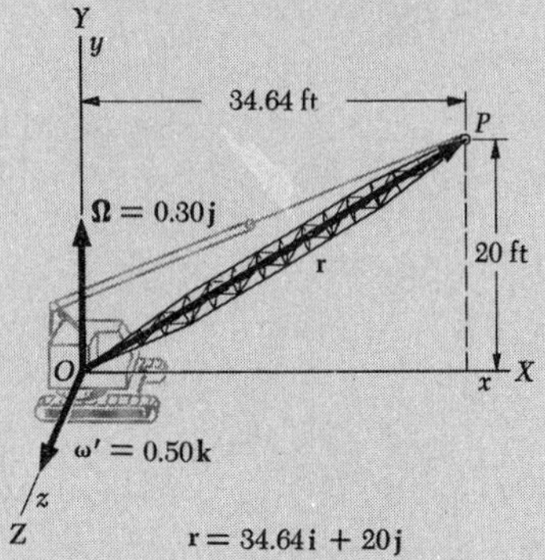

Frames of Reference. The frame $OXYZ$ is fixed; the frame $Oxyz$ is attached to the rotating cab. We observe that the rotating frame $Oxyz$ has an angular velocity $\boldsymbol{\Omega} = 0.30\mathbf{j}$ with respect to the frame $OXYZ$. The angular velocity of the boom relative to the cab and the rotating frame $Oxyz$ is $\boldsymbol{\omega}' = 0.50\mathbf{k}$.

Velocity $\mathbf{v}_P$. We denote by $\mathbf{r}$ the position vector of the tip P of the boom and write that the absolute velocity of P is the sum of the velocity $\mathbf{v}_{P'}$ of the point of the frame $Oxyz$ which coincides with P and of the velocity $\mathbf{v}_{P/\mathcal{F}}$ of P relative to $Oxyz$:

$$\mathbf{v}_P = \mathbf{v}_{P'} + \mathbf{v}_{P/\mathcal{F}} = \boldsymbol{\Omega} \times \mathbf{r} + \boldsymbol{\omega}' \times \mathbf{r} = (\boldsymbol{\Omega} + \boldsymbol{\omega}') \times \mathbf{r}$$

Noting that $(\boldsymbol{\Omega} + \boldsymbol{\omega}') = 0.30\mathbf{j} + 0.50\mathbf{k}$, we write

$$\mathbf{v}_P = \begin{vmatrix} \mathbf{i} & \mathbf{j} & \mathbf{k} \\ 0 & 0.30 & 0.50 \\ 34.64 & 20 & 0 \end{vmatrix} = -10\mathbf{i} + 17.32\mathbf{j} - 10.39\mathbf{k} \quad \text{(ft/sec)} \blacktriangleleft$$

The relative velocity of P with respect to the frame $Oxyz$ is

$$\mathbf{v}_{P/\mathcal{F}} = \boldsymbol{\omega}' \times \mathbf{r} = 0.50\mathbf{k} \times (34.64\mathbf{i} + 20\mathbf{j}) = 17.32\mathbf{j} - 10\mathbf{i}$$

Acceleration $\mathbf{a}_P$. Since the tip P of the boom moves with respect to the rotating frame $Oxyz$, we write

$$\begin{aligned} \mathbf{a}_P &= \mathbf{a}_{P'} + \mathbf{a}_{P/\mathcal{F}} + \mathbf{a}_c \\ &= \boldsymbol{\Omega} \times (\boldsymbol{\Omega} \times \mathbf{r}) + \boldsymbol{\omega}' \times (\boldsymbol{\omega}' \times \mathbf{r}) + 2\boldsymbol{\Omega} \times (\boldsymbol{\omega}' \times \mathbf{r}) \end{aligned}$$

Since the vectors $\boldsymbol{\omega}'$ and $\mathbf{r}$ are perpendicular, we may write $\boldsymbol{\omega}' \times (\boldsymbol{\omega}' \times \mathbf{r}) = -\omega'^2\mathbf{r}$. We thus have

$$\begin{aligned} \mathbf{a}_P &= \boldsymbol{\Omega} \times (\boldsymbol{\Omega} \times \mathbf{r}) - \omega'^2\mathbf{r} + 2\boldsymbol{\Omega} \times (\boldsymbol{\omega}' \times \mathbf{r}) \\ &= 0.30\mathbf{j} \times [0.30\mathbf{j} \times (34.64\mathbf{i} + 20\mathbf{j})] \\ &\quad - (0.50)^2(34.64\mathbf{i} + 20\mathbf{j}) + 2(0.30\mathbf{j}) \times [0.50\mathbf{k} \times (34.64\mathbf{i} + 20\mathbf{j})] \end{aligned}$$

$$\mathbf{a}_P = -3.12\mathbf{i} - 8.66\mathbf{i} - 5\mathbf{j} + 6\mathbf{k}$$

$$\mathbf{a}_P = -11.78\mathbf{i} - 5\mathbf{j} + 6\mathbf{k} \quad \text{(ft/sec}^2\text{)} \blacktriangleleft$$

Angular Velocity $\boldsymbol{\omega}$ and Angular Acceleration $\boldsymbol{\alpha}$

$$\boldsymbol{\omega} = \boldsymbol{\Omega} + \boldsymbol{\omega}' = 0.30\mathbf{j} + 0.50\mathbf{k} \quad \text{(radian/sec)} \blacktriangleleft$$

$$\boldsymbol{\alpha} = \frac{d\boldsymbol{\omega}}{dt} = \frac{d\boldsymbol{\Omega}}{dt} + \frac{d\boldsymbol{\omega}'}{dt} = 0 + \boldsymbol{\Omega} \times \boldsymbol{\omega}' = 0.30\mathbf{j} \times 0.50\mathbf{k} = 0.15\mathbf{i}$$

$$\boldsymbol{\alpha} = 0.15\mathbf{i} \quad \text{(radian/sec}^2\text{)} \blacktriangleleft$$

PROBLEMS

15.138 and 15.139. Two rotating rods are connected by a slider block P. Knowing that the rod attached at B rotates with a constant counterclockwise angular velocity of 5 radians/sec, determine for the position shown (*a*) the angular velocity of the rod attached at E, (*b*) the relative velocity of the slider block P with respect to the rod on which it slides.

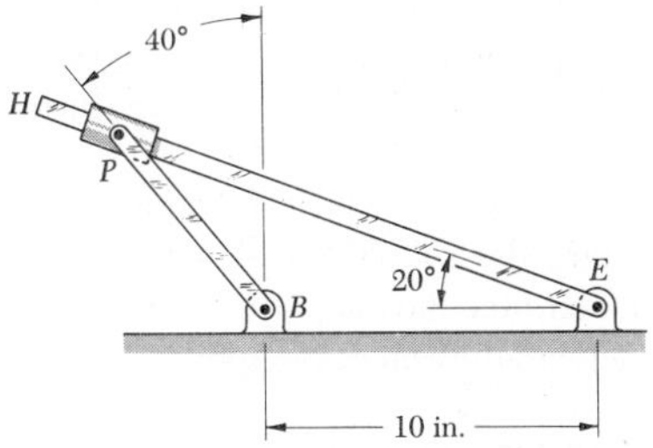

FIG. P 15.138 AND P 15.140

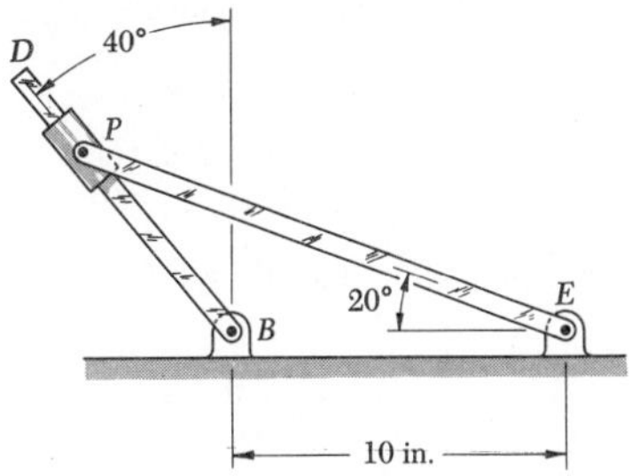

FIG. P 15.139 AND P 15.141

15.140 and 15.141. Two rotating rods are connected by a slider block P. Knowing that the velocity of the slider block relative to the rod on which it slides is 10 in./sec outward, determine the angular velocity of each rod for the position shown.

15.142. Two rods BD and EH pass through smooth holes drilled in a hexagonal block. (The holes are drilled in different planes so that the rods will not hit each other.) Knowing that rod BD rotates counterclockwise at the rate ω, determine the angular velocity of rod EH and the relative velocity of the block with respect to each rod when (*a*) $\theta = 90°$, (*b*) $\theta = 60°$.

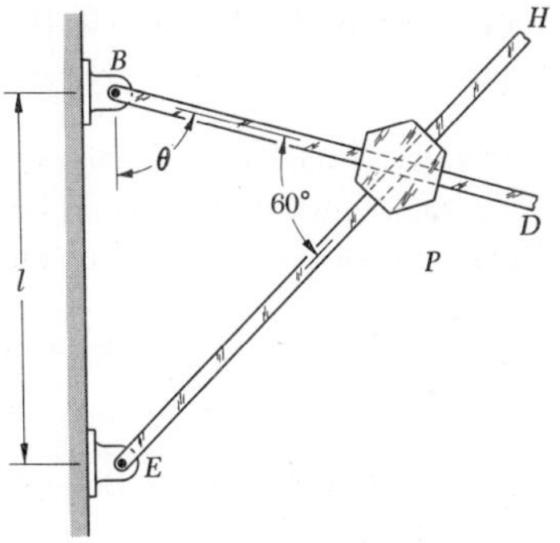

FIG. P 15.142

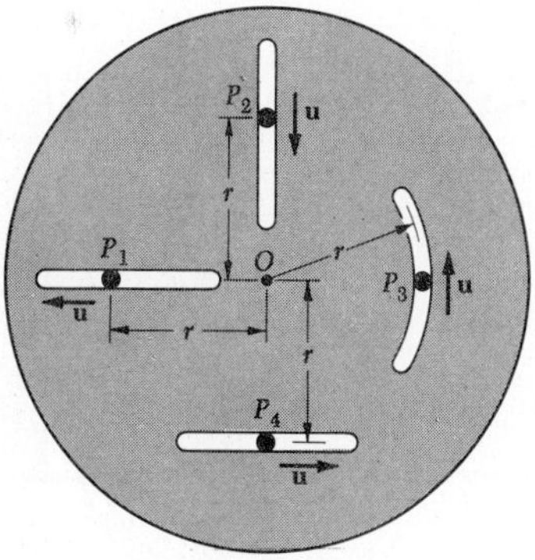

FIG. P 15.143

15.143. Four pins slide in four separate slots cut in a circular plate as shown. When the plate is at rest, each pin has a velocity directed as shown and of the same constant magnitude u. If each pin maintains the same velocity in relation to the plate when the plate rotates about O with a constant *counterclockwise* angular velocity ω, determine the acceleration of each pin.

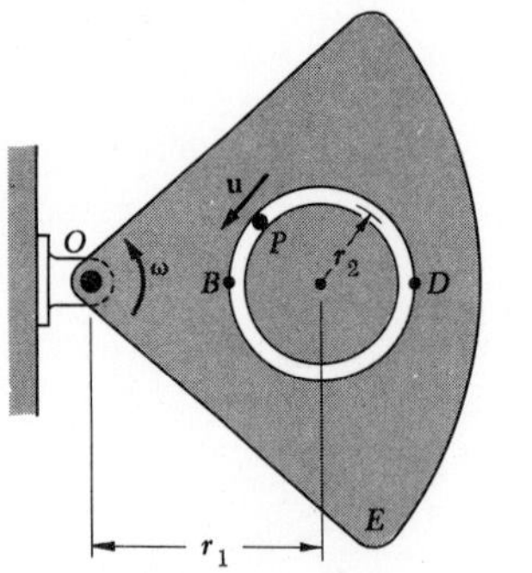

FIG. P 15.145

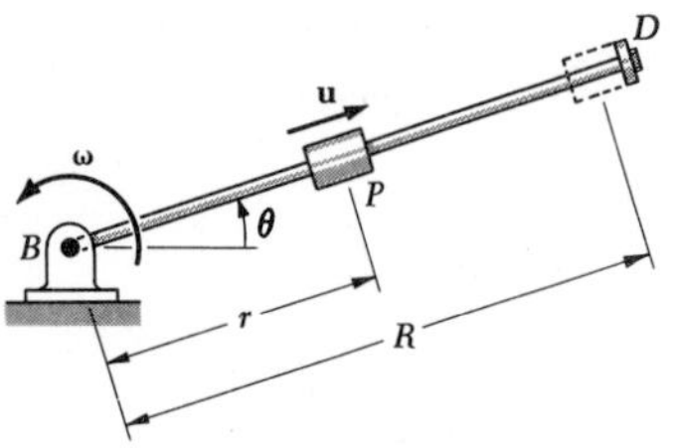

FIG. P 15.146 AND P 15.147

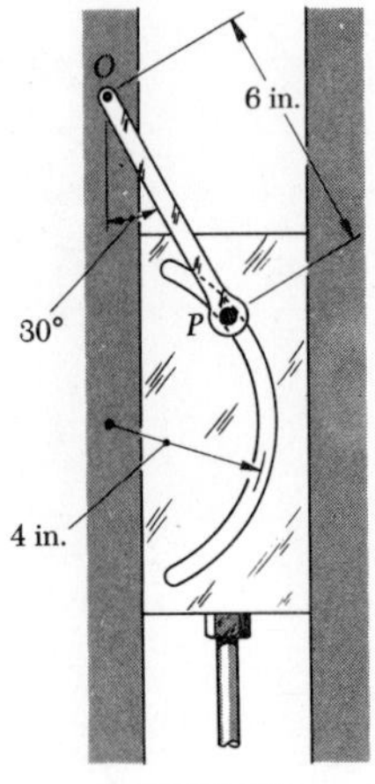

FIG. P 15.150

15.144. Solve Prob. 15.143 assuming that the plate rotates about O with a constant *clockwise* angular velocity ω.

15.145. A pin P slides in a circular slot of radius r_2 which is cut in the plate OE. The velocity of P relative to the plate is of constant magnitude u and is directed as shown. Knowing that the plate rotates counterclockwise with a constant angular velocity ω, derive an expression for (*a*) the magnitude u for which the acceleration of the pin is zero as it passes through point B, (*b*) the corresponding magnitude of the acceleration of the pin as it passes through point D.

15.146. The collar P slides outward at a constant relative speed u along the rod BD, which rotates at the constant angular velocity ω. Determine the magnitude of the acceleration of the collar P just before it reaches the end of the rod.

15.147. The collar P slides outward at a constant relative speed u along the rod BD, which rotates at the constant angular velocity ω. Knowing that $r = 0$ when $\theta = 0$ and that the collar reaches D when $\theta = \pi$, determine the magnitude of the acceleration of the collar P just before it reaches the end of the rod.

15.148. The cage of a mine elevator moves downward with a constant speed of 40 ft/sec. Determine the magnitude and direction of the Coriolis acceleration of the cage if the elevator is located (*a*) at the equator, (*b*) at latitude 40° north, (*c*) at latitude 40° south.

15.149. A rocket sled is tested on a straight track which is built along a meridian. Knowing that the track is located at a latitude of 40° north, determine the Coriolis acceleration of the sled when its speed is 600 mph.

15.150. At the instant shown, the slotted plate slides with a velocity of 10 in./sec upward and has an acceleration of 40 in./sec² downward. Determine the angular velocity and the angular acceleration of rod OP.

15.151. In Prob. 15.139, determine the angular acceleration of the rod attached at E.

15.152. In Prob. 15.138, determine the angular acceleration of the rod attached at E.

15.153. At the instant when $\theta = 90°$ in Prob. 15.142, rod BD has a counterclockwise angular velocity ω and no angular acceleration. Determine at that instant the angular acceleration of rod EH and the total acceleration of the block P.

15.154. Using the method of Sec. 15.13, solve Prob. 15.120.

15.155. Using the method of Sec. 15.13, solve Prob. 15.121.

15.156. Using the method of Sec. 15.13, solve Prob. 15.128.

15.157. One element of a space vehicle consists of a collar B which is made to move along a ring of radius R at a speed u relative to the ring. Knowing that the space vehicle rotates about the y axis at a constant angular velocity ω_1, determine the acceleration of the collar if (*a*) $\theta = 0$, (*b*) $\theta = 90°$.

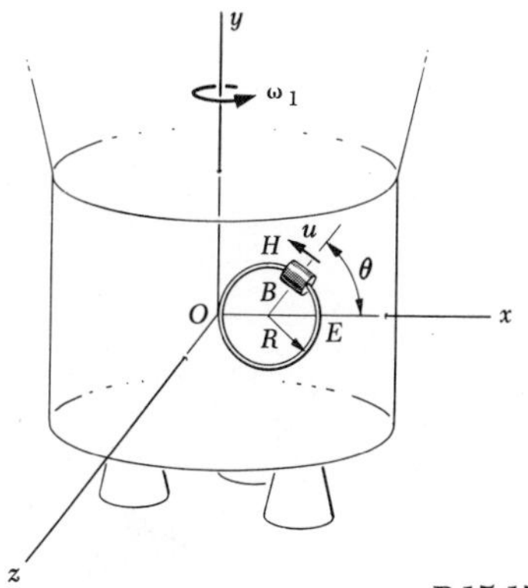

FIG. P 15.157

15.158. Solve Prob. 15.157 for the position $\theta = 30°$.

15.159. The elevator B of an ocean liner moves upward with a speed $\dot{R}$ and an acceleration $\ddot{R}$ while the liner is moving to the left with a constant velocity $\mathbf{v}_0$. Knowing that in the position shown the liner rolls at the rate ω_1 and pitches at the rate ω_3 with no angular acceleration, determine (*a*) the velocity of the elevator, (*b*) the acceleration of the elevator. (Note that frame $Oxyz$ is attached to the liner.)

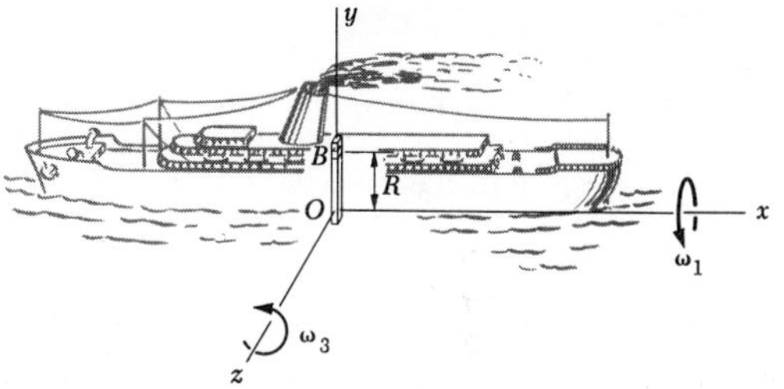

FIG. P 15.159

15.160. Solve Prob. 15.159 assuming $v_0 = 30$ ft/sec, $\omega_1 = 0.05$ radian/sec, $\omega_3 = 0.02$ radian/sec, $R = 50$ ft, $\dot{R} = 4$ ft/sec, and $\ddot{R} = -2$ ft/sec^2.

15.161 through 15.163. Two collars A and B are connected by a 10-in. rod AB as shown. Knowing that collar A moves toward point D with a constant speed of 24 in./sec, determine the velocities and accelerations of collars A and B for the constant rate of rotation indicated.

15.161. $\omega_1 = 20$ radians/sec, $\omega_2 = \omega_3 = 0$.
15.162. $\omega_2 = 20$ radians/sec, $\omega_1 = \omega_3 = 0$.
15.163. $\omega_3 = 20$ radians/sec, $\omega_1 = \omega_2 = 0$.

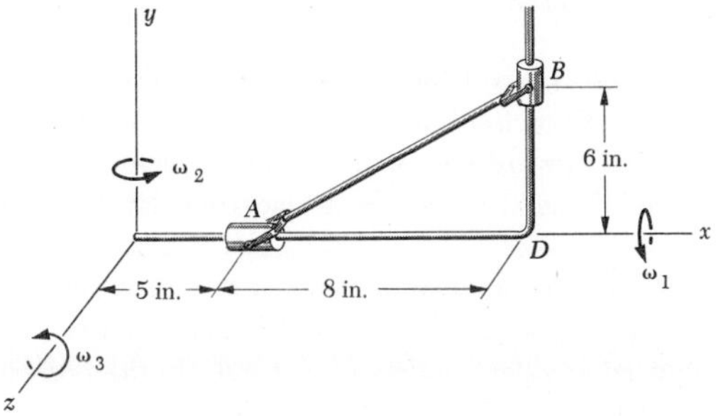

FIG. P 15.161, P 15.162, AND P 15.163

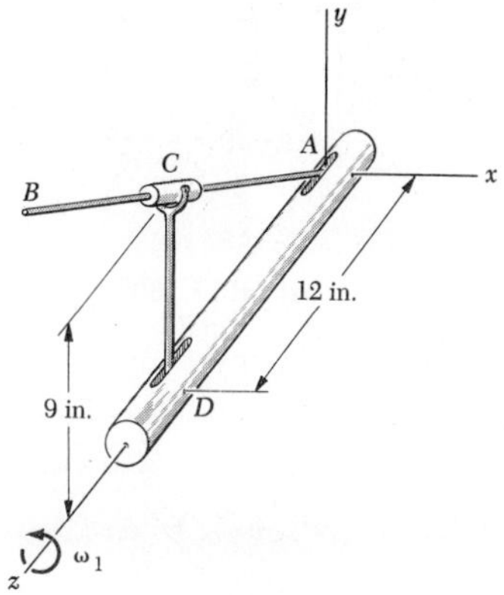

FIG. P 15.164

***15.164.** The entire assembly shown rotates about the z axis at a constant rate $\omega_1 = 3$ radians/sec. Knowing that collar C moves outward along the rod AB at a constant speed of 25 in./sec and that, in the position shown, the rod CD is vertical, determine (*a*) the velocity of collar C, (*b*) the acceleration of collar C.

*15.165. Solve Prob. 15.164 assuming that collar C moves inward along the rod AB at a constant speed of 25 in./sec.

REVIEW PROBLEMS

15.166. For the bevel-gear system shown, determine the required value of β if the ratio of ω_A to ω_B is to be 3.

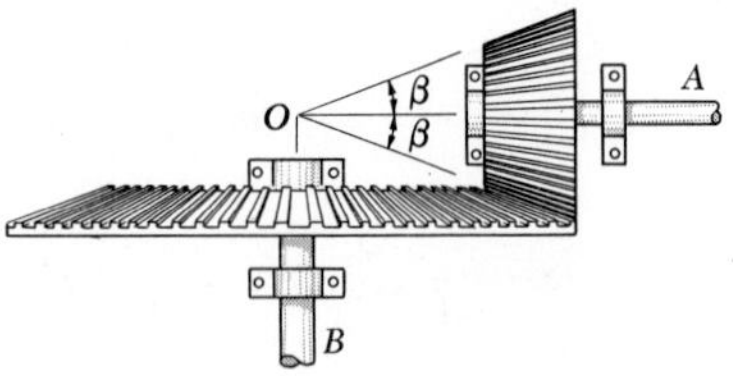

FIG. P 15.166

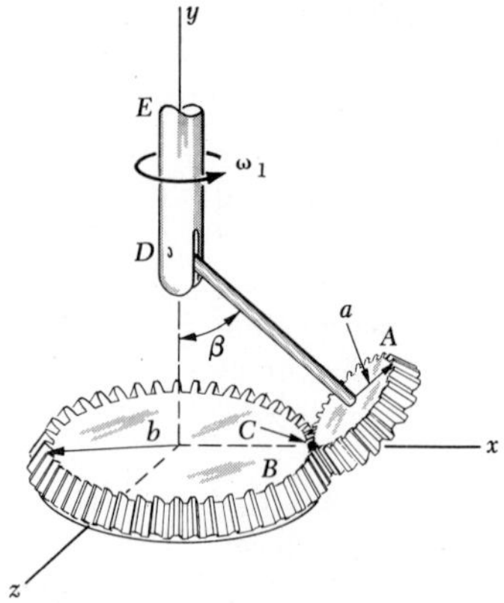

FIG. P 15.167

15.167. Gear A rolls on the fixed gear B and rotates about the axle AD which is rigidly attached at D to the vertical shaft DE. Knowing that shaft DE rotates with a constant angular velocity ω_1, determine (*a*) the rate of spin of gear A about the axle AD, (*b*) the angular acceleration of gear A, (*c*) the acceleration of tooth C of gear A.

15.168. Solve Prob. 15.167 assuming that $\omega_1 = 120$ rpm, $a = 3$ in., $b = 8$ in., and $\beta = 30°$.

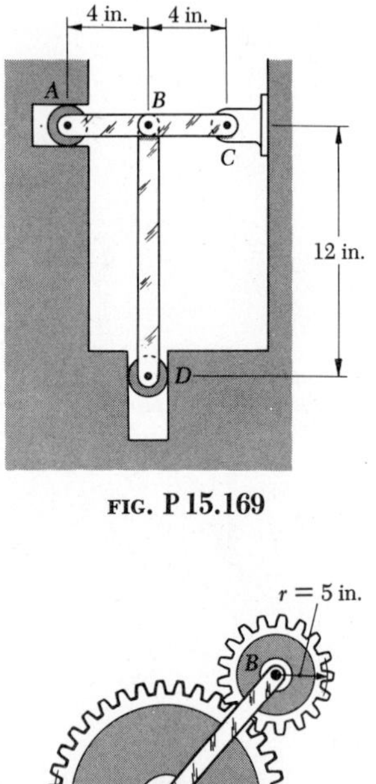

FIG. P 15.169

15.169. Three links AB, BC, and BD are connected by a pin B as shown. Knowing that at the instant shown point D has a velocity of 8 in./sec upward and no acceleration, determine (*a*) the angular acceleration of each link, (*b*) the accelerations of points A and B.

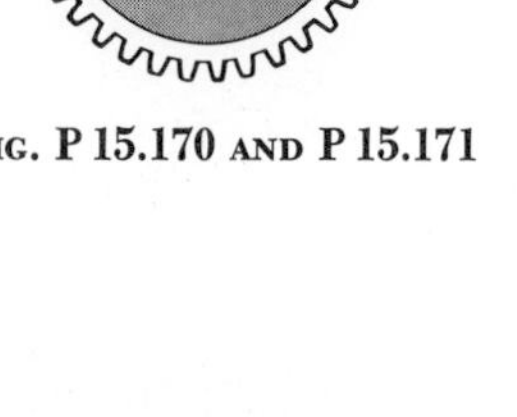

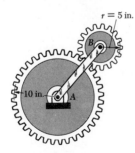

FIG. P 15.170 AND P 15.171

15.170. The angular velocity of gear A is 250 rpm clockwise. If the motion of gear B is to be a curvilinear translation, determine (*a*) the required angular velocity of rod AB, (*b*) the corresponding velocity of gear B.

15.171. Gear A rotates at the constant angular velocity of 120 rpm clockwise while rod AB rotates at the constant angular velocity of 60 rpm counterclockwise. Determine the magnitude of the accelerations of the two gear teeth which are in contact with each other.

15.172. The drive disk shown rotates about O with a constant angular velocity of 300 rpm counterclockwise. Knowing that $r = 3$ in. and $R = 6$ in., determine the velocity of member BCD when (*a*) $\theta = 0$, (*b*) $\theta = 60°$, (*c*) $\theta = 90°$.

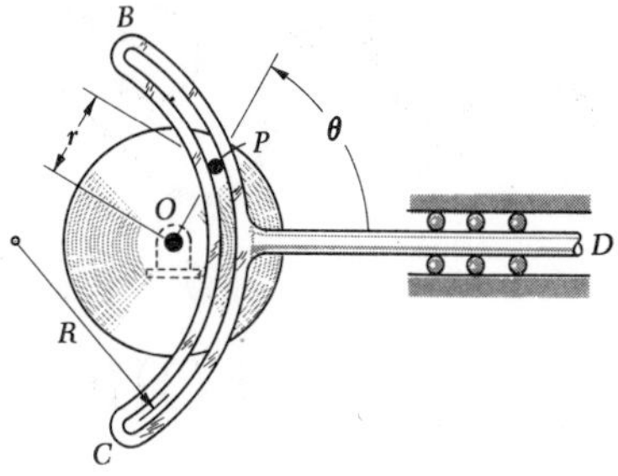

FIG. P 15.172

***15.173.** In Prob. 15.172, determine the acceleration of member BCD when (*a*) $\theta = 0$, (*b*) $\theta = 60°$, (*c*) $\theta = 90°$.

15.174. The angular acceleration of a disk is defined by the relation $\alpha = -4\omega$, where α is expressed in radians/sec^2 and ω in radians/sec. Knowing that at $t = 0$ the angular velocity is 2,000 rpm, determine (*a*) the number of revolutions executed by the disk before coming to rest, (*b*) the time required for the disk to come to rest, (*c*) the time required for the angular velocity of the disk to be reduced to 20 rpm.

15.175. A slender rod AB is attached to a collar at B and rests on a smooth circular cylinder of radius r. Knowing that the collar B moves upward with a constant velocity of magnitude v, derive an expression in terms of r, θ, and v (*a*) for the angular velocity of the rod, (*b*) for the angular acceleration of the rod.

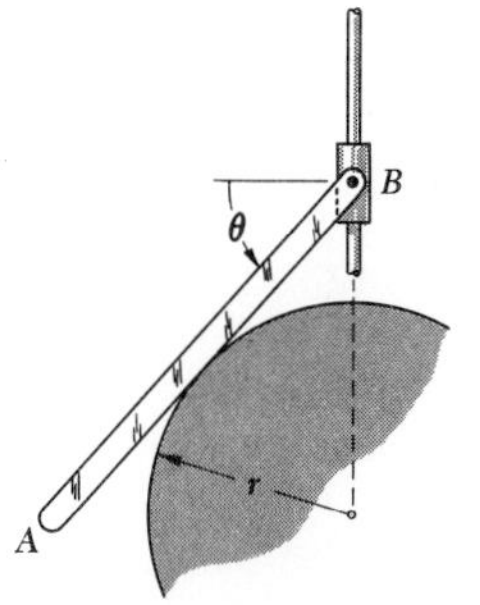

FIG. P 15.175

15.176. A straight rack rests on a gear of radius r and is attached to a block B as shown. Knowing that block B slides to the right at a constant speed v, derive an expression for the angular velocity of the rack in terms of r, θ, and v.

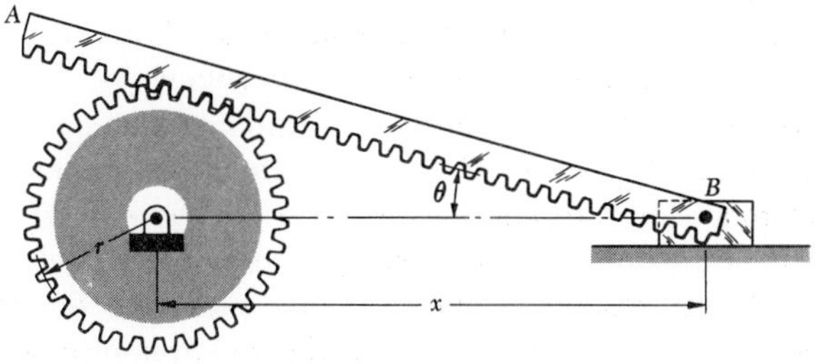

FIG. P 15.176

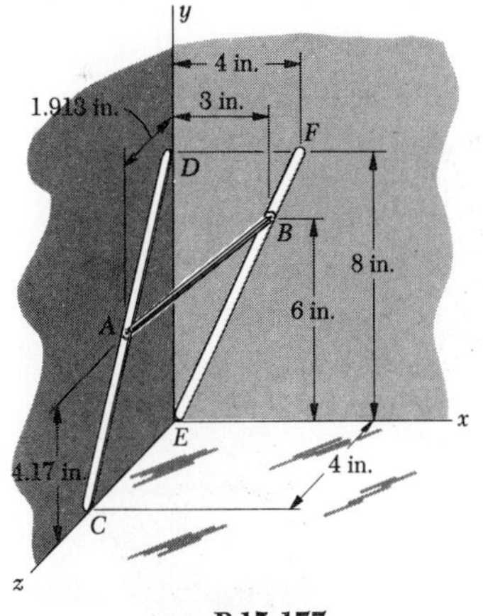

FIG. P 15.177

15.177. Rod AB is of length 4 in. and is guided by pins sliding in the slots CD and EF, which lie in the yz and xy planes, respectively. Knowing that in the position shown end A moves downward along slot CD with a speed of 10 in./sec, determine the velocity of end B of the rod.

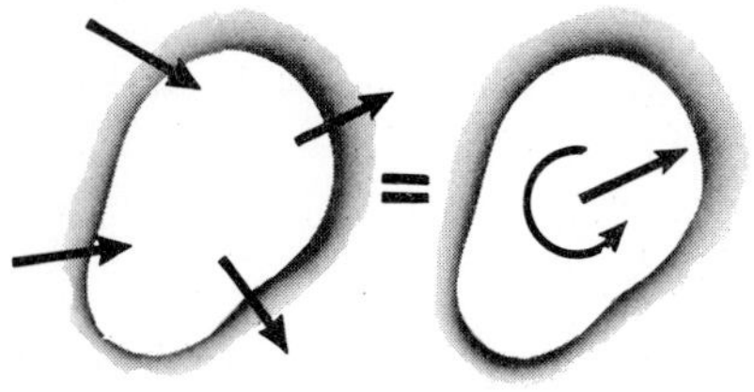

16. PLANE MOTION OF RIGID BODIES: FORCES AND ACCELERATIONS

16.1. Introduction. In this chapter and in Chaps. 17 and 18, we shall study the *kinetics of rigid bodies,* i.e., the relations existing between the forces acting on a rigid body, the shape and mass of the body, and the motion produced. In Chaps. 12 to 14, we studied similar relations, assuming then that the body could be considered as a particle, i.e., that its mass could be concentrated in one point and that all forces acted at that point. We shall now take the shape of the body into account, as well as the exact location of the points of application of the forces. Besides, we shall be concerned not only with the motion of the body as a whole but also with the motion of the body about its mass center.

In this chapter, our study will be based directly on the equation $\mathbf{F} = m\mathbf{a}$ and will be limited in two ways: (1) It will be restricted to the *plane motion* of rigid bodies, i.e., to a motion in which each particle of the body remains at a constant distance from a fixed reference plane. (2) The rigid bodies considered will consist only of plane slabs and of bodies which are symmetrical with respect to the reference plane.† The study of the plane motion of nonsymmetrical three-dimensional bodies and, more generally, the motion of rigid bodies in three-dimensional space will be postponed until Chap. 18.

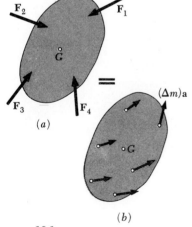

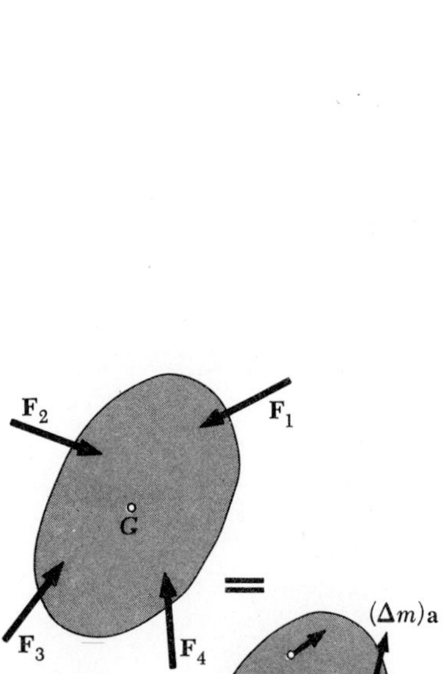

FIG. 16.1

16.2. Plane Motion of a Rigid Body. Consider a rigid slab of mass m in plane motion under the action of several forces $\mathbf{F}_1$, $\mathbf{F}_2$, $\mathbf{F}_3$, etc. According to D'Alembert's principle (Sec. 12.4), the external forces acting on the slab must be equivalent to the effective forces of the various particles forming the slab (Fig. 16.1). We recall that the *effective force* of a particle is

† Or, more generally, bodies which have a principal centroidal axis of inertia perpendicular to the reference plane.

defined as the product $(\Delta m)\mathbf{a}$ of its mass Δm and of its acceleration $\mathbf{a}$.

A more useful formulation of D'Alembert's principle for the plane motion of a rigid slab will be obtained if we reduce the system of the effective forces to an equivalent vector-and-couple system attached at the mass center G of the slab. The vector will be obtained by adding the effective forces of the various particles of the slab, and the moment of the couple by adding their moments about G.

We know from Sec. 15.8 that, if we choose the mass center G as a reference point, the acceleration $\mathbf{a}$ of a particle P of the slab may be expressed as the sum of the acceleration $\bar{\mathbf{a}}$ of G and of the acceleration $\mathbf{a}'$ of P relative to a frame attached to G and of fixed orientation. Denoting by $\mathbf{r}'$ the position vector of P relative to G, and recalling the relations (15.22), we write

$$\begin{aligned}\mathbf{a} &= \bar{\mathbf{a}} + \mathbf{a}' \\ &= \bar{\mathbf{a}} + \mathbf{a}'_t + \mathbf{a}'_n \\ &= \bar{\mathbf{a}} + \boldsymbol{\alpha} \times \mathbf{r}' - \omega^2\mathbf{r}'\end{aligned}$$

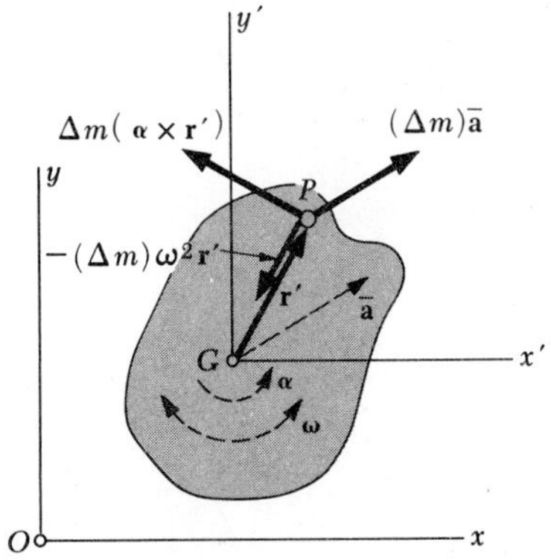

FIG. 16.2

where α and ω denote, respectively, the angular acceleration and the angular velocity of the slab at the instant considered. The effective force of the particle P may thus be resolved into the three vectors shown in Fig. 16.2. We have

$$(\Delta m)\mathbf{a} = (\Delta m)\bar{\mathbf{a}} + \Delta m(\boldsymbol{\alpha} \times \mathbf{r}') - (\Delta m)\omega^2\mathbf{r}' \qquad (16.1)$$

The sum of the effective forces of the various particles of the slab is

$$\begin{aligned}\Sigma\mathbf{a}\Delta m &= \Sigma\bar{\mathbf{a}}\Delta m + \Sigma(\boldsymbol{\alpha} \times \mathbf{r}')\Delta m - \Sigma\omega^2\mathbf{r}'\Delta m \\ &= \bar{\mathbf{a}}\Sigma\Delta m + \boldsymbol{\alpha} \times \Sigma\mathbf{r}'\Delta m - \omega^2\Sigma\mathbf{r}'\Delta m\end{aligned}$$

since $\bar{\mathbf{a}}$, $\boldsymbol{\alpha}$, and ω are independent of the particle considered. But the sum $\Sigma\Delta m$ is equal to the mass m of the slab, and, by (12.5), the sum $\Sigma\mathbf{r}'\Delta m$ is equal to $m\bar{\mathbf{r}}'$ and, thus, to zero, since the position vector $\bar{\mathbf{r}}'$ of G relative to itself is clearly zero. Therefore, the sum of the effective forces reduces to

$$\Sigma\mathbf{a}\Delta m = m\bar{\mathbf{a}} \qquad (16.2)$$

We note that Eq. (16.2) expresses the same result as Eq. (12.7), which was derived in the general case of the motion of a system of particles (Sec 12.5).

The sum of the moments about G of the effective forces of the slab is, by (16.1),

$$\begin{aligned}\Sigma(\mathbf{r}' \times \mathbf{a}\Delta m) &= \Sigma(\mathbf{r}' \times \bar{\mathbf{a}}\Delta m) + \Sigma[\mathbf{r}' \times (\boldsymbol{\alpha} \times \mathbf{r}')\Delta m] \\ &\qquad - \Sigma(\mathbf{r}' \times \omega^2\mathbf{r}'\Delta m) \\ &= (\Sigma\mathbf{r}'\Delta m) \times \bar{\mathbf{a}} + \Sigma[\mathbf{r}' \times (\boldsymbol{\alpha} \times \mathbf{r}')\Delta m] \\ &\qquad - \omega^2\Sigma(\mathbf{r}' \times \mathbf{r}')\Delta m\end{aligned}$$

As noted above, the sum $\Sigma\mathbf{r}'\Delta m$ is zero. Since each of the products $\mathbf{r}' \times \mathbf{r}'$ is also zero, the expression obtained reduces to its second term. Referring to Fig. 16.2, we easily verify that this term represents a vector of the same direction as $\boldsymbol{\alpha}$ (i.e., perpendicular to the slab) and of magnitude equal to $\alpha\Sigma r'^2\Delta m$. Recalling that the sum $\Sigma r'^2\Delta m$ represents the moment of inertia $\bar{I}$ of the slab about a centroidal axis perpendicular to the slab (Sec. 9.10), we find that the sum of the moments about G of the effective forces is

$$\Sigma(\mathbf{r}' \times \mathbf{a}\Delta m) = \bar{I}\boldsymbol{\alpha} \qquad (16.3)$$

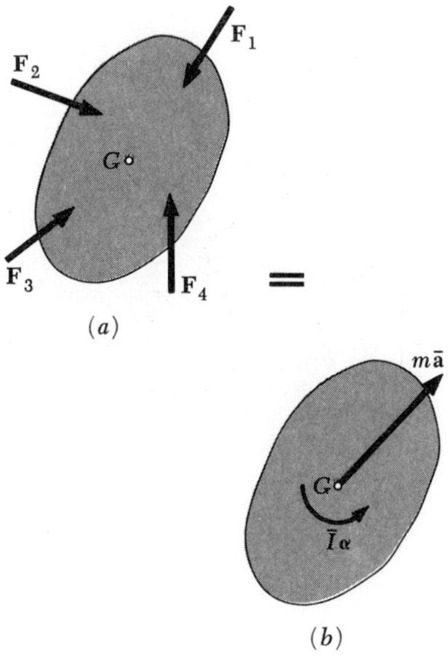

FIG. 16.3

Equations (16.2) and (16.3) show that the effective forces of the various particles of the slab reduce to a vector $m\bar{\mathbf{a}}$ attached at G and to a couple of moment $\bar{I}\boldsymbol{\alpha}$. Substituting this vector-and-couple system for the effective forces in Fig. 16.1, we obtain Fig. 16.3 and thus conclude that *the system of the external forces is equivalent to the vector $m\bar{\mathbf{a}}$ attached at G and to the couple $\bar{I}\boldsymbol{\alpha}$.* We note that, while our derivation was given for a slab, the results obtained are still valid in the case of a rigid body symmetrical with respect to the reference plane. These results do not hold, however, in the case of a three-dimensional nonsymmetrical body. In that case, the methods of Chap. 18 should be applied.

The relation shown in Fig. 16.3 may be expressed algebraically by writing three equations relating respectively the x and y components and the moments about any given point A of the forces and vectors in Fig. 16.3. If the moments are computed about the mass center G of the rigid body, these equations of motion read

$$\Sigma F_x = m\bar{a}_x \qquad \Sigma F_y = m\bar{a}_y \qquad \Sigma M_G = \bar{I}\alpha \qquad (16.4)$$

Translation. When a rigid body is constrained to move in translation, its angular acceleration is identically equal to zero and its effective forces reduce to the vector $m\bar{\mathbf{a}}$ attached at G (Fig. 16.4). Thus, the resultant of the external forces acting on a rigid body in translation passes through the mass center of the body and is equal to $m\bar{\mathbf{a}}$.

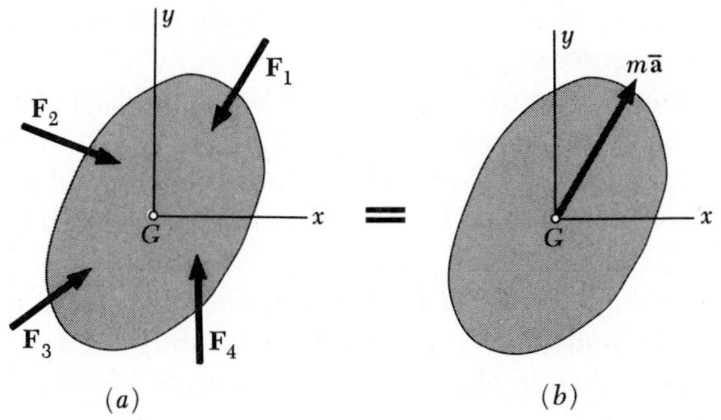

FIG. 16.4

Centroidal Rotation. When a slab, or, more generally, a body symmetrical with respect to the reference plane, is constrained to rotate about a fixed axis perpendicular to the reference plane and passing through its mass center G, we say that the body is in *centroidal rotation.* Since the acceleration $\bar{\mathbf{a}}$ is identically equal to zero, the effective forces of the body reduce to the couple $\bar{I}\alpha$ (Fig. 16.5). Thus, the external forces acting on a body in centroidal rotation are equivalent to a couple of moment $\bar{I}\alpha$.

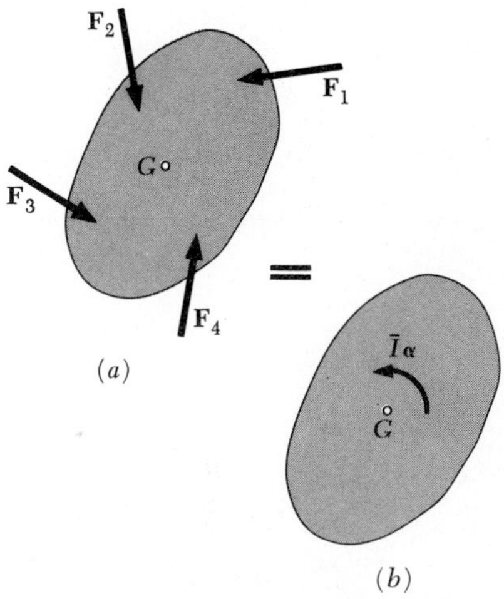

FIG. 16.5

General Plane Motion. Comparing Fig. 16.3 with Figs. 16.4 and 16.5, we observe that, from the point of view of *kinetics,* the most general plane motion of a rigid body symmetrical with respect to the reference plane may be replaced by the sum of a translation and a centroidal rotation. We should note that this statement is more restrictive than the similar statement made earlier from the point of view of *kinematics* (Sec. 15.5), since we now require that the mass center of the body be selected as the reference point.

Referring to Eqs. (16.4), we observe that the first two equations are identical with the equations of motion of a particle of mass m acted upon by the given forces $\mathbf{F}_1$, $\mathbf{F}_2$, $\mathbf{F}_3$, etc. We thus check that *the mass center G of a rigid body in plane motion moves as if the entire mass of the body were concentrated at that point, and as if all the external forces acted on it.* We recall that this result has already been obtained in Sec. 12.5 in the general case of a system of particles, the particles being not necessarily rigidly connected. We also note, as we did in Sec. 12.5, that the system of the external forces does not, in general, reduce to a single vector $m\bar{\mathbf{a}}$ attached at G. Therefore, in the general case of the plane motion of a rigid body, *the resultant of the external forces acting on the body does not pass through the mass center of the body.*

Finally, we may observe that the last of Eqs. (16.4) would still be valid if the rigid body, while subjected to the same applied forces, were constrained to rotate about a fixed axis through G. Thus, *a rigid body in plane motion rotates about its mass center as if this point were fixed.*

16.3. Solution of Problems Involving the Plane Motion of a Rigid Body. We saw in the preceding section that, when a rigid body is in plane motion, there exists a fundamental relation between the forces $\mathbf{F}_1$, $\mathbf{F}_2$, $\mathbf{F}_3$, etc., acting on the body, the acceleration $\bar{\mathbf{a}}$ of its mass center, and the angular acceleration $\boldsymbol{\alpha}$ of the body. This relation, which is represented in Fig. 16.3, may be used to determine the acceleration $\bar{\mathbf{a}}$ and the angular acceleration $\boldsymbol{\alpha}$ produced by a given system of forces acting on a rigid body or, conversely, to determine the forces which produce a given motion of the rigid body.

While the three algebraic equations (16.4) may be used to solve problems of plane motion,† our experience in statics suggests that the solution of many problems involving rigid bodies could be simplified by an appropriate choice of the point about which the moments of the forces are computed. It is therefore preferable to remember the relation existing between the forces and the accelerations in the vectorial form shown in Fig. 16.3, and to derive from this fundamental relation the components or moments equations which fit best the solution of the problem under consideration.

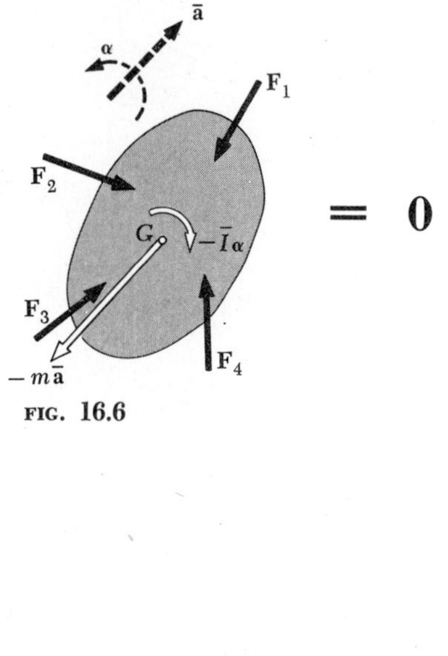

FIG. 16.6

The fundamental relation shown in Fig. 16.3 may be presented in an alternate form if we add to the external forces an inertia vector $-m\bar{\mathbf{a}}$ of sense opposite to that of $\bar{\mathbf{a}}$, attached at G, and an inertia couple $-\bar{I}\alpha$ of moment equal in magnitude to $\bar{I}\alpha$ and of sense opposite to that of $\boldsymbol{\alpha}$ (Fig. 16.6). The system obtained is equivalent to zero, and the rigid body is said to be in dynamic equilibrium.

Whether the principle of equivalence of external and effective forces is directly applied, as in Fig. 16.3, or whether the concept of dynamic equilibrium is introduced, as in Fig. 16.6, the use of free-body diagrams showing vectorially the relationship existing between the forces applied on the rigid body and the resulting linear and angular accelerations presents consider-

† We recall that the last of Eqs. (16.4) is valid only in the case of the plane motion of a rigid body symmetrical with respect to the reference plane. In all other cases, the methods of Chap. 18 should be used.

able advantages over the blind application of the formulas (16.4). These advantages may be summarized as follows:

1. First of all, a much clearer understanding of the effect of the forces on the motion of the body will result from the use of a pictorial representation.

2. This approach makes it possible to divide the solution of a dynamics problem into two parts: In the first part, the analysis of the kinematic and kinetic characteristics of the problem leads to the free-body diagrams of Fig. 16.3 or 16.6; in the second part, the diagram obtained is used to analyze by the methods of Chap. 3 the various forces and vectors involved.

3. A unified approach is provided for the analysis of the plane motion of a rigid body, regardless of the particular type of motion involved. While the kinematics of the various motions considered may vary from one case to the other, the approach to the kinetics of the motion is consistently the same. In every case we shall draw a diagram showing the external forces, the vector $m\bar{a}$ associated with the motion of G, and the couple $\bar{I}\alpha$ associated with the rotation of the body about G.

4. The resolution of the plane motion of a rigid body into a translation and a centroidal rotation, which is used here, is a basic concept which may be applied effectively throughout the study of mechanics. We shall use it again with the method of work and energy and the method of impulse and momentum (Chap. 17).

16.4. Systems of Rigid Bodies. The method described in the preceding section may also be used in problems involving the plane motion of several connected rigid bodies. A diagram similar to Fig. 16.3 or Fig. 16.6 may be drawn for each part of the system. The equations of motion obtained from these diagrams are solved simultaneously.

In some cases, as in Sample Prob. 16.4, a single diagram may be drawn for the entire system. This diagram should include all the external forces, as well as the vectors $m\bar{a}$ and the couples $\bar{I}\alpha$ associated with the various parts of the system. However, internal forces, such as the forces exerted by connecting cables, may be omitted, and the equations obtained will be more readily solved for the remaining unknowns.

This second approach may not be used in problems involving more than three unknowns, since only three equations of motion are available when a single diagram is used. We shall not elaborate upon this point, since the discussion involved would be completely similar to that given in Sec. 6.12 in the case of the equilibrium of a system of rigid bodies.

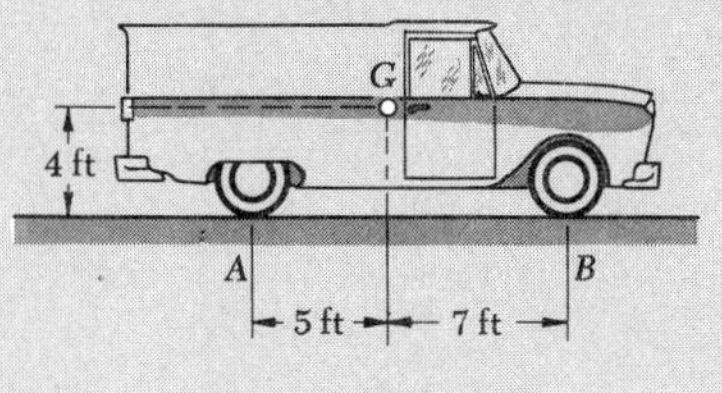

SAMPLE PROBLEM 16.1

When the forward speed of the truck shown was 30 ft/sec, the brakes were suddenly applied, causing all four wheels to stop rotating. It was observed that the truck skidded to rest in 20 ft. Determine the magnitudes of the normal reactions and of the friction forces at each wheel as the truck skidded to rest.

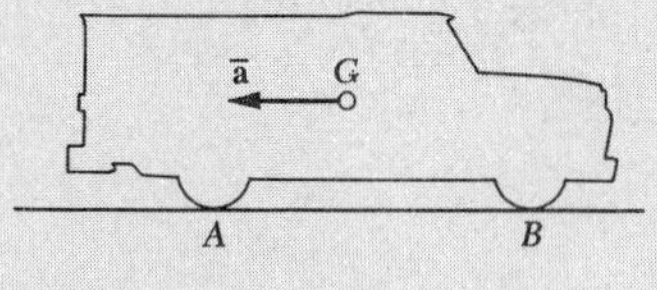

Kinematics of Motion. Choosing the positive sense to the right and using the equations of uniformly accelerated motion, we write

$$\bar{v}_0 = +30\text{ ft/sec} \qquad \bar{v}^2 = \bar{v}_0^2 + 2\bar{a}\bar{s} \qquad 0 = (30)^2 + 2\bar{a}(20)$$

$$\bar{a} = -22.5\text{ ft/sec}^2 \qquad \bar{\mathbf{a}} = 22.5\text{ ft/sec}^2 \leftarrow$$

Dynamic Equilibrium. The truck is in dynamic equilibrium under the action of its weight **W**, the normal reactions and friction forces at the wheels, and the inertia vector $-m\bar{\mathbf{a}}$ directed opposite to $\bar{\mathbf{a}}$ (i.e., directed to the right). The forces $\mathbf{N}_A$ and $\mathbf{F}_A$ represent the sum of the reactions at the rear wheels, while $\mathbf{N}_B$ and $\mathbf{F}_B$ represent the sum of the reactions at the front wheels.

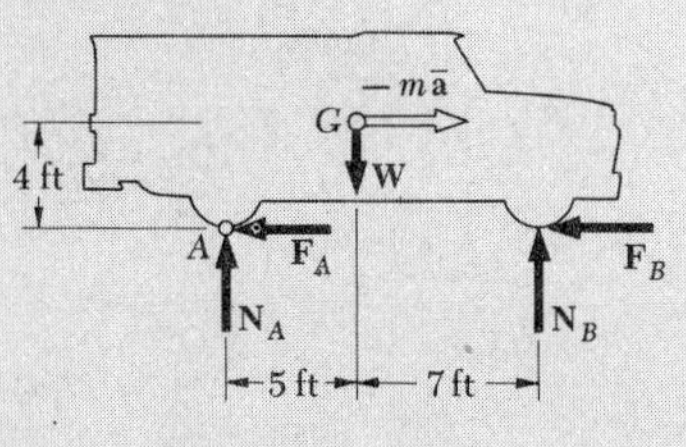

$$+\uparrow \Sigma F_y = 0: \qquad N_A + N_B - W = 0$$

Since $F_A = \mu N_A$ and $F_B = \mu N_B$, we find

$$F_A + F_B = \mu(N_A + N_B) = \mu W$$

Noting that the x component of the inertia vector $-m\bar{\mathbf{a}}$ is $+m\bar{a}$, we write

$$\overset{+}{\rightarrow} \Sigma F_x = 0: \qquad -(F_A + F_B) + m\bar{a} = 0$$

$$-\mu W + \frac{W}{g}(22.5) = 0 \qquad \mu = 0.699$$

$$+\circlearrowleft \Sigma M_A = 0: \qquad -W(5\text{ ft}) - m\bar{a}(4\text{ ft}) + N_B(12\text{ ft}) = 0$$

$$-5W - \frac{W}{g}(22.5)(4) + 12N_B = 0$$

$$N_B = 0.650W$$

$$F_B = \mu N_B = (0.699)(0.650W) \qquad F_B = 0.454W$$

$$+\uparrow \Sigma F_y = 0: \qquad N_A + N_B - W = 0$$

$$N_A + 0.650W - W = 0$$

$$N_A = 0.350W$$

$$F_A = \mu N_A = (0.699)(0.350W) \qquad F_A = 0.245W$$

Reactions at Each Wheel. Recalling that the values computed above represent the sum of the reactions at the two front wheels or the two rear wheels, we obtain the magnitudes of the reactions at each wheel by writing

$$N_{\text{front}} = \tfrac{1}{2}N_B = 0.325W \qquad N_{\text{rear}} = \tfrac{1}{2}N_A = 0.175W \blacktriangleleft$$

$$F_{\text{front}} = \tfrac{1}{2}F_B = 0.227W \qquad F_{\text{rear}} = \tfrac{1}{2}F_A = 0.122W \blacktriangleleft$$

SAMPLE PROBLEM 16.2

A 10-ft rod AB weighs 50 lb and is held in position by three inextensible wires AC, AD, and BE. Wire AC is then cut. Determine (*a*) the acceleration of the rod, (*b*) the tensions in wires AD and BE immediately after wire AC has been cut.

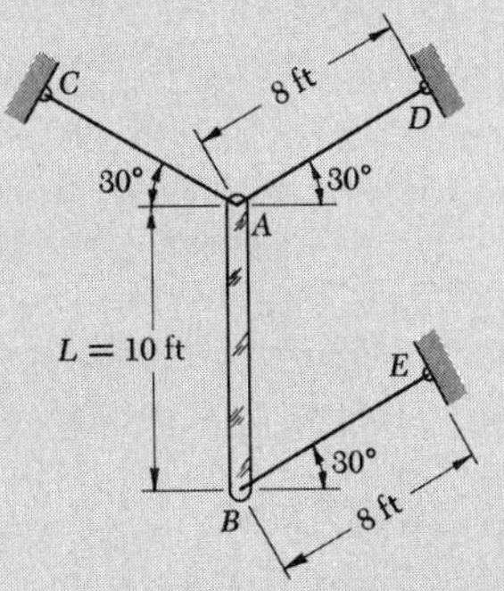

Motion of Rod. After wire AC is cut, we observe that ends A and B move along parallel circles of radius 8 ft centered, respectively, at D and E. The motion of the rod is thus a curvilinear translation; each particle of the rod moves along parallel circles of 8 ft radius.

At the instant wire AC is cut, the velocity of the rod is zero; the acceleration $\bar{\mathbf{a}}$ of the mass center G is thus tangent to the circular path of G.

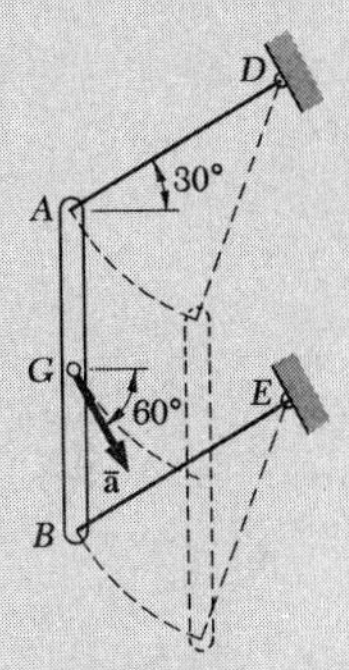

Equations of Motion. The weight $\mathbf{W}$ and the forces $\mathbf{T}_A$ and $\mathbf{T}_B$ are assumed to act on the rod as shown. Since the acceleration $\bar{\mathbf{a}}$ of the mass center of the rod must be directed along the t axis, we note that the system of forces $\mathbf{W}$, $\mathbf{T}_A$, and $\mathbf{T}_B$ must be equivalent to a vector $m\bar{\mathbf{a}}$ directed along the t axis. We write

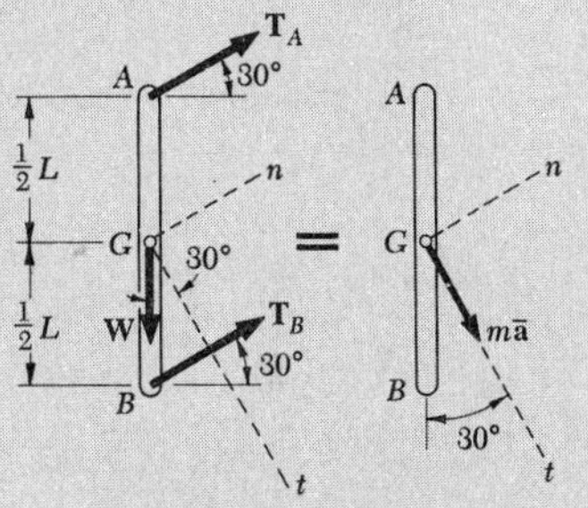

$+\searrow \Sigma F_t = m\bar{a}$: $\quad W \cos 30° = \dfrac{W}{g}\bar{a}$

$$\bar{a} = g \cos 30° = 27.9 \text{ ft/sec}^2$$

$$\bar{\mathbf{a}} = 27.9 \text{ ft/sec}^2 \;\searrow\; 60°$$

$+\circlearrowleft \Sigma M_G = 0$: $\quad -(T_A \cos 30°)\frac{1}{2}L + (T_B \cos 30°)\frac{1}{2}L = 0$

$$T_A = T_B$$

$+\nearrow \Sigma F_n = 0$: $\quad T_A + T_B - W \sin 30° = 0$

Since $T_A = T_B$, we have

$$T_A + T_A - W \sin 30° = 0$$

$$T_A = +\tfrac{1}{2}W \sin 30° = +\tfrac{1}{4}W$$

$$T_B = +\tfrac{1}{4}W$$

Recalling that $W = 50$ lb, we have

$$T_A = 12.5 \text{ lb} \qquad T_B = 12.5 \text{ lb} \quad ◄$$

SAMPLE PROBLEM 16.3

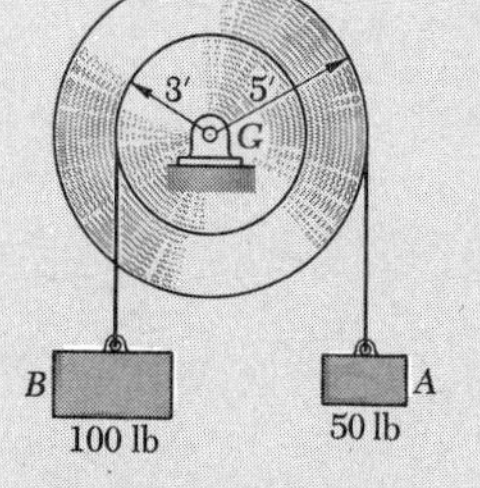

A pulley weighing 120 lb and with a radius of gyration of 4 ft is connected to two blocks as shown. Assuming no axle friction, determine the angular acceleration of the pulley.

Sense of Motion. Although an arbitrary sense of motion may be assumed (since no friction forces are involved) and later checked by the sign of the answer, we may prefer first to determine the actual sense of rotation of the pulley. We first find the weight of block B required to maintain the equilibrium of the pulley when it is acted upon by the 50-lb block A. We write

$$+\circlearrowleft \Sigma M_G = 0: \qquad W_B(3\text{ ft}) - (50\text{ lb})(5\text{ ft}) = 0 \qquad W_B = 83.3\text{ lb}$$

Since block B actually weighs 100 lb, the pulley will rotate counterclockwise.

Kinematics of Motion. Assuming α counterclockwise and noting that $a_A = r_A\alpha$ and $a_B = r_B\alpha$, we obtain

$$\mathbf{a}_A = 5\alpha \uparrow \qquad \mathbf{a}_B = 3\alpha \downarrow$$

Equations of Motion. A single system consisting of the pulley and the two blocks is considered. Forces external to this system consist of the weights of the pulley and the two blocks and of the reaction at G. (The forces exerted by the cables on the pulley and on the blocks are internal to the system considered.) Since the motion of the pulley is a centroidal rotation and the motion of each block is a translation, the effective forces reduce to the couple $\bar{I}\alpha$ and the two vectors $m\mathbf{a}_A$ and $m\mathbf{a}_B$. The centroidal moment of inertia of the pulley is

$$\bar{I} = mk^2 = \frac{120}{32.2}(4)^2 = 59.6\text{ lb-ft-sec}^2$$

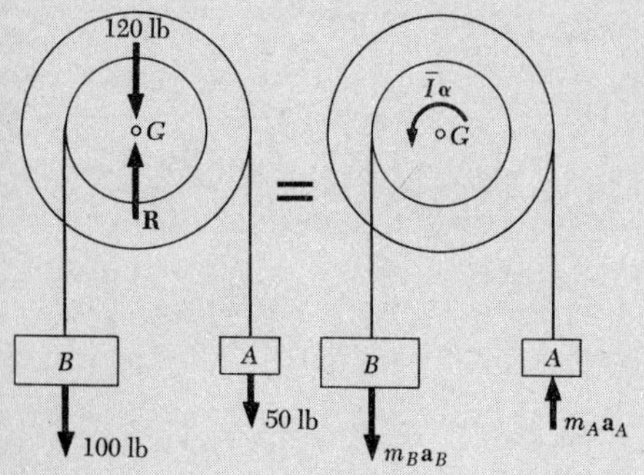

Since the system of the external forces is equivalent to the system of the effective forces, we write

$$+\circlearrowleft \Sigma M_G = \Sigma(M_G)_{\text{eff}}:$$

$$(100\text{ lb})(3\text{ ft}) - (50\text{ lb})(5\text{ ft}) = +\bar{I}\alpha + m_B a_B(3\text{ ft}) + m_A a_A(5\text{ ft})$$

$$(100)(3) - (50)(5) = +59.6\alpha + \frac{100}{g}(3\alpha)(3) + \frac{50}{g}(5\alpha)(5)$$

$$\alpha = +0.396\text{ radian/sec}^2 \qquad \alpha = 0.396\text{ radian/sec}^2 \circlearrowleft \blacktriangleleft$$

SAMPLE PROBLEM 16.4

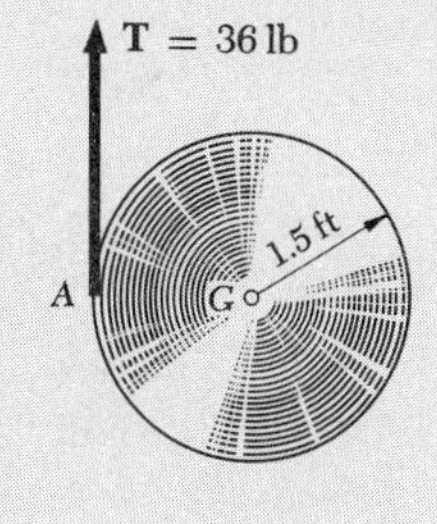

A cord is wrapped around a homogeneous disk of radius $r = 1.50$ ft and weight $W = 30$ lb. If the cord is pulled upward with a force **T** of magnitude 36 lb, determine (*a*) the acceleration of the center of the disk, (*b*) the angular acceleration of the disk, (*c*) the acceleration of the cord.

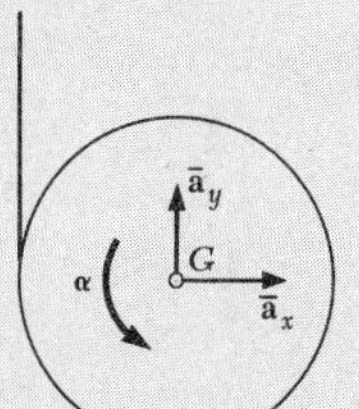

Solution. We assume that the components $\bar{\mathbf{a}}_x$ and $\bar{\mathbf{a}}_y$ of the acceleration of the center are directed, respectively, to the right and upward and that the angular acceleration of the disk is counterclockwise. The system of external forces acting on the disk consists of the weight **W** and the force **T** exerted by the cord. This system is equivalent to a vector of components $m\bar{\mathbf{a}}_x$ and $m\bar{\mathbf{a}}_y$ attached at G and a couple $\bar{I}\alpha$.

The mass and centroidal moment of inertia of the disk may be written as follows:

$$m = \frac{W}{g} \qquad \bar{I} = \tfrac{1}{2}mr^2 = \frac{1}{2}\frac{W}{g}r^2$$

Equations of Motion

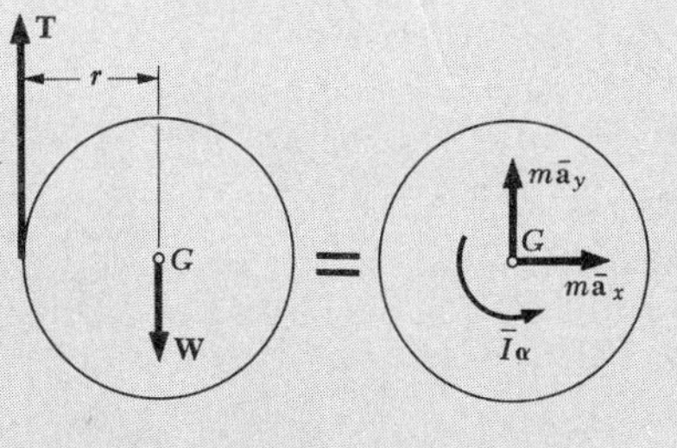

$\xrightarrow{+} \Sigma F_x = m\bar{a}_x$: $\qquad 0 = m\bar{a}_x \qquad\qquad \bar{\mathbf{a}}_x = 0$ ◄

$+\uparrow \Sigma F_y = m\bar{a}_y$: $\qquad T - W = m\bar{a}_y$

$$T - W = \frac{W}{g}\bar{a}_y$$

$$\bar{a}_y = \frac{T - W}{W}g$$

Since $T = 36$ lb and $W = 30$ lb, we have

$$\bar{a}_y = \frac{36 - 30}{30}g = +6.44 \text{ ft/sec}^2 \qquad \bar{\mathbf{a}}_y = 6.44 \text{ ft/sec}^2 \uparrow$$ ◄

$+\circlearrowleft \Sigma M_G = \bar{I}\alpha$: $\qquad -T(r) = \bar{I}\alpha$

$$-T(r) = \frac{1}{2}\frac{W}{g}r^2\alpha$$

$$\alpha = -\frac{2T}{W}\frac{g}{r} = -\frac{2(36)}{30}\frac{g}{1.5} = -51.5 \text{ radians/sec}^2$$

$$\alpha = 51.5 \text{ radians/sec}^2 \circlearrowright$$ ◄

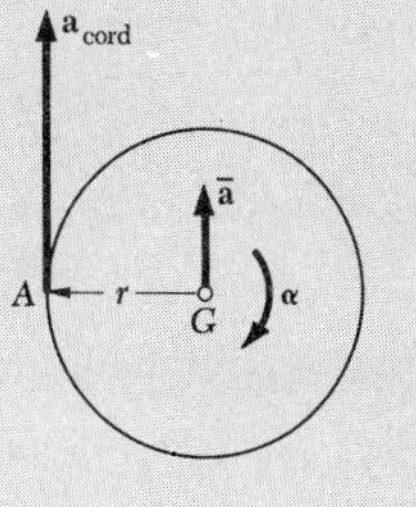

Acceleration of Cord. Since the acceleration of the cord is equal to the tangential component of the acceleration of point A on the disk, we write

$$\mathbf{a}_{cord} = (\mathbf{a}_A)_t = \bar{\mathbf{a}} + (\mathbf{a}_{A/G})_t$$
$$= [6.44\uparrow] + [(1.5)(51.5)\uparrow]$$

$$\mathbf{a}_{cord} = 83.7 \text{ ft/sec}^2 \uparrow$$ ◄

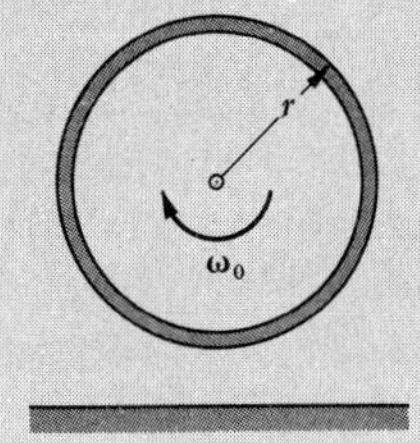

SAMPLE PROBLEM 16.5

A hoop of radius r and weight W is placed on a horizontal surface with no linear velocity but with a clockwise angular velocity ω_0. Denoting by μ the coefficient of friction between the hoop and the floor, determine (*a*) the time t_1 at which the hoop will start rolling without sliding, (*b*) the linear and angular velocities of the hoop at time t_1.

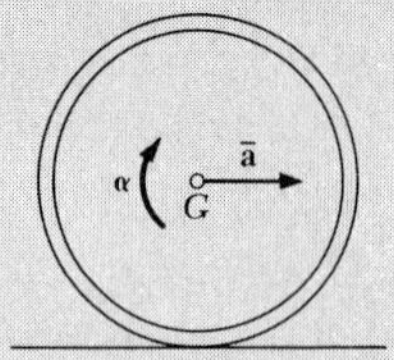

Solution. Since the entire mass, $m = W/g$, is located at a distance r from the center of the hoop, we write $\bar{I} = mr^2 = (W/g)r^2$.

Equations of Motion. The positive sense is chosen to the right for $\bar{\mathbf{a}}$ and clockwise for α. The system of external forces acting on the hoop consists of the weight **W**, the normal reaction **N**, and the friction force **F**. This system is equivalent to the vector $m\bar{\mathbf{a}}$ attached at G and the couple $\bar{I}\alpha$. While the hoop is sliding, the magnitude of the friction force is $F = \mu N$.

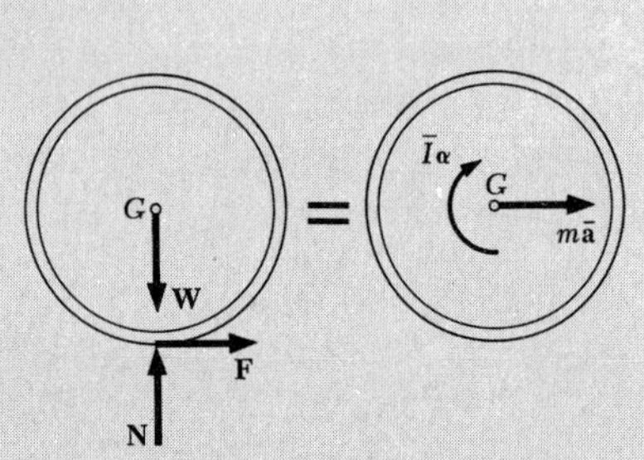

$$+\uparrow \Sigma F_y = 0: \qquad N - W = 0 \qquad N = W \qquad F = \mu N = \mu W$$

$$\xrightarrow{+} \Sigma F_x = m\bar{a}_x: \qquad F = m\bar{a} \qquad \mu W = \frac{W}{g}\bar{a} \qquad \bar{a} = +\mu g$$

$$+\circlearrowright \Sigma M_G = \bar{I}\alpha: \qquad -Fr = \bar{I}\alpha$$

$$-\mu W r = \left(\frac{W}{g}r^2\right)\alpha \qquad \alpha = -\frac{\mu g}{r}$$

Kinematics of Motion. As long as the hoop both rolls and slides, its linear and angular motions are uniformly accelerated.

$$t = 0, \bar{v}_0 = 0 \qquad \bar{v} = \bar{v}_0 + \bar{a}t = 0 + \mu g t \qquad (1)$$

$$t = 0, \omega = \omega_0 \qquad \omega = \omega_0 + \alpha t = \omega_0 + \left(-\frac{\mu g}{r}\right)t \qquad (2)$$

The hoop will start rolling without sliding when the velocity y_C of the point of contact is zero. At that time, $t = t_1$, point C becomes the instantaneous center of rotation, and we have

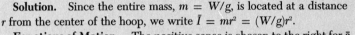

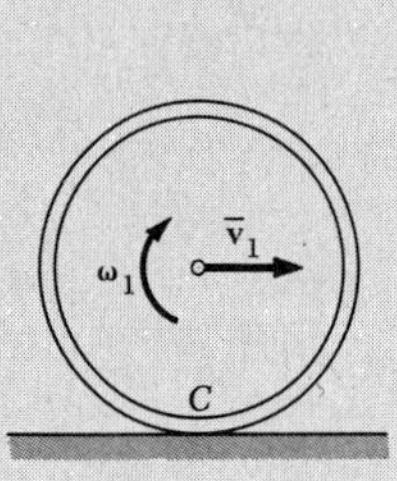

$$\bar{v}_1 = r\omega_1$$

$$\mu g t_1 = r\left(\omega_0 - \frac{\mu g}{r}t_1\right) \qquad t_1 = \frac{r\omega_0}{2\mu g} \blacktriangleleft$$

Substituting for t_1 into (1), we have

$$\bar{v}_1 = \mu g t_1 = \mu g \frac{r\omega_0}{2\mu g} \qquad \bar{v}_1 = \tfrac{1}{2}r\omega_0 \qquad \bar{\mathbf{v}}_1 = \tfrac{1}{2}r\omega_0 \rightarrow \blacktriangleleft$$

$$\bar{v}_1 = r\omega_1 \qquad \tfrac{1}{2}r\omega_0 = r\omega_1 \qquad \omega_1 = \tfrac{1}{2}\omega_0 \qquad \omega_1 = \tfrac{1}{2}\omega_0 \circlearrowright \blacktriangleleft$$

PROBLEMS

16.1. A 6-ft board is placed in a truck so that one end rests against a block A on the floor while the other end rests against a vertical wall. Determine the maximum possible uniform acceleration of the truck if the board is to remain in the position shown.

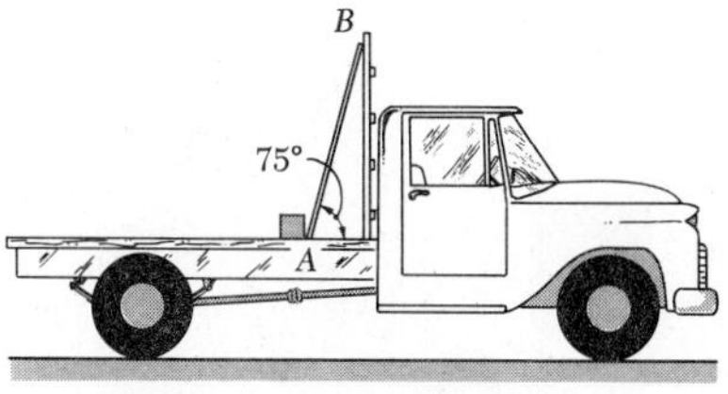

FIG. P 16.1

16.2. A uniform rod AB weighs 5 lb and is connected to two collars of negligible weight which slide freely on horizontal rods located in the same vertical plane. If a force **P** of magnitude 10 lb is applied at A, determine (*a*) the acceleration of the rod, (*b*) the reactions at A and B.

16.3. In Prob. 16.2 determine (*a*) the required magnitude of **P** if the reaction at B is to be zero, (*b*) the corresponding acceleration of the rod.

16.4. A 90-lb cabinet rests on a rough horizontal floor ($\mu = 0.30$). If a force **P** of magnitude 45 lb is applied as shown, determine (*a*) the acceleration of the cabinet, (*b*) the maximum distance h for which the cabinet will not tip about corner B.

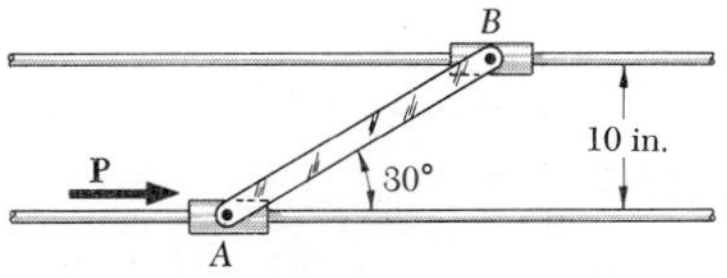

FIG. P 16.2

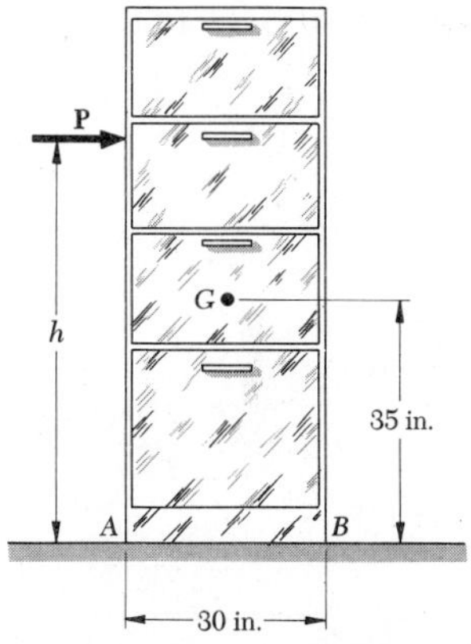

FIG. P 16.4 AND P 16.5

16.5. A horizontal force **P** is applied to the 90-lb cabinet shown at a distance $h = 45$ in. above the floor. Knowing that $\mu = 0.30$ between the cabinet and the floor, determine (*a*) the largest magnitude of **P** for which the cabinet will not tip about B, (*b*) the corresponding acceleration of the cabinet.

16.6. Cylindrical cans are transported from one elevation to another by the moving horizontal arms shown. Assuming that $\mu = 0.40$ between the cans and the arms, determine (*a*) the magnitude of the downward acceleration **a** for which the cans slide on the horizontal arms, (*b*) the smallest ratio h/d for which the cans tip before they slide.

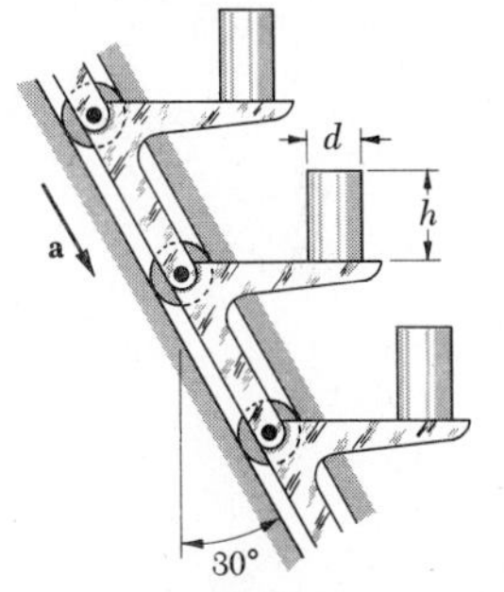

FIG. P 16.6

16.7. Solve Prob. 16.6 assuming that the acceleration **a** of the horizontal arms is directed upward.

16.8. A 15-lb cylinder, 10 in. high and 5 in. in diameter, can slide on a horizontal surface without friction. It is attached to a 30-lb weight as shown. (*a*) Determine the acceleration of the cylinder and the tension in the cord after the weight has been released. (*b*) What is the range of values of the distance h for which the cylinder will not tip during the motion?

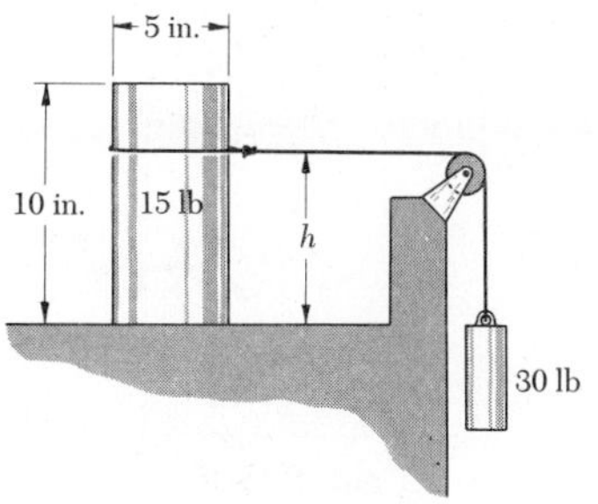

FIG. P 16.8

16.9. Solve Prob. 16.8 assuming the coefficient of friction between the block and the floor to be 0.20.

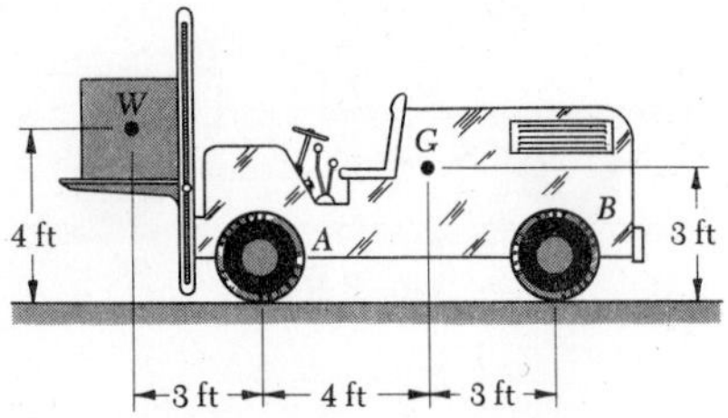

FIG. P 16.10 AND P 16.11

16.10. A fork-lift truck weighs 2,250 lb and is used to lift a crate of weight $W = 2{,}000$ lb. Determine the upward acceleration of the crate for which the reaction at the rear wheels B is zero.

16.11. The fork-lift truck shown weighs 2,250 lb and carries a crate of weight $W = 2{,}000$ lb. It is moving to the left with a speed of 15 ft/sec when the brakes are applied on all four wheels. Determine the shortest distance in which the truck can be brought to a stop if the crate is not to slide and if the truck is not to tip forward. The coefficient of friction between the crate and the fork lift is 0.30.

16.12. Determine the distance through which the truck of Sample Prob. 16.1 will skid if the rear-wheel brakes fail to operate.

16.13. Determine the distance through which the truck of Sample Prob. 16.1 will skid if the front-wheel brakes fail to operate.

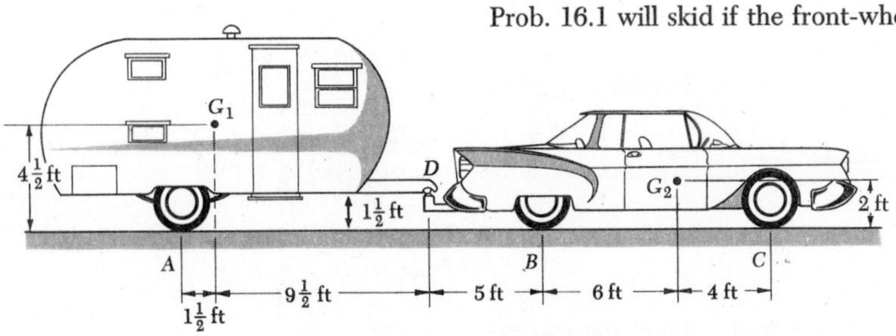

FIG. P 16.14 AND P 16.15

16.14. A trailer weighing 2,750 lb is attached to a 3,200-lb automobile by a ball-and-socket trailer hitch at D. Knowing that the car is being accelerated at the rate of 3 ft/sec², determine the components of the force exerted on the trailer by the hitch at D.

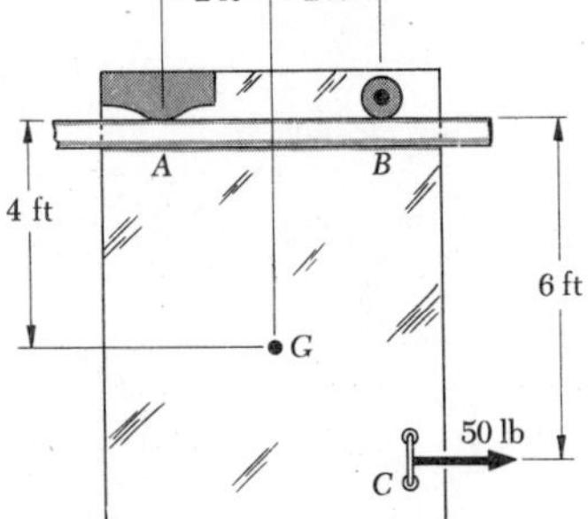

FIG. P 16.16

16.15. A trailer weighing 2,750 lb is attached to a 3,200-lb automobile by a ball-and-socket trailer hitch at D. The automobile and trailer are moving forward at a speed of 30 mph when the brakes are applied. Knowing that $\mu = 0.60$, determine the distance required to stop the automobile and trailer assuming (*a*) that the brakes are fully applied on all six wheels, (*b*) that the brakes are fully applied on the four automobile wheels but that the brakes on the trailer wheels A fail to operate.

16.16. A horizontal force of magnitude 50 lb is applied to the handle C of a 200-lb sliding door as shown. The coefficient of friction between the skid at A and the rail is 0.20. Neglecting the mass and friction of the wheel at B, determine (*a*) the acceleration of the door, (*b*) the components of the reactions at A and B.

16.17. Solve Prob. 16.16 assuming that the 50-lb force applied at C is directed horizontally to the left.

16.18. Disk AB and crank CD both rotate at a constant speed of 180 rpm. For the position $\phi = 30°$, determine the vertical components of the forces exerted on the 15-lb connecting rod BC by the pins B and C.

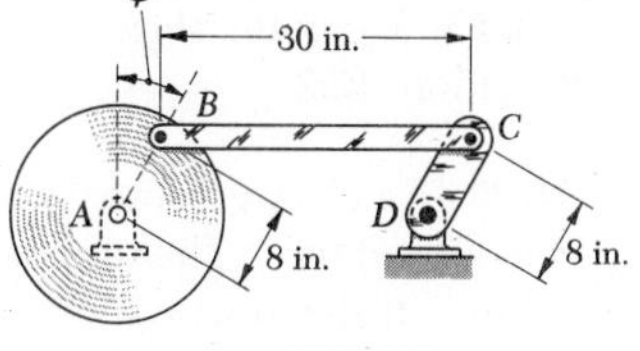

FIG. P 16.18

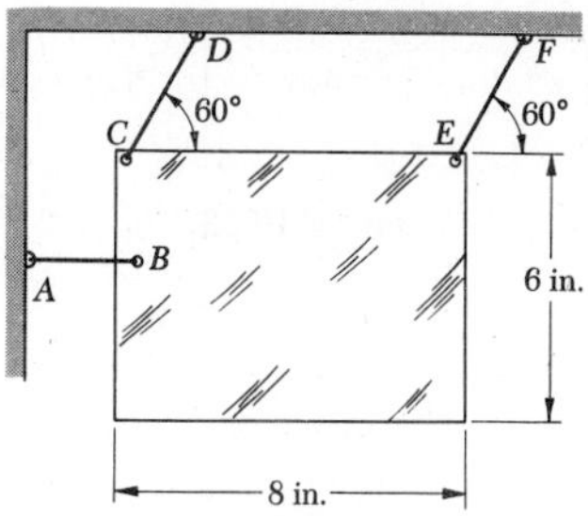

FIG. P 16.19

16.19. A homogeneous rectangular plate, 8 by 6 in. and weighing 10 lb, is held in the position shown by three wires. Determine the tension in wires CD and EF immediately after wire AB has been cut.

16.20. The motion of a 6- by 12-in. plate weighing 10 lb is guided by two pins which slide freely in parallel curved slots. At the instant shown, the velocity of each pin is 36 in./sec. Determine (*a*) the acceleration of the plate, (*b*) the pin reactions at A and B.

16.21. Members ACE and DCB are each 20 in. long and are connected by a pin at C. The mass center of the 10-lb member DE is located at G. Determine (*a*) the acceleration of DE immediately after the system has been released from rest in the position shown, (*b*) the corresponding force exerted by roller D on member DE. Neglect the weight of members ACE and DCB.

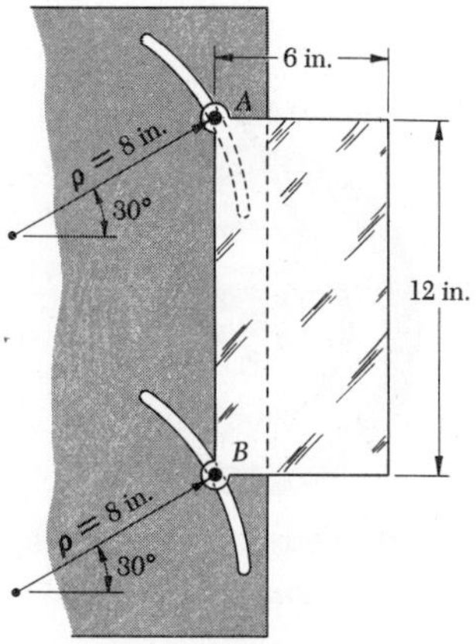

FIG. P 16.20

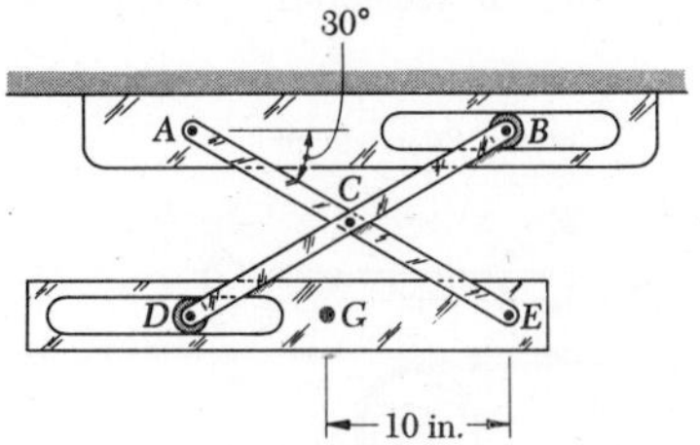

FIG. P 16.21

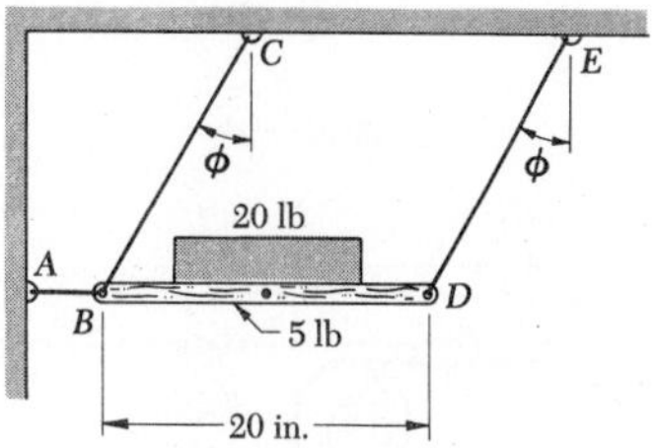

FIG. P 16.22

***16.22.** A 20-lb block is placed on a 5-lb platform BD which is held in the position $\phi = 30°$ by the three wires shown. Determine the accelerations of the block and the platform immediately after wire AB has been cut. Assume (*a*) that the block is rigidly attached to BD, (*b*) that $\mu = 0$ between the block and BD.

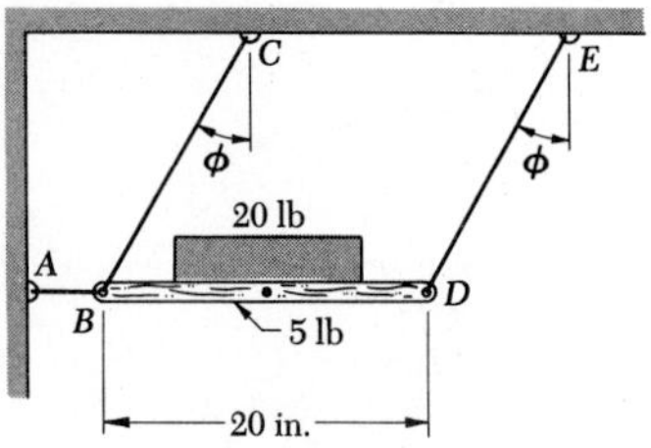

FIG. P 16.23

*16.23. The coefficient of friction between the 20-lb block and the platform BD is 0.50. Knowing that $\phi = 30°$, determine the accelerations of the block and of the platform immediately after wire AB has been cut.

*16.24. Draw the shear and bending-moment diagrams for the connecting rod of Prob. 16.18 when $\phi = 60°$.

*16.25. Draw the shear and bending-moment diagrams for the rod AB of Prob. 16.2.

16.26. An electric motor is rotating at 1,200 rpm when the load and power are cut off. The rotor weighs 200 lb and has a radius of gyration of 10 in. If the kinetic friction of the rotor produces a couple of magnitude 15 lb-in., how many revolutions will the rotor execute before stopping?

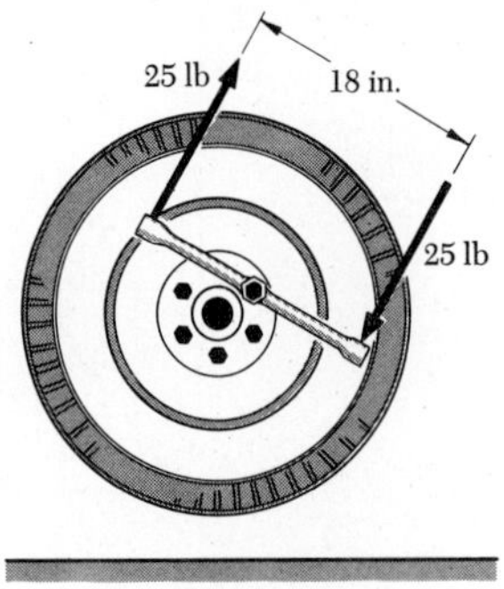

FIG. P 16.28

16.27. A 2,000-kva turbine-generator unit is shut off when its rotor is rotating at 3,600 rpm; it is observed that the rotor coasts to rest in 7.10 min. Knowing that the rotor weighs 4,100 lb and has a radius of gyration of 9.2 in., determine the average magnitude of the couple due to bearing friction.

16.28. A bolt located 2 in. from the center of an automobile wheel is tightened by applying the couple shown to a wrench. Assuming the wheel is free to rotate, determine the angular acceleration of the wheel. The wheel weighs 45 lb and has a radius of gyration of 11 in.

16.29. Disk A weighs 10 lb and is at rest when it is placed in contact with a conveyor belt moving at a constant speed. The link AB connecting the center of the disk to the support at B is of negligible weight. Knowing that $\mu = 0.40$, determine for each of the arrangements shown the angular acceleration of the disk while slipping occurs.

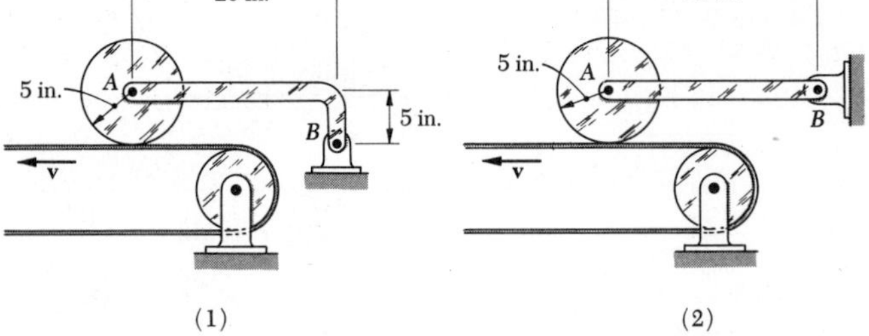

FIG. P 16.29

16.30. Solve Prob. 16.29 assuming that the direction of motion of the conveyor belt is reversed.

16.31. Referring to the Atwood machine of Prob. 12.20, derive a new formula for g, taking into account the centroidal moment of inertia $\bar{I}$ of the pulley.

16.32. A weight $W = 40$ lb is attached to a cord wrapped around the rim of a flywheel of radius $r = 3$ ft. The flywheel weighs 400 lb and has a radius of gyration of 2.50 ft. Knowing that the system is released from rest, determine the speed of the weight after it has moved 8 ft. Neglect bearing friction.

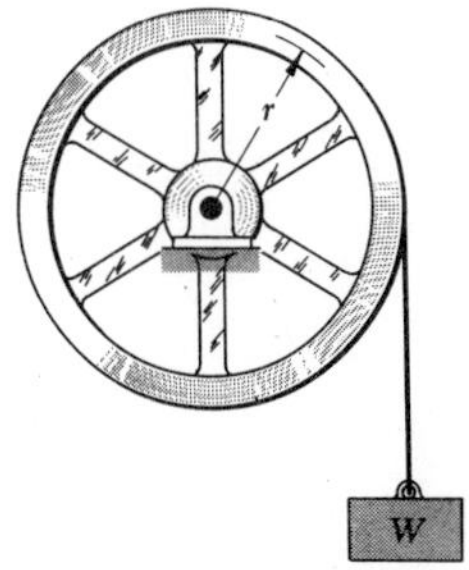

FIG. P 16.32 AND P 16.33

16.33. In order to determine the mass moment of inertia of a flywheel of radius $r = 2$ ft, a weight $W = 25$ lb is attached to a cord which is wrapped around the rim of the flywheel. The weight is released from rest and is observed to fall 10 ft in 4.80 sec. To eliminate bearing friction from the computation, a second weight $W = 50$ lb is used and is observed to fall 10 ft in 3.10 sec. Assuming that the moment of the couple due to bearing friction is constant, determine the mass moment of inertia of the flywheel.

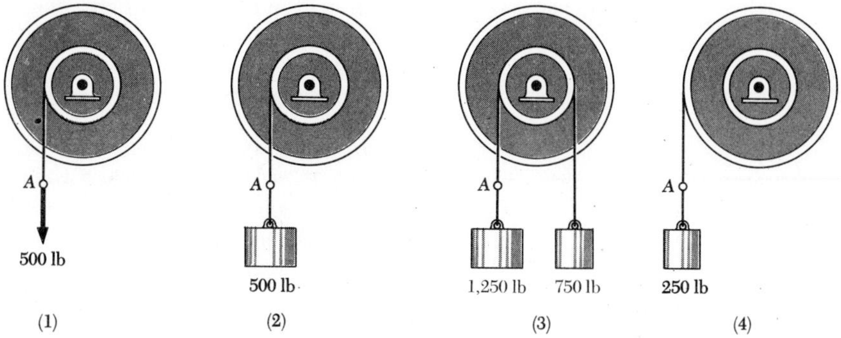

FIG. P 16.34

16.34. Each of the double pulleys shown has a mass moment of inertia of 20 lb-ft-sec^2 and is initially at rest. The outside radius is 2 ft, and the inner radius is 1 ft. Determine (*a*) the angular acceleration of each pulley, (*b*) the angular velocity of each pulley at $t = 2$ sec, (*c*) the angular velocity of each pulley after point *A* on the cord has moved 10 ft.

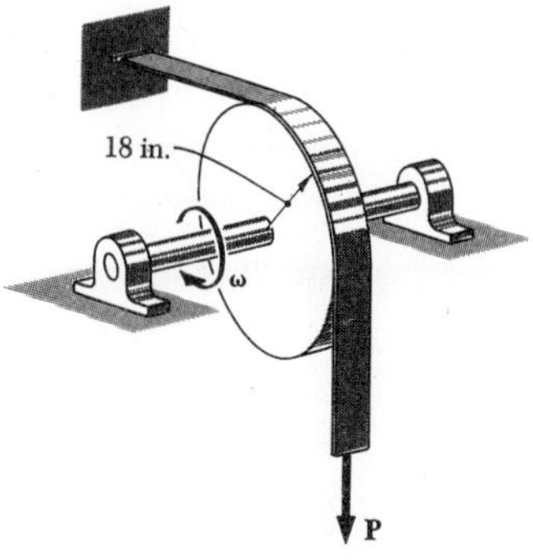

FIG. P 16.35

16.35. The flywheel shown consists of a 3-ft-diameter disk which weighs 300 lb. The coefficient of friction between the band and the flywheel is 0.30. If the initial angular velocity of the flywheel is 300 rpm clockwise, determine the magnitude of the force **P** required to stop the flywheel in 20 revolutions.

16.36. Solve Prob. 16.35 assuming that the initial angular velocity of the flywheel is 300 rpm counterclockwise.

16.37. Solve Sample Prob. 16.3 assuming that blocks A and B weigh 100 lb each.

16.38. A cylinder of radius r and weight W is placed in a corner with an initial counterclockwise angular velocity ω_0. Denoting by μ the coefficient of friction at A and at B, determine the angular acceleration α of the cylinder.

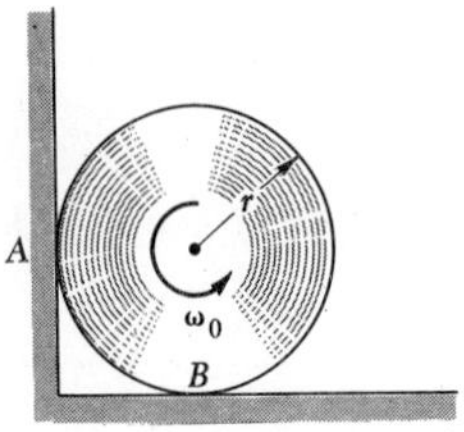

FIG. P 16.38

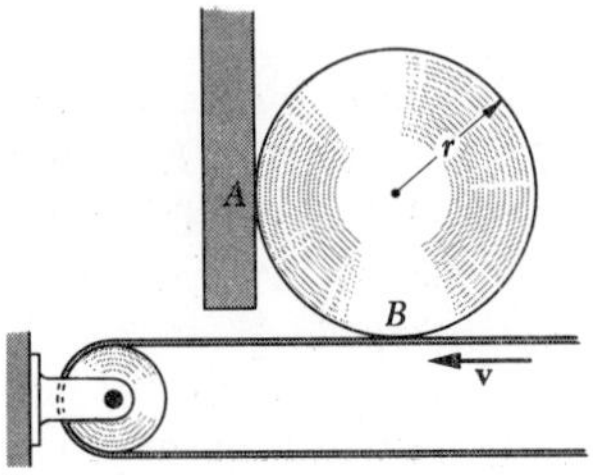

FIG. P 16.39

16.39. A cylinder of radius r and weight W is placed with no initial velocity on a belt as shown. Denoting by μ the coefficient of friction at A and at B and assuming that $\mu < 1$, determine the angular acceleration α of the cylinder.

16.40. A belt of negligible weight is pulled to the right with a force of magnitude P. Cylinder A weighs 5 lb and cylinder B 20 lb. The shaft of cylinder A is free to slide in the vertical slot shown. Knowing that $\mu = 0.50$ between the cylinders and the belt, determine the angular acceleration of each cylinder when $P = 2$ lb.

16.41. Solve Prob. 16.40 assuming $P = 4$ lb.

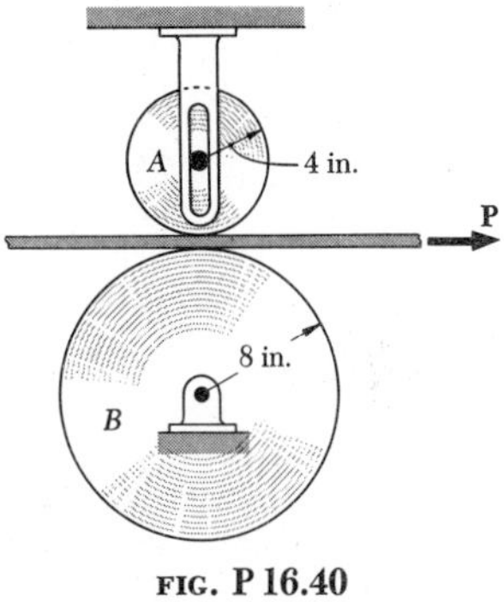

FIG. P 16.40

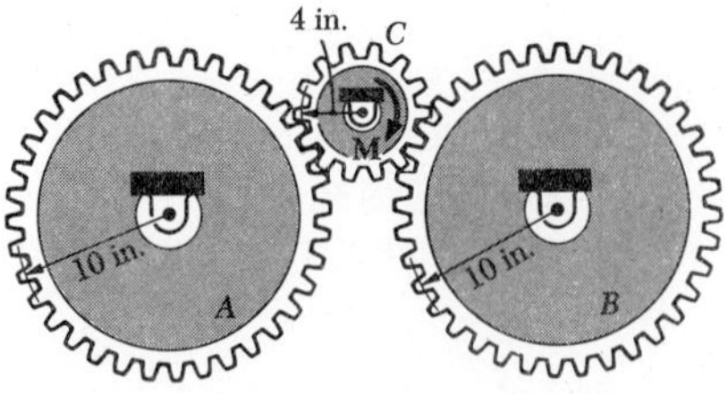

FIG. P 16.42

16.42. Gears A and B weigh 20 lb each and have each a radius of gyration of 9 in.; gear C weighs 5 lb and has a radius of gyration of 3 in. A couple of magnitude $M = 50$ lb-in. is applied to gear C. Determine (*a*) the angular acceleration of gear A, (*b*) the time required for the angular velocity of gear A to increase from 60 to 660 rpm.

16.43. Solve Prob. 16.42 assuming that the couple of magnitude $M =$ 50 lb-in. is applied to gear A.

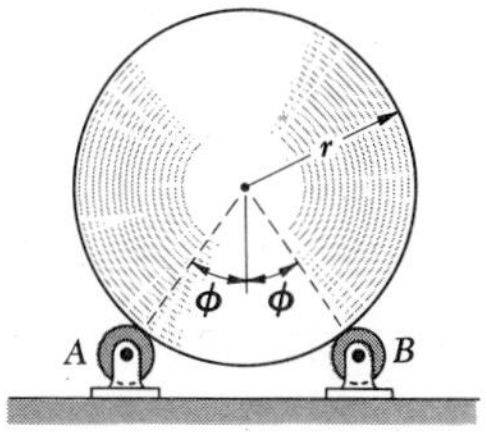

FIG. P 16.44

16.44. A cylinder of radius r and weight W rests on two small casters A and B as shown. Initially, the cylinder is at rest and is set in motion by rotating caster B clockwise at high speed so that slipping occurs between the cylinder and caster B. Denoting by μ the coefficient of friction and neglecting the moment of inertia of the free caster A, derive an expression for the angular acceleration of the cylinder.

16.45. In Prob. 16.44, assume that no slipping can occur between caster B and the cylinder (such a case would exist if the cylinder and caster had gear teeth along their rims). Derive an expression for the maximum counterclockwise acceleration α of the cylinder, if it is not to lose contact with the caster at A.

16.46. Show that the system of the effective forces for a rigid body in plane motion reduces to a single vector, and express the distance from the mass center G of the body to the line of action of this vector in terms of the centroidal radius of gyration $\bar{k}$ of the body, the magnitude $\bar{a}$ of the acceleration of G, and the angular acceleration α.

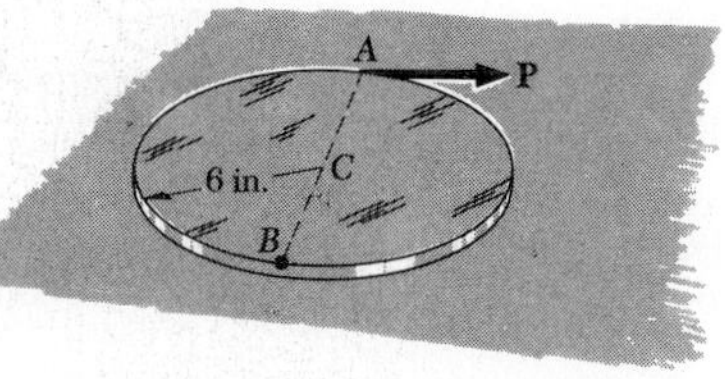

FIG. P 16.47

16.47. A 12-in.-diameter plate weighing 10 lb rests on a smooth horizontal table. A force $\mathbf{P}$ of magnitude 2 lb is applied to the plate at A in a horizontal direction perpendicular to the diameter AB. Determine (a) the angular acceleration of the plate, (b) the acceleration of the center C of the plate, (c) the point of the plate which has no acceleration.

16.48. In Prob. 16.47, determine the point on the diameter AB at which the force $\mathbf{P}$ should be applied if the acceleration of point B is to be zero. Knowing that the magnitude of $\mathbf{P}$ is 2 lb, determine the corresponding angular acceleration of the plate and the acceleration of the center C.

16.49. Shortly after being fired, the missile shown weighs 20,000 lb and is moving upward with an acceleration of 50 ft/sec². If, at this instant, the rocket engine A fails, while rocket engine B continues to operate, determine (a) the acceleration of the mass center of the missile, (b) the angular acceleration of the missile. Assume the missile to be a slender rod 48 ft long.

$\frac{ml^2}{12}$

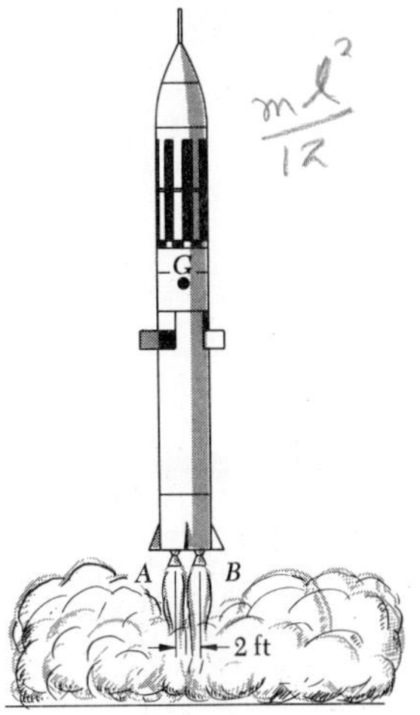

FIG. P 16.49

16.50. A 12-ft beam weighing 644 lb is lowered from a considerable height by means of two cables unwinding from overhead cranes. As the beam approaches the ground, the crane operators apply brakes to slow the unwinding motion. The deceleration of cable A is 4 ft/sec^2, while that of cable B is 28 ft/sec^2. Determine the tension in each cable.

16.51. Solve Prob. 16.50 assuming that the beam has been replaced by the 644-lb crate shown.

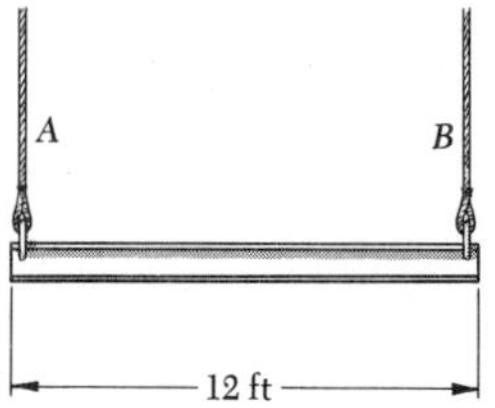

FIG. P 16.50 AND P 16.52

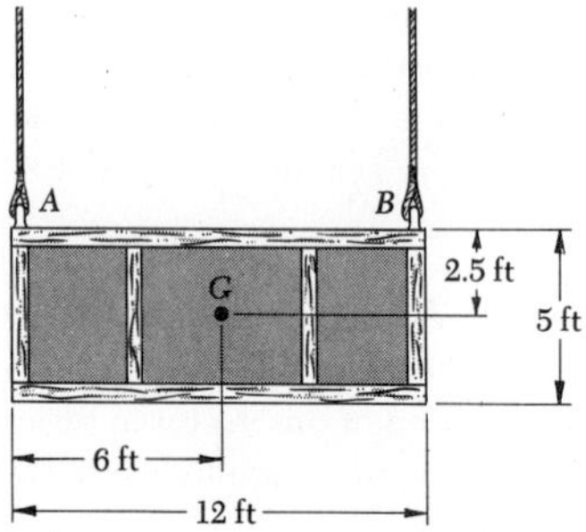

FIG. P 16.51 AND P 16.53

16.52. A 12-ft beam weighing 644 lb is lowered from a considerable height by means of two cables unwinding from overhead cranes. As the beam approaches the ground, the crane operators apply brakes to slow the unwinding motion. Determine the acceleration of each cable at that instant, knowing that $T_A = 502$ lb and $T_B = 542$ lb.

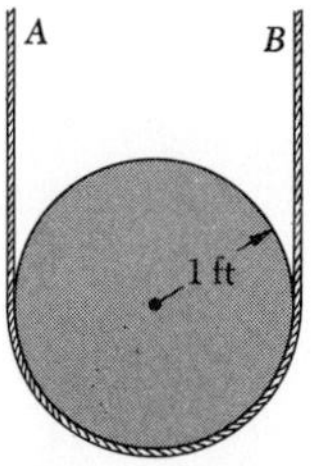

FIG. P 16.54

16.53. Solve Prob. 16.52 assuming that the beam has been replaced by the 644-lb crate shown.

16.54. A 50-lb cylinder of radius 1 ft is lifted by means of a cable wrapped around it. The two ends of the cable are pulled at different rates, so that the cylinder rotates with an angular acceleration of 6.44 radians/sec^2 counterclockwise, while moving up with an acceleration of 3.22 ft/sec^2. Find the tension in both sections of the cable.

16.55. A turbine disk and shaft have a combined weight of 200 lb and a centroidal radius of gyration of 2 in. The unit is lifted by two ropes looped around the shaft as shown. Knowing that for each rope $T_A = 55$ lb and $T_B = 65$ lb, determine the angular acceleration of the unit and the acceleration of its mass center.

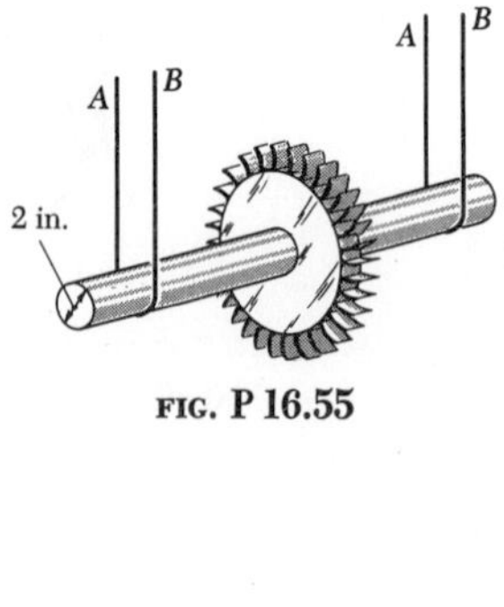

FIG. P 16.55

16.56. In Sample Prob. 16.4, determine (a) the magnitude of the force **T** for which the center of the disk has no acceleration, (b) the corresponding angular acceleration of the disk, (c) the corresponding acceleration of the cord.

16.57. By pulling on the cord of a yo-yo just fast enough, a man manages to make the yo-yo spin clockwise, while remaining at a constant height above the floor. Denoting the weight of the yo-yo by W, the radius of the inner drum on which the cord is wound by r, and the radius of gyration of the yo-yo by $\bar{k}$, determine (*a*) the tension in the cord, (*b*) the angular acceleration of the yo-yo.

16.58. A sphere of weight W and radius r is projected horizontally with a linear velocity $\mathbf{v}_0$ and with $\omega_0 = 0$. The sphere will decelerate and then reach a uniform motion. Denoting by μ the coefficient of friction, determine (*a*) the linear and angular acceleration of the sphere before it reaches a uniform motion, (*b*) the time required for the motion to become uniform, (*c*) the distance traveled before the motion becomes uniform, (*d*) the final linear and angular velocity of the sphere.

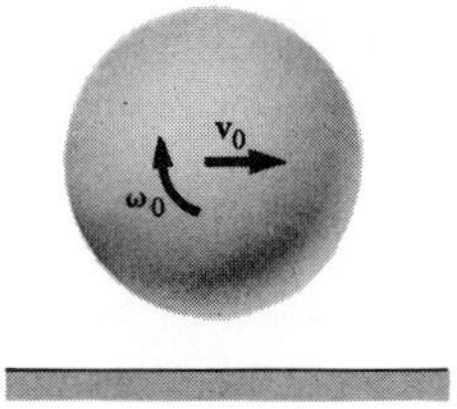

FIG. P 16.58

16.59. Solve Prob. 16.58 assuming that the sphere is replaced by a hoop of radius r and weight W.

16.60. A heavy square plate of weight W, suspended from four vertical wires, supports a small block E of much smaller weight w. The coefficient of friction between E and the plate is denoted by μ. If the coordinates of E are $x = \frac{1}{4}L$ and $z = \frac{1}{4}L$, derive an expression for the magnitude of the force $\mathbf{P}$ required to cause E to slip with respect to the plate. (*Hint.* Neglect w in all equations containing W.)

16.61. Solve Prob. 16.60 assuming that block E is placed at point D ($x = L$, $z = L$).

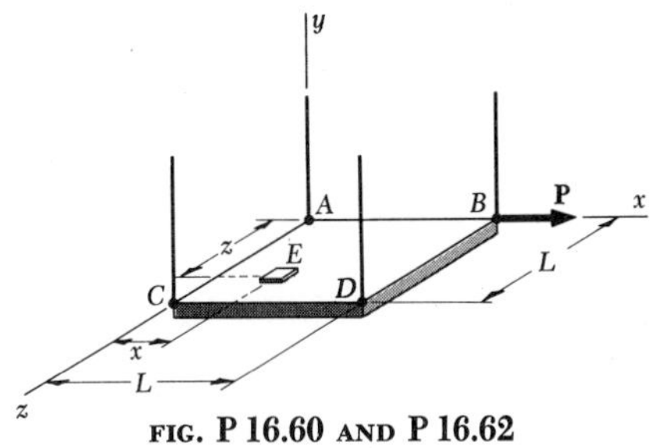

FIG. P 16.60 AND P 16.62

*__16.62.__ A square plate of weight $W = 20$ lb and side $L = 3$ ft is suspended from four wires and supports a block E of much smaller weight w. The coefficient of friction between E and the plate is 0.50. If a force $\mathbf{P}$ of magnitude 10 lb is applied as shown, determine the area of the plate where E should be placed if it is not to slip with respect to the plate. (*Hint.* Neglect w in all equations containing W.)

16.5. Constrained Plane Motion. Most engineering applications deal with rigid bodies which are moving under given constraints. Cranks, for example, are constrained to rotate about a fixed axis, wheels roll without sliding, connecting rods must describe certain prescribed motions. In all such cases, definite relations exist between the components of the acceleration $\bar{\mathbf{a}}$ of the mass center G of the body considered and its angular acceleration $\boldsymbol{\alpha}$; the corresponding motion is said to be a *constrained motion.*

The solution of a problem involving a constrained plane motion calls first for a *kinematic analysis* of the problem. Con-

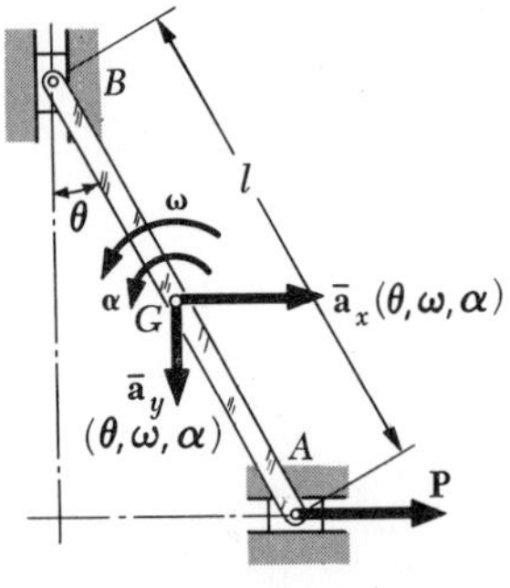

FIG. 16.7

sider, for example, a slender rod AB of length l and mass m whose extremities are connected to blocks of negligible mass which slide along horizontal and vertical frictionless tracks. The rod is pulled by a force **P** applied at A (Fig. 16.7). We know from Sec. 15.8 that the acceleration $\bar{\mathbf{a}}$ of the mass center G of the rod may be determined at any given instant from the position of the rod, its angular velocity, and its angular acceleration at that instant. Suppose, for instance, that the values of θ, ω, and α are known at a given instant and that we wish to determine the corresponding value of the force **P**, as well as the reactions at A and B. We should first *determine the components* $\bar{a}_x$ *and* $\bar{a}_y$ *of the acceleration of the mass center* G by the method of Sec. 15.8. We then carry the values obtained into Fig. 16.8 or Fig. 16.9, depending upon whether D'Alembert's principle is applied directly or the method of dynamic equilibrium is used. The unknown forces **P**, $\mathbf{N}_A$, and $\mathbf{N}_B$ may then be determined by writing and solving the appropriate equations.

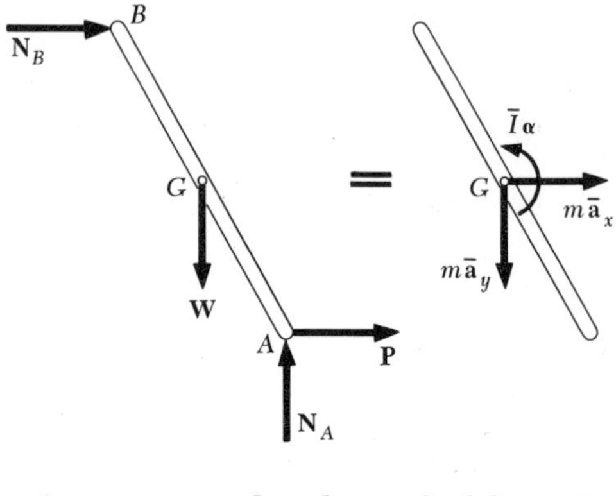

FIG. 16.8

Suppose now that the applied force **P**, the angle θ, and the angular velocity ω of the rod are known at a given instant and that we wish to find the angular acceleration α of the rod and the components $\bar{a}_x$ and $\bar{a}_y$ of the acceleration of its mass center at that instant, as well as the reactions at A and B. The preliminary kinematic study of the problem will have for its object *to express the components* $\bar{a}_x$ *and* $\bar{a}_y$ *of the acceleration of* G *in terms of the angular acceleration* α *of the rod.* This will be done by first expressing the acceleration of a suitable reference point such as A in terms of the angular acceleration α. The components $\bar{a}_x$ and $\bar{a}_y$ of the acceleration of G may then be determined in terms of α, and the expressions obtained carried into Fig. 16.8 or Fig. 16.9. Three equations may then be derived in terms of α, N_A, and N_B, and solved for the three unknowns (see Sample Prob. 16.10).

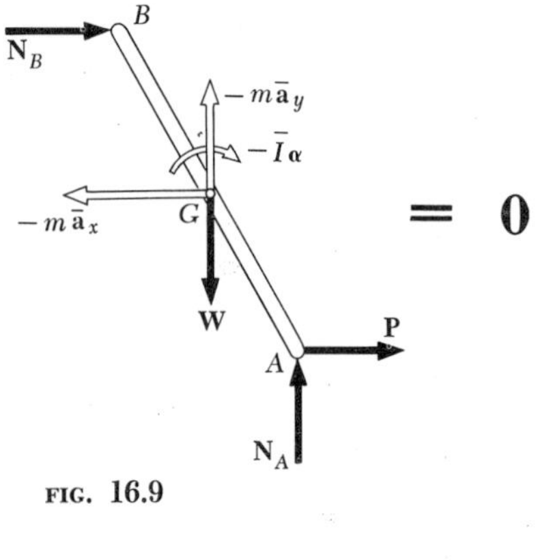

FIG. 16.9

When a mechanism consists of *several moving parts*, the method just described may be applied to each part of the mechanism. The procedure required to determine the various unknowns is then similar to the procedure followed in the case of the static equilibrium of a system of connected rigid bodies (Sec. 6.12).

We have analyzed earlier two particular cases of constrained plane motion, the translation of a rigid body, in which the angular acceleration of the body is constrained to be zero, and the centroidal rotation, in which the acceleration $\bar{\mathbf{a}}$ of the mass center of the body is constrained to be zero. Two other particular cases of constrained plane motion are of special interest, the *noncentroidal rotation* of a rigid body and the *rolling motion* of a disk or wheel. These two cases should be analyzed by one of the general methods described above. However, in view of the range of their applications, they deserve a few special comments.

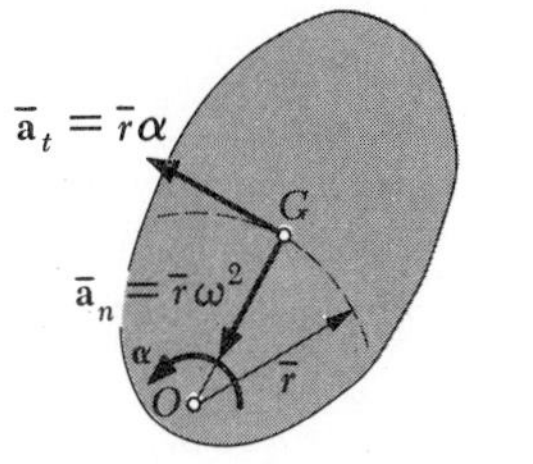

FIG. 16.10

Noncentroidal Rotation. This is the motion of a rigid body constrained to rotate about a fixed axis which does not pass through its mass center. Such a motion is called a *noncentroidal rotation.* The mass center G of the body moves along a circle of radius $\bar{r}$ centered at the point O, where the axis of rotation intersects the plane of reference (Fig. 16.10). Denoting, respectively, by ω and α the angular velocity and the angular acceleration of the line OG, we obtain the following expressions for the tangential and normal components of the acceleration of G:

$$\bar{a}_t = \bar{r}\alpha \qquad \bar{a}_n = \bar{r}\omega^2 \tag{16.5}$$

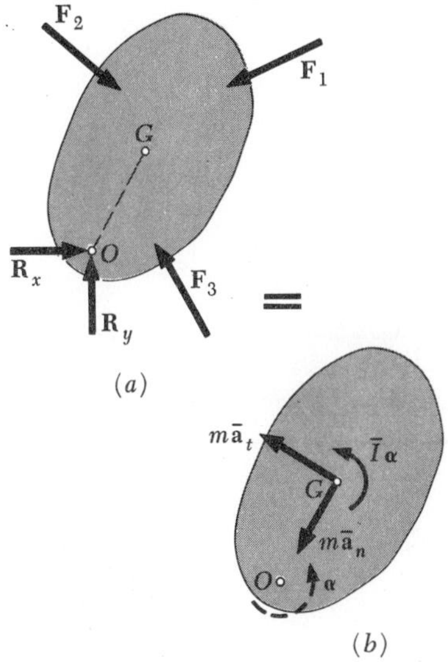

FIG. 16.11

Since line OG belongs to the body, its angular velocity ω and its angular acceleration α also represent the angular velocity and the angular acceleration of the body in its motion relative to G. Equations (16.5) define, therefore, the kinematic relation existing between the motion of the mass center G and the motion of the body about G. They should be used to eliminate $\bar{a}_t$ and $\bar{a}_n$ from the equations obtained by applying D'Alembert's principle (Fig. 16.11) or the method of dynamic equilibrium (Fig. 16.12).

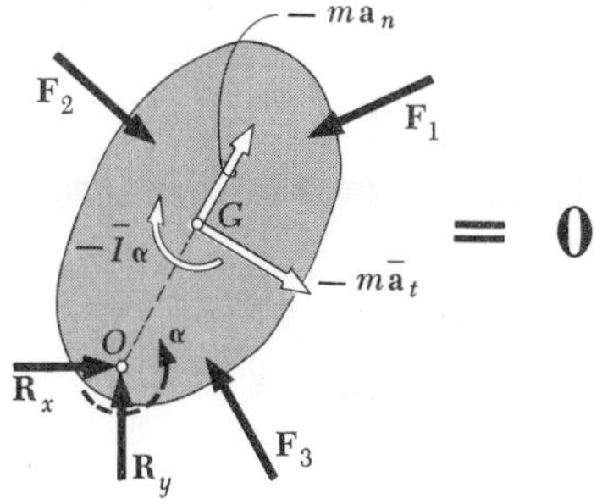

FIG 16.12

An interesting relation may be obtained by equating the moments about the fixed point O of the forces and vectors shown respectively in parts *a* and *b* of Fig. 16.11. We write

$$+\circlearrowleft \Sigma M_O = \bar{I}\alpha + (m\bar{r}\alpha)\bar{r} = (\bar{I} + m\bar{r}^2)\alpha$$

But, according to the parallel-axis theorem, we have $\bar{I} + m\bar{r}^2 = I_O$, where I_O denotes the moment of inertia of the rigid body about the fixed axis. We write, therefore,

$$\Sigma M_O = I_O\alpha \tag{16.6}$$

While formula (16.6) expresses an important relation between the sum of the moments of the external forces about the fixed point O and the product $I_O\alpha$, it should be clearly understood that this formula *does not mean* that the system of the external forces is equivalent to a couple of moment $I_O\alpha$. The system of the effective forces, and thus the system of the external forces, reduces to a couple only when O coincides with G, that is, *only when the rotation is centroidal* (Sec. 16.2). In the more general case of noncentroidal rotation, the system of the external forces does not reduce to a couple.

A particular case of noncentroidal rotation is of special interest: the case of *uniform rotation*, in which the angular velocity ω is constant. Since α is zero, the inertia couple in Fig. 16.12 vanishes and the inertia vector reduces to its normal component. This component (also called *centrifugal force*) represents the tendency of the rigid body to break away from the axis of rotation.

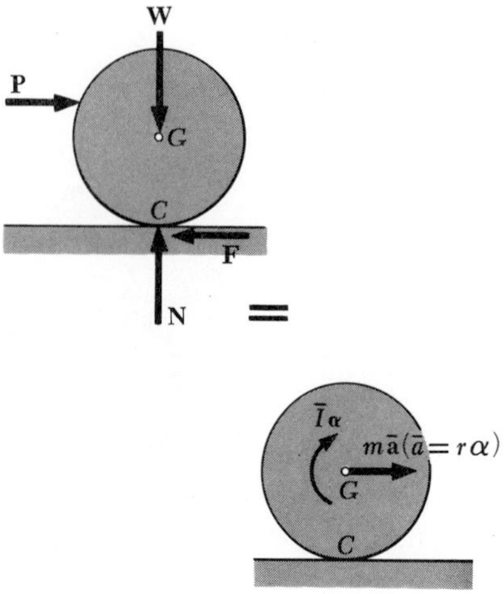

FIG. 16.13

Rolling Motion. Another important case of plane motion is the motion of a disk or wheel rolling on a plane surface. If the disk is constrained to roll without sliding, the acceleration $\bar{\mathbf{a}}$ of its mass center G and its angular acceleration α are not independent. Assuming the disk to be balanced, so that its mass center and its geometric center coincide, we first write that the distance $\bar{s}$ traveled by G during a rotation of θ radians of the disk is $\bar{s} = r\theta$, where r is the radius of the disk. Differentiating this relation twice, we write

$$\bar{a} = r\alpha \tag{16.7}$$

Recalling that the system of the effective forces in plane motion reduces to a vector $m\bar{\mathbf{a}}$ and a couple $\bar{I}\alpha$, we find that, in the particular case of the rolling motion of a balanced disk, the effective forces reduce to a vector of magnitude $mr\alpha$ attached at G and to a couple of magnitude $\bar{I}\alpha$. We may thus express that the external forces are equivalent to the vector and couple shown in Fig. 16.13. Considering the vector and couple of opposite sense, we may also express that the disk is in dynamic equilibrium under the action of the external forces and of the inertia vector and inertia couple shown in Fig. 16.14.

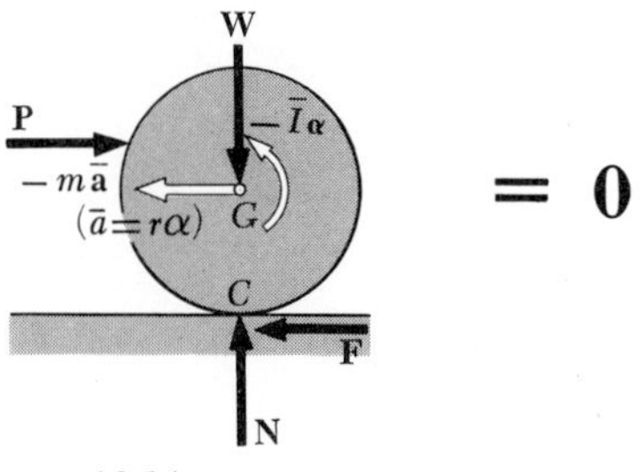

FIG. 16.14

When a disk *rolls without sliding*, there is no relative motion between the point of the disk which is in contact with the ground and the ground itself. As far as the computation of the friction force **F** is concerned, a rolling disk may thus be compared with a block at rest on a surface. The magnitude F of the friction force may have any value, as long as it does not exceed the maximum value $F_m = \mu_s N$, where μ_s is the coefficient of static friction and N the magnitude of the normal force. In the case of a rolling disk, the magnitude F of the friction force should therefore be determined independently of N by solving the equation obtained from Fig. 16.13 or Fig. 16.14.

When *sliding is impending,* the friction force reaches its maximum value $F_m = \mu_s N$ and may be obtained from N.

When the disk *rolls and slides* at the same time, a relative motion exists between the point of the disk which is in contact with the ground and the ground itself, and the force of friction has the magnitude $F_k = \mu_k N$, where μ_k is the coefficient of kinetic friction. In this case, however, the motion of the mass center G of the disk and the rotation of the disk about G are independent, and $\bar{a}$ is not equal to $r\alpha$.

These three different cases may be summarized as follows:

Rolling, no sliding:	$F \leq \mu_s N$	$\bar{a} = r\alpha$
Rolling, sliding impending:	$F = \mu_s N$	$\bar{a} = r\alpha$
Rolling and sliding:	$F = \mu_k N$	$\bar{a}$ *and* α *independent*

When it is not known whether a disk slides or not, it should first be assumed that the disk rolls without sliding. If F is found smaller than, or equal to, $\mu_s N$, the assumption is proved correct. If F is found larger than $\mu_s N$, the assumption is incorrect and the problem should be started again, assuming rolling and sliding.

When a disk is *unbalanced,* i.e., when its mass center G does not coincide with its geometric center O, the relation (16.7) does not hold between $\bar{a}$ and α. A similar relation will hold, however, between the magnitude a_O of the acceleration of the geometric center and the angular acceleration α,

$$a_O = r\alpha \tag{16.8}$$

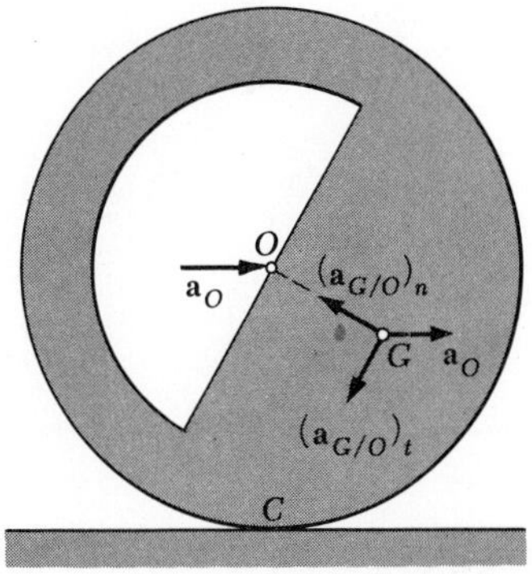

FIG. 16.15

To determine $\bar{a}$ in terms of the angular acceleration α and the angular velocity ω of the disk, we may use the relative-acceleration formula,

$$\begin{aligned}\bar{\mathbf{a}} = \mathbf{a}_G &= \mathbf{a}_O + \mathbf{a}_{G/O} \\ &= \mathbf{a}_O + (\mathbf{a}_{G/O})_t + (\mathbf{a}_{G/O})_n\end{aligned} \tag{16.9}$$

where the three component accelerations obtained have the directions indicated in Fig. 16.15 and the magnitudes $a_O = r\alpha$, $(a_{G/O})_t = (OG)\alpha$, and $(a_{G/O})_n = (OG)\omega^2$.

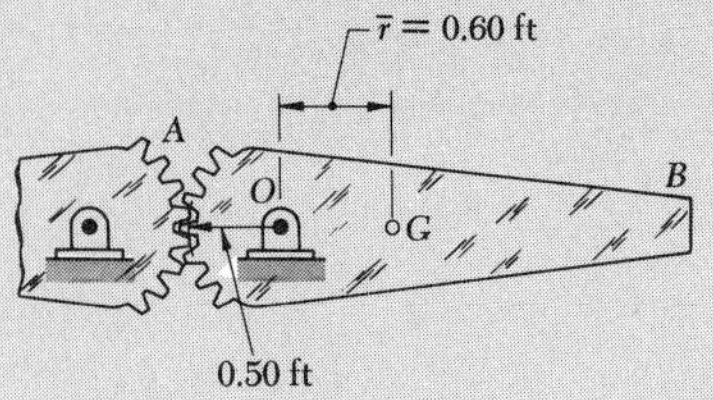

SAMPLE PROBLEM 16.6

At the instant shown, the lever AB rotates with a counterclockwise angular velocity of 10 radians/sec and with a clockwise angular acceleration of 50 radians/sec^2. Knowing that the lever weighs 30 lb and that its centroidal radius of gyration is 0.80 ft, determine (*a*) the tangential force exerted on the gear at A, (*b*) the components of the reaction at the shaft O.

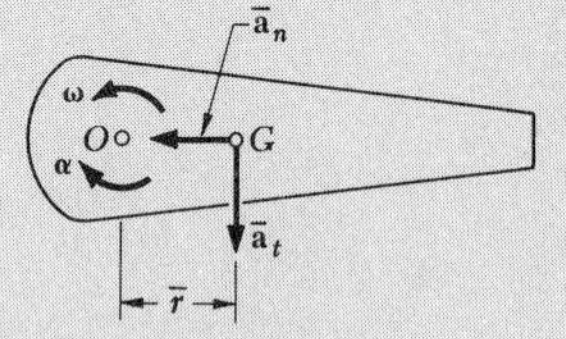

Acceleration of G. Since the lever rotates about O, we write

$$\bar{a}_n = \bar{r}\omega^2 = (0.60)(10^2) = 60 \text{ ft/sec}^2$$
$$\bar{a}_t = \bar{r}\alpha = (0.60)(50) = 30 \text{ ft/sec}^2$$

Equations of Motion. Two sketches of the lever are drawn showing all external forces, the couple $\bar{I}\alpha$, and the components $m\bar{\mathbf{a}}_n$ and $m\bar{\mathbf{a}}_t$ of the vector $m\bar{\mathbf{a}}$. Since the accelerations are known, we compute the magnitudes.

$$m\bar{a}_n = \frac{30}{32.2}(60) = 55.9 \text{ lb}$$

$$m\bar{a}_t = \frac{30}{32.2}(30) = 27.9 \text{ lb}$$

$$\bar{I}\alpha = m\bar{k}^2\alpha = \frac{30}{32.2}(0.80)^2(50) = 29.8 \text{ lb-ft}$$

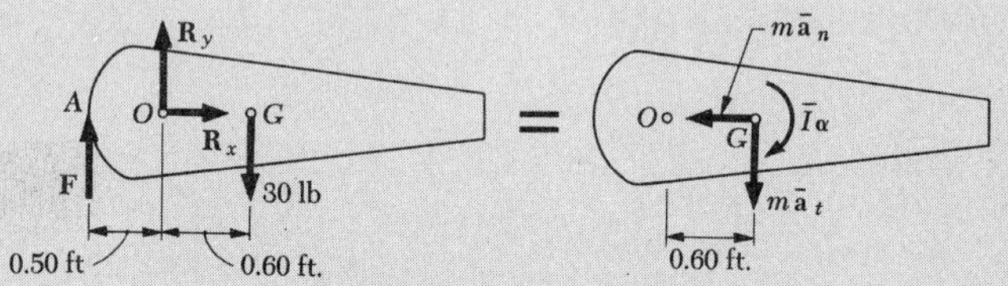

Expressing that the system of the external forces is equivalent to the system of the effective forces, we write the following equations of motion:

$+\circlearrowright \Sigma M_O = \Sigma(M_O)_{\text{eff}}$:

$$F(0.50 \text{ ft}) + (30 \text{ lb})(0.60 \text{ ft}) = m\bar{a}_t(0.60) + \bar{I}\alpha$$
$$0.50F + 18 = (27.9)(0.60) + 29.8$$
$$F = +57.1 \text{ lb} \qquad \mathbf{F} = 57.1 \text{ lb} \uparrow \blacktriangleleft$$

$\overset{+}{\rightarrow} \Sigma F_x = \Sigma(F_x)_{\text{eff}}$: $\quad R_x = -m\bar{a}_n$

$$R_x = -55.9 \text{ lb} \qquad \mathbf{R}_x = 55.9 \text{ lb} \leftarrow \blacktriangleleft$$

$+\uparrow \Sigma F_y = \Sigma(F_y)_{\text{eff}}$: $\quad F + R_y - 30 \text{ lb} = -m\bar{a}_t$

$$57.1 \text{ lb} + R_y - 30 \text{ lb} = -27.9 \text{ lb}$$
$$R_y = -55.0 \text{ lb} \qquad \mathbf{R}_y = 55.0 \text{ lb} \downarrow \blacktriangleleft$$

SAMPLE PROBLEM 16.7

A rectangular plate, 6 by 8 in., weighs 60 lb and is suspended from two pins A and B. If pin B is suddenly removed, determine (*a*) the angular acceleration of the plate, (*b*) the components of the reactions at pin A, immediately after pin B has been removed.

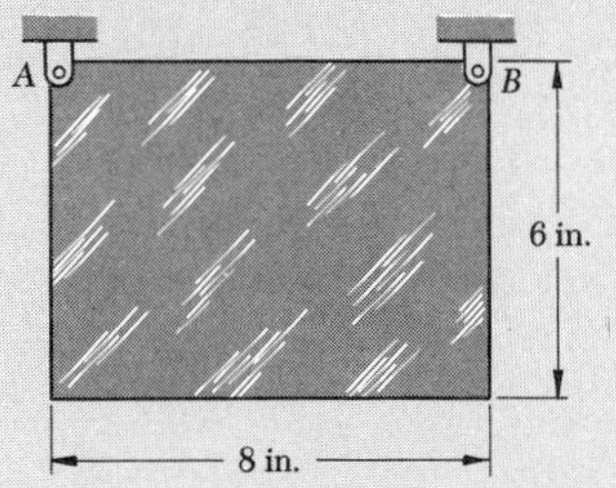

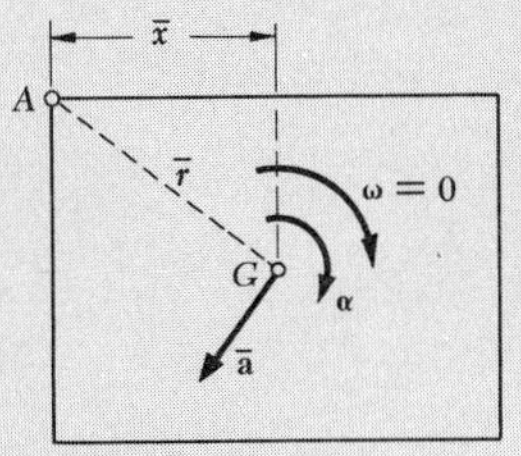

a. **Angular Acceleration.** We observe that as the plate rotates about point A, its mass center G describes a circle of radius $\bar{r}$ with center at A. Since the plate is released from rest ($\omega = 0$), the normal component of the acceleration of G is zero. The magnitude of the acceleration $\bar{\mathbf{a}}$ of the mass center G is thus $\bar{a} = \bar{r}\alpha$. We draw the diagram shown to express that the external forces are equivalent to the effective forces:

$$+\circlearrowright \Sigma M_A = \Sigma(M_A)_{\text{eff}}: \qquad W\bar{x} = (m\bar{a})\bar{r} + \bar{I}\alpha$$

Since $\bar{a} = \bar{r}\alpha$, we have

$$W\bar{x} = m(\bar{r}\alpha)\bar{r} + \bar{I}\alpha \qquad \alpha = \frac{W\bar{x}}{\frac{W}{g}\bar{r}^2 + \bar{I}} \tag{1}$$

The centroidal moment of inertia of the plate is

$$\bar{I} = \frac{m}{12}(a^2 + b^2) = \frac{60}{(12)(32.2)}[(\tfrac{8}{12})^2 + (\tfrac{6}{12})^2] = 0.1078 \text{ lb-ft-sec}^2$$

Substituting this value of $\bar{I}$ together with $W = 60$ lb, $\bar{r} = 5$ in., and $\bar{x} =$ 4 in. into Eq. (1), we obtain

$$\alpha = +46.3 \text{ radians/sec}^2 \qquad \boldsymbol{\alpha} = 46.3 \text{ radians/sec}^2 \circlearrowright \blacktriangleleft$$

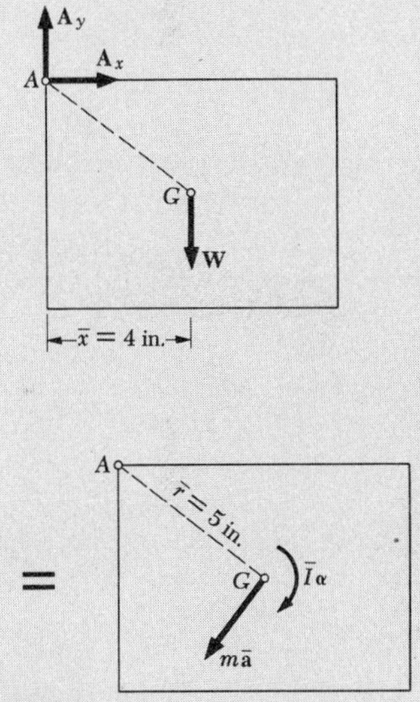

b. **Reaction at** A. Using the computed value of α, we determine the magnitude of the vector $m\bar{\mathbf{a}}$ attached at G,

$$m\bar{a} = m\bar{r}\alpha = \frac{60}{32.2}\frac{5}{12}(46.3) = 36.0 \text{ lb}$$

Showing this result on the diagram, we then write

$$\overset{+}{\rightarrow} \Sigma F_x = m\bar{a}_x: \qquad A_x = -\tfrac{3}{5}(36 \text{ lb})$$

$$A_x = -21.6 \text{ lb} \qquad \mathbf{A}_x = 21.6 \text{ lb} \leftarrow \blacktriangleleft$$

$$+\uparrow \Sigma F_y = m\bar{a}_y: \qquad A_y - 60 \text{ lb} = -\tfrac{4}{5}(36 \text{ lb})$$

$$A_y = +31.2 \text{ lb} \qquad \mathbf{A}_y = 31.2 \text{ lb} \uparrow \blacktriangleleft$$

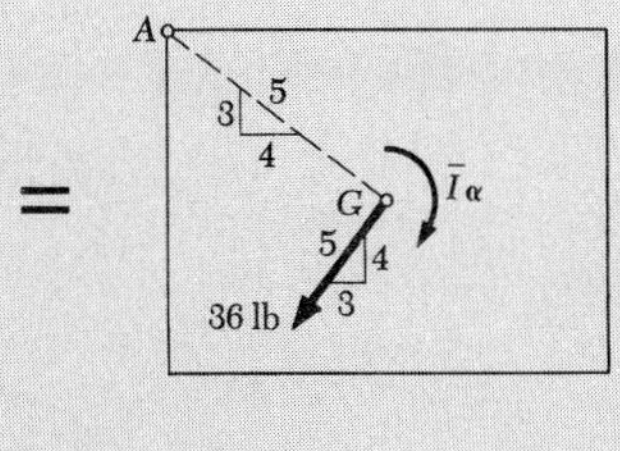

The couple $\bar{I}\alpha$ is not involved in the last two equations; nevertheless, it should be indicated on the diagram.

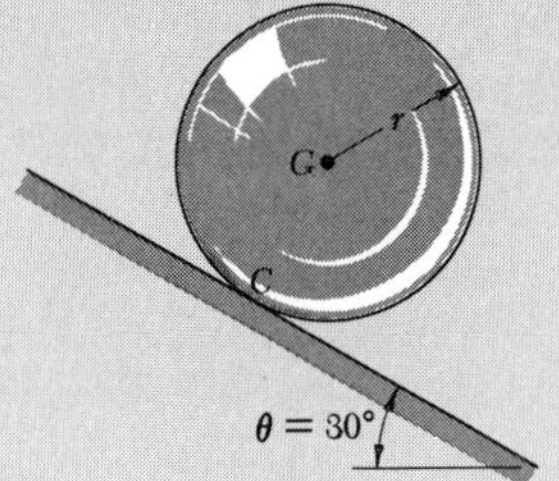

SAMPLE PROBLEM 16.8

A sphere of radius r and weight W is released with no initial velocity on the incline and rolls without slipping. Determine (*a*) the minimum value of the coefficient of friction compatible with the rolling motion, (*b*) the velocity of the center G of the sphere after the sphere has rolled 10 ft, (*c*) the velocity of G if the sphere were to move 10 ft down a frictionless 30° incline.

a. **Minimum μ for Rolling Motion.** The external forces **W**, **N**, and **F** form a system equivalent to the system of effective forces represented by the vector $m\bar{\mathbf{a}}$ and the couple $\bar{I}\boldsymbol{\alpha}$. Since the sphere rolls without sliding, we have $\bar{a} = r\alpha$.

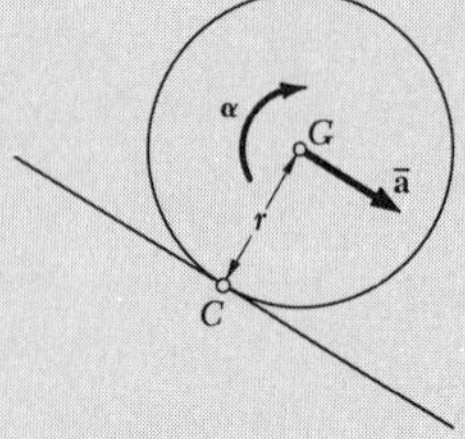

$$+\circlearrowright \Sigma M_C = \Sigma(M_C)_{\text{eff}}: \qquad (W \sin\theta)r = (m\bar{a})r + \bar{I}\alpha$$
$$(W \sin\theta)r = (mr\alpha)r + \bar{I}\alpha$$

Noting that $m = W/g$ and $\bar{I} = \frac{2}{5}mr^2$, we write

$$(W\sin\theta)r = \left(\frac{W}{g}r\alpha\right)r + \frac{2}{5}\frac{W}{g}r^2\alpha \qquad \alpha = +\frac{5g\sin\theta}{7r}$$

$$\bar{a} = r\alpha = \frac{5g\sin\theta}{7} = \frac{5g\sin 30°}{7} = +11.50 \text{ ft/sec}^2$$

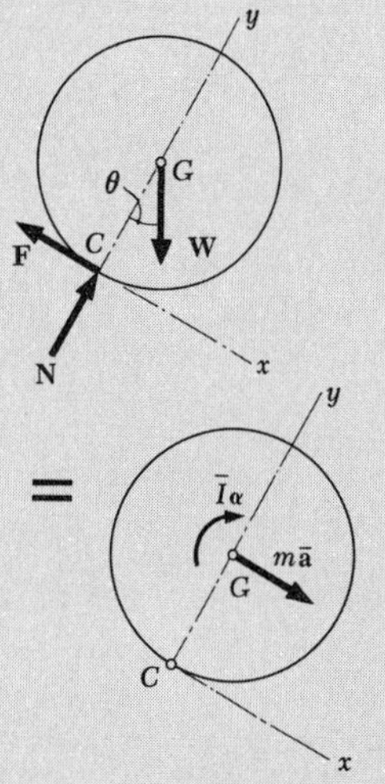

$$+\searrow \Sigma F_x = m\bar{a}: \qquad W\sin\theta - F = m\bar{a}$$
$$W\sin\theta - F = \frac{W}{g}\frac{5g\sin\theta}{7}$$

$$F = +\tfrac{2}{7}W\sin\theta = \tfrac{2}{7}W\sin 30° \qquad \mathbf{F} = 0.143\,W \nwarrow 30°$$

$$+\nearrow \Sigma F_y = 0: \qquad N - W\cos\theta = 0$$
$$N = W\cos\theta = 0.866W \qquad \mathbf{N} = 0.866W \nearrow 60°$$

$$\mu_{\min} = \frac{F}{N} = \frac{0.143\,W}{0.866\,W} \qquad \mu_{\min} = 0.165 \blacktriangleleft$$

b. **Velocity of Rolling Sphere.** We have uniformly accelerated motion,

$$\bar{v}_0 = 0 \qquad \bar{a} = 11.50 \text{ ft/sec}^2 \qquad \bar{s} = 10 \text{ ft} \qquad \bar{s}_0 = 0$$
$$\bar{v}^2 = \bar{v}_0^2 + 2\bar{a}(\bar{s} - \bar{s}_0) \qquad \bar{v}^2 = 0 + (2)(11.50)(10)$$
$$\bar{v} = 15.17 \text{ ft/sec} \qquad \bar{\mathbf{v}} = 15.17 \text{ ft/sec} \searrow 30° \blacktriangleleft$$

c. **Velocity of Sliding Sphere.** Assuming now no friction, we have $F = 0$ and obtain

$$+\circlearrowright \Sigma M_G = \Sigma(M_G)_{\text{eff}}: \qquad 0 = \bar{I}\alpha \qquad \alpha = 0$$

$$+\searrow \Sigma F_x = m\bar{a}: \qquad W\sin 30° = m\bar{a} \qquad 0.50W = \frac{W}{g}\bar{a}$$

$$\bar{a} = +16.1 \text{ ft/sec}^2 \qquad \bar{\mathbf{a}} = 16.1 \text{ ft/sec}^2 \searrow 30°$$

Substituting $\bar{a} = 16.1$ ft/sec² into the equations for uniformly accelerated motion, we obtain

$$\bar{v}^2 = \bar{v}_0^2 + 2\bar{a}(\bar{s} - \bar{s}_0) \qquad \bar{v}^2 = 0 + (2)(16.1)(10)$$
$$\bar{v} = 17.95 \text{ ft/sec} \qquad \bar{\mathbf{v}} = 17.95 \text{ ft/sec} \searrow 30° \blacktriangleleft$$

SAMPLE PROBLEM 16.9

A cord is wrapped around the inner drum of a wheel and pulled horizontally with a force of 40 lb. The wheel weighs 100 lb and has a radius of gyration of 3.5 in. Knowing that $\mu_s = 0.20$ and $\mu_k = 0.15$, determine the acceleration of G and the angular acceleration of the wheel.

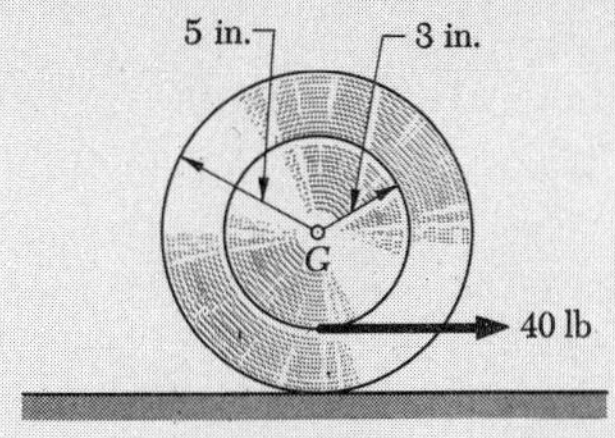

a. **Assume Rolling without Sliding.** In this case, we have

$$\bar{a} = r\alpha = \tfrac{5}{12}\alpha$$

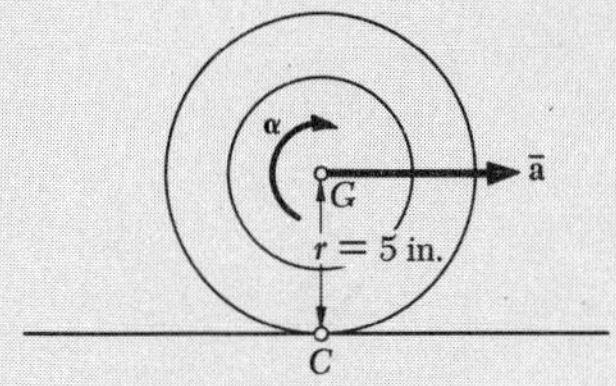

By comparing the friction force obtained with the maximum friction force, we shall determine whether this assumption is justified. The mass and moment of inertia of the wheel are

$$m = \frac{100}{32.2} = 3.11 \text{ lb-sec}^2/\text{ft}$$

$$\bar{I} = m\bar{k}^2 = \frac{100}{32.2}\left(\frac{3.5}{12}\right)^2 = 0.264 \text{ lb-ft-sec}^2$$

Equations of Motion

$+\circlearrowleft \Sigma M_C = \Sigma(M_C)_{\text{eff}}$: $\quad (40)(\tfrac{2}{12}) = m\bar{a}(\tfrac{5}{12}) + \bar{I}\alpha$

$$6.67 = (3.11)(\tfrac{5}{12}\alpha)(\tfrac{5}{12}) + 0.264\alpha$$

$$\alpha = +8.30 \text{ radians/sec}^2$$

$$\bar{a} = r\alpha = (\tfrac{5}{12})(8.30) = 3.46 \text{ ft/sec}^2$$

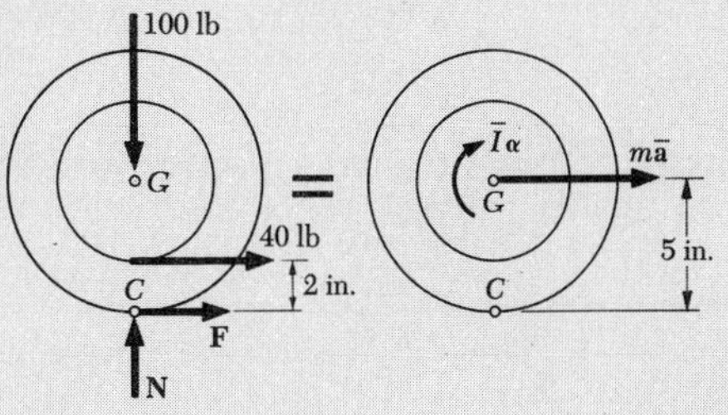

$\overset{+}{\rightarrow} \Sigma F_x = m\bar{a}$: $\quad F + 40 = m\bar{a}$

$$F + 40 = (3.11)(3.46)$$

$$F = -29.3 \text{ lb} \qquad \mathbf{F} = 29.3 \text{ lb} \leftarrow$$

$+\uparrow \Sigma F_y = 0$: $\quad N - 100 = 0 \qquad \mathbf{N} = 100 \text{ lb} \uparrow$

Maximum Available Friction Force

$$F_{\max} = \mu_s N = (0.20)(100) = 20 \text{ lb}$$

Since $F > F_{\max}$, the assumed motion is impossible.

b. **Rolling and Sliding.** Since the wheel must roll and slide at the same time, we draw a new diagram, where $\bar{a}$ and α are independent and where

$$F = F_k = \mu_k N = (0.15)(100) = 15 \text{ lb}$$

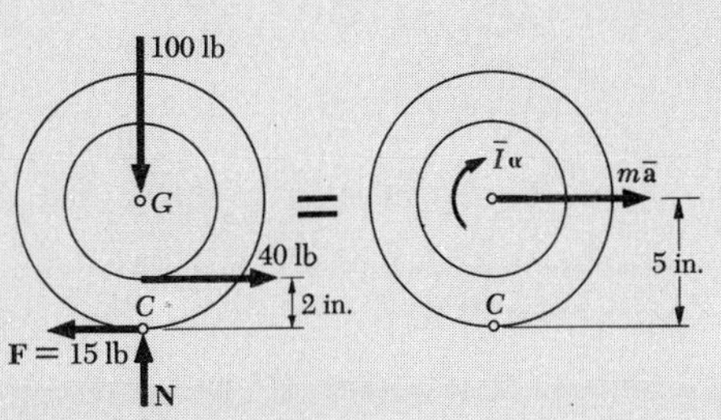

From the computation of part *a*, it appears that **F** should be directed to the left.

$\overset{+}{\rightarrow} \Sigma F_x = m\bar{a}$: $\quad 40 - 15 = 3.11\bar{a}$

$$\bar{a} = +8.04 \text{ ft/sec}^2 \qquad \bar{\mathbf{a}} = 8.04 \text{ ft/sec}^2 \rightarrow \blacktriangleleft$$

$+\circlearrowleft \Sigma M_G = \bar{I}\alpha$: $\quad (15)(\tfrac{5}{12}) - (40)(\tfrac{3}{12}) = 0.264\alpha$

$$\alpha = -14.2 \text{ radians/sec}^2 \qquad \boldsymbol{\alpha} = 14.2 \text{ radians/sec}^2 \circlearrowright \blacktriangleleft$$

SAMPLE PROBLEM 16.10

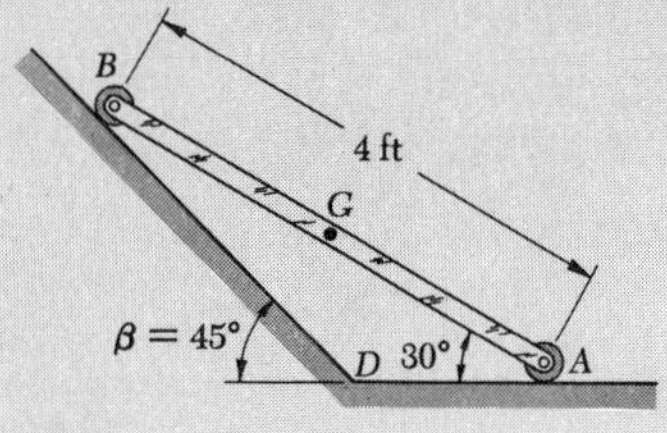

The extremities of a 4-ft rod, weighing 50 lb, may move freely and with no friction along two straight tracks as shown. If the rod is released with no velocity from the position shown, determine (*a*) the angular acceleration of the rod, (*b*) the reactions at *A* and *B*.

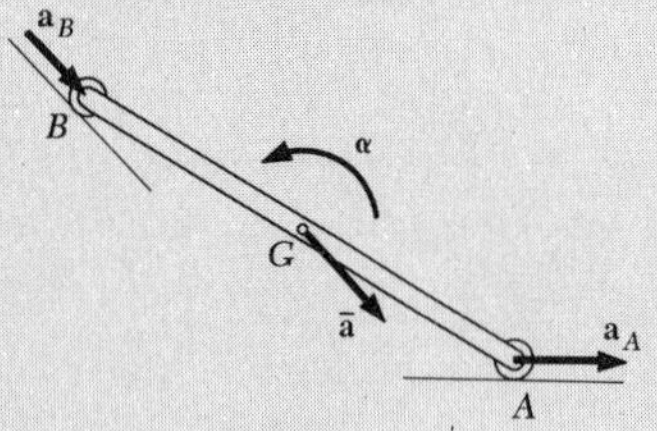

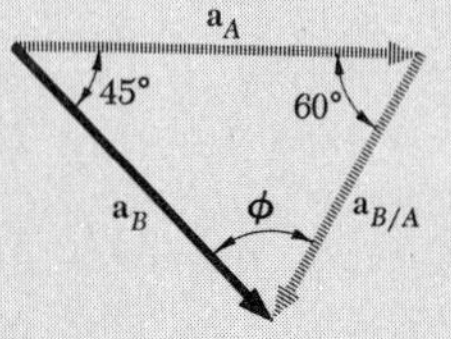

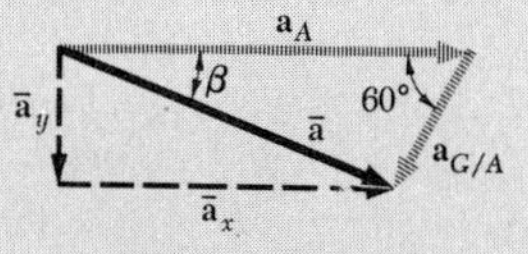

Kinematics of Motion. Since the motion is constrained, the acceleration of *G* must be related to the angular acceleration $\boldsymbol{\alpha}$. To obtain this relation, we shall first determine the magnitude of the acceleration $\mathbf{a}_A$ of point *A* in terms of α; assuming $\boldsymbol{\alpha}$ directed counterclockwise and noting that $a_{B/A} = 4\alpha$, we write

$$\mathbf{a}_B = \mathbf{a}_A + \mathbf{a}_{B/A}$$

$$[a_B \searrow 45°] = [a_A \rightarrow] + [4\alpha \nearrow 60°]$$

Noting that $\phi = 75°$ and using the law of sines, we obtain

$$a_A = 5.46\alpha \qquad a_B = 4.90\alpha$$

The acceleration of *G* is now obtained by writing

$$\bar{\mathbf{a}} = \mathbf{a}_G = \mathbf{a}_A + \mathbf{a}_{G/A}$$

$$\bar{\mathbf{a}} = [5.46\alpha \rightarrow] + [2\alpha \nearrow 60°]$$

Resolving $\bar{\mathbf{a}}$ into *x* and *y* components, we obtain

$$\bar{a}_x = 5.46\alpha - 2\alpha \cos 60° = 4.46\alpha \qquad \bar{\mathbf{a}}_x = 4.46\alpha \rightarrow$$

$$\bar{a}_y = -2\alpha \sin 60° = -1.732\alpha \qquad \bar{\mathbf{a}}_y = 1.732\alpha \downarrow$$

Kinetics of Motion. We draw the two sketches shown to express that the system of external forces is equivalent to the system of effective forces represented by the vector of components $m\bar{\mathbf{a}}_x$ and $m\bar{\mathbf{a}}_y$ attached at *G* and the couple $\bar{I}\alpha$. We compute the following magnitudes:

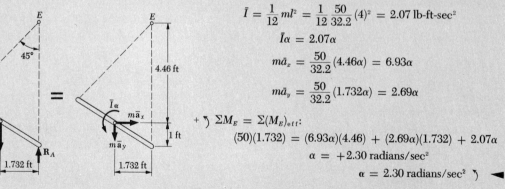

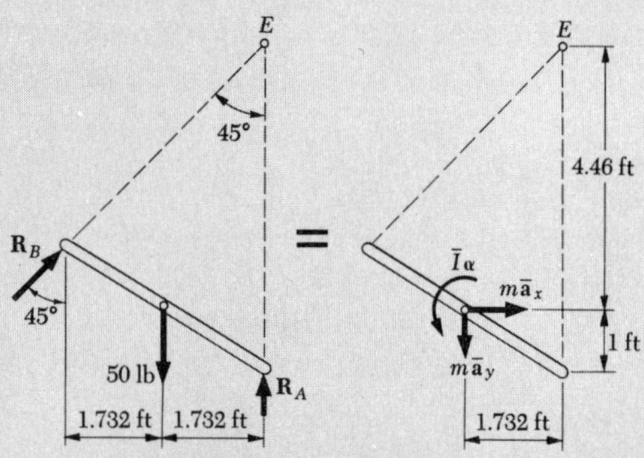

$$\bar{I} = \frac{1}{12}ml^2 = \frac{1}{12}\frac{50}{32.2}(4)^2 = 2.07 \text{ lb-ft-sec}^2$$

$$\bar{I}\alpha = 2.07\alpha$$

$$m\bar{a}_x = \frac{50}{32.2}(4.46\alpha) = 6.93\alpha$$

$$m\bar{a}_y = \frac{50}{32.2}(1.732\alpha) = 2.69\alpha$$

$$+\circlearrowleft \Sigma M_E = \Sigma(M_E)_{\text{eff}}:$$

$$(50)(1.732) = (6.93\alpha)(4.46) + (2.69\alpha)(1.732) + 2.07\alpha$$

$$\alpha = +2.30 \text{ radians/sec}^2$$

$$\boldsymbol{\alpha} = 2.30 \text{ radians/sec}^2 \circlearrowleft \quad ◀$$

Using the computed value of α and writing $\Sigma F_x = m\bar{a}_x$ and $\Sigma F_y = m\bar{a}_y$, we obtain

$$\mathbf{R}_A = 27.9 \text{ lb} \uparrow \quad ◀$$

$$\mathbf{R}_B = 22.5 \text{ lb} \angle 45° \quad ◀$$

PROBLEMS

16.63. Show that the couple $\bar{I}\alpha$ of Fig. 16.11 may be eliminated by attaching the vectors $m\bar{a}_t$ and $m\bar{a}_n$ at a point P called the *center of percussion*, located on line OG at a distance $GP = \bar{k}^2/\bar{r}$ from the mass center of the body.

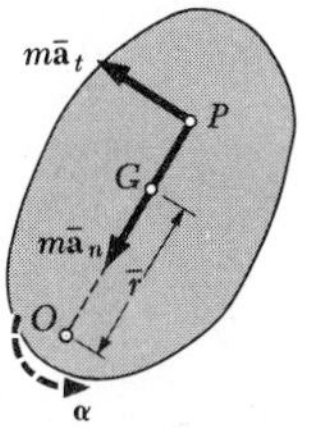

FIG. P 16.63

16.64. A uniform slender rod, of length $L = 48$ in. and weight $W = 16$ lb, hangs freely from a hinge at A. A horizontal force **P** of magnitude 30 lb is applied as shown. For $h = 48$ in., determine (a) the angular acceleration of the rod, (b) the components of the reaction at A.

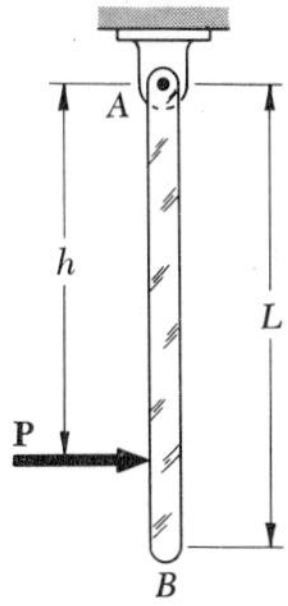

FIG. P 16.64

16.65. In Prob. 16.64, determine (a) the distance h for which the horizontal component of the reaction at A is zero, (b) the corresponding angular acceleration of the rod.

16.66. In Prob. 16.64, determine the range of values of h for which the magnitude of the *total* reaction at A does not exceed 20 lb.

16.67. A turbine disk weighing 155 lb rotates at a constant speed of 9,600 rpm; the mass center of the disk coincides with the center of rotation O. Determine the reaction at O after a single vane at A, weighing 1.50 oz, becomes loose and is thrown off.

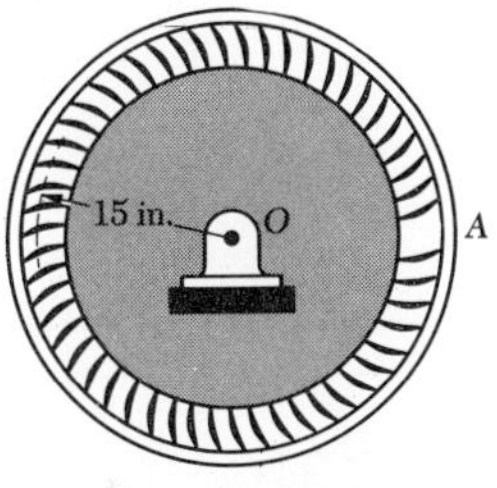

FIG. P 16.67

16.68. A 3,220-lb flywheel, of 4-ft diameter, is mounted on a fixed horizontal shaft. When the wheel rotates at a constant speed of 1,200 rpm, it exerts on the shaft a force varying from 12,580 lb upward to 19,020 lb downward. Determine the distance from the center of the shaft to the mass center of the flywheel.

16.69 and 16.70. A uniform slender beam of length L, weighing w lb/ft, is suspended from two cables as shown. If the cable at A suddenly breaks, determine (a) the tension in the cable at B, (b) the acceleration of end A.

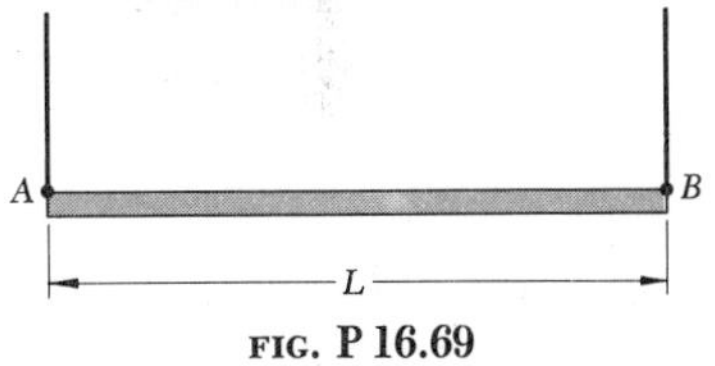

FIG. P 16.69

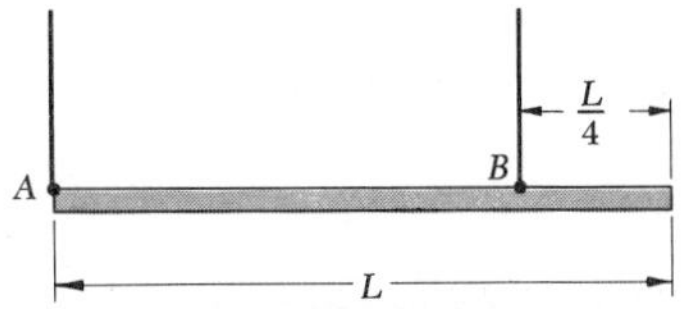

FIG. P 16.70

16.71. A collar C of weight W_C is rigidly attached to a uniform slender rod AB of length L and weight W. If the rod is released from rest in the position shown, determine the ratio d/L for which the reaction at B is independent of W_C.

***16.72.** A collar C of weight 2 lb is rigidly attached to a uniform slender rod AB of weight 12 lb and length $L = 20$ in. If the rod is released from rest in the position shown, determine the distance d for which the angular acceleration of the rod is maximum.

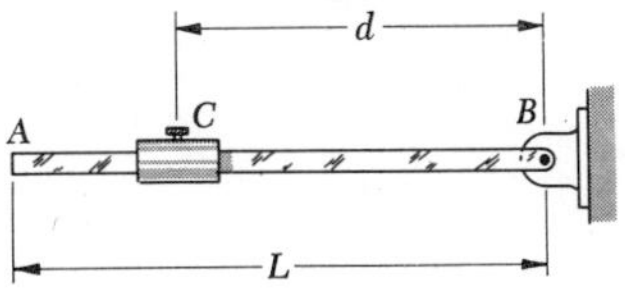

FIG. P 16.71 AND P 16.72

16.73. After being released, the plate of Sample Prob. 16.7 is allowed to swing through 90°. Knowing that at that instant the angular velocity of the plate is 4.82 radians/sec, determine (a) the angular acceleration of the plate, (b) the components of the reaction at A.

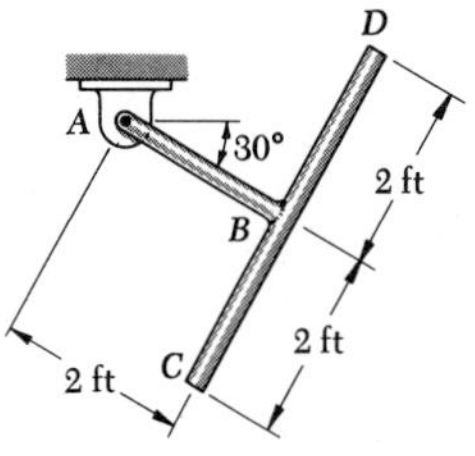

FIG. P 16.74

16.74. Two rods, each of weight 4 lb/ft, are welded together and rotate about A. In the position shown, the angular velocity of the rods is 5 radians/sec clockwise. Determine (a) the angular acceleration of the rods, (b) the components of the reaction at A.

°**16.75.** A uniform slender rod AB, of length $L = 4$ ft and weight 10 lb, is held in the position shown by three wires. If $\theta = 60°$, determine the tension in wires AC and BC immediately after wire AD has been cut.

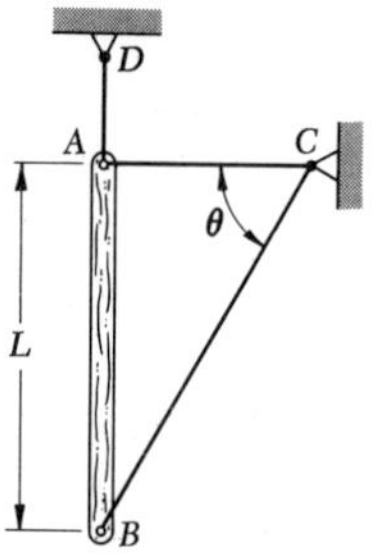

FIG. P 16.75

16.76. One end of a homogeneous rod of weight W rests on a rough horizontal surface. The rod is maintained at an angle $\beta = 60°$ by means of a string attached to its other end. The string is suddenly cut. Assuming that the friction between end A and the surface is large enough to prevent sliding, determine (a) the angular acceleration of the rod just after the string is cut, (b) the normal reaction and the friction force at A, (c) the minimum value of μ compatible with the described motion.

°**16.77.** Knowing that the coefficient of friction between the rod and the floor is 0.30, determine the range of values of β for which the rod *will* slip immediately after the string at B is cut.

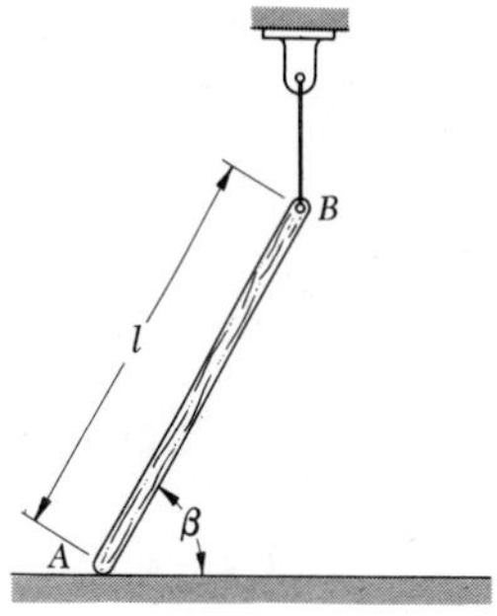

FIG. P 16.76 AND P 16.77

16.78. Derive the equation $\Sigma M_C = I_C\alpha$ for the rolling disk of Fig. 16.13, where ΣM_C represents the sum of the moments of the external forces about the instantaneous center C and I_C the moment of inertia of the disk about C.

16.79. Show that, in the case of an unbalanced disk, the equation derived in Prob. 16.78 is valid only when the mass center G, the geometric center O, and the instantaneous center C happen to lie in a straight line.

16.80. A cylinder of weight W and radius r rolls down an incline. Denoting by μ the coefficient of friction between the cylinder and the incline, determine the largest angle of inclination β for which no slipping will occur.

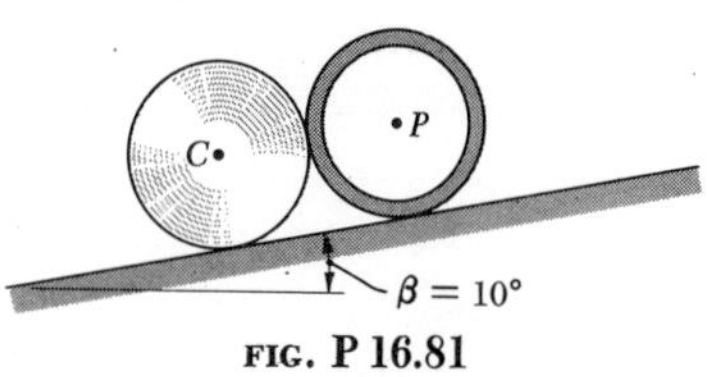

FIG. P 16.81

16.81. A cylinder C and a section of pipe P are in contact when they are released from rest. Knowing that both the cylinder and the pipe roll without slipping, determine the clear distance between them after 3 sec.

16.82. A flywheel is rigidly attached to a shaft of $1\frac{1}{2}$-in. radius which may roll along parallel rails as shown. When released from rest, the system rolls 16 ft in 40 sec. Determine the centroidal radius of gyration of the system.

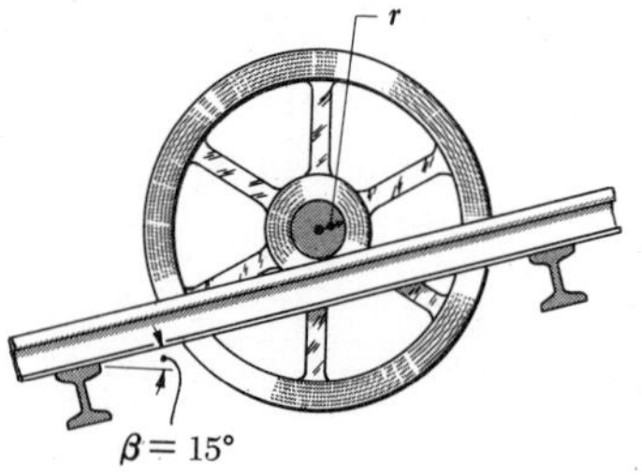

FIG. P 16.82 AND P 16.83

16.83. A flywheel of centroidal radius of gyration $\bar{k}$ is rigidly attached to a shaft of radius r which may roll along parallel rails. Denoting by μ the coefficient of friction between the shaft and the rails, derive an expression for the largest angle of inclination β for which no slipping will occur.

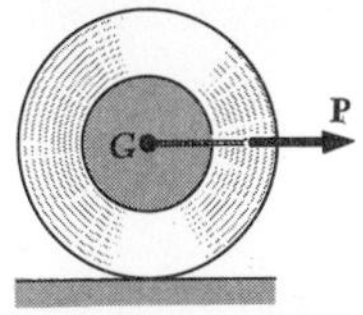

FIG. P 16.84 AND P 16.88

16.84 through 16.87. A drum of 6-in. radius is attached to a disk of 12-in. radius. The disk and drum have a total weight of 8 lb and a radius of gyration of 9 in. A cord is attached as shown and pulled with a force **P** of magnitude 4 lb. Knowing that the disk rolls without sliding, determine (*a*) the angular acceleration of the disk and the acceleration of *G*, (*b*) the minimum value of the coefficient of friction compatible with this motion.

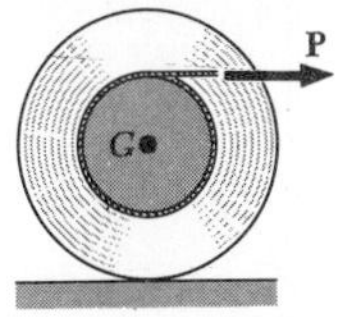

FIG. P 16.85 AND P 16.89

16.88 through 16.91. A drum of 6-in. radius is attached to a disk of 12-in. radius. The disk and drum have a total weight of 8 lb and a radius of gyration of 9 in. A cord is attached as shown and pulled with a force **P** of magnitude 4 lb. Knowing that $\mu = 0.20$, determine (*a*) whether or not the disk slides, (*b*) the angular acceleration of the disk and the acceleration of *G*.

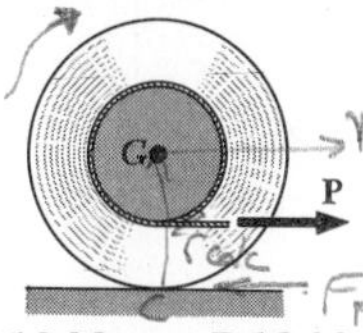

FIG. P 16.86 AND P 16.90

16.92. Find the magnitude of the maximum force **P** which may be applied to the disk of Prob. 16.91 if the disk is to roll without sliding.

16.93. The cord attached to the drum of Prob. 16.87 is pulled to the right in a direction forming an angle β with the horizontal and with a force **P** of magnitude 4 lb. Determine the range of values of β for which the disk (*a*) rolls to the right, (*b*) rolls to the left. Assume that μ is large enough to prevent sliding.

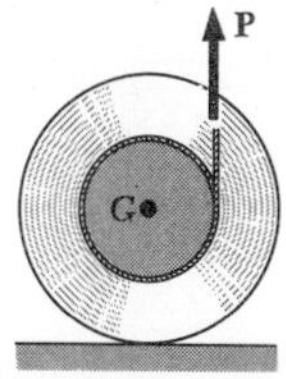

FIG. P 16.87 AND P 16.91

16.94. Two disks *A* and *B*, weighing 20 lb each, are connected by a rod *CD* of negligible weight. A couple **M** of magnitude 15 lb-ft is applied to disk *A*. Knowing that the disks roll without sliding, determine (*a*) the acceleration of the center of each disk, (*b*) the minimum value of μ for each disk compatible with the motion described.

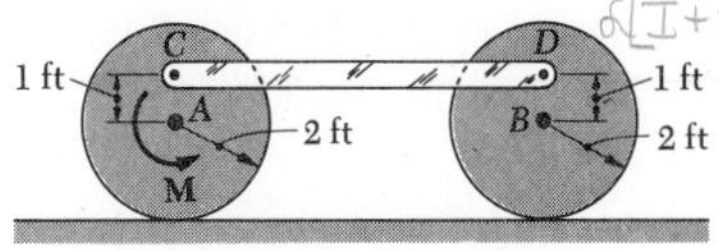

FIG. P 16.94

16.95. Solve Prob. 16.94 assuming that the disks have rotated through 180° so that points *C* and *D* are directly below points *A* and *B* respectively.

16.96. A hemisphere of weight *W* and radius *r* is released from rest in the position shown. Determine (*a*) the minimum value of μ for which the hemisphere starts to roll without sliding, (*b*) the corresponding acceleration of point *B*. [*Hint.* Note that $OG = \frac{3}{8}r$ and that, by the parallel-axis theorem, $\bar{I} = \frac{2}{5}mr^2 - m(OG)^2$.]

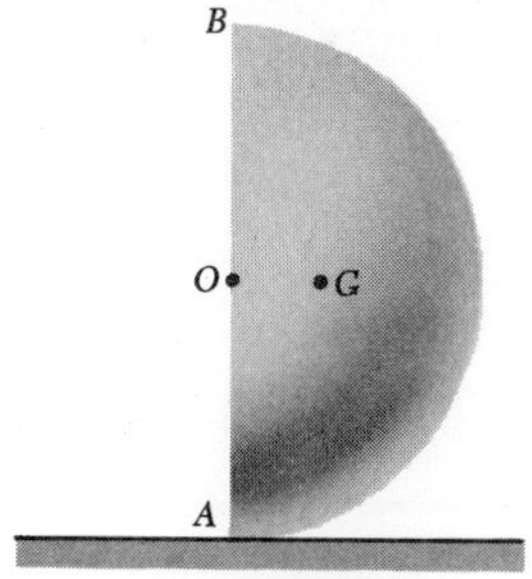

FIG. P 16.96

16.97. Solve Prob. 16.96, considering a half cylinder instead of a hemisphere. [*Hint.* Note that $OG = 4r/3\pi$ and that $\bar{I} = \frac{1}{2}mr^2 - m(OG)^2$.]

16.98. A slender rod *OA* of weight 10 lb is rigidly attached to a 10-lb disk as shown. At the instant when $\beta = 90°$, the center *O* of the disk has a velocity of 3 ft/sec and an acceleration of 4 ft/sec² both directed to the left. Knowing that the disk rolls without sliding, determine the magnitude of the force **P** applied to the disk.

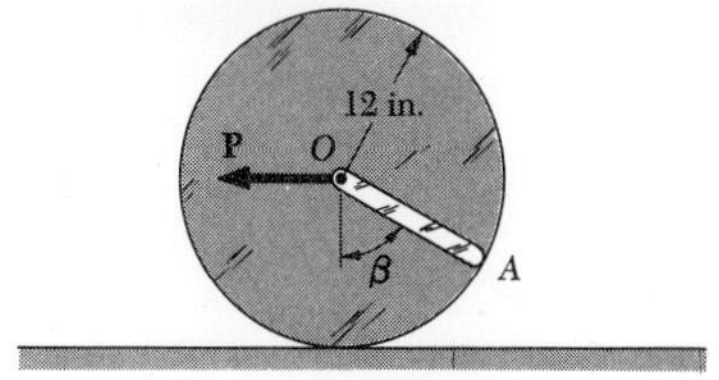

FIG. P 16.98

16.99. Solve Prob. 16.98 assuming $\beta = 270°$.

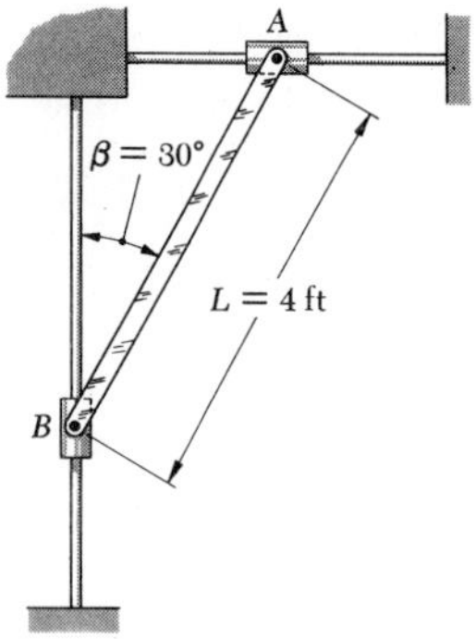

FIG. P 16.100

16.100. Ends A and B of a 10-lb slender rod are attached to collars which slide without friction along the rods shown. A horizontal force **P** is applied to collar A, causing the rod to start from rest with a clockwise angular acceleration of 3 radians/sec^2. Neglecting the weight of the collars, determine (a) the required magnitude of **P**, (b) the reactions at A and B.

16.101. Solve Prob. 16.100 assuming that at the instant considered the angular velocity of the rod is 2 radians/sec counterclockwise.

16.102. The motion of the rod of Sample Prob. 16.10 is to be controlled by a horizontal force **P** applied at A. If at the instant shown the angular velocity of the rod is 3 radians/sec clockwise and the angular acceleration of the rod is 2 radians/sec^2 counterclockwise, determine the required magnitude and sense of the force **P**.

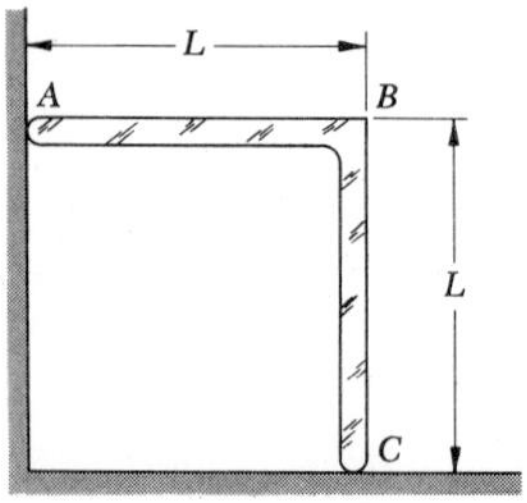

FIG. P 16.103 AND P 16.104

16.103. Two uniform rods AB and BC, each of length $L = 2$ ft, are welded together at B to form a rigid body of total weight 12 lb. A horizontal force **P** is applied at C, causing point C to start from rest with an acceleration of 10 ft/sec^2 to the left. Neglecting the effect of friction at A and at C, determine (a) the required magnitude of **P**, (b) the reactions at A and at C.

16.104. Two rods AB and BC, each of weight W and length L, are welded together at B and released from rest in the position shown. Neglecting the effect of friction at A and C, determine (a) the angular acceleration of the system, (b) the reactions at A and at C.

16.105. The rod of Prob. 16.100 is released from rest in the position shown. Determine (a) the angular acceleration of the rod, (b) the reactions at A and B.

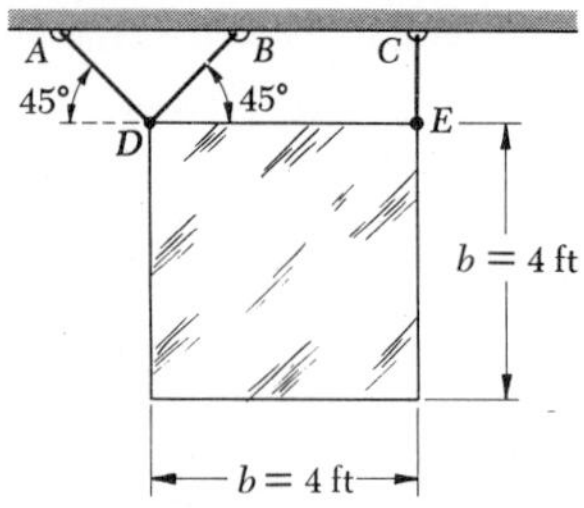

FIG. P 16.106 AND P 16.107

16.106. A 50-lb sign is held in place by the three cables shown. Determine the tension in cables BD and CE immediately after the cable AD has been cut.

16.107. A 50-lb sign is held in place by the three cables shown. Determine the tension in cables AD and CE immediately after cable BD has been cut.

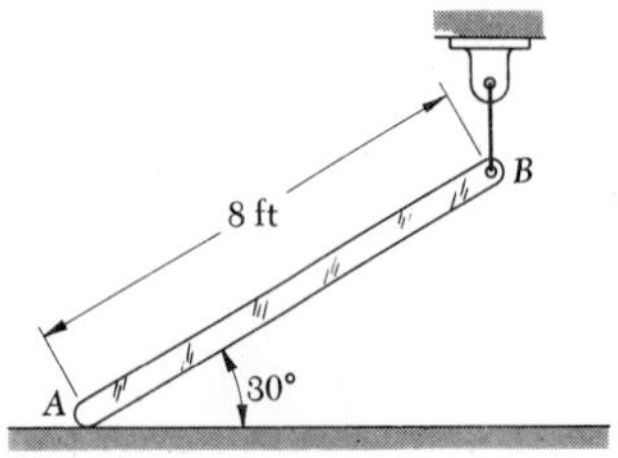

FIG. P 16.108

16.108. An 8-ft steel beam weighing 200 lb is being temporarily held in the position shown when the cable attached at B breaks. Determine the reaction at A immediately after the cable breaks, assuming that μ is zero at A.

***16.109.** Solve Prob. 16.108 assuming that $\mu = 0.30$ between end A and the horizontal surface.

*16.110. A uniform rod AB, of weight $W = 5$ lb and length $L = 4$ ft, is released from rest in the position shown. Knowing that $\beta = 30°$, determine the values immediately after release of (*a*) the angular acceleration of the rod, (*b*) the acceleration of end A, (*c*) the reaction at A. Neglect the weight and friction of the roller at A.

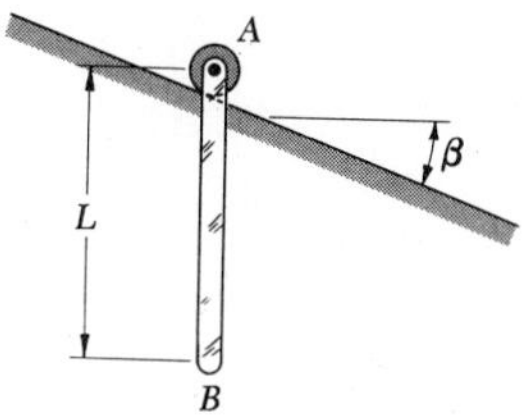

FIG. P 16.110 AND P 16.111

*16.111. A uniform slender rod of length L is released from rest in the position shown. Derive an expression for (*a*) the angular acceleration of the rod, (*b*) the acceleration of end A, (*c*) the reaction at A, immediately after release. Neglect the weight and friction of the roller at A.

16.112. Show that, for a rigid body in plane motion, the equation $\Sigma M_A = I_A \alpha$, where ΣM_A represents the sum of the moments of the external forces about point A and I_A the moment of inertia of the body about the same point A, is verified *if and only if* one of the following conditions is satisfied: (*a*) A is the mass center of the body, (*b*) A has zero acceleration, (*c*) the acceleration of A is directed along a line joining point A and the mass center G.

16.113. A 6-lb rod AB is attached to the disk shown which rotates about O with a constant clockwise angular velocity of 10 radians/sec. Determine the forces exerted on the rod at A and B when (*a*) $\beta = 0$, (*b*) $\beta = 180°$.

16.114. Solve Prob. 16.113 when $\beta = 90°$.

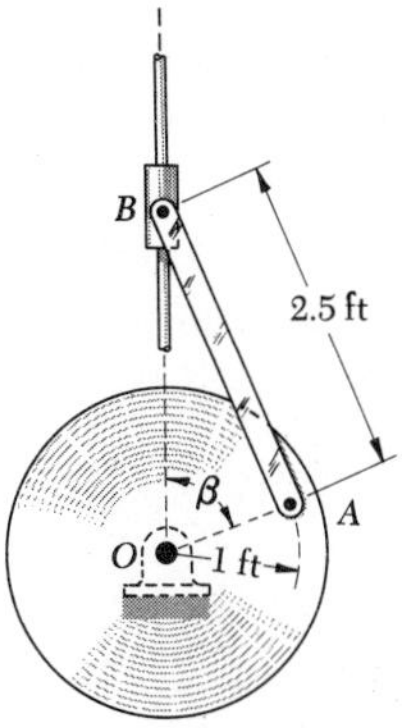

FIG. P 16.113

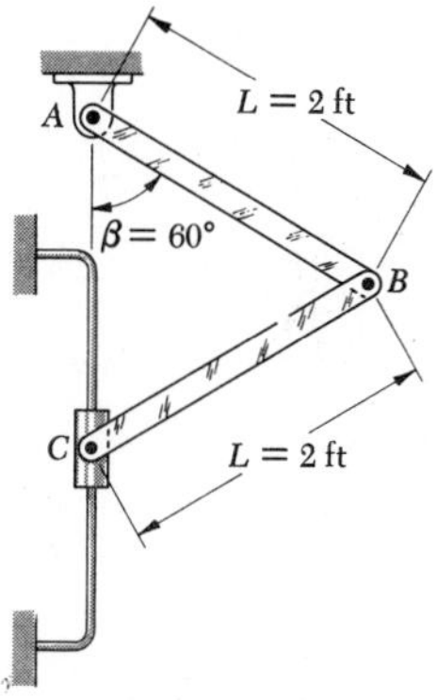

FIG. P 16.115 AND P 16.116

16.115. Each of the two bars shown is 2 ft long and weighs 10 lb. A vertical and variable force **P** is applied at C, causing point C to move up at a constant speed of 30 ft/sec. Determine the magnitude of **P** for the position shown.

16.116. The two bars AB and BC are released from rest in the position shown. Each bar is 2 ft long and weighs 10 lb. Determine the angular acceleration of each bar and the reactions at A and C immediately after release.

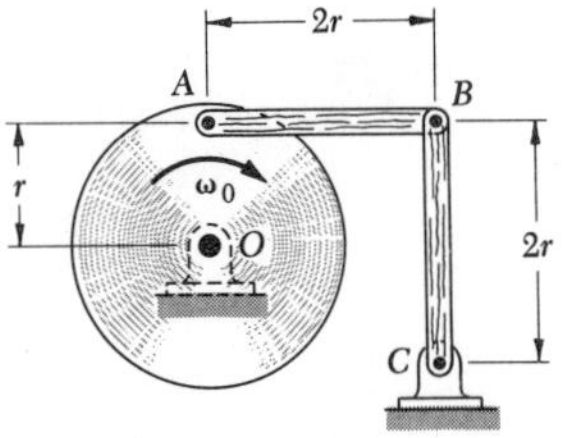

FIG. P 16.117

16.117. Two rods *AB* and *BC*, each of weight *W* and length $2r$, are connected as shown to a disk which is made to rotate in a vertical plane at a constant angular velocity ω_0. For the position shown, determine (*a*) the components of the forces exerted at *A* and *B* on rod *AB*, (*b*) the reaction at *C*.

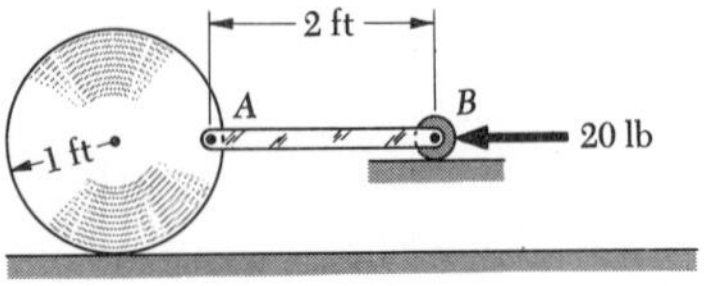

FIG. P 16.118

16.118. A 2-ft rod *AB* of weight 10 lb is attached to a 1-ft-radius disk of weight 10 lb as shown. When the system is at rest, a 20-lb force is applied at *B*. Knowing that the disk rolls without sliding, determine (*a*) the angular accelerations of the disk and of the rod, (*b*) the force exerted on the disk at *A*.

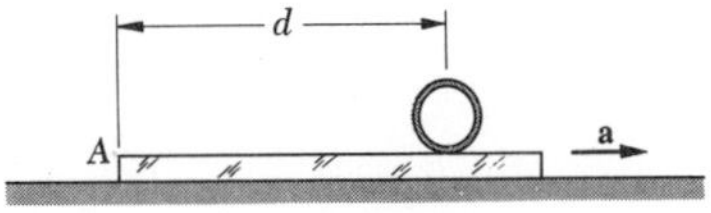

FIG. P 16.119

***16.119.** A section of pipe rests on a plate. The plate is then given a constant acceleration **a** directed to the right. Assuming that the pipe rolls on the plate, determine (*a*) the acceleration of the pipe, (*b*) the distance through which the plate will move before the pipe reaches end *A*.

***16.120.** Solve Prob. 16.119 assuming that the pipe is replaced (*a*) by a solid cylinder, (*b*) by a sphere.

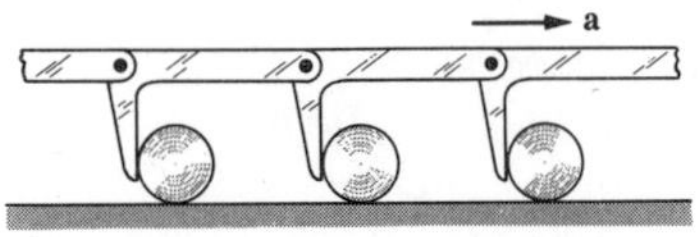

FIG. P 16.121 AND P 16.122

***16.121.** Identical cylinders of weight *W* and radius *r* are pushed by a series of moving arms. The coefficient of friction between all surfaces is μ. Denoting by *a* the magnitude of the acceleration of the arms, derive an expression for (*a*) the maximum allowable value of *a* if each cylinder is to roll without sliding, (*b*) the minimum allowable value of *a* if each cylinder is to move to the right without rotating.

***16.122.** Identical cylinders of weight 5 lb and radius 2 in. are pushed by a series of arms as shown. The coefficient of friction between all surfaces is 0.20. Determine the horizontal component of the force exerted on each cylinder when the acceleration of the cylinders is (*a*) 5 ft/sec^2 to the right, (*b*) 10 ft/sec^2 to the right.

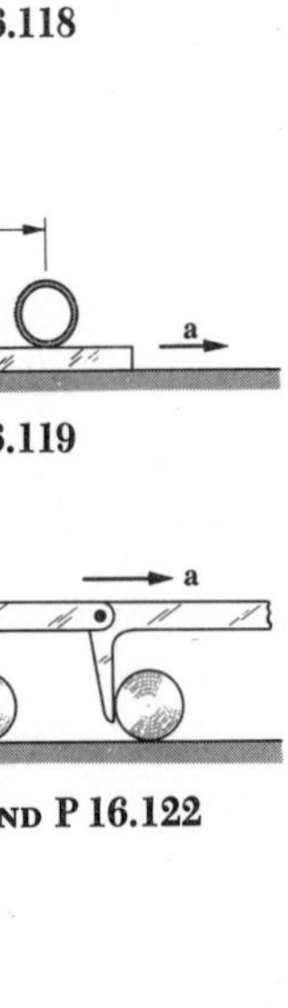

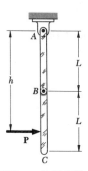

FIG. P 16.123 AND P 16.125

***16.123.** Two slender uniform bars *AB* and *BC* hang freely as shown. Each bar is of length $L = 2$ ft and weighs 5 lb. A horizontal force **P** of magnitude 3 lb is applied at *C*. Determine the angular acceleration of each bar.

***16.124.** Solve Prob. 16.123 assuming that the 3-lb force is applied at point *B*.

***16.125.** Two identical uniform bars *AB* and *BC* hang freely as shown. A horizontal force **P** is applied at a distance *h* below *A*. Determine the distance *h* for which the two bars start to move as if they formed a single rigid body. (*Hint.* The angular accelerations of the bars must be equal.)

***16.126.** Two disks of weight W and radius r are connected by a continuous chain belt as shown. The pin C is suddenly removed. Determine the value, immediately after the removal of C, (a) of the angular acceleration of each disk, (b) of the tension in the left-hand portion of the belt, (c) of the acceleration of point B.

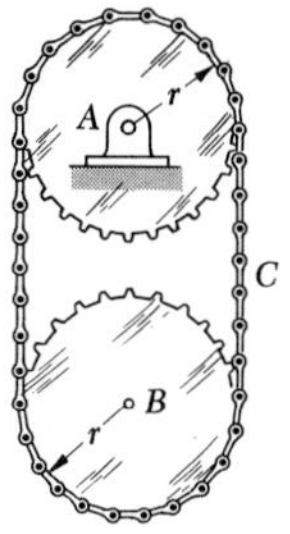

FIG. P 16.126

***16.127.** Two uniform bars AB and BC are connected by a pin at B and are held in a horizontal position by three wires as shown. Each bar is of length $L = 2$ ft and weighs 5 lb. The wires attached at D and B are cut simultaneously; determine at that instant (a) the angular acceleration of each bar, (b) the accelerations of points A and B, (c) the tension in the remaining wire attached at C.

***16.128.** Two identical uniform bars AB and BC are held in a horizontal position by three wires as shown. The wires attached at B and C are cut simultaneously; determine the distance d for which the two bars start to move as if they formed a single rigid body. (*Hint.* The angular accelerations of the bars must be equal.)

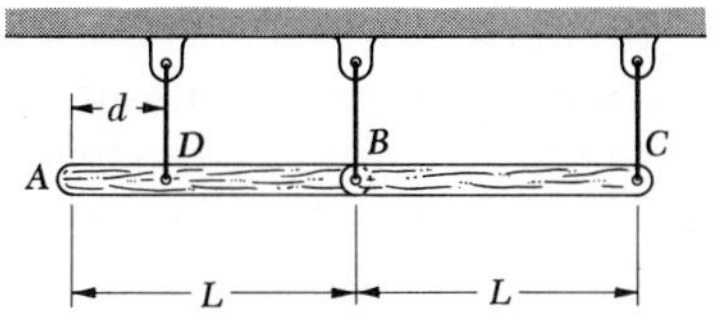

FIG. P 16.127 AND P 16.128

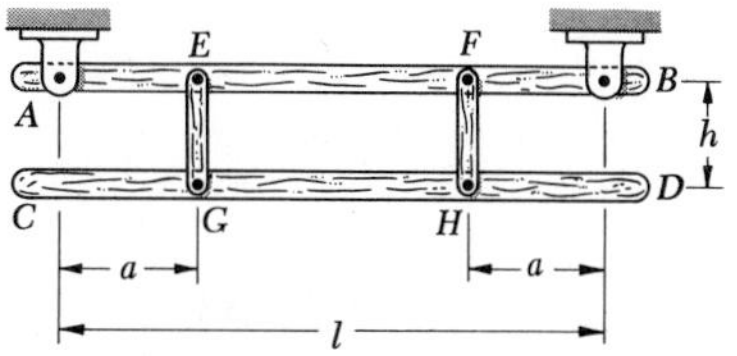

FIG. P 16.129

***16.129.** Two uniform slender rods AB and CD, each of weight W and length l, are connected by two weightless links EG and FH. If the pin support at B is suddenly removed, determine (a) the angular acceleration of each rod, (b) the accelerations of points B and D.

***16.130.** Solve Prob. 16.129 assuming that the connections at E, F, G, and H are welded so that no relative rotation can occur between the rods and the links.

***16.131.** Solve Prob. 16.129 assuming that the two vertical links are replaced by a single vertical link connecting the centers of rods AB and CD.

***16.132.** Draw the shear and bending-moment diagrams for the beam of Prob. 16.69 immediately after cable A breaks.

***16.133.** (a) Determine the magnitude and the location of the maximum bending moment in the rod of Prob. 16.64. (b) Show that the answer to part a is independent of the weight W of the rod.

*16.134. In Prob. 16.104, draw the shear and bending-moment diagrams for rod AB immediately after the rods have been released.

*16.135. In Prob. 16.104, draw the shear and bending-moment diagrams for rod BC immediately after the rods have been released.

REVIEW PROBLEMS

16.136. A uniform slender rod of length l, weighing w lb/ft, rotates about a vertical axis AA' at a constant angular velocity ω. Determine the tension in the bar at a distance x from the axis of rotation.

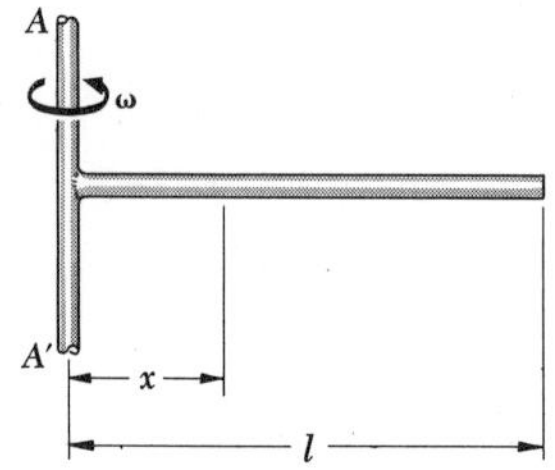

FIG. P 16.136

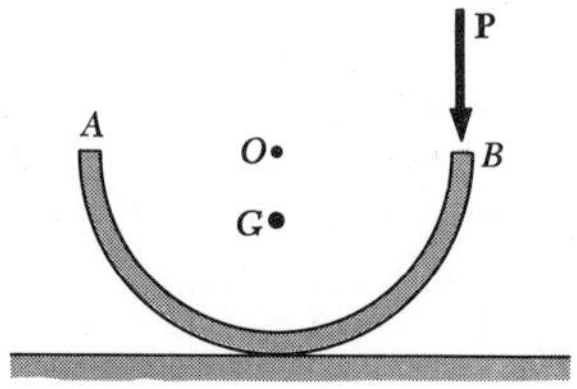

FIG. P 16.137

16.137. A half section of pipe of weight W and radius r rests on a rough horizontal surface. A vertical force **P** is applied as shown. Assuming that the section rolls without sliding, derive an expression (*a*) for its angular acceleration, (*b*) for the minimum value of μ compatible with this motion. [*Hint.* Note that $OG = 2r/\pi$ and that, by the parallel-axis theorem, $\bar{I} = mr^2 - m(OG)^2$.]

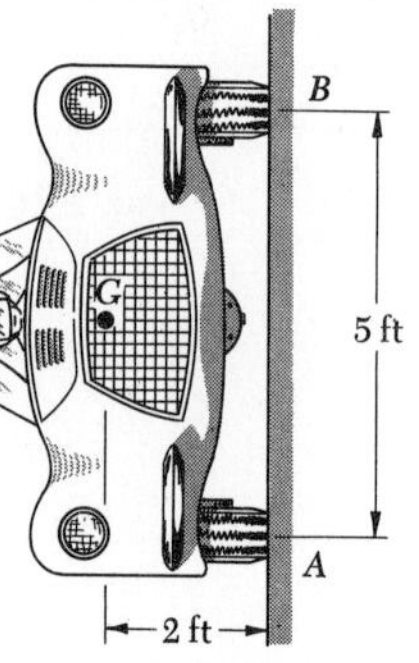

FIG. P 16.138

16.138. A daredevil drives a small automobile weighing 1,200 lb (driver included) on the vertical wall of a cylindrical pit of radius 32 ft at a speed of 30 mph. Knowing that this is the slowest speed at which he can perform this stunt, determine (*a*) the coefficient of friction between tires and wall, (*b*) the normal component of the reaction of the wall at each wheel.

16.139. If the coefficient of friction between the wall and the tires of the automobile of Prob. 16.138 is 0.40, determine (*a*) the lowest safe speed at which the stunt can be performed, (*b*) the normal component of the reaction of the wall at each wheel.

16.140. A block B of weight W is attached to a cord wrapped around a cylinder of the same weight W and of radius r. The cylinder rolls without sliding on a horizontal surface. Determine the components of the accelerations of the center A of the cylinder and of the block B immediately after the system has been released from rest if (*a*) the block hangs freely, (*b*) the motion of the block is guided by a rigid member DAE, frictionless and of negligible weight, which is hinged to the cylinder at A.

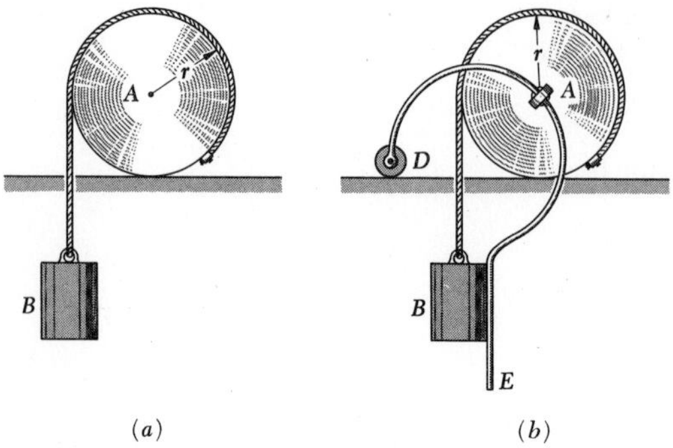

FIG. P 16.140

16.141. Knowing that the coefficient of friction between the tires and road is 0.75 for the car shown, determine the maximum possible acceleration on a level road, assuming (*a*) four-wheel drive, (*b*) conventional rear-wheel drive, (*c*) front-wheel drive.

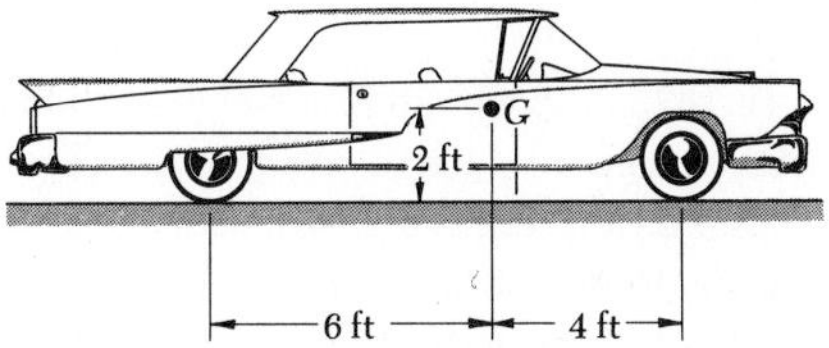

FIG. P 16.141

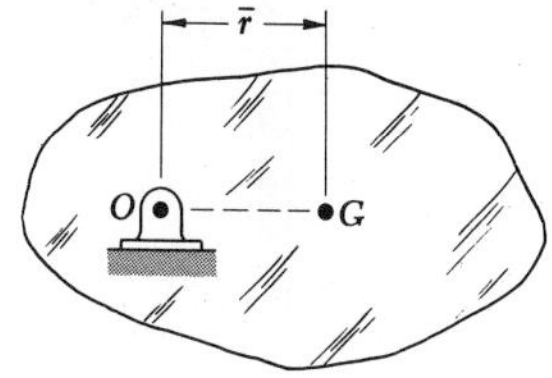

FIG. P 16.142

16.142. A body of weight W and centroidal radius of gyration $\bar{k}$ can rotate freely about a shaft O located at a distance $\bar{r}$ from its mass center G. If the body is released from rest in the position shown, determine (*a*) the distance $\bar{r}$ for which the angular acceleration of the body is maximum, (*b*) the corresponding vertical component of the reaction at O.

16.143. The flanged wheel shown rolls to the right with a constant velocity of 4 ft/sec. The rod AB is 4 ft long and weighs 10 lb. Knowing that point A slides without friction on the horizontal surface, determine the reaction at A (*a*) when $\beta = 0$, (*b*) when $\beta = 180°$.

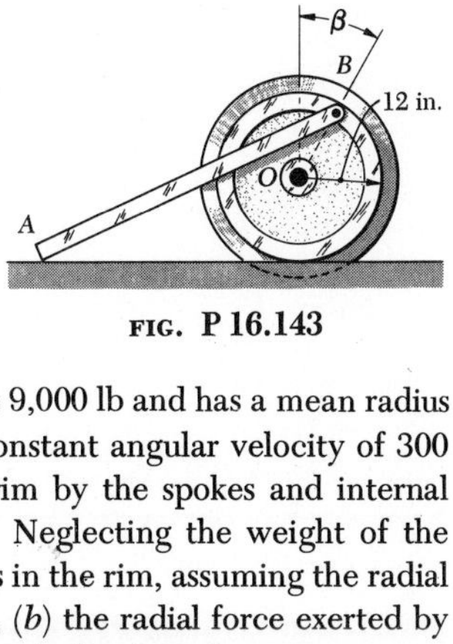

FIG. P 16.143

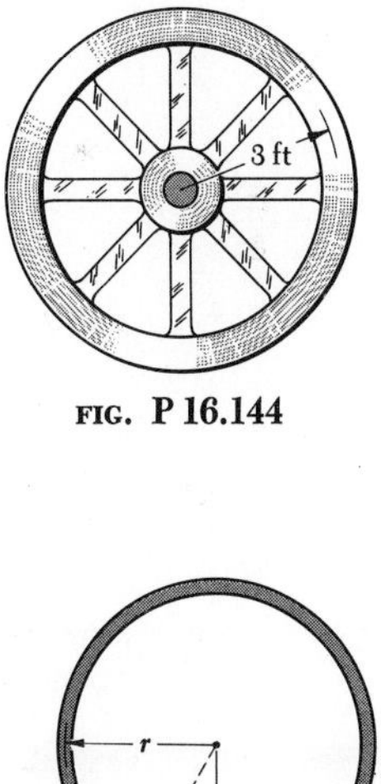

FIG. P 16.144

16.144. The rim of a flywheel weighs 9,000 lb and has a mean radius of 3 ft. As the flywheel rotates at a constant angular velocity of 300 rpm, radial forces are exerted on the rim by the spokes and internal forces are developed within the rim. Neglecting the weight of the spokes, determine (*a*) the internal forces in the rim, assuming the radial forces exerted by the spokes to be zero, (*b*) the radial force exerted by each spoke, assuming the tangential forces in the rim to be zero.

16.145. A section of pipe, of weight 100 lb and radius 1 ft, rests on two corners as shown. Assuming that μ between the corners and the pipe is sufficient to prevent sliding, determine (*a*) the angular acceleration of the pipe just after corner B is removed, (*b*) the corresponding magnitude of the reaction at A.

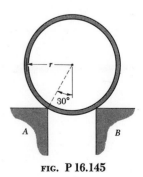

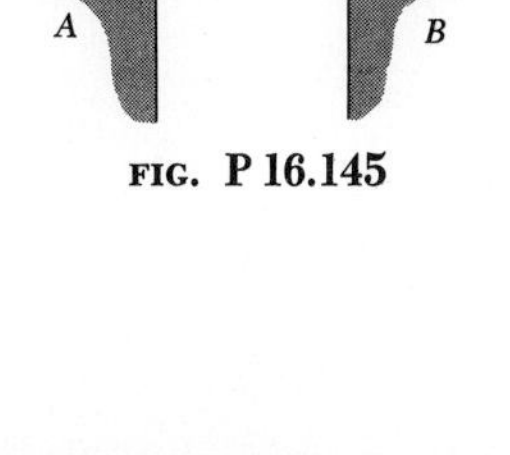

FIG. P 16.145

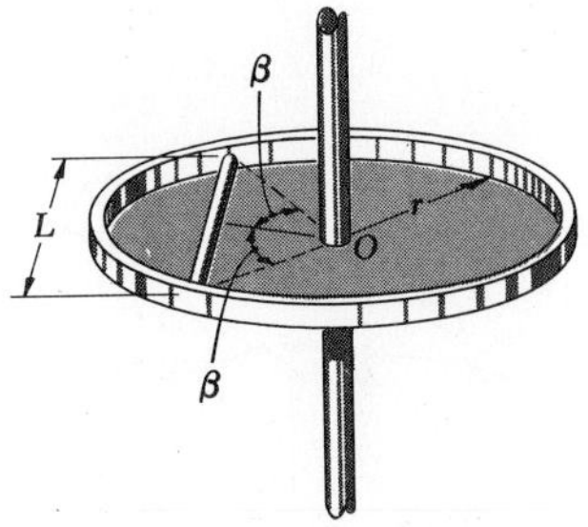

FIG. P 16.146

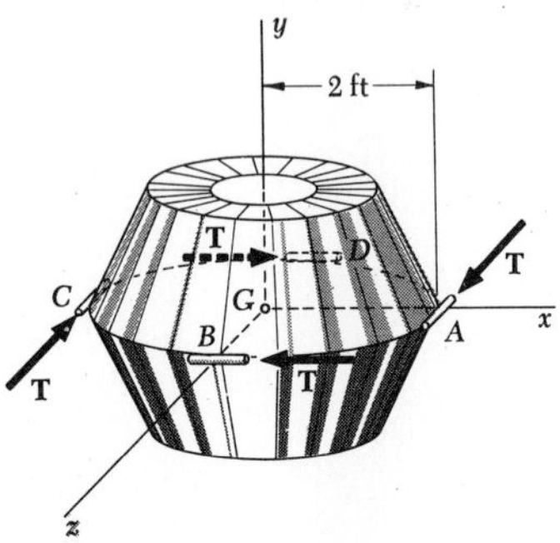

FIG. P 16.147

*16.146. A slender rod AB of weight w lb/ft is placed inside a shallow drum of radius r which rotates at a constant angular velocity ω about a vertical shaft through O. (*a*) Determine the ratio L/r for which the maximum bending moment in the rod is as large as possible. (*b*) Derive an expression for the corresponding value of the maximum bending moment.

16.147. A space satellite weighs 100 lb and has a radius of gyration of 1.50 ft with respect to the y axis. The orientation of the satellite is changed by firing four small rockets A, B, C, and D which are equally spaced around the perimeter of the satellite. While being fired, each rocket produces a thrust **T** of magnitude 2 lb directed as shown. Determine the angular acceleration of the satellite and the acceleration of the mass center G (*a*) when all four rockets are fired, (*b*) when all rockets except rocket D are fired.

17. PLANE MOTION OF RIGID BODIES: ENERGY AND MOMENTUM METHODS

17.1. Principle of Work and Energy for a Rigid Body. In the first part of this chapter, the principle of work and energy will be used to analyze the plane motion of rigid bodies and of systems of rigid bodies. As was pointed out in Chap. 13, the method of work and energy is particularly well adapted to the solution of problems involving velocities and displacements. Its main advantage resides in the fact that the work of forces and the kinetic energy of particles are scalar quantities.

Consider a rigid body of mass m, and let P be a particle of the body, of mass Δm. The kinetic energy of this particle is $\Delta T = \frac{1}{2}(\Delta m)v^2$, where v is the speed of the particle. Consider now a displacement of the rigid body during which the particle P moves from a position P_1 to a position P_2, and denote by $\Delta U_{1\to2}$ the work of all the forces acting on P during the displacement. We recall from Sec. 13.3 that the principle of work and energy for a particle states that

$$\Delta T_1 + \Delta U_{1\to2} = \Delta T_2$$

where ΔT_1 = kinetic energy of the particle at P_1
ΔT_2 = kinetic energy of the particle at P_2

Similar relations may be written for all the particles forming the body. Adding the kinetic energy of all the particles, and the work of all the forces involved, we write

$$T_1 + U_{1\to2} = T_2 \tag{17.1}$$

where T_1, T_2 = initial and final values of total kinetic energy of the particles forming the rigid body
$U_{1\to2}$ = work of all forces acting on the various particles of the body

The total kinetic energy

$$T = \Sigma\tfrac{1}{2}(\Delta m)v^2 \tag{17.2}$$

is obtained by adding positive scalar quantities and is itself a

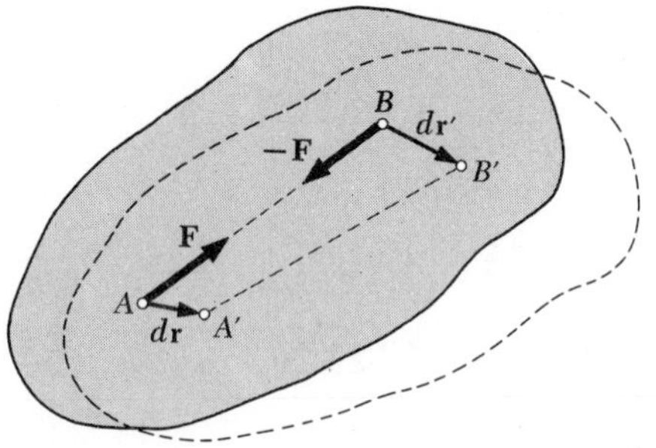

FIG. 17.1

positive scalar quantity. We shall see later how T may be determined for various types of motion of a rigid body.

The expression $U_{1\to2}$ in (17.1) represents the work of all the forces acting on the various particles of the body, whether these forces are internal or external. However, as we shall see presently, the total work of the internal forces holding together the particles of a rigid body is zero. Consider two particles A and B of a rigid body and the two equal and opposite forces **F** and −**F** they exert on each other (Fig. 17.1). While, in general, the displacements $d\mathbf{r}$ and $d\mathbf{r}'$ of the two particles are different, the components of these displacements along AB must be equal; otherwise, the particles would not remain at the same distance from each other, and the body would not be rigid. Therefore, the work of **F** is equal in magnitude and opposite in sign to the work of −**F**, and their sum is zero. Thus, the total work of the internal forces acting on the particles of a rigid body is zero, and *the expression $U_{1\to2}$ in Eq.* (17.1) *reduces to the work of the external forces* acting on the body during the displacement considered.

17.2. Work of Forces Acting on a Rigid Body. We saw in Sec. 13.2 that the work of a force **F** during a displacement of its point of application from A_1 to A_2 is

$$U_{1\to2} = \int_{A_1}^{A_2} \mathbf{F} \cdot d\mathbf{r} \tag{17.3}$$

or

$$U_{1\to2} = \int_{s_1}^{s_2} (F \cos \alpha)\, ds \tag{17.3'}$$

where F is the magnitude of the force, α the angle it forms with the direction of motion of its point of application A, and s the variable of integration which measures the distance traveled by A along its path.

In computing the work of the external forces acting on a rigid body, it is often convenient to determine the work of a couple

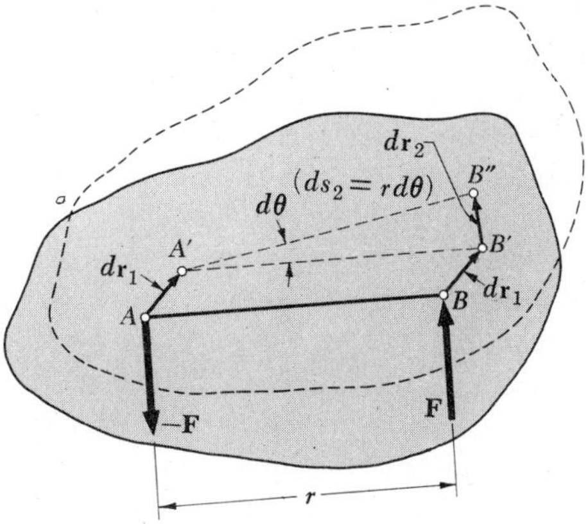

FIG. 17.2

without considering separately the work of each of the two forces forming the couple. Consider the two forces **F** and $-\mathbf{F}$ forming a couple of moment **M** and acting on a rigid body (Fig. 17.2). Any small displacement of the rigid body bringing A and B, respectively, into A' and B'' may be divided into two parts, one in which points A and B undergo equal displacements $d\mathbf{r}_1$, the other in which A' remains fixed while B' moves into B'' through a displacement $d\mathbf{r}_2$ of magnitude $ds_2 = r\,d\theta$. In the first part of the motion, the work of **F** is equal in magnitude and opposite in sign to the work of $-\mathbf{F}$ and their sum is zero. In the second part of the motion, only force **F** works, and its work is $dU = F\,ds_2 = Fr\,d\theta$. But the product Fr is equal to the magnitude M of the moment of the couple. Thus, the work of a couple of moment **M** acting on a rigid body is

$$dU = M\,d\theta \tag{17.4}$$

where $d\theta$ is the small angle expressed in radians through which the body rotates. We again note that work should be expressed in units obtained by multiplying units of force by units of length. The work of the couple during a finite rotation of the rigid body is obtained by integrating both members of (17.4) from the initial value θ_1 of the angle θ to its final value θ_2. We write

$$U_{1\to2} = \int_{\theta_1}^{\theta_2} M\,d\theta \tag{17.5}$$

When the moment **M** *of the couple is constant*, formula (17.5) reduces to

$$U_{1\to2} = M(\theta_2 - \theta_1) \tag{17.6}$$

It was pointed out in Sec. 13.2 that a number of forces encountered in problems of kinetics *do no work*. They are forces applied to fixed points or acting in a direction perpendicular to the displacement of their point of application. Among the forces which do no work the following have been listed: the reaction at a smooth pin when the body supported rotates about the pin, the reaction at a smooth frictionless surface when the body in contact moves along the surface, the weight of a body when its center of gravity moves horizontally. We should also indicate now that, *when a rigid body rolls without sliding on a fixed surface, the friction force* **F** *at the point of contact C does no work.* The velocity $\mathbf{v}_C$ of the point of contact C is zero, and the work of the friction force **F** during a small displacement of the rigid body is $dU = F\,ds_C = F(v_C\,dt) = 0$.

17.3. Kinetic Energy of a Rigid Body in Plane Motion. Consider a rigid body of mass m in plane motion. We recall from Sec. 13.5 that, if the absolute velocity $\mathbf{v}$ of each particle of the body is expressed as the sum of the velocity $\bar{\mathbf{v}}$ of the mass center G of the body and of the velocity $\mathbf{v}'$ of the particle relative to a frame $Gx'y'$ attached to G and of fixed orientation (Fig. 17.3*a*), the kinetic energy of the system of particles forming the rigid body may be written in the form

$$T = \tfrac{1}{2}(\Sigma\Delta m)\bar{v}^2 + \tfrac{1}{2}\Sigma(\Delta m)v'^2 \tag{17.7}$$

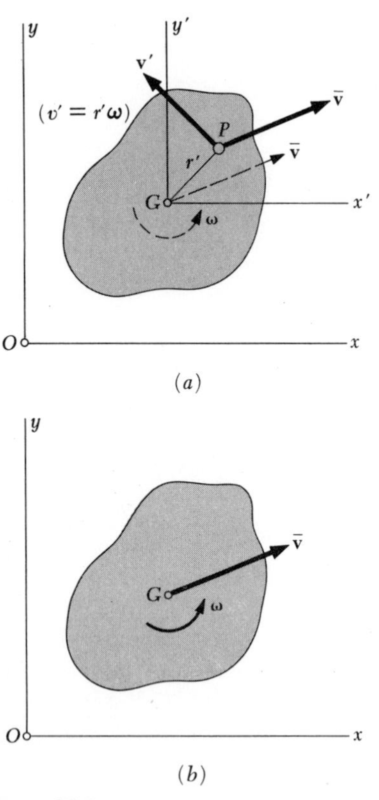

FIG. 17.3

But the magnitude v' of the relative velocity of a particle P of the rigid body is equal to the product $r'\omega$ of the distance r' of the particle from the axis through G perpendicular to the plane of motion and of the magnitude ω of the angular velocity of the body at the instant considered. Substituting into (17.7), we have

$$T = \tfrac{1}{2}(\Sigma\Delta m)\bar{v}^2 + \tfrac{1}{2}(\Sigma r'^2\Delta m)\omega^2 \tag{17.8}$$

or, since the sums $\Sigma\Delta m$ and $\Sigma r'^2\Delta m$ are equal, respectively, to the mass m of the body and to its moment of inertia $\bar{I}$ about the axis through G,

$$T = \tfrac{1}{2}m\bar{v}^2 + \tfrac{1}{2}\bar{I}\omega^2 \tag{17.9}$$

We note that, in the particular case of a body in translation ($\omega = 0$), the expression obtained reduces to $\frac{1}{2}m\bar{v}^2$, while, in the case of a centroidal rotation ($\bar{v} = 0$), it reduces to $\frac{1}{2}\bar{I}\omega^2$. We conclude that the kinetic energy of a rigid body in plane motion may be separated into two parts: (1) the kinetic energy $\frac{1}{2}m\bar{v}^2$ associated with the motion of the mass center G of the body, and (2) the kinetic energy $\frac{1}{2}\bar{I}\omega^2$ associated with the rotation of the body about G (Fig. 17.3*b*).

Noncentroidal Rotation. The relation (17.9) is valid for any type of plane motion and may, therefore, be used to express the kinetic energy of a rigid body rotating with an angular velocity ω about a fixed axis through O (Fig. 17.4). In that case, however, the kinetic energy of the body may be expressed more directly by noting that the speed v of a particle P of the body is equal to the product $r\omega$ of the distance r of P from the fixed axis and of the magnitude ω of the angular velocity of the body at the instant considered. Substituting into (17.2), we write

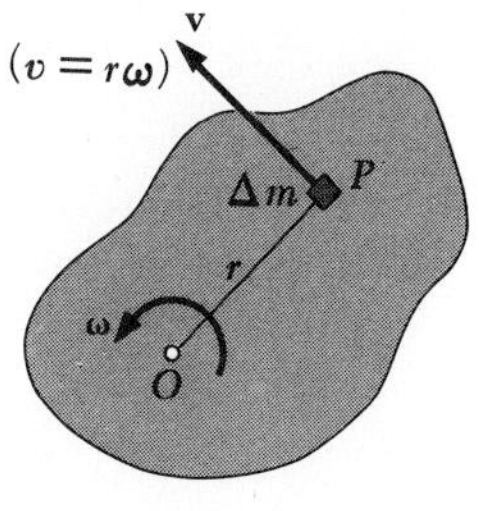

FIG. 17.4

$$T = \Sigma\tfrac{1}{2}(\Delta m)(r\omega)^2 = \tfrac{1}{2}(\Sigma r^2\Delta m)\omega^2$$

or, since the sum $\Sigma r^2\Delta m$ represents the moment of inertia I_O of the body about the fixed axis through O,

$$T = \tfrac{1}{2}I_O\omega^2 \qquad (17.10)$$

We note that the results obtained are not limited to the motion of plane slabs or to the motion of bodies which are symmetrical with respect to the reference plane. They may be applied to the study of the plane motion of any rigid body, regardless of its shape.

17.4. Systems of Rigid Bodies. When a problem involves several rigid bodies, each rigid body may be considered separately and the principle of work and energy may be applied to each body. Adding the kinetic energies of all the particles and considering the work of all the forces involved, we may also write the equation of work and energy for the entire system. We have

$$T_1 + U_{1\to2} = T_2 \qquad (17.11)$$

where T represents the arithmetic sum of the kinetic energies of the rigid bodies forming the system (all terms are positive) and $U_{1\to2}$ the work of all the forces acting on the various bodies, whether these forces are *internal* or *external* from the point of view of the system as a whole.

The method of work and energy is particularly useful in solving problems involving pin-connected members, or blocks and pulleys connected by inextensible cords, or meshed gears. In all these cases, the internal forces occur by pairs of equal and opposite forces, and the points of application of the forces in each pair *move through equal distances* during a small displacement of the system. As a result, the work of the internal forces is zero, and $U_{1\to2}$ reduces to the work of the *forces external to the system.*

17.5. Conservation of Energy. We saw in Sec. 13.6 that the work of conservative forces, such as the weight of a body or the force exerted by a spring, may be expressed as a change in potential energy. When a rigid body, or a system of rigid bodies, moves under the action of conservative forces, the principle of work and energy stated in Sec. 17.1 may be expressed in a modified form. Substituting for $U_{1\rightarrow 2}$ from (13.17′) into (17.1), we write

$$T_1 + V_1 = T_2 + V_2 \tag{17.12}$$

Formula (17.12) indicates that, when a rigid body, or a system of rigid bodies, moves under the action of conservative forces, *the sum of the kinetic energy and of the potential energy of the system remains constant.* It should be noted that, in the case of the plane motion of a rigid body, the kinetic energy of the body should include both the *translational* term $\frac{1}{2}m\bar{v}^2$ and the *rotational* term $\frac{1}{2}\bar{I}\omega^2$.

As an example of application of the principle of conservation of energy, we shall consider a slender rod AB, of length l and mass m, whose extremities are connected to blocks of negligible mass sliding along horizontal and vertical tracks. We assume that the rod is released with no initial velocity from a horizontal position (Fig. 17.5a), and we wish to determine its angular velocity after it has rotated through an angle θ (Fig. 17.5b).

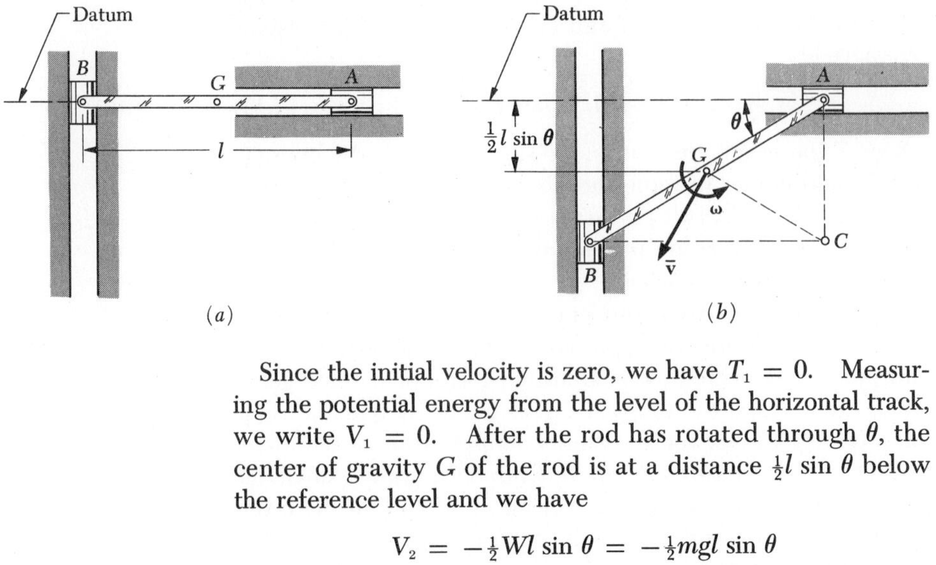

FIG. 17.5

Since the initial velocity is zero, we have $T_1 = 0$. Measuring the potential energy from the level of the horizontal track, we write $V_1 = 0$. After the rod has rotated through θ, the center of gravity G of the rod is at a distance $\frac{1}{2}l \sin\theta$ below the reference level and we have

$$V_2 = -\tfrac{1}{2}Wl \sin\theta = -\tfrac{1}{2}mgl \sin\theta$$

Observing that, in this position, the instantaneous center of the rod is located at C, and that $CG = \frac{1}{2}l$, we write $\bar{v}_2 = \frac{1}{2}l\omega$ and obtain

$$T_2 = \tfrac{1}{2}m\bar{v}_2^2 + \tfrac{1}{2}\bar{I}\omega_2^2 = \tfrac{1}{2}m(\tfrac{1}{2}l\omega)^2 + \tfrac{1}{2}(\tfrac{1}{12}ml^2)\omega^2$$
$$= \frac{1}{2}\frac{ml^2}{3}\omega^2$$

Applying the principle of conservation of energy, we write

$$T_1 + V_1 = T_2 + V_2$$
$$0 = \frac{1}{2}\frac{ml^2}{3}\omega^2 - \tfrac{1}{2}mgl\sin\theta$$
$$\omega = \left(\frac{3g}{l}\sin\theta\right)^{\frac{1}{2}}$$

We recall that the advantages of the method of work and energy, as well as its shortcomings, were indicated in Sec. 13.4. In this connection, we wish to mention that the method of work and energy must be supplemented by the application of D'Alembert's principle when reactions at fixed axles, at rollers, or at sliding blocks are to be determined. For example, in order to compute the reactions at the extremities A and B of the rod of Fig. 17.5*b*, a diagram should be drawn to express that the system of the external forces applied to the rod is equivalent to the vector $m\bar{\mathbf{a}}$ and the couple $\bar{I}\alpha$. The angular velocity ω of the rod, however, is determined by the method of work and energy before the equations of motion are solved for the reactions. The complete analysis of the motion of the rod and of the forces exerted on the rod requires, therefore, the combined use of the method of work and energy and of the principle of equivalence of the external and effective forces.

17.6. Power. *Power* was defined in Sec. 13.8 as the time rate at which work is done. In the case of a body acted upon by a force **F**, and moving with a velocity **v**, the power was expressed as follows [Eq. (13.24)],

$$\text{Power} = \frac{dU}{dt} = \mathbf{F}\cdot\mathbf{v}$$

In the case of a rigid body rotating at an angular velocity ω and acted upon by a couple of moment **M** parallel to the axis of rotation, we have, by (17.4),

$$\text{Power} = \frac{dU}{dt} = \frac{M\,d\theta}{dt} = M\omega \qquad (17.13)$$

The various units used to measure power, such as the horsepower and the kilowatt, were defined in Sec. 13.8.

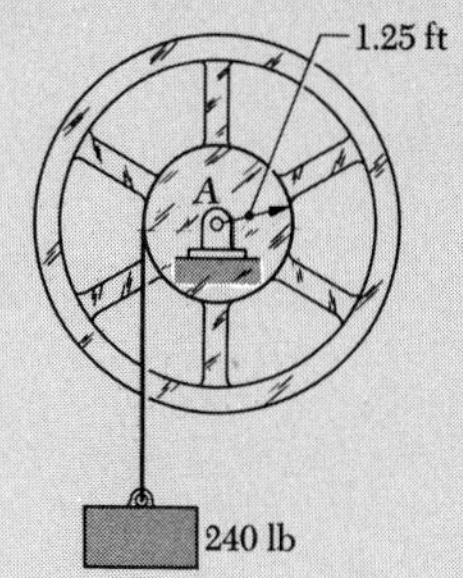

SAMPLE PROBLEM 17.1

A 240-lb block is suspended from an inextensible cable which is wrapped around a drum of 1.25-ft radius rigidly attached to a flywheel. The drum and flywheel have a combined centroidal moment of inertia $\bar{I} = 10.5$ lb-ft-sec^2. At the instant shown, the velocity of the block is 6 ft/sec directed downward. Knowing that the bearing at A is poorly lubricated and that the bearing friction is equivalent to a couple **M** of moment 60 lb-ft, determine the velocity of the block after it has moved 4 ft downward.

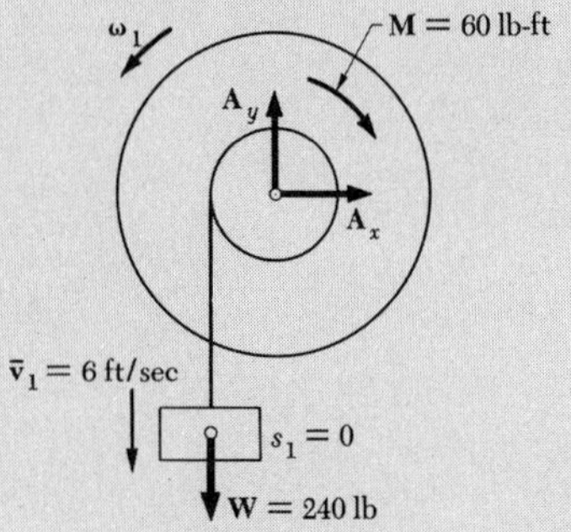

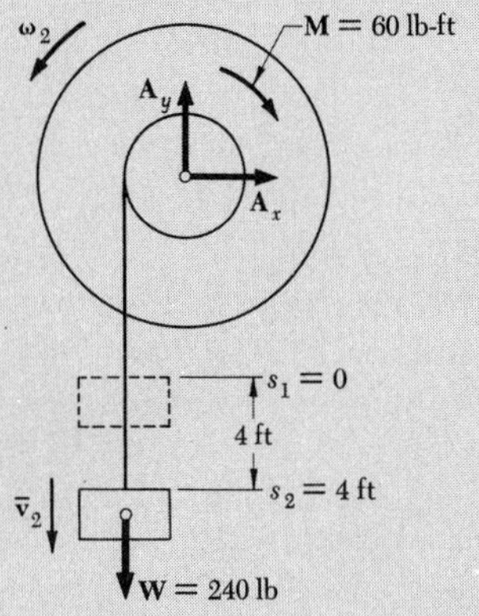

Solution. We consider the system formed by the flywheel and the block. Since the cable is inextensible, the work done by the internal forces exerted by the cable cancels. The initial and final positions of the system and the external forces acting on the system are as shown.

Kinetic Energy. *Position 1.* We have

$$\bar{v}_1 = 6 \text{ ft/sec} \qquad \omega_1 = \frac{\bar{v}_1}{r} = \frac{6}{1.25} = 4.80 \text{ radians/sec}$$

$$T_1 = \tfrac{1}{2}m\bar{v}_1^2 + \tfrac{1}{2}\bar{I}\omega_1^2$$

$$= \frac{1}{2}\frac{240}{g}(6)^2 + (\tfrac{1}{2})(10.5)(4.80)^2 = 255 \text{ ft-lb}$$

Position 2. Noting that $\omega_2 = \bar{v}_2/1.25$, we write

$$T_2 = \tfrac{1}{2}m\bar{v}_2^2 + \tfrac{1}{2}\bar{I}\omega_2^2$$

$$= \frac{1}{2}\frac{240}{g}(\bar{v}_2)^2 + (\tfrac{1}{2})(10.5)\left(\frac{\bar{v}_2}{1.25}\right)^2 = 7.09\bar{v}_2^2$$

Work. During the motion, only the weight **W** of the block and the friction couple **M** do work. Noting that **W** does positive work and that the friction couple **M** does negative work, we write

$$s_1 = 0 \qquad s_2 = 4 \text{ ft}$$

$$\theta_1 = 0 \qquad \theta_2 = \frac{s_2}{r} = 3.20 \text{ radians}$$

$$U_{1\to 2} = W(s_2 - s_1) - M(\theta_2 - \theta_1)$$

$$= (240 \text{ lb})(4 \text{ ft}) - (60 \text{ lb-ft})(3.20 \text{ radians})$$

$$= 768 \text{ ft-lb}$$

Principle of Work and Energy

$$T_1 + U_{1\to 2} = T_2$$

$$255 \text{ ft-lb} + 768 \text{ ft-lb} = 7.09\bar{v}_2^2$$

$$\bar{v}_2 = 12.01 \text{ ft/sec} \qquad \bar{\mathbf{v}}_2 = 12.01 \text{ ft/sec}\downarrow$$ ◄

SAMPLE PROBLEM 17.2

Gear A weighs 20 lb and has a radius of gyration of 9 in., while gear B weighs 5 lb and has a radius of gyration of 3 in. The system is at rest when a couple **M** of moment 4 lb-ft is applied to gear B. Neglecting friction, determine (a) the number of revolutions executed by gear B before its angular velocity reaches 600 rpm, (b) the tangential force which gear B exerts on gear A.

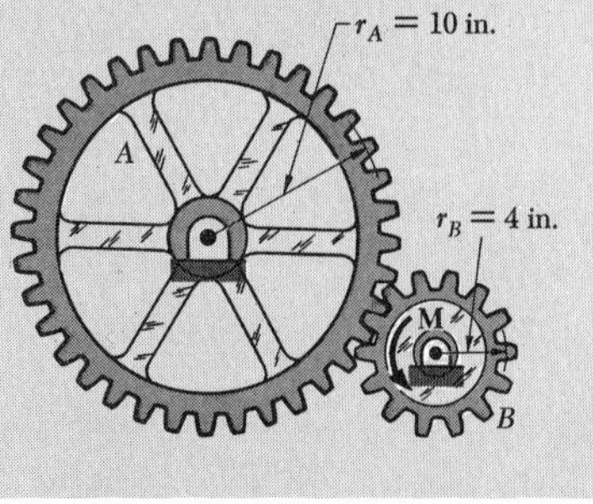

Motion of Entire System. Noting that the peripheral speeds of the gears are equal, we write

$$r_A\omega_A = r_B\omega_B \qquad \omega_A = \omega_B \frac{r_B}{r_A} = \omega_B \frac{4 \text{ in.}}{10 \text{ in.}} = 0.40\omega_B$$

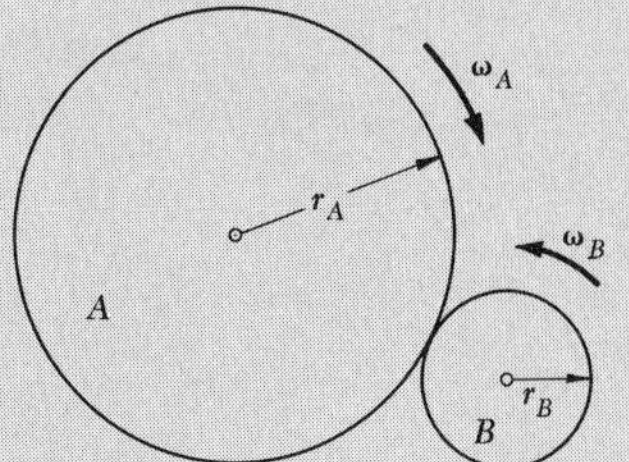

For $\omega_B = 600$ rpm, we have

$$\omega_B = 62.8 \text{ radians/sec} \qquad \omega_A = 0.40\omega_B = 25.1 \text{ radians/sec}$$

$$\bar{I}_A = m_A\bar{k}_A^2 = \frac{20}{g}\left(\frac{9}{12}\right)^2 = 0.349 \text{ lb-ft-sec}^2$$

$$\bar{I}_B = m_B\bar{k}_B^2 = \frac{5}{g}\left(\frac{3}{12}\right)^2 = 0.00970 \text{ lb-ft-sec}^2$$

Kinetic Energy. Since the system is initially at rest, $T_1 = 0$. Adding the kinetic energies of the two gears when $\omega_B = 600$ rpm, we obtain

$$T_2 = \tfrac{1}{2}\bar{I}_A\omega_A^2 + \tfrac{1}{2}\bar{I}_B\omega_B^2$$
$$= (\tfrac{1}{2})(0.349)(25.1)^2 + (\tfrac{1}{2})(0.00970)(62.8)^2 = 129.1 \text{ ft-lb}$$

Work. Denoting by θ_B the angular displacement of gear B, we have

$$U_{1\to2} = M\theta_B = (4 \text{ lb-ft})\theta_B$$

Principle of Work and Energy

$$T_1 + U_{1\to2} = T_2 \qquad 0 + 4\theta_B = 129.1 \text{ ft-lb}$$
$$\theta_B = 32.3 \text{ radians} \qquad\qquad \theta_B = 5.14 \text{ rev} \blacktriangleleft$$

Motion of Gear A. *Kinetic Energy.* Initially, gear A is at rest, $T_1 = 0$. When $\omega_B = 600$ rpm, the kinetic energy of gear A is

$$T_2 = \tfrac{1}{2}\bar{I}_A\omega_A^2 = (\tfrac{1}{2})(0.349)(25.1)^2 = 109.9 \text{ ft-lb}$$

Work. The forces acting on gear A are as shown. The tangential force **F** does work equal to the product of its magnitude and of the length $\theta_A r_A$ described by the point of contact. Since $\theta_A r_A = \theta_B r_B$, we have

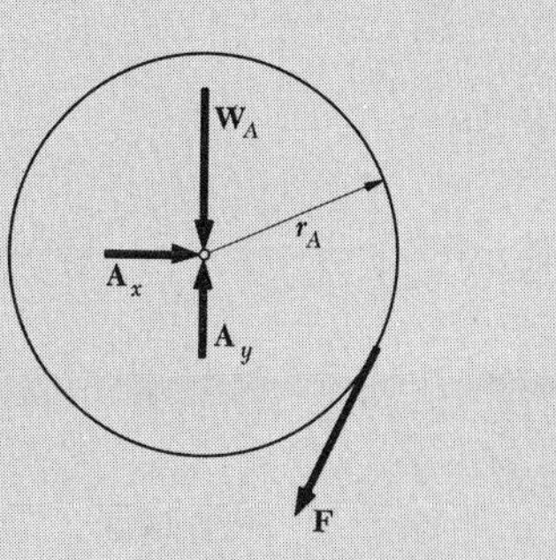

$$U_{1\to2} = F(\theta_B r_B) = F(32.3 \text{ radians})(\tfrac{4}{12} \text{ ft})$$

Principle of Work and Energy

$$T_1 + U_{1\to2} = T_2 \qquad 0 + F(32.3)(\tfrac{4}{12}) = 109.9$$
$$F = +10.21 \text{ lb} \qquad\qquad \mathbf{F} = 10.21 \text{ lb} \swarrow \blacktriangleleft$$

SAMPLE PROBLEM 17.3

A sphere, a cylinder, and a hoop are each released from rest on an incline. In each case, the weight is W and the radius is r. Determine the velocity of each body after it has rolled through a distance s.

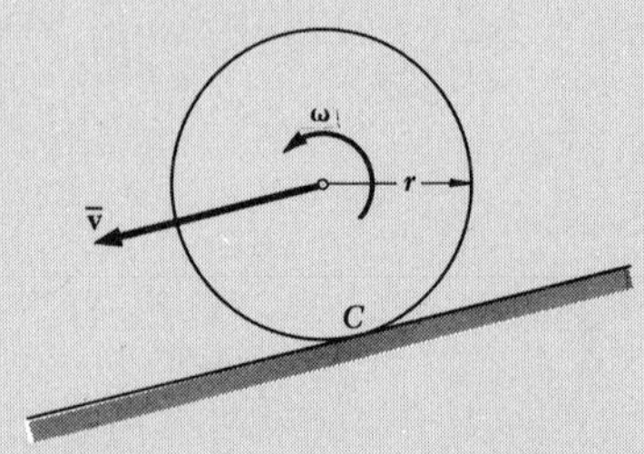

Solution. We shall first solve the problem in general terms and then find particular results for each body. We denote the centroidal moment of inertia by $\bar{I}$, the weight by W, and the radius by r.

Since each body rolls, the instantaneous center of rotation is located at C and we write

$$\omega = \frac{\bar{v}}{r}$$

Kinetic Energy

$$T_1 = 0$$

$$T_2 = \tfrac{1}{2}m\bar{v}^2 + \tfrac{1}{2}\bar{I}\omega^2$$

$$= \tfrac{1}{2}mv^2 + \tfrac{1}{2}\bar{I}\left(\frac{\bar{v}}{r}\right)^2 = \tfrac{1}{2}\left(m + \frac{\bar{I}}{r^2}\right)\bar{v}^2$$

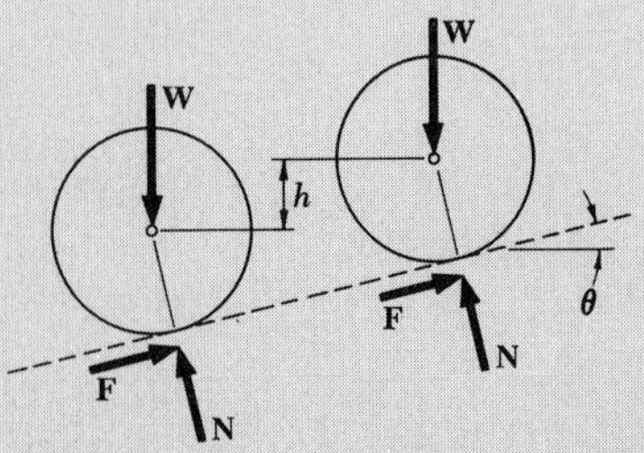

Work. Since the friction force **F** in rolling motion does no work, we have

$$U_{1\to2} = Wh$$

Principle of Work and Energy

$$T_1 + U_{1\to2} = T_2$$

$$0 + Wh = \tfrac{1}{2}\left(m + \frac{\bar{I}}{r^2}\right)\bar{v}^2 \qquad \bar{v}^2 = \frac{2Wh}{m + \bar{I}/r^2}$$

Noting that $W = mg$, we rearrange the result and obtain

$$\bar{v}^2 = \frac{2gh}{1 + \bar{I}/mr^2}$$

Velocities of Sphere, Cylinder, and Hoop. Introducing successively the particular expressions for $\bar{I}$, we obtain

Sphere:	$\bar{I} = \frac{2}{5}mr^2$	$\bar{v} = 0.845\sqrt{2gh}$
Cylinder:	$\bar{I} = \frac{1}{2}mr^2$	$\bar{v} = 0.817\sqrt{2gh}$
Hoop:	$\bar{I} = mr^2$	$\bar{v} = 0.707\sqrt{2gh}$

Remark. We may compare the results with the velocity attained by a frictionless block sliding through the same distance. The solution is identical to the above solution except that $\omega = 0$; we find $\bar{v} = \sqrt{2gh}$.

Comparing the results, we note that the velocity of the body is independent of both its weight and radius. However, the velocity does depend upon the quotient $\bar{I}/mr^2 = \bar{k}^2/r^2$, which measures the ratio of the rotational kinetic energy to the translational kinetic energy. Thus the hoop, which has the largest $\bar{k}$ for a given radius r, attains the smallest velocity, while the sliding block, which does not rotate, attains the largest velocity.

SAMPLE PROBLEM 17.4

A 30-lb slender rod AB is 5 ft long and is pivoted about a point O which is 1 ft from end B. The other end is pressed against a spring of constant $k = 1{,}800$ lb/in. until the spring is compressed 1 in. The rod is then in a horizontal position. If the rod is released from this position, determine its angular velocity and the reaction at the pivot O as the rod passes through a vertical position.

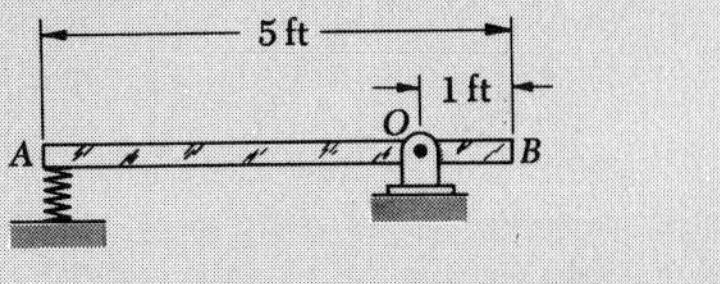

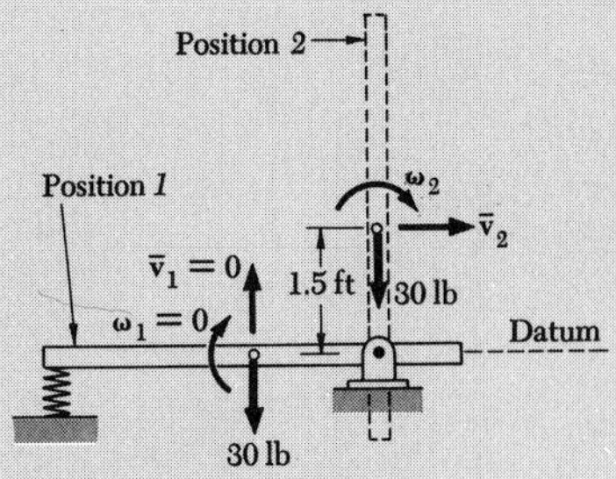

Position *1*. *Potential Energy.* Since the spring is compressed 1 in., we have $x_1 = 1$ in.

$$V_e = \tfrac{1}{2}kx_1^2 = \tfrac{1}{2}(1{,}800 \text{ lb/in.})(1 \text{ in.})^2 = 900 \text{ in.-lb}$$

Choosing the datum as shown, we have $V_g = 0$; therefore,

$$V_1 = V_e + V_g = 900 \text{ in.-lb} = 75 \text{ ft-lb}$$

Kinetic Energy. Since the velocity in position *1* is zero, we have $T_1 = 0$.

Position 2. *Potential Energy.* The elongation of the spring is zero, and we have $V_e = 0$. Since the center of gravity of the rod is now 1.5 ft above the datum,

$$V_g = (30 \text{ lb})(+1.5 \text{ ft}) = 45 \text{ ft-lb}$$
$$V_2 = V_e + V_g = 45 \text{ ft-lb}$$

Kinetic Energy. Denoting by ω_2 the angular velocity of the rod in position 2, we note that the rod rotates about O and write $\bar{v}_2 = \bar{r}\omega_2 = 1.5\omega_2$.

$$\bar{I} = \tfrac{1}{12}ml^2 = \frac{1}{12}\frac{30}{g}(5)^2 = 1.941 \text{ lb-ft-sec}^2$$

$$T_2 = \tfrac{1}{2}m\bar{v}_2^2 + \tfrac{1}{2}\bar{I}\omega_2^2 = \frac{1}{2}\frac{30}{g}(1.5\omega_2)^2 + (\tfrac{1}{2})(1.941)\omega_2^2 = 2.018\omega_2^2$$

Conservation of Energy

$$T_1 + V_1 = T_2 + V_2 \qquad 0 + 75 \text{ ft-lb} = 2.018\omega_2^2 + 45 \text{ ft-lb}$$

$$\omega_2 = 3.86 \text{ radians/sec} \circlearrowright \blacktriangleleft$$

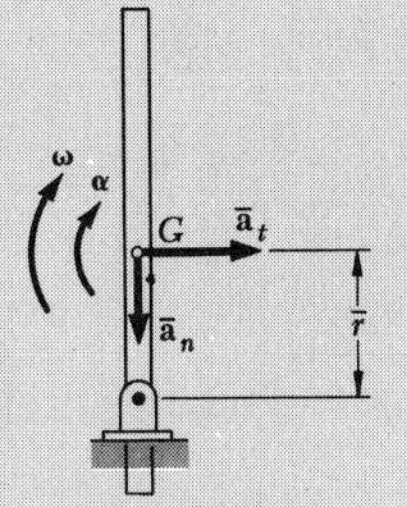

Reaction in Position 2. Since $\omega_2 = 3.86$ radians/sec, the components of the acceleration of G as the rod passes through position 2 are

$$\bar{a}_n = \bar{r}\omega_2^2 = (1.5)(3.86)^2 = 22.3 \text{ ft/sec}^2 \qquad \bar{\mathbf{a}}_n = 22.3 \text{ ft/sec}^2 \downarrow$$
$$\bar{a}_t = \bar{r}\alpha \qquad \bar{\mathbf{a}}_t = \bar{r}\alpha \rightarrow$$

We express that the system of external forces is equivalent to the system of effective forces represented by the vector of components $m\bar{\mathbf{a}}_t$ and $m\bar{\mathbf{a}}_n$ attached at G and the couple $\bar{I}\boldsymbol{\alpha}$.

$$+\circlearrowright \Sigma M_O = \Sigma(M_O)_{\text{eff}}: \qquad 0 = \bar{I}\alpha + m(\bar{r}\alpha)\bar{r} \qquad \alpha = 0$$
$$\xrightarrow{+} \Sigma F_x = \Sigma(F_x)_{\text{eff}}: \qquad R_x = m(\bar{r}\alpha) \qquad R_x = 0$$
$$+\uparrow \Sigma F_y = \Sigma(F_y)_{\text{eff}}: \qquad R_y - 30 = -m\bar{a}_n$$
$$R_y - 30 = -\frac{30}{g}(22.3)$$
$$R_y = +9.22 \text{ lb} \qquad \mathbf{R} = 9.22 \text{ lb} \uparrow \blacktriangleleft$$

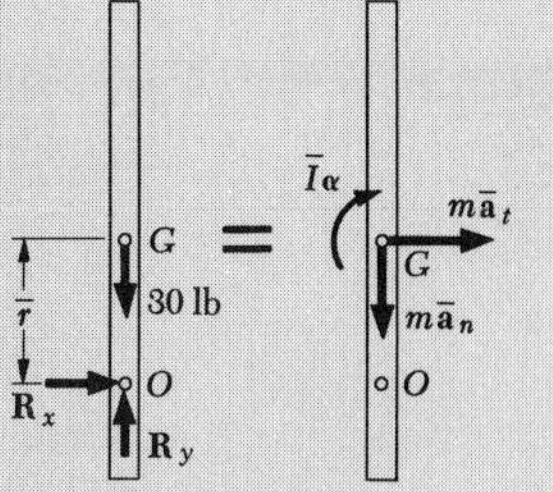

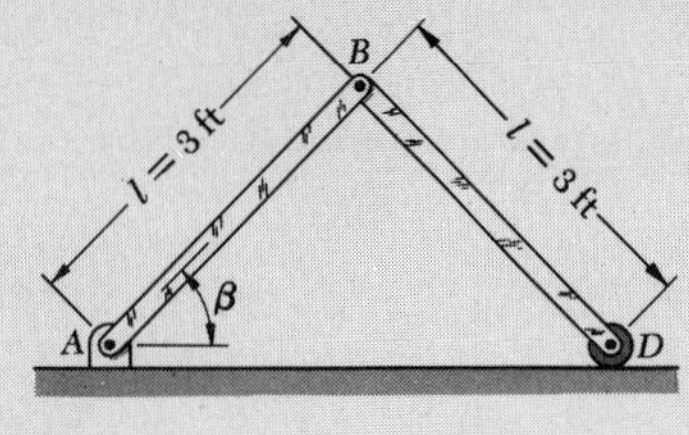

SAMPLE PROBLEM 17.5

Each of the two slender rods shown is 3 ft long and weighs 10 lb. If the system is released from rest when $\beta = 60°$, determine (*a*) the angular velocity of rod AB when $\beta = 20°$, (*b*) the velocity of point D at the same instant.

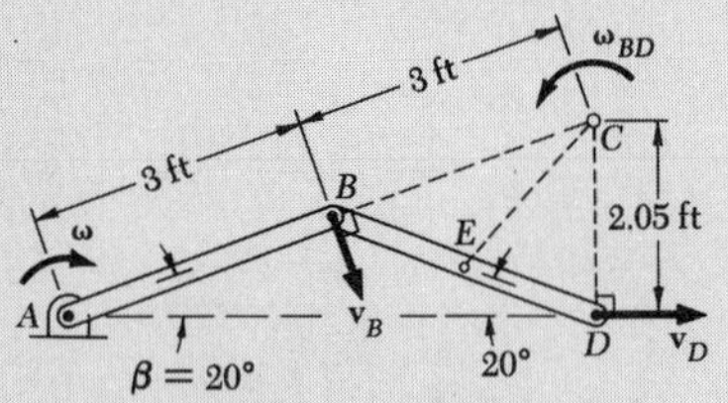

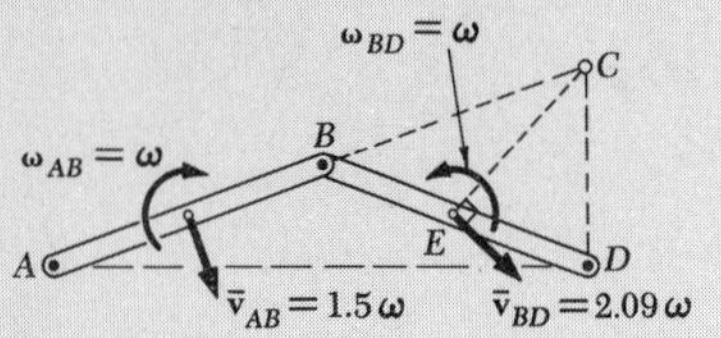

Kinematics of Motion When $\beta = 20°$. Since $\mathbf{v}_B$ is perpendicular to the rod AB and $\mathbf{v}_D$ is horizontal, the instantaneous center of rotation of rod BD is located at C. Considering the geometry of the figure, we obtain

$$BC = 3\text{ ft} \qquad CD = 2(3\text{ ft})\sin 20° = 2.05\text{ ft}$$

Solving the triangle CDE, where E is located at the mass center of rod BD, we find $EC = 2.09$ ft. Denoting by ω the angular velocity of rod AB, we have

$$\bar{v}_{AB} = (1.5\text{ ft})\omega \qquad \bar{\mathbf{v}}_{AB} = 1.5\omega \searrow$$
$$v_B = (3\text{ ft})\omega \qquad \mathbf{v}_B = 3\omega \searrow$$

Since rod BD seems to rotate about point C, we may write

$$v_B = (BC)\omega_{BD} \qquad (3\text{ ft})\omega = (3\text{ ft})\omega_{BD} \qquad \omega_{BD} = \omega \circlearrowleft$$
$$\bar{v}_{BD} = (EC)\omega_{BD} = 2.09\omega \qquad \bar{\mathbf{v}}_{BD} = 2.09\omega \searrow$$

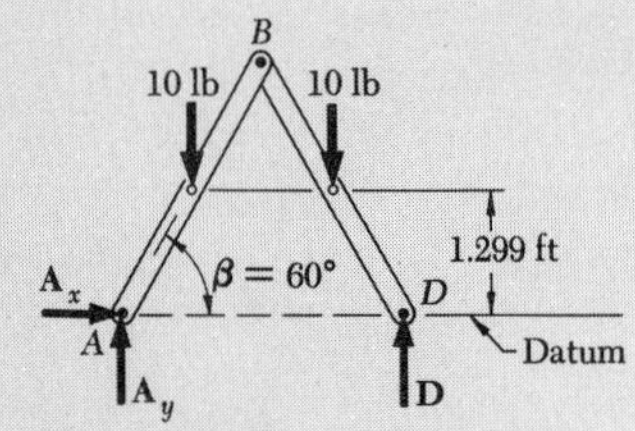

Position *1*

Position *1*. *Potential Energy.* Choosing the datum as shown, we have

$$V_1 = 2[(10\text{ lb})(1.299\text{ ft})] = 26.0\text{ ft-lb}$$

Kinetic Energy. Since the system is at rest, $T_1 = 0$.

Position 2. *Potential Energy*

$$V_2 = 2[(10\text{ lb})(0.513\text{ ft})] = 10.26\text{ ft-lb}$$

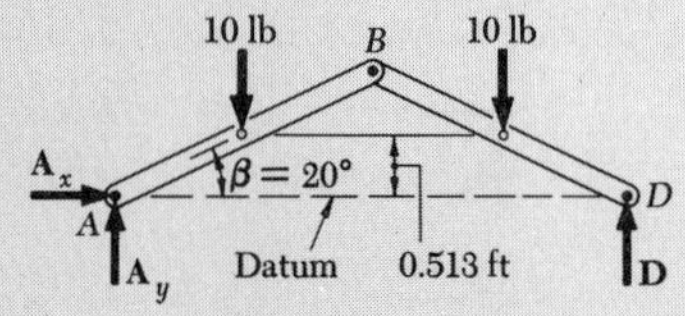

Position 2

Kinetic Energy

$$\bar{I}_{AB} = \bar{I}_{BD} = \tfrac{1}{12}ml^2 = \frac{1}{12}\frac{10}{g}(3)^2 = 0.233\text{ lb-ft-sec}^2$$

$$T_2 = \tfrac{1}{2}m\bar{v}_{AB}^2 + \tfrac{1}{2}\bar{I}_{AB}\omega_{AB}^2 + \tfrac{1}{2}m\bar{v}_{BD}^2 + \tfrac{1}{2}\bar{I}_{BD}\omega_{BD}^2$$
$$= \frac{1}{2}\frac{10}{g}(1.5\omega)^2 + (\tfrac{1}{2})(0.233)\omega^2 + \frac{1}{2}\frac{10}{g}(2.09\omega)^2 + (\tfrac{1}{2})(0.233)\omega^2$$
$$= 1.261\omega^2$$

Conservation of Energy

$$T_1 + V_1 = T_2 + V_2 \qquad 0 + 26.0\text{ ft-lb} = 1.261\omega^2 + 10.26\text{ ft-lb}$$
$$\omega = 3.53\text{ radians/sec} \qquad \omega_{AB} = 3.53\text{ radians/sec} \circlearrowright \blacktriangleleft$$

Velocity of Point D

$$v_D = (CD)\omega = (2.05\text{ ft})(3.53\text{ radians/sec})$$
$$v_D = 7.24\text{ ft/sec} \qquad \mathbf{v}_D = 7.24\text{ ft/sec} \rightarrow \blacktriangleleft$$

PROBLEMS

17.1. A large flywheel weighs 6,000 lb and has a radius of gyration of 36 in. It is observed that 1,500 revolutions are required for the flywheel to coast from an angular velocity of 300 rpm to rest. Determine the average magnitude of the couple due to kinetic friction in the bearings.

17.2. At a time when the rotor of an electric motor is rotating at 1,800 rpm, the load and power are cut off and the rotor coasts to rest. The rotor weighs 150 lb and has a radius of gyration of 6 in. If the kinetic friction of the rotor produces a couple of magnitude 5 lb-in., how many revolutions will the rotor execute before stopping?

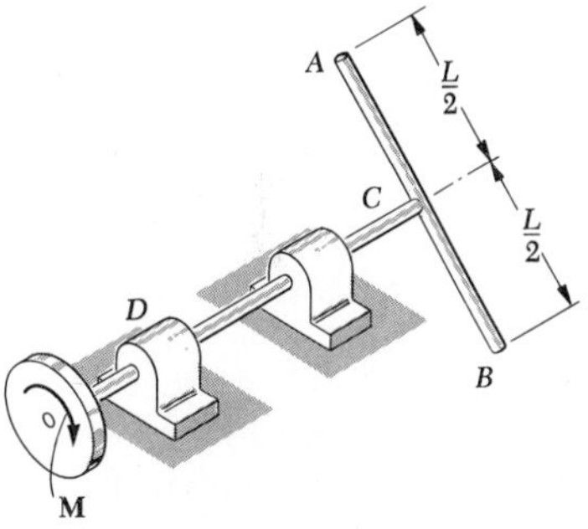

FIG. P 17.3 AND P 17.4

17.3. A 12-in.-diameter disk weighing 8 lb and a rod of length L weighing 2 lb/ft are attached to the shaft CD as shown. A couple **M** of magnitude 4 lb-ft is applied to the disk when the system is at rest. Determine the length L of rod AB if the angular velocity of the system is to be 300 rpm after two complete revolutions.

17.4. A rod AB weighing w lb/ft is to be attached to a shaft and disk as shown. A couple **M** of constant magnitude is applied to the disk when the system is at rest; after the system has executed one complete revolution the couple is removed. Denoting by I_0 the moment of inertia of the shaft and disk about the axis of rotation, derive an expression for the length L which results in the largest final speed of point A.

17.5. The flywheel of a small punch rotates at 180 rpm. It is known that 1,000 ft-lb of work must be done each time a hole is punched. It is desired that the speed of the flywheel after one punching be not less than 90 per cent of the original speed of 180 rpm. (*a*) Determine the required moment of inertia of the flywheel. (*b*) If a constant 25-lb-ft couple is applied to the shaft of the flywheel, determine the number of revolutions which must occur between each punching, knowing that the speed is to be 180 rpm at the start of each punching.

17.6. The flywheel of a punching machine weighs 600 lb and has a radius of gyration of 24 in. Each punching operation requires 2,000 ft-lb of work. (*a*) Knowing that the speed of the flywheel is 300 rpm just before a punching, determine the speed immediately after the punching. (*b*) If a constant 20-lb-ft couple is applied to the shaft of the flywheel, determine the number of revolutions executed before the speed is again 300 rpm.

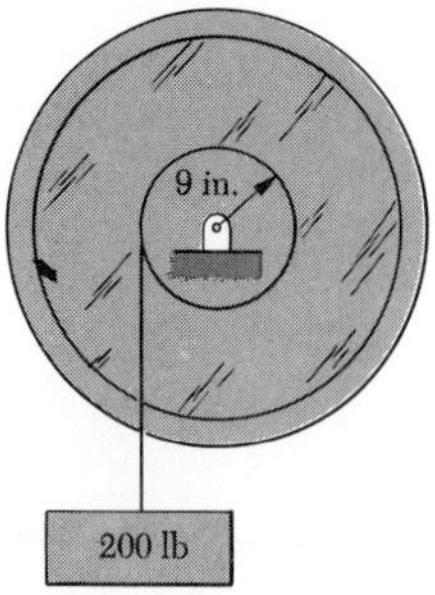

FIG. P 17.7 AND P 17.8

17.7. The flywheel of a small hoisting engine has a radius of gyration of 2 ft and weighs 800 lb. When the speed of the 200-lb load is 6 ft/sec upward, the power is cut off. Neglecting bearing friction, determine how far the load will rise before coming to rest.

17.8. The flywheel of a small hoisting engine has a radius of gyration of 2 ft and weighs 800 lb. When the speed of the 200-lb load is 6 ft/sec upward, the power is cut off. Knowing that the load rises 15 ft before coming to rest, determine the magnitude of the bearing-friction couple exerted on the shaft.

17.9. Using the principle of work and energy, solve Prob. 16.32.

17.10. Using the principle of work and energy, solve Prob. 16.34*c*.

17.11. Two blocks are attached to a double pulley of weight 200 lb and radius of gyration 2.5 ft as shown. If the system is released with no initial velocity, how far will the 100-lb block rise before coming to rest? What is the energy loss when the 200-lb block strikes the floor?

17.12. Solve Prob. 17.11 assuming that the weight of the pulley is increased to 400 lb.

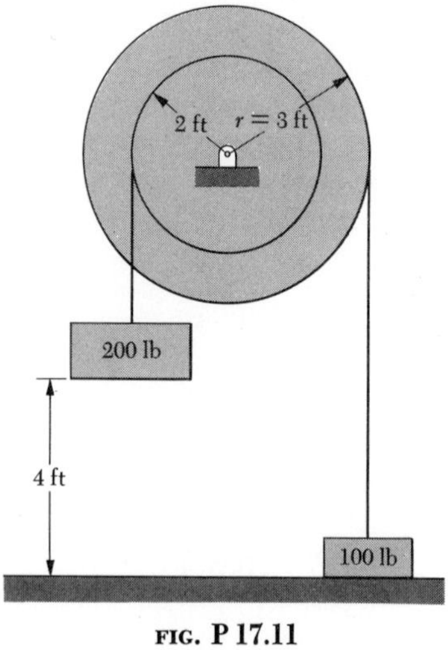

FIG. P 17.11

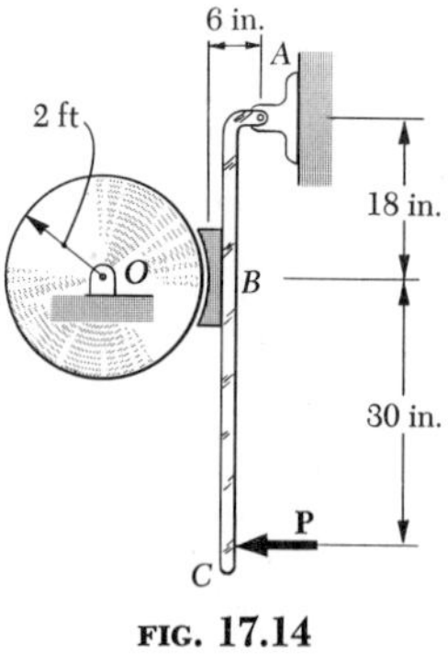

FIG. 17.14

17.13. In Prob. 17.11 determine the weight of the pulley for which the 100-lb block will rise 7.50 ft before coming to rest.

17.14. The flywheel shown consists of a disk which weighs 400 lb. The coefficient of friction between the brake shoe and the disk is 0.25. Determine the magnitude of the force **P** required to bring the flywheel to rest in 30 revolutions if the initial angular velocity is (*a*) 600 rpm clockwise, (*b*) 600 rpm counterclockwise.

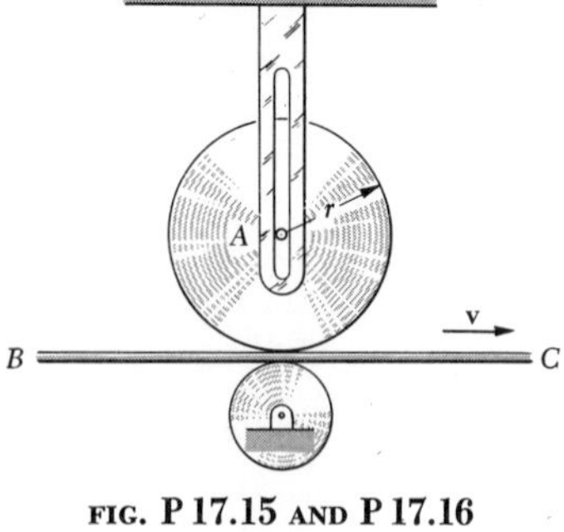

FIG. P 17.15 AND P 17.16

17.15. A disk of constant thickness and initially at rest is placed in contact with the belt *BC*, which moves with a constant velocity v. Denoting by μ the coefficient of friction between the disk and the belt, derive an expression for the number of revolutions executed by the disk before it reaches a constant angular velocity.

17.16. Disk *A*, of weight 10 lb and radius $r = 6$ in., is at rest when it is placed in contact with belt *BC*, which moves to the right with a constant speed $v = 40$ ft/sec. Knowing that $\mu = 0.20$ between the disk and the belt, determine the number of revolutions executed by the disk before it reaches a constant angular velocity.

17.17. A cord is wrapped around a cylinder of radius r and weight W as shown. If the cylinder is released from rest, determine the velocity of the center of the cylinder after it has moved through a distance s.

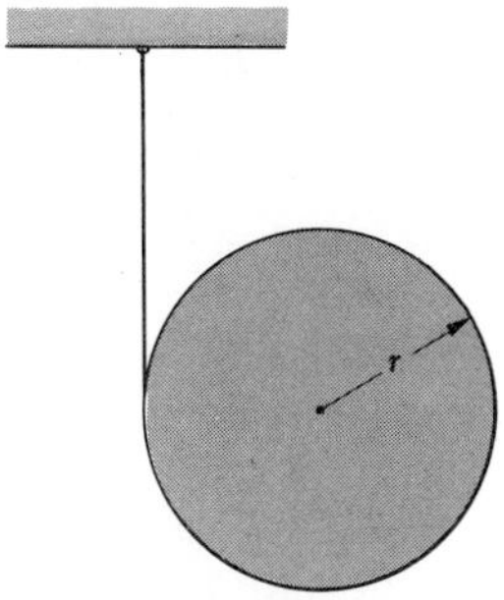

FIG. P 17.17

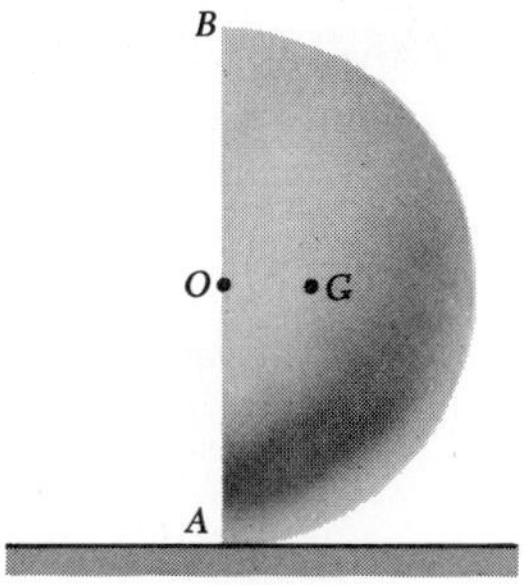

FIG. P 17.19

17.18. Solve Prob. 17.17 assuming that the cylinder is replaced by a hoop of weight W and radius r.

17.19. A hemisphere of weight W and radius r is released from rest in the position shown. Assuming that the hemisphere rolls without sliding, determine (*a*) the angular velocity of the hemisphere after it has rolled through 90°, (*b*) the normal reaction at the surface at the same instant. [*Hint.* Note that $GO = \frac{3}{8}r$ and that, by the parallel-axis theorem, $\bar{I} = \frac{2}{5}mr^2 - m(GO)^2$.]

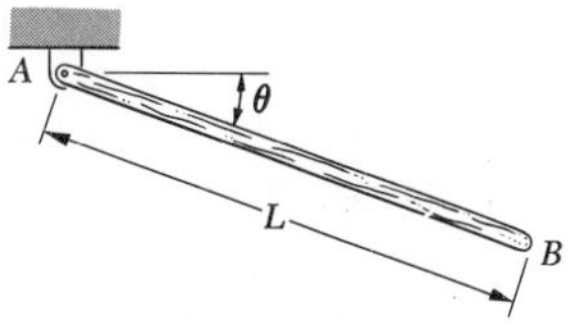

FIG. P 17.20

17.20. A slender rod of length L and weight W is pivoted at one end as shown. It is released from rest in a horizontal position and swings freely. (*a*) Determine the angular velocity of the rod and the reaction at the pivot when $\theta = 90°$. (*b*) Solve part *a* for $W = 20$ lb and $L = 6$ ft.

17.21. A 6- by 8-in. rectangular plate is suspended by two pins at A and B. The pin at B is removed and the plate swings about point A. Determine (*a*) the angular velocity of the plate after it has rotated through 90°, (*b*) the maximum angular velocity attained by the plate as it swings freely.

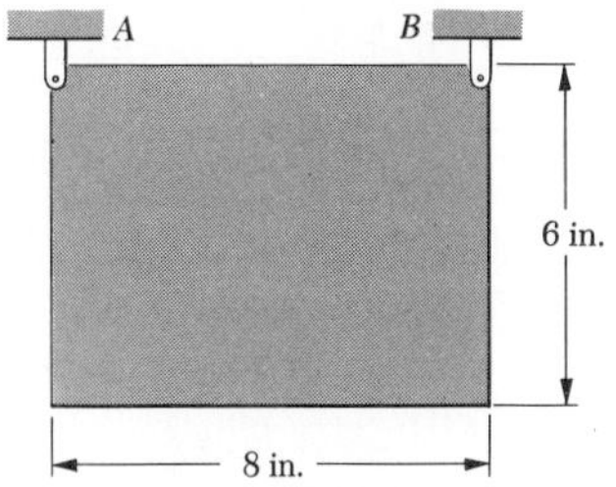

FIG. P 17.21

17.22. A collar of weight 2 lb is rigidly attached at a distance $d = 12$ in. from the end of a uniform slender rod AB. The rod weighs 6 lb and is of length $L = 24$ in. Knowing that the rod is released from rest in the position shown, determine the angular velocity of the rod after it has rotated through 90°.

***17.23.** A collar of weight 2 lb is rigidly attached to a slender rod AB of weight 6 lb and length $L = 24$ in. The rod is released from rest in the position shown. Determine the distance d for which the angular velocity of the rod is maximum after it has rotated through 90°.

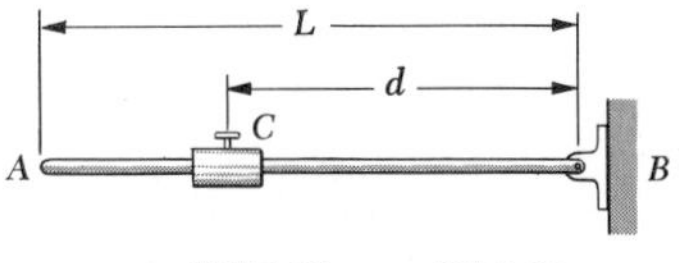

FIG. P 17.22 AND P 17.23

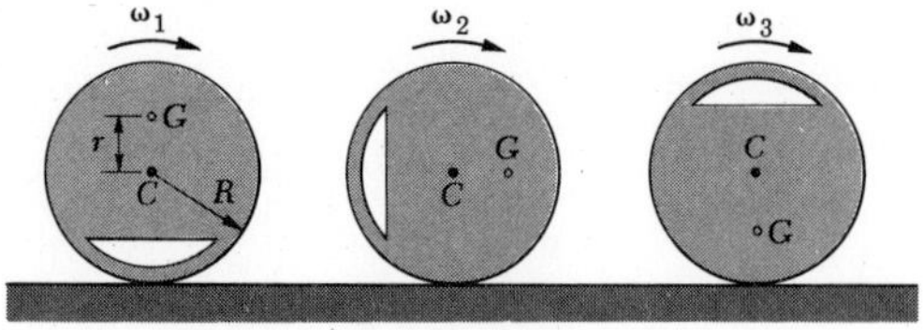

FIG. P 17.24 AND P 17.25

17.24. The mass center G of a wheel of radius R is located at a distance r from its geometric center C. The centroidal radius of gyration of the wheel is denoted by $\bar{k}$. As the wheel rolls freely and without sliding on a horizontal plane, its angular velocity is observed to vary. Denoting by ω_1, ω_2, and ω_3, respectively, the angular velocity of the wheel when G is directly above C, level with C, and directly below C, show that ω_1, ω_2, and ω_3 satisfy the relation

$$\frac{\omega_2^2 - \omega_1^2}{\omega_3^2 - \omega_2^2} = \frac{g/R + \omega_1^2}{g/R + \omega_3^2}$$

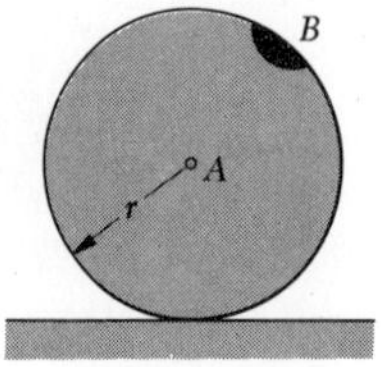

FIG. P 17.26

17.25. The mass center G of a 2-lb wheel of radius $R = 6$ in. is located at a distance $r = 2$ in. from its geometric center C. The centroidal radius of gyration of the wheel is $\bar{k} = 3$ in. As the wheel rolls without sliding, its angular velocity is observed to vary. Knowing that in position *1* the angular velocity is 10 radians/sec, determine the angular velocity of the wheel (*a*) in position 2, (*b*) in position 3.

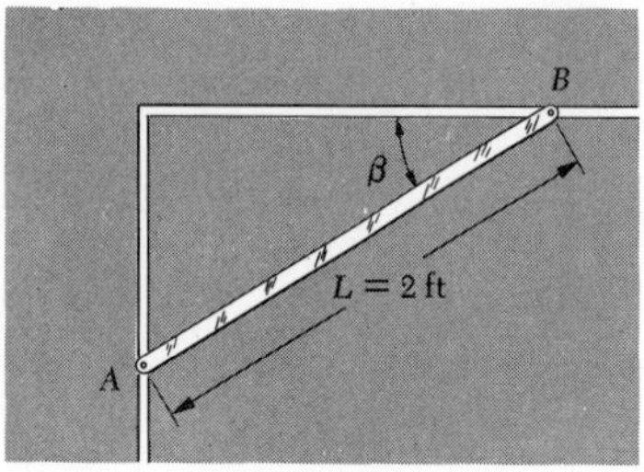

FIG. P 17.28

17.26. A weight W, of negligible dimensions, is attached at B to the rim of a disk of weight W and radius r. The disk rolls without sliding on a horizontal plane. Find the angular velocity ω_1 of the disk when B is directly above the center A in terms of g and r, knowing that the angular velocity of the disk is $3\omega_1$ when B is directly below A.

17.27. Solve Prob. 17.26 assuming that the disk is replaced by a hoop of weight W and radius r.

17.28. The motion of a 2-ft. slender rod is guided by pins at A and B which slide freely in the slots shown. Knowing that the rod is released from rest when $\beta = 0$, determine the velocity of A and of B (*a*) when $\beta = 30°$, (*b*) when $\beta = 90°$.

17.29. In Prob. 17.28, determine (*a*) the angle β for which the speed of end A is maximum, (*b*) the corresponding maximum speed of A.

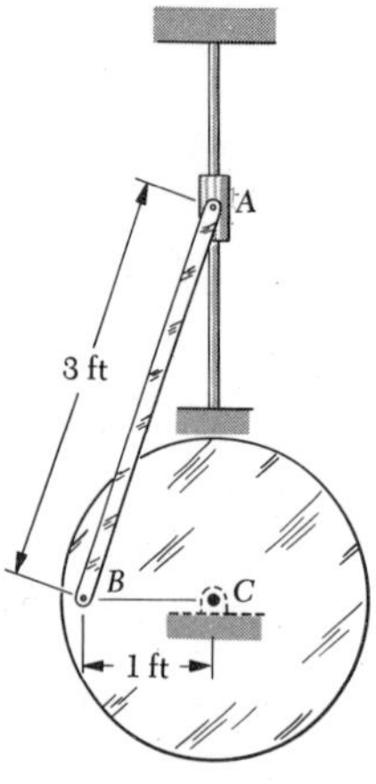

FIG. P 17.30

17.30. The connecting rod AB weighs 10 lb and is attached to a small collar of negligible weight at A and to a flywheel at B. The flywheel weighs 40 lb and has a radius of gyration of 9 in. Knowing that the angular velocity of the flywheel is 60 rpm clockwise in the position shown, determine the angular velocity of the flywheel (*a*) when B is directly above C, (*b*) when B is directly below C.

17.31. If in Prob. 17.30 the angular velocity of the flywheel is to be the same in the position shown and when point B is directly above C, determine its required angular velocity in the position shown.

17.32. The motion of a 20-lb sliding panel is guided by rollers at B and C. The counterweight A weighs 15 lb and is attached to a cable as shown. If the system is released from rest in the position shown, determine the velocity of the counterweight as it strikes the ground. Neglect the effect of friction.

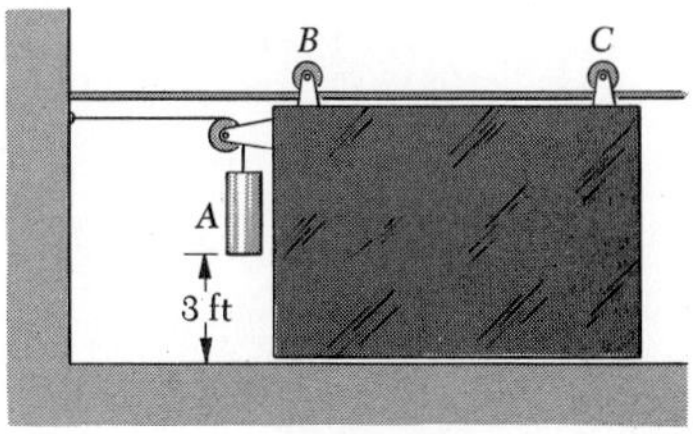

FIG. P 17.32

17.33. Determine the velocity of pin B as the rods of Sample Prob. 17.5 strike the horizontal surface.

17.34. A 2-ft rod AB of weight 10 lb is attached to a pin at A and to a spring of constant 6 lb/in. In the vertical position shown, the spring is unstretched and the angular velocity of the rod is 5 radians/sec clockwise. Determine the angular velocity of the rod after it has rotated through 90°.

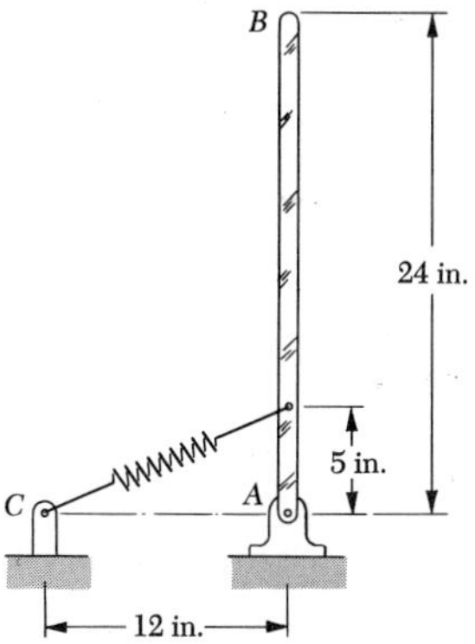

FIG. P 17.34

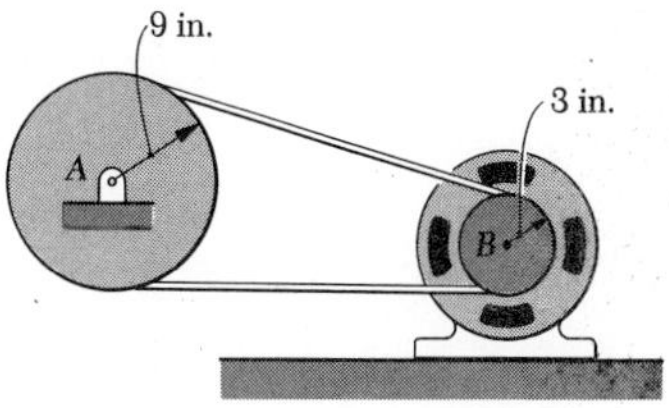

FIG. P 17.36

17.35. Solve Prob. 17.34 assuming that the rod rotates in a horizontal plane about a vertical axis (perpendicular to the page) through A.

17.36. The motor shown runs a machine attached to the shaft at A. The motor develops 4 hp and runs at a constant speed of 300 rpm. Determine the magnitude of the couple exerted (*a*) by the shaft on pulley A, (*b*) by the motor on pulley B.

17.37. Knowing that the magnitude of the maximum allowable couple which may be applied to a shaft is 80 kip-in., determine the maximum horsepower which may be transmitted by the shaft (*a*) at 60 rpm, (*b*) at 300 rpm.

17.38. Determine the magnitude of the couple which must be exerted by a motor to develop $\frac{3}{4}$ hp at a speed of (*a*) 720 rpm, (*b*) 7,200 rpm.

17.7. Principle of Impulse and Momentum for a Rigid Body. We shall now apply the principle of impulse and momentum to the analysis of the plane motion of rigid bodies and of systems of rigid bodies. As was pointed out in Chap. 14, the method of impulse and momentum is particularly well adapted to the solution of problems involving time and velocities. Moreover, the principle of impulse and momentum provides the only practicable method for the solution of problems of impact.

Since a rigid body of mass m may be considered as made of a large number of particles of mass Δm, Eq. (14.37), which was derived in Sec. 14.11 for a system of particles, may now be used to analyze the motion of a rigid body. We write

$$\textbf{Syst Momenta}_1 + \textbf{Syst Ext Imp}_{1\to2} = \textbf{Syst Momenta}_2 \quad (17.14)$$

This equation relates the three systems of vectors shown in Fig. 17.6. It expresses that the system formed by the momenta of the particles of the rigid body at time t_1 and the system of the impulses of the external forces applied to the body from t_1 to t_2 are together equivalent to the system formed by the momenta of the particles at time t_2.

We recall from Sec. 14.11 that, in the case of particles moving in the xy plane, three scalar equations are required to express the same relationship. The first two equations may be obtained by considering respectively the x and y components of the vectors shown in Fig. 17.6; they will relate the linear momenta of the particles and the linear impulses of the given forces in the x and y directions respectively. The third equation, which is obtained by computing the moments about O of the same vectors, will relate the angular momenta of the particles and the angular impulses of the forces.

Before we may conveniently apply the principle of impulse and momentum to the study of the plane motion of a rigid body,

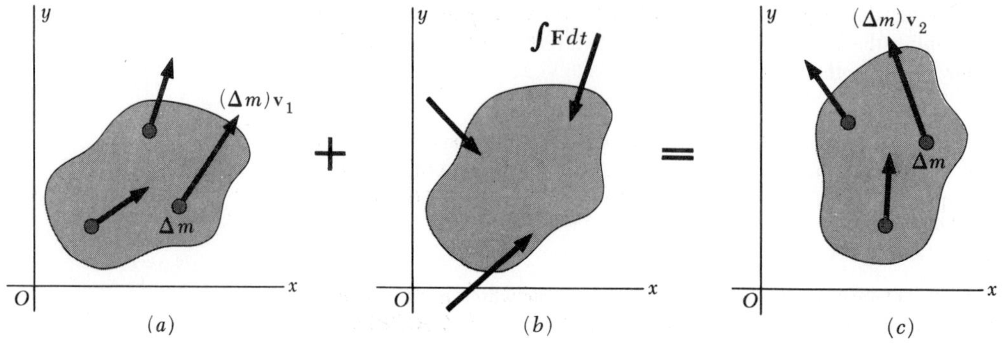

FIG. 17.6

we must learn to express more simply the systems of vectors representing the momenta of the particles forming the rigid body. This is the object of the next section.

17.8. Momentum of a Rigid Body in Plane Motion. We shall see in this section that the system of the momenta of the particles forming a rigid body may be replaced at any given instant by an equivalent system consisting of a *momentum vector* attached at the mass center of the body and a *momentum couple*. This reduction of the system of momenta to a vector and a couple is similar to the reduction of the system of effective forces described in Chap. 16. While the method involved is quite general, our present analysis will be limited to the plane motion of rigid slabs and of rigid bodies which are symmetrical with respect to the reference plane.†

Consider a rigid slab in plane motion. We know from Sec. 15.6 that, if we choose the mass center G of the slab as a reference point, the velocity $\mathbf{v}$ of a particle P of the slab may be expressed as the sum of the velocity $\bar{\mathbf{v}}$ of G and of the velocity $\mathbf{v}'$ of P relative to a frame attached to G and of fixed orientation. Denoting by $\mathbf{r}'$ the position vector of P relative to G, and recalling the relation (15.18), we write

$$\mathbf{v} = \bar{\mathbf{v}} + \mathbf{v}' = \bar{\mathbf{v}} + \boldsymbol{\omega} \times \mathbf{r}'$$

where $\boldsymbol{\omega}$ denotes the angular velocity of the slab at the instant considered. The momentum of the particle P may thus be resolved into the two vectors shown in Fig. 17.7. We have

$$(\Delta m)\mathbf{v} = (\Delta m)\bar{\mathbf{v}} + \Delta m(\boldsymbol{\omega} \times \mathbf{r}') \qquad (17.15)$$

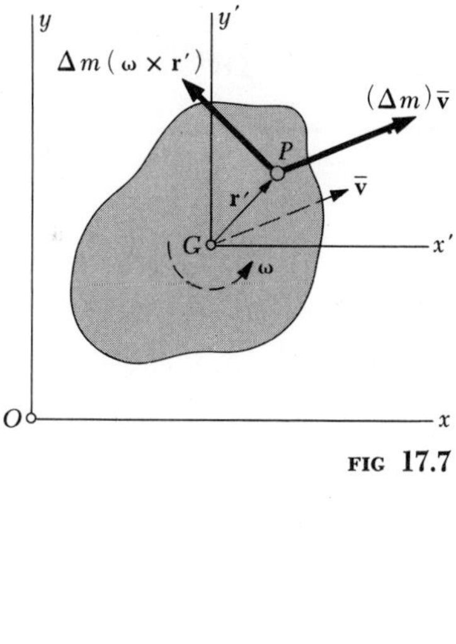

FIG 17.7

The sum of the momenta of the various particles of the slab is

$$\begin{aligned}\Sigma \mathbf{v}\Delta m &= \Sigma \bar{\mathbf{v}}\Delta m + \Sigma(\boldsymbol{\omega} \times \mathbf{r}')\Delta m \\ &= \bar{\mathbf{v}}\Sigma\Delta m + \boldsymbol{\omega} \times \Sigma \mathbf{r}'\Delta m\end{aligned}$$

since $\bar{\mathbf{v}}$ and $\boldsymbol{\omega}$ are independent of the particle considered. But the sum $\Sigma\Delta m$ is equal to the mass m of the slab, and, by (12.5), the sum $\Sigma\mathbf{r}'\Delta m$ is equal to $m\bar{\mathbf{r}}'$ and, thus, to zero, since the position vector $\bar{\mathbf{r}}'$ of G relative to itself is zero. Therefore, the sum of the momenta reduces to

$$\Sigma \mathbf{v}\Delta m = m\bar{\mathbf{v}} \qquad (17.16)$$

We note that Eq. (17.16) expresses the same result as Eq. (12.6), which was derived in the general case of the motion of a system of particles (Sec. 12.5).

† Or, more generally, to the motion of rigid bodies which have a principal axis of inertia perpendicular to the reference plane.

The sum of the moments about G of the momenta of the particles of the slab defines the *angular momentum* $\mathbf{h}_G$ of the slab about its mass center G. Recalling (17.15), we write

$$\begin{aligned}\mathbf{h}_G &= \Sigma(\mathbf{r}' \times \mathbf{v}\Delta m)\\ &= \Sigma(\mathbf{r}' \times \bar{\mathbf{v}}\Delta m) + \Sigma[\mathbf{r}' \times (\boldsymbol{\omega} \times \mathbf{r}')\Delta m]\\ &= (\Sigma\mathbf{r}'\Delta m) \times \bar{\mathbf{v}} + \Sigma[\mathbf{r}' \times (\boldsymbol{\omega} \times \mathbf{r}')\Delta m]\end{aligned}$$

As noted above, the sum $\Sigma\mathbf{r}'\Delta m$ is zero, and the expression obtained reduces to its last term.† Referring to Fig. 17.7, we easily verify that this term represents a vector of the same direction as $\boldsymbol{\omega}$ (i.e., perpendicular to the slab) and of magnitude equal to $\omega\Sigma r'^2\Delta m$. Recalling that the sum $\Sigma r'^2\Delta m$ represents the moment of inertia $\bar{I}$ of the slab about a centroidal axis perpendicular to the slab, we find that the angular momentum of the slab about its mass center is

$$\mathbf{h}_G = \bar{I}\boldsymbol{\omega} \tag{17.17}$$

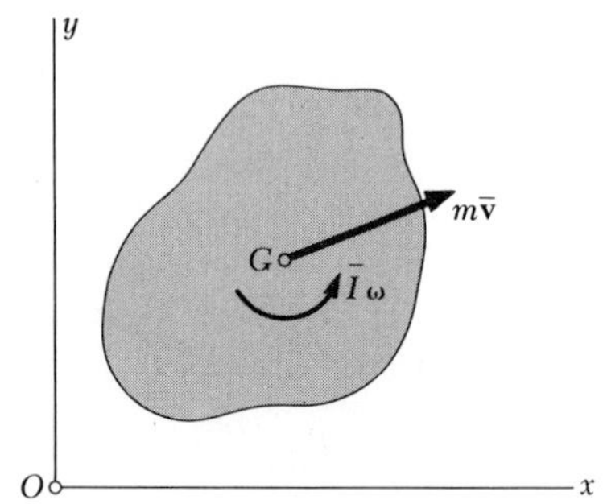

FIG. 17.8

Equations (17.16) and (17.17) show that the momenta of the various particles of the slab reduce to a momentum vector $m\bar{\mathbf{v}}$ attached at G and to a momentum couple $\bar{I}\boldsymbol{\omega}$ (Fig. 17.8).‡ We note that, while our derivation was given for a slab, the results obtained are still valid in the case of a rigid body symmetrical with respect to the reference plane.

Observing that the system of momenta reduces to the vector $m\bar{\mathbf{v}}$ attached at G in the particular case of a translation ($\boldsymbol{\omega} = 0$) and to the couple $\bar{I}\boldsymbol{\omega}$ in the particular case of a centroidal rotation ($\bar{\mathbf{v}} = 0$), we verify once more that the plane motion of a rigid body symmetrical with respect to the reference plane may be resolved into a translation with its mass center G and a rotation about G. The momentum vector is associated with the translation of the body with G and represents the *linear momentum* of the body. The momentum couple corresponds to the rotation of the body about G and its moment represents the *angular momentum* $\mathbf{h}_G$ *of the body about* G. Recalling the definition given in Sec. 14.10 for the angular momentum of a system of particles, we note that the angular momentum $\mathbf{h}_A$ of the body about an arbitrary point A may be obtained by adding

† We thus check that, in defining the angular momentum of the slab about its mass center G, we may determine the momenta of the particles of the slab indifferently with respect to a newtonian or a centroidal frame of reference. The equivalence of the two definitions was established in Prob. 14.88 in the general case of a system of particles.

‡ This vector and couple may in turn be reduced to a single vector (see Probs. 17.47 and 17.48).

the moment about A of the momentum vector $m\bar{\mathbf{v}}$ and the moment $\bar{I}\omega$ of the momentum couple.†

17.9. Application of the Principle of Impulse and Momentum to the Analysis of the Plane Motion of a Rigid Body. We saw in the preceding section that, in the case of the plane motion of a symmetrical rigid body, the system of the momenta of the particles of the body reduces to a vector $m\bar{\mathbf{v}}$ attached at G and a couple $\bar{I}\omega$. Replacing the system of momenta in parts a and c of Fig. 17.6 by the equivalent momentum vector and momentum couple, we obtain the three diagrams shown in Fig. 17.9. This figure expresses graphically, in the case of the plane motion of a rigid body, the fundamental relation

$$\textbf{Syst Momenta}_1 + \textbf{Syst Ext Imp}_{1\to 2} = \textbf{Syst Momenta}_2 \quad (17.14)$$

Three equations of motion may be derived from Fig. 17.9. Two equations are obtained by summing and equating the x and y *components* of the momenta and impulses, and the third by summing and equating the *moments* of these vectors *about any given point.* The coordinate axes may be chosen fixed in space, or they may be allowed to move with the mass center of the body while maintaining a fixed direction. In either case, the point about which moments are taken should keep the same position relative to the coordinate axes during the interval of time considered.

In deriving the three equations of motion for a rigid body, care should be taken not to add indiscriminately linear and angular momenta. Confusion will be avoided if it is kept in mind that $m\bar{v}_x$ and $m\bar{v}_y$ represent the *components of a vector,* namely, the linear momentum vector $m\bar{\mathbf{v}}$, while $\bar{I}\omega$ represents the *magnitude of a couple,* namely, the angular momentum couple $\bar{I}\omega$. Thus the quantity $\bar{I}\omega$ should be added only to the

† Note that, in general, $\mathbf{h}_A$ is *not* equal to $I_A\omega$ (see Prob. 17.49).

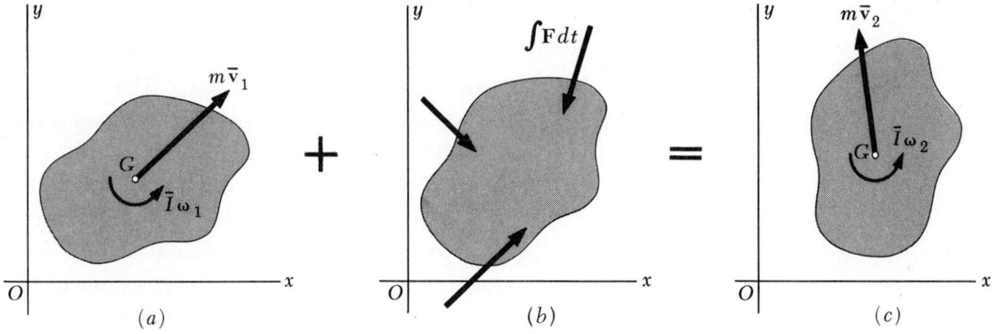

FIG. 17.9

moment of the linear momentum $m\bar{\mathbf{v}}$, never to this vector itself nor to its components. All quantities involved will then be expressed in the same units, namely, lb-ft-sec.

Noncentroidal Rotation. In this particular case of plane motion, the magnitude of the velocity of the mass center of the body is $\bar{v} = \bar{r}\omega$, where $\bar{r}$ represents the distance from the mass center to the fixed axis of rotation and ω the angular velocity of the body at the instant considered; the magnitude of the momentum vector attached at G is thus $m\bar{v} = m\bar{r}\omega$. Summing the moments about O of the momentum vector and momentum couple (Fig. 17.10) and using the parallel-axis theorem for moments of inertia, we find that the angular momentum of the body about O has the magnitude

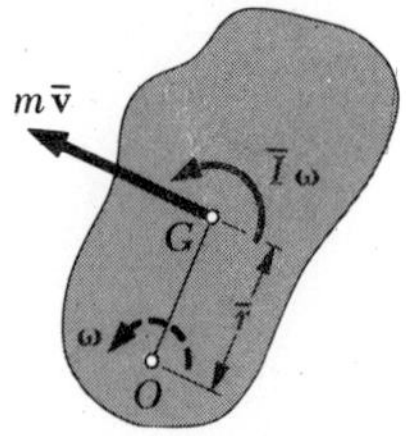

FIG. 17.10

$$\bar{I}\omega + (m\bar{r}\omega)\bar{r} = (\bar{I} + m\bar{r}^2)\omega = I_O\omega \qquad (17.18)$$

Equating the moments about O of the momenta and impulses in (17.14), we write

$$I_O\omega_1 + \Sigma \int_{t_1}^{t_2} M_O\, dt = I_O\omega_2 \qquad (17.19)$$

In the general case of plane motion of a rigid body, formula (17.18) may be used to determine the angular momentum of the body with respect to the instantaneous axis of rotation. Equation (17.19) may also be used with respect to the instantaneous axis of rotation under certain conditions of symmetry. It is recommended, however, that all problems of plane motion be solved by the general method described earlier in this section.

17.10. Systems of Rigid Bodies. The motion of several connected rigid bodies may be analyzed by applying the principle of impulse and momentum to each body separately (see Sample Prob. 17.6).

However, in solving problems involving no more than three unknowns (including the impulses of unknown reactions), it is often found more convenient to apply the principle of impulse and momentum to the system as a whole. We write Eq. (17.14) and draw the three corresponding momentum and impulse diagrams for the entire system of connected bodies. The diagrams of momenta should include a momentum vector, a momentum couple, or both, for each moving part of the system. Impulses of forces internal to the system, such as tensions in connecting cables, may be omitted from the impulse diagram (see Sample Prob. 17.7). Here again, care should be taken not to add indiscriminately linear and angular momenta; each equation should be checked to make sure that consistent units have been used.

SAMPLE PROBLEM 17.6

Gear A weighs 20 lb and has a radius of gyration of 9 in., while gear B weighs 5 lb and has a radius of gyration of 3 in. The system is at rest when a couple **M** of moment 4 lb-ft is applied to gear B. Neglecting friction, determine (*a*) the time required for the angular velocity of gear B to reach 600 rpm, (*b*) the tangential force which gear B exerts on gear A. These gears have been previously considered in Sample Prob. 17.2.

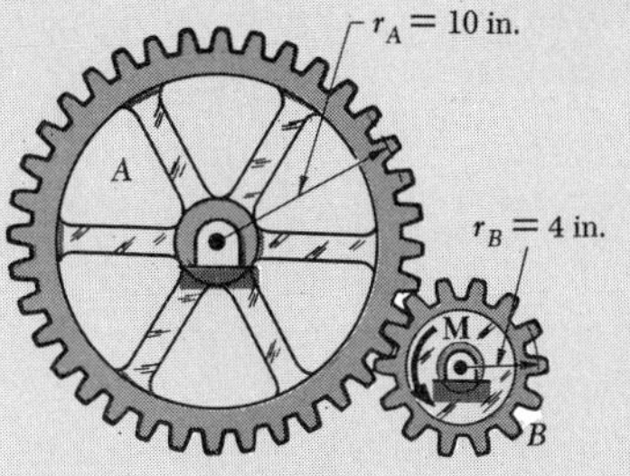

Solution. We apply the principle of impulse and momentum to each gear separately. Since all forces and the couple are constant, their impulses are obtained by multiplying them by the unknown time t. We recall from Sample Prob. 17.2 that the centroidal moments of inertia and the final angular velocities are

$$\bar{I}_A = 0.349 \text{ lb-ft-sec}^2 \qquad \bar{I}_B = 0.00970 \text{ lb-ft-sec}^2$$
$$(\omega_A)_2 = 25.1 \text{ radians/sec} \qquad (\omega_B)_2 = 62.8 \text{ radians/sec}$$

Principle of Impulse and Momentum for Gear A. The systems of initial momenta, impulses, and final momenta are shown in three separate sketches.

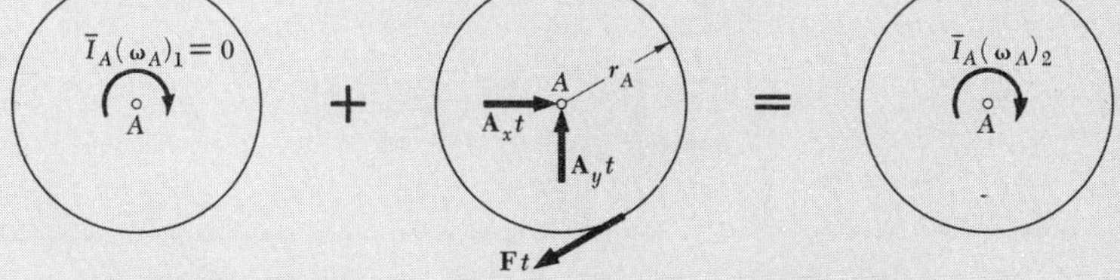

$$\textbf{Syst Momenta}_1 + \textbf{Syst Ext Imp}_{1\to2} = \textbf{Syst Momenta}_2$$

+↻ moments about A:
$$0 - Ftr_A = -\bar{I}_A(\omega_A)_2$$
$$Ft(\tfrac{10}{12}) = (0.349)(25.1)$$
$$Ft = 10.51 \text{ lb-sec}$$

Principle of Impulse and Momentum for Gear B

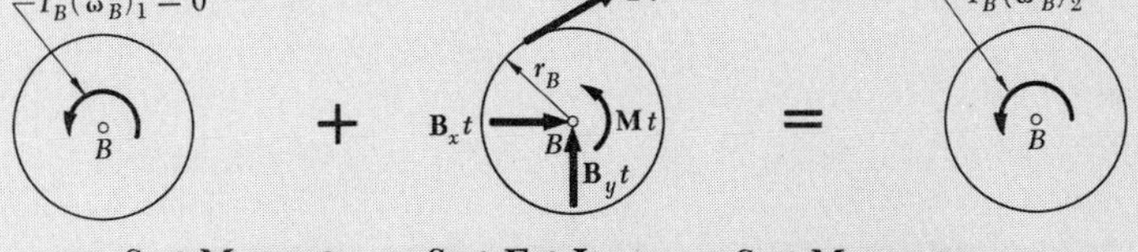

$$\textbf{Syst Momenta}_1 + \textbf{Syst Ext Imp}_{1\to2} = \textbf{Syst Momenta}_2$$

+↺ moments about B:
$$0 + Mt - Ftr_B = \bar{I}_B(\omega_B)_2$$
$$+4t - (10.51)(\tfrac{4}{12}) = (0.00970)(62.8)$$
$$t = 1.028 \text{ sec} \quad ◄$$

Recalling that $Ft = 10.51$ lb-sec, we write

$$F(1.028 \text{ sec}) = 10.51 \text{ lb-sec}$$
$$F = +10.22 \text{ lb}$$

Thus, the force exerted by gear B on gear A is

$$\mathbf{F} = 10.22 \text{ lb} \swarrow \quad ◄$$

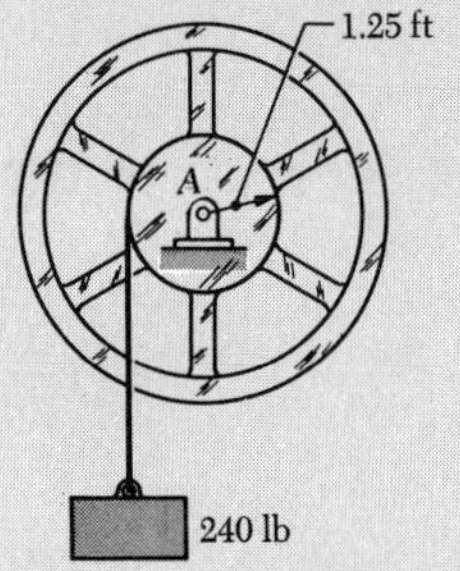

SAMPLE PROBLEM 17.7

A 240-lb block is suspended from an inextensible cable which is wrapped around a drum of radius 1.25 ft rigidly attached to a flywheel. The drum and flywheel have a combined moment of inertia $\bar{I} = 10.5$ lb-ft-sec^2. At the instant shown, the velocity of the block is 6 ft/sec directed downward. Knowing that the bearing at A is poorly lubricated and that the bearing friction is equivalent to a couple **M** of moment 60 lb-ft, determine the velocity of the block 2 sec later.

Solution. We consider the system formed by the flywheel and the block. Forces external to this system consist of the weight $\mathbf{W}_f$ of the flywheel, the weight **W** of the block, the reaction **A**, and the friction couple **M**. Since the magnitude and the line of action of each force are constant, the impulse of each force is equal to the product of the force and of the time interval t. Likewise, since the friction couple is constant, its angular impulse is $\mathbf{M}t$.

Principle of Impulse and Momentum. The systems of initial momenta, impulses, and final momenta are shown in three separate sketches.

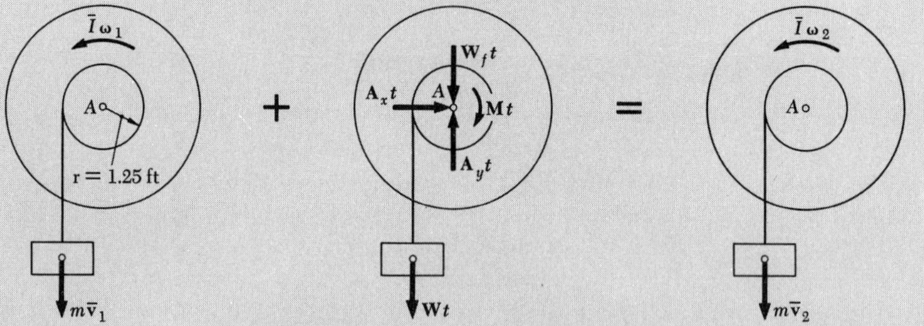

$$\textbf{Syst Momenta}_1 + \textbf{Syst Ext Imp}_{1\to 2} = \textbf{Syst Momenta}_2$$

$+\circlearrowright$ moments about A: $\quad \bar{I}\omega_1 + m\bar{v}_1 r + Wtr - Mt = \bar{I}\omega_2 + m\bar{v}_2 r$

We note that $\bar{v} = r\omega$ and write

$$\bar{v}_1 = 6 \text{ ft/sec} \qquad \omega_1 = \frac{\bar{v}_1}{r} = \frac{6}{1.25} = 4.80 \text{ radians/sec}$$

$$\omega_2 = \frac{\bar{v}_2}{r} = \frac{\bar{v}_2}{1.25}$$

Substituting these expressions together with the known values of W, $\bar{I}$, r, M, and t into the above equation, we obtain

$$(10.5)(4.80) + \frac{240}{g}(6)(1.25) + (240)(2)(1.25) - (60)(2) = (10.5)\frac{\bar{v}_2}{1.25} + \frac{240}{g}\bar{v}_2(1.25)$$

$$\bar{v}_2 = +33.1 \text{ ft/sec} \qquad \bar{\mathbf{v}}_2 = 33.1 \text{ ft/sec} \downarrow \blacktriangleleft$$

SAMPLE PROBLEM 17.8

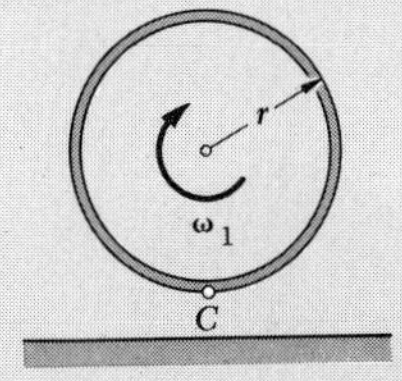

A hoop of radius r and weight W is placed on a horizontal surface with no linear velocity but with a clockwise angular velocity ω_1. Denoting by μ the coefficient of friction between the hoop and the surface, determine (*a*) the time t_2 at which the hoop will start rolling without sliding, (*b*) the linear and angular velocities of the hoop at time t_2.

Solution. Since the entire mass, $m = W/g$, is located at a distance r from the center of the hoop, we write $\bar{I} = mr^2 = (W/g)r^2$. While the hoop is sliding relative to the surface, it is acted upon by the normal force **N**, the friction force **F**, and its weight **W**.

Principle of Impulse and Momentum. We apply the principle of impulse and momentum to the hoop from the time t_1 when it is placed on the surface until the time t_2 when it starts rolling without sliding.

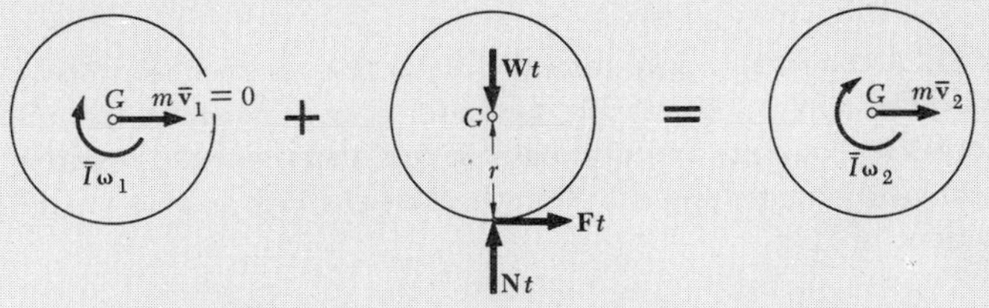

$$\textbf{Syst Momenta}_1 + \textbf{Syst Ext Imp}_{1\to2} = \textbf{Syst Momenta}_2$$

$+\uparrow$ y components: $\quad Nt - Wt = 0 \quad (1)$

$\xrightarrow{+}$ x components: $\quad Ft = m\bar{v}_2 \quad (2)$

$+\circlearrowright$ moments about G: $\quad -\bar{I}\omega_1 + Ftr = -\bar{I}\omega_2 \quad (3)$

From (1) we obtain $N = W$. For $t < t_2$, sliding occurs at point C and we have $F = \mu N = \mu W$. Substituting $F = \mu W$ into (2),

$$\mu W t = \frac{W}{g}\bar{v}_2 \qquad \bar{v}_2 = \mu g t \tag{4}$$

Substituting $F = \mu W$ into (3),

$$-\frac{W}{g}r^2\omega_1 + \mu W t r = -\frac{W}{g}r^2\omega_2 \qquad \omega_2 = \omega_1 - \frac{\mu g}{r}t \tag{5}$$

The hoop will start rolling without sliding when the velocity $\mathbf{v}_C$ of the point of contact is zero. At that time, $t = t_2$, point C becomes the instantaneous center of rotation, and we have $\bar{v}_2 = r\omega_2$. Substituting from (4) and (5), we write

$$\bar{v}_2 = r\omega_2 \qquad \mu g t_2 = r\left(\omega_1 - \frac{\mu g}{r}t_2\right) \qquad t_2 = \frac{r\omega_1}{2\mu g} \quad ◄$$

Substituting this expression for t_2 into (4),

$$\bar{v}_2 = \mu g t_2 = \mu g \frac{r\omega_1}{2\mu g} \qquad \bar{v}_2 = \tfrac{1}{2}r\omega_1 \qquad \bar{\mathbf{v}}_2 = \tfrac{1}{2}r\omega_1 \rightarrow \quad ◄$$

$$\omega_2 = \frac{\bar{v}_2}{r} \qquad \omega_2 = \tfrac{1}{2}\omega_1 \qquad \omega_2 = \tfrac{1}{2}\omega_1 \circlearrowright \quad ◄$$

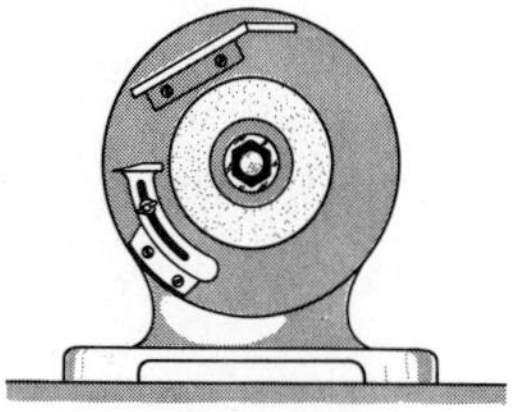

FIG. P 17.40

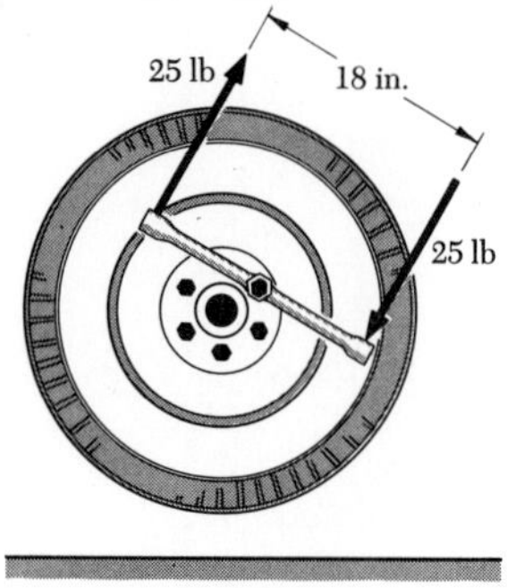

FIG. P 17.41

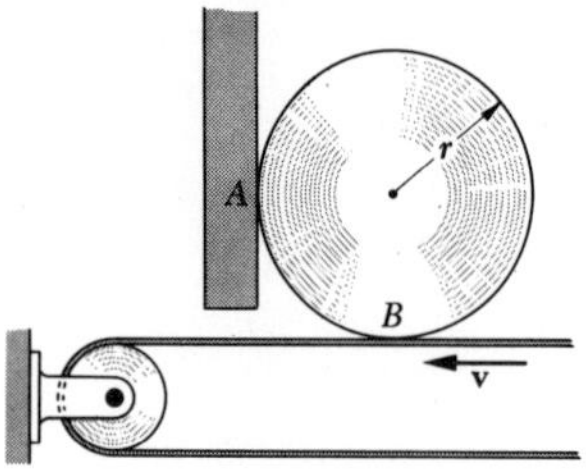

FIG. P 17.42

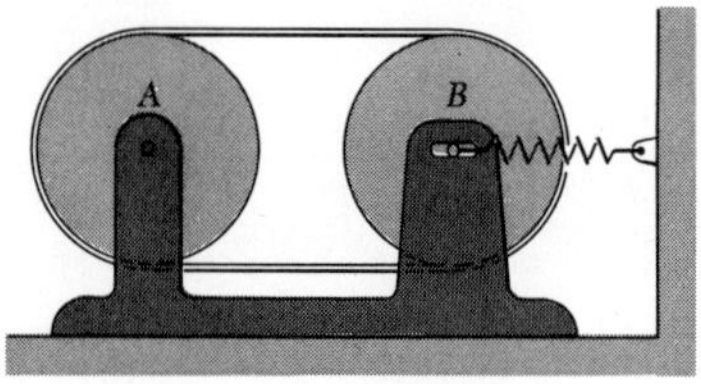

FIG. P 17.46

PROBLEMS

17.39. At a time when an electric motor is rotating at 1,200 rpm, the load and power are cut off and the rotor coasts to rest. The rotor weighs 75 lb and has a radius of gyration of 6 in. If the kinetic friction of the rotor produces a couple of magnitude equal to 6 lb-in., determine the time required for the rotor to coast to rest.

17.40. A small grinding wheel is attached to the shaft of an electric motor which has a rated speed of 3,600 rpm. When the power is turned off, the unit coasts to rest in 70 sec. The grinding wheel and rotor have a combined weight of 6 lb and a combined radius of gyration of 2 in. Determine the average magnitude of the couple due to kinetic friction in the bearings of the motor.

17.41. A bolt located 2 in. from the center of an automobile wheel is tightened by applying the couple shown for $\frac{1}{10}$ sec. Assuming that the wheel is free to rotate and is initially at rest, determine the resulting angular velocity of the wheel. The wheel weighs 45 lb and has a radius of gyration of 11 in.

17.42. A cylinder of radius r and weight W is placed with no initial velocity on a moving belt as shown. Denoting by μ the coefficient of friction at A and B, derive an expression for the time during which slippage occurs at B.

17.43. Using the principle of impulse and momentum, solve Prob. 16.34*b*.

17.44. Using the principle of impulse and momentum, solve Prob. 16.42*b*.

17.45. Using the principle of impulse and momentum, solve Prob. 16.43*b*.

17.46. Two disks A and B are connected by a belt as shown. Each disk weighs 30 lb and has a radius of 1.5 ft. The shaft of disk B rests in a slotted bearing and is held by a spring which exerts a constant force of 15 lb. If a couple of magnitude 20 lb-ft is applied to disk A, determine (*a*) the time required for the disks to attain a speed of 600 rpm, (*b*) the tension in both portions of the belt, (*c*) the minimum coefficient of friction if no slipping is to occur.

17.47. Show that the system of momenta for a rigid body in plane motion reduces to a single vector, and express the distance from the mass center G to the line of action of this vector in terms of the centroidal radius of gyration $\bar{k}$ of the body, the magnitude $\bar{v}$ of the velocity of G, and the angular velocity ω.

17.48. Show that, when a body rotates about a fixed axis through O, the system of momenta of its particles is equivalent to a single vector of magnitude $m\bar{r}\omega$, perpendicular to the line OG, and applied to a point P on this line, called the *center of percussion*, at a distance $GP = \bar{k}^2/\bar{r}$ from the mass center of the body.

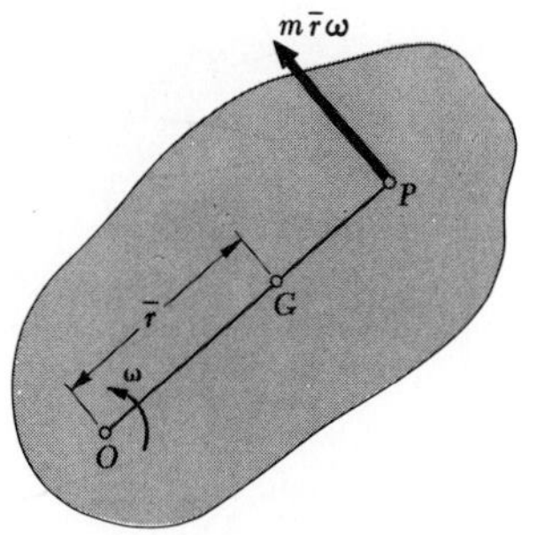

FIG. P17.48

17.49. Show that the angular momentum of a rigid body about a point A is equal to $I_A\omega$, where ω is the angular velocity of the body at the instant considered and I_A the moment of inertia of the body about A, *if and only if* one of the following conditions is satisfied: (*a*) A is the mass center of the body, (*b*) A is the instantaneous center of rotation, (*c*) the velocity of A is directed along a line joining point A and the mass center G.

17.50. Consider a rigid slab initially at rest and subjected to an impulsive force **F** contained in the plane of the slab. We define the *center of percussion P* as the point of intersection of the line of action of **F** with the perpendicular drawn from G. (*a*) Show that the instantaneous center of rotation C of the slab is located on line GP at a distance $GC = \bar{k}^2/GP$ on the opposite side of G. (*b*) Show that, if the center of percussion were located at C, the instantaneous center of rotation would be located at P.

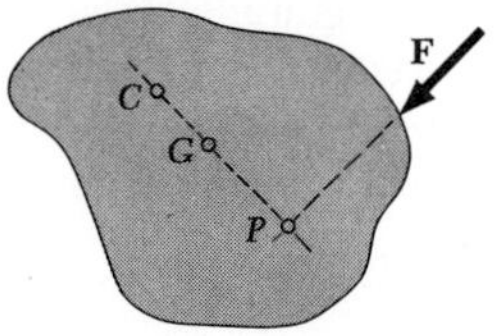

FIG. P17.50

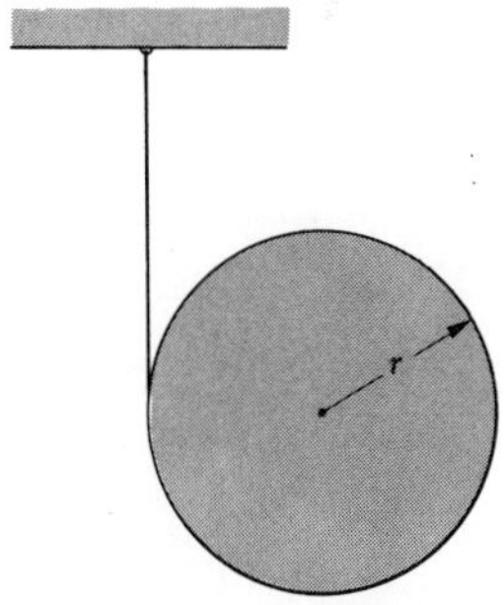

FIG. P17.51

17.51. A cord is wrapped around a solid cylinder of radius r and weight W as shown. If the cylinder is released from rest at time $t = 0$, determine the velocity of the center of the cylinder at a time t.

17.52. Solve Prob. 17.51 assuming that the solid cylinder is replaced by a hollow cylinder of outside radius r, weight W, and centroidal radius of gyration $\bar{k}$.

17.53. Two disks, each of weight 12 lb and radius 6 in., which roll without slipping, are connected by a drum of radius r and of negligible weight. A rope is wrapped around the drum and is pulled horizontally with a force **P** of magnitude 8 lb. Knowing that $r = 3$ in. and that the disks are initially at rest, determine (*a*) the velocity of the center G after 3 sec, (*b*) the friction force required to prevent slipping.

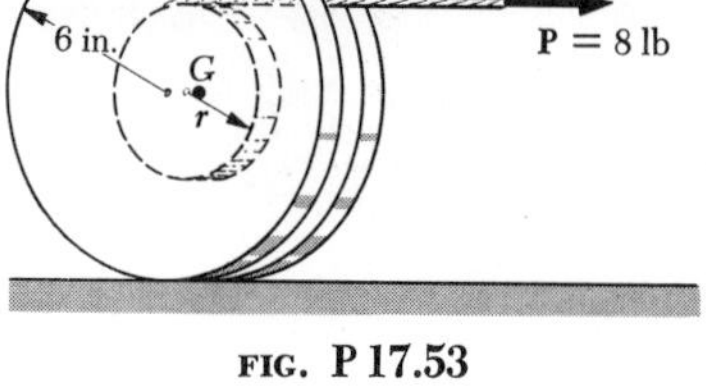

FIG. P17.53

17.54. In Prob. 17.53, determine the required value of r and the corresponding velocity after 3 sec if the friction force is to be zero.

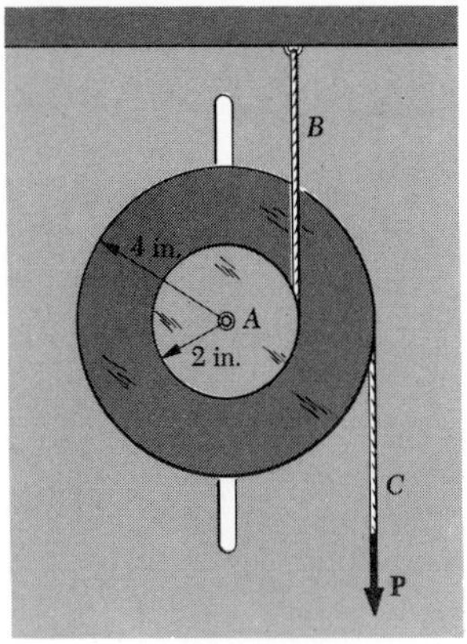

FIG. P 17.55

17.55. The double pulley shown weighs 6 lb and has a centroidal radius of gyration of 3 in. The 2-in.-radius inner pulley is rigidly attached to the 4-in.-radius outer pulley, and the motion of the center *A* is guided by a smooth pin at *A* which slides in a vertical slot. When the pulley is at rest, a force **P** of magnitude 8 lb is applied to cord *C*. Determine the velocity of the center of the pulley after 5 sec.

17.56. Solve Prob. 17.55 assuming that the force **P** is replaced by an 8-lb weight attached to cord *C*.

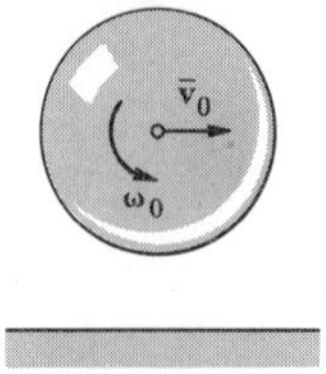

FIG. P 17.57

17.57. A sphere of weight *W* and radius *r* is projected along a rough horizontal surface with the initial velocities indicated. If the final velocity of the sphere is to be zero, express (*a*) the required ω_0 in terms of $\bar{v}_0$ and *r*, (*b*) the time required for the sphere to come to rest in terms of μ and $\bar{v}_0$.

17.58. In Prob. 17.57, assume $\omega_0 = 0$, and determine (*a*) the time at which the velocity of the sphere becomes constant, (*b*) the final velocity of the sphere.

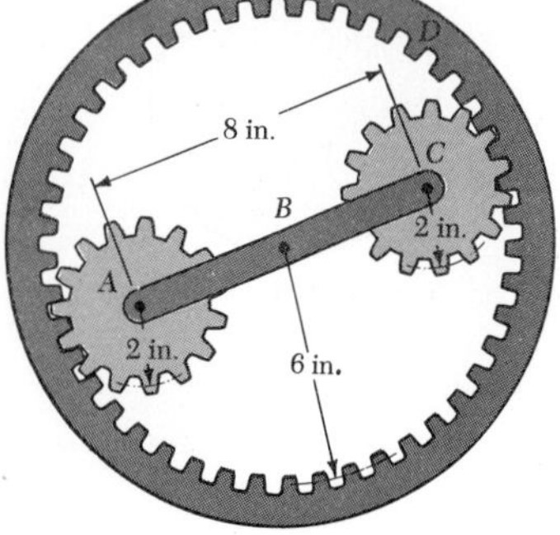

FIG. P 17.59

***17.59.** In the gear arrangement shown, the inner gears *A* and *C* are attached to the rod *ABC* which is free to rotate about *B*, while the outer gear *D* is fixed. Knowing that the system is initially at rest, determine the magnitude of the couple **M** which must be applied to rod *ABC* if 3 sec later the angular velocity of the rod is to be 300 rpm clockwise. Gears *A* and *C* weigh 3 lb each and may be considered as disks of radius 2 in.; rod *ABC* weighs 5 lb.

***17.60.** In the gear arrangement shown, gears *A* and *C* are attached to the rod *ABC*, which is free to rotate about *B*, while the inner gear *B* is fixed. Knowing that the system is at rest, determine the magnitude of the couple **M** which must be applied to rod *ABC*, if 3 sec later the angular velocity of the rod is to be 300 rpm clockwise. Gears *A* and *C* weigh 3 lb each and may be considered as disks of radius 2 in.; rod *ABC* weighs 5 lb.

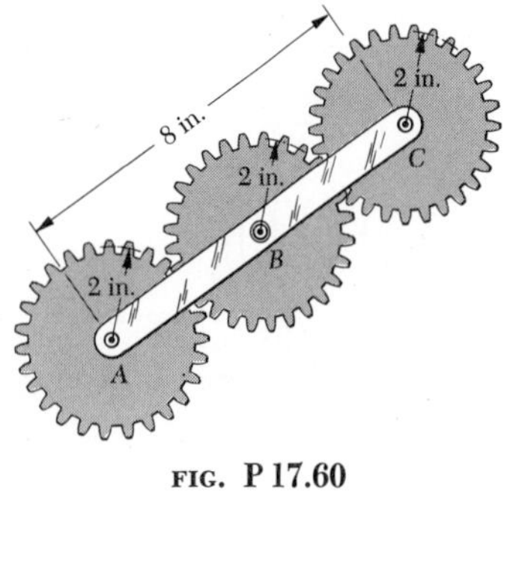

FIG. P 17.60

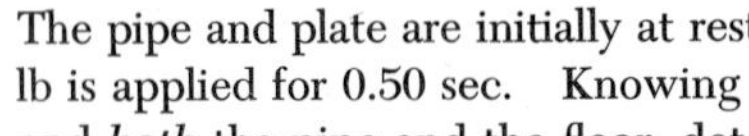

FIG. P 17.61

***17.61.** A 12-in.-diameter pipe weighing 40 lb rests on a 10-lb plate. The pipe and plate are initially at rest when a force **P** of magnitude 20 lb is applied for 0.50 sec. Knowing that $\mu = 0.20$ between the plate and *both* the pipe and the floor, determine the resulting velocities of the pipe and of the plate.

***17.62.** Solve Prob. 17.61 assuming that the magnitude of the force **P** is 30 lb.

17.11. Conservation of Angular Momentum. We recall the fundamental equation of impulse and momentum for a rigid body or a system of rigid bodies moving under the action of given forces:

$$\textbf{Syst Momenta}_1 + \textbf{Syst Ext Imp}_{1\to 2} = \textbf{Syst Momenta}_2 \quad (17.14)$$

When no external force acts on the system or, more generally, when the system of the impulses of the external forces is equivalent to zero, Eq. (17.14) reduces to

$$\textbf{Syst Momenta}_1 = \textbf{Syst Momenta}_2 \quad (17.20)$$

Summing and equating successively the x components, y components, and moments of the momenta in (17.20), we conclude that the total linear momentum of the system is conserved in any direction and that its total angular momentum is conserved about any point.

There are many engineering applications, however, in which *the linear momentum is not conserved,* yet in which *the angular momentum* $\mathbf{h}_O$ *of the system about a given point* O *is conserved:*

$$(\mathbf{h}_O)_1 = (\mathbf{h}_O)_2 \quad (17.21)$$

Such cases occur when the lines of action of all external forces pass through O or, more generally, when the sum of the angular impulses of the external forces about O is zero.

Problems involving *conservation of angular momentum* about a point O may be solved by the general method of impulse and momentum, i.e., by drawing the three diagrams corresponding to the fundamental equation (17.14). Equation (17.21) is then obtained by summing and equating moments about O. Two additional equations may be written by summing and equating x and y components; these equations may be used to determine two unknown linear impulses, such as the impulses of the reaction components at a fixed point (Sample Prob. 17.9).

There are many nonengineering applications of conservation of angular momentum which are familiar to all of us. By bringing his arms together or by extending them, a skater may vary his moment of inertia $\bar{I}$ and thus spin more or less rapidly (since $\bar{I}\omega$ must remain constant). A skier performing a high jump has no control over his *total* angular momentum once he has left the ground. Yet by revolving his arms he may change the *distribution* of his angular momentum and thus keep his body vertical. A cat dropped with no initial angular momentum spins its tail in one sense and thus causes its body to rotate in the other sense, with the result that it lands on its paws.

17.12. Eccentric Impact. We saw in Chap. 14 that the method of impulse and momentum is the only practicable method for the solution of problems involving impulsive forces. Now we shall also find that, compared with the various problems considered in the preceding sections, problems involving impulsive forces are particularly well adapted to a solution by the method of impulse and momentum. The computation of linear impulses and angular impulses is quite simple, since, the time interval considered being very short, the bodies involved may be assumed to occupy the same position during that time interval.

In Secs. 14.5 to 14.7, we learned to solve problems of *central impact*, i.e., problems in which the mass centers of the two colliding bodies are located on the line of impact. We shall now analyze the *eccentric impact* of two rigid bodies. Consider two bodies which collide, and denote by $\mathbf{v}_A$ and $\mathbf{v}_B$ the velocities before impact *of the two points of contact* A and B (Fig. 17.11*a*). Under the impact, the two bodies will *deform* and, at the end of the period of deformation, their velocities $\mathbf{u}_A$ and $\mathbf{u}_B$ will have equal components along the line of impact *nn* (Fig. 17.11*b*). A period of *restitution* will then take place, at the end of which the points of contact will have velocities $\mathbf{v}'_A$ and $\mathbf{v}'_B$ (Fig. 17.11*c*). Assuming the bodies perfectly smooth, we find that the forces they exert on each other are directed along the line of impact. Denoting, respectively, by $\int P\,dt$ and $\int R\,dt$ the magnitude of the impulse of one of these forces during the period of deformation and during the period of restitution, we recall that the coefficient of restitution e is defined as the ratio

$$e = \frac{\int R\,dt}{\int P\,dt} \tag{17.22}$$

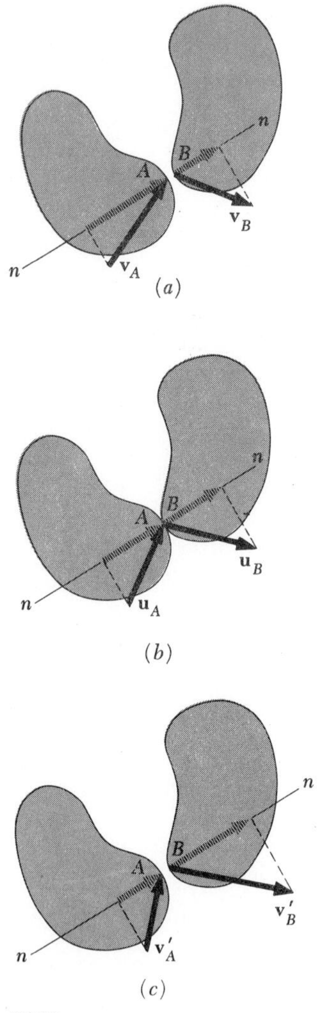

FIG. 17.11

We propose to show that the relation established in Sec. 14.6 between the relative velocities of two particles before and after impact also holds between the components along the line of impact of the relative velocities of the two points of contact A and B. We propose to show, therefore, that

$$(v'_B)_n - (v'_A)_n = e[(v_A)_n - (v_B)_n] \tag{17.23}$$

We shall first assume that the motion of each of the two colliding bodies of Fig. 17.11 is unconstrained. Thus the only impulsive forces exerted on the bodies during the impact are applied at A and B respectively. Consider the body to which point A belongs and draw the three momentum and impulse diagrams corresponding to the period of deformation (Fig. 17.12.)

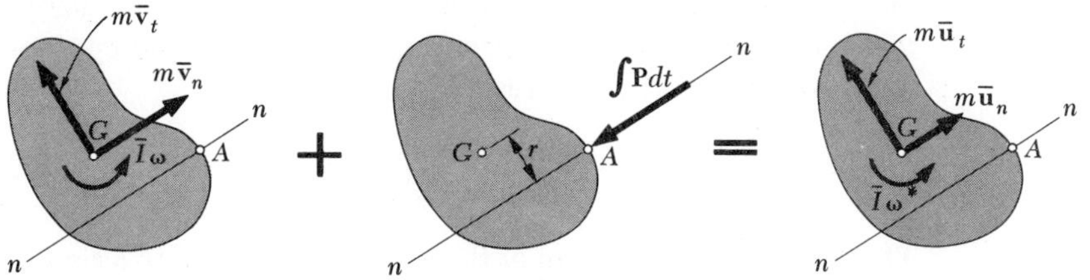

FIG. 17.12

We denote by $\bar{\mathbf{v}}$ and $\bar{\mathbf{u}}$, respectively, the velocity of the mass center at the beginning and at the end of the period of deformation, and by ω and ω^* the angular velocity of the body at the same instants. Summing and equating the components of the momenta and impulses along the line of impact nn, we write

$$m\bar{v}_n - \int P\,dt = m\bar{u}_n \tag{17.24}$$

Summing and equating the moments about G of the momenta and impulses, we also write

$$\bar{I}\omega - r\int P\,dt = \bar{I}\omega^* \tag{17.25}$$

where r represents the perpendicular distance from G to the line of impact. Considering now the period of restitution, we obtain in a similar way

$$m\bar{u}_n - \int R\,dt = m\bar{v}'_n \tag{17.26}$$

$$\bar{I}\omega^* - r\int R\,dt = \bar{I}\omega' \tag{17.27}$$

where $\bar{\mathbf{v}}'$ and ω' represent, respectively, the velocity of the mass center and the angular velocity of the body after impact. Solving (17.24) and (17.26) for the two impulses and substituting into (17.22), and then solving (17.25) and (17.27) for the same two impulses and substituting again into (17.22), we obtain the following two alternate expressions for the coefficient of restitution:

$$e = \frac{\bar{u}_n - \bar{v}'_n}{\bar{v}_n - \bar{u}_n} \qquad e = \frac{\omega^* - \omega'}{\omega - \omega^*} \tag{17.28}$$

Multiplying by r the numerator and denominator of the second expression obtained for e, and adding respectively to the numerator and denominator of the first expression, we have

$$e = \frac{\bar{u}_n + r\omega^* - (\bar{v}'_n + r\omega')}{\bar{v}_n + r\omega - (\bar{u}_n + r\omega^*)}$$

Observing that $\bar{v}_n + r\omega$ represents the component $(v_A)_n$ along nn of the velocity of the point of contact A and that, similarly, $\bar{u}_n + r\omega^*$ and $\bar{v}'_n + r\omega'$ represent, respectively, the components $(u_A)_n$ and $(v'_A)_n$, we write

$$e = \frac{(u_A)_n - (v'_A)_n}{(v_A)_n - (u_A)_n} \tag{17.29}$$

The analysis of the motion of the second body leads to a similar expression for e in terms of the components along nn of the successive velocities of point B. Recalling that $(u_A)_n = (u_B)_n$, and eliminating these two velocity components by a manipulation similar to the one used in Sec. 14.6, we obtain relation (17.23).

If one or both of the colliding bodies is constrained to rotate about a fixed point O, as in the case of a compound pendulum (Fig. 17.13*a*), an impulsive reaction will be exerted at O (Fig. 17.13*b*). We shall verify that, while their derivation must be modified, Eqs. (17.29) and (17.23) remain valid. Applying formula (17.19) to the period of deformation and to the period of restitution, we write

$$I_O\omega - r\int P\,dt = I_O\omega^* \tag{17.30}$$
$$I_O\omega^* - r\int R\,dt = I_O\omega' \tag{17.31}$$

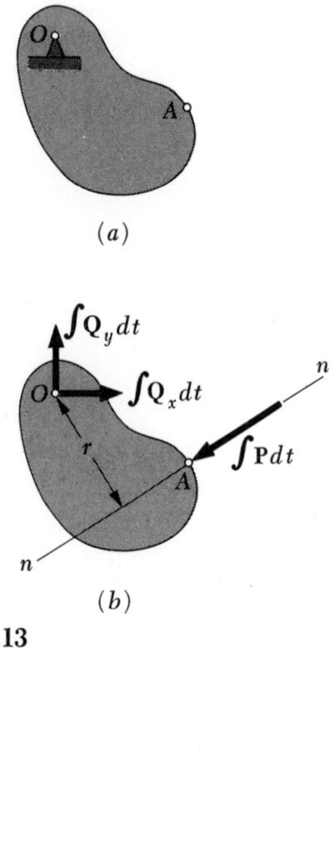

FIG. 17.13

where r represents the perpendicular distance from the fixed point O to the line of impact. Solving (17.30) and (17.31) for the two impulses and substituting into (17.22), and then observing that $r\omega$, $r\omega^*$, and $r\omega'$ represent the components along nn of the successive velocities of point A, we write

$$e = \frac{\omega^* - \omega'}{\omega - \omega^*} = \frac{r\omega^* - r\omega'}{r\omega - r\omega^*} = \frac{(u_A)_n - (v'_A)_n}{(v_A)_n - (u_A)_n}$$

and check that Eq. (17.29) still holds. Thus Eq. (17.23) remains valid when one or both of the colliding bodies is constrained to rotate about a fixed point O.

In order to determine the velocities of the two colliding bodies after impact, relation (17.23) should be used in conjunction with one or several other equations obtained by applying the principle of impulse and momentum (Sample Prob. 17.10).

SAMPLE PROBLEM 17.9

A 0.125-lb bullet A is fired with an initial velocity of 1,500 ft/sec into a 50-lb wooden beam B which is suspended from a hinge at O. Knowing that the beam is initially at rest, determine (a) the angular velocity of the beam immediately after the bullet becomes embedded in the beam, (b) the impulsive reactions at the hinge, assuming that the bullet becomes embedded in 0.0002 sec.

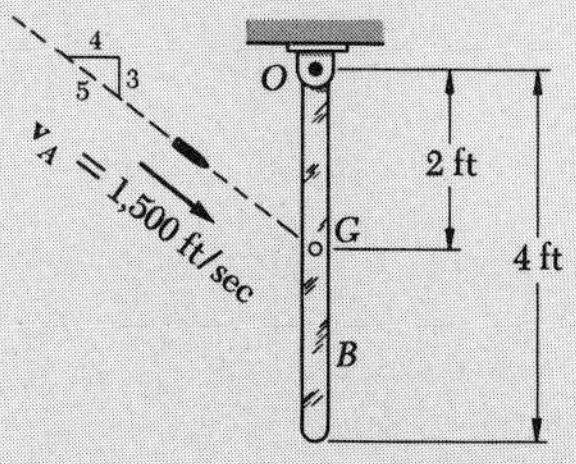

Solution. We consider the bullet and the beam as a single system. Since the time interval $\Delta t = 0.0002$ sec is very short, we neglect all nonimpulsive forces and consider only the external impulses $\mathbf{R}_x\,\Delta t$ and $\mathbf{R}_y\,\Delta t$.

Principle of Impulse and Momentum

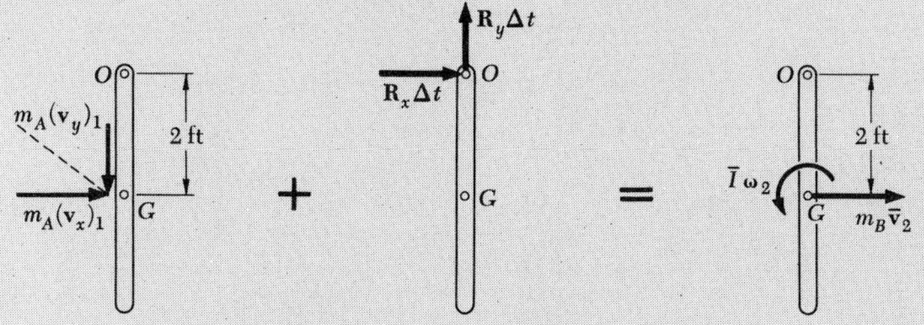

Syst Momenta$_1$ + Syst Ext Imp$_{1\to 2}$ = Syst Momenta$_2$

$+\circlearrowleft$ moments about O:	$m_A(v_x)_1(2\text{ ft}) + 0 = \bar{I}\omega_2 + m_B\bar{v}_2(2\text{ ft})$	(1)
$\xrightarrow{+}$ x components:	$m_A(v_x)_1 + R_x\,\Delta t = m_B\bar{v}_2$	(2)
$+\uparrow$ y components:	$-m_A(v_y)_1 + R_y\,\Delta t = 0$	(3)

The components of the velocity of the bullet and the centroidal moment of inertia of the beam are

$$(v_x)_1 = \tfrac{4}{5}(1{,}500) = 1{,}200\text{ ft/sec} \qquad (v_y)_1 = \tfrac{3}{5}(1{,}500) = 900\text{ ft/sec}$$

$$\bar{I} = \tfrac{1}{12}ml^2 = \frac{1}{12}\frac{50}{g}(4)^2 = 2.07\text{ lb-ft-sec}^2$$

Substituting these values into (1) and noting that $\bar{v}_2 = (2\text{ ft})\omega_2$, we obtain

$$\frac{0.125}{g}(1{,}200)(2) = 2.07\omega_2 + \frac{50}{g}(2\omega_2)(2)$$

$$\omega_2 = 1.125\text{ radians/sec} \qquad \omega_2 = 1.125\text{ radians/sec}\circlearrowleft \blacktriangleleft$$

Substituting $\bar{v}_2 = (2\text{ ft})(1.125\text{ radians/sec}) = 2.25$ ft/sec into (2), we solve Eqs. (2) and (3) for R_x and R_y, respectively.

$$\frac{0.125}{g}(1{,}200) + R_x(0.0002) = \frac{50}{g}(2.25)$$

$$R_x = -5{,}820\text{ lb} \qquad \mathbf{R}_x = 5{,}820\text{ lb}\leftarrow \blacktriangleleft$$

$$-\frac{0.125}{g}(900) + R_y(0.0002) = 0$$

$$R_y = +17{,}470\text{ lb} \qquad \mathbf{R}_y = 17{,}470\text{ lb}\uparrow \blacktriangleleft$$

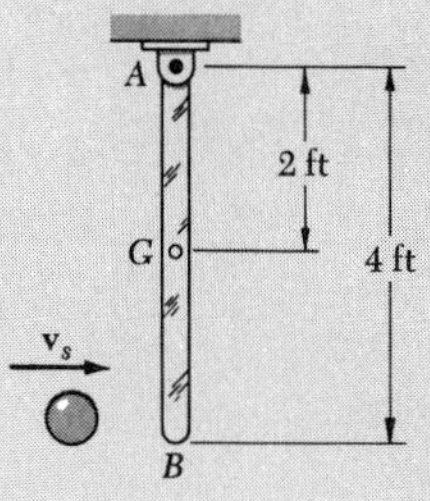

SAMPLE PROBLEM 17.10

A 3-lb sphere moving horizontally to the right with an initial velocity of 20 ft/sec strikes the lower end of a 12-lb rigid rod *AB*. The rod is suspended from a hinge at *A* and is initially at rest. Knowing that the coefficient of restitution between the rod and sphere is 0.80, determine the angular velocity of the rod and the velocity of the sphere immediately after the impact.

Principle of Impulse and Momentum. We consider the rod and sphere as a single system and apply the principle of impulse and momentum during the impact. The only impulsive force external to this system is the impulsive reaction at *A*.

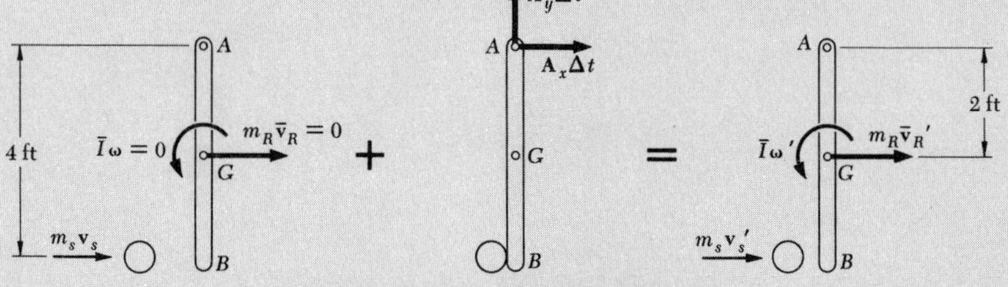

Syst Initial Momenta + Syst Ext Imp = Syst Final Momenta

+↺ moments about *A*: $m_s v_s(4\text{ ft}) = m_s v_s'(4\text{ ft}) + m_R\bar{v}_R'(2\text{ ft}) + \bar{I}\omega'$ (1)

Since the rod rotates about *A*, we have $\bar{v}_R' = \bar{r}\omega' = (2\text{ ft})\omega'$. Also,

$$\bar{I} = \frac{1}{12}\frac{12}{g}(4)^2 = 0.497\text{ lb-ft-sec}^2$$

Substituting these values and the given data into Eq. (1), we have

$$\frac{3}{g}(20)(4) = \frac{3}{g}v_s'(4) + \frac{12}{g}(2\omega')(2) + 0.497\omega'$$

$$7.45 = 0.373v_s' + 1.988\omega' \qquad (2)$$

Coefficient of Restitution. Choosing positive to the right, we write

$$v_B' - v_s' = e(v_s - v_B)$$

Substituting $v_s = 20$ ft/sec, $v_B = 0$, and $e = 0.80$, we obtain

$$v_B' - v_s' = (0.80)(20 - 0) \qquad (3)$$

Again noting that the rod rotates about *A*, we write

$$v_B' = (4\text{ ft})\omega' \qquad (4)$$

Solving Eqs. (2) to (4) simultaneously, we obtain

$\omega' = +3.86$ radians/sec $\qquad \omega' = 3.86$ radians/sec ↺ ◄

$v_s' = -0.58$ ft/sec $\qquad \mathbf{v}_s' = 0.58$ ft/sec ← ◄

SAMPLE PROBLEM 17.11

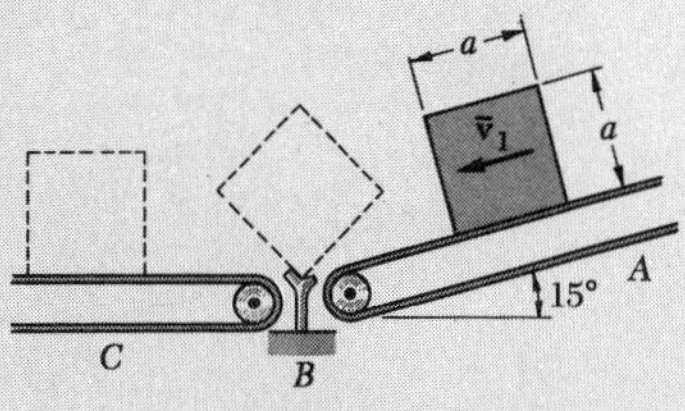

A square package of side a and weight W moves down a conveyor belt A with a constant velocity $\overline{\mathbf{v}}_1$. At the end of the conveyor belt, the corner of the package strikes a rigid support at B. Assuming that the impact at B is perfectly plastic, derive an expression for the smallest magnitude of the velocity $\overline{\mathbf{v}}_1$ for which the package will rotate about B and reach conveyor belt C.

Principle of Impulse and Momentum. Since the impact between the package and the support is perfectly plastic, the package rotates about B during the impact. We apply the principle of impulse and momentum to the package and note that the only impulsive force external to the package is the impulsive reaction at B.

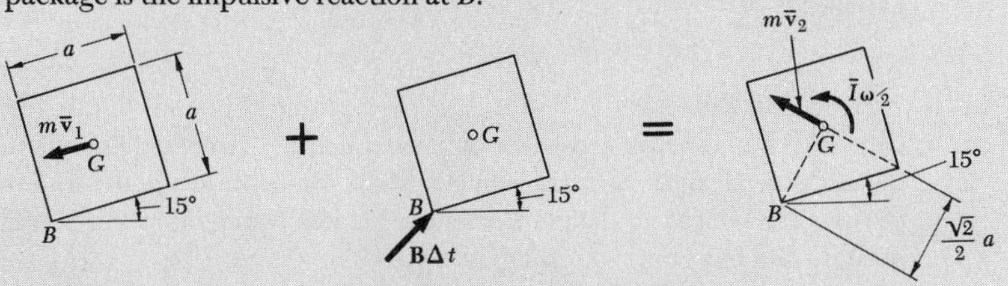

Syst Momenta$_1$ + Syst Ext Imp$_{1\to 2}$ = Syst Momenta$_2$

$+\circlearrowleft$ moments about B: $\quad (m\bar{v}_1)(\tfrac{1}{2}a) + 0 = (m\bar{v}_2)(\tfrac{1}{2}\sqrt{2}\,a) + \bar{I}\omega_2 \qquad (1)$

Since the package rotates about B, we have $\bar{v}_2 = (GB)\omega_2 = \frac{1}{2}\sqrt{2}\,a\omega_2$. We substitute this expression, together with $\bar{I} = \frac{1}{6}ma^2$, into Eq. (1):

$$(m\bar{v}_1)(\tfrac{1}{2}a) = m(\tfrac{1}{2}\sqrt{2}\,a\omega_2)(\tfrac{1}{2}\sqrt{2}\,a) + \tfrac{1}{6}ma^2\omega_2$$

$$\bar{v}_1 = \frac{4}{3}a\omega_2 \qquad (2)$$

Principle of Conservation of Energy. We apply the principle of conservation of energy between position 2 and position 3.

Position 2. $V_2 = Wh_2$. Recalling that $\bar{v}_2 = \frac{1}{2}\sqrt{2}\,a\omega_2$, we write

$$T_2 = \tfrac{1}{2}m\bar{v}_2^2 + \tfrac{1}{2}\bar{I}\omega_2^2 = \tfrac{1}{2}m(\tfrac{1}{2}\sqrt{2}\,a\omega_2)^2 + \tfrac{1}{2}(\tfrac{1}{6}ma^2)\omega_2^2 = \tfrac{1}{3}ma^2\omega_2^2$$

Position 2

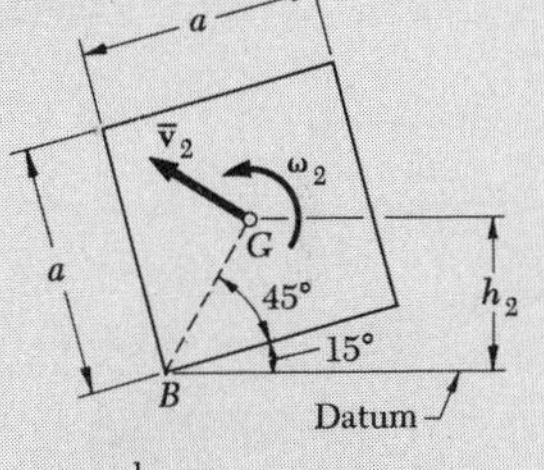

$GB = \frac{1}{2}\sqrt{2}a = 0.707a$
$h_2 = GB\sin(45° + 15°)$
$= 0.612\,a$

Position 3. Since the package must reach conveyor belt B, it must pass through position 3 where G is directly above B. Also, since we wish to determine the smallest velocity for which the package will reach this position, we choose $\bar{v}_3 = \omega_3 = 0$. Therefore $T_3 = 0$ and $V_3 = Wh_3$.

Conservation of Energy $\qquad T_2 + V_2 = T_3 + V_3$

$$\tfrac{1}{3}ma^2\omega_2^2 + Wh_2 = 0 + Wh_3$$

$$\omega_2^2 = \frac{3W}{ma^2}(h_3 - h_2) = \frac{3g}{a^2}(h_3 - h_2) \qquad (3)$$

Position 3

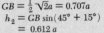

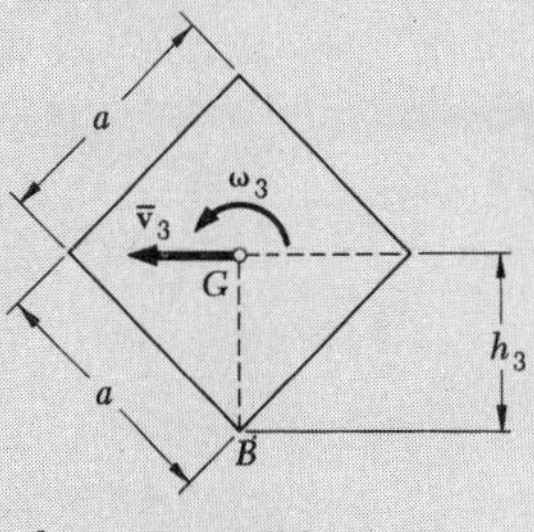

$h_3 = GB = 0.707a$

Substituting the computed values of h_2 and h_3 into Eq. (3), we obtain

$$\omega_2^2 = \frac{3g}{a^2}(0.707a - 0.612a) = \frac{3g}{a^2}(0.095a) \qquad \omega_2 = \sqrt{0.285g/a}$$

$$\bar{v}_1 = \frac{4}{3}a\omega_2 = \frac{4}{3}a\sqrt{0.285g/a} \qquad \bar{v}_1 = 0.713\sqrt{ga} \quad ◀$$

PROBLEMS

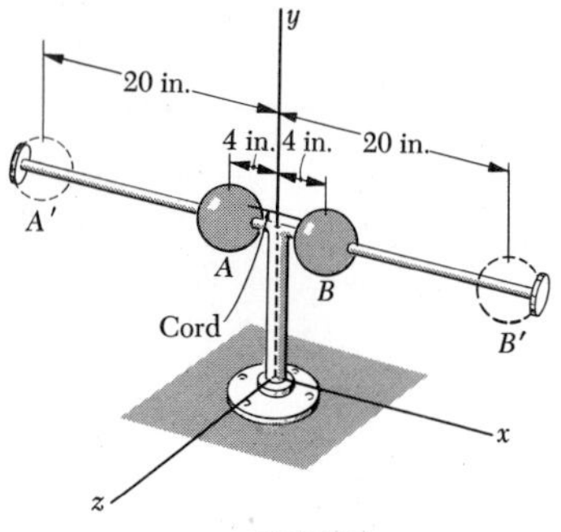

FIG. P 17.63

17.63. Two balls weighing 2 lb each are mounted at A and B on the horizontal rod $A'B'$, which rotates freely at 60 rpm about the vertical shaft. The balls are held in position by a cord which is suddenly cut. Knowing that the centroidal moment of inertia of the rod is 0.25 lb-ft-sec^2, determine the angular velocity of the rod after the balls have moved to positions A' and B'.

17.64. Solve Prob. 17.63 assuming that, after the cord is cut, ball B moves to position B' but that an obstruction prevents ball A from moving.

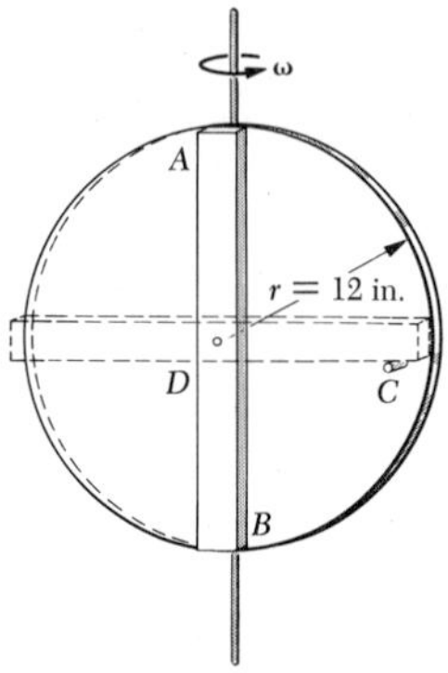

FIG. P 17.65

17.65. An 8-lb bar AB is attached by a pin at D to a 10-lb circular plate which may rotate freely about a vertical axis. Knowing that when the bar is vertical the angular velocity of the plate is 90 rpm, determine the angular velocity of the plate after the bar has swung into a horizontal position and has come to rest against pin C.

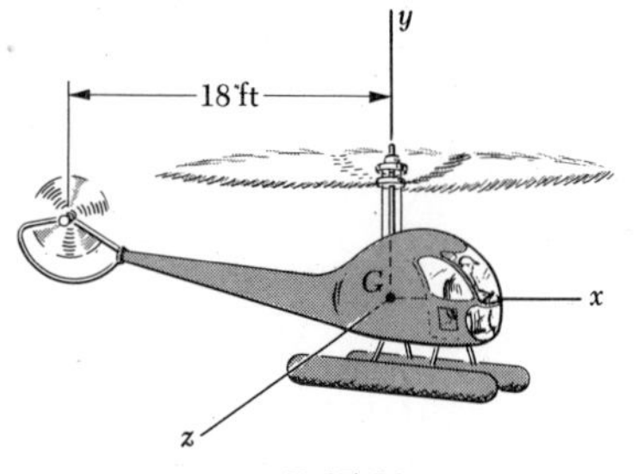

FIG. P 17.66

17.66. In the helicopter shown, a vertical tail propeller is used to prevent rotation of the cab as the speed of the main blades is changed. Assuming that the tail propeller is not operating, determine the final angular velocity of the cab after the speed of the main blades has been changed from 200 to 300 rpm. The speed of the main blades is measured relative to the cab, which has a centroidal moment of inertia of 800 lb-ft-sec^2. Each of the four main blades is assumed to be a 15-ft slender rod weighing 60 lb.

17.67. Assuming that the tail propeller in Prob. 17.66 is operating and that the angular velocity of the cab remains zero, determine the final horizontal velocity of the cab when the speed of the main blades is changed from 200 to 300 rpm. The cab weighs 1,500 lb and is initially at rest. Also determine the force exerted by the tail propeller if this change in speed takes places uniformly in 12 sec.

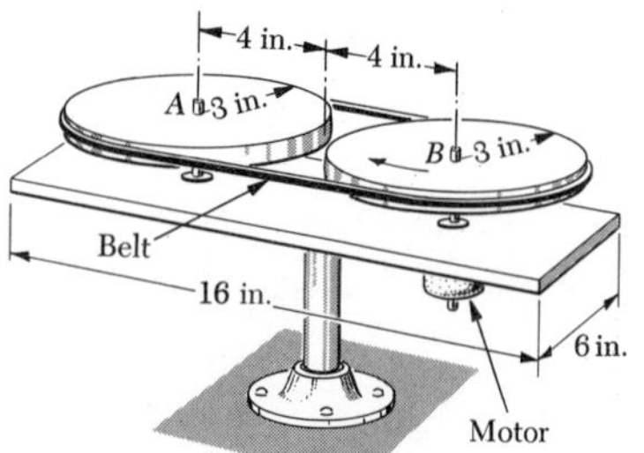

FIG. P 17.68

17.68. Two 10-lb disks and a small motor are mounted on a 15-lb rectangular platform which is free to rotate about a central vertical spindle. The normal operating speed of the motor is 180 rpm. If the motor is started when the system is at rest, determine the angular velocity of all elements of the system after the motor has attained its normal operating speed. Neglect the weight of the motor, and assume that the system is perfectly lubricated.

17.69. Solve Prob. 17.68 assuming (*a*) that the belt is removed, (*b*) that the belt is looped around the disks in a figure 8.

17.70. A slender tube weighing 4 lb rotates freely at 100 rpm about a vertical spindle as shown. A small ball weighing 1 lb is introduced in the tube at A with a very small velocity. Determine the angular velocity of the tube (*a*) just before the ball leaves the tube at B, (*b*) just after the ball has left the tube.

17.71. A slender tube weighing 4 lb rotates freely at 100 rpm about a vertical spindle as shown. A small ball weighing $\frac{1}{2}$ lb is introduced in the tube at A with a very small velocity; after this ball has left the tube at B, a second $\frac{1}{2}$-lb ball is introduced at A. Determine the angular velocity of the tube after the second ball has left the tube.

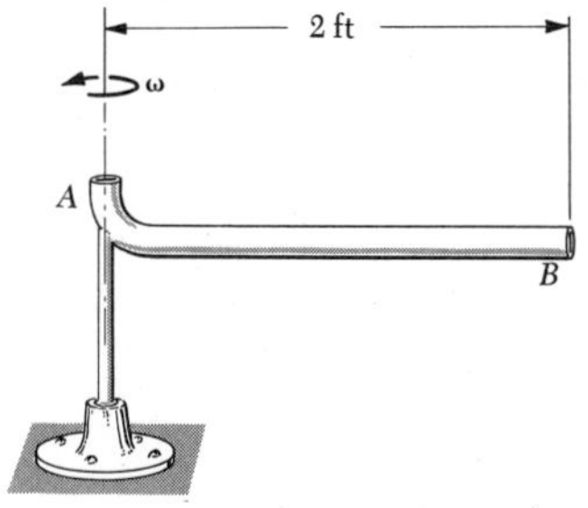

FIG. P 17.70 AND P 17.71

17.72. In Prob. 17.70, determine the radial and transverse components of the velocity of the ball as it leaves the tube at B.

17.73. In Prob. 17.65, determine the energy loss during the impact between the bar and pin C.

17.74. A bullet of mass m is fired with a horizontal velocity $\mathbf{v}_0$ and at a height $h = \frac{1}{2}R$ into a wooden disk of much larger mass M and radius R. The disk rests on a horizontal plane and the coefficient of friction between the disk and the plane is finite. (*a*) Determine the linear velocity $\mathbf{v}_1$ and the angular velocity ω_1 of the disk immediately after the bullet has penetrated the disk. (*b*) Describe the ensuing motion of the disk and determine its linear velocity after the motion has become uniform.

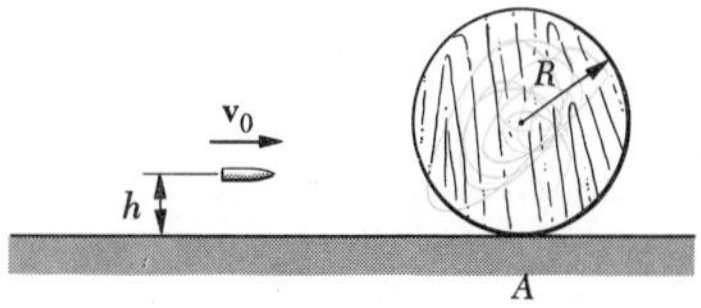

FIG. P 17.74

17.75. Determine the height h at which the bullet of Prob. 17.74 should be fired (*a*) if the disk is to roll without sliding immediately after impact, (*b*) if the disk is to slide without rolling immediately after impact.

17.76. Solve Prob. 17.74 assuming that the disk is fitted with a short spike at A which prevents it from slipping at the time of impact.

17.77. Knowing that $e = 0.70$ between the sphere and rod of Sample Prob. 17.10, determine the required weight of the rod if the velocity of the sphere after impact is to be zero. The weight of the sphere is unchanged.

17.78. Solve Sample Prob. 17.9 assuming that the bullet is fired so that its path forms the same angle with the horizontal but that it becomes embedded in the beam at its lower end.

17.79. A rigid rod of length l and weight W is released in the position shown. It is observed that the rod rebounds to a horizontal position after striking the vertical surface. (*a*) Determine the coefficient of restitution between the knob K and the surface. (*b*) Show that the same rebound may be expected for any position of the knob K.

17.80. In Prob. 17.79, determine the required distance r from end A to knob K if, during the impact, the impulsive reaction at A is to be zero.

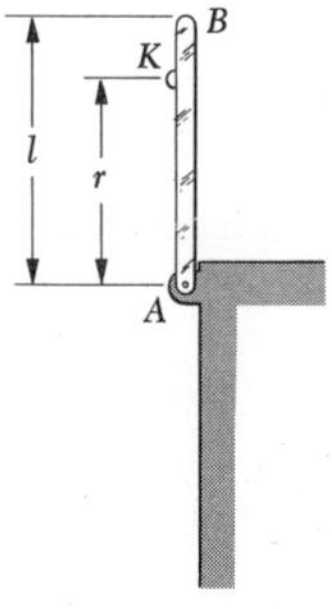

FIG. P 17.79

17.81. The plank CDE of weight W_P rests on top of a small pivot at D. A man A of weight W stands on the plank at end C; a second man B of the same weight W jumps from a height h and strikes the plank at E. Assuming perfectly plastic impact, determine the height to which man A will rise. (Assume that man A stands completely rigid.)

17.82. Solve Prob. 17.81 assuming that the impact between man B and the plank is perfectly elastic.

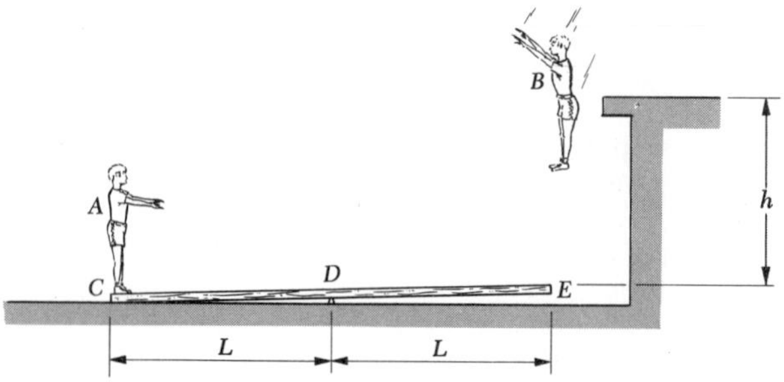

FIG. P 17.81

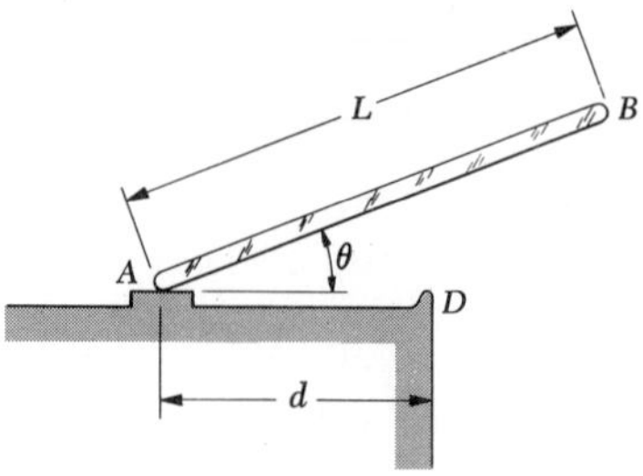

FIG. P 17.83

17.83. A slender rod of mass m and length L is released from rest in the position shown. The coefficient of friction is sufficient to prevent sliding at A. Assuming perfectly elastic impact ($e = 1$) at D, determine the distance d for which the rod will rebound with no angular velocity.

17.84. Assuming perfectly plastic impact ($e = 0$) at D in Prob. 17.83, determine the minimum value of d for which the rod will remain in contact with the ground at A and D after impact.

17.85. A uniformly loaded square crate is released from rest with its corner D directly above A; it rotates about A until its corner B strikes the floor, and then rotates about B. The floor is sufficiently rough to prevent slipping and the impact at B is perfectly plastic. Denoting by ω_0 the angular velocity of the crate immediately before B strikes the floor, find the angular velocity of the crate immediately after B strikes the floor. What fraction of the kinetic energy of the crate is lost during the impact?

17.86. In Prob. 17.85, determine the maximum value of the angle θ through which the crate will rotate after B strikes the floor.

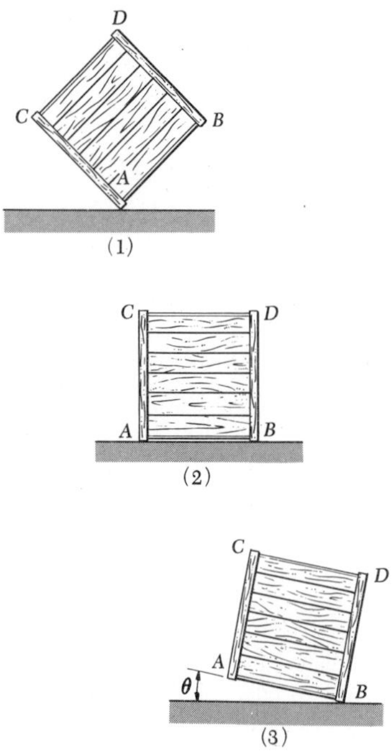

FIG. P 17.85

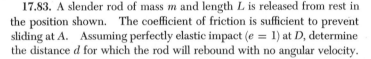

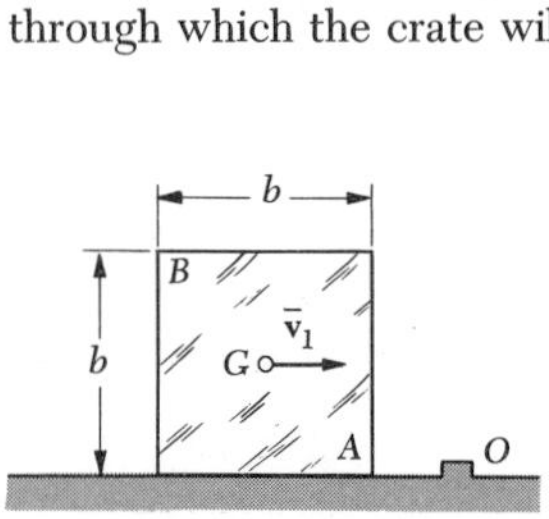

FIG. P 17.87

17.87. A square block of weight W moves along a smooth horizontal surface and strikes a small obstruction at O. Assuming that the impact between corner A and the obstruction O is perfectly *plastic*, determine the angular velocity of the block and the velocity of its mass center G immediately after the impact.

17.88. Solve Prob. 17.87 assuming that the impact between corner A and the obstruction O is perfectly *elastic*.

17.89. A uniform slender rod of length L is dropped onto rigid supports at A and B. Immediately before striking A the velocity of the rod is $\bar{v}_1$. Since support B is slightly lower than support A, the rod strikes A before it strikes B. Assuming perfectly *plastic* impact at both A and B, determine the velocity of each of the extremities of the rod immediately after the rod (a) strikes support A, (b) strikes support B.

17.90. Solve Prob. 17.89 assuming that the impact at both A and B is perfectly *elastic*.

17.91. In Prob. 17.89, determine the impulse exerted on the rod (a) at A as the rod strikes the support at A, (b) at A as the rod strikes the support at B, (c) at B.

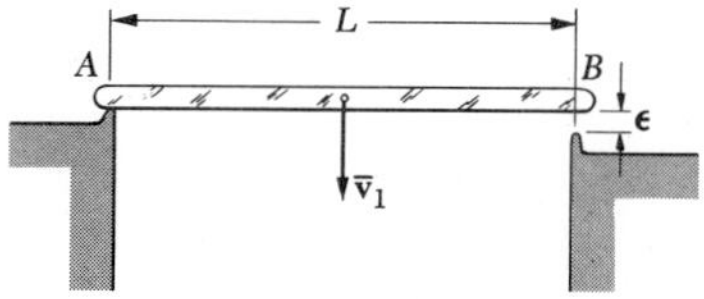

FIG. P 17.89

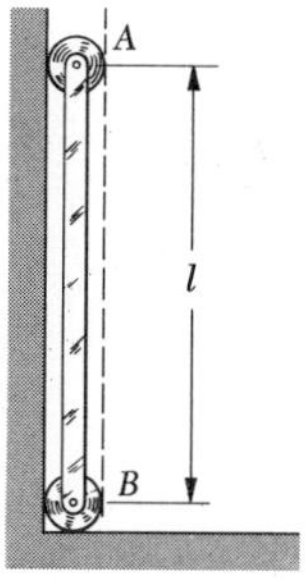

FIG. P 17.93

17.92. In Prob. 17.87, determine the line of action of the impulsive force exerted on the block by the obstruction at O.

17.93. A slender rod of weight W and length l is held in the position shown. Roller B is given a slight push to the right and moves along the horizontal plane, while roller A is constrained to move vertically. Determine the magnitudes of the impulses exerted on the rollers A and B as roller A strikes the ground. Assume perfectly plastic impact.

17.94. Solve Prob. 17.93 assuming that roller A is given a slight push to the right and describes a circular path, while roller B is maintained in a fixed position at the corner.

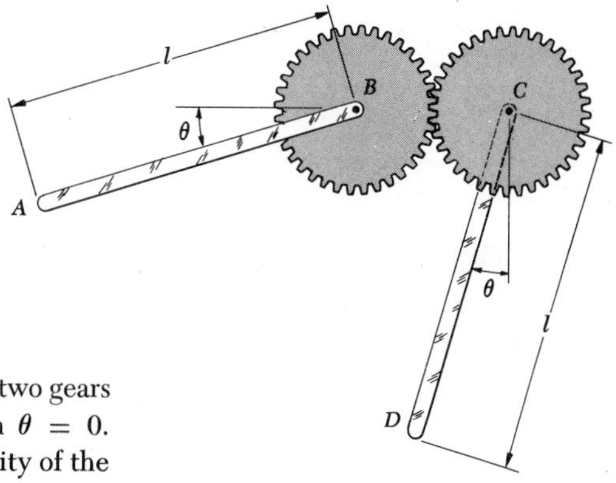

FIG. P 17.95

REVIEW PROBLEMS

17.95. Two uniform rods, each of weight W, are attached to two gears as shown. The rods are released from rest in the position $\theta = 0$. Neglecting the mass of the gears, determine the angular velocity of the rods when (a) $\theta = 30°$, (b) $\theta = 45°$, (c) $\theta = 60°$.

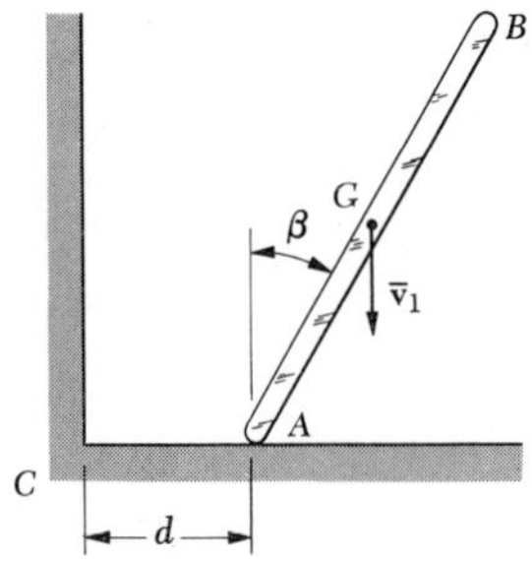

FIG. P 17.96

17.96. A slender rod of length l strikes a *smooth* floor at A with a vertical velocity $\bar{v}_1$ and no angular velocity. Assuming that end A does not rebound, derive an expression (*a*) for the angular velocity of the rod immediately after impact, (*b*) for the corresponding velocity of end A of the rod.

17.97. Solve part *a* of Prob. 17.96 assuming that the distance d is zero so that end A strikes the corner C.

17.98. Gear B weighs 4 lb and has a centroidal radius of gyration of 5 in. Rod AB is 12 in. long and weighs 3 lb. If the system is released from rest in the position shown, determine the velocity of point B after rod AB has rotated through 90°. Assume that gear A is fixed and cannot rotate.

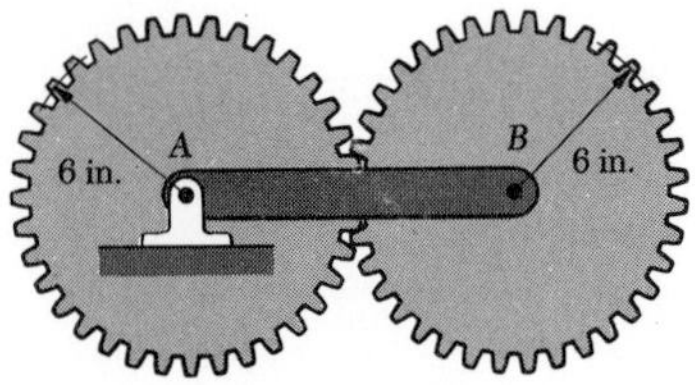

FIG. P 17.98

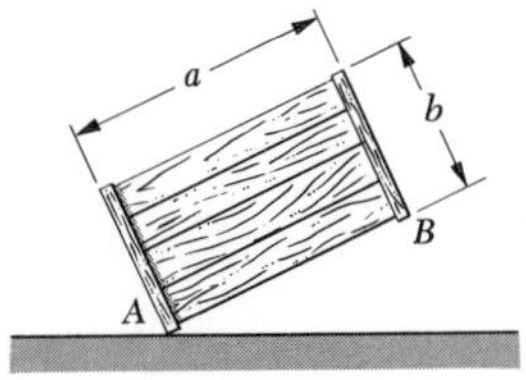

FIG. P 17.99

17.99. A uniformly loaded rectangular crate is released from rest in the position shown. Assuming that the floor is sufficiently rough to prevent slipping and that the impact at B is perfectly plastic, determine the largest value of the ratio b/a for which corner A will remain in contact with the floor.

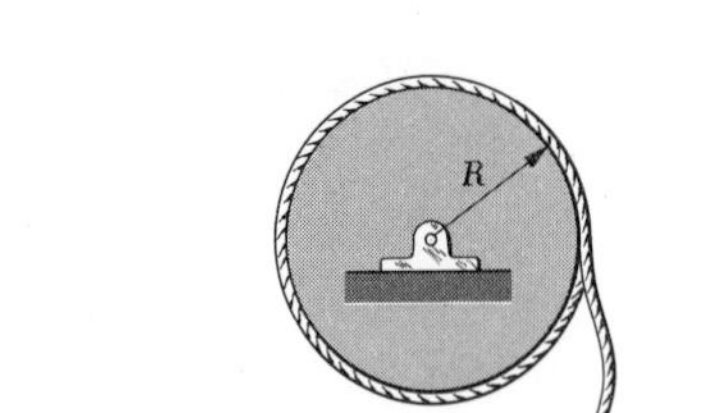

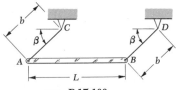

FIG. P 17.100

17.100. A uniform rod of length L and weight W is attached to two wires, each of length b. The rod is released from rest when $\beta = 0$ and swings to the position $\beta = 90°$ at which time wire BD suddenly breaks. Determine the tension in wire AC (*a*) immediately before wire BD breaks, (*b*) immediately after wire BD breaks.

***17.101.** In Prob. 17.100, draw the shear and bending-moment diagrams for rod AB (*a*) immediately before wire BD breaks, (*b*) immediately after wire BD breaks.

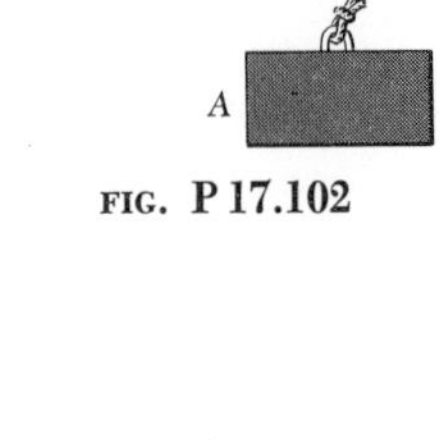

FIG. P 17.102

17.102. Block A of mass m is attached to a cord which is wrapped around a uniform disk of mass M. The block is released from rest and falls through a distance h before the cord becomes taut. Derive expressions for the velocity of the block and the angular velocity of the disk immediately after the impact. Assume that the impact is (*a*) perfectly plastic, (*b*) perfectly elastic.

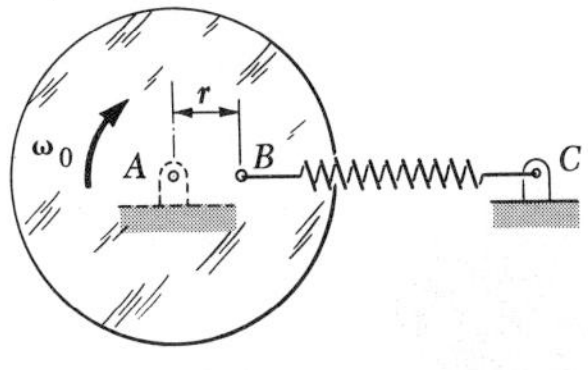

FIG. P 17.103

17.103. A spring of constant k is attached to a pin located at a distance r from the center of a flywheel of moment of inertia $\bar{I}$. Knowing that in the position shown the tension in the spring is zero, determine the smallest initial angular velocity ω_0 which will permit continuous (although not uniform) rotation of the flywheel.

17.104. For the system of Prob. 17.103, determine the speed ω_0 so that the speed variation during each revolution will be limited to 2 per cent. Assume $\bar{I} = 15$ lb-ft-sec², $k = 100$ lb/in., $r = 2$ in.

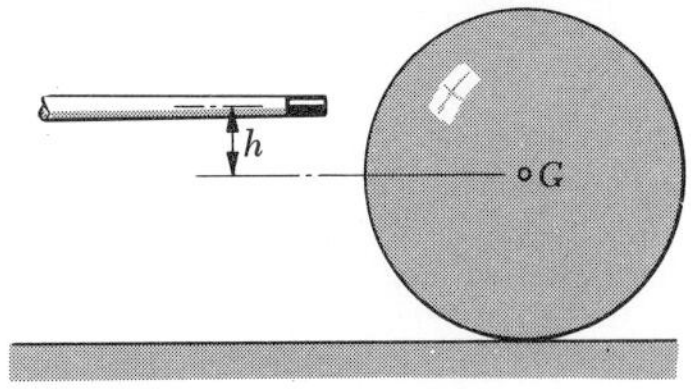

FIG. P 17.105

17.105. At what height h above its center G should a billiard ball of radius r be struck horizontally by a cue if the ball is to start rolling without sliding?

17.106. Two identical slender rods swing freely from the pivots shown. Rod A is released from rest in a horizontal position and swings to a vertical position at which time the small knob K strikes rod B. If $h = \frac{1}{2}l$ and $e = \frac{1}{2}$, determine the angle through which rod B will swing.

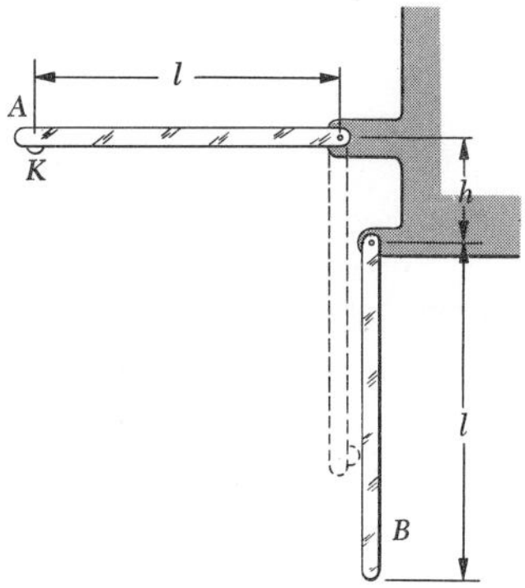

FIG. P 17.106

18. KINETICS OF RIGID BODIES IN THREE DIMENSIONS

***18.1. Introduction.** In Chaps. 16 and 17, we analyzed the *plane motion* of rigid bodies and of systems of rigid bodies. In Chap. 16 and in the second half of Chap. 17 (momentum method), our study was further restricted to that of plane slabs and of bodies symmetrical with respect to the reference plane. We shall now develop a general method for the analysis of the motion of a rigid body, which will enable us to analyze more difficult problems, such as the rotation of a nonsymmetrical body about a fixed axis and the motion of a gyroscope.

Since a rigid body of mass m may be assumed to consist of a large number of particles of mass Δm, we may apply to the analysis of its motion the fundamental principles established in Chaps. 12, 13, and 14 for the motion of a system of particles. For example, recalling from Sec. 12.5 that the mass center of a system of particles moves as if the entire mass of the system and all the external forces were concentrated at that point, we find that the acceleration $\bar{\mathbf{a}}$ of the mass center G of a rigid body is defined by the relation

$$\Sigma \mathbf{F} = m\bar{\mathbf{a}} \tag{18.1}$$

where $\Sigma \mathbf{F}$ represents the sum of the forces applied to the rigid body, and where $\bar{\mathbf{a}}$ is measured with respect to a newtonian frame of reference $OXYZ$ (Fig. 18.1).

Recalling, on the other hand, the relations established in Sec. 14.10 between the moments of the external forces and the rate of change of the angular momentum of a system of particles, we write

$$\Sigma \mathbf{M}_O = \frac{d\mathbf{h}_O}{dt} \tag{18.2}$$

where $\Sigma \mathbf{M}_O$ represents the sum of the moments about O of the forces applied to the rigid body, and $\mathbf{h}_O$ the angular momentum of the body about O when its motion is observed from the newtonian frame $OXYZ$. Considering the sum $\Sigma\mathbf{M}_G$ of the moments of the forces about the mass center G of the body and the

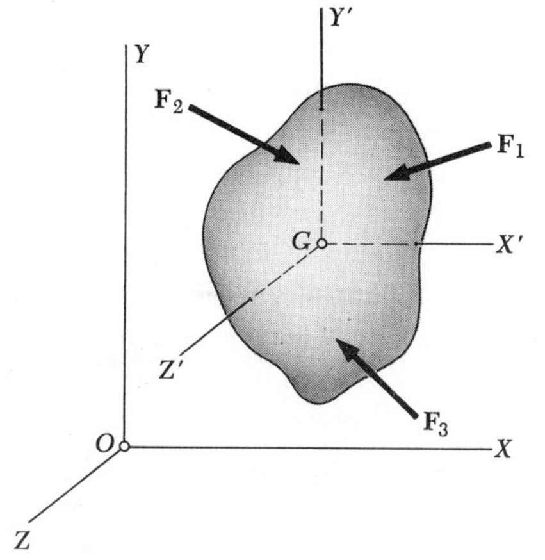

FIG. 18.1

angular momentum $\mathbf{h}'_G$ of the body about G when its motion is observed from the frame $GX'Y'Z'$ (Fig. 18.1), we may also write

$$\Sigma\mathbf{M}_G = \frac{d\mathbf{h}'_G}{dt} \tag{18.3}$$

The six scalar equations defined by the relations (18.1) and (18.2)—or by the relations (18.1) and (18.3)—may be used to determine the motion of a rigid body subjected to given forces, as well as the reactions at its supports. Consider, for example, a rigid body with a fixed point O. As we shall see later (Sec. 18.7), three angles are required to define the position of the body at a given instant. These angles may be determined by integrating the three differential equations defined by (18.2); the three components of the reaction at O may then be obtained by solving the three scalar equations corresponding to (18.1). In the case of a rigid body moving freely in space under the action of given forces, it is more convenient to use the relations (18.1) and (18.3). The three scalar equations corresponding to (18.1) define the motion of the mass center G of the body, while the three equations corresponding to (18.3) define the motion of the body about G.

In some problems, it will be found advantageous to replace

one of the six equations discussed above by the equation

$$T + V = \text{constant} \tag{18.4}$$

derived from the principle of conservation of energy (Sec. 13.7). However, before we can use this equation, we must learn to compute the kinetic energy of a rigid body in three-dimensional motion (Sec. 18.4).

In problems of impact, it will be convenient to apply the generalized principle of impulse and momentum (Sec. 14.11) and to represent the system of the momenta of the particles of the body by a momentum vector $m\bar{\mathbf{v}}$ attached at the mass center G of the body and a momentum couple $\mathbf{h}'_G$.

***18.2. Angular Momentum of a Rigid Body in Three Dimensions.** In order to make an effective use of the relations (18.2) and (18.3) of the preceding section, we should develop a practical method for determining the angular momentum of a rigid body at any given instant.

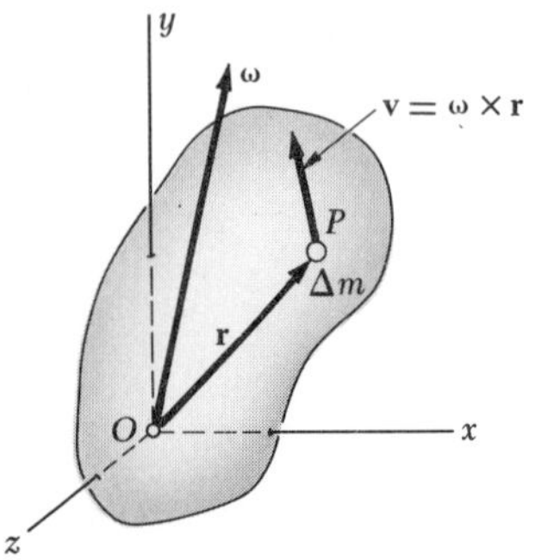

FIG. 18.2

Let us consider the case of a rigid body with a fixed point O (Fig. 18.2). According to (14.30), the angular momentum of the body about O is

$$\mathbf{h}_O = \Sigma[\mathbf{r} \times (\Delta m)\mathbf{v}] \tag{18.5}$$

where $\mathbf{r}$ and $\mathbf{v}$ denote, respectively, the position vector and the velocity of a particle P of mass Δm. But $\mathbf{v} = \boldsymbol{\omega} \times \mathbf{r}$, where $\boldsymbol{\omega}$ is the angular velocity of the body at the instant considered. Substituting into (18.5) we have

$$\mathbf{h}_O = \Sigma[\mathbf{r} \times (\boldsymbol{\omega} \times \mathbf{r})\Delta m]$$

Recalling the rule for determining the rectangular components of a vector product (Sec. 3.4), we obtain the following expression for the x component of the angular momentum:

$$\begin{aligned} h_x &= \Sigma[y(\boldsymbol{\omega} \times \mathbf{r})_z - z(\boldsymbol{\omega} \times \mathbf{r})_y]\,\Delta m \\ &= \Sigma[y(\omega_x y - \omega_y x) - z(\omega_z x - \omega_x z)]\,\Delta m \\ &= \omega_x \Sigma(y^2 + z^2)\,\Delta m - \omega_y \Sigma xy\,\Delta m - \omega_z \Sigma xz\,\Delta m \end{aligned}$$

Replacing the sums by integrals in this expression and in the two similar expressions which are obtained for h_y and h_z, we have

$$\begin{aligned} h_x &= \omega_x \textstyle\int (y^2 + z^2)\,dm - \omega_y \int xy\,dm - \omega_z \int xz\,dm \\ h_y &= -\omega_x \textstyle\int yx\,dm + \omega_y \int (z^2 + x^2)\,dm - \omega_z \int yz\,dm \\ h_z &= -\omega_x \textstyle\int zx\,dm - \omega_y \int zy\,dm + \omega_z \int (x^2 + y^2)\,dm \end{aligned} \tag{18.6}$$

We note that the integrals containing squares represent the *mass moments of inertia* of the body about the x, y, and z axes, respectively; we have

$$I_x = \int (y^2 + z^2)\,dm \qquad I_y = \int (z^2 + x^2)\,dm \qquad I_z = \int (x^2 + y^2)\,dm \tag{18.7}$$

Using the integrals containing products of coordinates to define the *mass products of inertia* of the body, we set

$$\begin{array}{lll} P_{xy} = \int xy\,dm & P_{yz} = \int yz\,dm & P_{zx} = \int zx\,dm \\ P_{yx} = \int yx\,dm & P_{zy} = \int zy\,dm & P_{xz} = \int xz\,dm \end{array} \tag{18.8}$$

It is clear from this definition that $P_{xy} = P_{yx}$, $P_{yz} = P_{zy}$, and $P_{zx} = P_{xz}$. Substituting from (18.7) and (18.8) into (18.6), we obtain the components of the angular momentum $\mathbf{h}_O$ of the body about the fixed point O:

$$\begin{aligned} h_x &= I_x\omega_x - P_{xy}\omega_y - P_{xz}\omega_z \\ h_y &= -P_{yx}\omega_x + I_y\omega_y - P_{yz}\omega_z \\ h_z &= -P_{zx}\omega_x - P_{zy}\omega_y + I_z\omega_z \end{aligned} \tag{18.9}$$

Similar relations, involving centroidal moments and products of inertia, may be obtained for the components of the angular momentum $\mathbf{h}'_G$ of the body about its mass center.

The relations (18.9) show that the operation which transforms the vector $\boldsymbol{\omega}$ into the vector $\mathbf{h}_O$ (Fig. 18.3) is characterized by the array of moments and products of inertia

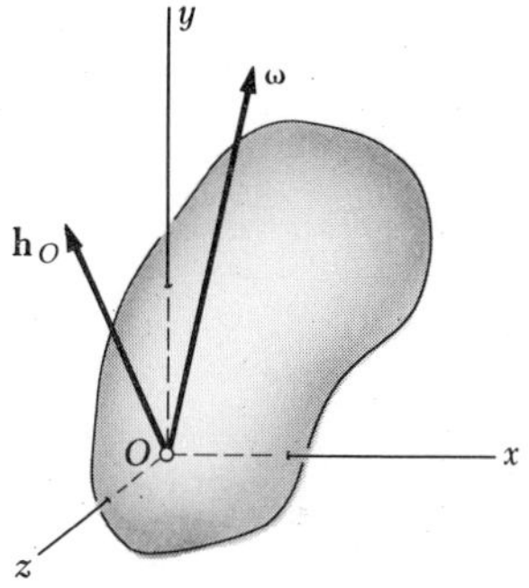

FIG. 18.3

$$\begin{pmatrix} I_x & -P_{xy} & -P_{xz} \\ -P_{yx} & I_y & -P_{yz} \\ -P_{zx} & -P_{zy} & I_z \end{pmatrix} \tag{18.10}$$

The array (18.10) defines the *inertia tensor* of the body at point O.† A new array of moments and products of inertia would be

† Setting $I_x = I_{11}$, $I_y = I_{22}$, $I_z = I_{33}$, and $-P_{xy} = P_{12}$, $-P_{xz} = P_{13}$, etc., we may write the inertia tensor in the standard form

$$\begin{pmatrix} I_{11} & I_{12} & I_{13} \\ I_{21} & I_{22} & I_{23} \\ I_{31} & I_{32} & I_{33} \end{pmatrix}$$

Denoting by h_1, h_2, h_3 the components of the angular momentum $\mathbf{h}_O$ and by ω_1, ω_2, ω_3 the components of the angular velocity $\boldsymbol{\omega}$, we may write the relations (18.9) in the form

$$h_i = \sum_j I_{ij}\omega_j$$

where i and j take the values 1, 2, 3. The quantities I_{ij} are said to be the *components* of the inertia tensor. Since $I_{ij} = I_{ji}$, the inertia tensor is a *symmetric tensor of the second order.*

obtained if a different system of axes were used. The transformation characterized by this new array, however, would still be the same. Clearly, the angular momentum $\mathbf{h}_O$ corresponding to a given angular velocity $\boldsymbol{\omega}$ is independent of the choice of the coordinate axes. As it will be shown in Sec. 18.3, it is always possible to select a system of axes $Ox'y'z'$, called *principal axes of inertia,* with respect to which all the products of inertia of a given body are zero. The array (18.10) takes then the diagonalized form

$$\begin{pmatrix} I_{x'} & 0 & 0 \\ 0 & I_{y'} & 0 \\ 0 & 0 & I_{z'} \end{pmatrix} \tag{18.11}$$

where $I_{x'}$, $I_{y'}$, $I_{z'}$ represent the *principal moments of inertia* of the body, and the relations (18.9) reduce to

$$h_{x'} = I_{x'}\omega_{x'} \qquad h_{y'} = I_{y'}\omega_{y'} \qquad h_{z'} = I_{z'}\omega_{z'} \tag{18.12}$$

We note that, if the three principal moments of inertia $I_{x'}$, $I_{y'}$, $I_{z'}$ are equal, the components $h_{x'}$, $h_{y'}$, $h_{z'}$ of the angular momentum about O are proportional to the components $\omega_{x'}$, $\omega_{y'}$, $\omega_{z'}$ of the angular velocity, and the vectors $\mathbf{h}_O$ and $\boldsymbol{\omega}$ are collinear. In general, however, the principal moments of inertia will be different, and the vectors $\mathbf{h}_O$ and $\boldsymbol{\omega}$ *will have different directions,* except when two of the three components of $\boldsymbol{\omega}$ happen to be zero, i.e., when $\boldsymbol{\omega}$ is directed along one of the coordinate axes. Thus, *the angular momentum* $\mathbf{h}_O$ *of a rigid body and its angular velocity* $\boldsymbol{\omega}$ *have the same direction if, and only if,* $\boldsymbol{\omega}$ *is directed along a principal axis of inertia.*† Since this condition is satisfied in the case of the plane motion of a rigid body symmetrical with respect to the reference plane,we were able in Sec. 17.8 to represent the angular momentum $\mathbf{h}_G$ of such a body by the vector $\bar{I}\boldsymbol{\omega}$. We must realize, however, that this result cannot be extended to the case of the plane motion of a nonsymmetrical body, or to the case of the three-dimensional motion of a rigid body. Except when $\boldsymbol{\omega}$ happens to be directed along a principal axis of inertia, the angular momentum and angular velocity of a rigid body have different directions, and the relation (18.9) or (18.12) must be used to determine $\mathbf{h}_O$ from $\boldsymbol{\omega}$.

***18.3. Ellipsoid of Inertia.** In order to understand better

† In the particular case when $I_{x'} = I_{y'} = I_{z'}$, any line through O may be considered as a principal axis of inertia, and the vectors $\mathbf{h}_O$ and $\boldsymbol{\omega}$ are always collinear.

the properties of the inertia tensor (18.10) which characterizes the transformation of $\boldsymbol{\omega}$ into $\mathbf{h}_O$, we shall determine the moment of inertia I_{OL} about an axis OL of the rigid body considered in Sec. 18.2. Denoting by $\boldsymbol{\lambda}$ the unit vector along OL and by $\mathbf{r}$ the position vector of a particle P of the body (Fig. 18.4), we observe that the perpendicular distance p from P to OL is equal to the magnitude $r \sin \theta$ of the vector product $\boldsymbol{\lambda} \times \mathbf{r}$. Denoting by Δm the mass of the particle, we write

$$I_{OL} = \Sigma p^2 \, \Delta m = \Sigma(\boldsymbol{\lambda} \times \mathbf{r})^2 \, \Delta m \tag{18.13}$$

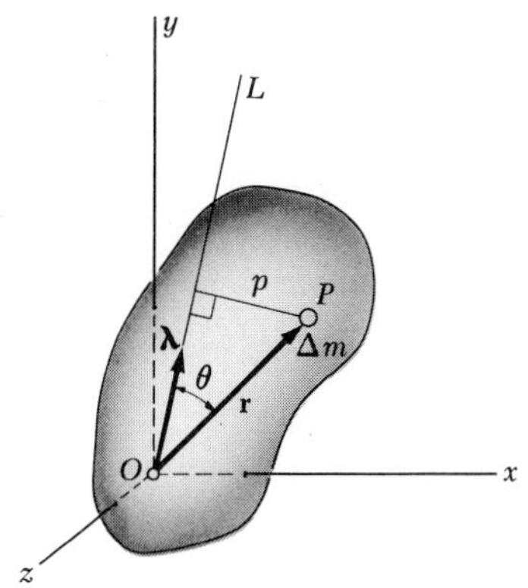

FIG. 18.4

Expressing the square of the vector product in terms of its rectangular components, and replacing the sums by integrals, we have

$$\begin{aligned} I_{OL} &= \int [(\lambda_x y - \lambda_y x)^2 + (\lambda_y z - \lambda_z y)^2 + (\lambda_z x - \lambda_x z)^2] dm \\ &= \lambda_x^2 \int (y^2 + z^2) dm + \lambda_y^2 \int (z^2 + x^2) dm + \lambda_z^2 \int (x^2 + y^2) dm \\ &\qquad - 2\lambda_x \lambda_y \int xy \, dm - 2\lambda_y \lambda_z \int yz \, dm - 2\lambda_z \lambda_x \int zx \, dm \end{aligned}$$

or, recalling the relations (18.7) and (18.8),

$$\begin{aligned} I_{OL} = I_x \lambda_x^2 + I_y \lambda_y^2 + I_z \lambda_z^2 &- 2P_{xy} \lambda_x \lambda_y \\ &- 2P_{yz} \lambda_y \lambda_z - 2P_{zx} \lambda_z \lambda_x \end{aligned} \tag{18.14}$$

Let us now assume that the moment of inertia of the body has been determined about a large number of axes OL through the fixed point O, and that a point Q has been plotted on each axis OL at a distance $OQ = 1/\sqrt{I_{OL}}$ from O. The locus of the points Q thus obtained forms a surface (Fig. 18.5). The equation of that surface may be obtained by substituting $1/(OQ)^2$ for I_{OL} in (18.14) and multiplying both sides of the equation by $(OQ)^2$. Observing that

$$(OQ)\lambda_x = \xi \qquad (OQ)\lambda_y = \eta \qquad (OQ)\lambda_z = \zeta$$

where ξ, η, ζ denote the rectangular coördinates of a point Q of the surface, we write

$$I_x \xi^2 + I_y \eta^2 + I_z \zeta^2 - 2P_{xy} \xi \eta - 2P_{yz} \eta \zeta - 2P_{zx} \zeta \xi = 1 \tag{18.15}$$

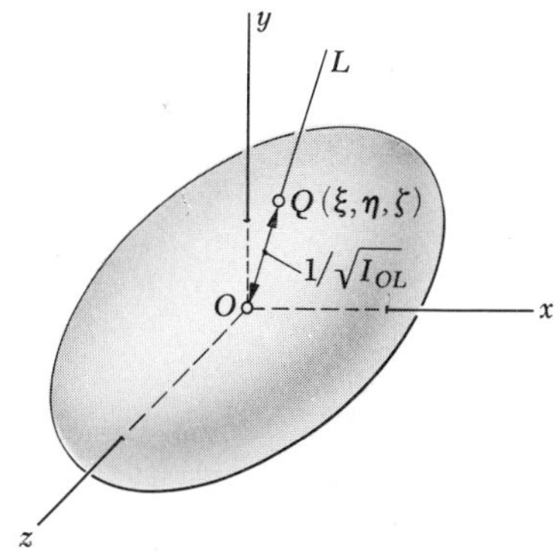

FIG. 18.5

The equation obtained is that of a *quadric*. Since the moment of inertia I_{OL} is different from zero for every axis OL, no point Q may be at an infinite distance from O. Thus, the quadric obtained is an *ellipsoid*. This ellipsoid, which characterizes the moment of inertia of the body about any axis through O, is known as the *ellipsoid of inertia* of the body at O.

Comparing Eq. (18.15) and the array (18.10), we observe that the ellipsoid of inertia and the inertia tensor of a given body at

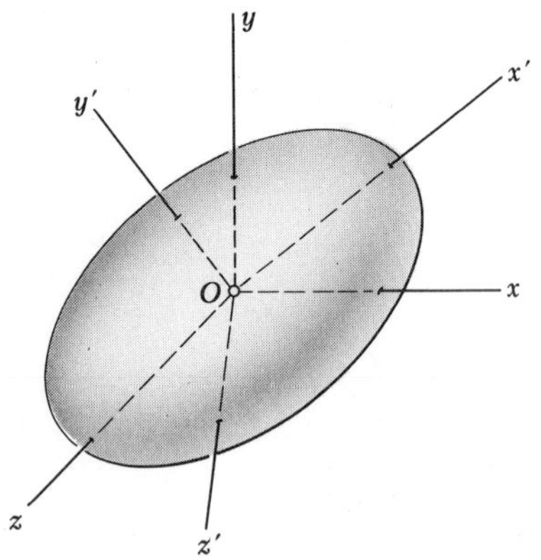

FIG. 18.6

O are defined by the same coefficients. Thus, we may use the ellipsoid of inertia to represent the inertia tensor and the corresponding transformation of ω into $\mathbf{h}_O$, in much the same way as an arrow is used to represent a vector. We note that, if the axes in Fig. 18.5 are rotated, *the coefficients of the equation defining the ellipsoid change, but the ellipsoid itself remains unaffected*, just as the arrow representing a vector remains unchanged in a rotation of axes, while the *components* of the vector are transformed. Choosing x', y', and z' axes which coincide with the principal axes of the ellipsoid of inertia (Fig. 18.6), we write the equation of the ellipsoid in the form

$$I_{x'}\xi'^2 + I_{y'}\eta'^2 + I_{z'}\zeta'^2 = 1 \qquad (18.16)$$

which does not contain any product of coordinates. We thus verify that, whatever the shape of the body and the point O considered, we may always select a system of axes with respect to which the products of inertia of the body are zero. The inertia tensor is then represented by the array (18.11) and the relations defining the transformation of ω into $\mathbf{h}_O$ take the reduced form (18.12). The x', y', and z' axes are the *principal axes of inertia* of the body at O, and the moments of inertia $I_{x'}$, $I_{y'}$, and $I_{z'}$ are the *principal moments of inertia* of the body at O. Recalling the manner in which the ellipsoid of inertia was constructed, we check that the three principal moments of inertia include the largest and the smallest moments of inertia of the body about any axis through O.

While the determination of the principal axes of inertia of a body of arbitrary shape is somewhat involved and requires solving a cubic equation,† there are many cases when these axes may be spotted immediately. Consider, for instance, the homogeneous cone of elliptical base shown in Fig. 18.7; this cone possesses two mutually perpendicular planes of symmetry OAA' and OBB'. We check from the definition (18.8) that, if the $x'y'$ and $y'z'$ planes are chosen to coincide with the two planes of symmetry, all the products of inertia are zero. The x', y', and z' axes thus selected are therefore the principal axes of inertia of the cone at O and the reduced relations (18.12) may be used to determine the angular momentum of the cone about O when its angular velocity is known. In the case of the homogeneous regular tetrahedron $OABC$ shown in Fig.

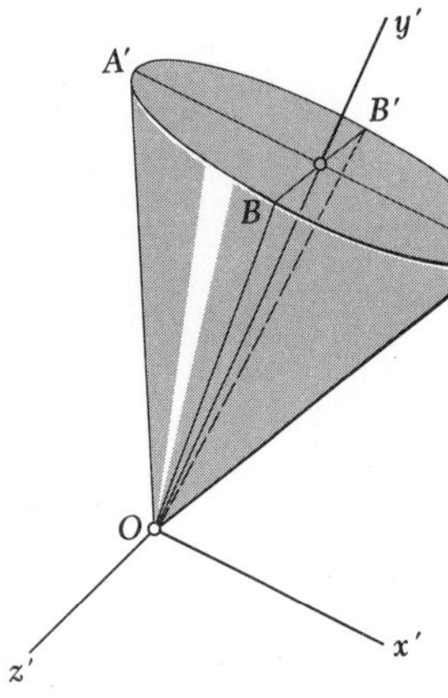

FIG. 18.7

† Cf. Synge and Griffith, *Principles of Mechanics*, McGraw-Hill Book Company, Inc., sec. 11.3.

18.8, the line joining the corner O to the center D of the opposite face is a principal axis of inertia at O and any line through O perpendicular to OD is also a principal axis of inertia at O. This property may be recognized if we observe that a rotation through 120° about OD leaves the shape and the mass distribution of the tetrahedron unchanged. It follows that the ellipsoid of inertia at O also remains unchanged under this rotation. The ellipsoid, therefore, is of revolution about OD, and the line OD, as well as any perpendicular line through O, must be a principal axis of the ellipsoid.

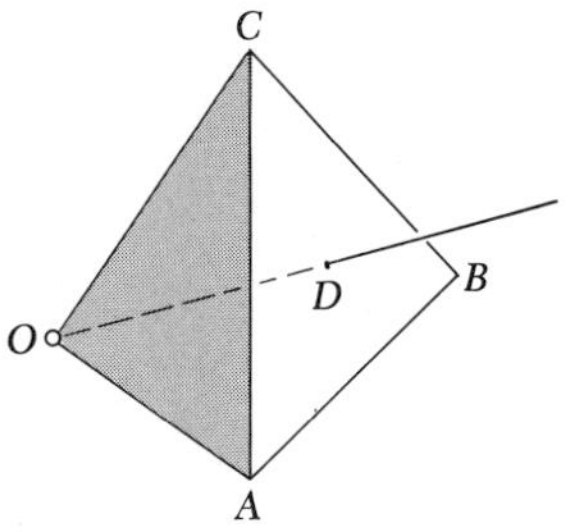

FIG. 18.8

***18.4. Kinetic Energy of a Rigid Body in Three Dimensions.** Consider a rigid body with a fixed point O (Fig. 18.9). Denoting by $\boldsymbol{\omega}$ the angular velocity of the body at a given instant, and by $\mathbf{r}$ the position vector of a particle P of mass Δm of the body, we recall that the speed v of the particle P is equal to the magnitude of the vector $\mathbf{v} = \boldsymbol{\omega} \times \mathbf{r}$. The kinetic energy of the body at the instant considered is therefore

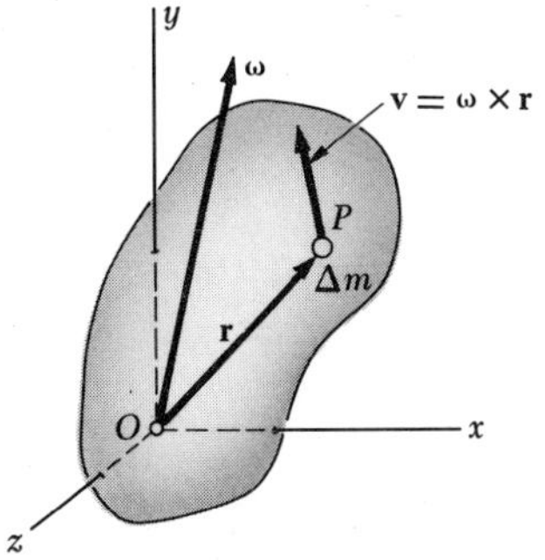

FIG. 18.9

$$T = \tfrac{1}{2}\Sigma(\Delta m)v^2 = \tfrac{1}{2}\Sigma(\boldsymbol{\omega} \times \mathbf{r})^2\Delta m \qquad (18.17)$$

Manipulations similar to those used to derive (18.14) from (18.13) in the preceding section lead us to the fundamental relation

$$T = \tfrac{1}{2}(I_x\omega_x^2 + I_y\omega_y^2 + I_z\omega_z^2 - 2P_{xy}\omega_x\omega_y - 2P_{yz}\omega_y\omega_z - 2P_{zx}\omega_z\omega_x) \qquad (18.18)$$

If the principal axes of inertia x', y', z' of the body are chosen as coordinate axes, the relations obtained reduce to

$$T = \tfrac{1}{2}(I_{x'}\omega_{x'}^2 + I_{y'}\omega_{y'}^2 + I_{z'}\omega_{z'}^2) \qquad (18.19)$$

In the case of a rigid body in general motion, the relation (18.18) or (18.19) may be used to determine the kinetic energy of the body with respect to a centroidal frame of reference. Recalling the results obtained in Sec. 13.5 for a system of particles, and choosing a centroidal frame of reference which coincides at the instant considered with the principal axes of inertia of the body, we express the kinetic energy of a rigid body in general motion as follows:

$$T = \tfrac{1}{2}m\bar{v}^2 + \tfrac{1}{2}(\bar{I}_{x'}\omega_{x'}^2 + \bar{I}_{y'}\omega_{y'}^2 + \bar{I}_{z'}\omega_{z'}^2) \qquad (18.20)$$

where $\bar{\mathbf{v}}$ = velocity of mass center
$\boldsymbol{\omega}$ = angular velocity
m = mass of rigid body
$\bar{I}_{x'}, \bar{I}_{y'}, \bar{I}_{z'}$ = principal centroidal moments of inertia

SAMPLE PROBLEM 18.1

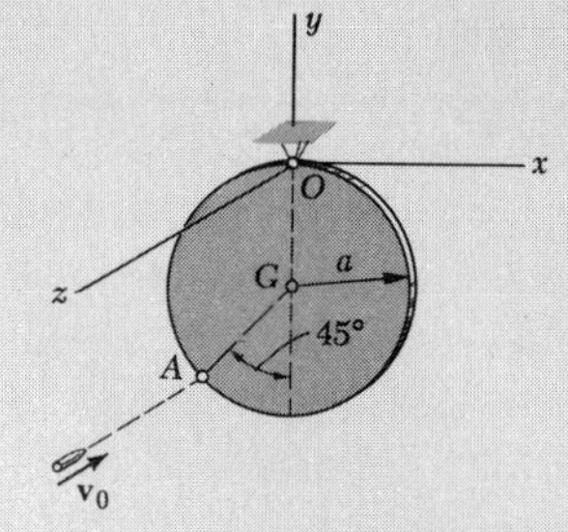

A bullet of mass m_0 is fired with an initial velocity $\mathbf{v}_0$ into a heavy circular plate of mass m which is suspended from a ball-and-socket joint at O. Knowing that the bullet strikes point A and becomes embedded in the plate, determine immediately after impact (*a*) the angular momentum of the plate about O, (*b*) the angular velocity and instantaneous axis of rotation of the plate, (*c*) the kinetic energy of the plate.

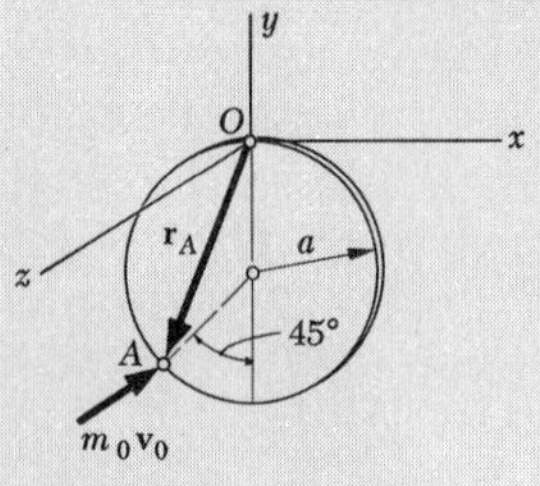

a. **Angular Momentum about** O. We consider the plate and the bullet as a single system. Since the only external impulsive force is the reaction at O, which has no moment about O, the angular momentum about O of the plate and bullet immediately after impact must be equal to the initial angular momentum of the bullet about O.

$$\mathbf{h}_O = \mathbf{r}_A \times m_0\mathbf{v}_0 = (-0.707a\mathbf{i} - 1.707a\mathbf{j}) \times (-m_0v_0\mathbf{k})$$

$$\mathbf{h}_O = m_0v_0a(1.707\mathbf{i} - 0.707\mathbf{j}) \quad ◄$$

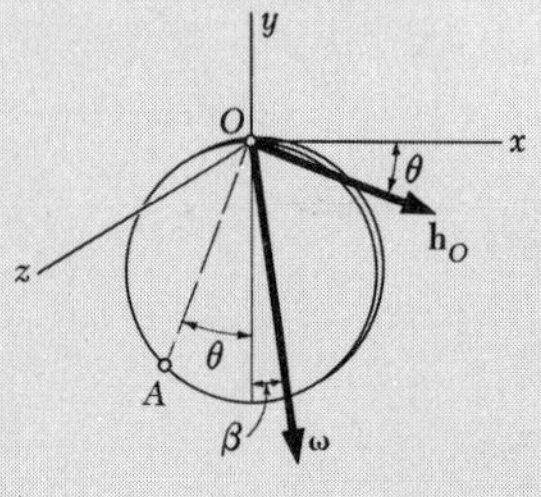

b. **Angular Velocity and Instantaneous Axis.** Neglecting the effect of m_0 on the inertia of the plate, we note that the coordinate axes shown are principal axes of inertia.

$$I_x = \tfrac{1}{4}ma^2 + ma^2 = \tfrac{5}{4}ma^2 \qquad I_y = \tfrac{1}{4}ma^2 \qquad I_z = \tfrac{1}{2}ma^2 + ma^2 = \tfrac{3}{2}ma^2$$

Since the inertia tensor reduces to the diagonalized form of Eq. (18.11), we write

$$h_x = I_x\omega_x: \quad 1.707\, m_0v_0a = \tfrac{5}{4}ma^2\omega_x \qquad \omega_x = +1.366m_0v_0/ma$$

$$h_y = I_y\omega_y: \quad -0.707\, m_0v_0a = \tfrac{1}{4}ma^2\omega_y \qquad \omega_y = -2.828m_0v_0/ma$$

$$h_z = I_z\omega_z: \quad 0 = \tfrac{3}{2}ma^2\omega_z \qquad \omega_z = 0$$

$$\boldsymbol{\omega} = \frac{m_0v_0}{ma}(1.366\mathbf{i} - 2.828\mathbf{j}) \quad ◄$$

The instantaneous axis lies in the plane of the plate and forms an angle β with the vertical.

$$\tan\beta = \frac{\omega_x}{-\omega_y} = \frac{1.366}{2.828} = 0.483 \qquad \beta = 25.8° \quad ◄$$

c. **Kinetic Energy.** Again noting that the axes chosen are principal axes of inertia, we write

$$T = \tfrac{1}{2}(I_x\omega_x^2 + I_y\omega_y^2 + I_z\omega_z^2)$$

$$= \tfrac{1}{2}[\tfrac{5}{4}ma^2(1.366m_0v_0/ma)^2 + \tfrac{1}{4}ma^2(-2.828m_0v_0/ma)^2 + 0]$$

$$T = 2.166\,\frac{m_0^2v_0^2}{m} \quad ◄$$

PROBLEMS

18.1. Determine the principal moments of inertia of a solid cube of mass m and side a about one of its corners.

18.2. Determine the moment of inertia of a solid rectangular parallelepiped about one of its diagonals, (*a*) in terms of a, b, and c and the total mass m, (*b*) if the parallelepiped weighs 30 lb and $a = 18$ in., $b = 15$ in., and $c = 12$ in.

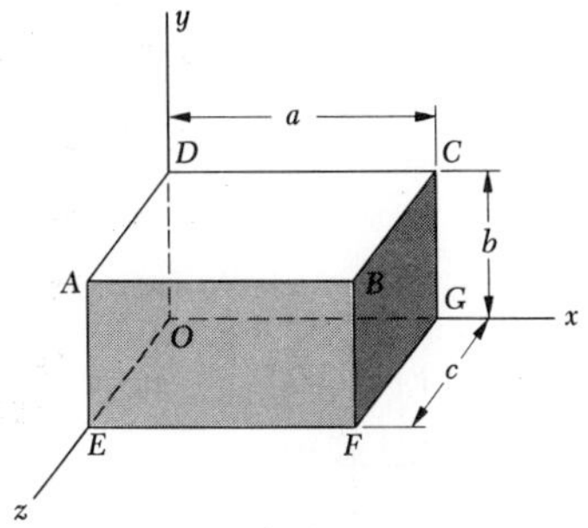

FIG. P 18.2

18.3. Determine the angular momentum of the parallelepiped of Prob. 18.2 when it rotates about the diagonal OB at the rate $\omega = 20$ radians/sec.

18.4. A thin homogeneous disk of mass m and radius a is mounted on the vertical axle AB. The plane of the disk forms an angle β with the horizontal. Knowing that the axle rotates with an angular velocity ω, (*a*) derive an expression for the angle θ formed by the axle and the angular momentum of the disk about O, (*b*) determine the value of β for which θ is maximum.

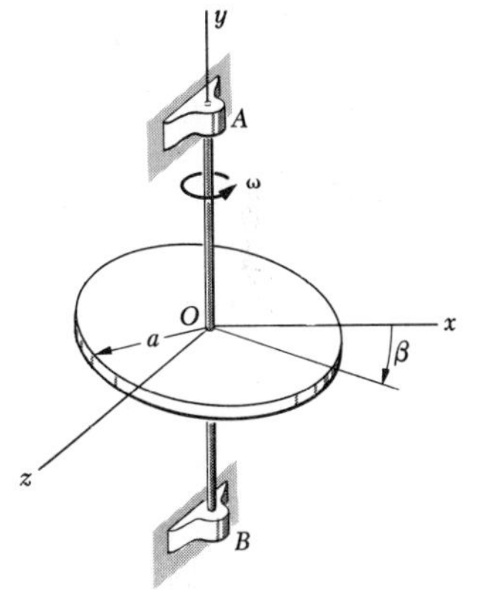

FIG. P 18.4

18.5. Denoting respectively by $\boldsymbol{\omega}$, $\mathbf{h}_O$, and T the angular velocity, the angular momentum, and the kinetic energy of a rigid body with a fixed point O, (*a*) prove that

$$\mathbf{h}_O \cdot \boldsymbol{\omega} = 2T$$

(*b*) show that the angle θ between $\boldsymbol{\omega}$ and $\mathbf{h}_O$ will always be acute.

18.6. Determine the kinetic energy of the parallelepiped of Prob. 18.2 knowing that it rotates about one of its diagonals at a rate $\omega = 20$ radians/sec.

18.7. In the portion of a differential gear system shown, gears A and B are free to rotate about the rod AB while the rod itself is free to rotate in the zx plane about its midpoint O. Gear D is fixed while gear C rotates with a constant angular velocity ω_1. Assuming that gear B can be approximated by a thin disk of weight W and radius r, determine (*a*) the angular velocity of gear B, (*b*) the angular momentum of gear B about point O, (*c*) the kinetic energy of gear B.

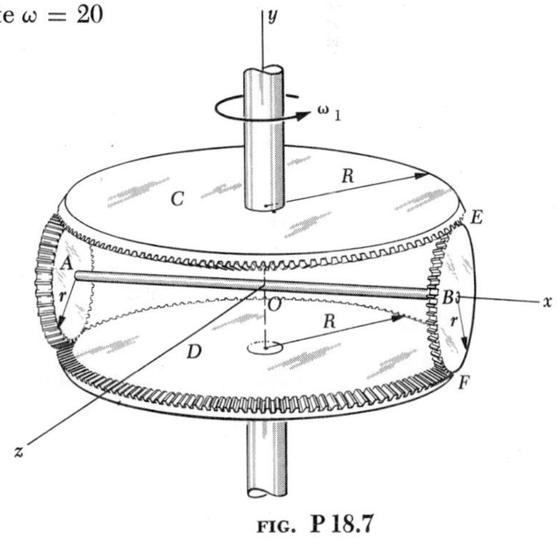

FIG. P 18.7

18.8. Solve Prob. 18.7 assuming that gear B weighs 2 lb and that $\omega_1 = 600$ rpm, $r = 1.50$ in., and $R = 7.50$ in.

18.9. Gear A rolls on the fixed gear B and rotates about the axle AD of length L which is rigidly attached at D to the vertical shaft DE. The shaft DE is made to rotate with a constant angular velocity ω_1. Assuming gear A can be approximated by a thin disk of weight W and radius a, determine (a) the angular velocity of gear A, (b) the angular momentum of gear A about point D, (c) the kinetic energy of gear A.

18.10. Solve Prob. 18.9 assuming that gear A weighs 4 lb and that $\omega_1 = 90$ rpm, $a = 3$ in., $b = 8$ in., and $\beta = 30°$.

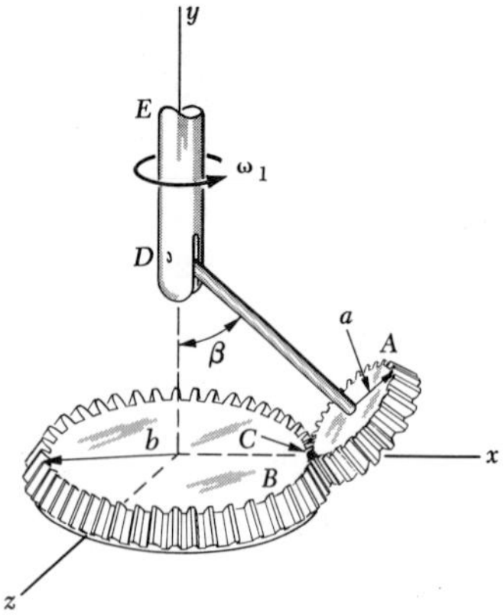

FIG. P 18.9

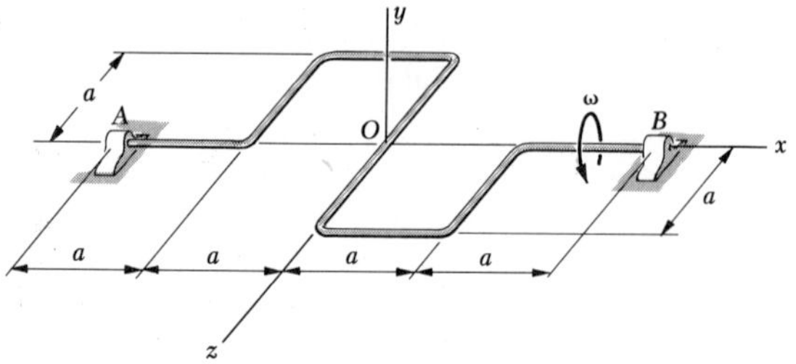

FIG. P 18.11

18.11. Each element of the crankshaft shown is a homogeneous rod weighing w lb/ft. Knowing that the crankshaft rotates with a constant angular velocity ω, determine (a) the angular momentum of the crankshaft about O, (b) the angle formed by the angular momentum and the axis AB.

18.12. Solve Prob. 18.11 assuming $w = 4.00$ lb/ft, $a = 3$ in., and $\omega = 1{,}200$ rpm.

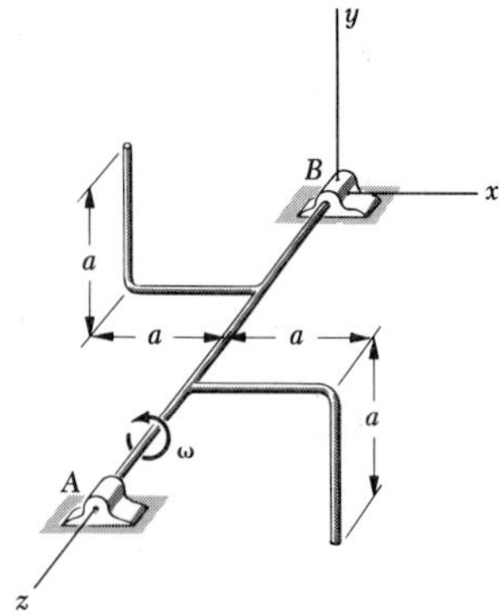

FIG. P 18.13

18.13. Two L-shaped arms, each weighing w lb/ft, are welded to shaft AB. The shaft is of length $3a$ and the arms are welded to the third points of the shaft. Knowing that shaft AB rotates with a constant angular velocity ω, determine (a) the angular momentum of the body about B, (b) the angle formed by the angular momentum and the shaft AB.

18.14. Solve Prob. 18.13 assuming $w = 0.75$ lb/ft, $a = 6$ in., and $\omega = 300$ rpm.

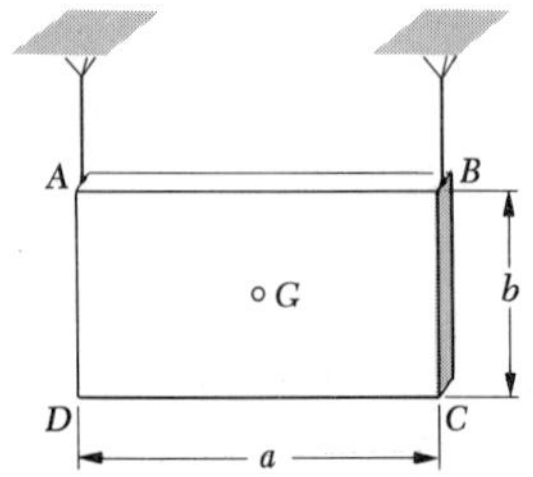

FIG. P 18.15 AND P 18.16

18.15. A 20-lb rectangular plate of sides $a = 3$ ft and $b = 2$ ft is hit at D in a direction perpendicular to the plate. If the impulse applied to the plate is 2.50 lb-sec, determine immediately after impact (a) the angular momentum of the plate about its mass center, (b) the angular velocity of the plate, (c) the two points on the edge of the plate which have zero velocity.

18.16. A bullet is fired into the rectangular plate shown from a direction perpendicular to the plate. Knowing that the angular velocity of the plate immediately after impact is parallel to the diagonal BD, determine the locus of the possible points of impact.

18.17. A uniform rod of total weight W is bent into the shape shown and is suspended by a wire attached at B. The bent rod is hit at C in a direction perpendicular to the plane containing the rod. Determine immediately after impact (a) the angle formed by the instantaneous axis of rotation and the vertical, (b) the points of the rod which have no velocity.

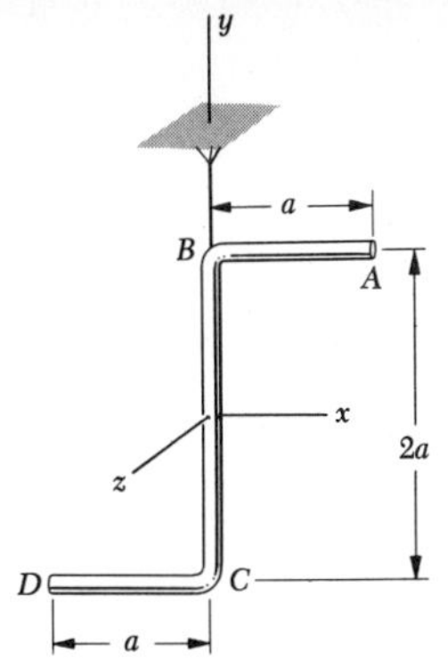

FIG. P 18.17

18.18. The impulse applied to the rod of Prob. 18.17 is known to be 1.50 lb-sec. If $W = 10$ lb and $a = 2$ ft, determine immediately after impact (a) the angular velocity and instantaneous axis of rotation of the rod, (b) the velocity of points A and D.

18.19. The rectangular plate shown is falling with a velocity $\bar{\mathbf{v}}_0$ and no angular velocity when its corner A strikes an obstruction. Assuming the impact at A is perfectly plastic, determine immediately after impact (a) the angular velocity of the plate, (b) the velocity of the mass center G of the plate.

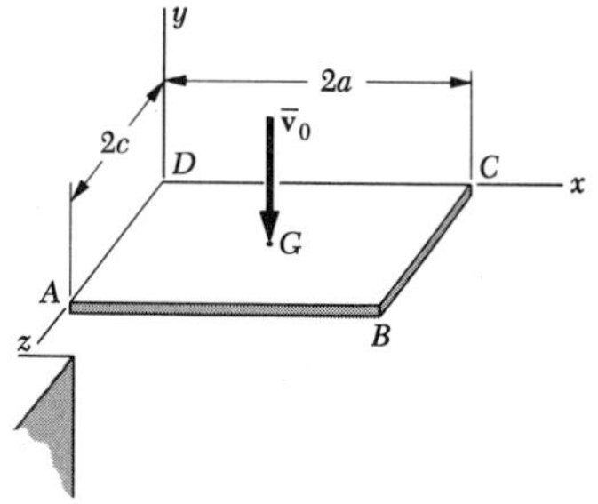

FIG. P 18.19

***18.20.** Solve Prob. 18.19 assuming that the impact at A is perfectly elastic.

18.21. The angular velocity of a 400-lb space capsule is zero when a 0.50-lb projectile is fired from A in a direction parallel to the z axis and with a velocity $\mathbf{v}_0$ of 4,000 ft/sec. Knowing that the radii of gyration of the capsule are $\bar{k}_x = \bar{k}_z = 1.50$ ft and $\bar{k}_y = 2.00$ ft, determine the angular velocity of the capsule immediately after the projectile has been fired.

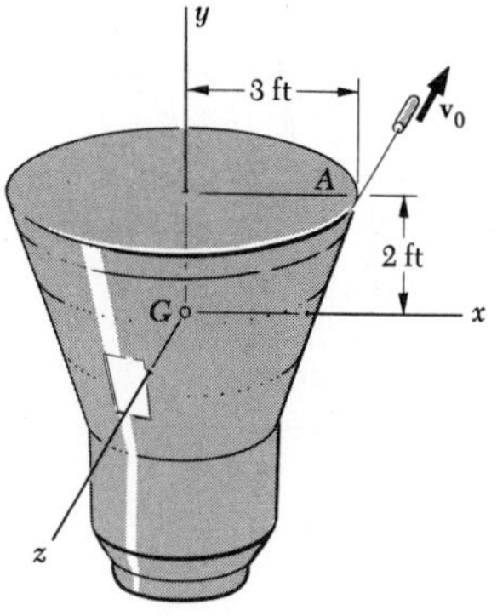

FIG. P 18.21

18.22. A satellite of total weight 200 lb has no angular velocity when it is struck by a 0.02-lb meteorite traveling with a velocity $\mathbf{v}_0 = -4{,}500\mathbf{i} + 6{,}000\mathbf{k}$ (ft/sec) relative to the satellite. Knowing that the radii of gyration of the satellite are $\bar{k}_x = 1.50$ ft and $\bar{k}_y = \bar{k}_z = 3.00$ ft, determine the angular velocity of the satellite immediately after the meteorite has become embedded.

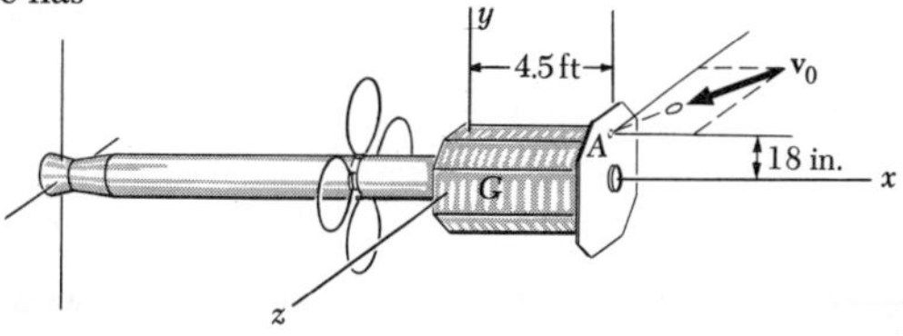

FIG. P 18.22

18.23. Solve Prob. 18.21 assuming that, initially, the capsule was spinning with an angular velocity of 100 rpm counterclockwise as viewed from the positive y axis.

18.24. Solve Prob. 18.22 assuming that, initially, the satellite was spinning about its axis of symmetry with an angular velocity of 10 rpm clockwise as viewed from the positive x axis.

18.25. Determine the kinetic energy of the space capsule of Prob. 18.21 in its motion about its mass center after the projectile has been fired.

18.26. Determine the change in the kinetic energy of the satellite of Prob. 18.22 in its motion about its mass center due to the impact of the meteorite, knowing that before the impact the satellite was spinning about its axis of symmetry with an angular velocity of 10 rpm clockwise as viewed from the positive x axis.

18.27. Determine the change in the total kinetic energy of the plate of Prob. 18.19 due to its impact with the obstruction.

18.28. Determine the kinetic energy of the rod of Prob. 18.18 immediately after impact.

***18.5. Equations of Motion of a Rigid Body about a Fixed Point or about Its Mass Center.** Returning to the fundamental equation (18.2), we recall that the motion of the rigid body, and thus its angular velocity ω, should be defined with respect to a newtonian, or fixed, frame of reference. It would seem natural, therefore, to use components of ω along fixed x, y, and z axes in writing the relations (18.9) which define $\mathbf{h}_O$. But, since the body rotates, its moments and products of inertia would change continuously, and it would be necessary to determine their values as functions of the time. It is therefore more convenient to attach the x, y, and z axes to the body, thus making sure that its moments and products of inertia will maintain the same values during the motion (Fig. 18.10). This is permissible since, as indicated earlier, the transformation of ω into $\mathbf{h}_O$ is independent of the system of coordinate axes which has been selected. The angular velocity vector ω, however, should still be *defined* with respect to a fixed frame $OXYZ$; the vector ω may then be *resolved* into components along the rotating x, y, and z axes. Applying the relations (18.9), we obtain the *components of the vector* $\mathbf{h}_O$ *along the rotating axes.* The vector $\mathbf{h}_O$, however, represents the angular momentum about O of the body *in its motion relative to the fixed frame OXYZ.*

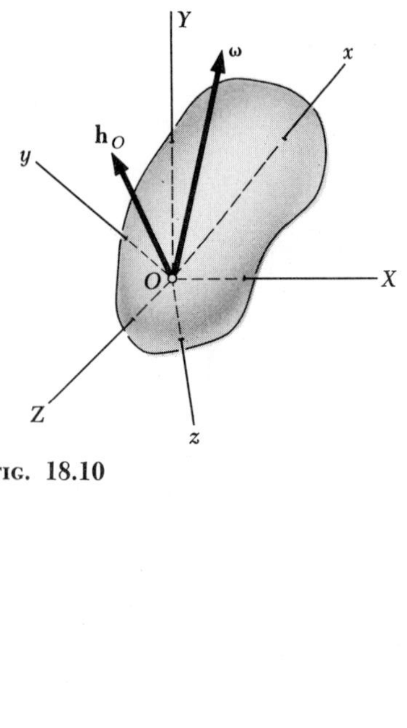

FIG. 18.10

Differentiating with respect to t the components of the angular momentum in (18.9), we define the rate of change $\delta\mathbf{h}_O/\delta t$ of the vector $\mathbf{h}_O$ with respect to the rotating frame $Oxyz$. We have

$$\frac{\delta \mathbf{h}_O}{\delta t} = \frac{dh_x}{dt}\mathbf{i} + \frac{dh_y}{dt}\mathbf{j} + \frac{dh_z}{dt}\mathbf{k} \tag{18.21}$$

where $\mathbf{i}$, $\mathbf{j}$, $\mathbf{k}$ are the unit vectors along the rotating axes. Recalling from Sec. 15.12 that the rate of change of the vector $\mathbf{h}_O$ with respect to the fixed frame $OXYZ$ may be obtained by adding to $\delta\mathbf{h}_O/\delta t$ the vector product $\mathbf{\Omega} \times \mathbf{h}_O$, where $\mathbf{\Omega}$ denotes the angular velocity of the rotating frame, we rewrite (18.2) as follows:

$$\Sigma \mathbf{M}_O = \frac{\delta \mathbf{h}_O}{\delta t} + \mathbf{\Omega} \times \mathbf{h}_O \tag{18.22}$$

where $\Sigma \mathbf{M}_O$ = sum of the moments about O of the forces applied to the rigid body

$\mathbf{h}_O$ = angular momentum of the body with respect to the fixed frame $OXYZ$

$\dfrac{\delta \mathbf{h}_O}{\delta t}$ = rate of change of $\mathbf{h}_O$ with respect to the rotating frame $Oxyz$, to be computed from the relations (18.9) and (18.21)

$\mathbf{\Omega}$ = angular velocity of the rotating frame

If, as it has been assumed in this discussion, the rotating frame $Oxyz$ is attached to the body, its angular velocity $\mathbf{\Omega}$ is identically equal to the angular velocity $\boldsymbol{\omega}$ of the body. There are many applications, however, where it is advantageous to use a frame of reference which is not actually attached to the body, yet rotates in such a way that the moments and products of inertia of the body with respect to the frame remain constant (Sec. 18.7). In such cases, the angular velocity $\mathbf{\Omega}$ of the rotating frame and the angular velocity $\boldsymbol{\omega}$ of the body are different.

The relation (18.22) is equivalent to three scalar equations and may be used to determine the motion of a rigid body with a fixed point, or to determine the forces which should be applied to such a body to produce a given motion. Starting from (18.3), we derive in a similar way the relation

$$\Sigma \mathbf{M}_G = \frac{\delta \mathbf{h}'_G}{\delta t} + \mathbf{\Omega} \times \mathbf{h}'_G \tag{18.23}$$

which may be used to determine the motion of a rigid body about its mass center.

Euler's Equations of Motion. If the x, y, and z axes are chosen to coincide with the principal axes of inertia of the body, the simplified relations (18.12) may be used to determine the components of the angular momentum $\mathbf{h}_O$. Omitting the primes from the subscripts, we write

$$\mathbf{h}_O = I_x\omega_x\mathbf{i} + I_y\omega_y\mathbf{j} + I_z\omega_z\mathbf{k} \tag{18.24}$$

where I_x, I_y, and I_z denote the principal moments of inertia of the body. Substituting for $\mathbf{h}_O$ from (18.24) into (18.22) and setting $\mathbf{\Omega} = \boldsymbol{\omega}$, we obtain the three scalar equations

$$\begin{aligned} \Sigma M_x &= I_x\dot{\omega}_x - (I_y - I_z)\omega_y\omega_z \\ \Sigma M_y &= I_y\dot{\omega}_y - (I_z - I_x)\omega_z\omega_x \\ \Sigma M_z &= I_z\dot{\omega}_z - (I_x - I_y)\omega_x\omega_y \end{aligned} \tag{18.25}$$

These equations, called *Euler's equations of motion* after the Swiss mathematician Leonhard Euler (1707–1783), may be used to analyze the motion of a rigid body with a fixed point; similar equations may be obtained for the motion of a body about its mass center. In the following sections, however, we shall use Eq. (18.22) in preference to Eqs. (18.25), since the former is more general and the compact vectorial form in which it is expressed is easier to remember.

***18.6. Rotation of a Rigid Body about a Fixed Axis. Balancing of Shafts.** We shall use the fundamental equation (18.22) derived in the preceding section to analyze the motion of a rigid body constrained to rotate about a fixed axis AB (Fig. 18.11). First, we note that the angular velocity of the body with respect to the fixed frame $OXYZ$ is represented by the vector $\boldsymbol{\omega}$ directed along the axis of rotation. Attaching the moving frame of reference $Oxyz$ to the body, with the z axis along AB, we have $\boldsymbol{\omega} = \omega\mathbf{k}$. Substituting $\omega_x = 0$, $\omega_y = 0$, $\omega_z = \omega$ into the relations (18.9), we obtain the components along the rotating axes of the angular momentum $\mathbf{h}_O$ of the body about O:

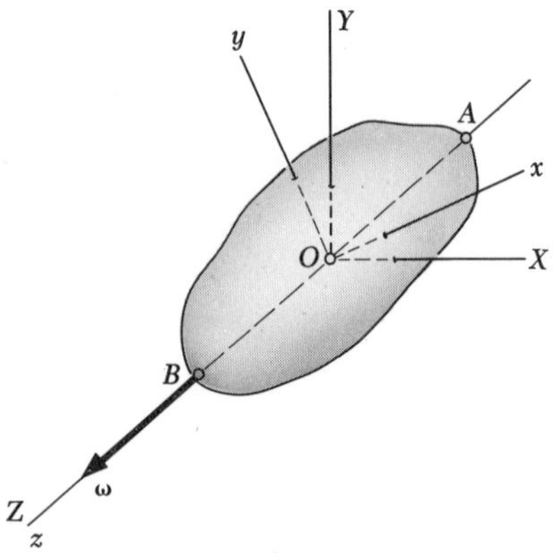

FIG. 18.11

$$h_x = -P_{xz}\omega \qquad h_y = -P_{yz}\omega \qquad h_z = I_z\omega$$

Since the frame $Oxyz$ is attached to the body, we have $\boldsymbol{\Omega} = \boldsymbol{\omega}$ and Eq. (18.22) yields

$$\begin{aligned}\Sigma\mathbf{M}_O &= \frac{\delta\mathbf{h}_O}{\delta t} + \boldsymbol{\omega}\times\mathbf{h}_O \\ &= (-P_{xz}\mathbf{i} - P_{yz}\mathbf{j} + I_z\mathbf{k})\dot{\omega} + \omega\mathbf{k}\times(-P_{xz}\mathbf{i} - P_{yz}\mathbf{j} + I_z\mathbf{k})\omega \\ &= (-P_{xz}\mathbf{i} - P_{yz}\mathbf{j} + I_z\mathbf{k})\alpha + (-P_{xz}\mathbf{j} + P_{yz}\mathbf{i})\omega^2\end{aligned}$$

The result obtained may be expressed by the three scalar equations

$$\begin{aligned}\Sigma M_x &= -P_{xz}\alpha + P_{yz}\omega^2 \\ \Sigma M_y &= -P_{yz}\alpha - P_{xz}\omega^2 \\ \Sigma M_z &= I_z\alpha\end{aligned} \tag{18.26}$$

When the forces applied to the body are known, the angular acceleration α may be obtained from the last of Eqs. (18.26). The angular velocity ω is then determined by integration and the values obtained for α and ω may be substituted into the first two equations (18.26). These equations, plus the three equations defining the motion of the mass center of the body (Sec. 18.1), may then be used to determine the reactions at the bearings A and B.

It should be noted that axes other than the ones shown in Fig. 18.11 may be selected to analyze the rotation of a rigid body about a fixed axis. In many cases, the principal axes of inertia of the body will be found more advantageous (see Sample Prob. 18.3). It is wise, therefore, to revert to the fundamental equation (18.22) and to select the system of axes which fits best the problem under consideration.

If the rotating body is symmetrical with respect to the *xy* plane, the products of inertia P_{xz} and P_{yz} are equal to zero and Eqs. (18.26) reduce to

$$\Sigma M_x = 0 \qquad \Sigma M_y = 0 \qquad \Sigma M_z = I_z\alpha \tag{18.27}$$

which is in accord with the results obtained in Chap. 16. If, on the other hand, the products of inertia P_{xz} and P_{yz} are different from zero, the sum of the moments of the external forces about the *x* and *y* axes will also be different from zero, even when the body rotates at a constant rate ω. Indeed, in the latter case, Eqs. (18.26) yield

$$\Sigma M_x = P_{yz}\omega^2 \qquad \Sigma M_y = -P_{xz}\omega^2 \qquad \Sigma M_z = 0 \tag{18.28}$$

This last observation leads us to discuss the *balancing of rotating shafts.* Consider a shaft of length *l* held in bearings at *A* and *B* and supporting two equal spheres of weight *W* (Fig. 18.12*a*). We first observe that, when the system is at rest, the shaft exerts no lateral thrust on its supports, since the center of gravity *G* is located directly above *A*. The reaction at *A* is therefore vertical and its magnitude is equal to $2W$; the system is said to be *statically balanced.* Let us now assume that the shaft rotates with a constant angular velocity ω. Attaching our frame of reference to the shaft, with its origin at *G*, the *z* axis along *AB*, and the *y* axis in the plane of symmetry of the system (Fig. 18.12*b*), we note that P_{xz} is zero and that P_{yz} is positive. According to Eqs. (18.28), the external forces must include a couple of moment $P_{yz}\omega^2\mathbf{i}$. Since this couple is formed by the reaction at *B* and the horizontal component of the reaction at *A*, we have

$$\mathbf{A}_y = (P_{yz}\omega^2/l)\mathbf{j} \qquad \mathbf{B} = -(P_{yz}\omega^2/l)\mathbf{j} \tag{18.29}$$

The bearing reactions being proportional to ω^2, the shaft will have a tendency to tear away from its bearings when rotating at high speeds. Moreover, since the bearing reactions are contained in the *yz* plane, they rotate with the shaft and cause it to vibrate. These undesirable effects will be avoided if, by rearranging the distribution of mass around the shaft, or by adding corrective masses, we let P_{yz} become equal to zero. The reactions at the bearings will then reduce to the vertical component $\mathbf{A}_z$; the shaft will be *dynamically as well as statically balanced.*

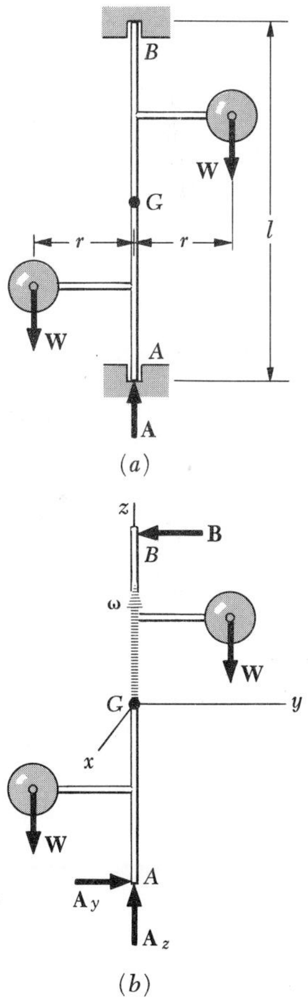

FIG. 18.12

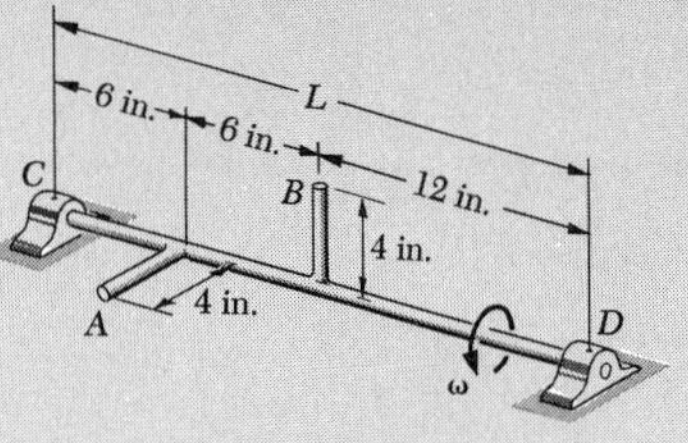

SAMPLE PROBLEM 18.2

Two 4-in. rods A and B, each weighing 3 lb, are welded to the shaft CD which rotates at a constant rate of 1,200 rpm. Determine the dynamic reactions at C and D.

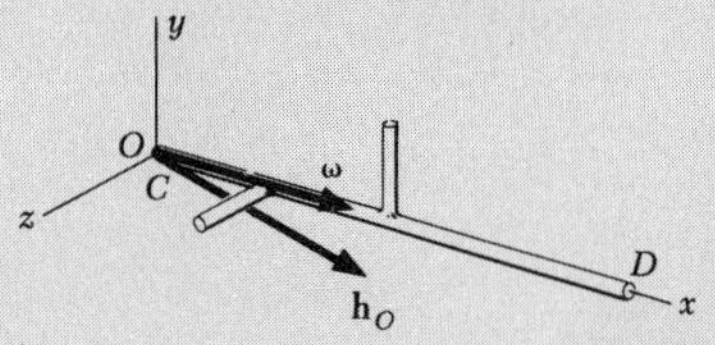

Angular Momentum about O. We attach to the body the frame of reference $Oxyz$ and note that the axes chosen are not principal axes of inertia for the body. Since the body rotates about the x axis, we have $\omega_x = \omega$ and $\omega_y = \omega_z = 0$. Substituting into Eqs. (18.9), we write

$$h_x = I_x\omega \qquad h_y = -P_{xy}\omega \qquad h_z = -P_{xz}\omega$$

$$\mathbf{h}_O = (I_x\mathbf{i} - P_{xy}\mathbf{j} - P_{xz}\mathbf{k})\omega$$

Moments of the External Forces about O. Recalling that the frame of reference rotates with the angular velocity $\boldsymbol{\omega}$, we write

$$\Sigma\mathbf{M}_O = \frac{\delta\mathbf{h}_O}{\delta t} + \boldsymbol{\omega} \times \mathbf{h}_O$$

$$= (I_x\mathbf{i} - P_{xy}\mathbf{j} - P_{xz}\mathbf{k})\dot{\omega} + \omega\mathbf{i} \times (I_x\mathbf{i} - P_{xy}\mathbf{j} - P_{xz}\mathbf{k})\omega$$

Since the angular velocity of the body is constant, $\dot{\omega} = 0$, and we find

$$\Sigma\mathbf{M}_O = -P_{xy}\omega^2\mathbf{k} + P_{xz}\omega^2\mathbf{j} \tag{1}$$

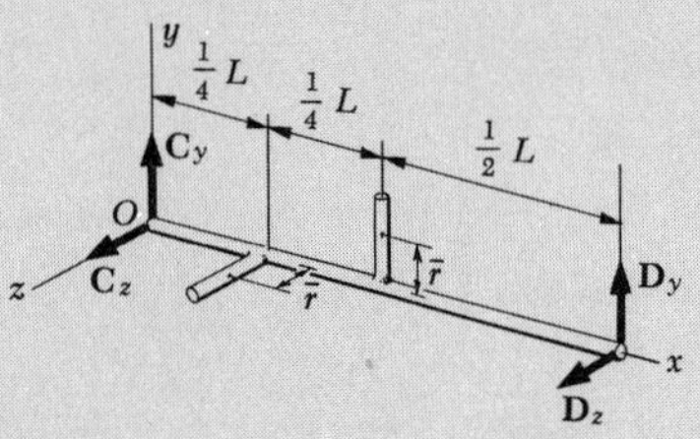

Dynamic Reaction at D. The external forces consist of the weights of the rods, the static reactions at C and D, and the dynamic reactions at C and D. Since the weights and the static reactions are balanced, the system of external forces reduces to the dynamic reactions $\mathbf{C}$ and $\mathbf{D}$ shown in the figure. Taking moments about O, we have

$$\Sigma\mathbf{M}_O = \mathbf{r}_D \times \mathbf{D} = (L\mathbf{i}) \times (D_y\mathbf{j} + D_z\mathbf{k}) = D_yL\mathbf{k} - D_zL\mathbf{j} \tag{2}$$

Equating the right-hand members of (1) and (2), we write

$$D_yL\mathbf{k} - D_zL\mathbf{j} = -P_{xy}\omega^2\mathbf{k} + P_{xz}\omega^2\mathbf{j}$$

from which it follows that

$$D_y = -(P_{xy}\omega^2)/L \qquad D_z = -(P_{xz}\omega^2)/L \tag{3}$$

Using the parallel-axis theorem, and noting that the product of inertia of each rod is zero with respect to centroidal axes, we have

$$P_{xy} = \Sigma m\bar{x}\bar{y} = m(\tfrac{1}{2}L)\bar{r} \qquad P_{xz} = \Sigma m\bar{x}\bar{z} = m(\tfrac{1}{4}L)\bar{r}$$

Substituting into (3), we write

$$D_y = -\tfrac{1}{2}m\bar{r}\omega^2 \qquad D_z = -\tfrac{1}{4}m\bar{r}\omega^2$$

Substituting $\omega = 1{,}200$ rpm $= 126.3$ radians/sec, $\bar{r} = 2$ in., and $m = 3/g$, we have

$$D_y = -122.5 \text{ lb} \qquad D_z = -61.3 \text{ lb} \blacktriangleleft$$

Dynamic Reaction at C. Using a frame of reference attached at D, we may determine the dynamic reaction at C in a similar manner.

$$C_y = -122.5 \text{ lb} \qquad C_z = -183.7 \text{ lb} \blacktriangleleft$$

SAMPLE PROBLEM 18.3

A slender rod AB of length $L = 8$ ft and weight $W = 40$ lb is pinned at A to a vertical axle DE which rotates with a constant angular velocity ω of 15 radians/sec. The rod is maintained in position by means of a wire BC attached to the axle and to the end B of the rod. Determine the tension in the wire and the reaction at A.

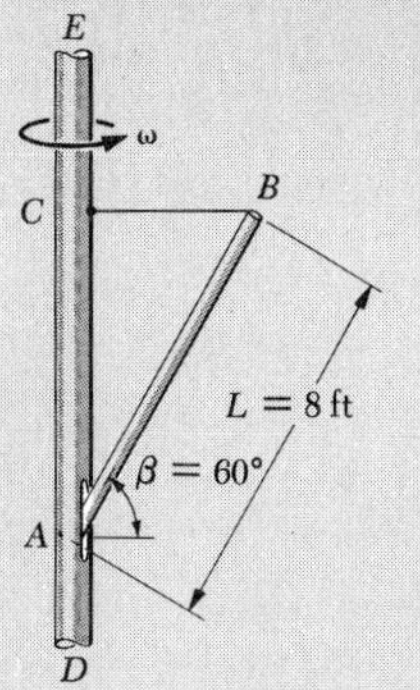

Angular Momentum about O. We attach to the rod a frame of reference $Ox'y'z'$ as shown, with the y' axis along the rod and the z' axis perpendicular to the vertical plane containing the rod. Since the axes chosen are principal axes of inertia for the rod, we may use the simplified relations (18.12) to determine $\mathbf{h}_O$. We write

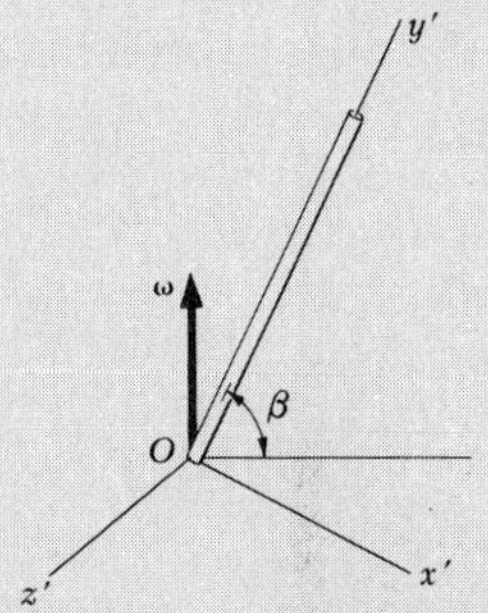

$$I_{x'} = \tfrac{1}{3}mL^2 \qquad I_{y'} = 0 \qquad I_{z'} = \tfrac{1}{3}mL^2$$

$$\omega_{x'} = -\omega \cos \beta \qquad \omega_{y'} = \omega \sin \beta \qquad \omega_{z'} = 0$$

$$\mathbf{h}_O = I_{x'}\omega_{x'}\mathbf{i}' + I_{y'}\omega_{y'}\mathbf{j}' + I_{z'}\omega_{z'}\mathbf{k}'$$

$$\mathbf{h}_O = -\tfrac{1}{3}mL^2\omega \cos \beta \, \mathbf{i}'$$

Moments of the External Forces about O. Since the frame of reference rotates with the same angular velocity ω as the rod, and since $\mathbf{h}_O$ remains constant with respect to the rotating frame, we write

$$\Sigma \mathbf{M}_O = \frac{\delta \mathbf{h}_O}{\delta t} + \boldsymbol{\omega} \times \mathbf{h}_O = \boldsymbol{\omega} \times \mathbf{h}_O$$

$$\Sigma \mathbf{M}_O = (-\omega \cos \beta \, \mathbf{i}' + \omega \sin \beta \, \mathbf{j}') \times (-\tfrac{1}{3}mL^2\omega \cos \beta \, \mathbf{i}')$$

$$\Sigma \mathbf{M}_O = \tfrac{1}{3}mL^2\omega^2 \sin \beta \cos \beta \, \mathbf{k}' \tag{1}$$

Tension in the Wire DE. Introducing a new system of rotating axes x, y, and z with the y axis along the vertical axle and the z axis coinciding with z', we compute the moments about O of the external forces:

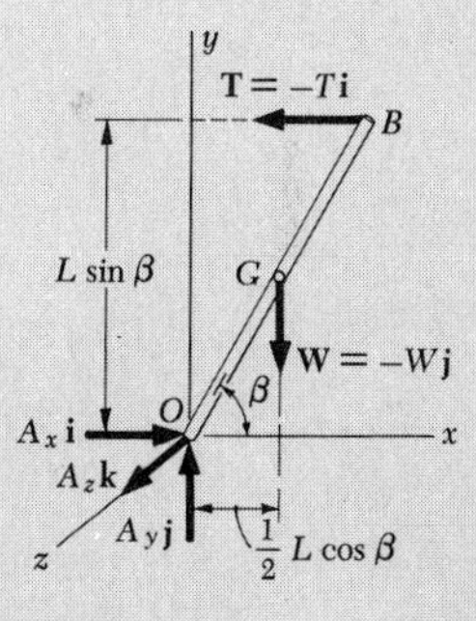

$$\Sigma \mathbf{M}_O = (TL \sin \beta - \tfrac{1}{2}WL \cos \beta)\mathbf{k} \tag{2}$$

Equating the right-hand members of (1) and (2), and noting that the unit vectors $\mathbf{k}$ and $\mathbf{k}'$ are identically equal, we obtain

$$T = \tfrac{1}{2}W \cot \beta + \tfrac{1}{3}mL\omega^2 \cos \beta \tag{3}$$

For the rod considered, we have $W = 40$ lb, $L = 8$ ft, $\beta = 60°$, and $\omega = 15$ radians/sec; substituting these values into (3), we obtain

$$T = 384 \text{ lb} \quad ◄$$

Reaction at A. Since the mass center G moves in a horizontal circle of radius $\bar{r} = \tfrac{1}{2}L \cos \beta$, the acceleration of G is

$$\bar{\mathbf{a}} = -(\tfrac{1}{2}L \cos \beta)\omega^2\mathbf{i} = -(450 \text{ ft/sec}^2)\mathbf{i}$$

We express that the sum of the external forces is equal to the vector $m\bar{\mathbf{a}}$.

$$\Sigma \mathbf{F} = m\bar{\mathbf{a}}: \qquad A_x\mathbf{i} + A_y\mathbf{j} + A_z\mathbf{k} - 384\mathbf{i} - 40\mathbf{j} = -\frac{40}{g}(450)\mathbf{i}$$

$$A_x = -175 \text{ lb} \qquad A_y = +40 \text{ lb} \qquad A_z = 0 \quad ◄$$

Since the system of axes $Oxyz$ rotates with the rod, we note that the reaction at O also rotates and remains in the plane of the rod.

PROBLEMS

18.29. One end of a slender rod of length l and weight W is welded to a vertical rotating shaft. Knowing that the shaft rotates with a constant angular velocity ω, determine the reaction at end A of the rod.

18.30. Rod AB is of length $l = 2$ ft and of weight $W = 10$ lb; it is welded to the vertical shaft, which rotates with a constant velocity of 60 rpm. Determine the moment of the couple exerted by the rod on the shaft if $\beta = 60°$.

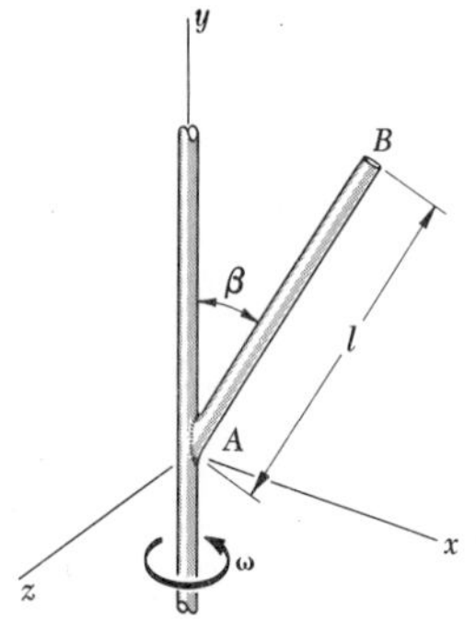

FIG. P 18.29 AND P 18.30

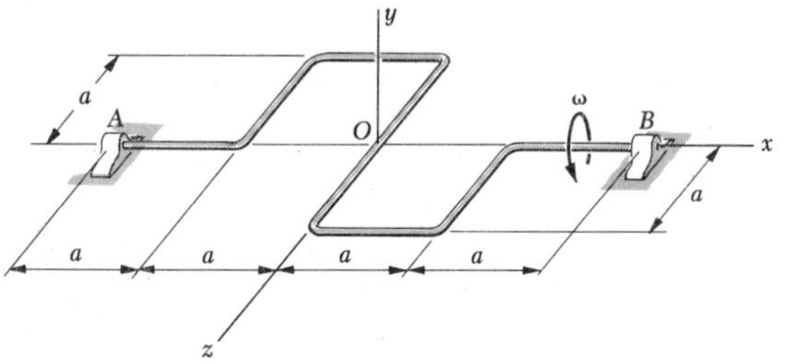

FIG. P 18.31

18.31. Each element of the crankshaft shown is a homogeneous rod weighing w lb/ft. Knowing that the crankshaft rotates with a constant angular velocity ω, determine the dynamic reactions at A and B.

18.32. Solve Prob. 18.31 assuming $w = 4.00$ lb/ft, $a = 3$ in., and $\omega = 1{,}200$ rpm.

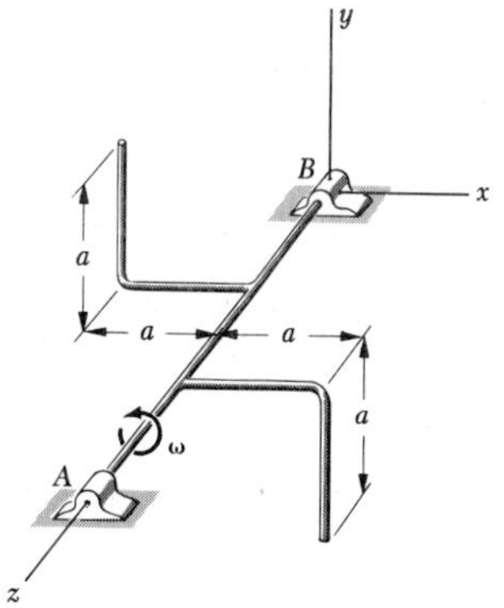

FIG. P 18.33

18.33. Two L-shaped arms, each weighing w lb/ft, are welded to shaft AB. The shaft is of length $3a$ and the arms are welded at the third points of the shaft. Knowing that shaft AB rotates with a constant angular velocity ω, determine the dynamic reactions at A and B.

18.34. Solve Prob. 18.33 assuming $w = 0.75$ lb/ft, $a = 6$ in., and $\omega = 300$ rpm.

18.35. The shaft of Prob. 18.31 is initially at rest ($\omega = 0$) and is accelerated at the rate $\alpha = \dot{\omega} = 100$ radians/sec^2. Knowing that $w = 4$ lb/ft and $a = 3$ in., determine (*a*) the moment of the couple required to cause the acceleration, (*b*) the corresponding dynamic reactions at A and B.

18.36. The shaft of Prob. 18.33 is initially at rest ($\omega = 0$) when a couple $\mathbf{M} = (7.50 \text{ lb-ft})\mathbf{k}$ is applied to the shaft AB. Knowing that $w = 0.75$ lb/ft and $a = 6$ in., determine (*a*) the angular acceleration of the shaft, (*b*) the corresponding dynamic reactions at A and B.

18.37. A thin rectangular plate weighing 15 lb is attached to a shaft as shown. If a 20-lb-ft couple **M** is applied to the shaft when the plate is at rest in a horizontal position, determine (*a*) the angular acceleration of the plate, (*b*) the dynamic reactions at *A* and *C*.

18.38. Solve Prob. 18.37 assuming that the angular velocity of the plate is 200 rpm when the couple **M** is applied.

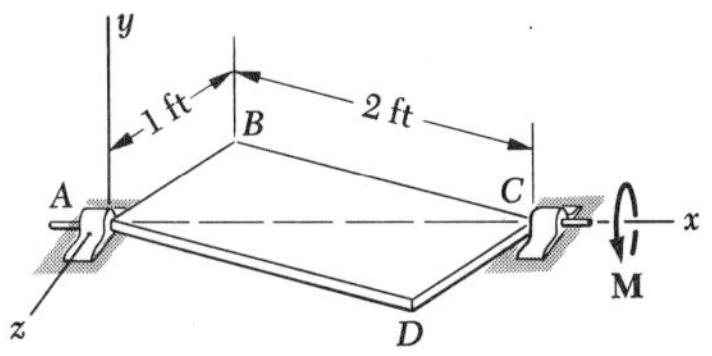

FIG. P 18.37

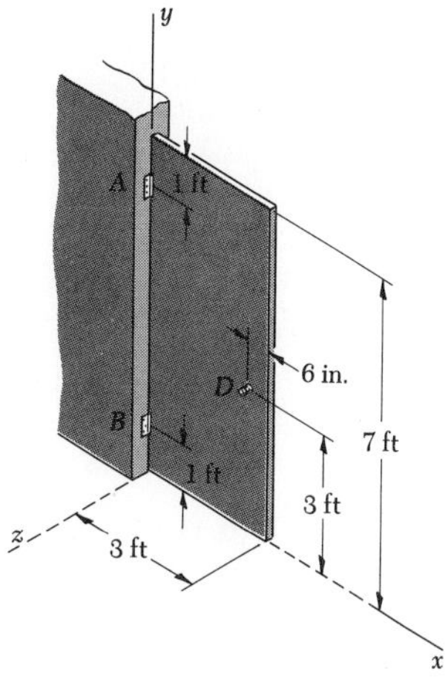

FIG. P 18.39

18.39. A door is made of a solid homogeneous panel 3 by 7 ft, weighing 80 lb. A man pushes on the knob *D* with a 10-lb force directed perpendicularly to the door. Determine (*a*) the angular acceleration of the door, (*b*) the horizontal components of the reactions at the hinges.

18.40. Locate the point on the face of the door of Prob. 18.39 at which a force of 10 lb may be applied perpendicularly to the door without affecting the horizontal components of the reactions at the hinges.

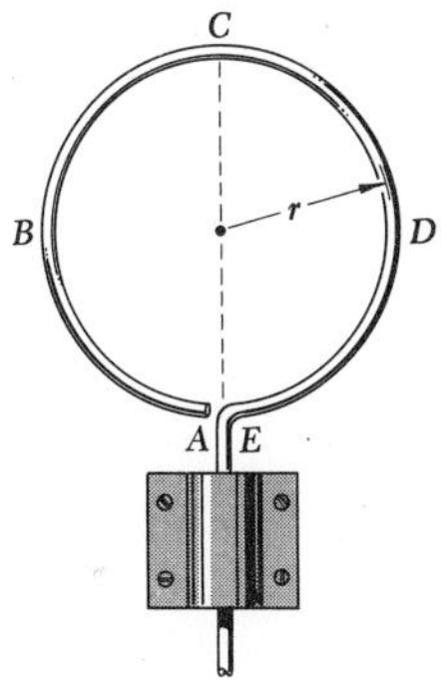

FIG. P 18.41

18.41. A thin homogeneous wire, of weight w lb/ft and in the shape of a circle of radius r, is made to rotate about a vertical shaft with a constant angular velocity ω. Determine the bending moment in the wire (*a*) at point *C*, (*b*) at point *E*, (*c*) at point *B*. (Neglect the effect of gravity.)

18.42. Denoting by L the length of shaft AB in Prob. 18.4 and knowing that the disk is mounted at the mid-point of AB, determine the dynamic reactions at A and B.

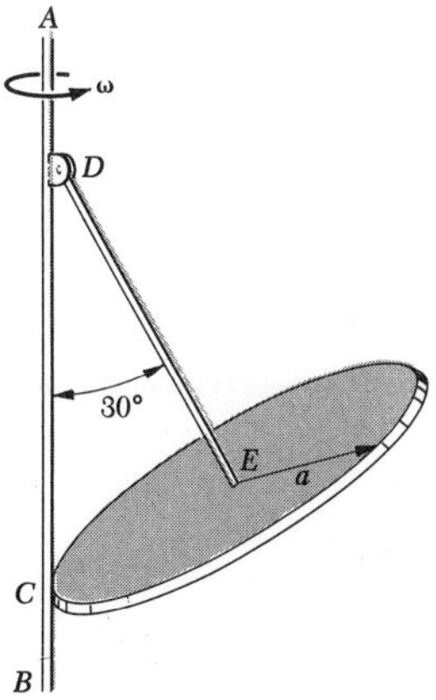

FIG. P 18.43

18.43. A disk of mass m and radius a is rigidly attached to a rod DE of negligible mass. The rod DE is attached to a vertical shaft AB at D and the disk leans against the shaft at C. Noting that, when the shaft AB is made to rotate, the same point of the disk will remain in contact with the shaft at C, determine the angular velocity ω for which the reaction at C will be zero.

18.44. Determine the reactions at C and D for the disk and rod of Prob. 18.43, assuming that the weight of the disk is 25 lb, $\omega = 40$ rpm, and $a = 9$ in.

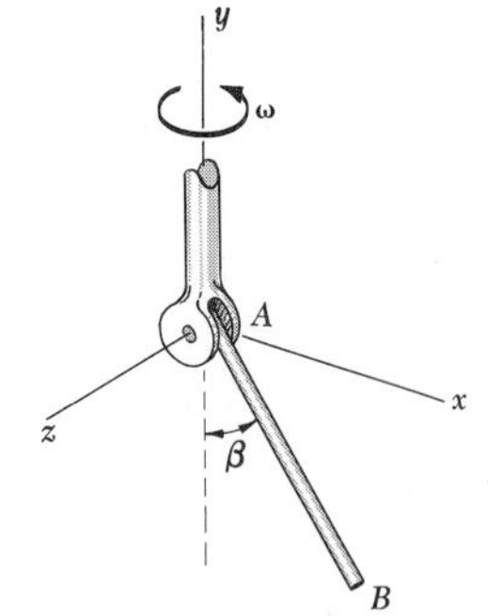

FIG. P 18.45 AND P 18.46

18.45. A uniform rod AB of length l and weight w lb/ft is attached to the pin of a clevis which rotates with a constant angular velocity ω. Derive an expression (*a*) for the angle β that the rod forms with the vertical, (*b*) for the maximum value of ω for which the rod will remain vertical.

18.46. A 2-ft uniform rod AB is attached at A to the pin of a clevis which rotates with a constant angular velocity ω. Determine (*a*) the angle β that the rod forms with the vertical when $\omega = 10$ radians/sec, (*b*) the maximum value of ω for which the rod will remain vertical.

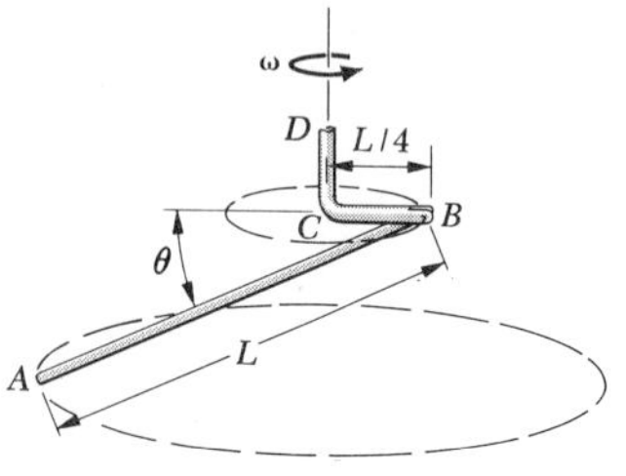

FIG. P 18.47

18.47. A slender rod AB of length L is attached to the arm BC by a clevis at B and is made to rotate about the vertical with an angular velocity ω. Knowing that the rod forms an angle $\theta = 30°$ with the horizontal, derive an expression for the corresponding magnitude of the angular velocity.

***18.48.** For the rod of Prob. 18.47, show that, if there exists a stable position of equilibrium with $\theta < 90°$, then there also exist two other positions of equilibrium, namely, a stable position with $\theta > 90°$ and an unstable position with $\theta < 90°$. Derive an expression for the largest angular velocity for which only one position of equilibrium is possible.

***18.49.** For the angular velocity corresponding to $\theta = 30°$ in Prob. 18.47, find two additional values of θ corresponding to positions of equilibrium. Show that only one of these additional positions is stable.

***18.7. Motion of a Gyroscope. Eulerian Angles.** A *gyroscope* consists essentially of a rotor which may spin freely about its geometric axis. When mounted in a Cardan's suspension (Fig. 18.13), a gyroscope may assume any orientation, but its mass center must remain fixed in space. In order to define the position of a gyroscope at a given instant, we shall select a fixed frame of reference $OXYZ$, with the Z axis directed along the line defined by the bearings A and A' of the outer gimbal, and we shall consider a reference position of the gyroscope in which the two gimbals and a given diameter DD' of the rotor are located in the fixed YZ plane (Fig. 18.13*a*). The gyroscope may be brought from this reference position into any arbitrary position (Fig. 18.13*b*) by means of the following steps: (1) a rotation of the outer gimbal through an angle ϕ about the axis AA', (2) a rotation of the inner gimbal through θ about BB', (3) a rotation of the rotor through ψ about CC'. The angles ϕ, θ, and ψ are called the *Eulerian angles;* they completely characterize the position of the gyroscope at any given instant. Their derivatives $\dot{\phi}$, $\dot{\theta}$, and $\dot{\psi}$ define, respectively, the rate of *precession*, the rate of *nutation*, and the rate of *spin* of the gyroscope at the instant considered.

In order to compute the components of the angular velocity and of the angular momentum of the gyroscope, we shall use a rotating system of axes *Oxyz attached to the inner gimbal*, with the y axis along BB' and the z axis along CC' (Fig. 18.14). These axes are principal axes of inertia for the gyroscope but, while they follow it in its precession and nutation, they do not spin. For that reason, they are more convenient to use than axes actually attached to the gyroscope. We shall now express the angular velocity $\boldsymbol{\omega}$ of the gyroscope with respect to the fixed frame of reference $OXYZ$ as the sum of three partial angular velocities corresponding respectively to the precession, the nutation, and the spin of the gyroscope. Denoting by **i**, **j**, **k** the unit vectors along the rotating axes, and by **K** the unit vector along the fixed Z axis, we have

$$\boldsymbol{\omega} = \dot{\phi}\mathbf{K} + \dot{\theta}\mathbf{j} + \dot{\psi}\mathbf{k} \tag{18.30}$$

Since the vector components obtained for $\boldsymbol{\omega}$ in (18.30) are not orthogonal (Fig. 18.14), we shall resolve the unit vector **K** into components along the x and z axes; we write

$$\mathbf{K} = -\sin\theta\,\mathbf{i} + \cos\theta\,\mathbf{k} \tag{18.31}$$

and, substituting for **K** into (18.30),

$$\boldsymbol{\omega} = -\dot{\phi}\sin\theta\,\mathbf{i} + \dot{\theta}\mathbf{j} + (\dot{\psi} + \dot{\phi}\cos\theta)\mathbf{k} \tag{18.32}$$

Since the coordinate axes are principal axes of inertia, the components of the angular momentum $\mathbf{h}_O$ may be obtained by multiplying the components of $\boldsymbol{\omega}$ by the moments of inertia of the rotor about the x, y, and z axes, respectively. Denoting by I the moment of inertia of the rotor about its spin axis, by I' its moment of inertia about a transverse axis through O, and neglecting the mass of the gimbals, we write

$$\mathbf{h}_O = -I'\dot{\phi}\sin\theta\,\mathbf{i} + I'\dot{\theta}\mathbf{j} + I(\dot{\psi} + \dot{\phi}\cos\theta)\mathbf{k} \tag{18.33}$$

Recalling that the rotating axes are attached to the inner gimbal, and thus do not spin, we express their angular velocity as the sum

$$\boldsymbol{\Omega} = \dot{\phi}\mathbf{K} + \dot{\theta}\mathbf{j} \tag{18.34}$$

or, substituting for **K** from (18.31),

$$\boldsymbol{\Omega} = -\dot{\phi}\sin\theta\,\mathbf{i} + \dot{\theta}\mathbf{j} + \dot{\phi}\cos\theta\,\mathbf{k} \tag{18.35}$$

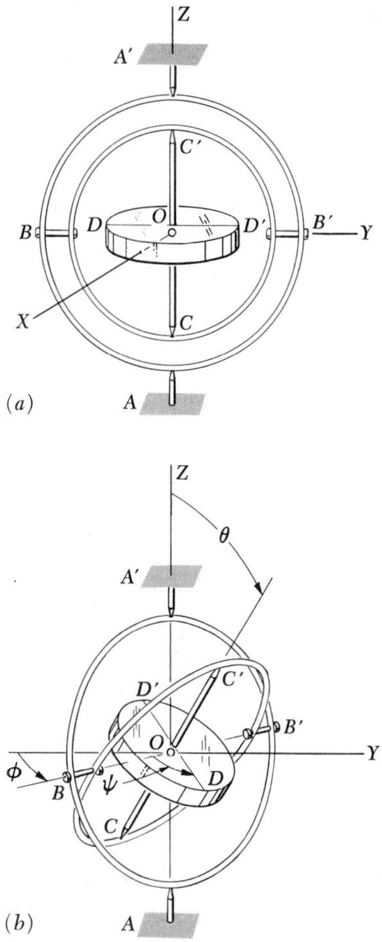

FIG. 18.13

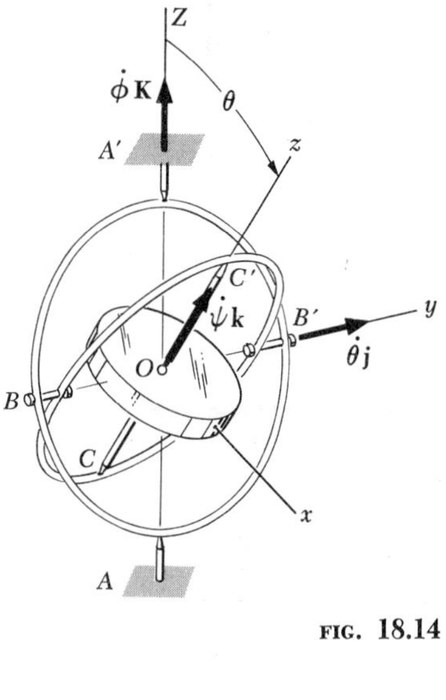

FIG. 18.14

Substituting for $\mathbf{h}_O$ and $\mathbf{\Omega}$ from (18.33) and (18.35) into the fundamental equation

$$\Sigma \mathbf{M}_O = \frac{\delta \mathbf{h}_O}{\delta t} + \mathbf{\Omega} \times \mathbf{h}_O \tag{18.22}$$

we obtain the three differential equations

$$\begin{aligned} \Sigma M_x &= -I'(\ddot{\phi} \sin \theta + 2\dot{\theta}\dot{\phi} \cos \theta) + I\dot{\theta}(\dot{\psi} + \dot{\phi} \cos \theta) \\ \Sigma M_y &= I'(\ddot{\theta} - \dot{\phi}^2 \sin \theta \cos \theta) + I\dot{\phi} \sin \theta(\dot{\psi} + \dot{\phi} \cos \theta) \\ \Sigma M_z &= I\frac{d}{dt}(\dot{\psi} + \dot{\phi} \cos \theta) \end{aligned} \tag{18.36}$$

The equations (18.36) define the motion of a gyroscope subjected to a given system of forces when the mass of its gimbals is neglected. They may also be used to define the motion of an *axisymmetrical body* (or body of revolution) attached at a point of its axis of symmetry, or the motion of an axisymmetrical body about its mass center. While the gimbals of the gyroscope helped us visualize the Eulerian angles, it is clear that these angles may be used to define the position of any rigid body with respect to axes centered at a point of the body, regardless of the way in which the body is actually supported.

Since the equations (18.36) are nonlinear, it will not be possible, in general, to express the Eulerian angles ϕ, θ, and ψ as analytical functions of the time t, and numerical methods of solution may have to be used. However, as we shall see in the following sections, there are several particular cases of interest which may be analyzed easily.

***18.8. Steady Precession of a Gyroscope.** We shall consider in this section the particular case of gyroscopic motion in which the angle θ, the rate of precession $\dot{\phi}$, and the rate of spin $\dot{\psi}$ remain constant. We propose to determine the forces which must be applied to the gyroscope to maintain this motion, known as the *steady precession* of a gyroscope.

Instead of applying the general equations (18.36), we shall determine the sum of the moments of the required forces by computing the rate of change of the angular momentum of the gyroscope in the particular case considered. We first note that the angular velocity ω of the gyroscope, its angular momentum $\mathbf{h}_O$, and the angular velocity $\mathbf{\Omega}$ of the rotating frame of reference (Fig. 18.15) reduce respectively to

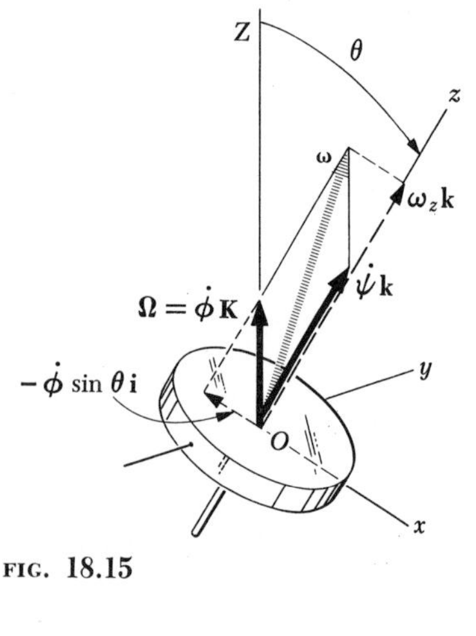

FIG. 18.15

$$\omega = -\dot{\phi} \sin \theta \, \mathbf{i} + \omega_z \mathbf{k} \tag{18.37}$$
$$\mathbf{h}_O = -I'\dot{\phi} \sin \theta \, \mathbf{i} + I\omega_z \mathbf{k} \tag{18.38}$$
$$\mathbf{\Omega} = -\dot{\phi} \sin \theta \, \mathbf{i} + \dot{\phi} \cos \theta \, \mathbf{k} \tag{18.39}$$

where $\omega_z = \dot{\psi} + \dot{\phi}\cos\theta$ = component along the spin axis of the total angular velocity of the gyroscope

Since θ, $\dot{\phi}$, and $\dot{\psi}$ are constant, the vector $\mathbf{h}_O$ is constant in magnitude and direction with respect to the rotating frame of reference, and its rate of change $\delta\mathbf{h}_O/\delta t$ with respect to that frame is zero. Thus, the fundamental equation (18.22) reduces to

$$\Sigma\mathbf{M}_O = \mathbf{\Omega} \times \mathbf{h}_O \tag{18.40}$$

which yields, after substitutions from (18.38) and (18.39),

$$\Sigma\mathbf{M}_O = (I\omega_z - I'\dot{\phi}\cos\theta)\dot{\phi}\sin\theta\,\mathbf{j} \tag{18.41}$$

Since the mass center of the gyroscope is fixed in space, we have, by (18.1), $\Sigma\mathbf{F} = 0$; thus, the forces which must be applied to the gyroscope to maintain its steady precession reduce to a couple of moment equal to the right-hand member of Eq. (18.41). We note that *this couple should be applied about an axis perpendicular to the precession axis and to the spin axis of the gyroscope* (Fig. 18.16).

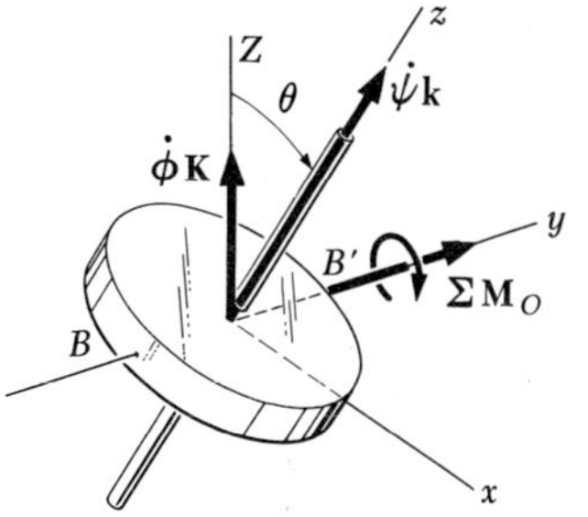

FIG. 18.16

In the particular case when the precession axis and the spin axis are at a right angle to each other, we have $\theta = 90°$ and Eq. (18.41) reduces to

$$\Sigma\mathbf{M}_O = I\dot{\psi}\dot{\phi}\mathbf{j} \tag{18.42}$$

Thus, if we apply to the gyroscope a couple $\mathbf{M}_O$ about an axis perpendicular to its axis of spin, the gyroscope will precess about an axis perpendicular to both the spin axis and the couple axis, in a sense such that the vectors representing respectively the spin, the couple, and the precession form a right-handed triad (Fig. 18.17).

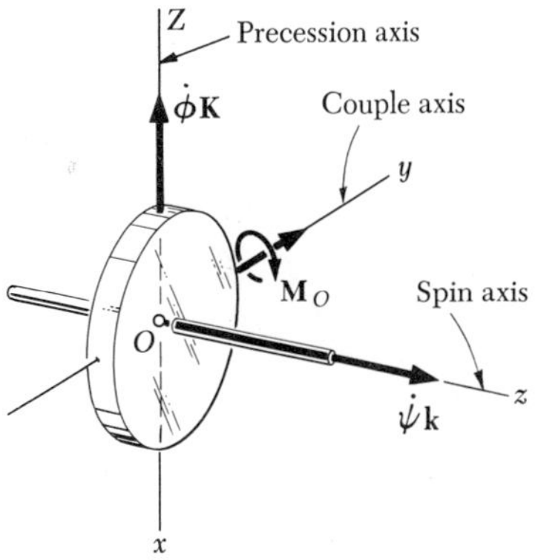

FIG. 18.17

Because of the relatively large couples required to change the orientation of their axles, gyroscopes are used as stabilizers in torpedoes and ships. Spinning bullets and shells remain tangent to their trajectory because of gyroscopic action. And a bicycle is easier to keep balanced at high speeds because of the stabilizing effect of its spinning wheels. However, gyroscopic action is not always welcome and must be taken into account in the design of bearings supporting rotating shafts subjected to forced precession. The reactions exerted by its propellers on an airplane which changes its direction of flight must also be taken into consideration and compensated for whenever possible.

18.9. Motion of an Axisymmetrical Body under No Force. We shall consider in this section the motion about its mass center of an axisymmetrical body under no force, except its own weight. Examples of such a motion are furnished by projec-

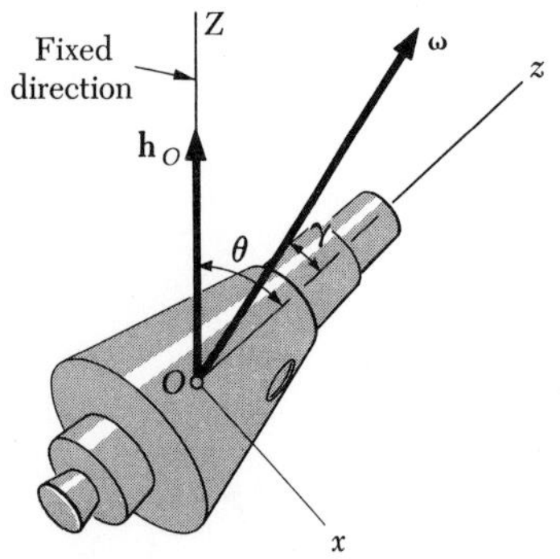

FIG. 18.18

tiles, if air resistance is neglected, and by artificial satellites and space vehicles after burnout of their launching rockets.

Denoting by O the mass center of the body, we observe that the vector $\mathbf{h}_O$ which represents the angular momentum of the body about O must be constant, since the moments of the external forces about O are zero. Thus, the direction of $\mathbf{h}_O$ is fixed in space and may be used to define the Z axis, or axis of precession (Fig. 18.18). Selecting a rotating system of axes $Oxyz$ with the z axis along the axis of symmetry of the body and the x axis in the plane defined by the Z and z axes, we have

$$h_x = -h_O \sin\theta \qquad h_y = 0 \qquad h_z = h_O \cos\theta \quad (18.43)$$

where θ represents the angle formed by the Z and z axes, and h_O denotes the constant magnitude of the angular momentum of the body about O. Since the x, y, and z axes are principal axes of inertia for the body considered, we may write

$$h_x = I'\omega_x \qquad h_y = I'\omega_y \qquad h_z = I\omega_z \quad (18.44)$$

where I denotes the moment of inertia of the body about its axis of symmetry, and I' its moment of inertia about a transverse axis through O. It follows from Eqs. (18.43) and (18.44) that

$$\omega_x = -(h_O \sin\theta)/I' \qquad \omega_y = 0 \qquad \omega_z = (h_O \cos\theta)/I \quad (18.45)$$

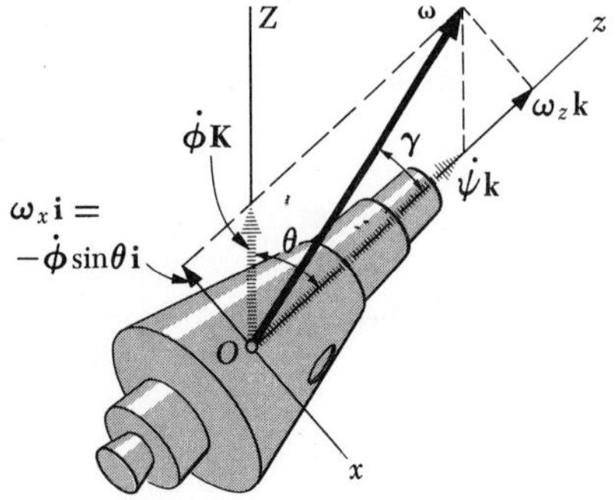

FIG. 18.19

The second of the relations obtained shows that the angular velocity $\boldsymbol{\omega}$ has no component along the y axis, i.e., along an axis perpendicular to the Zz plane. Thus, the angle θ formed by the Z and z axes remains constant and *the body is in steady precession about the Z axis.* Recalling that $\omega_x = -\dot{\phi}\sin\theta$ (Fig. 18.19), substituting this value into the first of the relations (18.45), and using the third of the same relations to eliminate h_O, we find the following expression for the rate of precession:

$$\dot{\phi} = \frac{I\omega_z}{I'\cos\theta} \quad (18.46)$$

where θ = angle between precession axis Z and axis of symmetry z

I, I' = axial and transverse moments of inertia†

Dividing the first and third of the relations (18.45) member by member, and observing from Fig. 18.19 that $-\omega_x/\omega_z =$

† We may verify as follows that the condition (18.41) for steady precession is satisfied by an axisymmetrical body under no force: On one hand we have $\Sigma\mathbf{M}_O = 0$ and, on the other hand, it follows from (18.46) that

$$I\omega_z - I'\dot{\phi}\cos\theta = 0$$

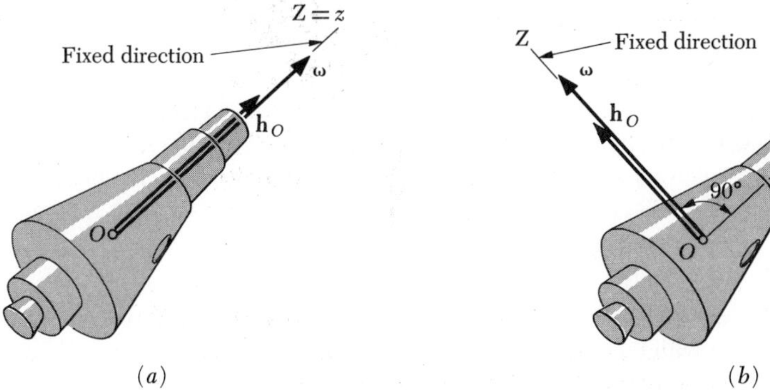

FIG. 18.20

tan γ, we obtain the following relation between the angles γ and θ that the vectors ω and $\mathbf{h}_O$ respectively form with the axis of symmetry of the body:

$$\tan \gamma = \frac{I}{I'} \tan \theta \tag{18.47}$$

There are two particular cases of motion of an axisymmetrical body under no force which involve no precession: (1) If the body is set to spin about its axis of symmetry, we have $\omega_x = 0$ and, by (18.44), $h_x = 0$; the vectors ω and $\mathbf{h}_O$ have the same orientation and the body keeps spinning about its axis of symmetry (Fig. 18.20*a*). (2) If the body is set to spin about a transverse axis, we have $\omega_z = 0$ and, by (18.44), $h_z = 0$; again ω and $\mathbf{h}_O$ have the same orientation and the body keeps spinning about the given transverse axis (Fig. 18.20*b*).

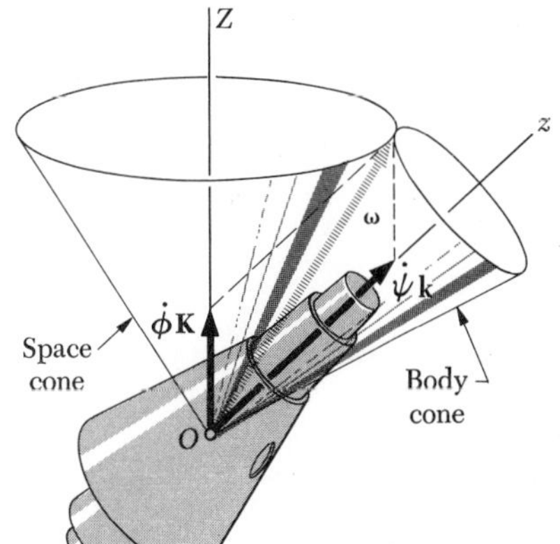

FIG. 18.21

Considering now the general case represented in Fig. 18.19, we recall from Sec. 15.10 that the motion of a body about a fixed point—or about its mass center—may be represented by the motion of a body cone rolling on a space cone. In the case of steady precession, the two cones are circular, since the angles γ and θ − γ that the angular velocity ω forms, respectively, with the axis of symmetry of the body and with the precession axis are constant. Two cases should be distinguished:

1. $I < I'$. This is the case of an elongated body, such as the space vehicle of Fig. 18.21. By (18.47) we have $\gamma < \theta$; the vector ω lies inside the angle *ZOz*; the space cone and the body cone are tangent externally; the spin and the precession are both observed as counterclockwise from the positive *z* axis. The precession is said to be *direct*.

2. $I > I'$. This is the case of a flattened body, such as the satellite of Fig. 18.22. By (18.47) we have $\gamma > \theta$; since ω must lie outside the angle *ZOz*, the vector $\dot{\psi}\mathbf{k}$ has a sense opposite to that of the *z* axis; the space cone is inside the body cone; the precession and the spin have opposite senses; the precession is said to be *retrograde*.

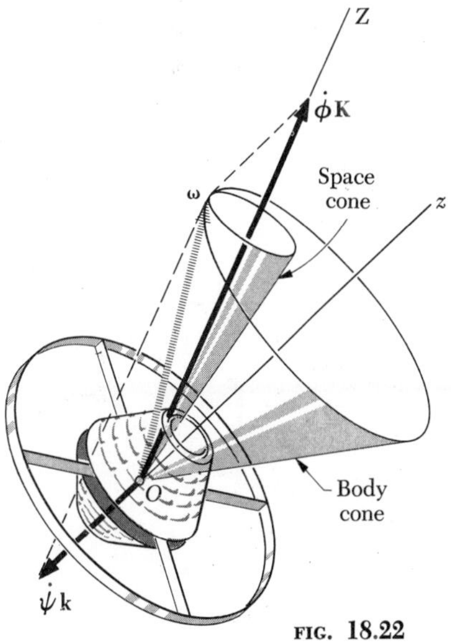

FIG. 18.22

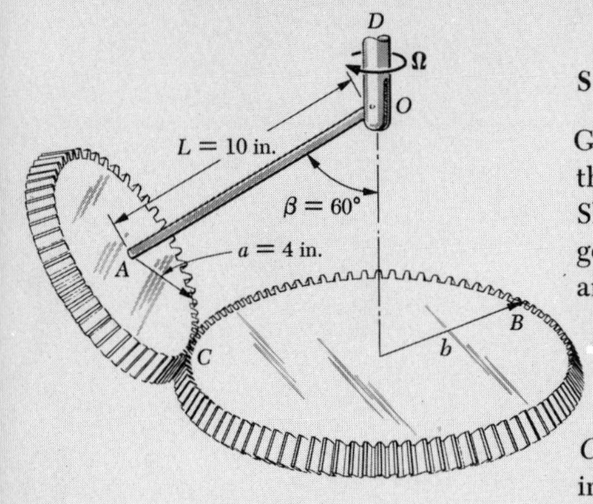

SAMPLE PROBLEM 18.4

Gear A, of weight $W = 10$ lb, rolls on the fixed gear B and rotates about the axle OA which is connected to the vertical shaft OD by a clevis at O. Shaft OD rotates with a constant angular velocity $\mathbf{\Omega}$. Assuming that gear A is equivalent to a thin disk of radius a, determine the maximum angular velocity $\mathbf{\Omega}$ for which gear A remains in contact with gear B.

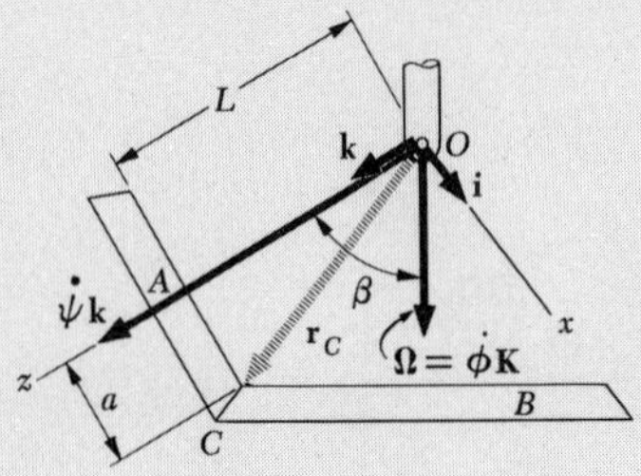

Angular Velocity of Gear A. We choose the frame of reference $Oxyz$ with the z axis directed along the axle OA and the x axis contained in the vertical plane OAC. We note that these axes are principal axes of inertia for gear A and that, while they rotate about the vertical, they do not spin with gear A about the axle OA. Resolving the angular velocity $\mathbf{\Omega} = \dot{\phi}\mathbf{K}$ of the frame $Oxyz$ into x and z components, we write

$$\mathbf{\Omega} = \dot{\phi} \sin \beta \, \mathbf{i} + \dot{\phi} \cos \beta \, \mathbf{k} \tag{1}$$

The angular velocity $\boldsymbol{\omega}$ of gear A is obtained by adding the spin $\dot{\psi}\mathbf{k}$ to $\mathbf{\Omega}$.

$$\boldsymbol{\omega} = \dot{\phi} \sin \beta \, \mathbf{i} + (\dot{\phi} \cos \beta + \dot{\psi})\mathbf{k} = \dot{\phi} \sin \beta \, \mathbf{i} + \omega_z \mathbf{k} \tag{2}$$

Observing that the velocity of point C is zero, we write

$$\boldsymbol{\omega} \times \mathbf{r}_C = (\dot{\phi} \sin \beta \, \mathbf{i} + \omega_z \mathbf{k}) \times (a\mathbf{i} + L\mathbf{k}) = (a\omega_z - L\dot{\phi} \sin \beta)\mathbf{j} = 0$$

from which it follows that $\omega_z = (L/a)\dot{\phi} \sin \beta$. Substituting into (2):

$$\boldsymbol{\omega} = \frac{\dot{\phi} \sin \beta}{a}(a\mathbf{i} + L\mathbf{k}) \tag{3}$$

Denoting by I and I' the moments of inertia of gear A with respect to the z and x axes, respectively, we write

$$\mathbf{h}_O = I'\omega_x \mathbf{i} + I\omega_z \mathbf{k} = \frac{\dot{\phi} \sin \beta}{a}(I'a\mathbf{i} + IL\mathbf{k}) \tag{4}$$

Moments of the External Forces about O. Observing that $\mathbf{h}_O$ is constant with respect to the frame $Oxyz$, and using (1) and (4), we have

$$\Sigma \mathbf{M}_O = \frac{\delta \mathbf{h}_O}{\delta t} + \mathbf{\Omega} \times \mathbf{h}_O = \mathbf{\Omega} \times \mathbf{h}_O$$

$$\Sigma \mathbf{M}_O = \dot{\phi}(\sin \beta \, \mathbf{i} + \cos \beta \, \mathbf{k}) \times \frac{\dot{\phi} \sin \beta}{a}(I'a\mathbf{i} + IL\mathbf{k})$$

$$\Sigma \mathbf{M}_O = \frac{\dot{\phi}^2 \sin \beta}{a}(I'a \cos \beta - IL \sin \beta)\mathbf{j} \tag{5}$$

Maximum Angular Velocity. The maximum value $\dot{\phi}$ for which contact is maintained between the gears occurs when the force $\mathbf{F}$ exerted by gear B on gear A is zero. The weight $\mathbf{W}$ is then the only force having a moment about O.

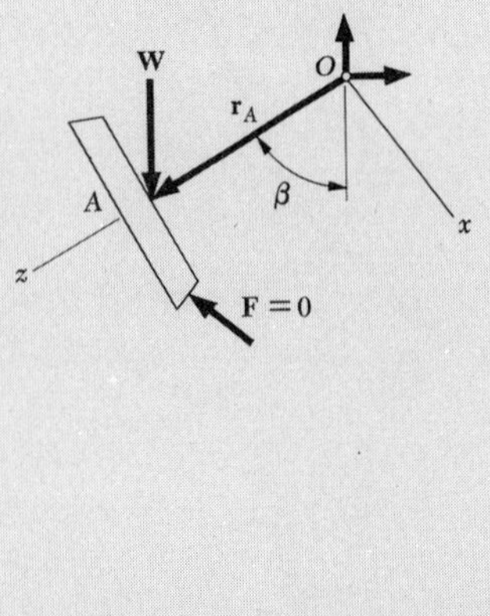

$$\Sigma \mathbf{M}_O = \mathbf{r}_A \times \mathbf{W} = L\mathbf{k} \times (W \sin \beta \, \mathbf{i} + W \cos \beta \, \mathbf{k}) = WL \sin \beta \, \mathbf{j} \tag{6}$$

Equating the right-hand members of (5) and (6), solving for $\dot{\phi}^2$, and substituting the appropriate numerical values, we have

$$\dot{\phi}^2 = \frac{WaL}{I'a \cos \beta - IL \sin \beta} = 111.3 \qquad \Omega = \dot{\phi} = 10.55 \text{ radians/sec} \quad ◄$$

SAMPLE PROBLEM 18.5

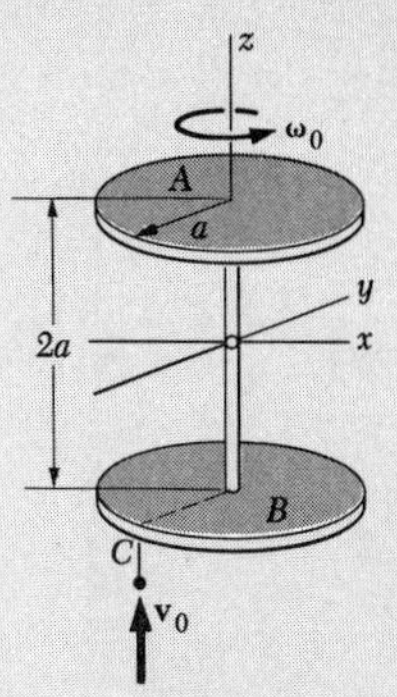

A space satellite of mass m is known to be dynamically equivalent to two thin disks of equal mass. The disks are of radius $a = 3$ ft and are rigidly connected by a light rod of length $2a$. Initially the satellite is spinning freely about its axis of symmetry at the rate $\omega_0 = 60$ rpm. A meteorite, of mass $m_0 = m/1{,}000$ and traveling with a velocity $\mathbf{v}_0$ of 7,500 ft/sec relative to the satellite, strikes the satellite and becomes embedded at C. Determine (*a*) the angular velocity of the satellite immediately after impact, (*b*) the precession axis of the ensuing motion, (*c*) the rates of precession and spin of the ensuing motion.

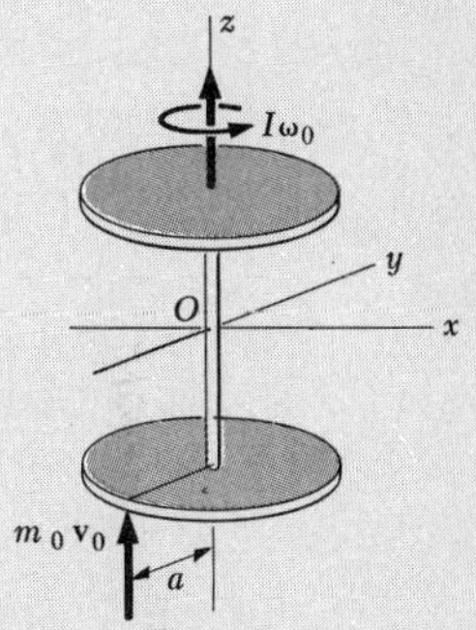

Solution. *Moments of Inertia.* We note that the axes shown are principal axes of inertia for the satellite and write

$$I = I_z = \tfrac{1}{2}ma^2 \qquad I' = I_x = I_y = 2[\tfrac{1}{4}(\tfrac{1}{2}m)a^2 + (\tfrac{1}{2}m)a^2] = \tfrac{5}{4}ma^2$$

Angular Momentum about O. We consider the satellite and the meteorite as a single system. Since no external force acts on this system, the angular momentum of the system about O is conserved, and we have

$$\mathbf{h}_O = -a\mathbf{j} \times m_0v_0\mathbf{k} + I\omega_0\mathbf{k} = -m_0v_0a\mathbf{i} + I\omega_0\mathbf{k}$$

$$h_x = -m_0v_0a \qquad h_y = 0 \qquad h_z = I\omega_0 \qquad (1)$$

Angular Velocity after Impact. Substituting the values obtained for the components of $\mathbf{h}_O$ and for the moments of inertia into

$$h_x = I_x\omega_x \qquad h_y = I_y\omega_y \qquad h_z = I_z\omega_z$$

we write

$$-m_0v_0a = I'\omega_x = \tfrac{5}{4}ma^2\omega_x \qquad 0 = I'\omega_y \qquad I\omega_0 = I\omega_z$$

$$\omega_x = -\frac{4}{5}\frac{m_0v_0}{ma} \qquad \omega_y = 0 \qquad \omega_z = \omega_0 \qquad (2)$$

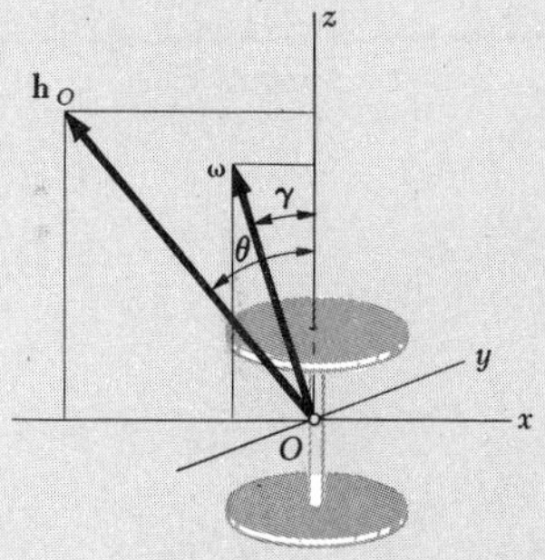

For the satellite considered we have $\omega_0 = 60$ rpm $= 6.28$ radians/sec, $m_0/m = 1/1{,}000$, $a = 3$ ft, and $v_0 = 7{,}500$ ft/sec; we find

$$\omega_x = -2 \text{ radians/sec} \qquad \omega_y = 0 \qquad \omega_z = 6.28 \text{ radians/sec}$$

$$\omega = \sqrt{\omega_x^2 + \omega_z^2} = 6.59 \text{ radians/sec} \qquad \tan\gamma = \frac{-\omega_x}{\omega_z} = +0.318$$

$$\omega = 63.0 \text{ rpm} \qquad \gamma = 17.6° \quad ◀$$

Precession Axis. Since, in free motion, the direction of the angular momentum $\mathbf{h}_O$ is fixed in space, the satellite will precess about this fixed direction. The angle θ formed by the precession axis and the z axis is

$$\tan\theta = \frac{-h_x}{h_z} = \frac{m_0v_0a}{I\omega_0} = \frac{2m_0v_0}{ma\omega_0} = 0.796 \qquad \theta = 38.5° \quad ◀$$

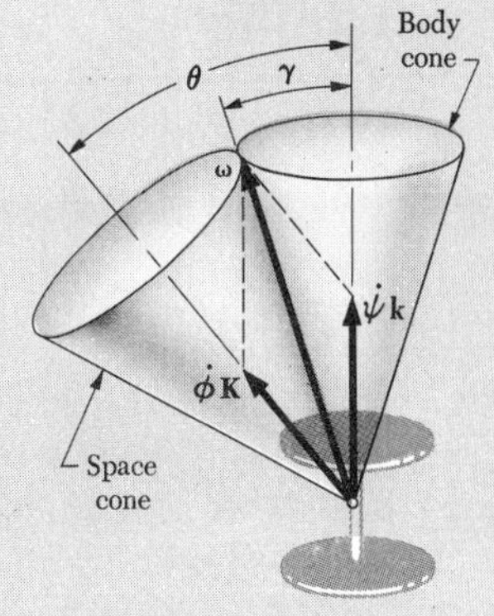

Rates of Precession and Spin. We sketch the space and body cones for the free motion of the satellite. Using the law of sines, we compute the rates of precession and spin.

$$\frac{\omega}{\sin\theta} = \frac{\dot\phi}{\sin\gamma} = \frac{\dot\psi}{\sin(\theta - \gamma)}$$

$$\dot\phi = 30.6 \text{ rpm} \qquad \dot\psi = 36.1 \text{ rpm} \quad ◀$$

PROBLEMS

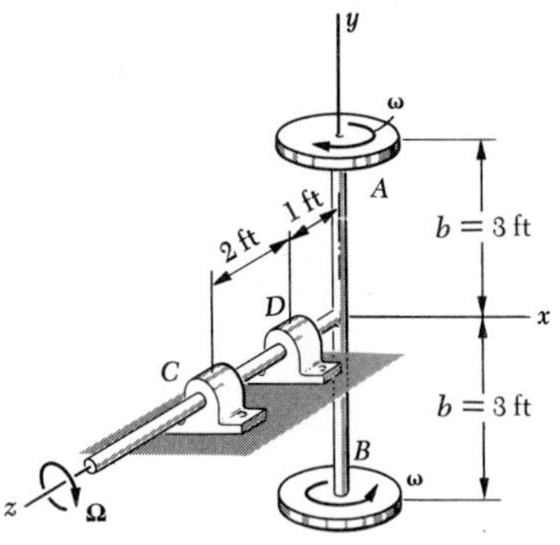

FIG. P 18.50

18.50. Two disks, each of weight 10 lb and radius 12 in., spin as shown at 1,200 rpm about the rod *AB*, which is attached to shaft *CD*. The entire system is made to rotate about the *z* axis with an angular velocity **Ω** of 60 rpm. (*a*) Determine the reactions at *C* and *D* due to gyroscopic action as the system passes through the position shown. (*b*) Solve part *a* assuming that the direction of spin of disk *B* is reversed.

18.51. A stationary horizontal plate is attached to the ceiling by means of a fixed vertical tube. A wheel of radius *a* and mass *m* is mounted on a light axle *AC* which is attached by means of a clevis at *A* to a rod *AB* fitted inside the vertical tube. The rod *AB* is made to rotate with a constant angular velocity **Ω** causing the wheel to roll on the lower face of the stationary plate. Determine the minimum angular velocity **Ω** for which contact is maintained between the wheel and the plate. Consider the particular cases (*a*) when the mass of the wheel is concentrated in the rim, (*b*) when the wheel is equivalent to a thin disk of radius *a*.

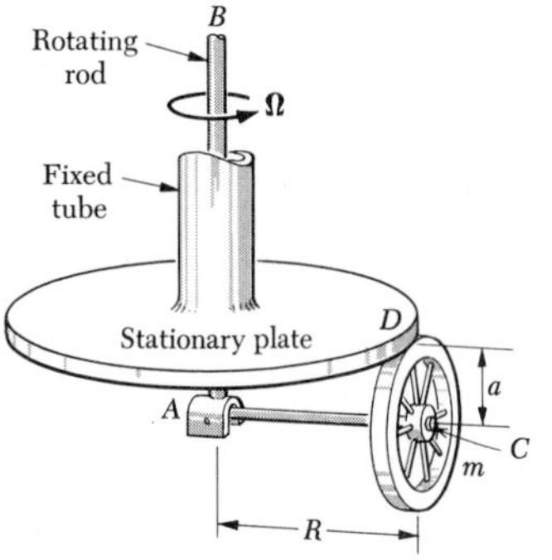

FIG. P 18.51

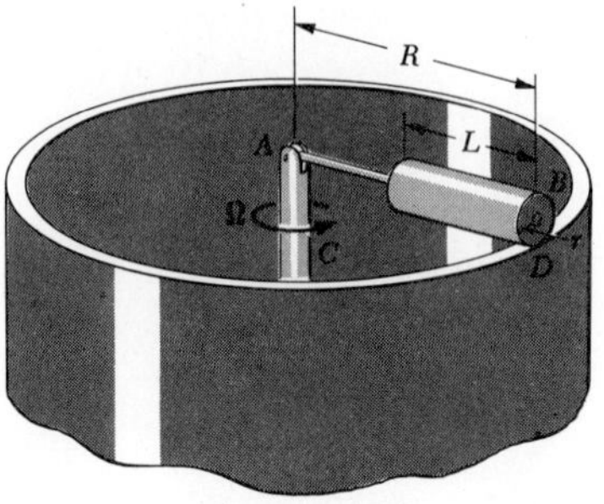

FIG. P 18.53

18.52. Solve Prob. 18.51 assuming that the wheel weighs 5 lb and that $R = 15$ in. and $a = 3$ in.

18.53. A solid cylinder of weight *W*, length *L*, and radius *r* is mounted on a light axle *AB* which is attached to a vertical shaft *AC* by means of a clevis at *A*. The shaft *AC* and the horizontal axle *AB* are made to rotate with a constant angular velocity **Ω** causing the cylinder to roll on the edge of a vertical tube of radius *R*. Assuming that the reaction at *D* is vertical, determine (*a*) the angular velocity **Ω** for which the reaction at *A* is horizontal, (*b*) the corresponding magnitude of the horizontal reaction at *A*.

18.54. Solve Prob. 18.53 assuming that $W = 5$ lb, $r = 3$ in., $L = 8$ in., and $R = 12$ in.

18.55. The essential features of a type of crusher are shown. A disk of weight *W* is mounted on a shaft *AB* about which it can rotate freely.

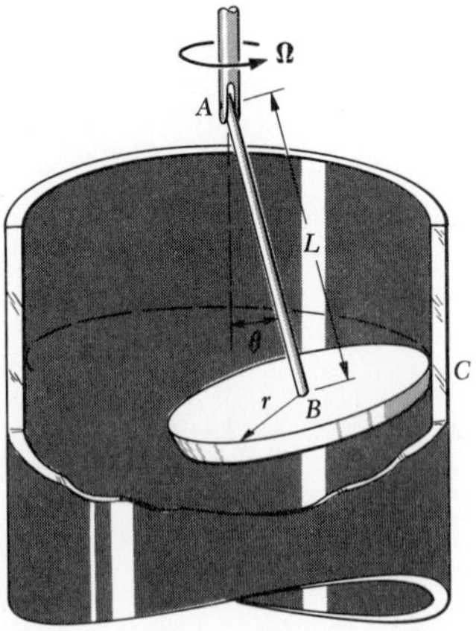

FIG. P 18.55

The shaft AB is attached by means of a clevis to a vertical shaft which is made to rotate at a constant angular velocity $\boldsymbol{\Omega}$. The disk rolls on the inside of a vertical cylinder. (Only one half of the cylinder is shown.) Determine the minimum angular velocity $\boldsymbol{\Omega}$ for which contact is maintained between the disk and the cylinder.

18.56. In Sample Prob. 18.4 determine the magnitude of the force $\mathbf{F}$ exerted on gear A at point C when shaft OD rotates with a constant angular velocity of 6 radians/sec. Assume that the force $\mathbf{F}$ is perpendicular to the line joining O and C.

18.57. A right circular cone of weight W, height h, and base radius r is supported by a ball-and-socket joint at A. The cone spins at the rate $\dot{\psi}$ about its axis of symmetry and precesses at the constant rate $\dot{\phi}$ about the vertical axis. Derive an expression for $\dot{\psi}$ in terms of $\dot{\phi}$, β, h, and r.

18.58. The rate of steady precession $\dot{\phi}$ of the cone shown is observed to be 30 rpm. Knowing that $r = 3$ in. and $h = 12$ in., determine the rate of spin $\dot{\psi}$ of the cone about its axis of symmetry if (*a*) $\beta = 45°$, (*b*) $\beta = 90°$, (*c*) $\beta = 135°$.

18.59. The top shown is supported at the fixed point O. Show that the condition for steady precession is

$$(I\omega_z - I'\dot{\phi}\cos\theta)\dot{\phi} = Wc$$

where $\dot{\phi}$ is the rate of precession and ω_z the component of the angular velocity along the axis of symmetry of the top.

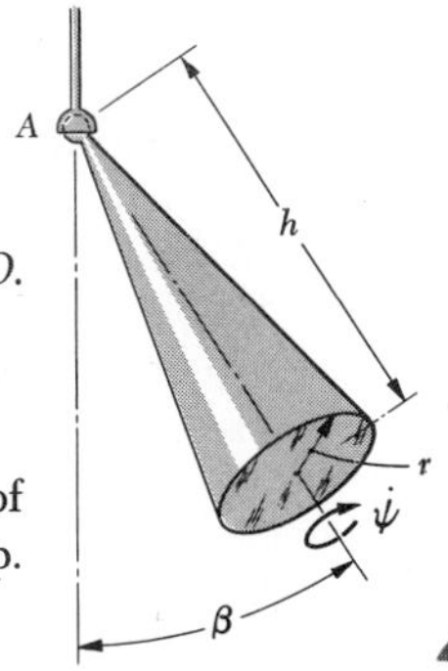

FIG. P 18.57 AND P 18.58

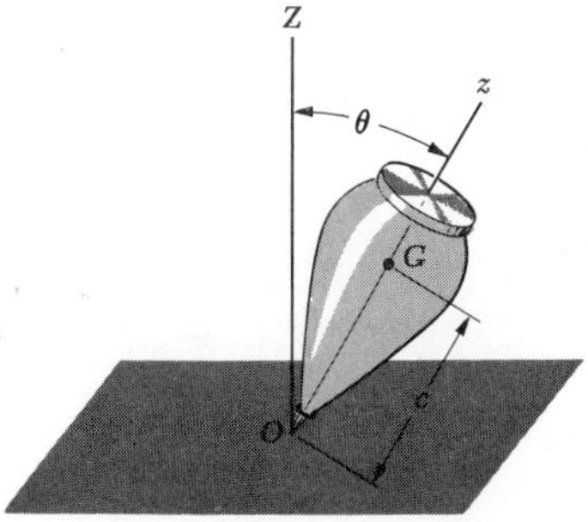

FIG. P 18.59, P 18.60, AND P 18.61

18.60. Show that, if the rate of spin $\dot{\psi}$ of a top is very large compared to its rate of precession $\dot{\phi}$, the condition for steady precession is $I\dot{\psi}\dot{\phi} \approx Wc$.

18.61. The top shown weighs 0.15 lb and is supported at the fixed point O. The radii of gyration of the top with respect to its axis of symmetry and with respect to a transverse axis through O are 0.75 in. and 1.75 in., respectively. It is known that $c = 1.50$ in. and that the rate of spin of the top with respect to its axis of symmetry is 1,600 rpm. (*a*) Using the relation of Prob. 18.59, determine the two possible rates of steady precession corresponding to $\theta = 30°$. (*b*) Determine the relative error introduced when the slower of the two rates obtained in part *a* is approximated by the relation of Prob. 18.60.

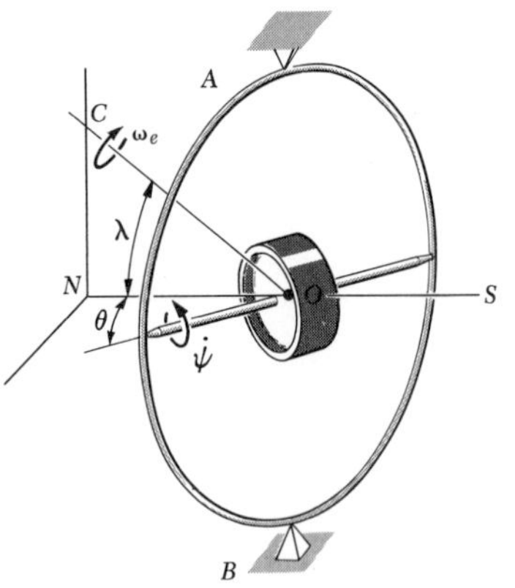

FIG. P 18.62

18.62. The essential features of the gyrocompass are shown. The rotor spins at the rate $\dot\psi$ about an axis mounted in a single gimbal, which may rotate freely about the vertical axis AB. The angle formed by the axis of the rotor and the plane of the meridian is denoted by θ and the latitude of the position on the earth is denoted by λ. We note that the line OC is parallel to the axis of the earth and we denote by ω_e the angular velocity of the earth about its axis.

(*a*) Show that the equations of motion of the gyrocompass are

$$I'\ddot\theta + I\omega_z\omega_e \cos\lambda \sin\theta - I'\omega_e^2 \cos^2\lambda \sin\theta \cos\theta = 0$$
$$I\dot\omega_z = 0$$

where ω_z is the component of the total angular velocity along the axis of the rotor, and I and I' are the moments of inertia of the rotor with respect to its axis of symmetry and a transverse axis through O, respectively.

(*b*) Neglecting the term containing ω_e^2, show that, for small values of θ, we have

$$\ddot\theta + \frac{I\omega_z\omega_e \cos\lambda}{I'}\theta = 0$$

and that the axis of the gyrocompass oscillates about the north-south direction.

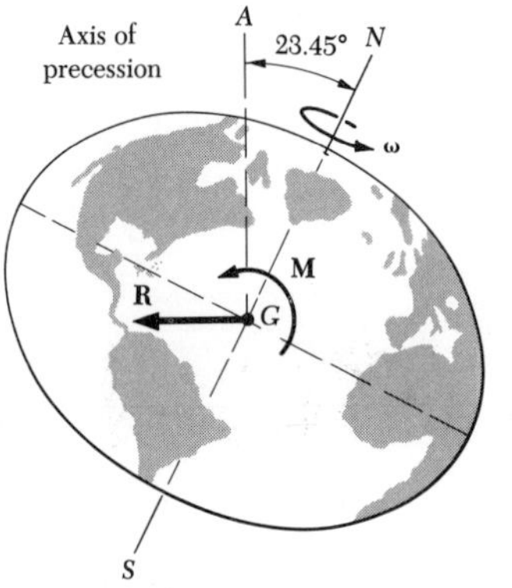

FIG. P 18.63

18.63. If the earth were a sphere, the gravitational attraction of the sun, moon, and planets would at all times be equivalent to a single force **R** acting at the mass center of the earth. However, the earth is actually an oblate spheroid and the gravitational system acting on the earth is equivalent to a force **R** and a couple **M**. Knowing that the effect of the couple **M** is to cause the axis of the earth to precess about the axis GA at the rate of one revolution in 25,800 years, determine the average magnitude of the couple **M** applied to the earth. Assume that the average density of the earth is 5.51, that the average radius of the earth is 3,960 miles, and that $\bar I = \frac{2}{5}mR^2$. (*Note.* This forced precession is known as the precession of the equinoxes and is not to be confused with the free precession discussed in Prob. 18.66.)

18.64. For an axisymmetrical body prove (*a*) that the rate of retrograde precession can never be less than twice the rate of spin of the body about its axis of symmetry, (*b*) that in Fig. 18.22 the axis of symmetry of the body can never lie within the space cone.

18.65. Show that the angular velocity vector ω of an axisymmetrical body under no force is observed from the body itself to rotate about the axis of symmetry at the constant rate

$$n = \frac{I' - I}{I'}\omega_z$$

where ω_z is the component of ω along the axis of symmetry of the body.

18.66. Using the relation given in Prob. 18.65, determine the period of precession of the north pole of the earth about the axis of symmetry of the earth. The earth may be approximated by an oblate spheroid of axial moment of inertia I and of transverse moment of inertia $I' = 0.9967I$. (*Note.* Actual observations show a period of precession of the north pole of about 432.5 mean solar days; the difference between the observed and computed periods is due to the fact that the earth is not a perfectly rigid body. The free precession considered here should not be confused with the much slower precession of the equinoxes, which is a forced precession. See Prob. 18.63.)

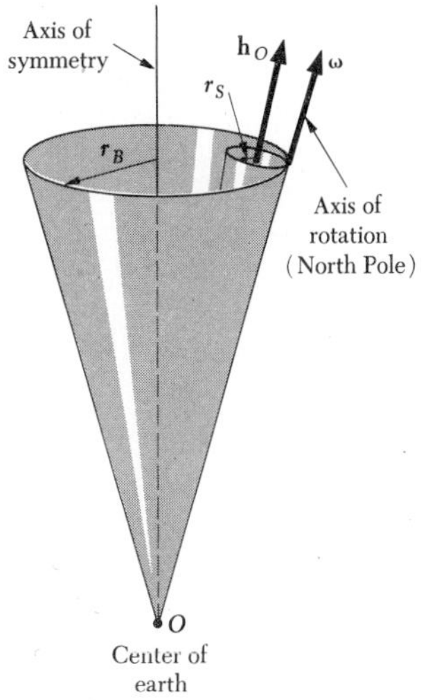

FIG. P 18.66 AND P 18.67

18.67. Actual measurements of the variation of the latitude of fixed points on the earth's surface indicate that the intersection of the body cone and the surface of the earth is a circle of radius $r_B \approx 14$ ft. Using the relation given in Prob. 18.65, determine the radius r_S of the space conc. (See Prob. 18.66.)

18.68. The angular velocity vector of a football which has just been kicked is horizontal, and its axis of symmetry OC is oriented as shown. Knowing that the magnitude of the angular velocity is 180 rpm and that the ratio of the axial and transverse moments of inertia is $I/I' = 1/3$, determine (*a*) the orientation of the axis of precession OA, (*b*) the rates of precession and spin.

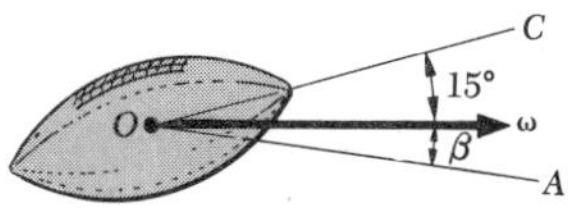

FIG. P 18.68

18.69. A coin is tossed into the air. During the free motion the angle β between the plane of the coin and the horizontal is observed to be constant. (*a*) Derive an expression for the angle formed by the angular velocity of the coin and the vertical. (*b*) Denoting by $\dot{\psi}$ the rate of spin of the coin about its axis of symmetry, derive an expression for the rate of precession. (*c*) Solve parts *a* and *b* for the case $\beta = 10°$.

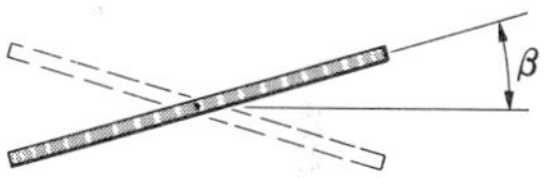

FIG. P 18.69

18.70. Determine the precession axis and the rates of precession and spin of the satellite of Prob. 18.22 after the impact.

18.71. Determine the precession axis and the rates of precession and spin of the space capsule of Prob. 18.21 after the projectile has been fired.

18.72. Determine the precession axis and the rates of precession and spin of the satellite of Prob. 18.22 knowing that, before impact, the angular velocity of the satellite was $\omega_0 = -(10 \text{ rpm})\mathbf{i}$.

18.73. Determine the precession axis and the rates of precession and spin of the space capsule of Prob. 18.21 knowing that, before the projectile was fired, the angular velocity of the capsule was $\omega_0 = (100 \text{ rpm})\mathbf{j}$.

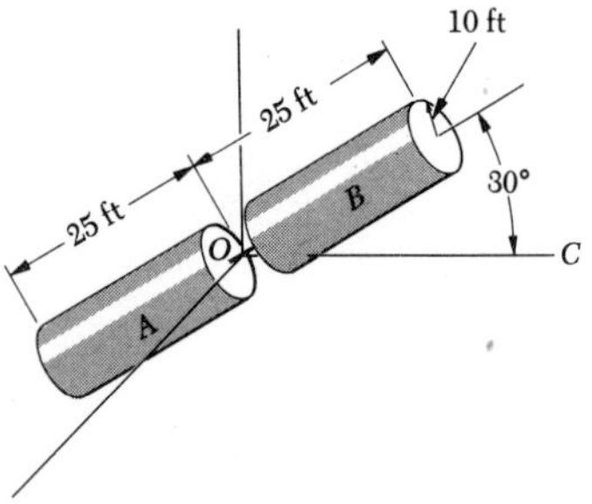

FIG. P 18.74

18.74. The space station shown is known to precess about the fixed direction OC at the rate of one revolution per hour. Assuming that the station is dynamically equivalent to a homogeneous cylinder of length 50 ft and radius 10 ft, determine the rate of spin of the station about its axis of symmetry.

18.75. The link connecting portions A and B of the space station of Prob. 18.74 may be severed to allow each portion to move freely. Each portion of the station is dynamically equivalent to a cylinder of length 25 ft and radius 10 ft. Knowing that, when the link is severed, the station is oriented as shown, determine for portion B the axis of precession, the rate of precession, and the rate of spin about the axis of symmetry.

18.76. Solve Sample Prob. 18.5 assuming that the meteorite strikes the satellite at C with a velocity $\mathbf{v}_0 = -(7{,}500 \text{ ft/sec})\mathbf{i}$.

18.77. After the motion determined in Sample Prob. 18.5 has been established, the rod connecting disks A and B of the satellite breaks, and disk A moves freely as a separate body. Knowing that the rod and the z axis coincide when the rod breaks, determine the precession axis, the rate of precession, and the rate of spin for the ensuing motion of disk A.

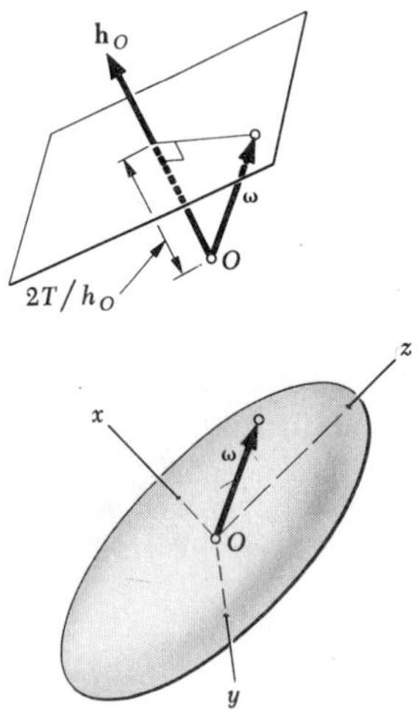

FIG. P 18.78

***18.78.** Consider a rigid body of arbitrary shape, which is attached at its mass center O and subjected to no force other than its weight and the reaction of the support at O. (*a*) Prove that the angular momentum $\mathbf{h}_O$ of the body about the fixed point O is constant in magnitude and direction, that the kinetic energy T of the body is constant, and that the projection along $\mathbf{h}_O$ of the angular velocity $\boldsymbol{\omega}$ of the body is constant. (*b*) Show that the tip of the vector $\boldsymbol{\omega}$ describes a curve on a fixed plane in space (called the *invariable plane*), which is perpendicular to $\mathbf{h}_O$ and at a distance $2T/h_O$ from O. (*c*) Show that, with respect to a frame of reference attached to the body and coinciding with its principal axes of inertia, the tip of the vector $\boldsymbol{\omega}$ appears to describe a curve on an ellipsoid of equation

$$I_x\omega_x^2 + I_y\omega_y^2 + I_z\omega_z^2 = 2T = \text{constant}$$

This ellipsoid (called the *Poinsot ellipsoid*) is rigidly attached to the body and is of the same shape as the ellipsoid of inertia, but of a different size.

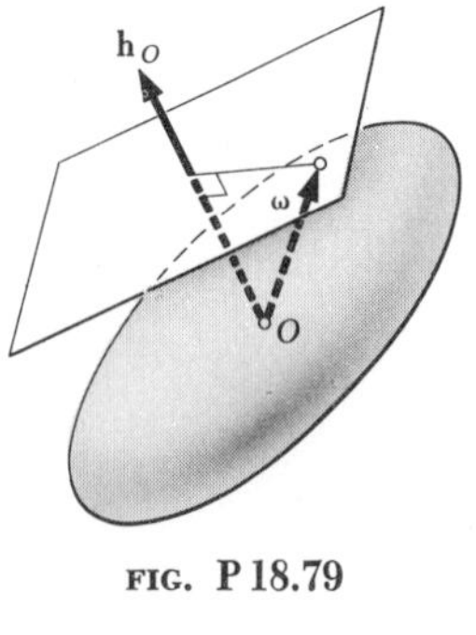

FIG. P 18.79

***18.79.** Referring to Prob. 18.78, (*a*) prove that the Poinsot ellipsoid is tangent to the invariable plane, (*b*) show that the motion of the rigid body must be such that the Poinsot ellipsoid appears to roll on the invariable plane. (*Hint.* In part *a*, show that the normal to the Poinsot ellipsoid at the tip of $\boldsymbol{\omega}$ is parallel to $\mathbf{h}_O$. It is recalled that the direction of the normal to a surface of equation $F(x,y,z) = \text{constant}$ at a point P is the same as that of **grad** F at point P.)

*18.80. Using the results obtained in Probs. 18.78 and 18.79, show that, for an axisymmetrical body attached at its mass center O and under no force other than its weight and the reaction at O, the Poinsot ellipsoid is an ellipsoid of revolution and the space and body cones are both circular and are tangent to each other. Further show that (*a*) the two cones are tangent externally, and the precession is direct, when $I < I'$, where I and I' denote, respectively, the axial and transverse moment of inertia of the body, (*b*) the space cone is inside the body cone, and the precession is retrograde, when $I > I'$.

*18.81. Referring to Probs. 18.78 and 18.79, (*a*) show that the curve (called *polhode*) described by the tip of the vector ω with respect to a frame of reference coinciding with the principal axes of inertia of the rigid body is defined by the equations

$$I_x\omega_x^2 + I_y\omega_y^2 + I_z\omega_z^2 = 2T = \text{constant} \tag{1}$$
$$I_x^2\omega_x^2 + I_y^2\omega_y^2 + I_z^2\omega_z^2 = h_O^2 = \text{constant} \tag{2}$$

and that this curve may, therefore, be obtained by intersecting the Poinsot ellipsoid with the ellipsoid defined by Eq. (2). (*b*) Further show, assuming $I_x > I_y > I_z$, that the polhodes obtained for various values of h_O have the shapes indicated in the figure. (*c*) Using the result obtained in part *b*, show that a rigid body under no force can rotate about a fixed centroidal axis if, and only if, that axis coincides with one of the principal axes of inertia of the body, and that the motion will be stable if the axis of rotation coincides with the major or minor axis of the Poinsot ellipsoid (z or x axis in the figure) and unstable if it coincides with the intermediate axis (y axis).

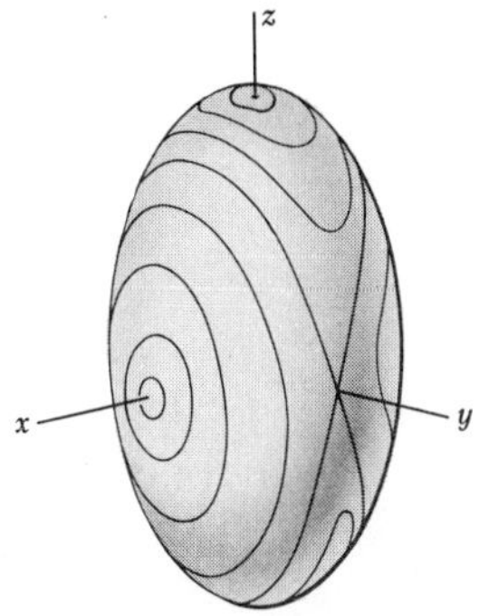

FIG. P 18.81

REVIEW PROBLEMS

18.82. The top shown is supported at the fixed point O. We denote by ϕ, θ, and ψ the Eulerian angles defining the position of the top with respect to a fixed frame of reference. We shall consider the general motion of the top in which all Eulerian angles vary.

(*a*) Observing that $\Sigma M_Z = 0$ and $\Sigma M_z = 0$, and denoting by I and I', respectively, the moments of inertia of the top about its axis of symmetry and about a transverse axis through O, derive the two first-order differential equations of motion

$$I'\dot{\phi}\sin^2\theta + I(\dot{\psi} + \dot{\phi}\cos\theta)\cos\theta = \alpha \tag{1}$$
$$I(\dot{\psi} + \dot{\phi}\cos\theta) = \beta \tag{2}$$

where α and β are constants which depend upon the initial conditions.

(*b*) Use Eqs. (1) and (2) to show that the component ω_z of the angular velocity of the top is constant and that the rate of precession $\dot{\phi}$ depends upon the value of the angle of nutation θ.

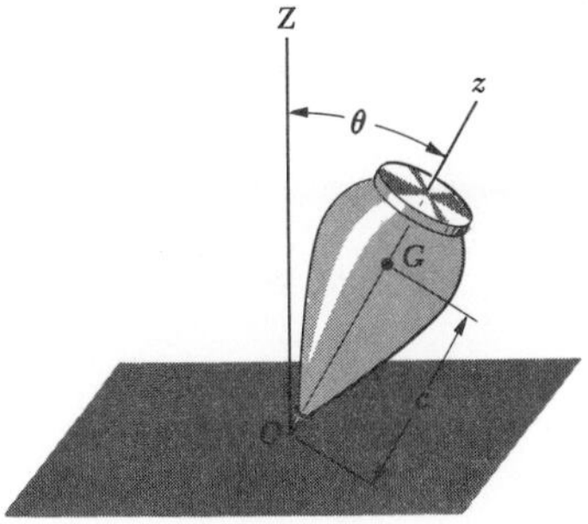

FIG. P 18.82

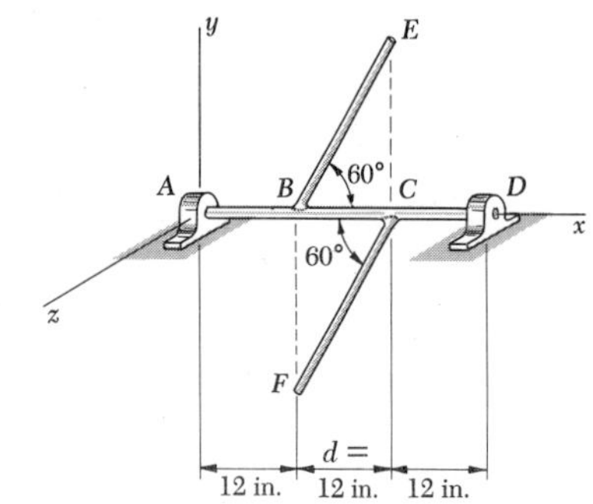

FIG. P 18.84 AND P 18.85

18.83. (*a*) Applying the principle of conservation of energy, derive a third differential equation for the general motion of the top of Prob. 18.82. (*b*) Eliminating the derivatives $\dot{\phi}$ and $\dot{\psi}$ from the equation obtained and from the two equations of Prob. 18.82, express the rate of nutation $\dot{\theta}$ as a function of the angle θ.

18.84. Two 24-in. rods *BE* and *CF*, each weighing 10 lb, are attached to the shaft *AD* which rotates at a constant speed of 30 radians/sec. Knowing that the two rods and the shaft lie in the same plane, determine the dynamic reactions at *A* and *D*.

18.85. Two 24-in. rods *BE* and *CF*, each weighing 10 lb, are attached to the shaft *AD* which is at rest. A couple $\mathbf{M} = (600 \text{ lb-ft})\mathbf{i}$ is then applied to the shaft *AD*. Knowing that the two rods and the shaft lie in the same plane, determine (*a*) the angular acceleration of the shaft, (*b*) the dynamic reactions at *A* and *B*.

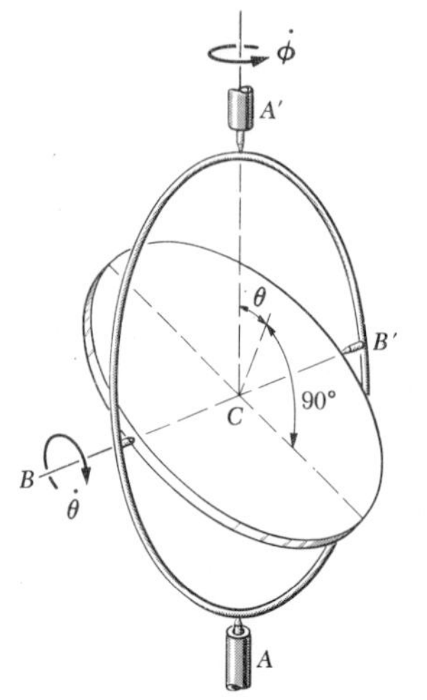

FIG. P 18.86

18.86. The gimbal $ABA'B'$ is of negligible mass and may rotate freely about the vertical AA'. The uniform disk of radius *a* and mass *m* may rotate freely about its diameter BB', which is also the horizontal diameter of the gimbal. (*a*) Applying the principle of conservation of energy, and observing that, since $\Sigma M_{AA'} = 0$, the component of the angular momentum of the disk along the fixed axis AA' must be constant, write two first-order differential equations defining the motion of the disk. (*b*) Given the initial conditions $\theta_0 \neq 0$, $\dot{\phi}_0 \neq 0$, and $\dot{\theta}_0 = 0$, express the rate of nutation $\dot{\theta}$ as a function of θ. (*c*) Show that the angle θ will never be larger than θ_0 during the ensuing motion.

18.87. The rectangular box shown is falling vertically with a velocity of 10 ft/sec and no angular velocity when its corner hits an obstruction A. Assuming perfectly plastic impact, determine immediately after impact (*a*) the angular velocity of the box, (*b*) the velocity of the mass center of the box.

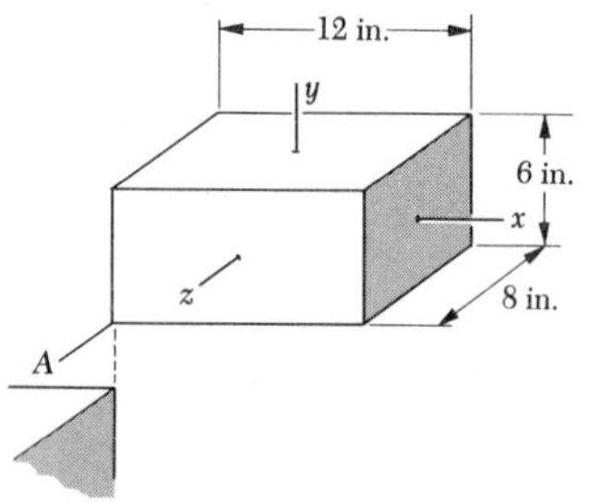

FIG. P 18.87

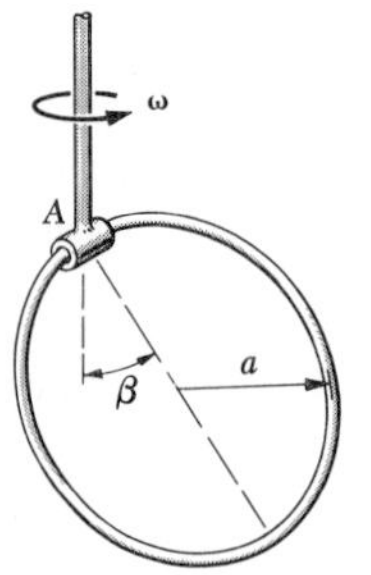

FIG. P 18.88

18.88. A thin ring of radius *a* is attached by a collar at *A* to a vertical shaft which rotates with a constant angular velocity ω. Derive an expression for (*a*) the constant angle β that the plane of the ring forms with the vertical, (*b*) the maximum value of ω for which the ring will remain vertical.

18.89. A high-speed photographic record shows that a certain projectile was fired with a horizontal velocity $\bar{\mathbf{v}}$ of 2,000 ft/sec and with its axis of symmetry forming an angle $\beta = 3°$ with the horizontal. The rate of spin of the projectile was $\dot{\psi} = 6{,}000$ rpm, and the atmospheric drag was equivalent to a force **D** of 25 lb acting at the center of pressure C_P located at a distance $c = 3$ in. from G. (*a*) Knowing that the projectile weighs 40 lb and has a radius of gyration of 2 in. with respect to its axis of symmetry, determine its approximate rate of precession. (*b*) If it is further known that the radius of gyration of the projectile with respect to a transverse axis through G is 8 in., determine the exact values of the two possible rates of precession.

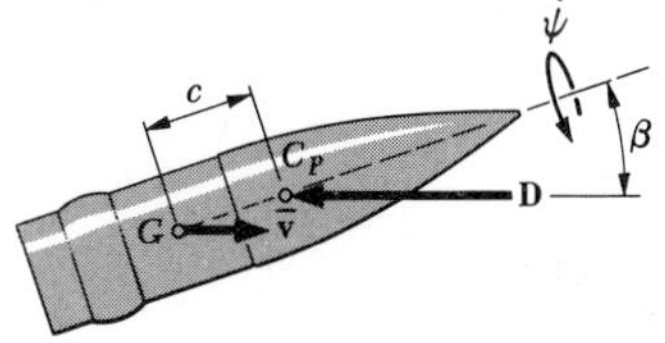

FIG. P 18.89

18.90. A circular plate of radius a and mass m supported by a ball-and-socket joint at O was rotating about the y axis with a constant angular velocity $\boldsymbol{\omega} = \omega_0\mathbf{j}$ when an obstruction was suddenly introduced at A. Assuming that the impact at A is perfectly plastic, determine immediately after impact (*a*) the angular velocity of the plate, (*b*) the velocity of the mass center G.

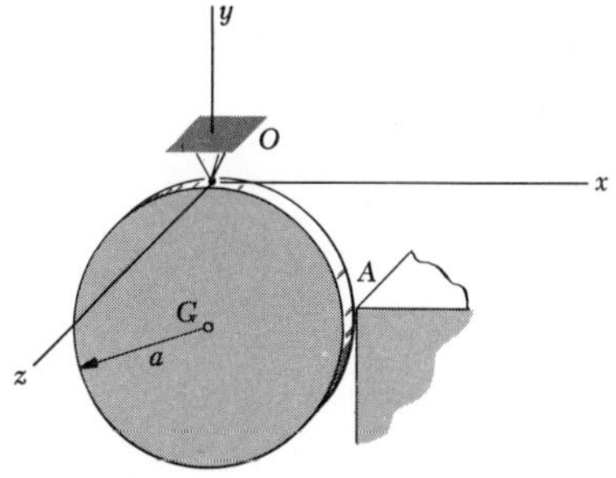

FIG. P 18.90

18.91. Solve Prob. 18.90 assuming that, before the obstruction was introduced, the plate was rotating about the x axis with a constant angular velocity $\boldsymbol{\omega} = \omega_0\mathbf{i}$.

18.92. A homogeneous sphere of radius a and mass m is attached to a light rod of length $4a$. The rod forms an angle of 30° with the vertical and rotates about AC with a constant angular velocity $\boldsymbol{\Omega}$. (*a*) Assuming that the sphere does not spin about the rod ($\dot{\psi} = 0$), determine the tension in the cord BC and the kinetic energy of the sphere. (*b*) Determine the spin $\dot{\psi}$ (magnitude and sense) which should be given to the sphere if the tension in the cord BC is to be zero. What is the corresponding kinetic energy of the sphere?

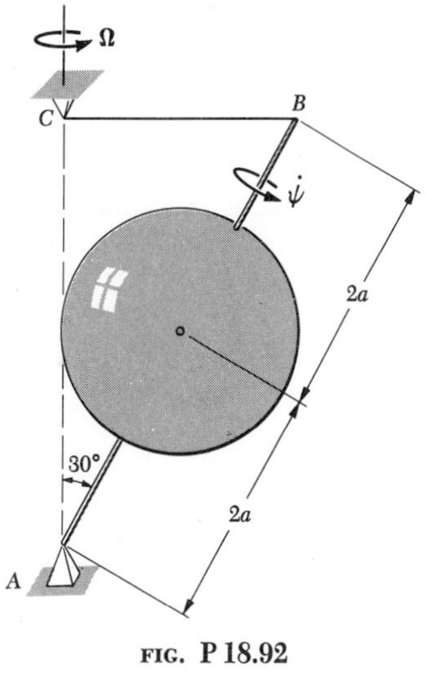

FIG. P 18.92

18.93. A disk of mass m and radius a is mounted on a horizontal axle of length R and of negligible mass. The disk rolls without sliding on a horizontal floor, and the center of the disk describes a horizontal circle of radius R with a speed $\bar{v}_0$. Determine (*a*) the angular velocity of the disk, (*b*) the angular momentum of the disk about B, (*c*) the kinetic energy of the disk, (*d*) the reaction at B and the reaction of the floor on the disk.

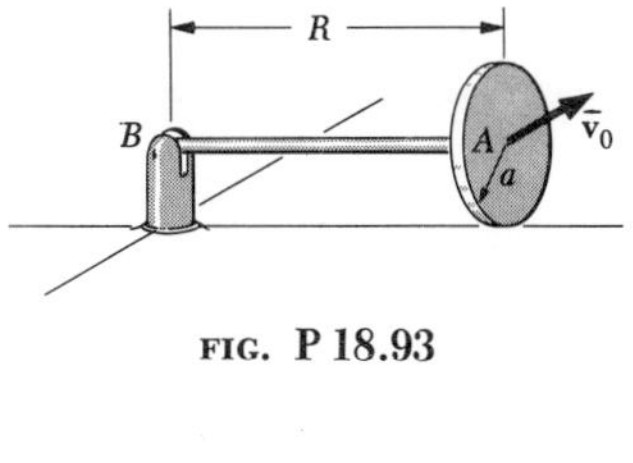

FIG. P 18.93

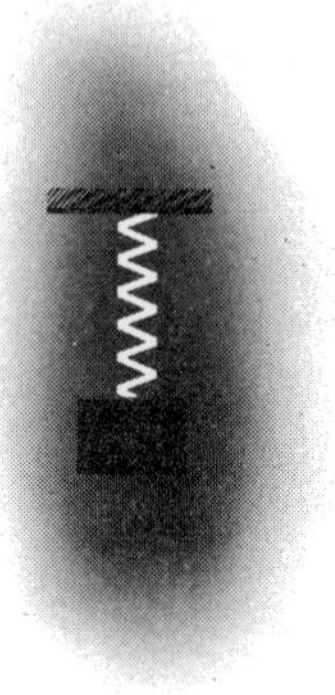

19. MECHANICAL VIBRATIONS

19.1. Introduction. A *mechanical vibration* is the motion of a particle or a body which oscillates about a position of equilibrium. Most vibrations in machines and structures are undesirable because of the increased stresses and energy losses which accompany them. They should therefore be eliminated or reduced as much as possible by appropriate design. The analysis of vibrations has become increasingly important in recent years owing to the current trend toward higher-speed machines and lighter structures. There is every reason to expect that this trend will continue and that an even greater need for vibration analysis will develop in the future.

The analysis of vibrations is a very extensive subject to which entire texts have been devoted.† We shall therefore limit our present study to the simpler types of vibrations, namely, the vibrations of a body or a system of bodies with one degree of freedom.

A mechanical vibration generally results when a system is displaced from a position of stable equilibrium. The system tends to return to this position under the action of restoring forces (either elastic forces, as in the case of a mass attached to a spring, or gravitational forces, as in the case of a pendulum). But the system generally reaches its original position with a certain acquired velocity which carries it beyond that position. Since the process can be repeated indefinitely, the system keeps moving back and forth across its position of equilibrium. The time interval required for the system to complete a full cycle of motion is called the *period* of the vibration. The number of cycles per unit time defines the *frequency*, and the maximum displacement of the system from its position of equilibrium is called the *amplitude* of the vibration.

† See, for example, Den Hartog, "Mechanical Vibrations," 4th ed., McGraw-Hill Book Company, Inc.

When the motion is maintained by the restoring forces only, the vibration is said to be a *free vibration* (Secs. 19.2 to 19.6). When a periodic force is applied to the system, the resulting motion is described as a *forced vibration* (Sec. 19.7). When the effects of friction may be neglected, the vibrations are said to be *undamped.* However, all vibrations are actually *damped* to some degree. If a free vibration is only slightly damped, its amplitude slowly decreases until, after a certain time, the motion comes to a stop. But damping may be large enough to prevent any true vibration; the system then slowly regains its original position (Sec. 19.8). A damped forced vibration is maintained as long as the periodic force which produces the vibration is applied. The amplitude of the vibration, however, is affected by the magnitude of the damping forces (Sec. 19.9).

VIBRATIONS WITHOUT DAMPING

19.2. Free Vibrations of Particles. Simple Harmonic Motion. Consider a body of mass m attached to a spring of constant k (Fig. 19.1a). Since, at the present time, we are concerned only with the motion of its mass center, we shall refer to this body as a particle. When the particle is in static equilibrium, the forces acting on it are its weight **W** and the force **T** exerted by the spring, of magnitude $T = k\delta_{st}$, where δ_{st} denotes the elongation of the spring. We have, therefore,

$$W = k\delta_{st} \tag{19.1}$$

Suppose now that the particle is displaced through a distance x_m from its equilibrium position and released with no initial velocity. If x_m has been chosen smaller than δ_{st}, the particle will move back and forth through its equilibrium position; a vibration of amplitude x_m has been generated. Note that the vibration may also be produced by imparting a certain initial velocity to the particle when it is in its equilibrium position $x = 0$ or, more generally, by starting the particle from any given position $x = x_0$ with a given initial velocity $\mathbf{v}_0$.

To analyze the vibration, we shall consider the particle in a position P at some arbitrary time t (Fig. 19.1b). Denoting by x the displacement OP measured from the equilibrium position O (positive downward), we note that the forces acting on the particle are its weight **W** and the force **T** exerted by the spring which, in this position, has a magnitude $T = k(\delta_{st} + x)$. Recalling (19.1), we find that the magnitude of the resultant **F** of the two forces (positive downward) is

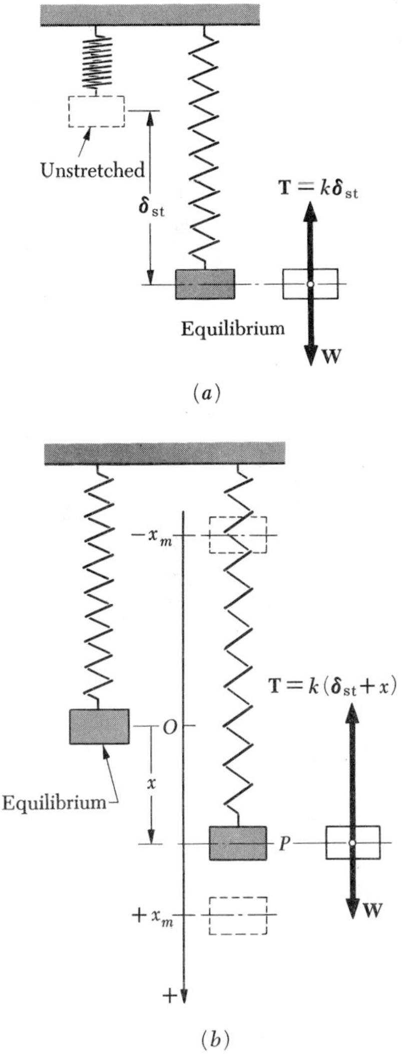

FIG. 19.1

$$F = W - k(\delta_{st} + x) = -kx \qquad (19.2)$$

Thus the *resultant* of the forces exerted on the particle is proportional to the displacement *OP measured from the equilibrium position.* Recalling the sign convention, we note that **F** is always directed *toward* the equilibrium position *O*. Substituting for *F* into the fundamental equation $F = ma$ and recalling that $a = d^2x/dt^2$, we write

$$m\frac{d^2x}{dt^2} + kx = 0 \qquad (19.3)$$

Note that the same sign convention should be used for the acceleration d^2x/dt^2 and for the displacement x, namely, positive downward.

Equation (19.3) is a linear differential equation of the second order. Setting

$$p^2 = \frac{k}{m} \qquad (19.4)$$

we write (19.3) in the form

$$\frac{d^2x}{dt^2} + p^2x = 0 \qquad (19.5)$$

The motion defined by Eq. (19.5) is called *simple harmonic motion.* It is characterized by the fact that *the acceleration is proportional to the displacement and of opposite direction.* We note that each of the functions $x_1 = \sin pt$ and $x_2 = \cos pt$ satisfies (19.5). These functions, therefore, constitute two *particular solutions* of the differential equation (19.5). As we shall see presently, the *general solution* of (19.5) may be obtained by multiplying the two particular solutions by arbitrary constants *A* and *B* and adding. We write

$$x = Ax_1 + Bx_2 = A \sin pt + B \cos pt \qquad (19.6)$$

Differentiating, we obtain successively the velocity and acceleration at time *t*,

$$v = \frac{dx}{dt} = Ap \cos pt - Bp \sin pt \qquad (19.7)$$

$$a = \frac{d^2x}{dt^2} = -Ap^2 \sin pt - Bp^2 \cos pt \qquad (19.8)$$

Substituting from (19.6) and (19.8) into (19.5), we verify that the expression (19.6) provides a solution of the differential equation (19.5). Since this expression contains two arbitrary constants *A* and *B*, the solution obtained is the general solution of the differential equation. The values of the constants A and B depend upon the *initial conditions* of the motion. For example, we have $A = 0$ if the particle is displaced from its equilibrium position and released at $t = 0$ with no initial velocity, and we have $B = 0$ if P is started from O at $t = 0$ with a certain initial velocity. In general, substituting $t = 0$ and the initial values x_0 and v_0 of the displacement and velocity into (19.6) and (19.7), we find $A = v_0/p$ and $B = x_0$.

The expressions obtained for the displacement, velocity, and acceleration of a particle may be written in a more compact form if we observe that (19.6) expresses that the displacement $x = OP$ is the sum of the x components of two vectors of magnitude A and B, directed as shown in Fig. 19.2*a*. As t varies,

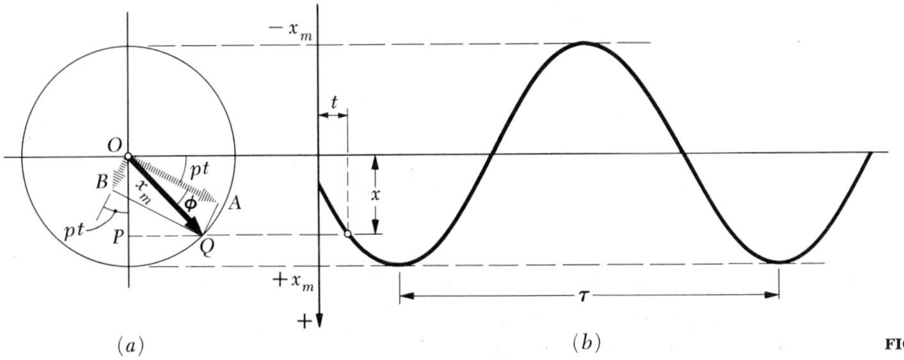

FIG. 19.2

both vectors rotate clockwise; we also note that the magnitude of their resultant $\overrightarrow{OQ}$ is equal to the maximum displacement x_m. The simple harmonic motion of P along the x axis may thus be obtained by projecting on this axis the motion of a point Q describing an *auxiliary circle* of radius x_m *with a constant angular velocity* p. Denoting by ϕ the angle formed by the vectors OQ and A, we write

$$OP = OQ \sin (pt + \phi) \tag{19.9}$$

which leads to new expressions for the displacement, velocity, and acceleration of P,

$$x = x_m \sin (pt + \phi) \tag{19.10}$$

$$v = \frac{dx}{dt} = x_m p \cos (pt + \phi) \tag{19.11}$$

$$a = \frac{d^2x}{dt^2} = -x_m p^2 \sin (pt + \phi) \tag{19.12}$$

The displacement-time curve is represented by a sine curve (Fig. 19.2*b*), and the maximum value x_m of the displacement is called the *amplitude* of the vibration. The angular velocity p of the point Q which describes the auxiliary circle is known as the *circular frequency* of the vibration and is measured in radians/sec, while the angle ϕ which defines the initial position of Q on the circle is called the *phase angle.* We note from Fig. 19.2 that a full *cycle* has been described after the angle pt has increased by 2π radians. The corresponding value of t, denoted by τ, is called the *period* of the vibration and is measured in seconds. The number of cycles described per unit of time is denoted by f and known as the *frequency* of the vibration. Frequencies are measured in cycles/sec (or cps, or sec^{-1}, since cycles are dimensionless units).

$$\text{Period} = \tau = \frac{2\pi}{p} \tag{19.13}$$

$$\text{Frequency} = f = \frac{1}{\tau} = \frac{p}{2\pi} \tag{19.14}$$

Recalling that p was defined in (19.4) in terms of the constant k of the spring and the mass m of the particle, we observe that the period and the frequency are independent of the initial conditions and of the amplitude of the vibration. Note that τ and f depend on the *mass* rather than on the *weight* of the particle and thus are independent of the value of g.

The velocity-time and acceleration-time curves may be represented by sine curves of the same period as the displacement-time curve, but with different phase angles. From (19.11) and (19.12), we note that the maximum values of the magnitudes of the velocity and acceleration are

$$v_m = x_m p \qquad a_m = x_m p^2 \tag{19.15}$$

Since the point Q describes the auxiliary circle, of radius x_m, at the constant angular velocity p, its velocity and acceleration are equal, respectively, to the expressions (19.15). Recalling Eqs. (19.11) and (19.12), we find, therefore, that the velocity and acceleration of P may be obtained at any instant by projecting on the x axis vectors of magnitudes $v_m = x_m p$ and $a_m = x_m p^2$ representing respectively the velocity and acceleration of Q at the same instant (Fig. 19.3).

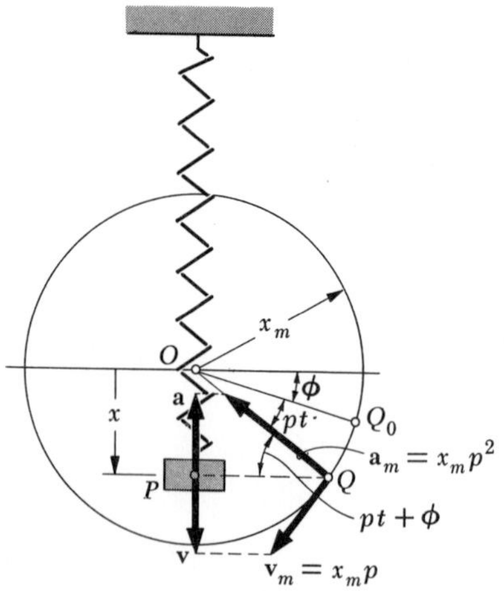

FIG. 19.3

The results obtained are not limited to the solution of the problem of a mass attached to a spring. They may be used to analyze the rectilinear motion of a particle *whenever the resultant* **F** *of the forces acting on the particle is proportional* *to the displacement x and directed toward O.* The fundamental equation of motion $F = ma$ may then be written in the form (19.5), which characterizes simple harmonic motion. Observing that the coefficient of x in (19.5) represents the square of the circular frequency p of the vibration, we easily obtain p and, after substitution into (19.13) and (19.14), the period τ and the frequency f of the vibration.

19.3. Simple Pendulum (Approximate Solution). Most of the vibrations encountered in engineering applications may be represented by a simple harmonic motion. Many others, although of a different type, may be *approximated* by a simple harmonic motion, provided that their amplitude remains small. Consider for example a *simple pendulum,* consisting of a bob of mass m attached to a cord of length l, which may oscillate in a vertical plane (Fig. 19.4*a*). At a given time t, the cord forms an angle θ with the vertical. The forces acting on the bob are its weight **W** and the force **T** exerted by the cord (Fig. 19.4*b*). Using tangential components (positive to the right) and observing that $a_t = l(d^2\theta/dt^2)$, we write

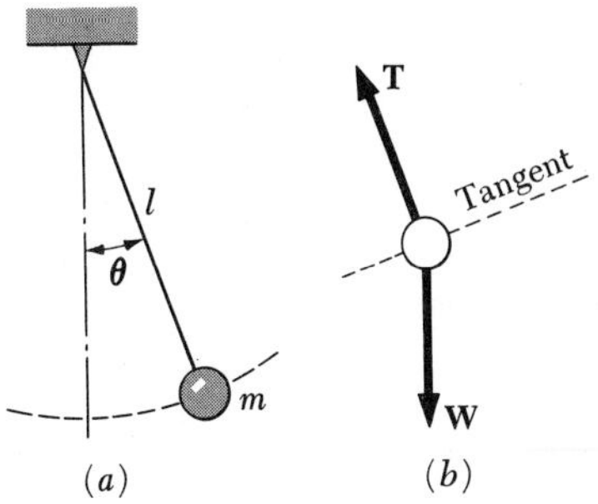

FIG. 19.4

$$F_t = ma_t: \qquad -W \sin\theta = ml\frac{d^2\theta}{dt^2}$$

Noting that $W = mg$ and dividing through by ml, we obtain

$$\frac{d^2\theta}{dt^2} + \frac{g}{l}\sin\theta = 0 \tag{19.16}$$

For oscillations of small amplitude, we may replace $\sin\theta$ by θ, expressed in radians, and write

$$\frac{d^2\theta}{dt^2} + \frac{g}{l}\theta = 0 \tag{19.17}$$

Comparison with (19.5) shows that the equation obtained is that of a simple harmonic motion and that the circular frequency p of the oscillations is equal to $(g/l)^{\frac{1}{2}}$. Substitution into (19.13) yields the period of the small oscillations of a pendulum of length l,

$$\tau = \frac{2\pi}{p} = 2\pi\sqrt{\frac{l}{g}} \tag{19.18}$$

***19.4. Simple Pendulum (Exact Solution).** Formula (19.18) is only approximate. To obtain an exact expression for the period of the oscillations of a simple pendulum, we must return to (19.16). Multiplying both terms by $2\,d\theta/dt$ and integrating from an initial position corresponding to the maximum deflection, i.e., $\theta = \theta_m$ and $d\theta/dt = 0$, we write

$$\left(\frac{d\theta}{dt}\right)^2 = \frac{2g}{l}(\cos\theta - \cos\theta_m)$$

Replacing $\cos\theta$ by $1 - 2\sin^2(\theta/2)$ and $\cos\theta_m$ by a similar expression, solving for dt, and integrating over a quarter period from $t = 0$, $\theta = 0$ to $t = \tau/4$, $\theta = \theta_m$, we have

$$\tau = 2\sqrt{\frac{l}{g}}\int_0^{\theta_m}\frac{d\theta}{\sqrt{\sin^2(\theta_m/2) - \sin^2(\theta/2)}}$$

The integral in the right-hand member is known as an *elliptic integral;* it cannot be expressed in terms of the usual algebraic or trigonometric functions. However, setting

$$\sin(\theta/2) = \sin(\theta_m/2)\sin\phi$$

we may write

$$\tau = 4\sqrt{\frac{l}{g}}\int_0^{\pi/2}\frac{d\phi}{\sqrt{1 - \sin^2(\theta_m/2)\sin^2\phi}} \tag{19.19}$$

where the integral obtained, commonly denoted by K, may be found in *tables of elliptic integrals* for various values of $\theta_m/2$.† In order to compare the result just obtained with that of the preceding section, we write (19.19) in the form

$$\tau = \frac{2K}{\pi}\left(2\pi\sqrt{\frac{l}{g}}\right) \tag{19.20}$$

Formula (19.20) shows that the actual value of the period of a simple pendulum may be obtained by multiplying the approximate value (19.18) by the correction factor $2K/\pi$. Values of the correction factor are given in Table 19.1 for various values

TABLE 19.1. *Correction Factor for the Period of a Simple Pendulum*

θ_m	0°	10°	20°	30°	60°	90°	120°	150°	180°
K	1.571	1.574	1.583	1.598	1.686	1.854	2.157	2.768	∞
$2K/\pi$	1.000	1.002	1.008	1.017	1.073	1.180	1.373	1.762	∞

of the amplitude θ_m. We note that for ordinary engineering computations the correction factor may be omitted as long as the amplitude does not exceed 10°.

† See, for example, Dwight, "Table of Integrals and Other Mathematical Data," The Macmillan Company, p. 208, or Peirce, "A Short Table of Integrals," Ginn and Company, p. 121.

SAMPLE PROBLEM 19.1

A 100-lb block moves between vertical guides as shown. The block is pulled 2 in. down from its equilibrium position and released. For each spring arrangement, determine the period of the vibration and the maximum velocity of the block.

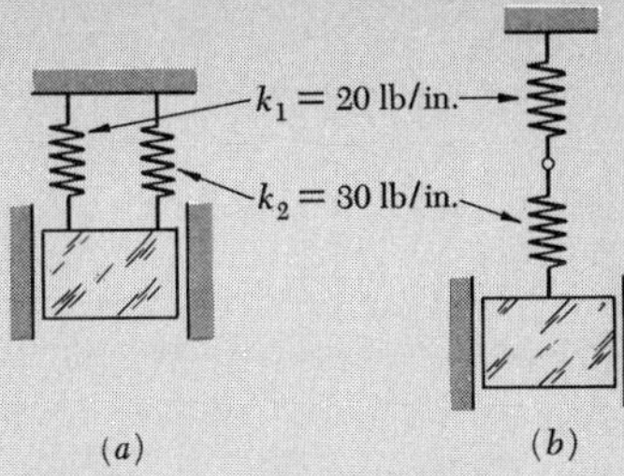

a. **Springs Attached in Parallel.** We first determine the constant k of a single spring equivalent to the two springs *by finding the magnitude of the force* **P** required to cause a deflection of 1 in. Since for a deflection of 1 in. the forces exerted by the springs are, respectively, equal in magnitude to k_1 and k_2, we have

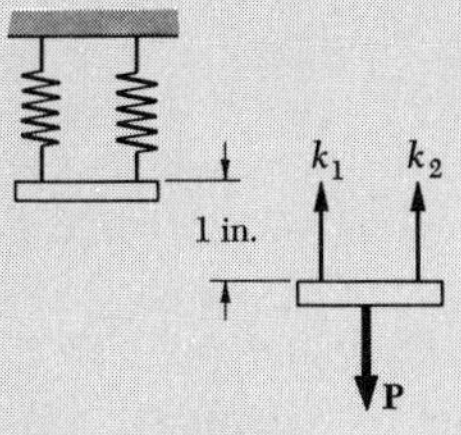

$$P = k_1 + k_2$$

The constant k of the single equivalent spring is

$$k = \frac{P}{1 \text{ in.}} = k_1 + k_2$$

$$k = 20 \text{ lb/in.} + 30 \text{ lb/in.} = 50 \text{ lb/in.} = 600 \text{ lb/ft}$$

Period of Vibration. Since $m = 100/g = 3.11$ lb-sec²/ft, Eq. (19.4) yields

$$p^2 = \frac{k}{m} = \frac{600}{3.11} \qquad p = 13.89 \text{ radians/sec}$$

$$\tau = \frac{2\pi}{p} \qquad \tau = 0.452 \text{ sec} \blacktriangleleft$$

Maximum Velocity

$$v_m = x_m p = (2 \text{ in.})(13.89 \text{ radians/sec})$$

$$\mathbf{v}_m = 27.8 \text{ in./sec} \updownarrow \blacktriangleleft$$

b. **Springs Attached in Series.** We first determine the constant k of a single spring equivalent to the two springs *by finding the total elongation* δ of the springs under a given static load. To facilitate the computation, a static load of magnitude $P = 60$ lb is used.

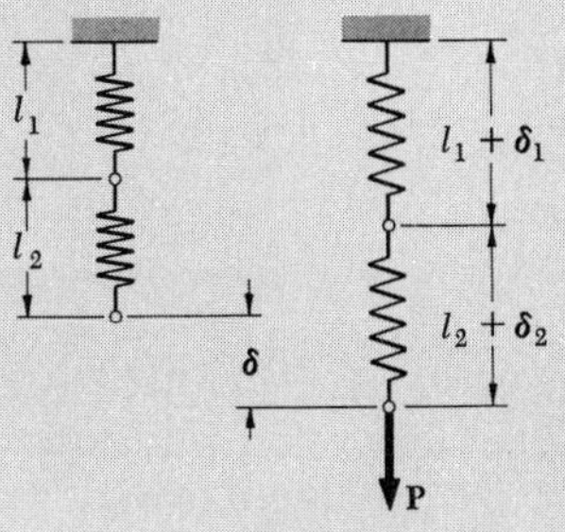

$$\delta = \delta_1 + \delta_2 = \frac{P}{k_1} + \frac{P}{k_2} = \frac{60}{20} + \frac{60}{30} = 5 \text{ in.}$$

$$k = \frac{P}{\delta} = \frac{60 \text{ lb}}{5 \text{ in.}} = 12 \text{ lb/in.} = 144 \text{ lb/ft}$$

Period of Vibration

$$p^2 = \frac{k}{m} = \frac{144}{3.11} \qquad p = 6.80 \text{ radians/sec}$$

$$\tau = \frac{2\pi}{p} \qquad \tau = 0.924 \text{ sec} \blacktriangleleft$$

Maximum Velocity

$$v_m = x_m p = (2 \text{ in.})(6.80 \text{ radians/sec})$$

$$\mathbf{v}_m = 13.60 \text{ in./sec} \updownarrow \blacktriangleleft$$

PROBLEMS

19.1. A particle is known to move with a simple harmonic motion. The maximum acceleration is 40 ft/sec^2, and the maximum velocity is 5 ft/sec. Determine the amplitude and the frequency of the motion.

19.2. A particle moves in simple harmonic motion with an amplitude of 4 in. and a period of 0.75 sec. Find the maximum velocity and the maximum acceleration.

19.3. Collar A of weight 8 lb rests on a spring of constant $k = 2$ lb/in. as shown. If the collar is depressed 2 in. and released, determine the period, the maximum velocity, and the maximum acceleration of the resulting motion.

19.4. Collar A of weight 8 lb rests on, but is not attached to, a spring as shown. The collar is to move in simple harmonic motion with an amplitude of 2 in. Determine (*a*) the largest permissible value of the spring constant k, (*b*) the corresponding frequency of the motion.

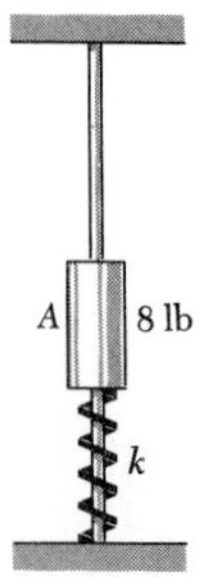

FIG. P 19.3 AND P 19.4

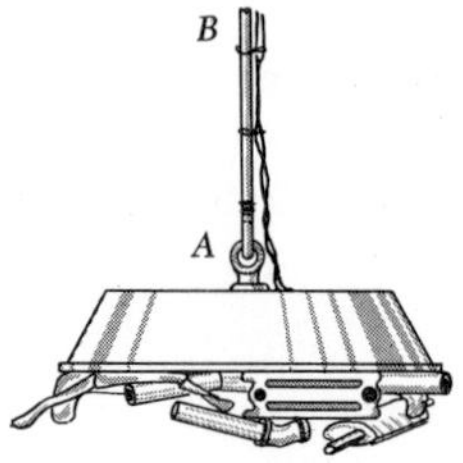

FIG. P 19.5

19.5. A 300-lb electromagnet is at rest and is holding 200 lb of scrap steel when the current is turned off and the steel is dropped. Knowing that the cable and the supporting crane have a total stiffness equivalent to a spring of constant 1,000 lb/in., determine (*a*) the frequency, the amplitude, and the maximum velocity of the resulting motion, (*b*) the minimum tension which will occur in the cable during the motion.

19.6. In Prob. 19.5, determine the largest weight of scrap steel which the electromagnet can hold and then drop, if the cable is to remain taut during the resulting motion. What is the corresponding frequency of the resulting motion?

19.7. In Prob. 19.3, determine the position, velocity, and acceleration of the collar 0.10 sec after it has been released.

19.8. In Prob. 19.3, determine (*a*) the time required for the collar to move 1 in. upward after it has been released from rest, (*b*) the corresponding velocity and acceleration of the collar.

19.9 and 19.10. A 100-lb block is supported by the spring arrangement shown. If the block is moved vertically downward and released, determine (*a*) the period and frequency of the resulting motion, (*b*) the maximum velocity and acceleration of the block if the amplitude of the motion is 3 in.

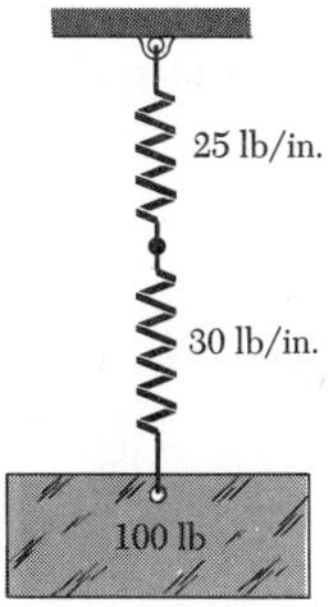

FIG. P 19.9

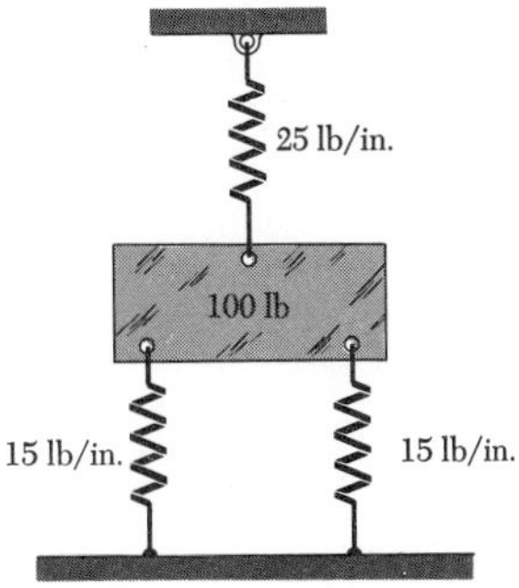

FIG. P 19.10

19.11. Denoting by δ_{st} the static deflection of a beam under a given weight, show that the frequency of vibration of the weight is

$$f = \frac{1}{2\pi}\sqrt{\frac{g}{\delta_{st}}}$$

Neglect the mass of the beam, and assume that the weight remains in contact with the beam.

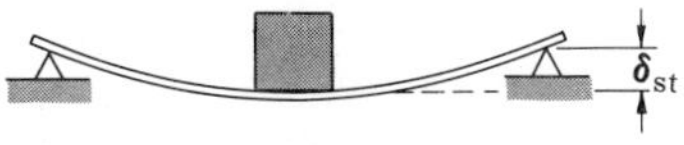

FIG. P 19.11

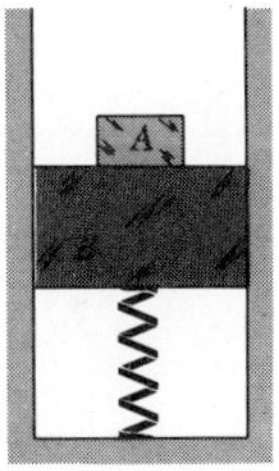

FIG. P 19.12

19.12. The period of vibration of the system shown is observed to be 0.80 sec. If block *A* is removed, the period is observed to be 0.70 sec. Knowing that block *A* weighs 1 lb, determine the weight of block *B*.

19.13. Determine the required length *l* of a simple pendulum if the period of small oscillations is to be 2 sec.

19.14. Determine the amplitude of a simple pendulum of length 4 ft if the maximum velocity of the bob is (*a*) 6 in./sec, (*b*) 12 in./sec.

19.15. A small bob is attached to a cord of length 4 ft and is released from rest when $\theta_A = 5°$. Knowing that $d = 2$ ft, determine (*a*) the time required for the bob to return to point *A*, (*b*) the amplitude θ_C.

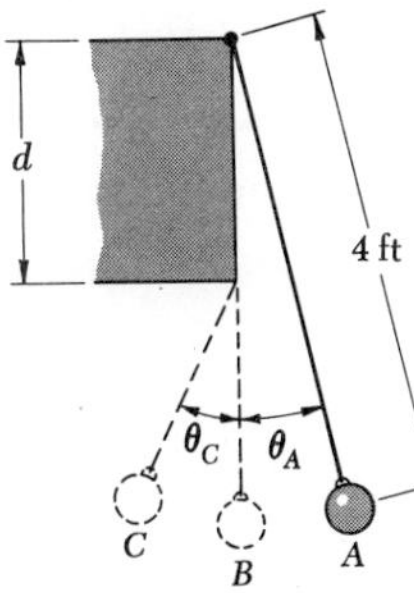

FIG. P 19.15

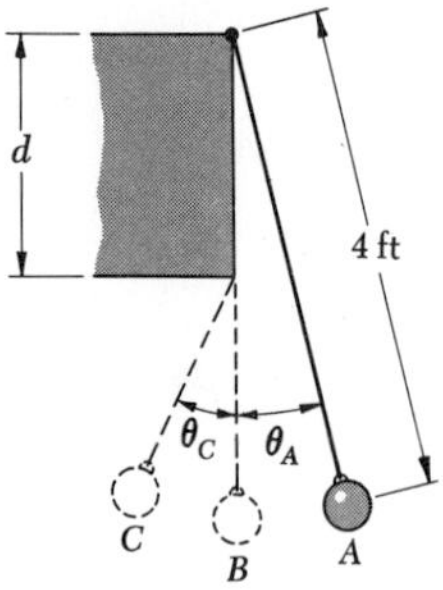

FIG. P 19.16

19.16. A small bob is attached to a cord of length 4 ft and released from rest at A when $\theta_A = 4°$. Determine the distance d for which the bob will return to point A in 2 sec.

19.17. A small weight W rests on a smooth horizontal surface and is attached to a taut string. Denoting by T the tension in the string, determine the period and frequency of small oscillations of the weight in a direction perpendicular to the string. Show that the longest period occurs when $a = b = \frac{1}{2}l$.

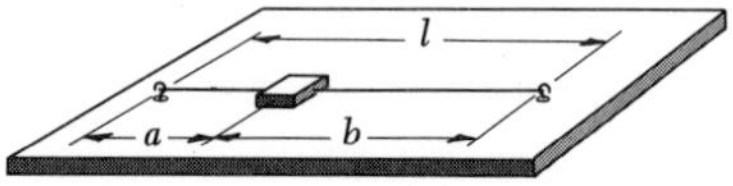

FIG. P 19.17

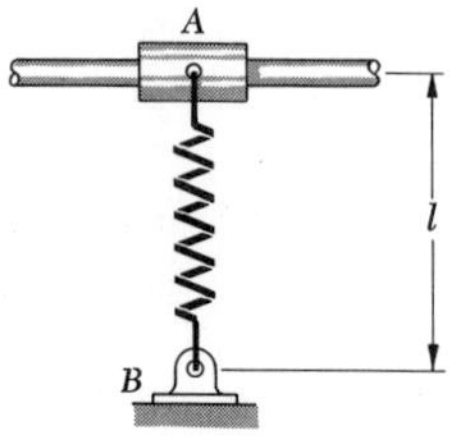

FIG. P 19.18

***19.18.** A collar of weight W slides without friction on a horizontal rod and is attached to a spring AB of constant k. (*a*) If the unstretched length of the spring is just equal to l, show that the collar does not execute simple harmonic motion even when the amplitude of the oscillations is small. (*b*) If the unstretched length of the spring is less than l, show that the motion may be approximated by a simple harmonic motion for small oscillations.

***19.19.** A particle is placed with no initial velocity on a smooth *plane* tangent to the surface of the earth. (*a*) Show that the particle will theoretically execute simple harmonic motion with a period of oscillation equal to that of a simple pendulum of length equal to the radius of the earth. (*b*) Knowing that the radius of the earth is 3,960 miles, compute the theoretical period of oscillation.

***19.20.** Using the data of Table 19.1, determine the period of a simple pendulum of length 48 in. (*a*) for small oscillations, (*b*) for oscillations of amplitude $\theta_m = 60°$, (*c*) for oscillations of amplitude $\theta_m = 120°$.

***19.21.** Expanding the integrand in (19.19) into a series of even powers of $\sin\phi$ and integrating, show that the period of a simple pendulum of length l may be approximated by the formula

$$\tau = 2\pi\sqrt{\frac{l}{g}}\left(1 + \tfrac{1}{4}\sin^2\frac{\theta_m}{2}\right)$$

where θ_m is the amplitude of the oscillations.

*19.22. Using the formula given in Prob. 19.21, determine the amplitude θ_m for which the period of a simple pendulum is $\frac{1}{2}$ per cent longer than the period of the same pendulum for small oscillations.

*19.23. Using a table of elliptic integrals, determine the period of a simple pendulum of length $l = 36$ in. if the amplitude of the oscillations is $\theta_m = 40°$.

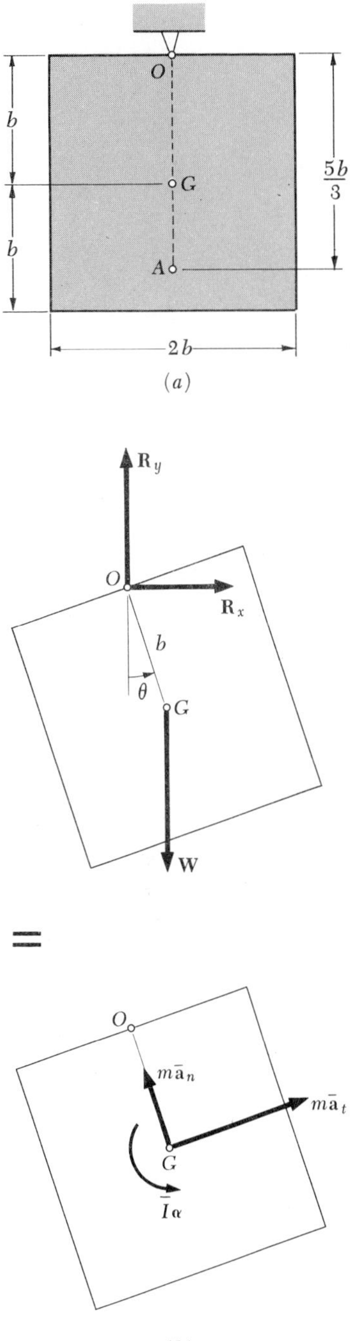

FIG. 19.5

19.5. Free Vibrations of Rigid Bodies. The analysis of the vibrations of a rigid body or of a system of rigid bodies possessing a single degree of freedom is similar to the analysis of the vibrations of a particle. An appropriate variable, such as a distance x or an angle θ, is chosen to define the position of the body or system of bodies, and an equation relating this variable and its second derivative with respect to t is written. If the equation obtained is of the same form as (19.5), i.e., if we have

$$\frac{d^2x}{dt^2} + p^2x = 0 \qquad \text{or} \qquad \frac{d^2\theta}{dt^2} + p^2\theta = 0 \qquad (19.21)$$

the vibration considered is a simple harmonic motion. The period and frequency of the vibration may then be obtained by identifying p and substituting into (19.13) and (19.14).

In general, a simple way to obtain one of Eqs. (19.21) is to express that the system of the external forces is equivalent to the system of the effective forces by drawing a diagram of the body for an arbitrary value of the variable and writing the appropriate equation of motion. We recall that our goal should be *the determination of the coefficient* of the variable x or θ, *not* the determination of the variable itself or of the derivatives d^2x/dt^2 or $d^2\theta/dt^2$. Setting this coefficient equal to p^2, we obtain the circular frequency p, from which τ and f may be determined.

The method we have outlined may be used to analyze vibrations which are truly represented by a simple harmonic motion, or vibrations of small amplitude which can be *approximated* by a simple harmonic motion. As an example, we shall determine the period of the small oscillations of a square plate of side $2b$ which is suspended from the mid-point O of one side (Fig. 19.5*a*). We consider the plate in an arbitrary position defined by the angle θ that the line OG forms with the vertical and draw a diagram to express that the weight $\mathbf{W}$ of the plate and the components $\mathbf{R}_x$ and $\mathbf{R}_y$ of the reaction at O are equivalent to the vectors $m\bar{\mathbf{a}}_t$ and $m\bar{\mathbf{a}}_n$ and to the couple $\bar{I}\alpha$ (Fig. 19.5*b*). Since the angular velocity and angular acceleration of the plate are equal, respectively, to $d\theta/dt$ and $d^2\theta/dt^2$, the magnitudes of the two vectors are, respectively, $mb(d^2\theta/dt^2)$ and $mb(d\theta/dt)^2$, while the magnitude of the couple is $\bar{I}(d^2\theta/dt^2)$. In previous applications of this method (Chap. 16), we tried whenever possible to assume the correct sense for the acceleration. Here, however, we should assume the same positive sense for θ and $d^2\theta/dt^2$ in order to obtain an equation of the form (19.21). Consequently, the angular acceleration $d^2\theta/dt^2$ will be assumed positive counterclockwise, even though this assumption is obviously unrealistic. Equating moments about O, we write

$$+\circlearrowleft \qquad -W(b\sin\theta) = \left(mb\frac{d^2\theta}{dt^2}\right)b + \bar{I}\frac{d^2\theta}{dt^2}$$

Noting that $\bar{I} = \frac{1}{12}m[(2b)^2 + (2b)^2] = \frac{2}{3}mb^2$ and $W = mg$, we obtain

$$\frac{d^2\theta}{dt^2} + \frac{3}{5}\frac{g}{b}\sin\theta = 0 \tag{19.22}$$

For oscillations of small amplitude, we may replace $\sin\theta$ by θ, expressed in radians, and write

$$\frac{d^2\theta}{dt^2} + \frac{3}{5}\frac{g}{b}\theta = 0 \tag{19.23}$$

Comparison with (19.21) shows that the equation obtained is that of a simple harmonic motion and that the circular frequency p of the oscillations is equal to $(3g/5b)^{\frac{1}{2}}$. Substituting into (19.13), we find that the period of the oscillations is

$$\tau = \frac{2\pi}{p} = 2\pi\sqrt{\frac{5b}{3g}} \tag{19.24}$$

The result obtained is valid only for oscillations of small amplitude. A more accurate description of the motion of the plate is obtained by comparing Eqs. (19.16) and (19.22). We note that the two equations are identical if we choose l equal to $5b/3$. This means that the plate will oscillate as a simple pendulum of length $l = 5b/3$, and the results of Sec. 19.4 may be used to correct the value of the period given in (19.24). The point A of the plate located on line OG at a distance $l = 5b/3$ from O is defined as the *center of oscillation* corresponding to O (Fig. 19.5*a*).

SAMPLE PROBLEM 19.2

A cylinder of weight W and radius r is suspended from a looped cord as shown. One end of the cord is attached directly to a rigid support, while the other end is attached to a spring of constant k. Determine the period and frequency of vibration of the cylinder.

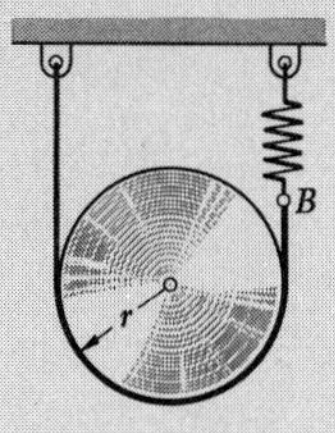

Kinematics of Motion. We express the linear displacement and the acceleration of the cylinder in terms of the angular displacement θ. Choosing the positive sense clockwise and measuring the displacements from the equilibrium position, we write

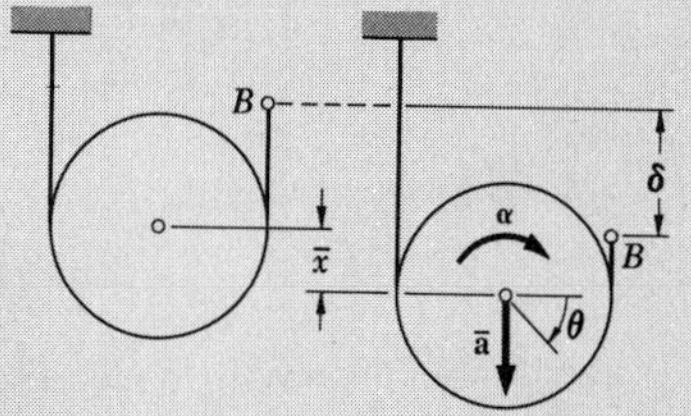

$$\bar{x} = r\theta \qquad \delta = 2\bar{x} = 2r\theta$$

$$\alpha = \frac{d^2\theta}{dt^2} \curvearrowright \qquad \bar{a} = r\alpha = r\frac{d^2\theta}{dt^2} \qquad \bar{\mathbf{a}} = r\frac{d^2\theta}{dt^2} \downarrow \tag{1}$$

Equations of Motion. The system of external forces acting on the cylinder consists of the weight **W** and of the forces $\mathbf{T}_1$ and $\mathbf{T}_2$ exerted by the cord. We express that this system is equivalent to the system of effective forces represented by the vector $m\bar{\mathbf{a}}$ attached at G and the couple $\bar{I}\alpha$.

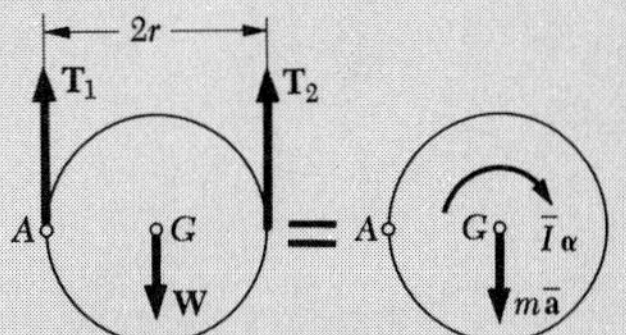

$$+\curvearrowright \Sigma M_A = \Sigma(M_A)_{\text{eff}}: \qquad Wr - T_2(2r) = m\bar{a}r + \bar{I}\alpha \tag{2}$$

When the cylinder is in its position of equilibrium, the tension in the cord is $T_0 = \frac{1}{2}W$. We note that, for an angular displacement θ, the magnitude of $\mathbf{T}_2$ is

$$T_2 = T_0 + k\delta = \tfrac{1}{2}W + k\delta = \tfrac{1}{2}W + k(2r\theta) \tag{3}$$

Substituting from (1) and (3) into (2), and recalling that $\bar{I} = \frac{1}{2}mr^2$, we write

$$Wr - (\tfrac{1}{2}W + 2kr\theta)(2r) = m\left(r\frac{d^2\theta}{dt^2}\right)r + \tfrac{1}{2}mr^2\frac{d^2\theta}{dt^2}$$

$$\frac{d^2\theta}{dt^2} + \frac{8}{3}\frac{k}{m}\theta = 0$$

The motion is seen to be simple harmonic, and we have

$$p^2 = \frac{8}{3}\frac{k}{m} \qquad p = \sqrt{\frac{8}{3}\frac{k}{m}}$$

$$\tau = \frac{2\pi}{p} \qquad \tau = 2\pi\sqrt{\frac{3}{8}\frac{m}{k}} \blacktriangleleft$$

$$f = \frac{p}{2\pi} \qquad f = \frac{1}{2\pi}\sqrt{\frac{8}{3}\frac{k}{m}} \blacktriangleleft$$

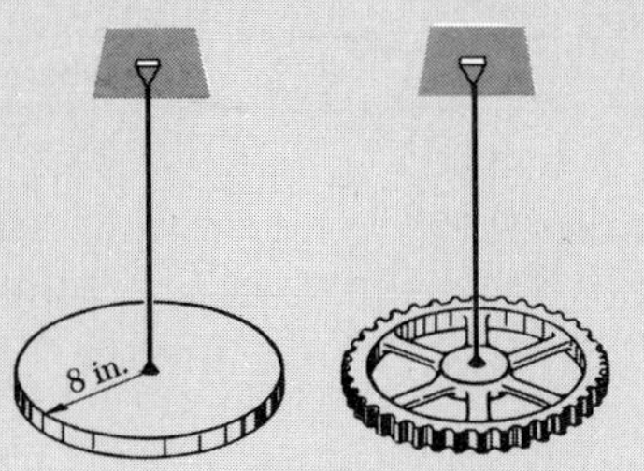

SAMPLE PROBLEM 19.3

A circular disk, weighing 20 lb and of radius 8 in., is suspended from a wire as shown. The disk is rotated (thus twisting the wire) and then released; the period of the torsional vibration is observed to be 1.13 sec. A gear is then suspended from the same wire, and the period of torsional vibration for the gear is observed to be 1.93 sec. Assuming that the moment of the couple exerted by the wire is proportional to the angle of twist, determine (*a*) the torsional spring constant of the wire, (*b*) the centroidal moment of inertia of the gear.

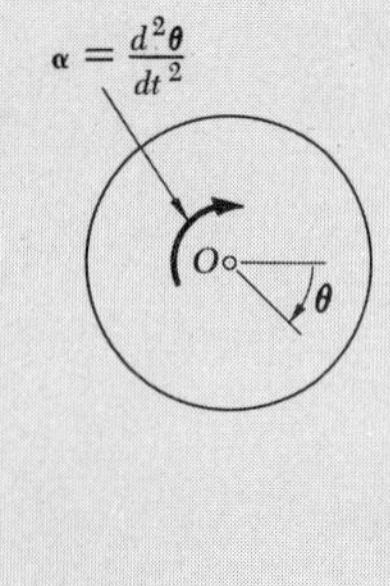

a. **Vibration of Disk.** Denoting by θ the angular displacement of the disk, we express that the magnitude of the couple exerted by the wire is $M = K\theta$, where K is the torsional spring constant of the wire. Since this couple must be equivalent to the couple $I\alpha$ representing the effective forces of the disk, we write

$$+\circlearrowleft \Sigma M_O = \Sigma(M_O)_{\text{eff}}: \qquad +K\theta = -I\frac{d^2\theta}{dt^2}$$

$$\frac{d^2\theta}{dt^2} + \frac{K}{I}\theta = 0$$

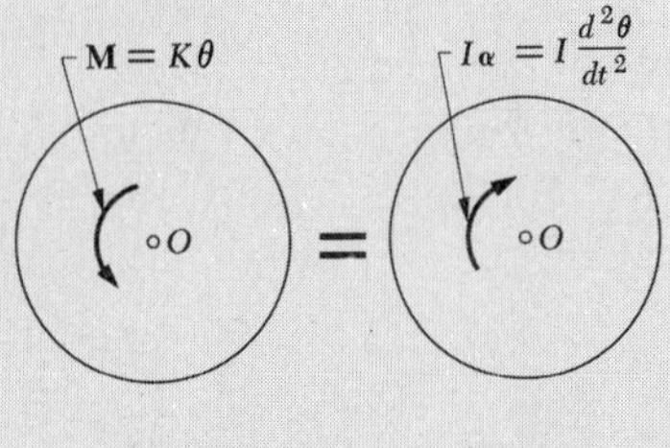

The motion is seen to be simple harmonic, and we have

$$p^2 = \frac{K}{I} \qquad p = \sqrt{\frac{K}{I}}$$

$$\tau = \frac{2\pi}{p} \qquad \tau = 2\pi\sqrt{\frac{I}{K}} \tag{1}$$

For the disk, we have

$$\tau = 1.13 \text{ sec} \qquad I = \tfrac{1}{2}mr^2 = \frac{1}{2}\left(\frac{20}{32.2}\right)\left(\frac{8}{12}\right)^2 = 0.138 \text{ lb-ft-sec}^2$$

Substituting into (1), we obtain

$$1.13 = 2\pi\sqrt{\frac{0.138}{K}} \qquad K = 4.27 \text{ lb-ft/radian} \blacktriangleleft$$

b. **Vibration of Gear.** Since the period of vibration of the gear is 1.93 sec and $K = 4.27$ lb-ft/radian, Eq. (1) yields

$$1.93 = 2\pi\sqrt{\frac{I}{4.27}} \qquad I_{\text{gear}} = 0.403 \text{ lb-ft-sec}^2 \blacktriangleleft$$

Note. It is shown in mechanics of materials that the torsional spring constant of a cylindrical rod of length L is $K = L/JG$, where J is the polar moment of inertia of the circular cross-sectional area of the rod and G the shearing modulus of elasticity of the material.

PROBLEMS

19.24. A 600-lb flywheel has a diameter of 4 ft and a radius of gyration of 20 in. A belt is placed over the rim and attached to two springs, each of constant $k = 75$ lb/in. The initial tension in the belt is sufficient to prevent slipping. If the end C of the belt is pulled 1 in. to the right and released, determine (*a*) the period of vibration, (*b*) the maximum angular velocity of the flywheel.

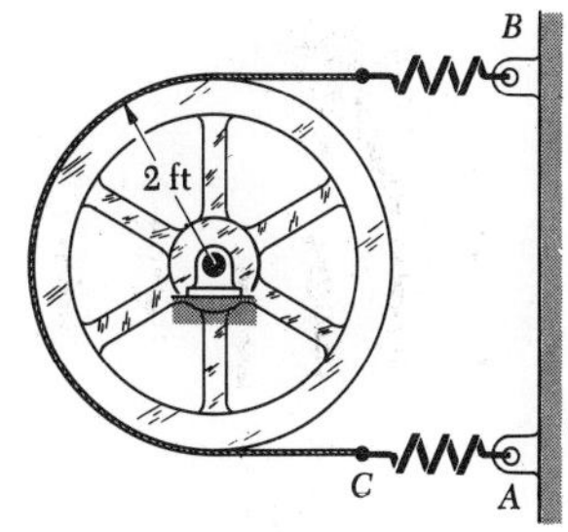

FIG. P 19.24

19.25. A disk is rigidly attached to a gear of radius r which may roll on the gear rack shown. The disk and gear have a total weight W and a combined radius of gyration $\bar{k}$. A spring of constant K is attached to the center of the gear. If the disk is released from rest when the tension in the spring is zero, derive an expression (*a*) for the amplitude and frequency of the resulting vibration, (*b*) for the maximum velocity of the center of the gear.

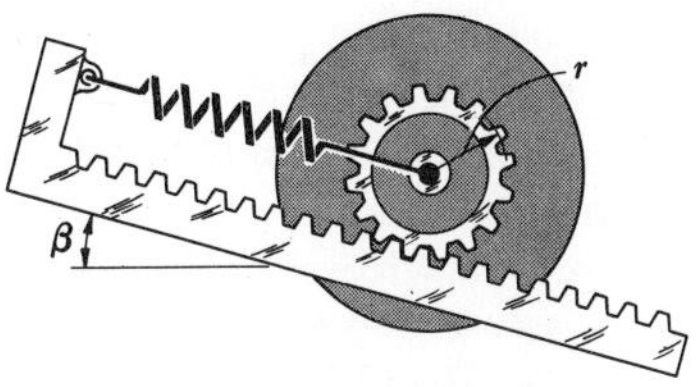

FIG. P 19.25

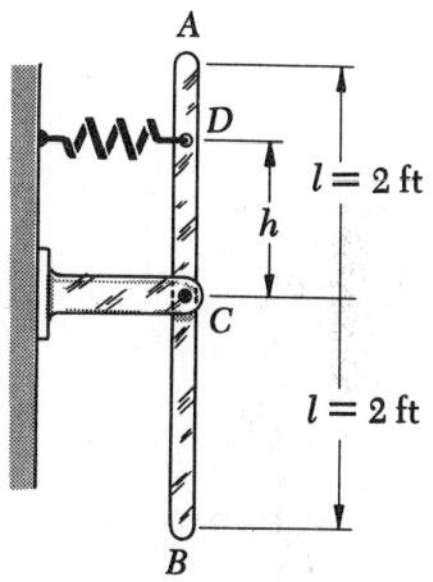

FIG. P 19.27

19.26. Solve Prob. 19.25 assuming $r = 3$ in., $\bar{k} = 4$ in., $W = 20$ lb, $K = 2$ lb/in., and $\beta = 30°$.

19.27. A 4-ft rod AB weighing 15 lb is attached to a hinge at its center C and to a spring of constant $k = 3$ lb/in. at D. Determine the distance h for which the period of vibration of the rod is 1 sec.

19.28 and 19.29. Two slender rods, each of weight W and length L, are welded together at B to form an L-shaped bracket. The bracket is supported in the horizontal plane by a hinge at B and by a spring of constant k as shown. If the spring is compressed by a small amount and released, determine the period of the resulting motion.

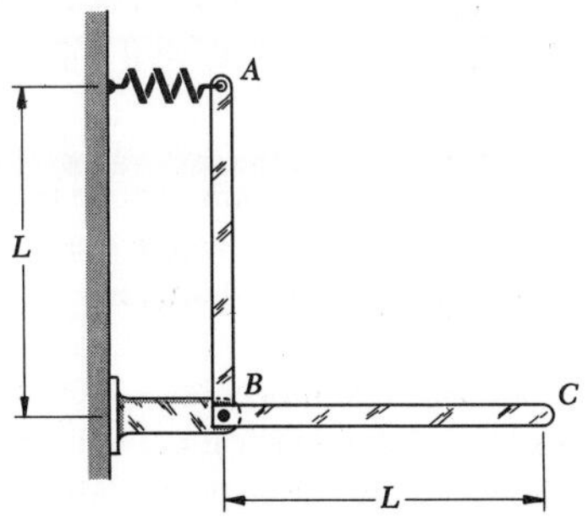

FIG. P 19.28

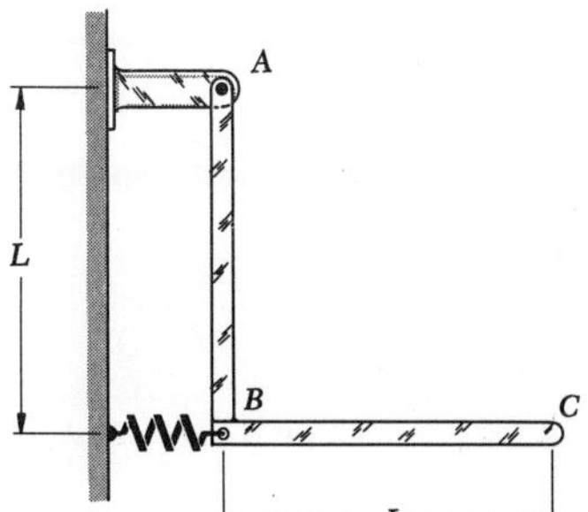

FIG. P 19.29

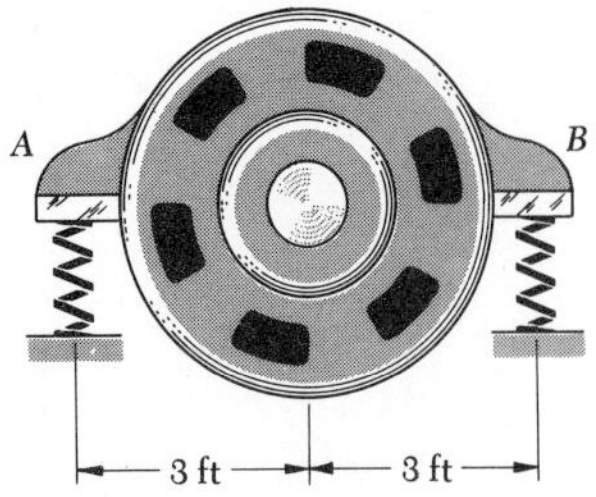

FIG. P 19.30

19.30. During the normal operation of a single-phase generator, the transmission of undesirable vibrations is prevented by four springs mounted as shown (two springs at A and two springs at B). Knowing that the stator of the generator weighs 400 lb and has a centroidal radius of gyration of 24 in., determine the required constant of each spring if the frequency of the free *angular* vibration of the stator is to be 15 cycles/sec.

19.31. The *rotor* of the generator of Prob. 19.30 weighs 300 lb and has a centroidal radius of gyration of 18 in. Knowing that the springs have been chosen so that the angular frequency of the *stator* alone is 15 cycles/sec, determine the frequency of the *angular* vibration of the generator if the bearings are frozen so that the rotor and stator move as a single rigid body.

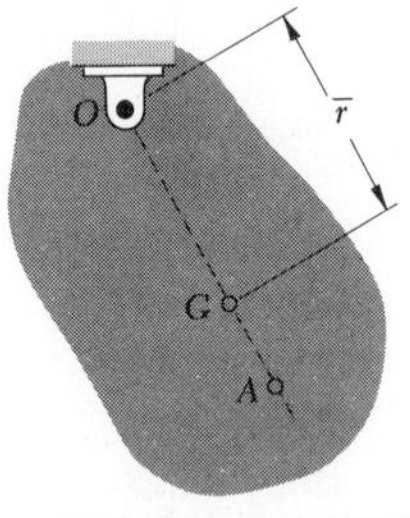

FIG. P 19.32 AND P 19.34

19.32. A *compound pendulum* is defined as a rigid body which oscillates about a fixed point O called the center of suspension. Show that the period of oscillation of a compound pendulum is equal to the period of a simple pendulum of length OA, where the distance from A to the mass center G is $GA = \bar{k}^2/\bar{r}$. Point A is defined as the center of oscillation and coincides with the center of percussion defined in Prob. 18.10.

19.33. Show that, if the compound pendulum of Prob. 19.32 is suspended from A instead of O, the period of oscillation is the same as before and the new center of oscillation is located at O.

19.34. A rigid body oscillates about a fixed point O. Show that the smallest period of oscillation occurs when the distance $\bar{r}$ from point O to the mass center G is equal to $\bar{k}$.

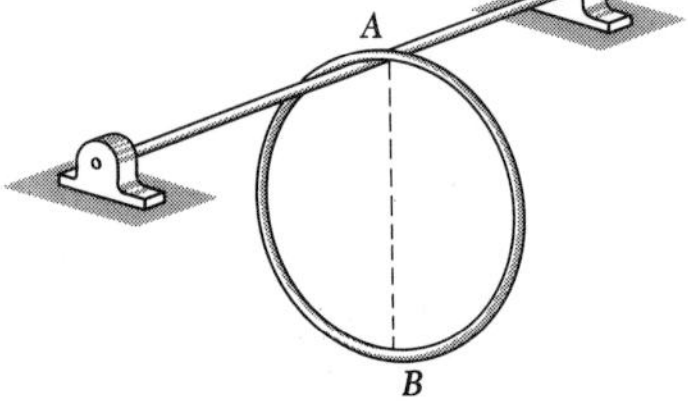

FIG. P 19.35

19.35. A thin hoop of radius r and weight W is suspended from a rough rod as shown. Determine the frequency of small oscillations of the hoop (*a*) in the plane of the hoop, (*b*) in a direction perpendicular to the plane of the hoop. Assume that μ is sufficiently large to prevent slipping at A.

19.36. Solve Prob. 19.35 assuming that a small collar of weight W is rigidly attached to the hoop at point B.

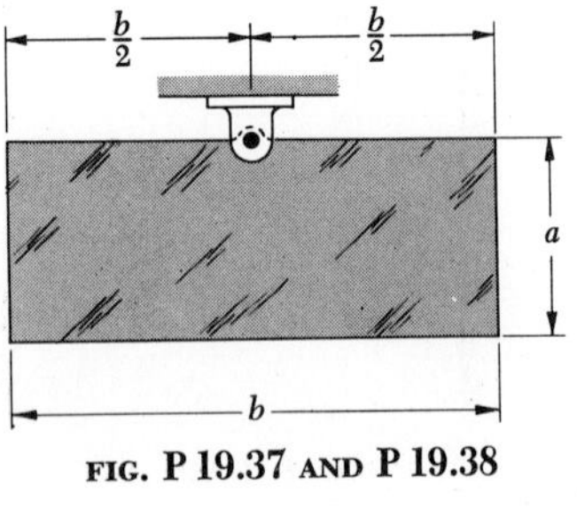

FIG. P 19.37 AND P 19.38

19.37. A homogeneous rectangular plate is suspended from a pin located at the mid-point of one edge as shown. Considering the dimension b constant, determine the ratio a/b for which the period of oscillation of the plate is minimum.

19.38. A homogeneous rectangular plate is suspended from a pin located at the mid-point of one edge as shown. Determine the ratio a/b for which the period of oscillation of the plate is the same as the period of a simple pendulum of length a.

19.39. The period of small oscillations about A of a connecting rod is observed to be 1.12 sec. Knowing that the distance r_a is 7.50 in., determine the centroidal radius of gyration of the connecting rod.

19.40. A connecting rod is supported by a knife-edge at point A; the period of small oscillations is observed to be 0.945 sec. The rod is then inverted and supported by a knife-edge at point B and the period of small oscillations is observed to be 0.850 sec. Knowing that $r_a + r_b =$ 11.50 in., determine (*a*) the location of the mass center G, (*b*) the centroidal radius of gyration $\bar{k}$.

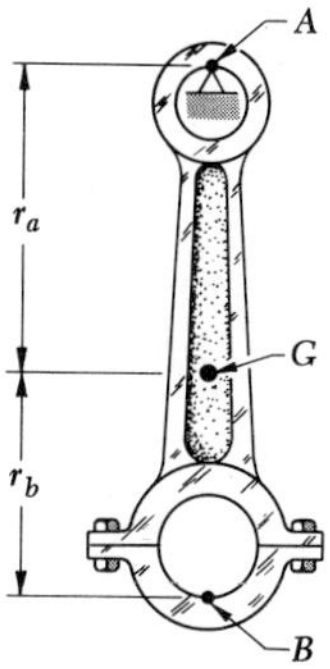

FIG. P 19.39 AND P 19.40

19.41. A slender bar of length L is attached by a smooth pin at A to a collar of negligible weight as shown. Assuming that the coefficient of friction between the collar and the horizontal rod is sufficient to prevent any movement of the collar, determine the period of small oscillations of the rod.

19.42. Solve Prob. 19.41 assuming that the coefficient of friction between the collar and the horizontal rod is zero.

19.43. Solve Prob. 19.35 assuming that $\mu = 0$.

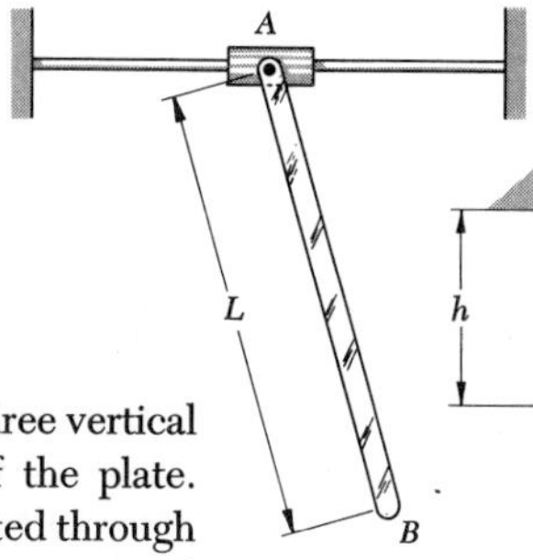

FIG. P 19.41

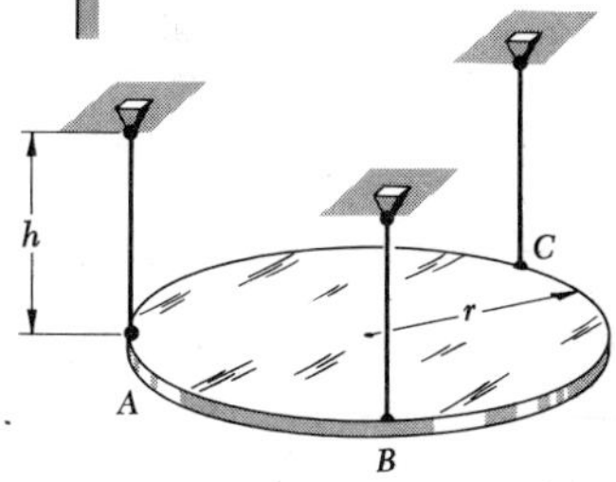

FIG. P 19.44

19.44. A thin circular plate of radius r is suspended from three vertical wires of length h equally spaced around the perimeter of the plate. Determine the period of oscillation when (*a*) the plate is rotated through a small angle about a vertical axis passing through its mass center and released, (*b*) the plate is given a small horizontal translation and released.

19.45. In Prob. 19.44, the points of attachment of the three vertical wires are changed so that they are *unequally* spaced around the perimeter of the plate. Show that this change does not affect the answers to either part *a* or *b* of Prob. 19.44, as long as the points A, B, and C are not on the same side of a given diameter of the plate.

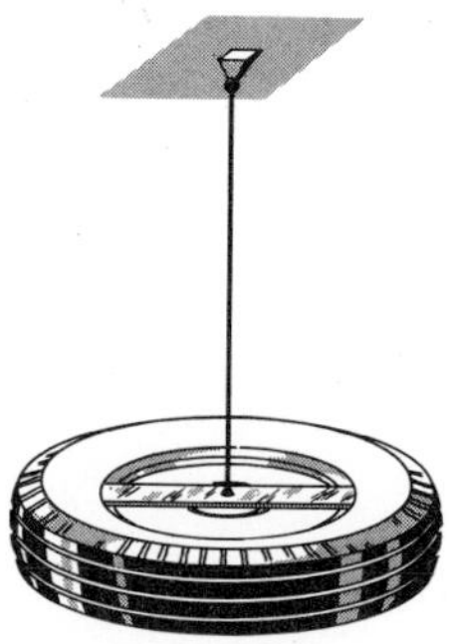

FIG. P 19.46

19.46. An automobile wheel-and-tire assembly of total weight 47 lb is attached to a mounting plate of negligible weight which is suspended from a steel wire. The torsional spring constant of the wire is known to be $K = 0.40$ lb-in./radian. The wheel is rotated through 90° about the vertical and then released. Knowing that the period of oscillation is observed to be 30 sec, determine the centroidal mass moment of inertia and the centroidal radius of gyration of the wheel-and-tire assembly.

19.47. A disk of radius 12 in. weighing 20 lb is attached to a horizontal shaft which is rigidly held at B. It is known that the disk rotates through 5° when a 10-lb-ft static couple is applied to the disk. If the disk is rotated through 3° and then released, determine (*a*) the period of the resulting vibration, (*b*) the maximum angular velocity of the disk.

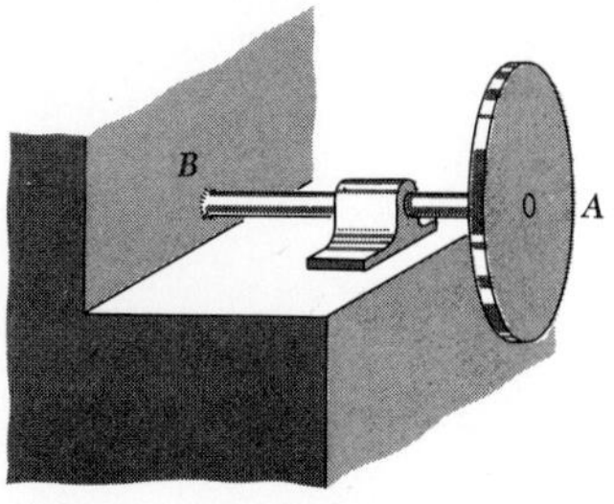

FIG. P 19.47

19.48. An instrument is rigidly bolted to the disk of Prob. 19.47. Knowing that the period of torsional vibration of the disk and instrument is 0.410 sec, determine the moment of inertia of the instrument with respect to the shaft AB.

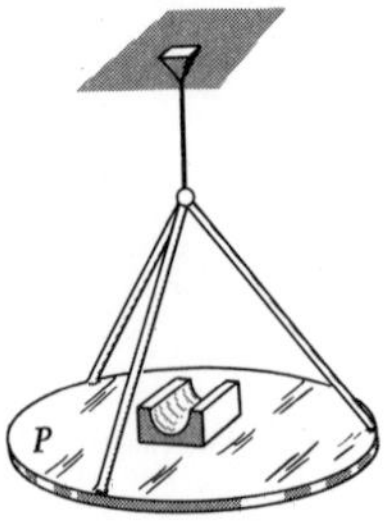

FIG. P 19.49

19.49. A torsion pendulum may be used to determine experimentally the moment of inertia of a given object. The horizontal platform P is held by several rigid bars which are connected to a vertical wire. The period of oscillation of the platform is found equal to τ_0 when the platform is empty and to τ_A when an object of known moment of inertia I_A is placed on the platform so that its mass center is directly above the center of the plate. (*a*) Show that the moment of inertia I_0 of the platform and its supports may be expressed as $I_0 = I_A\tau_0^2/(\tau_A^2 - \tau_0^2)$. (*b*) If a period of oscillation τ_B is observed when an object B of unknown moment of inertia I_B is placed on the platform, show that

$$I_B = I_A(\tau_B^2 - \tau_0^2)/(\tau_A^2 - \tau_0^2)$$

19.6. Application of the Principle of Conservation of Energy. We saw in Sec. 19.2 that, when a particle of mass m is in simple harmonic motion, the resultant **F** of the forces exerted on the particle has a magnitude proportional to the displacement x measured from the position of equilibrium O and is directed toward O; we wrote $F = -kx$. Referring to Sec. 13.6, we note that **F** is a *conservative force* and that the corresponding potential energy is $V = \frac{1}{2}kx^2$, where V is assumed equal to zero in the equilibrium position $x = 0$. Since the velocity of the particle is equal to dx/dt, its kinetic energy is $T = \frac{1}{2}m(dx/dt)^2$ and we may express that the total energy of the particle is conserved by writing

$$T + V = \text{constant} \qquad \frac{1}{2}m\left(\frac{dx}{dt}\right)^2 + \frac{1}{2}kx^2 = \text{constant}$$

Setting $p^2 = k/m$ as in (19.4), where p is the circular frequency of the vibration, we have

$$\left(\frac{dx}{dt}\right)^2 + p^2x^2 = \text{constant} \tag{19.25}$$

Equation (19.25) is characteristic of simple harmonic motion; it may be obtained directly from (19.5) by multiplying both terms by $2(dx/dt)$ and integrating.

The principle of conservation of energy provides a convenient way for determining the period of vibration of a rigid body or of a system of rigid bodies possessing a single degree of freedom. Choosing an appropriate variable, such as a distance x or an angle θ, we consider two particular positions of the system:

1. *The displacement of the system is maximum;* we have $T_1 = 0$, and V_1 may be expressed in terms of the amplitude x_m or θ_m (choosing $V = 0$ in the equilibrium position).

2. *The system passes through its equilibrium position;* we have $V_2 = 0$, and T_2 may be expressed in terms of the maximum velocity $(dx/dt)_m$ or $(d\theta/dt)_m$.

We then express that the total energy of the system is conserved and write $T_1 + V_1 = T_2 + V_2$. Recalling from (19.15) that for simple harmonic motion the maximum velocity is equal to the product of the amplitude and of the circular frequency p, we find that the equation obtained may be solved for p.

As an example, we shall consider again the square plate of Sec. 19.5. In the position of maximum displacement (Fig. 19.6*a*), we have

$$T_1 = 0 \qquad V_1 = W(b - b\cos\theta_m) = Wb(1 - \cos\theta_m)$$

or, since $1 - \cos\theta_m = 2\sin^2(\theta_m/2) \approx 2(\theta_m/2)^2 = \theta_m^2/2$ for oscillations of small amplitude,

$$T_1 = 0 \qquad V_1 = \tfrac{1}{2}Wb\theta_m^2 \tag{19.26}$$

As the plate passes through its position of equilibrium (Fig. 19.6*b*), its velocity is maximum and we have

$$T_2 = \tfrac{1}{2}m\bar{v}_m^2 + \tfrac{1}{2}\bar{I}\omega_m^2 = \tfrac{1}{2}mb^2\left(\frac{d\theta}{dt}\right)_m^2 + \tfrac{1}{2}\bar{I}\left(\frac{d\theta}{dt}\right)_m^2 \qquad V_2 = 0$$

or, recalling from Sec. 19.5 that $\bar{I} = \frac{2}{3}mb^2$,

$$T_2 = \tfrac{1}{2}\tfrac{5}{3}mb^2\left(\frac{d\theta}{dt}\right)_m^2 \qquad V_2 = 0 \tag{19.27}$$

Substituting from (19.26) and (19.27) into $T_1 + V_1 = T_2 + V_2$, and noting that the maximum velocity $(d\theta/dt)_m$ is equal to the product $\theta_m p$, we write

$$\tfrac{1}{2}Wb\theta_m^2 = \tfrac{1}{2}\tfrac{5}{3}mb^2\theta_m^2 p^2 \tag{19.28}$$

which yields $p^2 = 3g/5b$ and

$$\tau = \frac{2\pi}{p} = 2\pi\sqrt{\frac{5b}{3g}} \tag{19.29}$$

as previously obtained.

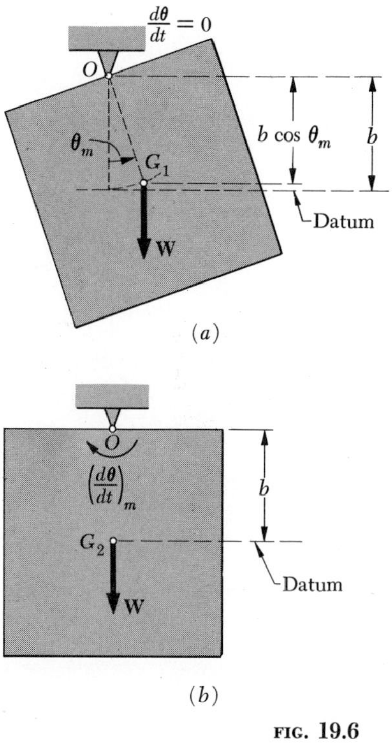

FIG. 19.6

SAMPLE PROBLEM 19.4

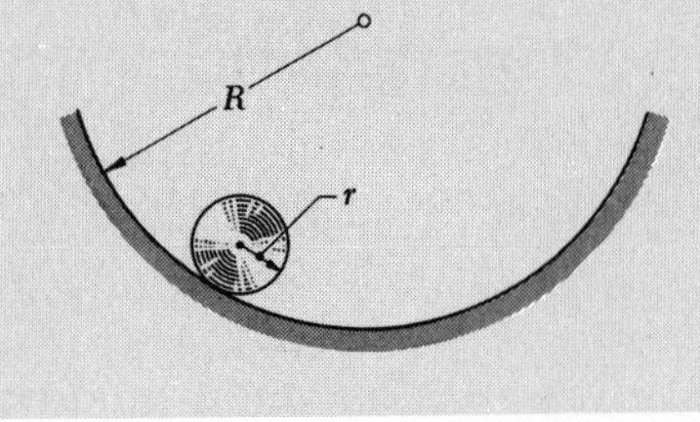

Determine the period of oscillation of a cylinder of radius r which rolls without slipping inside a curved surface of radius R.

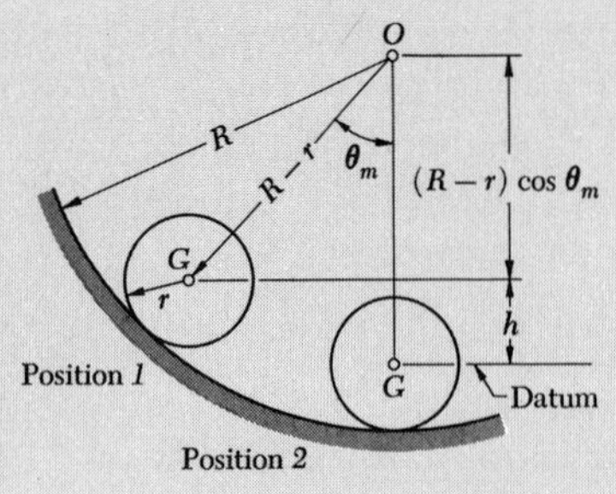

Solution. We denote by θ the angle which line OG forms with the vertical. Since the cylinder rolls without slipping, we may apply the principle of conservation of energy between position *1*, where $\theta = \theta_m$, and position 2, where $\theta = 0$.

Position *1*. *Kinetic Energy.* Since the velocity of the cylinder is zero, we have $T_1 = 0$.

Potential Energy. Choosing a datum as shown and denoting by W the weight of the cylinder, we have

$$V_1 = Wh = W(R - r)(1 - \cos\theta)$$

Noting that for small oscillations $(1 - \cos\theta) = 2\sin^2(\theta/2) \approx \theta^2/2$, we have

$$V_1 = W(R - r)\frac{\theta_m^2}{2}$$

Position 2. Denoting by $(d\theta/dt)_m$ the angular velocity of line OG as the cylinder passes through position 2, and observing that point C is the instantaneous center of rotation of the cylinder, we write

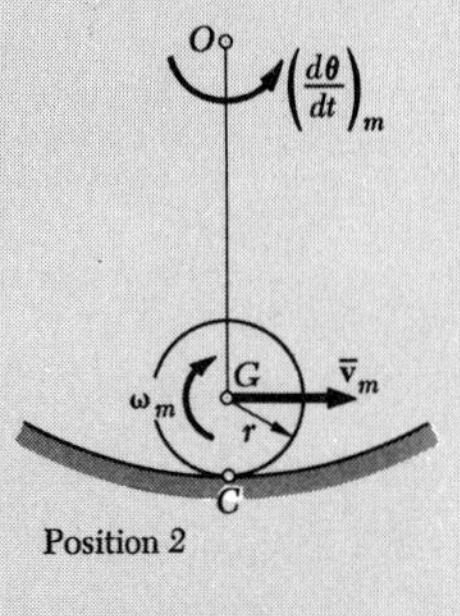

$$\bar{v}_m = (R - r)\left(\frac{d\theta}{dt}\right)_m \qquad \omega_m = \frac{\bar{v}_m}{r} = \frac{R - r}{r}\left(\frac{d\theta}{dt}\right)_m$$

Kinetic Energy:

$$\begin{aligned} T_2 &= \tfrac{1}{2}m\bar{v}_m^2 + \tfrac{1}{2}\bar{I}\omega_m^2 \\ &= \tfrac{1}{2}m(R - r)^2\left(\frac{d\theta}{dt}\right)_m^2 + \tfrac{1}{2}(\tfrac{1}{2}mr^2)\left(\frac{R - r}{r}\right)^2\left(\frac{d\theta}{dt}\right)_m^2 \\ &= \tfrac{3}{4}m(R - r)^2\left(\frac{d\theta}{dt}\right)_m^2 \end{aligned}$$

Potential Energy: $V_2 = 0$

Conservation of Energy

$$T_1 + V_1 = T_2 + V_2$$

$$0 + W(R - r)\frac{\theta_m^2}{2} = \tfrac{3}{4}m(R - r)^2\left(\frac{d\theta}{dt}\right)_m^2 + 0$$

Since $(d\theta/dt)_m = p\theta_m$ and $W = mg$, we write

$$mg(R - r)\frac{\theta_m^2}{2} = \tfrac{3}{4}m(R - r)^2(p\theta_m)^2 \qquad p^2 = \frac{2}{3}\frac{g}{R - r}$$

$$\tau = \frac{2\pi}{p} \qquad \tau = 2\pi\sqrt{\frac{3}{2}\frac{R - r}{g}} \quad ◄$$

PROBLEMS

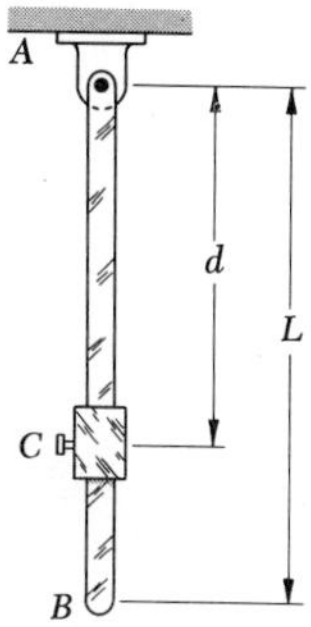

FIG. P 19.50

19.50. A small collar weighing 2 lb is rigidly attached to a 6-lb uniform rod of length $L = 3$ ft. Determine the period of oscillation of the rod when (*a*) $d = 3$ ft, (*b*) $d = 2$ ft.

19.51. Solve Prob. 19.50 assuming that the collar weighs 1 lb.

19.52. Using the method of Sec. 19.6, solve Prob. 19.5.

19.53. Using the method of Sec. 19.6, solve Prob. 19.9.

19.54. Using the method of Sec. 19.6, solve Prob. 19.10.

19.55. Using the method of Sec. 19.6, solve Prob. 19.11.

19.56. Using the method of Sec. 19.6, solve Prob. 19.12.

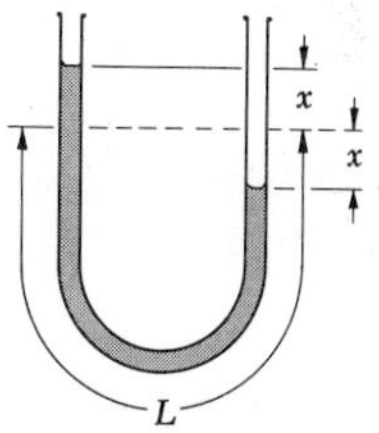

FIG. P 19.57

19.57. Neglecting fluid friction, determine the frequency of oscillation of the liquid in the U-tube manometer shown. Show that this frequency is independent of the density of the liquid and of the amplitude of the oscillation.

19.58. Two small weights w are attached at A and B to the rim of a uniform disk of radius r and weight W. Denoting by τ_0 the period of small oscillations when $\beta = 0$, determine the angle β for which the period of small oscillations is $2\tau_0$.

19.59. Two $\frac{1}{10}$-lb weights are attached at A and B to the rim of a 3-lb uniform disk of radius $r = 4$ in. Determine the frequency of small oscillations when $\beta = 60°$.

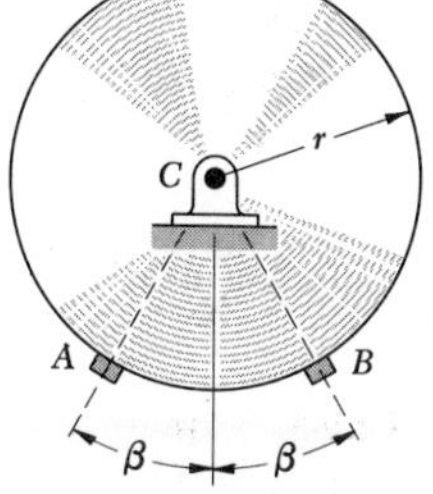

FIG. P 19.58 AND P 19.59

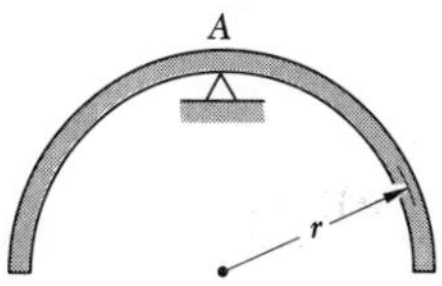

FIG. P 19.60

19.60. A half section of pipe is suspended as shown. Determine the frequency of small oscillations. Assume that μ is sufficiently large to prevent slipping at A.

19.61. Using the method of Sec. 19.6, solve Prob. 19.41.

19.62. The motion of the uniform rod AB is guided by the cord AC and by the small roller at B. Determine the frequency of oscillation when the end B of the rod is given a small horizontal displacement and released.

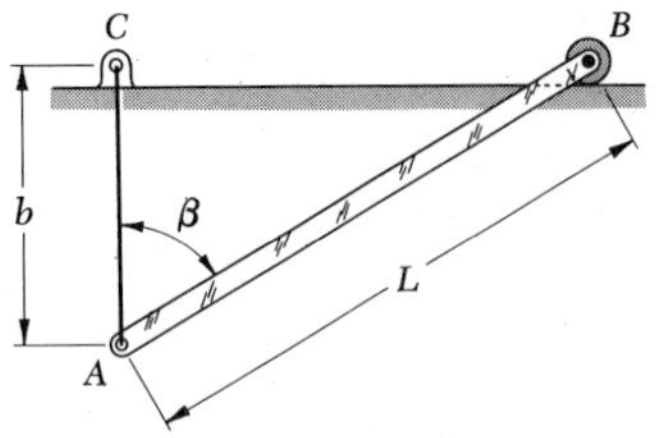

FIG. P 19.62

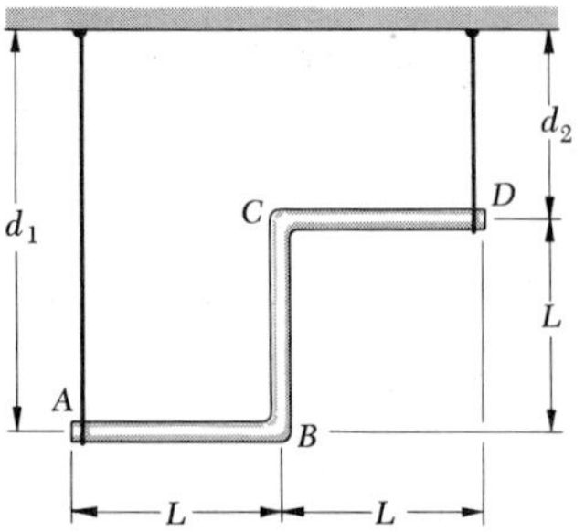

FIG. P 19.63

19.63. A section of uniform pipe bent in the shape shown is suspended from two vertical cables attached at A and D. Determine the period of oscillation when point D is given a small horizontal displacement to the right and released.

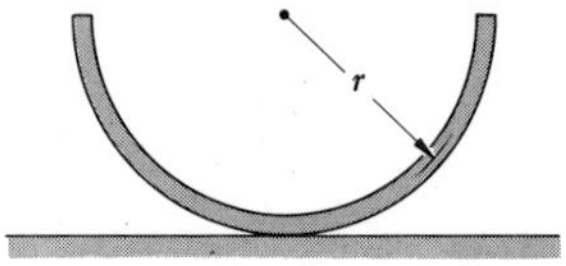

FIG. P 19.64

19.64. A half section of pipe is placed on a rough surface, rotated through a small angle, and then released. Assuming that μ is sufficiently large to prevent sliding, determine the period of oscillation.

19.65. Using the method of Sec. 19.6, solve Prob. 19.25.

19.66. Solve Sample Prob. 19.4 assuming that the cylinder is replaced by a sphere of radius r.

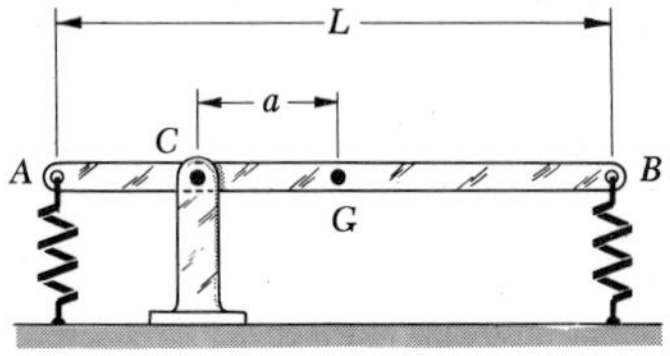

FIG. P 19.67

19.67. A slender bar of weight W and length L is attached to a pin support at C and to two springs each of constant k. Knowing that end B is depressed slightly and then released, determine the frequency of vibration if (*a*) $a = 0$, (*b*) $a = \frac{1}{4}L$, (*c*) $a = \frac{1}{2}L$.

19.68. Solve Prob. 19.67 assuming $W = 20$ lb, $L = 5$ ft, and $k = 10$ lb/in.

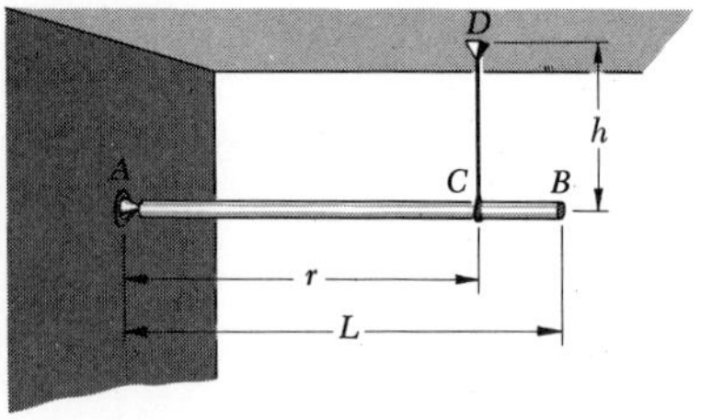

FIG. P 19.69

19.69. A uniform rod of length L is supported by a ball-and-socket joint at A and by the vertical wire CD. Derive an expression for the period of oscillation of the rod if end B is given a small horizontal displacement and then released.

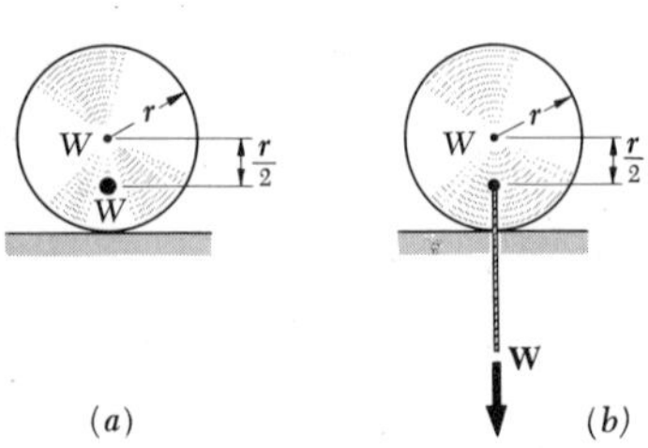

FIG. P 19.71

19.70. Using the method of Sec. 19.6, solve Prob. 19.44.

19.71. A uniform disk of weight W and radius r may roll on the horizontal surface shown. In case a, a weight W of negligible dimensions is bolted to the disk at a distance $\frac{1}{2}r$ from the geometric center of the disk. In case b, a vertical force of constant magnitude W is applied to a cord which is attached to the disk at a distance $\frac{1}{2}r$ from the center of the disk. Determine the ratio τ_b/τ_a of the two periods of oscillation.

***19.72.** As a submerged body moves through a fluid, the particles of the fluid flow around the body and thus acquire kinetic energy. In the case of a sphere moving in an ideal fluid, the total kinetic energy acquired by the fluid is $\frac{1}{4}\rho V v^2$, where ρ is the mass density of the fluid, V the volume of the sphere, and v the velocity of the sphere. Consider a 1-lb hollow spherical shell of radius 3 in. which is held submerged in a tank of water by a spring of constant 3 lb/in. (a) Neglecting fluid friction, determine the period of vibration of the shell when it is displaced vertically and then released. (b) Solve part a assuming that the tank is accelerated upward at the constant rate of 10 ft/sec^2.

FIG. P 19.72

***19.73.** The shell of Prob. 19.72 is held submerged by an inextensible cord of length 3 ft instead of a spring. (a) Neglecting fluid friction, determine the period of small oscillations of the shell when it is moved slightly to the side and then released. (b) Solve part a assuming that the tank is accelerated upward at the constant rate of 10 ft/sec^2.

***19.74.** A thin plate of length l rests on a half cylinder of radius r. Derive an expression for the period of small oscillations of the plate.

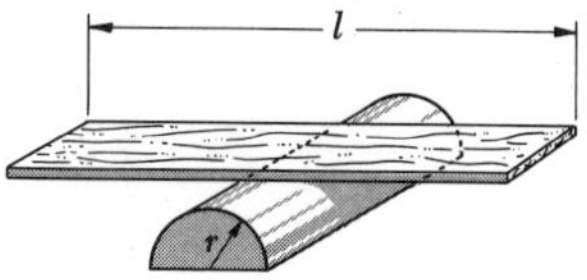

FIG. P 19.74

19.7. Forced Vibrations.

The most important vibrations from the point of view of engineering applications are the *forced vibrations* of a system. These vibrations occur when a system is subjected to a periodic force or when it is elastically connected to a support which has an alternating motion.

Consider first the case of a body of mass m suspended from a spring and subjected to a periodic force $\mathbf{P}$ of magnitude $P = P_m \sin \omega t$ (Fig. 19.7). This force may be an actual external force applied to the body, or it may be a centrifugal force produced by the rotation of some unbalanced part of the body. (See Sample Prob. 19.5.) Denoting by x the displacement of the body measured from its equilibrium position, we write the equation of motion,

$$+\downarrow\Sigma F = ma: \qquad P_m \sin \omega t + W - k(\delta_{st} + x) = m\frac{d^2x}{dt^2}$$

Recalling that $W = k\delta_{st}$, we have

$$m\frac{d^2x}{dt^2} + kx = P_m \sin \omega t \qquad (19.30)$$

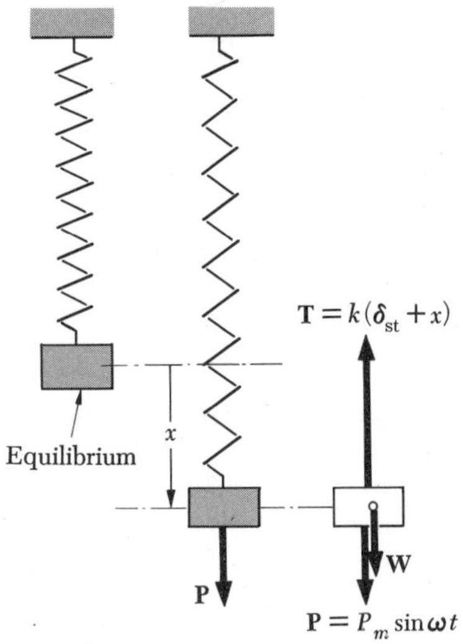

FIG. 19.7

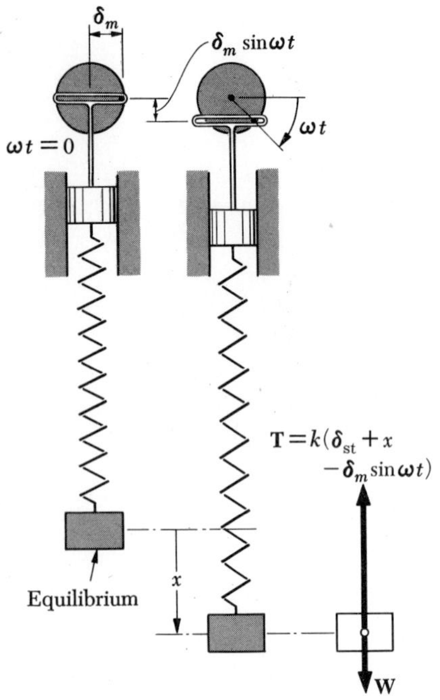

FIG. 19.8

Next we consider the case of a body of mass m suspended from a spring attached to a moving support whose displacement δ is equal to $\delta_m \sin \omega t$ (Fig. 19.8). Measuring the displacement x of the body from the position of static equilibrium corresponding to $\omega t = 0$, we find that the total elongation of the spring at time t is $\delta_{st} + x - \delta_m \sin \omega t$. The equation of motion is thus

$$+\downarrow\Sigma F = ma: \qquad W - k(\delta_{st} + x - \delta_m \sin \omega t) = m\frac{d^2x}{dt^2}$$

Recalling that $W = k\delta_{st}$, we have

$$m\frac{d^2x}{dt^2} + kx = k\delta_m \sin \omega t \tag{19.31}$$

We note that Eqs. (19.30) and (19.31) are of the same form and that a solution of the first equation will satisfy the second if we set $P_m = k\delta_m$.

A differential equation like (19.30) or (19.31), possessing a right-hand member different from zero, is said to be *nonhomogeneous*. Its general solution is obtained by adding a particular solution of the given equation to the general solution of the corresponding *homogeneous* equation (with right-hand member equal to zero). A *particular solution* of (19.30) or (19.31) may be obtained by trying a solution of the form

$$x_{\text{part}} = x_m \sin \omega t \tag{19.32}$$

Substituting x_{part} for x into (19.30), we find

$$-m\omega^2 x_m \sin \omega t + kx_m \sin \omega t = P_m \sin \omega t$$

which may be solved for the amplitude,

$$x_m = \frac{P_m}{k - m\omega^2}$$

Recalling from (19.4) that $k/m = p^2$, where p is the circular frequency of the free vibration of the body, we write

$$x_m = \frac{P_m/k}{1 - (\omega/p)^2} \tag{19.33}$$

Substituting from (19.32) into (19.31), we obtain in a similar way

$$x_m = \frac{\delta_m}{1 - (\omega/p)^2} \tag{19.33$'$}$$

The homogeneous equation corresponding to (19.30) or (19.31) is Eq. (19.3), defining the free vibration of the body.

Its general solution, called the *complementary function,* was found in Sec. 19.2,

$$x_{\text{comp}} = A \sin pt + B \cos pt \qquad (19.34)$$

Adding the particular solution (19.32) and the complementary function (19.34), we obtain the *general solution* of Eqs. (19.30) and (19.31),

$$x = A \sin pt + B \cos pt + x_m \sin \omega t \qquad (19.35)$$

We note that the vibration obtained consists of two superposed vibrations. The first two terms in (19.35) represent a free vibration of the system. The frequency of this vibration, called the *natural frequency* of the system, depends only upon the constant k of the spring and the mass m of the body, and the constants A and B may be determined from the initial conditions. This free vibration is also called a *transient* vibration since, in actual practice, it will soon be damped out by friction forces (Sec. 19.9).

The last term in (19.35) represents the *steady-state* vibration produced and maintained by the impressed force or impressed support movement. Its frequency is the *forced frequency* imposed by this force or movement, and its amplitude x_m, defined by (19.33) or (19.33′), depends upon the *frequency ratio* ω/p. The ratio of the amplitude x_m of the steady-state vibration to the static deflection P_m/k caused by a force P_m, or to the amplitude δ_m of the support movement, is called the *magnification factor.* From (19.33) and (19.33′), we obtain

$$\text{Magnification factor} = \frac{x_m}{P_m/k} = \frac{x_m}{\delta_m} = \frac{1}{1 - (\omega/p)^2} \qquad (19.36)$$

The magnification factor has been plotted in Fig. 19.9 against the frequency ratio ω/p. We note that, when $\omega = p$, the amplitude of the forced vibration becomes infinite. The impressed force or impressed support movement is said to be in *resonance* with the given system. Actually, the amplitude of the vibration remains finite because of damping forces (Sec. 19.9); nevertheless, such a situation should be avoided, and the forced frequency should not be chosen too close to the natural frequency of the system. We also note that for $\omega < p$ the coefficient of $\sin \omega t$ in (19.35) is positive, while for $\omega > p$ this coefficient is negative. In the first case the forced vibration is *in phase* with the impressed force or impressed support movement, while in the second case it is 180° *out of phase.*

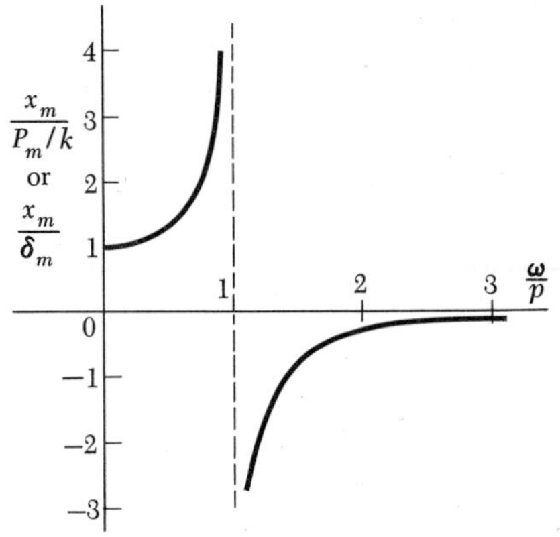

FIG. 19.9

SAMPLE PROBLEM 19.5

A motor weighing 350 lb is supported by four springs having each a constant of 750 lb/in. The unbalance of the rotor is equivalent to a weight of 1 oz located 6 in. from the axis of rotation. Knowing that the motor is constrained to move vertically, determine (*a*) the speed in rpm at which resonance will occur, (*b*) the amplitude of the vibration of the motor at a speed of 1,200 rpm.

a. **Resonance Speed.** The resonance speed is equal to the circular frequency (in rpm) of the free vibration of the motor. The mass of the motor and the equivalent constant of the supporting springs are

$$m = \frac{350 \text{ lb}}{32.2 \text{ ft/sec}^2} = 10.87 \text{ lb-sec}^2\text{/ft}$$

$$k = 4(750 \text{ lb/in.}) = 3{,}000 \text{ lb/in.} = 36{,}000 \text{ lb/ft}$$

$$p = \sqrt{\frac{k}{m}} = \sqrt{\frac{36{,}000}{10.87}} = 57.5 \text{ radians/sec} = 549 \text{ rpm}$$

Resonance speed = 549 rpm ◄

b. **Amplitude of Vibration at 1,200 rpm.** The angular velocity of the motor and the mass of the equivalent 1-oz weight are

$$\omega = 1{,}200 \text{ rpm} = 125.6 \text{ radians/sec}$$

$$m = (1 \text{ oz})\frac{1 \text{ lb}}{16 \text{ oz}}\,\frac{1}{32.2 \text{ ft/sec}^2} = 0.00194 \text{ lb-sec}^2\text{/ft}$$

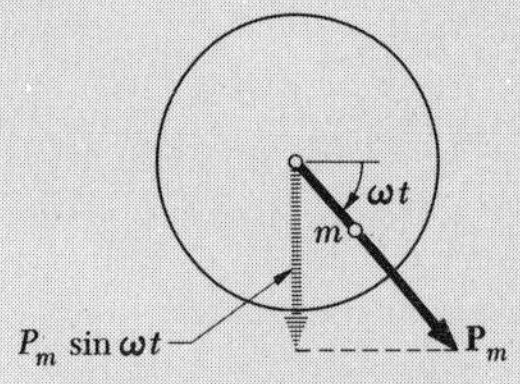

The magnitude of the centrifugal force due to the unbalance of the rotor is

$$P_m = ma_n = mr\omega^2 = (0.00194)\left(\tfrac{6}{12}\right)(125.6)^2 = 15.3 \text{ lb}$$

The static deflection that would be caused by a constant load P_m is

$$\frac{P_m}{k} = \frac{15.3 \text{ lb}}{3{,}000 \text{ lb/in.}} = 0.00510 \text{ in.}$$

Substituting the value of P_m/k together with the known values of ω and p into Eq. (19.33), we obtain

$$x_m = \frac{P_m/k}{1-(\omega/p)^2} = \frac{0.00510 \text{ in.}}{1-(125.6/57.5)^2}$$

$x_m = 0.00135$ in. ◄

PROBLEMS

19.75. A block of weight W is suspended from a spring of constant k and is acted upon by a vertical periodic force of magnitude $P = P_m \sin \omega t$. Determine the range of values of ω for which the amplitude of the vibration exceeds twice the static deflection caused by a constant force of magnitude P_m.

19.76. In Prob. 19.75, determine the range of values of ω for which the amplitude of the vibration is less than the static deflection caused by a constant force of magnitude P_m.

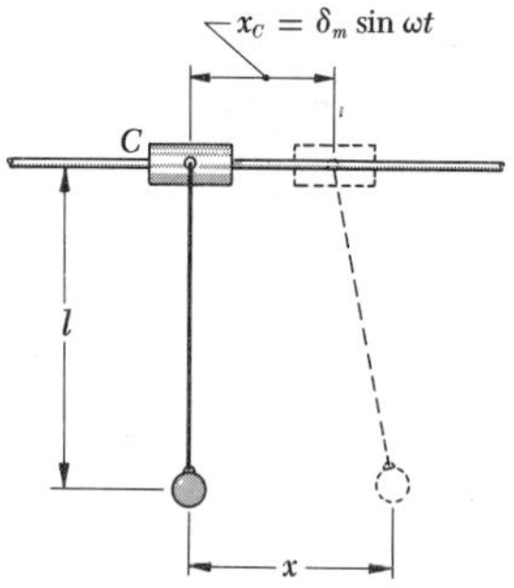

FIG. P 19.77

19.77. A simple pendulum of length l is suspended from a collar C which is forced to move horizontally according to the relation $x_C = \delta_m \sin \omega t$. Determine the range of values of ω for which the amplitude of the motion of the bob exceeds $2\delta_m$. (Assume δ_m is small compared to the length l of the pendulum.)

19.78. In Prob. 19.77, determine the range of values of ω for which the amplitude of the motion of the bob is less than δ_m.

FIG. P 19.79

19.79. A motor weighing 200 lb is supported by four springs having each a constant of 50 lb/in. The unbalance of the rotor is equivalent to a weight of 2 oz located 5 in. from the axis of rotation. Knowing that the motor is constrained to move vertically, determine (*a*) the speed (in rpm) at which resonance will occur, and (*b*) the amplitude of the steady-state vibration of the motor at a speed of 240 rpm.

19.80. Solve Prob. 19.79 assuming now that the 200-lb motor is directly supported by a light horizontal beam and that the static deflection of the beam due to the weight of the motor is 0.250 in.

19.81. A motor weighing 300 lb is supported by four springs having each a constant of 300 lb/in. The motor is constrained to move vertically, and the amplitude of its movement is observed to be 0.090 in. at a speed of 600 rpm. Knowing that the rotor weighs 120 lb, determine the distance between the mass center of the rotor and the axis of the shaft.

19.82. In Prob. 19.81, determine the amplitude of the vertical movement of the motor at a speed of (*a*) 100 rpm, (*b*) 800 rpm, (*c*) 375 rpm.

19.83. Rod AB is rigidly attached to the frame of a constant-speed motor. When a collar of weight W is placed on the spring, it is observed to vibrate with an amplitude of 0.10 in. When two collars, each of weight W, are placed on the spring, the amplitude is observed to be 0.12 in. What amplitude of vibration should be expected when three collars, each of weight W, are placed on the spring? (Obtain two answers.)

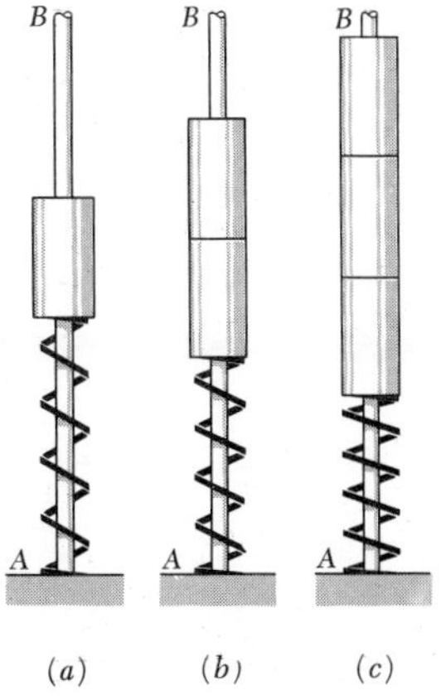

FIG. P 19.83

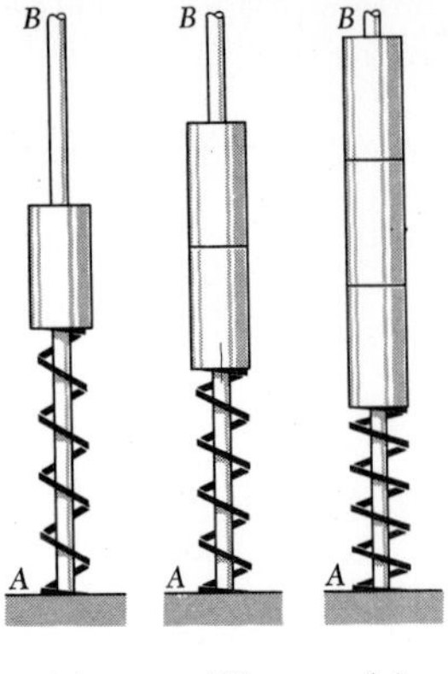

FIG. P 19.84

19.84. Rod AB is rigidly attached to the frame of a constant-speed motor. When a collar of weight W is placed on the spring, it is observed to vibrate with an amplitude of 0.30 in. When two collars, each of weight W, are placed on the spring, the amplitude is observed to be 0.10 in. What amplitude of vibration should be expected when three collars, each of weight W, are placed on the spring? (Obtain two answers.)

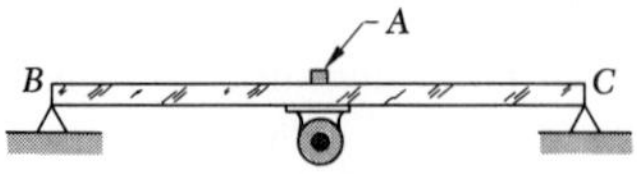

FIG. P 19.85

19.85. A variable-speed motor is rigidly attached to the beam BC. The rotor is slightly unbalanced and causes the beam to vibrate. When the speed of the motor is less than 1,000 rpm or more than 2,000 rpm, a small object placed at A is observed to remain in contact with the beam. For speeds between 1,000 and 2,000 rpm the object is observed to "dance" and actually to lose contact with the beam. Determine the amplitude of the motion of A when the speed of the motor is (*a*) 1,000 rpm, (*b*) 2,000 rpm.

19.86. In Prob. 19.85, determine the speed at which resonance will occur.

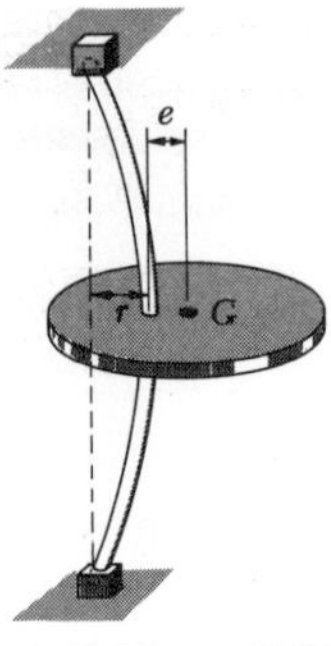

FIG. P 19.87 AND P 19.88

19.87. A disk of mass m is attached to the mid-point of a vertical shaft which revolves at an angular velocity ω. Denoting by k the spring constant of the system for a horizontal movement of the disk and by e the eccentricity of the disk with respect to the shaft, show that the deflection of the center of the shaft may be written in the form

$$r = \frac{e(\omega/p)^2}{1 - (\omega/p)^2}$$

where $p = \sqrt{(k/m)}$.

19.88. A disk weighing 75 lb is attached to the mid-point of a shaft. Knowing that a static force of 100 lb will deflect the shaft 0.050 in., determine the speed of the shaft in rpm at which resonance will occur.

19.89. Knowing that the disk of Prob. 19.88 is attached to the shaft with an eccentricity $e = 0.075$ in., determine the deflection r of the shaft at a speed of 800 rpm.

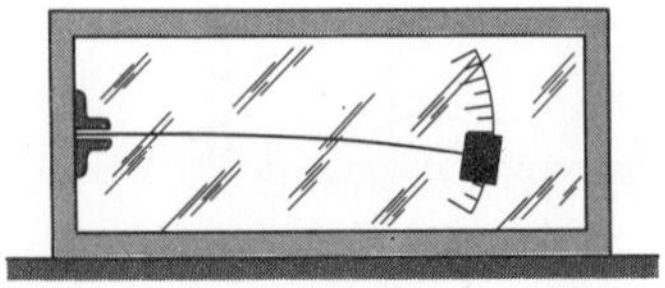

FIG. P 19.90

19.90. A certain vibrometer used to measure vibration amplitudes consists essentially of a box containing a slender rod to which a mass m is attached; the natural frequency of the mass-rod system is known to be 5 cycles/sec. When the box is rigidly attached to the casing of a motor rotating at 600 rpm, the mass is observed to vibrate with an amplitude of 0.060 in. relative to the box. Determine the amplitude of the vertical motion of the motor.

19.91. Solve Prob. 19.90 assuming that the speed of the motor is 150 rpm and that the other data are unchanged.

19.92. A small trailer weighing 600 lb is supported by two springs, each of constant 100 lb/in. The trailer is pulled over a road, the surface of which may be approximated by a sine curve of amplitude $1\frac{1}{2}$ in. and of period 16 ft (i.e., the distance between two successive crests is 16 ft, and the vertical distance from a crest to a trough is 3 in.). Determine (*a*) the speed at which resonance will occur, (*b*) the amplitude of the vibration of the trailer at a speed of 40 mph.

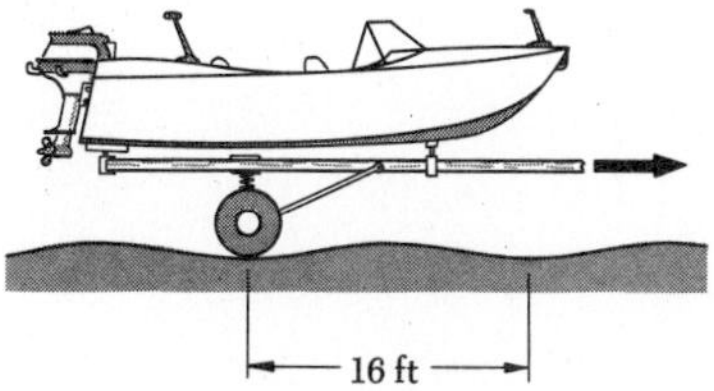

FIG. P 19.92

19.93. Knowing that the amplitude of the vibration of the trailer of Prob. 19.92 is not to exceed $\frac{3}{4}$ in., determine the smallest speed at which the trailer can be pulled over the road.

19.94. The amplitude of the motion of the pendulum bob in Prob. 19.77 is observed to be 2 in. when the amplitude of the motion of collar C is 1.0 in. Knowing that the length of the pendulum is $l = 36$ in., determine the two possible values of the frequency of the horizontal movement of the collar C.

DAMPED VIBRATIONS

***19.8. Damped Free Vibrations.** The vibrating systems considered in the first part of this chapter were assumed free of damping. Actually all vibrations are damped to some degree by friction forces. These forces may be caused by *dry friction*, or *Coulomb friction*, between rigid bodies, by *fluid friction* when a rigid body moves in a fluid, or by *internal friction* between the molecules of a seemingly elastic body.

A type of damping of special interest is the *viscous damping* caused by fluid friction at low and moderate speeds. Viscous damping is characterized by the fact that the friction force is *directly proportional to the speed* of the moving body. As an example, we shall consider again a body of mass m suspended from a spring of constant k, and we shall assume that the body is attached to the plunger of a dashpot (Fig. 19.10). The magnitude of the friction force exerted on the plunger by the surrounding fluid is equal to $c(dx/dt)$, where the constant c, expressed in lb-sec/ft and known as the *coefficient of viscous damping*, depends upon the physical properties of the fluid and the construction of the dashpot. The equation of motion is

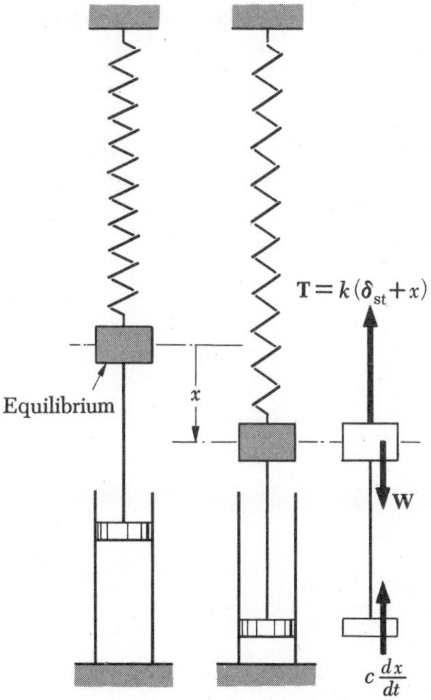

FIG. 19.10

$$+\downarrow \Sigma F = ma: \qquad W - k(\delta_{st} + x) - c\frac{dx}{dt} = m\frac{d^2x}{dt^2}$$

Recalling that $W = k\delta_{st}$, we write

$$m\frac{d^2x}{dt^2} + c\frac{dx}{dt} + kx = 0 \tag{19.37}$$

Substituting $x = e^{\lambda t}$ into (19.37), we write the *characteristic equation*

$$m\lambda^2 + c\lambda + k = 0 \tag{19.38}$$

and obtain the roots

$$\lambda = -\frac{c}{2m} \pm \sqrt{\left(\frac{c}{2m}\right)^2 - \frac{k}{m}} \tag{19.39}$$

Defining the *critical damping coefficient* c_c as the value of c which makes the radical in (19.39) equal to zero, we write

$$\left(\frac{c_c}{2m}\right)^2 - \frac{k}{m} = 0 \qquad c_c = 2m\sqrt{\frac{k}{m}} = 2mp \tag{19.40}$$

where p is the natural frequency of the system in the absence of damping. We may distinguish three different cases of damping, depending upon the value of the coefficient c.

1. *Heavy Damping:* $c > c_c$. The roots λ_1 and λ_2 of the characteristic equation (19.38) are real and distinct, and the general solution of the differential equation (19.37) is

$$x = Ae^{\lambda_1 t} + Be^{\lambda_2 t} \tag{19.41}$$

This solution corresponds to a nonvibratory motion. Since λ_1 and λ_2 are both negative, x approaches zero as t increases indefinitely. However, the system actually regains its equilibrium position after a finite time.

2. *Critical Damping:* $c = c_c$. The characteristic equation has a double root $\lambda = -c_c/2m = -p$, and the general solution of (19.37) is

$$x = (A + Bt)e^{-pt} \tag{19.42}$$

The motion obtained is again nonvibratory. Critically damped systems are of special interest in engineering applications since they regain their equilibrium position in the shortest possible time without oscillation.

3. *Light Damping:* $c < c_c$. The roots of (19.38) are complex and conjugate, and the general solution of (19.37) is of the form

$$x = e^{-(c/2m)t}(A \sin qt + B \cos qt) \tag{19.43}$$

where q is defined by the relation

$$q^2 = \frac{k}{m} - \left(\frac{c}{2m}\right)^2$$

Substituting $k/m = p^2$ and recalling (19.40), we write

$$q = p\sqrt{1 - \left(\frac{c}{c_c}\right)^2} \tag{19.44}$$

where the constant c/c_c is known as the *damping factor*. A substitution similar to the one used in Sec. 19.2 enables us to write the general solution of (19.37) in the form

$$x = x_m e^{-(c/2m)t} \sin (qt + \phi) \tag{19.45}$$

The motion defined by (19.45) is vibratory with diminishing amplitude (Fig. 19.11). Although this motion does not actually repeat itself, the time interval $\tau = 2\pi/q$ corresponding to two successive points where the curve (19.45) touches one of the limiting curves shown in Fig. 19.11 is commonly referred to as the period of the damped vibration. Recalling (19.44), we observe that τ is larger than the period of vibration of the corresponding undamped system.

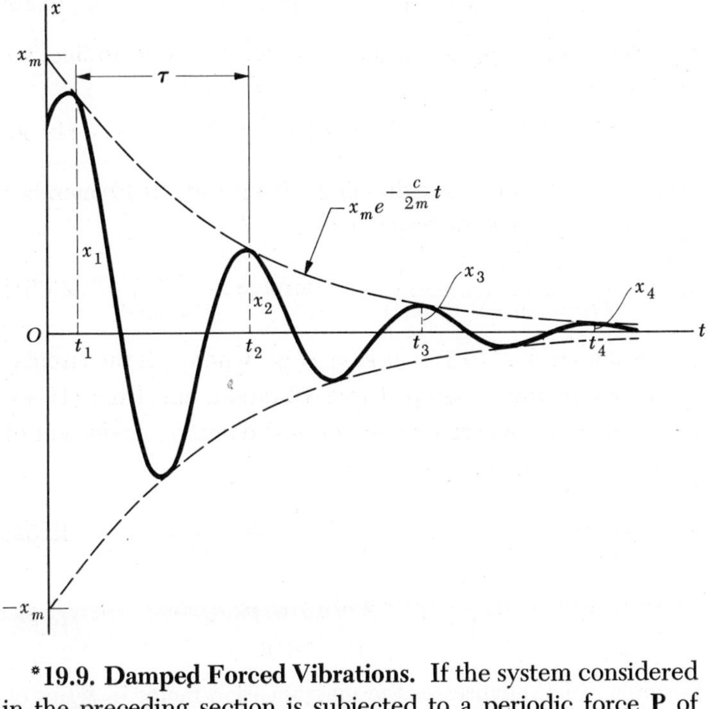

FIG. 19.11

***19.9. Damped Forced Vibrations.** If the system considered in the preceding section is subjected to a periodic force **P** of magnitude $P = P_m \sin \omega t$, the equation of motion becomes

$$m\frac{d^2x}{dt^2} + c\frac{dx}{dt} + kx = P_m \sin \omega t \tag{19.46}$$

The general solution of (19.46) is obtained by adding a particular solution of (19.46) to the complementary function or general solution of the homogeneous equation (19.37). The complementary function is given by (19.41), (19.42), or (19.43), depending upon the type of damping considered. It represents a *transient* motion which is eventually damped out.

Our interest in this section is centered on the steady-state vibration represented by a particular solution of (19.46) of the form

$$x_{\text{part}} = x_m \sin(\omega t - \varphi) \tag{19.47}$$

Substituting x_{part} for x into (19.46), we obtain

$$-m\omega^2 x_m \sin(\omega t - \varphi) + c\omega x_m \cos(\omega t - \varphi) + kx_m \sin(\omega t - \varphi) = P_m \sin \omega t$$

Making $\omega t - \varphi$ successively equal to 0 and to $\pi/2$, we write

$$c\omega x_m = P_m \sin\varphi \tag{19.48}$$

$$(k - m\omega^2)x_m = P_m \cos\varphi \tag{19.49}$$

Squaring both members of (19.48) and (19.49) and adding, we have

$$[(k - m\omega^2)^2 + (c\omega)^2]x_m^2 = P_m^2 \tag{19.50}$$

Solving (19.50) for x_m and dividing (19.48) and (19.49) member by member, we obtain, respectively,

$$x_m = \frac{P_m}{\sqrt{(k - m\omega^2)^2 + (c\omega)^2}} \qquad \tan\varphi = \frac{c\omega}{k - m\omega^2} \tag{19.51}$$

Recalling from (19.4) that $k/m = p^2$, where p is the circular frequency of the undamped free vibration, and from (19.40) that $2mp = c_c$, where c_c is the critical damping coefficient of the system, we write

$$\frac{x_m}{P_m/k} = \frac{x_m}{\delta_m} = \frac{1}{\sqrt{[1 - (\omega/p)^2]^2 + [2(c/c_c)(\omega/p)]^2}} \tag{19.52}$$

$$\tan\varphi = \frac{2(c/c_c)(\omega/p)}{1 - (\omega/p)^2} \tag{19.53}$$

Formula (19.52) expresses the magnification factor in terms of the frequency ratio ω/p and damping factor c/c_c. It may be used to determine the amplitude of the steady-state vibration produced by an impressed force of magnitude $P = P_m \sin \omega t$ or by an impressed support movement $\delta = \delta_m \sin \omega t$. Formula

(19.53) defines in terms of the same parameters the *phase difference* φ between the impressed force or impressed support movement and the resulting steady-state vibration of the damped system. The magnification factor has been plotted against the frequency ratio in Fig. 19.12 for various values of the damping factor. We observe that the amplitude of a forced vibration may be kept small by choosing a large coefficient of viscous damping c or by keeping the natural and forced frequencies far apart.

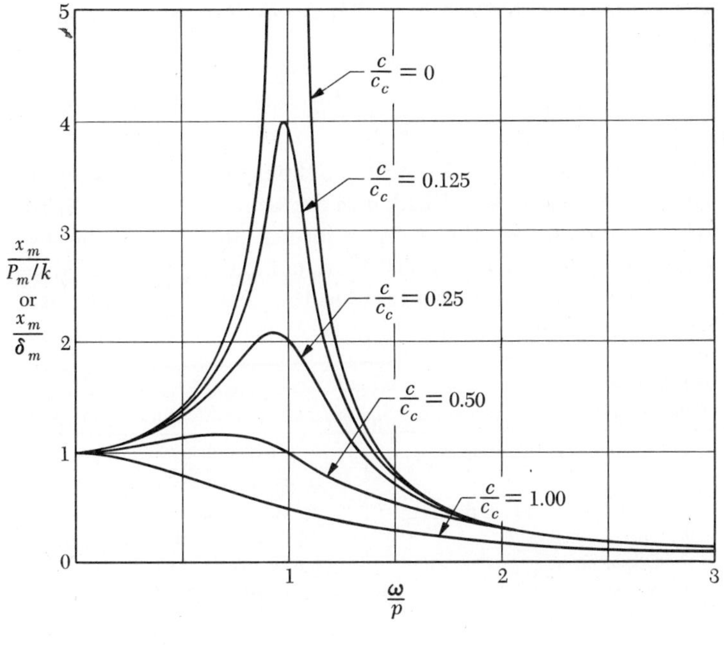

FIG. 19.12

***19.10. Electrical Analogues.** Oscillating electrical circuits are characterized by differential equations of the same type as those obtained in the preceding sections. Their analysis is therefore similar to that of a mechanical system and the results obtained for a given vibrating system may be readily extended to the equivalent circuit. Conversely, any result obtained for an electrical circuit will also apply to the corresponding mechanical system.

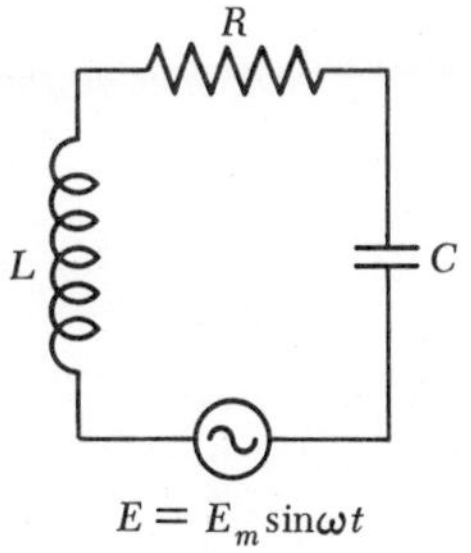

FIG. 19.13

Consider an electrical circuit consisting of an inductor of inductance L, a resistor of resistance R, and a capacitor of capacitance C, connected in series with a source of alternating voltage

$E = E_m \sin \omega t$ (Fig. 19.13). It is recalled from elementary electromagnetic theory† that, if i denotes the current in the circuit and q the electric charge on the capacitor, the drop in potential is $L(di/dt)$ across the inductor, Ri across the resistor, and q/C across the capacitor. Expressing that the algebraic sum of the applied voltage and of the drops in potential around the circuit loop is zero, we write

$$E_m \sin \omega t - L\frac{di}{dt} - Ri - \frac{q}{C} = 0 \qquad (19.54)$$

Rearranging the terms and recalling that, at any instant, the current i is equal to the rate of change dq/dt of the charge q, we have

$$L\frac{d^2q}{dt^2} + R\frac{dq}{dt} + \frac{1}{C}q = E_m \sin \omega t \qquad (19.55)$$

We verify that Eq. (19.55), which defines the oscillations of the electrical circuit of Fig. 19.13, is of the same type as Eq. (19.46), which characterizes the damped forced vibrations of the mechanical system of Fig. 19.10. By comparing the two equations, we may construct a table of the analogous mechanical and electrical expressions.

TABLE 19.2
Characteristics of a Mechanical System and of Its Electrical Analogue

Mechanical System	Electrical Circuit
m Mass	L Inductance
c Coefficient of viscous damping	R Resistance
k Spring constant	$1/C$ Reciprocal of capacitance
x Displacement	q Charge
v Velocity	i Current
P Applied force	E Applied voltage

Table 19.2 may be used to extend to their electrical analogues the results obtained in the preceding sections for various mechanical systems. For instance, the amplitude i_m of the current in the circuit of Fig. 19.13 may be obtained by noting that it corresponds to the maximum value v_m of the velocity in the analogous mechanical system. Recalling that $v_m = \omega x_m$, substituting for x_m from Eq. (19.51), and replacing the constants of the mechanical system by the corresponding electrical expressions, we have

† See Hammond, "Electrical Engineering," McGraw-Hill Book Company, Inc., chap. 1.

$$i_m = \frac{\omega E_m}{\sqrt{\left(\frac{1}{C} - L\omega^2\right)^2 + (R\omega)^2}}$$

$$i_m = \frac{E_m}{\sqrt{R^2 + \left(L\omega - \frac{1}{C\omega}\right)^2}} \tag{19.56}$$

The radical in the expression obtained is known as the *impedance* of the electrical circuit.

The analogy between mechanical systems and electrical circuits holds for transient as well as steady-state oscillations. The oscillations of the circuit shown in Fig. 19.14, for instance, are analogous to the damped free vibrations of the system of Fig. 19.10. As far as the initial conditions are concerned, we may note that closing the switch S when the charge on the capacitor is $q = q_0$ is equivalent to releasing the mass of the mechanical system with no initial velocity from the position $x = x_0$. We should also observe that, if a battery of constant voltage E is introduced in the electrical circuit of Fig. 19.14, closing the switch S will be equivalent to suddenly applying a force of constant magnitude P to the mass of the mechanical system of Fig. 19.10.

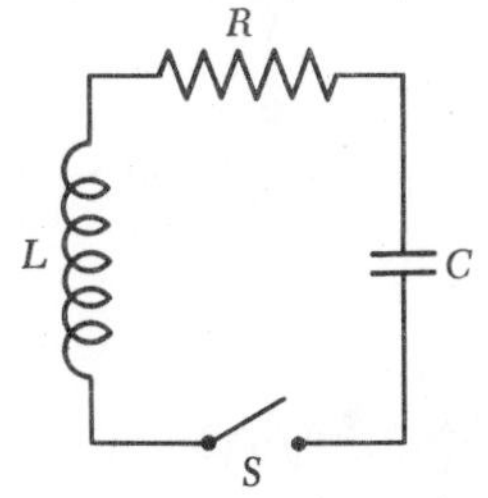

FIG. 19.14

The above discussion would be of questionable value if its only result were to make it possible for mechanics students to analyze electrical circuits without learning the elements of electromagnetism. It is hoped, rather, that this discussion will encourage the students to apply to the solution of problems in mechanical vibrations the mathematical techniques they may learn in later courses in electrical circuits theory. The chief value of the concept of electrical analogue, however, resides in its application to *experimental methods* for the determination of the characteristics of a given mechanical system. Indeed, an electrical circuit is much more easily constructed than a mechanical model, and the fact that its characteristics may be modified by varying the inductance, resistance, or capacitance of its various components makes the use of the electrical analogue particularly convenient.

To determine the electrical analogue of a given mechanical system, we shall focus our attention on each moving mass in the system and observe which springs, dashpots, or external forces are applied directly to it. An equivalent electrical loop may then be constructed to match each of the mechanical units thus defined; the various loops obtained in that way will form together the desired circuit. Consider, for instance, the mechanical system of Fig. 19.15. We observe that the mass m_1

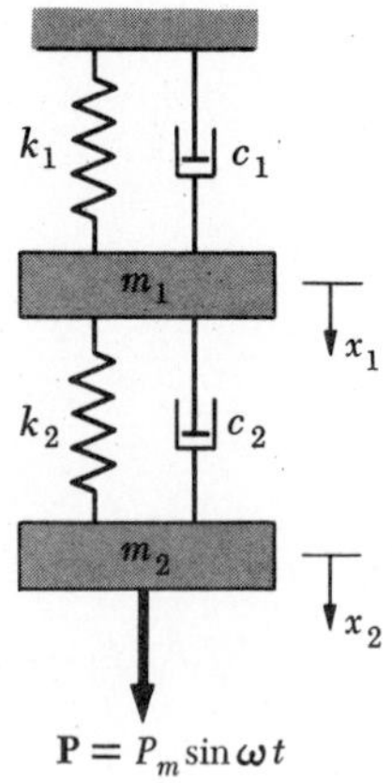

FIG. 19.15

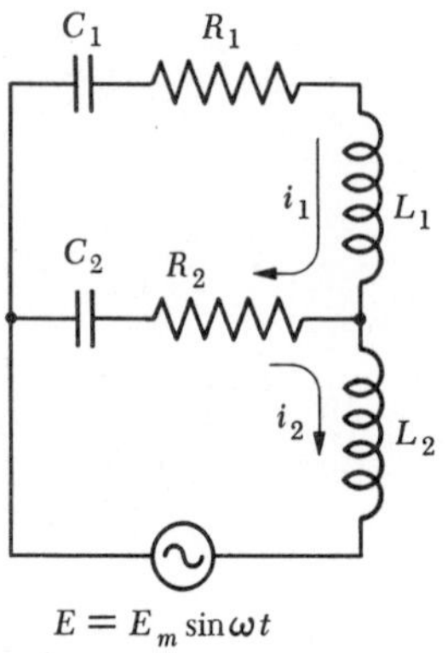

FIG. 19.16

is acted upon by two springs of constants k_1 and k_2 and by two dashpots characterized by the coefficients of viscous damping c_1 and c_2. The electrical circuit should therefore include a loop consisting of an inductor of inductance L_1 proportional to m_1, of two capacitors of capacitance C_1 and C_2 inversely proportional to k_1 and k_2 respectively, and of two resistors of resistance R_1 and R_2, proportional to c_1 and c_2 respectively. Since the mass m_2 is acted upon by the spring k_2 and the dashpot c_2, as well as by the force $P = P_m \sin \omega t$, the circuit should also include a loop containing the capacitor C_2, the resistor R_2, the new inductor L_2, and the voltage source $E = E_m \sin \omega t$ (Fig. 19.16).

To check that the mechanical system of Fig. 19.15 and the electrical circuit of Fig. 19.16 actually satisfy the same differential equations, we shall first derive the equations of motion for m_1 and m_2. Denoting respectively by x_1 and x_2 the displacements of m_1 and m_2 from their equilibrium positions, we observe that the deflection of the spring k_1 (measured from the equilibrium position) is equal to x_1, while the deflection of the spring k_2 is equal to the relative displacement $x_1 - x_2$ of m_1 with respect to m_2. The equations of motion for m_1 and m_2 are therefore

$$m_1 \frac{d^2x_1}{dt^2} + c_1 \frac{dx_1}{dt} + c_2 \frac{d}{dt}(x_1 - x_2) + k_1 x_1 + k_2 (x_1 - x_2) = 0 \tag{19.57}$$

$$m_2 \frac{d^2x_2}{dt^2} + c_2 \frac{d}{dt}(x_2 - x_1) + k_2 (x_2 - x_1) = P_m \sin \omega t \tag{19.58}$$

Consider now the electrical circuit of Fig. 19.16; we denote respectively by i_1 and i_2 the current in the first and second loops, and by q_1 and q_2 the integrals $\int i_1\,dt$ and $\int i_2\,dt$. Noting that the charge on the capacitor C_1 is q_1, while the charge on C_2 is $q_1 - q_2$, we express that the sum of the potential differences in each loop is zero:

$$L_1 \frac{d^2q_1}{dt^2} + R_1 \frac{dq_1}{dt} + R_2 \frac{d}{dt}(q_1 - q_2) + \frac{q_1}{C_1} + \frac{q_1 - q_2}{C_2} = 0 \tag{19.59}$$

$$L_2 \frac{d^2q_2}{dt^2} + R_2 \frac{d}{dt}(q_2 - q_1) + \frac{q_2 - q_1}{C_2} = E_m \sin \omega t \tag{19.60}$$

We easily check that Eqs. (19.59) and (19.60) reduce to (19.57) and (19.58), respectively, when the substitutions indicated in Table 19.2 are performed.

PROBLEMS

19.95. Show that, in the case of heavy damping ($c > c_c$), a body never passes through its position of equilibrium O. (*a*) if it is released with no initial velocity from an arbitrary position or (*b*) if it is started from O with an arbitrary initial velocity.

19.96. Show that, in the case of heavy damping ($c > c_c$), a body released from an arbitrary position with an arbitrary initial velocity cannot pass more than once through its equilibrium position.

19.97. In the case of light damping, the displacements x_1, x_2, x_3, etc., shown in Fig. 19.11 may be assumed equal to the maximum displacements. Show that the ratio of any two successive maximum displacements x_n and x_{n+1} is a constant and that the natural logarithm of this ratio, called the *logarithmic decrement*, is

$$\ln \frac{x_n}{x_{n+1}} = \frac{2\pi(c/c_c)}{\sqrt{1 - (c/c_c)^2}}$$

19.98. In practice, it is often difficult to determine the logarithmic decrement defined in Prob. 19.97 by measuring two successive maximum displacements. Show that the logarithmic decrement may also be expressed as $(1/n) \ln (x_1/x_{n+1})$, where n is the number of cycles between readings of the maximum displacement.

19.99. In a system with light damping ($c < c_c$), the period of vibration is commonly defined as the time interval $\tau = 2\pi/q$ corresponding to two successive points where the displacement-time curve touches one of the limiting curves shown in Fig. 19.11. Show that the interval of time (*a*) between a maximum positive displacement and the following maximum negative displacement is $\frac{1}{2}\tau$, (*b*) between two successive zero displacements is $\frac{1}{2}\tau$, (*c*) between a maximum positive displacement and the following zero displacement is greater than $\frac{1}{4}\tau$.

19.100. The barrel of a field gun weighs 1,400 lb and is returned into firing position after recoil by a recuperator of constant $k = 10{,}000$ lb/ft. Determine the value of the coefficient of damping of the recoil mechanism which causes the barrel to return into firing position in the shortest possible time without oscillation.

19.101. A critically damped system is released from rest at an arbitrary position x_0 when $t = 0$. (*a*) Determine the position of the system at any time t. (*b*) Apply the result obtained in part *a* to the barrel of the gun of Prob. 19.100, and determine the time at which the barrel is halfway back to its firing position.

19.102. Assuming that the barrel of the gun of Prob. 19.100 is modified, with a resulting increase in weight of 400 lb, determine the constant k of the recoil mechanism which should be used with the same recuperator if the system is to remain critically damped.

19.103. In the case of the forced vibration of a system with a given damping factor c/c_c, determine the frequency ratio ω/p for which the amplitude of the vibration is maximum.

19.104. Show that for a small value of the damping factor c/c_c (*a*) the maximum amplitude of a forced vibration occurs when $\omega \approx p$, (*b*) the corresponding value of the magnification factor is approximately $\frac{1}{2}(c_c/c)$.

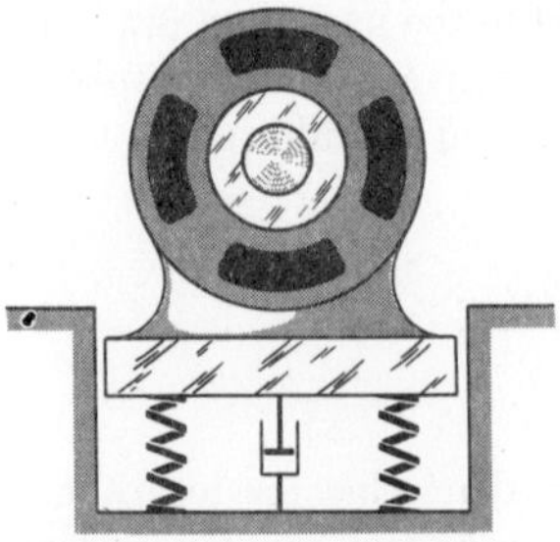

FIG. P 19.105

19.105. A motor weighing 50 lb is supported by four springs having each a constant of 1,000 lb/in. The unbalance of the rotor is equivalent to a weight of 1 oz located 5 in. from the axis of rotation. Knowing that the motor is constrained to move vertically, determine the amplitude of the steady-state vibration of the motor at a speed of 1,800 rpm, assuming (*a*) that no damping is present, (*b*) that the damping factor c/c_c is equal to 0.125.

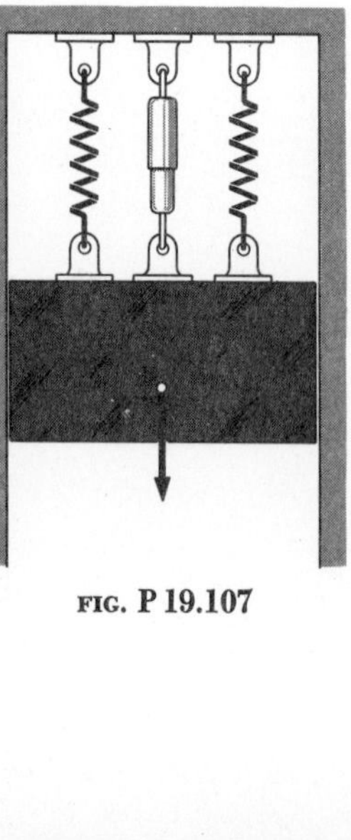

FIG. P 19.107

19.106. Assume that the 50-lb motor of Prob. 19.105 is directly supported by a light horizontal beam. The static deflection of the beam due to the weight of the motor is observed to be 0.230 in., and the amplitude of the vibration of the motor is 0.02 in. at a speed of 400 rpm. Determine (*a*) the damping factor c/c_c, (*b*) the coefficient of damping c.

19.107. A machine element weighing 800 lb is supported by two springs having each a constant of 200 lb/in. A periodic force of maximum value 20 lb and of frequency 2.5 cycles/sec is applied to the element. Knowing that the coefficient of damping is 8 lb-sec/in., determine the amplitude of the steady-state vibration of the element.

19.108. In Prob. 19.107, determine the required value of the coefficient of damping if the amplitude of the steady-state vibration of the element is to be 0.15 in.

19.109. A platform of weight 200 lb, supported by a set of springs equivalent to a single spring of constant $k = 400$ lb/in., is subjected to a periodic force of maximum magnitude 100 lb. Knowing that the coefficient of damping is 10 lb-sec/in., determine (*a*) the natural frequency in rpm of the platform *if* there were no damping, (*b*) the frequency in rpm of the periodic force corresponding to the maximum value of the magnification factor, assuming damping, (*c*) the amplitude of the *actual* motion of the platform for each of the frequencies found in parts *a* and *b*.

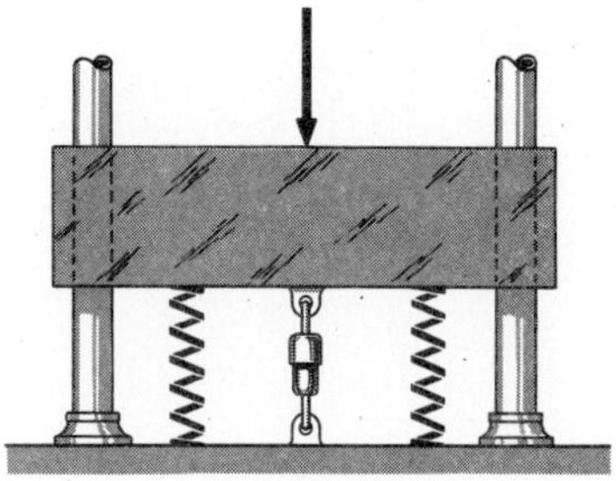

FIG. P 19.109

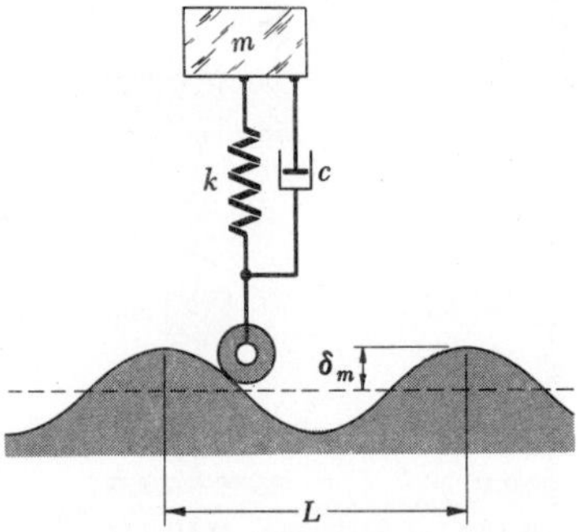

FIG. P 19.110

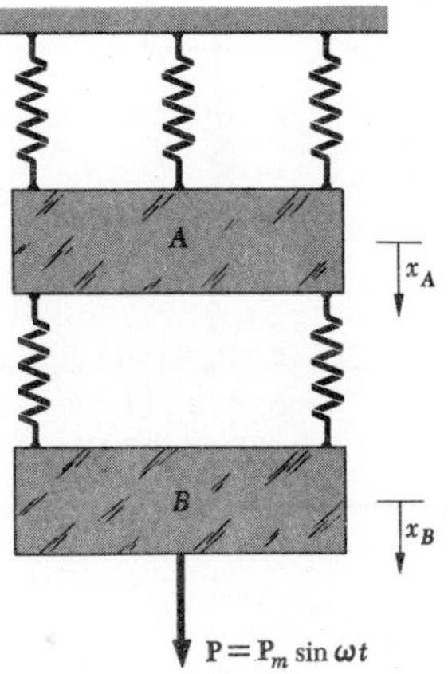

FIG. P 19.111

*19.110. The suspension of an automobile may be approximated by the simplified spring-and-dashpot system shown. (*a*) Write the differential equation defining the absolute motion of the mass m when the system moves at a speed v over a road of sinusoidal cross section as shown. (*b*) Derive an expression for the amplitude of the absolute motion of m.

*19.111. Two loads A and B, each of mass m, are suspended as shown by means of five springs of the same constant k. Load B is subjected to a force of magnitude $P = P_m \sin \omega t$. Write the differential equations defining the displacements x_A and x_B of the two loads from their equilibrium positions.

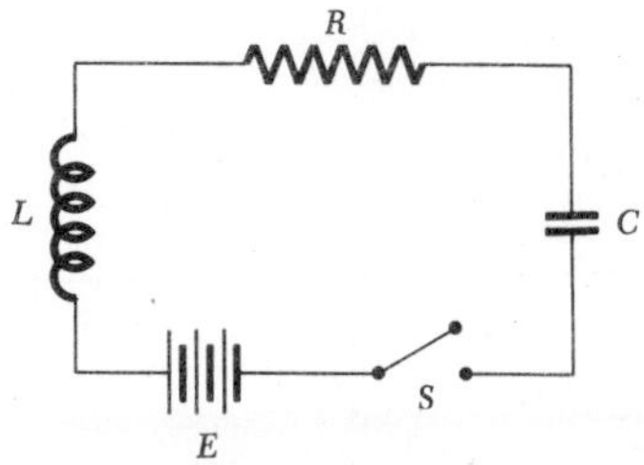

FIG. P 19.112

19.112. Determine the range of values of the resistance R for which oscillations will take place in the circuit shown when the switch S is closed.

19.113. Consider the circuit of Prob. 19.112 when the capacitance C is equal to zero. If the switch S is closed at time $t = 0$, determine (*a*) the final value of the current in the circuit, (*b*) the time t at which the current will have reached $(1 - 1/e)$ times its final value. (The desired value of t is known as the *time constant* of the circuit.)

19.114 through 19.117. Draw the electrical analogue of the mechanical system shown. (*Hint.* In Probs. 19.114 and 19.115, draw the loops corresponding to the free bodies m and A.)

19.118 and 19.119. Write the differential equations defining (*a*) the displacements of mass m and point A, (*b*) the currents in the corresponding loops of the electrical analogue.

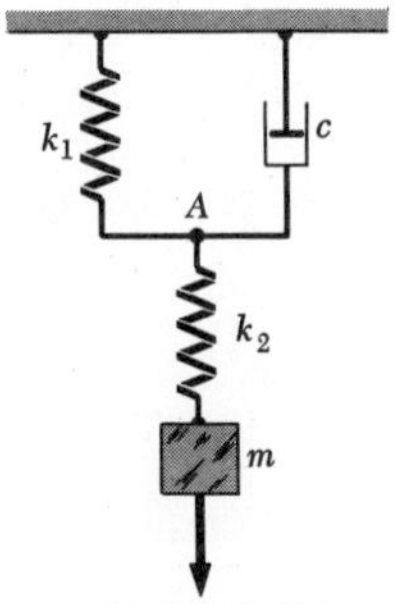

$P = P_m \sin \omega t$

FIG. P 19.114 AND P 19.118

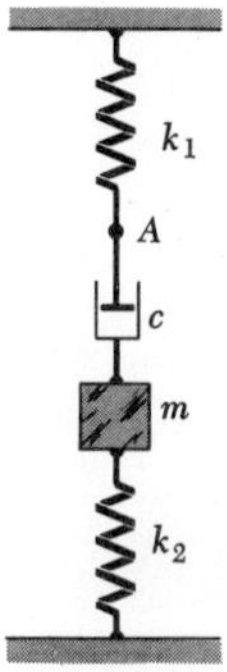

FIG. P 19.115 AND P 19.119

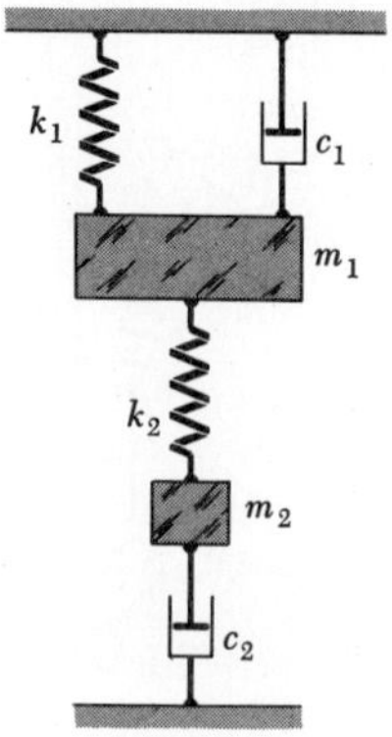

FIG. P 19.116 AND P 19.120

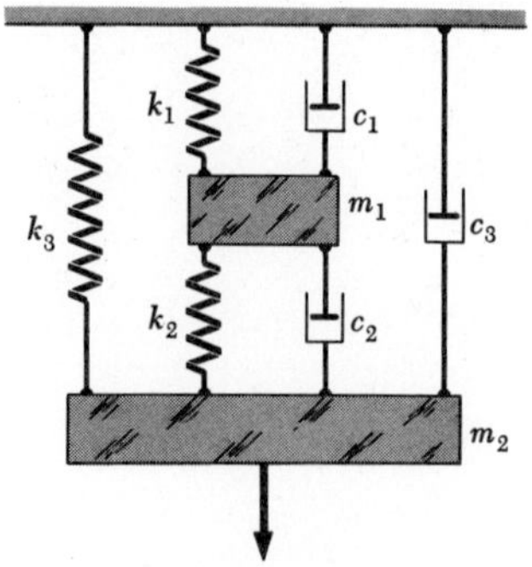

$P = P_m \sin \omega t$

FIG. P 19.117 AND P 19.121

19.120 and 19.121. Write the differential equations defining (*a*) the displacements of the masses m_1 and m_2, (*b*) the currents in the corresponding loops of the electrical analogue.

REVIEW PROBLEMS

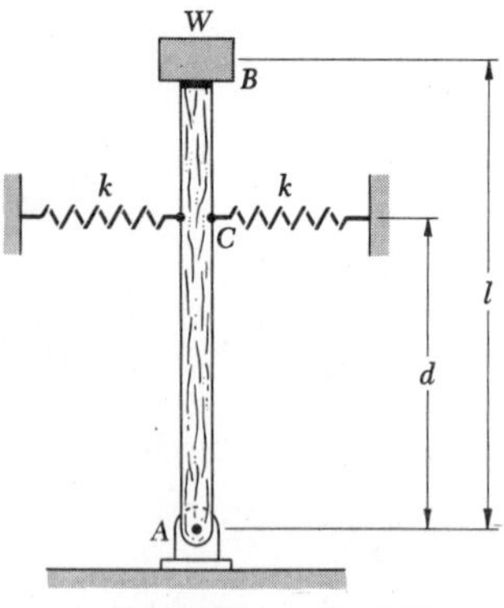

FIG. P 19.122 AND P 19.123

19.122. The rod AB is attached to a hinge at A and to two springs each of constant k. When l = 20 in., d = 15 in., and W = 225 lb, determine the value of k for which the period of small oscillations is (*a*) 1 sec, (*b*) infinite. Neglect the weight of the rod and assume that each spring can act in either tension or compression.

19.123. If d = 16 in., l = 24 in., and each spring has a constant k = 4 lb/in., determine the load W for which the period of small oscillations is (*a*) 0.50 sec, (*b*) infinite. Neglect the weight of the rod and assume that each spring can act in either tension or compression.

19.124. A simple pendulum of length l is suspended in an elevator. A weight W is attached to a spring of constant k and is carried in the same elevator. Determine the periods of vibration of the pendulum and of the weight if the elevator has an acceleration a directed (*a*) upward, (*b*) downward.

19.125. The centroidal moments of inertia $\bar{I}_x$ and $\bar{I}_z$ of an airplane weighing 1,600 lb are determined by letting the airplane oscillate as a compound pendulum. In the arrangement shown, the distance from the mass center G to the point of suspension O is known to be 6 ft. Knowing that the observed periods of oscillation about axes through O parallel to the x and z axes are, respectively, 3.10 sec and 3.25 sec, determine the centroidal moments of inertia $\bar{I}_x$ and $\bar{I}_z$.

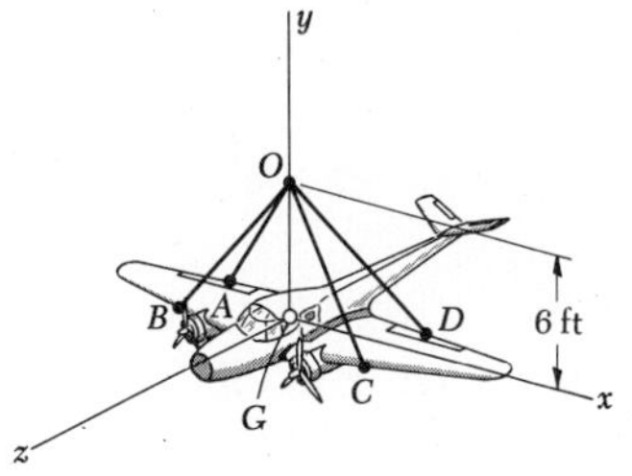

FIG. P 19.125

19.126. The centroidal moment of inertia $\bar{I}_y$ of an airplane weighing 1,600 lb is determined by suspending the airplane by two cables of length 6 ft as shown. The airplane is rotated through a small angle about the vertical through G and then released. Knowing that the observed period of oscillation is 2.60 sec, determine the centroidal moment of inertia $\bar{I}_y$.

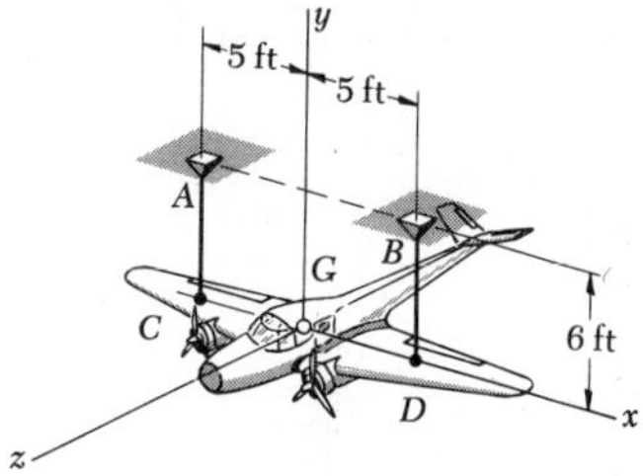

FIG. P 19.126

19.127. As the speed of a spring-supported motor is slowly increased from 150 to 200 rpm, the amplitude of the vibration due to the unbalance of the rotor is observed to decrease continuously from 0.150 to 0.080 in. Determine the speed at which resonance would occur, assuming no damping.

19.128. In Prob. 19.127, determine the speed of the motor for which the amplitude of the vibration is 0.200 in.

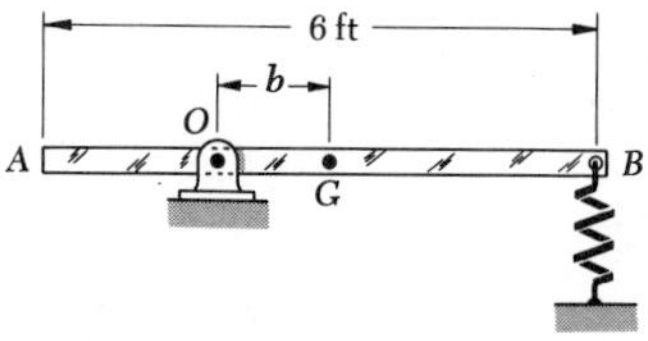

FIG. P 19.129

19.129. A slender rod AB of length 6 ft and weight $W = 40$ lb is attached to a pin at O and to a spring of constant $k = 40$ lb/in. at B. Determine (*a*) the distance b for which the largest frequency of vibration occurs, (*b*) the corresponding value of the frequency.

19.130. If either a simple or a compound pendulum is used to determine experimentally the acceleration of gravity g, difficulties are encountered. In the simple pendulum, the string is not truly weightless, while, in the compound pendulum, the exact location of the mass center is difficult to establish. In the case of a compound pendulum, the difficulty may be eliminated by using a reversible, or Kater, pendulum. Two knife-edges A and B are placed so that they are obviously not at the same distance from the mass center G, and the distance l is measured with great precision. The position of a counterweight D is then adjusted so that the period of oscillation τ is the same when either knife-edge is used. Show that the period τ obtained is equal to that of a true simple pendulum of length l and that $g = 4\pi^2 l/\tau^2$.

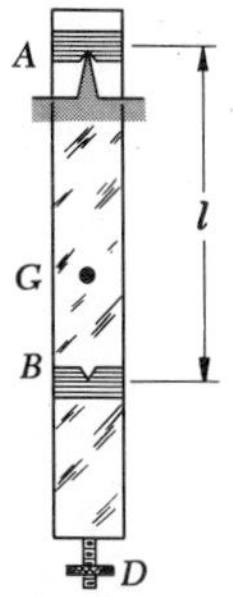

FIG. P 19.130

19.131. A period of 4.10 sec is observed for the angular oscillations of a 1-lb gyroscope rotor suspended from a wire as shown. Knowing that a period of 6.20 sec is obtained when a 2-in.-diameter steel sphere is suspended in the same fashion, determine the centroidal moment of inertia and the centroidal radius of gyration of the rotor. (Specific weight of steel = 490 lb/ft^3.)

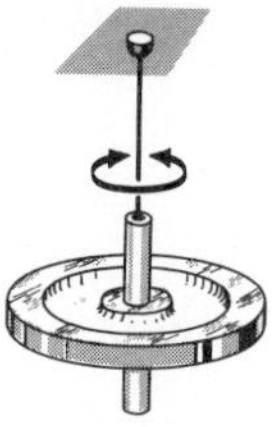
FIG. P 19.131

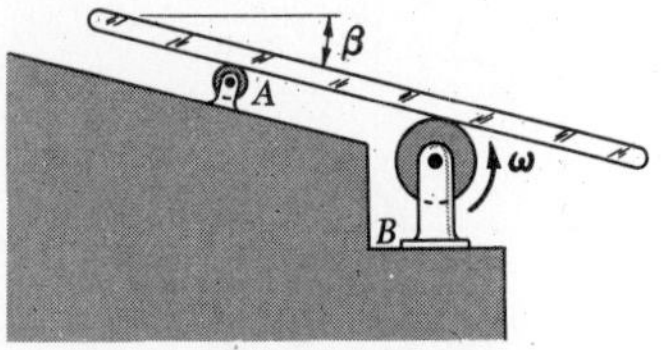

FIG. P 19.132

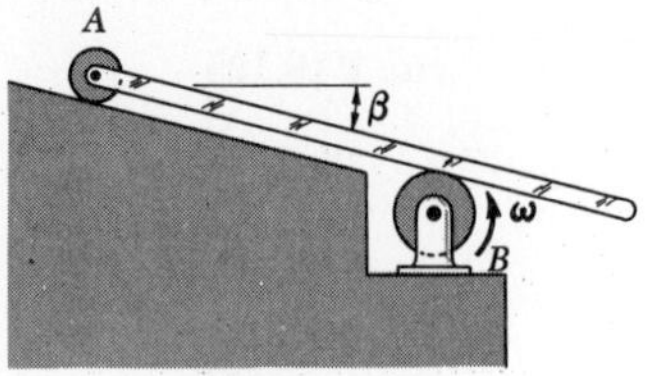

FIG. P 19.133

19.132 and 19.133. A plank of weight W is supported by a small wheel A of negligible weight and by a wheel B which rotates with a large counterclockwise angular velocity. The coefficient of friction between wheel B and the plank is μ and the distance between the two wheels is L. If the plank is displaced slightly from its equilibrium position, (*a*) show that the resulting motion is simple harmonic, (*b*) derive an expression for the frequency of the vibration.

Slender rod	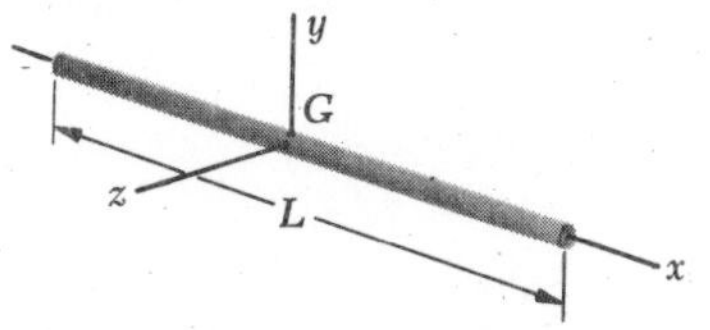	$I_y = I_z = \frac{1}{12}mL^2$
Thin rectangular plate	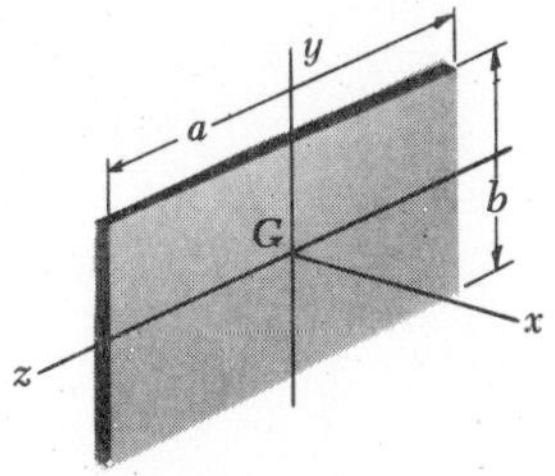	$I_x = \frac{1}{12}m(a^2 + b^2)$ $I_y = \frac{1}{12}ma^2$ $I_z = \frac{1}{12}mb^2$
Rectangular prism	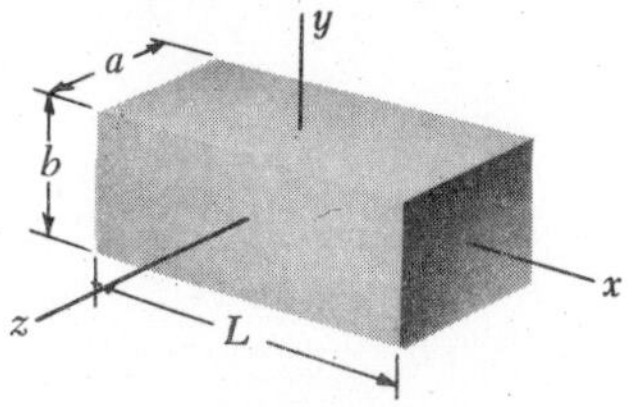	$I_x = \frac{1}{12}m(a^2 + b^2)$ $I_y = \frac{1}{12}m(a^2 + L^2)$ $I_z = \frac{1}{12}m(b^2 + L^2)$
Thin disk	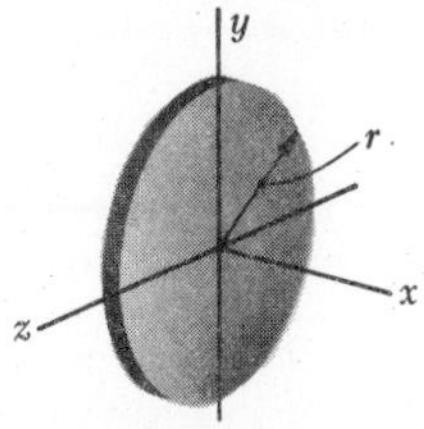	$I_x = \frac{1}{2}mr^2$ $I_y = I_z = \frac{1}{4}mr^2$
Circular cylinder	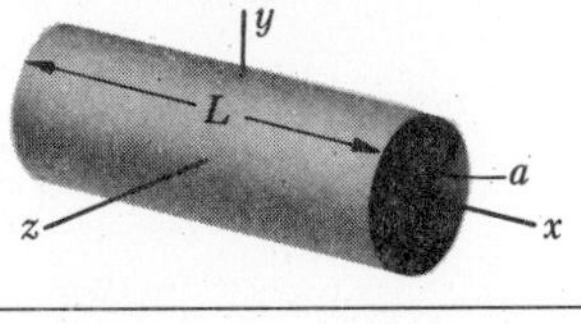	$I_x = \frac{1}{2}ma^2$ $I_y = I_z = \frac{1}{12}m(3a^2 + L^2)$
Circular cone	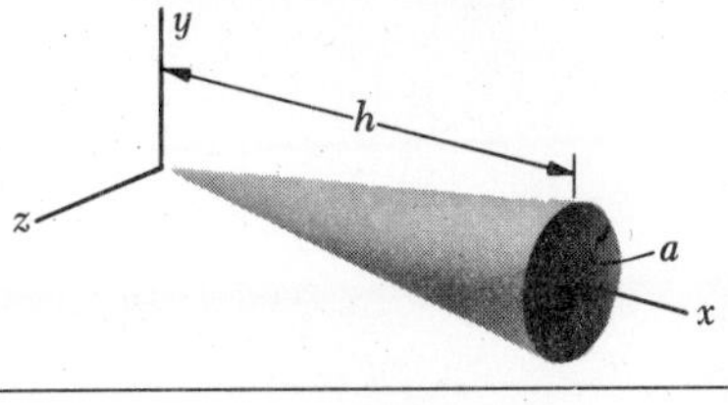	$I_x = \frac{3}{10}ma^2$ $I_y = I_z = \frac{3}{5}m(\frac{1}{4}a^2 + h^2)$
Sphere	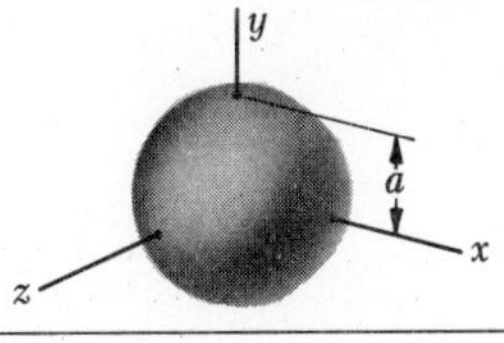	$I_x = I_y = I_z = \frac{2}{5}ma^2$

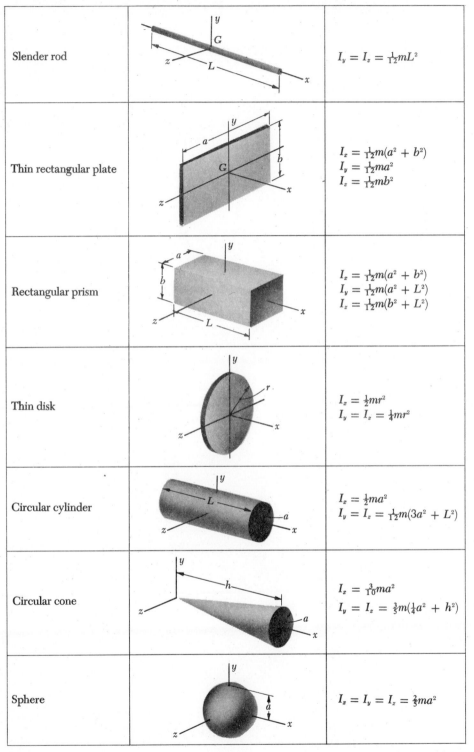

Mass moments of inertia of common geometric shapes

Appendix. GRAPHICAL METHODS IN STATICS

A.1. A Graphical Method for the Reduction of a System of Forces. A system of coplanar forces acting on a rigid body may be reduced graphically to one force or one couple by making use of the principle of transmissibility and the parallelogram law. Consider, for instance, the three forces $\mathbf{F}_1$, $\mathbf{F}_2$, and $\mathbf{F}_3$ (Fig. A.1*a*). The forces $\mathbf{F}_1$ and $\mathbf{F}_2$ may be moved along their lines of action until they act at the same point *A* (Fig. A.1*b*). They may then be added into their resultant $\mathbf{R}_{1,2}$ (Fig. A.1*c*). The forces $\mathbf{R}_{1,2}$ and $\mathbf{F}_3$ may in turn be moved along their lines of action until they act at the same point *B* (Fig. A.1*d*) and added into their resultant $\mathbf{R}_{1,2,3}$ (Fig. A.1*e*). If there were more than three forces, it would be possible to repeat this procedure until all the forces were added together.

This method is simple to understand and easy to remember; yet it is not always practical. Indeed, the construction may

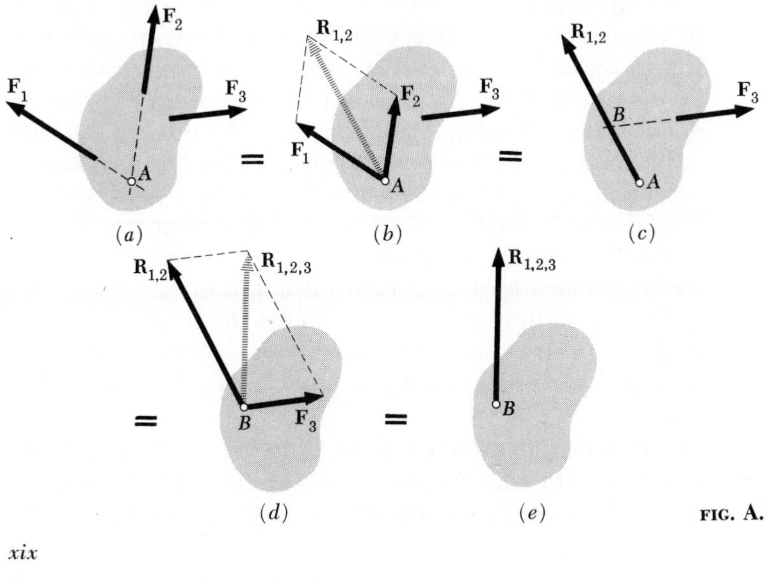

FIG. A.1

become quite cumbersome if many forces are involved. Besides, lines of action will perhaps intersect off the paper; and, obviously, the method fails completely if all the forces are parallel. We shall consider next another method for the graphical reduction of a system of forces, which is less direct but more effective.

A.2. Resultant of a System of Forces by the Method of the Force Polygon and String Polygon. Consider four forces $\mathbf{F}_1$, $\mathbf{F}_2$, $\mathbf{F}_3$, and $\mathbf{F}_4$ acting on a rigid body (Fig. A.2*a*). We draw the lines of action of the forces, extending them as far as possible on one side of the rigid body to divide the space outside the rigid body into four distinct regions. We write the letter *a* in one of these regions, and, moving clockwise around the body, we write successively *b, c, d,* and finally *e* in the region from which we started. The line of action of $\mathbf{F}_1$, which separates regions *a* and *b,* will be referred to as *line ab.* The lines of action of $\mathbf{F}_2$, $\mathbf{F}_3$, and $\mathbf{F}_4$ will be denoted similarly by *bc, cd,* and *de,* each time reading the letters clockwise around the body. This is *Bow's notation.*

We shall now draw the four given forces in tip-to-tail fashion in a separate diagram (Fig. A.2*b*). The tail of the first force is denoted by *A* and its tip, which is also the tail of the second force, by *B; C, D,* and *E* are defined in a similar way. We shall refer to each of these forces by the names of the points they join, naming first the letter corresponding to the tail and last the letter corresponding to the tip. Thus, the four given forces will be called $\overrightarrow{AB}$, $\overrightarrow{BC}$, $\overrightarrow{CD}$, and $\overrightarrow{DE}$, respectively.

Comparing the two figures we have drawn (Fig. A.2*a* and *b*), we note that a correspondence exists between *regions* in Fig. A.2*a* and *points* in Fig. A.2*b*. Each force *joins two points* in Fig. A.2*b*, while its line of action *separates two regions* of corresponding names in Fig. A.2*a*; thus, to the force $\overrightarrow{AB}$ joining points *A* and *B* corresponds the line of action *ab* separating regions *a* and *b;* to the force $\overrightarrow{BC}$ corresponds the line *bc*, to $\overrightarrow{CD}$ corresponds *cd,* and to $\overrightarrow{DE}$ corresponds *de.*

The magnitude, direction, and sense of the resultant are easily obtained by joining points *A* and *E* in Fig. A.2*b*. We shall see next how the line of action of the resultant $\overrightarrow{AE}$ may be determined by using the two figures simultaneously. We note that, according to the notation used, this line will be named *ae.*

We choose an arbitrary point *O*, called a *pole* (Fig. A.2*d*), and draw lines from *O* to each of the vertices of the force polygon. The lines *OA, OB, OC, OD,* and *OE* are called *rays.* We

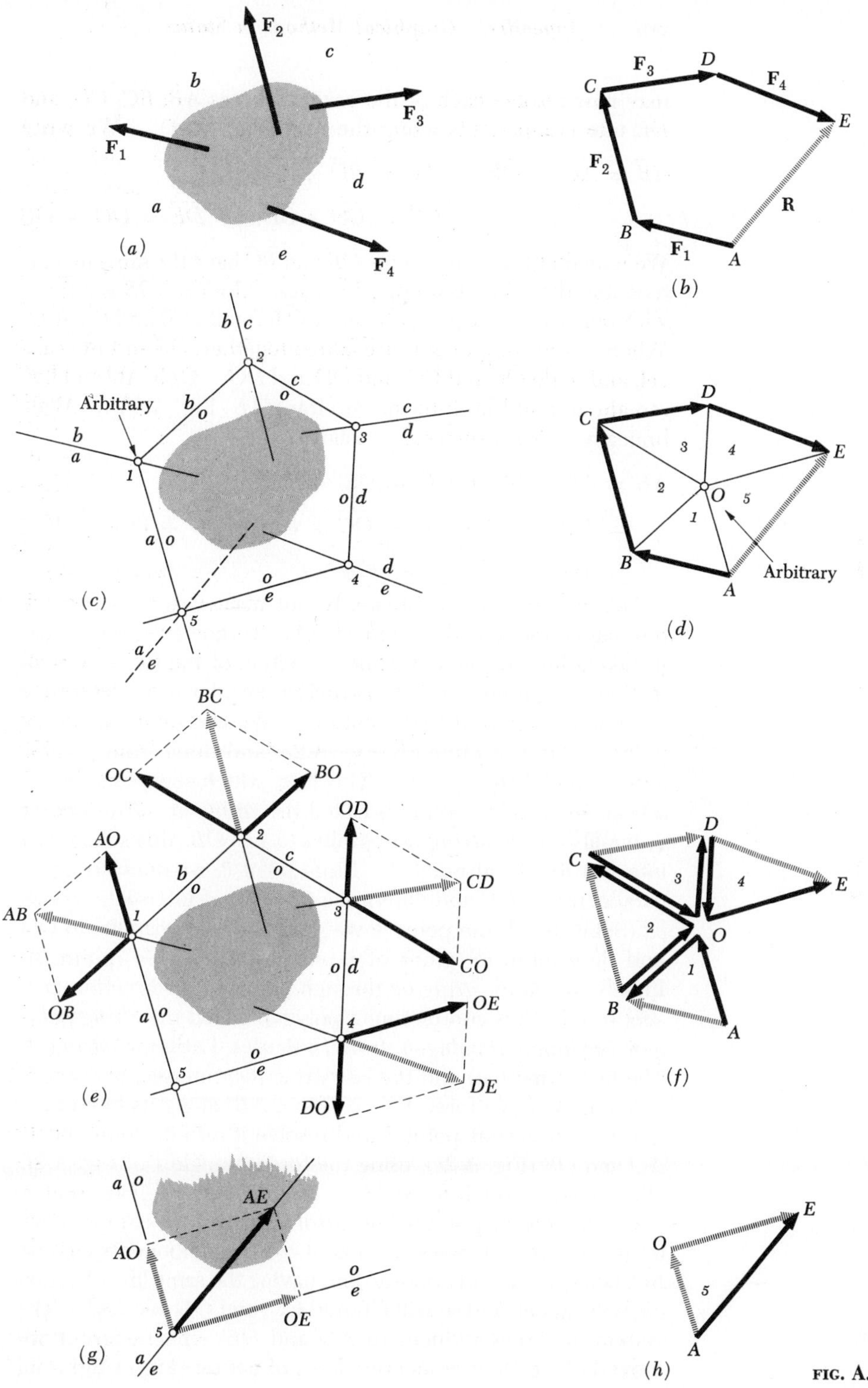

F2
b
c
F3
F1
d
a
(a)
e
F4
C
F3
D
F4
E
F2
R
B
F1
A
(b)
b
c
2
Arbitrary
b
o
c
o
c
d
3
b
a
1
o
d
a
o
d
4
o
e
e
(c)
5
a
e
D
C
3
4
E
2
O
5
1
B
A
Arbitrary
(d)
BC
OC
BO
OD
AO
2
b
o
c
o
CD
AB
1
3
CO
o
d
OB
a
o
OE
4
o
e
5
DE
(e)
DO
D
C
3
4
E
2
O
1
B
A
(f)
a
o
AE
AO
o
e
OE
5
(g)
a
e
E
O
5
A
(h)

FIG. A.2

may now resolve each of the original forces $\overrightarrow{AB}$, $\overrightarrow{BC}$, $\overrightarrow{CD}$, and $\overrightarrow{DE}$ into components along the rays (Fig. A.2*f*). We write

$$\overrightarrow{AB} = \overrightarrow{AO} + \overrightarrow{OB} \qquad \overrightarrow{BC} = \overrightarrow{BO} + \overrightarrow{OC}$$

$$\overrightarrow{CD} = \overrightarrow{CO} + \overrightarrow{OD} \qquad \overrightarrow{DE} = \overrightarrow{DO} + \overrightarrow{OE}$$

We note that the components $\overrightarrow{OB}$ and $\overrightarrow{BO}$ have the same magnitude and direction, but opposite sense. Indeed, $\overrightarrow{OB}$ is a force with tail at O and tip at B, while $\overrightarrow{BO}$ has tail at B and tip at O. When all the components are added together, $\overrightarrow{OB}$ and $\overrightarrow{BO}$ cancel, and so do $\overrightarrow{OC}$ and $\overrightarrow{CO}$, and $\overrightarrow{OD}$ and $\overrightarrow{DO}$. Only $\overrightarrow{AO}$ and $\overrightarrow{OE}$ remain and add up into the resultant $\overrightarrow{AE}$ (Fig. A.2*h*). Algebraically, this is expressed as follows:

$$\begin{aligned}\overrightarrow{AE} &= \overrightarrow{AB} + \overrightarrow{BC} + \overrightarrow{CD} + \overrightarrow{DE} \\ &= \overrightarrow{AO} + \overrightarrow{OB} + \overrightarrow{BO} + \overrightarrow{OC} + \overrightarrow{CO} + \overrightarrow{OD} + \overrightarrow{DO} + \overrightarrow{OE} \\ &= \overrightarrow{AO} + \overrightarrow{OE}\end{aligned}$$

This construction is obviously not necessary to determine the magnitude and direction of $\overrightarrow{AE}$. If, however, we repeat it, taking into account the lines of action of the forces as well as their magnitudes, this construction enables us to determine the line of action of the resultant. We choose an arbitrary point (point *1*) on line *ab* (Fig. A.2*c*) and draw from point *1* a line parallel to ray *OA*. This line, which separates region *a* from a central region *o*, is called the *string oa*. From point *1*, we also draw *string ob* parallel to ray *OB*; this string will intersect line *bc* at point *2*. From point *2*, we draw *string oc* parallel to ray *OC* and determine its point of intersection with *cd* (point *3*). From point *3*, we draw *string od* parallel to *OD* and determine its point of intersection with *de* (point *4*). Finally, we draw *string oe* through point *4* in a direction parallel to *OE*, thus completing a polygon called the *string polygon*, or *funicular polygon* (from *funiculus*, Latin for "*string*"). The first string (*oa*) and the last string (*oe*) intersect at point 5.

We now move force $\mathbf{F}_1$ (i.e., force $\overrightarrow{AB}$) along its line of action until it acts at point *1* and resolve it into its components $\overrightarrow{AO}$ and $\overrightarrow{OB}$ (Fig. A.2*e*), using the force triangle *1* of Fig. A.2*f*. We similarly attach force $\overrightarrow{BC}$ at point *2*, force $\overrightarrow{CD}$ at point *3*, and force $\overrightarrow{DE}$ at point *4* and resolve them into components, using the force triangles *2*, *3*, and *4*. The components $\overrightarrow{OB}$ and $\overrightarrow{BO}$, being equal and opposite and having the same line of action *ob*, will cancel, and so will $\overrightarrow{OC}$ and $\overrightarrow{CO}$, and $\overrightarrow{OD}$ and $\overrightarrow{DO}$. The system of forces reduces to $\overrightarrow{AO}$ and $\overrightarrow{OE}$. These forces are moved along their respective lines of action (Fig. A.2g) until they act at point 5. They may then be added into the resultant AE, using the force triangle 5 of Fig. A.2*h*. The line of action of the resultant is the line *ae* drawn through point 5 in a direction parallel to $\overrightarrow{AE}$.

Once the construction has been understood, it may be reduced to a few steps. Since the magnitude and direction of the resultant are obtained from the force polygon, the string polygon will be used to determine only its line of action. The necessary steps are the following:

1. Denote the various regions defined by the lines of action of the given forces, using lower-case letters and moving clockwise around the rigid body (Fig. A.2*a*).
2. Draw the force polygon, using capital letters corresponding to the lower-case letters used in step 1, and determine the magnitude, direction, and sense of the resultant (Fig. A.2*b*).
3. Choose an arbitrary pole O (either inside or outside the force polygon), and draw rays from O to each of the vertices of the force polygon (Fig. A.2*d*).
4. Starting from an arbitrary point on the line of action *ab*, draw the string polygon, each string parallel to the corresponding ray. Through the point of intersection of the first and last strings (here *oa* and *oe*), draw a line parallel to the resultant; this is the line of action of the resultant (Fig. A.2*c*).

The shape of the string polygon depends upon the choice of the pole, and care should be taken to choose the pole so that no string will be parallel to the line of action it is supposed to intersect. The size of the polygon generally depends upon the choice of its first vertex (unless all forces are parallel). The line of action of the resultant does not, however, depend upon the choice of the pole or of the first vertex.

It may happen that *the resultant of the force polygon is zero.* In this case, the first and last vertices of the force polygon (here A and E) coincide. The first and last rays (here OA and OE) also coincide, and the corresponding two strings (here *oa* and *oe*) have the same direction. Two cases may be distinguished:

1. *The Two Strings Coincide.* The forces they carry (here $\overrightarrow{AO}$ and $\overrightarrow{OE}$) may be canceled, and the given system of forces reduces to zero. The rigid body is in equilibrium (see Sec. A.3).
2. *The Two Strings Are Parallel and Distinct.* The given system reduces to the two forces they carry, i.e., to a couple. The moment of this resultant couple is equal to the product of the common ray OA and the perpendicular distance between the two parallel strings (see Sample Prob. A.2).

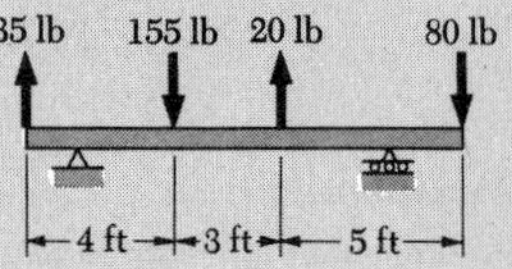

SAMPLE PROBLEM A.1

A 12-ft beam is subjected to the forces shown. Determine graphically the resultant of the given system of forces. (*Note.* This problem is the same as Sample Prob. 3.9. Again the reactions at the supports are not included in the given system of forces.)

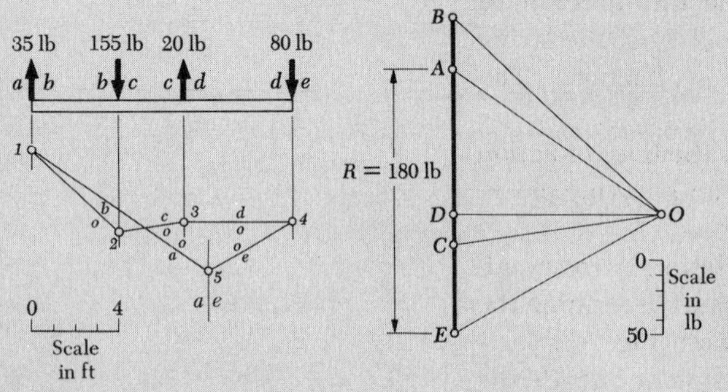

Solution. 1. Moving clockwise around the beam, we write the lower-case letters *a*, *b*, *c*, *d*, and *e*. Note that *a* and *e* are written in the same region.

2. Using the corresponding capital letters, we draw the force polygon *ABCDE*. Since all the forces are vertical, the polygon reduces to a vertical line. The resultant $\overrightarrow{AE}$ is directed downward, and its magnitude is 180 lb.

3. We choose an arbitrary pole *O* and draw rays *OA*, *OB*, *OC*, *OD*, and *OE*.

4. We choose an arbitrary point *1* on line *ab* and draw the following strings:

From point *1* on *ab*, we draw string *oa* parallel to *OA*.

From point *1* on *ab*, we draw string *ob* parallel to *OB* and obtain point *2* on *bc*.

From point *2* on *bc*, we draw string *oc* parallel to *OC* and obtain point *3* on *cd*.

From point *3* on *cd*, we draw string *od* parallel to *OD* and obtain point *4* on *de*.

From point *4* on *de*, we draw string *oe* parallel to *OE*.

5. The line of action *ae* of the resultant passes through the point of intersection (point *5*) of strings *oa* and *oe*. Since the resultant is vertical (see step *b*), we draw the line of action of the resultant *ae* vertically through point *5*.

SAMPLE PROBLEM A.2

In order to move a 173-lb crate, two men push on it while two other men pull on it by means of ropes. The force exerted by man A is 150 lb, and that exerted by man B is 50 lb; both forces are horizontal. Man C pulls with a force equal to 80 lb and man D with a force equal to 120 lb. Both cables form an angle of 30° with the vertical. Determine graphically the resultant of all forces acting on the crate.

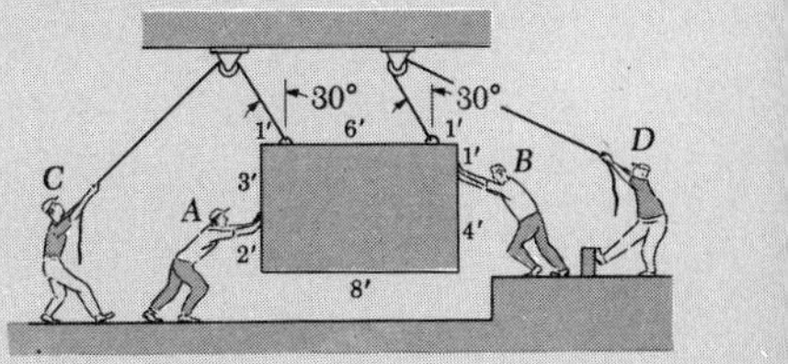

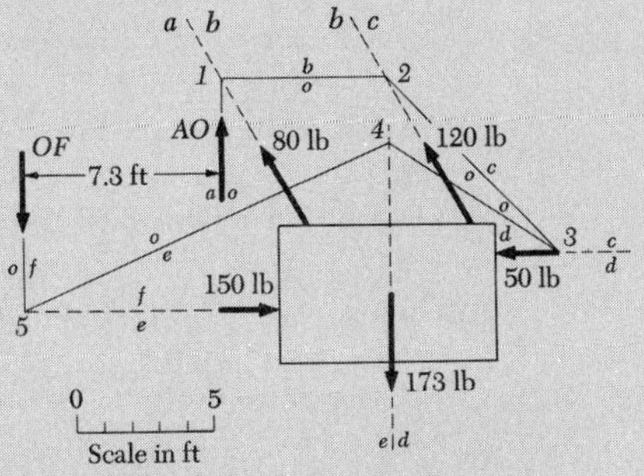

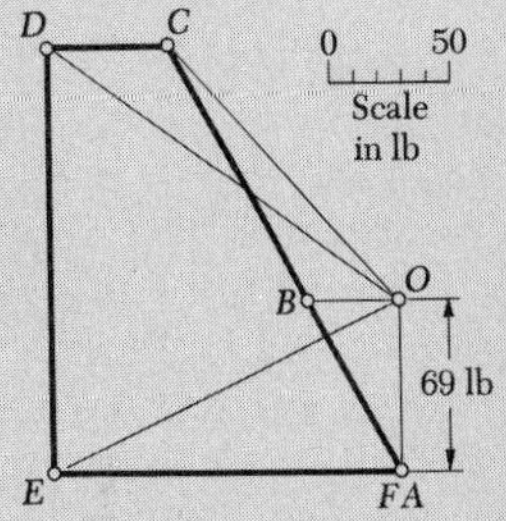

Solution. 1. We draw the free-body diagram of the crate and write the lower-case letters a, b, c, d, e, and f, moving clockwise around the crate.

2. Using the corresponding capital letters, we draw the force polygon $ABCDEF$ and note that F coincides with A. The polygon is closed, and the resultant $\overrightarrow{AF}$ is zero. The given forces must thus reduce either to a couple or to zero.

3. We choose pole O and draw the various rays; the rays OA and OF coincide.

4. Starting from an arbitrary point *1* on line ab, we draw the string polygon, obtaining successively the vertices *2*, *3*, *4*, and *5*. The strings oa and of are parallel but distinct, and the forces $\overrightarrow{AO}$ and $\overrightarrow{OF}$ that they carry have the same magnitude and opposite sense. The system of forces thus reduces to a counterclockwise couple. The moment of the couple is obtained by multiplying the common magnitude

$$AO = OF = 69 \text{ lb}$$

of the forces $\overrightarrow{AO}$ and $\overrightarrow{OF}$ by the perpendicular distance between strings oa and of (7.3 ft); the moment is found to be 504 lb-ft ↺.

PROBLEMS

A.1. Solve Prob. 3.77*a* graphically.

A.2. Solve Prob. 3.76 graphically.

A.3. Solve Prob. 3.59 graphically.

A.4. Solve Prob. 3.77*b* graphically.

A.5. Solve Sample Prob. 3.10*b* graphically.

A.6. Solve Prob. 3.82 graphically.

A.7. Solve Prob. 3.81 graphically.

A.8. Solve Prob. 3.84 graphically.

A.9. Solve Prob. 3.83*b* graphically.

A.10. Solve Prob. 3.77*c* graphically.

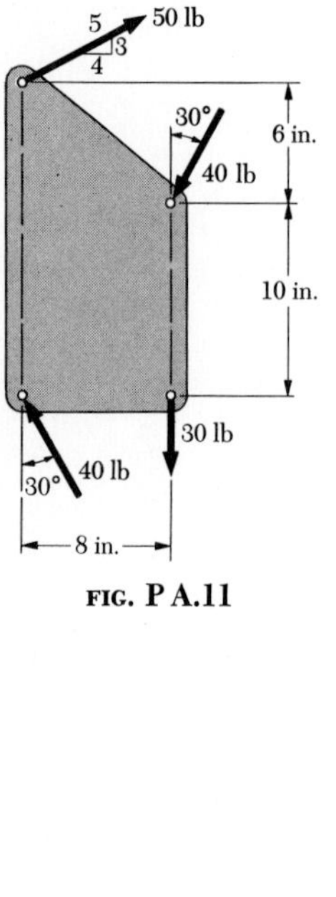

FIG. P A.11

A.11 and A.12. Determine graphically the resultant of the force system shown.

A.13. Solve Prob. A.12 assuming that the 20-kip force acts downward.

***A.14.** The 20-kip force in Prob. A.12 is removed and replaced by a vertical force **P** acting at the same point. Determine graphically the required magnitude and sense of **P** if the resultant of the four forces is to pass through a point 24 in. from the left end of the beam.

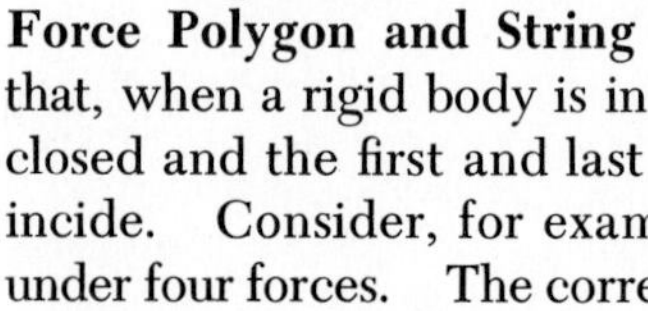

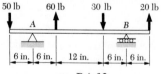

FIG. P A.12

A.3. Equilibrium of a Rigid Body by the Method of the Force Polygon and String Polygon.

We saw in Sec. A.2 that, when a rigid body is in equilibrium, the force polygon is closed and the first and last strings of the string polygon coincide. Consider, for example, a rigid body in equilibrium under four forces. The corresponding string polygon and force polygon are shown in Fig. A.3. Note that, since the force polygon is closed, the same letter A is used to denote the tail of the first force and the tip of the last force. Similarly, the first and last regions that we meet while moving clockwise around the rigid body we denote by a single letter a and not by two different letters a and e as we did in Sec. A.2 when the rigid body was not in equilibrium.

Problems concerning the equilibrium of rigid bodies usually call for the determination of two unknown forces.† The force polygon, therefore, cannot be drawn completely at the outset of the solution; one of its vertices is unknown, and the object of the solution is to determine this vertex graphically. The exact procedure to follow varies from one problem to another, and the student is advised to turn now to the Sample Problems. A general outline of the method is described here for later reference.

1. The lines of action of all external forces are named according to Bow's notation, moving clockwise around the rigid body. If necessary, the lines of action of some of the forces are extended to the other side of the body, so that all known forces may be denoted by successive letters (see Sample Prob. A.3).
2. The force polygon is drawn, starting with the known forces. All the vertices of the force polygon may be plotted except one.
3. A pole O is chosen, and all the rays corresponding to known vertices are drawn.
4. Next, we draw the string polygon, choosing the first vertex on the line of action of one of the two unknown forces, and ending with the vertex located on the second unknown force. The last side of the string polygon is obtained by joining the first and last vertices. It should be noted that, if a force is unknown in magnitude and direction, the string polygon *must* be started at the point of application of that force (see Sample Prob. A.4).
5. We draw a ray from pole O in a direction parallel to the last side of the string polygon, thus defining the unknown vertex of the force polygon. The force polygon may now be completed and the unknown forces determined.

Note that, if a rigid body is in equilibrium under three nonparallel forces, the unknown forces may be determined more conveniently by observing that the lines of action of the three forces must be concurrent (Sec. 4.7).

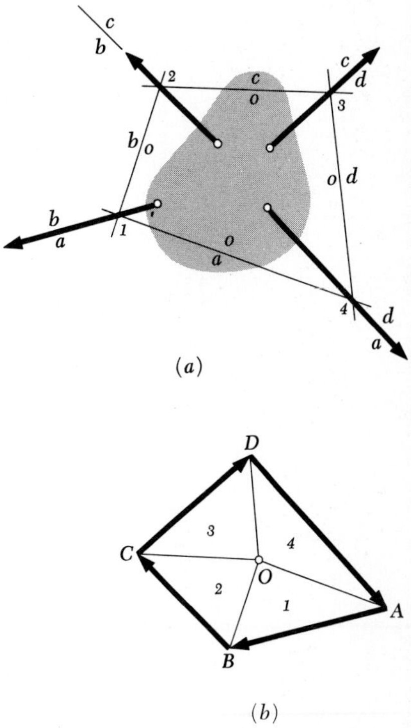

FIG. A.3

†If three forces are unknown, their lines of action must be known. Two of the forces may then be replaced by a single force applied at the point of intersection of their lines of action.

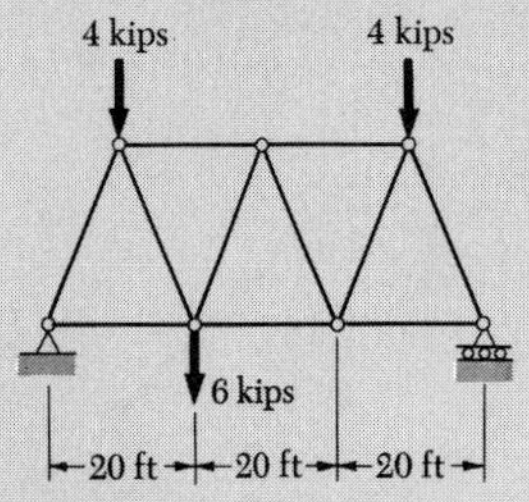

SAMPLE PROBLEM A.3

Determine graphically the reactions at the points of support of the truss shown.

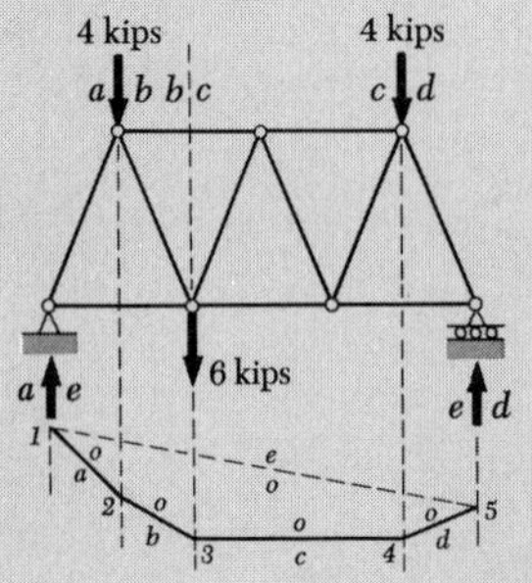

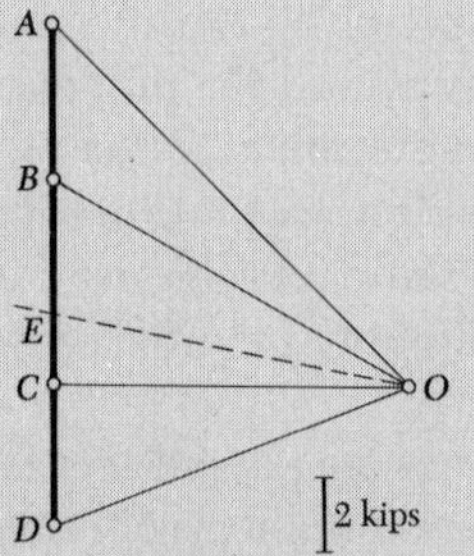

Solution. 1. The truss is drawn to scale, and the lines of action of the given loads and of the two unknown reactions are named according to Bow's notation, moving clockwise around the truss. The line of action of the 6-kip load has been extended to the other side of the truss, so that all known forces may be denoted by successive letters.

2. The force polygon is drawn, starting with load $\overrightarrow{AB}$ and proceeding with loads $\overrightarrow{BC}$ and $\overrightarrow{CD}$. The reaction $\overrightarrow{DE}$ at the roller is vertical, and so must be the reaction $\overrightarrow{EA}$ at the pin, since all applied loads are vertical. The location of point *E*, however, is not known, and the force polygon is incomplete.

3. A pole *O* is chosen, and the rays *OA*, *OB*, *OC*, and *OD* are drawn.

4. The string polygon is drawn. Point *1* is chosen on the line of action *ea* of one of the unknown reactions, and strings *oa*, *ob*, *oc*, and *od* are drawn in directions parallel, respectively, to the known rays *OA*, *OB*, *OC*, and *OD*. The vertices *2*, *3*, *4*, and *5* are thus successively obtained. The last string *oe* may then be drawn by joining point *1* and point *5*.

5. Ray *OE* is drawn from *O* in a direction parallel to string *oe*, thus defining point *E*. The force polygon is completed, and the reactions are measured on the force polygon. They are found to be

$$\overrightarrow{DE} = 6 \text{ kips} \uparrow \qquad \overrightarrow{EA} = 8 \text{ kips} \uparrow \quad ◄$$

SAMPLE PROBLEM A.4

A fixed crane weighs 2,000 lb and is used to lift a load of 5,000 lb. The center of gravity of the crane is located at *G*. Determine graphically the reactions at the points of support.

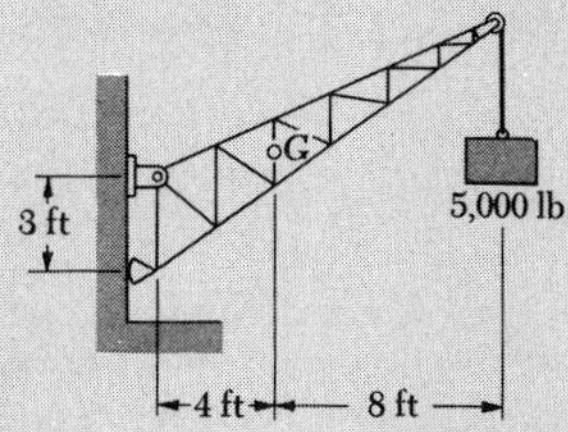

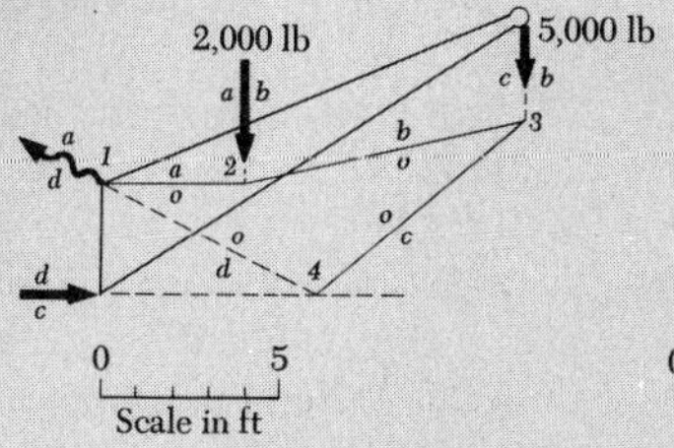

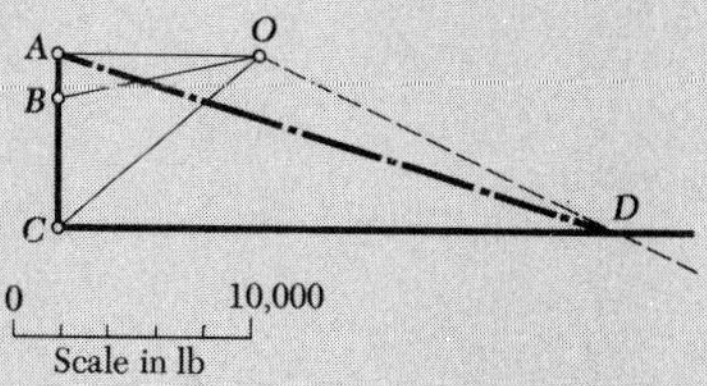

Solution. 1. A free-body diagram of the crane is drawn to scale. The lines of action of the given load, of the weight of the crane, and of the two unknown reactions are named according to Bow's notation, moving clockwise around the crane.

2. The force polygon is drawn, starting with the 2,000-lb weight $\overrightarrow{AB}$ and proceeding with the 5,000-lb load $\overrightarrow{BC}$. The reaction $\overrightarrow{CD}$ at the rocker is horizontal, but its magnitude is not known, and point *D* cannot be plotted. The reaction $\overrightarrow{DA}$ at the pin is unknown in magnitude and in direction and cannot be drawn. The force polygon is incomplete.

3. A pole *O* is chosen, and the rays *OA*, *OB*, and *OC* are drawn.

4. The string polygon is drawn. The line of action *da* of the reaction at the pin is not known, except for the fact that it passes through the pin. We must then choose the first vertex of the string polygon at the pin. If the string polygon were started at any other point, we would eventually have to find the point of intersection of a string with line *da*. This would be impossible since line *da* is not known. Having thus chosen point *1* at the pin, we draw strings *oa*, *ob*, and *oc* in directions parallel, respectively, to the known rays *OA*, *OB*, and *OC*. The vertices *2*, *3*, and *4* are obtained, respectively, on lines *ab*, *bc*, and *cd*. The last string *od* may then be drawn by joining point *1* and point *4*.

5. We draw ray *OD* from *O* in a direction parallel to string *od*, and, since *CD* must be horizontal, we determine the vertex *D* of the force polygon. Side *DA* may now be drawn to complete the force polygon. The reactions $\overrightarrow{CD}$ and $\overrightarrow{DA}$ (magnitude and direction) are determined from the force polygon. We find

$$\overrightarrow{CD} = 22{,}700 \text{ lb}\rightarrow \qquad \overrightarrow{DA} = 23{,}700 \text{ lb} \measuredangle\ 17^\circ \quad ◀$$

PROBLEMS

A.15. Solve Prob. 4.21 graphically.

A.16. Determine graphically the reactions for the truss and loading of Prob. 3.76.

A.17. Solve Sample Prob. 4.2 graphically.

A.18. Determine graphically the reactions for the beam and loading of Prob. A.12.

A.19. Solve Prob. 4.9 graphically.

A.20. Determine graphically the reactions for the truss and loading of Prob. 3.84.

A.21. Solve Prob. 4.23*a* and *b* graphically.

A.22. Solve Prob. 4.24*a* and *b* graphically.

***A.23.** Solve Prob. 4.13 graphically. (*Hint.* Start the string polygon at the point of intersection of two of the unknown forces.)

***A.24.** Solve Prob. 4.14*a* graphically (see hint of Prob. A.23).

***A.25.** Solve Prob. 4.15 graphically (see hint of Prob. A.23).

***A.26.** Solve Prob. 4.29 graphically. (*Hint.* Since the belt tensions are known to be equal, the line of action of their resultant may easily be determined.)

INDEX

ANSWERS TO EVEN-NUMBERED PROBLEMS

CHAPTER 2

2.2. 409 lb ⊽ 26.6°.
2.4. 4,000 lb ⊽ 9.2°.
2.6. 26.1 lb ⊾ 86.7°.
2.8. 67.4 lb ∠ 35.2°.
2.10. 27.2°.
2.12. 604 lb.
2.14. 64.7 lb ←; 241 lb ↑.
2.16. P = 69.3 lb; 34.6 lb ↙.
2.18. 150 lb →; 360 lb ↑.
2.20. 502 lb ⊽ 4.6°.
2.22. 111.8 lb ⊽ 8.8°.
2.26. (*a*) α = 48.2°. (*b*) Impossible.
2.28. 53.6 lb ⊾ 51.8°.
2.30. T_{AC} = 175.9 lb; T_{BC} = 130.5 lb.
2.32. T_{AC} = 240 lb; T_{BC} = 320 lb.
2.34. (*a*) 30°. (*b*) T_{AC} = 300 lb; T_{BC} = 520 lb.
2.36. 6.09 lb ⊾ 7.5°.
2.38. $T_{AC} = T_{BC}$ = 174.5 lb.
2.40. P = 270 lb; Q = 642 lb.
2.42. (*a*) 300 lb. (*b*) 300 lb. (*c*) 200 lb. (*d*) 200 lb. (*e*) 150 lb.
2.44. (*a*) 938 lb. (*b*) 1,250 lb.
2.46. 1.252 in.
2.48. 201 lb ∠ 39.7° or 414 lb ⊽ 39.7°.
2.50. (*a*) +113.3 lb; +217 lb; +52.8 lb. (*b*) 63.1°; 30°; 77.8°.
2.52. (*a*) −260 lb; −410 lb; −121.2 lb. (*b*) 121.3°; 145.1°; 104.0°.
2.54. 45.7°. +279 lb; +69.5 lb; +278 lb.
2.56. +600 lb; −300 lb; −200 lb.
2.58. 261 lb. 54.9°; 106.7°; 40.0°.
2.60. 31.0°; 115.4°; 106.6°.
2.62. −1,200 lb; +600 lb; −400 lb.
2.64. T_{AB} = 13,000 lb; T_{AD} = 10,000 lb.
2.66. 655 lb.
2.68. T_{AD} = 168 lb; T_{BD} = 80 lb; T_{CD} = 90 lb.
2.70. T_{AD} = 31.2 lb; T_{BD} = 10.39 lb; T_{CD} = 22.9 lb.
2.72. $T_{AD} = T_{BD} = T_{CD}$ = 25 lb.
2.74. P = 125 lb. $T_{AC} = T_{BC}$ = 331 lb.
2.76. T_{AD} = 0; $T_{CD} = T_{ED}$ = 43.8 lb.
2.78. (*a*) 6 ft. (*b*) A must be on or inside the circle $x^2 + z^2 = 64$.
2.80. (*a*) 462 lb. (*b*) 454 lb.
2.82. 800 lb.
2.84. (*a*) 48.2°; 109.5°; 131.8°. (*b*) 48.2°; 109.5°; 48.2°. (*c*) 153.4°; 116.6°; 90.0°.
2.86. aa = 4,320 lb ↙; cc = 4,320 lb ↗.
2.88. (*a*) 120°. (*b*) 100 lb.
2.90. P = 115.5 lb; R = 200 lb.

CHAPTER 3

3.2. −960 lb-in.; α = 15°.
3.4. (*a*) −643 lb-in.; (*b*) 68.4 lb ←; (*c*) 64.3 lb ⊽ 20°.
3.6. −510 lb-in.
3.8. +3,300 lb-in.
3.10. $M_B = (x_1 - x_2)F_y - (y_1 - y_2)F_x$.
3.12. $d = (xF_y - yF_x)/(F_x^2 + F_y^2)^{\frac{1}{2}}$.
3.14. (*a*) $\mathbf{M}_O = -58\mathbf{i} + 4\mathbf{j} + 32\mathbf{k}$. (*b*) $\mathbf{M}_O = +6\mathbf{i} - 4\mathbf{k}$. (*c*) $\mathbf{M}_O = -30\mathbf{i} + 12\mathbf{j}$.
3.16. $\mathbf{M}_O$ = (3,600 lb-ft)**i** − (3,600 lb-ft)**k**.
3.18. M_x = 600 lb-ft, M_y = 3,800 lb-ft, M_z = −1,300 lb-ft.
3.20. $\mathbf{M}_O$ = −(1,200 lb-in.)**i** + (1,800 lb-in.)**j** − (1,200 lb-in.)**k**.
3.22. 3.53 in.
3.28. 56.4°.
3.30. 400 lb.
3.32. (*a*) 32.5°. (*b*) 177.1 lb.

3.34. 4.00.
3.36. 1,146 lb.
3.40. (*a*) −328 lb-in. (*b*) 288 lb-in.
3.42. (*a*) zero. (*b*) 1,460 lb-in. (*c*) 396 lb-in.
3.44. (*a*) 4,800 lb-ft. (*b*) −1,662 lb-ft.
3.48. 5.91 in.
3.50. (*a*) 50 lb. (*b*) 72 lb. (*c*) 46.2 lb.
3.52. 1.50 in.
3.54. $M = 6{,}180$ lb-in.;
$\phi_x = 104.0°, \phi_y = 90.0°, \phi_z = 14.0°$.
3.56. $(0.555\,M)\mathbf{i} + (1.279\,M)\mathbf{j} + (0.894\,M)\mathbf{k}$.
3.58. (*a*) 65 lb ∠ 60°; 457 lb-in. ↻.
(*b*) 65 lb ∠ 60°; 288 lb-in. ↻.
3.60. 22.0°.
3.62. $\mathbf{F}_A = Pb/(a+b)\downarrow$; $\mathbf{F}_B = Pa/(a+b)\downarrow$.
3.66. **F** = (3,000 lb)**i**;
M = −(4,050 lb-in.)**j** − (7,950 lb-in.)**k**.
3.68. (*a*) **F** = (600 lb)**i** − (300 lb)**j** − (200 lb)**k**,
M = (3,600 lb-ft)**i** + (9,600 lb-ft)**j**
− (3,600 lb-ft)**k**.
(*b*) **F** = (600 lb)**i** − (300 lb)**j** − (200 lb)**k**,
M = −(1,200 lb-ft)**i** − (3,600 lb-ft)**k**.
3.70. system at *C*.
3.72. **F** = (9 lb)**i** + (20 lb)**j** − (12 lb)**k**,
M = (150 lb-in.)**i** + (108 lb-in.)**j** − (20 lb-in.)**k**.
3.74. *b* and *d*.
3.76. 9 kips ↓; 14.22 ft to right of *A*.
3.78. 130 lb ∠ 67.4°; 60 lb-in. ↻.
3.80. **R** = 0; **M** = 504 lb-ft ↺.
3.82. 88.9 lb ∠ 13.0°. (*a*) 10.50 in. to left of *B*.
(*b*) 2.42 in. below *B*.
3.84. 65.8 kips ∠ 61.7°; 22.7 ft to right of *A*.
3.86. (*a*) 46.2 lb ∠ 60°. (*b*) 46.2 lb ∠ 60°.
3.88. (*a*) $\mathbf{F} = P \angle \theta$; $\mathbf{M}_E = Pa\cos\theta\sin 2\theta$ ↻.
(*b*) 35.3°.
3.90. **R** = −(55 lb)**j** + (8.66 lb)**k**;
M = −(17.32 lb-in)**i** + (416 lb-in.)**j**
− (960 lb-in.)**k**.
3.92. **P** = (40.0 lb)**j** + (17.32 lb)**k**.
3.94. 80 kips; $x = 1.75$ ft, $z = -1.75$ ft.
3.96. 152 kips;
on edge *AC* at a point 10.53 ft from *A*.
3.98. (*a*) **F** = −(30 lb)**i** − (30 lb)**k**,
M = (40 lb-ft)**i** − (40 lb-ft)**k**.
(*b*) Horizontal, 1.333 ft below *C*, forming 45° angle with the *xy* plane.
3.100. $R = \sqrt{3}\,P$, $M = -\sqrt{3}\,Pa$; at origin,
direction of axis, $\theta_x = \theta_y = \theta_z = 54.7°$.
3.102. (*a*) **R** = −(5 lb)**j**;
M = (40 lb-in.)**i** − (50 lb-in.)**j** − (35 lb-in.)**k**.
(*b*) $R = -5$ lb, $M = -50$ lb-in.; parallel to the *y* axis at $x = 7$ in., $z = 8$ in.;
pitch = 10 in.
3.104. (*a*) $\mathbf{R} = \sqrt{2}\,P\,\mathbf{i}$; $\mathbf{M} = (Pa/\sqrt{2})(\mathbf{i} + \mathbf{j} - \mathbf{k})$.
(*b*) $R = \sqrt{2}\,P$, $M = Pa/\sqrt{2}$;
parallel to the *x* axis at $y = z = \frac{1}{2}a$;
pitch = $\frac{1}{2}a$.
3.106. **R** = −55 **j** + 8.66 **k**,
$\mathbf{M} = 30\sqrt{3}\,(20 - a)\mathbf{j} - 30(20 + a)\mathbf{k}$;
$a = 10$ in.
3.108. $\mathbf{F}_B$ = −(20 lb)**i** + (30 lb)**j** + (60 lb)**k**,
$\mathbf{F}_{xz}$ = (80 lb)**i** − (40 lb)**k**, at $x = 1.50$ in.,
$y = z = 0$.
3.112. **R** = 300 lb, $\theta_x = \theta_z = 48.2°, \theta_y = 109.5°$;
M = 9,900 lb-in., $\phi_x = 45°, \phi_y = 90°, \phi_z = 135°$.
3.114. **R** = 88.9 lb ∠ 13.0°; (*a*) 1.086 in. below *B*;
(*b*) 4.70 in. to right of *B*; (*c*) 2.61 in. above *D*.
3.116. (*a*) **R** = (150 lb)**i**; **M** = (520 lb-in.)**i**
+ (300 lb-in.)**j** + (600 lb-in.)**k**.
(*b*) $R = 150$ lb, $M = 520$ lb-in.;
parallel to the *x* axis at $y = -4$ in.,
$z = +2$ in.; pitch = 3.47 in.
3.118. (*a*) $\mathbf{M}_O$ = −(900 lb-in.)**i** + (3,600 lb-in.)**j**
+ (2,800 lb-in.)**k**.
(*b*) 3,180 lb-in.
3.120: **Q** = (90 lb)**i** − (77.3 lb)**j**.
3.122. 40 lb at *B* and 30 lb at *F*.

CHAPTER 4

4.2. $T = 250$ lb, $\mathbf{B}_x = 275$ lb →, $\mathbf{B}_y = 217$ lb ↑.
4.4. (*a*) $T = \frac{1}{2}W(1 - r_1/r_2)$. (*b*) 200 lb.
4.6. (*a*) $T = (Pa/r)\sin\theta$. (*b*) 115.9 lb.
4.8. 467 lb.
4.10. **A** = 2.89 kips ∠ 60°, $\mathbf{B}_x$ = 2.56 kips →,
$\mathbf{B}_y$ = 7.50 kips ↑.
4.12. **A** = 0.833 kip ↑, $\mathbf{B}_x$ = 4.00 kips ←,
$\mathbf{B}_y$ = 9.17 kips ↑.
4.14. (*a*) $T = 800$ lb, **A** = 200 lb →, **D** = 200 lb ←.
(*b*) 12.5 in.
4.16. (*a*) **B** = 360 lb ↗, **C** = 360 lb ↙,
D = 200 lb ↑. (*b*) 2 and 3.
4.18. (*a*) **A** = 0, $\mathbf{M}_A = M$ ↻. (*b*) **B** = 0, $\mathbf{M}_B = M$ ↻.
(*c*) $\mathbf{A} = 2M/\sqrt{3}L \uparrow$, $\mathbf{B} = 2M/\sqrt{3}L \downarrow$.
(*d*) $\mathbf{A} = M/L$ ∠ 60°, $\mathbf{B} = M/L$ ∠ 60°.
(*e*) $\mathbf{A} = 2M/L \leftarrow$, $\mathbf{B} = 2M/L \rightarrow$.

(*f*) $\mathbf{A} = 2\sqrt{3}M/L \uparrow, \mathbf{B} = 2M/L \leftarrow$,
$\mathbf{D} = 4M/L \searrow$.

4.20. (*a*) $\mathbf{B}$ = 90 lb ↑, $\mathbf{D}$ = 90 lb ↓.
(*b*) $\mathbf{B}$ = 120 lb ←, $\mathbf{D}$ = 120 lb →.
(*c*) $\mathbf{B} = 0$, $\mathbf{M}_B$ = 900 lb-in. ↺.

4.22. 1,029 lb.

4.24. (*a*) $\mathbf{A}$ = 15.61 lb ∡ 73.9°, $\mathbf{B}$ = 4.33 lb ←.
(*b*) $\mathbf{A} = \mathbf{B}$ = 7.5 lb ↑. (*c*) $\mathbf{A}$ = 18.75 lb ↑,
$\mathbf{B}$ = 6.50 lb ←, $\mathbf{C}$ = 7.50 lb ⊽ 30°.
(*d*) $\mathbf{A}$ = 15 lb ↑, $\mathbf{M}_A$ = 90 lb-in. ↻.

4.26. (*a*) $\mathbf{A}_x$ = 89.9 lb ←, $\mathbf{A}_y$ = 20 lb ↑,
$\mathbf{C}$ = 3.33 lb →. (*b*) $\mathbf{A}$ = 47.5 lb ↓,
$\mathbf{C}_x$ = 86.6 lb ←, $\mathbf{C}_y$ = 67.5 lb ↑.
(*c*) $\mathbf{C}_x$ = 86.6 lb ←, $\mathbf{C}_y$ = 20 lb ↑,
$\mathbf{M}_C$ = 569 lb-in. ↻.

4.28. (*a*) $\mathbf{R}_A$ = 175 lb ↑, $\mathbf{M}_A$ = 2,625 lb-in. ↻.
(*b*) 1,313 lb.

4.30. T = 62.6 lb, $\mathbf{D}$ = 50.9 lb ⊽ 63.3°.

4.32. 82.8°.

4.34. (*a*) 31.0°. (*b*) 34.7°. (*c*) Impossible.

4.36. $\sin\theta = (2M/WL)\cot\alpha$.

4.38. (*a*) 90°. (*b*) 90°. (*c*) 60°. (*d*) 20.3 in.

4.40. (1) Completely constrained; det.;
$\mathbf{A}$ = 12.02 kips ∡ 56.3°; $\mathbf{B}$ = 6.67 kips ←.
(2) Improperly constrained; indet.; no equil.
(3) Completely constrained; det.;
$\mathbf{A} = \mathbf{C}$ = 5 kips ↑.
(4) Completely constrained; indet.;
$\mathbf{A}_x$ = 6.67 kips →; $\mathbf{B}_x$ = 6.67 kips ←;
($\mathbf{A}_y + \mathbf{B}_y$ = 10 kips ↑).
(5) Improperly constrained; indet.; no equil.
(6) Partially constrained; det.; equil.;
$\mathbf{A} = \mathbf{C}$ = 5 kips ↑.
(7) Completely constrained; det.;
$\mathbf{A}$ = 5 kips ↑; $\mathbf{B}$ = 8.33 kips ⦣ 36.9°;
$\mathbf{C}$ = 6.67 kips →.
(8) Completely constrained; indet.;
$\mathbf{A}_y$ = 5 kips ↑.

4.48. (*a*) 32.6°. (*b*) $\mathbf{C}$ = 210 lb ↙; $\mathbf{D}$ = 234 lb ↑.

4.50. $\mathbf{P} = Wa/b \leftarrow$,
$\mathbf{B} = W(1 + a^2/b^2)^{\frac{1}{2}}$ ∡ $\tan^{-1}(b/a)$.

4.52. (*a*) 1,252 lb. (*b*) 406 lb.

4.54. α = 68.1°, θ = 51.2°.

4.56. $\sin^3\theta = 2a/L$.

4.58. (*a*) 5 lb ↑. (*b*) 5.32 lb along leg.

4.60. (*a*) 1,800 lb. (*b*) $\mathbf{A} = 0$.

4.62. $T_{AD} = T_{ED}$ = 262.5 lb, T_{CD} = 474 lb.

4.64. $\mathbf{A} = -(1{,}025\text{ lb})\mathbf{i} + (3{,}250\text{ lb})\mathbf{j} - (1{,}680\text{ lb})\mathbf{k}$,
T_{ECF} = 725 lb, T_{FBG} = 2,175 lb.

4.66. (*a*) 36.9°, (*b*) 53.1°.

4.68. W = 90 lb; x = 0.889 ft, z = 2.44 ft.

4.70. P = 24.2 lb, $\mathbf{A} = (9.45\text{ lb})\mathbf{i} - (15.76\text{ lb})\mathbf{k}$,
$\mathbf{B} = (11.76\text{ lb})\mathbf{i} + (40\text{ lb})\mathbf{j} + (18.79\text{ lb})\mathbf{k}$.

4.72. F_{CD} = 3 lb, $\mathbf{A} = -(2.94\text{ lb})\mathbf{i} + (6.90\text{ lb})\mathbf{j}$,
$\mathbf{B} = (7.50\text{ lb})\mathbf{j}$.

4.74. T = 70 lb, $\mathbf{A} = (10\text{ lb})\mathbf{i} + (15\text{ lb})\mathbf{j} + (20\text{ lb})\mathbf{k}$.
$\mathbf{B} = (50\text{ lb})\mathbf{i} + (15\text{ lb})\mathbf{j}$.

4.76. $\mathbf{A}_y = (5.39\text{ lb})\mathbf{j}$, $\mathbf{B}_y = (16.2\text{ lb})\mathbf{j}$,
$\mathbf{C}_y = (38.4\text{ lb})\mathbf{j}$.

4.78. $\theta = M_0 h/Wr^2$.

4.80. $M_0 = Wr\sin\theta/(h^2/r^2 - 4\sin^2\frac{1}{2}\theta)^{\frac{1}{2}}$.

4.82. T_{CD} = 25 lb, $\mathbf{A} = (20\text{ lb})\mathbf{i}$,
$\mathbf{B} = (12\text{ lb})\mathbf{j} + (9\text{ lb})\mathbf{k}$.

4.84. $\mathbf{D} = (75\text{ lb})\mathbf{i}$.

4.86. 180.3 lb.

4.88. P = 21.0 lb, θ_x = 65.2°, θ_y = 69.6°,
θ_z = 33.1°.

4.90. $\mathbf{A}_x$ = 522 lb ←, $\mathbf{A}_y$ = 777 lb ↓; T = 455 lb.

4.92. $\mathbf{Q} = -(150\text{ lb})\mathbf{i}$, $\mathbf{B} = (180\text{ lb})\mathbf{i} + (52.0\text{ lb})\mathbf{j}$,
$\mathbf{C} = -(30\text{ lb})\mathbf{i} - (52.0\text{ lb})\mathbf{j}$.

4.94. (*a*) $T = M_0/[r(\cos\phi - c)]$,
where $c = 1/\sqrt{3 + 2\cos\phi}$.
(*b*) $T = 1.809\,M_0/r$,
$\mathbf{D} = \mathbf{E} = -(1.309\,M_0/r)\mathbf{j} + (0.809\,M_0/r)\mathbf{k}$.
(*c*) $-60° < \phi < 60°$.

4.96. Case 1: (*a*) 90°, (*b*) 40 lb, $\mathbf{A}$ = 56.6 lb ∡ 45°,
(*c*) 0°.
Case 2: (*a*) 26.6°, (*b*) 17.89 lb,
$\mathbf{A}$ = 25.3 lb ∡ 71.6°, (*c*) −63.4°.
Case 3: (*a*) 45°, (*b*) 14.14 lb,
$\mathbf{A}$ = 28.3 lb ∡ 45°, (*c*) −45°.

4.98. $\mathbf{B} = 2P/\sqrt{3}$ ∡ 60°, $\mathbf{C} = 2P/\sqrt{3}$ ⦣ 60°,
$\mathbf{D} = P \downarrow$.

4.100. $\mathbf{A} = (222\text{ lb})\mathbf{j}$,
$\mathbf{B} = -(800\text{ lb})\mathbf{i} + (222\text{ lb})\mathbf{j} - (600\text{ lb})\mathbf{k}$,
$\mathbf{C} = +(1{,}050\text{ lb})\mathbf{i} + (556\text{ lb})\mathbf{j} + (600\text{ lb})\mathbf{k}$.

CHAPTER 5

5.2. $\bar{x}$ = 5.94 in.; $\bar{y}$ = 2.62 in.

5.4. $\bar{x}$ = 0; $\bar{y}$ = 0.459 in.

5.6. $\bar{x}$ = 0; $\bar{y}$ = 3.36 in.

5.8. $\bar{x}$ = −0.774 in.; $\bar{y}$ = 0.

5.10. $\bar{x}$ = 4.80 in.; $\bar{y}$ = 0.

5.12. $\bar{x}$ = 8.00 in.; $\bar{y}$ = 2.29 in.

5.14. $\bar{x} = \dfrac{4r}{3}\dfrac{\sin^3\alpha}{2\alpha - \sin 2\alpha}$.
5.16. $\bar{x} = 0$; $\bar{y} = 0.206$ in.
5.18. $\bar{x} = \dfrac{r\sin\alpha\,(1 + \cos\alpha)}{\alpha + \sin\alpha}$; $\bar{y} = 0$.
5.20. 0.494.
5.24. $\tan\theta = \dfrac{2W}{\pi\,(W + 2W_1)}$.
5.26. $\alpha = 43.9°$; $\theta_{max} = 46.1°$.
5.28. $\bar{x} = 0.56$ in.; $\bar{y} = 0$.
5.30. $\bar{x} = 0.7666a$; 2.22%.
5.32. $\bar{x} = \frac{2}{3}b$; $\bar{y} = \frac{1}{3}h$.
5.34. $\bar{x} = \frac{4}{7}a$; $\bar{y} = \frac{2}{5}b$.
5.42. $\bar{x} = \bar{y} = \frac{9}{20}$.
5.44. $\bar{x} = L/\pi$; $\bar{y} = \pi a/8$.
5.46. $\bar{x} = c$; $\bar{y} = \frac{1}{4}a$.
5.48. $\bar{x} = \bar{y} = (2a^2 - 1)/2a(1 + 2\ln a)$.
5.50. (*a*) 792 in.^{3} (*b*) 1,263 in.^{3}
5.52. $A = 4\pi^2 rR$; $V = 2\pi^2 r^2 R$.
5.54. 28.3 ft^2.
5.56. 8,200 ft^3.
5.58. $V = 17.84$ in.^{3}; $A = 58.0$ in.^{2}
5.60. $\pi/4$.
5.62. 0.1737 in.
5.64. 0.436.
5.66. $\mathbf{R} = 2{,}500$ lb ↓, 9.80 ft to right of A;
$\mathbf{A} = 969$ lb ↑, $\mathbf{B} = 1{,}531$ lb ↑.
5.68. $\mathbf{A} = 18.30$ kips ↑, $\mathbf{B} = 15.70$ kips ↑.
5.70. $\mathbf{A} = 2{,}740$ lb ↑, $\mathbf{B} = 3{,}660$ lb ↑.
5.72. (*a*) 0.500; $\mathbf{B} = \frac{1}{4}w_B L$ ↑, $\mathbf{M}_B = 0$.
(*b*) 1.000; $\mathbf{B} = 0$, $\mathbf{M}_B = \frac{1}{6}w_B L^2$ $\circlearrowright$.
5.74. (*a*) $\mathbf{R} = \frac{1}{2}(w_A + w_B)L$ ↓,
$\bar{X} = (w_A + 2w_B)L/3(w_A + w_B)$.
(*b*) $\mathbf{A} = \frac{1}{6}L(2w_A + w_B)$ ↑,
$\mathbf{B} = \frac{1}{6}L(w_A + 2w_B)$ ↑.
5.76. (*a*) $\mathbf{R} = 1{,}966$ lb ←, 1.714 ft below A.
(*b*) $\mathbf{B} = 1{,}123$ lb →.
5.78. 9 in.
5.80. $\mathbf{A} = 1{,}191$ lb →, $\mathbf{B} = 1{,}200$ lb →.
5.82. $\mathbf{R} = 19.90$ kips ←, 7.52 ft above B.
5.84. $\tan\theta = \dfrac{2}{3}\dfrac{\gamma b r^2}{W}$.
5.86. 3.94 ft.
5.88. 8.36 ft.
5.90. 0.792.
5.92. 6,350 lb $\measuredangle$ 38.2°, through center of drum.
5.94. $7h/9$ above base of cylinder.
5.96. 4.31 in. from right end.
5.98. $\bar{x} = 0.0313$ in., $\bar{y} = 0.376$ in., $\bar{z} = 0$.
5.100. 1.457 in. above the base of the aluminum part.
5.102. $\bar{x} = 2$ in., $\bar{y} = 0.223$ in., $\bar{z} = 0.584$ in.
5.104. $\bar{x} = \bar{z} = 5.05$ in., $\bar{y} = 10.81$ in.
5.106. $\frac{1}{2}r$ above base.
5.110. $\bar{x} = 5h/8$.
5.112. $\bar{x} = 5h/6$, $\bar{y} = 20a/21\pi$, $\bar{z} = 0$.
5.114. $\bar{y} = 0.422$ in.
5.116. $0.785a$.
5.118. $\bar{y} = (\pi + 2)h/16$.
5.120. $\bar{x} = 0$, $\bar{y} = 5h/16$, $\bar{z} = -a/4$.
5.122. 17.66 in.^{3}
5.124. $\mathbf{A} = 81.3$ lb ↑, $\mathbf{B} = 518.7$ lb ↑.
5.126. 1.645 ft.
5.128. 784 lb.
5.130. 1.412 ft.
5.132. $-10/9$.

CHAPTER 6

6.2 and 6.22. *1-2* = *2-4* = 240 lb *T*;
1-3 = *3-4* = 260 lb *C*; *2-3* = 100 lb *C*.
6.4 and 6.24. *1-2* = *3-4* = 8 kips *T*;
2-3 = 16 kips *T*; *2-6* = *3-7* = 4 kips *C*;
other members = 10 kips *C*.
6.6 and 6.26. *1-2* = *1-6* = *6-7* = 1 kip *C*;
1-4 = *4-7* = *2-4* = *4-6* = 1.414 kips *T*;
2-3 = *7-8* = 1 kip *T*;
2-5 = *5-8* = *3-5* = *5-7* = 1.414 kips *C*.
6.8 and 6.28. *1-2* = *2-3* = 200 lb *T*;
1-4 = *4-6* = 150 lb *T*; *3-5* = *5-6* = 250 lb *C*;
2-4 = *2-5* = *4-5* = 0.
6.10 and 6.30. *1-2* = 1,200 lb *T*; *1-4* = 1,300 lb *C*;
2-3 = *5-6* = 0; *2-4* = 2,400 lb *C*;
2-6 = 2,680 lb *T*; *3-6* = 1,500 lb *C*;
4-5 = 1,700 lb *C*; *4-6* = 1,697 lb *C*.
6.12 and 6.32. *1-2* = *2-4* = 30 kips *T*;
1-3 = *3-4* = 40 kips *C*; *2-3* = 36 kips *T*.
6.14. *2-3*; *3-4*; *9-10*; *9-12*; *11-12*; *12-13*; *13-14*.
6.16. All simple trusses except 6.14 and 6.15.
6.18. $AB = AC = AD = P/\sqrt{6}$ *comp.*;
$BC = CD = DB = P/3\sqrt{6}$ *ten.*
6.20. (*a*) $A_x = +192$ lb, $A_y = 0$; $A_z = -144$ lb,
$B_x = -384$ lb, $B_y = +576$ lb, $C_y = -576$ lb.
(*b*) $AB = BC = 240$ lb *C*; $BE = 576$ lb *C*;
$CE = 624$ lb *T*; other members = 0.
6.34. *1-2* = *2-3* = 30 kips *C*; *1-4* = *2-6* = *4-9* = 0;
1-5 = *5-9* = 10 kips *C*; *1-6* = 31.6 kips *T*;
3-6 = 31.6 kips *C*; *3-7* = *7-10* = 70 kips *T*;

3-8 = 84.8 kips *C*; 4-5 = 5-6 = 20 kips *T*;
6-7 = 7-8 = 80 kips *T*, 8-10 = 63.2 kips *C*.

6.36. 1-2 = 3-4 = 874 lb *T*; 1-5 = 614 lb *C*;
2-3 = 897 lb *T*; 2-5 = 3-5 = 346 lb *C*;
4-5 = 980 lb *C*; 4-6 = 1,225 lb *T*.

6.38. 1-2 = 6-8 = 21.2 kips *C*;
1-3 = 3-5 = 5-7 = 7-8 = 15.0 kips *T*;
2-3 = 2-5 = 4-5 = 5-6 = 6-7 = 0;
2-4 = 4-6 = 15.8 kips *C*.

6.40. F_{DF} = 66.7 kips *C*; F_{DG} = 16.67 kips *C*.

6.42. F_{EF} = 12 kips *C*; F_{CE} = 9 kips *T*.

6.44. 6 kips *T*.

6.46. F_{DF} = 8.25 kips *T*; F_{DE} = 3 kips *C*;
F_{CE} = 8 kips *C*.

6.48. F_{BD} = 39 kips *T*; F_{BE} = 23.4 kips *C*;
F_{CE} = 18 kips *C*.

6.50. F_{BE} = 2.50 kips *C*; F_{DE} = 4.50 kips *T*.

6.52. 6.67 kips *C*.

6.54. $F_{AB} = 0$; $F_{EJ} = \frac{4}{3}P$ *comp.*

6.56. $F_{AB} = Q$ *comp.*; $F_{EJ} = \frac{2}{3}Q$ *comp.*

6.58. F_{CE} = 10 kips *C*; F_{DF} = 5 kips *T*;
F_{CF} = 7.07 kips *T*.

6.60. F_{CD} = 12 kips *C*; F_{CG} = 20 kips *T*;
for this loading both F_{AD} and F_{BC} are zero.

6.62. (*a*) Completely constrained, indet.
(*b*) Partially constrained.
(*c*) and (*d*) Completely constrained, det.

6.64. (*a*) Partially constrained.
(*b*) Completely constrained, indet.
(*c*) and (*d*) Completely constrained, det.

6.66. $\mathbf{A}_x$ = 600 lb ←; $\mathbf{A}_y$ = 800 lb ↑; **C** = 900 lb ↓;
$\mathbf{E}_x$ = 600 lb →; $\mathbf{E}_y$ = 900 lb ↑.

6.68. $\mathbf{A}_x$ = 175 lb ←; $\mathbf{A}_y$ = 200 lb ↑; **B** = 220 lb →,
D = 375 lb →; $\mathbf{E}_x$ = 420 lb ←, $\mathbf{E}_y$ = 200 lb ↓.

6.70. **A** = 86.7 lb $\measuredangle$ 63.5°; **E** = 44.7 lb $\measuredangle$ 30°;
C = 29.8 lb $\measuredangle$ 30°; **D** = 74.5 lb $\measuredangle$ 30°.

6.72. (*a*) **A** = 13 lb $\measuredangle$ 22.6°; **B** = 13 lb $\measuredangle$ 22.6°.
(*b*) **A** = 13 lb $\measuredangle$ 22.6°; **B** = 13 lb $\measuredangle$ 22.6°.
(*c*) **A** = 5 lb ↓, **B** = 55 lb ↓.

6.74. **E** = 132.0 lb $\measuredangle$ 16.5°; **F** = 169.3 lb $\measuredangle$ 41.6°;
C = 339 lb $\measuredangle$ 41.6°.

6.76. $\mathbf{A}_x$ = 750 lb ←; $\mathbf{A}_y$ = 1,000 lb ↑;
$\mathbf{E}_x$ = 750 lb →, $\mathbf{E}_y$ = 400 lb ↓.

6.78. **A** = 200 lb ↑, **E** = 200 lb ↑, $\mathbf{M}_E$ = 0.

6.80. 40.9°.

6.82. (0 < *a* < 30 ft): $A_x = 1{,}000(a/30)$;
$A_y = 1{,}000(1 - a/75)$.
(30 ft < *a* < 50 ft): $A_x = 1{,}000(50 - a)/20$;
$A_y = 1{,}000(50 - a)/33.3$.

6.84. *At each wheel:* (*a*) **A** = 1,188 lb ↑;
B = 921 lb ↑; **C** = 866 lb ↑.
(*b*) **B** = 281 lb ↑; **C** = 93.8 lb ↓.

6.86. (*a*) *T* = 491 lb.
(*b*) *At each wheel:*
A = 1,277 lb ↑; **B** = 689 lb ↑; **C** = 1,009 lb ↑.

6.88. $a \geqslant 7.20$ ft.

6.90. $F_{AF} = 3M_0/4a$ *ten.*;
$F_{BG} = F_{GD} = M_0/\sqrt{2}a$ *comp.*;
$F_{EH} = M_0/4a$ *ten.*

6.92. (*a*) Rigid; **A** = 2.24 kips $\measuredangle$ 26.6°;
B = 3.61 kips $\measuredangle$ 56.3°. (*b*) Not rigid.

6.94. (*a*) Rigid; **A** = 4.00 kips →,
B = 5.66 kips $\measuredangle$ 45°. (*b*) Not rigid.

6.96. $\mathbf{C}_x$ = 200 lb ←, $\mathbf{C}_y$ = 150 lb ↑, **D** = 300 lb ↓,
$\mathbf{E}_x$ = 400 lb →, $\mathbf{E}_y$ = 300 lb ↑,
$\mathbf{F}_x$ = 200 lb ←, $\mathbf{F}_y$ = 150 lb ↓.

6.98. **B** = 17.07 lb ←; $\mathbf{E}_x$ = 36.3 lb →;
$\mathbf{E}_y$ = 32.0 lb ↓; $\mathbf{H}_x$ = 19.20 lb ←;
$\mathbf{H}_y$ = 32.0 lb ↑.

6.100. $\mathbf{D} = 2M_0/3r$ $\measuredangle$ 30°;
$\mathbf{E} = M_0(r + a)/3ra$ $\measuredangle$ 30°;
$\mathbf{F} = M_0(r - a)/3ra$ $\measuredangle$ 30°.

6.102. (*a*) 6 in. (*b*) 7.07 in.

6.104. 15 lb; **B** = 40 lb ↓.

6.106. **D** = 515 lb $\measuredangle$ 29.1°; **C** = 950 lb →.

6.108. (*a*) 175 lb-ft ↻. (*b*) 75 lb-ft ↻.

6.110. (*a*) $\mathbf{M}_B = M_D \cos^2 \theta$ ↺.
(*b*) $\mathbf{B} = (M_D \cos \theta)/h$ $\measuredangle$ θ;
$\mathbf{D} = (M_D \cos \theta)/h$ $\measuredangle$ θ.

6.112. 14,625 lb.

6.116. T_1 = 350 lb, T_2 = 4,150 lb.

6.118. (*a*) **B** = **D** = 500 lb ↑; **C** = 1,000 lb ↓.
(*b*) 320 lb. (*c*) 8 in.

6.120. F_{AD} = 0; F_{BC} = 192.4 lb *T*;
F_{DG} = 1,052 lb *C*.

6.122. (*a*) 240 lb-ft. (*b*) *B* = 0; M_B = −450 lb-ft,
parallel to the *x* axis.

6.124. (*a*) $\mathbf{M}_S = 4M_A$ ↺. (*b*) $\mathbf{M}_E = 3M_A$ ↻.

6.126. (*a*) M_A = 577 lb-in. (*b*) *B* = 0;
$D_x = D_y = E_x = E_y = 0$; D_z = −28.8 lb;
E_z = +28.8 lb.

6.128. 15.6°.

6.130. **G** = 480 lb ↓; **D** = 200 lb ↙, **F** = 400 lb ↘,
$\mathbf{H}_x$ = 120 lb ←, $\mathbf{H}_y$ = 480 lb ↑.

6.132. 1,600 lb.

6.134. F_{AB} = 2.47 kips *T*; F_{AC} = 9.00 kips *C*;

F_{GH} = 1.50 kips *C*.

6.136. $\mathbf{C}_x = \mathbf{F}_x$ = 500 lb →, $\mathbf{C}_y = \mathbf{F}_y$ = 200 lb ↑, **D** = **E** = 500 lb ←.

6.138. *On the frame:* **F** = 1,611 lb ↑, **A** = 500 lb ←, $\mathbf{D}_x$ = 500 lb →, $\mathbf{D}_y$ = 861 lb ↓.

6.140. *1-2* = *2-7* = *6-11* = *3-8* = 6 kips *C*;
1-6 = 4.5 kips *C*; *1-7* = 7.5 kips *T*;
2-3 = 10 kips *C*; *2-8* = 5 kips *T*;
6-7 = 2 kips *C*; *6-12* = 2.5 kips *T*;
7-8 = 4 kips *T*; *7-12* = 1.50 kips *C*;
11-12 = 0.

CHAPTER 7

7.2. (On *JG*) **F** = 480 lb ↙; **V** = 360 lb ↖; **M** = 1,800 lb-ft ↻.

7.4. (On *JA*) **F** = 38.7 lb →; **V** = 77.6 lb ↓; **M** = 310 lb-in. ↺.

7.6. (On *JA*) **F** = **V** = 0; **M** = 1,000 lb-ft ↺.

7.8. (On *CB*) (*a*) **F** = **V** = 0; **M** = $\frac{1}{8}wL^2 \cos\theta$ ↻. (*b*) **F** = **V** = 0; **M** = 450 lb-ft ↻.

7.10. At *J* (On *JB*) **F** = 0; **V** = 90 lb ↑; **M** = 900 lb-in. ↺. At *K* (On *KD*) **F** = 0; **V** = 30 lb ↓; **M** = 300 lb-in. ↺.

7.12. (On *JC*) 54.5 lb-in. ↻.

7.14. (On *JC*) **F** = $(\frac{1}{2}W - W\theta/\pi)\cos\theta$ ↘;
V = $(\frac{1}{2}W - W\theta/\pi)\sin\theta$ ↙;
M = $\frac{1}{2}Wr(1 - \cos\theta) - (Wr/\pi)(\sin\theta - \theta\cos\theta)$ ↻.

7.16. $M_B = +Pab/L$.

7.18. $M_B = +wa^2/2$.

7.20. $M_B = -wL^2/2$.

7.22. M_A = −2,500 lb-ft.

7.24. M_C = +13.5 kip-ft.

7.26. 5.00 ft.

7.28. M_C = −1,200 lb-ft.

7.30. M_E = +960 lb-in.

7.32. M_D = −500 lb-ft.

7.34. $a = 0.207L$.

7.46. M_D = +132 kip-ft.

7.48. $M_B = -w_0L^2/3$.

7.50. M = +3,600 lb-ft, 6 ft to the right of *A*; M = −4,500 lb-ft at *C*.

7.52. M = +200 lb-ft, 8 ft to the right of *A*; M = −7,000 lb-ft at *B*.

7.54. $V = -wx$; $M = -wx^2/2$.

7.56. $V = w_0(L/\pi)\cos(\pi x/L)$,
$M = w_0(L/\pi)^2 \sin(\pi x/L)$;
$M_{\max} = w_0(L/\pi)^2$, at $x = \frac{1}{2}L$.

7.58. (*a*) 1.500.
(*b*) $V = w_0L[\frac{1}{4} - (x/L) + \frac{3}{4}(x/L)^2]$,
$M = w_0L^2[\frac{1}{4}(x/L) - \frac{1}{2}(x/L)^2 + \frac{1}{4}(x/L)^3]$.
(*c*) $M_{\max} = w_0L^2/27$, at $x = L/3$.

7.60. V_D = +100 lb, M_C = −100 lb-ft.

7.62. (*a*) $\mathbf{A}_x$ = 1,000 lb ←, $\mathbf{A}_y$ = 400 lb ↑. (*b*) h_B = 4 ft, h_D = 5 ft.

7.64. 5 ft.

7.66. $\mathbf{E}_x$ = 800 lb →, $\mathbf{E}_y$ = 300 lb ↑, T_E = 854 lb.

7.68. 50,200 kips, 47,200 kips.

7.70. 22.5 ft.

7.72. 8.66 ft.

7.74. 15 in. to the left of *B*, 1.940 in.

7.76. h = 0.1429 ft, θ_A = 38.2° ∡, θ_C = 35.5° ∡.

7.78. For $x \geqslant 0$: $y = 2h[3(x/L)^2 - 2(x/L)^3]$; $T_0 = w_0L^2/12h$.

7.84. 495 ft, 1,125 lb.

7.86. 199.48 ft.

7.88. 628 ft, 2,230 lb.

7.90. 7.96 ft, 20.5 lb.

7.92. 15.02 in. to the left of *B*, 1.953 lb.

7.96. 2.05 ft, 33.4 ft.

7.98. h/L = 0.338, θ_B = 56.5°, $T_m = 0.754wL$.

7.100. M_A = −240 lb-in.; M_D = +720 lb-in.

7.102. (*a*) 230 ft. (*b*) 63.0 lb.

7.104. $y = (L/\delta)x$.

7.106. (On *JA*) $\mathbf{M}_{\max} = \frac{1}{4}PL$ ↻, at $a = \frac{1}{2}L$.

7.108. (*a*) $\mathbf{A}_x$ = 267 lb ←, $\mathbf{A}_y$ = 100 lb ↑, $\mathbf{B}_x$ = 228 lb →, $\mathbf{B}_y$ = 171 lb ↑. (*b*) T_{ACB} = 285 lb. (*c*) T_{DE} = 48.5 lb.

7.110. a = 3 ft, b = 9 ft.

CHAPTER 8

8.2. 5.77 lb.

8.4. (*a*) 28.0 lb ∡ 34.0°. (*b*) 5.23 lb ∡ 6.0°.

8.6. All packages move; $\mathbf{F}_A$ = 1.932 lb ↗, $\mathbf{F}_B$ = 0.773 lb ↗, $\mathbf{F}_C$ = 1.932 lb ↗.

8.8. Moves; 48.7 lb.

8.10. (*a*) 27.0 lb. (*b*) 22.5 lb. (*c*) 9.64 lb.

8.12. (*a*) 59.1 lb. (*b*) Slide.

8.14. 51.4 lb ←.

8.16. **B** = 612 lb →.

8.18. 2.86 in.

8.20. 135.0 lb.

8.22. 72.4 lb (motion impending at *C*).

8.24. (*a*) 11.43 lb. (*b*) Motion impending at *C*.

8.26. 12 in.

8.28. 0.353.
8.30. $\mu_B = \mu_C = \tan \frac{1}{2}\theta$; $\mu_A =$ any value.
8.32. (*a*) $P = W(\mu^2 \cos^2 \theta - \sin^2 \theta)^{\frac{1}{2}}$.
(*b*) $\tan \beta = (\mu^2 \cot^2 \theta - 1)^{\frac{1}{2}}$, where β is the angle between the direction of motion and the line of greatest slope of the plane.
(*c*) 6.52 lb, $\beta = 26.7°$.
8.34. $2L/3$.
8.36. All forces, tensions, and displacements are zero, except as follows:
Case 1: (*a*) $\mathbf{F}_A = 0.40$ lb ←, $\mathbf{F}_B = 0.10$ lb ←.
(*b*) $T_{AB} = 0.10$ lb. (*c*) $\Delta_A = 0.50$ in. →.
Case 2: (*a*) $\mathbf{F}_A = 0.10$ lb →, $\mathbf{F}_B = 0.10$ lb ←.
(*b*) $T_{AB} = 0.10$ lb. (*c*) $\Delta_A = 0.50$ in. →.
8.38. Straight line segments connecting the following points: (0, 0), (0.40 lb, 0), (0.80 lb, 2 in.), (1.00 lb, 4 in.), (0.20 lb, 4 in.), (0, 3 in.).
8.40. 1.300 lb ↗, *C* rolls.
8.42. $0 < \theta < 14.0°$.
8.46. (*a*) 111.3 lb →. (*b*) $\mathbf{B}_x = 511$ lb ←, $\mathbf{B}_y = 500$ lb ↓.
8.48. 0.635 lb.
8.50. 473 lb.
8.52. (*a*) 4.50 lb-in. ⤸. (*b*) 6.60 lb-in. ⤸.
8.54. (*a*) 115.6 lb →. (*b*) Machine will not move.
8.56. (*a*) Wedge is forced up and out from between plates. (*b*) Wedge will become self-locked at $\theta = 4.0°$.
8.58. 0.378.
8.60. 3.71 lb-ft.
8.62. 10.08 lb-in.
8.64. (*a*) First adjust *A*. (*b*) 6.37 lb-in.
8.66. 0.12.
8.68. (*a*) 72.8 lb. (*b*) 62.8 lb.
8.70. $T_{AB} = 72.5$ lb, $T_{CD} = 77.5$ lb, $T_{EF} = 82.7$ lb.
8.72. 11.95 in.
8.74. 4.69 lb/ton.
8.76. 2.22 lb.
8.78. 60 lb, 240 lb.
8.84. 0.026 in.
8.86. 7.19 lb/ton.
8.88. 4.14 ft.
8.90. (*a*) 39.0 lb. (*b*) 42.3°.
8.92. 113.5 lb-ft.
8.94. 0.441.
8.96. (*a*) 73.0 lb. (*b*) 39.0 lb. (*c*) 73.0 lb.
8.98. 3.17 ft.
8.102. 75.8°.
8.104. 185.1 lb-ft.
8.106. $T_A = 11.5$ lb, $T_B = 18.5$ lb.
8.108. (*a*) 3 lb. (*b*) 4.5 lb. (*c*) 6 lb.
8.110. 36.7 lb-ft.
8.112. (*a*) 2,860 lb. (*b*) 3.37 turns.
8.114. $M = Wr\mu(1 + \mu)/(1 + \mu^2)$.
8.116. $M = \frac{1}{4}\mu WL$.

CHAPTER 9

9.2. $3a^3b/10$.
9.4. $2a^3b/15$.
9.6. $ab^3/6$.
9.8. $2ab^3/7$.
9.10. $\pi a^3b/8$, $a/2$.
9.12. $a\sqrt{2/3}$.
9.14. $(b^2 + h^2)bh/3$, $\sqrt{(b^2 + h^2)/3}$.
9.16. (*a*) $\frac{1}{2}\pi(R_2^4 - R_1^4)$. (*b*) $\frac{1}{4}\pi(R_2^4 - R_1^4)$.
9.20. 56.0 in.^{4}, 2.18 in.
9.22. 29.0 in.^{4}, 1.555 in.
9.24. 2,040 in.^{4}
9.26. $A = 40$ in.^{2}, $J_C = 300$ in.^{4}, $d = 5$ in.
9.28. 283 in.^{4}
9.30. (*a*) 77.1 in.^{4} (*b*) 74.9 in.^{4}
9.32. 6.24 in.
9.34. 339 in.^{4}, 4.89 in.; 31.3 in.^{4}, 1.485 in.
9.36. $h/2$.
9.38. $3\pi r/16$.
9.40. $h + (r^2/4h)$.
9.44. $+b^2h^2/4$.
9.46. $+a^2b^2/6$.
9.48. +30.0 in.^{4}
9.50. −32.3 in.^{4}
9.52. $\bar{I}_u = \bar{I}_v = bh(b^2 + h^2)/24$, $\bar{P}_{uv} = -bh(b^2 - h^2)/24$.
9.54. (*a*) $(\pi - \sqrt{3})a^4/16$, $(\pi + \sqrt{3})a^4/16$, $+a^4/16$.
(*b*) $(\pi - 2)a^4/16$, $(\pi + 2)a^4/16$, 0.
9.56. −32.9°, 75.4 in.^{4}, 9.6 in.^{4}
9.58. +28.5°, 98.3 in.^{4}, 21.3 in.^{4}
9.60. (*a*) $0.0881a^4$, $0.305a^4$, $0.0625a^4$.
(*b*) $0.0713a^4$, $0.321a^4$, 0.
9.64. +28.5°, 98.3 in.^{4}, 21.3 in.^{4}.
9.66. −32.9°, 75.4 in.^{4}, 9.6 in.^{4}.
9.70. −18.4°, 50.0 in.^{4}
9.74. (*a*) $I_{AA'} = ma^2/4$, $I_{BB'} = mb^2/4$.
(*b*) $I_{CC'} = m(a^2 + b^2)/4$.
9.76. $I_{DD'} = m(b^2/24 + d^2)$, $I_{EE'} = m(h^2/18 + d^2)$.
9.78. $8\pi\rho a^5/15$, $\sqrt{2/5}\,a$.

9.80. $5ma^2/18$.
9.82. $\pi\rho a^2L(3a^2 + 4L^2)/12$, $\sqrt{(3a^2 + 4L^2)/12}$.
9.84. $5m(a^2/36 + h^2/7)$.
9.86. $(134.0)\rho$, 2.34 in.
9.88. $ma^2/20$.
9.90. $m(R^2 + \frac{3}{4}a^2)$.
9.94. $0.360a$ or $-1.110a$.
9.96. $2ma^2/3$.
9.98. 1.622 in.
9.100. 0.000424 lb-ft-sec^2, 0.644 in.
9.102. 0.000283 lb-ft-sec^2, 1.031 in.
9.104. 1.743 lb-ft-sec^2, 6.54 in.
9.106. 0.890.
9.108. $m(3a^2 + 2h^2)/20$.
9.110. 1.643 in.
9.112. 69.6 in.^{4}, 11.64 in.^{4}; 2.52 in., 1.029 in.
9.114. $I_x = 0.01553$ lb-ft-sec^2,
$I_y = I_z = 0.0621$ lb-ft-sec^2;
$k_x = 0.236$ ft, $k_y = k_z = 0.471$ ft.
9.116. (*a*) $P_{xy} = +r^4/8$.
(*b*) $\bar{P}_{x'y'} = r^4(1/8 - 4/9\pi) = -0.01647r^4$.
9.118. 0.1944.

CHAPTER 10

10.4. 50 lb ↑.
10.6. 480 lb-in. ↺.
10.8. $Q = P(AD)/(AC)$, where AC = distance from A to C, and AD = distance A to D.
10.10. $(Pl/r)\cos^2\theta$.
10.12. $\frac{1}{2}Pd\sin\theta$.
10.14. $\frac{1}{2}Pd\cos\theta$.
10.16. 173.2 lb.
10.18. 904 lb.
10.20. 52.2°.
10.22. 26.6°.
10.24. 11.8 in.
10.26. 30.7°.
10.28. 78.7°, 323.8°, 379.1°.
10.30. $\tan\theta/\tan(\theta + \phi_s)$.
10.32. 143.2 lb, 203.2 lb.
10.34. 280 lb ↑, 1,280 lb-ft ↻.
10.36. $\tan\theta_1 = 2P/3W$, $\tan\theta_2 = 2P/W$.
10.38. 0.356 in. ↓.
10.40. 0.625 in. →.
10.44. 78.7°, unstable; −101.3°, stable.
10.46. 78.7° and 379.1°, stable; 323.8°, unstable.
10.48. (*a*) $2W/P = \cot\theta\,(5 - 4\cos\theta)^{\frac{1}{2}}$. (*b*) 32.5°.
10.52. kr^2/l.
10.54. 11.18 in.
10.56. (*a*) 2. (*b*) $\frac{2}{3}$. (*c*) $\frac{2}{3} < P/W < 2$.
10.58. $0.382kl$.
10.60. 7.50 lb.
10.64. 60°.
10.66. 11.0°, stable; 79.0°, unstable.
10.68. $ka^2/2l$.
10.70. $\mathbf{A} = 100$ lb ↑, $\mathbf{E} = 300$ lb ↑,
$\mathbf{M}_E = 2{,}000$ lb-ft ↻.
10.72. 18.4°.

CHAPTER 11

11.2. $t = 2$ sec, $s = 1$ in., $a = -6$ in./sec^2;
$t = 3$ sec, $s = 0$, $a = 6$ in./sec^2.
11.4. 6 sec, −13 ft, 46 ft.
11.6. $a = 2t$, $v = t^2 - 9$, $s = \frac{1}{3}t^3 - 9t + 18$.
11.8. (*a*) 3 sec. (*b*) 5 ft, −28 ft/sec. (*c*) 32.5 ft.
11.10. (*a*) 9.17 ft/sec. (*b*) 5 ft. (*c*) 2.89 ft.
11.12. (*a*) 80 in.^{3}/sec^2. (*b*) 12 in./sec.
11.14. (*a*) 10 ft. (*b*) Infinite. (*c*) 0.230 sec.
11.16. (*b*) $v^2 = (1/k^2)(1 - e^{-2k^2gs})$.
(*c*) The velocity approaches this value as a limit for large values of t.
11.18. (*a*) $v = (kT/\pi)(1 - \cos \pi t/T)$,
$s = (kT^2/\pi^2)[(\pi t/T) - \sin(\pi t/T)]$.
(*b*) $v_{max} = 2kT/\pi$. (*c*) $s = 2kT^2/\pi$.
(*d*) $v_{av} = kT/\pi$.
11.20. (*a*) 15,540 ft. (*b*) 1,677,000 ft. (*c*) Infinite.
11.22. (*a*) 25,950 ft/sec. (*b*) 34.5 min.
11.24. (*a*) 15 ft/sec. (*b*) 45 ft/sec. (*c*) 225 ft.
11.26. (*a*) 1.115 sec, 35.9 ft/sec.
(*b*) 2.74 sec, 14.57 ft/sec. (*c*) 59.1.
11.28. (*a*) 314 ft. (*b*) 13.60 ft/sec.
11.30. (*a*) 14.93 sec, 334 ft. (*b*) $v_A = 44.8$ ft/sec,
$v_B = 51.7$ ft/sec.
11.32. 0.816 sec, 276 ft below ground level.
11.34. (*a*) 24 ft/sec ↓. (*b*) 12 ft/sec ↓.
(*c*) 36 ft/sec ↓. (*d*) 24 ft/sec ↓.
11.36. (*a*) 12 in./sec ↓, 12 in./sec ↑, 36 in./sec ↓,
36 in./sec ↑. (*b*) 48 in./sec ↑.
(*c*) 48 in./sec ↑.
11.38. (*a*) 6 sec. (*b*) $s_A = 54$ in. →, $s_B = 72$ in. →,
$s_C = 18$ in. ↓.
11.40. $v_A = 24$ in./sec →, $v_B = 28$ in./sec →.
11.42. $v_A = 5$ ft/sec ↓, $v_B = 1$ ft/sec ↑,
$v_C = 8$ ft/sec ↑.

11.44. (*a*) 40 ft/sec. (*b*) 288 ft.
11.46. (*a*) 120 in. (*b*) 0, 8, 16, and 22 sec.
11.48. (*a*) 5.33 ft/sec^2. (*b*) 22.7 mph.
11.50. 15 sec.
11.52. (*a*) 2 sec. (*b*) 1,500 ft.
11.54. 55.4 mph.
11.56. 22.5 ft/sec^2.
11.58. 25 sec.
11.60. (*a*) 135 in./sec. (*b*) 540 in. (*c*) 90 in./sec.
11.62. (*a*) 8 sec. (*b*) 72 ft.
11.64. (*a*) 12.00 sec. (*b*) 383 ft.
11.66. (*a*) -63 ft/sec^2. (*b*) -73 ft/sec^2.
11.68. 288 ft.
11.70. (*a*) 60 in. (*b*) 120 in.
11.74. $\mathbf{v}_{min} = 2.828$ ft/sec ⊽ 45°, $t = 1.500$ sec, $x = y = -1.500$ ft.
11.76. (*a*) $x = y = 0$, $\mathbf{v} = 14.14$ in./sec ∡ 45°, $\mathbf{a} = 22.4$ in./sec^2 ⊽ 63.4°. (*b*) $x = 6.32$ in., $y = 5$ in., $\mathbf{v} = 4.45$ in./sec ∡ 34.2°, $\mathbf{a} = 4.45$ in./sec^2 ⊽ 34.2°.
11.80. $v = \sqrt{c^2 + R^2p^2}$, $a = Rp^2$.
11.82. (*a*) 42.4°. (*b*) Directly above target.
11.84. 3.47 ft/sec $< v_0 <$ 11.57 ft/sec.
11.86. 25.8 ft.
11.88. $d <$ 19.1 ft.
11.90. 8.0° or 72.5°.
11.92. $R = v_0^2/g$, $\alpha = 45°$.
11.94. 36.5 ft.
11.96. (*a*) 93.1 ft. (*b*) 75.9°.
11.100. (*a*) 26.0 ft. (*b*) 22.4°.
11.102. 18.54 mph from 62.8° west of south.
11.104. (*a*) 30.8 mph ∡ 76.9°. (*b*) 452 ft ∡ 76.9°. (*c*) 818 ft.
11.106. 35.1 ft/sec ⊽ 81.2°.
11.108. (*a*) 63.9°. (*b*) 1,195 ft/sec ↑, 32.2 ft/sec^2 ↓.
11.110. (*a*) 6.21 ft/sec ↖. (*b*) 1.153 ft/sec ↖.
11.112. (*a*) 4.84 ft/sec^2. (*b*) 63.6 mph.
11.114. 299,000 ft/sec^2.
11.116. 347 ft.
11.118. 43.8 sec.
11.120. 14,580 ft.
11.122. $R + c^2/Rp^2$.
11.124. 17,060 mph.
11.126. 84.4 min.
11.128. $v = 4$ in./sec, $\gamma = 0°$; $a = 64.5$ in./sec^2, $\gamma = 82.9°$; where γ is measured counterclockwise from the positive r axis.
11.130. (*a*) $v = k\pi/\sqrt{2}$, $\gamma = 135°$; $a = \sqrt{5}\,k\pi^2/4$, $\gamma = -116.5°$. (*b*) $v = 0$; $a = k\pi^2/4$, $\gamma = 0°$.
11.132. $a = d\sec^2\theta\,[(d^2\theta/dt^2) + 2\tan\theta\,(d\theta/dt)^2]$.
11.134. (*a*) $v = b\sqrt{1+\theta^2}\,(d\theta/dt)$. (*b*) $a = b\omega^2\sqrt{\theta^2 + 4}$.
11.136. (*a*) $v = e^{b\theta}\sqrt{1+b^2}\,(d\theta/dt)$. (*b*) $a = (b^2+1)\omega^2 e^{b\theta}$.
11.138. (*a*) helix with vertical axis ($\theta = 0$, $R = k$). (*b*) $v = \sqrt{4k^2 + p^2}$, $a = 4k$. (*c*) $\rho = k + p^2/4k$.
11.140. $v = 2\pi\sqrt{A^2 + B^2n^2\cos^2(2\pi nt)}$, $a = 4\pi^2\sqrt{A^2 + B^2n^4\sin^2(2\pi nt)}$.
11.142. $\tan^{-1}(Rp/c)$.
11.144. (*a*) 15.83 ft/sec ∡ 50°. (*b*) 0.983 sec.
11.146. (*a*) 42 sec. (*b*) 1,848 ft.
11.148. (*a*) 4.50 sec. (*b*) 101.25 in./sec.
11.150. $\alpha = 5.7°$, $\beta = 1.0°$ (or $\alpha = 84.3°$, $\beta = 10.0°$).
11.152. ($\alpha = 29.5°$) $\rho = 22{,}900$ ft; ($\alpha = 70.0°$) $\rho = 58{,}100$ ft.
11.154. 240 ft/sec.

CHAPTER 12

12.2. 16.50 lb, 100.00 lb, 3.11 lb-sec^2/ft.
12.4. 3.86 ft/sec^2 ↓, 25 lb.
12.6. (*a*) 150.3 ft. (*b*) 18.97 mph.
12.8. (*a*) 0.152. (*b*) 16.00 ft/sec.
12.10. 4.4°.
12.12. Block A: (*a*) 3.43 ft/sec^2. (*b*) 34.3 ft/sec. (*c*) 18.52 ft/sec. Block B: (*a*) 6.00 ft/sec^2. (*b*) 60.0 ft/sec. (*c*) 24.5 ft/sec.
12.14. (*a*) 11.3°. (*b*) 6.69 ft/sec^2.
12.16. $F_{AB} = 2{,}000$ lb C, $F_{BC} = 3{,}000$ lb C.
12.18. (1) 33.3 lb added, (2) 33.3 lb taken away, (3) 1,367 lb added.
12.20. $g = \dfrac{v^2}{2h}\dfrac{m_2 + m_1}{m_2 - m_1}$.
12.22. (*a*) 7.00 ft/sec ↑. (*b*) 22.9 ft.
12.24. (*a*) 59.7 lb. (*b*) Impossible, since a_B cannot be greater than g.
12.26. $T_1 = 502.5$ lb, $T_2 = 47.5$ lb.
12.28. 2 min 59 sec.
12.30. 13.23 ft/sec ←.
12.32. (*a*) 75 lb. (*b*) 8.05 ft/sec^2 ←.
12.34. (*a*) 16.10 ft/sec^2 ←. (*b*) 4.83 ft/sec^2 ←. (*c*) 11.27 ft/sec^2 ←.

12.36. 14.18 ft/sec $\rightarrow$.
12.38. $s = (Wv_0^2/2gF_0)\ln 2$.
12.40. $v = \sqrt{gk/W}[\sqrt{x_0^2 + l^2} - l] \leftrightarrow$.
12.42. $\mathbf{a}_A = 13.25$ ft/sec² $\uparrow$, $\mathbf{a}_B = 1.889$ ft/sec² $\downarrow$.
$\mathbf{a}_C = 9.47$ ft/sec² $\downarrow$;
block C strikes ground first.
12.44. $W_A = 11.25$ lb, $W_B = 22.5$ lb.
12.46. $\mathbf{a}_A = \frac{1}{2}g\uparrow$, $\mathbf{a}_B = \frac{1}{4}g\downarrow$, $\mathbf{a}_C = 0$.
12.48. (*a*) 22.7 ft/sec. (*b*) 2.62 ft.
12.50. 10.56 ft/sec.
12.52. 3.74 lb.
12.54. (*a*) $T_{CD} = W$. (*b*) $T_{CD} = \frac{1}{2}W$,
$\mathbf{a} = 0.866\,g \searrow 60°$.
12.56. (*a*) 947 ft. (*b*) 219 lb.
12.58. 19.4°.
12.60. $v_{\min} = \sqrt{gr\tan(\theta - \phi)}$,
$v_{\max} = \sqrt{gr\tan(\theta + \phi)}$.
12.62. 31.7°.
12.64. $1/h - 1/y = c^2 \ln(x/b)$.
12.66. (*a*) 59.9 mph. (*b*) 139.1 mph.
12.68. 9.96 ft.
12.70. Length of plates must be doubled.
12.72. $x = L, y = 0, z = -eBL^2/2mv_0$.
12.74. (*a*) $F_r = -1.242$ lb, $F_\theta = 0$.
(*b*) $F_r = 0.932$ lb, $F_\theta = -1.242$ lb.
12.76. (*a*) $F_r = -4.60$ lb, $F_\theta = 0$.
(*b*) $F_r = -1.533$ lb, $F_\theta = -3.07$ lb.
12.78. $n = 0$: uniform circular motion;
$n = 1$: uniform rectilinear motion.
12.80. 1.317×10^{25} lb (or 4.09×10^{23} lb-sec²/ft).
12.82. 5.32 ft/sec².
12.84. (*a*) 16,860 mph. (*b*) 1.2 per cent.
12.86. 22,300 mph, 3,240 mph.
12.88. (*a*) 5,790 mph. (*b*) 2,640 mph.
(*c*) 10,020 mph.
12.90. 12 hr 42 min.
12.92. 3 hr 5 min.
12.94. (*a*) $8r_0$. (*b*) 9.54.
12.96. (*a*) 24,000 mph. (*b*) 164.6°.
(*c*) 3,220 mph, 7.7°. (*d*) 50 hr 48 min.
12.98. A: 12.86 ft/sec². B: 25.8 ft/sec².
C: 19.32 ft/sec².
12.100. $\bar{v} = \sqrt{2gh(1 - h/l)}$, $v_{\max} = \sqrt{gl/2}$.
12.102. $t = (m/\sqrt{Tk})[\tanh^{-1}(v\sqrt{k/T}) - \tanh^{-1}(v_0\sqrt{k/T})]$. If v were greater than $\sqrt{T/k}$, the drag would be larger than the thrust and the speed could not be maintained.
12.104. $a = (P/m)\,e^{-kt/m}$.
12.106. 0.665.
12.108. 26,200 miles.

CHAPTER 13

13.2. 376×10^6 ft-lb.
13.4. 321 lb.
13.8. $v_A^2 = 4(P_1a + P_2b + P_3c)/\pi m$.
13.10. 143.2 ft, $F_{AB} = 12.6$ kips T,
$F_{BC} = 5.40$ kips T.
13.12. 2.27 ft.
13.14. 15.10 ft/sec.
13.16. 2.51 lb.
13.22. 21.1°.
13.24. 77 mph.
13.26. 2.8 ft.
13.28. 3,520 lb/in.
13.30. (*a*) 8 in. (*b*) 0. (*c*) -1 in.
13.32. Loop 1: (*a*) $\sqrt{5gr} \leftarrow$. (*b*) $3W \rightarrow$.
Loop 2: (*a*) $\sqrt{4gr} \leftarrow$. (*b*) $2W \rightarrow$.
13.36. (*a*) 29.7 ft/sec. (*b*) 20.2 in.
13.38. (*a*) 7,580 mph. (*b*) 5 per cent.
13.40. 8,730 mph $\uparrow$.
13.42. (*a*) $\frac{1}{2}kl^2[(5 - 4\cos\theta)^{\frac{1}{2}} - 1]^2$.
(*b*) $-Wl\sin\theta$.
13.44. (*b*) $V = -\ln\sqrt{x^2 + y^2}$.
13.46. (*b*) $V = -\ln(x^3 + y^3 + z^3)^{\frac{1}{3}}$.
13.48. Paths ABC and ADC, $U = a^4/3$;
path AC, $U = a^4/2$.
13.50. 12.07 in. above floor.
13.52. (*a*) 19.69 in. (*b*) 14.40 in.
13.54. (*a*) 11.58 ft/sec. (*b*) 19.79 ft/sec.
13.56. 7.04 ft/sec.
13.58. $1.091\sqrt{gl}$.
13.60. (*a*) 41.8°. (*b*) 3.38 ft.
13.62. 0.615 lb $\rightarrow$.
13.64. 1.600 in., 16 lb $\uparrow$.
13.66. (*a*) $\frac{1}{2}L$. (*b*) $\frac{1}{4}L$.
13.68. 36,700 ft/sec.
13.70. (*a*) $\frac{1}{2}mgR$. (*b*) mgR.
13.72. (*a*) 87.4×10^8 ft-lb. (*b*) 6.72×10^8 ft-lb.
13.74. 0.818 hp, 0.955 hp.
13.76 $t < 14.67$ sec: $1{,}708t$ ft-lb/sec;
$t > 14.67$ sec: 3,170 ft-lb/sec.
13.78. (*a*) 36.4 hp. (*b*) 60.1 hp.
13.80. (*a*) 9.09 hp. (*b*) 42.8 hp.
13.82. (*a*) Zero. (*b*) 720,000 hp.

13.84. 27.4 sec, 1,525 ft.
13.86. (*b*) $s = (W/3kg) \ln [(P_2 - kv_0^3)/(P_2 - kv_1^3)]$.
13.88. (*a*) 3.11 ft-lb. (*b*) 6.21 ft-lb. (*c*) Part *b* includes both the work done by the boy and the work done by the elevator motor in maintaining the constant velocity.
13.90. (*a*) 533 hp
(*b*) 7.37 mph, 984 hp.
(*c*) 5.93 mph, 33,700 lb.
13.94. (*a*) $\frac{1}{2}mgR$. (*b*) $\frac{3}{4}mgR$.
13.96. $W(1 + h/L)$.
13.98. (*a*) 60.0 ft. (*b*) 0.161.

CHAPTER 14

14.2. 34,200 lb-sec.
14.4. (*a*) 151.8 sec. (*b*) 151.8 sec.
14.6. $\mathbf{v} = 760\mathbf{i} + 1{,}409\mathbf{j} + 1{,}739\mathbf{k}$ (ft/sec).
14.8. (*a*) $\mathbf{v} = (F_1\mathbf{i} + F_2\mathbf{j} + F_3\mathbf{k})/\pi m$. (*b*) $\mathbf{v} = 0$.
14.10. (*a*) 1.553 sec. (*b*) 3.11 sec.
14.12. (1) 25.8 ft/sec ↓. (2) 42.9 ft/sec ↓.
(3) 2.86 ft/sec ↓.
14.16. 33.6 ft/sec ↘.
14.20. (*a*) 29.1 ft/sec. (*b*) Zero.
14.24. 4,270 lb.
14.26. 45.2 lb ↘ 20.1°.
14.28. 10.42 ft/sec.
14.30. (*a*) 2,188 ft/sec →. (*b*) 1,548 ft/sec →.
14.32. 0.40 mph, 7,290 lb.
14.34. (*a*) 3 ft/sec ←. (*b*) 3 ft/sec ←.
14.36. (*a*) 4 ft/sec ←. (*b*) 49.7 lb ←.
14.38. (*a*) 3.47 mph →. (*b*) 2.88 mph →.
(*c*) 2.60 mph →.
14.40. (*a*) 24.9 lb-sec. (*b*) 19.94 lb-sec.
14.42. (*a*) $\mathbf{v}_A = 23$ ft/sec ←, $\mathbf{v}_B = 1$ ft/sec →.
(*b*) 13.04 ft-lb.
14.44. 0.400 lb.
14.46. $\mathbf{v}'_D = \frac{1}{8}v_A(1 + e)^3$ →.
14.48. (*a*) $1.621\mathbf{v}_1$. (*b*) $1.333\mathbf{v}_1$. (*c*) $0.571\mathbf{v}_1$.
14.50. $a = r\sqrt{2}$, $\mathbf{v}'_B = v/\sqrt{2} \measuredangle 45°$.
14.52. 0.330.
14.56. (*a*) $\tan\theta = \sqrt{e}$. (*b*) $\sqrt{e}\, v$.
14.58. (*a*) 0.945. (*b*) 12.94 in.
14.60. $d/(1 - e^2)$.
14.62. $\theta_A = 79.7°$.
14.64. 1.331 ft.
14.66. (*a*) 1.892 in. (*b*) 6.67 ft-lb.
14.68. $W_A = W_B$.
14.70. (*a*) 200 ft-lb. (*b*) 160 ft-lb.
14.72. (*a*) 3.98 ft-lb. (*b*) 3.62 ft-lb.
14.74. 2.86 in., 20.2 in.
14.76. (*a*) 12.50 in./sec. (*b*) $T_{\text{final}} = \frac{1}{16}T_1$.
(*c*) Straight line, $x = 5$ in.
14.78. (*a*) $v_2 = 2v_1$. (*b*) +100 per cent. (*c*) Zero.
(*d*) +300 per cent.
14.80. (*a*) 27.3 ft/sec. (*b*) 1.099 ft.
14.82. 22.7 ft/sec.
14.84. 8.01 in.
14.86. (*a*) $\mathbf{h}_O = 2.48\mathbf{i}$ (lb-sec-ft).
(*b*) $\mathbf{h}_O = 1.863\mathbf{i} - 2.24\mathbf{j} - 7.08\mathbf{k}$ (lb-sec-ft).
14.96. $3r_0$.
14.98. 30°.
14.100. 11,280 miles, 1,018 miles.
14.102. 26,700 ft/sec, 26.9°.
14.104. (*b*) $\frac{1}{3}\sqrt{6}\, v_{\text{esc}}$, $\frac{1}{2}\sqrt{2}\, v_{\text{esc}}$.
14.106. 776 lb ↘ 30°.
14.108. 327 lb.
14.110. $\rho Q v$ ↘ θ.
14.112. (*a*) 7,360 lb. (*b*) 21,090 hp. (*c*) 12,750 hp.
14.114. 7.5°.
14.116. (*a*) $F = (w/g)(u - v)$.
14.118. (*a*) 4,100 lb. (*b*) 6,450 lb.
14.120. (*a*) $\gamma A v^2/g$. (*b*) $\gamma A v^3/2g$.
14.122. 11.86 lb →.
14.124. 278 ft³/sec.
14.126. 40.9 ft/sec ↓.
14.128. (*a*) 1,138 lb. (*b*) 136.6 hp.
14.130. (*a*) wv/g. (*b*) 9.32 lb.
14.132. (*a*) $w(l - vt)$. (*b*) $wvt + wv^2/g$.
14.134. u/g.
14.136. (*a*) 180 ft/sec². (*b*) 720 ft/sec².
14.138. 10,060 ft/sec.
14.140. (*a*) 1,540 ft/sec. (*b*) 11,600 ft/sec.
14.142. (*a*) 30,320 ft/sec →. (*b*) 13,680 ft/sec →
14.144. (*a*) $\frac{1}{2}v_1$ →.
(*b*) Max power $= \frac{1}{4}A\rho(1 - \cos\theta)v_1^3$.
(*c*) $\eta = 2(V/v_1)(1 - V/v_1)(1 - \cos\theta)$.
14.146. 80,700 ft.
14.152. (*a*) 6 oz. (*b*) 75 per cent.
14.156. $\sqrt{hg}$.
14.158. $v^2 = (2PgL/W) \ln 2$.
14.160. (*a*) 0.388 sec. (*b*) 0.518 sec.

CHAPTER 15

15.2. (*a*) 0, +0.200 radian/sec, −0.050 radian/sec².

(*b*) 0.506 radian, +0.0736 radian/sec, −0.01839 radian/sec^2. (*c*) 0.800 radian, 0, 0.

15.4. (*a*) 1,440 rpm. (*b*) 12.60 sec.

15.6. $\mathbf{v}_C = -6\mathbf{i} + 12\mathbf{k}$ (in./sec), $\mathbf{a}_C = -24\mathbf{i} - 30\mathbf{j} - 12\mathbf{k}$ (in./sec^2).

15.8. $\mathbf{v}_C = -6\mathbf{i} + 12\mathbf{k}$ (in./sec.), $\mathbf{a}_C = -12\mathbf{i} - 30\mathbf{j} - 36\mathbf{k}$ (in./sec^2).

15.10. 66,700 mph, 0.01947 ft/sec^2.

15.12. 1.362 sec, 5.45 radians/sec.

15.14. (*a*) 20 ft/sec^2. (*b*) 80.2 ft/sec^2. (*c*) 200 ft/sec^2.

15.16. (*a*) 1.047 radians/sec^2. (*b*) 19.44 revolutions.

15.18. (*a*) 3.95 radians/sec^2. (*b*) 3.18 sec.

15.20. (*a*) $\alpha_A = 8.38$ radians/sec^2 ↻, $\alpha_B = 13.96$ radians/sec^2 ↻. (*b*) 2.25 sec.

15.22. (*a*) $a_B = r\theta_0(2\pi/T)^2\sqrt{\theta_0^2\cos^4(2\pi t/T) + \sin^2(2\pi t/T)}$. (*b*) Maximum: For $\theta_0 \leqslant 1$, $a_B = r\theta_0(2\pi/T)^2$, at $\theta = \pm\theta_0$; for $\theta_0 \geqslant 1$, $a_B = r\theta_0^2(2\pi/T)^2$, at $\theta = 0$. Minimum: For $\theta_0^2 \leqslant \frac{1}{2}$, $a_B = r\theta_0^2(2\pi/T)^2$, at $\theta = 0$; for $\theta_0^2 \geqslant \frac{1}{2}$, $a_B = r(2\pi/T)^2(\theta_0^2 - \frac{1}{4})^{\frac{1}{2}}$, at $\theta = \pm(\theta_0^2 - \frac{1}{2})^{\frac{1}{2}}$.

15.24. $\mathbf{v}_B = 176$ ft/sec →, $\mathbf{v}_C = 0$, $\mathbf{v}_D = 170.0$ ft/sec ∠ 15°, $\mathbf{v}_E = 124.5$ ft/sec ∠ 45°.

15.26. (*a*) 1.121 radians/sec ↻. (*b*) 22.0 in./sec ∠ 60°.

15.28. $(x - 3.5)^2 + (y + 2)^2 = 16$.

15.30. (*a*) $\frac{1}{4}\omega_A$ ↺. (*b*) $\frac{1}{2}\omega_A$ ↻.

15.32. $\omega_B = 40$ rpm ↺, $\omega_C = 20$ rpm ↻.

15.34. (*a*) 0, 26.2 radians/sec ↻. (*b*) 209 in./sec ↓, 0. (*c*) 0, 26.2 radians/sec ↺.

15.36. 205 in./sec ↓, 13.41 radians/sec ↻.

15.38. $\omega_{BD} = 5$ radians/sec ↺, $\omega_{DE} = 3$ radians/sec ↻.

15.40. $\omega_{BD} = 1.5$ radians/sec ↻, $\omega_{DE} = 4$ radians/sec ↻.

15.42. (*a*) 0, 0. (*b*) 0.934 radian/sec ↺, 4.60 ft/sec →.

15.46. $v_P = b\omega\sin\omega t\,[1 + (b\cos\omega t)/\sqrt{l^2 - b^2\sin^2\omega t}\,]$.

15.48. (*a*) 2 in. above center of disk. (*b*) 56 in./sec →.

15.50. (*a*) 2.50 radians/sec ↺. (*b*) 15 in./sec →. (*c*) 10 in. wound per sec.

15.52. 0.80 radians/sec ↻, 5.29 ft/sec ∠ 49.1°

15.54. (*a*) 5 radians/sec ↻. (*b*) 40 in./sec ↑. (*c*) 25 in./sec ∠ 53.1°.

15.58. (*a*) 3 radians/sec ↺. (*b*) 27 in./sec ↑.

15.60. Space centrode: circle of radius l, with center at intersection of vertical and horizontal rods. Body centrode: circle of radius $\frac{1}{2}l$, with center at midpoint of rod AB.

15.66. (*a*) 22 in./sec →. (*b*) 0.833 radian/sec ↻.

15.72. 12 ft/sec^2 ↑, 0.500 radian/sec^2 ↻.

15.74. (*a*) 12 in./sec^2 ←. (*b*) 12 in./sec^2 →.

15.76. $\mathbf{a}_C = 7{,}150$ ft/sec^2 ↑, $\mathbf{a}_D = 7{,}150$ ft/sec^2 ∠ 60°.

15.78. $\mathbf{a}_A = 6$ in./sec^2 →, $\mathbf{a}_B = 25.1$ in./sec^2 ∠ 85.4°, $\mathbf{a}_C = 37.5$ in./sec^2 ↑.

15.80. $\mathbf{a}_A = 6$ in./sec^2 ↓, $\mathbf{a}_B = 66.5$ in./sec^2 ∠ 15.7°.

15.82. $\omega_{AB} = 0$, $\alpha_{AB} = \frac{1}{4}\omega_0^2$ ↻, $\omega_{BC} = \frac{1}{2}\omega_0$ ↺, $\alpha_{BC} = 0$.

15.84. (*a*) 877 ft/sec^2 ←. (*b*) 233 ft/sec^2 →.

15.86. $\mathbf{a}_D = 36$ in./sec^2 ↑, $\mathbf{a}_E = 36$ in./sec^2 ↓, $\mathbf{a}_F = 36$ in./sec^2 ←.

15.88. (*a*) 30.0 radians/sec^2 ↺. (*b*) 54.0 radians/sec^2 ↻.

15.90. (*a*) 2.81 radians/sec^2 ↻. (*b*) 18 in./sec^2 ←, 150.5 in./sec^2 ↑.

15.92. (*a*) $\alpha_{BC} = 40$ radians/sec^2 ↻, $\alpha_{CD} = 20$ radians/sec^2 ↻. (*b*) $\mathbf{a}_C = 256$ in./sec^2 ∠ 51.3°, $\mathbf{a}_D = 0$.

15.94. (*a*) $\alpha_{BC} = 40$ radians/sec^2 ↻, $\alpha_{CD} = 5$ radians/sec^2 ↻. (*b*) $\mathbf{a}_C = 167.6$ in./sec^2 ∠ 17.4°, $\mathbf{a}_D = 0$.

15.98. $\omega = (v_B\sin\beta)/(l\cos\theta)$.

15.100. $v_B = r\omega\cos\theta$, $a_B = r\alpha\cos\theta - r\omega^2\sin\theta$.

15.102. $v_B = R\omega\sec^2\theta$, $a_B = R\sec^2\theta\,(\alpha + 2\omega^2\tan\theta)$.

15.104. $\alpha = -2(v_A^2/b^2)\sin\theta\cos^3\theta$.

15.106. $v_P = 2r\omega\sin\omega t$, $a_P = 2r\omega^2\cos\omega t$.

15.108. −17 in./sec.

15.110. $v_x = z\omega_y - y\omega_z$, $v_y = x\omega_z - z\omega_x$, $v_z = y\omega_x - x\omega_y$.

15.112. $\boldsymbol{\alpha} = -377\mathbf{i} - 3\mathbf{j}$ (radians/sec^2).

15.114. (*a*) $\boldsymbol{\omega} = -\frac{1}{2}(R/r)\omega_1\mathbf{i} + \frac{1}{2}\omega_1\mathbf{j}$. (*b*) $\boldsymbol{\alpha} = \frac{1}{4}(R/r)\omega_1^2\mathbf{k}$.

15.116. $\omega_2 = \omega_1\cos 30°$.

15.118. (*a*) $\omega_1/\sin\beta$. (*b*) $\boldsymbol{\omega} = -(\omega_1/\tan\beta)\mathbf{i}$. (*c*) $\boldsymbol{\alpha} = (\omega_1^2/\tan\beta)\mathbf{k}$.

15.120. (*a*) $\boldsymbol{\omega} = -0.1745\mathbf{i} - 0.524\mathbf{j}$ (radians/sec). (*b*) $\boldsymbol{\alpha} = -0.0914\mathbf{k}$ (radians/sec^2). (*c*) $\mathbf{v}_P = -5.44\mathbf{i} + 1.814\mathbf{j} - 1.047\mathbf{k}$

(ft/sec),
$\mathbf{a}_P = 1.097\mathbf{i} - 0.1828\mathbf{j} - 3.17\mathbf{k}$ (ft/sec²).

15.122. (*a*) $\omega = 21.6\mathbf{i} - 5.24\mathbf{j}$ (radians/sec).
(*b*) $\omega_{FH} = 24.2\mathbf{i}$ (radians/sec).

15.124. (*a*) $\omega = -4\mathbf{i} - 8\mathbf{j}$ (radians/sec).
(*b*) $\alpha = -32\mathbf{k}$ (radians/sec²).
(*c*) $\mathbf{v}_A = -160\mathbf{i} + 80\mathbf{j}$ (in./sec).
(*d*) $a_A = -1{,}600\mathbf{k}$ (in./sec²).

15.126. (*a*) $\omega = \omega_0\mathbf{i} + (v_0/R)\mathbf{j}$, $\alpha = (-\omega_0 v_0/R)\mathbf{k}$.
(*b*) $\mathbf{v}_B = v_0\mathbf{i} + \omega_0 r\mathbf{k}$,
$\mathbf{a}_B = (2\omega_0 v_0 r/R)\mathbf{i} - r\omega_0^2\mathbf{j} - (v_0^2/R)\mathbf{k}$.

15.128. (*a*) $\omega = \omega_1\mathbf{i} + \omega_2\mathbf{j} + \omega_3\mathbf{k}$,
$\alpha = \omega_2\omega_3\mathbf{i} - \omega_1\omega_3\mathbf{j} - \omega_1\omega_2\mathbf{k}$.
(*b*) $\mathbf{v}_E = -r\omega_3\mathbf{i} + (r\omega_1 - R\omega_2)\mathbf{k}$,
$\mathbf{a}_E = (2r\omega_1 - R\omega_2)\omega_2\mathbf{i} - r(\omega_1^2 + \omega_3^2)\mathbf{j}$
$+ 2r\omega_2\omega_3\mathbf{k}$.

15.130. $\mathbf{v}_B = 20\mathbf{j}$ (in./sec).

15.132. (*a*) $\omega = 0.30\mathbf{i} + 2.00\mathbf{j} - 0.40\mathbf{k}$
(radians/sec). (*b*) $\mathbf{v}_B = -12\mathbf{k}$ (in./sec),
$\mathbf{v}_D = 5\mathbf{j} + 13\mathbf{k}$ (in./sec).

15.134. $\mathbf{a}_B = -125\mathbf{j}$ (in./sec²).

15.136. (*a*) $\alpha = -5.60\mathbf{i} - 3.00\mathbf{j} + 5.80\mathbf{k}$
(radians/sec²). (*b*) $\mathbf{a}_B = 50\mathbf{k}$ (in./sec²),
$\mathbf{a}_D = -82.5\mathbf{j} - 37.5\mathbf{k}$ (in./sec²).

15.138. (*a*) 1.933 radians/sec ↻.
(*b*) 17.10 in./sec ◺ 20°.

15.140. $\omega_{BP} = 2.92$ radians/sec ↻,
$\omega_{EF} = 1.130$ radians/sec ↻.

15.142. (*a*) $\omega_{EF} = \omega_{BD}$, $\mathbf{v}_{P/BD} = l\omega \leftarrow$, $\mathbf{v}_{P/EF} = 0$.
(*b*) $\mathbf{v}_{P/BD} = l\omega/\sqrt{3}$ ◺ 30°,
$\mathbf{v}_{P/EF} = l\omega/\sqrt{3}$ ∠ 30°.

15.144. $\mathbf{a}_1 = r\omega^2\mathbf{i} + 2u\omega\mathbf{j}$, $\mathbf{a}_2 = -2u\omega\mathbf{i} - r\omega^2\mathbf{j}$,
$\mathbf{a}_3 = (2u\omega - r\omega^2 - u^2/r)\mathbf{i}$,
$\mathbf{a}_4 = (r\omega^2 - 2u\omega)\mathbf{j}$.

15.146. $a = R\omega^2\sqrt{1 + (2u/R\omega)^2}$.

15.148. (*a*) 0.00582 ft/sec² west.
(*b*) 0.00446 ft/sec² west.
(*c*) Same as *b*.

15.150. 1.124 radians/sec ↻, 8.07 radians/sec² ↺.

15.152. 1.266 radians/sec² ↻.

15.158. $\mathbf{a}_P = -(1.866R\omega_1^2 + 0.866u^2/R)\mathbf{i}$
$- (0.500u^2/R)\mathbf{j} + u\omega_1\mathbf{k}$.

15.160. (*a*) $\mathbf{v}_B = -31\mathbf{i} + 4\mathbf{j} + 2.50\mathbf{k}$ (ft/sec).
(*b*) $\mathbf{a}_B = -0.160\mathbf{i} - 2.145\mathbf{j} + 0.400\mathbf{k}$
(ft/sec²).

15.162. $\mathbf{v}_A = 24\mathbf{i} - 100\mathbf{k}$ (in./sec),
$\mathbf{v}_B = 32\mathbf{j} - 260\mathbf{k}$ (in./sec);
$\mathbf{a}_A = -2{,}000\mathbf{i} - 960\mathbf{k}$ (in./sec²),
$\mathbf{a}_B = -5{,}200\mathbf{i} - 267\mathbf{j}$ (in./sec²).

15.164. (*a*) $\mathbf{v}_C = -27\mathbf{i} + 31.25\mathbf{k}$ (in./sec).
(*b*) $\mathbf{a}_C = -189.5\mathbf{j} + 52.1\mathbf{k}$ (in./sec²).

15.166. 18.4°.

15.168. (*a*) 320 rpm. (*b*) $\alpha = 211\mathbf{k}$ (radians/sec²).
(*c*) $\mathbf{a}_C = 4{,}180\mathbf{i} + 1{,}685\mathbf{j}$ (in./sec²).

15.170. (*a*) 166.7 rpm ↺. (*b*) 21.8 ft/sec ↘.

15.172. (*a*) 0. (*b*) 58.9 in./sec ←.
(*c*) 94.3 in./sec ←.

15.174. (*a*) 8.33 revolutions. (*b*) infinite.
(*c*) 1.151 sec.

15.176. $\omega = -(v \sin^2\theta)/(r \cos\theta)$.

CHAPTER 16

16.2. (*a*) 64.4 ft/sec² →. (*b*) **A** = 5.387 lb ↑,
B = 0.387 lb ↓.

16.4. (*a*) 6.44 ft/sec² →. (*b*) 44.0 in.

16.6. (*a*) 15.22 ft/sec². (*b*) 2.50.

16.8. (*a*) 21.5 ft/sec² →, 10.0 lb.
(*b*) 1.25 in. $\leqslant h \leqslant$ 8.75 in.

16.10. 16.1 ft/sec² ↑.

16.12. 36.8 ft.

16.14. 256 lb →, 305 lb ↑.

16.16. (*a*) 3.02 ft/sec² →.
(*b*) $\mathbf{A}_x$ = 31.3 lb ←,
$\mathbf{A}_y$ = 156.3 lb ↑, **B** = 43.7 lb ↑.

16.18. $\mathbf{B}_y = \mathbf{C}_y$ = 40.3 lb ↓.

16.20. (*a*) $\bar{\mathbf{a}}$ = 31.0 ft/sec² ◸ 85.8°.
(*b*) **A** = 0.288 lb ∠ 30°, **B** = 0.520 lb ∠ 30°.

16.22. (*a*) 0.500 g ◸ 30°.
(*b*) Platform: 1.250 g ◸ 30°, block: 0.625 g ↓.

16.24. V_B = −20.1 lb,
M = −150.7 lb-in. at center of *BC*.

16.26. 4,340 revolutions.

16.28. 31.9 radians/sec² ↺.

16.30. Case 1: 56.2 radians/sec² ↻.
Case 2: 61.8 radians/sec² ↻.

16.32. 8.05 ft/sec.

16.34. (1) 25 radians/sec² ↻, 50 radians/sec ↻,
22.4 radians/sec ↻; (2) 14.07 radians/sec² ↻,
28.14 radians/sec ↻, 16.77 radians/sec ↻;
(3) 6.09 radians/sec² ↻, 12.18 radians/sec ↻,
11.04 radians/sec ↻; (4) 9.79 radians/sec² ↻,
19.58 radians/sec ↻, 9.89 radians/sec ↻.

16.36. 73.0 lb.

16.38. $\alpha = \dfrac{2g}{r}\dfrac{\mu(1+\mu)}{1+\mu^2}$ ↙.

16.40. $\alpha_A = 15.46$ radians/sec² ↶,
$\alpha_B = 7.73$ radians/sec² ↙.

16.42. (*a*) 13.72 radians/sec² ↶. (*b*) 4.58 sec.

16.44. $\alpha = \dfrac{2\mu g \sin\phi}{r(\sin 2\phi - \mu\cos 2\phi)}$ ↶.

16.46. $\bar{k}^2\alpha/\bar{a}$.

16.48. 3 in. from *A* on line *AB*, 12.88 radians/sec² ↙,
6.44 ft/sec² →.

16.50. $T_A = 442$ lb, $T_B = 522$ lb.

16.52. $\mathbf{a}_A = 14$ ft/sec² ↑, $\mathbf{a}_B = 26$ ft/sec² ↑.

16.54. $T_A = 25$ lb, $T_B = 30$ lb.

16.56. (*a*) 30 lb. (*b*) 42.9 radians/sec² ↙.
(*c*) 64.4 ft/sec² ↑.

16.58. (*a*) $\bar{\mathbf{a}} = \mu g$ ←, $\alpha = \dfrac{5}{2}\dfrac{\mu g}{r}$ ↙. (*b*) $t = \dfrac{2}{7}\dfrac{v_0}{\mu g}$.
(*c*) $s = \dfrac{12}{49}\dfrac{v_0^2}{\mu g}$. (*d*) $\bar{\mathbf{v}} = \dfrac{5}{7}v_0$ →,
$\omega = \dfrac{5}{7}\dfrac{v_0}{r}$ ↙.

16.60. $P = 4\mu W/\sqrt{58}$.

16.62. Inside a circle of radius 1 ft with center at
$x = 1.5$ ft, $z = 2.5$ ft.

16.64. (*a*) 45.3 radians/sec² ↶. (*b*) $\mathbf{A}_x = 15$ lb →,
$\mathbf{A}_y = 16$ lb ↑.

16.66. 1.600 ft $\leqslant h \leqslant$ 3.73 ft.

16.68. 0.120 in.

16.70. (*a*) $4wL/7$. (*b*) $9g/7$ ↓.

16.72. 6.33 in.

16.74. (*a*) 11.62 radians/sec² ↙.
(*b*) $\mathbf{A}_x = 34.1$ lb ←, $\mathbf{A}_y = 27.0$ lb ↑.

16.76. (*a*) $\frac{3}{4}g/l$ ↙. (*b*) $\mathbf{N} = 13W/16$ ↑,
$\mathbf{F} = (3\sqrt{3}/16)W$ →. (*c*) 0.400.

16.80. $\tan\beta = 3\mu$.

16.82. 2.55 ft.

16.84. (*a*) 10.30 radians/sec² ↙, 10.30 ft/sec² →.
(*b*) 0.180.

16.86. (*a*) 5.15 radians/sec² ↙, 5.15 ft/sec² →.
(*b*) 0.340.

16.88. (*a*) Does not slide. (*b*) 10.30 radians/sec² ↙,
10.30 ft/sec² →.

16.90. (*a*) Slides. (*b*) 2.86 radians/sec² ↶,
9.66 ft/sec² →.

16.92. 3.08 lb.

16.94. (*a*) 4.03 ft/sec² ←. (*b*) $\mu_A = 0.25$, $\mu_B = 0$.

16.96. (*a*) 0.298. (*b*) $15g/28$ →.

16.98. 9.92 lb.

16.100. (*a*) 4.32 lb.
(*b*) $\mathbf{A} = 10.93$ lb ↑, $\mathbf{B} = 2.71$ lb ←.

16.102. 5.41 lb →.

16.104. (*a*) $3g/4L$ ↶. (*b*) $\mathbf{A} = 3W/8$ →,
$\mathbf{C} = 13W/8$ ↑.

16.106. $T_{BD} = 19.89$ lb, $T_{CE} = 31.3$ lb.

16.108. 61.5 lb ↑.

16.110. (*a*) 11.95 radians/sec² ↙.
(*b*) 36.8 ft/sec² ↘. (*c*) 2.47 lb ↗.

16.114. $\mathbf{A}_x = 8.70$ lb ←, $\mathbf{A}_y = 10.07$ lb ↑,
$\mathbf{B} = 0.613$ lb ←.

16.116. $\alpha_{AB} = 12.87$ radians/sec² ↙,
$\alpha_{BC} = 12.87$ radians/sec² ↶,
$\mathbf{A}_x = 4.66$ lb ←, $\mathbf{A}_y = 6.16$ lb ↑,
$\mathbf{C} = 0.666$ lb →.

16.118. (*a*) $\alpha_{\text{disk}} = 17.05$ radians/sec² ↶,
$\alpha_{AB} = 8.52$ radians/sec² ↙.
(*b*) $\mathbf{A}_x = 14.71$ lb ←, $\mathbf{A}_y = 6.77$ lb ↓.

16.120. Cylinder: $\mathbf{a}_c = a/3$ →, $s = 3d/2$.
Sphere: $\mathbf{a}_s = 2a/7$ →, $s = 7d/5$.

16.122. (*a*) 1.456 lb →. (*b*) 2.66 lb →.

16.124. $\alpha_{AB} = 16.56$ radians/sec² ↶.
$\alpha_{BC} = 24.8$ radians/sec² ↙.

16.126. (*a*) $\alpha_A = 2g/5r$ ↶, $\alpha_B = 2g/5r$ ↙.
(*b*) $W/5$. (*c*) $4g/5$ ↓.

16.128. $\frac{1}{2}L$.

16.130. (*a*) $\alpha_{AB} = \alpha_{CD} = \dfrac{3g}{2l}\left[1 + \dfrac{3h^2}{2l^2}\right]^{-1}$ ↙.
(*b*) $\mathbf{a}_B = l\alpha_{AB}$ ↓, $\mathbf{a}_D = [h\alpha_{AB}$ ←$] + [l\alpha_{AB}$ ↓$]$.

16.132. $M_{\max} = +wL^2/27$, at $2L/3$ to right of *A*.

16.134. $V_B = -5W/8$, $M_B = -WL/4$.

16.136. $T = w^2(l^2 - x^2)/2g$.

16.138. (*a*) 0.50. (*b*) $\mathbf{A}_n = 841$ lb ←,
$\mathbf{B}_n = 361$ lb ←.

16.140. (*a*) $\mathbf{a}_A = 2g/5$ ←, $\mathbf{a}_B = 2g/5$ ↓.
(*b*) $\mathbf{a}_A = 2g/7$ ←, $(\mathbf{a}_B)_x = 2g/7$ ←,
$(\mathbf{a}_B)_y = 2g/7$ ↓.

16.142. (*a*) $\bar{r} = \bar{k}$. (*b*) $\frac{1}{2}W$ ↑.

16.144. (*a*) 131.7 kips. (*b*) 100.8 kips.

16.146. (*a*) 1.634. (*b*) $0.1925\, w\omega^2 r^3/g$.

CHAPTER 17

17.2. 7,900 revolutions.

17.4. $L^3 = 24I_0 g/w$.

17.6. (*a*) 292 rpm. (*b*) 15.92 revolutions.

17.8. 14.60 lb-ft.

17.12. 7.62 ft, 38.1 ft-lb.

17.14. (*a*) 211 lb. (*b*) 178.9 lb.
17.16. 19.77 revolutions.
17.18. $\mathbf{v} = (gs)^{\frac{1}{2}} \downarrow$.
17.20. (*a*) $\sqrt{3g/l}$, $2.50W$. (*b*) 4.01 radians/sec, 50 lb.
17.22. 7.18 radians/sec ↺.
17.26. $\sqrt{g/2r}$.
17.28. (*a*) $\mathbf{v}_A = 8.51$ ft/sec $\downarrow$, $\mathbf{v}_B = 4.91$ ft/sec $\leftarrow$.
(*b*) $\mathbf{v}_A = 0$, $\mathbf{v}_B = 13.90$ ft/sec $\leftarrow$.
17.30. (*a*) 45.3 rpm ↻.
(*b*) 81.3 rpm ↻.
17.32. 10.76 ft/sec ⦩ 45°.
17.34. 7.35 radians/sec ↻.
17.36. (*a*) 210 lb-ft. (*b*) 70.0 lb-ft.
17.38. (*a*) 5.47 lb-ft. (*b*) 0.547 lb-ft.
17.40. 0.335 lb-in.
17.42. $v(1 + \mu)/2g\mu$.
17.46. (*a*) 6.58 sec. (*b*) 10.83 lb, 4.17 lb. (*c*) 0.304.
17.52. $gr^2t/(r^2 + \bar{k}^2) \downarrow$.
17.54. (*a*) 3 in. (*b*) $\bar{\mathbf{v}} = 32.2$ ft/sec $\rightarrow$,
$\omega = 64.4$ radians/sec ↻.
17.56. 11.71 ft/sec $\uparrow$.
17.58. (*a*) $2\bar{v}_0/7\mu g$. (*b*) $5\bar{v}_0/7 \rightarrow$.
17.60. 0.385 lb-ft ↻.
17.62. Pipe: $\bar{\mathbf{v}} = g/10 \rightarrow$, $\omega = g/5$ ↺.
Plate: $\mathbf{v} = 3g/5 \rightarrow$.
17.64. 36.9 rpm.
17.66. 41.1 rpm.
17.68. $\omega_A = \omega_B = 159.1$ rpm ↻, $\omega_P = 20.9$ rpm ↺.
17.70. (*a*) 57.1 rpm. (*b*) 57.1 rpm.
17.72. $v_r = 15.84$ ft/sec, $v_\theta = 11.96$ ft/sec.
17.74. (*a*) $\bar{\mathbf{v}}_1 = mv_0/M \rightarrow$, $\omega_1 = mv_0/MR$ ↺.
(*b*) $mv_0/3M \rightarrow$.
17.76. (*a*) $\bar{\mathbf{v}}_1 = mv_0/3M \rightarrow$, $\omega_1 = mv_0/3MR$ ↻.
(*b*) $mv_0/3M \rightarrow$.
17.78. (*a*) 2.25 radians/sec ↺.
(*b*) $\mathbf{R}_x = 11{,}650$ lb $\rightarrow$, $\mathbf{R}_y = 17{,}470$ lb $\uparrow$.
17.80. $2L/3$.
17.82. $h_A = h\left(\dfrac{6W}{6W + W_P}\right)^2$.
17.84. $2L/3$.
17.86. 1.5°.
17.88. $\omega = 3\bar{v}_1/2b$ ↻, $\bar{\mathbf{v}}_x = \bar{v}_1/4 \leftarrow$, $\bar{\mathbf{v}}_y = 3\bar{v}_1/4 \uparrow$.
17.90. (*a*) $\mathbf{v}_A = \bar{v}_1 \uparrow$, $\mathbf{v}_B = 2\bar{v}_1 \downarrow$.
(*b*) $\mathbf{v}_A = \bar{v}_1 \downarrow$, $\mathbf{v}_B = 2\bar{v}_1 \uparrow$.
17.92. 31.0° ⦣.
17.94. $\mathbf{A}\Delta t = W\sqrt{l/3g} \uparrow$, $\mathbf{B}\Delta t = W\sqrt{l/12g} \uparrow$.
17.96. (*a*) $\omega = \dfrac{6\bar{v}_1}{l}\dfrac{\sin\beta}{3\sin^2\beta + 1}$ ↻.
(*b*) $\mathbf{v}_A = 3\bar{v}_1\dfrac{\sin\beta\cos\beta}{3\sin^2\beta + 1} \leftarrow$.
17.98. 6.75 ft/sec $\leftarrow$.
17.100. (*a*) $3W/2$. (*b*) $3W/4$.
17.102. (*a*) $\mathbf{v}_A = \dfrac{2m}{2m + M}\sqrt{2gh} \downarrow$,
$\omega = \dfrac{2m}{2m + M}\dfrac{\sqrt{2gh}}{R}$ ↻.
(*b*) $\mathbf{v}_A = \dfrac{2m - M}{2m + M}\sqrt{2gh} \downarrow$,
$\omega = \dfrac{4m}{2m + M}\dfrac{\sqrt{2gh}}{R}$ ↻.
17.104. 143.0 rpm.
17.106. 50.2°.

CHAPTER 18

18.2. (*a*) $I_{\text{diagonal}} = \dfrac{m}{6}\dfrac{a^2b^2 + b^2c^2 + c^2a^2}{a^2 + b^2 + c^2}$.
(*b*) 0.236 lb-ft-sec².
18.4. (*a*) $\tan\theta = \dfrac{\sin 2\beta}{3 + \cos 2\beta}$. (*b*) 54.7°.
18.6. 47.2 ft-lb.
18.8. (*a*) $\omega = -157.1\mathbf{i} + 31.4\mathbf{j}$ (radians/sec).
(*b*) $\mathbf{h}_O = -0.0762\mathbf{i} + 0.770\mathbf{j}$ (lb-sec-ft).
(*c*) 18.08 ft-lb.
18.10. (*a*) $\omega = -12.57\mathbf{i} + 31.2\mathbf{j}$ (radians/sec).
(*b*) $\mathbf{h}_D = 1.525\mathbf{i} + 1.030\mathbf{j}$ (lb-sec-ft).
(*c*) 6.50 ft-lb.
18.12. (*a*) $\mathbf{h}_O = 0.813\mathbf{i} - 0.488\mathbf{k}$ (lb-sec-ft).
(*b*) 31.0°.
18.14. (*a*) $\mathbf{h}_B = -0.1372\mathbf{i} + 0.0457\mathbf{j} + 0.305\mathbf{k}$ (lb-sec-ft). (*b*) 25.4°.
18.16. along diagonal AC.
18.18. (*a*) $\omega = 8.28\mathbf{i} + 12.42\mathbf{j}$ (radians/sec),
$y = 0.583 + 1.500x$.
(*b*) $\mathbf{v}_A = -13.11\mathbf{k}$ (ft/sec),
$\mathbf{v}_D = 3.45\mathbf{k}$ (ft/sec).
18.20. (*a*) $-\dfrac{6}{7}v_0\left(\dfrac{1}{c}\mathbf{i} + \dfrac{1}{a}\mathbf{k}\right)$. (*b*) $-\dfrac{5}{7}v_0\mathbf{j}$.
18.22. $3.82\mathbf{i} - 2.86\mathbf{j} + 0.716\mathbf{k}$ (rpm).
18.24. $-6.18\mathbf{i} - 2.86\mathbf{j} + 0.716\mathbf{k}$ (rpm).
18.26. -2.06 ft-lb.
18.28. 16.04 ft-lb.
18.30. $-15.74\mathbf{k}$ (lb-ft).
18.32. $\mathbf{A} = 61.3\mathbf{k}$ (lb), $\mathbf{B} = -61.3\mathbf{k}$ (lb).
18.34. $\mathbf{A} = -2.87\mathbf{i} + 0.958\mathbf{j}$ (lb), $\mathbf{B} = -\mathbf{A}$.

18.36. $\mathbf{A} = 0.75\mathbf{i} + 2.25\mathbf{j}$ (lb), $\mathbf{B} = -\mathbf{A}$.
18.38. (*a*) 322**i** (radians/sec^2).
(*b*) $\mathbf{A} = 6.71\mathbf{j} + 9.12\mathbf{k}$ (lb), $\mathbf{C} = -\mathbf{A}$
18.40. $x =$ 2 ft, $y = 3.50$ ft.
18.42. $\mathbf{A} = (1/8L)m\omega^2a^2 \sin 2\beta\, \mathbf{i}$, $\mathbf{B} = -\mathbf{A}$.
18.44. $\mathbf{C} = 4.74$ lb $\rightarrow$, $\mathbf{D} = [13.60$ lb $\leftarrow] + [25$ lb $\uparrow]$
18.46. (*a*) 76.0°. (*b*) 4.91 radians/sec.
18.48. $2.12\,(g/L)^{\frac{1}{2}}$.
18.50. (*a*) zero. (*b*) $\mathbf{C} = 122.6\mathbf{j}$ (lb),
$\mathbf{D} = -122.6\mathbf{j}$ (lb).
18.52. (*a*) 11.35 radians/sec. (*b*) 16.05 radians/sec.
18.54. (*a*) 9.27 radians/sec. (*b*) 8.89 lb.
18.56. 5.44 lb.
18.58. (*a*) 3,250 rpm. (*b*) 3,920 rpm.
(*c*) 4,580 rpm.
18.66. 302 days.
18.68. (*a*) $\beta = 23.8°$.
(*b*) precession, 74.3 rpm; spin, 115.9 rpm.
18.70. Precession Axis: $\theta_x = 72.1°$, $\theta_y = 157.4°$,
$\theta_z = 76.7°$; precession, 3.10 rpm;
spin, 2.87 rpm.
18.72. Precession Axis: $\theta_x = 117.6°$, $\theta_y = 149.3°$,
$\theta_z = 77.6°$; precession, 3.33 rpm;
spin, 4.64 rpm.
18.74. 3.18 revolutions per hour.
18.76. (*a*) $\omega = 22.7$ rpm; $\theta_x = 90°$, $\theta_y = 32.7°$,
$\theta_z = 57.3°$.
(*b*) $\theta_x = 90°$, $\theta_y = 14.4°$, $\theta_z = 75.6°$.
(*c*) precession, 19.72 rpm; spin, 7.36 rpm.
18.84. $\mathbf{A} = (26.9\text{ lb})\mathbf{j}$, $\mathbf{D} = -(26.9\text{ lb})\mathbf{j}$.
18.86. (*b*) $\dot{\theta} = \dot{\phi}_0\sqrt{\dfrac{(1+\cos^2\theta_0)(\cos^2\theta - \cos^2\theta_0)}{1+\cos^2\theta}}$.
18.88. (*a*) $\cos\beta = 2g/3a\omega^2$. (*b*) $\sqrt{2g/3a}$.
18.90. (*a*) $\omega = \frac{1}{6}\omega_0(-\mathbf{i} + \mathbf{j})$. (*b*) $\bar{\mathbf{v}} = \frac{1}{6}\omega_0 a\mathbf{k}$.
18.92. (*a*) tension $= \frac{1}{2}ma\Omega^2 + (\sqrt{3}/6)mg$,
kinetic energy $= \frac{7}{10}ma^2\Omega^2$.
(*b*) spin $= +5g/a\Omega + 5\sqrt{3}\Omega$.

CHAPTER 19

19.2. 2.79 ft/sec, 23.4 ft/sec^2.
19.4. (*a*) 4 lb/in. (*b*) 2.21 cps.
19.6. 300 lb, 5.71 cps.
19.8. (*a*) 0.1065 sec. (*b*) 1.419 ft/sec ↑,
8.05 ft/sec^2 ↑.
19.10. (*a*) 0.431 sec, 2.32 cps. (*b*) 3.65 ft/sec,
53.1 ft/sec^2.
19.12. 3.27 lb.
19.14. (*a*) 2.52°. (*b*) 5.04°.
19.16. 1.400 ft.
19.20. (*a*) 2.21 sec. (*b*) 2.37 sec. (*c*) 3.03 sec.
19.22. 16.3°.
19.24. (*a*) 0.533 sec. (*b*) 0.491 radian/sec.
19.26. (*a*) 5 in., 0.594 cps. (*b*) 1.554 ft/sec.
19.28. $\tau = 2\pi\sqrt{2W/3gk}$.
19.30. 1,022 lb/in.
19.36. (*a*) $f = (1/2\pi)\sqrt{g/2r}$.
(*b*) $f = (1/2\pi)\sqrt{6g/11r}$.
19.38. 0.707.
19.40. (*a*) $r_a = 7.09$ in. (*b*) 3.42 in.
19.42. $\tau = 2\pi\sqrt{L/6g}$.
19.44. (*a*) $\tau = 2\pi\sqrt{h/2g}$. (*b*) $\tau = 2\pi\sqrt{h/g}$.
19.46. 0.760 lb-ft-sec^2, 8.66 in.
19.48. 0.1774 lb-ft-sec^2.
19.50. (*a*) 1.715 sec. (*b*) 1.566 sec.
19.52. (*a*) 5.71 cps, 0.20 in., 7.18 in./sec.
(*b*) 100 lb.
19.58. 75.5°.
19.60. $f = (1/2\pi)\sqrt{g/2r}$.
19.62. $f = (1/2\pi)\sqrt{g/2b}$.
19.64. $\tau = 2\pi\sqrt{r(\pi - 2)/g}$.
19.66. $\tau = 2\pi\sqrt{7(R - r)/5g}$.
19.68. (*a*) 5.42 cps. (*b*) 4.58 cps.
(*c*) 3.83 cps.
19.72. (*a*) 0.322 sec. (*b*) 0.322 sec.
19.74. $\tau = \pi l/\sqrt{3gr}$.
19.76. $\omega > \sqrt{2kg/W}$.
19.78. $\omega > \sqrt{2g/l}$.
19.80. (*a*) 375.3 rpm. (*b*) 0.00216 in.
19.82. (*a*) 0.00420 in. (*b*) 0.0711 in. (*c*) ∞.
19.84. 0.060 in. or 0.0429 in.
19.86. 1,085 rpm.
19.88. 969 rpm.
19.90. 0.045 in.
19.92. (*a*) 19.70 mph. (*b*) 0.480 in.
19.94. 0.369 cps, 0.639 cps.
19.100. 1,320 lb-sec/ft.
19.102. 7,780 lb/ft.
19.106. (*a*) 0.1582. (*b*) 20.1 lb-sec/ft.
19.108. 4.73 lb-sec/in.
19.110. (*a*) $m\dfrac{d^2x}{dt^2} + c\dfrac{dx}{dt} + kx$
$= (k \sin \omega t + c\omega \cos \omega t)\delta_m$.
(*b*) $x_m = \dfrac{\sqrt{k^2 + c^2\omega^2}\,\delta_m}{\sqrt{(k - m\omega^2)^2 + (c\omega)^2}}$,
with $\omega = 2\pi v/L$.
19.112. $R < 2\sqrt{L/C}$.

19.118. (*a*) $m\dfrac{d^2x_m}{dt^2} + k_2(x_m - x_A) = P_m \sin \omega t,$

$c\dfrac{dx_A}{dt} + k_1x_A + k_2(x_A - x_m) = 0.$

(*b*) $L\dfrac{d^2q_m}{dt^2} + \dfrac{(q_m - q_A)}{C_2} = E_m \sin \omega t,$

$R\dfrac{dq_A}{dt} + \dfrac{q_A}{C_1} + \dfrac{(q_A - q_m)}{C_2} = 0.$

19.120. (*a*) $m_1\dfrac{d^2x_1}{dt^2} + c_1\dfrac{dx_1}{dt}$

$+ k_1x_1 + k_2(x_1 - x_2) = 0,$

$m_2\dfrac{d^2x_2}{dt^2} + c_2\dfrac{dx_2}{dt} + k_2(x_2 - x_1) = 0.$

(*b*) $L_1\dfrac{d^2q_1}{dt^2} + R_1\dfrac{dq_1}{dt} + \dfrac{q_1}{C_1}$

$+ \dfrac{(q_1 - q_2)}{C_2} = 0,$

$L_2\dfrac{d^2q_2}{dt^2} + R_2\dfrac{dq_2}{dt} + \dfrac{(q_2 - q_1)}{C_2} = 0.$

19.122. (*a*) 30.4 lb/in. (*b*) 10 lb/in.

19.124. (*a*) $\tau = 2\pi\sqrt{l/(g + a)}$, $\tau = 2\pi\sqrt{m/k}$.
(*b*) $\tau = 2\pi\sqrt{l/(g - a)}$, $\tau = 2\pi\sqrt{m/k}$.

19.126. 1,141 lb-ft-sec^2.

19.128. 141.4 rpm or 109.5 rpm.

19.132. (*b*) $f = (1/2\pi)\sqrt{(\mu g/L)\cos\beta}$.

APPENDIX ON GRAPHICAL METHODS

A.4. 150 lb ←, 50.7 in. above *A*.

A.10. Resultant is a couple; 4,000 lb-in. ↻.

A.12. **R** = 0, **M** = 720 lb-in. ↻.

A.14. 40 lb ↓.

A.16. **A** = 5 kips ↑, **B** = 4 kips ↑.

A.18. **A** = 30 lb ↑, **B** = 30 lb ↓.

A.20. **A** = 31.5 kips ↙ 8.6°, **B** = 62.7 kips ↑.

A.26. T = 74.8 lb, **C** = 168 lb ↖ 39.8°.